TH
GOOD
BEER
GUIDE
2025

MANAGING EDITOR
Emma Haines

EDITORS
Katie Button, Alan Murphy, Claire-Michelle Taverner-Pearson

PROJECT ASSISTANCE
Stewart Campbell

SALES & MARKETING
Toby Langdon

© Campaign for Real Ale Ltd, 2024
www.camra.org.uk

Special thanks to the 150,000 CAMRA members who carried out research for the pub entries; the Campaign's Regional Directors and Area Organisers, who co-ordinated the pub entries; the Campaign's Brewery Liaison Coordinators and Brewery Liaison Officers, who carried out research for the brewery entries; Rick Pickup for assistance coordinating the brewery entries; Alex Presland for technical support; Iain Barker, Christine Beatty and Simon Mather at AMA Dataset; Iain MacLeod, Alison Sinclair and AJ Dean at ITV Studios; Paul Ainsworth, Phil Gregg, Maddy Hardman, Alex Metcalfe, Sarah Newson, Roger Protz, Annabel Smith and Camilla Weddell for supplying articles, images and information for the Guide; Lily Haines and Geoff Strawbridge for proofreading assistance; all CAMRA's staff and CAMRA's National Executive for their help and support. In memory of Ian 'Dickie' Dickinson.

Thanks also to the publicans, breweries, CAMRA members and others who have kindly contributed their photographs.

Photo credits: [Key: t = top; b = bottom; c = centre; l = left; r = right] p4 Nicci Peet; p5 ITV Studios; p7 (tr) Stuart Grahame; p8 Pablo Merchán Montes; p9 (tr) Amelia Claudia, (bl) Phil Tragen; p12 (bl) Brittani Burns/Unsplash; p13 (tl) Matthew Curtis, (cr) Bill Bradshaw; p14 Jane Carrodus/Flickr; p15 (tl) John Corser; p622 Les Taylor; p623 Greene King; p839 Emma Haines; p840 George Greenaway; p841 Emma Haines; p896 (cr) Stuart McMahon; p897 (bl) Don Croker, (br) Christopher Crowther; p898 (cl) Stephen Tubb, (tr) Bob Smith, (b) George Greenaway; p899 (tr) Mark Bates, (br) Stuart McMahon; p900 Dave Pickersgill; p901 (all) Stuart McMahon; p910 Richard Adam.
https://creativecommons.org/licenses

Design: Cover photography: ITV Studios. Jacket designs: Jack Pemberton.

Colour and extra mono pages: Dale Tomlinson.

Production: Database, maps, typesetting of listings and indexes: AMA Dataset Ltd, Preston.

Printing: Printed and bound in the UK by CPI William Clowes, Beccles, Suffolk.

Published by the Campaign for Real Ale Ltd, 230 Hatfield Road, St Albans, Herts, AL1 4LW. www.camra.org.uk

© Campaign for Real Ale 2024/2025. All rights reserved.

ISBN 978-1-85249-391-2 / 978-1-85249-393-6

MIX
Paper | Supporting
responsible forestry
FSC
www.fsc.org
FSC® C013604

Pilot Boat and Rock Point Inn, Lyme Regis, Dorset (p114). *Photo:* Emma Haines

CONTENTS

ABOUT THE GOOD BEER GUIDE

Your Guide to the best pubs and beer in the UK.

For more than five decades, the *Good Beer Guide* has been a comprehensive guide to the UK's breweries, their ales and the best outlets to find them in around the country.

There may be other pub guides out there, but this book is different. Where other guides might have a small editorial board pulling together entries, the *Good Beer Guide* has a huge volunteer team, based around the country, all regularly using their local pubs, trying out the beers on offer and recommending the best of them to other beer- and pub-lovers.

We strive hard to ensure that all areas of the country are covered. Each county or region has a listing allocation based on a scientific calculation of its population, number of licensed premises and levels of tourism. As a result, the Guide's reach is unparalleled.

The *Good Beer Guide* is also proudly independent. Inclusion in this book is dependent on merit, not on payment. No pubs or breweries paid to be in this book.

VOLUNTEER INVOLVEMENT

CAMRA has 150,000 members across more than 200 branches around the UK. It's within these branches that entries are democratically selected, with beer quality being the foremost criterion. All members are invited to rate beers served to them via the National Beer Scoring System (see p902). These scores are used by branches to identify pubs consistently serving the best real ale. Not only is the quality of the cask beer monitored, but also factors that could affect the range on offer, and the overall standard of the pub, such as change of ownership or management.

While the core purpose of the Guide is to seek out quality real ale, it also considers other things such as history, architecture, food, family and disabled facilities, gardens and special events (such as beer festivals). The pub listings you find in these pages paint a full picture of what you can expect before you embark on a trip to visit them.

The listings are checked many times before publication, to ensure they are accurate and up to date.

BREWERY LISTINGS

The *Good Beer Guide* includes a comprehensive listing of the more than 1,700 breweries currently operating in the UK – not just those producing real ale – and their core cask-conditioned beers available.

Each one is appointed a local CAMRA volunteer as soon as they come on stream. These volunteer officers regularly keep in touch with the brewery to stay abreast of what's being brewed and developments that may be taking place.

OPENING HOURS

Opening hours are not listed in the Guide as they are subject to significant change. Please phone ahead if you are travelling.

THE PUB IS THE HUB

On an imaginary TV Soap Monopoly board, the Rovers Return and the Woolpack would be Mayfair and Park Lane: the most significant pieces of real estate in their respective fictional worlds.

There's good reason for this. In the Soaps, as in the real world, the pubs are where all of life's rich pageant plays out. They are where relationships are formed (and sometimes consummated!). They are where marriages are celebrated, and deaths commemorated. But most importantly, they are where friends and family congregate to talk about – or distract themselves from – the daily dramas of their lives.

And let's face it – Soap characters and the pubs they drink in see more than their fair share of drama. Both the Woolpack and the Rovers, across their 50–60 years on screen, have been nearly destroyed many times by numerous fires, a lightning strike, a gas explosion, a flood, a lorry crashing through a wall and even being hit by a falling plane! Time to find a new local, you might think.

But the story which threatened one of our pubs the most was also the one which most resonated with our times. In 2023, the Rovers Return closed its doors. A combination of the lingering legacy of the Covid lockdowns and the cost-of-living crisis meant that landlady Jenny Bradley couldn't afford to keep it open. The characters – and the viewers – lamented the news like the loss of a loved one. If it were needed, it was a timely reminder of the central place the nation's pubs have in our lives and in our affections.

Recently, Coronation Street character Steve McDonald calculated on-screen that he'd drunk more than 17,000 pints of Newton and Ridley (Corrie's fictional beer) in the Rovers over his many decades on the show. On Emmerdale and Coronation Street, the Woolpack and the now reopened Rovers will remain central to our characters' lives, so that he and others can enjoy thousands more. Let's hope the same will be true for the many pubs under threat across the country.

Iain MacLeod *Executive Producer, Continuing Drama, ITV Studios*

CONSUMER CHAMPIONS

For more than 50 years the *Good Beer Guide* has represented the pinnacle of the brewing and hospitality industry. It is the joy of everyone at CAMRA to be able to highlight the best of the best, and it couldn't be done without the dedication of thousands of volunteers who scour the country for the finest places to enjoy a pint.

CAMPAIGNING CHALLENGES

Over the past 12 months the Campaign has come up against challenges in the trade that have required commitment and enthusiasm from staff and members alike. When the Crooked House in Himley was gutted by fire and unlawfully torn down in 2023, CAMRA immediately acted. In 2024 we heard the news that Carlsberg Marston's Brewing Company decided to introduce a new 'Fresh Ale', which turned out to be a ploy to serve kegged beer through cask dispensers. This handpump hijack deliberately misleads consumers and boots a genuine cask beer off the bar, depriving customers of choice. Carlsberg Marston's Brewing Company claim to champion cask beer but have instead closed breweries and removed cask lines from bars.

Carlsberg Marston's 'Fresh Ale' is simply a ploy to serve keg beer through cask dispensers

In Northern Ireland, volunteers have been battling against archaic licensing laws, severely restricted consumer choice and, more often than not, a lack of government to lobby about it. Happily, the Assembly and Executive are back up and running. We now have plans for campaigning on reforms to the new producer's licence, and the abolition of the 'Surrender Principle', which fixes the number of licences available for pubs, bars, and off licences.

This year has made it clear that our members are capable of stepping up to any challenge.

PUBLICATIONS

Year on year our publishing arm CAMRA Books creates a roster of fantastic titles, and this year has been no different. A hugely successful Kickstarter campaign on behalf of author Adam Wells saw the publishing of *Perry: A Drinker's Guide* which for the first time ever tells the full international story of perry – the drinks world's best kept secret. Adam then set off on a whirlwind tour, imparting his unrivalled knowledge of perry to enthusiasts across the UK, with an official CAMRA launch event in London.

Another success story from this year was the comprehensive history of women in brewing written by Dr Christina Wade. *The Devil's in the Draught Lines* features interviews from beer writers including Laura Hadland, Ruvani de Silva, Natalya Watson and Jane Peyton, plus women in the industry such as Helena Adedipe of Eko Brewery, Lizzie and Lucy Stevens of Closet Brewing Project, and

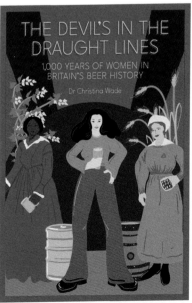

CAMRA published a history of women in brewing by Dr Christina Wade

Talia Chain of Sadeh Farm. The book busts some of the myths that have perpetuated over the past 1,000 years and charts the rise and fall – and rise – of women in Britain's brewing trade.

We were also very proud to publish Matthew Curtis's *Manchester's Best Beer Pubs and Bars*. Many of the establishments listed in his comprehensive guide will be found in this one, as well as plenty of hidden gems from across the city. With a foreword by the Mayor of Greater Manchester, Andy Burnham, the guide is a love letter to the beer scene in the North West.

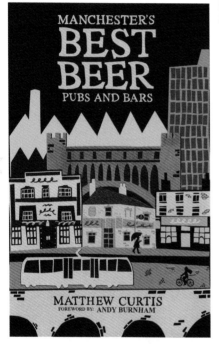

CHAMPIONING LOCAL FESTIVALS

While our flagship event the Great British Beer Festival took a fallow year, we have been shining a spotlight on the 180+ local events organised by passionate volunteers. Over 7,000 people offer their time, hard work and expertise to ensure that the thousands of visitors to CAMRA festivals leave with a smile on their face and a better knowledge of beer and cider.

Our Learn & Discover platform has been on the road, visiting festivals across the UK to entertain and educate festival goers. Attendees have been getting their hands on real ingredients, speaking to brewers and cider producers, and getting a taste for special beers and ciders from all over the country.

We can't wait to welcome the Great British Beer Festival back in 2025.

CAMRA's Learn & Discover platform has been on the road at beer festivals across the UK

OUR DIGITAL FUTURE

Our volunteers live in every corner of all four nations of the UK and, because of that, we're committed to ensuring we're all as connected as possible. Our shiny new website has been custom built to show off everything we do best. Visitors can find their favourite beer and the closest CAMRA recommended pub that stocks it. It allows you to navigate with ease, find Good Beer Guide content and create personalised trips and beer wish lists. Plus, you can access beer and brewery information to help you choose where to go and what beers to try.

WHAT'S NEXT?

Campaigning, education and community are at the heart of what CAMRA offers. The past year has been full of challenges and new beginnings, and the next is sure to be the same. At the time of writing this the country is preparing to vote in a national election, after which we'll be forging new relationships to ensure our voice is heard in the highest offices. Our commitment, as ever, will be to the consumer, and with that comes our unending support for the publicans, brewers and producers that supply us with the beer, cider and perry that we love.

Nik Antona, *National Chairman*

WOMEN IN BEER

Would it surprise you if you found out the beer you were drinking was brewed by a woman? Would it make you think differently about that beer?

It would not have even crossed your mind if you were drinking beer a few hundred years ago because almost all beer was brewed by women up until the 18th century. It was seen as women's work to produce a refreshing, intoxicating liquid to slake the thirst of the male agricultural workers returning from a hard day's toil on the land. Much like making bread, it was the responsibility of women to provide nourishment for the village menfolk (and children), and this tradition was rooted in history.

This tradition stretches back into history. Sumerian women brewed low-alcohol beer for religious ceremonies as well as for daily food rations. (For the geography-geeks, Sumer is modern-day Iraq). Ancient Egyptians worshipped a beer goddess named Tenenet, and hieroglyphics have been found depicting women brewing and drinking beer. Baltic and Slavic mythology both include a goddess, named Raugutiene, who provided protection over beer. And the Finnish told of a legendary woman named Kalevatar who invented beer by mixing honey with bear saliva. Sounds delicious.

WOMEN'S WORK

This image of women as ale-makers persisted well into the Middle Ages, moving from a sacred role to an everyday necessity of homemaking, historically typified as 'women's work.'

Water was unsanitary, at times bringing with it deadly diseases. But the process of fermentation created a sterile drink, so beer was considered a safe option. Without doubt, nearly all women in England knew how to brew ale.

But as beer gradually moved from a cottage industry into a money-making one, most women were moved out of the brewing industry. Whilst some women continued to make ale for their family's daily consumption, the Industrial Revolution saw massive advances in science, technology, and engineering in the brewing sector. This made buying beer cheaper and easier than whipping up a batch of home brew.

Smear campaigns demonised ale-wives, painting them as dishonest, unsanitary and morally suspect. And just to make sure women got the message, the marketing campaigns of the 1950s and 1960s branded beer as a 'man's drink'. Case closed: beer is not for women.

DEA LATIS

That's a huge amount of history to unravel, and it's reflected in two pieces of recent research. A 2024 survey commissioned by the Dea Latis group revealed only 8% of British women choose beer as their favourite drink (a long way behind wine and spirits), and only 14% of women drink it regularly (that is, once a week or more). The SIBA Independent Beer Report 2024

The Gender Pint Gap: Revisited

A FURTHER STUDY INTO GB WOMENS ATTITUDES AND BEHAVIOURS TOWARDS BEER

DeaLatis in association with the drinks business

A 2024 survey revealed only 8% of British women choose beer as their favourite drink

disclosed just 6% of head brewing roles are held by women in the UK independent sector.

I'm not a mathematician, but could there be a little bit of a connection between these statistics? If women are more visible in brewing roles and have an active say in the way beer is packaged, marketed, and presented, it makes it a better industry for everyone, both societally and commercially.

Unpicking some of the information in the Dea Latis Gender Pint Gap Revisited report, it is obvious that the taste of beer is not a problem for women. It was cited as the most likeable aspect about beer, above refreshment and the sociability factor. The vast range of flavours in beer, from zesty grapefruity pale ales to the chewy toffee-ness of a best bitter, and the silky-smooth chocolate flavours in stouts and porters scored a huge tick for women of all ages.

Fancy a glass of beer?

However, they felt these attractive flavour attributes were seldom communicated through menus, point of sale, or pump clips. (The words 'likeable,' 'more-ish' and 'thirst-quenching' aren't taste descriptors by the way, they're opinions). It's elitist to assume everyone knows the difference between a West Coast IPA and an imperial stout, so more inclusive language on beer boards and lists is a great way of getting everyone, not just women, to choose beer.

The way beer is presented and served was also an issue for women. The traditional pint of beer served up in pubs conjured up negative images of a voluminous, calorie-laden, bloat-inducing liquid. It's not a good look, is it? However, change the phrase 'fancy a pint' to 'fancy a glass of beer' and it's a game-changer. In Belgium, for example, where beer is served in smaller measures and in attractive glassware specifically designed for the brand, female beer drinkers equal their male counterparts.

CHANGING THE NARRATIVE

The promotion and marketing of beer is always going to be a thorny issue to tackle. In the Gender Pint Gap report 67% women strongly agreed or tended to agree with the statement that beer is a drink for men. This is a reflection on the way that beer has been historically advertised and marketed. There are now guidelines and recommendations set out by the beer industry about acceptable advertising and marketing standards, but these just restrict actively exclusionary communications.

Commenting on this, Emma Inch, an award-winning beer writer and broadcaster says, "It's simply not enough to reach out to young, white, cisgender, heterosexual, able-bodied women. It requires a concerted effort on the part of everyone in the industry to check the messages they are putting out in the world and ask themselves 'are we leaving some people out?'" Positive representation of all types of women enjoying beer, on their own terms, is an opportunity we should all embrace and capitalise on. Over half the UK's population are women, why exclude them from enjoying beer?

The Gender Pint Gap Revisited report examined many more of the challenges, perceptions, and attitudes of women towards beer and it's essential reading if you hold the opinion that beer is a 'man's drink'.

Women do exist in the beer world. They brew, package, sell, serve, drink, and enjoy beer every day. Women brew some of the UK's most well-loved beers: Sara Barton from Brewsters, George Young at St Austell, Julie O'Grady at Neptune, and Jaega Wise from Wild Card to name a few. Female beer educators, writers, broadcasters and commentators are changing the narrative, creating a landscape in which everyone can – and should – enjoy beer without prejudice or bias.

Beer is one of the most sociable drinks in the world and, to quote Dea Latis, it's far too good to be enjoyed only by men.

Annabel Smith is an award-winning Beer Sommelier, educator, writer, and broadcaster. Having managed several renowned cask ale pubs for 12 years, she worked as a trainer for Guinness before becoming the first female beer inspector for the Cask Marque Trust. In 2015 she founded BeerBelle, a company specialising in designing and delivering bespoke beer training courses and events. She is the founder member of Dea Latis, an organisation that educates women about beer and conducts research into female attitudes and opinions about the beer category. For more information see **beerbelle.co.uk** and **dealatisuk.wordpress.com**

THERE'S NO MATCHING A SCRATCHING
with a great pint, in a great pub

TRADITIONAL

Pork Scratchings

CAMRA'S BEER STYLES

We are very lucky in the UK to enjoy a rich variety of traditional beer styles developed by brewers over the past few hundred years. The number of brewers brewing international recipes and experimenting with new styles means that there are ever more beers to choose from. Such a wide range of styles, names and variations can be a little overwhelming, so CAMRA have cut through the jargon and have come up with 12 beer style categories to help you navigate the choices at the bar.

Over the next few pages, we take you through the beer style categories, with advice on some of the flavour profiles you can expect.

1. Milds
up to and including 4% ABV

Look: There are two types of mild: light/pale milds, and dark milds. Milds can be dark brown to black to pale amber or even gold.

Taste: Light drinking and not very hoppy. Pale milds are lightly hopped and can have a light fruitiness and sweet taste with a little butterscotch/toffee. Dark milds are frequently sweet with a light bitterness with malt and roasted notes of chocolate, coffee, and liquorice.

Scottish 60 shillings or Scottish light beer also fits into this category and can be dark brown to black in colour with flavours of malt with butterscotch/toffee notes.

2. Session Bitters
up to and including 4.3% ABV

Look: Amber to dark brown in colour.

Taste: Bitterness can range from light to strong. These are 'traditional bitters' with a thin to average body, a malt character with noticeable hops; typically earthy, spicy and peppery, they can also be floral or piny. Fruitiness, sometimes citrus, can be present.

3. Premium Bitters
4.4%–6.4% ABV

Look: Usually amber to dark brown in colour.

Taste: Premium bitters are traditionally stronger bitters with an average to thick body. They have medium to strong malt flavour with noticeable hops; typically earthy, spicy and peppery, they can also be floral, piny, or citrus. Fruitiness can be medium to strong.

Stronger bitters can have estery notes such as pear drops, and the bitterness can range from medium to strong.

4. Session Pale, Blond & Golden Ales
up to and including 4.3% ABV

Look: Pale ales are dark gold to amber in colour. Blond ales are straw to golden in colour.

Taste: These are refreshing, light-drinking beers. Malt flavours are light in character, with hop flavours more noticeable and varying from earthy or spicy to citrus and tropical.

Pale ales can be fruitier than a session bitter. Malt is minimal with low to moderate fruit flavours. Hops again can vary but will not have a strong citrus character. Golden ales have pronounced fruity, citrus hop notes and can have strong bitterness.

5. **Premium Pale, Blond & Golden Ales**: 4.4%–6.4% ABV

Look: Pale ales are dark gold to amber. Blond and golden ales are straw to gold in colour.

Taste: These beers are refreshing but fuller-bodied than the session varieties. Malt is light to medium in character and not dominant. Fruit can vary from minimal to strong and is often citrus or tropical. Hops are noticeable and vary from earthy and spicy to citrus.

6. **British & New World IPAs** 5.5% ABV and above

Look: British IPAs are usually amber to pale brown. New World IPAs are straw to pale brown. Black IPAs are typically dark brown or black.

Taste: These are strong, hoppy beers. The finish is long and complex.

British IPAs often have a biscuit malt aroma and peppery, spicy, earthy, piny or floral hop notes.

New World IPAs are noticeably fruitier with citrus, tropical or white wine flavours. The malt tends to make less of an impact. Black IPAs have a lighter roasted character which complements rather than dominating the hops and fruit in the flavour profile.

7. **Brown & Red Ales, Old Ales & Strong Milds**: up to 6.4% ABV

Look: Darker in colour, from deep red to dark brown.

Taste: These beers tend to have malty notes.

Brown ales have malt to the fore, often with roasted, smoky or nut-like flavours. Hops are sometimes evident, and they can have a moderately bitter or dry finish. Fruity flavours such as raisins or sultanas can be present. American brown ales tend to be much fruitier, sometimes with pronounced bittering.

Red ales have malt to the fore, often with roast or nutty flavours. Rye can be present, creating a balanced tartness. American red ales are fruitier and hoppier. Strong milds and unaged old ales have a light to rich malt character, sometimes with caramel and fruit notes such as raisins and sultanas.

8. **Session Stouts & Porters** up to and including 4.9% ABV

Look: Dark ruby to jet black.

Taste: Stouts are typically black and less hopped than porters. Their flavour and aroma results from the roasted grain malts, for example chocolate, caramel and coffee notes. They have minimal hop and fruit notes. There are several different types of stout brewed, each with a slightly different flavour profile. These include dry stouts, oyster stouts, oatmeal stouts and milk stouts.

Porters also have roasted notes of coffee or chocolate but are balanced by a hoppy character.

11. **Speciality Beers**: differently produced

Look: Varies.

Taste: Differently produced speciality beers are those brewed with non-standard ingredients or techniques, as opposed to flavoured speciality beers, which have flavour added. Non-conventional ingredients and techniques are only limited by the brewer's imagination. They can include styles such as Pilsners, Vienna lagers, Märzen, dark lagers and Kölsch, wheat beers, sours, saisons, wood-aged and smoked beers.

9. **Strong Stouts & Porters**
5% ABV and above

Look: Dark ruby to jet black.

Taste: Grain, burnt fruit, fresh leather, espresso coffee, bitter chocolate, molasses and liquorice notes. Warming alcohol is often noticeable due to the high alcohol content. These are stronger, dry versions of the session varieties, usually with a smoother, fuller mouthfeel. Flavours range from sweet to dry but with a rich, full body.

Imperial stouts and Baltic (or Imperial) porters are deep and complex with roast grain, burnt fruit and fresh leather notes.

10. **Barley Wines & Strong Ales**
6.5% ABV and above

Look: Pale gold, amber, ruby to black.

Taste: Strong beer used to be produced to allow it to be kept, particularly to provide beer when it was too warm to brew. Many of the beers in this category are still aged before selling, leading to wine-like notes. They are rich, complex, and full-bodied with noticeable alcohol, but can vary from dry to sweet. Bitterness can be medium to strong.

12. **Speciality Beers**: flavoured

Look: Varies.

Taste: Flavoured speciality beers are beers with a flavour added. They can be similar to other styles in that any beer style can be adapted by a flavour addition to become a speciality beer. They include fruit beers or beers brewed with herbs, spices or other culinary ingredients. The latter can include ginger, coriander, mint, elderflower or ingredients such as honey, coffee, chocolate, vanilla or fortified wines and spirits.

The character of a base beer will influence the final taste of a fruit beer but the wide range of fruit available to brewers means that tastes can vary from sour (typical of lemons and some cherries), to bitter (such as bergamot), through to sweet (such as mango or strawberry).

To help you find your favourite beers more easily we now include beer style information next to each beer listed in the brewery section of the Guide. Please see p625 for more information, or the CAMRA website **camra.org.uk/learn-discover**

TAKING ACTION

Go behind the headlines and see how CAMRA has been campaigning for beer and pubs over the past 12 months.

THE CROOKED HOUSE

On 5 August 2023 the Crooked House – well known as Britain's wonkiest pub – was gutted by fire and the remaining shell of the building was bulldozed shortly after.

The local outpouring of shock and loss soon attracted the attention of the national media and calls were made for this historic gem to be rebuilt. Sorrow turned to anger as it became clear that the pub had been torn down unlawfully.

CAMRA's response was immediate.

Our campaigners met with the Mayor of the West Midlands and the West Midlands Combined Authority to discuss ways to increase their focus on protecting heritage pubs and drew up plans for the 'List Your Local' campaign. This campaign asked West Midlands residents to suggest pubs they believed were of historical significance which, along with CAMRA's target list, were examined on a case-by-case basis to explore all ways they could be protected. Options included local listing, nominating pubs as Assets of Community Value, or community ownership bids. Seventeen pubs even went forward to Heritage England to be considered for heritage listing.

Our network of pub data coordinators, CAMRA members, and members of the public create the UK's most comprehensive pub database by taking the time to submit updates to CAMRA's WhatPub site. This meant we were also able to use this crowdsourced data to raise the profile of unlawful demolitions and conversions across the whole of the UK. Our figures showed that up to a third of conversions and demolitions may be happening without all the required permissions.

CAMRA met with the Housing and Planning Minister to call for legislative changes that would create meaningful penalties for unscrupulous developers, who are currently free to play fast and loose with planning regulations without consequence. We called for Councils to be obligated to investigate reports of pubs being redeveloped without permission, rather than being able to do this at their discretion, and for the creation of a specific offence of illegal demolition of a pub.

Taking the Campaign all the way to Parliament, MP Marco Longhi even brought forward a Private Members Bill, on the protection of heritage public houses.

In April, the brilliant news broke that the owners of the Crooked House had been ordered to rebuild the pub brick-by-brick. This not only means that this unique building should literally rise from the ashes, but also sends a powerful message that enforcement action will be taken in cases like this.

The Crooked House, Himley, was well known as Britain's wonkiest pub

The Crooked House after it was gutted by fire and demolished

The owners have appealed this order, and any hearing on their appeal will be delayed until after the separate court action relating to the fire. Despite the delays CAMRA will keep working to see the building restored to its original, wonky glory.

Shockingly, planning protections in England are still stronger than in Wales and Scotland. CAMRA is calling for similar protections for pubs in the planning system in Wales, and for a tightening of loopholes in Scotland to prevent pubs being allowed to be demolished without planning permission.

HANDPUMP HIJACK

CAMRA has been standing up against misleading practices on the bar too.

This year saw the launch of 'Fresh Ale' from the Carlsberg Marston Brewing Company – one of the world's largest brewing conglomerates.

Part of what makes cask unique is that it doesn't leave the brewery as a finished product. Instead, the conditioning that completes the brewing process is done at the pub, and relies on the skills, timing and experience of the staff and licensee.

On the other hand, most beers, including 'Fresh Ale' are ready to drink when they leave the brewery, making them easier to serve.

Brewers often make both these types of beer, but CAMRA believes they should market them accordingly, so consumers know what they're getting. Unfortunately, 'Fresh Ale' is little more than a deceptive marketing gimmick.

The 'Fresh Ale' product is designed to be served through a handpump, imitating cask, or as Carlsberg Marston Brewing Company put it "preserving the beloved hand pull ritual that delivers the traditional theatre of serve that ale is famed for".

Consumers deserve better than play acting at cask, and CAMRA believes it is a basic consumer right to know what you're getting at the bar.

'Fresh Ale' is simply not a cask beer, and selling it as if it was, by hijacking a handpump, is unfair and misleading to pub-goers.

In response to this insidious handpump hijack CAMRA took the campaign to Trading Standards, calling for them to investigate whether 'Fresh Ale' breached the Consumer Protection from Unfair Trading Regulations 2008.

Despite having acted on misleading dispense in the past, Trading Standards and Trading Standards Scotland responded to let us know that they would be unable to investigate without being first directed by government.

CAMRA took this straight to the then Business Secretary, calling for her to allow Trading Standards to investigate, but this campaign was paused by the calling of a General Election.

Our priority for the new UK Parliament will be to forge new relationships with incoming politicians, and resume working with all parties for pubs, pints and people.

Until then, remember your power as a consumer. Make sure to ask what you're getting at the bar, and if the answer is 'Fresh Ale', choose something else to drink and make sure you let the licensee know why. You won't find any pubs that serve beer in a misleading way in the pages of the Good Beer Guide and soon, hopefully, you won't find them elsewhere either.

To find out more about CAMRA's campaigning activities, please visit **camra.org.uk/take-action**

Be *part* of the CAMRA story

Real ale is just the start...

CAMRA members get more. Join or sign someone up with gift membership and get...

- £30 worth of beer vouchers as a single member
- Discounts on pints at over 3,500 pubs
- Reduced entry to CAMRA beer festivals
- Exclusive partner offers and discounts, plus more...

**Join today
camra.org.uk/join**

Real stories, real people, real ale

Scan me to find out more

The Pubs

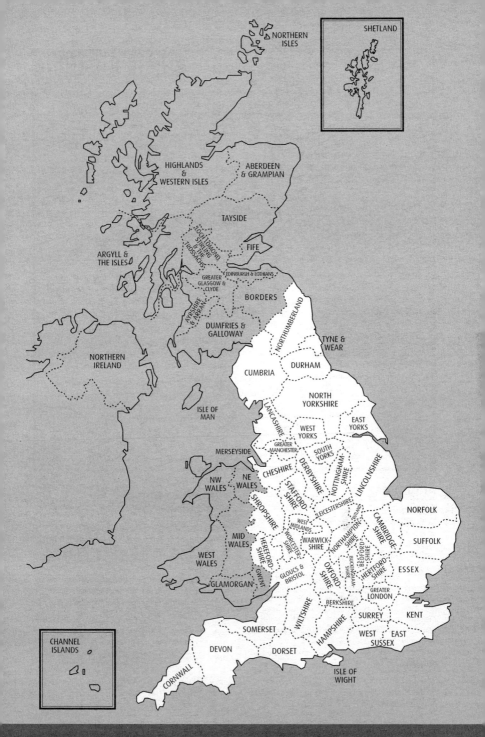

NORTHERN ISLES

SHETLAND

HIGHLANDS & WESTERN ISLES

ABERDEEN & GRAMPIAN

TAYSIDE

LOCH LOMOND STIRLING & THE TROSSACHS

FIFE

ARGYLL & THE ISLES

GREATER GLASGOW & CLYDE

EDINBURGH & LOTHIANS

AYRSHIRE & ARRAN

BORDERS

NORTHERN IRELAND

DUMFRIES & GALLOWAY

ISLE OF MAN

NORTHUMBERLAND

TYNE & WEAR

CUMBRIA

DURHAM

NORTH YORKSHIRE

LANCASHIRE

WEST YORKS

EAST YORKS

MERSEYSIDE

GREATER MANCHESTER

SOUTH YORKS

NW WALES

NE WALES

CHESHIRE

DERBYSHIRE

NOTTINGHAMSHIRE

LINCOLNSHIRE

STAFFORDSHIRE

LEICESTERSHIRE

NORFOLK

SHROPSHIRE

WEST MIDLANDS

WARWICKSHIRE

NORTHAMPTONSHIRE

RUTLAND

CAMBRIDGESHIRE

SUFFOLK

MID WALES

WORCESTERSHIRE

BEDFORDSHIRE

WEST WALES

HEREFORDSHIRE

GWENT

GLOUCS & BRISTOL

OXFORDSHIRE

BUCKINGHAMSHIRE

HERTFORDSHIRE

ESSEX

GLAMORGAN

GREATER LONDON

WILTSHIRE

BERKSHIRE

SURREY

KENT

SOMERSET

HAMPSHIRE

WEST SUSSEX

EAST SUSSEX

DEVON

DORSET

CORNWALL

ISLE OF WIGHT

CHANNEL ISLANDS

England

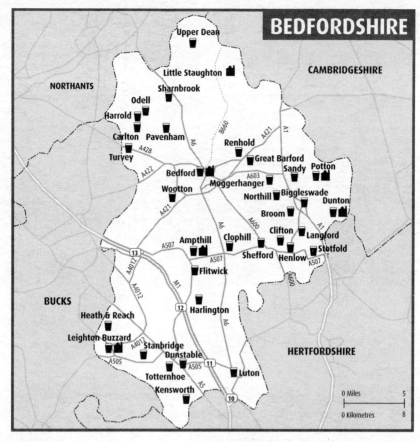

BEDFORDSHIRE

(Map of Bedfordshire showing locations: Upper Dean, Little Staughton, Sharnbrook, Odell, Harrold, Carlton, Pavenham, Turvey, Renhold, Great Barford, Sandy, Potton, Bedford, Wootton, Moggerhanger, Northill, Biggleswade, Dunton, Broom, Clifton, Langford, Ampthill, Clophill, Shefford, Henlow, Stotfold, Flitwick, Harlington, Heath & Reach, Leighton Buzzard, Stanbridge, Dunstable, Totternhoe, Kensworth, Luton, bordered by NORTHANTS, CAMBRIDGESHIRE, BUCKS, HERTFORDSHIRE)

0 Miles 5
0 Kilometres 8

Ampthill

Albion
36 Dunstable Street, MK45 2JT
☎ (01525) 643126
Everards Tiger; 3 changing beers (sourced nationally) Ⓗ
A proper narrow-fronted Victorian pub, which includes one large bar and various handpumps serving Everards Tiger and three or four guest cask ales from other breweries. There are two or three changing craft keg beer taps, as well as ciders. There's a small 'snug' meeting room and secluded patio garden towards the rear. A varied selection of local clubs and groups are supported. ⟡⟡⟡(2,34)⟡⟡⟡

Bedford

Castle Ⓛ
17 Newnham Street, MK40 3JR
☎ (01234) 353295 ⊕ castlebedford.co.uk
Brewpoint Anchorman; 4 changing beers (sourced nationally; often Adnams, Black Sheep, Timothy Taylor) Ⓗ
Lively town pub with a pleasant walled patio garden, close to the town centre and convenient for the Bedford Blues rugby ground. Lunches and light evening meals are served. Current guest beers are listed on the website and social media. Open mic features on a Monday evening, with a quiz and Irish folk music monthly. A guesthouse behind the pub provides five en-suite bedrooms. ⟡⟡⟡⟡⟡⟡⟡⟡⟡⟡⟡

Devonshire Arms Ⓣ Ⓛ ✓
32 Dudley Street, MK40 3TB (1 mile E of town centre S of A4280)
☎ (01234) 301170 ⊕ devonshirearmsbedford.co.uk
Adnams Ghost Ship; Brewpoint Anchorman; Fuller's London Pride; St Austell Tribute; Timothy Taylor Landlord; 1 changing beer (sourced nationally; often Brewpoint) Ⓗ
Pleasant late-Victorian pub in a residential area, a Wells house for over 125 years. The front bar has bare floorboards and an open fire, while there is a separate rear bar. The garden has a gazebo for smokers and a non-smoking paved area covered by a marquee in winter. Beer and cider festivals are held twice a year, and a range of wines is sold. Local CAMRA Town Pub of the Year 2022 and 2024. Q⟡⟡⟡⟡(4)⟡⟡⟡

Pilgrim's Progress ✓
42 Midland Road, MK40 1QB
☎ (01234) 363751
Greene King Abbot; Ruddles Best Bitter; Sharp's Doom Bar; 6 changing beers (sourced nationally) Ⓗ
A former furniture store, this architecturally significant building, on the far side of the pedestrianised area from the High Street, has been converted to a Wetherspoon hotel. The bar was extensively remodelled and is divided into five distinct areas on the ground floor. A mezzanine gives access to the upper (non-smoking) outside area with a garden below. it attracts a wide age range and is a good place from which to watch the world go by. ⟡⟡⟡⟡⟡⟡⟡⟡⟡

Wellington Arms

40-42 Wellington Street, MK40 2JX (N of town centre)
☎ 07340 116929
8 changing beers (sourced regionally) ⓗ

The Welly has been a key part of the local real ale scene for many years. Now free of the Banks & Taylor tie, full use is being made of the freedom to source beers from different breweries. A wide selection of pumpclips and bottles, including some from now closed breweries, is among the breweriana on display. A selection of Belgian and other beers is kept in the fridge. Well worth searching out. Local CAMRA Pub of the Year 2023. ❀❀🐾♫

Biggleswade

Crown Hotel ●

23 High Street, SG18 0JE
☎ (01767) 310510
Greene King Abbot; Ruddles Best Bitter; Sharp's Doom Bar; 3 changing beers (sourced nationally) ⓗ

A relatively small frontage on the High Street belies the deceptively spacious, open-plan interior of this Wetherspoon outlet. The stillage is across a passageway at the front of the building and has a Victorian postbox built into the wall. The walls are adorned with pictures reflecting some of the history of the town. On the eve of each of the chain's beer festivals, CAMRA members are welcomed by the manager for pre-festival tastings. ☎❀❀❐♿🛏️🖵(73,74) 🛜

Golden Pheasant ⓛ ●

71 High Street, SG18 0JH
☎ (01767) 313653 ⊕ goldenpheasantbiggleswade.co.uk
Young's London Original; 3 changing beers (sourced nationally; often Adnams, St Austell, Timothy Taylor) ⓗ

Step down from street level into the single room bar of this historic Grade II listed building, which was originally built in the 18th century and first licensed in 1851. Beams and wooden pillars feature in the pleasantly furnished interior with the serving area to the right of the entrance while, at the rear, is a large patio area. Darts is popular and Sky TV is available for sporting events. A meat raffle is held every Friday evening and there are monthly quizzes. Q❀🛜🚆♣♠🖵❀🛜♫

Broom

Cock ★

23 High Street, SG18 9NA
☎ (01767) 314411 ⊕ thecockinnbroom.com
Greene King Abbot; 3 changing beers (sourced nationally; often Adnams, St Austell, Tring) ⓖ

This Grade II-listed pub has been identified by CAMRA as having a nationally important historic pub interior. Drinks are served directly from the cellar, and include real cider from Apple Cottage. To one side of the serving area are two snug rooms, with a third playing host to traditional pub games. To the other side, past further seating, is a dining room. The courtyard and garden areas are popular in the summer. There is a large field used for camping, classic car meets and the pub's beer and music festivals. Q☎❀❀❐🍴▲♣♠🖵(200) ❀🛜♫

Carlton

Fox ⓨ ⓛ

High Street, MK43 7LA (off Turvey Rd, S of village centre)
☎ (01234) 720235 ⊕ thefoxatcarlton.pub

Potbelly Best; Timothy Taylor Landlord; 2 changing beers (sourced regionally; often Buntingford, Tring, Vale) ⓗ

A charming, thatched community pub with a warm welcome and an attractive garden popular with families. Guest beers are often from local microbreweries. Good-value, home-cooked lunches are served Tuesday to Sunday, and evening meals Tuesday to Saturday. There is a regular Thursday evening quiz. Spring and summer bank holiday festivals are held, plus a sausage and cider festival in April and a gin festival in June. Local CAMRA Pub of the Year 2022 and Community Pub of the Year 2024. Q☎❀❀❐♿♣🖵(25)❀🛜♫

Clifton

Admiral

1 Broad Street, SG17 5RJ
☎ (01462) 811069
Greene King IPA; Morland Old Speckled Hen; 5 changing beers (sourced nationally; often Butcombe, Courage, Young's) ⓗ

Friendly single-room free house dating to 1867, serving a selection of changing beers from six handpumps on the small bar. There is a wood-burning stove for winter warmth and an outdoor patio for finer weather (where the annual June beer festival is held). Two TVs regularly show sporting events, and meat raffles, darts, quiz nights and occasional live music entertain the clientele in this locals' pub. The fourth week of every month features a themed food week. ☎❀❐♣🖵(9A,9B)❀🛜♫

Clophill

Stone Jug ⓨ ⓛ

10 Back Street, MK45 4BY (500yds off A6 at N end of village) TL083381
☎ (01525) 860526 ⊕ stonejug.co.uk
Vale Wychert Ale; 4 changing beers (sourced regionally; often Buntingford, Nethergate, Vale) ⓗ

Originally three 16th-century cottages, this popular village local has an L-shaped bar serving two drinking areas and a family/function room. Excellent home-made lunches are available Tuesday to Saturday. Changing beers are usually from local microbreweries. Picnic benches at the front and a rear patio garden offer outdoor drinking space in fine weather. Parking can be difficult at busy times. A good refreshment stop for the nearby Greensand Ridge Walk. Local CAMRA Pub of the year 2024. Q☎❀❀❐♣🖵(44,MK1)❀

Dunstable

Gary Cooper ●

Grove Park, Court Drive, LU5 4GP
☎ (01582) 471452
Greene King Abbot; Ruddles Best Bitter; Sharp's Doom Bar; 5 changing beers ⓗ

Situated in Grove Park leisure area, not far from the Grove Theatre, is this modern Wetherspoon bar, serving a selection of up to five guest ales, plus the usual range of craft beers. There is a large outdoor patio area overlooking the Grove House gardens. The pub is named

REAL ALE BREWERIES	
Brewpoint ♦	Bedford
Crown 🍺	Little Staughton
Kelchner	Ampthill
Leighton Buzzard	Leighton Buzzard
March Hare 🍺	Dunton
Potton	Potton

after the Hollywood star, who attended the local grammar school between 1910 and 1913. It gets busy at weekends. Many bus routes stop nearby. ☎◖◗⑁☕☆

Globe
43 Winfield Street, LU6 1LS
☎ (01582) 512300
6 changing beers (sourced locally) Ⓗ
Friendly, popular beer destination and community local where the handpumps dispense a good range of six constantly changing microbrewery beers, often local. A range of Belgian beers is also available. Bare boards, bar stools, breweriana and a famous plank at the end of the bar create a traditional town pub atmosphere; the place is buzzing with conversation. It is also dog friendly. A former local CAMRA Pub of the Year.
Q☕⚘(70) ❀☆♪

Victoria ⓛ
69 West Street, LU6 1ST
☎ (01582) 668759
House beer (by Tring); 3 changing beers (sourced nationally) Ⓗ
The Victoria (Vic) is a popular town-centre pub near the police station on West Street. Three varying ales from microbreweries are usually offered, plus house beer Victoria Ale from the local Tring brewery. Darts, dominoes and crib are popular, as well as televised sports in the bar. There is a separate function room available next to the rear courtyard. ☎❀⚘❀♪

Dunton

March Hare Brewpub ⓛ
34 High Street, SG18 8RN
☎ (01767) 318121
Digfield Chiffchaff; March Hare BGB; 3 changing beers (sourced nationally; often March Hare, Nene Valley, Otter) Ⓗ
Standing next to the church in the centre of the village is this local CAMRA Rural Pub of the Year. The beers brewed on the premises by the landlord are kept in excellent condition and there are always two or three available, alongside ales from smaller breweries. The comfortable, spacious interior plays host to quizzes, occasional beer festivals and regular social gatherings, and there is a garden at the side. The pub is poorly served by public transport. ☎❀⚘◖☕(188,189)❀☆♪

Flitwick

Crown
Station Road, MK45 1LA
☎ (01525) 713737 ● crownflitwick.co.uk
4 changing beers (sourced nationally) Ⓗ
Large and thriving two-bar pub where the tenants are very keen on their real ales, with three or four changing ales and a craft keg beer usually available. The front bar has TV, a jukebox, pool and darts, and hosts Saturday evening music nights. There is a large garden with a patio, children's play area and table tennis. Food is served at lunchtimes, but only on Sundays in winter months. ☎❀◖⚘≈P☕(200)❀♪

Great Barford

Anchor Inn ⓛ ✔
High Street, MK44 3LF (by river, 1 mile S of village centre) TL134517
☎ (01234) 870364 ● anchorinngreatbarford.co.uk

Adnams Ghost Ship; Brewpoint Anchorman; 2 changing beers (sourced nationally; often Fuller's, Timothy Taylor) Ⓗ
Busy inn next to the church, looking over a medieval bridge across the River Great Ouse. At least two guest beers are usually available from an extensive range offered by the pub company. Good home-cooked food is served in the bar and restaurant, as well as a fine selection of wines. The pub is popular with river users in the summer. Occasional themed food nights are held, mainly during the winter months. Q☕❀◖◗P☕(27)☆

Harlington

Old Sun
34 Sundon Road, LU5 6LS
☎ 07468 617866
Adnams Ghost Ship; St Austell Tribute, Proper Job; Timothy Taylor Landlord Ⓗ
A traditional, half-timbered, Grade II-listed pub, a short walk from the railway station. The pub dates back to at least 1785 and has two bars, both featuring sports TVs, plus an upper level side room. There is a pleasant garden and patio with an outside bar in summer. Events are held nightly and include quizzes, games and music. It hosts beer festivals on bank holidays in May and August. Q☕❀≈P☕(X42) ❀☆♪

Harrold

Oakley Arms ⓛ
98 High Street, MK43 7BH (next to Harrold Institute)
☎ (01234) 720166 ● theoakleyharrold.co.uk
Tring Ridgeway; 1 changing beer (sourced regionally; often Tring) Ⓗ
Attractive, 400-year-old village inn with a modest bar and large lounge. The various seating areas include a private dining room for up to 10. Board games are available. Food is prepared to order, with a preference for locally sourced ingredients, and the menu varies daily according to what is in season. The ales are usually from Tring or other local microbreweries. There is no car park, but street parking nearby is usually available. ☎❀◖⚘☕(25) ❀☆

Heath & Reach

Axe & Compass ⓛ
23 Leighton Road, LU7 0AA
☎ (01525) 237394 ● theaxeandcompass.pub
2 changing beers (sourced nationally) Ⓗ
This Grade II-listed village community pub has been a free house since 2014. The older front bar, with its low beams, is a lounge and dining area while the rear public bar has gaming machines, pool table and a TV screen. The large garden includes a pétanque court. Regularly appearing guest beers mostly come from local breweries such as Tring, Vale and Chiltern. Accommodation is available in a separate lodge to the rear. ☎❀⌂◖⚘P☕(X4) ❀☆

Henlow

Engineers Arms ⛷ ⓛ
68 High Street, SG16 6AA
☎ (01462) 812284 ● engineersarms.co.uk
10 changing beers (sourced nationally; often Church End, Grainstore, Tring) Ⓗ
Friendly, multi award-winning pub, popular with a wide range of customers. The main bar is usually populated by sports enthusiasts watching the two large screens. To the right is a door leading to a quieter bar containing a library

and games. At the rear is a large patio. Real cider is served, typically from Seacider and The Garden Cider. Tap takeovers, mini beer festivals, trips, poker, quizzes and live music are regular attractions. Bar snacks are available. Local CAMRA Pub of the Year 2024. Q✿✦Å♣●🖫(9B,74) ✿🛈🎵

Kensworth

Farmer's Boy
216 Common Road, LU6 2PJ
☎ (01582) 872207 ⊕ farmersboykensworth.co.uk
Fuller's London Pride; Gale's HSB; 2 changing beers (sourced nationally; often Fuller's) Ⓗ
Located at the Whipsnade Zoo end of the village, this traditional 19th-century pub is well run and has several drinking and dining areas. The feature windows were installed in the 1930s when the pub was purchased by Mann, Crossman and Paulin. It is popular for its food, especially Sunday roasts (booking advisable), with pub classics available in varying portion sizes. Children and pets are welcome, and a large selection of board games is available for use. ✿✦◑♿P🖫(40)✿🛈🎵

Langford

Plough
77 Church Street, SG18 9QA
☎ (01462) 700348
Greene King Abbot; 1 changing beer (sourced nationally; often Purity, Timothy Taylor, Wadworth) Ⓗ
Winner of the local CAMRA Most Improved Pub in 2022, this pub continues to provide a welcoming environment for a strong following of regulars, as well as visitors. Activities include pool, darts, pétanque, quizzes, live music and televised sports, plus a diverse range of events. It features an open-plan design with an L-shaped bar and exposed beams. The large garden accommodates their main beer festival in September, with additional cider, gin and rum festivals held during the course of the year. Burger or pizza nights are provided by visiting food vendors. Real cider from Sheppy's is served. ✿✿♣●P🖫(74)✿🛈🎵

Leighton Buzzard

Bald Buzzard Micropub Ⓛ
6 Hockliffe Street, LU7 1HJ
☎ 07538 903753
2 changing beers (sourced nationally) Ⓖ
Popular micropub that first opened its doors in 2015 and provides the discerning beer enthusiast with a superb selection of ales and cider. It has a bespoke chiller room, and six KeyKeg dispensers serving a constantly changing selection of keg and cask beers not normally found locally. Three ciders are also available, plus a selection of craft, bottled and canned beers. The cosy seating layout encourages conversation. Q✿✿♿♣●🖥🖫(F70,X4)✿

Black Lion
20 High Street, LU7 1EA
☎ (01525) 853725 ⊕ blacklionlb.com
Draught Bass; Nethergate Suffolk County Best Bitter; Vale VPA; 5 changing beers (sourced nationally) Ⓗ
Grade II-listed with 17th-century origins, this traditional alehouse features exposed beams, wooden floors and an open fire. Eight handpumps dispense beers from North Cotswold, Slaters and Purity. Eight changing real ciders are available, and there is an impressive bottled and canned beer menu featuring continental and British beers. Outside is a large paved garden, and a separate

craft bar with 14 keg taps. Bar snacks are served and BYO lunches are welcome. Local CAMRA Pub of the Year from 2015 to 2023. Q✿✿◑♣●🖫(F70,X4)✿

Buckingham Arms
92 Old Road, Linslade, LU7 2RB
☎ (01525) 374665
Morland Old Speckled Hen; Woodforde's Wherry Ⓗ
Traditional two-bar pub on a street corner close to the railway station. Built in the 1830s as the Railway Tavern, its name was changed to the Buckingham Arms in 1848. There is a small, quiet saloon bar at the front and a games-oriented public bar at the rear, with pool, dominoes and darts, plus a largescreen TV and gaming machines. Two regular cask ales are served – Woodforde's Wherry and Morland Old Speckled Hen. Q✿♿≍♣P🖫(F70,L1)✿🛈

Leighton Buzzard Brewing Company Brewery Tap Ⓛ
Unit 31 Harmill Industrial Estate, Grovebury Road, LU7 4FF (2nd left from Grovebury Rd)
☎ 07538 903753 ⊕ leightonbuzzardbrewing.co.uk
6 changing beers (sourced locally; often Kelchner, Leighton Buzzard) Ⓖ
The Brewery Tap of Leighton Buzzard brewery. The brewery's beers are dispensed directly from casks in the cool room, with bottles available to drink on the premises or to take home. A range of guest beers and real cider is also available. Beer can be delivered within Leighton Buzzard and surrounding areas. Brewery comedy nights and live music Saturdays usually take place once a month between March and December (check website for details), often with with local food offerings. ✿♿♣●P🖥🖫(L1)✿🛈🎵

Stag ⬤
1 Heath Road, LU7 3AB
☎ (01525) 372710 ⊕ stagleightonbuzzard.co.uk
4 changing beers (often Fuller's) Ⓗ
A traditional Fuller's pub, a short walk from the town centre, which has a larger interior than its exterior would suggest. The traditional long, wood-panelled bar attracts a good cross-section of drinkers and diners, and serves three Fuller's and one guest beer. Good-value meals are also served daily. The pub holds a quiz night every Tuesday, and occasional bingo evenings. ✿✿◑♣P🖫(L2,L3)✿🛈

Swan Hotel ⬤
50 High Street, LU7 1EA
☎ (01525) 380170
Greene King Abbot; Ruddles Best Bitter; Sharp's Doom Bar; 4 changing beers (sourced nationally) Ⓗ
Grade II-listed former coaching inn and a local landmark which was renovated by Wetherspoon. Friendly service comes from one long bar serving two rooms, a conservatory and a courtyard. Guest beers may feature local microbreweries, and real cider is available in summer months. The hotel also serves good-value food and has 39 guest rooms, so is busy for much of the week. Families are welcome until 11pm. Events include bi-annual beer festivals. Q✿✿✦◑♿🖫(F70,X4)🛈

White Horse
9 New Road, Linslade, LU7 2LS
☎ (01525) 635739 ⊕ whitehorsebandb.co.uk
3 changing beers (sourced nationally) Ⓗ
This is a genuine backstreet free house, close to the Grand Union Canal and the railway station. The L-shaped bar features several sports TV screens, and there is a small courtyard to the rear. Guest beers are often from North Cotswold and Vale. An interesting and varied

selection of bottled and canned beers is also offered. Accommodation comprises seven rooms in a converted stable block. There is a small public car park opposite. ⑤🍴🏠&≉🚗♿😊🛜

Luton

Black Horse 🅛
23 Hastings Street, LU1 5BE
4 changing beers (sourced nationally; often Leighton Buzzard, Oakham, Tring) Ⓗ
Characterful backstreet pub near Luton town centre. The pub is popular with music fans, featuring DJ nights and live bands on Saturday evening, and is usually open until late at weekends. There is a large covered, outdoor seating area for smokers at the rear of the pub. It is also very popular on Luton Town match days as it is the closest ale pub to the Kenilworth Road ground. ⑤🌞≉♣♿P🖥😊♪

Bricklayers Arms 🏆
16-18 High Town Road, LU2 0DD
☎ (01582) 611017
6 changing beers (sourced nationally; often Oakham) Ⓗ
Quirky pub in the High Town that has been run by the same landlady for over 30 years. There are sports TVs in both bars and a popular quiz night is held every Monday. The six handpumps serve a variety of guest beers, with a choice of light, amber and usually a mild. Draught Belgian beers and real ciders are also available. The extension of the outdoor drinking area is a bonus on Luton Town match days. 🌞≉♦🖥(14)😊🛜

Globe ✅
26 Union Street, LU1 3AN
☎ (01582) 482259
3 changing beers (sourced nationally) Ⓗ
Friendly and homely street-corner local, just outside Luton town centre. There is an L-shaped bar offering three constantly changing beers from micro and regional breweries. Sport is shown on several TVs. Food is served on Saturday match days and roasts on Sunday lunchtimes. Occasional beer festivals are held. An enclosed patio area with a function room stands to the rear of the small car park. ⑤🌞&🍴≉♣P😊🛜♪

Great Northern ★
63 Bute Street, LU1 2EY
☎ (01582) 729311
St Austell Tribute Ⓗ
This may be the smallest pub in Luton. Its name was changed in the 1860s when the Great Northern Railway was built right on its doorstep. It still retains Victorian green wall tiles, and has been identified by CAMRA as having a nationally important historic pub interior. St Austell Tribute is regularly served. The front door opens onto a pedestrianised area of the Hat District where occasional live events are held. ≉♣🛜

White House 🅛 ✅
1 Bridge Street, LU1 2NB
☎ (01582) 454608
Greene King Abbot; Ruddles Best Bitter; Sharp's Doom Bar; 6 changing beers (sourced nationally) Ⓗ
A large, two-bar, town-centre Wetherspoon pub with the usual keenly priced food and drinks. There are six different guest ales on the two separate bars. Local ales often include something from Tring or Kelchner breweries. The pub is located in the Galaxy Centre and has a large outdoor drinking area facing St Georges Square. Q⑤🌞&🍴≉🖥😊

Moggerhanger

Guinea ✅
Bedford Road, MK44 3RG
☎ (01767) 640388 ⊕ guineamoggerhanger.co.uk
Adnams Southwold Bitter; 2 changing beers (sourced nationally) Ⓗ
Large 18th-century pub with beamed ceilings, in a prominent position at the heart of the village. There is a garden at the front and car parks at the side and rear. The main bar has a drinking area and two areas beyond for diners. A separate games bar has hood skittles and darts. There is a regular quiz on Thursday. Freshly prepared food is available Tuesday to Saturday, and Sunday lunchtime. Q⑤🌞&🍴&♣P🖥😊♪

Northill

Crown Inn ✅
2 Ickwell Road, SG18 9AA
☎ (01767) 627337 ⊕ crownnorthill.co.uk
Greene King IPA, Abbot; 1 changing beer Ⓗ
Pub/restaurant tucked away between the church and village pond, a stone's throw from the Greensand Ridge Walk. The main bar and its adjoining snug are traditional and welcoming, with antique bay windows, low beams, flagstones and copper-topped counter. The restaurant has a more contemporary and elegant feel. There is a sunny patio and a large garden with children's play area. Freshly-prepared food is served in all areas. The pub can accommodate private functions for up to 60 guests. ⑤🌞🍴&P🖥(74)😊

Odell

Bell
81 High Street, MK43 7AS
☎ (01234) 910850 ⊕ thebellinodell.co.uk
Greene King IPA, Abbot; 3 changing beers (sourced nationally; often Ruddles, St Austell) Ⓗ
Handsome, thatched village pub with a large garden near the River Great Ouse. A series of linked but distinct seating areas helps retain a traditional pub atmosphere. Good-value, quality food includes a Sunday roast, steak and chips Monday evening, pie and chips Tuesday, and fish and chips all day Thursday. Tea and cakes are also available all day. The pub is a popular stop for walkers, with the Harrold-Odell Country Park just down the lane. Local CAMRA Lockdown Hero 2020. Q⑤🌞🍴&P🖥(25)😊🛜♪

Pavenham

Cock
High Street, MK43 7NJ
☎ (01234) 822834 ⊕ thecockatpavenham.co.uk
Marston's 61 Deep, Pedigree; Wainwright Gold; 1 changing beer (sourced nationally; often Draught Bass, Fuller's, Timothy Taylor) Ⓗ
A friendly village pub with a warm welcome and a choice of cask ales. The bar has a late Art Deco look, mirrored in the pub sign outside. The large rear garden connects through a rear gate to the Ouse Valley Way and John Bunyan Trail public footpaths. Food is not available on a regular basis, but there are occasional food-related events such as pie nights. ⑤🌞♣P🖥(25,29)😊🛜

Potton

Rising Sun 🅛 ✅
11 Everton Road, SG19 2PA
☎ (01767) 260231 ⊕ risingsunpotton.co.uk

Eagle Bombardier; 6 changing beers (sourced nationally; often Fyne Ales, Nene Valley, Ossett) Ⓗ
Licensed since 1836, this spacious pub is popular with diners for its well-regarded home-cooked food, as well as being home to many local social groups. Both current and future ales are listed on the pub's website and on a board by the rear entrance. The comfortable interior has numerous separate seating areas, with exposed beams, and music memorabilia and local photos adorning the walls. There is an upstairs function room with a west-facing roof terrace. Q ಎ ❀ ⓓ Ⓐ P ☐ ❀ ☂ ♪

Renhold

Polhill Arms

25 Wilden Road, MK41 0JP (at Salph End)
☎ (01234) 771398 ⏀ polhillarms.co.uk
Hardys & Hansons Bitter; 2 changing beers (sourced nationally; often Greene King, St Austell) Ⓗ
A family-friendly village local with a welcoming atmosphere. It has a large garden and children's play area. Regular events include quiz nights, live music and a monthly meat raffle. The light-bites menu includes ploughman's, home-made soup, paninis and more. The bar has recently been refurbished to create more space without losing the cosy country feel. Local CAMRA Most Improved Pub 2024. ಎ ❀ ⓓ ♣ P ☐ (27) ❀ ☂ ♪

Sandy

Sir William Peel

39 High Street, SG19 1AG
☎ (01767) 843026
Batemans XB; Nethergate Stour Valley Gold; 4 changing beers (sourced nationally) Ⓗ
This welcoming, traditional pub has been taken over and the new management have extended and revitalised the beer range. There are now six handpulled beers, all kept in excellent condition. Changes have also been made to the interior, which now features rare enamel brewery and beer signs. The rear patio and barn are popular and host beer festivals and music events, making the pub an excellent venue. Winner of the local CAMRA Most Improved Pub of the Year 2024. Excellent transport links.
Q ಎ ❀ ⁂ ♣ ♣ P ☐ (72,73) ❀ ☂ ♪

Sharnbrook

Swan With Two Nicks

38 High Street, MK44 1PF
☎ (01234) 781585 ⏀ swanwithtwonicks.com
Adnams Southwold Bitter; Fuller's London Pride; 1 changing beer (sourced nationally) Ⓗ
Friendly village pub with an attractive, enclosed rear courtyard and patio garden. Home-cooked quality lunches and evening meals are served, using locally sourced ingredients where possible and including daily specials and home-made pies. A selection of award-winning wines is available by the glass or bottle. The pub is a good base for local walks and visiting the nature reserves near the River Great Ouse. Walking groups and cyclists are welcome. ಎ ❀ ⓓ P ☐ ❀ ☂ ♪

Shefford

Brewery Tap

14 Northbridge Street, SG17 5DH
☎ (01462) 628448
6 changing beers (sourced nationally; often 3 Brewers of St Albans) Ⓗ
Previously the tap for the now closed B&T brewery, this is primarily a drinkers' pub. Six handpumps feature

changing beers mainly from independent breweries. Light lunches are available on weekdays, and breakfast on Saturday. The wood-panelled, open-plan front bar features breweriana, and there is also a rear area with more seating. The gravel beer garden has ample seating and a covered smoking area with heaters. Car park access is through an archway at the side of the pub.
ಎ ❀ ⓓ ♣ P ☐ ❀ ☂ ♪

Stanbridge

Five Bells

Station Road, LU7 9JF
☎ (01525) 210224 ⏀ fivebellsstanbridge.co.uk
Fuller's London Pride; Gale's Seafarers Ale, HSB Ⓗ
A Fuller's-owned country pub with wooden floors, real fire, cosy snug and low beams. It has a separate 80-seater restaurant in the 18th-century wing, which can be used for weddings and other functions. It is set in extensive and attractive grounds and named after the nearby church which once had five bells but subsequently acquired an additional one.
ಎ ❀ ⓓ � ♣ P ☐ (F70) ❀ ☂

Stotfold

Stag ⊘

35 Brook Street, SG5 4LA
☎ (01462) 731098 ⏀ thestagpubstotfold.co.uk
Adnams Southwold Bitter; Fuller's London Pride; 1 changing beer Ⓗ
The comfortable front bar of this pub is U-shaped, with a longer, quieter area to the right. Three real ale handpulls, plus one serving Saxby's Original cider, face the front door. Large-screen TVs show live sports, and towards the rear of the pub is a dining area where generously sized, good-quality meals are served, with breakfasts at weekends. A dartboard, plus dominoes and cribbage are available. At the rear is a small patio area. The licensees are supporters of charities, many local organisations, and vulnerable local individuals. Local CAMRA Community Pub of the Year. ಎ ❀ ⓓ ♣ P ☐ ♪

Totternhoe

Old Farm Inn ★

16 Church Road, LU6 1RE
☎ (01582) 674053 ⏀ oldfarmpub.com
Dark Star American Pale Ale; Fuller's London Pride; 2 changing beers (sourced nationally) Ⓗ
Charming village pub in the conservation area of Church End, boasting two inglenooks. Dogs are welcome in the front bar and there is a child-friendly garden. There are bingo nights every Monday and quizzes are held on alternate Thursdays. Tasty, home-cooked food is served, including popular Sunday roasts (no food Sun eve) Beer festivals are held at Easter and in May and August.
Q ಎ ❀ ⓓ � ♣ P ☐ (61) ❀ ☂ ♪

Turvey

Three Cranes

High Street, MK43 8EP
☎ (01234) 881365 ⏀ thethreecranes.com
5 changing beers (sourced nationally; often Black Sheep, Eagle, Fuller's) Ⓗ
Comfortable 17th-century coaching inn which reopened in 2014 as a free house offering a good choice of cask beers. A split-level bar provides inviting corners for drinking and conversation. Home-cooked food is served daily in the bar and restaurant, with the kitchen using locally supplied seasonal produce where possible. There

are five luxury bedrooms upstairs. The restaurant is available to hire for private events.
Q ☺ ✿ ⛺ ◖ P ⛟ (41) ☻ 📶 ♫

Upper Dean

Three Compasses ✔

High Street, PE28 0NE (S of village on road to Melchbourne)
☎ (01234) 708346 ⊕ thethreecompasses.co.uk
Greene King IPA; St Austell Tribute; Timothy Taylor Landlord ⊞
Attractive, thatched and partly-boarded pub on the southern edge of the village. The main bar is to the left of the entrance, with a games area behind. A small lounge bar on the right is used mainly for dining, and there is a large garden at the rear. Since reopening the pub several years ago, the current owners have

successfully created a popular rural venue for food and drink. Local CAMRA Most Improved Pub 2019.
☺ ✿ ◖ ♣ P ⛟ (28) ☻ 📶 ♫

Wootton

Chequers

Hall End, MK43 9HP (at NW edge of village) TL001458
⊕ thechequersinnwootton.co.uk
1 changing beer (sourced nationally) ⊞
Originally a farmhouse, this handsome old free house retains a wealth of period features, including heavy wooden beams. The large, pleasant garden is popular in fine weather. A range of meals is available at weekends in the bar and separate restaurant, given a Gallic twist by the French landlord. The menu may feature dedicated seafood days (see Facebook page for details).
Q ☺ ✿ ◖ ◔ ♣ P ✿

Vikki and Mark Stevens receiving the local CAMRA Pub of the Year award at the Stone Jug, Clophill

Public transport information

Leave the car behind and travel to the pub by bus, train, tram or even ferry…

Using public transport is an excellent way to get to the pub, but many people use it irregularly, and systems can be slightly different from place to place. So, below are some useful websites and phone numbers where you can find all the information you might need.
Bus Services: The maximum fare in England will be held at £2 single until the end of 2024.

Combined travel information

The national **Traveline** system gives information on all rail and local bus services throughout England, Scotland and Wales. Calls are put through to a local call centre and if necessary your call will be switched through to a more relevant one. There are also services for mobiles, including a next-bus text service and smart-phone app. The website offers other services including timetables and a journey planner with mapping.

- 0871 200 22 33
  traveline.info

LONDON

In London use Traveline or **Transport for London (TfL)** travel services. TfL provides information and route planning for all of London's Underground and Overground, Docklands Light Railway, National Rail, buses, River Buses, Tramlink. Detailed ticketing information helps you find the most cost-effective ways to travel.

- 0343 222 1234
  tfl.gov.uk

Train travel

National Rail Enquiries covers the whole of Great Britain's rail network and provides service information, ticketing, online journey planning and other information.

- 03457 48 49 50
  nationalrail.co.uk

Coach travel

The two main UK coach companies are **National Express** and **Scottish Citylink**. Between them, they serve everywhere from Cornwall to the Highlands. Their websites offer timetables, journey planning, ticketing, route mapping, and other useful information.

- National Express: 08717 81 81 81
  nationalexpress.com

- Scottish Citylink: 0141 352 4444
  citylink.co.uk

Megabus

(A Stagecoach Company) operate various long-distance services between major cities and towns in England and Scotland, also Cardiff in Wales.

- **uk.megabus.com**

Scottish ferries

Caledonian MacBrayne (CalMac) operate throughout Scotland's islands, stretching from Arran in the south to Lewis in the north.

- 0800 066 5000
  calmac.co.uk

Northern Ireland & islands

For travel outside mainland Britain but within the area of this Guide, information is available from the following companies:

NORTHERN IRELAND

- Translink: 028 9066 6630
  translink.co.uk

ISLE OF MAN

- Isle of Man Transport: 01624 662525
  iombusandrail.im

ISLE OF WIGHT

- Southern Vectus Bus services covering all the Island: 0330 0539 182
  islandbuses.info

JERSEY

- Liberty Bus: 01534 828555
  libertybus.je

GUERNSEY

- Island Coachways: 01481 700456
  buses.gg

Public transport symbols in the Guide

Pub entries in the Guide include helpful symbols to show if there are stations and/or bus routes close to a pub. There are symbols for railway stations (≉); tram or light rail stations (Ⓡ); London Underground, Overground or DLR stations (⊖); and bus routes (🚌). See the 'Key to symbols' on the inside front cover for more details.

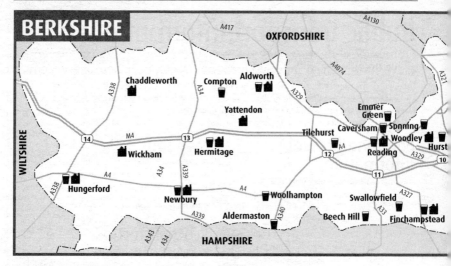

BERKSHIRE

Aldermaston

Aldermaston Recreational Society 🅛

Reading Road, RG7 4PR
☎ (0118) 982 4544 ● recsoc.co.uk
2 changing beers 🄷
On the Hampshire/Berkshire border, this sports and social club is on the site of the AWE facility but operates independently. CAMRA members with a current card are welcome. There are play facilities on a grassy area outside, which is also used for drinking. Two or three handpumps serve mainly local ales. Live events are featured, and food is served. Entry is via the West Gate of AWE with adjacent parking. The bus stop is a 10-minute walk away in Tadley. 🌣🏮🕭🕭⛳🅟🚆♪

Aldworth

Bell Inn 🍺 ★ 🅛

Bell Lane, RG8 9SE (250yds off B4009)
☎ (01635) 578272
Aldworth Five Giants; Amwell Springs Chairman Dave; Arkell's 3B; Indigenous Baldrick; Rebellion Roasted Nuts; 1 changing beer (sourced locally) 🄷
The unspoilt, quirky interior, large beer garden and off-the-beaten track village location make this a popular 'destination' pub that offers a genuine warm welcome to all customers. It now boasts its own on-site microbrewery producing fine ales that are served from the bar. Warm, crusty rolls with various tasty fillings are available at all times. Twice winner of CAMRA's National Pub of the Year award and a consistent Guide entry. Q🌣🏮🕭♣⛳🐾♪

Beech Hill

Elm Tree ✅

Beech Hill Road, RG7 2AZ SU6950364118
☎ (0118) 988 3505 ● theelmtreebeechhill.co.uk
Ringwood Razorback; Timothy Taylor Landlord 🄷
Part pub, part restaurant, the Elm Tree is popular both with locals and those from further afield. The cosy interior of this popular gastropub features open fires, wood beams and a central bar. Spectacular countryside views can be enjoyed from the covered decking. Though food is a major attraction, drinkers are equally welcome at the bar. May close early on Sunday if quiet. 🌣🏮🕭🕭⛳🐾♪🖥

Binfield

Victoria Arms

Terrace Road North, RG42 5JA (100yds S of jct with Tilehurst Ln)
☎ (01344) 483856 ● victoriaarmsbinfield.co.uk
Dark Star Hophead; Fuller's London Pride, ESB; 1 changing beer (sourced nationally; often Fuller's) 🄷
This popular and busy Fuller's local at the centre of the village community offers a warm welcome to all. In winter, an open fire warms the pub, while in summer the terrace and garden offers a great outdoor space. There is an extensive traditional pub menu and food service is to the fore, with a children's menu and Sunday roasts on offer. The garden has a heated marquee, which is available to hire for private functions. 🌣🏮🕭🅟🚆🐾🛜

Bracknell

Cannie Man 🅛 ✅

Bywood, RG12 7RF
☎ (01344) 307620 ● cannieman.co.uk
Dartmoor Legend; Sharp's Doom Bar; 1 changing beer (sourced nationally; often Hogs Back) 🄷
An estate wet-led pub where good beer is given top priority with four handpumps serving a session bitter, a local ale and guests. Largescreen TVs in the L-shaped bar show sporting events and there is frequent live music. The landlady prides herself on offering a warm welcome to all. The pub supports many sports teams and its charity fundraising is renowned for supporting local people and community projects. 🌣♣⛳🅟🚆(171,172)🐾🛜♪

Newtown Pippin 🍺 🅛

Ralphs Ride, Harmans Water, RG12 9LR
☎ (01344) 426298 ● thenewtownpippin.com
3 changing beers (sourced nationally; often Purity, Rebellion, Windsor & Eton) 🄷
A two-bar pub that is a genuine local asset, highly valued by the community. Up to three real ales from local and regional breweries are served. Home-made food is available lunchtimes and evenings and includes gluten-free and vegan options. Outside are patio areas with benches and a surrounding garden, allowing for alfresco dining and drinking. Regular quiz nights, live music, themed events and occasional beer festivals are all hosted, plus regular charity fundraising for local and national charities. A function room is available for hire. Current local CAMRA Pub of the Year. 🌣🏮🕭♣🚆🐾🛜♪

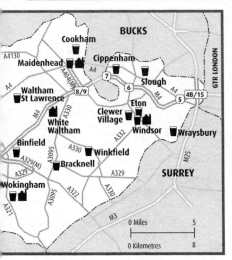

Old Manor 🍺 ✓
Grenville Place, RG12 1BP (at College roundabout jct with Church Rd)
☎ (01344) 304490
Greene King Abbot; Ruddles Best Bitter; Sharp's Doom Bar; 5 changing beers (sourced nationally; often Loddon, Rebellion, Windsor & Eton) 🅗
Weatherspoon pub occupying a building that dates from Tudor times, containing several historic features including its own priest hole. It is a favourite with locals of all ages and has been in the Guide for over 20 years. It has a variety of indoor and outdoor drinking areas, and an excellent range of regular changing guest beers supplement their regular offerings, all served by friendly and knowledgeable staff who are always welcome to suggestions for new beers. Parking on-site is in a Pay & Display car park. 🛏️🍴🍽️❤♿🅿🚆🛜

Caversham

Clifton Arms
12 Gosbrook Road, RG4 8BS
☎ (0118) 947 1775
Brakspear Gravity; 1 changing beer 🅗
A local Brakspear pub in the heart of Caversham, run by the same landlady since 1995. Entertainment is available in the form of a jukebox and most sporting events are shown on one of three TVs. Their pool and darts teams compete in the local leagues. It has a covered and heated smoking area. 🛏️🍴🍽️❤🍴♣🅿🚆🛜🎵

Fox & Hounds 🍺 🍺
51 Gosbrook Road, RG4 8BN
☎ 07915 540926 🌐 thefoxcaversham.com
6 changing beers (often Oakham, Siren, Wild Weather) 🅗
A popular and lively community hub, offering six changing beers and eight craft keg lines from local and independent breweries, plus up to four ciders and perries and a good selection of cans and bottles. Extensive outside areas are covered and heated. A blue plaque commemorates the day in 1960 that John Lennon and Paul McCartney performed a gig here as the Nerk Twins. 🛏️🍴🍽️♣❤🅿🚆🛜🎵

Griffin 🍺
10-12 Church Road, RG4 7AD
☎ (0118) 947 5018

Greene King IPA, Abbot; 3 changing beers (often Loddon, Rebellion) 🅗
There has been a pub on this site since the 1800s, with the current building dating from 1916. It is convenient for Caversham town centre, and therefore gets busy, but it is surprisingly spacious inside. A heated rear patio garden offers level access. An extensive Chef and Brewer menu is available all day, with specials on chalkboards. 🛏️🍴🍽️♿🅿🚆🛜🎵

Cippenham

Barleycorn 🍺
151 Lower Cippenham Lane, SL1 5DS
☎ (01628) 603115
Rebellion IPA; 3 changing beers 🅗
A cosy, traditional, single-bar pub, with seating on one side and a pool table on the other, catering for a strong local following. Four guest beers include one from Rebellion and another local brewery, plus two nationals. In the summer they also offer real and fruit ciders. A large collection of bottles and jugs is displayed on the walls. Occasional live music and two sports TVs provide the entertainment. The nearby public car park is free. 🍴♣🅿🚆(5) ❤🛜🎵

Clewer Village

Swan 🍺
9 Mill Lane, SL4 5JG
☎ 07458 300026 🌐 theswanwindsor.co.uk
Windsor & Eton Guardsman; 2 changing beers (sourced regionally; often Windsor & Eton) 🅗
Just 15 minutes' walk from Windsor town centre, this 18th-century village free house has been renovated following a closure of over three years. Purchased as a community interest company, it has become the hub of the village and now provides coffee mornings, cribbage, quiz nights, a cycle hub, occasional music and a book club. Major renovations are now completed and the new kitchen serves freshly cooked food. 🅠🛏️🍴🍽️♿❤🚆(8,702) ❤🛜🎵

Compton

Swan at Compton
High Street, RG20 6NJ
☎ (01635) 885700

Hardys & Hansons Olde Trip; Morland Original Bitter; Timothy Taylor Landlord Ⓗ
This popular village pub reverted to its original name in 2023, after four years as the Foinavon under previous management. There are several extensive bar areas, one with a grand piano, and there is also a real fire. Food is served in the bar and in the spacious restaurant. The large beer garden, accessed from the car park and rear entrance, includes an outdoor climbing frame, slide and swings. ≿⊛⋈⋈①♣P♈

Cookham

Old Swan Uppers
The Pound, SL6 9QE
☎ (01628) 523573 ⊕ theoldswanuppers.co.uk
Fuller's London Pride; Rebellion IPA Ⓗ
Friendly, cosy pub with flagstone floors and a wood-burning stove. Its name stems from the ancient activity of 'Swan Upping' or marking of the swans on the River Thames. The front bar accommodates drinkers, with a separate restaurant and lounge to the rear. Food comes from a traditional pub menu (burgers, fish & chips, pies, steaks) and a tapas-style menu of around 20 dishes.
≿⊛①⇌P♈(7) ♠♥

Emmer Green

Black Horse
16 Kidmore End Road, RG4 8SE (just off B481, next door to Village Tandoori restaurant)
☎ (0118) 947 4111
Courage Best Bitter; Young's London Original; 1 changing beer (sourced nationally; often Sharp's) Ⓗ
Well-kept two-bar local with a pool table and sports TV in its public bar, while the quieter lounge bar has a real fire. You can sit outside the front, or in the enclosed rear patio. The pub has been run by the same licensee for many years, ensuring a timeless continuity. The pub moved to its present site before 1870, allegedly to remove temptation from the nearby chapel-goers at its original location in old Peppard Road. In Victorian times the pub yard doubled as the local fire station.
Q⊛♣♈♥♠♥♪

Eton

George Inn Ⓛ ✔
77 High Street, SL4 6AF
☎ (01753) 861797 ⊕ georgeinn-eton.co.uk
Windsor & Eton Knight of the Garter, Windsor Knot, Guardsman; 2 changing beers (sourced locally; often Windsor & Eton) Ⓗ
Windsor & Eton brewery's first pub is popular with tourists and locals alike. It hosts six of the brewery's ales, the range subject to change when special or seasonal ales become available. Wooden floors and lighting supplied by carriage lamps and candles help to create a warm, comfortable ambience. Breakfast is served every day. There is a quiz every Wednesday. The Hop House, a separate building in the beer garden, is available for private functions. Accommodation is in eight en-suite rooms.
Q≿⊛⋈①⇌(Windsor & Eton Riverside) ♈(15) ♠♥

Finchampstead

Elusive Brewing Tap Room Ⓛ
Unit 5, Marino Way, Hogwood Industrial Estate, RG40 4RF
☎ (0118) 973 2153 ⊕ elusivebrewing.com

Elusive Microball, Level Up, Oregon Trail, Spellbinder; 8 changing beers (sourced nationally) Ⓗ
New and improved taproom for this award-winning, innovative microbrewery established in 2016 on an industrial estate. Seven KeyKeg taps and one handpull showcase their own excellent brews, and there are also many brewery collaborations and tap takeovers. During warmer months covered tables are set up outside. Retro video games can be played for free. Cans, bottles and growler-fills are available to take away. Check in advance for latest opening times. Card payment only.
Q≿⊛P♈(3) ♠♥

Hermitage

Fox Inn Ⓛ ✔
High Street, RG18 9RB (on B4009 at jct with Yattendon Rd)
☎ (01635) 200772 ⊕ thefoxhermitage.com
Renegade Good Old Boy; Sharp's Doom Bar; Timothy Taylor Landlord; 2 changing beers (often Courage, Wadworth) Ⓗ
A popular, welcoming village pub converted from three artisan cottages dating from the 16th century. It has a restaurant and a bar, and drinking/eating areas with real fires, plus a covered outside area. The Fox shares its name with a book by D. H. Lawrence, who briefly lived in the village at the end of World War I. Traditional, home-cooked food is available in generous portions. Dogs are welcome except in the restaurant area. The main bar areas can be reserved for private functions.
≿⊛①&♣♈(6,6A) ♠♥♪

Hungerford

Hungerford Club ✔
3 The Croft, RG17 0HY (on foot via Church Ln, by road via Church St and Croft Rd)
☎ (01488) 682357 ⊕ hungerford-club.co.uk
Fuller's London Pride; 2 changing beers (sourced nationally) Ⓗ
A friendly sports and social club in the quiet Croft, just a short distance from the High Street. Three cask ales are usually available, two of which are changing guests. Indoor games include darts and snooker. Hot food is served at the weekend and comprises Friday steak nights, Saturday brunch, and Sunday roasts. Cold snacks are available on weekday lunchtimes. An annual beer festival is held over the August bank holiday. CAMRA members are welcome. Q≿⊛⇌♣P♈♥

John O'Gaunt Ⓛ
21 Bridge Street, RG17 0EG (30yds N of canal bridge)
☎ (01488) 683535 ⊕ john-o-gaunt-hungerford.co.uk
House beer (by INNformal); 7 changing beers (sourced regionally; often Siren) Ⓗ
A 16th-century listed town-centre free house and brew pub which has been sympathetically restored, keeping many original features. There are up to eight cask ales on offer, half of which are from the pub's own brewery, INNformal. The range changes constantly and is complemented by up to 10 real ciders. Outside are heated Tiki tents and a seated garden area with a bar and kitchen. Food is available lunchtimes and evenings and all day at weekends. Q≿⊛①⇌♣♣P♈♠♥

Hurst

Castle Inn Ⓛ
Church Hill, RG10 0SJ
☎ (0118) 934 0034 ⊕ castlehurst.co.uk
3 changing beers (sourced locally) Ⓗ

Parts of this free house, owned by the church opposite, date back to the 10th century. It provides good beer and good food. There are three changing ales on handpumps, with at least one Rebellion and one other local cask ale. Access to the garden is between the pub and the neighbouring bowling green, and there's an outside bar during summer. It may close early if quiet, so check in advance. Q ♿ 🍴 ◐ ♣ P ☐ (129) 🐾 ❄ 🛜

Maidenhead

A Hoppy Place Maidenhead 🍷 🅻

Units 1-3, Trinity Place, Park Street, SL6 1TJ
☎ (01753) 206802 🌐 ahoppyplace.co.uk
Siren Broken Dream Breakfast Stout; Stardust English Bitter; 2 changing beers (often Howling Hops, Verdant) 🄷
A beer emporium that opened in 2022, with four cask lines, 14 keg lines, four types of traditional cider, and over 150 chilled cans and bottles. Food is available to eat in from Knead Napolean Pizzeria. There is lots of seating inside, and more outside, as well as plenty of standing room. They offer 10% off all product with their 'A Hoppy Friend' membership card. Local CAMRA Pub of the Year 2023 and 2024. ♿ 🐾 ♿ ≉ ♥ P 🐾 🛜

Bear 🅻 ✅

8-10 High Street, SL6 1QJ
☎ (01628) 763030
Greene King IPA, Abbot; Sharp's Doom Bar; 3 changing beers (sourced nationally) 🄷
A short walk from the town hall, this former coaching inn became a Wetherspoon in 2010. It has an open-plan bar, with several different seating areas, including a licensed outside area to the front. There is additional seating on the upper floor. The 10 handpumps dispense up to six guest ales, many from local breweries, plus ciders are available. Only assistance dogs are allowed on the premises. ♿ 🐾 ◐ ♿ ≉ ♥ 🛜

Craufurd Arms 🅻

15 Gringer Hill, SL6 7LY
☎ (01628) 675410 🌐 craufurdarms.com
Rebellion IPA; 3 changing beers (sourced locally; often Stardust, Windsor & Eton) 🄷
This pint-sized local, well known for its friendly atmosphere and selection of local real and craft ales, is the 50th community owned pub in the country. The building dates back to the 1800s and is just outside the town centre. It hosts activities including cribbage (Mon), darts (Wed), quiz (Thu), live music (Fri and Sat). Two TV screens show live sports. Evening meals are served on Friday and Saturday only. A former local CAMRA Pub of the Year. ♿ 🐾 ◐ ≉ (Furze Platt) ♣ P ☐ (9) 🐾 🛜 ♫

Maiden's Head 🅻

34 High Street, SL6 1QE
☎ (01628) 784786 🌐 themaidenshead.co.uk
4 changing beers (often Rebellion, Stardust, Windsor & Eton) 🄷
Large single-room town-centre pub, with separate seating areas. It offers four constantly rotating guest ales, with an emphasis on local breweries, plus keg craft beers, as well as a range of world bottled beers. Food is served, including locally sourced beef burgers, chicken and wraps. Outside, there is a large beer garden at the back of the pub. Terrestrial TV shows some events and live music is hosted at the weekend. Dogs are welcome outside. ♿ 🐾 ◐ ♿ ≉ ♣ ♥ 🛜 ♫

North Star 🅻

91 Westborough Road, SL6 4AP
☎ (01628) 622711

Timothy Taylor Landlord; 1 changing beer (sourced locally) 🄷
A friendly, traditional, back-street pub with two bars: a busy public bar with TV and darts, and a lovely, quiet lounge. It is an Asset of Community Value (ACV) with the local council. Darts and cribbage are played, and there is a quiz every other Thursday evening. Occasional live bands also feature. There is a patio area to the front of the pub. Q ♿ 🐾 ♣ ☐ (3) 🐾 🛜 ♫

Newbury

Bowler's Arms

Enborne Street, Wash Common, RG14 6TW (between Enborne Lodge Ln and Wheatlands Ln)
☎ (01635) 47658 🌐 thebowlersarms.co.uk
Fuller's London Pride; St Austell Tribute; Timothy Taylor Landlord 🄷
Located within the clubhouse for Falkland Cricket Club, the modern, open-plan bar area caters for drinkers, diners and community activities. There are TV screens for sporting events and a pool table, and outside seating at ground-floor and first-floor levels allow views over the cricket pitch. A seasonal menu includes toasted sandwiches at lunchtimes. The pub is good base for local walks and for visiting the nearby Civil War battlefield. ♿ 🐾 ◐ ♿ ♣ P ☐ (2) 🛜

Catherine Wheel 🅻

35 Cheap Street, RG14 5DB
☎ (01635) 569897 🌐 thecatherinewheel.com
6 changing beers (sourced regionally; often Loddon, Sherfield Village, Wild Weather) 🄷
Popular and lively town-centre pub, with six beers on handpumps, always including local ales. A blackboard lists draught ciders, and there are bottled ciders in the fridge, as well as a range of non-alcoholic and other drinks. The partly covered courtyard area features a cocktail bar. A Pieminister-based menu includes vegetarian/vegan and other pub grub options. Several live music events are held every month, and there are annual beer festivals, including one over Easter. A six-time winner of the local CAMRA Cider Pub of the Year. ♿ 🐾 ◐ ≉ ♣ ♥ 🐾 🛜 ♫

Cow & Cask 🅻

1 Inches Yard, Market Street, RG14 5DP (SE of pedestrian crossing at corner of Market St and Bartholomew St)
☎ 07517 658071
3 changing beers (sourced regionally; often Indigenous, Loddon, XT) 🄶
Berkshire's first micropub – now 10 years old – is a friendly little establishment in a quiet, town-centre location, where conversation flourishes. The focus is on local breweries, and over 840 different beers have been served since opening. Breweries often featured include Indigenous, Loddon, Ramsbury and Vale. Three cask beers and one keg are usually available, with a good range of local ciders, plus non-alcoholic options, bottled beers, wine and spirits. Q ≉ ♣ ♥ ☐ (2,LINK) 🐾

Hatchet Inn 🅻 ✅

12 Market Place, RG14 5BD
☎ (01635) 277560
Greene King Abbot; Ruddles Best Bitter; Sharp's Doom Bar; 5 changing beers (sourced nationally; often Loddon, Stonehenge) 🄷
This Grade II-listed Wetherspoon hotel, opened in 2011, overlooks the pedestrianised Market Place. Ales are served from two sets of handpumps positioned at each end of the bar, with boxed real cider in the fridge behind. There are outside tables at the front, and a large rear

patio offers a variety of seating options. Regular beer and cider festivals are held, and food is available all day, including breakfast. Q♿🏡🅿🍴◑🕑♿🚲🚉🌳🛜

Lion ✅

39 West Street, RG14 1BD
☎ (01635) 528468 ⊕ thelionatnewbury.co.uk
Wadworth 6X, Horizon; 5 changing beers (sourced nationally; often Oakham, Rudgate, Tiny Rebel) Ⓗ
This popular back-street local was rebuilt in 1988 by Wadworth brewery to replace the previous Lion pub. It has gone from strength to strength under the stewardship of a father and son team since 2019. Up to four nationally sourced guest beers may be available and an occasional guest cider. Tex-Mex food is served Thursdays to Sundays until 9pm. Regular live music features, and there is a popular quiz on Thursdays. Sport is shown on several TV screens. ♿🏡◑🚲🌳🛒♿🛜🎵

Lock, Stock & Barrel

104 Northbrook Street, RG14 1AA (in alleyway 20yds NW of canal bridge)
☎ (01635) 580550 ⊕ lockstockandbarrelnewbury.co.uk
Fuller's London Pride, ESB; 1 changing beer (sourced regionally; often Dark Star, Fuller's) Ⓗ
Just off Newbury's main shopping street, next to the Kennet and Avon Canal, this popular, comfortably furnished pub with an open-plan interior. The attractive setting makes the garden popular on sunny days. In addition to London Pride and ESB, Fuller's seasonal beers and one or two guest beers are usually available. Traditional, freshly cooked pub classics are served until 8pm Tuesdays to Saturdays and until 5pm Sundays and Mondays. Occasional live music is featured and Six Nations rugby is shown on TV. ♿🏡◑&🚲🛒♿🛜🎵

Reading

Alehouse Ⓛ

2 Broad Street, RG1 2BH
☎ (0118) 950 8119
9 changing beers (sourced locally) Ⓗ
Popular drinking establishment which always leaves an impression on visitors with its quirky wooden fixtures and reclaimed wooden floor. As a champion of microbreweries, both local and further afield, rare and unusual ales are frequently found on the pumps. A selection of real ciders, perries and mead is also available. It is often busy around the bar area, but those wishing for a more peaceful drink can take advantage of the secluded snugs at the back of the pub.
♿🚲Θ♠◑🛒♿

Allied Arms Ⓛ

57 St Mary's Butts, RG1 2LG
☎ (0118) 958 3323 ⊕ allied-arms.co.uk
Loddon Hullabaloo; 4 changing beers Ⓗ
A town-centre pub dating from around 1828, with two cosy bars entered through the side passage, not the front door. A range of up to 10 ales is available each weekend. The large walled garden is a popular refuge from the bustle of the town, with patio heaters for colder nights. A wide and interesting selection of music is available on the jukebox. The pub hosts a regular charity quiz.
♿🏡🚲Θ♠🛒♿🛜

Foresters Arms Ⓛ

79-81 Brunswick Street, RG1 6NY
☎ (0118) 304 3648
Timothy Taylor Landlord; 3 changing beers (often Rebellion) Ⓗ
This pub was reopened following a complete refurbishment that knocked the two bars into one while

retaining the old side corridor. It has a traditional feel and is more popular than ever with local residents. Usually three ales are available. The rear garden is a pleasant suntrap on summer evenings.
♿🏡&🚲(West)♠🛒♿🛜🎵

Hop Leaf

163-165 Southampton Street, RG1 2QZ
☎ (0118) 931 4700
Downton New Forest Ale; Hop Back Crop Circle, Summer Lightning; 2 changing beers (sourced regionally; often Hop Back) Ⓗ
A traditional, beer-focused pub with a warm and welcoming atmosphere. Most of the Hop Back core range is usually available, as well as a couple of ciders. A good selection of pub games such as bar billiards, darts, crib and backgammon are available alongside a growing and eclectic mix of board games. ♿♠♿🚲(5,6A)♿🛜

Nag's Head Ⓛ

5 Russell Street, RG1 7XD
☎ 07765 880137 ⊕ thenagsheadreading.co.uk
12 changing beers Ⓗ
With a wide range of real ales, real cider and perry always on offer, visitors are sure to find something to suit their taste here. There is also a craft beer wall, with vessel and dispense clearly indicated on the adjacent blackboard. A selection of board games is available for those wanting to while away a few sociable hours. The pub gets busy on Reading FC match days. Basic hot food (toasties, sausage rolls, pulled pork or beef rolls) is available. ♿🏡◑🚲(West)Θ♠🛒♿🛜🎵

Retreat ★ ✅

8 St John's Street, RG1 4EH
☎ (0118) 957 2130 ⊕ theretreat.pub
Harvey's Sussex Best Bitter; 4 changing beers (often Butcombe, Sharp's) Ⓗ
This much-loved back-street boozer was refurbished in 2020/21. A good range of real ales are squeezed onto the small bar. The landlord tends to concentrate on well-known regional brands, though there is a good range of interesting options available in bottled form, including continental beers, as well as a number of ciders. It is renowned locally for its regular live music and hosts various events (including a pickled onion competition).
Q♿◑&♠🛒🎵

Three Guineas

Station Approach, RG1 1LY
☎ (0118) 957 2743 ⊕ three-guineas.co.uk
Fuller's Oliver's Island, London Pride, ESB; Gale's Seafarers Ale; 4 changing beers (often Butcombe, Windsor & Eton) Ⓗ
A Grade II-listed pub in the old ticket hall of Reading railway station. It was completely refurbished by Fuller's a few years ago and features ornate tiling, old railway memorabilia and a selection of classic clocks. There's a large outdoor seating area in front, but you cannot access the platforms directly, so make sure you leave enough time for your train! ♿🏡◑&🚲Θ🛒♿🛜

Slough

Moon & Spoon Ⓛ ✅

86 High Street, SL1 1EL (close to jct with Windsor Rd)
☎ (01753) 531650
Greene King Abbot; Ruddles Best Bitter; Sharp's Doom Bar; 4 changing beers (sourced nationally) Ⓗ
This Wetherspoon establishment has 12 handpumps offering three regulars beers, accompanied by up to four changing guest ales, including one from a local brewery. A couple of ciders are also usually available, often Old

Rosie and Black Dragon. At the entrance is an eye-catching sculpture made of 1,148 spoons. The usual Wetherspoon all-day food menu is served. The rear of the pub has a cosy feel with separated seating areas and an interesting ceiling light feature. ♿🍴🕹♿⮌♿🚪(8,2)🅿🛜

Sonning

Bull Inn
High Street, RG4 6UP (next to St Andrew's Church)
☎ (0118) 969 3901 ⊕ bullinnsonning.co.uk
Dark Star Hophead; Fuller's London Pride; Gale's HSB; 1 changing beer (sourced nationally) Ⓗ
This delightful and characterful 16th-century pub is leased to Fuller's by the adjacent church. Most of the interior is set for dining, but there is a separate Village Bar drinking area, also used as a function room. The regular beers and changing guests are mainly from the Fuller's range. An excellent selection of quality food, from snacks to fine dining, is available daily. A good stop-off for those taking a walk alongside the Thames.
Q♿🕹⊛♿🚪🅿♿🛜♪

Swallowfield

George & Dragon Ⓛ
Church Road, RG7 1TJ
☎ (0118) 988 4432 ⊕ georgedragonpub.com
Siren Yu Lu; Timothy Taylor Landlord; 1 changing beer (often Siren) Ⓗ
Just outside Swallowfield centre itself, this 17th-century Grade II-listed pub was recently taken over by nearby Siren Craft Brew. The relaxed country gastropub serves real ales, excellent wines and good food. Tables are mainly set for dining but drinkers are more than welcome, with up to three cask ales available.
♿⊛🕹🅿♿🛜

Tilehurst

Fox & Hounds
116 City Road, RG31 5SB
☎ (0118) 942 2982 ⊕ thefoxandhoundstilehurst.co.uk
Timothy Taylor Landlord Ⓗ**; 2 changing beers (often Butcombe, Purity)** Ⓗ/Ⓖ
Right on the edge of Tilehurst, this low-beamed village pub is popular with locals and visitors walking open fields to Sulham Woods via the dovecote tower at Nunhide Manor. It is worth visiting in all weathers, with a dartboard and pool table, a garden gazebo, a conservatory and a recently-uncovered fireplace now containing a wood-burning stove.
♿⊛♿♣♿🅿🚪(33)🛜♪

Victoria Ⓛ
1 Norcot Road, RG30 6BP
☎ (0118) 941 5064
Rebellion IPA; 2 changing beers (sourced nationally; often Timothy Taylor, Theakston) Ⓗ
Formerly a Blatch's of Theale establishment called the White House, this pub was extensively refurbished in 2014, with the addition of a conservatory, and scenes of historic Reading displayed throughout. It now serves food, including excellent Sunday roasts (booking advisable), and real ale. It was the winner of Reading Chronicle's Pub of the Year Award in 2022. Buses stop right outside or just around the corner of the adjacent road junction. ♿⊛🕹♿♣♿🅿🚪(17)♿🛜♪

Waltham St Lawrence

Bell ★ Ⓛ
The Street, RG10 0JJ
☎ (0118) 934 1788 ⊕ thebellwalthamstlawrence.co.uk
Loddon Hoppit; 4 changing beers (often Loose Cannon, Stardust) Ⓗ
A classic half-timbered 14th-century pub, bequeathed to the village in 1608 by Sir Ralph Newbury. It doubles as the village local, promoting real ales from small independent breweries, and a quality restaurant, producing exceptionally good food from fresh, seasonal ingredients. It also offers up to eight ciders and perries served from their cellar. You'll find log fires in the winter and a good-sized beer garden for sunny summer days.
Q♿🕹⊛♿♣♿🚪(234)♿🛜♪

Windsor

A Hoppy Place Ⓛ
11 St Leonard's Road, SL4 3BN
☎ (01753) 206802 ⊕ ahoppyplace.co.uk
2 changing beers (sourced locally; often Stardust) Ⓟ
Windsor's first micropub, twice winner of local CAMRA Pub of the Year. In addition to the two casks, there are 11 keg lines, plus six ciders on tap. A highlight are the five fridges of bottled and canned beer which are arranged by beer style, including one fridge for cider and many alcohol-free options. The pub has a canning machine to can cask and keg beer for a takeaway. There is also a retro games console for customers to play on.
⊛⇌(Windsor & Eton Central) ♣♿🚪♿🛜

Carpenters Arms
4 Market Street, SL4 1PB
☎ (01753) 863739
St Austell Nicholson's Pale Ale; Sharp's Doom Bar; 4 changing beers (sourced nationally) Ⓗ
Situated on a narrow cobbled street close to the castle, this excellent Nicholson's pub has been voted local CAMRA Pub of the Year several times. The elegantly decorated interior is on three levels, the lowest of which is reputed to house a passageway to the castle. Ashby's brewery tiles are on the floor by the entrance, harking back to the pub's former owners. The two regular beers are supplemented by four interesting guests, often including something dark.
♿🕹⇌(Windsor & Eton Central) 🚪🛜

Windsor & Eton Brewery Unit 4 Taproom Ⓛ
4 Vansittart Estate, Duke Street, SL4 1SE
☎ (01753) 392495 ⊕ webrew.co.uk
Windsor & Eton Knight of the Garter, Windsor Knot, Guardsman; 5 changing beers (sourced regionally; often Windsor & Eton) Ⓗ
Newly opened in 2021, the brewery taproom features eight handpumps dispensing six of their beers, plus two guests and 22 keg lines. There is also Devon Red cider by Sandford Orchards, plus one other, and an interesting range of cans and bottles. The decor is modern and relaxing, and includes a mezzanine floor and a stage for events. Regular brewery tours are available, and tasty pub grub.
♿⊛🕹♿⇌(Windsor & Eton Central) ♿🅿🚪♿🛜

Windsor Trooper ✪
97 St Leonards Road, SL4 3BZ
☎ (01753) 670122 ⊕ thewindsortrooper.com
Adnams Southwold Bitter; Oakham Citra; 3 changing beers (sourced regionally) Ⓗ

Popular pub within walking distance of Windsor town centre. It has been pleasantly refurbished in traditional style with a collection of original brewery mirrors. Five cask beers are available plus nine traditional ciders. There is a large room at the rear that also serves as a function room and venue for Thursday night live music. Outside is a sizeable beer garden. Accommodation is available in nine en-suite rooms. Local CAMRA Cider Pub of the Year 2023 and 2024.
✿🛏🍴🕽≠(Windsor & Eton Central) ●🖪🌢🛜♬

Winkfield

Duke of Edinburgh ✔
Woodside Road, SL4 2DP (off Woodside Rd, 150yds N of A332) SU928709
☎ (01344) 882736 🌐 thedukeofedinburgh.com
Arkell's 3B, Hoperation IPA; 1 changing beer (often Arkell's) Ⓗ
This Arkell's tied house, near Ascot Racecourse, is over 200 years old and has been run by the same licensees since 1998. The low beams give it a cosy atmosphere and customers can choose from a wide variety of food on offer. Mottos and proverbs adorn the walls, and one corner features football memorabilia. There are two TVs in the lounge area showing football matches and other sporting events. Note that it can get busy on race days.
✿🕽&♣P🌢🛜

Wokingham

Crispin Ⓛ
45 Denmark Street, RG40 2AY (opp Denmark St car park)
☎ (0118) 978 0309
Hogs Back TEA; Rebellion Overthrow; 1 changing beer (sourced regionally; often Stardust) Ⓗ
A traditional, cosy, real ale and cider pub named after the patron saint of cobblers, championing LocAle and friendly conversation. Regular charity events are held and occasional beer festivals in the garden, which has covered seating. The pub does not serve food, but plates and cutlery are provided to consume your own food with a drink purchased from the bar. Closes early evening Sunday to Wednesday. 🏃✿≠♣🗍🖪🌢🛜♬

Outhouse Brewery Ⓛ
Unit 4, Southgate House, Alexandra Court, RG40 2SL
🌐 theouthousebrewery.com
4 changing beers (sourced locally; often Outhouse)
Town-centre brewery and taproom with the brewing equipment on display. Beers served from a tap wall are unfiltered and unpasturised from membrane kegs. The bar staff are knowledgeable and will happily provide guidance. There is plenty indoor seating plus a small outdoor eating area. It is open at weekends and most weekday evenings, but closed Mondays and Tuesdays for brewing; check for latest opening times. Local artists' work is displayed on the walls. Coffee is served Friday to Sunday daytime. ✿&🖪🌢🛜

Queen's Head ★ Ⓛ
23 The Terrace, RG40 1BP
☎ (0118) 978 1221
Greene King Abbot; 2 changing beers (sourced locally; often Greene King, Rebellion, Stardust) Ⓗ
Grade II-listed 15th-century cruck-framed inn nestling in a terrace close to the station. The characterful, cosy single bar has low ceilings and timber floors, and a log fire provides a welcome retreat. It is a Greene King Local Hero pub, with local ales available alongside their Abbot Ale and house beer. The pleasant rear patio and garden hosts the annual beer festival, and there is further seating on the terrace. 🏃✿≠♣🖪🌢🛜

Ship Inn
104 Peach Street, RG40 1XH (jct with London Rd, on entrance to Wokingham one-way system)
☎ (0118) 978 0389 🌐 shipwokingham.co.uk
Fuller's London Pride, ESB; 2 changing beers (sourced regionally; often Dark Star, Fuller's) Ⓗ
A large, popular Fuller's establishment on the south corner of Wokingham's ring road, with three bars plus a spacious outside area that has been extended in recent years. The pub is especially busy at weekends, and when live sports events are screened. Good food is served at lunchtimes and evenings. It has a strong community focus, and offers tea, coffee and chat for senior citizens in the morning. 🏃✿🕽🖪🌢🛜

Woolhampton

Rowbarge Ⓛ
Station Road, RG7 5SH
☎ (0118) 971 2213
House beer (by St Austell); 5 changing beers (sourced regionally; often Delphic, Loddon, Renegade) Ⓗ
A cottage that was first licensed in 1830 is now a destination pub with a separate dining area in the rear extension. It is set in a large paddock by the Kennet and Avon Canal, with plenty of outdoor seating and a large car park. The Brunning & Price pub's new manager keeps the rapidly turning over beers well. An annual beer festival is held in July. Midgham station and bus stops are nearby. Q🏃✿🕽&≠(Midgham)♣●P🖪🌢🛜♬

Wraysbury

Perseverance
2 High Street, TW19 5DB
☎ (01784) 482375 🌐 thepercy.co.uk
Stardust Red Rocket; 2 changing beers Ⓗ
Comfortable pub now free of tie. The larger front room has a piano and a large inglenook fireplace, with a real log fire. Another seating area with an open fire leads to the rear dining area. The rear garden is delightful. Two guest ales are always varied and are from interesting breweries, both LocAle and around the country. Regular beer festivals are held. Quiz night is Thursday and live music features on Sunday afternoon.
Q🏃✿🕽♣●P🖪(305)🌢🛜♬

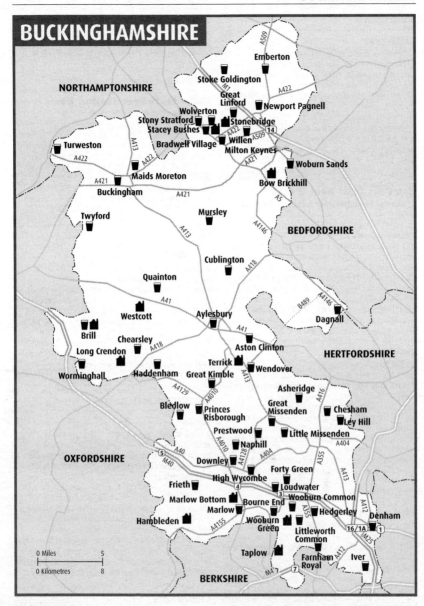

BUCKINGHAMSHIRE

Asheridge

Blue Ball Ⓛ

Asheridge Road, HP5 2UX

☎ (01494) 758305

Adnams Ghost Ship; Fuller's London Pride; Tring Side Pocket for a Toad Ⓗ

Dating from the late 17th century, this rural family pub is situated in a hamlet two miles north-west of Chesham. The L-shaped bar serves well-kept beers from three handpumps. There are two wood-burning stoves, one at each end of the main bar area. A restaurant serves good food at lunchtimes (no evening meals are available). The extensive garden has seating, including a heated enclosure, with fine views across the adjacent valley.

🛉🏵🖤🌢🍴🖤🅿🏵🛜

Aston Clinton

Oak

119 Green End Street, HP22 5EU

☎ (01296) 630466 ⊕ oakastonclinton.co.uk

Fuller's London Pride; 1 changing beer (often Fuller's) Ⓗ

A thatched, 500-year-old half-timbered pub, the Royal Oak is steeped in history. It has a large, comfortable L-shaped bar with low beams, a wooden floor and plenty of seating. The pub boasts an extensive beer garden outside with attractive, leafy trees in season. While not completely separate, the smaller, tiled bar to the left operates like a public bar, full of local characters and chit-chat. The other larger areas of the bar are low-beamed with open fires. 🏵🕽&🅿🚃(500,61)🏵🛜

Aylesbury

Aristocrat
1 Wendover Road, HP21 7SZ (on the gyratory)
☎ (01296) 415366 ⊕ aristocrataylesbury.com
Dark Star Hophead; Fuller's London Pride ⊞
This Grade II-listed building dates back to the 17th century but is now stranded in the centre of Aylesbury's infamous traffic gyratory system, about 500 yards from the town centre. The low ceilings and oak beams give the open-plan interior a sense of smaller interconnected rooms. The pub is lively and popular with locals, regularly featuring entertainment such as live music, DJs and sports on TV. A small public car park (free in the evenings) is immediately outside. ❀❤️◖◗♣≠P🚃♬

Hop Pole Craft Beer & Grill ⊾
83 Bicester Road, HP19 9AZ (near Gatehouse Industrial Area)
☎ (01296) 482129
9 changing beers ⊞
Well worth a short stroll out of the town centre, this temple of beer regularly sports nine cask ales, varied in style and provenance, including three or four guest ales among the Vale family beers. There is also a good range of mostly Belgian bottled beers. It hosts a long-running quiz on Tuesday night and ukulele sessions on the second and fourth Wednesday of each month. There is also occasional live music at the weekend, as well as seasonal beer festivals. ❀◖◗♣🚃❀🛜♬

King's Head ⊾
Market Square, HP20 2RW
☎ (01296) 718812 ⊕ kingsheadaylesbury.co.uk
Chiltern Pale Ale, Beechwood Bitter; 3 changing beers ⊞
This magnificent building is owned by the National Trust and the bar is run by the Chiltern brewery as a de facto brewery tap. It is the oldest courtyard inn in England, complete with cobbles, and a converted stables occupies one side. The bar has up to four Chiltern ales, two of which often change, and a guest beer – often a stout or porter in winter – and also a cider. Beer festivals are held periodically. There is plenty of outside seating. Q❀🛏◖◗♿≠❀🛜

White Hart ✓
Unit 4, Exchange Street, HP20 1UR
☎ (01296) 468440
Ruddles County; Sharp's Doom Bar; 4 changing beers (sourced nationally) ⊞
Wetherspoon pub on the site of the old cattle market and opposite the Aylesbury Waterside Theatre. It is named after a pub that stood nearby, now long since demolished. A younger crowd frequents the pub at night, but during the day and early evening, it attracts the usual Wetherspoons crowd as well as theatre goers. It serves an interesting range of real ales. ❀◖◗♿≠🚃🛜

Bledlow

Lions of Bledlow ⊾
Church End, HP27 9PE (from M40 jct 6 go through Chinnor to Bledlow village on B4009, take 2nd left through village on B4009, pub is signposted)
☎ (01844) 343345 ⊕ thelionsofbledlow.co.uk
4 changing beers (sourced locally; often Tring, Wadworth) ⊞
A charming 16th-century free house at the foot of the Chiltern Hills, between the Icknield Way and the Chinnor and Princes Risborough Steam Railways Line, popular with ramblers, dog walkers and cyclists. Its five handpumps offer a rotating variety of local, regional and

natiional beers. The traditional dark oak beams and quarry tiles of its interior have seen it used as a filming location for the ITV detective drama series, Midsomer Murders, on several occasions. Q🛏❀◖◗♿P🚃❀🛜

Bourne End

KEG – Craft Beer Tasting Bar ⊾
12 Oakfield Road, SL8 5QN
☎ (01628) 529369 ⊕ kegcraftbeer.co.uk
2 changing beers (often Stardust)
Small, welcoming bar named KEG after the initials of its owner Kim E Georgiou. The bar offers two cask beers from Stardust, plus six craft keg beers and real ciders. Kim and her husband, Carl, enjoyed sampling venues around the country, and decided to emulate them, offering top-quality beer, cider, gin and wine in their own town. Card payment only. ≠❀🚃(6)❀🛜

Brill

Pointer ⊾
27 Church Street, HP18 9RT
☎ (01844) 238339 ⊕ thepointerbrill.co.uk
Vale Best IPA; house beer (by XT); 2 changing beers ⊞
Not only a destination eatery, this fee house has become a destination ale house as well, thanks to the skilled cellarwoman. Its four handpumps offer a reliable choice, which often features a stout or porter and another guest ale. The pub supports the Brill beer festival in August. An open-walled kitchen serves wonderful, locally sourced food to a separate vaulted dining room. Q❀🛏◖◗♣🚃❀🛜

Buckingham

Mitre
2 Mitre Street, MK18 1DW
☎ (01280) 813080 ⊕ themitrepub.co.uk
Ossett Yorkshire Blonde; Timothy Taylor Boltmaker; 3 changing beers (sourced nationally; often Five Points, Harbour, Tring) ⊞
Buckingham's oldest pub is a 17th-century stone-built free house. The cosy and friendly atmosphere is enhanced by an open fire in winter. It offers changing and interesting beers, regularly including local ales, from five handpumps during winter months, with one replaced by still ciders in summer. Largescreen TVs show major events, and live music also features regularly. A large stretch-tent covers the garden. Steet parking only. Local CAMRA Pub of the Year 2023. 🛏❀♣♣🚃❀🛜♬

Chearsley

Bell
Church Lane, HP18 0DJ
☎ (01844) 208077 ⊕ thebellchearsley.co.uk

Fuller's London Pride; Gale's Seafarers Ale; 2 changing beers ⊞

Attractive thatched pub on the edge of the village green, often featured in Midsomer Murders. The cosy interior has settles, flagstones, bric-a-brac, a real fire, and an interesting clock. The large garden is suitable for children and perfect for sunny summer's days. This Fuller's house is well known both for its ales and its good, wholesome food. Q❀◑ᴾ🖵(110)

Chesham

Queen's Head 🅛

120 Church Street, HP5 1JD

☎ (01494) 778690 ⊕ queensheadchesham.co.uk

Fuller's London Pride, ESB; 3 changing beers (sourced regionally; often Dark Star, Gale's) ⊞

In Chesham's Old Town alongside the River Chess, is this characterful 18th-century pub. It is divided into several distinct rooms: real fires warm the cosy lounge and lively public bar, while another room to the rear and a yard provide further seating. Three changing ales usually come from the Fuller's range. Authentic Thai cuisine dominates the menu in both the pub and separate restaurant. There is a popular quiz night on Thursdays. ᗡ❀◑&⊖(Chesham) ♣ᴾ🖵(1,1A) ❀🛜

Cublington

Unicorn 🅛

High Street, LU7 0LQ

☎ (01296) 681261 ⊕ theunicornpub.co.uk

3 changing beers (sourced locally) ⊞

A 16th-century village free house in a quiet location. It has been tastefully restored, with exposed beams and rustic furniture. The long single bar has real fires at either end and serves predominantly LocAle beers from Tring, Vale, XT, Chiltern and others. The restuarant section is extremely popular, and there is a function room, where many clubs and societies meet regularly. Boules and Aunt Sally are played in the large secure garden. ❀◑&♣ᴾ🖵(651) ❀🛜

Dagnall

Red Lion 🅛

21 Main Road North, HP4 1QZ

☎ (01442) 843020 ⊕ theredliondagnall.co.uk

Greene King IPA; Tring Side Pocket for a Toad; Vale VPA; 1 changing beer (sourced locally) ⊞

A welcoming and cosy community-focused local. Two log-burning stoves serve both the front bar and rear dining room. The latter is decorated with local photographs, including some of the adjoining National Trust Ashridge Estate. Four well-kept, mostly local real ales are available, with a full range of other drinks including low/no-alcohol beers. First-class meals are served lunchtimes and evenings, and use locally sourced ingredients where possible. The garden to the rear is an oasis of calm. There are quiz nights every other Thursday. Qᗡ❀◑&♣ᴾ❀🛜

Denham

Falcon Inn ✅

Village Road, UB9 5BE

☎ (01895) 832125 ⊕ falcondenham.com

St Austell Proper Job; Timothy Taylor Landlord; 1 changing beer (sourced regionally; often Brakspear) ⊞

Small one-bar pub in Denham village conservation area. Though the building dates from the 18th century, it has a smart interior. The entrance has interesting old steps straight off the road, leading into the welcoming bar. A lower dining area leads to a sunny terrace garden with an area of covered seating. There are four high-quality B&B bedrooms. Parking in the village is limited. the nearest rail station is 750 yards along the South Bucks Way footpath. Qᗡ❀🛏≉🖵❀🛜♪

Downley

De Spencer Arms

The Common, HP13 5YQ (across common from village on a flint track beyond end of Plomer Green Ln)

☎ (01494) 535317 ⊕ ledespencers.co.uk

Fuller's London Pride, ESB; 2 changing beers (sourced nationally) ⊞

Busy, friendly local on the edge of Downley Common, offering a warm welcome to all, including dogs and children. The pub is a favourite of walkers and cyclists. The garden is a lovely place to sit during the summer months, and the surrounding Area of Outstanding Natural Beauty offers many walks. Car parking is to the rear of the pub. ᗡ❀◑♣ᴾ🖵❀🛜♪

Emberton

Bell & Bear

12 High Street, MK46 5DH

☎ (01234) 385537 ⊕ thebellandbear.co.uk

House beer (by XT); 3 changing beers (sourced locally; often Phipps NBC, Tring, XT) ⊞

Rescued from closure by community purchase, this friendly stone-built village pub houses a long narrow bar with high stools and, past the real fire, tables, chairs and settees at the far end. The comfortable lounge is behind the bar, providing a quieter area, which is also used for eating from visiting food vans. Five handpumps offer the regular house ale, with a rotating selection of three guests, usually from eight local breweries, plus a cider. ᗡ❀Å♣ᴾ🖵(21) ❀🛜♪

Farnham Royal

Emperor 🅛

Blackpond Lane, SL2 3EG SU959842

☎ (01753) 643006 ⊕ theemperorpub.co.uk

Rebellion IPA, Overthrow; 1 changing beer (sourced locally) ⊞

An old pub with a contemporary look. The front area is furnished with comfortable seating, and there is a cosy lower area around a large table. To the rear is a room dedicated to dining. Outside is a pleasant garden and a covered seating area. There is usually live music on Saturdays once a month. All real ales are from Rebellion. No food served on Sunday evening. Qᗡ❀◑ᴾ🖵(X74) ❀🛜

Forty Green

Royal Standard of England ★ 🅛

Forty Green Road, HP9 1XT

☎ (01494) 673382 ⊕ theoldestpub.com

Chiltern Pale Ale; Rebellion IPA; Windsor & Eton Knight of the Garter; 2 changing beers (sourced locally) ⊞

This historic hostelry, which claims to be the oldest free house in England, has a fascinating pedigree and is well worth a detour. A barrel-shaped wooden partition wall/ noticeboard leads to rooms containing log fires or cast iron stoves. The architecture and furniture is eclectic and rustic, with hops adorning the bar areas. As well three regular ales, ir offers two guest local beers, and a range of bottled beers from craft breweries. It also serves excellent food. The area is great for walking. Terry Pratchett hailed from the village and Bekonscot Model Village is nearby. Q❀◑●P

Frieth

Prince Albert
Moors End, RG9 6PY
☎ (01494) 881683
Brakspear Gravity Ⓗ
This charming, cloistered Brakspear country local, is a stone's throw from Frieth village, and well worth seeking out for its cosy, old-fashioned atmosphere. The small bar area boasts a log fire in the winter and leads to further rooms and seating. The beer garden offers secluded summer family drinking. This is a classic example of a quaint, rural inn in good hiking country. Check out the rustic outside gents' toilets. Q❀◑▶P⊒❀

Great Kimble

Swan Ⓛ
Grove Lane, HP17 9TR
☎ (01844) 275288
1 changing beer (sourced locally; often Tring) Ⓗ
A family-owned free-house that dates back to the 18th century. It adjoins the children's playground on the green in this village at the foot of the Chiltern Hills, in excellent hiking and cycling country. Sunday lunchtimes are popular and live music and quizzes are occasionally staged. The back garden features a wood-fired pizza oven and barbecue. Opening times during the week are limited. The ale range can be restricted, although what's available is reliably well kept.
🐾❀◪◑ಈ⇌(Little Kimble) ♣P⊒(300) ❀✿♪

Great Missenden

George Ale House
94 High Street, HP16 0BG
☎ (01494) 865185
4 changing beers (sourced nationally) Ⓗ
A lovely pub with a great atmosphere and ales that are always in excellent condition. There are three seating areas, some with comfortable sofas and real fires, and a small patio beer garden at the back. Normally there is no music, but occasionally live acts play on Saturday nights. Multiple local CAMRA award winner, including Pub of the Year in 2023. Q❀⇌●P⊒❀✿♪

Haddenham

Rising Sun Ⓛ ✅
9 Thame Road, HP17 8EN
☎ (01844) 291744 ⊕ risingsunhaddenham.co.uk
XT Four; 3 changing beers (sourced locally) Ⓗ
This bustlng community pub offers at least three cask-conditioned ales (predominantly from local brewery XT) and a selection of craft beers. The friendly locals inhabit an area to the left of the bar known as Compost Corner. An enclosed beer garden with marquee extends the pub on busier days. A weekly pub quiz is well attended, so booking is encouraged. This dog-friendly pub also offers treats for your four-legged friends.
Q🐾⇌❀⇌(Haddenham & Thame Parkway) ●⊒(280) ❀✿

Hedgerley

White Horse ★ Ⓛ
Village Lane, SL2 3UY (in old village, near church)

☎ (01753) 643225 ⊕ thewhitehorsehedgerley.co.uk
Rebellion IPA; 7 changing beers (often Mighty Oak, Oakham) Ⓖ
This village local offers an impressive range of real ales. New breweries often feature, as well as favourite ales from Oakham and Mighty Oak. Two craft beers and three real ciders/perries are also available. This classic pub has a well-tended garden and a heated, covered patio area. Regular beer festivals are held, the largest of which is over the Whitsun weekend and is a must for real ale enthusiasts. Local CAMRA Pub of the Year on numerous occasions. Q🐾❀◪♣●P❀✿✦

High Wycombe

Rose & Crown Ⓛ ✅
Desborough Road, HP11 2PR
4 changing beers Ⓗ
This friendly, L-Shaped pub next to the Eden shopping centre and bus station has steadily built up its real ale offering over the past few years and now has an extensive range. Many sporting events are displayed on two largescreen TVs. The pub holds an acoustic jam once a month and runs darts teams on Tuesday nights. Local CAMRA Pub of the Year runner-up 2024. ❀♣⊒❀✦♪

Iver

Red Lion
Langley Park Road, SL0 0JZ (jct Wood Ln and B470)
☎ (01753) 654257
Greene King IPA; St Austell Tribute; 2 changing beers (sourced nationally; often Greene King) Ⓗ
On the outskirts of Iver Village, on the mini roundabout between Wood Lane and Langley Park Road, the Red Lion has a rich and fascinating history. It was originally built in the 16th century by the local Parish council (who served their own ale to the community), and has maintained much of its character, with original wooden beams, open fires and flagstone floors. There is a Chef and Brewer pub restaurant with a separate drinking area where you can enjoy four real ales. There are two EV charging points in the car park. Q🐾❀◑●P⊒(3)❀✦

Ley Hill

Crown Ⓛ
The Common, HP5 1UY (just off Blackwell Hall Ln)
SP9898201932
☎ (01494) 783910 ⊕ thecrownleyhill.co.uk
3 changing beers (sourced nationally) Ⓗ
Standing in the heart of the Chilterns, the Crown welcomes cyclists, walkers, classic car and motorcycle enthusiasts. The kitchen is open daily and serves traditional pub food. In the summer you can enjoy your drinks and food on the village green. In August, it hosts an annual music and beer festival with bands, food and lots of great beer. The pub is dog and child friendly.
🐾❀◑⇌P⊒❀✦♪

Little Missenden

Crown Inn
HP7 0RF (off A413, between Amersham and Great Missenden)
☎ (01494) 957265
4 changing beers (sourced nationally) Ⓗ
A warm welcome is assured in this traditional free house, which is popular with locals and walkers alike. The long-standing Guide entry continues to offer superb beers in an idyllic setting. Four handpumps dispense a good range of well-kept cask ales, including occasional guests. Light

lunchtime food is available, except on Sundays. The pub is dog-friendly despite the resident cats. Three en-suite rooms are available. Q🌢⛱🛏🍽◖♣P🖵(55)🐾🗢

Littleworth Common

Blackwood Arms

Common Lane, SL1 8PP SU937863

☎ (01753) 645672 ⊕ theblackwoodarms.co.uk

Brakspear Gravity, Oxford Gold; 2 changing beers (sourced regionally; often Oakham) Ⓗ

A delightful Victorian country pub brought back to life by an enthusiastic couple after a long period of closure. It is close to Burnham Beeches and popular with walkers and diners. The large and attractive garden has plenty of seating, including a covered heated area, and is well used in summer. In winter a roaring log fire burns. Tuesday is Pie and Pint night. Dog and horse friendly; treats and hay are provided. Closed on Monday. Q🌢🌝◖♣P🐾🗢

Loudwater

General Havelock

114 Kingsmead Road, HP11 1HZ

☎ (01494) 520391 ⊕ generalhavelock.co.uk

Fuller's London Pride, ESB; Gale's Seafarers Ale; 1 changing beer Ⓗ

The General Havelock has been run by the same family since Fuller's acquired it in 1986, and it remains popular with groups of all ages. The interior is adorned with an eclectic selection of bric-a-brac and antiques. There are four ales available at all times on handpump, including a range of seasonal and guest beers. The pub has a cosy feel in winter while the garden makes for a peaceful haven in summer. Thai food is served on Thursday and Saturday evenings. 🌢🌝◖♣P🖵(5,5A)🐾🗢

Maids Moreton

Wheatsheaf

Main Street, MK18 1QR

☎ (01280) 822903

Tring Side Pocket for a Toad; 1 changing beer (sourced nationally; often Butcombe, Roman Way) Ⓗ

This family-run, traditional village pub has been in continuous use as a pub since the 18th century; it has also functioned as a village store, a blacksmiths and a butcher's shop. It is full of character, with a thatched roof, low ceilings and exposed beams. The bar has an inglenook fireplace with a log-burning stove and an old dutch oven with a flintstone hearth. A separate room can be hired for private parties. There is a large garden at the back. Q🌝♣P🖵(60)🐾🗢

Marlow

Royal British Legion Ⓛ

Station Approach, SL7 1NT (50yds from Marlow railway station)

☎ (01628) 486659 ⊕ rblclubmarlow.co.uk

6 changing beers Ⓗ

Situated next door to Marlow railway station is this friendly and popular Royal British Legion club. It has a wide range of cask ales available, and holds two excellent beer festivals every year. Various other events are held here, including jazz and music nights. Although a private members' club, entry is permitted on production of a copy of the Good Beer Guide or a CAMRA membership card. A regular winner of CAMRA Regional Club of the Year. 🌝&🚲♣P🖵🗢♫

Two Brewers Ⓛ ⊘

St Peter Street, SL7 1NQ

☎ (01628) 484140

Rebellion IPA; 3 changing beers (often Rebellion) Ⓗ

Beautifully set on the banks of the River Thames down, this pub is in a quiet street, a few minutes' walk from the bustling high street, close to T.S. Eliot's former residence. A bright seating area at the front leads to a smaller snug area at a lower level to the right. A large terrace at the side of the pub gives space for outdoor drinking. The pub serves a selection of Rebellion regular beers in addition to its seasonal range. 🌢🌝◖&🚲🖵🐾🗢♫

Milton Keynes: Bradwell Village

Victoria Inn 🍸

6 Vicarage Road, MK13 9AQ

☎ (01908) 312769

3 changing beers (sourced regionally; often Grainstore, Vale, XT) Ⓗ

A cosy, traditional, 17th-century stone-built pub, whose exposed beams, low ceilings and blue half-panelled walls offer a comfortable and relaxed atmosphere. Four handpumps on the bar serve mainly regional beers that are chosen by the regulars. To the right is a a room with a pool table and dartboard, while the left-hand room has two levels with tables and chairs and an open fireplace. There is plenty of seating on the paved terrace at the front. Local CAMRA Pub of the Year 2024. Q🌢♣🖵(33) 🐾🗢

Milton Keynes: Great Linford

Nag's Head

30 High Street, MK14 5AX

☎ (01908) 607449 ⊕ nagsheadgreatlinford.com

Greene King IPA, Abbot; Timothy Taylor Landlord; 1 changing beer (sourced nationally; often Belhaven, Greene King, St Austell) Ⓗ

Pretty, thatched-roof pub dating from the 18th century (though the building is older). The low ceilings and exposed beams give its two bars a cosy feel, especially when the log-burning stove is lit in the saloon bar. Traditional and craft ales are served, with guests from local breweries. Freshly-prepared food is offered at reasonable prices. Customers enjoy monthly quiz nights, regular live music and the newly refurbished large front and rear patio gardens. It is popular with ramblers, dog-walkers, narrow-boaters and the local community. 🌢🌝◖♣P🐾🗢♫

Milton Keynes: Stacey Bushes

Blackened Sun Brewery Tap Ⓛ

Unit 3, Heathfield, MK12 6HP

☎ (01908) 990242 ⊕ blackenedsunbrewing.co.uk

Blackened Sun Hédoné Ⓗ; 5 changing beers (sourced locally; often Blackened Sun) Ⓟ

A warm welcome brightens the rather austere surroundings of this taproom, in an award-winning microbrewery housed in an unpretentious trading-estate unit. Furniture consists of long tables, bench seating and some stools. The six taps serve Blackened Sun beers, which often include a collaboration brew. All are real ales, many brewed with Belgian yeasts, and usually vegan, served from KeyKeg. Bottled beers are also available, including for takeaway, and growlers can be refilled. Under-18s are welcome until 8pm with an adult. The taproom is dog friendly. Q🌢P🖵(6)🐾

Milton Keynes: Stony Stratford

Stony Stratford Conservative Club

77 High Street, MK11 1AY
☎ (01908) 567105 ⊕ stonyconclub.co.uk
Brains Rev James Original; Vale VPA; 2 changing beers (often Fuller's, Phipps NBC, Timothy Taylor) ⊞
Multi-roomed social club for Conservative Party members. Card-carrying CAMRA members and those with a current copy of this Guide are admitted as guests. It offers up to four cask-conditioned ales, often local. Members enjoy regular events and activities, including live music. Occasionally events are open to the general public, and the restaurant/lounge is available to the public at lunchtime when food is available. The car park is restricted to members and their guests; parking outside can be difficult. ⏴❀◑ᒪ♣Ρ⏢ᕼ(6,X60)❀❄♪

Milton Keynes: Willen

Ship Ashore

Granville Square, MK15 9JL
☎ (01908) 694360
Brains Rev James Original; Fuller's London Pride; Timothy Taylor Landlord; 1 changing beer (sourced nationally; often Black Sheep, Rudgate, Titanic) ⊞
Smart, modern, Ember Inns pub on a residential estate close to Willen Lake. The pub comprises one large bar, but pillars and half-walls give a more intimate feel. It offers three regular beers, plus a changing guest ale, often a dark beer, all of which are reduced in price on Monday and Thursday. Food is served at lunchtime and evenings, with a dedicated vegetarian/vegan menu. Drinkers and diners are made equally welcome. Weekly quizzes are held. It has a small garden and ample free parking. ❀◑ᒪΡ⏢(1)❀❄

Milton Keynes: Wolverton

MK Biergarten

Unit 3, The Triangle, Wolverton Park Road, MK12 5FJ
☎ (01908) 990127 ⊕ mkbiergarten.co.uk
1 changing beer (sourced nationally; often Brew York, Roman Way, Tring) ⊞
Milton Keynes' first micropub and bottle shop opened in 2016 in a retail unit in a prestigious residential development alongside the Grand Union Canal, close to Wolverton station. A wide and interesting range of bottles and cans are stocked in chiller units and all can be drunk on-site or purchased to take away. There is a small corner bar with six taps and one handpump, often serving a local ale. Q⏴ᒪ≑♣●Ρ⏢❀♪

Mursley

Green Man

22 Main Street, MK17 0RT
☎ (01296) 720389
3 changing beers (sourced nationally; often Settle, Tring, XT) ⊞
This nice little village pub reopened under new local ownership in 2023 after it was rescued from development. Its one bar usually offers a choice of three well-kept and regularly changing beers. The drinking area has plenty of chairs and tables in front of the bar and to the left. At the rear is a further room with beams, comfortable settees, more chairs and tables, plus a largescreen TV. There is a beer garden, plus front and rear patios with seating. ⏴❀♣Ρ⏢(50,67)❀❄

Naphill

Wheel ◢

100 Main Road, HP14 4QA
☎ (01494) 562210 ⊕ thewheelnaphill.com
Greene King Abbot; house beer (by Hardys & Hansons); 2 changing beers ⊞
Friendly and popular local with a large garden, opposite the village hall. It has two regular and two changing beers. There are two bar areas and an extension that's used as a eating area towards the rear of the pub. Occasionally sport is shown on TV. Dogs and muddy boots are welcome. The pub is a regular in the Guide. Convenient for the X9 bus route. ❀◑▶Å♣Ρ⏢(X9)❀❄

Newport Pagnell

Frog & Nightgown

33A High Street, MK16 8AR
☎ (01908) 610565 ⊕ swanrevived.co.uk
St Austell Tribute; 1 changing beer (sourced nationally; often Fuller's, Ringwood, Windsor & Eton) ⊞
This busy one-room bar is part of the Swan Revived Hotel. Entrance to the pub is by the side-entry (the original coach entrance). Interesting knick-knacks adorn the walls, and there is a comfortable, quiet courtyard outside with sheltered tables and chairs, which also serves as a smoking area. Three handpumps dispense ales, though only two are in use. Accommodation and meeting rooms in the hotel are accessible from within the pub. A quiz night is held on Thursday, with live music every other Friday. Q⏴❀◑ᒪΡ⏢❀❄♪

Ousebank House

High Street, MK16 8AN
☎ (01908) 462618 ⊕ ousebankhouse.co.uk
Courage Directors; 2 changing beers (often Marston's, Wychwood) ⊞
Formerly the Royal British Legion Club, this 17th-century building with 19th-century extension is now a community-owned pub. It has two bars: a front lounge and the larger main bar. Friendly bar staff serve one regular ale and two changing guests – these are rotating beers from the Marston's stable or Phipps NBC. Food is only available on Sundays. They also hold a monthly Armed Forces and Veterans Breakfast and Drop-in hub. Current local CAMRA Club of the Year. ⏴◑ᒪ♣Ρ⏢(21,C10)❀❄♪

Prestwood

Green Man

2 High Street, HP16 9EB (on A4128 near Great Missenden)
☎ (01494) 327128 ⊕ greenmanprestwood.co.uk
Hook Norton Old Hooky; Timothy Taylor Landlord; Tring Ridgeway ⊞
Reopened in 2023 after extensive refurbishment following a long period of closure, the pub originally dates back to 1861. I has an L-shaped bar with a snug to the right boasting a wood-burning stove. The left-hand side of the pub leads to a small outside drinking area with tables at the rear. The pub is in superb walking countryside and is dog and child friendly. ⏴❀◑ᒪΡ⏢(41) ❀❄

Princes Risborough

Bird in Hand ᒪ ◢

47 Station Road, HP27 9DE
☎ (01844) 345602 ⊕ birdinhandprincesrisborough.co.uk

Chiltern Beechwood Bitter; Thame Hoppiness; 2 changing beers ⎔

Thriving community local in a residential area near the station. This Oak Taverns house has gone from strength to strength and offers an excellent selection of real ales on handpump. The compact, L-shaped drinking area is supplemented by a beer garden and outside drinking space that hosts pub quizzes, live music, and pop-up food vans at weekends. Parking nearby can be tricky. Local CAMRA Pub of the Year 2023. ✿≉♣●🅰♿🐾🎵

Quainton

George & Dragon 🗎

32 The Green, HP22 4AR

☎ (01296) 655436 ● georgeanddragonquainton.co.uk

4 changing beers (sourced locally) ⎔

Delightful free house with an adjoining coffee shop. It is split between public and saloon bars, both offering home-cooked food at lunchtime. The friendly public bar has darts, a jukebox and a TV, while the saloon is dedicated to dining. Four LocAles are served, plus two guests. Parts of this well-maintained pub date back to the 1700s; traditional features include inglenook fireplaces, beams and a quarry-tiled floor. ♿✿◑♿♣🅿 (16) 🐾🎵

Stoke Goldington

Lamb 🗎

16-20 High Street, MK16 8NR

☎ (01908) 551233

Tring Moongazing, Death or Glory; 1 changing beer (sourced regionally; often Oakham, Phipps NBC, Tring) ⎔

Family-run pub in a peaceful village between Milton Keynes and Northampton, offering a warm and friendly welcome. Its main bar has six handpumps, usually serving three ales and a cider, with a smaller room beyond, a restaurant bar, and a large garden for holding the annual music festival. Home-cooked food uses local produce and includes award-winning pies, with steak and ale a favourite. the pub has featured in the Guide for 22 consecutive years, winning many CAMRA awards, including local Pub of the Year. Q♿✿◑♿♣🅿🐾🎵

Turweston

Stratton Arms ✅

Main Street, NN13 5JX

☎ (01280) 704956

Sharp's Doom Bar; Timothy Taylor Boltmaker, Landlord; 2 changing beers (sourced nationally; often Fuller's, St Austell, Woodforde's) ⎔

Early 18th-century stone-built pub on edge of a quiet village. It was the village morgue before it became a pub; the tunnel to the church is now its cellar. Five real ales are usually available (the pub is a member of the Timothy Taylor Champion Club). Food is available throughout the week, but only pizzas Monday and Tuesday evenings. There are seats and tables outside, with several marquee-covered areas and an extensive grassed area. It is popular with walkers, and there is free overnight parking for motor homes (call ahead to book). Q♿✿◑🅰♣🅿 (131,132) 🐾🎵

Twyford

Crown Inn

The Square, MK18 4EG

☎ (01296) 730216

2 changing beers ⎔

A freehold locals' pub central to the life of the village. The present landlady has seen the others decline and close. The pub is deceptively large; a spacious bar area leads through to an even larger lounge/function area on the left. It serves one frequently changing beer from the barrel, and it is normal to have seven different beers on during the week. ♿✿◑♿♣🅰 (16) 🐾🎵

Wendover

King & Queen ✅

17 South Street, HP22 6EF

☎ (01296) 696872 ● thekingandqueenwendover.co.uk

Timothy Taylor Landlord; Young's London Original; 1 changing beer ⎔

Situated just off the High Street, within easy reach of the station, this three-roomed pub has a pleasant, homely ambience. There is an impressive wall map of the local countryside in one room. A wood-burning fire helps to provide a warm winter welcome for cold walkers returning from exploring the nearby Chiltern Hills. It hosts occasional tap takeovers and events such as comedy nights. Q♿✿♿≉🅿🐾

Woburn Sands

Station Tavern

146 Station Road, MK17 8SG

☎ (01908) 582495 ● stationwoburnsands.co.uk

Phipps NBC Phipps IPA; 1 changing beer (sourced nationally; often Brains, Phipps NBC, Sharp's) ⎔

A friendly, traditional pub next to the station. It retains many original features, such as the horseshoe-shaped bar and railway memorabilia. Although it only has two handpumps the beer is always fresh and very drinkable. Its barn and covered courtyard both offer pleasant dining areas that can also be booked for private functions.The publicans received a local CAMRA award in 2022 for 36 years' service. ♿✿🛏◑≉♣🅿 (450) 🐾🎵

Wooburn Common

Royal Standard 🗎

Wooburn Common Road, HP10 0JS (follow signs to Odds Farm)

☎ (01628) 521121 ● theroyalstandard.biz

Caledonian Deuchars IPA; Dark Star Hophead; Hop Back Summer Lightning ⎔; St Austell Tribute ⎔/🅶; 6 changing beers ⎔

A warm welcome is guaranteed at this regular award-winning pub set in the countryside near Burnham Beeches and Cliveden House. It serves five beers on handpump and another five on gravity, as well as real cider. Outside at the front is a disused phone box with books that patrons can borrow. There is no public transport but the pub has a large car park. Q♿✿◑♿♣🅿🐾🎵

Worminghall

Clifden Arms 🗎

Clifden Road, HP18 9JR

☎ (01844) 338090 ● theclifdenarms.co.uk

House beer (by Rebellion); 3 changing beers (sourced locally) ⎔

A characterful country local in a timber-framed building with brick noggin and thatched roof. The older part is medieval, with a newer wing added in the 17th century. A restaurant offers a varied menu that is focused on local ingredients. The bar on the other side has comfy seating and a log fire. The regular beer is Rebellion IPA rebadged as Clifden IPA. Q♿✿🛏◑♣🅿🐾🎵

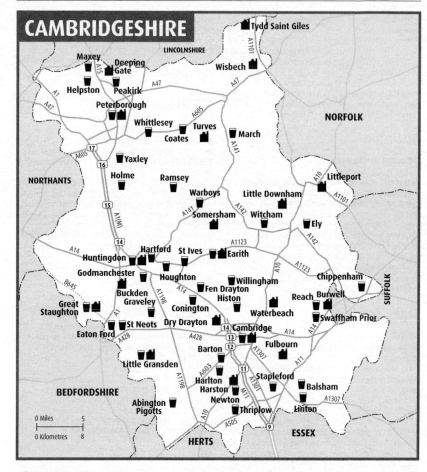

CAMBRIDGESHIRE

(Map showing locations including: Tydd Saint Giles, Maxey, Deeping Gate, Wisbech, Helpston, Peakirk, Peterborough, Whittlesey, Turves, March, Coates, Yaxley, Holme, Ramsey, Warboys, Little Downham, Littleport, Somersham, Witcham, Ely, Hartford, St Ives, Earith, Huntingdon, Godmanchester, Houghton, Willingham, Chippenham, Buckden, Fen Drayton, Histon, Reach, Burwell, Great Staughton, Graveley, Conington, Waterbeach, Swaffham Prior, St Neots, Dry Drayton, Cambridge, Eaton Ford, Fulbourn, Little Gransden, Barton, Stapleford, Balsham, Harlton, Harston, Newton, Linton, Abington Pigotts, Thriplow; surrounding counties LINCOLNSHIRE, NORFOLK, NORTHANTS, SUFFOLK, BEDFORDSHIRE, HERTS, ESSEX; roads A1, A15, A47, A605, A141, A142, A10, A1101, A14, A1123, A428, A603, A1307, A505, M11; scale 0 Miles 5, 0 Kilometres 8)

Abington Pigotts

Pig & Abbot
High Street, SG8 0SD (off A505 through Litlington)
☎ (01763) 853515 ⊕ pigandabbot.co.uk
Adnams Southwold Bitter; Fuller's London Pride; 2 changing beers (often Mighty Oak, Woodforde's) Ⓗ
Located in a remote part of south Cambridgeshire, this Queen Anne period pub offers a warm welcome. The interior has exposed oak beams, with two fires, including a large inglenook featuring a wood-burning stove. A comfortable restaurant offers home-made traditional pub food and specialises in fresh fish & chips, and steak and kidney puddings and pies. Two guest beers are stocked, often including beers from Burton Bridge, Humpty Dumpty, Mighty Oak, Timothy Taylor or Woodforde's. A former local CAMRA Pub of the Year. Q ▓ ⊛ ◖◗ ◇ ♣ P ✿

Balsham

Bell Inn
2 West Wickham Road, CB21 4DZ
☎ (01223) 892999
Greene King IPA; 3 changing beers Ⓗ
Popular community two-bar pub. The wood-panelled lounge bar has tables suitable for diners or drinkers, and the public bar has a jukebox, pub games and TV. Reasonably priced home-made pub food is available, with food vans on Mondays. The changing beers always

include a mild or other dark beer. There is often a locally produced cider in the line-up. A large beer garden to the rear of the pub contains cosy sheds that provide shelter when needed. Q ▓ ⊛ ◖◗ ♣ ♠ P ⊟ (19) ✿ 🖦 ♪

Barton

Hoops ✓
1 School Lane, CB23 7BD
☎ (01223) 344995 ⊕ the-hoops.co.uk
Greene King Abbot Ⓖ; 4 changing beers (often Belhaven, Oakham) Ⓗ
A traditional village pub whose current licensee took over in 2022 and continues its reputation for good beer. The Abbot is served direct from the cask, while guest ales are sourced from the Greene King and SIBA lists. The cosy little public bar, with its tiled floor, enormous fireplace, and upholstered benches, is a delight. The lounge has less character but is pleasant enough, with a bar billiards table and music. There is a large beer garden with a mature walnut tree. Q ▓ ⊛ ♣ P ⊟ (18) ✿ ♪

Cambridge

Alexandra Arms
22 Gwydir Street, CB1 2LL
☎ (01223) 324441 ⊕ thealexcambridge.com
4 changing beers Ⓗ

A modern refurbishment of a backstreet corner pub. Inside there are three distinct areas across two levels, with wooden flooring and plenty of tables. In the attractive enclosed garden there are covered booths and a recently-added garden room, which can be booked for functions. It is a Greene King local hero pub that is mainly free of tie, so guest beers frequently feature local breweries alongside Greene King beers. Food is home-made and focused on burgers. ▷※❶▶●Ұ♣🐾🌐

Cambridge Blue
85-87 Gwydir Street, CB1 2LG
☎ (01223) 471680 ⊕ cambridge.pub/the-blue
14 changing beers Ⓗ/Ⓖ
Popular pub in the Mill Road 'beer quarter'. The bar area has an extension leading to a sizeable garden, where there is a heated marquee in winter. The walls and ceiling are adorned by breweriana and pumpclips. Up to 14 beers are dispensed on handpump or by gravity, from microbreweries nationwide. Gluten-free beer are usually available, as well as a choice of ciders and perries, and a large selection of international bottled beers. Its main beer festival is held in June. Food consists of burgers. ▷※❶◐&♣●Ұ🐾🌐

Champion of the Thames ♈ ★
68 King Street, CB1 1LN
☎ (01223) 351464 ⊕ thechampionofthethames.com
Greene King IPA, Abbot; 3 changing beers Ⓗ
Small, two-room, city-centre pub with a welcoming atmosphere. Etched windows portray the oarsman from the pub's name. The rooms are separated by a part-glazed partition, and there are wooden floors and wood-panelled walls with fixed benches throughout. The pub has been identified by CAMRA as having a historic interior of national importance. The chatter of customers predominates, and there is a popular Tuesday pub quiz. Local CAMRA Pub of the Year 2024. Q※♣🌐🐾🌐

Devonshire Arms Ⓛ
1 Devonshire Road, CB1 2BH
☎ (01223) 316610
Milton Pegasus; 5 changing beers (sourced locally) Ⓗ
Rescued from decline and reopened in 2010 as Milton brewery's first pub in Cambridge. A wide range of Milton beers is always stocked, including dark and strong selections, plus guest beers. A wide selection of real ciders is also available, many from local producers. Deceptively large inside, with outside seating at both front and rear, the pub retains a traditional feel and attracts a wide range of customers. A beer festival coinciding with Mill Road Winter Fair is held in early December. ▷※❶➤♣●Ұ🐾🌐 ♪

Elm Tree
16A Orchard Street, CB1 1JT
☎ (01223) 322553 ⊕ elmtreecambridge.co.uk
7 changing beers (sourced nationally; often Brewpoint, Roughacre) Ⓗ
Back-street pub close to Parker's Piece, owned by Charles Wells. A short bar near the entrance has seating around and beyond, and a few tables are available outside. It is decorated with breweriana, bric-a-brac, photos and Belgian flags. The pub always has the current Brewpoint special, and a further six pumps offer changing guests, frequently local and always including a dark beer. A local real cider is also served, and there is a range of around 40 bottled Belgian beers. There is regular live music. ▷♣●Ұ🐾🌐♪

Free Press
7 Prospect Row, CB1 1DU
☎ (01223) 368337 ⊕ freepresscambridge.com

Greene King IPA, Abbot; Timothy Taylor Landlord; 4 changing beers Ⓗ
Friendly, intimate pub serving high-quality food and great beer. A pub since 1834, it survived the 1970s redevelopment of the area. Only the tiny snug is original; the other two rooms are a loving reconstruction and the quality of the restoration means that the pub is included on CAMRA's list of pubs that are outstanding conversions or restorations. It is named after a temperance movement newspaper that lasted for just one edition. There is bench seating outside at the front and a walled garden at the rear. The 'press room' in the garden is a recent addition, providing additional sheltered seats. ▷※❶➤♣●Ұ🌐

Geldart Ⓛ ✔
1 Ainsworth Street, CB1 2PF
☎ (01223) 314264 ⊕ the-geldart.co.uk
Adnams Ghost Ship; Oakham Citra; St Austell Tribute Ⓗ**; 5 changing beers (sourced nationally)** Ⓗ/Ⓖ
Tucked away in the back streets, with mostly dining and live music to one side, a drinkers' bar to the other, and an enclosed patio garden. A music and film theme dominates, with musical instruments as handpumps and menus on LPs. It has a good reputation for its food and drinks, with six beers on offer, plus cider, and a selection of malt whiskies and rums. Changing guest beers often include a locally sourced dark beer. Live music events are held frequently. Local CAMRA Pub of the Year 2023. ▷※❶●Ұ🐾🌐♪

Haymakers Ⓛ
54 High Street, CB4 1NG
☎ (01223) 311077
Milton Pegasus; 5 changing beers (often Milton) Ⓗ
The second of Milton brewery's three Cambridge pubs, this is popular with employees from the nearby science park as well as local residents. Dark wood and warm colours abound. There are drinking areas either side of the door, plus a snug, and a good-sized beer garden behind. Eight real ales are served, including at least one dark, plus guests, and three real ciders or perries, often from local producers, as well as Moravka unpasteurised lager. Food is mainly pizzas. It boasts the largest pub cycle park in Cambridge ▷※❶◐&♣●Ұ🐾🌐♪

REAL ALE BREWERIES

Bowler's Deeping Gate
BrewBoard ✦ Harston
Burwell Burwell
Calverley's ✦ Cambridge
Cambridge 🍺 Cambridge
Downham Isle ✦ Littleport
Draycott Buckden
Elgood's Wisbech
IVO Somersham
Lord Conrad's Dry Drayton
Milton ✦ Waterbeach
Moonshine Fulbourn
Oakham Peterborough
Papworth Earith
Pastore ✦ Waterbeach
Rocket Great Staughton
Secret Project Turves
Son of Sid 🍺 Little Gransden (brewing suspended)
Three Blind Mice Little Downham
Tydd Steam Tydd Saint Giles
Wheatsheaf ✦ Huntingdon
Xtreme Peterborough

Kingston Arms
33 Kingston Street, CB1 2NU
☎ (01223) 323962 ⊕ thekingstonarms.co.uk
Draught Bass; Ossett White Rat; Tring Side Pocket for a Toad; 5 changing beers ⊞
Classic, cosy, side-street pub which was reopened in 2023. The windows and mirrors keep the interior light and welcoming, with seating at simple tables and chairs or on bar stools. There are real fires in winter, and the walled rear garden has canopies and heaters for colder months. Up to eight cask ales are offered, including at least one dark beer, and the four still ciders include real ones. Pork pies and snacks are served, and pizzas delivered. Cribbage and skittles on Tuesdays.
ᗷ⊛◐➳♣⊕🖫♿🏳

Live & Let Live
40 Mawson Road, CB1 2EA
☎ (01223) 460261
Oakham Citra; 5 changing beers ⊞
An unassuming Victorian street-corner local, just off Mill Road. With a single wood-panelled bar area and a small snug furnished with simple wooden tables and chairs, plus a few bar-stools at one end of the long bar counter, this is a pub made for conversation. There is a wood-burner in the fireplace. The six handpumps regularly feature Oakham and Nethergate beers. The 10 keg taps feature both unusual and well-known beers. The six still ciders include some real ones. ➳♣⊕🖫♿🏳

Maypole ⌧
20A Portugal Place, CB5 8AF
☎ (01223) 352999 ⊕ maypolefreehouse.co.uk
16 changing beers ⊞
The Maypole has been in the capable hands of the Castiglione family since 1982, initially as tenants, latterly as owners. It has a busy front bar, a quieter back bar, an upstairs function room and a large covered patio. The 16 ever-changing beers come mainly from microbreweries, including locals. The cask range is joined by interesting live keg beers and cocktails. The pub holds a festival to coincide with the nearby Cambridge Beer Festival in May. Food focuses on home-cooked Italian dishes and English pub classics. ⊛◐🖫🏳

Queen Edith ⌧
Wulfstan Way, CB1 8QN
☎ (01223) 318536
Milton Justinian, Pegasus, Sparta, Minerva, Nero; 3 changing beers ⊞
The third of Cambridge's Milton brewery pubs, built after the demolition of a pub of the same name at the rear of the site. It is named after Edith the Fair, wife of the ill-fated King Harold II. The style is mock Georgian, inside and out. The large bar to the left of the entrance has large windows on two sides and a wood-burning stove, while the other bar has wooden booths down one side. Regular and changing Milton beers are served, plus guests. Q ᗷ⊛◐♿🖫♿🏳

Royal Standard ⌧
292 Mill Road, CB1 3NL
☎ (01223) 569065 ⊕ cambridge.pub/royal-standard
4 changing beers ⊞
A well-designed renovation of a former two-bar Victorian local that had not been a pub for some time. It is popular with local residents. The entrance, with eating on either side, leads to a single bar; to the right a partly covered and heated patio. It offers a selection of three or four draught beers and many ciders, plus keg beers that frequently include locals. Greek food is available to eat in or take away. ⊛◐♿🖫(Citi2)♿🏳

Chippenham

Tharp Arms
46 High Street, CB7 5PR
☎ (01638) 720234
2 changing beers ⊞
Grade II-listed Georgian pub that takes its name from a local eminent family who lived at Chippenham Park. A straightforward village pub with two bar rooms and a further room to the rear. It is frequented by the popular village cricket team as well as others further afield. The only food comes from occasional pop-up food vans in the evening. The pub was purchased in 2014 by a community keen to support local brewers, and is also listed as an Asset of Community Value. ⊛♣P

Coates

Vine ⌧
4 South Green, PE7 2BJ
☎ (01733) 840343
3 changing beers (often Bakers Dozen, Nene Valley, Salopian) ⊞
Overlooking the village green, this free house was refurbished and extended in 2019. There are three rooms: the lively main sports bar/lounge; a conservatory with pool table at the rear; and a conference suite at the front. The varying beer list always includes a LocAle. The large outdoor area includes pétanque terrains and a children's play area. The pub raises money for the Royal British Legion and Coates War Memorial Fund, particularly on Coates Day in late August. ᗷ⊛♿♣⊕P🖫(33)♿🏳♪

Conington

White Swan
Elsworth Road, CB23 4LN
☎ (01954) 267251 ⊕ thewhiteswanconington.co.uk
Adnams Southwold Bitter, Ghost Ship �servedG**, Broadside** ⊞
Classic 19th-century village pub, fronted by a large lawn and children's play area. The main bar has a tiled floor and a brick fireplace occupied by a fine cast-iron stove. The wheelchair friendly bar is notably lower than usual. Two of the three ales are served by gravity. The pub is owned by Conington Pub Co and run free of tie since being sold by Greene King in 2013. A permanent marquee allows alfresco drinking in all weathers. Q ᗷ⊛◐♣⊕P♿🏳

Earith

Crystal Ship ⌧
32 Earith Business Park, PE28 3QF
☎ (01487) 740634 ⊕ papworthbrewery.com
10 changing beers (sourced locally; often Papworth) ⒼG
This is the Papworth brewery tap, housed in an industrial unit next door to the brewery. It is open for indoor and outdoor drinking, serving up to 11 changing Papworth ales and a guest ale, alongside ciders, wines and spirits. Pizzas are available Thursday and Saturday evenings. Occasional events such as quizzes, live music and food and drink tastings are held (see Facebook for details). There is also a bottle shop selling a range of Papworth beers and Cromwell ciders. Q♿Å⊕P♿🏳♪

Eaton Ford

Barley Mow ⊘
27 Crosshall Road, PE19 7AB
☎ (01480) 474435

Greene King IPA, Abbot; 2 changing beers (often St Austell, Timothy Taylor) ⊞
Simple, one-bar community pub with a wide variety of activities focused on the regulars, plus live music events and seasonal celebrations. The decor is a mix of plaster, brick and wood panel and a long service counter dominates the centre of the bar. Images of past pub social events adorn the walls. There is a garden room, and large beer garden with an extensive children's play area. The two changing beers are not normally from the Greene King range. ⏷❀◑♣P🚃(905)❀🛜♫

Ely

Drayman's Son 🅛
29A Forehill, CB7 4AA
☎ (01353) 662920 ⊕ draymansely.com
12 changing beers (sourced nationally; often Three Blind Mice) ⊞
Small and welcoming micropub in former shop premises nostalgically themed with old railway and enamel signs. Drinks are generally delivered to your table. Twelve beers are mostly available – four on handpump and up 11 on KeyKeg and craft keg – sourced mainly from Three Blind Mice and microbreweries. A large range of 20-plus ciders are also available, many sourced locally. The cellar is in a temperature-controlled back room. Local CAMRA Pub of the Year 2023 and local Cider Pub of the Year 2022. ⏷≠❀📗🚃❀🛜

Prince Albert 🅛 ⊘
62 Silver Street, CB7 4JF (opp cathedral car park)
☎ (01353) 663494 ⊕ princealbertely.co.uk
Black Sheep Bitter; Greene King IPA, Abbot; Three Blind Mice Old Brown Mouse; 3 changing beers (sourced nationally) ⊞
This pub has two distinct areas: the front part is a music-free drinkers' pub, with a friendly atmosphere, a loyal crowd of regulars, and a mixture of bench seating and stools; the rear half is a restaurant serving meals and snacks (booking advisable on Sundays). There is also a separate function room, and a garden at the rear, which is secluded and perfect for summer days. The pub is a short walk from Ely Cathedral and just over half a mile from the railway station. Q⏷❀◑♿❀●🚃❀🛜

West End House 🍷 ⊘
16 West End, CB6 3AY
☎ (01353) 662907 ⊕ westendhouseely.co.uk
Lacons Encore; Woodforde's Wherry; 2 changing beers (often St Austell, Timothy Taylor) ⊞
The Westie is a local drinkers' pub in a small community area, a short distance from the cathedral and Oliver Cromwell's House. It is a snug pub with low ceilings, and has four distinct drinking areas and an enclosed patio area. There is a fireplace that is used in the winter, which adds to the atmosphere. In the summer local bands sometimes perform. An excellent pub, very welcoming and also dog friendly. ❀≠❀🛜

Fen Drayton

Three Tuns 🅛
High Street, CB24 4SJ
☎ (01954) 230242 ⊕ threetunsfendrayton.co.uk
Woodforde's Wherry; 3 changing beers (often Nethergate, Timothy Taylor) ⊞
An 18th-century thatched pub, with a traditional bar, complete with stone floor and inglenook fireplace, sitting between two large dining areas. The pub is food oriented and serves locally sourced produce. It also serves up to four well-kept beers, three of which are changing guests.

The large garden is very popular in summer months. The pub was purchased from Greene King in 2019 by a village resident who renovated it and persuaded the popular former licensees to return. The pub gets busy on Sundays. ⏷❀◑P🚃❀🛜♫

Godmanchester

Comrades Club
58 Cambridge Street, PE29 2AY
☎ (01480) 453991 ⊕ godmanchestercomradesclub.co.uk
Sharp's Doom Bar; 2 changing beers (sourced regionally) ⊞
The Comrades Club (Working Men's and Social Club) which started life in 1920 for the Comrades of the Great War, is a respected and established part of the Godmanchester community and is committed to providing members, their families, and visitors with the best facilities, services and entertainment options. It often stocks beers from the north of England as well as national favourites. Bar bingo and karaoke on Friday nights, cash bingo on Tuesdays and Fridays (available to members and non-members). ♿●P♫

Graveley

Three Horseshoes
23 High Street, PE19 6PL
☎ (01480) 700320 ⊕ thethreehorseshoesgraveley.co.uk
2 changing beers (sourced regionally; often Black Sheep, Greene King, Morland) ⊞
A late addition to the village, the pub was built in the early 20th century after the other village pubs closed or burnt down. Graveley airbase was used by RAF bomber squadrons until 1946. Two changing ales are from a regional or microbrewery. Food is served lunchtimes and evenings, except Sunday when there is a three meat carvery at lunchtime only. Quiz nights and a meat raffle are held every Sunday evening. Q⏷❀◑♿♣P🛜

Great Staughton

White Hart
56 The Highway, PE19 5DA (on B645)
☎ (01480) 861131
Batemans XB, XXXB; 1 changing beer ⊞
Passing through the narrow entrance of this fine small former coaching inn, dating back to 1630, takes you back to the days of horse-drawn coaches. The building has been extended and altered, but still warrants a Grade II listing. As well as the main bar there is a small pool room at the front of the pub and a restaurant at the rear. Traditional pub food is served at lunchtime Thursday-Sunday, and on Saturday evening. Q⏷❀◑P❀🛜♫

Harlton

Hare & Hounds
60 High Street, CB23 1ES
☎ (01223) 264698 ⊕ hareandhoundsharlton.co.uk
3 changing beers ⊞
Thatched single-bar 18th-century pub with half-timbered walls, a beamed ceiling and a large fireplace. The large garden has views over the countryside, plus a children's play area and a pétanque pitch. The pub has been owned by a community interest company since 2017. Three changing beers come mainly from local and regional breweries. Cider and perry include locally produced ones. Home-cooked food has a strong reputation, especially Sunday lunch. Quiz night on Sunday, bridge on Tuesday and cribbage on Thursday. Local CAMRA Cider Pub of the Year 2022. Q⏷❀◑♣●P🚃(75)❀🛜♫

Hartford

King of the Belgians ♥ Ⓛ
27 Main Street, PE29 1XU (on old village high steet, parallel to the B1514 from Huntingdon to St Ives)
☎ (01480) 52030 ⊕ kingofthebelgians.com
4 changing beers (sourced locally; often Digfield, Nene Valley, St Austell) Ⓗ
A 16th-century pub at the heart of the community and which actively supports local charities. It hosts beer festivals in May and late August. An ever-changing selection of four real ales and up to 10 local ciders is served, alongside good-value food. The public bar features low oak beams and a copper-topped bar, and there's a separate dining area. Regular quizzes and games nights are held, with an open mic night on the first Monday of each month, a BYO cheese night every second Thursday, and a monthly themed food night.
Q✿⭄❀❀❀➤P➤❀♪

Helpston

Bluebell Ⓛ
10 Woodgate, PE6 7ED
☎ (01733) 252394 ⊕ bluebellhelpston.co.uk
Black Sheep Best Bitter; Woodforde's Wherry; 2 changing beers (sourced locally; often Bowler's, Tydd Steam) Ⓗ
Quaint 17th-century stone village pub, extensively refurbished in 2014, with the main entrance at the side. There are two wood-panelled bars, a number of dining areas, and a snug named after local poet John Clare, who worked in the pub as a pot boy and lived next door 200 years ago. The pub serves beers from Woodforde's and Black Sheep, plus two rotating guests from local breweries. Good-value food is served lunchtime and evenings. Q✿⭄❀❀❀➤P➤❀

Histon

Red Lion Ⓛ ✅
27 High Street, CB24 9JD
☎ (01223) 564437 ⊕ theredlionhiston.co.uk
Adnams Ghost Ship; Oakham Citra; 6 changing beers (sourced regionally) Ⓗ
Two-bar free house adorned with a wonderful collection of breweriana and historical photos. The nine handpumps are in the quieter, chid-free right-hand bar, while the left-hand bar is family- and dog-friendly. There is also a large beer garden with an accommodation block at the rear, and an outside pizza shed. Two beer festivals are held each year: the Easter aperitif, and the main event in September, which raise money for local charitable causes. Q✿⭄❀❀❀❀➤P➤❀♪

Holme

Admiral Wells Ⓛ
41 Station Rd, PE7 3PH (jct of B660 and Yaxley Rd)
☎ (01487) 831214 ⊕ admiralwells.co.uk
Adnams Southwold Bitter, Ghost Ship; Digfield Fools Nook; 1 changing beer (often Adnams, Wadworth) Ⓗ
Officially the lowest level pub in the UK, this Victorian inn was named after one of Nelson's pallbearers. It has two bar/lounge areas in a contemporary style, plus a conservatory and function room at the rear. There is a beer garden outside at the front, a large car park to the side, a marquee with its own bar in the summer, and a children's play area. Four ales are available, one of which is from the local Digfield brewery. The pub received a '20 Years in the Guide' award in 2023. Q✿⭄❀❀❀➤P➤❀

Houghton

Three Horseshoes ✅
The Green, PE28 2BE (off A1123)
☎ (01480) 462410 ⊕ threehorseshoesinnhoughton.co.uk
Greene King IPA; Sharp's Doom Bar; 1 changing beer (often Milton) Ⓖ
Characterful Grade II-listed 17th-century building in a picturesque village, popular with locals as well as walkers and cyclists. The lane opposite leads to the river and the historic Houghton Mill. There are two bar areas and plenty of space for diners. The real ales, which always include one from a local brewery, are served by gravity dispense from a taproom behind the bar. Home-cooked food is available every day, except Monday and Tuesday in winter months. Opens at 5pm on Monday and Tuesday in winter. Q✿⭄❀❀❀➤PȦ➤❀♪

Huntingdon

Old Bridge Hotel Ⓛ ✅
1 High Street, PE29 3TQ (at S end of High St on ring road, by river)
☎ (01480) 424300 ⊕ oldbridgehuntingdon.co.uk
3 changing beers (sourced locally; often Adnams, Lacons, Nene Valley) Ⓗ
An ivy-clad hotel in an 18th-century former private bank at the southern end of the High Street with a prominent position on the banks of the River Great Ouse. Enjoy imaginative and high-quality food in the Terrace Restaurant, the covered patio and the garden area, or simply relax with a drink in the bar or lounge. The award-winning Old Bridge Wine Shop offers wine tasting as a diversion and the bus station is a short walk away.
Q✿⭄❀❀❀Ȧ P➤❀

Sandford House ✅
George Street, PE29 3AD
☎ (01480) 432402
Greene King IPA, Abbot; Sharp's Doom Bar; 3 changing beers (sourced nationally; often Adnams, Oakham, Titanic) Ⓗ
A stylish conversion of two Victorian buildings by JD Wetherspoon, offering several different drinking and eating areas. Sandford House is built on the site of the original Huntingdon Theatre, and a chapel dating from 1848, and was the home of the local Victorian industrialist Charles Sandford Windover. More recent uses include the town's post office and a furniture retailer. It serves the usual Wetherspoon's range of good-value food and drinks, and there is a 22-room hotel is at the rear of the pub. Q✿⭄❀❀❀Ȧ❀➤❀

Linton

Wylde Sky Taproom Ⓛ
Unit 8A, The Grip Industrial Estate, CB21 4XN
☎ (01223) 778350 ⊕ wyldeskybrewing.com
House beer (by Wylde Sky) Ⓗ
Opened in 2018 in an industrial estate on the outskirts of Linton, Wylde Sky started by brewing a wide range of craft keg beers, which are available in the taproom, along with guest beers from KeyKegs. Recently, they have started brewing cask ales. Their first brew is a traditional English Best Bitter, and the range will be extended gradually. Various gourmet food vans attend the taproom in the evenings, and DJs and other music is featured. ⭄❀P➤(13)❀♪

Little Gransden

Chequers ★ 🄻
71 Main Road, SG19 3DW
☎ (01767) 677348 ⊕ chequersgransden.co.uk
Lacons Norfolk Gem, Legacy; 1 changing beer (sourced locally) 🄷
Village pub owned and run by the same family for over 70 years (and in this Guide for 29). The unspoilt middle bar, with its wooden benches and roaring fire, is a favourite spot to pick up on the local gossip. When brewing, the pub's Son of Sid brewhouse supplies the pub and local beer festivals. Home-made pizzas are available on Friday nights (booking essential). Winner of numerous CAMRA awards and finalist for the National CAMRA Pub of the Year 2018. Q❀🕭⋏⬥P🛏🖵❀🛜

March

Rose & Crown 🄻
41 St Peters Road, PE15 9NA
☎ (01354) 652077
St Austell Tribute; 4 changing beers (often Adnams, St Austell, Tydd Steam) 🄷
150-year-old traditional community pub with two carpeted rooms and low-beamed ceilings. Ale lovers prepared to make the walk away from the town centre will receive a warm welcome, and there's a real fire in the main bar. Normally five real ales are on offer from mainly small breweries, with at least one St Austell beer. There is also a large selection of gins and single malt whiskies. Good-quality food is served at lunchtimes and evenings. Quiz night is Thursday. It received a '10 Years in the Guide' award in 2023. Q❀🕭P🖵(33,46)🛜♪

Ship Inn 🄻
1 Nene Parade, PE15 8TD
☎ (01354) 607878
Timothy Taylor Landlord; 3 changing beers (often Church End, Lacons, Tydd Steam) 🄷
Thatched Grade II-listed riverside pub built in 1680, with extensive riverside moorings. It reopened in 2010 as a free house after a major refit. The unusual carved beams are said to have 'fallen off a barge' during the building of Ely Cathedral. A quaint wobbly floor and wall lead to the toilets and a small games room. Friendly and welcoming, the Ship is a Guide regular and winner of CAMRA Gold Awards in 2012 and 2019. Q🌤❀♣🖵(33,46.)❀🛜♪

Maxey

Blue Bell 🄻
39 High Street, PE6 9EE
☎ (01778) 348182
Abbeydale Absolution; Fuller's London Pride, ESB; Oakham Bishops Farewell; 4 changing beers (sourced regionally; often Grainstore, Ossett, Woodforde's) 🄷
Originally a limestone barn, the building was converted many years ago and reflects its rural setting. Paraphernalia of country life adorns the stone walls and shelves of the two-roomed interior. Nine handpumps dispense a range of quality ales from large and small breweries far and wide. The pub is a popular meeting place for several groups including birdwatchers and golfers. A former local CAMRA Pub of the Year and Gold Award winner. Opening hours may reduce in winter. Q❀♣P🖵(22,413) ❀🛜

Newton

Queen's Head ★
Fowlmere Road, CB22 7PG
☎ (01223) 870436 ⊕ queensheadnewton.co.uk
Adnams Southwold Bitter; 2 changing beers (sourced regionally) 🄶
This village local is one of only a handful of pubs to have appeared in every edition of the Guide, and a list of landlords displayed in the public bar has only 18 entries since 1729. The cosy lounge has a welcoming fire in the colder months. Adnams Bitter and up to three other beers are available from the stillage directly behind the bar, and there's real cider from Crone's. A monthly Saturday bistro night and Wednesday night food vans have been added to the standard soup and sandwiches, and an expanded menu is available Thursday-Saturday evenings and on Sundays. Q❀🕭♣⬥P🖵(31)❀🛜

Peakirk

Ruddy Duck
12 St Pegas Road, PE6 7NF
☎ (01733) 252426 ⊕ ruddyduckpeakirk.co.uk
Digfield Barnwell Bitter; Hop Back Summer Lightning; 2 changing beers (often Black Sheep, Tydd Steam) 🄷
Formerly the Black Bull, this Grade II-listed stone building is the last of the three pubs in Peakirk. Well-known for its food while retaining some of the feel of a village local, the pub consists of three rooms: a small, basic bar; a long, comfortable bar/lounge with a low-beamed ceiling; and a small dining room. Two pairs of handpumps at either end of the bar dispense four different ales at any time. Outside is a large patio area where occasional live music and beer festivals are held. ❀🕭P🖵(411,413) ♪

Peterborough

Blue Bell 🄻
6 The Green, Werrington, PE4 6RU
☎ (01733) 571264
Elgood's Cambridge Bitter; 3 changing beers (often Dark Star, Fuller's, Hop Back) 🄷
An 1890s brick-built pub on the village green, with a light, airy front bar and a comfortable lounge restaurant providing meals from an extensive home-cooked menu. It has a large garden with an outdoor bar, lots of seating and family pods. It serves possibly the best Elgood's beer in the city, and interesting guest ales from a restricted list. There is regular live entertainment, and darts, pool and cribbage are played. Sunday is quiz night. Winner of local CAMRA Gold Award in 2022 and City Pub of the Year 2023. Q❀🕭&♣⬥P🖵(1)❀♪

Bumble Inn 🏆
46 Westgate, PE1 1RE
⊕ thebimbleinn.wordpress.com
5 changing beers (sourced regionally; often North Riding (Brewery), Rockingham, Rooster's) 🄷
This micropub opened in 2016 as a former chemist's shop. Minimalist in style, it has five handpumps dispensing quality ales from far and wide, so expect the unusual from regional and national brewers. Taster paddles of three thirds are available, as are bottled and canned beers, plus two craft keg beers, and two ciders. Also serves a small selection of wines, spirits and soft drinks. Nepalese food is available to order from next door. Local CAMRA Pub of the Year 2024. ⇌⬥🖵🛜

Charters 🄻
Town Bridge, PE1 1FP (down steps at Town Bridge)
☎ (01733) 315700 ⊕ charters-bar.com
Oakham JHB, Inferno, Citra, Bishops Farewell; 4 changing beers (often Nene Valley) 🄷/🄶

This converted Dutch grain barge sits on the River Nene near the city centre. An oriental restaurant is on the upper deck and food is also served in the bar. The large garden, with covered areas, a bar and landing stage for boats, is popular in summer. Up to 10 ales are available, plus ciders. Live music plays most weekends, outside the pub in summer. Popular with football fans on match days. Close to the Nene Valley Railway. Dogs are welcome. Local CAMRA Gold Award winner in 2023. ⍟⍟⍟⍟⍟⍟⍟⍟(1,3) ⍟ ⍟ ♪

Draper's Arms ⃞

29-31 Cowgate, PE1 1LZ

☎ (01733) 847570

Brewster's Hophead; Grainstore Ten Fifty; Greene King Abbot; Ruddles Best Bitter; Sharp's Doom Bar; Titanic Plum Porter; 4 changing beers (often Brewster's, Grainstore, Newby Wyke) ⃞

A converted former draper's shop, built in 1899 and one of the two Wetherspoon pubs in the city. The beer range, with many from local microbreweries, is dispensed through 12 handpumps. The interior is broken up, with intimate wood-panelled spaces and dividers, and there is a new roof terrace. Food is served all day and regular beer and cider festivals are held throughout the year. A quiz is held on Wednesday evening. A regular top 10-listed real ale pub within the company's chain. Close to bus and railway stations. Q⍟⍟⍟⍟⍟⍟⍟⍟

Frothblowers ⃞

78 Storrington Way, Werrington, PE4 6QP

☎ 07756 066503 ⊕ frothblowers.site

7 changing beers (sourced regionally; often Bowler's, Brewster's, Tydd Steam) ⃞

This micropub is easily accessed by bus from the city centre. It has five handpumps, and more beers available in the cellar, with at least 25 ciders and bottled beers. Alcohol-free beers are also available. A hub of the local community, activities include tap takeovers, acoustic music, bus tours, a summer cycling club and a knitting club. A regular local CAMRA award winner including Cider Pub of the Year in 2023. Cash only.
⍟⍟⍟⍟⍟⍟P⍟⍟(1) ⍟ ♪

Hand & Heart ★ ⃞

12 Highbury Street, PE1 3BE

☎ (01733) 564653

6 changing beers (sourced regionally; often Brewster's, Rockingham, Tydd Steam) ⃞/⃞

Rebuilt in 1938, this Art Deco-style community local has been identified by CAMRA as having a nationally important historic pub interior. A drinking corridor connects the rear room to the main public bar, with its war memorial and real fire. Traditional pub games are played. Up to six handpumped ales are served, with more from the cellar. The range is eclectic and forever changing. Beer festivals with live music are held in the large garden. A former local and county CAMRA Pub of the Year and winner of a '20 years in the Guide' award in 2023. Q⍟⍟⍟⍟⍟⍟(1,62)⍟ ♪

Ostrich Inn ⃞

17 North Street, PE1 2RA

☎ 07307 195560 ⊕ ostrichinnpeterborough.com

5 changing beers (sourced regionally; often Nene Valley, Thornbridge, Tiny Rebel) ⃞

Refurbished in 2009, the pub reopened with its original name restored. A U-shaped bar in this one-room pub has up to five regularly changing beers on offer, many from local breweries, alongside craft keg and KeyKeg lines. A large gin selection is also available. Live music is played up to four evenings most weeks, including weekends. The small enclosed patio is a sun trap. Hot pies are

available. Busy on Peterborough United match days. Local CAMRA City Pub of the Year 2022. ⍟⍟⍟⍟⍟⍟⍟⍟P⍟⍟ ♪

Palmerston Arms ⃞

82 Oundle Road, PE2 9PA

☎ (01733) 565865

Batemans XB ⃞/⃞**; Castle Rock Harvest Pale; Oakham Citra; 4 changing beers (sourced regionally; often Lacons, Ossett, St Austell)** ⃞

Popular 400-year old listed stone-built locals' pub. Owned by Batemans, two of their beers are rotated alongside four or more other real ales, including Oakham Ales or Nene Valley brewery. Traditional cider, perries and an extensive range of malt whiskies are available. Most beers are served straight from the cellar, which can be seen through a large glass screen. Rolls and a variety of snacks are served. Can get busy on football match days. ⍟⍟⍟⍟⍟(1,24)⍟ ⍟

Wonky Donkey ⃞

102C High Street, Fletton, PE2 8DR

☎ 07919 470635

Dancing Duck Abduction; 4 changing beers (sourced locally; often Digfield, Mile Tree, Tydd Steam) ⃞/⃞

Housed in two rooms of a former florists, this is Peterborough's latest micropub, situated in a previously pub-free area. Run by the brothers of one of the Frothblowers licencees, it usually offers five beers, many straight from the cask, mostly LocAles. It also stocks a large range of ciders, wines and gins, along with several quality bottled lagers. Themed evenings include pop-up food nights. The pub regularly helps to brew house specials with local brewery, Mile Tree. Local CAMRA Gold Award recipient in 2021. ⍟⍟⍟⍟⍟⍟(5)⍟ ♪

Woolpack ⍟

29 North Street, Stanground, PE2 8HR (in old part of Stanground village by river Nene)

☎ (01733) 753544 ⊕ thewoolpack.pub

Timothy Taylor Landlord; 3 changing beers (sourced regionally; often Nene Valley, Ossett, Tydd Steam) ⃞

Originally built in 1711, a medieval wall remains in the garden and the old barn used to be the village mortuary (last used in the 1850s). The covered beer garden is used for live music and leads to the old River Nene, with boat moorings available. The L-shaped bar has TVs and a dartboard and is adorned with old photos and prints. At least two guest beers are available. The pub is on the city Green Wheel cycle route. Former local CAMRA Pub of the Year. Q⍟⍟⍟⍟⍟⍟⍟ ♪

Yard of Ale

72 Oundle Road, PE2 9PA

☎ (01733) 348000 ⊕ theyardofalepub.co.uk

Sharp's Doom Bar; house beer (by Digfield); 4 changing beers (often Rooster's, Tydd Steam) ⃞

Built on land that was part of the nearby Palmerston Arms stable yard, this 120-year-old pub was refurbished and reopened in 2017. Tastefully decorated in shades of grey with a warm wooden bar and surround, the large, open-plan single room is split into four distinct areas. Entertainment includes sports TV, darts, a pool table, and live music most weekends. A large beer garden with pizza oven operates in the summer months. A former local CAMRA Pub of the Year. ⍟⍟⍟⍟⍟(1)⍟ ♪

Ramsey

Angel

76 High Street, PE26 1BS

☎ (01487) 711968

Adnams Ghost Ship; Greene King Abbot; 2 changing beers (often Lacons, Orkney, Tydd Steam) [H]
This traditional brick-built two-room pub was refurbished in 2019. The main bar area contains two dartboards, a jukebox, pool table and plenty of seating and is accessed from the rear car park and beer garden. The lounge is accessed from the main road and the rear. Friendly staff and locals make this a great place to enjoy a drink or two, with a LocAle always being available, usually from Tydd Steam. 🛋❀♣P🚌(31)🐾📶

Reach

Dyke's End
8 Fair Green, CB25 0JD
☎ (01638) 743816 🌐 dykesendreach.co.uk
Woodforde's Wherry; 2 changing beers (sourced regionally) [H]
Quintessential village pub. The interior has a cosy taproom, and a larger dining area serving freshly prepared meals. Photos and art of local interest adorn the walls. The front garden overlooks the village green where the Reach Fair takes place on the early May bank holiday Monday. Its cask ales are sourced from small and medium-sized regional breweries, sometimes including the nearby Moonshine brewery.
Q🛋❀◐♿♣P🚌(11)🐾📶♫

St Ives

Nelson's Head [L]
Merryland, PE27 5ED
☎ (01480) 494146 🌐 nelsonsheadpubstives.co.uk
Greene King IPA, Abbot; Oakham JHB; Timothy Taylor Landlord [H]
Popular pub in a picturesque narrow street in the town centre. Alongside the beers from Greene King there are two other regulars. The interior has two distinct areas and there is a large outdoor patio. Lunchtime food is available daily. Live bands play on Sunday afternoons, when the pub gets very busy. ❀◐🚌🐾📶♫

Swan & Angel ✔
Market Hill, PE27 5AL
☎ (01480) 499060
Greene King Abbot; Ruddles Best Bitter; Sharp's Doom Bar; 3 changing beers (sourced nationally) [H]
Large open-plan pub in St Ives town centre, converted from a shop unit in 2017. It has a rear outdoor drinking area, and a few pavement tables at the front. Good-value meals from the standard Wetherspoon menu are available throughout the day. Six real ales are served from 12 handpumps; three regular and three changing beers from around the country. Two annual beer festivals are held, which add to the selection of ales on sale.
🛋❀◐♿🚌📶

St Neots

Ale Taster
25 Russell Street, PE19 1BA
☎ (01480) 581368
4 changing beers (sourced regionally) [G]
A small back-street pub in the style of a micropub. It features up to three changing beers, which are served from stillage behind the bar. There are also up to nine real ciders and perry, all sourced from local producers where possible. Three large fridges display a wide selection of bottled beers from around the world. The pub encourages conversation, with quiet background music and no electronic machines. Traditional bar games can be played. Q🛋❀♣🍎P🚌(905)🐾

> When you have lost your inns, drown your empty selves, for you will have lost the last of England.
> **Hilaire Belloc, The Four Men, 1912**

Pig 'n' Falcon [L]
9 New Street, PE19 1AE (behind Barretts department store in town centre)
☎ 07591 296155 🌐 pignfalcon.co.uk
6 changing beers (sourced locally; often Lacons, Potbelly, Three Blind Mice) [G]
Busy town-centre pub serving up to six real ales and several real ciders, focusing on microbreweries and unusual beers including milds, porters and stouts. It also has a good range of bottled ciders, and UK and foreign bottled beers including Trappist ales. Live blues and rock nights are hosted on Wednesday, Friday, Saturday and Sunday. Outside is a large, imaginatively created covered and heated beer garden. Three Blind Mice beers are real ale served in Keykegs. 🛋❀🍎🍺🚌(905)🐾♫

Weeping Ash ✔
15 New Street, PE19 1AE (off town centre)
☎ (01480) 408330
Greene King Abbot; Ruddles Best Bitter; 6 changing beers [H]
Wetherspoon conversion of the old Victorian town post office, named after a large weeping ash tree that used to be on the site before the post office was built. A large, open, wood-panelled bar area with period decor leads to separate dining areas, and an outdoor patio at the rear. It features lots of local history and postal memorabilia, including post boxes, and one long bar with a mural above depicting the local area. 🛋❀◐♿🚌(905)📶

Stapleford

Three Horseshoes
2 Church Street, CB22 5DS
☎ (01223) 503402 🌐 threehorseshoes-pub.co.uk
Stancill Barnsley Bitter; 4 changing beers (sourced regionally) [H]
Friendly village local just south of Cambridge, which is popular with the local community and visitors from surrounding villages. The central bar area is popular with drinkers, while food is normally served in the large room on the right-hand side. There is a sheltered beer garden at the back, including a barbecue. Beers are sourced from various breweries, including Nene Valley, Church End and Buntingford. A variety of food is available, with the accent on traditional Cypriot and Greek dishes.
🛋❀◐🚆(Shelford) 🍎P🚌🐾♫

Swaffham Prior

Red Lion
43 High Street, CB25 0LD
☎ (01223) 650999
Batemans Gold; 3 changing beers (often Batemans) [H]
Attractive 17th-century country pub in the centre of the village. Steps lead up to the front door, beyond which is a brick-faced main bar, a red and cream tiled floor, and exposed ceiling and wall beams. To the left is the dining area, and to the right a cosy public bar with an open fire and TV. The village's two churches can been seen from the raised enclosed rear garden. Four handpumps offer Batemans beers and others from their guest list.
🛋❀◐♣P🚌(11)🐾📶♫

Thriplow

Green Man 🅛
2 Lower Street, SG8 7RJ
☎ (01763) 208855 ⊕ thegreenmanthriplow.co.uk
Buntingford Hurricane; Woodforde's Wherry; 1 changing beer (sourced regionally) Ⓗ
Purchased by villagers in 2013, this pub has a reputation for good food and beer. The ales tend to come from smaller regional breweries. The light interior is in two sections: to the left is a village pub area complete with open fire, while to the right a larger area is mostly for dining. There is outside seating on the green in front of the pub and in the pleasant rear garden. A former local CAMRA Rural Pub of the Year. Q🛏🏵🕙🌑&P🖵(31)🐾🎵

Warboys

Royal Oak ✅
70 Mill Green, PE28 2SB
☎ (01487) 824848 ⊕ royaloakwarboys.com
Fuller's London Pride; 1 changing beer (sourced nationally) Ⓗ
This popular village pub reopened in 2022. There is a large main bar and a separate dining room. Outside there is a large beer garden at the front of the pub. One regular and one changing real ale are always available. A good selection of traditional pub food is cooked to order, with roasts on a Sunday. Regular events are held, including live music nights. Q🛏🏵🕙🌑♣P🖵🐾🎵

Whittlesey

Boat Inn 🅛
2 Ramsey Road, PE7 1DR
☎ (01733) 202488 ⊕ quinnboatinn.wordpress.com
4 changing beers (sourced regionally; often Parkway, Tydd Steam) Ⓗ/Ⓖ
This corner pub consists of two rooms: a public bar with sports TV, and a cosy lounge. The pub hosts a whisky club on the second Friday of the month, and organises regular trips to tasting events. A large number of traditional ciders and perries supplement the real ales, some of which are served direct from the cask. Outside is a pétanque terrain which is used by dancers at the Straw Bear Festival in January. 🛏🏵🚄&♣P🖵(31)🐾🎵

Letter B 🅛
53-57 Church Street, PE7 1DE
☎ (01733) 206975 ⊕ theletterb.co.uk
Sharp's Atlantic; 4 changing beers (often Digfield, Nene Valley) Ⓗ
This 200-year-old pub has two bars, a small side room with a bar billards table, and a decked rear patio area. A beer festival is held in January during the Straw Bear Festival weekend, which is very popular with locals and

visitors. Over recent years the cider range has expanded rapidly to support the five real ales. Winner of numerous local CAMRA. Accommodation is sometimes available. Q🛏🏵🕙🌑♣P🖵(31,33)🐾🎵

Willingham

Bank Micropub
9 High Street, CB24 5ES
☎ (01954) 200045 ⊕ thebankmicropub.co.uk
3 changing beers Ⓖ
Formerly a village bank, this single-room micropub has a short bar rescued from a closed Cambridge pub. Its walls are decorated with photos of local interest. A wide range of beers are available, direct from the cask, from membrane keg or from keg. There's also a fridge well-stocked with cans. Ciders include local Foxhay in bottles. The Bank offers a warm welcome and the casual visitor is certain to be included in local conversation. Q♣🐶🖵🐾

Witcham

White Horse Inn
7 Silver Street, CB6 2LF (1 mile from A142 jct, then first left)
☎ (01353) 777999
Elgood's Cambridge Bitter; 2 changing beers (sourced regionally; often Parkway, Rocket Ales, Wolf) Ⓗ
Popular, family-friendly village pub with a constantly changing selection of real ales, mostly from East Anglia. As well as the main bar, there is a dining area and pool table area. Witcham village is famous for hosting the annual world pea-shooting championship, normally on the second weekend in July. The pub sign is unique, depicting the current world champion in battle dress astride a white horse and with pea shooter held aloft. Q🛏🏵🕙🌑♣🖵🎵

Yaxley

Farmers
200 Broadway, PE7 3NT
☎ (01733) 244885 ⊕ thefarmersyaxley.co.uk
Grainstore Ten Fifty; 3 changing beers (sourced locally; often Xtreme) Ⓗ
A spacious 1930s red-brick pub and multi-room restaurant, with large outdoor areas. Four handpumps serve a minimum of three beers at any one time. Xtreme Ales are from the landlord's brother's brewery. There's ample room to sit and drink but no space at the bar to stand. The emphasis is on dining, with an extensive menu available every day. The pub holds mini beer and music festivals at various times. A large function room is available for parties and weddings. 🛏🏵🕙🌑&♣P🖵(5)🎵

This real ale is locally-brewed

Many entries in the Guide refer to pubs' support for CAMRA's LocAle scheme. The ᴸ symbol is used where a pub has LocAle accreditation. The aim of the scheme is to get publicans to stock at least one cask beer that comes from a local brewery, usually no more than 30 miles away.

The aim is a simple one: to cut down on 'beer miles'. Research by CAMRA shows that food and drink transport accounts for 25 per cent of all HGV vehicle miles in Britain. Taking into account the miles that ingredients have travelled on top of distribution journeys, an imported lager produced by a multi-national brewery could have notched up more than 24,000 'beer miles' by the time it reaches a pub.

Supporters of LocAle point out that £10 spent on locally-supplied goods generates £25 for the local economy. Keeping trade local helps enterprises, creates more economic activity and jobs, and makes other services more viable. The scheme also generates consumer support for local breweries.

Support for LocAle has grown at a rapid pace since it was created in 2007. It's been embraced by pubs and CAMRA branches throughout England and has now crossed the borders into Scotland and Wales.

For more information, see camra.org.uk/locale

What is CAMRA LocAle?

- An initiative that promotes pubs which sell locally-brewed real ale

- The scheme builds on a growing consumer demand for quality local produce and an increased awareness of 'green' issues

Everyone benefits from local pubs stocking locally brewed real ale...

- Public houses, as stocking local real ales can increase pub visits

- Consumers, who enjoy greater beer choice and locally brewed beer

- Local brewers, who gain from increased sales and get better feedback from consumers

- The local economy, because more money is spent and retained in the local economy

- The environment, due to fewer 'beer miles' resulting in less road congestion and pollution

- Tourism, due to an increased sense of local identity and pride – let's celebrate what makes our locality different

CHESHIRE

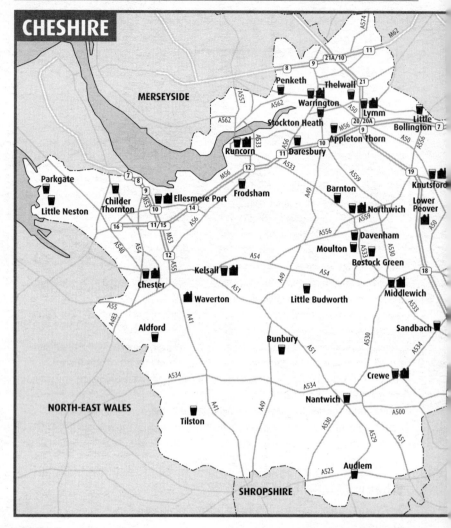

Map of Cheshire showing: MERSEYSIDE, Parkgate, Little Neston, Childer Thornton, Ellesmere Port, Frodsham, Runcorn, Penketh, Warrington, Stockton Heath, Thelwall, Lymm, Appleton Thorn, Daresbury, Little Bollington, Barnton, Northwich, Lower Peover, Knutsford, Davenham, Moulton, Bostock Green, Middlewich, Kelsall, Chester, Waverton, Little Budworth, Sandbach, Aldford, Bunbury, Crewe, NORTH-EAST WALES, Tilston, Nantwich, Audlem, SHROPSHIRE

Aldford

Grosvenor Arms ⓛ
Chester Road, CH3 6HJ (on B5130)
☎ (01244) 620228
Timothy Taylor Landlord; Weetwood Eastgate; house beer (by Brightside); 3 changing beers (sourced nationally) Ⓗ
A spacious, stylish and characterful pub that is unashamedly upmarket. The decor in this multi-roomed pub is modern-traditional, with lots of bare wood, bookcases, pictures and chalkboards. A pleasant garden room leads to an outside terrace and garden, which in turn leads on to the village green. Three changing beers, which occasionally include a mild, complement the house beer brewed by Brightside, plus Weetwood and Timothy Taylor. High-quality food from an imaginative menu is served all day. Q🏠🕭🕭◐🚶♣🅿🚌(5)🐾☀🛜

Alsager

Lodge Inn ⓨ
88 Crewe Road, ST7 2JA (jct Crewe Rd/B5077 and Station Rd, opp Church Rd) ⊕ thelodgeinnalsager.co.uk

Oakham Citra; house beer (by Marston's); 6 changing beers (sourced nationally) Ⓗ
This deservedly popular town-centre pub has been sympathetically modernised by the current owners. On entering, there is a smart lounge on the right and a more rustic room on the left, with a real fire. The bar, whose excellent range of real ales and ciders is the main attraction, opens onto both rooms. A third room stretches to the rear and borders the pleasant patio and garden area. Although there is no food, large pork pies are available. Q🏠🕭🕭🚌(3,317)🐾🛜♪

Appleton Thorn

Appleton Thorn Village Hall
Stretton Road, WA4 4RT
☎ (01925) 261187 ⊕ appletonthornvillagehall.co.uk
7 changing beers (sourced nationally) Ⓗ
This award-winning club (CAMRA National Club of the Year winner more than once) in the heart of the community boasts a wide range of independently-brewed real ales which can be served in third-pint paddles. Real ciders, perries and craft beers are also available. The hall comprises a sizeable function room, a

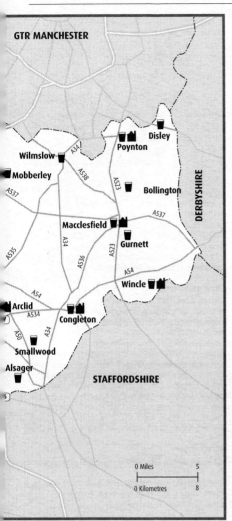

GTR MANCHESTER

Disley
Poynton
Wilmslow
Mobberley
Bollington
DERBYSHIRE
Macclesfield
Gurnett
Wincle
Arclid
Congleton
Smallwood
Alsager
STAFFORDSHIRE

0 Miles 5
0 Kilometres 8

cosy lounge and a small pool room with a garden to the rear. Show a CAMRA card for admission (a small fee may be payable). Closed Monday to Wednesday.
Q🍂❄🐶♣🚭🖶P🚃(Cat8,Cat7)🌮🛜♪

Audlem

Shroppie Fly ✓
Audlem Wharf, Shropshire street, CW3 0DX (on the Shropshire Union Canal bank; follow path from bridge where A525 crosses canal)
☎ (01270) 421396
Salopian Shropshire Gold; Timothy Taylor Landlord; Wye Valley Butty Bach; 3 changing beers (sourced nationally) Ⓗ
Situated near lock 13 on the Audlem flight, outdoor seating makes this an ideal spot to sit and watch the passing narrowboats while enjoying a pint of real ale. Inside, there are two distinct drinking areas and one for diners. The bar servery takes the form of a wooden 'Joey boat', with six handpumps serving a good range of real ales. A good choice of meals is available at reasonable prices. 🍂🌐P🚃(71,73)🌮🛜

Barnton

Barnton Cricket Club Ⓛ
Broomsedge, Townfield Lane, CW8 4QL (200yds from A533, down narrow drive to left of Barnton Community Primary School)
☎ (01606) 77702 🌐 barntoncc.co.uk
Sharp's Doom Bar; 3 changing beers (sourced nationally) Ⓗ
A sport-based club with two main areas: the member's bar has TVs (sound muted) showing live sport; the large lounge overlooking the patio and cricket pitch accommodates family parties and sporting audiences. Cricket predominates in summer but at other times it's a good place to watch the big match of choice. Crown green bowls, squash, darts and dominoes may all be played and there are quiz and bingo nights and occasional music events. Show your CAMRA membership card for admission. 🍂❄🌐♣🚭P🚃(Cat9,N4)🛜♪

Bollington

Cotton Tree ✓
3-5 Ingersley Road, SK10 5RE
☎ 07458 302857
Draught Bass; Timothy Taylor Landlord; Theakston Best Bitter; Wainwright Gold; 2 changing beers (sourced nationally) Ⓗ
Traditional, welcoming wet-led local, the Cotton is a family-run pub with a collection of memorabilia based on local transport and agriculture complimented by a roaring fire and stone floor. Six real ales are available, including two guests that change weekly, and several ciders and perries. No food, except local pies on Friday and Saturday. Apart from a monthly jamming session there is no music or TV. Cash preferred. The pub is next to the bus terminus (last bus leaves around 6.30pm).
Q🍂❄🐶🚃(10,391)🌮🛜

Poachers Inn Ⓛ
95 Ingersley Road, SK10 5RE
☎ (01625) 572086 🌐 thepoachers.org
Beartown Glacier; Storm Desert Storm; 3 changing beers (sourced locally) Ⓗ
The Poachers is a flagship real ale pub at the heart of the local community. It hosts many local groups and is popular with walkers and cyclists. The guest beers, which always include a dark beer, come from a wide range of microbreweries, many local, and are complemented by locally sourced, fresh home-made food. The real fire, suntrap garden and sumptuous sofas provide added conviviality. Quiz nights for local charities are on the second and last Sunday of each month. Dogs welcome.
🍂❄🌐🚭P🚃(10,391)🌮🛜♪

Vale Inn Ⓛ
29-31 Adlington Road, SK10 5JT
☎ (01625) 575147 🌐 valeinn.co.uk
Bollington White Nancy, Long Hop, Bollington Best, Oat Mill Stout, Eastern Nights Ⓗ
Terraced 1860s pub with an open-plan single room and a cosy corner featuring a real fire. The garden overlooks the cricket ground and has its own bar in summer. Excellent home-cooked food is served, and Bollington brewery beers are available to take away (pre-order advisable). The pub is close to the Macclesfield Canal and Middlewood Way. 🍂❄🌐♣🚭P🚃(10,391)🌮🛜

Bostock Green

Hayhurst Arms Ⓛ
London Road, CW10 9JP (off A533 Bostock Rd)
☎ (01606) 541810

Weetwood Cheshire Cat, Eastgate; house beer (by Brightside); 4 changing beers (sourced locally) H
Built in 1845, this was previously a social club before being purchased by pubco Brunning & Price. In common with their other pubs, a relaxed atmosphere prevails. Walls are festooned with period framed photographs and art throughout (even in the toilets!). It is largely open plan, with exposed beams, but there are several smaller areas for a quiet pint. Dining is popular (booking recommended). A private dining room is available for free hire by groups. 🛏️🕗🍴⛲♿♣P🐾🎵🛜

Bunbury

Dysart Arms L
Bowe's Gate Road, CW6 9PH (jct Bowe's Gate Rd, College Ln and Wyche Ln)
☎ (01829) 260183 ⊕ dysartarms-bunbury.co.uk
House beer (by Brightside); 3 changing beers (sourced regionally; often Big Hand, Twisted Wheel, Weetwood) H
Pleasant, 19th-century village pub opposite St Boniface's church. The pub was named after the local landowners, the Tollemache family, who were the Earls of Dysart. The decor is mainly wood, with bookcases, and pictures adorning the walls. Beers are Brunning & Price Original Bitter and three varying beers from local breweries. Good food is served, sourced from local produce. There are also regular dog walks on Sunday mornings and charitable events. Q🛏️🕗🍴♿P🐾🛜

Chester

Bluestone
117 Christleton Road, CH3 5UQ (on main A41 road out of Chester)
☎ (01244) 738149 ⊕ bluestonebar.co.uk
3 changing beers (sourced nationally) H
Small community micropub in the Boughton area of Chester. Real ale is dispensed from three handpumps, and there are 10 keg beer lines. Up to four real ciders are on offer and a wide selection of canned and bottled beers are available from fridges next to the bar. The interior has a mixture of high stools and low-level upholstered bench seats. There is also some seating on the pavement outside. Children are welcome until 7pm. 🛏️♣🍴🖥🐾🛜

Brewery Tap L
52-54 Lower Bridge Street, CH1 1RU
☎ (01244) 340999 ⊕ spittingfeathers.co.uk/the-brewery-tap
Spitting Feathers Thirstquencher, Special Ale; 5 changing beers (sourced nationally; often Castle Rock, Magic Rock, Northern Monk) H
Stunning Jacobean great hall with high barrel-vaulted ceiling. Its features include an ornate sandstone fireplace, tapestries, and stone floors that create a terrific ambience. A fitting winner of CAMRA's Heritage Conservation and Conversion to Pub Use award. Inventive, freshly prepared food is locally sourced. Eight ales are available, with several of their own Spitting Feathers beers complemented by a range of guests which are often from other regional microbreweries. The pub is reached by a flight of stone steps from street level. Q🍴♣🖥🐾🛜

Cavern of the Curious Gnome 🏆
61 Bridge Street Row East, CH1 1NW
☎ (01244) 641704 ⊕ thecavernofthecuriousgnome.co.uk
Ossett White Rat; 3 changing beers (sourced nationally; often Vocation) H

Belgian-themed bar on Chester's famous Rows. Enter via Paysan wine bar then climb the steps up to the bar where a colourful large papier-mâché gnome gazes down on proceedings. Red-and-white spotted toadstool seats plus tables with bench seating catch the eye, with more quirkiness to be found among the decor. Four handpumps serve changing cask ales from all over the UK. Belgian offerings include lambics, gueuzes and Trappist ales, plus Duvel on draught. 🕗♿🍴🖥🛜

Cellar
19-21 City Road, CH1 3AE
☎ (01244) 318950 ⊕ thecellarchester.co.uk
Timothy Taylor Landlord; 5 changing beers (sourced nationally; often Marble, Salopian, Vocation) H
Friendly street-level bar whose name relates to the function room in the cellar below. It is deservedly renowned for its excellent selection of cask ales. A regular beer such as Timothy Taylor Landlord is complented by five guest beers and three real ciders. There is also an extensive range of keg and bottled beers from around the world. Sport features on three large TV screens. The food offering consists of pizzas and meat and cheese platters. 🍴≈♣🖥🐾🛜

Cornerhouse
4-8 City Road, CH1 3AE
☎ (01244) 347518 ⊕ cornerhousechester.com
Salopian Oracle; 3 changing beers (sourced nationally) H
Situated in Chester's thriving Canal Quarter, this attractive, candlelit, mock-Tudor building features lots of bare brick and wood flooring. It offers one regular beer and three changing ales – usually one dark – plus an extensive bottled beer selection. Live music is hosted Thursday to Saturday and a quiz on Sunday. There is a a free-to-hire function room upstairs. Outside seating is at the front of the pub. Food consists of platters (meats and cheeses), tapas, pizzas and snacks. 🕗🍴≈♣🐾🖥🛜🎵

Deva Tap
121 Brook Street, CH1 3DU (at city end of Hoole Bridge, close to railway station)
☎ (01244) 314440 ⊕ thedevatap.co.uk
Ossett White Rat; 2 changing beers (sourced regionally; often Thornbridge) H

REAL ALE BREWERIES

4Ts ⚓ Warrington	
Beartown ⚓ Congleton	
Bollington Macclesfield	
Brewhouse & Kitchen 🍴 Chester	
Coach House Warrington	
Four Priests Middlewich	
Happy Valley Macclesfield (brewing suspended)	
Hush ⚓ Northwich	
Lymm ⚓ Lymm	
MBH Beer Lower Peover	
Merlin Arclid	
Neighbourhood Poynton	
Norton Runcorn	
Oaks Ellesmere Port	
Pied Bull 🍴 Chester	
RedWillow Macclesfield	
Spitting Feathers Waverton	
Spookton ⚓ Chester (NEW)	
Storm Macclesfield	
Tatton Knutsford	
Tay Brew Middlewich (NEW)	
Tom's Tap ⚓ Crewe	
Weetwood ⚓ Kelsall	
Wincle ⚓ Wincle	

This popular venue near the railway station has three distinct seating areas: a small one by the entrance; a large one in the middle; and the bar at the far end. The White Rat is complimented by two guest beers and ciders and a variety of keg and bottled beers. Good-value food includes vegetarian and gourmet burgers. Quiz night is Wednesday and an Oktoberfest is held annually. There is outside seating in a small courtyard at the front. ♿✪❶❺⇆🍴🚪❀🛜🎵

Old Harkers Arms ℐ

1 Russell Street, CH3 5AL (down steps off City Rd to canal towpath)
☎ (01244) 344525
Weetwood Cheshire Cat, Eastgate; house beer (by Brightside); 6 changing beers (sourced nationally) ℍ
Upmarket pub converted from the ground floor of a former Victorian canalside warehouse. Timber flooring, traditional wooden furniture and cast iron pillars provide an insight to its history. Blackboards list real ales, with tasting notes. Three regular and up to six guest ales always offer a good range of styles. Up to four ciders and perries are served from the cellar. Food is available all day (booking is advisable at weekends). Outside seating is alongside the canal. Q✪❶❺⇆🍴🚪❀🛜

Olde Cottage

34-36, Brook Street, CH1 3DZ
☎ (01244) 324065 ⊕ oldecottagechester.co.uk
Otter Bitter; Wye Valley HPA; 2 changing beers (sourced nationally; often Butcombe, Weetwood) ℍ
Welcoming and traditional community local on Brook Street, between the city centre and railway station and popular for eating and drinking. To the left is the games room with pool, darts and a bagatelle table (rarely seen outside Chester). The main bar has another dartboard, small TV, and a real fire for the colder weather. Two regular beers are supplemented by two guests, one of which is free of tie. ✪⇆🍴🚪❀🛜

Telford's Warehouse ℐ

Canal Basin, Tower Wharf, CH1 4EZ (just off city walls)
☎ (01244) 390090 ⊕ telfordswarehousechester.com
Salopian Oracle; Weetwood Cheshire Cat; 2 changing beers (sourced nationally) ℍ
Converted warehouse with large glass frontage overlooking the Shropshire Union canal basin. Some walls retain their original features and are adorned with interesting industrial artefacts. Up to six changing beers are available, usually from microbreweries. The pub is a popular live music venue, charging admission on some evenings after 9pm. Good-quality food is served, and the upstairs restaurant can also be hired for private functions. Outside seating is popular in good weather. ♿✪❶🚪🚌(1A)❀🛜🎵

Childer Thornton

Halfway House

Chester Road, CH66 1QN (on A41, S of M53 jct 5)
☎ (0151) 339 2202
Weetwood Best Bitter; 3 changing beers (sourced regionally) ℍ
Friendly, traditional former coaching inn dating from the 1770s. Although now open plan, it retains much of its original character and intimacy with old prints adorning the walls. The community feel is evident, with darts and domino teams plus a golf society. This smallish pub can be busy when sporting events are on TV. Now free of tie, beers are usually sourced from smaller breweries and change frequently. Quiz night is Thursday. ✪🚪🚌(1,X1)❀🛜🎵

Congleton

BarleyHops

29 High Street, CW12 1BG
☎ (01260) 295247
4 changing beers (sourced regionally) ℍ
This popular beer café relocated in 2021 to a former shop in the centre of town and has quickly re-established its place in this Guide thanks to its excellent cask beers and a laid-back ambience. There are usually four handpumps in use, together with some interesting keg beers and a cider. There are regular live music, vinyl records and games evenings. The fridge contains an enticing range of cans and bottles. ♿❶❀🚪❀🛜🎵

Beartown Tap ℐ

18 Willow Street, CW12 1RL
☎ (01260) 270775
Beartown Glacier, Kodiak, Skinful, Kahuna, Lit, Creme Bearlee; 1 changing beer (sourced locally; often Abbeydale, Beartown, Purple Moose) ℍ
Now independently owned, this continues to be the flagship pub for the nearby Beartown brewery and has won multiple CAMRA awards. Six Beartown beers are always on offer plus a guest ale and cider. There is something happening most nights at this community local, whether it's street food, quiz night, pub games or live music. Conversation thrives downstairs, with a log-burner for the winter, and there is an upstairs area with dartboard and outdoor terrace for the summer. ♿✪❀🚪(92)❀🎵

Queen's Head ℐ

Park Lane, CW12 3DE
☎ (01260) 272546
Draught Bass; Greene King Abbot; Timothy Taylor Landlord; house beer (by Beartown); 2 changing beers (sourced regionally) ℍ
Independent free house opposite the railway station and by bridge 75 on the Macclesfield Canal. The pub was saved from closure a few years ago, and the current owners have focused on quality food offering, while maintaining an excellent reputation for beer. Guest beers are generally from local and regional breweries. Outside seating area can get busy with families during the summer. Live music is played at least once a month, and a music group meets here. It also hosts a popular board-gaming group. ♿✪❶⇆🚪🚌(94)❀🛜🎵

Throstle's Nest

11 Buxton Road, CW12 2DW
☎ (01260) 221725
Draught Bass; 4 changing beers (sourced regionally) ℍ
This pub reopened in 2023 following a high-quality refurbishment by Caldmore Taverns, which included the rooftop terrace. Five cask beers are available, and there are various discounts on offer. Pub games include darts and pool, and there is bingo on the first Tuesday of the month. The pub is a two-mile walk from Congleton station via Macclesfield Canal and Biddulph Valley Way. Winner of the local CAMRA Newcomer award in 2023. ♿✪❀🚪(92)❀🛜🎵

Crewe

Borough Arms ℐ

33 Earle Street, CW1 2BG (on Earle St rail bridge, with entrance up steps in adjoining Thomas St)
10 changing beers (sourced nationally; often Fyne, Oakham, Thornbridge) ℍ
Popular town-centre pub with 10 ever-changing real ales on handpump, normally including a dark beer, and a

good selection of Belgian beers on tap and in bottles. It has three distinct drinking areas on two levels: the upstairs is open plan while downstairs has a large room with a wood-burner in one alcove. This room leads to the sheltered beer garden, which is popular on warm sunny days. Q ☺ 🕏 ♣ 🖢 P 🖪 😾 🗢 ☂

Earl of Chester 🗓

104 Wistaston Road, CW2 7RE (jct Flag Ln/Wistaston Rd)

☎ (01270) 488244

Merlin Merlin's Gold, Excalibur; 1 changing beer (sourced regionally) 🖽

Small, friendly, traditional two-roomed corner pub selling reasonably-priced beers. There are bar and lounge areas plus a pool room that can be used for functions. TVs throughout show a variety of sporting events. The pub hosts darts, dominoes and pool teams, and has regular live music, plus quiz, bingo and karaoke evenings. The main bar area is decorated to reflect the landlady's love of classic rock music. ☺ 🕏 ♣ 🖪 (8) 😾 🗢 🎵

Hops 🗓

Prince Albert Street, CW1 2DF (opp Lifestyle Centre at S end of Prince Albert St)

☎ (01270) 211100 ⊕ hopsbelgianbar.co.uk

6 changing beers (sourced nationally; often Neptune, Thornbridge, Townhouse) 🖽

Friendly, welcoming, family-run café-bar, popular with a wide range of clientele and a great place for conversation. It serves real ales from local and regional breweries, and up to six real ciders or perries from mainly small producers. There is also a great selection of bottled beers, especially Belgian. Hops is an accredited Orval Ambassador, one of only 24 such premises in the UK. A Guide entry continuously since 2007.
Q ☺ 🕏 🕏 ♣ 🖢 🖪 😾 🗢

Raven

Brookhouse Drive, CW2 6NA (jct Brookhouse Dr and Davenport Ave/Broadleigh Way)

☎ (01270) 668004

Sharp's Doom Bar; 4 changing beers (sourced nationally; often Ossett, Titanic, Wye Valley) 🖽

This dog- and family-friendly estate pub, once owned by Boddington's, has an excellent community spirit. The spacious lounge has comfortable seating and a removable stage that is used for live music events at weekends. Outside is a covered terrace and a roof terrace that is open when weather permits. Traditional pub games are played in the separate bar. TVs in all areas show mainly major sporting events.
☺ 🕏 🕏 ♣ P 🖪 (12,39) 😾 🗢 🎵

Daresbury

Ring o' Bells 🗓

Chester Road, WA4 4AJ (just off the A56, in centre of village)

☎ (01925) 740256

Greene King IPA; 6 changing beers (sourced regionally; often Weetwood, Titanic, Phoenix) 🖽

Another year in the Guide for this half-timbered 19th-century building. Once the village courthouse, the pub still retains many of its original features. Although food orientated, this LocAle-accredited Chef & Brewer pub has five handpumps that dispense beers mainly from the Weetwood range. Charles Lutwidge Dodgson, aka Lewis Carroll, was born nearby (his father was the curate of the church opposite) and associated memorabilia features prominently. There is a large beer garden to the rear, and well-behaved dogs are welcome.
☺ 🕏 🕪 ♪ 🕭 P 🖪 (X30) 😾 🗢

Davenham

Davenham Cricket Club 🗓

Butchers Stile, Hartford Road, CW9 8JF (down narrow, signed driveway near brick post box)

☎ (01606) 48922 ⊕ davenham.play-cricket.com

4 changing beers (sourced regionally; often MBH Beer, RedWillow, Salopian) 🖽

This friendly, welcoming community club is hidden away in an idyllic setting on the edge of the village. The outdoor seating terrace is an ideal place to enjoy the cricket and soak up the sun, while sampling a quality ale. Ever-changing local and regional real ales are dispensed from four handpumps. Two beer festivals are held each year. A largescreen TV shows sporting events. During the cricket season the opening hours are extended. Show your CAMRA card for admission. ☺ 🕏 ♿ P 🖪 (37) 😾 🗢

Disley

Malt Disley

22 Market Street, SK12 2AA

☎ (01663) 308020 ⊕ maltdisley.com

Ossett White Rat; 3 changing beers (sourced locally; often RedWillow, Titanic, Torrside) 🖽

Vibrant and friendly converted shop on the A6 in the village centre. This spacious micropub includes a downstairs room/games room. It is open for coffee and cakes at 11am (alcoholic drinks from noon). Four cask beers are available, plus 10 KeyKeg beers, including continental beers and a cider, as well as a range of British and continental bottled beers. A former local CAMRA Pub of the Year, and Cheshire Pub of the Year.
☺ 🕏 🕭 ♣ 🖪 (199) 😾 🗢 🎵

Ellesmere Port

Bondie's Bar 🗓

2 Chester Road, Whitby, CH65 6RU

☎ (0151) 345 8560

House beer (by Coach House); 3 changing beers (sourced locally; often Oaks) 🖽

Ellesmere Port's first micropub, opened in 2021 just outside the town centre, is named after a former landlord of the Sportsman's Arms which stood nearby. It serves a good variety of drinks. The smart, wood-panelled downstairs bar has simple wooden chairs and stools and is complemented by an upstairs lounge with comfortable leather sofas and a variety of games. There are a few outside seats at the front and back.
☺ 🕏 ♣ 🖢 P 🖯 🖪 😾

Frodsham

Helter Skelter 🗓

31 Church Street, WA6 6PN

☎ (01928) 733361 ⊕ thehelterskelter.co.uk

Ossett White Rat; Salopian Oracle, Darwins Origin; Weetwood Best Bitter; 4 changing beers (sourced nationally; often Thornbridge) 🖽

Located close to the railway station, this small and lively single-room bar is a multiple winner of local CAMRA Pub of the Year awards. There are four regular cask ales and a further four changing guest ales from local and national breweries. Dark beers feature regularly. Other beers include rotating craft kegs, imported bottled beers, and a rotating guest cider. Food is served Wednesday to Sunday in the bar and the upstairs Grill@31 restaurant.
Q 🕪 🕭 🖪 😾 🗢 🎵

Gurnett

Olde King's Head 🄻

30 Bradley Smithy, Byrons Lane, SK11 0HD (100yds E of canal on Macclesfield to Sutton road)
☎ (01625) 611444

Timothy Taylor Landlord; house beer (by Wincle); 3 changing beers (often Bollington, Draught Bass, Storm) 🄷

This 17th-century former smithy is well known for good food, served in the bar or dining areas towards the rear of the pub. There is outdoor seating on terracing to the side. The pub has a Champion Club award for its Timothy Taylor Landlord. The house beer is Gurnett Glory, brewed locally by Wincle. Guest beers include at least one LocAle from breweries such as Storm or Red Willow. The pub is next to the Gurnett canal aqueduct, with Macclesfield Forest nearby. 🛇✿🄾🄿➡(14A)🌣🛜♫

Kelsall

Weetwood Tap

Common Lane, CW6 0PY
☎ (01829) 752377 ● weetwoodales.co.uk

Weetwood Best Bitter, Cheshire Cat; 2 changing beers (sourced locally) 🄷

Opened in 2023, this newly built taproom is next to the eponymous brewery, a short walk down country lanes from the village. It comprises a smart and tidy single room with sturdy tables, simple chairs and large windows. Trestles outside cater for warmer weather, when it can be popular with casual cyclists. It stocks a diverse range of Weetwood products for takeout, including their own spirits. There are usually at least three cask ales on handpump. 🛇✿🅟🌣

Knutsford

Wine & Wallop

76 King Street, WA16 6ED
☎ (01565) 228429 ● wineandwallop.co.uk

Brightside Odin Blonde; 2 changing beers (sourced locally; often Marble, Ossett) 🄷

Stylish bar at the heart of Knutsford's busy King Street, offering three or four cask beers from Manchester, Cheshire and Yorkshire, mainly lower strength and pale varieties. The bar benefits from a terrace area on the first floor. The pub has been extended into the premises next door, providing additional seating and the opportunity for occasional live music. Card payment only. 🛇✿🄾➥➡(88,89)🌣🛜♫

Little Bollington

Swan with Two Nicks 🄻 ✅

Park Lane, WA14 4TJ (signposted off A56)
☎ (0161) 928 2915 ● swanwithtwonicks.co.uk

Dunham Massey Little Bollington Bitter; Timothy Taylor Landlord; house beer (by Coach House) 🄷

This quaint country pub has been around since the 1800s and has a rustic and traditional feel, with open fires, original wood beams, brasswear decorations, comfy seating and low-level music playing in the background. The pub serves food and snacks from noon. It is close to the Bridgewater Canal and 10 minutes' walk from the National Trust's Dunham Park. It is accessible by a footpath from the park's Bollin Gate across a footbridge over the river. Family and dog friendly. 🛇✿🄾🄿➡(X5)🌣

Little Budworth

Egerton Arms 🄻

Pinfold Lane, CW6 9BS (on edge of village near Oulton Park and Budworth Common) SJ5942465422
☎ (01829) 760765 ● egerton-arms.co.uk

Weetwood Best Bitter, Cheshire Cat; 4 changing beers (sourced regionally; often Bank Top, Salopian) 🄷

A change of ownership in 2021 has resurrected this friendly, vibrant country pub on the edge of the village. A wood-burner helps to create a cosy atmosphere in winter, while in summer outdoor seating and a beer garden gives the opportunity to watch cricket. Regular quizzes, musical events and beer festivals contribute to the ambience. It has a widescreen TV for sports events. 🛇✿🄾🄸🄰♣🅿🌣🛜♫

Little Neston

Harp 🄻 ✅

19 Quayside, CH64 0TB (turn left at bottom of Marshlands Rd, pub is 300yds on left overlooking marshes)
☎ (0151) 336 6980

Joseph Holt Bitter; Peerless Triple Blond; Timothy Taylor Landlord; 2 changing beers (sourced nationally; often Butcombe, Titanic) 🄷

A former coal miners' inn converted from two cottages, near to the site of Neston Colliery, which closed in 1927. It has a public bar with a real fire in winter and a basic lounge. Set in a glorious location on the Deeside to Neston part of the National Cycle Network, the pub overlooks the Dee Marshes and North Wales, with a large garden and a drinking area abutting the edge of the marshes. No food in the evening, except for a popular curry night every Tuesday; booking advisable. Q🛇✿🄾🄿➡(22,487)🌣

Lymm

Brewery Tap 🍷 🄻

18 Bridgewater Street, WA13 0AB
☎ (01925) 755451 ● lymmbrewing.co.uk

Dunham Massey Dunham Dark; Lymm Bitter, Bridgewater Blonde; 4 changing beers (sourced locally; often Dunham Massey, Lymm) 🄷

A former red-brick post office in the centre of Lymm village near the Bridgewater Canal, on the same site as Lymm brewery. Fully refurbished in 2022, it has cosy seating areas, complemented by subdued lighting, and a wood-burning stove. A dark beer is usually available among four changing beers, plus three regular ales. There is live music at the weekend and a twice-monthly open mic night. Renowned local pies are available at all times. Local CAMRA Pub of the Year 2024. 🛇✿🄾➡🌣🛜♫

Macclesfield

Castle ★ 🄻 ✅

25-27 Church Street, SK11 6LB (walk up cobbled street from Waters Green Car Park, pub is to the left as road bends right)
☎ (01625) 462646

3 changing beers (sourced locally; often RedWillow, Storm, Wincle) 🄷

Tucked away on a cobbled street near the station, this 18th-century listed pub was sympathetically restored in 2021 and has been identified by CAMRA as having a nationally important historic pub interior. Small from the outside but with plenty of seating inside, it has four separate rooms, two of which are served from a handsome bar area. The beer range from the three handpulls is often local and always includes a good mix of styles. An imaginative food menu is available daily (no hot food Mon-Wed). 🛇🏵🅿🌙♿➴⬥🍴🐶🎐🛜🎵

Jack in the Box 🅛

Picturedrome, 102-104 Chestergate, SK11 6DU
Blackjack Irk Street Pale Ale, Jack In The Box Blonde,
Pub Ale: Best Bitter; 4 changing beers (sourced
locally; often Blackjack) Ⓗ
Blackjacks brewery bar is housed in the Picturedrome, which was originally the town's oldest cinema (1911). The bar overlooks a popular seating/dining area surrounded by stalls serving varied types of street food. You can also take your drink down to the eating areas. House beers are provided by Blackjack, plus there is a good range of guests from independent breweries and a wide selection of craft keg, and real cider (from boxes). 🛇🏵🅞🔥➴⬥🚌(88,130) 🐶🎐

Park Tavern 🅛

158 Park Lane, SK11 6UB
☎ (01625) 667846 🌐 park-tavern.co.uk
Bollington White Nancy, Long Hop, Best, Oat Mill
Stout, Eastern Nights Ⓗ
Mid-terrace pub owned by Bollington brewery, a short walk from the town centre. Up to six beers from the Bollington range are served, plus two real ciders. This popular community pub is a great place for conversation, and hosts regular events including film nights in a mini-cinema function room upstairs, plus quizzes or science evenings downstairs. An opened-out area surrounds the bar, with a snug by the front door, and a small outdoor area at the rear. Food is available Thursday to Sunday, 🛇🏵🍴➴⬥🚌(38,3) 🐶🎐

RedWillow 🅛

32A Park Green, SK11 7NA
☎ (01625) 830718 🌐 redwillowbrewery.com
RedWillow Headless; 3 changing beers (often
RedWillow) Ⓗ
This popular bar is the tap for the nearby Redwillow brewery. The original frontage with large glass windows has been kept, with pavement seating, and a mix of sofas, chairs and tables inside. Beers on offer are displayed above the bar. Regular and special brews from the brewery are on handpull and keg, plus a changing range of guest keg beers, usually including at least one dark beer. Up to four traditional ciders are available. Pizzas are served till 8pm. 🛇🏵🅞♿➴⬥🐶🎐🛜

Middlewich

King's Lock 🅛

1 Booth Lane, CW10 0JJ (cross the canal off A533, Booth Ln)
☎ (01606) 836894
4 changing beers (sourced regionally) Ⓗ
Pub on the Trent and Mersey canal with extensive canalside seating, a separate beer garden with marquee, and indoor seating in an opened-out bar area. The bar counter resembles a narrowboat, and alongside the four handpumps serving mainly local ales, homemade cakes are displayed. Locals and visitors, typically narrowboaters, are welcomed and the pub is popular during the town's annual festival and the pub's own regular live music events. 🛇🏵🅞♣🅿🚌(37,42)🐶🎐🛜🎵

White Bear Hotel 🅛

Wheelock Street, CW10 9AG (on right, lower end of Wheelock St, just off the A54/St Michael's Way)
☎ (01606) 837666 🌐 thewhitebearmiddlewich.co.uk
4 changing beers (sourced locally) Ⓗ

A 17th-century coaching inn in the town centre, not far from the canal, which was comprehensively restored in 2011 by the current owner. Its local real ales always include a dark ale and an IPA. It has a large open-plan room off the bar, a separate restaurant, an alfresco patio and an upstairs function room. Convenient for local bus services to Winsford, Northwich, Congleton, Sandbach and Crewe. It appeals to a wide-ranging clientele and is now in its 11th consecutive year in the Guide
🛇🏵🛇🅞🅞🚌(37,42)🐶🎐

Mobberley

Bull's Head 🅛

Mill Lane, WA16 7HX
☎ (01565) 873395 🌐 thebullsheadpub.co.uk
Weetwood Cheshire Cat; house beer (by Weetwood);
3 changing beers (sourced locally) Ⓗ
An excellent country inn, with two open fires, stone floor, candlelit tables, low beams, exposed Cheshire brick and an old back-to-back fireplace. Six Cheshire beers are part of the pub's offering, and house beers are brewed by Weetwood. Each handpump has tasting notes and tasters in tiny mugs are available to help you decide. Much of its good, freshly cooked food is locally sourced. Tables can't be reserved. 🛇🏵🅞♿🚌(88)🐶🎐🛜🎵

Moulton

Lion 🅛

74 Main Road, CW9 8PB
☎ (01606) 606049
Wainwright Gold; 2 changing beers (sourced locally;
often Merlin, Ossett) Ⓗ
Featuring in the Guide for 10 consecutive years, this former local CAMRA Pub of the Year is at the heart of the community. Drinking is the focus here and the pub is a rare local outlet for real cider. Stonebaked pizzas are available daily in the early evening, and there is a smartphone quiz held on a Thursday evening, as well as monthly music quizzes, occasional party nights, singo bingo and karaoke. Key sporting events are shown on the TV. 🛇🏵🅞🅰♣⬥🐶🎐🛜🎵

Nantwich

Black Lion 🅛

29 Welsh Row, CW5 5ED (on Welsh Row, opp Cheshire Cat)
☎ (01270) 628711 🌐 blacklionnantwich.co.uk
Weetwood Best Bitter, Cheshire Cat, Old Dog; 3
changing beers (sourced regionally; often Coach
House) Ⓗ
Grade II-listed black and white pub dating from 1664. It consists of a through bar and lounge with a real fire during colder months. There is an upstairs dining room with extra seating. The outside area includes covered and open seating, with an enclosed area linking it to the pub. Children are welcome till 5pm; over 12s only after that time. Well-behaved dogs are welcome.
Q🏵🅞🅰➴♣⬥🚌(84) 🐶🎐🛜🎵

Crown 🅛

High Street, CW5 5AS (on High St, between Natwest and Café Nero)
☎ (01270) 625283 🌐 crownhotelnantwich.com
Salopian Shropshire Gold; 4 changing beers (sourced
nationally; often Sandstone, Spitting Feathers) Ⓗ
An impressive Grade I-listed black and white timbered building. The entrance in Crown Mews at the side gives way to a comfortable front lounge with a real fire. Seating extends alongside the bar to the rear. Original

beams abound and there are some sloping floors. Food is available all day in the bar and the restaurant at the rear. The relaxed lunchtime atmosphere can become livelier in the evenings. Dogs are welcome, except in the restaurant. ♘🛏◑⇌🚌🐾📶

Vine Inn ✔

42 Hospital Street, CW5 5RP (near St Mary's church in town centre)

☎ (01270) 619055 🌐 vineinnnantwich.co.uk

Hydes Dark Ruby, Hopster, Original, Lowry; 2 changing beers (sourced regionally) Ⓗ

A 17th-century Grade II-listed building on three distinct open-plan levels. It serves a full range of consistently well-conditioned Hydes beer, including craft beers from the Beer Studio. It is a welcoming, family- and dog-friendly pub serving good food, with sports TV in most rooms and a quiet board games room with a real fire at the back. There is also a small beer garden. Now a regular Guide entry. ♘❀◑⇌♣🚌🐾📶♫

Wickstead Arms 🄻 ✔

5 Mill Street, CW5 5ST (jct Mill St and Barker St)

☎ (01270) 610196 🌐 wicksteadpubnantwich.co.uk

6 changing beers (sourced regionally) Ⓗ

A busy back-street pub, a short stroll from Nantwich town centre. There is a sports TV bar and a quieter lounge. The latter features a large poster with a map of the Battle of Nantwich (fought on 25 January 1644), as well as old pictures of Nantwich. Six handpumps serve a range of changing regional and national beers from the Punch Taverns list, the majority of which are LocAle. The bar is dog friendly and has free treats. ♘◑♿⇌🚌🐾

Northwich

Salty Dog 🄻

21-23 High Street, CW9 5BY (in pedestrianised town centre) 🌐 salty-dog.co.uk

Merlin Gold; 3 changing beers (sourced locally; often Hush Brewing Co, RedWillow) Ⓗ

Housed in one of the town's black and white timbered buildings is this pub and award-winning independent music venue. The co-owner is a drummer in punk bands and hosts weekly gigs featuring top names as well as new talent. In addition to music, spoken word and comedy nights feature regularly. Alongside the real ales there is an extensive range of bottled and canned British and European beers. ♘❀♿♣🚌🐾📶♫

Parkgate

Boat House

1 The Parade, CH64 6RN

☎ (0151) 336 4187 🌐 theboathouseparkgate.co.uk

Hydes Original, Lowry; 1 changing beer (sourced regionally) Ⓗ

Attractive half-timbered building on the Dee Estuary overlooking an RSPB nature reserve. Bought by Hydes in 2016, and refurbished and reopened in 2017, the pub has retained its character with nooks and recesses, old photos of Parkgate and old-style lamps. It has a spacious and comfortable interior, good food, and an outside terrace to sit and enjoy a pint in good weather. Occasional high tides can lap up against the pub walls. Q♘❀◑♿P🚌(22)🐾📶

Penketh

Ferry Tavern

Station Road, WA5 2UJ (from car park at bottom of Station Rd cross the railway and canal bridge) SJ5634986649

☎ (01925) 791117 🌐 theferrytavern.com

Ossett White Rat; house beer (by Ossett); 4 changing beers (sourced regionally; often Hawkshead, RedWillow, Titanic) Ⓗ

In a scenic location next to the River Mersey, this pub is popular with cyclists as it is close to the Trans Pennine Trail. The atmospheric interior has low-beamed ceilings and a balcony area which can be sectioned off for private functions. Outside is a large seating area in the extensive beer garden which overlooks the river and is popular in summer. ♘❀P🚌(32)🐾♫

Poynton

Kingfisher ✔

London Road South, SK12 1NJ

☎ (01625) 870990

Greene King Abbot; Ruddles Best Bitter; Sharp's Doom Bar; Thornbridge Jaipur; 6 changing beers (sourced regionally; often Beartown, Peerless, Titanic) Ⓗ

Popular pub on the main road through Poynto. It is fairly unusual for a Wetherspoon as it was built and run as a pub prior to them taking it over. Local and regional cask beers feature on 10 handpumps. Two beer festivals each year showcase many real ales, and Meet the Brewer nights are also held here. Internal features include a an industrial-style fireplace and a window onto the cellar. Two large beer gardens at the front incorporate a heated smoking area. Q♘❀◑♿P🚌(391,392)📶

Runcorn

Ferry Boat ✔

10 Church Street, WA7 1LR

☎ (01928) 583380

Greene King Abbot; Ruddles Best Bitter; Sharp's Doom Bar; 2 changing beers (sourced nationally) Ⓗ

Large busy Wetherspoon pub opposite Runcorn old town bus station. The pub takes its name from the river crossing that used to operate between the towns of Runcorn and Widnes (on the opposite bank of the River Mersey) before the building of the Manchester Ship Canal in the 1890s. The award-winning Brindley theatre is 200 yards away. ♘◑♿⇌P🚌📶

Norton Arms 🏆

125-127 Main Street, WA7 2AD

☎ (01928) 567642 🌐 thenortonarms.co.uk

Greene King IPA; 3 changing beers (sourced nationally; often Hardys & Hansons) Ⓗ

This is the 11th year in the Guide for this Grade II-listed two-roomed pub in the centre of Halton village. Sports TV dominates, except on Sundays when the sound is turned down in the lounge. Its attractions include open mic nights, live music, quiz nights, and a bowling green. It can get busy at weekends. Disabled access is difficult as the only public entrance is up a flight of stone steps. A former local CAMRA Pub of the Year. ♘❀◑♿♣P🚌(52)🐾📶♫

Sandbach

Beer Emporium 🄻

8 Welles Street, CW11 1GT (off Hightown roundabout, down one-way street)

☎ (01270) 760113 ⊕ thebeeremporium.com
5 changing beers Ⓗ
Large micropub and bottle shop with a friendly welcome. Seating is in the front window, beneath a large mural of taps, plus a small room to the rear. Five changing cask ales are available, supplemented by four craft keg lines. A dark beer is usually available, as well as ones from local breweries. One wall is dedicated to a wide selection of bottles and cans available to drink in or take away. Knowledgeable bar staff are always willing to help.
Q🕭🖵❀🛜

Smallwood

Bull's Head ♈
Newcastle Road, CW11 2TY (on the A50)
☎ (01477) 500247 ⊕ thebullsheadatsmallwood.co.uk
3 changing beers (sourced locally; often Merlin, Spitting Feathers, Storm) Ⓗ
A former coaching inn with sensitively maintained features. The dining area is separate from the bar and periodically hosts acoustic music evenings. Three regularly changing cask ales are available, together with a selection of keg ales and ciders. Occasional outdoor beer and music festivals are held in the summer in the extensive garden area. Good car parking facilities are provided. The pub is highly regarded locally and regularly hosts various group meetings in separate meeting rooms or the conservatory. 🕭🏠🕽♿▲P❀🛜♪

Stockton Heath

Costello's Bar Ⓛ
23 Walton Road, WA4 6NJ
☎ (01925) 600910 ⊕ costellosbar.co.uk/stocktonheath
Dunham Massey Dunham Dark, Big Tree Bitter; Lymm Bridgewater Blonde; 4 changing beers (sourced locally; often Dunham Massey, Lymm) Ⓗ
A relaxed, modern bar in a former shop unit by the traffic lights at the main cross roads in the village centre, close to the bus stops. Owned by Dunham Massey brewing, the bar was fully refurbished in 2023. Seven handpumps serve cask ales, with three regular and four changing beers all from the Dunham Massey or Lymm stables. Live music features on Sunday evenings. Q🕭🏠♿🖵❀🛜♪

Red Lion ✅
60 London Road, WA4 6HN
☎ (01925) 861041 ⊕ redlionstocktonheath.co.uk
Thwaites Original, IPA, Gold, Amber; 1 changing beer (sourced regionally) Ⓗ
Popular multi-roomed community pub in the village centre, next to the bus stops. This brick-built former Georgian coaching inn features a separate vault and snug, with competitive darts played in the Stables Bar. Screens in all rooms show sporting events and live music can feature on Sunday afternoons. Scan the QR code on your table to order food from local takeaways for delivery direct to your table. Q🕭🏠♣🖵❀🛜♪

Thelwall

Little Manor Ⓛ
Bell Lane, WA4 2SX
☎ (01925) 212070 ⊕ littlemanor-thelwall.co.uk
Hawkshead Windermere Pale; house beer (by Brightside; Lancaster); 5 changing beers (sourced regionally; often 4Ts, Coach House, Timothy Taylor) Ⓗ
Built in the 1660s as a home for the Percival family, this Brunning & Price pub is typical of pubco's style. A previous local CAMRA Pub of the Year, it offers excellent food and real ale, with the large beer garden and

covered patio perfect for alfresco dining and drinking. The house beers are B&P Original brewed by Brightside and Lancaster Blonde, rebadged as Little Manor Blonde. Close to the M6 viaduct over the River Mersey and Manchester Ship Canal, the Little Manor is an oasis of peace in the heart of the historic village.
Q🕭🏠🕽♿♣P🖵❀🛜♪

Tilston

Carden Arms Ⓛ
Church Road, SY14 7HB
☎ (01829) 250900 ⊕ cardenarms.co.uk
Coach House Gunpowder Premium Mild; Salopian Shropshire Gold; Weetwood Eastgate; 2 changing beers (sourced locally; often Big Hand, Spitting Feathers) Ⓗ
Impressive rural free house at the crossroads in the village. The interior has rug-covered wood and tiled floors, real fires, traditional furniture and attractive framed pictures on the plain white walls. In addition to three regular beers there are up to two guests, often from local microbreweries. High-quality food is served in the bar area and the stylish dining room. Two adjoining Georgian rooms upstairs can be booked for groups. Accommodation is available in five bedrooms.
Q🛏🕽♿♣P🖵(41)❀🛜

Warrington

Albion Ⓛ
94 Battersby Lane, WA2 7EG (200yds N of A57/A49 jct)
4 changing beers (sourced locally; often Merlin) Ⓗ
Victorian, Grade II-listed pub on the edge of town. Inside, it has exposed original floors and crackling fireplaces, and a games room with pool table. Outside is a courtyard surrounded by the original stables. Up to four independently brewed and often local ales are served. Live music plays on Thursdays, and weekly entertainment (quiz, bingo, stand-up comedy) is on Wednesdays. This community hub is a previous local CAMRA award winner and embraces local causes.
🕭🏠🚲(Central)♣🖵(17,25)❀♪

Costello's Bar Ⓛ
36 Time Square, WA1 2NT
☎ (01925) 954846 ⊕ costellosbar.co.uk/timesquare
8 changing beers (sourced locally; often Dunham Massey, Lymm) Ⓗ
Modern, smart and eco-friendly single-room bar in Time Square, next to the cinema and opposite Warrington market. The fourth in Dunham Massey's chain of bars, it has an impressive specialist ventilation system which makes sure the bar is always full of fresh, clean air. An array of 10 handpumps serves up to eight changing cask ales from the Dunham Massey and Lymm Brewing portfolios. 🕭🏠♿🚲(Central)🖵❀🛜♪

Hop Emporium
Unit 14 Warrington New Market, Time Square, Academy Way, WA1 2NT
House beer (by Ossett); 3 changing beers (sourced regionally) Ⓗ
This new bar in Warrington market opened in 2020 and goes from strength to strength. Three rotating guest beers, usually including one dark beer, are offered alongside a house beer. There is plenty of seating and food options from the Cookhouse in the market area. The bar gets busy on Saturday when there is live music. A popular tap takeover is held on alternate months.
🕭🏠🕽♿🚲(Central)🖵❀🛜♪

Lower Angel 🅛

27 Buttermarket Street, WA1 2LY (in pedestrianised town centre)
☎ 07375 881706
Liverpool Brewing Company Dark Mode; house beer (by Liverpool Brewing Company); 7 changing beers (sourced locally) Ⓗ
Taken over by Liverpool Brewing Company in 2022, this former Peter Walker pub still retains some of it previous ownership history including stained-glass windows from the former Walker's brewery. The pub has a traditional vault, lounge, sheltered beer garden to the rear and outdoor seating in front. The seven rotating guest beers are mainly from Liverpool Brewing Company's extensive range and usually including a dark mild and a stout or porter. ❀≠(Central)🚲🛒🅿🐾🛜🎵

Tavern 🅛

25 Church Street, WA1 2SS
☎ 07747 668817
8 changing beers (sourced regionally; often 4Ts, Abbeydale, Mallinsons) Ⓗ
The Tavern is the brewery tap for 4Ts. The single-roomed pub offers a changing range of 4Ts beers, as well as other beers from around the country, and has tap takeovers once a month. It is very popular for watching sports on the multiple TVs, especially rugby league, and the pub hosts thriving darts and dominoes teams. There is an outdoor drinking area in the yard to the rear, with heaters if required. A long-term Guide entry. ❀≠(Central)🛒🚲🛒🐾🛜

Wilmslow

Coach & Four 🅛

69-71 Alderley Road, SK9 1PA
☎ (01625) 525046 ⊕ thecoachandfour.co.uk
Hydes Original, Lowry; 2 changing beers (sourced locally; often Hydes) Ⓗ
Large, comfortable old coaching inn near the centre of Wilmslow, catering to a wide-ranging clientele. The large single room is divided into secluded alcoves, and there is a restaurant on the right as you enter. Food is served all day either in the restaurant or the bar area. Four Hyde's cask beers are available. Outside is a covered and heated patio for smokers. Quiz nights, music and comedy are held, as well as charity and community events. There is also lodge-style accommodation. 🛏❀🛌🍴🚻♿≠🅿🚲🅿(130,88) 🐾🛜🎵

Wincle

Wincle Brewery Shop 🅛

Tolls Farm Barn, Dane Bridge, SK11 0QE
☎ (01260) 227777 ⊕ winclebeer.co.uk
3 changing beers (sourced locally; often Wincle) Ⓗ
With a breathtaking view across the Dane valley from the beer garden, this brewery shop is well worth a visit and a great end to a Peak District walk. There are three cask beers on handpump and a good selection of bottles from the adjacent Wincle brewery, plus soft drinks and a few spirits, including gin from the nearby Forest Gin distillery. A log-burning stove keeps you warm in winter, though indoor seating is limited. Cakes are offered at weekends and ice-creams in summer. Q🛌❀🐾🛜

White Bear Hotel, Middlewich (Photo: Marc Holmes)

CORNWALL

ISLES OF SCILLY

ST MARTIN'S

TRESCO

ST MARY'S

ST AGNES

Trebarwith Strand

St Minver
Rock

Padstow

St Mabyn

Edmonton

Bodmin

Newquay

A3059

A392

A39

A30

A391

Indian Queens

Polmear

Perranporth

A3075

Zelah

A3058

St Austell

A39

A3078

A390

Grampound

Trevaunance Cove

Threemilestone

A30

Truro

Mevagissey

Bridge

Redruth

Vogue

Frogpool

St Ives

Treen

A393

Perranwell

Piece

Mylor Bridge

Ponsanooth

Hayle

Pendeen

Trewellard

Newbridge

Crowlas

Penryn

Portscatho

St Just

A3071

Long Rock

A394

Nancenoy

Falmouth

Penzance

Rosudgeon

A30

Helston

Porthleven

A3083

Pednavounder

Blisland

Blisland Inn

The Green, PL30 4JF (off A30 E of Bodmin) SX100732
☎ (01208) 850739
House beer (by Tintagel) H; **4 changing beers (sourced nationally)** H/G
A friendly rural community pub by the village green, on the edge of Bodmin Moor, the Blisland retains its reputation as a real ale destination. Having served well over 3,000 different real ales, it usually has at least five or six beers available, with several brewed locally, and frequently changing draught ciders including more

unusual varieties. An annual 'Mild Month' festival is held in May, where many mild ales from around the country are featured. Freshly prepared meals use local produce. Popular with walkers and cyclists on the nearby Camel Trail, it also welcomes well-behaved children and dogs. A former CAMRA National Pub of the Year.
Q❄️🐕♿🅿️🚶🍴🍽️🎵

Bodmin

Hole in the Wall 🍷

16 Crockwell Street, PL31 2DS (entrance from town car park)

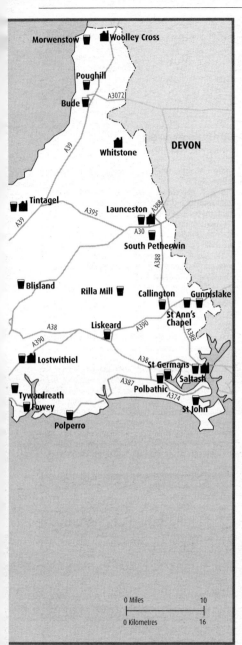

Morwenstow
Woolley Cross
Poughill
Bude
A3072
Whitstone
DEVON
Tintagel
A39
A395
Launceston
A389
A30
South Petherwin
A388
Blisland
Rilla Mill
Callington
Gunnislake
St Ann's Chapel
A38
Liskeard
A390
A388
Lostwithiel
A38
St Germans
A387
Saltash
Polbathic
A374
Tywardreath
St John
Fowey
Polperro

0 Miles 10
0 Kilometres 16

Bridge

Bridge Inn

Bridge Row, TR16 4QW
☎ (01209) 842532
2 changing beers (often Brains, Dartmoor, Skinner's) Ⓗ

This former 18th-century hunting lodge, now a small, traditional Cornish granite inn, is reputedly haunted. The atmosphere in its L-shaped bar is warm and friendly, with a local character. Traditional brown hues dominate, with partly wood-cladded walls, carpeted floor, and a few local pictures on display. The riverside beer garden has a fishpond, while the nearby old Portreath tramroad offers a delightful coast to coast walk through Cornish mining history. Buses to Redruth, Portreatn and Camborne stop outside during the day.
Q ☺ ❀ ▲ ♣ P ☒ (48,49) ✿ 🛜

Bude

Barrel at Bude

36 Lansdown Road, EX23 8BN
☎ (01288) 356113
5 changing beers (sourced locally) Ⓖ

This small micropub opened in 2017 in a former shop. All beers and ciders are sourced from within Cornwall by the owner/proprietor without recourse to the wholesale trade. The beers in place on opening on Thursday should all be consumed by the Sunday, ready for restocking for the following week. Cornish organic gins and wines are also available. Live music plays every Sunday, plus on the last Thursday and Friday and first Monday of the month. Sunday closing time may be adjusted if necessary.
❀ ● ☒ ✿ ♪

Bencoolen

Bencoolen Road, EX23 8PJ
☎ (01288) 354694
Dartmoor Legend; St Austell Proper Job; Sharp's Doom Bar Ⓖ

This friendly and spacious pub has a huge bar welcoming all ages and varieties of customer. Despite three handpumps, the beer is usually fetched from the cellar and gravity-fed. The pub is named after a ship that was wrecked nearby in 1862. Some of the ship's timbers were used in the pub's construction, and an account of the wreck is displayed on one of the walls. As well as bar food there is a restaurant serving à la carte international cuisine. ☺ ❀ ◑ ♿ P ☒ ✿ 🛜 ♪

Callington

Cornish Ancestor

6 Newport, PL17 7AS (just off A386)
☎ (01579) 208300
3 changing beers (sourced regionally; often Cotleigh, Exmoor, Otter) Ⓖ

This town centre micropub, housed in a former pet shop, serves three real ales by gravity dispense and up to seven varying real ciders depending on demand. It is a quiet pub, with conversation the main entertainment and no distracting noisy machines. The bar area has a serving worktop, with a beer and cider menu chalkboard. The interestingly shaped pub is furnished throughout with functional barrels, wooden furniture, and walls adorned with local pictures. No food served, but local takeaways will deliver. Q ☺ ❀ ♿ ♣ ● ☒ (12,79) ✿ 🛜

☎ (01208) 72397 ⊕ theholeinthewallbodmin.co.uk
Dartmoor Jail Ale; Draught Bass; Sharp's Atlantic; 3 changing beers (sourced nationally) Ⓗ

Popular locals' pub built in the 18th century as a debtors' prison, so called due to food being passed through a hole in the wall. The pub can be accessed direct from the public car park or through a secluded, leafy garden containing its own hop bine and stream, and presided over by a rather bleached stuffed lion. The single bar, which is subdivided by archways, contains a large and eclectic collection of antiques and military memorabilia. Upstairs is a separate function room. Current local CAMRA Pub of the Year. Q ☺ ❀ ♿ ☒ (26,11) ✿ 🛜

Edmonton

Quarryman Inn

PL27 7JA (just off A39 near the Royal Cornwall showground)
☎ (01208) 816444 ⊕ thequarryman.co.uk
Otter Bitter; Padstow May Day; 2 changing beers (sourced locally) Ⓗ
This characterful and convivial free house is an ever-popular gem, renowned for the excellent quality of its food and local ales. Its quiet and comfortable interior divides into a small public bar with a flagstone floor, and larger carpeted lounge, with dining permitted in both. The eclectic decor features local art and sporting memorabilia. Conversation and friendly banter thrive here, and with up to four ales on offer, enough to slake most thirsts, a visit is well worthwhile.
Q ♿ 🐕 🕰 🕒 ⛲ ♣ 🚪 🚌 (11,95) 🍴 🛜 🎵

Falmouth

'front

Custom House Quay, TR11 3JT
Firebrand West Coast Session IPA; Sharp's Sea Fury; Tintagel Pendragon; 7 changing beers (sourced locally; often Tintagel, Treen's, Verdant) Ⓗ
A warm welcome is guaranteed at this lively cellar-style bar on Custom House Quay. The bar front is decorated with old wooden cask sections, while a large range of ales is dispensed from the impressive array of 10 handpumps. Usually sourced from Cornwall, they cater for all styles and tastes. There is a popular Sunday evening quiz. No food is available, but you may bring your own. A discount on real ales is offered before 6pm daily. ♿ 🐕 ♿ ⇌ (Town) ♣ 🍴 🎵

Beerwolf Books

3-4 Bells Court, TR11 3AZ (up side alley off the shopping street next to Santander)
☎ (01326) 618474
6 changing beers (sourced nationally; often Penzance, Treen's) Ⓗ
Is this a pub or a bookshop? Actually, it's both. Popular with all ages, this former maritime storage loft with a pleasant outside courtyard is tucked away off the main street. It is accessed via a flight of stairs, at the top of which is the bookshop. To the right is the bar, furnished with six handpulls dispensing a constantly changing and adventurous selection of beers from near and far. Food is not served but you may bring your own.
♿ 🐕 ♣ 🍴 🚪 🚌 🛜 🎵

Boathouse Ⓛ

Beacon Street, Trevethan Hill, TR11 2AG (top of High St)
☎ (01326) 315425 ⊕ theboathousefalmouth.co.uk
3 changing beers (sourced locally; often St Austell, St Ives, Treen's) Ⓗ
This bright and airy maritime-themed pub has impressive views across Carrick Roads to Flushing and beyond. The bar area itself is traditional, but the main dining area to the front has a more modern vibe, with large windows. An additional room at the rear features floor-to-ceiling windows, allowing customers to admire the views. The large patio area outside has heaters, making it suitable for year-round use. Three local real ales are usually available. ♿ 🐕 🕰 ♣ 🚪 🚌 🛜 🎵

Moth & the Moon

31 Killigrew Street, TR11 3PW
☎ (01326) 315300
4 changing beers (sourced locally; often Firebrand, Tintagel, Treen's) Ⓗ

This small town-centre pub has a dark yet modern cosy interior. Downstairs, the bar room is open plan with an intimate snug. More seating upstairs surrounds a tiny glass-sided outdoor smoking area in the centre. To the rear of the pub is a large suntrap terrace, which is popular in summer. Up to four changing ales are generally available from local breweries. On Tuesdays there is a folk, acoustic and song session night, and an open mic night on Wednesdays. ♿ 🕰 ⛲ 🚪 🚌 🛜 🎵

Oddfellows Arms

2 Quay Hill, TR11 3HA
☎ (01326) 218611
Sharp's Atlantic, Sea Fury; 1 changing beer (sourced nationally) Ⓗ
This small, unpretentious and traditional single-bar community pub is tucked away up a hilly side street off the town centre. Popular with locals and visitors, it has a convivial atmosphere in which to enjoy the three beers normally on offer. The front room has a dartboard while the small room at the back hosts a pool table and a real fire in winter. It is decorated throughout with old photographs. It holds popular jam sessions and quiz nights. ⇌ (Town) ♣ 🚌 🍴 🛜 🎵

Seven Stars ★

The Moor, TR11 3QA
☎ (01326) 312111 ⊕ thesevenstarsfalmouth.com
Draught Bass; Sharp's Atlantic, Sea Fury; 3 changing beers (sourced nationally; often Padstow, Penzance) Ⓖ
This timeless, unspoilt town centre pub has been in the same family for over 170 years and is a real gem. It has had a sympathetic makeover and has been identified by CAMRA as having a nationally important historic pub interior. It has a narrow taproom where the beers are served on gravity, and two rooms at the back, further supplemented by an upstairs drinking area created from an old bottle store. In 2023 the pub celebrated 50 consecutive years in the Guide. Q ♿ 🐕 ⛲ 🚪 🚌 🍴 🛜

REAL ALE BREWERIES

Atlantic ⏺ Indian Queens
Black Flag ⏺ Perranporth
Blue Anchor 🍺 Helston
Bluntrock ⏺ St Minver
Castle Lostwithiel
Cornish Crown Penzance
Driftwood Spars Trevaunance Cove
Dynamite Valley Ponsanooth
Firebrand ⏺ Launceston
Forge Woolley Cross
Hidden 🍺 Penryn
Ideal Day Saltash
Keltek Redruth
Lizard Pednavounder
Longhill Whitstone
Mason ⏺ Threemilestone (NEW)
Mine St Ives
Newquay Brewing Project Zelah
Padstow Padstow
Penzance 🍺 Crowlas
Sharp's Rock
Shoals ⏺ Porthleven
Skinner's ⏺ Truro
St Austell ⏺ St Austell
St Ives ⏺ Hayle
Tintagel Tintagel
Treen's Ponsanooth
Tremethick Grampound
Verdant ⏺ Penryn

CORNWALL

Fowey

Galleon Inn
12 Fore Street, PL23 1AQ (in centre of town)
☎ (01726) 833014 ⊕ galleon-inn.co.uk
Sharp's Doom Bar; Tintagel Castle Gold; 3 changing beers (sourced locally; often Firebrand, Sharp's, Tintagel) ⊞
This riverside pub in the town centre dates back 400 years. Now fully modernised, it is reached off Fore Street through a glass-covered corridor with a colourful marine life mural. The only free house in Fowey, it features mainly Cornish ales and offers delightful harbour views from the main bar and conservatory. Tables outside overlook the water and there is a heated, sheltered courtyard. A wide range of meals is available daily. Accommodation is en-suite, with some rooms affording river views. ✿❀🚲◐♿♣●🚐(24,25)✿❖♪

Frogpool

Cornish Arms
TR4 8RP (between Perranwell and United Downs) SW760401
☎ (01872) 863445 ⊕ cornisharmsfrogpool.com
St Austell Tribute; 2 changing beers (often Greene King, Treen's) ⊞
This long-established community inn has been recently modernised but retains its olde-worlde charm. Its wood-beamed bar is warm and cosy with alcoves and open fires, and adorned with brasses and other bric-a-brac. A distinctly separate area at one end houses the pool table. Home-cooked meals are served in the bar or in a separate dining area at busy times; call ahead if you wish to eat. The pub also offers a takeaway service. The two changing beers vary frequently. Q❀◐♣●🚐(36A)✿

Gunnislake

Rising Sun Inn
Calstock Road, PL18 9BX (off A390) SX432711
☎ (01822) 832201
Dartmoor Legend, Jail Ale; 2 changing beers (sourced regionally) ⊞
Friendly, oak-beamed 17th-century country inn with much charm and character, in a conservation area in a rural setting off the beaten track. It serves a good choice of up to four real ales, mainly from Devonian or other West Country breweries. Exposed stone walls and wooden beams allow an extensive display of chinaware, and a beautiful terraced garden affords views over the Tamar Valley. A true community pub, hosting various local activities. Q❀❀◐≈♣●🚐(79,118)✿❖♪

Helston

Blue Anchor ★
50 Coinagehall Street, TR13 8EL
☎ (01326) 562821 ⊕ spingoales.com
Blue Anchor Flora Daze, Jubilee IPA, Spingo Middle, Spingo Special; 2 changing beers (sourced locally; often Blue Anchor) ⊞
A former monks' rest, this 15th-century brewpub is one of the oldest in Britain, changing little over the years and retaining much of its original character. Two separate small bars are found to the right of the central passageway, one with an open fire, and two sitting rooms to the left, all with slate floors. To the rear are a skittle alley and partly covered garden area with its own bar. Commemorative brews may appear on special occasions. Q❀❀♣●🚐✿♪

Launceston

Bell Inn
1 Tower Street, PL15 8BQ (in town centre next to parish church tower)
☎ (01566) 779970 ⊕ bellinnlaunceston.co.uk
House beer (by Holsworthy Ales); 4 changing beers (sourced regionally) ⊞
Cosy 16th-century town pub, originally built to house stonemasons erecting the nearby church, with an ever-changing range of mostly local beers and two ciders, although the available selection may be reduced out of season. A separate family room, available for local groups to use, has some interesting frescoes uncovered when previous owners stripped away decades of modernisation. Conversation rules in the pub. Pub games include cribbage and other board games. Food is limited to pasties and pork pies. Q❀❀♣●🚐(78,97)✿❖♪

Liskeard

Red Lion Inn
5 Lower Lux Street, PL14 3JL
☎ (01579) 344354
Bays Devon Dumpling, Topsail; 1 changing beer (sourced regionally) ⊞
Traditional town pub with a character all of its own. Interior decoration is a little sparse, but behind the bar is a large collection of breweriana. The L-shaped main bar is to the right of the entrance; it is mostly carpeted and hosts a pool table and jukebox. To the left is a small snug with two dartboards, one of which is above the fireplace. Euchre and pool are played, with pub teams being supported. ❀❀♣●🚐✿❖

Long Rock

Mexico Inn
Gladstone Terrace, TR20 8JB (off A30 just E of Penzance)
☎ (01736) 710625 ⊕ themexicoinn.com
4 changing beers (sourced regionally) ⊞
Near a beach is this lively, welcoming and popular free house. Its homely interior features a single L-shaped, wood-beamed bar with adjacent restaurant, and a spacious conservatory to the rear. Wood-burning fires, wooden flooring and furnishings create character. Various events are held including 'Wobbly Wednesday' when regulars enjoy discounted drinks. Up to four ales are available from an ever-changing menu. An interesting food menu is served in both bar and restaurant. Roadside parking is limited but bus services are frequent. Q❀❀🚲◐♿♣●🚐(T1,17)✿❖♪

Lostwithiel

Globe Inn
3 North Street, PL22 0EG (near railway station, on town side of river bridge)
☎ (01208) 872501 ⊕ globeinn.com
Otter Ale; Skinner's Betty Stogs; 2 changing beers (sourced regionally) ⊞
In the narrow streets of an old stannary town lies this cosy, relaxing 13th-century pub, whose welcoming atmospheric interior accommodates a single bar and several distinct drinking and dining areas. Towards the rear is an intimate, stylish restaurant with adjoining sheltered suntrap patio, where an extensive home-cooked menu is served. Up to four real ales are offered. This is an ideal place for a pint or two or a tasty meal, and well worth seeking out. Q❀❀🚲◐♿≈♣●✿❖♪

Royal Oak

Duke Street, PL22 0AG

☎ (01208) 872552 🌐 royaloakcornwall.com

St Austell Tribute, Proper Job; Sharp's Doom Bar; 1 changing beer (sourced regionally) Ⓗ

Located just off the main road through the town, this historic 13th-century inn is welcoming and friendly. Internally, the stone-floored traditional public bar contrasts with a comfortable lounge and adjoining restaurant, where good-value food is served. Traditional pub games are played regularly, supplemented by occasional quiz nights and live music. Accommodation is available, also ample parking. There is reputedly a tunnel running under the pub to the dungeons of nearby Restormal Castle, alleged to have been used for smuggling. Q🐴❀🛏◑▲⇌♣●P🚌(28)🐾📶♫

Mevagissey

Fountain Inn

3 Cliff Street, PL26 6QH

☎ (01726) 842320

St Austell Cornish Best Bitter, Tribute, Hicks; 1 changing beer (sourced locally; often St Austell) Ⓗ

Friendly two-bar 15th-century inn near the harbour, with slate-flagged floors, exposed stone walls and low-beamed ceilings. The decor includes historic photographs and paintings of old Mevagissey. The back Smugglers Bar once housed a pilchard press – a glass plate in the floor covers the former fish-oil sump, which also served as a store for contraband. The menu offers a range of home-cooked dishes using local produce. Nearby buses connect with St Austell and the Lost Gardens of Heligan.
Q🐴🛏◑♣●🚌(24)🐾📶♫

Morwenstow

Bush Inn

Crosstown, EX23 9SR (off A39, N of Kilkhampton)
SS208150

☎ (01288) 331242 🌐 thebushinnmorwenstow.com

St Austell Tribute, Hicks; house beer (by St Austell) Ⓗ

This ancient former chapel dates in parts back to 950AD. Unassuming externally, it is a gem internally and is simply furnished, with slate floors, granite walls and exposed beams in the two small bar rooms, one of which is subdivided into separate drinking areas. Conversation is the main entertainment, although there is occasional live music. A large garden, with children's play area, at the back offers outstanding views over the Tidna Valley and out to sea. 🐴❀🛏◑♣●P🚌(217)🐾📶♫

Mylor Bridge

Lemon Arms

Lemon Hill, TR11 5NA (off A393 from Penryn)
SW805362

☎ (01326) 373666

St Austell Tribute, Proper Job, Hicks; 1 changing beer (sourced locally; often Bath Ales, St Austell) Ⓗ

There has been a hostelry on this site since 1765. Once called the Griffin Inn, it became the Red Lion in 1829 and took its present name in 1837. This friendly one-bar pub in the centre of the village is home to local sports teams. Good home-cooked food is available (booking for the popular Sunday lunches is advisable). Families with children are made most welcome. Daytime buses run from Falmouth and Truro during the week.
🐴❀◑♿♣P🚌(66,69)

Nancenoy

Trengilly Wartha Inn

Nancenoy, TR11 5RP (off B3291 near Constantine)
SW732283

☎ (01326) 340332 🌐 trengilly.co.uk

3 changing beers (sourced nationally; often Penzance, Tintagel) Ⓗ

This versatile converted farmhouse inn sits in a steeply wooded valley – the pub's name means 'settlement above the trees'. The bar beams are covered in many pumpclip labels from brews sold over the years. A conservatory extension doubles as a family room. An extra beer appears in summer, and cider is locally made. The Trengilly also offers an imaginative menu, prepared where possible with Cornish produce and presented with flair. Live entertainment features occasionally; Wednesday is 'jamming night'.
Q🐴❀🛏◑♣●P🐾📶♫

Newbridge

Fountain Inn

TR20 8QH (on A3071)

☎ 07825 889645 🌐 thefountainnewbridge.co.uk

2 changing beers (sourced locally; often Penzance) Ⓗ

A traditional cottage-style Cornish inn situated in a quiet hamlet on the Penzance to St Just road. A warm welcome is assured, and the atmosphere is boosted by exposed granite walls and a spectacular inglenook with log-burner. Sunday lunches are served (booking advised) as well as lunchtime and evening meals, and bar snacks Wednesday to Saturday. There are traditional musical jam sessions on the first and third Tuesdays of the month, and occasional quizzes and bingo nights.
🐴❀🛏◑▲P🚌(17)🐾📶♫

Newquay

Great Western Hotel

Cliff Road, TR7 2NE

☎ (01637) 872010 🌐 greatwesternnewquay.co.uk

St Austell Tribute, Proper Job; 1 changing beer (sourced locally; often St Austell) Ⓗ

Art Deco-style hotel with a modern, spacious, open-plan bar and dining area that can be segmented into more private function rooms. Large windows to the side and rear give spectacular views to the beach below and across to the harbour and coastline. There is an extensive garden area with similar views. The hotel, which offers comfortable accommodation, is family and dog friendly, and has a strong community focus. It is only two minutes' walk from the railway station.
🐴❀🛏◑♿⇌♣P🚌🐾📶♫

Pendeen

North Inn

Pendeen, TR19 7DN (on B3306)

☎ (01736) 788417 🌐 thenorthinnpendeen.co.uk

St Austell Tribute, Proper Job; 1 changing beer (sourced locally; often St Austell) Ⓗ

This welcoming single-bar locals' pub stands in an old mining village near the coastal path and Geevor and Levant mines, and close to spectacular cliff walks. Its wood-beamed ceiling adds to the cosy ambience of the large bar area, where a good-value menu features a range of home-cooked curries – which are the landlord's speciality – as well as traditional fare. The inn offers accommodation in four double rooms, as well as its own campsite, an award-winning garden and a pétanque piste. 🐴❀🛏◑♿▲♣P🚌(17,17E)🐾📶♫

Penryn

Famous Barrel

St Thomas Street, TR10 8JP
☎ (01326) 373505
Dartmoor Jail Ale; Treen's Sunbeam; 1 changing beer (sourced locally; often Skinner's (Goodh Brewing Co)) H
A historic and cosy back-street pub situated in a conservation area beside a small river. The front door is barrel-shaped and leads into a traditional low-beamed bar, heated in winter by a wood-burning stove in the original granite fireplace. To the left on entry is the main drinking area, while to the right is a games area with darts and pool. A beer garden is at the rear of the pub. Parking is limited, so best to come by bus.
๒❀♣P🖭🏮🤝🎵

Penzance

Crown 🅛

Victoria Square, TR18 2EP (on Bread St, just behind Market Jew St)
☎ (01736) 351070 ⊕ thecrownpenzance.co.uk
Cornish Crown Causeway, Madagascan Vanilla Porter; 1 changing beer (sourced locally; often Cornish Crown) H
Close to the railway and bus stations, and tap for the Cornish Crown brewery, this back-street local offers a relaxing atmosphere and is well worth searching out. It has a comfortable bar with upholstered window seats and a huge mirror covering one wall. To the rear is a cosy snug with sofas and board games, while outside there is a roadside patio with benches and tables. No food is served, but you may bring your own, with plates provided. ๒❀≠♣🖭🏮🤝🎵

Dock Inn

17 Quay Street, TR18 4BD
☎ (01736) 362833 ⊕ thedockinnpenzance.co.uk
Blue Anchor Spingo Middle; Penzance Potion No 9; Sharp's Doom Bar H
This old former fishermen's pub lies near the dockside and close to the Isles of Scilly ferry pier. The pub extends through two old cottages, with the bar in the upper level and a comfortable lounge/dining area in the lower, beyond which is a pool room. The decor includes a mix of nautical and mining pictures and artefacts. Sunday lunches are served. The pub holds its own beer festival every Penzance Mazey Day in late June.
๒❀🔊≠♣P🖭🏮🤝🎵

Farmer's Arms

38 Causewayhead, TR18 2ST
☎ (01736) 362627
Sharp's Sea Fury; Timothy Taylor Landlord; 1 changing beer H
At the top of a pedestrianised shopping street, this quirky traditional pub is not to be missed. The long, narrow bar area has a beamed ceiling and wooden floor, tables and old fixed bench seating and wood panelling. On one wall at the rear is a collection of posters of famous films but with a difference - they have been given Cornish themes! A music area hosts live bands on Friday evenings and an open mic Sunday afternoons.
❀≠♣🖭🤝🎵

Perranwell

Royal Oak

TR3 7PX
☎ (01872) 863175 ⊕ theroyaloakperranwellstation.co.uk

4 changing beers (sourced regionally; often Exeter, Padstow, Penzance) H
This small, low-beamed, 18th-century community pub prioritises both good food and good beer. Most tables are set for dining, but drinkers are equally welcome. Bookings for meals are advisable, especially in the evenings. The beers listed are constantly varied, but are almost invariably from Cornish or Devon breweries. Buses stop close by for Truro and Helston, while the railway station is about 15 minutes' walk away.
Q๒❀🕙≠♣🖭P🖭(36,46)🏮🤝🎵

Piece

Countryman Inn

TR16 6SG (on Four Lanes-Pool road) SW679398
☎ (01209) 215960 ⊕ countrymaninns.com
Courage Directors H/G**; St Austell Tribute; Theakston Old Peculier; 1 changing beer (sourced locally; often Treen's)** H
This former miners' shop is now a lively rural pub set among former copper mines near the distinctive landmark of Carn Brea. The larger bar is overlooked by a granite fireplace and massive cast-iron coal-fired cooking range, while the smaller one also serves as a family room. There is also a spacious games room. The pub hosts some form of live entertainment most nights, as well as Sunday lunchtime when there is a raffle in support of local charities. ๒❀🕙♦♣P🖭(42)🏮🤝🎵

Polbathic

Halfway House

PL11 3EY (on A387 between Trerulefoot and Torpoint)
☎ (01503) 232986 ⊕ halfwayhousepolbathic.co.uk
St Austell Proper Job; house beer (by Salcombe); 2 changing beers (sourced nationally; often Draught Bass, Firebrand) H
A 16th-century former coaching inn, village local and community library. It is surprisingly large inside, with separate public and lounge bars, and further rooms beyond that are used for dining. The smallish 'public' is the normal focus of the pub's daily life, hosting the pool table and dartboard. It also boasts an unusual stone fireplace, above which is mounted an old wagon wheel. A large beer garden at the rear is on a steep hillside and reached via flights of steps. ๒❀🕙♦🦽♣P🖭🏮🎵

Polmear

Ship Inn ✅

Polmear Hill, PL24 2AR (on A3082)
☎ (01726) 812540 ⊕ theshipinnpar.co.uk
Dartmoor Jail Ale; St Austell Proper Job; Sharp's Doom Bar; 2 changing beers (sourced regionally; often Keltek, Skinner's) H
A cosy free house offering five cask beers. Its L-shaped bar has a beamed ceiling decorated with beer pumpclips. There are several separate areas for drinking and eating, with wagon wheels forming an unusual partition, and a fireplace featuring a Cornish range. A function room upstairs is available for hire. The spacious garden features a play area, ideal for families and featuring music events in summer. It is close to Par beach and the South West Coast Path. Q๒❀🕙♦🦽♣P🖭(25)🏮🤝🎵

Polperro

Blue Peter Inn

Quay Road, PL13 2QZ (far end of W side of harbour)
☎ (01503) 272743 ⊕ thebluepeterinn.com

Firebrand Patchwork Rocket Pale; Otter Ale; St Austell Tribute; 4 changing beers (sourced regionally) ⊞
Next to the harbour is this welcoming pub, reached up a flight of steps that passes a small patio seating area. The pub is named after the naval flag, which flies outside. Inside, there are wooden floors, low beams (sporting whimsical sayings/rhymes) and interesting nooks and crannies. It is the only pub in the village that boasts sea views. It offers many Cornish beers, as well as guest beers from Devon breweries. ♿☕❀♣◐❀✿♫

Crumplehorn Inn
The Old Mill, Crumplehorn, PL13 2RJ (on A387, top of town near coach park)
☎ (01503) 272348 ⊕ thecrumplehorninn.co.uk
St Austell Tribute, Proper Job; 2 changing beers (sourced locally; often Sharp's, Tintagel) ⊞
Once a farmhouse and mill and mentioned in the Domesday Book, this 14th-century inn at the entrance to the village still has a working overshot waterwheel outside. The split-level bar has three comfortable areas with low-beamed ceilings and flagstone floors. A spacious outside patio by the millstream offers large parasols as sunshades in summer. A varied menu includes locally sourced food. B&B or self-catering accommodation is available. It is half a mile's walk from the pub down to the harbour.
♿☕❀♣◐▶▲🚌(72,73)❀✿♫

Portscatho
Plume of Feathers ★
The Square, TR2 5HW
☎ (01872) 580321 ⊕ plumeoffeathers-roseland.com
St Austell Tribute, Proper Job; 1 changing beer (sourced locally; often St Austell) ⊞
Originally a lively old smugglers' and fishermen's pub, the Plume is now a popular watering hole and dining venue for locals and tourists. Inside are two beamed bars, a snug with a part-circle bar, and a dining room upstairs. The main bar is a sociable centre of village life; it has a quiz team and takes part in the annual regatta. Food is varied, locally sourced and home cooked with occasional themed events. Parking is in the public car park nearby. Q♿☕❀♣◐▶▲♣🚌(50)❀✿

Poughill
Preston Gate Inn
Poughill Road, EX23 9ET (just outside Bude, on Sandymouth Bay road) SS224077
☎ (01288) 354017 ⊕ prestongateinn.co.uk
Sharp's Sea Fury; 3 changing beers (sourced regionally; often Firebrand, Otter, Tintagel) ⊞
This cosy 16th-century building became a village pub in 1983. Its spacious room hosts the dartboard at one end of the bar, while the other end has more seating and a roaring log fire in a stove in winter. There are four beers, one permanent and three changing. Meals include winter curry nights, steak nights and lunchtime fish & chips. Conversation rules, and the pub supports darts and quiz teams, folk music, live bands, and jam sessions.
Q♿◐▲♣♣🚌(128,219)❀✿♫

Rilla Mill
Manor House Inn
PL17 7NT (N and E of Liskeard, off B3254)
☎ (01579) 362354 ⊕ manorhouserilla.co.uk
Dartmoor Legend, Jail Ale; 1 changing beer (sourced locally) ⊞

The Manor House is a comfortable 17th-century community pub in the Lynher Valley, on the edge of Bodmin Moor. It has three rooms, one of which has slated and carpeted flooring, the other two comprising the restaurant areas, where meals generally use local produce. The changing beers are mainly from Cornish breweries. The pub, which is allegedly haunted by three ghosts, is situated near the Sterts open air theatre and a dairy that makes a variety of Cornish cheeses.
Q♿❀◐♣P🚌(236)❀✿

Rosudgeon
Coach & Horses
Kenneggy Downs, TR20 9AW (on A394 Penzance-Helston road)
☎ (01736) 763089 ⊕ coachandhorsespenzance.com
St Austell Tribute; 2 changing beers (sourced regionally; often Exeter) ⊞
A large granite freehouse, built in 1752 and refurbished in 2016, on the A394 between the towns of Helston and Penzance. It features a wood-floored interior with exposed stone walls and wooden beams, as well as a cosy fireplace. Seating is in front of the bar and to the right, with comfy chairs and tables. The cottage is available for private parties. A large car park is in front with an overflow to the right-hand side.
♿❀◐▲♣P🚌❀✿♫

St Ann's Chapel
Rifle Volunteer Inn
PL18 9HL (on A390)
☎ (01822) 851551 ⊕ riflevolunteer.com
St Austell Tribute; 2 changing beers (sourced regionally; often Dartmoor, Exmoor) ⊞
Former mine captain's house, converted to a coaching inn during the mid-19th century. The main bar has been extended to accommodate a conservatory, which is popular with diners for the view over the garden. Meals are cooked using locally sourced ingredients. A separate public bar caters for more dedicated drinkers and hosts a pool table and dartboard. The changing beers, usually from local breweries, are regularly varied. The pub offers panoramic views across the Tamar Valley and is in good walking country. Q♿❀◐♣♣♣P🚌(79)❀✿

St Germans
Eliot Arms
Fore Street, PL12 5NR
☎ (01503) 232733 ⊕ thebestpubincornwall.com
3 changing beers (sourced regionally; often Dartmoor, Exmoor, Salcombe) ⊞
Everyone is welcome in this 'local of the local gentry', whose presence is underlined by two beautiful leaded stained-glass windows depicting the family crests. The smaller public bar hosts a pool table and dartboard and has a large screen for special events. Entertainment includes live groups and occasional karaoke. The main bar is the 'quiet' refuge and is beamed and carpeted. Outdoor drinking takes place on a patio area. Food is locally sourced, and served in a separate dining area.
Q♿❀❀◐▶▲≠♣❀✿♫

St Ives
Pilchard Press Alehouse
Wharf Road, TR26 1LF (in alleyway between Talay Thai and the Cornish Pasty Shop)
☎ (01736) 791665

3 changing beers (sourced locally; often Penzance, St Ives, Treen's) Ⓗ/Ⓖ
Located up an alleyway off the harbourside near the Lifeboat Inn, this tiny bar in an old stone-walled cellar is Cornwall's first micropub. It can be difficult to find, but is nevertheless worth seeking out. A friendly little pub, it has a wood-topped bar and is furnished with bar stools and a few tables with chairs, offering space for around 20-25 customers. Do not miss the mural or webcam. It typically offers three real ales, mainly from Cornish microbreweries, and two ciders. Q❀▲≈●🚐🏵

St John

St John Inn
PL11 3AW
☎ 07816 502201 ⊕ stjohninn.co.uk
Draught Bass; 2 changing beers (sourced nationally; often Teignworthy, Woodforde's) Ⓗ
Reached down narrow country lanes, this 16th-century village pub and community shop is constructed from two former cottages. The pub is cosy, with an L-shaped bar room with beamed ceiling and red-tiled floor, wooden furniture and a warming open fire for winter. A cosy snug opposite the bar, a patio with seating at the front, and an attractive beer garden set the scene for this picturesque and welcoming pub. A semi-permanent marquee is used to host live events. Q❀🌞♣●P🏵🐾🏵

St Just

Star Inn ★ ✔
1 Fore Street, TR19 7LL
☎ (01736) 788767
St Austell Cornish Best Bitter, Tribute, Proper Job; 3 changing beers (sourced regionally; often St Austell) Ⓗ
No food, just excellent beer and friendly banter at this traditional old pub, identified by CAMRA as having a nationally important historic pub interior. The atmospheric bar is enhanced by its dark, quirky decor, open fire and mining artefacts, with flags of the Celtic nations adorning the ceiling. A room opposite doubles as a meeting place for community groups, and there is an enclosed beer garden to the rear. Part of St Austell's select Cask Club, the pub serves small batch brews when available. 🌞🏵&▲🚐🏵🔅

St Mabyn

St Mabyn Inn
Churchtown, PL30 3BA
☎ (01208) 841266 ⊕ stmabyninn.com
Firebrand Bootleg Billy, Patchwork Rocket Pale; Sharp's Doom Bar; Tintagel Cornwall's Pride Ⓗ
A warm welcome is assured in this charming, traditional village local, where chat and banter flourish. A 17th-century free house, it features a single bar with adjoining snug, games room, well-appointed restaurant and an extensive beer garden. Wooden furnishings, open fires, stained-glass partitions and windows are complemented by interesting collections of toby jugs, brassware and vintage advertising signage. With quality ales, local cider and an ever-changing food menu including Thai nights, a visit here is a must. Q❀🌞🍴◑&▲♣●P🚐(96)🏵🔅🎵

St Mary's: Isles of Scilly

Atlantic
Hugh Street, TR21 0PL
☎ (01720) 422417 ⊕ atlanticinnscilly.co.uk

St Austell Cornish Best Bitter, Tribute, Proper Job, Hicks; 1 changing beer (sourced regionally) Ⓗ
Don't be put off by the 'restaurant' sign outside – this is a busy pub and hotel. The spacious, open-plan interior, with beamed ceilings, has distinct drinking areas and a separate dining room offering a good range of food. Bar meals are also available. Food is an important part of the operation, but this is also a pub for beer and conversation. Children are welcome until 9pm. A small back patio overlooks the harbour. Q❀🌞🏵🍴◑▲🏵🔅

Saltash

Cockleshell
73 Fore Street, PL12 6AF
☎ 07776 343673
House beer (by Atlantic); 3 changing beers (often Castle, Firebrand, Padstow) Ⓖ
This independently owned micropub in the centre of Saltash was newly opened in the summer of 2020 in a converted retail unit. It has no TV, loud music or electronic gaming machines to distract from the convivial atmosphere. A selection of unusual real ales and ciders are on offer, as well as a range of wines and gins, plus six craft keg beers. Q≈♣🚐(2,72)🏵

Two Bridges
13 Albert Road, PL12 4EB
☎ (01752) 242244
3 changing beers (sourced locally) Ⓗ
On a steep hill above the River Tamar and adjacent to Saltash railway station, this small attractive building is a real locals' pub, but still welcoming to visitors. It features wooden furniture and bench seats along the walls, together with old photos of the area. Three ever-changing beers are on offer, usually from local breweries. Up some steps at the rear is a pleasant well-furnished garden with fine views of the famous Tamar bridges that span the river. 🌞🏵≈♣●🚐(2,72)🏵🔅🎵

South Petherwin

Frog & Bucket
PL15 7LP (just off B3254)
☎ (01566) 776988 ⊕ frogandbucket.net
5 changing beers (sourced nationally) Ⓗ
This roomy, purpose-built village pub was opened in 1989, despite local opposition, but now gives a warm community welcome to all. With up to five changing real ales on offer, it provides a friendly focus for village social life. Off the main bar are a separate lounge, a games room, and two other rooms, one of which can double as a restaurant or function room. The pub offers fine Dartmoor views, and also becomes a focus for vintage vehicles in summer. Q❀🌞🍴◑&♣●P🚐(236)🏵🔅

Tintagel

Olde Malt House
Fore Street, PL34 0DA
☎ (01840) 770461 ⊕ malthousetintagel.com
Tintagel Cornwall's Pride, Harbour Special; 1 changing beer (sourced locally; often Tintagel) Ⓗ
This charming 14th-century inn at the heart of the village of Tintagel retains many original features, and boasts a suntrap front courtyard offering country views and spectacular sunsets. The pub serves three real ales from the local brewery (two in the winter) and also offers a varied food menu. There are three distinct drinking areas, each seating up to 20 people. Accommodation is also available at reasonable prices. Check website for seasonal opening hours. Q🌞🏵🍴◑▲♣🚐(95)🏵🔅

Trebarwith Strand

Mill House Inn

Mill Hill, PL34 0HD (off B3263, near Tintagel) SX058865
☎ (01840) 770200 ⊕ themillhouseinn.co.uk
Tintagel Castle Gold, Sir Lancelot, Harbour Special ⊞
Converted 16th-century corn mill and water wheel set beside a stream in a deep, wooded valley. This friendly inn has a stone-flagged main bar accessible up a flight of steps by an adjacent drinking terrace. The restaurant extension offers an imaginative menu that changes daily; Thursday is steak night. Though primarily a food and accommodation establishment, the bar nevertheless functions as a pub for drinkers, with a range of beers from nearby Tintagel brewery. Occasional live music.
Q❄️☺🛏️ⁱ◑♣P🏮🐾♿🎵

Treen (Zennor)

Gurnard's Head

TR26 3DE (on B3306, Lands End to St Ives coast road)
☎ (01736) 796928 ⊕ gurnardshead.co.uk
4 changing beers (sourced locally; often St Ives) ⊞
Welcoming and strikingly-coloured free house which takes its name from the nearby headland and draws custom from near and far. Its characterful interior boasts a large single bar with log fire in winter, a cosy snug and a stylish restaurant. Wooden furnishings and local artwork enhance the relaxing ambience. Up to four changing beers are available, all from local breweries. An ever-changing food menu features local produce. The availability of accommodation makes this a popular stopover with tourists and walkers.
Q❄️☺🛏️◑🅰️♣P🏮🐾♿🎵

Trevaunance Cove

Driftwood Spars ✅

Quay Road, TR5 0RT
☎ (01872) 552428 ⊕ driftwoodspars.co.uk
6 changing beers (sourced locally; often Driftwood Spars) ⊞
Welcoming community-orientated free house with accommodation. The interior of this 17th-century former sail loft and mine warehouse features three wood-beamed bars on different levels, lead light windows, granite fireplaces, and nautical-themed decor throughout. An upstairs restaurant affords panoramic cove views. There are two beer gardens: an upper cliffside garden and a lower one opposite the brewery, whose beers always appear on the lower bar. Regular entertainment includes theatre. Three annual beer festivals are held.
Q❄️☺🛏️◑♿♣P🏮(U1A,316)🐾♿🎵

Trewellard

Trewellard Arms

Trewellard Road, TR19 7TA (on B3318/B3306 jct)
☎ (01736) 788634 ⊕ goodpubfoodlandsend.com
4 changing beers (sourced regionally; often Exeter, Tintagel) ⊞
A warm welcome is assured at this family-run free house in what was formerly a mining counthouse, then a hotel. There is a cosy, beamed single bar, and a restaurant with a secluded dining space. Taste of the West Gold Award winning home-cooked food is served, while log burners enhance the homely atmosphere. The beer menu varies constantly with up to four regionally sourced ales and two ciders. Beer festivals are held outside on the patio every Whitsun bank holiday weekend.
Q❄️☺◑🅰️♣P🏮🐾♿🎵

Truro

Old Ale House

7 Quay Street, TR1 2HD (near the bus station)
☎ (01872) 719462 ⊕ theoldalehousetruro.co.uk
8 changing beers (sourced nationally) ⊞
Friendly and lively two-storey city-centre pub housed in a former milliner's shop. The lower main bar is atmospheric, with wooden flooring, beamed ceilings, subtle lighting, various artefacts and plentiful wooden seating. With up to eight real ales and eight ciders on offer, there is something here for everyone. No food is served, but customers may bring their own. The upper floor is an events room with its own bar. Live music features frequently. Q❄️☺♿♣🍽️🏮🐾♿🎵

Rising Sun

Mitchell Hill, TR1 1ED
☎ (01872) 240003 ⊕ therisingsuntruro.co.uk
Fuller's London Pride ⒼE; **Sharp's Doom Bar, Sea Fury; 1 changing beer (sourced locally)** ⊞
Near the city centre up a steep hill, this award-winning gastro-pub is worth seeking out. Its narrow frontage belies a spacious interior, accommodating a small public bar with adjacent dining space, a lounge bar, and a stylish raised restaurant. Comfortably furnished throughout, the decor includes old Truro scenes. The changing beer menu offers four ales, two on gravity dispense, while the wide-ranging food menu features locally-sourced ingredients; booking essential. Outside is a sheltered patio where beer festivals are sometimes held. Q❄️☺◑🍽️P🏮🐾♿🎵

Tywardreath

New Inn ★

Fore Street, PL24 2QP
☎ (01726) 813073 ⊕ thenewinncornwall.co.uk
Draught Bass Ⓖ; **St Austell Tribute, Proper Job; 1 changing beer (sourced locally; often St Austell)** ⊞
A classic village pub, built in the mid-18th century by mine owners, and a perfect example of a community local and village hub. Groups meet here regularly, and fêtes are held in the extensive gardens. Although tied to a brewery, the bar offers a guest beer, often Draught Bass when available. Good conversation provides the main entertainment. There is a separate restaurant area to the rear, and a function room, decorated with posters of former pop stars. Q❄️☺◑🅰️P🏮(24)🐾🎵

Vogue

Star at Vogue

St Day Road, TR16 5NP (on road between Redruth and St Day)
☎ (01209) 820242 ⊕ starinnvogue.biz
5 changing beers (sourced nationally; often Camerons, Exmoor, Padstow) ⊞
Innovative, community-orientated village inn hosting a library branch, hairdressing salon, boules court, campsite, meetings and social events, plus music, quizzes and karaoke. This lively, welcoming and family-friendly pub slakes the thirst of a diverse custom, offering an ever-changing range of beers (including taster paddles) and home-cooked food. The cosy, relaxed and characterful interior accommodates a single bar, quiet lounge and separate dining area. Outside is sheltered seating, an extensive garden with reinforced marquee, and ample parking. Worth seeking out.
☺◑♿🅰️♣P🏮(40)🐾♿🎵

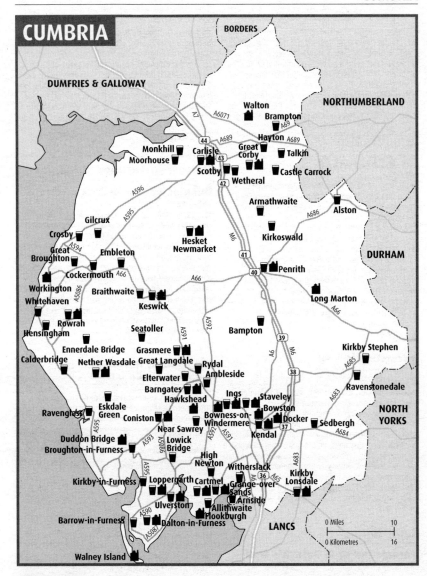

CUMBRIA

BORDERS

DUMFRIES & GALLOWAY

NORTHUMBERLAND

Walton
Brampton
Hayton
Monkhill
Carlisle
Great
Corby
Talkin
Moorhouse
Scotby
Castle Carrock
Wetheral
Armathwaite
Alston
Kirkoswald
Gilcrux
Crosby
Hesket
Newmarket
DURHAM
Great
Broughton
Embleton
Penrith
Cockermouth
Workington
Braithwaite
Whitehaven
Keswick
Long Marton
Rowrah
Seatoller
Hensingham
Bampton
Ennerdale Bridge
Grasmere
Kirkby Stephen
Calderbridge
Nether Wasdale
Great Langdale
Rydal
Ambleside
Ravenstonedale
Elterwater
Barngates
NORTH
YORKS
Ravenglass
Eskdale
Green
Hawkshead
Ings
Staveley
Bowston
Coniston
Bowness-on-
Windermere
Docker
Sedbergh
Near Sawrey
Kendal
Duddon Bridge
Lowick
Bridge
Broughton-in-Furness
High
Newton
Witherslack
Kirkby
Lonsdale
Kirkby-in-Furness
Loppergarth
Cartmel
Grange-over-
Sands
Arnside
Ulverston
Allithwaite
Barrow-in-Furness
Flookburgh
Dalton-in-Furness
LANCS
Walney Island

0 Miles 10
0 Kilometres 16

Allithwaite

Pheasant Inn 🅛

LA11 7RQ
☎ (015395) 32239 ⊕ thepheasantinnallithwaite.co.uk
Cumbrian Ales Loweswater Gold; house beer (by Banks's); 2 changing beers (sourced nationally; often Marston's, Unsworth's Yard) Ⓗ
This extensively refurbished free house now boasts an extension with stunning views over Humphrey Head to Morecambe Bay. The emphasis is very much on good-quality and good-value food. Disabled access via a lift that is accessed from outside. There is a separate bar area where dogs are welcome if on a lead.
🚫❀🛏❶♿🅰♣🅿🚃(530) ☻ 🤶

Alston

Cumberland Inn 🅛

Townfoot, CA9 3HX
☎ (01434) 381875 ⊕ cumberlandalston.co.uk
Firebrick Pagan Queen; 2 changing beers Ⓗ
Close to the Sea to Sea cycle route and Pennine Way, this 19th-century inn overlooking the South Tyne river is an ideal base to explore the highest market town in England. Guest beers are dispensed from four handpumps. The Cumberland has won many local CAMRA awards, including cider awards and always has a wide selection of beers, ciders and perries to choose from. It was refurbished in 2022 to provide a second bar.
Q❀🛏❶♣🅿🚃☻🤶

Ambleside

Golden Rule

Smithy Brow, LA22 9AS
☎ (015394) 32257 ⊕ goldenrule-ambleside.co.uk
Robinsons Dizzy Blonde, Cascade IPA; 3 changing beers (sourced regionally; often Robinsons) Ⓗ

Grade II-listed traditional inn at the bottom of the infamous 'Struggle', leading up to Kirkstone Pass. An exceptionally cosy multi-roomed pub with a real fire, bench seating, and historical rock-climbing photos decorating the walls. It serves a good range of well-kept Robinsons ales, occasionally featuring their award-winning Old Tom. There is an attractive snug, popular with families, and a rear courtyard with outdoor tables. Regularly packed with locals, students from the nearby university, and walkers and climbers. Q ➳ ❀ ❅ ♣ ⌂ ❀ ☎

Armathwaite

Fox & Pheasant ✓
CA4 9PY
☎ (016974) 72162 ⊕ foxandpheasantarmathwaite.co.uk
Robinsons Dizzy Blonde, Cumbria Way, Unicorn; 1 changing beer (sourced nationally; often Hawkshead, Robinsons) Ⓗ
Atmospheric 17th-century coaching inn overlooking the River Eden. The main bar has a flagstone floor and inglenook fire place. The former stables have been converted into a bar and eating area, and booking is recommended if dining. Original wooden beams, exposed stonework and stable stalls all add to the ambience. Friendly, welcoming service is assured. The guest beer is usually Robinsons seasonal beer but others are frequently seen. ➳ ❀ ⇔ ❪ Å ⇔ ♣ P ❀ ☎ ♪

Arnside

JJ Crossfield's Ⓛ ✓
35 The Promenade, LA5 0HA
⊕ jjcrossfields.com
Lancaster Amber, Blonde, IPA, Black; 2 changing beers (often Lancaster, Marston's) Ⓗ
This café-bar occupies a delightful position with views of Arnside Viaduct and across Morecambe Bay. Inside is a mixture of high bench and table seating, dining tables, low tables and armchairs, with a quiet snug area above the main bar. The 1960s-era bar fittings are sourced from the now-closed Holyrood Bar in Edinburgh. A restored antique beer engine is the centrepiece of the main room. It champions ales from the local Lancaster brewery. Food, mainly pizzas and beer snacks, is served all day. ➳ ❪ ⇔ ❀ ☎

Bampton

Mardale Inn at St Patrick's Well Ⓛ
CA10 2RQ (follow signs to Haweswater from Shap village)
☎ (01931) 719202 ⊕ themardaleinn.com
Cumbrian Ales Loweswater Gold; 2 changing beers (sourced locally; often Bowness Bay, Cumbrian Ales, Hawkshead) Ⓗ
Typical whitewashed Lakeland pub overlooking the Bampton valley and situated in a small hamlet close to Haweswater. It is a successful community free house offering good local ale, food, and welcome to everyone, and is well worth seeking out. The 2023 refurbishment is to a high standard, with flagstone floors and open fires. Lakeland pictures and photos include features about the nearby red squirrels. Six cosy en-suite rooms are ideal for walkers and cyclists. ➳ ❀ ⇔ ❪ ❅ ♣ ❀ ☎

Barngates

Drunken Duck Inn Ⓛ
LA22 0NG (signed off the B5286 Hawkshead to Ambleside road)

☎ (015394) 36347 ⊕ drunkenduckinn.co.uk
Barngates Brathay Gold, Cat Nap, Tag Lag; 2 changing beers (sourced locally; often Barngates) Ⓗ
High above Ambleside, this traditional Lakeland dwelling reflects the simplicity, beauty and longevity of its natural environment. It draws water from the fells for the beers brewed on-site by Barngates brewery. The bar has four handpumps and serves one of the other Barngates beers. The outside seating area at the front offers dramatic views of the fells to the north-east. Dogs are allowed except in the restaurant or bedrooms. Q ➳ ❀ ⇔ ❪ ❅ P ❀ ☎

Barrow-in-Furness

Duke of Edinburgh Ⓛ ✓
Abbey Road, LA14 5QR
☎ (01229) 821039 ⊕ dukeofedinburghhotel.co.uk
Lancaster Amber, Blonde, Red; Wainwright Gold; 3 changing beers (sourced nationally) Ⓗ
An impressive building on the edge of the town centre, near the station. It has an airy feel, with modern, comfortable furniture and a fine open fire, and is not as noisy as similar bars in the town. Good-quality, reasonably priced bar meals are available; there is also a separate restaurant, and accommodation. Beers are mainly from Lancaster brewery, with guest ales plus three craft keg ales, and bottled beers from around the world. ➳ ⇔ ❪ ❅ ⇔ P ⊠ ❀ ☎

King's Arms Hawcoat Ⓛ
Quarry Brow, Hawcoat, LA14 4HY
☎ (01229) 828137
Cumbrian Ales Loweswater Gold; Kirkby Lonsdale Monumental; Moorhouses White Witch; Wainwright

REAL ALE BREWERIES

Barngates ▤ Barngates
Bowness Bay ⚲ Kendal
Carlisle Carlisle
Coastline Walney Island
Coniston Coniston
Cumbrian Hawkshead
Eden River Penrith
Ennerdale ⚲ Rowrah
Fell Flookburgh
Gan Yam ⚲ Kendal
Grasmere Grasmere
Great Corby Great Corby
Handsome Bowston
Hawkshead ⚲ Staveley
Healey's ▤ Loppergarth
Hesket Newmarket Hesket Newmarket
Keswick ⚲ Keswick
Kirkby Lonsdale ⚲ Kirkby Lonsdale
Lakes ⚲ Kendal
Langdale Docker
Logan Beck Duddon Bridge
Old Friends ▤ Ulverston
Old Vicarage ⚲ Walton
Shaws of Grange Grange-over-Sands
Strands ▤ Nether Wasdale
Tirril Long Marton
Townhouse Dalton-in-Furness
Tractor Shed ⚲ Workington
Ulverston ⚲ Ulverston
Unsworth's Yard ⚲ Cartmel
Westmorland Kendal
Wild Boar ▤ Bowness-on-Windermere
Windermere ▤ Ings

Gold; 2 changing beers (sourced locally; often Bowness Bay, Kirkby Lonsdale) Ⓗ
Popular local pub conveniently situated near the number 1 bus route in Hawcoat village that runs between the main town centre and the hospital. It sells ales mainly from Cumbrian micros. A beer menu on a chalkboard lists forthcoming attractions. The pub, which has been on these premises since the 1860s, has been extensively extended and renovated, and features an open bar with adjacent separate rooms. Friendly staff give a warm welcome. Well-behaved dogs are allowed in one of the rooms. Q✖&♣🖿😊🛜

Braithwaite

Coledale Inn
CA12 5TN (at top of village, off Whinlatter Pass)
☎ (017687) 78272 ⊕ coledale-inn.co.uk
Great Corby Blonde; 2 changing beers (sourced regionally) Ⓗ
The Coledale Inn was built in 1824 as a woollen mill, later becoming a pencil mill. This late Georgian building became a hotel in the 1970s, prior to which it had been a country club with accommodation. It has been in the hands of the same family for about 40 years. The hotel has two bars, 21 rooms and great views. Note the typical lakeland carved oak bar and unusual 'Cumbrian life' mural Q✖😊🖿◑&♠P🖿(X5,77A)😊🛜

Brampton

Howard Arms ✅
Front Street, CA8 1NG
☎ (016977) 42758 ⊕ howardarms.co.uk
Thwaites IPA, Gold, Amber; house beer (by Thwaites) Ⓗ
Modernised 18th-century country inn situated in the town centre. Four handpumps dispense beers from the Thwaites range including one badged as Howard Arms. Charles Dickens is reputed to have slept here. Meeting and function rooms are available, with a separate games room upstairs. Breakfasts are served daily and the main menu shows a commitment to local produce and home-made cooking. ✖😊◑&♠P🖿(685)😊🛜♫

Broughton-in-Furness

Manor Arms Ⓛ
The Square, LA20 6HY
☎ (01229) 716286 ⊕ manorarmsthesquare.co.uk
Great Corby Blonde; Lakes Pale; 5 changing beers (sourced regionally; often Townhouse) Ⓗ
Outstanding free house owned by the Varty family for more than 30 years. Set in an attractive Georgian square, it has been the recipient of many CAMRA awards. Real ale dominates, always including a dark beer, along with traditional cider and perry, making every day a mini beer festival. Two fires keep the pub warm and the bar staff are always friendly. Q✖😊♣🗓😊🛜

Calderbridge

Stanley Arms Hotel
CA20 1DN (on the A595)
☎ (01946) 841235 ⊕ stanleyarmshotel.com
Wychwood Hobgoblin Gold; 2 changing beers (sourced nationally; often Bowness Bay, Wychwood) Ⓗ
Located on the western edge of the Lake District National Park the Stanley Arms has 14 en-suite hotel rooms and offers conference facilities, a popular restaurant, two bars and probably the best river-fronted beer garden in

Cumbria. Between two and four ales are available, usually including Wychwood Hobgoblin Gold and Bowness Bay Swan Blonde. Q✖😊🖾◑♣P😊🛜

Carlisle

King's Head Inn Ⓛ
Fisher Street, CA3 8RF
⊕ kingsheadcarlisle.co.uk
Cumbrian Ales Esthwaite Bitter; 3 changing beers (sourced regionally) Ⓗ
Excellent city-centre pub and winner of many CAMRA awards, it serves a range of guest ales from four handpumps. Pictures of old Carlisle adorn the internal walls and outside is an explanation of why the city isn't in the Domesday Book. Good-value meals are served at lunchtime. The covered outdoor courtyard has a largescreen TV and regularly features live music. No children or dogs allowed. 😊◑➹♣🖿😊🛜♫

Last Zebra
Lowther Street, CA3 8DA
☎ (01228) 593600 ⊕ thelastzebra.co.uk
Cumbrian Ales Loweswater Gold; Hawkshead Windermere Pale Ⓗ
Rebranded and reopened in 2014 this is a posh wine bar in the centre of town, originally a pub. Over the years it has undergone many changes of name and styles, and is now aimed at the 25-35 age group. The original glazed high roof has now been exposed allowing lots of natural light. Food is available all day, specialising in steaks cooked on an Inka charcoal grill. Up to four handpumps are available serving local ales, seasonal brews and a nationally-known beer. ✖◑&➹🗓🛜

Milbourne Arms
150 Milbourne Street, CA2 5XB
☎ (01228) 541194
2 changing beers (sourced locally) Ⓗ
Former State Management pub which, when built in 1853, served the thriving surrounding textile industry. Hand looms, spinning wheels, bobbins and shuttles from Linton Tweeds which would have been used in the nearby mills, along with archive photos of the industry are to be found throughout the pub. This is a cosy and friendly single-room pub arranged around a central bar. On local bus routes, it is a 12-minute walk from Carlisle train station. ✖◑&➹🗓😊🛜♫

Spinners Arms Ⓛ
Cummersdale, CA2 6BD
☎ (01228) 532928
Carlisle Cumbrian Bitter, Spun Gold; 2 changing beers (often Carlisle) Ⓗ
Cosy family-friendly hostelry, an original Redfern pub with unique and original features. It is situated less than half a mile from Carlisle's south-western boundary, close to the Cumbrian Way and National Cycle Route 7, which run alongside the picturesque river Caldew. There is regular live music, with Irish music sessions every first and third Wednesday. Children are welcome until 9pm and well-behaved dogs are permitted. The pub is the brewery tap for Carlisle Brewing Co, showcasing their beer on three pumps. ✖😊&♣P🗓(75)😊🛜♫

Sportsman Inn ✅
Heads Lane, CA3 8AQ
☎ (01228) 533799
3 changing beers Ⓗ
The oldest recorded pub in Carlisle, dating from 1747, although there is a copy of a 15th-century map of the area on display in the pub which suggests there was a building on the site at that time. The pub has one large

room. It was formerly a State Management pub – a plaque above the bar states it was part of the scheme between August 1916 and May 1973. 🏮🏠🍴➹⚒♿🚗🚃🛜

Woodrow Wilson 🗓 ✅

48 Botchergate, CA1 1QS
☎ (01228) 819942
Great Corby Blonde; Greene King Abbot; Ruddles Best Bitter; Sharp's Doom Bar; Wainwright Gold; 7 changing beers (sourced nationally; often Great Corby, Theakston, Thornbridge) Ⓗ
One of two almost adjacent Wetherspoons, this pub is in a refurbished Co-op building named after the former US president, whose mother was born in Carlisle. Up to 14 handpumps offer the largest range of real ales to be found in Carlisle. Food is available all day until 11pm. At the rear there is a spacious outdoor seating area, heated patio and smokers' area. Children are welcome in some areas until 8pm. 🏮🏠🍴♿➹⚒🅿🚃🛜

Cartmel

Royal Oak Inn 🗓

The Square, LA11 6QB
☎ (015395) 36692
Fell Ghyll, Crag; 4 changing beers (sourced nationally; often Fell) Ⓗ
Traditional inn in the village square within five minutes walk of the famous priory and racecourse. A firm favourite with locals and tourists alike, the meals, decor and atmosphere are all excellent. A welcoming log fire and oak beams (some so low as to carry headroom warnings) give a rustic appeal. The extensive enclosed riverside garden at the rear is an attraction for families. Q🏠🏮🍴🌳♿🚃(530,532) ❀🛜♫

Unsworth Yard Brewery 🗓

4 Unsworth's Yard, LA11 6PG
☎ 07810 461313 ● unsworthsyard.co.uk/brewery
Unsworth's Yard Crusader Gold; 3 changing beers (sourced locally; often Bowness Bay, Unsworth's Yard) Ⓗ
Tasting room at the front of a five-barrel brewery, with up to three of the brewery's beers available at all times. The tasting room, which is available for functions by appointment, opens out on to a courtyard with extensive outdoor seating. Other businesses, including high quality bread and cheese shops, as well as a shop specialising in fine wines, surround the courtyard giving this an almost continental ambience. 🏮🍴♿🚃(532,530)♫

Castle Carrock

Duke of Cumberland 🗓

CA8 9LU
☎ (01228) 670341 ● the-dukeofcumberland.com
Twice Brewed Gallia, Sycamore Gap; 1 changing beer (sourced locally) Ⓗ
At the heart of this charming village, the Duke reopened in 2009 and is now successfully re-established, with a strong local following. It is the centre for the annual Marr Folk Festival in July. At the foot of the northern Pennines, it is ideally located for outdoor activity enthusiasts, who can enjoy real ale and sample the home-made food which has a growing reputation. The layout separates the games/TV area from the dining area. Dogs are not allowed inside the pub. 🏮🏠🍴🏮🅿🛜♫

Cockermouth

Bitter End

15 Kirkgate, CA13 9PJ

☎ (01900) 828993 ● bitterend.co.uk
6 changing beers (sourced nationally) Ⓗ
This award-winning pub features six handpumps which dispense beer from well-respected Cumbrian breweries. The house beer is brewed by various different breweries, including Marston's and Tirril. The cosy bar comprises of three areas, with seating mostly given over to dining; the food is deservedly popular. A unique collection of Old Cockermouth photographs are displayed on the walls. There is a popular quiz every Tuesday evening. It has a small seating area in front, next to the road. Q🏠🏮🚃❀🛜

Cock & Bull

7 South Street, CA13 9RT (centre of town opp Sainsburys)
☎ (01900) 827999 ● thenewcockandbull.co.uk
Coniston Bluebird Bitter; Great Corby Blonde, Fox Brown Ale; 2 changing beers (sourced regionally) Ⓗ
Community pub in the centre of town with a constantly changing range of real ales on two of the handpumps, mainly from smaller Cumbrian breweries. The venue is on three levels with the main area having bar stools plus two seating areas, with a TV showing sports in the front corner. The top level has pool table and dartboard. Below this, off the main bar, is a quieter small room. No food is served. 🏮🏠❀🛜♫

Coniston

Black Bull Inn & Hotel 🗓

LA21 8DU
☎ (015394) 41668 ● blackbullconiston.co.uk
Coniston Oliver's Light Ale, Bluebird Bitter, Bluebird Premium XB, Old Man Ale, Special Oatmeal Stout, No 9 Barley Wine; 3 changing beers (sourced locally; often Coniston) Ⓗ
This 16th-century coaching inn is Coniston Brewing Company's on-site taphouse, also serving good food in comfortable surroundings. A full menu is served from noon. Six regular beers are supplemented by other beers from the brewery on a rotation basis – try a tasting paddle. The spacious bar and lounge are frequented by tourists in this popular, spectacular location near Coniston Old Man. The outside seating area is perfect in summer. Dogs are not allowed in the restaurant. 🏠🏮🏮🍴♿🅿(X12,505) ❀🛜

Crosby

Stag Inn ✅

Lowside, CA15 6SH
☎ (01900) 812549 ● staginncrosby.com
Greene King IPA; Timothy Taylor Landlord Ⓗ
Friendly and welcoming inn that is popular with locals and visitors alike. It is run by a knowledgable owner with a nucleus of long-term, experienced staff. The pub has a large bar with two serving points and quiet corners. There is also a dinning area which serves a wide range of meals, catering for all tastes. You can enjoy views over the Solway Firth to Scotland from the beer garden. Q🏠🏮🍴🏮🅿(300) ❀🛜♫

Dalton-in-Furness

Clarence

33 Ulverston Road, LA15 8EF
☎ 07974 467615
2 changing beers (sourced nationally; often Logan Beck, Townhouse) Ⓗ
You will receive a warm welcome from all in this recently refurbished friendly and community-focused pub. The

owners are enthusiastic about cask ales and hope to showcase more local breweries. They have regular music sessions, and have enthusiastic teams in the local darts and pool leagues. Check their Facebook page for details of special and charity events.
≠(Dalton) ♣🚌(6,X6) 🌸🛜🎵

Elterwater

Britannia Inn ★ 🅛 ✓
LA22 9HP
☎ (015394) 37210 🌐 britinn.co.uk
Coniston Bluebird Bitter; Langdale Elterwater Gold; house beer (by Langdale); 3 changing beers (sourced locally) 🅷
A brilliant, friendly and deservedly popular pub, its small rooms soon fill up, and walkers and their dogs will be seen around the benches in front most days of the year. Beers are mostly local, with the core range supplemented by up to three guests in summer. Langdale brewery is the sister business. Food is available all day, with dining room bookings advised (by phone) for evening meals. There are nine bedrooms. The 516 bus stops just outside. 🏴🌸🛏️🍽️🚃(516)🌸🛜

Embleton

Embleton Spa
CA13 9YA (just off A66 in Embleton village)
☎ (017687) 76606 🌐 embletonspa.co.uk
Cumbrian Ales Loweswater Gold; 2 changing beers (sourced locally; often Coniston) 🅷
Originally an 18th Century lakeland farm house. With grandstand views of Sale Fell, Skiddaw and Ullock Pike from a thoughtfully laid out patio area, or via large panoramic windows in the cozy, well equipped bar/dining areas, this is an ideal place to simply relax or use the swimming pool, jacuzzi and gym. There are many interesting walks on the doorstep, including Whinlatter Forest Park, and a warm welcome from friendly, helpful staff who strive to serve the best cask ales Cumbrian breweries can provide. 🏴🌸🛏️🍽️🅿️🚃(X4,X5)🌸🛜

Ennerdale Bridge

Fox & Hounds Inn 🅛
4 Post Office Row, CA23 3AR (follow signposted route from Wath Brow for approx 3 miles)
☎ (01946) 861373 🌐 foxandhoundsinn.org
Wainwright Gold; 5 changing beers (sourced nationally; often Bowness Bay, Keswick) 🅷
Lovely country pub on the Coast-to-Coast walking route and only minutes away from Ennerdale Lake. The village is mentioned in the Wordsworth poem The Brothers. Ennerdale valley is currently undergoing a pioneering rewilding project. The pub has three seperate areas and has five handpumps at all times with increased numbers in the summer months. Q🏴🌸🛏️🍽️♿🏕️♣🅿️🅿️🛜

Eskdale Green

Bower House Inn
CA19 1TD (short walk from Irton Road station La'al Ratty)
☎ (019467) 23244 🌐 bowerhouseinn.com
Cumbrian Ales Loweswater Gold; Timothy Taylor Landlord; 5 changing beers (sourced nationally; often Hawkshead) 🅷
Situated on the edge of the village of Eskdale Green, close to the famous Outward Bound school, this popular and well-managed tourist pub is renowned for its good food and a wide range of well-kept cask ales. Staff are helpul and courteous. There is an open fire in winter

months and excellent outdoor seating areas and a childrens' play area for warmer days.
Q🏴🌸🛏️🍽️🅰️≠(Irton Road) ♣🅿️🌸🛜

Gilcrux

Mason's Arms
CA7 2QX
☎ (016973) 23267 🌐 themasonsarmsgilcrux.co.uk
Kirkby Lonsdale Ruskin's; 1 changing beer (sourced locally; often Cumbrian Ales) 🅷
Welcoming village pub with a sizeable L-shaped bar and seperate games room. The building, with reclaimed ships' timbers in its structure, dates back to 1865 and was originally a boot and shoe makers. It is run by an experienced couple who take pride in serving a range of beers and good home-made food. Regular themed food evenings cover European and Asian dining. There is a large beer garden outside. Q🏴🌸🍽️♣🅿️🌸🛜🎵

Grange-over-Sands

Keg & Kitchen 🅛
Main Street, LA11 6AB
☎ (015395) 83003 🌐 kegandkitchen.co.uk
Unsworth's Yard Sir Edgar Harrington's Last Wolf; 2 changing beers (sourced nationally; often Bowness Bay, Oakham, Unsworth's Yard) 🅷
Situated in the centre of Grange opposite the post office, the main bar and entrance of this family-run pub are on the middle floor. The upstairs has been converted to a games area containing a pool table. The lower area, called the Gin Pig, can be accessed from the pub or from a separate entrance. It hosts open mic and cinema nights and is also available for hire. 🏴🌸🍽️🅰️≠♣🚃🌸🛜🎵

Grasmere

Tweedies Bar & Lodge 🅛
Red Bank Road, LA22 9SW
☎ (015394) 35300 🌐 tweediesgrasmere.com
Coniston Old Man Ale; Cumbrian Ales Loweswater Gold; Fell Crag; Lakes Pale Ale; 3 changing beers (sourced nationally) 🅷
A legend in these parts, the bar is a must-go attraction for regular visitors who seek advice from the knowledgeable bar staff on the wide-ranging selection of excellent ales. The beer list is updated daily on their website, and in addition to the cask ales will also feature a number of craft ales. Ideal for walkers with muddy boots and even muddier dogs, it has an incredible number of outdoor tables and seating in the garden which is a real pleasure to sit down and relax in. 🏴🌸🛏️🍽️♿♣🅿️🚃(555,599) 🌸🛜🎵

Great Broughton

Punch Bowl Inn
19 Main Street, CA13 0YJ
☎ (01900) 267070
3 changing beers (sourced nationally) 🅷
Committee-run cosy community pub that prides itself on the range and number of beers they continue to source both nationally and from within Cumbria. Originally a 17th-century coaching inn, it has a welcoming atmosphere and the beers are consistently well kept. This is very much a drinkers pub for locals and visitors alike. It has limited opening hours so check before visiting. Q🏴♣🅿️🌸🛜

Great Corby

Queen Inn L
The Green, CA4 8LR
☎ (01228) 832032 ● thequeeninn-greatcorby.co.uk
Great Corby Corby Ale, Blonde Ⓗ
Refurbished village pub with two restaurant areas. The focus is on food and booking is essential if you wish to eat. A conference room is available and a private dining room. There is a separate room for sports TV. It serves a range of ales from the next door Great Corby Brewhouse. The pub occasionally hosts live music. Q✿☻❀◐⟨P❀ 🐾 ？

Great Langdale

Old Dungeon Ghyll Hotel ★ L
LA22 9JY
☎ (015394) 37272 ● odg.co.uk
Cumbrian Ales Loweswater Gold; 5 changing beers (sourced locally; often Barngates, Cumbrian Ales, Fell) Ⓗ
The Climbers' Bar is famous as a timeless watering hole for generations of weary walkers, and the atmosphere and the beer always hits the spot. It is in a stunningly beautiful location beneath the surrounding fells and is naturally popular with walkers. Local ales are featured on the bar with occasional outsiders for variety. The fare is limited yet enjoyable, as are the facilities. Plenty of tables in the garden give the best views. The bus from Ambleside is an added bonus for the less-active visitor. Q✿☻❀◀◐⟨P❰(516) ❀ ？ ♫

Hayton

Stone Inn
CA8 9HR
☎ (01228) 670896 ● stoneinnhayton.co.uk
2 changing beers (sourced locally) Ⓗ
Traditional, family-run, community pub in the village of Hayton, and home to the local leek club! There is an upstairs dining room which can be hired for small gatherings. A fine pair of 1904 Christ Church boat club oars adorn one wall. Ask to see the CAMRA mirror. There is usually a choice of two real ales at weekends, occasionally from a local brewery. ☻◐♣P❀ ？

Hensingham

Globe Inn
95 Main Street, CA28 8QX (take the A595 from Whitehaven and follow signs for Cleator Moor)
☎ (01946) 443853
Cumbrian Ales Loweswater Gold Ⓗ
An unassuming pub from the outside, as soon as you walk in the friendly character takes hold. The pub is open plan, with a real fire in winter and a function room upstairs. The beer range on the two handpumps changes frequently. Sports TV is available, also a dartboard and jukebox. Very much a local's pub but always welcoming to strangers and their dogs. Card payments are now accepted. Food is not served but customers can bring in a takeaway from across the street. ☻❀❀ ？ ♫

Hesket Newmarket

Old Crown L ✔
CA7 8JG
☎ (016974) 78288 ● theoldcrownpub.co.uk
Hesket Newmarket Black Sail, Helvellyn Gold, Brim Fell IPA; 3 changing beers (sourced locally; often Hesket Newmarket) Ⓗ

Sitting in the heart of this lovely fellside village, the Old Crown is a showcase for the Hesket Newmarket brewery, which is immediately behind the pub. It is famous as the first co-operatively owned pub in the country and is popular with locals and visitors alike, with King Charles and Sir Chris Bonnington among its supporters. Opening hours are subject to change, please check the pub website before travelling. Q☻❀◐⟨♣❀❀ ？

High Newton

Heft L
Newton in Cartmel, LA11 6JH (turn off High Newton bypass into hamlet; pub is in centre, near X6 bus stop) SD402829
☎ (015395) 30017 ● hefthighnewton.co.uk
Fell Ghyll; Lakes Pale; 2 changing beers (sourced nationally; often Farm Yard) Ⓗ
This village local with a large restaurant area is worth a detour off the A590 High Newton bypass or a stop off the X6 bus from Kendal to Barrow-in-Furness. The three regular local beers are complemented by a varied selection of beers, both local and from further afield, including a range of styles. Excellent locally produced food is also served. The restaurant area can be reached by a door to the rear of the pub, which has disabled access. Q☻❀❀◀ ▲ⵔ(X6)❀ ？

Ings

Watermill Inn L
LA8 9PY
☎ (01539) 821309 ● watermillinn.co.uk
Windermere Collie Wobbles, A Bit'er Ruff, Windermere Blonde; 8 changing beers (sourced locally; often Windermere) Ⓗ
This village pub with rooms, in a converted watermill, is a long-established gateway to the Lakes. The many Windermere brewery beers, brewed on the premises, have dog-themed names, and, unsurprisingly, four legs are as welcome as two in the pub; menus cater for both, as do the bedrooms. There is a nearby campsite and the Lakes 555 bus stops outside – handy if you're sampling the renowned Shi Tzu Faced at 7% ABV. Q☻❀❀◀◐ ♣▲P❀ ？

Kendal

Barrel House L
Unit 10 Castle Mills, Aynam Road, LA9 7DE
☎ 07379 437125 ● bownessbaybrewing.co.uk
Bowness Bay Swan Blonde, Fell Walker, Raven Red, Swan Gold, Swan Black Ⓗ
The tap house for Bowness Bay Brewing is hidden in an old mill complex across the river from the town centre. At the back of the walled yard are self-contained beer booths, then a large folding glass door opens to reveal a two-storey modern conversion with a snug bar and upstairs comfy lounge. The bar showcases the full range of beers brewed on site on five handpumps. Food is supplied by various vendors at the weekends. Open Thursday-Sunday only, with changing seasonal hours – see website for details. ❀◐⟨P❀ ♫

Factory Tap L
5 Aynam Road, LA9 7DE
☎ (015394) 82541 ● thefactorytap.co.uk
Fyne Jarl; 9 changing beers (sourced nationally; often Brass Castle, Fell, Gan Yam) Ⓗ
A friendly, welcoming pub that proudly showcase ales from local breweries on six handpumps and four keg taps, alongside guests ales, which can be sourced from

anywhere in the country. Pizzas are available every Tuesday and Friday, with street food served on the last Saturday of the month. Just a short walk from the town centre, this place is well worth a visit.
ᗰ❀⬤◖ᴥ🅿️🖳❀🛜♪

Fell Bar L
3 Lowther Street, LA9 4DH
☎ 07904 488014 ⊕ fellbrewery.co.uk
Fell Ghyll Ⓗ; 11 changing beers (sourced regionally; often Fell, Fyne, Gan Yam) Ⓗ/Ⓚ
This four-storey house by the town hall is a tap bar for artisan Fell brewery and offers an extensive choice of house and guest ales on six handpumps and eight keg lines, plus a selection of spirits, natural wines and soft drinks. The selection includes unctuous stouts and fruity sours alongside more traditional styles. Live music and Jim's pizzas are hosted on the first and second floors and the staff are enthusiastic and knowledgeable.
ᗰ◖≉♣🖳❀♪

Indie Craft Beer L
32 Finkle Street, LA9 4AB
☎ (01539) 721450 ⊕ indiecraftbeer.co.uk
Lakes Pale Ale Ⓗ; 12 changing beers (sourced nationally; often Arbor, Cloudwater, Northern Monk) Ⓚ
Quirky beer shop and bar in the centre of Kendal on the pedestrianised Finkle Street, with outdoor tables and benches. There is one handpump serving cask ale and 12 keg lines offering a wide selection of craft ales, many of which are live beers brewed by independent breweries from around the UK and further afield. Around 200 bottles and cans line the shelves and fridges including Belgian and other European beers. Ranging over three floors, the micropub gives a nod to Manchester with its music and décor. A vinyl selection is available for customer requests. ❀≉⬤🖳🖳(555,X6)❀🛜♪

New Union L
159 Stricklandgate, LA9 4RF
☎ (01539) 726019 ⊕ thenewunion.co.uk
Fyne Jarl; 3 changing beers (sourced regionally; often Bowness Bay, Kirkby Lonsdale, Thornbridge) Ⓗ
The multi award-winning New Union is famed for its huge drinks selection. There is a strong focus on the promotion of local breweries and championing of real cider, for which it has won national accolades. It is a real community pub, hosting Meet the Brewer and distiller events, beer festivals, whisky nights, regular live music and more. Four handpumps serve a constantly changing selection, with beers from further afield often featuring alongside local ales. ᗰ❀≉♣⬤🖳(555)❀🛜♪

Keswick

Dog & Gun ✓
2 Lake Road, CA12 5BT
☎ (017687) 73463
Cumbrian Ales Loweswater Gold; Theakston Old Peculier; 5 changing beers (sourced nationally; often Greene King) Ⓗ
Refurbished during 2023 to a more modern style this town-centre pub is popular with dogs and their owners, becoming really busy, especially around meal times. The slate and wooden floors combine with other features to maintain a characterful appearance, as does the long bar with eight handpumps providing a mix of Cumbrian and national cask ales. There is a typical pub food menu whilst the beef or vegetarian goulash provide an interesting option. ᗰ◖♣🖳❀🛜

Fox Tap ♆ L
Brewery Lane, CA12 5BY
☎ (017687) 80700 ⊕ keswickbrewery.co.uk
Keswick Gold, Fox Pale; 5 changing beers (sourced locally) Ⓗ
There has been a brewery on the site since 1875. The tap serves all the brewery beers with usually six cask ales and four keg beers on offer. Staff will guide drinkers through the beers on offer if required. Brewery tours are available, and need to be prebooked. Social events are held. Situated just outside the town centre, there is an outside seating area and monthly social events are held. Dogs are welcome. Q❀⬤🖳❀♪

Wainwright L
Lake Road, CA12 5BZ
☎ (017687) 44927 ⊕ thewainwright.pub
Fell Tinderbox IPA; 7 changing beers (sourced nationally; often Kirkby Lonsdale, Ulverston, Marston's) Ⓗ
Having achieved national fame as a walkers pub with local real ales, good food, cosy atmosphere and warm welcome, this oak floored traditional pub is not to be missed. With nine handpumps serving a diverse range of cask ales, at least one gluten-free, and a map depicting locations of the Cumbrian breweries, it is an ideal place to relax after a long or short walk. A TV above the bar displays many iconic hikes and climbs in the area.
Qᗰ❀🚐◖♣⬤🖳❀🛜

Kirkby Lonsdale

Orange Tree L ✓
9 Fairbank, LA6 2BD (turn left past the churchyard, and the Orange Tree is on your right)
☎ (015242) 71716 ⊕ theorangetreehotel.co.uk
Kirkby Lonsdale Ruskin's, Monumental; 3 changing beers (sourced locally; often Bowness Bay, Handsome, Kirkby Lonsdale) Ⓗ
Formerly the Fleece, this is a warm, welcoming pub near the church in a peaceful part of this bustling little town. Six handpumps on the bar have Kirkby Lonsdale beers and usually one local guest. A still cider is also available. There's accommodation in six en-suite rooms and a strong food offering. The owner's love of Rugby Union is reflected in the Orange Tree name, borrowed from a pub near Twickenham, and in the framed pictures on the walls. ᗰ🚐◖♣🖳(567)❀🛜

Royal Barn L ✓
New Road, LA6 2AB
☎ (015242) 71918
Kirkby Lonsdale Tiffin Gold, Stanley's, Ruskin's, Singletrack, Monumental, Jubilee; 4 changing beers (sourced locally; often Kirkby Lonsdale) Ⓗ
From the outside the tap house for Kirkby Lonsdale brewery is a plain barn, but once inside you'll discover a buzzing hive of beer activity. The bar showcases 12 handpumps and eight keg lines, alongside a handful of ciders often including Hogan's. An underground kitchen produces fresh pizzas, and coffee is roasted on site. Occasional live music and other events are listed on social media. ᗰ◖⬤🖳❀♪

Kirkby Stephen

La'l Nook L
1 Croft Street, CA17 4QJ
☎ 07506 075625
5 changing beers (sourced locally; often Keswick, Langdale, Tirril) Ⓗ

This cosy micropub is a local hub for good beer and good conversation. It is located at the end of a side alley on the main street just above the centre of this little town. The five handpumps supply weekly-changing ales from every brewery in the surrounding area, and you can check out the updated beer menu on social media to inform your visit. The unisex toilet facility is up steep stairs and is regulated by a novel entry system. Last orders are 30 minutes before closing times shown. Tasting paddles are available. Q ★ ◆ (S5)❦

Taggy Man L
4 Market Street, CA17 4QS
☎ (017683) 72531 ⊕ taggyman.co.uk
House beer (by Kirkby Lonsdale); 2 changing beers (sourced locally; often Cross Bay, Keswick, Rudgate) Ⓗ
Traditional old Cumbrian free house below the town centre that is praised for its friendly welcome and easy hospitality. The pub is named after the medieval watchman who called the nightly curfew. A good selection of local ales sits alongside popular national beers with good pub grub; the tasty handmade pies are the house speciality. Weekly live music events and a Tuesday quiz are advertised on social media. Dogs and muddy boots are welcome. ★ ◑ ▲ ♣ ➡ (S5)❦ ⚞ ♪

Kirkby-in-Furness

Ship Inn L
Askew Gate Brow, LA17 7TE
☎ 07733 276451
Townhouse Meg's Mild; 4 changing beers (sourced regionally; often Townhouse) Ⓗ
This traditional family-run 300-year-old village inn is situated on the Cumbria Cycle Way. Only a two minute walk from the station, and a short stroll from the crossroads on the main A595, there are magnificent views from the outside terrace over the Duddon estuary. There is a warm, friendly atmosphere, enhanced by the log burner and a good choice of local ales, which always includes a dark beer. Simple home-cooked food is served in the evening at the weekend. Closed Tuesday and Wednesday. ★ ◑ ◐ ➾ ♣ P ❦ ⚞ ♪

Kirkoswald

Fetherston Arms
The Square, CA10 1DQ
☎ (01768) 898284 ⊕ fetherston-arms.co.uk
Theakston Best Bitter; 3 changing beers (often Allendale, Hesket Newmarket) Ⓗ
Situated in the centre of this historic village, the friendly enthusiasm of the owners, plus the extensive alterations, have helped convert the Fethers into a truly outstanding pub with an excellent reputation for food. Three changing real ales are available from breweries such as Allendale and Hesket Newmarket. Although the village is not on a bus route it is 20 minutes' stroll from Lazonby station on the Carlisle to Settle Line. Opening hours may vary in winter. Q ★ ◐ ◑ ❦ ❦ ⚞

Loppergarth

Wellington Inn L
Main Street, LA12 0JL (1 mile from A590 between Lindal and Pennington)
☎ (01229) 582388
Healey's Blonde, Mild; 4 changing beers (sourced locally; often Healey's) Ⓗ
Superb village local with its own microbrewery (Healey's), a custom-made stainless steel plant which is

viewable from the snug. Two handpumps dispense Healey's beers with one of the regular beers replaced occasionally with a darker best bitter. Wood-burning stoves make this a cosy pub with games, books and good conversation. There is a quiz on alternate Saturdays. Well-behaved dogs on leads are welcome. ★ ◑ ◐ ♣ ❦ ⚞

Lowick Bridge

Red Lion Inn L
LA12 8EF (just off the A5084 on the Ulverston to Torver road)
☎ (01229) 885366 ⊕ redlion-lowick.co.uk
Bank Top Flat Cap; Great Corby Corby Ale; 1 changing beer (sourced locally) Ⓗ
This former Hartleys ale house, worth finding just off the road from Greenodd to Coniston, was purchased by the present owners from Robinsons in 2014. It is now a charming, comfortable and welcoming country inn, popular with both locals and visitors to the Lakes, and makes an ideal base to explore the hidden corners of the Southern Lakes and the Furness and Cartmel Peninsulas. The changing beer is often a dark beer. Q ★ ◑ ◰ P ❦ ⚞ ♪

Monkhill

Drovers Rest ♥
CA5 6DB
☎ (01228) 576141
4 changing beers Ⓗ
A traditional country pub, close to the popular Hadrian's Wall Path, with a strong community focus. Although opened up, the interior still has the feel of three distinct rooms. The bar area is cosy and welcoming with a roaring fire in winter. Some interesting historical State Management Scheme documents adorn the walls. The Drovers is an oasis for lots of different and sometimes obscure (for the area) real ales. Winner of many CAMRA awards including at regional level. ★ ◑ ◐ ▲ ♣ P ➡ (93)❦

Moorhouse

Royal Oak
CA5 6EZ
☎ (01228) 576475
Cumbrian Ales Loweswater Gold; Timothy Taylor Landlord; 1 changing beer Ⓗ
This small country pub on the outskirts of Carlisle is over 250 years old, so be prepared to duck as you go through some of the doors. Log-burning stoves help provide a rustic atmosphere. A traditional home-cooked menu is available along with ale from local breweries. ◐ ◑ ❦ ⚞

Near Sawrey

Tower Bank Arms L
LA22 0LF (on B5285 2 miles S of Hawkshead)
☎ (015394) 36334 ⊕ towerbankarms.co.uk
Barngates Tag Lag; Cumbrian Ales Loweswater Gold; Hawkshead Bitter; 4 changing beers (sourced locally; often Barngates, Cumbrian Ales, Hawkshead) Ⓗ
This 17th-century Lakeland inn, with slate floors, oak beams and a cast-iron range creating a lovely atmosphere isnext to the National Trust's Hill Top which was Beatrix Potter's home. Four handpumps serve local beer, with cider and perry dispensed by gravity. Booking is essential for evening meals. Families and dogs are welcomed. There is a seasonal bus service connecting to the Windermere ferry and Hawkshead. Accommodation is available in four en-suite rooms. Closed on Mondays in winter. Q ★ ◑ ◰ ◑ ♣ P ➡ ❦ ⚞

Nether Wasdale

Strands Inn [L]
CA20 1ET
☎ (019467) 26237 🌐 strands-brewery.co.uk
Strands Brown Bitter, Errmmm...; 6 changing beers (sourced locally) [H]
Home of Strands brewery and gin distillery, this inn has an extensive food and beer menu of which they are justifiably proud. A range of around 40 beers is brewed on site – of which six are available on the main bar all year round. Visit during the annual May festival of beers to try the entire range. Children are welcome as well as dogs. The owners also run the Screes Inn opposite which serves up to six more beers during summer months.
Q🐴✿🛏◑♿⛺♣P🐾📶

Penrith

Dog Beck ✔
21-22 Southend Road, CA11 8JH
☎ (01768) 840491
Greene King Abbot; Ruddles Best Bitter; changing beers [H]
Named after the historic Dog Beck that ran nearby, this Wetherspoon pub is situated conveniently between the main car park and centre of Penrith. It has the usual large range of real ales and food is served all day every day. The bar and downstairs area is a single open-plan room on different levels. There is a large upstairs outside courtyard area in which meals can be taken alfresco on warm summer days. Q🐴✿◑♿🚆(North Lakes)🚌📶

Fell Bar [L]
52 King Street, CA11 7AY
☎ (01768) 866860
6 changing beers [H]
A small and intimate pub on three floors in the centre of Penrith which was only turned into a pub in 2012. Brewery tap for Fell brewery, it serves a range of other cask ales and craft beers as detailed on the blackboard near the bar. The Fell holds regular quiz, comedy and music nights, as advertised on the well-kept Facebook page. A former local CAMRA Pub of the Year.
🐴🚆(North Lakes) 🚌🐾📶♫

George Hotel (1597 Bar)
Devonshire Street, CA11 7SU
☎ (01768) 862696 🌐 thegeorgehotelpenrith.co.uk
4 changing beers [H]
The 1597 Bar is at the front of the George Hotel on Devonshire Street and has the appearance of a separate and very modern microbar. The date 1597 refers to the year when the hotel was established. The bar staff will happily bring beers through to 1597 from Dappers (another bar in the hotel with two real ale handpumps). Both bars can be accessed through the main reception area via some fine revolving doors, or from the car park behind the hotel with entry off Burrowgate, just past the Pinny. Q🐴🛏◑♿🚆(North Lakes)P🚌

Ravenglass

Inn at Ravenglass
Main Street, CA18 1SQ (N end of village, overlooking Irish Sea)
☎ (01229) 717230
Fyne Ales Jarl; 3 changing beers (sourced regionally; often Ennerdale Craft) [H]
A 17th-century inn adjacent to Ravenglass mainline station and the Ravenglass and Eskdale steam railway. Its outdoor seating area has wonderful views overlooking the estuary which, in Roman and Viking times, was one of the five main ports in the country. This dog-friendly pub offers a good choice of up to four real ales all year round and high-quality dining serving local produce.
Q🐴✿🛏◑⛺🚆♣P🚌(6) 🐾📶

Pennington Hotel
Main Street, CA18 1SD
☎ (01229) 717222 🌐 penningtonhotels.com
Hawkshead Bitter; 3 changing beers (often Marston's) [H]
The Pennington Hotel is a renovated 16th-century coaching inn with 22 high-quality contemporary rooms. It sits adjacent to Ravenglass station and the Ravenglass and Eskdale steam railway. The Estuary Bar & Grill provides friendly service from local staff. It offers casual or formal dining in the bar, outside courtyard and separate dining rooms, providing quality affordable food using fresh, locally sourced ingredients. It is dog friendly and now serves two, permanently local, real ales all year round. Q🐴✿🛏◑♿⛺🚆P🐾📶

Ratty Arms
CA18 1SN
☎ (01229) 717676 🌐 ravenglass-railway.co.uk/plan-your-visit/the-ratty-arms
2 changing beers (sourced regionally; often Great Corby, Hawkshead, Keswick) [H]
This converted former railway station building is located on the platform of Ravenglass station on the scenic Cumbrian Coast Line. It sits adjacent to Ravenglass and Eskdale steam railway and Ravenglass campsite. This cosy and welcoming pub has a real fire, is dog friendly and is wheelchair accessible with disabled toilet facilities. It has a choice of indoor and outdoor seating. It offers five ever-changing real ales from Cumbrian breweries and one cider. Food is served daily, using the finest local suppliers. Q🐴✿◑♿⛺🚆♣P🐾📶

Ravenstonedale

Black Swan Hotel [L] ✔
CA17 4NG
☎ (015396) 23204 🌐 blackswanhotel.com
3 changing beers (sourced locally; often Eden River, Kirkby Lonsdale, Settle) [H]
Victorian inn, rebuilt in 1899, in a tranquil conservation village in the Eden valley. This family-owned hotel has a cosy bar serving three cask ales – mainly from local breweries. There is a comfortable lounge with a log fire, and two dining areas serving excellent and imaginative home-cooked food. Across the road is the garden area beside the village stream, with picnic tables and three yurts. Q🐴✿🛏◑♣P🚌(S5)🐾📶

Rowrah

Ennerdale Brewery Tap [L]
Chapel Row, CA26 3XS
☎ (01946) 862977 🌐 ennerdalebrewery.co.uk
Ennerdale Craft Blonde, Pale, Darkest, Wild [H]
This brewery tap is a café by day and a bistro pub in the evening. It offers a warm, friendly setting with four main ales and four seasonal ales available, and also has speciality beers on offer. The brewery is on site and tours can be booked in advance via the website. The village is on the Sea to Sea cycle route, but public transport is extremely limited. The brewery received the Best Business award in 2023 from England's Business Awards.
🐴◑♿♣P🐾📶♫

Rydal

Badger Bar (Glen Rothay Hotel) ★ 🗓
LA22 9LR
☎ (015394) 34500 ⊕ theglenrothay.co.uk
Barngates Goodhew's Dry Stout; Bowness Bay
Lakeland Blonde, Swift Best; Great Corby Tizzie
Whizie; Handsome Hound 🔣
Quaint old inn that meets visitor expectations of a typical
Lakes hostelry. The bar has a handful of interesting local
ales and the oldest room is especially popular with
walkers and their dogs who dry out round the blazing
fire. In summer, the garden and car park will be busy – so
take the 555 or open-top 599 bus. In the evening, try
feeding the badgers – otherwise watch them on the
webcam. Q ☎ 🌟 🛏 🕪 ▲ ♣ P 🚌 (555,599) 🌸 🎵

Scotby

Royal Oak
47 Scotby Village, Village Green, CA4 8BT
☎ (01228) 498117 ⊕ royaloakscotby.co.uk
Great Corby Blonde, Lakeland Summit 🔣
Refurbished pub opposite the village green and hall, at
the heart of the village. It is popular with locals as well as
visitors who travel from Carlisle and further afield for
their meals and well-kept beers. The staff work tirelessly
in support of local charities with various events organised
throughout the year. ☎ 🌟 🕪 ♣ P 🎵

Seatoller

Glaramara Hotel
CA12 5XQ
☎ (017687) 77222 ⊕ glaramara.co.uk
Cumbrian Ales Loweswater Gold; Tirril Borrowdale
Bitter 🔣
At the gateway to Scafell Pike and Honister Pass, this
independently owned 33-bedroom hotel has been
managed by the same family for 22 years. A warm and
friendly welcome awaits visitors and guests alike, from
reception to dining and bar areas, where quality meals
are available. Two handpumps serve Cumbrian cask ales,
perfect after a day fell-walking, cycling or rambling.
There is a regular bus service to/from Keswick and a
summer route over Honister/Whinlatter passes, via
Buttermere. Q ☎ 🌟 🛏 🕪 ᜒ P 🚌 🌸 🎵

Sedbergh

Dalesman 🗓
Main Street, LA10 5BN
☎ (015396) 21183 ⊕ thedalesman.co.uk
Barngates Brathay Gold; Cumbrian Ales Loweswater
Gold; house beer (by Settle); 2 changing beers
(sourced locally; often Coniston, Dark Horse,
Hawkshead) 🔣
Small town-centre free house with comfortable rooms
that makes a great base for the Dalesway Walk and
Cumbria Cycleway. The bar stocks an interesting selection
of ales from Cumbria and Yorkshire, complemented by
local food in the two dining rooms. The front
seating has been extended with a spacious courtyard at
the rear. Up to five cask beers, reducing to three during
winter, are sourced within a 30-mile radius.
☎ 🌟 🛏 🕪 ▲ 🚌 🎵

Thirsty Rambler 🗓
14-16 Main Street, LA10 5BN
☎ 07874 838816 ⊕ thethirstyrambler.co.uk
3 changing beers (sourced locally; often Fell, Settle,
Wensleydale)

Light and airy micropub with young, enthusiastic owners,
where conversation and mingling are encouraged.
Excellent local ales are served in top-rate condition from
three handpumps and two keg lines. The pub is close to
the Lakeland Fells and Yorkshire Dales, so there is always
an interesting mix of customers who relish a good pint
and a good natter. Popular with walkers and their well-
behaved dogs. ᜒ 🍺 🌟 🌸 🎵

Staveley

Beer Hall 🗓 ✅
Hawkshead Brewery, Mill Yard, LA8 9LR
☎ (01539) 822644 ⊕ hawksheadbrewery.co.uk
Hawkshead Bitter; 12 changing beers (sourced
locally; often Hawkshead) 🔣
The Beer Hall is the flagship tap for the award-winning
Hawkshead brewery, attracting large numbers of
families alongside more serious walkers and drinkers,
with a new pool table upstairs attracting younger
customers. Expect a warm welcome from the personable
and efficient staff at the bar counter. Food is served
every day and up to 14 cask ales are served on
handpump from their core range, enjoyed by the pint or
in thirds, alongside a selection of keg beers. Easily
accessed by bus or train. Brewery tours must be booked
in advance. Card payment only.
☎ 🌟 ᜒ ▲ ⇌ ♣ P 🚌 (555) 🌸 🎵

Talkin

Blacksmiths Arms 🗓
CA8 1LE
☎ (016977) 42111 ⊕ blacksmithstalkin.co.uk
Black Sheep Best Bitter; Hawkshead Windermere
Pale, Bitter; 1 changing beer 🔣
Since taking over in 1997, the present owners have
made this probably the most popular pub in the vicinity.
The winning formula includes four real ales, a superbly-
stocked bar, friendly efficient staff, no television and
meticulous attention to detail. With a golf course and
country park within two miles and plenty of outdoor
activities locally, it attracts visitors from far
outside north Cumbria to this Area of Outstanding Natural
Beauty. Q ☎ 🌟 🛏 🕪 ᜒ ♣ P 🌸

Ulverston

Devonshire Arms 🗓
Braddyll Terrace, Victoria Road, LA12 0DH (next to
railway bridge in town centre)
3 changing beers (sourced regionally; often Logan
Beck) 🔣
Conveniently situated between the bus and train
stations, the Dev is a real locals' pub with a welcoming
atmosphere. Four TVs provide comprehensive sports
coverage, and there are two dartboards and a pool table.
Three constantly changing cask ales are all dispensed on
handpump and often include a dark beer. The outside
seating area is popular in summer. A meat raffle is held
on Sunday evening. Winner of numerous CAMRA awards
over the years. ☎ 🌟 ᜒ ▲ ⇌ ♣ P 🚌 🌸 🎵

Farmers Arms
3 Market Place, LA12 7BA
☎ (01229) 584469 ⊕ the-farmers-ulverston.co.uk
Cumbrian Ales Loweswater Gold; 4 changing beers
(sourced regionally; often Timothy Taylor, Bowness
Bay) 🔣
Smart, busy, centrally-located pub with a heated covered
terrace at the front. Six beers are available, along with a
good selection of wines. It opens early for breakfasts and

coffee, with quality meals served lunchtime and evenings (see blackboards over the fireplace for daily specials). There's a raised area to the rear which is mainly for diners. Meals can be also taken in the comfortable bar area, although this can get busy at weekends. Q👶❀◖◗♿🚆🚌(X6,6)

Gather [L]

7 Market Street, LA12 7AY

☎ (01229) 318393 🌐 gatherbeers.co.uk

2 changing beers (sourced nationally) [H]

Micropub and bottle shop owned by a CAMRA member. It has two handpumps plus nine KeyKeg beers, with an extensive range of interesting local, national and international bottled and canned beers and ciders. Tap takeovers and other events are occasionally held – check the Facebook page for details. Recently refurbished to give more seating downstairs, with additional seating upstairs making for a pleasant and relaxing atmosphere. Pizzas are available. 🚆🍎🚌🐾📶♫

Mill [L] ✔

Mill Street, LA12 7EB

☎ (01229) 581384 🌐 mill-at-ulverston.co.uk

Lancaster Amber, Blonde, Black, Red; 6 changing beers (sourced nationally) [H]

The Mill has an interesting characterful layout centred around a restored original, but now static, waterwheel. The Cask Bar is on the ground floor. On Friday and Saturday both the Loft Bar on the second floor, serving evening cocktails, and the first-floor Terrace Bar with a separate outdoor patio area and largescreen TV, are open. Deservedly popular for quality food; booking is essential for the restaurant. There are picnic tables outside to the front. 👶❀◖◗🚆🚌(6,X6)🐾📶♫

Old Friends [L]

49 Soutergate, LA12 7ES

☎ (01229) 208195 🌐 oldfriendsulverston.co.uk

Old Friends New Acquaintance; 3 changing beers (sourced regionally; often Old Friends) [H]

A 17th-century Grade II-listed locals' pub near the town centre. It has a cosy snug with an open fire in front of the bar. Another room with a TV is separated by a passageway with a hatch to the bar. Beers are mostly local, including those from the pub's own brewery. The changing beers typically include a darker beer. A popular quiz is held every Tuesday. A wonderful beer garden has heating in the winter. 👶❀♣🚌🐾📶♫

Stan Laurel Inn [L]

31 The Ellers, LA12 0AB

☎ (01229) 582814 🌐 thestanlaurel.co.uk

House beer (by Marston's); 3 changing beers (sourced regionally; often Ulverston) [H]

Just off the centre of Stan Laurel's home town, this pub offers a warm welcome to locals and visitors. Three handpulls serve a variety of mainly locally brewed beers, often featuring Ulverston brewery. Excellent-value, quality food is available throughout the week. In winter, two log-burning stoves add to the pub's comfortable ambience. Well-behaved dogs are welcome in the bar. 👶❀🛏◖◗🚆P🚌(6,X6)🐾📶

Swan Inn 🏆 [L]

Swan Street, LA12 7JX

☎ (01229) 582519

8 changing beers (sourced nationally) [H]

On the edge of the town centre, overlooking the A590, this pub has an open-plan feel, despite its three distinct drinking areas. Premier League football and major sports events are screened, live music features occasionally, and a jukebox allows for all genres of music. A Sunday night quiz rounds off the entertainment. The beer garden is popular, especially in summer. Children are allowed until 8pm. 👶❀♿🚌(6,X6)🐾📶♫

Wetheral

Wheatsheaf Inn [L] ✔

CA4 8HD

☎ (01228) 560686 🌐 wheatsheafwetheral.co.uk

Great Corby Corby Ale; 2 changing beers [H]

Deservedly popular with locals and visitors, this early 19th-century village pub is just a few minutes' walk from the village green and railway station. Along with Corby Ale from the local Great Corby Brewhouse there are two changing ales sourced from local breweries. Good-value bar meals are served Wednesday to Sunday, with booking advisable at weekends. The regular Tuesday quiz nights are well supported. 👶❀◖◗🚆♣P🚌(75)🐾📶

Whitehaven

Candlestick

21-22 Tangier Street, CA28 7UX

☎ (01946) 599032

3 changing beers (sourced nationally; often Cross Bay, Titanic) [H]

This down-to-earth boozer welcomes everyone warmly, with great beer and good service. A pub of two halves: afternoons feature older customers who include all in cross-bar chat; in the evenings it attracts a younger, and louder, crowd. The only pub for miles around that sources new beers, this is the pub to find darker and stronger beers. 👶♿🚆🚌🐾📶

Vagabond

9 Marlborough Street, CA28 7LL (on a continuation of Lowther St, leading to the harbour)

☎ (01946) 66653 🌐 thevagabondpub.co.uk

3 changing beers (sourced nationally; often Bowness Bay, Cumbrian Ales, Fyne Ales) [H]

This family-run pub is highly popular for food, especially the pizzas cooked in a wood-fired oven. Beers are well kept and change, with favourites returning often. Golden ales are popular but but dark beers do appear. It is popular for group meals and celebrations. Staff and regulars are friendly and welcoming and conversation in the bar is inclusive. The harbour and marina are spectacularly lit at night. 👶◖◗🚆🍎🚌🐾📶♫

Witherslack

Derby Arms Hotel [L]

LA11 6RH

☎ (015395) 52207 🌐 derbyarms.co.uk

Bowness Bay Swan Blonde, Fell Walker; 3 changing beers (sourced locally; often Fell, Keswick, Kirkby Lonsdale) [H]

Possibly the best pub you've never visited – although it is easily accessible from Kendal by bus or car. The central bar serves five traditionally-furnished rooms with a wide range of local ales in tip-top condition and good home-cooked food. Most rooms have a fire and the games room has a pool table. Walkers and cyclists mix with regulars and diners to ensure a welcoming atmosphere of lively buzz. Dogs like to visit too! 👶❀🛏◖◗♿♣P🚌(X6)🐾📶♫

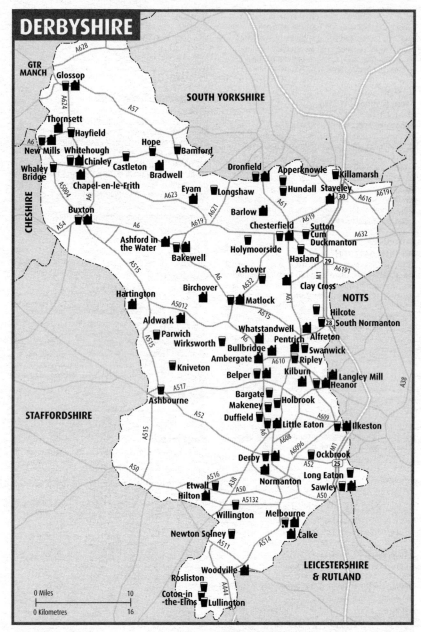

DERBYSHIRE

Map of Derbyshire showing towns and brewery/pub locations:

GTR MANCH · Glossop · Thornsett · Hayfield · New Mills · Whitehough · Chinley · Whaley Bridge · Chapel-en-le-Frith · Buxton · Hope · Bamford · Castleton · Bradwell · Eyam · Longshaw · Barlow · Ashford in the Water · Bakewell · Hartington · Birchover · Ashover · Matlock · Aldwark · Parwich · Wirksworth · Kniveton · Ashbourne · Whatstandwell · Bullbridge · Pentrich · Ambergate · Belper · Bargate · Makeney · Duffield · Holbrook · Little Eaton · Derby · Normanton · Etwall · Hilton · Willington · Newton Solney · Melbourne · Calke · Woodville · Rosliston · Coton-in-the-Elms · Lullington

SOUTH YORKSHIRE · CHESHIRE · STAFFORDSHIRE · NOTTS · LEICESTERSHIRE & RUTLAND

Dronfield · Apperknowle · Killamarsh · Hundall · Staveley · Chesterfield · Sutton Cum Duckmanton · Holymoorside · Hasland · Clay Cross · Hilcote · South Normanton · Alfreton · Swanwick · Ripley · Kilburn · Langley Mill · Heanor · Ilkeston · Ockbrook · Long Eaton · Sawley

0 Miles 10
0 Kilometres 16

Apperknowle

Traveller's Rest 🄻

High Street, S18 4BD SK384782

☎ (01246) 460169

Bradfield Farmers Blonde; Timothy Taylor Landlord; 4 changing beers (sourced regionally) Ⓗ

The Travs, also referred to locally as the Corner Pin, is a traditional country inn with several seating areas around a corner bar. Usually six real ales are available, together with numerous ciders. Good quality hot food is on offer, along with its popular cheese and pork pie platters. The outdoor roadside seating area affords sweeping views of the Drone Valley. Q ☾ ❀ ◑ ▣ ➡ (15) ❀ 🛜

Ashbourne

Smith's Tavern

36 St John Street, DE6 1GH

☎ (01335) 300809

Banks's Sunbeam; Brakspear Gravity; Marston's Pedigree; Ringwood Fortyniner; 1 changing beer (sourced locally) Ⓗ

Small, highly traditional town-centre pub, with at least four real ales always on from Marston's range. Its front bar-room leads to two further rooms, one with an upright piano. One free choice guest ale is served at weekends, usually from a local brewery. Locally sourced pork pies are usually available. There is a good selection of around 25 malt whiskies, plus tutored tastings regularly throughout year. Winner of local CAMRA Pub of the Year six out of last 10 years. Q☺☮♣♨?

Ashover

Old Poets' Corner L

Butts Road, S45 0EW (downhill from church)
☎ (01246) 590888
Everards Tiger; Titanic Iceberg, Plum Porter, Captain Smith's Strong Ale; 6 changing beers (sourced regionally; often Castle Rock, Everards, Thornbridge) Ⓗ
This popular village pub has a warm welcoming atmosphere, with open fires on cold days. A Titanic brewery pub, it offers 10 hand-pulled ales, normally including four Titanic beers, along with changing guest ales, traditional ciders, draught and bottled Belgian beers and country wines. The pub has five rooms as well as a holiday cottage. Winner of CAMRA national Cider Pub of the Year in 2006 and four-time local CAMRA Pub of the Year. Dogs are welcome.
Q❀⛺️◑&♣●P☱(63,64) ☺?♪

Bakewell

Manners Hotel L

Haddon Road, DE45 1EP
☎ (01629) 812756
3 changing beers (sourced regionally; often Robinsons) Ⓗ
Traditional Robinsons hotel and pub, situated close to Bakewell town centre. There is a separate tap room which is popular with the locals. It has a large beer garden and parking facilities. There are three cask offerings, with Trooper, Unicorn and Dizzy Blond as regulars. Food is served at lunchtimes and early evenings. Entertainment is provided by regular live music and a weekly pub quiz. A range of accommodation is available, check out their website for details.
☺❀⛺️◑&P☱☺

Thornbridge Brewery Tap Room

Buxton Road, DE45 1GS
☎ (01629) 815994 ⊕ thornbridgebrewery.co.uk
Thornbridge Lord Marples; 4 changing beers (sourced locally; often Thornbridge) Ⓗ
The Tap Room, situated at the Thornbridge brewery, features a spacious shop and a comfortable seating area. It is a 15-minute stroll from Bakewell town centre, on the Riverside Industrial Estate. Excellent freshly handmade pizzas are served daily. The bar showcases a selection of four cask and 16 keg lines, available in thirds, halves, and pints, with options for beer flights with three selections. Regular music and social events are held monthly. Pre-booked brewery tours to explore the brewing process are also available. ☺◑P☺?♪

Bamford

Anglers Rest L ✔

Main Road, S33 0DY
☎ (01433) 659317 ⊕ anglers.rest
Black Sheep Best Bitter; house beer (by Torrside); 4 changing beers (sourced locally; often Abbeydale, Bradfield, Little Critters) Ⓗ
At the heart of Bamford and not far from Ladybower Reservoir, this is a community hub in every sense, where the locals have been running the pub (and associated post office and café) since 2013. The main bar is the focal point and extremely popular with families, walkers and particularly cyclists who have access to dedicated cycle

parking and a DIY repair shop. There is also a quieter snug. A lunch and dinner menu is served Wednesday to Saturday 12-8pm; Sunday lunches available until sold out. Q☺❀◑&♣▲P☱(257)☺?♪

Bargate

White Hart

Sandbed Lane, DE56 0JA
☎ (01773) 827397
Draught Bass; Oakham Citra; St Austell Tribute; 3 changing beers (sourced regionally) Ⓗ
The White Hart is a cosy two-roomed pub in the heart of Bargate. With a reputation for friendly staff, good beer and a welcoming atmosphere, the pub is popular with locals and has an excellent selection of changing cask and keg ales. It has a large beer garden to the rear, and

REAL ALE BREWERIES

14 Lock ▤ Bullbridge
3P's Woodville
Aldwark Artisan Aldwark
Alter Ego Alfreton
Ashover Clay Cross
Bad Bunny Ambergate
Bang The Elephant Langley Mill
Beestonia ✦ Ilkeston (NEW)
Bentley Brook Matlock
Big Stone Chinley
Birch Cottage Sawley
Birchover ▤ Birchover
Black Hole Little Eaton
Bottle Brook Kilburn
Brampton Chesterfield
Brunswick ▤ Derby
Buxton ✦ Buxton
Chapel-en-le-Frith Chapel-en-le-Frith
Collyfobble ▤ Barlow
Crich ✦ Belper (NEW)
Dancing Duck Derby
Derby Derby
Drone Valley Dronfield
Dungeon Hilton (NEW)
Emperor's Langley Mill
Eyam Eyam
Falstaff ▤ Derby: Normanton
Furnace Derby
Globe ▤ Glossop
Grasshopper Langley Mill
Hollow Tree Whatstandwell
Intrepid Bradwell
Leadmill Heanor
Little Brewing ✦ Derby
Marlpool ▤ Heanor
Moot ▤ Matlock
Morgan Brewmasters ▤ Melbourne
Muirhouse Ilkeston
Peak Ashford in the Water
Pentrich Pentrich
RBA Derby
Red Dog Ilkeston
Resting Devil ▤ Chesterfield
Shiny ✦ Little Eaton
Silver Brewhouse Chesterfield
Temper ▤ Dronfield
Thornbridge Bakewell
Thornsett ✦ Thornsett
Tollgate ✦ Calke
Torrside New Mills
Townes ▤ Staveley
Urban Chicken Ilkeston
Whim Hartington

walkers are welcome. Bar snacks are usually available with occasional visits by street food vendors (see Facebook). A previous local CAMRA Pub of the Year.
Q ঌ ⚘ ♣ ♠ P ⧠ (71) ✿ 🛜

Belper

Angels Micro Pub
29 Market Place, DE56 1FZ (top right hand side of Market Place)
☎ 07527 163316
Oakham Citra; Thornbridge Jaipur IPA; Titanic Plum Porter; 5 changing beers (sourced nationally) Ⓖ
A quirky, friendly and popular micropub that has a selection of at least eight cask ales, gradually decreasing by Sunday when the majority have been consumed. Tap takeovers or beer style events are a frequent feature. Ten real ciders plus bar snacks are also available. Local CAMRA awards include Cider Pub of the Year 2020 and 2023 and Pub of the Year 2023.
ঌ ⚘ ঌ ≈ ♣ ♠ P ⧠ (sixes) ✿ 🛜

Arkwright's Real Ale Bar
6 Campbell Street, DE56 1AP
☎ (01773) 823117
7 changing beers (sourced nationally) Ⓗ
Situated in the centre of Belper and named after Sir Richard Arkwright, an important 18th-century mill owner, Arkwright's is a modern friendly one-roomed real ale bar with constantly changing cask ales, often from less well-known breweries. A popular pub with local drinkers, good quality home-made bar snacks always available. A no under-14s rule ensures a quiet and relaxing environment for adults, often with live acoustic music at weekends. Regular beer festivals are held in conjunction with local events.
⚘ ঌ ≈ ♣ ♠ ⧠ (sixes) ✿ 🛜 ♪

Railway ⊘
25 King Street, DE56 1PW
☎ (01773) 689987 ⊕ railwaybelper.co.uk
Lincoln Green Marion, Archer, Hood, Tuck; 4 changing beers (sourced nationally; often Lincoln Green) Ⓗ
Large town-centre pub, operated by Lincoln Green brewery, offering eight cask and six keg ales, which are mostly but not always from Lincoln Green. It operates a loyalty card scheme on cask ales. Bar meals are available until early evening and there is popular live music on some Saturdays. Located on the main shopping street of Belper, it has a large sunny beer garden to the rear. As the name suggests, this is the nearest pub to the railway station and is also close to the bus station, with some buses stopping almost adjacent.
ঌ ⚘ ◐ ঌ ≈ ♠ P ⧠ (sixes) ✿ 🛜 ♪

Buxton

Ale Stop Ⓛ
Chapel Street, SK17 6HX
☎ 07801 364619
4 changing beers (sourced nationally) Ⓗ
The first micropub in the High Peak, this is a two-room converted shop off Buxton Market Place. Beer is the main event here, with four changing ales from microbreweries up and down the country, as well as two boxed ciders. The objective is to bring to Buxton beers that are rarely, if ever, seen in the town. The enthusiastic staff ensure a warm and friendly welcome. An eclectic choice of background music on vinyl is played. A log-burning stove is a welcome addition for the winter. ঌ ঌ ♠ 🖵 ✿ 🛜 ♪

Buxton Tap House Ⓛ
11-16 The Old Court House, George Street, SK17 6AT
☎ (01298) 214085
4 changing beers (sourced locally; often Buxton) Ⓗ
The Tap House is in Buxton's café quarter at the rear of the crescent. The tap for Buxton brewery, it has four handpumps serving a regularly changing range of the brewery's cask beers, and up to 16 fonts serve a variety of KeyKeg beers in different styles and strengths. The beers available are listed on the beer blackboard. A varied food menu is also available. The next-door Cellar Bar is also owned by Buxton brewery.
ঌ ⚘ ◐ ঌ ≈ ♣ ♠ 🖵 ✿ 🛜 ♪

Cheshire Cheese Ⓛ
37-39 High Street, SK17 6HA
☎ (01298) 212453
Everards Tiger; Titanic Steerage, Iceberg, White Star, Plum Porter, Captain Smith's Strong Ale; 4 changing beers (sourced nationally; often Ashover, Bradfield, Eyam) Ⓗ
A double-fronted building of considerable age, which was refurbished before reopening under the management of Titanic in 2013. The pub is essentially open plan but is split into several distinct areas. Low ceilings with original beams add to the cosy atmosphere and there are two open fires. The bar boasts an array of 10 handpumps serving a range of Titanic beers and guests. Home-made food is available. Entertainment is provided on Saturday evenings and there is a quiz on Sundays. ঌ ⚘ ◐ ঌ A P 🖵 ✿ 🛜 ♪

RedWillow Buxton Ⓛ
1 Cavendish Circus, SK17 6AT
☎ (01298) 807582
RedWillow Wreckless; 3 changing beers (sourced locally; often RedWillow) Ⓗ
Opened in 2017 and located in a former bank in the centre of Buxton, this is RedWillow brewery's second bar. Original features have been retained such as etched windows and the mahogany and glass office, alongside a new bar and smaller mezzanine area. Four of the brewery's cask ales are served from handpumps on the bar, and craft keg beers from various breweries are available. Cider is from Hogan's. Live music plays weekly.
ঌ ঌ ≈ ♣ ♠ 🟦⧠ ✿ 🛜 ♪

Castleton

Olde Cheshire Cheese Ⓛ
How Lane, S33 8WJ
☎ (01433) 620330 ⊕ cheshirecheeseinn.co.uk
Abbeydale Moonshine; Acorn Barnsley Bitter; Bradfield Farmers Blonde; 3 changing beers (often Abbeydale, Intrepid, Peak Ales) Ⓗ
Excellent traditional village inn offering six cask beers from local brewers. A central servery separates the restaurant and the bustling bar area, and the names of landlords since 1746 are inscribed on the low wooden beams. Accommodation is offered in 10 en-suite rooms. Home-made food is served every day. Walkers are welcome, with dogs allowed in the bar.
ঌ ⇌ ঌ A P ⧠ (173,272) ✿ 🛜

Chesterfield

Beer Parlour Ⓛ
1 King Street North, Whittington Moor, S41 9BA
☎ 07870 693411 ⊕ the-beer-parlour.co.uk
4 changing beers (sourced nationally; often Abbeydale, Draught Bass) Ⓗ

The Beer Parlour is a cosy, popular drinking establishment which is slightly tucked away off the main road and close to the home stadium of Chesterfield FC. Up to four changing real ales are available via handpump to drink in or take out, with an extensive selection of fonts dispensing continental ales and ciders. Bottled continental and local beers, and box cider and perries also available to drink in or take away. 🌛&♿P🛏️🚍🏵️🌳🛜

Brampton Bierhuis
Unit 6, Chatsworth Business Park, Chatsworth Road, Brampton, S40 2AR
☎ (01246) 221680 ⏺ bramptonbrewery.co.uk
4 changing beers (often Brampton) Ⓗ
The Brampton brewery tap room is situated at the Brampton brewery and features a comfortable seating area. Located along the Brampton Mile, a stroll from Chesterfield town centre, it is open on Fridays and Saturday afternoons only. Four Brampton brewery beers are served on cask as well as a range of continental kegs, traditional cider, wines and spirits. Pre-booked brewery tours are also available to explore the brewing process. The venue is available for private hire. QP🚍🏵️

Chesterfield Alehouse Ⓛ
37 West Bars, S40 1AG
4 changing beers Ⓗ
A popular micropub with good friendly staff and an excellent selection of beers and locally-produced ciders. It has four lines of cask ales, eight KeyKegs and an extensive bottle range. Regular tap takeovers feature breweries not often seen in the area. A seating area upstairs is available for booking and free-to-air sports are often shown in the upstairs room. Local CAMRA Cider Pub of the Year 2023. Q&♣♿🚍🏵️🛜

Chesterfield Arms Ⓛ
40 Newbold Road, S41 7PH
☎ (01246) 236634 ⏺ chesterfieldarms.co.uk
Draught Bass; Everards Tiger; Timothy Taylor Landlord; 6 changing beers (sourced nationally; often Abbeydale, Oakham, Thornbridge) Ⓗ
Multi-award winning real ale pub in Chesterfield serving home-made pizzas alongside real ales, craft beers, ciders, and everything else in between. With the introduction of its own brewery the Resting Devil in 2022, their house brew, Twisted Pale, is a permanent addition to the bar alongside up to 10 cask ales. A weekly quiz is held on Wednesday, and there is regular live music and beer festivals. Conservatory doors open on warm summer evenings, extending the outdoor seating area. Local CAMRA Pub of the Year 2022 and 2023. Q🌛🏵️🍽️&🚍(10)🏵️🛜♫

Glassworks Ⓛ
388 Sheffield Road, Whittington Moor, S41 8LF
☎ (01246) 768688 ⏺ theglassworkschesterfield.co.uk
Brampton Golden Bud; 6 changing beers (sourced nationally) Ⓗ
The third pub from Chesterfield-based Brampton brewery was acquired in 2019, situated opposite the Technique Stadium, home of Chesterfield FC. The bar has up to eight handpulls, one for the regular ale, one for rotating popular ciders, and the remaining for the wide range of Brampton ales plus ever-changing guests. The main bar area has two sports TV screens, historical photos adorning its walls and a snug to the rear. An outside bar opens on home match days. 🌛🏵️♣🚍🏵️🛜♫

Market Pub Ⓛ
95 New Square, S40 1AH
☎ (01246) 273641 ⏺ themarketpub.co.uk
8 changing beers (sourced nationally) Ⓗ

Premium gastro-pub located in the Chesterfield's market square. Typically eight changing cask ales are on offer, with quality home-cooked food made with local produce served lunchtime and early evening. Regular events held include murder mysteries, gourmet food nights, wine, whisky and spirit tastings, and general knowledge and music quizzes. Several small beer festivals are held throughout the year – check Facebook and their website for details. 🏵️🍽️🚍♣🚍🏵️♫

Pig & Pump Ⓛ
16 St Mary's Gate, S41 7TJ
☎ (01246) 229570 ⏺ pigandpump.co.uk
Oakham Citra; Ossett White Rat; Peak Ales Chatsworth Gold; Thornbridge Jaipur; 6 changing beers (sourced nationally; often Abbeydale, Peak Ales, Thornbridge) Ⓗ
Previously named the White Swan, this welcoming pub is located in the heart of town, directly across from Chesterfield's iconic crooked spire parish church. With a selection of up to 10 cask ales, including many LocAles, the pub is open-plan, divided into two areas, one slightly elevated. The upstairs function room is available for hire. This is a popular spot for home-cooked locally sourced food. Live music is regularly available on Friday evenings and lively quizzes are held on Tuesday. 🌛🏵️🍽️&≠P🚍🏵️

Portland Hotel Ⓛ ✅
West Bars, S40 1AY
☎ (01246) 245410
Greene King Abbot; Ruddles Best Bitter; Sharp's Doom Bar; 6 changing beers (sourced nationally) Ⓗ
Constructed in 1899 to cater to the new Market Place railway station, it bears the name of the Duke of Portland, as the railway ran through his estate. Currently operated by JD Wetherspoon, it boasts a mock-Tudor façade, with large interior and exterior seating areas that get busy due to its central location. There are three consistent beers and a rotating selection of up to six guest beers, frequently sourced from local breweries. Open daily at 7am for breakfast, with the bar open from 9am. Q🌛🏵️🍽️🍴&≠🚍🛜

Rose & Crown 🍷 Ⓛ ✅
104 Old Road, Brampton, S40 2QT (1¼ miles from Chesterfield town centre on jct of Old Rd and Old Hall Rd)
☎ (01246) 563750 ⏺ roseandcrownbrampton.co.uk
Brampton Golden Bud, Best; 7 changing beers (sourced nationally; often Brampton, Everards) Ⓗ
This award-winning Everards Project William pub, is a Brampton brewery tied house, situated at the top end of the Brampton Mile. It hosts regular real ale festivals and weekly quizzes every Tuesday. The drinks selection includes bottled Belgian beers, nine changing cask beers, keg beer and up to 10 ciders and perries. Featuring a compact snug, memorabilia from the old brewery festoons the walls. Local CAMRA Pub of the Year 2024. Q🌛🏵️🍽️♣♿P🚍(170)🏵️🛜

Tap House
318 Chatsworth Road, Brampton, S40 2BY
☎ (01246) 234731
Draught Bass; 7 changing beers (sourced nationally) Ⓗ
Traditional friendly pub with a central bar, etched windows and tiled flooring. It has a wide choice of up to eight changing beers local and national, normally including Draught Bass. A quiet room is available to the rear of the pub and there is also a covered outdoor area. Hot and cold snacks are available during the day. 🏵️♿🚍🏵️🛜

Coton-in-the-Elms

Black Horse

17 Burton Road, DE12 8HJ (centre of village)
☎ (01283) 761843
Draught Bass; Marston's Pedigree; 1 changing beer (sourced nationally) ⊞

Lively and popular free house, owned by the licensee, with a bright and airy main room, with an open fire, divided into bar and lounge areas by glass-topped wood partitions and featuring a bar billiards table. A small snug, served through a hatch, acts as a children's room. Over 30 ciders and perries are available. A free cheese board is provided Monday and Friday evenings. Quiz night is Tuesday, plus occasional live music. Beer festivals are usually held on spring and August bank holiday weekends. Accommodation available in a self-catering flat. Q ❀ ☀ ✿ ♠ Å ♣ ♠P ❏ (22)❀ ❖ ♪

Derby

Alexandra Hotel ⎣

203 Siddals Road, DE1 2QE
☎ (01332) 293993
Castle Rock Harvest Pale, Preservation; 6 changing beers (sourced nationally) ⊞

A Castle Rock pub serving their own beers, guest ales and craft beers, across a good range of styles. There is also a wide range of UK and continental bottled and canned beers of varying styles. The tall freestanding building offers some en-suite accommodation. The lounge is adorned with local breweriana and the bar with railway memorabilia. A Class 37 railway locomotive cab resides in the car park. The pub was the birthplace of the local branch of CAMRA in 1974. Q ❀ ☀ ✿ ♠ ≈ ♣ ♠P ❏ ❀ ❖

Brunswick Inn ⎣

1 Railway Terrace, DE1 2RU
☎ (01332) 290677 ⊕ brunswickderby.co.uk
Brunswick White Feather, Triple Hop, The Usual; Everards Beacon Hill, Tiger; Timothy Taylor Landlord; 8 changing beers (sourced nationally) ⊞

Built in 1841, this is the oldest purpose-built railway inn in the UK and it truly unmissable. The flatiron-style pub is part of the North Midland Railway village, it was restored from a derelict condition and reopened in 1987 (see press-cuttings in the main bar). The Brunswick brewery was added in 1991 and is visible at one end of the pub. The large pub features four separate rooms, flagstone floors and an upstairs function area. It gets busy on match days. Q ❀ ☀ ✿ ♠ ♦ ≈ ♣ ♠P ❏ ❀ ❖ ♪

Creaky Floorboard ⎣

179 Kedleston Road, DE22 1FT
☎ 07974 749517
Dancing Duck Ay up; 3 changing beers (sourced locally) ⊞

Wonderful conversion of a 19th-century domestic dwelling which, being end-of-terrace, is inconspicuous to passers-by. The two front rooms off the tiled entrance hall do not disappoint, with quirky decor and a pleasing ambience. Pork pies, rolls and four-pint takeaways are available. Books and card games are offered and open mic nights are hosted every Tuesday. The delightful courtyard garden to the rear has a water feature.
Q ❀ ♠ ❏ ❀

Exeter Arms ⎣ ⊘

13 Exeter Place, DE1 2EU
☎ (01332) 605323 ⊕ exeterarms.co.uk
Dancing Duck Ay up; Marston's Pedigree; 4 changing beers (sourced nationally) ⊞

This quirky, multi-roomed pub was born from a number of different buildings and the interior boasts numerous sections as a result, including a raised area. The site has been a licensed premises for over 100 years. Contemporary, cutting-edge food is one of the major selling points of this gem of a pub, which also boasts a secluded courtyard garden and memorabilia from the punk rock band Anti-Pasti. ❀ ❀ ◐ ▶ ❏ ❀ ❖ ♠

Falstaff ★ ⎣

74 Silverhill Road, Normanton, DE23 6UJ
☎ (01332) 342902 ⊕ falstaffbrewery.co.uk
Falstaff Fist Full of Hops, Phoenix, Smiling Assassin; 1 changing beer (sourced locally) ⊞

Originally a coaching inn before the Normanton neighbourhood was built up, this is now the Falstaff brewery tap and the only real ale house in the area. This three-roomed corner pub sits awkwardly among traditional terrace housing. The rear lounge is a shrine to Offiler's brewery, with a large display of memorabilia. Other collectables can be viewed in the games room and second bar room. Q ❀ ☀ ♣ ❏ (4,7)❀

Five Lamps ⎣

25 Duffield Road, DE1 3BH
☎ (01332) 730380
Dancing Duck Ay up; Draught Bass; Oakham Citra; house beer (by Thornbridge); 7 changing beers (sourced regionally) ⊞

In a now primarily student area to the north of the city centre, this pub showcases an excellent range of styles, usually featuring Derbyshire breweries. There is a house beer from Thornbridge. The Lamps is essentially open plan, but has many little nooks and crannies giving it a homely feel. It has been tastefully refurbished in a traditional style with wood panelling and leather seating. A patioed area is at the front and a large covered area at rear. ❀ ☀ ♣ ♠P ❏ ❀ ❖ ♪

Flowerpot ⎣

23-25 King Street, Cathedral Quarter, DE1 3DZ
☎ (01332) 204955 ⊕ flowerpotderby.com
Marston's Pedigree; Oakham Bishops Farewell; Whim Hartington IPA ⊞; 5 changing beers (sourced nationally) ⊞/Ⓖ

Dating from around 1800, but much expanded from its original premises into the neighbouring car tyre centre, this vibrant pub reaches back from the roadside frontage and divides into several interlinking rooms. One room provides the stage for regular live bands; another has a glass cellar wall revealing stillaged casks. Their popular Gurkha curry nights take place every Tuesday and Wednesday evening. An attractive outside seating area hosts summer entertainment. ❀ ☀ ✿ ♦ ♣ ♠ ❏ ❀ ❖ ♪

Furnace Inn ⎣

9 Duke Street, DE1 3BX
☎ (01332) 385981
Furnace Fun Sponge; Shiny 4 Wood; 6 changing beers (sourced nationally) ⊞

A former Hardy & Hansons pub that reopened in 2012, it has been transformed into a real ale mecca. It is now the tap for the Furnace brewery, featuring up to eight real ales and three ciders/perries complimented by a variety of UK craft beers. There are two distinct open-plan rooms, with a central bar and a large rear garden. Poker, quiz and cheese nights feature weekly with regular beer festivals held throughout the year. ❀ ☀ ◐ ♣ ♠P ❀ ❖ ❖

Golden Eagle ⎣

55 Agard Street, DE1 1DZ
☎ (01332) 230600
5 changing beers (sourced nationally) ⊞

A stand-alone corner building in an area of student accommodation on the west side of the city. A large mural on the outside pays homage to Derby's history. Inside, the long single room has a wooden floor throughout. The low ceiling makes it feel comfortable and welcoming. A walled paved area at the back provides pleasant outdoor seating. The upstairs function room is also a cocktail bar and boasts a terrace. ▓✿♣♠P♬☼✿♪

Hole in the Wall L

24 Uttoxeter Road, Mickleover, DE3 0ZQ
☎ (01332) 501301
Derby Hop Till You Drop, Business As Usual; 4 changing beers (sourced regionally) Ⓗ
Opened in 2020, this is a former NatWest bank building on the corner with Station Road in the centre of Mickleover. The pub has a large pleasant single room with the bar to one side at the back. It is operated by the Derby Brewing Co, whose beers are prominent among the six hand-pulled beers on offer. There is an excellent selection of bar snacks. ♠☼✿

Hoptimist L

91 Sitwell Street, Spondon, DE21 7FH
4 changing beers (sourced nationally) Ⓗ
Spondon's first micropub was converted from a hardware store in the centre of the village and opened in 2021. Entrance is into the front room, which hosts the bar and provides a selection of comfortable high and low seating. The back room, set slightly lower, provides more seating in a bright atmosphere. The bar features a changing range of beers, normally including some local ales. ♿☼

Old Silk Mill L ✓

19 Full Street, Cathedral Quarter, DE1 3AF
☎ (01332) 320851 ⊕ theoldsilkmill.co.uk
Dancing Duck Ay up, Dark Drake; Draught Bass; Oakham Citra; 1 changing beer (sourced nationally) Ⓗ
Built in the 1920s and close to the Museum of Making, a major city tourist attraction, the colourful, gable-end mural above the raised panel depicts the 1933 Silk Mill Lock-out. Tastefully decorated throughout with a step separating the drinking and dining areas, this is not the only pub to be rescued from closure by a local entrepreneur and Dancing Duck brewery. A well-appointed first-floor room is available for hire. ▓✿☼♠P☼(sixes) ☼

Pot Hole

Park Farm Shopping Centre, Park Farm Drive, Allestree, DE22 2QQ
☎ 07947 242710
Falstaff Fist Full of Hops, Phoenix; 3 changing beers (sourced nationally) Ⓗ
Formerly a dry cleaners, the premises was transformed into Allestree's first micropub in 2017; a welcome return of a licensed venue in the Park Farm shopping area. This friendly single-roomed pub serves six real ales including at least three from the local Falstaff brewery who took over the running in 2020, and three guests. Café-style outdoor seating is available. Q✿♣♠P☼✿

Smithfield L

Meadow Road, DE1 2BH
☎ (01332) 986601 ⊕ smithfieldderby.co.uk
Draught Bass; 9 changing beers (sourced nationally) Ⓗ
This well-proportioned imposing building is situated on the banks of the River Derwent (which has caused problems), and a short walk from the main bus station. The bar boasts an eclectic range of ever-changing

interesting beers, including two darks, supported by Draught Bass. There is a nice subtle collection of breweriana on view. A separate quiet room with a real fire overlooks the patio, itself against the river. The pub has regular live music and many beer-related activities. ▓✿♣♠P☼✿☼♪

Standing Order ✓

28-32 Iron Gate, Cathedral Quarter, DE1 3GL
☎ (01332) 207591
Greene King Abbot; Marston's Pedigree; Oakham Citra; Ruddles Best Bitter; Sharp's Doom Bar; 11 changing beers (sourced nationally) Ⓗ
This large, recently-refurbished, city-centre pub is located between the Market Place and the cathedral. A long horseshoe bar sits in a huge and splendid ex-banking hall featuring high-level paintings. At the side are a number of partitioned bays with banquette seating. There are also quieter and more private areas away from the main hall to one side and at the back. At the rear, a large patio has further seating. Q▓◐♿♠☼

Victoria Inn

12 Midland Place, DE1 2RR
☎ 07506 705463
Leatherbritches Bounder, Dovedale; 4 changing beers (sourced nationally) Ⓗ
Locally known as the Vic, this pub is situated on Midland Place across the road from the railway station. On the right of the entrance way is a small cosy bar with leather seating and a fireplace. The walls show many pictures of old Derby. On the left is a larger room, served by the end of the bar, which leads to the back of the pub and the function room. One of the few live music venues in Derby. ⇌✿♠☼☼♪

Dronfield

Coach & Horses L

Sheffield Road, S18 2GD
☎ (01246) 413269 ⊕ mycoachandhorses.co.uk
Thornbridge Lord Marples, Jaipur; 4 changing beers (sourced locally; often Thornbridge) Ⓗ
This Thornbridge-owned, single-roomed, comfortable and welcoming pub is situated in the northern part of Dronfield next to the Sheffield FC ground, who are reputed to be the world's oldest football club. It showcases a good range of their ales and keg beers, along with the occasional guest. There is a large, popular outdoor drinking area with a heated, covered section, and a weekly quiz night. Dronfield train station is under a mile away. Q▓✿♣♠P☼(43)✿☼

Dronfield Arms L

Chesterfield Road, S18 2XE
☎ 07923 808332
Abbeydale Moonshine; Temper Relacite; 2 changing beers (sourced locally; often Temper) Ⓗ
This unusually shaped freehouse also houses a brewery downstairs. Originally installed by Hopjacker in 2015 (see the etched panel in front window) it is now operated by Temper and can be viewed through a window in the main bar. The pub features a long bar leading to a large, comfortable seating area. Up to four real ales are usually available, with several keg fonts including KeyKeg. Above the rear car park there is an outside drinking area. Darts, quiz and pizza nights are held. ✿⇌♣P☼✿☼♪

Duffield

Town Street Tap 🄻
17 Town Street, DE56 4EH
☎ 07925 461706
4 changing beers (sourced nationally) Ⓖ
Situated on the main road in Duffield, this micropub is the tap for Tollgate brewery. The pub consists of a large room vaguely split into two sides. Real ales are kept on a stillage in a room to the back of the pub and served from direct from the cask. It has a nicely decorated interior with a mixture of high and normal height tables. There are occasional street food nights. The rear pub entrance and toilets have level access. Walkers and their boots are welcome. Q➪♣♠Ⓟ🚃🐾

Etwall

Spread Eagle
28 Main Street, DE65 6LP
☎ (01283) 735224
Draught Bass; Oakham Citra; Thornbridge Jaipur; Timothy Taylor Landlord; 2 changing beers (sourced regionally) Ⓗ
This large 18th-century village pub near the church in the middle of Etwall was originally several different buildings. As a result there are three distinct areas inside, all served by an elongated semicircular bar. Each has screens showing sporting events but the volume is generally muted. There is usually one beer (often Thornbridge Jaipur) served by gravity and fetched from the cellar – do ask. Tables in front of the pub are used in good weather. 🌳♣Ⓟ🖥🛜

Glossop

Bar 2 🄻
9 High Street East, SK13 8DA
☎ 07597 704447
Bradfield Farmers Blonde; 5 changing beers (sourced locally; often Bradfield, Bridge Beers, Ossett) Ⓗ
Smart bar opened in 2018 in converted shop. This comfortable micropub is a good size and has six handpulls with ever-changing beers typically from local breweries. Craft KeyKeg and lagers are also available, plus a good selection of wines and gins. Discrete background music, traditional pub games such as cards and dominoes, and retro video games table are available. Discounted beers are served on Monday and Wednesday. Bar 1, a cocktail and wine bar, has now opened next door and is connected to Bar 2. 🕭🌳♿➪♣🖥🐾🛜

Queens Arms
1 Shepley Street, SK13 7RZ
☎ (01457) 853005 ⊕ queens-arms-hotel-old-glossop.co.uk
Joseph Holt Bitter; Morland Old Speckled Hen; Robinsons Unicorn; Wainwright Gold; 2 changing beers (sourced locally; often Ossett, Thornbridge) Ⓗ
A traditional warm and welcoming pub in a historic area of Old Glossop, which caters for walkers from the nearby hill-walking areas in addition to locals, plus visitors from far and wide. Food is popular, particularly the upstairs Indian restaurant. Regular music events are held on Tuesday and Saturday evenings and a charity quiz on Thursday evenings. Coach parties are welcome by appointment. Accommodation is available and consists of five luxury en-suite letting rooms. 🕭🌳🛏🌀♿🅰🖥(390)🐾🛜♪

Smithy Fold ⦿
Unit 11 Howard Town Shopping Park, Victoria Street, SK13 8HS

☎ (01457) 890070
Greene King Abbot; Ruddles Best Bitter; Sharp's Doom Bar; 5 changing beers (sourced nationally; often Coach House, Phoenix, Sharp's) Ⓗ
This popular and welcoming Wetherspoon pub is situated in the town centre on the ground floor of an old cotton mill. Some original features of the building remain and interesting artwork is displayed showing the history of the mill and some notable figures from Glossop. Open for breakfast, food is served all day. Beers usually consist of three national brands with others from both national and regional breweries. 🌳🕭🌀♿🍴🚃🖥🛜

Star Inn ⦿
2 Howard Street, SK13 7DD (next to railway station)
☎ (01457) 761816
Oakham Citra; Timothy Taylor Boltmaker, Landlord; 3 changing beers (sourced regionally; often Abbeydale, Pictish) Ⓗ
A popular town-centre pub, next to the railway station. A comfortable main room, where conversation predominates, features wood panelling. A smaller room is located to the rear and includes a large map of part of the Peak District National Park on one wall. Guest beers are sourced mainly from regional breweries. The pub is ideally situated as a starting or finishing point for walking or cycling in the Dark Peak. Camping is available nearby at Windy Harbour Farm. Q🌳♿🅰➪♣Ⓟ🖥🐾🛜♪

Hasland

Hasland Working Mens Club
Hampton Street, S41 0LH
☎ (01246) 273660
6 changing beers Ⓗ
Hasland Club is a community resource, committed to providing a safe environment for members. The club welcomes non-members and CAMRA members. There are no regular cask ales, but five or six different ales are on at any time, with pales, ambers and stouts featuring. The Club organises charity and community events. Tap takeovers featuring local and national breweries and live music at weekends are also regular events. 🌳♿♣🖥(54)🐾🛜♪

Hayfield

Kinder Lodge 🄻
10 New Mills Road, SK22 2JG
☎ (01663) 743613 ⊕ kinder-lodge.co.uk
4 changing beers (often Greene King, Morland, Thornbridge) Ⓗ
Terraced stone-built pub dating from 1778 located on the edge of Hayfield village and close to the end of the Sett Valley Trail and the Hayfield Visitor Centre in the heart of the Peak District. Four regularly-changing beers are served. The on-site parking is limited, but the public Pay & Display car park and the bus station are close by. There are five guest bedrooms. 🌳🕭🌀🅰♣Ⓟ🖥🛜♪

Heanor

Redemption Ale House 🄻
Ray Street, DE75 7GE
☎ 07887 568576
8 changing beers Ⓗ
A large open-plan micropub, on two floors. Formerly a butcher's shop; old framed photographs illustrate the pub's previous life. Up to eight regularly changing beers are served, and real cider is sometimes available. The ground-floor room is warmed by a stove in the winter months, and there is a variety of board games available

in the upstairs room. A large collection of pumpclips adorn the walls. There is an attractive courtyard drinking area. Q🏠🍴🍽️👵🎵

Hilcote

Hilcote Arms
New Lane, DE55 5HT
☎ (01773) 862696
2 changing beers (sourced locally; often Dancing Duck, Welbeck Abbey) Ⓗ
The Hilcote Arms reopened in 2017, after being closed since 2014. Extensive refurbishment has seen the introduction of four handpulls, a log burner, and new interiors throughout. Local ales are featured on the bar. Dog-friendly, children are welcome until 8pm. Public transport is frequent from a stop one mile away at the East Midlands Designer Outlet shopping centre. Q🕭🍽️👵

Holbrook

Dead Poets Inn
38 Chapel Street, DE56 0TQ
☎ (01332) 780301
Draught Bass; Everards Old Original; Oakham Citra; 5 changing beers (sourced regionally; often Brunswick, Everards) Ⓗ
Now owned by Everards brewery and leased by the Brunswick brewery, discounted ales from both breweries feature regularly on the bar. The pub prides itself on being one of the top cider pubs in the area, with up to two dozen available. A main stone-flagged bar area with low ceilings and a large open fire is flanked by a cosy snug. A newer airy conservatory extension sits at the back, which leads to an outside garden drinking area. Two annual beer and cider festivals are held. Local CAMRA Pub of the Year 2023. Q🕭🏠🍽️🚆(71)👵🎵

Holymoorside

Lamb Inn
16 Loads Road, S42 7EU
☎ (01246) 566167
Peak Ales Swift Nick, Bakewell Best Bitter, Chatsworth Gold; 3 changing beers Ⓗ
This quaint, traditional country pub is owned by Peak Ales and serves their own cask ales alongside beers from other regional breweries. Warm up next to the log fire on winter days or enjoy the paved drinking area on warm summer evenings. This is a traditional locals' pub unspoilt by progress where all are welcome, including dogs and walkers – although not their muddy boots. Finalist for local CAMRA Pub of the Year 2024. Q🏠🍴P🚆(84)👵

Hope

Cheshire Cheese Inn Ⓛ
Edale Road, S33 6ZF
☎ (01433) 620381 ⊕ thecheshirecheeseinn.co.uk
Black Sheep Best Bitter; Bradfield Farmers Blonde; Peak Ales Bakewell Best Bitter; 1 changing beer (sourced locally; often Abbeydale, Bradfield, Little Critters) Ⓗ
A cosy country inn dating from 1578 with an open-plan bar area and a smaller room at a lower level that was probably originally used to house animals, but now is mainly used as a dining area. Home-cooked meals using local produce are served lunchtimes and evenings. The pub is situated in good walking country but the parking is limited as the road outside is narrow. Closed Monday apart from bank holidays. Q🕭🏠🍴P🚆👵🎵

Old Hall Hotel 🏅
Market Place, S33 6RH
☎ (01433) 620160 ⊕ oldhallhotelhope.co.uk
Theakston Best Bitter, Lightfoot, Old Peculier; 3 changing beers (sourced nationally) Ⓗ
Set in the heart of the village of Hope, this large and atmospheric 16th-century building has been an inn since 1730. It is popular for its locally sourced food and has five letting rooms together with extra facilities in the adjoining tearooms. Home of the Hope Valley Beer and Cider Festival held on three bank holiday weekends a year, it also boasts a large collection of malt whiskies. Q🕭🏠🍴🍽️▲P🚆👵🎵

Hundall

Miner's Arms Ⓛ
Hundall Lane, S18 4BS
☎ (01246) 414505
Drone Valley Dronny Bottom Bitter; Pictish Alchemists Ale; 3 changing beers (sourced nationally) Ⓗ
A comfortable, cosy, traditional open-plan village pub that has won numerous CAMRA awards at local and county levels. It offers a wide range of ales, a genuine cider from Sandford Orchards, and several fruit-based ciders. The two permanent and three ever-changing ales often include a dark and are served in oversized glasses. There is extra seating in the conservatory and in the extensive beer garden. A largescreen TV is mainly used for sports. The pub is dog friendly. Q🕭🏠🍴♣P🚆(15)👵🎵♪

Ilkeston

Burnt Pig Ⓛ
53 Market Street, DE7 5RB
☎ 07812 158219
6 changing beers Ⓗ
A well established, friendly and popular micropub, extended over three rooms, with a collection of historical pub memorabilia. A regular entry in this Guide, five frequently changing cask ales are at the bar, and there is a good selection of continental bottled beers. Real cider is sometimes available. Bar snacks include a selection of excellent cheeses and pork pies to eat in or take away, and its famous pork scratchings. Customers may bring in their own food. There are good bus connections. Q♣🚆👵

Dew Drop Inn ★ Ⓛ
24 Station Street, DE7 5TE
☎ (0115) 932 9684
Full Mash Warlord; Thornbridge Jaipur; 5 changing beers (sourced nationally; often Castle Rock, Dancing Duck, Ossett) Ⓗ
A welcoming and deservedly popular local, and an enduring real ale haven. Formerly a hotel, Sir Barnes Wallis stayed here on a visit to the area during WWII. A regular entry in this Guide, it has been identified by CAMRA as having a nationally important historic pub interior. The lounge bar is warmed by an impressive stove during the winter months. Its close proximity to Ilkeston railway station makes the pub a convenient port of call on a visit to Ilkeston. Q🕭🏠🍴≠♣👵🚆(27)👵

Killamarsh

Guzzle Micropub
193A Sheffield Road, S21 1DX
5 changing beers (sourced locally; often Little Critters, Stancill, Welbeck Abbey) Ⓗ

Micropub serving local products including cask and keg beer, lager, gins, wines and prosecco. Five regularly changing cask beers are available from local breweries such as Stancill, Welbeck Abbey, Little Critters and Don Valley. Seating is availabe indoors, as well as on outdoor benches. It is the sister micropub to Guzzle in Woodseats which opened several years earlier. ❀

Kniveton

Red Lion at Kniveton ♈
Main Street, DE6 1JH
☎ (01335) 345554
Marston's Pedigree; 2 changing beers Ⓗ
Attractive stone pub on the main road through the village. It changed hands in 2020 and is now run by a local couple who also own a cider company. It serves a good, well-kept range of beers from local breweries including Wincle & Aldwark, with a great emphasis on ciders, including their own brand. Friendly and welcoming staff, good range of excellent food served at most times. Local CAMRA Pub of the Year 2024, and regional Cider Pub of the Year 2023 and 2024.
🌠❀🛲◑●P❀🎵

Little Eaton

Shiny Tap
10 Old Hall Mill Business Park, Alfreton Road, DE21 5EJ
⊕ shinybrewing.com/shiny-tap
Shiny 4 Wood, Disco Balls Ⓖ; 2 changing beers (sourced locally) Ⓗ
Situated in a business park hidden from the main road in the centre of Little Eaton, the building is principally the Shiny brewery. The front room has bloomed from a beer shop into a single-room pub with a cosy wooden feel and plenty of seating. There is a pleasant seating area outside the front of the building bounded by a small sunken brook. The well-kept real ales are complimented by interesting craft ales to try. ❀P🛲(Comet)●

Long Eaton

Mill & Brook 🅛 ✅
101 Derby Road, NG10 4QB
☎ (0115) 998 7518
Lincoln Green Marion, Archer, Hood, Tuck; 2 changing beers (sourced nationally) Ⓗ
A late-Victorian two-bar pub located adjacent to the impressive Harrington Mill, an historic Victorian tenement lace factory. Now managed by the Lincoln Green brewery, it is a welcome addition to the real ale presence in Long Eaton, and a wide range of Lincoln Green's beers are available on the bar. An interesting range of tapas and bar snacks is available every day except Sunday. The pub is easily reached from the neighbouring Erewash Canal and Erewash Valley Trail.
🌠❀P🛲●🎵

Rowells Drinking Emporium 🅛
22 High Street, NG10 1LL
☎ 07809 627286
6 changing beers Ⓖ
A spacious micropub in the Long Eaton's iconic former draper's shop of the same name. The pub retains many of the original features and has been refurbished to a high standard, creating a relaxed and cosy atmosphere. Up to six real ales are dispensed by gravity; casks can be seen in the temperature-controlled cool room next to the bar. Occasional real cider as well as tea and coffee are available. Q♿🛲(15,Sky)●🎵🎵

Longshaw

Grouse
S11 7TZ
☎ (01433) 630423 ⊕ thegrouseinn-froggatt.co.uk
Banks's Amber Ale; Marston's Pedigree, Old Empire; 1 changing beer Ⓗ
In the same family for over 50 year, this free house stands in isolation on bleak moorland southwest of Sheffield, and is a welcome refuge for walkers as well as climbers from the nearby Froggatt Edge. The comfortable lounge and bar are at the front with separate room at the rear reached through the conservatory in which vines manage to grow. Well known for their excellent steak pie. Both children and dogs are welcome and a children's menu is available. Closed Monday evening.
Q🌠❀◑♿P●🎵

Lullington

Colvile Arms
Main Street, DE12 8EG (centre of village)
☎ 07510 870980 ⊕ thecolvilearms.com
Draught Bass; Marston's Pedigree; 2 changing beers (sourced regionally) Ⓗ
Once owned by the Lullington Estate, seat of the Colvile family until the early 1900s, but now leased from a private owner, this popular 18th-century free house is at the heart of an attractive hamlet at the southern tip of the county. The public bar incorporates an adjoining hallway and features high-backed settles with wood panelling. The bar and a comfortable lounge are situated on opposite sides of a central serving area. A snug/function room overlooks the beer garden. Pop-up food vans visit some Wednesdays and most Fridays. Quiz night is the last Sunday of month. Q🌠❀◑♣●P●🎵

Makeney

Holly Bush ★ ✅
Holly Bush Lane, DE56 0RX
☎ (01332) 841729 ⊕ hollybushinnmakeney.co.uk
Marston's Pedigree Ⓖ; Thornbridge Jaipur IPA; Timothy Taylor Landlord; Whim Hartington IPA; house beer (by Thornbridge); 3 changing beers (sourced nationally) Ⓗ
The Holly Bush is a late 17th-century Grade II-listed pub with great character. Dick Turpin reputedly drank here. It has been identified by CAMRA as having a nationally important historic pub interior, with various stone-flagged hideaways with welcoming fires in winter. Eight cask and five keg ales are usually available with even more at the regular beer festivals. Walkers, families and dogs are all welcome, and there is plenty of outdoor seating. Q🌠❀♿♣●P🛲(sixes)●🎵

Matlock

bod Matlock
22 Dale Road, DE4 3LT
☎ (01629) 580382 ⊕ bodcafebars.co.uk/matlock
Everards Tiger; Titanic Steerage, Iceberg, Plum Porter; 2 changing beers (often Titanic) Ⓗ
A smart, sympathetic conversion of what was most recently a furniture shop, it comprises of a main room with two smaller rooms off. There are some original features including exposed brickwork. Built in the 1920s specifically for Boots the Chemist, a mural of the original frontage can be seen on the Garden Room wall. It's primarily a café bar which serves alcohol from 11am. There are up to six real ales, with 10 craft beers and Titanic gins on the bar. Q🌠◑♿🛲●🎵

Farmacy 🅛

76 Smedley Street, DE4 3JJ (jct of Bank Rd and Smedley St)

☎ (01629) 583350 ⊕ aaabrewery.co.uk

5 changing beers (often Aldwark Artisan Ales) Ⓗ

Up the hill from the town centre, behind the County Hall on Smedley Street, this cosy, split-level micropub is the tap for Aldwark Artisan Ales. They have five handpulls, one dispensing real cider, and usually feature several of their own beers. A range of Aldwark bottled beers are always available. They serve a range of gins and wines. Regular quiz nights take place. Dogs are welcome. Ᏸ≠🅟❀🐾🛜

Newsroom 🅛

75-77 Smedley Street East, DE4 3FQ

☎ (01629) 583625

4 changing beers (sourced locally) Ⓗ

This smart conversion from a newsagent to a micropub is an L-shaped room with some exposed brickwork and renovated sash windows. There are four real ales from interesting local, and sometimes national, microbreweries. Six craft ales normally feature a stout and a lager; at least one will be KeyKeg. There are also over 60 different bottled and canned beers for drinking or takeaway, alongside a good range of gins and wines. ♿≠🅟❀

Red Lion 🅛

65 Matlock Green, DE4 3BT

☎ (01629) 584888 ⊕ theredlionmatlock.co.uk

7 changing beers (often Moot Ales Brewery) Ⓗ

Set back from the A615 behind the bus stop and shops in the Matlock Green area of Matlock, just a short walk past the football ground away from the town centre. It is a large, impressive open-plan building with a dining area to the left of the central entrance. Seven handpulls often dispense up to four ales from the onsite Moot Ales brewery. Dogs are welcome. Q Ᏸ❀🖨🕮🍴♿Å≠♣🅟🖃

Twenty Ten 🅛

16 Dale Road, DE4 3LT

☎ (01629) 259793

4 changing beers (sourced regionally) Ⓗ

Located a stone's throw from the local train and bus station, this busy town-centre bar sits on the lively Dale Road. It serves four regularly-changing real ales, with LocAles often available. These are complemented by an impressive range of draught ales, 10 of which are craft keg options. Live sports are screened throughout the week with live music on Friday and Saturday evenings. Ᏸ❀≠🅟❀🛜♫

Melbourne

Spirit Vaults 🅛

53 Church Street, DE73 8EJ

☎ (01332) 300542 ⊕ thespiritvaults.co.uk

House beer (by Morgan Brewmasters); 4 changing beers (sourced locally) Ⓗ

The multi-roomed Spirit Vaults dates from the 19th century and is well located for visitors to the Hall and Norman parish church which can be seen from the outdoor heated drinking area. The pub was extensively refurbished in 2020 with copious quantities of polished wood. An in-house brewhouse, Morgan Brewmaster, was installed which is visible from one side. House-brewed cask beers are complimented by a good range of guests, craft and Belgian beers. ❀🖨🕮♣❀🅟(2,9)❀🛜

New Mills

Beer Shed

47B Market Street, SK22 4AA

4 changing beers (sourced locally; often Black Iris, Abbeydale, Torrside) Ⓗ

The ownership and running of the Beer Shed was transferred in 2023 from the owner over the last eight years to nearby Torrside Brewing. Their intention is very much to continue business as usual, and not to create a Torrside Tap. The Beer Shed is a narrow micropub on two levels offering a range of interesting beers from the Peak District and beyond on four handpulls. A real cider is available, six craft beers and German Rothaus on draught plus a range of bottled beers. ≠(Central)🖐🅟🐾❀

Mason's Arms

57 High Street, SK22 4BR

☎ 07745 575472

Wainwright Gold; 4 changing beers (sourced locally; often Silver Brewhouse, Storm) Ⓗ

The only pub in the conservation area of New Mills, it is situated close to the Sett River Valley and Torrs Millennium Bridge. It was extensively refurbished after a takeover from Robinsons. The pub offers a good selection of good-value cask ales, predominantly from local micros. It is a lively friendly pub with a strong sports orientation and regular live music at weekends featuring local bands. There is a small drinking area outside the pub. ❀≠(Central)♣🅟🐾❀🛜♫

Newton Solney

Brickmakers Arms

9-11 Main Street, DE15 0SJ (on B5008; opp jct with Trent Ln)

☎ 07525 220103 ⊕ brickmakersarms.pub

Burton Bridge Sovereign Gold, Bridge Bitter, Top Dog Stout, Stairway to Heaven; 1 changing beer (sourced regionally) Ⓗ

This cosy local at the end of an 18th-century terrace of cottages was converted into a pub in the early 19th century for workers at a nearby brickworks. It features a narrow central bar leading at one end to a room served through a hatch, and at the other to an impressive oak-panelled room. The street entrance hallway houses a small bring-and-take library, beyond which is a small function/meeting room. Q Ᏸ❀♣🅟(V3)❀🛜♫

Ockbrook

Royal Oak ★ 🅛

55 Green Lane, DE72 3SE

☎ (01332) 662378 ⊕ royaloakockbrook.com

Draught Bass; 4 changing beers (sourced nationally) Ⓗ

Attractive 18th-century pub with a number of small rooms. Run by the Wilson family since 1953, they have brought about many improvements while retaining the original character and features. Excellent home-cooked food is served every day. A large function room allows the pub to host many community and public events including live music and open mic nights. Outside there are two pleasant gardens, one with an enclosed play area for children. Q Ᏸ❀🕮♣❀🖐🅟🐾❀🛜♫

Parwich

Parwich Royal British Legion Club

Dam Lane, DE6 1QJ

☎ (01335) 390501

Dancing Duck Ay up; 2 changing beers Ⓗ

Sitting in the heart of the village, not far from the local pub, this welcoming club is open to all visitors. At least three real ales are usually on, one tapped direct from the cellar room, from local breweries such as Dancing Duck or Wincle. Local CAMRA Club of the Year 2022-24, and reached the final four of the National Club of the Year 2023. 🐴❀♿♣🐾

Ripley

Groovers Arms

151 Peasehill, DE5 3JN
☎ 07896 832141
Alter Ego Mr Brown; Blue Monkey Infinity IPA; Dancing Duck Dark Drake [H], Abduction; 5 changing beers (often Bradfield, Oakham, Thornbridge) [G]
A mile from the town centre, this smart new-build two-roomed bar opened in late 2023. It is within the garden area of the former Beehive Inn, on the site of the former Honeypot Bar. It serves up to nine cask ales and a plethora of keg beers and ciders, with the majority sourced from Derbyshire and local breweries within 30 miles. There is regular live music in summer, with occasional vinyl music nights.
🐴❀♿♣🍎P🚌(nines) 🐾📶♫

Red Lion ✔

Market Place, DE5 3BR
☎ (01773) 512875
Greene King Abbot; Ruddles Best Bitter; Sharp's Doom Bar; 4 changing beers (sourced nationally) [H]
A large former Home Brewery pub built in the 1960s and easily identified by the large red lion rampant on the pub frontage. Facing the Victorian Ripley Town Hall and Market Place at the centre of this busy market town, it is close to the main bus stops. With a typical Wetherspoon's interior layout, the pub serves several changing ales and the regular food menu is available all day.
🐴❀◖◗♿P🚌(nines,sixes) 📶

Talbot

1 Butterley Hill, DE5 3LT
☎ 07494 767374
7 changing beers (sourced nationally) [H]
A traditional Victorian flatiron-shaped pub, the Talbot is a welcoming and popular community pub, a short walk from the town centre. It has a real fire in winter and an excellent selection of at least seven changing real ales, often from breweries less-seen locally, pulled from casks stored on an original stone stillage, plus at least four real ciders. A previous local CAMRA Pub of the Year and Cider Pub of the Year. Q🐴♿🍎P🚌(nines,90)🐾📶♫

Rosliston

Bull's Head

19 Burton Road, DE12 8JU (NW edge of village)
☎ (01283) 762642 🌐 bullsheadrosliston.co.uk
Draught Bass; Marston's Pedigree; 2 changing beers (sourced regionally) [H]
Late 19th-century brick-built free house with a comfortable public bar and smart, cosy lounge, both featuring open fires and beamed ceilings. There is also a large function room in a converted stable block. A collection of china bulls is displayed behind the bar, and intricate encased models of a Burton union brewing system can be found in both the public bar and the function room. Bingo is played on alternate Wednesday evenings; with open mic night Thursday.
🐴❀◖⛺♣🍎P🚌(22) 🐾📶♫

Sawley

Sawley Junction [L]

176 Tamworth Road, NG10 3JU
☎ 07966 757407
6 changing beers (sourced regionally) [G]
Renovated to a high standard, this micropub has the feel of a traditional station bar and tea shop (the pub takes nearby Long Eaton railway station's former name). Historic railway artefacts adorn the walls. It has up to six gravity-dispensed cask beers on offer. Bar snacks and hot drinks are available throughout the day. A popular local, its proximity to the railway station also makes it handy for commuters. Closed Monday and Tuesday except bank holiday Mondays. 🐴🚆(Long Eaton)P🚌(Sky,15)🐾

White Lion [L]

Tamworth Road, NG10 3AT
☎ (0115) 946 3061 🌐 whitelion-sawley.co.uk
Draught Bass; 5 changing beers (sourced regionally) [H]
Located in the Sawley conservation area and dating back to the 18th century, this spacious two-roomed pub is near the River Trent and marina. Bass is a regular beer and there are up to five other handpumps on the bar. Beers are sourced from all types of breweries, from local to national. Locally produced savoury snacks are on offer and are a tasty filler to go with the beers and chat with other pubgoers. 🐴❀P🚌(Sky,15)🐾📶♫

South Normanton

Clock Inn

107 Market Street, DE55 2AA
☎ (01773) 811396 🌐 theclockinn.co.uk
Burton Bridge XL Bitter; 2 changing beers [H]
Multi-room pub with a lounge and public bar area with a central bar serving both rooms. Up to three beers are available. There is a nice lawn and garden to the rear, with outdoor seating and a covered smoking area. Sky Sports and TNT Sports are available in both rooms on large projection screens. Dogs are welcome in both rooms. 🐴❀P🚌(9.1)🐾📶

Market Tavern [L]

41 High Street, DE55 2BP
5 changing beers (often Blue Monkey, Marble, Thornbridge) [H]
Two-roomed micropub lovingly renovated from a former charity shop. Located on the High Street just off the Market Place, this pub offers up to five ever-changing real ales, usually sourced from local breweries, and up to six traditional ciders. A range of craft cans is also available. Dogs and children are welcome at all times.
Q🐴♣🍎P🚆🚌(9.1) 🐾📶

Sutton cum Duckmanton

Arkwright Arms [L]

Chesterfield Road, S44 5JG (on A632 between Chesterfield and Bolsover)
☎ 07803 006926 🌐 arkwrightarms.co.uk
House beer (by Whim); 5 changing beers (sourced locally; often Ashover, Thornbridge, Whim) [H]
There is always a warm welcome at this mock-Tudor fronted free house, with three cosy rooms all with open fires and comfortable furniture. The impressive wood-panelled bar is adorned by an excellent range of guest ales, many from local breweries. Regular beer festivals are held at Easter and bank holidays. Good food is served every day except Monday and Tuesday. Local CAMRA Pub of the Year 2022. 🐴❀◖◗⛺♣🍎P🚌🐾

Swanwick

Steampacket Inn

Derby Road, DE55 1AB
☎ (01773) 607771
Draught Bass; 5 changing beers (sourced nationally; often Ashover, Blue Monkey, Nottingham) ⓗ
A friendly Pub People Co pub situated in the centre of Swanwick, the Steampacket boasts an excellent and constantly-changing range of real ales and ciders, many of them from local microbreweries. Beer festivals are held in winter and summer. It is a popular and lively pub at the weekends, with TV sport and regular live music. It has a welcoming fire in winter wth outdoor tables in summer. ⏥♿♣♠P🖵(nines,Comet)♨🛜♪

Whaley Bridge

Whaley Nook

20 Old Road, SK23 7HR (turn up Old Rd opp Co-op, bar is on the left)
Abbeydale Deception; 3 changing beers (sourced locally; often Big Stone, Eyam, Thornbridge) ⓗ
Two-room pub, with a small cosy front bar and another small room at the rear. There is also a little French café-style seating outside on the pavement. Four handpumps offer one regular beer and three changing beers from local breweries, plus six craft beers and a real cider on fonts. An interesting selection of gins from far and wide are available and works of art by local artists are displayed on the walls and are for sale.
Q♨≉♠🖵(199,61)

Whitehough

Old Hall Inn ⓛ

SK23 6EJ (nr Chinley; 750yds off B6062)
☎ (01663) 750529 ⊕ old-hall-inn.co.uk
Abbeydale Deception; Wainwright Gold; 5 changing beers (sourced locally; often Ossett, Thornbridge, Torrside) ⓗ

The 16th-century Whitehough Hall forms part of this superb quintessential country inn which has previously won the CAMRA Regional Pub of the Year, the Great British Pub award for best cask pub in the region for several years, and is a regular entry within this Guide. Eight ales, including six regularly changing beers from quality local micros, complement those available at the adjacent Paper Mill Inn (under the same ownership). A well-regarded menu features dishes using local produce. Popular beer festival in September.
⏥♨♿⏽A≉(Chinley)♠P🖵(190)♨🛜

Willington

Dragon ⓛ

13 The Green, DE65 6BP
☎ (01283) 704795 ⊕ thedragonatwillington.co.uk
Draught Bass; Marston's Pedigree; Sharp's Doom Bar; 3 changing beers (sourced locally) ⓗ
This pub's origins can be traced back to when the Trent and Mersey Canal was constructed. The rear garden overlooks the canal while the front garden has a fenced childrens' play area. The pub has been expanded into the adjacent cottage for an additional dining area but retains an old, low-ceilinged feel. The Bridgeside restaurant doubles as a function room.
⏥♨♿⏽♿≉♠P🖵(V3) ♨🛜♪

Wirksworth

Feather Star ⓛ

Market Place, DE4 4ET
☎ 07931 424117 ⊕ thefeatherstar.co.uk
5 changing beers ⓗ
There are five regularly changing beers on handpumps, sourced locally and regionally, and the tap wall offers up to 13 craft beers and lagers, plus five real ciders. The owners have joined forces with Umami, a restaurant in the same building, to provide hot bar snacks and their takeaway food can be eaten in the bar. The pub is named for a Crinoid fossil found locally in the limestone around Wirksworth. Q⏥♨≉(Ecclesbourne Valley)P🖵(6.1)♨♪

Old Poets' Corner, Ashover (Photo: Emma Haines)

DEVON

Map locations: Ilfracombe, Lee Bay, Lee, Yarde Down, Braunton, Barnstaple, Appledore, Yelland, Instow, Abbotsham, Bideford, Chittlehampton, Parkham, Umberleigh, Chittlehamholt, Kings Nympton, Beaford, Chulmleigh, Tiverton, Shebbear, Dolton, Meeth, Iddesleigh, Cullompton, Black Torrington, Hatherleigh, North Tawton, Bow, Cheriton Fitzpaine, Sandford, Clawton, Exbourne, Spreyton, Yeoford, Crediton, Stoke Canon, Newton St Cyres, Woodbury Salterton, Lewdown, South Zeal, Chagford, Christow, Ide, Exeter, Topsham, Clyst St Mary, St Giles on the Heath, Hennock, Cockwood, Dawlish, Exmouth, Postbridge, Widecombe-in-the-Moor, Holcombe, Teignmouth, Peter Tavy, Horsebridge, Tavistock, Princetown, Bishopsteignton, Sigford, Walkhampton, Ashburton, Newton Abbot, Abbotskerswell, Morwellham, Buckfastleigh, Staverton, Kingskerswell, Avonwick, Littlehempston, Torquay, Paignton, Plympton, Ivybridge, South Brent, Totnes, Stoke Gabriel, Plymouth, Lee Mill, Ashprington, Billacombe, Bittaford, Brixton, Brixham, Turnchapel, Dartmouth, Ledstone, Stoke Fleming, Kingsbridge, Salcombe

CORNWALL

Abbotskerswell

Two Mile Oak Inn L

Totnes Road, TQ12 6DF (on A381 between Newton Abbot and Ipplepen)
☎ (01803) 812411 • twomileoakinn.co.uk
Dartmoor Jail Ale; Otter Bitter; 1 changing beer G
A two-bar olde-worlde pub, formerly a farmhouse then licensed in 1703. It is still sympathetic to its heritage, with wooden floors, oak beams and a log fire. A large collection of shiny brasses and original ornaments can be found displayed on the open stone walling, shelves and in the many nooks around the pub. Otter Bitter, Dartmoor Jail Ale plus a guest are served straight from casks on the bar. The pleasant garden has views across Dartmoor.
Q❄️🐕🍴🚆♿🅿️🚆(7,177)🐾📶🎵

Appledore

Champ L

Meeting Street, EX39 1RJ (just off The Quay)

☎ (01237) 421662
4 changing beers (sourced locally) H
Open mainly in the evenings, this cosy and quirky pub is the brewery tap for nearby Clearwater brewery and up to four of their ales are generally available. The Champ is renowned for live music which features regularly on Fridays and Saturdays, together with popular open-mic evenings on Tuesday, Wednesday and Thursday. Customers are welcome to bring in food for consumption on the premises, while a nearby public car park accommodates camper vans overnight for a modest fee.
🚆♿♣️🍴🅿️🚆🐾📶🎵

Ashburton

Old Exeter Inn L

26 West Street, TQ13 7DU (on main road through the centre of Ashburton, opp church)
☎ (01364) 652013 • oldexeterinn.com
1 changing beer G

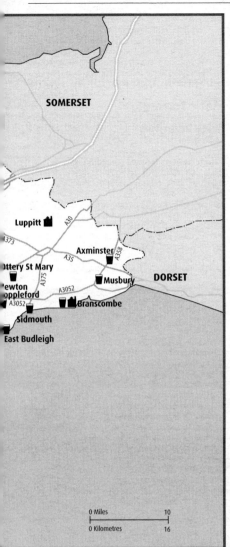

SOMERSET

Luppitt

Axminster

DORSET

Ottery St Mary

A35

newton
poppleford

A3052

Musbury

Branscombe

Sidmouth

East Budleigh

| 0 Miles | 10 |
| 0 Kilometres | 16 |

Ashprington

Durant Arms
TQ9 7UP (exit Totnes on the A381; left turn signposted after 1 mile)
☎ (01803) 732240 ⊕ durantarms.co.uk
Dartmoor Jail Ale; Noss Beer Works Church Ledge Ⓗ; **2 changing beers (sourced regionally; often Teignworthy, Otter)** Ⓗ/Ⓖ
A traditional, family-run 18th-century inn with wood-burning fires and slate floors. Beers include local offerings alongside some from as far afield as Yorkshire. A beer festival is held in September and frequent events include Burns Night among others. En-suite B&B accommodation and a restaurant serving local produce attract visitors. The pub is close to the River Dart and only three miles along the Dart Valley scenic walking trail from Totnes. It is on the South Devon National Cycle Route 28. Q🏠🍴♿◑●🚆(B2C)♣🐾🌳♪

Avonwick

Avon Inn Ⓛ
TQ10 9NB
☎ (01364) 73475 ⊕ avon-inn.org.uk
Dartmoor Legend; Timothy Taylor Landlord; 1 changing beer (sourced regionally) Ⓗ
Situated at the crossroads in the centre of the village, the Avon Inn is open until at least 10.30 daily, but may close later. The former lounge is now a restaurant. The pub is the centre of the community with occasional events including quiz nights, live music and barbecues taking place – see website for details. Up to 10 ciders from producers such as Ashridge, Countryman and Sandford Orchards are also on offer.
🏠🍴◑♿Å♣●P🚆(91) 🐾🌳♪

Axminster

Axminster Inn Ⓛ ✔
Silver Street, EX13 5AH
☎ (01297) 34947 ⊕ axminsterinn.pub
Palmers Copper Ale, IPA, Dorset Gold, 200; 1 changing beer (sourced locally) Ⓗ
The Axminster Inn is a friendly traditional pub, lying just off the town centre. It has a real log fire for the winter months and a lovely enclosed beer garden to enjoy in warmer weather. It's a Palmers house, offering a good range of their real ales and ciders. Live music is featured. Free Wi-Fi is available and there is a skittle alley and dartboard. The pub is dog friendly. Children are welcome up until 7pm. Local CAMRA Pub of the Year 2022.
🏠🍴♿♣●P🚆🐾🌳♪

Barnstaple

Beer Matters Community Micropub
7 Tuly Street, EX31 1DH
⊕ beermatters.uk
4 changing beers (sourced nationally) Ⓖ
A community micropub opened in late 2022 close to the town centre, the pub is renowned for its unfailingly welcoming atmosphere. It offers a wide range of constantly changing cask conditioned ales, many not usually seen in North Devon, plus numerous bottled beers and ciders. With no TV and children not admitted, the bar furniture and decor encourage friendly conversation, even among strangers. There are regular acoustic music evenings. A large public car park is directly opposite. ●P🚆(21)🐾♪

This friendly local is the oldest pub in Ashburton, originally built in 1130 to house the workers building the nearby church, with additions in 17th century. There is a wood-panelled L-shaped bar with a granite shelf behind for serving the gravity-fed ales. There are two seated areas either side of the entrance plus two rear seating areas and flagstoned corridor leading to the secluded walled garden at the back. Local cider is sold. Open till 10pm all week in summer. Q🏠🍴◑●🚆(38,88)🐾🌳

Silent Whistle
34 St Lawrence Lane, TQ13 7DD
☎ (01364) 716327
Dartmoor Jail Ale; 1 changing beer (sourced locally) Ⓗ
This pub became the Silent Whistle in 1962 when the branch line from Totnes was closed, save for a brief period in the late 80s when it became the Fleece & Firkin, reverting to the Silent Whistle in 1994. Now a free house, it has a large bar area with plenty of seating plus a snug and a rear room with pool table and sports screen. Real ales are rotated and come mainly from Dartmoor brewery. 🏠🍴♣🚆(88,38)🐾🌳♪

Panniers 🅛 ✅

33-34 Boutport Street, EX31 1RX (opp Queen's Theatre)
☎ (01271) 329720
Greene King Abbot; Ruddles Best Bitter; Sharp's Doom Bar; 4 changing beers (sourced regionally) 🅗
Centrally located opposite the Queen's Theatre and close to the historic Pannier Market, this popular JD Wetherspoon pub maintains an ever-changing selection of real ales from local and West Country breweries, as well as those from further afield. Framed prints, hung throughout the comfortable premises, depict various items relating to the history of Barnstaple. To the rear, a pleasant courtyard garden drinking area is a suntrap in summer. ►❄️🕙🔥🚃🛜

Reform Inn 🅛

Reform Street, Pilton, EX31 1PD
☎ (01271) 323164 🌐 reforminn.co.uk
Barum Original, Breakfast; 1 changing beer (sourced locally) 🅗
Well-established, popular community local and brewery tap for Barum brewery. From the main road, look above roof level for the pub sign to locate it. The skittle alley is the location for the annual Green Man beer festival in July and other regular beer festivals are held during the year. In the public bar there is a pool table and dartboard. Music events are held occasionally, see the website or facebook page for details. ♣🚃❄️🛜🎵

Beaford

Globe Inn 🅛

Exeter Road, EX19 8LR (on main road in centre of village)
☎ (01805) 603920 🌐 globeinnpub.co.uk
3 changing beers (sourced regionally) 🅗
Traditional and cosy country inn, with a passion for serving real ale and craft beers to suit all tastes. Three changing and mainly local ales are usually available, alongside a comprehensive drinks menu that includes more than 40, often legendary, bottled and bottle-conditioned beers from around the globe. Proud of its environmental credentials, the pub also offers a seasonal and attractively-priced food menu, using the best ingredients from local producers. Local CAMRA Pub of the Year 2022 and 2023. Q►❄️🍴🕙♣🚃(5B)❄️🛜🎵

Bideford

Joiners Arms

EX39 2DR
☎ (01237) 472675
Sharp's Doom Bar; 2 changing beers (sourced regionally) 🅗
The Joiners Arms is a friendly old-style English pub with accommodation. Local ales, lagers and cider are on offer. Situated in the heart of the town, next to the historic Pannier Market, the pub hosts a number of pub teams and is the focus of regular community events including popular music nights. There is a skittle alley and function room, and live music every weekend. ❄️♣P❄️🛜🎵

Bittaford

Horse & Groom 🅛

Exeter Road, PL21 0EL
☎ (01752) 892358 🌐 horseandgroombittaford.com
Dartmoor Jail Ale; house beer (by Summerskills); 4 changing beers (sourced locally; often Exmoor, South Hams, Summerskills) 🅗
A family-owned pub run by Dawn, son Pierre and husband Oliver, who is a real ale enthusiast. Good home-cooked food is served, and six pumps predominantly offer ales from local breweries in Devon and Cornwall, with two dedicated to real cider. Third-pint tapas is available. There is a long bar and separate dining area. A beer festival, and a cider and sausage festival, are hosted during the year, in aid of local charities. ►❄️🕙🆕🍴♣🚃P🚃(38,Gold) ❄️🎵

Black Torrington

Black River Inn

Broad Street, EX21 5PT SS465056
☎ (01409) 231888 🌐 blackriverinn.co.uk
3 changing beers (sourced regionally) 🅗
Village pub with a growing reputation for real ale and good food. Three regularly changing real ales are served, together with two local ciders. The tastefully decorated public bar with adjacent eating area leads through to the separate restaurant, sometimes used as a function room. Outside, the attractive garden has views over the Torridge valley and surrounding countryside. Near to both the Tarka Trail and Ruby Way, the pub is attractive to walkers and cyclists. Bar snacks only are available on Tuesday and Wednesday. Q►❄️🕙🆕P❄️🛜🎵

REAL ALE BREWERIES

Barnaby's Staverton
Barum 🍺 Barnstaple
Bays Paignton
Beer Engine 🍺 Newton St Cyres
Branscombe Branscombe
Bridgetown Totnes
Checkstone 🍺 Exmouth
Clearwater Bideford
Combe 🍷 Ilfracombe
Copperhead Totnes (NEW)
Cottage Beer Project Tiverton
Country Life Abbotsham
Crossed Anchors 🍺 Exmouth
Dartmoor Princetown
Devil's Pleasure Sigford
Exeter 🍷 Exeter
Grampus 🍺 Lee Bay
GT Braunton
Hanlons 🍷 Newton St Cyres
Hatherland Tiverton
Holsworthy Clawton
Isca Holcombe
Ivybridge 🍷 Ivybridge
Morwellham Morwellham
Noss Beer Works Lee Mill
Otter 🍷 Honiton: Luppitt
Powderkeg Woodbury Salterton
Red Rock 🍷 Bishopsteignton (brewing suspended)
Riviera Totnes: Stoke Gabriel
Roam 🍷 Plymouth
Salcombe 🍷 Ledstone
South Hams Kingsbridge
Stannary 🍷 Tavistock
Steel Brew 🍷 Plymouth
Summerskills Plymouth: Billacombe
Tally Ho! 🍺 Hatherleigh
Tavistock Peter Tavy
Taw Valley 🍷 North Tawton
Teignmouth Teignmouth
Teignworthy Newton Abbot
Topsham 🍷 Exeter
Totnes 🍺 🍷 Totnes
TQ Beerworks 🍷 South Brent
Turk's Head 🍺 Exeter
Utopian Bow
Yelland Manor 🍷 Barnstaple: Yelland

Branscombe

Fountain Head Inn L

EX12 3BG (on the outskirts of the village on the road from the Donkey Sanctuary to Beer, off the main A3052)
☎ (01297) 680359 ⊕ fountainheadinn.com
Branscombe Branoc, Golden Fiddle; 1 changing beer (sourced locally) Ⓗ
Set in a beautiful coastal valley, this walker-friendly old pub is at the west end of one of England's longest villages, approximately a mile and a quarter from Branscombe beach. Ancient features such as the inglenook fireplace, wood panelling and flagstone floors greet customers, while the bar offers Branscombe brewery ales and ciders. Good-value home-cooked food is served. A beer festival is held on the closest weekend to the summer solstice. Q❀☀➊➍♣♠P🚲(899)☀♫

Brixham

Queen's Arms L

31 Station Hill, TQ5 8BN (from Brixham Library go up Church Hill East, then Station Hill)
☎ (01803) 852074 ⊕ thequeensarmsbrixham.co.uk
6 changing beers (sourced nationally; often Branscombe, Salcombe, Teignworthy) Ⓗ
This unpretentious back street boozer with its highly sought-after range of cask beers and ciders, has been local CAMRA Pub of the Year four times and is a regular entrant in this Guide. It features live music on Wednesdays and at weekends, with a Friday meat draw and a Sunday evening quiz. In early December it hosts a charity beer festival with more than 50 real ales and ciders. ❀☀♣♠🚲(17)♫

Vigilance L ✔

5 Bolton Street, TQ5 9DE
☎ (01803) 850489
Dartmoor Jail Ale; Greene King IPA, Abbot; Sharp's Doom Bar; 4 changing beers (sourced nationally) Ⓗ
Named after the last sailing ketch to be built in Brixham's Upham Shipyard, which was subsequently redeveloped into a marina in the 1980s, this town-centre Wetherspoon pub features prints of the town's nautical heritage and historical personalities, including Rev Francis Lyte, composer of Abide With Me and one N Bonaparte. An imposing ship's figurehead surveys customers as they enjoy food and drink which is served all day. Regular beer and cider festivals are held throughout the year. ❀➊♿🚲♠

Brixton

Foxhound Inn L

Kingsbridge Road, PL8 2AH
☎ (01752) 880271 ⊕ foxhoundinn.co.uk
Dartmoor Jail Ale; house beer (by Summerskills); 3 changing beers (sourced nationally; often Caledonian, Salcombe, Summerskills) Ⓗ
An 18th-century former coaching house in a rural village just east of Plymouth, with two separate bars and a small restaurant. Traditional English meals are served daily, featuring locally sourced ingredients. Lookout for Red Coat, an ale crafted by the landlord, among four guest ales. A monthly charity quiz night is held. The village is served by a frequent daytime bus service. Q❀☀➊♿♣♠P🚲(3,94)☀

Buckfastleigh

King's Arms

14-15 Fore Street, TQ11 0BT (in centre of town)

☎ (01364) 643432
Bridgetown Shark Island Stout; Teignworthy Gun Dog; 1 changing beer (sourced locally) Ⓗ
This freehouse has been fully refurbished following its purchase from Admiral Taverns a few years ago. From the entrance hallway is a small public sports bar with a pool table at the front of the pub, and a small function room opposite. A larger lounge bar also showing sports is at the rear, with plenty of comfortable seating. There is a pleasant beer garden at rear with plenty of seating. The ales on sale are mainly local. ❀☀➜♣♠🚲(38,88)☀🛜♫

Chagford

Globe Inn ★ L

9 High Street, TQ13 8AJ
☎ (01647) 433485 ⊕ theglobeinnchagford.co.uk
Dartmoor IPA, Jail Ale; Otter Bitter Ⓗ
Grade II-listed pub built in 1833 on site of an earlier inn. It is a focal point of this historic Dartmoor stannary town, providing good food, music and other functions. The public bar, with its Victorian counter and bar-back thought to date from the 1930s, has been identified by CAMRA as having a regionally important historic interior. This, the lounge bar and dining room have open log fires. There is also a rear courtyard garden. Cider is from Sam's. ☀❀♿➊♠🚲(173,178)☀🛜♫

Cheriton Fitzpaine

Ring of Bells L

EX17 4JG
☎ (01363) 860111 ⊕ theringofbells.com
2 changing beers (sourced regionally) Ⓗ
This thatched Grade II-listed pub sits at one end of this picturesque village, by the parish church. Two changing beers and local real ciders are normally available at the single bar. Fine food, largely locally sourced, is available lunchtimes and evenings but those seeking a snack, a quiet pint by the fire or a few drinks with friends in the garden are equally welcome. Binka the landlady has made this a pub for everyone, including their children and the dog. ☀❀➊♣♠P☀

Chittlehamholt

Exeter Inn L

EX37 9NS
☎ (01769) 540281 ⊕ exeterinn.co.uk
GT Ales Thirst of Many; Otter Ale; St Austell Proper Job Ⓗ
Traditional 16th-century coaching inn on the old road from Barnstaple to Exeter with four cosy eating areas and a pleasant south-facing patio. The food is locally sourced, home cooked and varies with the seasons. The pub retains many original architectural features including a real fire with a bread oven, and various past photographs of the village adorn the walls. There is a popular quiz night once a month and accommodation is available, see the website and facebook page for details. Holiday accommodation is available. Q☀❀♿➊♿♣♠P☀♫

Chittlehampton

Bell Inn L

The Square, EX37 9QL (opp St Hieritha's church)
SS636254
☎ (01769) 540368 ⊕ thebellatchittlehampton.co.uk
Butcombe Original; 1 changing beer (sourced regionally) Ⓗ
In the same family since 1975, and popular with locals and visitors alike, this busy village local has been in the

Guide continuously since 1997. It has won several local CAMRA awards in recent years, including Pub of the Year. The bar area contains notable sporting memorabilia and there is a games room downstairs. The good-value food is home cooked and is served both in the bar and adjoining restaurant. The gardens outside are extensive with long views and are ideal for children.
🏠🕱🛏🕪🕹🧡🚲P🚍(658,859) 🏵🛜🎵

Christow

Teign House Inn 🅛
Teign Valley Road, EX6 7PL
☎ (01647) 252286 ⊕ teignhouseinn.co.uk
Otter Bitter; 3 changing beers (sourced regionally; often Exeter, Powderkeg, South Hams) 🅷
A welcoming and atmospheric country pub on the edge of Dartmoor in the scenic Teign Valley, it has exposed wood beams and log fires. The pub has strong local support and serves as a real hub of the community. The huge garden attracts families and locals, while the adjoining field has space for caravans, campers and tents. There's regular live music, a monthly quiz and great home-cooked food available including a special Asian inspired menu also available for takeaways.
Q🏠🕱🛏🕪🕹🧡🚲P🚍(360) 🏵🛜🎵

Chulmleigh

Old Court House
South Molton Street, EX18 7BW
☎ (01769) 580045 ⊕ oldcourthouseinn.co.uk
Butcombe Original; Dartmoor IPA 🅷
Charles I stayed here in 1634 when he held court (hence the name) and this is commemorated with an original coat of arms in one of the bedrooms, while a replica hangs above the fireplace in the main bar. Today this friendly, cosy local features two regular real ales, usually joined by a guest beer in summer. Good home-cooked food can be taken in the bar area, the separate dining room, or the pretty cobbled courtyard garden.
🏠🛏🕪🕹🧡🚲🚍(377) 🏵🛜

Clyst St Mary

Half Moon Inn
Frog Lane, EX5 1BR
☎ (01392) 873515 ⊕ thehalfmoonclyst.co.uk
Exeter Ferryman; 1 changing beer 🅷
Friendly village pub with a great atmosphere, it was completely refurbished in 2020. Reasonably priced locally sourced food is available lunchtime and evenings, with smaller portions available. Two real ales are on offer. The pub is within walking distance of Exeter Chiefs Rugby Club and Westpoint Exhibition Arena. The garden has some covered seating. Dogs are welcome in the bar area. Q🏠🕱🛏🕪🕹🧡🚍(9)🏵🛜

Cockwood

Anchor Inn 🅛
EX6 8RA (just off the A379, outside Starcross, next to Cockwood harbour) SX9756480692
☎ (01626) 890203 ⊕ anchorinncockwood.com
Otter Ale; 3 changing beers (sourced locally) 🅷
On the picturesque Cockwood harbour, this 450-year-old inn and former seaman's mission has old settles, timber panelling, low beams and snugs, with an impressive display of old nautical memorabilia. Mussels are a speciality on the extensive award-winning seafood menu. Up to five ales and a real cider from Sandford Orchards are usually offered. Haunted by a friendly ghost

and his dog, this is an atmospheric Devon gem. Close to the main GWR line, it is a steam train spotters' paradise. Limited parking; the bus stop is over the bridge.
Q🏠🕱🛏🕪🕹🧡🚲P🚍(2) 🏵

Ship Inn 🅛
Church Road, EX6 8NU (just off the A379, outside Starcross, close to Cockwood harbour)
☎ (01626) 890373 ⊕ shipinncockwood.co.uk
2 changing beers (sourced nationally) 🅷
A busy family-run pub, close to the picturesque harbour at Cockwood, with a roaring log fire in winter and a large beer garden with views of the estuary in warmer weather. Popular with drinkers and diners alike, it offers a choice of three regular ales and usually two rotating guests, and has an excellent food menu. Meals are prepared with local produce where possible including a varied choice of locally caught fish. The bus stops 100 yards across the bridge. Q🏠🕱🛏🕪🕹🧡🚲P🚍(2)🏵🛜

Crediton

Crediton Inn
28A Mill Street, EX17 1EZ
☎ (01363) 530451
4 changing beers (sourced nationally) 🅷
The framed indenture dates this inn to 1878, with windows etched with the ancient town seal. It is a genuine free house serving two to four real ales and a local cider. The skittle alley doubles as a function room. No food except bar snacks such as crisps and nuts. Well-behaved dogs are welcome. Opening times may vary, please phone to check. Children under 14 are not allowed as per the licence. 🕱🛥🧡🚲P🚍(5)🏵🛜

Duke of York 🅛
74 High Street, EX17 3JX
☎ (01363) 775289
Dartmoor IPA; 2 changing beers (sourced regionally) 🅷
One-bar, Grade II-listed pub at the top of the high street, it has been a family-run free house since 2002. One regular beer and one or two changing beers are on offer, mainly from different breweries, depending on demand. Sky, BT and Amazon sports can be shown on three screens. Mens and womens darts teams play here, and there is a south-facing garden. The number 5 bus passes the door. 🕱🧡🚍🏵🛜

Cullompton

Pony & Trap 🅛 ✅
10 Exeter Hill, EX15 1DJ (on B3181 S of town)
☎ (01884) 34182
Bays Devon Dumpling; Dartmoor Jail Ale; Draught Bass; 5 changing beers (sourced regionally) 🅷
A traditional local with good atmosphere and mixed clientele. Many local darts and skittles teams are based here. It has a smart interior featuring a logburner, making it cosy in winter; flowers and ornaments give it a homely feel. Up to eight real ales are on offer, plus three real ciders from Sandford Orchard. There is a garden and outside seating area. Pub games are played.
Q🕱🧡🚍🏵

Dartmouth

Cherub Inn
13 Higher Street, TQ6 9RB
☎ (01803) 832571 ⊕ the-cherub.co.uk
5 changing beers (sourced locally; often Otter, St Austell) 🅷

Situated in the centre of Dartmouth, a nautical town famous for its medieval buildings, the Cherub is one of the best and the oldest, a Grade II-listed 14th-century former merchant's house. Beams made from old ships' timbers feature in the bar which boasts six handpumps serving local and national cask ales. An intricate winding staircase leads to the cosy restaurant and facilities on the two upper floors. May open later on Monday and Tuesday in winter. ♿🍴▲≷(Kingswear)♣🚐☀🛜

Dawlish
Brunswick Arms 🅛
9-10 Brunswick Place, EX7 9PB
☎ (01626) 862181 ⊕ thebrunswickarms.co.uk
Otter Ale; 2 changing beers (sourced locally) 🅷
Family orientated pub overlooking The Brook and The Lawn. It offers outside seating and is a a good spot to sit in the afternoon sun watching the famous black swans of Dawlish. Two guest ales are usually on offer, plus a real cider which changes. Food is available. Skittles, pool and darts are played; children and dogs are welcome. Happy hour is 5-6 all week, but an hour earlier on except Sunday. ♿☀🍴♿≷♣🚐☀🛜♪

Swan Inn
94 Old Town Street, EX7 9AT
☎ (01626) 863677
St Austell Tribute, Proper Job; 1 changing beer (sourced regionally) 🅷
This is a friendly locals pub, reputedly the oldest of Dawlish's pubs, dating from 1642, and is situated in the old part of town. It has a large patio and garden, and a covered heated smoking area. A real cider is always available and there is an outside bar during the summer months from May onwards. Dogs are welcome.
Q♿☀♣♿P☀🛜♪

Dolton
Royal Oak Inn
EX19 8QF (on village square behind church)
☎ (01805) 439214 ⊕ royaloakdolton.co.uk
3 changing beers (sourced regionally; often Bays, Otter) 🅷
A warm welcome is assured in this traditional village pub. A roaring log fire awaits in the main bar, and there is also a snug and a games room with pool, skittles and darts regularly played. Two real ales from Bays usually available, one is their charity beer of the month, and other local brews appear. Good home-cooked food usually available, often locally sourced.
Q♿☀🍴♿♣P🚐☀🛜♪

East Budleigh
Sir Walter Raleigh Inn 🅛
22 High Street, EX9 7ED (off B3178 opp Hayes Ln)
☎ (01395) 442510
Teignworthy Gun Dog; 3 changing beers 🅷
This gem of a community-run pub can be found in East Budleigh, the birthplace of Sir Walter Raleigh. The quirky thatched building has numerous nooks and crannies inside with a rear walled beer garden at the back. Four real ales and real cider are served to quench your thirst, with award-winning locally produced food served at meal times. The pub hosts an annual autumn beer festival plus monthly events of all sorts. A free car park can be found in Hayes Lane opposite the pub.
Q♿☀🍴▲♿(157)☀

Exbourne
Red Lion 🅛
High Street, EX20 3RY (200m N of jct with A3072)
SS602018
☎ (01837) 851551 ⊕ theredlionexbourne.co.uk
Dartmoor IPA, Legend; 1 changing beer (sourced regionally) 🅖
This friendly village local has a well deserved reputation for the quality and consistency of its ales and has been local CAMRA Pub of the Year several times in recent years. Casks are set on stillage at the end of the L-shaped bar and feature Legend from Dartmoor and other locally brewed ales. The pub does not serve food but customers can bring their own snacks or get a takeaway delivered. There is always good conversation to be enjoyed here.
Q♿☀P🚐(5A)☀🛜♪

Exeter
Bowling Green 🅛 ✅
29-30 Blackboy Road, EX4 6ST
☎ (01392) 490300
3 changing beers (sourced locally) 🅷
Originally called the Ropemakers, the Bowling Green is situated away from the city centre close to Exeter City Football Club at St James Park. It opens at noon on home match days. An extensive selection of reasonably priced pub food is served, including pizzas and gluten-free vegan and vegetarian options. Four real ales are available – three are rotating and supporting local breweries – along with changing bag in box ciders.
Q♿☀🍴♿≷(St James Park)♣♿🚐☀🛜

George's Meeting House 🅛 ✅
38 South Street, EX1 1ED (near bottom of South St)
☎ (01392) 454250
Greene King IPA, Abbot; Sharp's Doom Bar; 4 changing beers 🅷
This Wetherspoon opened in 2005 having been sympathetically converted from a Unitarian Chapel dating from 1760. Many of the original features remain unaltered; these include two upstairs galleries with seating, a pulpit and stained-glass windows. A range of national, regional and local real ales are served. Food is available throughout the day and evening. A newer extension with a real fire, which is at the rear of the main building, leads to an outdoor seating area on two levels.
Q♿☀🍴♿≷(Central)🚐🛜

Hour Glass Inn 🅛
21 Melbourne Street, EX2 4AU (300yds from Exeter Quayside)
☎ (01392) 258722 ⊕ hourglassexeter.co.uk
Exeter Lighterman, Avocet, 'fraid Not, Ferryman, Darkness; 1 changing beer (sourced locally) 🅷
Established in 1848, this traditional hostelry in the back streets of Exeter is in a hub of the local area, close to the Quay and about five minutes' walk from the main city centre. It is now operated by Exeter brewery and also offers two real keg ciders. The newly refurbished dining room is open and dinner is available Thursday, Friday and Saturday evenings, and lunch on Friday, Saturday and Sunday. Snacks and light meals are available at all other times. 🍴♿🚐☀🛜

Imperial 🅛 ✅
New North Road, EX4 4AH
☎ (01392) 434050
Greene King IPA, Abbot; 7 changing beers 🅷
This pub features a range of beers from local and national breweries. It was built in 1810 as a private house, converted to a hotel, and opened as a Wetherspoon pub

in 1996. It has an orangery, and a large beer garden. It is located close to the university. Regular beer and cider festivals are held, featuring local, national and international breweries. Food is served all day.
Q♨❀◐◑♿🚆(St David's) 🍎P🚌📶

Port Royal

Weirfield Path, Larkbeare Road, EX2 4DR
☎ (01392) 272360 🌐 theportroyal.co.uk
Exeter Ferryman; Powderkeg Speak Easy Pale Ale; 1 changing beer [H]
Friendly riverside pub with several areas, including a large restaurant and a function room, spread over a long narrow site offering splendid views of the water and the distant countryside. There is plenty of outside seating overlooking the river, perfect on a summer evening. Changing beers are likely to be from local breweries such as Exeter. There is a pool table in the first bar and a small car park at the rear. ♨❀◐◑♿♣P🚌🐾📶

Sawyer's Arms [L] ✔

121 Cowick Street, EX4 1JD (opp St Thomas church)
☎ (01392) 269520
Greene King IPA, Abbot; Sharp's Doom Bar; 5 changing beers (sourced nationally) [H]
This 1960s pub on the main street off St Thomas replaced an earlier pub at a different location. It is a Wetherspoon pub, following all conventions of the well-established chain. Beer festivals and meet the brewer events are held. Roomy, with good sized bar, it has plenty of tables and seating both inside and outside. Large televisions mostly show BBC News 24 on mute with subtitles.
Q♨❀◐◑♿🚆(St Thomas) 🚌📶

Ship Inn ✔

1-3 Martins Lane, EX1 1EY
☎ (01392) 272040
Exeter Avocet; Greene King IPA, Abbot; house beer (by Greene King); 2 changing beers (sourced regionally) [H]
A historic city centre pub situated along a narrow passage way between the High Street and Cathedral Green. It is one of the oldest pubs in Exeter and Sir Francis Drake used to visit. Four regular ales feature along with two guests, mostly local. The cider is Sandford Orchards Devon Red in keg. The pub offers good value food served all day, including a children's menu. Live entertainment features on Wednesdays, Fridays and Saturdays. ♨◐◑♿🚆(Central)🍎🚌🐾📶♫

Thatched House Inn 🏆 [L] ✔

Exwick Road, EX4 2BQ
☎ (01392) 272920 🌐 thatchedhouse.net
Greene King Abbot; house beer (by Greene King); 4 changing beers (sourced locally; often Hanlons) [H]
This thatched building dates from the 1600s and is a community establishment next to Exwick playing fields, opposite the Exeter College Sports Hub. It is close to the river and convenient for dog walkers, cyclists and sightseers. Up to six real ales and one real cider are usually available together with great value home-cooked food featuring local ingredients and producers. On-street parking is available nearby. ♨❀◐◑♣🍎🚌(E2)🐾📶

Topsham Brewery Taproom

Haven Road, EX2 8GR
☎ (01392) 275196
3 changing beers [G]
A historic stone building on the Haven Banks side of Exeter Quay, a popular visitor area outside the city centre. It has an outside garden seating area that attracts passers-by, and is often busy with families and walkers during the day. Inside, the brewery can be seen from the bar. There is regular live music or DJs in the evenings, and a contracted pizza van outside most days.
❀◐◑🚆(St Thomas) 🍎🐾

Exmouth

Bicton Inn [L]

5 Bicton Street, EX8 2RU
☎ (01395) 272589 🌐 bictoninn.co.uk
Dartmoor Jail Ale; Hanlons Citra IPA, Port Stout; 3 changing beers (sourced locally) [H]
A friendly and popular back-street local, offering good beer and chat. It has won local CAMRA Community Pub of the Year several times and has previously been branch Pub of the Year. Regular live music including a weekly folk night takes place, as well as a monthly quiz. The pub hosts an annual beer festival, usualy in late winter. Up to six real ales, including several LocAles, and two or three real ciders are normally on offer. ♨🚆♣🍎🚌(57)🐾📶♫

First & Last Inn [L]

10 Church Street, EX8 1PE (off B3178 Rolle St)
☎ (01395) 263275
Dartmoor Jail Ale; Otter Ale; Teignworthy Neap Tide; 2 changing beers (sourced locally; often Checkstone) [H]
Victorian pub near the town centre with a public car park opposite. A genuine free house, with three distinct areas and a courtyard patio with heated awnings. Checkstone brewery started here in 2016 and supplies the pub with changing ales from an increasing range. Changing real ciders are available, including their own Checkstone Cider on occasion. Games include pool and darts and there is a skittle alley. Televised sport is prominent and there is regular live music early on Sunday evenings.
❀♿🚆♣🍎🚌(57) 🐾📶♫

Grapevine [L]

2 Victoria Road, EX8 1DL
☎ (01395) 222208 🌐 thegrapevineexmouth.com
Crossed Anchors Bitter Exe, American Pale Ale; 3 changing beers (sourced locally; often Crossed Anchors) [H]
Situated in the centre of Exmouth, and home to Crossed Anchors brewery and Ruby Diner burgers, the Grapevine is a stylish Victorian building, with several distinct seating areas. There are six handpumps, 12 craft taps and bottle conditioned Crossed Anchor beers. Three ciders are available on keg along with some bag in box and bottled offerings. Bottled German and Belgian beers are also available. There is live music on the first Saturday of the month and live international rugby shown on the big screen. ♨❀◐◑♿🚆🍎🚌(57)🐾♫

GWRSA Railway Club [L]

3-5 Royal Avenue, EX8 1EN
☎ (01395) 274010 🌐 exmouthrailwayclub.com
Greene King Abbot; Hanlons Yellow Hammer; 2 changing beers [H]
A community focused club with several small outdoor seated areas and superb views of the Exe Estuary. This club has frequently been local CAMRA Club of the Year and in 2023 was the regional runner-up. It has four real ales on handpump, two of which are changing beers usually from local breweries. One real cider is available on keg and usually one bag in box. Traditional games are played, live music is usually on Saturday night and quiz nights every Thursday. Bar snacks are available. Open to the public, everyone is welcome.
♨❀◐♿🚆♣🍎🚌(57,157) 🐾📶♫

Holly Tree

161 Withycombe Village Road, EX8 3AN (leave A376 at Gipsy Lane lights; turn left at roundabout)

☎ (01395) 273740
Dartmoor Jail Ale; Otter Ale; 3 changing beers (sourced nationally) Ⓗ
A popular pub about one mile from the town centre, run by Nigel and family who have been there for 5 years. Ales are now predominately from Otter and Dartmoor, though guest beers may be from further afield. The real cider is Sandford Orchards Devon Red in keg. There are several rooms off the large open bar, one housing the pool table and dartboards. This vibrant pub supports four darts teams and two pool teams. Families are welcome until 7pm. ⛲☸♣Pᗕ(97)♨

Powder Monkey Ⓛ ✅
2-2A The Parade, EX8 1RJ
☎ (01395) 280090
Bays Devon Dumpling; Dartmoor Jail Ale; Greene King Abbot; Ruddles Best Bitter; Sharp's Doom Bar; 4 changing beers Ⓗ
A Wetherspoon pub named after Nancy Perriam, whose sewing skills earned her a berth in the navy where she also acted as a powder monkey. Nancy lived in nearby Tower Street. Powder monkey was a naval slang term for the boys and girls who filled shells and cartridges with gunpowder on board ships of war. The building was converted from local newspaper offices. The bar, wih its good selection of ales, is adjacent to the central seating areas, with a number of rooms off it.
Q⛲☸①ᕼ&⇌ᗕ(57) 🛜

Hennock

Palk Arms Ⓛ
Church Road, TQ13 9QB (take B3344 from A38 to Chudleigh Knighton; follow signs for Hennock)
☎ (01626) 836584 ⊕ thepalkarms.co.uk
Bays Devon Dumpling; Dartmoor Legend; Teignworthy Gun Dog; 1 changing beer (sourced locally; often Dartmoor, Otter, Teignworthy) Ⓗ
A prime example of a village pub, overlooking the Teign Valley. Supposedly haunted, this friendly free house enjoys stunning views over the countryside. Hearty home-cooked meals can be enjoyed by the comforting warmth of log-burning stoves. An in-house brewery is due to open in 2024. The pub is popular with cyclists and walkers as a base from which to explore Henock's mining heritage and the surrounding countryside. The red phonebox opposite houses the village's unique public library. Q⛲☸①ᕼ&ᐁ♣●Pᗕ♨🛜♪

Horsebridge

Royal Inn ★
PL19 8PJ (off the A384 Tavistock-Launceston road) SX401748
☎ (01822) 870214 ⊕ royalinn.co.uk
St Austell Proper Job; 4 changing beers (sourced nationally; often Otter, Salcombe, Timothy Taylor) Ⓖ
Originally built as a nunnery in 1437 by French Benedictine monks, and reported to have been visited by Charles I, the pub overlooks an old bridge on the River Tamar, connecting Devon to Cornwall. It features half-panelling, stone floors, log fires and traditional styling in the bar and lounge, with another larger room off the lounge. It has a terraced garden with sheltered seating. All the beers are served on gravity; the locally sourced food is recommended. Free Wi-Fi is provided.
Q☸①●Pᗕ(115) ♨🛜

Iddesleigh

Duke of York ★
EX19 8BG (off B3217, next to church) SS570083
☎ (01837) 810253 ⊕ dukeofyorkdevon.co.uk
Bays Topsail; Otter Bitter; 1 changing beer (sourced nationally) Ⓖ
A 15th-century traditional thatched village inn with old beams, inglenook fireplaces and an unfailingly friendly atmosphere. Real ales are dispensed on gravity, while cider comes from nearby Sam's. The pub is renowned for its generous portions of locally sourced, home-cooked food. Close to the Tarka Trail, River Torridge and Stafford Moor Fishery, there are seven en-suite rooms for visitors. A popular beer festival is held every August bank holiday weekend. Q⛲☸ᕼ①●&▲●ᗕ♨🛜

Ide

Poachers Inn Ⓛ
55 High Street, EX2 9RW (3 miles from M5 jct 31, via A30)
☎ (01392) 273847 ⊕ poachersinn.co.uk
Branscombe Branoc; Exeter Tomahawk; 3 changing beers (sourced locally) Ⓖ
Typical busy village pub, with a friendly atmosphere, serving a varied menu of home-made locally sourced produce, including excellent-value fish & chips to eat in or take away on Wednesday evenings. Dogs are welcome in the comfortably furnished bar, with old sofas, chairs and a big log fire in winter. There is also a large beer garden overlooking the glorious Devon countryside. The landlord is a keen rugby fan and games are shown on the television in the bar.
Q⛲☸ᕼ①●▲Pᗕ(360) ♨🛜

Ilfracombe

Hip@No.8 Ⓛ
8 St James Place, EX34 9BH
☎ (01271) 549651
Draught Bass; Greene King Abbot; 1 changing beer (sourced nationally) Ⓗ
This extensively modernised old Georgian house has a nautical theme, with the flooring a special feature. It shows the bay around Ilfracombe in pictorial form, with local landmarks and shipwrecks plotted, together with an impressive pub logo shown in an image of a compass. Outside there is a pleasant beer garden in front of the pub. A good selection of real ales, ciders and food offerings is available. The pub is only 50 yards from Ilfracombe bus terminus. ⛲☸①&▲●🍴ᗕ(21)♨🛜

Wellington Arms Ⓛ
66-67 High Street, EX34 9QE
☎ (01271) 862206
Butcombe Gold; Greene King Abbot; Sharp's Doom Bar Ⓗ
A friendly town local, originally two pubs and now a listed building. There are separate public and lounge bars and a games room. The cosy lounge retains its original beams and large open fire. TVs and music sound systems enable different channels to be shown, making the pub popular with sports enthusiasts. Up to five competitively priced ales are usually available. Regular live music sessions, quiz nights and beer festivals are held. No under-18s allowed. ☸▲♣ᗕ♨🛜♪

Instow

Quay Inn Ⓛ ✅
Marine Parade, EX39 4HY

☎ (01271) 860624 ⊕ thequayinninstow.co.uk
2 changing beers (sourced nationally) Ⓗ
Delightful contemporary riverfront bar that serves three nationally sourced beers, one of which is usually from a local brewery, and two ciders. There is a 20-seater function room and separate restaurant upstairs. Food is traditional pub fare, but with fresh fish a speciality. Sunday roast is popular all year round. A family and dog friendly pub that claims to be the first in the village to be Cask Marque accredited. ⏾❍⅊♿🐾🅿🚭🌝🛜

Kings Nympton

Grove Inn 🍷 Ⓛ

EX37 9ST (in centre of village) SS683194
☎ (01769) 580406 ⊕ thegroveinn.co.uk
Exmoor Ale; 2 changing beers (sourced regionally) Ⓗ
Thatched, Grade II-listed 17th-century inn, with low beams, flagstoned floors, an open fire in winter, and a pretty enclosed terrace to enjoy in summer. A recent local CAMRA Pub of the Year and Cider Pub of the Year, it usually has three real ales available, together with a good range of ciders. The pub also has a reputation for its excellent home-cooked food, which can be enjoyed in the dining area, adjacent to the bar.
Q⏾❍⅊♣🅿🌝🛜

Kingsbridge

Hermitage Inn

8 Mill Street, TQ7 1ED
☎ (01548) 853234 ⊕ the-hermitage-inn.edan.io
3 changing beers (sourced locally; often Summerskills, Teignworthy) Ⓗ
Situated in the centre of town, two minutes walk from the bus station, this is an extremely friendly pub, popular with both the locals of Kingsbridge and visitors. The pub boasts an eclectic range of local beers, normally two or three at any given time. It has log fires, a traditional interior and an enclosed, pleasant beer garden to the rear. ⏾🌝♿♣🅿🚭🛜♪

Kingskerswell

Lord Nelson

47 Fore Street, TQ12 5JB
☎ (01803) 875628
3 changing beers (sourced nationally; often Exmoor, St Austell) Ⓗ
Known colloquially as the Nellie, this is a cosy two-bar pub in the centre of the village. The lounge bar has upholstered high back bench settle seating, tables, a fireplace and a snug, the Admirals Cabin. The other bar has two open stone fireplaces and alcove seating. The bar walls are adorned with Trafalgar memorabilia, horse brasses and 1960s-era photographs of the village. The garden has views across the valley. Guest beers supplement the regular offerings. ⏾🌝♣🚭🌝🛜♪

Lee

Grampus Inn Ⓛ

EX34 8LR (at end of lane; keep left of the post office) SS483463
☎ (01271) 862906 ⊕ thegrampusinn.co.uk
Grampus Bitter, Ale Ⓗ
With parts dating back to the 14th century, a cosy interior and an attractive garden with outdoor table tennis table, this dog-friendly pub is particularly popular with tourists, especially walkers. Three real ales from West Country breweries are kept, including those from its own onsite brewery, together with a real cider, usually from

Sandford Orchards, and Westons Country Perry. Good, locally sourced home-made food is served daily. The landlord, an accomplished fiddle player, encourages local musicians in open mike session on Friday evenings. Winter hours may vary. Q⏾🌝❍♿🅰♣🅿🚭🌝🛜♪

Lewdown

Blue Lion Inn Ⓛ

EX20 4DL
☎ (01566) 783238
Dartmoor IPA, Jail Ale; 2 changing beers (sourced regionally) Ⓗ
Family-owned and run roadside inn, set on the old, now bypassed A30 between Okehampton and Launceston. Originally a 17th-century farmhouse on the Lewtrenchard Estate, the property was extended in the early 1900s. Now home to numerous local groups, several pub teams are also supported. Although predominantly wet sales oriented, good-value food is also served Tuesday to Saturday in the evenings. There are two well-appointed rooms offering accommodation.
⏾🌝🛏❍♿♣🅿🚭🌝🛜♪

Littlehempston

Tally Ho Ⓛ

TQ9 6LY SX813627
☎ (01803) 862316 ⊕ tallyhoinn.co.uk
Dartmoor Legend; 2 changing beers (sourced locally; often Exmoor) Ⓗ
Located in Littlehempston, nestled in rolling hills and only five minutes from Totnes, this 14th-century pub has been known as the Tally Ho since 1957. Becoming South Devon's first community pub in 2014, with the freehold acquired by the current licensees Kelly and Mike Joiner in 2018, they continue to deliver superb real ales. The olde-worlde interior has black timber beams, stone walls and open fires. It's been in the Good Beer Guide since 2016 and won local CAMRA Pub of the Year in 2022. There is a beer garden and car park to the rear.
Q⏾🌝❍♿♣🅿🚌(X64,177) 🌝🛜♪

Meeth

Bull & Dragon Ⓛ

EX20 3EP (on A386)
☎ (01837) 811742 ⊕ thebullanddragon-meeth.business.site
3 changing beers (sourced regionally) Ⓗ
This friendly traditional thatched pub has been an inn since around 1490 and sits at the end of the Tarka Trail cycling route, on the A386 between Torrington and Hatherleigh. There is a lounge area with a piano which hosts a monthly singalong, and regular quiz nights are held. Good local homemade food adds to the offering. The garden and car park are at the front of the pub. Local CAMRA Cider Pub of the Year 2023.
Q⏾🌝❍♣🅿🚭🌝🛜♪

Musbury

Hind Ⓛ

The Street, EX13 8AU
☎ (01297) 553553 ⊕ thehindmusbury.co.uk
3 changing beers Ⓗ
The Hind is a free house situated on the crossroads of the A358, on The Street, in the village of Musbury, three miles south of Axminster. One real cider usually available in keg. There is a public bar, and a lounge/restaurant, where good-value home-cooked food is available lunchtimes and evenings (not Mon-Wed or Sun eve). On Saturday mornings breakfast is available. There is a front

courtyard with stunning views over the Axe Valley. A good-sized function room/skittle alley has recently opened. Q🏠🍴🛏♿♣●P🚲(885)🛜♪

Newton Abbot

Dartmouth Inn
63 East Street, TQ12 2JP
☎ (01626) 202309
Dartmoor Legend, Jail Ale; 1 changing beer (sourced locally; often Exeter, Teignworthy) 🅗
Historic pub dating from 1674, when it was known as the Great Dane and acted as a recruitment centre for men wanting to join the Newfoundland fishing fleets. The narrow entrance belies the depth of this establishment which has split-level separate drinking areas and two fireplaces, all surrounded by solid stone walls with timber beams and columns. There are some sofas and comfy seating options opposite the bar.
Q🏠🍴♿≢♣P🚲🐾🛜♪

Maltings Taphouse & Bottle Shop
Tuckers Maltings, Teign Road, TQ12 4AA (500yds from Newton Abbot railway station)
☎ (01626) 334734 ⊕ themaltingstaphouse.co.uk
House beer (by Teignworthy); 2 changing beers (sourced nationally) 🅗
A spacious no-frills pub, just a short walk from Newton Abbot railway station and the Templer Way footpath and cycle route. Established in 2016 it occupies part of the old maltings building. The furniture in the large ground floor bar is wooden tables and benches which add to the rustic simplicity. Upstairs are an outside area and a function room. Three handpumps dispense real ale, often from the neighbouring Teignworthy brewery. Keg beers, real cider and bottled beers also available.
Q🍴♿≢●🚲(12)🐾🛜♪

Newton Poppleford

Cannon Inn
High Street, EX10 0DW
☎ (01395) 568266 ⊕ cannoninn.co.uk
2 changing beers (sourced nationally) 🅖
Cheery, welcoming, two-bar pub with tables for dining in the lounge bar and restaurant area. Real ales are served by gravity from stillage behind the bar. This is a friendly locals' pub with busy passing trade. Good-value home-cooked food comprising of traditional pub favourites is served lunchtimes and evenings. Well-behaved dogs are allowed. There are two large gardens and a skittle alley. This is the only pub in the village and a real community hub. 🏠🍴♿♣▲●P🚲(52,157)🐾🛜♪

Newton St Cyres

Beer Engine 🅛
EX5 5AX (beside railway station, N of A377)
☎ (01392) 851282 ⊕ thebeerengine.co.uk
Beer Engine Rail Ale, Piston Bitter; 3 changing beers 🅗
Victorian pub, built in 1850 on the Exeter to Barnstaple Tarka Line. A destination pub for its home-cooked food which is made with locally sourced produce and served lunchtimes and evenings. Part of the downstairs area has been converted into a second bar to accommodate sports fans and to serve those in the large, covered area between the pub and the railway line. The downstairs bar also allows views of the brewery. The pub brews its own ales and five are usually available. Real cider from Sandford Orchards is available in keg and bottles.
Q🏠🍴♿≢●🐾

North Tawton

Railway Inn 🅛
Whiddon Down Road, EX20 2BE (1 mile S of town, just off A3124, next to the old North Tawton railway station) SS666000
☎ (01837) 82789 ⊕ therailwaynorthtawton.co.uk
Teignworthy Reel Ale; 1 changing beer (sourced regionally) 🅗
Good value and a warm welcome always await you at this friendly Devon local. Long running Guide entry and frequent local CAMRA Pub of the Year finalist. Adjacent to the former North Tawton railway station, there are numerous old railway photos on the walls. Reel Ale from Teignworthy is normally joined by a guest ale from one of the other West Country breweries, together with a real cider in summer. The dining room is popular in the evening (no food Thu), also Sunday lunchtimes. Guide dogs only. Q🏠🍴♿♣●P🚲(51)🛜

Ottery St Mary

Volunteer Inn
Broad Street, EX11 1BZ
☎ (01404) 814060 ⊕ volunteerinnottery.co.uk
Otter Bitter; 3 changing beers (sourced regionally) 🅖
The pub has been part of Ottery St Mary's history since 1810, when it opened as a dwelling, hostelry and recruitment centre for the Napoleonic Wars. In the centre of the town, it is deservedly popular. The front bar has been kept traditional and the rear bar is more modern. All real ales, mainly sourced from local breweries, are delivered by gravity. Real cider from Sandford Orchards is available. Food is served seven days a week, including traditional Sunday roast, in the refurbished and extended restaurant. 🏠🍴♿♣●🚲(4)🐾🛜♪

Paignton

Henry's Bar 🅛 ✅
53 Torbay Road, TQ4 6AJ
☎ (01803) 551190 ⊕ henrysbarpaignton.co.uk
Sharp's Doom Bar; 2 changing beers (sourced nationally; often Dartmoor, Exmoor, Teignworthy) 🅗
This long-established warm and welcoming town-centre pub is situated on the main street of Paignton, close to local transport links, and is renowned for its real ale and cider. It features a long bar with four handpumps serving local/national ales, plus a fifth dedicated to traditional cider. There are two regular beers, two guest ales, plus various bottles/polyboxes of cider. Home-cooked food is served daily with a renowned roast on Sundays. Families are welcome until 10pm. The pub is dog-friendly and offers free Wi-Fi. 🏠🍴≢●🐾🛜

Paignton Conservative Club
34 Palace Avenue, TQ3 3HB
☎ (01803) 551065
Dartmoor Jail Ale; 2 changing beers (often Exmoor, Salcombe, Skinner's (Goodh)) 🅗
Established as a private members club in 1885, this historic building features a stone-carved entrance. On the bar, three handpumps serve real ales from local and national brewers with a long reputation of consistent quality. Downstairs there's a spacious function room where many events such as bingo, cabaret and quiz nights take place. Upstairs is another function room plus a snooker hall with two tables. Q🏠♿≢♣P🚲🛜♪

Torbay Inn ✅
34 Fisher Street, TQ4 5ER (300yds from The Big Tree bus stop)
☎ (01803) 392729

St Austell Tribute; Sharp's Sea Fury; Wye Valley HPA; 1 changing beer (often St Austell) ⊞
Paignton's oldest inn has an old-fashioned layout featuring separate lounge and public bars boasting four handpumps each, all serving national and local real ale. It dates back to the early 1600s when the sea was on its doorstep and the fish market opposite, hence the address of Fisher Street. Time is called via a ship's bell recovered from a wreck by a local diver. The Roundhead General Fairfax stayed here prior to a Civil War battle in Exeter. Q⍟⏚⊛&⇌♣P🚃(12,120)❀❀?♪

Parkham

Bell Inn ⓛ ✅
Rectory Lane, EX39 5PL (½ mile S of the A39 at Horns Cross; on the opp corner to the village primary school) SS387212
☎ (01237) 451201 ⊕ thebellinnparkham.co.uk
3 changing beers (sourced regionally) ⊞
Sympathetically restored after a serious fire in 2017, this 13th-century thatched inn, with its cob walls, oak beams and woodburner fires, has retained all of its olde-worlde charm. Three and sometimes four changing real ales are available, with usually at least one of these coming from a local brewery. Good home-cooked food is served lunchtimes and evenings Thursday to Saturday, either in the bar or the adjacent raised restaurant area, while the Sunday roast is also popular.
Q⍟⊛⊯⏶⏚♣P🚃(372) ❀?

Peter Tavy

Peter Tavy Inn
Lane Head, PL19 9NN
☎ (01822) 810348 ⊕ petertavyinn.co.uk
Dartmoor IPA, Jail Ale; 3 changing beers (sourced locally; often Tavistock) ⊞
In a quiet village on the edge of Dartmoor, this inn has a small central bar serving a varying range up to five local beers including Dartmoor and Tavistock ales. It also has two larger rooms, traditionally attired throughout, with slate, beams and log burners. A patio and hidden garden are added attractions. The pub is renowned for its food, but drinkers are made welcome. The inn is situated on the National Cycle Route 27 and is open all day in spring and summer. Q⍟⊛⊯⏶A♣P🚃(118,122)❀?

Plymouth

Artillery Arms ⓛ
6 Pound Street, Stonehouse, PL1 3RH (behind Stonehouse Barracks and Millbay Docks)
☎ (01752) 262515
Draught Bass; 1 changing beer (sourced locally; often Dartmoor, South Hams, Summerskills) ⊞
Cracking backstreet local tucked away in the old quarter of Stonehouse, close to the magnificent Grade I-listed Royal William Yard and reflecting the area's military connections. One South West guest beer from breweries such as Dartmoor, South Hams and Summerskills, and at least one varying real cider or perry are normally available and supplement the Draught Bass. An out of season beach party takes place on the last weekend of February, and charity monkey racing also features.
⊛⏶🚃(34) ❀?♪

Bread & Roses ⓛ
62 Ebrington Street, City Centre, PL4 9AF
☎ (01752) 659861 ⊕ breadandrosesplymouth.co.uk
Exeter Avocet; 2 changing beers (sourced regionally; often Hanlons, Salcombe, Summerskills) ⊞

This friendly, sympathetically restored late-Victorian pub is popular with university staff, but also has a mixed clientele. Up to three live beers are available, which are organic or Fairtrade wherever possible, just like the snacks. The beers are selected from local and regional breweries, including small batch and speciality beers unusual for the area. The pub promotes artistic and musical creativity, and is a vibrant music hub for local talent. ⊛⏶🚃(23,24)❀❀?♪

Clifton Inn ⓛ
35 Clifton Street, Greenbank, PL4 8JB
☎ 07831 165938
Dartmoor Jail Ale; 3 changing beers (sourced regionally; often Sharp's, St Austell) ⊞
This is a spacious back-street local which is not far from the city centre. Up to four ales may be available, along with at least one real cider dispensed from the bank of five handpumps. Pool and dart teams play here regularly, while live televised sport provides sporting entertainment for the less energetic, with a very large projection TV screen. A large heated patio area is provided for those who smoke. ⍟⊛⇌♣⏶🚃❀?♪

Dolphin Hotel ⓛ ✅
14 The Barbican, PL1 2LS
☎ (01752) 660876
Dartmoor Jail Ale; Draught Bass; St Austell Proper Job; Sharp's Atlantic, Doom Bar; Timothy Taylor Landlord; 2 changing beers (sourced regionally; often Otter, Sharp's, St Austell) Ⓖ
A Plymouth institution, this unpretentious hostelry is steeped in history. Up to eight ales are all dispensed by gravity from the cask. Full of character, this charming pub has tiled floors, well-used wooden benches and a traditional open fire, all creating the perfect ambience. The walls are adorned with paintings by local artist, the late Beryl Cook, who painted many of the characters she encountered in the Dolphin. Local CAMRA City Pub of the Year 2022. ⏶🚃(25)❀

Duchy of Cornwall ⓛ
14 Anstis Place, Stonehouse, PL1 5JT
☎ (01752) 954045
1 changing beer (sourced locally; often Dartmoor, Salcombe, Summerskills) ⊞
Michelle and Rob welcome you to this traditional backstreet pub with modern décor that has truly bounced back. This vibrant establishment champions the local community and hosts regular live music along with pool and darts teams. One rotating cask ale, kept in excellent condition, is available to enjoy. Beers are mainly sourced from Devon breweries, although some national favourites also appear. Look out for offerings from Bays, Dartmoor, Salcombe and Plymouth-based brewery Summerskills. ♣🚃❀♪

Fawn Private Members Club ⓛ
39 Prospect Street, Greenbank, PL4 8NY
☎ (01752) 226385
Bays Topsail; Dartmoor Legend; 3 changing beers (sourced regionally; often Sharp's, St Austell, Teignworthy) ⊞
This mid-19th century establishment was originally the Fawn Inn/Hotel, prior to converting to a club. CAMRA members are welcome with a valid membership card; regular visitors will be required to join. Up to four guest ales from the local area are generally served, as well as a rotating range of local cider from Countryman. The club is popular for rugby and other televised sports, and supports multiple dart and euchre teams. Local CAMRA Club of the Year 2024. ⇌♣⏶🚃❀♪

Ferry House Inn L ✓

888 Wolseley Road, Saltash Passage, PL5 1LA
☎ (01752) 361063 ⊕ ferryhouseinn.com
Dartmoor IPA, Legend, Jail Ale Ⓗ
A warm welcome awaits you and your dog from the
landlord and locals at this picturesque riverside pub on
the River Tamar. Three regular West Country ales are
served, as well as good home-cooked food. A decking
area on the edge of the river gives spectacular views of
both road bridge and Brunel's iconic 1859 railway bridge.
Photos, some dating back to the turn of the 20th century,
adorn the walls. Quiz night is Sunday.
⊅❀✿◑&➓♖(13) ✿♠

Fisherman's Arms L

31 Lambhay Street, Barbican, PL1 2NN
☎ (01752) 268243 ⊕ fishermansarms.co.uk
**House beer (by Summerskills); 2 changing beers
(sourced regionally; often Dartmoor, Salcombe, South
Hams)** Ⓗ
Owner Donna turned this former St Austell pub back into
a free house serving great food back in 2014. The house
beer is brewed by Summerskills and is supplemented
with two ales sourced from Devon and Cornwall. The
interior is cosy and the décor is regularly updated.
Traditional pub grub at affordable prices is supplemented
by specials. Close to the Royal Citadel and the Barbican,
first timers should turn right on exiting the pub, and head
down the steps towards the Barbican to save time.
⊅◑♣➓♖(25) ✿♠♪

Fortescue Hotel ♥ L ✓

37 Mutley Plain, PL4 6JQ
☎ (01752) 660673
**Bays Devon Dumpling; Dartmoor Legend; Exeter
County Best; Salcombe Lifesaver; South Hams
Eddystone; 5 changing beers (sourced nationally;
often Exeter, Salcombe, Summerskills)** Ⓗ
This multi award-winning and lively local is frequented
by a broad section of the community, and conversation
flourishes. Up to eight live beers are usually available on
tap including four or five beers from the local area, and
up to eight real ciders. Live evening entertainment takes
place regularly, and a quiz is held on Sunday evenings.
The patio beer garden draws crowds in the summer and
is heated in winter. Terrestrial televised sport is also
shown. Local CAMRA City Pub of the Year 2024.
⊅❀✿➣♣♖➓✿♠♪

Indian Inn

82 Devonport Road, Stoke, PL3 4DF
☎ (01752) 556438
**2 changing beers (sourced locally; often
Summerskills)** Ⓗ
A small cosy family-run one-bar pub in the Stoke Village
area of Plymouth, with a large welcome. The current
licensees have presided over this pub for over 30 years.
Two varying live beers are available, mostly from local
Plymouth brewer Summerskills. There are lots of
Indigenous American ornaments featuring in the pub.
Darts matches take place most weekday evenings, and
there is a real fire in winter with comfortable armchairs
from which to enjoy it. The pub is dog-friendly.
Q❀➣(Devonport)♣➓(34) ✿

Lounge

7 Stopford Place, Devonport, PL1 4QT
☎ (01752) 561330
**Draught Bass; 2 changing beers (sourced regionally;
often Otter)** Ⓗ
Located in a quiet residential area, this street-corner local
is situated near to Devonport Park, and offers a warm
welcome. The wood-panelled bar is comfortable and

relaxing, although may be busy at times with Plymouth
Albion RFC's ground nearby. 'One weaker, one stronger'
than the regular Bass is the rule for guest ales, with
lighter and darker brews alternating. A secluded
garden at the front offers a retreat for smokers. Good
value food is also available daily.
Q⊅❀✿◑➣(Devonport)♣●➓♖(34,36)✿♠♪

Mannamead L ✓

61 Mutley Plain, PL4 6JH
☎ (01752) 825610
**Dartmoor Jail Ale; Greene King Abbot; Ruddles Best
Bitter; Sharp's Doom Bar; changing beers (sourced
nationally; often Bays, South Hams, Summerskills)** Ⓗ
This typical Wetherspoon establishment was converted
from a former NatWest bank in 2002. A wide range of
ales from near and far can be found, with at least two
local brews usually on the pumps. There is also a small
range of real cider and perry. Beer and cider festivals
take place several times a year. The weekly quiz is held
on Wednesday at 8pm and games night on Sundays.
Local CAMRA City Pub of the Year runner-up in 2024.
⊅❀◑&➣♣➓♖♠

Prince Maurice L

3 Church Hill, Eggbuckland, PL6 5RJ
☎ (01752) 658388
**Dartmoor Jail Ale; St Austell Tribute, Proper Job, Hicks;
South Hams Sherman; 2 changing beers (sourced
locally; often Hanlons, Summerskills, Teignworthy)** Ⓗ
There is very much a village feel to this four-times local
CAMRA Pub of the Year, which sits between the church
and village green. The five regular ales are
supplemented by a changing guest ale. It is named after
the Royalist General, the King's nephew, who had his
headquarters nearby during the siege of Plymouth in the
Civil War. Two log fires keep you warm in winter, adding
to the ambience. No food at weekends.
Q⊅❀✿◑♣●➓♖(60,61)✿♠♪

Providence L

20 Providence Street, Greenbank, PL4 8JQ
☎ (01752) 946251
**3 changing beers (sourced regionally; often
Bridgetown, Holsworthy Ales, Summerskills)** Ⓗ
This welcoming hostelry, tucked-away within the
backstreet labyrinth of Greenbank, is well worth seeking
out. One of the smallest pubs in Plymouth, what it lacks
in size it makes up for in atmosphere and character. The
interior is smart but comfortable and the real fire in
winter is wonderful. Three competitively priced live
beers, from a range of breweries, are generally available
as are two or three real ciders. There are no fruit
machines here; the sound is generated by conversation.
Q➣♣➓♖➓♠

Queen's Arms

55 Southside Street, Barbican, PL1 2LA
☎ (01752) 662915
**Dartmoor Jail Ale; Otter Amber; St Austell Proper Job;
1 changing beer (often Otter, St Austell, Timothy
Taylor)** Ⓗ
A public house has stood on this site in Southside Street
since the mid-19th century. The current building dates
from the mid-1960s after the area was blitzed in 1941. It
is a traditional pub and tends to attract older customers.
Up to four live beers are usually available. The Otter
Amber may alternate with Otter Ale, as may the Proper
Job and Tribute. The walls are adorned with pictures of
monarchs, mostly queens obviously. Q⊅♣➓(25)✿♪

Roam Brewery Tap L

New Victoria House, Western Park Road, Peverell, PL3 4NU
☎ (01752) 251059 ⊕ roambrewco.uk
Roam Tavy IPA; 2 changing beers (sourced locally; often Roam) ⊞
Situated in the former New Victoria Brewery Company premises, the taproom has a light and airy feel, with two large tinted windows allowing the sunshine to flood in. One live beer from the range will usually be available, supplementing the seven craft beers also on tap, including guest beers. Third-pint tapas is also available. As well as the brewery itself, there is an on-site brewery shop and bakery serving pastries and pizzas when the tap is open. ⏱🏵️🌶️🍽️♿️🅿️🚌(35,35A)🌺

Tamar L

1-7 Morshead Road, Crownhill, PL6 5AD
☎ (01752) 771445
Greene King IPA, Abbot; 2 changing beers (sourced nationally; often Dartmoor, Otter, Salcombe) ⊞
Popular pub in the Crownhill area of the city, serving up to four live beers. As well as some national favourites, a good range of guest ales from Devon and beyond appear regularly. Real cider is from Sandford Orchards range. Live entertainment takes place weekly. Open for breakfast, food is served all day until 9pm (8pm on Sun). Pool and darts are played, with Sky Sports and TNT Sport also shown. The nearby car park is Pay & Display.
⏱🏵️🌶️🍽️♿️🍺🅿️🚌🌺🛜♪

Vessel Beer Shop

184 Exeter Street, St Jude's, PL4 0NQ
☎ 07796 667449 ⊕ vesselbeer.co.uk
Changing beers (sourced nationally)
An independent bar and bottle shop, located a few minutes' walk from Plymouth city centre and opposite St Judes Retail Park. It stocks over 300 different beers from some of the best breweries in Britain and around the world. Bottle- and cask-conditioned live beers are sold with some craft beer on draught. Regular events include Meet the Brewer or Food Producers; and beer tastings and beer styles. See social media for up-to-date activities. Q⏱🏵️🚌

Plympton

London Inn L ✅

8 Church Road, Plympton St Maurice, PL7 1NH
☎ (01752) 343322 ⊕ londoninnpub.co.uk
Draught Bass; changing beers (sourced regionally; often Bays, Dartmoor, South Hams) ⊞
This friendly 16th-century pub, situated next to the church, is the epitome of a typical village inn. The pub serves up to eight live beers, supplemented by several real ciders. The cosy lounge bar is adorned with a large collection of Royal Naval memorabilia, while the public bar boasts a pool table, dartboard and TVs for sports enthusiasts. Regular beer festivals are held. The pub is allegedly haunted, by Captain Hinds. Dogs welcome.
Q⏱🏵️🌶️🍽️🅿️🚌🌺🛜♪

Union Inn L

17 Underwood Road, Underwood, PL7 1SY
☎ (01752) 336756
4 changing beers (sourced regionally; often Salcombe, South Hams, Teignmouth) ⊞
A warm welcome is assured at this traditional, cosy, early 19th-century hostelry. The landlord of this family-run community pub is a beer hunter, sourcing changing brews to charm his regulars' palates, and create a year-round beer festival. The four beers on offer are sourced

regionally, but could be from almost anywhere. It is the same with the cider selection which is also sourced from far and wide. Q⏱🏵️🌶️🍽️🅿️🚌(21,21A)🌺🛜♪

Postbridge

Warren House Inn L

PL20 6TA (on the B3212 between Postbridge and Bennett's Cross) SX674809
☎ (01822) 880208 ⊕ warrenhouseinn.co.uk
Otter Ale; 2 changing beers (sourced regionally; often Exeter, Hanlons, Summerskills) ⊞
Isolated and exposed at 1,425 feet above sea level, this is one of England's highest pubs. Up to three varying guest beers, mainly sourced from the West Country, are stocked. The characterful main bar boasts two log fires – one never goes out! Excellent-value home-made food includes the famous rabbit pie, local lamb and delicious puddings with clotted cream. There is a large family room, and tables outside give breathtaking views over the moors. Open all day in summer. Q⏱🏵️🌶️🍽️⛺🅿️🌺

St Giles on the Heath

Pint & Post L

PL15 9SA (just off main road through village, on opp side of road to village shop)
☎ (01566) 779933
2 changing beers (sourced locally; often Dartmoor) ⊞
This thatched village local, was once two cottages, then a pub and post office, hence the name. A friendly family-run pub close to the Cornish border, offering good home-cooked food, including takeaways, and a regular Wednesday quiz night. Legend from Dartmoor is one of the two well-kept ales, joined by a locally sourced guest beer. See their Facebook page for extra opening hours. Dog friendly throughout the pub.
Q⏱🏵️🌶️♿️⛺🌶️🅿️🌺🛜♪

Salcombe

King's Arms

18-20 Fore Street, TQ8 8BU
☎ (01548) 842202 ⊕ boatswainsattheka.com
Salcombe Gold, Lifesaver; Sharp's Doom Bar ⊞
A town-centre pub with a main bar that maintains a traditional feel about it. The Milton family who run it operate a seafood restaurant and wine merchant in Salcombe and previously ran an Ei Publican Partnerships site in the town for many years. A recent refurbishment features a revamped bar and terrace and a new kitchen. The upstairs restaurant has a terrace and offers locally sourced seafood, while the downstairs restaurant and bar focus on traditional pub classics.
⏱🏵️🌶️🌶️🅿️🚌(606)🌺🛜♪

Sandford

Lamb Inn

The Square, EX17 4LW
☎ (01363) 773676 ⊕ lambinnsandford.co.uk
Powderkeg Speak Easy Transatlantic Pale Ale; 2 changing beers (sourced locally; often Dartmoor, Powderkeg, Teignworthy) ⊞
A 16th-century coaching house with open fires and comfy sofas, this busy free house in the village centre offers a warm, welcoming atmosphere and is well supported by locals and visitors alike. Ales are generally sourced from the South West and real ciders from Sandford Orchards. There is a large tiered garden, seven B&B rooms, and a skittle alley also used as a cinema and for live music and events. The short, changing menu

features local and fresh produce and is popular – book ahead. Hours extend in summer and school holidays.
Q⮾☕♿◗①♿♣⊕P🖵(369)☀🛜♪

Shebbear

Devil's Stone Inn 🄻

EX21 5RU (in village square opp church) SS438094
☎ (01409) 281210
Dartmoor Jail Ale; Otter Amber; St Austell Tribute; 1 changing beer (sourced regionally) 🄷
Allegedly haunted, this 17th-century former coaching inn at the heart of the village is warm, cosy venue with wood beams, flagstone floors and open fireplaces. The single bar has four handpumps serving three regular ales and a guest. The new owners have been gradually increasing the range of food which now includes evenings and Saturday breakfast, locally sourced where possible. It has a large garden, games room and separate dining room. In the church opposite you will find the Devil's Stone that is turned every year on 5th November to ward off evil spirits. Q⮾☕♿◗①♣P🖵(72)☀🛜♪

Sidmouth

Anchor Inn

Old Fore Street, EX10 8LP
☎ (01395) 514129 ⊕ theanchorinn-sidmouth.co.uk
St Austell Tribute, Proper Job; Sharp's Doom Bar; 1 changing beer (sourced locally)
Large welcoming pub, situated just off the Esplanade, with a good ambience and friendly helpful staff. Popular with tourists and locals alike, it has seating outside, and a garden at the rear. It gets especially busy during Sidmouth Folk Week when the garden and car park are given over to events. Three regular ales are usually on tap with a guest added in summer. Good-value home-cooked food is served. Dogs are welcome outside but not inside. ⮾☕◗①♿♣P🖵🛜♪

Swan Inn ✅

37 York Street, EX10 8BY
☎ (01395) 512849 ⊕ swaninnsidmouth.co.uk
3 changing beers (sourced nationally) 🄷
A traditional and quiet back-street inn, established around 1770, that lies just off the centre of this picturesque town, a short walk from the seafront. An old-style wood-paneled bar with an open fire attracts a strong local trade, and leads to a dedicated dining area serving good food. Three changing beers are normally available. Dogs, but not children, are welcome indoors. Hosts the King of Chit – a traditional competition – and the Black Rod fishing contest. Q☕◗①♿♣🖵(52,157)☀🛜

South Zeal

King's Arms 🄻

EX20 2JP (centre of village) SX649936
☎ (01837) 840300 ⊕ thekingsarmssouthzeal.com
Dartmoor IPA, Legend; 1 changing beer (sourced regionally) 🄷
Thatched 14th-century village local, which is not only at the hub of the community, but also attracts many visitors exploring the area. Well-behaved dogs are made particularly welcome here. The regular Dartmoor beers are accompanied by a changing guest ale and locally made cider during summer months. Good food is served lunchtimes and evenings every day. Regular live music sessions are held throughout the year and the pub plays a central role during the Dartmoor Folk Festival in August.
Q⮾☕◗①♿♣P🖵☀🛜♪

Spreyton

Tom Cobley Tavern 🄻

EX17 5AL (off A3124 in village) SX6986096761
☎ (01647) 231314 ⊕ tomcobleytavern.co.uk
Clearwater Eric's ESB; Utopian Bow 🄷**; 6 changing beers (sourced regionally; often Parkway)** 🄷/🄶
Built in the 16th century and named after a local folklore figure, the Tom Cobley won National Cider Pub of the Year in 2023. The bar has an open fire and at the rear is a restaurant and garden. Four ales are stocked in winter and up to 10 in summer, with a dark beer always available. Fifteen or more real ciders are served from the cellar. It's the only pub in the UK to win both National Pub of the Year (in 2006) and Cider Pub of the Year, a truly unique achievement. Q⮾☕♿◗①♣⊕P☀🛜

Stoke Canon

Stoke Canon Inn

High Street, EX5 4AR (on A396 between Exeter and Tiverton)
☎ (01392) 840063 ⊕ stokecanoninn.com
St Austell Tribute; 3 changing beers (sourced nationally) 🄷
The Stoke Canon Inn is a community owned and run pub, saved from extinction by a dedicated team of volunteers from the village and surrounding area. It offers a spacious beer garden for the warmer weather, and a woodburner for the winter months. One real cider is usually available. Good-quality home-cooked food is served. Live events are featured (check website for details). Opening hours may vary. The pub was awarded the Queen's Award for Voluntary Service in 2020.
⮾☕◗①♿♣⊕P🖵(55,355)☀🛜♪

Stoke Fleming

Green Dragon

Church Road, TQ6 0PX (opp village church)
☎ (01803) 770238
House beer (by Otter); 2 changing beers (sourced locally) 🄷
Conveniently positioned on both a cross-roads and the South West Coastal Path, with Blackpool Sands half a mile away, this quintessential village pub, a focus for the village, features a large log-burning open fire. The background music is subdued and there are no gaming machines. Local legend suggests there is a tunnel underneath the floor to the nearby beach and, some say, a ghost. The extensive garden has benefited from a recent makeover and now has an outside bar.
⮾☕◗①♣P🖵(93)☀🛜♪

Tavistock

Queen's Head Hotel 🄻 ✅

80 West Street, PL19 8AQ
☎ (01822) 612455
Dartmoor Jail Ale; Greene King Abbot; Ruddles Best Bitter; Sharp's Doom Bar; changing beers (sourced nationally; often Dartmoor, Roam, Summerskills) 🄷
The oldest licensed premises in Tavistock, the Queen's Head was a formerly an 18th-century coaching inn with extensive stabling and yards, situated on one of Tavistock's main thoroughfares. Latterly Brown's Hotel, it was acquired by JDW in 2015 as one of their growing number of hotels, and reverted to its former name. The usual Wetherspoon range of food and drink is served. Several beer and cider festivals are held, including a Devon real ale festival. ⮾☕♿◗①♿♣⊕🖵🛜

Teignmouth

Blue Anchor Inn L
Teign Street, TQ14 8EG
☎ (01626) 772741
6 changing beers (sourced regionally; often Exeter, Palmers, Teignmouth) ⊞
Superb free house and one of the best for many a mile with a range of constantly changing real ales both local and from much further afield and often including something dark. The one bar can become crowded, especially during international rugby matches. The excellent outside areas, served from a hatch in summer, include sheltered areas for non-smokers. One of only a few pubs with a VR postbox outside. Buses 2 and 22 pass nearby. ❀&≠🚲(2,22)♣ ♫

Tiverton

White Ball Inn ✅
8 Bridge Street, EX16 5LY
☎ (01884) 251525
Bays Devon Dumpling; Greene King Abbot; Ruddles Best Bitter; Sharp's Doom Bar; 6 changing beers (sourced regionally) ⊞
Former coaching inn, situated just off the town centre, next to the Exe Bridge. Built around 1823, it became a Wetherspoon in 1998. It was restyled in 2019 to include upstairs toilets and a downstairs extension with doors to the large rear seating area and terrace. Look out for the glass-covered walk over well. Pay & Display car park at the rear. Up to 10 real ales, plus one real cider are served. ➤❀🕻&♦🚲🛜

Topsham

Bridge Inn ★ L
Bridge Hill, EX3 0QQ
☎ (01392) 873862
Branscombe Branoc; changing beers (sourced regionally) Ⓖ
This cosy historic 16th-century inn overlooking the River Clyst, has been run by five generations of the same family since 1897. It was visited by the late Queen Elizabeth in 1998 and is a delight for real ale fans with a varying range of beers dispensed by gravity direct from the cellar. There are two rooms in the unspoilt interior plus the malthouse which is used at busy times and for functions. Traditional lunches such as ploughman's and sandwiches are served. Q❀🕻≠♦🚲🚌(57,T)♣ ♫

Torquay

Hole in the Wall L
6 Park Lane, TQ1 2AU
☎ (01803) 200755 ⊕ holeinthewalltorquay.co.uk
Dartmoor Jail Ale; Exeter Ferryman; Timothy Taylor Landlord; 4 changing beers (sourced regionally) ⊞
Torquay's oldest inn, circa 1540, is an atmospheric pub popular with tourists and locals. It is tucked behind the harbour in one of the town's oldest areas. The interior has cobbled floors and low-beamed ceilings and the walls are adorned with placards and artefacts from Torbay's maritime history. It has an extensive bar area serving a variety of beers for all tastes. This pub is a hotspot for real ale drinkers with local and national beers on throughout the year. Q➤🕻&🚌♣🛜 ♫

TQ Beerworks Taphouse
1A Abbey Cresecent, TQ2 5HB
☎ (01803) 364925 ⊕ tqbeerworks.com

5 changing beers (sourced nationally; often TQ Beerworks) ⊞
About 20 metres from the beach and with splendid sea views, the taphouse to TQ Beerworks brewery, South Brent, producers of cask and craft keg beers opened in January 2022 in the premises of the former Cru Cocktail lounge. There is seating for approximately 30 people downstairs, 40 upstairs and 50 outside. There are 10 keg lines and four cask lines which are regularly rotated with fresh brews. One is devoted to cider and usually two from TQ and one guest. ➤❀≠♦🚲🚌(12,22)♣🛜 ♫

Totnes

Albert Inn L
32 Bridgetown, TQ9 5AD (from Totnes centre cross river, pub is 100yds on left)
☎ (01803) 863214 ⊕ albertinntotnes.com
Bridgetown Albert Ale, Bitter, Cheeky Blonde, Shark Island Stout, Westcountry IPA; 2 changing beers (sourced locally) ⊞
An excellent example of a community pub, this welcoming hostelry is the sole pub on the 'other' side of the River Dart in Totnes. Housed in a former chapel of rest it has a secluded beer garden and is also the tap for Bridgetown brewery, both found at the rear of the pub. As well as its famed Sunday lunches, the pub also hosts culinary evenings, beer festivals, open-mic nights and live music. Q➤❀🕻&♣♦🚲🚌♣🛜 ♫

Bay Horse Inn L
8 Cistern Street, TQ9 5SP (at the top of the main shopping street in Totnes)
☎ (01803) 862088 ⊕ bayhorsetotnes.com
House beer (by Teignworthy); 2 changing beers (sourced locally; often Bays, Otter, Salcombe) ⊞
This Grade II-listed, 15th-century, elegant community hostelry at the top of historic Totnes has been in this Guide repeatedly, and is well worth seeking out. As well as holding occasional beer and cider festivals, this welcoming pub also holds jazz and open-mic nights and is home to the renowned 'purl a pint' knitting club. The pub also has a charming, spacious, and well-kept beer garden to the rear of the building where many diverse events are held. While food is not available, patrons are welcome to bring in takeaway food. Q➤❀🚲&≠♣♦🚲🚌(92,164)♣🛜 ♫

King William IV
45 Fore Street, TQ9 5HN
☎ (01803) 866689 ⊕ kingwilliamtotnes.co.uk
Dartmoor Jail Ale; St Austell Proper Job; 1 changing beer (sourced locally) ⊞
Popular with both locals and shoppers, this is a substantial building of brick and stone with a pretty curved glass and timber window frontage at ground floor level. Inside it is now one large room, the left-hand side has the feel of a lounge whereas the right side is more like a bar, with high stools looking out of the curved window at Totnes. Three real ales, an excellent range of quality food, and en-suite accommodation are on offer. ➤🚲🕻&♣🚲🚌♣🛜 ♫

Steam Packet Inn L
St Peters Quay, TQ9 5EW
☎ (01803) 863880 ⊕ steampacketinn.co.uk
Dartmoor Jail Ale; Sharp's Doom Bar; 2 changing beers (often Exeter, Salcombe) ⊞
This Buccaneer Inns family-run pub-restaurant with accommodation is a substantial stone building on the Totnes bank of the River Dart, just five minutes walk from the centre of the historic town of Totnes. It has a waterside terrace with ample seating and a conservatory

dining area overlooking Vire Island. It serves good food including pub classics with modern flair. Guest ales change regularly and are usually from local breweries.
ㅎ송녀⏏▲P무ꗚ☞

Turnchapel

Boringdon Arms 🅛 ✅

13 Boringdon Terrace, PL9 9TQ
☎ (01752) 402053 ⊕ boringdon-arms.net
Dartmoor Jail Ale; Fuller's London Pride; Sharp's Atlantic, Sea Fury; 1 changing beer (sourced regionally) Ⓗ
The Bori is a traditional and dog friendly former Regional Pub of the Year. It sits in a waterside village on the South West Coastal Footpath, and benefits from a regular bus service from Plymouth or a short water taxi from the Barbican in Plymouth. Four live beers are usually available. Good value, home-cooked food is served daily. There are two secluded gardens to the rear.
Q ㅎ송①♣무(2,2A)ꗚ☞♫

Umberleigh

Rising Sun Inn 🅛

EX37 9DU (on A377 opp Umberleigh bridge)
☎ (01769) 560447 ⊕ theriser.online
3 changing beers (sourced regionally) Ⓗ
Under new ownership from 2021, this is a village free house and hotel on the River Taw and close to Umberleigh Railway Station. An ideal base for fishing (including an extensive stretch of the river exclusive to the pub), as well as shooting, walking and cycling breaks. Regular house beer The Riser is usually accompanied by two locally sourced ales. The bar has an adjoining eating area and there is also a separate restaurant. Accommodation comprises eight en-suite rooms, seven of which are doubles. Outside an attractive patio area overlooks the river and the A377.
Q ㅎ송녀①▲≠♣♠P무ꗚ☞♫

Walkhampton

Walkhampton Inn 🍷 🅛

PL20 6JY
☎ (01822) 258697 ⊕ walkhamptoninn.co.uk
3 changing beers (sourced regionally; often Exeter, Firebrand, Salcombe) Ⓗ
Set in the centre of the village, this welcoming 17th-century local displays traditional features throughout the bar, dining areas and snug. Up to four ever-changing live beers are available, and up to nine real ciders. There are quiz, live music and open mic nights throughout the year, with annual live beer and cider festivals. The pleasant courtyard beer garden hosts summer events.

This is a good, old fashioned, dog-friendly country pub. Local CAMRA Rural and Cider Pub of the Year 2024.
Q ㅎ①♣♠P무(55,56)ꗚ☞♫

Widecombe-in-the-Moor

Rugglestone Inn ★ 🅛

TQ13 7TF (¼ mile from the centre of the village)
☎ (01364) 621327 ⊕ rugglestoneinn.co.uk
Dartmoor Legend; house beer (by Teignworthy); 3 changing beers (sourced regionally) Ⓖ
This Grade II-listed building was converted from a cottage to an inn back in 1823. Just a few minutes walk from the centre of the village it is surrounded by peaceful moorland. Inside, there is a cosy bar with a wood burner and two further rooms, one of which has an open log fire. Outside is a large sheltered garden with picnic tables and a car park just down the road. Ciders include local Hunt's Cider. Q ㅎ송녀①▲♣♠P무(271,672)ꗚ

Yarde Down

Poltimore Arms 🅛

Brayford, EX36 3HA (2 miles E of Brayford on jct with unclassified road from South Molton to Simonsbath)
SS725356
☎ (01598) 710381
Exeter Lighterman Ⓗ; **1 changing beer (sourced regionally)** Ⓖ
Dating back from the 13th century, this old coaching inn lies in a remote area of glorious Exmoor countryside. This ivy-clad beamed pub is so remote it needs to generate its own electricity, and water is from a spring. The Poltimore Arms is an atmospheric and welcoming locals' pub, which retains many interesting and original features, including, it is said, a friendly ghost.
Q ㅎ송▲♣Pꗚ☞

Yeoford

Duck ✅

EX17 5JD (right out of train station)
☎ (01392) 85273 ⊕ theduckatyeoford.co.uk
House beer (by Hardys & Hansons); 2 changing beers (sourced locally) Ⓗ
Set in beautiful countryside, this multi-roomed, 19th-century free house is easily accessible from the train station on The Tarka Line connecting Exeter and Barnstaple. The Duck serves three, mostly local, cask ales, local cider from Sandford Orchards, and an extensive food menu including vegetarian and vegan options and a children's menu. It has an outdoor play area. There is also a small shop on the pub premises, open at the same times as the pub. ㅎ송①ঙ≠♠Pꗚ☞

Ale conner

The official ale-tester wore leather breeches. He would enter an inn without warning, draw a glass of ale, pour it on a wooden bench, and then sit down in the puddle he had made. He would sit for half an hour and would not change his position. At the end of the half hour, he would make as if to rise, and this was the test of the ale; for if the ale was impure, if it had sugar in it, the tester's leather breeches would stick fast to the bench, but if there was no sugar in the liquor, no impression would be present – in other words, the tester would not stick to the seat.

17th-century description of the work of the ale conner, a public official who inspected inns, taverns and ale houses to test the quality of the beer. William Shakespeare's father was an ale conner.

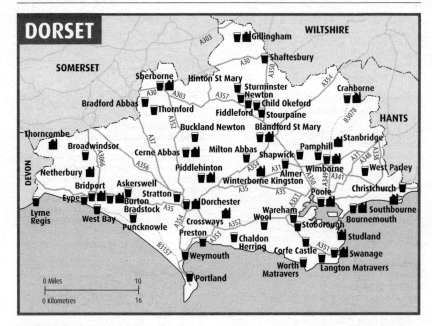

DORSET

Almer

Worlds End 🄻
DT11 9EW (off B3075 nr jct with A31)
☎ (01929) 459036 ⊕ worldsendalmer.co.uk
2 changing beers (sourced regionally; often Eight Arch, Lyme Regis, Sandbanks) 🄷
A large thatched country pub believed to be about 600 years old, arguably one of the oldest in Dorset. Churchill and Eisenhower are said to have met here prior to D-day to discuss invasion plans. There is a long bar split into two, one for diners and one predominantly for drinkers, with cosy fireplaces and wooden beams. For the summer months there is also an extensive garden and a play area. Dogs are welcome. Q🏠🅟🕭🍴🍷🅿🌼

Askerswell

Spyway Inn
DT2 9EP
☎ (01308) 485250 ⊕ thespywayinn.com
3 changing beers (sourced locally; often Cerne Abbas, Exmoor, Otter) 🄶
Family-friendly 16th-century smuggler's inn perched on the lower slopes of Eggardon Hill on the outskirts of Askerswell. The gravity-served real ales are sourced from local and West Country brewers, typically Cerne Abbas, Otter and Exmoor. Local cider is also available. There is a compact main bar, and further rooms for dining. A low doorway leads into the large garden, with plenty of seating, including six covered pods with superb views across the countryside. Closed on Monday and Tuesday.
Q🏠🕭🛏🍷🍴🅿🌼🍽🎵

Blandford St Mary

Stour Inn
5 Blandford St Mary, DT11 9LH
☎ (01258) 268188
4 changing beers (sourced nationally) 🄷
A 400-plus-year-old Grade II-listed free house with a community feel, conveniently located in the town. The cosy bar area, with an open fire, has a rotating selection

of four ales, primarily from independent breweries, plus real ciders sourced from Dorset makers. To the left of bar there is a mix of low- and high-level wooden seating leading to a larger area with dining tables and access to the secluded garden. 🏠🕭🍷🍴♣🛏🖼(X8,CR8)🌼🍽🎵

Bournemouth

Acorn
1492 Wimborne Road, BH11 9AD
☎ (01202) 575062
6 changing beers (sourced regionally; often Goddards, Hattie Brown's, Sixpenny) 🄷
Imposing 17th-century pub, originally a coaching inn, and rich in history. It was previously named Gulliver's due its connection with Isaac Gulliver, a local smuggler. It is now in the safe hands of a family who previously ran an award-winning pub nearby, and offers a well-chosen selection of ales from an L-shaped bar that serves two distinct areas. Pub games include shove-ha'penny and darts. A local DJ plays at weekends. No children after 6pm. 🕭♣🛏🅿🌼

All Hail Ale
10 Queens Road, BH2 6BE
☎ 07786 045996 ⊕ allhailale.com
4 changing beers (sourced nationally) 🄷
A vibrant micropub and bottle shop, this former restaurant has been skilfully converted, with wooden flooring and polished-wood bar and tables. Five handpumps serve a range of ales from independent breweries nationwide, alongside a real cider. Ten keg pumps offer a varied and well-chosen selection of beers. Popular tap takeovers are held to showcase some of the major new craft ales available; a large blackboard lists the beers available. ▶🛏🌼🍽🎵♪

Firkin Shed
279 Holdenhurst Road, BH8 8BZ
☎ (01202) 302340
4 changing beers (sourced regionally) 🄷
The Shed is a quirky, friendly, family-run micropub and a former CAMRA National Cider Pub of the Year. Tables and

benches hug the walls of the main bar area and snug, which are decorated with flags, musical instruments, puppets and skulls. A shed is used as the bar, hosting a constantly changing range of cask and keg beers alongside an impressive cider range. The garden area is a great place to relax and enjoy the summer sunshine.
🏵🌢🖳(2) 🌢

Goat & Tricycle 🗸

27-29 West Hill Road, BH2 5PF
☎ (01202) 314220 ⊕ goatandtricycle.co.uk
Butcombe Adam Henson's Rare Breed, Original, Gold; Liberation Ale, Herm Island Gold, IPA; 4 changing beers (sourced regionally) Ⓗ
An award-winning traditional pub, popular with drinkers and diners. It was originally two adjoining pubs, the left of which is listed and has a fine tiled frontage. Eleven handpumps serve mostly Butcombe and Liberation Ales, as well as Stan's cider. Good, freshly cooked food is served daily, except Sunday evenings, with gluten-free options available. A partly covered courtyard caters for smokers and alfresco drinkers. Sunday is quiz night. Under-18s are not admitted. 🏵🕦🌢🖳🌢🛜

Silverback Alehouse

518 Wimborne Road, BH9 2EX
☎ (01202) 510988 ⊕ silverbackalehouse.co.uk
4 changing beers (sourced regionally; often Brew Shack, Gritchie) Ⓖ
This long, narrow micropub is a friendly and relaxed place to enjoy a drink. Just take a seat on a bench or at one of the high set tables and the staff will come and take your order. You have a choice from four regionally sourced ales, five at weekends, and ciders that are all always in good order. There are bar snacks on offer, or you can bring your own. Closing time may be later than advertised depending on demand. Q&♣🌢🖳🌢🛜

Bradford Abbas

Rose & Crown 🗸

Church Road, DT9 6RF
☎ (01935) 423199
Otter Bitter; Sharp's Doom Bar, Sea Fury Ⓗ
This 14th-century former monk's house is now run by experienced licensees. The interior has been completely updated, including a refurbishment of the toilets. Regular league skittles can be played in the historic alley, and the attractive garden has a play area. The real ales are from the Admiral list, and the pub also sells Camden Town keg beers. Quality food is served, with a Sunday carvery where booking is essential. Closed on Monday.
🌢🏵🕦&♣P🌢🛜

Bridport

Pursuit of Hoppiness

15 West Street, DT6 3QJ
☎ (01308) 427111
House beer (by Lyme Regis); 5 changing beers (sourced nationally; often Bristol Beer Factory, Eight Arch, Vibrant Forest) Ⓗ
Near the town hall is this small, one-room micropub accommodates up to two dozen people, with the same number seated outside. A fast-changing range of beers from local, regional and national breweries are supplemented by various bottled and canned beers in the fridge. Beers and ciders can be sampled before purchase, and even canned to take away. Ciders are usually from Isaac or Dorset Nectar. Card payment only.
Q🌢🏵🌢P🖳🌢🛜

Ropemakers Ⓛ 🗸

36 West Street, DT6 3QP
☎ (01308) 421255 ⊕ theropemakers.com
Palmers Copper Ale, IPA, Dorset Gold, 200, Tally Ho!; 1 changing beer (sourced locally; often Palmers) Ⓗ
A busy town-centre pub tied to local Palmers brewery, with the full range of their ales including seasonal specials when available. A full menu of locally sourced food is available daily, with a roast on Sundays. Entertainment includes a popular weekly quiz, monthly meat draw, cheese club and book club. Live music can be open mic, traditional jazz or folk. There are lots of nooks and crannies so it's possible to find a cosy seat.
🌢🏵🕦🗛♣🌢P🖳🌢🛜♪

Tiger Inn 🗸

14-16 Barrack Street, DT6 3LY
☎ (01308) 427543 ⊕ tigerinnbridport.co.uk
6 changing beers (sourced regionally; often Exeter, Fine Tuned, Hattie Brown's) Ⓗ
A busy Victorian pub tucked away just off the town centre. The changing real ales are predominantly from the West Country. The main bar is decorated with dried hops and beer mats, and boasts a large TV screen showing mainly sporting events, plus a dartboard. To the rear is a smaller, quieter bar and a cocktail bar/function room. Outside are two well-maintained seating areas. Look for the rare Groves Brewery etched window. Accommodation is in seven en-suite rooms.
🌢🏵🛏♣🖳🌢🛜

Woodman Inn 🏆

61 South Street, DT6 3NZ
☎ (01308) 456455 ⊕ thewoodman.pub
4 changing beers (sourced nationally; often Cerne Abbas, Copper Street, Exmoor) Ⓗ
A friendly community pub with a focus on quality beers, and up to 12 real ciders. The real ales turn over very quickly and are announced on the pub's Facebook page. There is a stone-floored single bar with fire, and a skittle alley to the rear. Tables at the front make the most of the sunny aspect, with a pleasant, quieter garden to the rear. Regular events include folk nights and storytelling. Handy for the twice-weekly local markets. Local and

---

REAL ALE BREWERIES

Apex Sherborne
Big Dig 🍂 Winterborne Kingston (NEW)
Bredy Burton Bradstock (NEW)
Brewers Folly 🍂 Stanbridge
Brewhouse & Kitchen 🍺 Bournemouth
Brewhouse & Kitchen 🍺 Dorchester
Brewhouse & Kitchen 🍺 Poole
Brewhouse & Kitchen 🍺 Southbourne
Cerne Abbas 🍂 Cerne Abbas
Copper Street 🍂 Dorchester
Dorset 🍂 Crossways
Eight Arch 🍂 Wimborne
Gyle 59 Thorncombe
Hall & Woodhouse (Badger) 🍂 Blandford St Mary
Hattie Brown's Swanage
Isle of Purbeck 🍺 Studland
Lyme Regis Netherbury
Palmers Bridport
Piddle Piddlehinton
Poole Hill 🍂 Bournemouth
Remedy Oak 🍂 Wimborne
Sandbanks 🍂 Poole
Sixpenny 🍂 Cranborne
Small Paul's Gillingham
Way Outback 🍂 Southbourne

Regional CAMRA Cider Pub of the Year 2023, and local CAMRA Pub of the Year and Cider Pub of the Year 2024.
&⌂Å♠P🖂♣?

Broadwindsor

White Lion 🅛 ✅
The Square, DT8 3QD
☎ (01308) 867070 ⊕ whitelionbroadwindsor.co.uk
Palmers Copper Ale, Tally Ho!; 1 changing beer (sourced locally) 🄷
This 17th-century inn was threatened with closure, but in 2022 was successfully taken over by the community on a tenancy agreement with local brewers Palmers. Food is available Wednesday to Sunday, including a Sunday roast, for dining or takeaway. Live music features at this family- and dog-friendly pub, which is volunteer run on a Tuesday evening (bring your fish & chips from the van, plates and cutlery are provided). Closed on Monday. Local CAMRA Pub of the Year 2023.
Q&⌂⊕♣♠🖂(CB3)♣♪

Buckland Newton

Gaggle of Geese
Buckland Newton, DT2 7BS
☎ (01300) 345249 ⊕ gaggleofgeese.co.uk
Sharp's Doom Bar; 3 changing beers (sourced locally; often Cerne Abbas, Wriggle Valley) 🄷
Substantial country pub on the outskirts of the village with a large garden featuring camping facilities and shepherd huts. Entry is via a small drinking area, leading to another raised room set out for dining, though drinkers are welcome here. A separate skittle alley is adjacent. Decoration is pastel shades, having many up-cycled decorative features, local changing artwork for sale and a collection of vintage pub games. Events are held in the garden in the summer. Closed Monday.
Q&⌂⊕&Å♠P♣♪

Burton Bradstock

Three Horseshoes 🅛 ✅
Mill Street, DT6 4QZ
☎ (01308) 897259 ⊕ threehorseshoesburtonbradstock.co.uk
Palmers Copper Ale, IPA, Dorset Gold, 200, Tally Ho!; 1 changing beer (sourced locally; often Palmers) 🄷
An attractive thatched pub on the Jurassic Coast road catering for villagers and visitors to nearby Hive beach. It serves excellent food, and the full range of local Palmers beers and real cider are available. There is a suntrap beer garden for the summer and log fires for the winter. The car park is opposite and the village shop/post office is next door. Open all day throughout April to September; winter hours are more restricted. Closed on Mondays.
Q&⌂⊕Å♠♣P🖂(X53)♣?

Cerne Abbas

Cerne Abbas Brewery Tap
Chescombe Barn, Barton Meadows Farm, DT2 7JS
☎ (01300) 341999 ⊕ cerneabbasbrewery.com
5 changing beers (sourced locally; often Cerne Abbas) 🄶
The brewery was founded in 2014 on a farm in the Cerne Valley. Their beers are always brewed using local ingredients and are served in the quirky, rustic-style tap house, which is used for numerous local events (ticket holders only), from charity concerts to car shows. You are welcome to bring your own picnic, though on occasional weekends they have Papa Cheese kitchen available. Well worth a visit. &⌂♠P🖂(X11,CR5)♣♪

Giant Inn 🅛 ✅
24 Long Street, DT2 7JF
☎ (01300) 341441 ⊕ thegiantcerneabbas.co.uk
Butcombe Adam Henson's Rare Breed; 3 changing beers (sourced locally; often Cerne Abbas, Exmoor, Ringwood) 🄷
Traditional brick-built village pub dating from the 15th century but remodelled in the Victorian era by the Groves and Sons brewery. This friendly, open-plan pub offers local ales and serves a good range of home-cooked food. Note the Cerne Abbas Giant nostalgia on the walls. Outside there is a sunny beer garden, a covered passageway with tables, and a skittle alley. Definitely worth a visit. Closed on Monday.
Q&⌂⊕♣♠🖂(X11,CR5)♣?

Chaldon Herring

Sailor's Return 🅛
DT2 8DN
☎ (01305) 854441 ⊕ sailorsreturnpub.com
Cerne Abbas Ale; Otter Ale; Palmers Copper Ale; 1 changing beer (sourced regionally; often Exmoor, Nuttycombe, Palmers) 🄷
Historic thatched inn on the edge of a tranquil village, a few miles from the Jurassic Coast. The pub dates from the 1860s but the buildings are much earlier. There are several dining and drinking areas, with flagstone floors throughout. An original inn sign hangs in the main bar. Wednesday is pie night, with roasts on Sunday. On Friday night food is only served in the restaurant area (booking advisable). Closed Monday and Tuesday. The range of beers increases in summer and autumn.
Q&⌂⊕♠P♣?

Child Okeford

Saxon Inn
Gold Hill, DT11 8HD
☎ (01258) 860310 ⊕ saxoninn.co.uk
Butcombe Original; Gritchie English Lore; Palmers Copper Ale; 1 changing beer (sourced regionally; often Eight Arch) 🄷
A newly renovated 300-year-old inn hidden behind a row of cottages. The bar and dining areas are cosy, with a log fire, and are popular with locals and visitors. As well as three permanent ales, a guest is also available. Excellent home-cooked food is available at lunchtime and evenings (booking is essential), and the large garden is perfect for alfresco dining. The pub also does B&B and is an ideal base for exploring the surrounding Dorset countryside. Closed Monday and Tuesday.
&⌂⊛⊕♣P🖂(X10)♣?

Christchurch

Saxon Bar
5 The Saxon Centre, Fountain Way, BH23 1QN
☎ (01202) 488931
4 changing beers (sourced nationally) 🄶
A friendly, single-room micropub close to the town centre, offering a variety of well-chosen cask ales, and up to 10 real ciders, all served direct to your table. The perimeter seating, and the high table, are all made from wood reclaimed from Bournemouth Pier. Speciality bar snacks, local and international spirits and four KeyKeg beers are also available. Winter hours may vary. Regional CAMRA Cider Pub of the Year and local CAMRA Pub of the Year 2023. ⊛≈♠🖂♣

Corfe Castle

Corfe Castle Club

70 East Street, BH20 5EQ (off A351)
☎ (01929) 480591
Butcombe Original; Timothy Taylor Landlord; 1 changing beer (sourced nationally; often Dartmoor) Ⓗ
This friendly, award-winning club is a real community asset and a regular entry in this Guide. It is located in the centre of the village and is famed for its traditional filled rolls. The main bar has a TV for sporting events, and darts and shove-ha'penny are played. An upstairs room is available for hire, and the garden boasts a boules court. Visitors are welcome with CAMRA membership or a copy of this Guide. Regional CAMRA Club of the year 2023 and local CAMRA Club of the Year 2024.
❀≹♣P🚌(40,30)🐾📶

Fox Inn 🄻

8 West Street, BH20 5HD
☎ (01929) 480449 🌐 thefoxinncorfecastle.com
Butcombe Adam Henson's Rare Breed; Hattie Brown's Moonlite; 1 changing beer (often Exmoor, Fuller's) Ⓗ
Delightful 16th-century inn nestled in the heart of historic Corfe Castle. It retains many original features and links to the stone industry for which the area is famous. The front door opens into a small traditional snug with steps down to the main bar area where good pub food is served. Towards the rear is an elongated garden with a barbecue shack and fine views over the castle and surrounding Purbeck hills. The heritage Swanage Steam Railway is just a stone's throw away.
Q❀◑⛺≹🚌(40,30)

Cranborne

Sixpenny Tap 🄻

Holwell Farm, Holwell, BH21 5QP (1 mile from village centre on B3078)
☎ (01725) 762006 🌐 sixpennybrewery.co.uk
Sixpenny 6d Best Bitter, 6d Gold, 6d IPA; 1 changing beer (sourced locally; often Sixpenny) Ⓗ
Housed in a converted stables and packed full of miscellaneous quirky items, Sixpenny Tap has established itself at the heart of the local community. The Sixpenny brewery is next door and their popular range of ales is served with pride and enthusiasm. The pub hosts many successful and colourful community and charity events in their extensive courtyard, and a warm welcome awaits everyone. This little gem is nestled in the picturesque Cranborne Area of Outstanding Natural Beauty, and even has its own Tardis.
Q❀♿♣●P🐾📶♫

Dorchester

Blue Raddle

9 Church Street, DT1 1JN
☎ (01305) 267762 🌐 blueraddle.co.uk
Cerne Abbas Blonde; St Austell Tribute; 3 changing beers (sourced regionally; often Bath Ales, Dartmoor, Palmers) Ⓗ
Very much a locals' pub, reflected by the quirky photos and paraphernalia that adorn the walls and bar, but strangers are made equally welcome. The bar dominates and is decorated with covers of Private Eye and old pumpclips. Seating is on soft furnished benches alongside wooden tables and chairs. Food is locally sourced and cooked by the publican's wife. Note that the pub is only open at weekends and is closed when the owners are on holiday, so phone ahead.
Q◑≹(South)🚌🐾📶

Convivial Rabbit

1 Trinity House, Trinity Street, DT1 1TT (down the alley to the left of Pennywise)
☎ 07717 158853 🌐 convivialrabbit.co.uk
6 changing beers (sourced nationally) Ⓖ
This popular micropub serves a changing selection of around six real ales of varying styles and strengths, sourced from micro and independent British breweries. Local ciders, lagers, wines, gins and tea and coffee are also available. The regular live music includes folk night on Sunday. The pub is tucked away in an alley off Trinity Street, but easily accessed from South or West stations and is well worth seeking out. Closed Monday.
Q❀≹(South)♣●🚌🐾📶♫

Copper Street Brewery Tap Room 🄻

8 Copper Street, DT1 1GH
☎ 07395 664390
3 changing beers (often Copper Street) Ⓖ
The glass-fronted taproom is opposite Dorchester South railway station. The comfortably furnished bar, which serves three of the brewery's own beers and one guest, as well as tea and coffee, can accommodate 20 customers, with more seating outside. It is partitioned off from the brewery, which is visible through a viewing window. There is a wall-mounted bottle shop stocking the brewery's full range, and a TV showing sporting events. Q❀♿≹(South)🚌(10)🐾📶

Royal Oak ✔

20 High West Street, DT1 1UW
☎ (01305) 755910
Greene King Abbot; Ruddles Best Bitter; Sharp's Doom Bar; 5 changing beers (sourced nationally; often Dorset, Otter) Ⓗ
A busy town-centre Wetherspoon pub offering a wide selection of frequently changing local and national ales on handpump, with regular beer festivals adding to the range. The pub offers a full food menu and is open daily for breakfast, welcoming children and families. It has a number of separate areas for both diners and drinkers. To the rear is a sunny patio area with wheelchair access to the main internal area. Q❀◑♿≹(West)🚌📶

Tom Browns 🄻

47 High East Street, DT1 1HU
☎ (01305) 264020 🌐 tombrownspub.co.uk
Copper Street Saxon Gold; Dorset Tom Brown's; 2 changing beers (sourced regionally; often Cerne Abbas, Copper Street) Ⓗ
Town-centre alehouse with wood-floored public bar, a real fire, and basic furinshings. The pub is a keen supporter of local breweries and makes the perfect starting point for a walk along the river Frome via the secluded garden. It gets lively on Saturday nights when it hosts live bands. Occasionally food is available from external caterers. There is a skittle alley at the rear. This pub is well worth a visit, but is currently under threat of redevelopment. ❀≹(West)♣●🚌🐾📶♫

Eype

New Inn ✔

Mount Lane, DT6 6AP
☎ (01308) 423254 🌐 newinneype.com
Palmers Copper Ale, IPA, Dorset Gold, 200, Tally Ho! Ⓗ
Friendly, family-run pub halfway down a lane from the Bridport bypass (A35) to Eype beach. The superb home-cooked meals and snacks use local suppliers. The full range of Palmers beers are usually stocked, but it can be more limited in winter. There is a lovely garden with a

beautiful view, particularly at sunset. Takeaway meals are also available, with fish & chips on Friday and Sunday roasts. Closed on Monday. Q➰⊛❍❸♣♠P🌸 ♫

Fiddleford

Fiddleford Inn

off A357, DT10 2BX (off A357 between Sturminster Newton and Blandford)
☎ (01258) 472886 ⊕ thefiddlefordinn.net
4 changing beers (sourced nationally) Ⓗ
Recently refurbished inn dating from around 1740 and retaining some of its original features. The building has, over the years, been a malt house and an old coaching stop, and also housed a brewery in the 18th and 19th centuries. The pub has a relaxing atmosphere and serves great food in the bar and the separate restaurant. Ideally sited for country walks and the nearby Fiddleford Manor (English Heritage). Q➰⊛❍❸❍P🌸 ♫

Gillingham

Phoenix

The Square, SP8 4AY
☎ (01747) 823277
St Austell Proper Job; Sharp's Doom Bar; 1 changing beer (sourced locally; often Hattie Brown's) Ⓗ
Originally a 15th-century coaching inn with its own brewery and stable, this pub was rebuilt and renamed the Phoenix following a fire in the 17th century. It has an open-plan layout with two areas and an open fire. In addition to the two regular beers there is always a dark beer from Dorset brewery Hattie Browns. A hand-pulled cider is also usually available. There is seating outside and two public car parks nearby. ➰⊛▲⇌🚌(CR2)🌸🛜

Hinton St Mary

White Horse

White Horse Lane, DT10 1NA
☎ (01258) 915001 ⊕ thewhitehorsehinton.co.uk
Butcombe Original; 3 changing beers (sourced regionally; often Gritchie, Palmers, Salcombe) Ⓗ
This recently renovated and redecorated 16th-century Grade II-listed free house is situated on the Pitt-Rivers estate, which explains the equestrian themes. With wooden beams throughout, the bar area features stone flooring and a log-burner, while the other areas of the pub are used as a restaurant. The bar stocks a rotating selection of cask ales from the south-west, along with locally sourced gins and soft drinks. There is a lovely outside patio area. Accommodation is available.
Q➰⊛❍❸♣🚌(CR4)🌸🛜

Langton Matravers

King's Arms ★

27 High Street, BH19 3HA
☎ (01929) 422979
Butcombe Original; 3 changing beers (sourced nationally; often Hattie Brown's, St Austell) Ⓗ
Dating back to 1743, this Grade II-listed, Purbeck stone-built pub features rooms off a central bar area with original flagstone floors. It is a family-friendly community pub that welcomes dogs and is popular with visitors. It serves fine pub food and hosts a village shop. The rear garden is a suntrap. The seaside town of Swanage is close by, as are many fine walks where you can explore the Purbecks and the South West Coast Path.
Q➰⊛❍▲🚌(40)🌸🛜

Lyme Regis

Lyme Regis Brewery Tap

Mill Lane, DT7 3PU
☎ (01297) 444354 ⊕ lymeregisbrewery.com
3 changing beers (sourced locally) Ⓗ/Ⓖ
The brewery taproom can be found in the Town Mill courtyard off Coombe Street. Previously, the premises were a malthouse and the town's first power station. There are three changing cask ales available, plus up to eight keg beers, all from the brewery, and the occasional guest. Seating is limited inside but there is more in the charming courtyard. An annual Oktoberfest beer festival is held, with imported German beers. No disabled access but there is an accessible toilet off the courtyard.
➰⊛▲🚌🌸🛜♫

Pilot Boat ✪

1 Bridge Street, DT7 3QA
☎ (01297) 443157 ⊕ thepilotboat.co.uk
Palmers Copper Ale, IPA, Dorset Gold, 200, Tally Ho! Ⓗ
A spacious, family-orientated pub predominantly dedicated to dining. It features a large main bar opening out to a courtyard which is overlooked by a roof terrace with glimpses of the sea. The full range of Palmers beers are normally available. Food is available all day from the open-plan kitchen, which includes a pizza oven. The excellent accommodation comprises three sea-view rooms, all named after Palmers beers.
➰⊛❍❸♣▲♣🚌(x51,x53)🌸🛜♫

Rock Point Inn

1-2 Broad Street, DT7 3QD
☎ (01297) 443153 ⊕ rockpointinn.co.uk
St Austell Tribute, Proper Job; 2 changing beers (sourced regionally; often Bath Ales, St Austell) Ⓗ
An 18th-century town-centre inn with fabulous sea views from inside the pub and the split-level outdoor balconies. The outside space has gas heaters for those cold evenings, but can be closed in rough weather. Proper Job and Tribute are regulars, with two changing beers from the St Austell and Bath Ales ranges, including a changing monthly cask club ale. There are nine bedrooms, some with a sea view. Q➰⊛❍❸▲🚌🌸🛜

Milton Abbas

Hambro Arms

DT11 0BP
☎ (01258) 880233 ⊕ hambroarms.com
Otter Bitter; 2 changing beers (sourced regionally; often Dark Star) Ⓗ
Located in the picturesque village of Milton Abbas, with its identical thatched cottages and unique history. It is believed to be the first 'planned village' in England. The pub has been recently updated, but retains many of the original features, including a large fireplace. Regular events are held, including charity quizzes, racing evenings, live music and open mic nights, and major sporting events are shown on TV. ⊛🚌♣P

Pamphill

Vine Inn ★

Vine Hill, BH21 4EE (off B3082)
☎ (01202) 882259
2 changing beers (sourced regionally; often Otter) Ⓗ/Ⓖ
Identified by CAMRA as having a nationally important historic pub interior, this multi-award winning country pub is owned by the National Trust. It has been managed by the same family for 120 years – and by the current

landlady for over 30 years. There are two cosy bars, an upstairs room, and a large patio and garden. Light snacks of ploughman's and toasties are served during lunchtimes. This is a real gem, and popular with walkers and cyclists. Opening times may vary in winter. Q✿◑♣P✿

Piddlehinton

Thimble Inn ℒ ✓

14 High Street, DT2 7TD
☎ (01300) 348270 ⊕ thimbleinn.co.uk
Palmers Copper Ale, IPA, Dorset Gold; 1 changing beer (sourced locally; often Palmers) ℍ
A popular, thatched Palmers village pub, a short drive from Dorchester, sitting beside the River Piddle. Tastefully refurbished a few years ago, its features include a roaring log burner, flagstone flooring in the low-beamed bar area, and an internal well that rises with the water table. It is set out for diners, but drinkers are made welcome. Palmers seasonal beer or Tally Ho! is often available. A former local CAMRA Pub Garden of the Year winner. Closed Mondays, including bank holidays. ➷✿◑&▲♣P✿�� ♪

Poole

Barking Cat Alehouse ♥

182-184 Ashley Road, BH14 9BY
☎ (01202) 258465 ⊕ thebarkingcatalehouse.co.uk
8 changing beers (sourced nationally) ℍ
Popular, multi award-winning pub with 12 keg/KeyKegs and four ciders on handpump complementing the eight cask beers, which are mainly sourced from both local and national independent breweries. Regular beer festivals and occasional live music also feature. The back room can be booked for functions. Customers can order food next door, or from elsewhere. A popular fortnightly pub quiz is held on Sundays. Note the ornate granite pillars between the two rooms. Current local CAMRA Pub of the Year. ➷&⇌(Branksome)♣●🖪⛔🖪(M1,15)✿🛜 ♪

Bermuda Triangle

10 Parr Street, BH14 0JY
☎ (01202) 402672 ⊕ bermudatrianglepub.com
5 changing beers (sourced nationally; often Dartmoor, Oakham, Palmers) ℍ
A beautifully quirky and popular Victorian pub themed around the Bermuda Triangle legend. Every piece of space has been fully utilised, including an upstairs cocktail bar accessed through a bookcase. There is a partially heated outside area and a roof terrace. The outside area includes a café serving speciality coffees, teas, breakfast, lunch, homemade treats and weekly evening specials (Wed-Fri). Five changing cask ales are served, and live music features three nights a week. Popular with all ages. ✿◑⇌(Parkstone) 🖪(M1,M2)✿🛜 ♪

Brewhouse ✓

68 High Street, BH15 1DA
☎ (01202) 685288
Frome Funky Monkey, The Usual; 2 changing beers (sourced nationally; often Brentwood, Elgood's, Frome) ℍ
This multi award-winning pub is an established feature of Poole High Street, offering interesting ales from Frome brewery, well-chosen ales from national microbreweries, and locally sourced real cider. Gourmet burgers, pasties and ploughman's are available at lunchtime and evenings and can be eaten at the tables by the window or the alfresco seating area on the High Street. At the

rear is an area for pool and darts, and occasional sporting events are televised. This community-focused pub welcomes locals, visitors, and well-behaved dogs. Local CAMRA Cider Pub of the Year 2024. ✿⇌♣●🖪✿🛜

Crown Hotel

23 Market Street, BH15 1NB
☎ (01202) 672137 ⊕ crownhotelpoole.co.uk
2 changing beers (sourced nationally; often Sandbanks, St Austell) ℍ
Situated in Poole old town, the hotel has been recently refurbished and tastefully decorated in a traditional style. The bar area is open plan, with small, cosy areas with sofas. One of the two beers served is usually locally produced. Reasonably priced food is served all afternoon, Wednesday to Sunday, and includes Sunday lunches. The pub is dog friendly (with biscuits supplied). The hotel has five en-suite rooms and one apartment available for guests. ◄⇌🖪✿

Poole Arms ℒ ✓

19 The Quay, BH15 1HJ
☎ (01202) 673450 ⊕ poolearms.co.uk
Dorset Jurassic; Flack Manor Flack's Double Drop; St Austell Proper Job; 1 changing beer (sourced regionally; often Stonehenge) ℍ
Originating from 1635 and steeped in history, this distinctive green-tiled quayside pub is popular with locals and tourists. Wood-panelled walls adorned with photographs of old Poole dominate the cosy single room bar area where up to five real ales are served. The extensive menu offers locally sourced, award-winning seafood. Quayside bench seating at the front provides a great space to watch the many activities taking place around the bustling harbour. Q✿◑🖪(8)

Portland

George Inn ★

133 Reforne, DT5 2AP
☎ (01305) 820011
Greene King Abbot; 3 changing beers (sourced nationally; often Butcombe, St Austell, Timothy Taylor) ℍ
Standing directly opposite the cricket ground, the George is housed in one of the oldest dwellings on Portland and has been a pub since 1805. It consists of three separate drinking areas and a large beer garden. There are usually three guest ales on offer. Meals are served, and there is an occasional themed food night. The pub is close to some spectacular cliff walks and a restored 18th-century church. Dogs are welcome. ➷✿◑🖪(1)✿🛜 ♪

Preston

Spice Ship Inn

240 Preston Road, DT3 6BJ
☎ (01305) 516099 ⊕ prestonspiceship.com
Sharp's Doom Bar; Timothy Taylor Landlord ℍ
Family-friendly Grade II-listed coaching house with wood panelling and low beams. A central bar separates the restaurant from the dog-friendly bar, where televised sport is shown. The restaurant serves quality food from a seasonal menu and adjoins a covered, elevated patio overlooking a large beer garden. A quiz is held on Monday, Thursday is curry night, and live music plays most Fridays. There is an outside TV for those who wish to watch their sport in the fresh air. Q➷✿◄◑▲♣P✿🛜 ♪

Puncknowle

Crown Inn L ✔
Church Street, DT2 9BN
☎ (01308) 897711 ⊕ crowninndorset.co.uk
Palmers IPA, Dorset Gold, 200 Ⓗ
Popular, thatched pub at the heart of this village (pronounced 'Punnel') consisting of two bars, with log fires and a further dining room off the main drinking area. Wheelchair access is via the back door from the car park and into the main bar. Well-kept Palmers ales are served, occasionally including Tally Ho!, and food is traditional pub fare with a specials menu. Outside is a large garden with extensive views across the Bride Valley. Closed Monday. Q ❄ 🛏 ① ⅍ ♣ P ● 🐾 🎵

Shaftesbury

Grosvenor Arms
The Commons, SP7 8JA
☎ (01747) 850580 ⊕ grosvenorarms.co.uk
2 changing beers (sourced nationally; often Otter) Ⓗ
Located close to Gold Hill and an inn since Medieval times. The original timber framed building was a busy coaching inn, originally the Red Lion. It was bought by the Grosvenor family, rebuilt and re-named the Grosvenor Arms Hotel in the early 19th century. It is a comfortable hotel with a courtyard, a large, cosy club style bar and fine restaurant dining. Food is served every day including breakfast (9-11). Changing local ales and West Country ciders are available.
Q ❄ 🛏 ① ⅍ 🖭 ● 🎵

Ship Inn ★ ✔
24 Bleke Street, SP7 8JZ
☎ (01747) 853219
Butcombe Original; Sixpenny 6d IPA; 2 changing beers Ⓗ
Stone-built town pub at the top of the steep Tout Hill. The single bar serves the four different areas: the main bar; a games room with pool, darts, fruit machine and jukebox; a snug with an open fire; and a lounge bar. Outside is a sunny patio and covered smoking area. No hot food is available, but they will order food for you from local takeaways, or you can bring your own. ❄ 🖭 🐾 ●

Shapwick

Anchor Inn
West Street, DT11 9LB
☎ (01258) 857269 ⊕ anchorshapwick.co.uk
3 changing beers (often Downton, Gritchie, Otter) Ⓗ
This community-owned pub was rescued from closure about 17 years ago by locals who couldn't contemplate their village without a pub. Good beer, good food and the close proximity to local attractions – including Kingston Lacy, the Badbury Rings and the Stour Valley Way – are all reasons you need to visit. There is a pleasant roadside seating area at the front where you can relax and watch the world go by, when the sun is shining. Q ❄ ① ● P 🐾

Sherborne

Digby Tap ★ ✔
Cooks Lane, DT9 3NS
☎ (01935) 813148 ⊕ digbytap.co.uk
4 changing beers (sourced regionally; often Cerne Abbas, Otter, Teignworthy) Ⓗ
A lively, friendly and deservedly popular 16th-century ale house situated close to the famous abbey and railway station. The owners of over 20 years have retained the

character of the building, with its four separate drinking areas, flagged floors and cosy corners. The four changing beers are sold at reasonable prices, as are the lunchtime meals. This real drinkers' pub is a step back in time, and an institution in the town and surrounding area.
Q ❄ ① ≠ ♣ 🛏 🖭 (58,5) ● 🎵

Stoborough

King's Arms
3 Corfe Road, BH20 5AB
☎ (01929) 552705 ⊕ thekingsarms-stoborough.co.uk
Isle of Purbeck Best Bitter; Ringwood Razorback; 2 changing beers (sourced nationally) Ⓗ
Historic and attractive thatched pub at the gateway to the Isle of Purbeck. This 17th-century village inn hosted Cromwell's troops in 1642. An excellent menu of modern and traditional classics is served in the beamed bar or the dedicated restaurant. Four handpumps dispense two regular beers and two well-chosen guests. The garden and patio area are a great place to relax in the summer sunshine and host the annual beer festival and bonfire party. Q ❄ ① ⅍ A P 🖭 (40) ● 🐾 🎵

Stourpaine

White Horse Inn ✔
Shaston Road, DT11 8TA
☎ (01258) 453535 ⊕ whitehorse-stourpaine.co.uk
Sharp's Doom Bar; house beer (by Flack Manor); 3 changing beers (sourced regionally; often Gritchie, Palmers, Salcombe) Ⓗ
A warm welcome awaits at this village free house at the heart of the community. Dating back to the 18th century, the pub was originally two buildings converted into one. The wooden furniture and open fire create a cosy feel and the pub appeals to both diners and drinkers, with lovely food, regional cask ales, local ciders, good conversation, pub games and regular live music nights. There is outdoor seating to front and rear of this gem of a pub, which is located just off the North Dorset Trailway. ❄ ① ♣ ● P 🖭 (CR7) ● 🐾 🎵

Stratton

Saxon Arms
20 The Square, DT2 9WG
☎ (01305) 260020 ⊕ thesaxon-stratton.co.uk
Butcombe Original; Timothy Taylor Landlord; 1 changing beer (sourced regionally; often Butcombe, St Austell) Ⓗ
Next to the church and village hall, the Saxon is a stunning-looking thatched, flint and stone pub. The popular venue is the hub of the village and offers a good range of ales, local and national, ciders and lagers. It enjoys a good reputation for its locally sourced food, and there are numerous themed evenings throughout the year. In winter there is a welcoming wood-burner in the rustic, open-plan bar and restaurant. The outside seating area is great in summer. Q ❄ ① ⅍ ♣ ● P 🐾 ●

Sturminster Newton

White Hart Alehouse
Market Cross, DT10 1AN
☎ (01258) 472558
6 changing beers (sourced nationally; often Eight Arch, Gritchie) Ⓗ
Built in 1708, this thatched Grade II-listed public house sits in the heart of the town. The interior is open plan, but with two defined areas; at one end is a large TV, and at the other a large open fire. The pub offers up to six

real ales and 10 craft beers, and good quality pub food is available at reasonable prices. There is a secure beer garden at the rear, formerly the car park. Live music features occasionally. ♿🛇🌢🌓🅿️🖥️(X4,X10)♣🔊📶♪

Swanage

Black Swan 🅛 ⊘

159 High Street, BH19 2NE

☎ (01929) 423846 ⊕ blackswanswanage.co.uk

Dorset Knob; 2 changing beers (sourced nationally) ⏣
A traditional Grade II-listed pub on the High Street, about half a mile from the seafront and near the terminus of the Swanage Steam Railway. There are two bars with stone floors and log fires, serving three well-kept ales. It is renowned for its quality food, and booking for tables is essential (phone reservations only). The pub garden catches the evening sunshine.
Q♿🌢🌓◑≉🅿️🖥️(40,50) ♣📶

Royal British Legion ⊘

150 High Street, BH19 2PA

☎ (01929) 422722 ⊕ therblswanage.co.uk

Hattie Brown's Moonlite; Sharp's Doom Bar; 2 changing beers ⏣
A busy, friendly and well-supported social club that welcomes members and non-members. There are pool tables, darts, and social events including quiz nights, as well as regular live music on Saturday evening and Sunday afternoon. Televised sporting events are shown regularly. Food is served from Wednesday to Sunday and includes midweek burger and steak nights as well as a Sunday carvery. ♿🌓◑🖐️♿≉♣🖥️(40,50)📶♪

Thornford

King's Arms 🅛

Pound Road, DT9 6QD

☎ (01935) 872294 ⊕ kingsarmsthornford.com

Butcombe Original; Palmers Tally Ho!; 2 changing beers (sourced regionally; often Exmoor, Nuttycombe, Parkway) ⏣
The pub stands next to an unusual red-brick Victorian clock tower, which was erected to commemorate Queen Victoria's Diamond Jubilee. Inside is a traditional bar and a separate restaurant; the menu includes vegetarian and gluten-free options. Outside, there are pleasant seating areas, children's play facilities and a large skittle alley. The car park is small, but on-road parking is also available. News of the pub's guest ale is posted weekly on their Facebook page. Closed Monday and Tuesday.
♿🌢🌓♣🅿️📶♪

Wareham

Horse & Groom 🍸 🅛 ⊘

St Johns Hill, BH20 4LZ

☎ (01929) 552222

5 changing beers (sourced regionally; often Butcombe, Hattie Brown's, Palmers) ⏣
Situated in the heart of Wareham is this cosy pub with a reputation for good food and service. In winter customers can enjoy a real fire, while the pleasant courtyard garden can be enjoyed in summer. Five real ales are offered, plus real cider. The pub hosts charity quiz nights and their famed curry evening. They are proud to be the local CAMRA Rural Pub of the Year 2023 and 2024.
♿🌢🌓◑♣🖥️(40,X54) ♣📶

West Bay

George Hotel 🅛 ⊘

18 George Street, DT6 4EY

☎ (01308) 423191 ⊕ georgewestbay.com

Palmers Copper Ale, IPA, Dorset Gold, 200; 1 changing beer (sourced locally; often Palmers) ⏣
A large and welcoming pub next to a picturesque harbour. It consists of a separate public bar, a dedicated eating area and a riverside garden with its own bar in the summer. Wholesome, reasonably priced pub food is available. It serves local cider and at least four Palmers beers, which are brewed nearby in their historic thatched brewery. Open every day, even in winter. There are six en-suite bedrooms. Q♿🌢🛏️◑ A♣🖐️🖥️(X53)♣📶

West Parley

Owls Nest

196 Christchurch Road, BH22 8SS

☎ (01202) 572793

4 changing beers (sourced regionally) ⏣
Cosy, two-roomed pub with an owl theme. It is popular with diners and booking is recommended. The reasonably priced, varied menu includes their famous homemade pies with gluten-free and vegan food also available. There is also an area set out for those who just want a drink, and the bar features up to four changing, local/regional beers. A log burner will keep you warm in colder weather. Live music most Wednesdays. Closed Monday and Tuesday. ♿🌢🌓🅿️🖥️(13,X6)♣📶♪

Weymouth

Dolphin Hotel

67 Park Street, DT4 7DE

☎ (01305) 839273

Hop Back Crop Circle, Entire Stout, Summer Lightning; 1 changing beer (sourced regionally; often Hop Back) ⏣
A Hop Back brewery pub situated only a few minutes' walk to the beach and close to the railway station and bus routes. The pub is light, airy and divided into three rooms: two lounge rooms, both with TVs showing either sports or various music videos, and a function room at the rear with a pool table. Summer Lightning and Crop Circle are the regular beers, usually with Entire Stout and a seasonal ale. There are five en-suite bedrooms.
♿🛏️≉♣🖥️(1)♣♪

Globe Inn

24 East Street, DT4 8BN

☎ (01305) 786061

Butcombe Original; Dartmoor Jail Ale; St Austell Proper Job; Sharp's Sea Fury; 2 changing beers (sourced regionally; often Cerne Abbas, Fine Tuned, Quantock) ⏣
Free house with a friendly welcome, tucked away on a street corner close to the iconic harbourside. It is only a short distance from the town centre, the beach and the esplanade, and offers a quiet refuge from the busy waterside. The bar has a jukebox and photos of old Weymouth on the walls. There is a separate games room for darts and pool players. Guest ales are mainly from local or regional breweries ≉♣🖥️♣📶

William Henry ⊘

1 Frederick Place, DT4 8HQ

☎ (01305) 763730

Greene King IPA; Ruddles Best Bitter; Sharp's Doom Bar; Thornbridge Jaipur IPA; 4 changing beers (sourced nationally; often Milestone, Oakham, Orkney) ⏣

Centrally located close to the main transport links, this popular Wetherspoon pub stands in the gardens of the summer residence of Prince William Henry, Duke of Gloucester, brother of George III. It has an excellent range of ales, plus ciders and craft beers. At least two beer festivals and four tap takeovers are held every year in the gravity-fed festival bar. Wheelchair access is good, including toilets. Family friendly and appealing to all ages. 🐴◑♿🚆🚌📶

Wimborne

Green Man ✔
1 Victoria Road, BH21 1EN
☎ (01202) 881021 🌐 greenmanwimborne.com
Wadworth Henry's IPA, 6X, Swordfish [H]
A friendly, traditional 18th-century pub in the centre of town, with one bar and four separate drinking areas. It features award-winning floral displays, a wood-burner, ubiquitous brasses and the infamous Green Man in the entranceway floor. Games are available on the patio and there is regular live music. The food offered includes steak nights, fish Fridays and Sunday roasts.
🐴❀◑P🚌(3,13) 🐾📶♫

Wool

Black Bear
High Street, BH20 6BP
☎ (01929) 405541
House beer (by Flack Manor); 2 changing beers (sourced nationally) [H]
Friendly community pub in the heart of Wool village, close to the many attractions of the Isle of Purbeck, including Lulworth Cove and Durdle Door. In addition to the cask ales, traditional pub food is on offer. It is welcoming both to locals and visitors, and is family- and dog-friendly. The outside seating area is perfect for relaxing and enjoying the summer sun. Opening times may vary seasonally. Q🐴❀◑🚆P🚌(X54)🐾📶

Worth Matravers

Square & Compass ★ [L]
BH19 3LF (off B3069)
☎ (01929) 439229 🌐 squareandcompasspub.co.uk
Hattie Brown's HBA, Moonlite; 3 changing beers (sourced regionally) [G]
A real gem, this multi award-winning pub has been identified by CAMRA as having a nationally important historic pub interior. It has been in the same family since 1907 and has appeared in every edition of the Guide. Two rooms either side of a serving hatch convey an impression that little has changed over the years. The sea-facing garden offers fantastic views across the Purbecks, and fossils are displayed in the small adjacent museum. Pasties are available. Beer and cider festivals are held in October and November respectively.
Q🐴❀♿🍏🐾♫

George Hotel, West Bay (Photo: Emma Haines)

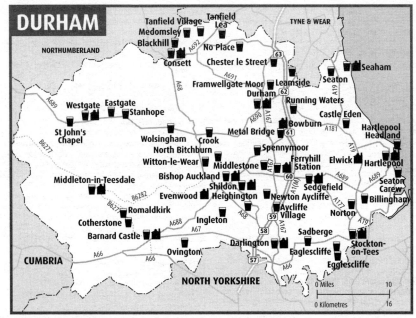

Co Durham incorporates part of the former county of Cleveland

Aycliffe Village

County
13 The Green, DL5 6LX
☎ (01325) 312273 ⊕ thecountyaycliffevillage.com
3 changing beers (sourced nationally) Ⓗ
Overlooking the green in a picturesque village, this attractive, cream-coloured, country free house was originally three 17th-century cottages. It is now open plan, with the bar and three dining areas unified by a bright, modern decor that is complemented by older beams and log fireplaces. The current owners took over in 2020 and have a passion to marry good food with excellent beers. Up to three guests are served along with three craft beers. There is accommodation in seven rooms. Q🕏🖨🌓P🛜

Barnard Castle

Old Well Inn Ⓛ ●
21 The Bank, DL12 8PH
☎ (01833) 690130 ⊕ theoldwellinn.co.uk
Timothy Taylor Landlord, Golden Best; house beer (by Mithril); 1 changing beer (sourced locally) Ⓗ
The boundary of this award-winning 17th-century town-centre inn incorporates part of the medieval castle wall. The pub has a cosy front bar and a comfortable lounge, a separate restaurant and an airy conservatory, plus an enclosed beer garden. At least five well-kept beers are available including two guests from local micros. The house beer is Cummings and Goings from Mithril. Excellent food is served daily, including tasty curries and Chinese. Accommodation in seven en-suite rooms.
Q🕏🏵🖨🌓👌♿🖨(75,76) ✦🛜♪

Billingham

Billingham Catholic Club Ⓛ
37 Wolviston Road, TS23 2RU (on E side of old A19, just S of Roseberry Rd roundabout, next to bus stop)
☎ (01642) 901143

3 changing beers (sourced regionally) Ⓗ
Now in its 16th year in the Guide, this Victorian mansion and former school is a friendly club that actively supports the local community. Dedicated volunteers ensure that the club's reputation for serving 150 different beers every year continues. Three beers are normally served, with eight available throughout the popular bank holiday beer and music festivals. Superb outdoor drinking facilities are provided. A local CAMRA Community Award winner and current Club of the Year.
🏵♿♣P🖨(35,36) ✦♪

Crafty Cock Ⓛ
113 Station Road, TS23 2RL (at N end of Station Rd, close to level crossing)
☎ (01642) 881478
2 changing beers (sourced locally) Ⓗ
This small, cosy bar affords a warm welcome, with friendly and knowledgeable bar staff. Two beers are served, mainly from local breweries, as well as an extensive gin menu. Third-pint tasting paddles are available. Tapas, meze and Mexican food are served Thursday to Saturday evenings, as well as Sunday lunches, and a takeaway and local delivery service are available. The bar is renowned locally for its regular live bands. Quiz night is alternate Wednesdays.
🍺♿P🖨(36,X10) ♪

Bishop Auckland

Bay Horse ●
38-40 Fore Bondgate, DL14 7PE (50yds N of bus station)
☎ (01388) 609765 ⊕ dorbiere.co.uk/the-bay-horse
Timothy Taylor Landlord; Maxim Double Maxim; 1 changing beer (sourced nationally) Ⓗ
There has been a pub on this site since 1530, and this lively, open-plan bar is a quiet relief from shopping during the week. With live music on Friday, speed quizzing on Thursday, and karaoke on Saturday, it becomes joyfully boisterous at the weekend, and is

119

popular for televised sport. It retains its roots as a long-established proper pub, with pub games teams, and an open fire when needed. 🏰👍♣🚌🏡🛜♪

Pollards 🅛
104 Etherley Lane, DL14 6TU (400yds W of railway station)
☎ (01388) 603539
5 changing beers (sourced nationally) 🅗
This comfortable and busy establishment is a great combination of traditional pub and pleasant diner, and is a 10-minute stroll from the town centre. Two of the four original areas, including the bar, boast open fires or log-burners, and there is a spacious restaurant to the rear where the famous Sunday carvery can be enjoyed. Five well-kept ales are augmented by good conversation. Q🌳🏰🕀👍🚌♣P🐾

Stanley Jefferson ✅
5 Market Place, DL14 7NJ
☎ (01388) 452830
Ruddles Best Bitter; Greene King Abbot; 6 changing beers (sourced nationally) 🅗
All the usual Wetherspoon facilities are on offer at this interesting conversion of former solicitors' offices. Several separate but linked drinking areas and a glass-roofed bar area provide the opportunity for privacy or company. Close to the Bishop of Durham's palace and park, the pub takes its name from locally schooled Mr Jefferson – better known as Stan Laurel. There is a large walled garden to the rear and a small pavement patio to the front. Quiz night is Wednesday. 🌳🏰🕀👍🚌

Blackhill

Scotch Arms 🅛 ✅
48 Derwent Street, DH8 8LZ
☎ (01207) 593709
3 changing beers (sourced nationally; often Big Lamp, Mordue, Moorhouse's) 🅗
A welcoming, traditional community hostelry off the main street in Blackhill. The interior of this large, L-shaped bar was freshened up to celebrate the licensee's 10-year anniversary in 2018. Up to three cask ales are on offer, always including local beers. The pub is home to pool and darts teams, a local football team, and is popular for sports TV. Charity nights and other live events often feature. Toasted sandwiches are available. 🌳🕀👍♣🚌🐾🛜♪

Castle Eden

Castle Eden Inn
Stockton Road, Castle Eden, TS27 4SD
☎ (01429) 835954 🌐 castleedeninn.co.uk
2 changing beers (sourced nationally) 🅗
Castle Eden village is famous for the eponymous former brewery. This refurbished old coaching inn has a large bar offering a good selection of ales. The lounge has a spacious and comfortable seating area. Quality food featuring local produce is served in the bar, lounge or the more formal restaurant. There is also a private function room which can comfortably seat 60 people. 🌳🏰🕀P🐾

Chester le Street

Butchers Arms
Middle Chare, DH3 3QD (off Front St, on left from Market Place)
☎ (0191) 388 3605
4 changing beers (sourced nationally; often Ringwood, Wainwright, Wychwood) 🅗

A cosy pub acknowledged for the quality and quantity of its beers, selling at least four cask ales from the Marston's range. The pub is also noted for its food, with home-cooking a speciality; Sunday lunches are popular and good value. Teas and coffees are also served. Dogs are welcome and it is convenient for the railway station and all buses through the town. Quiz night is Tuesday. Q🌳🏰🕀👍🚋♣(Chester-le-Street) ♣🚌(21,50) 🐾

Masonic Centre 🅛 ✅
Station Road, DH3 3DU
☎ (0191) 388 4905 🌐 clsmasoniccentre.co.uk
Black Sheep Best Bitter; 4 changing beers (sourced nationally; often Cheviot, Marston's, Oakham) 🅗
Guests are more than welcome at the Masonic Centre just off Front Street in the heart of the town. As well as up to five changing real ales, you will also find one of the biggest selections of single malt whisky in the area. Sunday lunches and Friday fish suppers are popular. Local CAMRA Club of the Year 2020, 2022 and 2023, and regional Club of the Year runner-up 2023. 🌳🕀👍♣(Chester-le-Street) P🚌(21) 🐾🛜

Wicket Gate 🅛 ✅
193 Front Street, DH3 3AX
☎ (0191) 387 2960
Ruddles Best Bitter; Greene King Abbot; 5 changing beers (sourced nationally) 🅗
This modern Wetherspoon pub reopened in 2020 after major refurbishment. The name acknowledges the strong connection the town has with cricket. It is located near the county cricket ground at the Riverside, and various items of cricket memorabilia decorate the walls. It is very roomy inside, with a single long bar championing local beers. 🌳🏰🕀👍♣(Chester-le-Street) ♣🚌(21) 🛜

Consett

Grey Horse 🏆 🅛 ✅
115 Sherburn Terrace, DH8 6NE (A692, then right along Sherburn Tce)
☎ (01207) 502585 🌐 consettaleworks.co.uk/the-grey-horse
Consett Ale Works Steeltown, White Hot, Red Dust; 6 changing beers (sourced nationally) 🅗
Traditional pub dating back to 1848. The interior comprises a lounge and L-shaped bar with a wood-beamed ceiling. Consett Ale Works brewery is located at the rear. Beer festivals are held twice a year, with a quiz each Wednesday and open mic on Sunday. The coast to coast cycle route is close by. There is some bench seating

REAL ALE BREWERIES

Camerons Hartlepool
Caps Off 🚲 Bishop Auckland
Castle Eden Seaham
Consett 🍺 Consett
Crafty Monkey Elwick
Crafty Pint 🍺 Darlington
Dark Sky Middleton-in-Teesdale
Durham 🚲 Bowburn
George Samuel 🚲 Shildon
Hill Island 🚲 Durham
Hopper House Brew Farm 🚲 Sedgefield
Mad Scientist 🍺 Darlington
McColl's Evenwood
Second Sun Barnard Castle (NEW)
Three Brothers 🚲 Stockton-on-Tees
Village Brewer Brew 22 🍺 Darlington
Weard'ALE 🍺 Westgate
Yard of Ale 🍺 Ferryhill Station

outside at the front of the pub. A repeat local CAMRA Town Pub of the Year, including 2024, and regional Pub of the Year 2023. Q✿♣🖩🌢🏠📶🎵

Cotherstone

Red Lion ★ ℾ
Main Street, DL12 9QE
☎ 07871 865118 ⊕ theredlionhotel.blogspot.com
Yorkshire Dales Butter Tubs, Aysgarth Falls 🖪
An 18th-century Grade II-listed coaching inn, built in stone and set in an idyllic village. Simply furnished, this homely local has changed little since the 1960s. There's no TV, jukebox or one-armed bandit, just good beer and conversation – and two real fires. Children, dogs and clean boots are welcome. It is used by various local clubs, and the small garden is a suntrap. Up to five real ciders are served, including local cider producer Kemps. A former local CAMRA Cider Pub of the Year and Community Pub of the Year. 🌢✿♣🖩(95)🌢📶

Crook

Horse Shoe ℾ ✅
4 Church Street, DL15 9BG
☎ (01388) 744980
Ruddles Best Bitter; Maxim Double Maxim; Greene King Abbot; 5 changing beers (sourced nationally) 🖪
A busy and tastefully refurbished pub with four interlinked drinking areas making up the main part of the pub, and a pleasant, sheltered patio to the side. There is the usual Wetherspoon acknowledgement of previous use, in this case a butcher's, in the metal bar top. Local history is reflected in the decor, with a surprise at the top of the stairs in the shape of old mining equipment. 🌢✿🌢(X1,X46)📶

Darlington

Crafty Merlin's Bottle Shop & Micropub
6 Bucktons Yard, DL3 7QL
☎ 07428 769106 ⊕ craftymerlins.co.uk
3 changing beers (sourced nationally) 🖪
This one-man operation opened during the pandemic as a bottle shop ordering online. The micropub has one room downstairs and one upstairs, as well as outside drinking in the yard. Up to three handpulls serve real ales, with an equal number of keg beers also available. The pub has a homely atmosphere, with conversation very much to the fore. This could become the quirky real ale star of Darlington. Q✿🌢📶

Darlington Snooker Club ℾ
1 Corporation Road, DL3 6AE (corner of Northgate)
☎ (01325) 241388
4 changing beers (sourced nationally) 🖪
First-floor, family-run and family-oriented private snooker club which celebrated its centenary in 2015. A cosy, comfortable TV lounge is available for those not playing on one of the 10 snooker tables. Twice-yearly, the club plays host to a professional celebrity. Four guest beers are stocked from micros countrywide, and two beer festivals are held annually. Frequently voted CAMRA Regional Club of the Year, and a finalist for National Club in 2014, it welcomes CAMRA members on production of a membership card or copy of this Guide. 🌢◑🚌

Half Moon ℾ
130 Northgate, DL1 1QS
☎ 07804 305175
6 changing beers (sourced nationally) 🖪

Old-school local pub just across the ring road from the town centre. It reopened in 2013 as a real ale pub following a long period of closure. Six changing cask ales are served, including ones from micros unusual for the area and occasional ales from their own Crafty Pint nanobrewery, plus two ever-changing real ciders. It has a relaxed, friendly atmosphere and welcomes dogs. There is a library section for borrowing and exchanging books. 🌢♣🌢🌢📶

House of Hop ℾ
4B Houndgate, DL1 5RL
4 changing beers (sourced nationally) 🖪
Smart, contemporary bar in the town centre's Imperial Quarter, with links to the local Three Brothers brewery. There are four ever-changing real ales, usually from across the North East and beyond. You can also find one of the widest ranges of craft keg beers in the town, plus ciders and cocktails. The pub also regularly features live music. Q🌢📶🎵

Number Twenty 2 ℾ ✅
22 Coniscliffe Road, DL3 7RG
☎ (01325) 354590
Village White Boar, Bull, Old Raby; 7 changing beers (sourced nationally) 🖪
Town-centre ale house with a passion for cask beer and winner of many CAMRA awards. Ales are dispensed from up to 16 handpumps, including two real ciders and a stout or porter, along with 10 European beers on draught. Huge curved windows, stained-glass panels and a high ceiling give the interior an airy, spacious feel. It is home to the Village Brewer beers (including Zetland Pale), commissioned from Hambleton by the licensee. To the rear is the in-house nano distillery and microbrewery producing ales, gin and vodka. Sandwiches and snacks are available at lunchtime. Q🌢✿🌢🌢📶

Old Yard Tapas Bar ℾ
98 Bondgate, DL3 7JY
☎ (01325) 467385 ⊕ tapasbar.co.uk
Bradfield Farmers Blonde; Fuller's London Pride; Timothy Taylor Landlord; 2 changing beers (sourced nationally) 🖪
An interesting mixture of a bar and Mediterranean taverna offering real ales alongside a fascinating blend of international wines and spirits in a friendly setting. Five guest beers from local micros and breweries countrywide are stocked, with an extra two sometimes available in further room. Although this is a thriving restaurant, you are welcome to pop in for a beer and tapas. The pavement café is popular in good weather. Food is served lunchtime and evening Sunday to Friday and all day Saturday. Q🌢✿◑🌢📶

ORB Micropub ℾ
28 Coniscliffe Road, DL3 7RG
☎ 07903 237246
7 changing beers (sourced nationally) 🖪
Darlington's first micropub, in a former beauty salon, provides the highest quality local real ales, craft beers and a large range of single malt whiskies. The friendly, knowledgeable staff serve seven local real ales, 10 craft beers, and two real ciders. With no TV or loud music, this is somewhere to engage in conversation. ORB stands for Orchard Road Brewery. A former local CAMRA Pub of the Year. Q🌢

Quakerhouse ♥ ℾ
2 Mechanics Yard, DL3 7QF (off High Row)
⊕ quakerhouse.co.uk
9 changing beers (sourced nationally) 🖪

This friendly, welcoming gem of a pub is located in one of the towns historic Yards. A lively bar with nine handpulled guest beers from local and regional breweries and two changing real ciders. The pub is a popular live music venue, catering for all tastes, and entry is free. There is a music quiz every first Tuesday, when the pub opens late. Home to Mad Scientist microbrewery and Egor. Multiple winner of local CAMRA Town Pub of the Year. ❀♿♣●🚌🐾 ♫

Travellers Rest ★

2 West Auckland Road, DL3 9ER

☎ (01325) 468177

4 changing beers (sourced nationally) Ⓗ

This welcoming, Edwardian-era local is in the heart of Cockerton village, on the outskirts of Darlington. It consists of the traditional bar and lounge arrangement, with an outside drinking area. Some original features remain: tiling in the entrance lobby, fielded panelling in the corridor and, in the public bar, a bar counter with mirrored bar back. The wood surround fireplace and fixed seating are also from the same period. Up to four well-kept guest beers are served. ❀♿♫

Vesuvio

Houndgate, DL1 5RL

☎ (01325) 788564

1 changing beer (sourced nationally) Ⓗ

A recently reopened cosy wine bar in the centre of town. It always has at least one ever-changing real ale available on handpump, typically from local breweries. The welcoming downstairs bar also has an extensive range of wines, spirits and cocktails, and is a popular venue for live music. There are plans to serve food in the future. ≷🐾

Durham

Dun Cow ★ Ⓛ ✔

37 Old Elvet, DH1 3HN

☎ (0191) 386 9219

Castle Eden Ale; Timothy Taylor Landlord; 1 changing beer (sourced nationally; often Castle Eden, Moorhouse's) Ⓗ

A Grade II-listed pub, parts of which date back to the 15th century. In 995AD, Lindisfarne monks searching for a resting place for the body of St Cuthbert came across a milkmaid looking for her lost cow. She directed them to Dun Holm (Durham), and the pub is named after the historic animal. There is a small front snug with a larger lounge to the rear. An occasional guest beer is available. Q♣🚌(6,X12) 🐾

Half Moon Inn ★ ✔

86 New Elvet, DH1 3AQ

☎ (0191) 374 1918 🌐 thehalfmooninndurham.co.uk

Draught Bass; Sharp's Doom Bar; 2 changing beers (sourced nationally; often St Austell, Timothy Taylor, Wainwright) Ⓗ

Popular city-centre pub, reputedly named after the crescent-shaped bar that runs through it. The decor throughout is traditional, featuring photos of the pub at the beginning of the 20th century. A friendly venue with a relaxed atmosphere, it offers a good selection of ales. The large beer garden overlooks the river. ❀♿🚌(6)🐾

Head of Steam Ⓛ

3 Reform Place, DH1 4RZ (through archway from North Rd)

☎ (0191) 383 2173

5 changing beers (sourced nationally; often Camerons, Leeds) Ⓗ

This vibrant pub has a continental feel, attracting beer lovers of all ages. As well as five real ales, it offers an extensive choice of draught and bottled beers from around the world. Tasting events are often held featuring a wide choice of ales and ciders. Excellent, good-value food is available and families are welcome during the day. Improved outdoor seating in the courtyard was installed recently. ❀◑♿≷🚌

Holy GrAle

57 Crossgate, DH1 4PR

☎ (0191) 386 3851

Allendale Pennine Pale Ⓗ

A former board-games café, this craft beer bar was opened in 2019 by the previous landlord of Ye Old Elm Tree, just up the hill. A friendly open-plan venue with several keg taps and two handpulls (though the second is rarely used), all serving an ever-changing range of good beer, alongside large fridges showcasing a range of bottles and cans. A vaulted basement is used for occasional live music. ≷●🚌🐾 ♫

Old Elm Tree 🏆 Ⓛ

12 Crossgate, DH1 4PS

☎ (0191) 386 4621

5 changing beers (sourced nationally; often Abbeydale, Consett Ale Works, Cullercoats) Ⓗ

One of Durham's oldest inns, dating back to at least 1600, this pub has a friendly atmosphere and attracts a good mix of locals, students and visitors to the city. The interior comprises an L-shaped bar and a top room linked by stairs. The pub hosts a Wednesday quiz (arrive early), hosts acoustic nights, and there is a good sized outdoor patio with heaters. Local CAMRA City Pub of the Year 2023 and 2024. ❀◑≷P🚌🐾 ♫

Station House Ⓛ

North Road, DH1 4SE

🌐 stationhousedurham.co.uk

4 changing beers (sourced nationally; often Fyne Ales, Yorkshire Dales) Ⓗ/Ⓖ

Opened in 2015 by a couple who are passionate about real ale, the pub is a totally independent operation. It is friendly, with a back-to-basics approach and an emphasis on conversation. Handpumps have been installed, with gravity remaining an option for a changing range of beer and cider. A dark beer is always available. Closed Mondays. Runner-up in the national CAMRA Pub of the Year awards in 2022. Q♿≷●🚌🐾

Victoria Inn ★ Ⓛ

86 Hallgarth Street, DH1 3AS

☎ (0191) 386 5269 🌐 victoriainn-durhamcity.co.uk

Big Lamp Bitter; 4 changing beers (sourced regionally; often Durham, Fyne Ales) Ⓗ

This warm and welcoming Grade II-listed pub has remained almost unchanged since it was built in 1899, and has been in he same family for over 40 years. The quaint decor, coal fires, cosy snug and genuine Victorian cash drawer help create an olde-worlde feel. No meals are served but toasties are available. The pub is popular with locals, students and visitors, and is a frequent local CAMRA City Pub of the Year winner. Q🛏♣🚌(6,PR2) 🐾

Waiting Room Ⓛ

Northbound Platform, Durham Railway Station, DH1 4RB

☎ (0191) 386 7773

Firebrick Pagan Queen; 1 changing beer (sourced locally; often Durham, Hadrian Border, Yard of Ale) Ⓗ

This attractive venue on Durham railway station's northbound platform is an interesting relaunch of the original 1872 Ladies' Waiting Room, which was out of use for many years other than as a storage facility. In keeping with the building's Grade II-listed status, the design is traditional, with Chesterfield-style seating, original floorboards and fireplaces, wood panelling and a dark-wood bar. Three handpumps showcase local beers. Q✿&♿P🖳(40) ✿ ❦

Woodman Inn

23 Gilesgate, DH1 1QW
☎ (0191) 697 5369 ⊕ thewoodmaninndurham.co.uk
Timothy Taylor Landlord; 1 changing beer (sourced nationally; often Adnams, Maxim, Titanic) Ⓗ
Traditional pub with a twist, just outside the city centre and very much a locals' favourite. It reopened in 2022 after a major refurbishment. It boasts arguably the city's best pub garden, which is a real suntrap in the summer. This pub is family- and dog-friendly and well worth a visit. ☺♿&♣🖳✿ ❦ ♪

Eaglescliffe

Cleveland Bay

718 Yarm Road, TS16 0JE (jct of A67 and A135, N of Tees bridge)
☎ (01642) 780275 ⊕ clevelandbay.co.uk
Timothy Taylor Landlord; Wainwright Gold; 2 changing beers Ⓗ
This three-roomed locals' pub, now with extensive outdoor drinking facilities, has been under the proud stewardship of an enthusiastic licensee, with an enviable reputation for serving fine premium bitters for over 20 years. Third-pint glasses and tasting notes are available for the four handpumps. Their Blues at the Bay music evenings feature bands of national and international repute, covering the various blues styles. A free lunch is served on Sundays. A former local CAMRA Community Pub of the Year. Q✿&♣P🖳(7,17)✿ ❦ ♪

Eastgate

Cross Keys Ⓛ

A689, DL13 2HW (on main road)
☎ (01388) 517234 ⊕ crosskeyseastgate.co.uk
2 changing beers (sourced locally; often Allendale) Ⓗ
A proper family-run Weardale pub, popular with holidaymakers and locals, adjacent to the A689. The ancient 17th-century building has a pleasant interior with a lively, welcoming bar and a restaurant providing relaxed dining. Allendale brewery beers feature regularly, and there is a pleasant beer garden to the rear. Comfortable B&B accommodation is available for those wishing to explore the beautiful surrounding countryside. Q☺✿&♿▲♣P🖳(101) ✿

Egglescliffe

Pot & Glass ★

Church Road, TS16 9DQ (300yds E of A167, opp parish church)
☎ (01642) 651009
Brains Rev James Original; Greene King Abbot; Theakston Old Peculier; Wainwright Gold; Wychwood Hobgoblin Gold, Hobgoblin Ruby; 1 changing beer (sourced nationally) Ⓗ
This classic, old-fashioned, multi-roomed local dates from the 17th century and is situated in a quiet cul-de-sac, high above the River Tees and opposite the 11th-century village church. A former licensee and cabinet maker Charlie Abbey, whose resting place lies in the churchyard, fashioned the ornate bar fronts from old country furniture. Seven handpulls are available, while

the Heng Heng kitchen serves good value home-cooked Thai and Cambodian food. The pub is family-owned and ever-popular, and has pleasant outdoor facilities. Q☺✿&♿🖳(7,17) ❦

Ferryhill Station

Surtees Arms ♥ Ⓛ

Chilton Lane, DL17 0DH
☎ (01740) 655933 ⊕ yardofalebrewery.com
Yard of Ale One Foot In The Yard; 4 changing beers (sourced locally; often Yard of Ale) Ⓗ
Traditional pub serving local and national ales and ciders, as well as beers from the on-site Yard of Ale brewery. Annual beer festivals are held in the summer and at Halloween. Live music and charity nights are regular events. Lunches are served on Sunday only. A large function room is available. Local CAMRA Country Pub of the Year 2023 and 2024 and a former regional Pub of the Year. Q☺✿&♿🖳✿ ❦ ♪

Framwellgate Moor

Fram Ferment Ⓛ

29B Front Street, DH1 5EE
⊕ framferment.co.uk
3 changing beers (sourced nationally; often Cullercoats, Durham, Fyne Ales) Ⓟ
A former NHS clinic converted to a bottle shop and taproom in 2019. Large fridges full of bottles and cans of beer and cider line one wall. A large oak bar, believed to have previously been a Methodist pulpit, sits in front of a tiled tap wall, through which both the cask and keg beers are served. Seating options include a Monk's bench, cinema seats and pub stools, along with a couple of tables outside the front window. ☺✿&⇌(Durham) ●🖳✿ ❦

Hartlepool

Anchor Tap Room & Bottle Shop Ⓛ

Stockton Street, TS24 7QS (on A689, in front of Camerons brewery)
☎ (01429) 868686 ⊕ cameronsbrewery.com
Camerons Strongarm; 1 changing beer Ⓗ
When Camerons brewery discovered that it owned the adjacent derelict pub, its future was secured after it was converted into the brewery's visitor centre. Now in its 21st successful year, it has reverted to its original 1865 name and rebranded as a tap and bottle shop. Strongarm and the brewery's specials are always available, together with an array of limited edition and continental bottled beers. Located close to Stranton All Saints Church, which is possibly of Saxon origin. ✿&⇌P🖳(1,36)✿

Hops & Cheese

9-11 Tower Street, TS24 7HH (100yds S of bus interchange/railway station)
☎ 07704 660417
3 changing beers Ⓗ
Run by an enthusiastic licensee, this unique, modern venue definitely offers 'something quite different', and represents a complete breath of fresh air. Combining beers and cider with top-class cheeses and charcuterie, served with all the trimmings, and available to take away if required. Comedy club, jazz and open-mic sessions, cheese/wine nights and vinyl nights are becoming more popular and all add to the experience. Some events are pre-bookable/ticket only, making the venue occasionally closed to the passing visitor. ☺♿&⇌🖳(1,36) ✿

Rat Race Ale House

Station Approach, Hartlepool Railway Station, TS24 7ED (on Platform 1)

☎ 07903 479378 ⊕ ratracealehouse.co.uk

4 changing beers (sourced nationally) Ⓗ

The second micropub in the country, now celebrating 15 years of continuous Guide recognition. It adheres to the original micropub norms: no lager; no spirits/alcopops; no TV/jukebox; no one-arm-bandit; even no bar! Since opening in 2009, more than 2,000 beers, sourced from over 550 different breweries, have been served direct to customers' tables by the landlord himself. A porter or a stout is always available as well as two real ciders. A winner of multiple local CAMRA awards.

Q♿☕♣🅿️🚃(1,36)

Hartlepool Headland

Fisherman's Arms Ⓛ

Southgate, TS24 0JJ (on headland close to Fish Quay, in Old Hartlepool)

☎ 07847 208599 ⊕ thefishhartlepool.co.uk

3 changing beers Ⓗ

This local CAMRA multi-award winner is a friendly, one-room locals' pub, recognised by the local council for its charitable support to the community. Now free of tie, it serves three changing beers. The pub's theme is 'keeping music alive', and it hosts well-supported open mic nights, with regular live music also featuring. A popular quiz is held on Sunday. There is no TV, jukebox, or one-armed-bandit. Two beer festivals, also with live music, are held annually. Winter opening hours may vary. Q🚃🚃(7)🐾🐕♫

Heighington

Bay Horse Inn

28 West Green, DL5 6PE (5 mins from A1 at jct 58 with the A68)

☎ (01325) 312312 ⊕ bayhorseheighington.co.uk

Pennine Millie George; Timothy Taylor Landlord; 1 changing beer (sourced nationally) Ⓗ

Picturesque 300-year-old pub overlooking the award-winning village's large green. Its traditional interior, with exposed beams and stone walls, is partitioned into distinct drinking and dining areas, and a large restaurant extends from the lounge. Drinkers in the bar can enjoy the good beer range in the evening, with up to three guest ales. The pub steps away from traditional fare to offer a butcher's counter of meaty delights, cut and cooked to personal preference. 🐕🍴🕑🕛♿🅿️🚃

Ingleton

Black Horse Ⓛ

Front Street, DL2 3HS

☎ (01325) 730374

4 changing beers (sourced locally) Ⓗ

Free house and restaurant set back from the road in a picturesque village. This is a popular community hostelry with a relaxed atmosphere, and the friendly bar runs into the dining area. Four guest ales come from local micros within a 30-mile radius of the pub. Excellent Italian food is served Wednesday to Sunday in the restaurant. Local darts team are supported. A weekly Sunday night quiz is held. It has a large car park. Q🐕🍴🕑🕛♿♣🅿️🚃(84)🐾🐕

Leamside

Three Horseshoes ★ Ⓛ

Pit House Lane, DH4 6QQ (about ½ mile N of A690, just outside West Rainton)

☎ (0191) 584 2394 ⊕ threehorseshoesleamside.co.uk

Timothy Taylor Landlord; 5 changing beers (sourced nationally) Ⓗ

A country pub with an excellent restaurant, the Back Room (booking advisable). The traditional bar has open fires in winter and a large TV for sport. Five real ales are served. The pub is home to a local cycle club and hosts a quiz on Sunday evening. A former local CAMRA Country Pub of the Year and runner-up in 2023.

Q🐕🍴🍴🕑🕛♿🅿️🐕📶

Medomsley

Royal Oak Ⓛ

7 Manor Road, DH8 6QN

☎ (01207) 560336

Hadrian Border Tyneside Blonde; Mordue Workie; 1 changing beer (sourced nationally) Ⓗ

Traditional country-style pub with a warm, welcoming feel. It has a large bar with a selection of seating including soft sofas and leather chairs, and plenty of dining space. The pub serves a rotation of quality beers as well as good food. There is a large, attractive rear garden and ample parking to the front.

Q🐕🍴🕑🕛♿🅿️🚃🐕📶

Metal Bridge

Old Mill Ⓛ

Thinford Road, DH6 5NX (off A1M jct 61, follow signs on A177)

☎ (01740) 652928 ⊕ oldmilldurham.co.uk

4 changing beers (sourced nationally; often Bowland, Durham, Rudgate) Ⓗ

Originally an early 19th-century paper mill, the pub offers good-quality food and well-kept ales. Four handpumps serve a diverse range, with local breweries supplying at least one of the beers. The food menu is extensive, with daily specials written on a board above the bar. Larger groups are welcome in the conservatory. Accommodation is of a high standard, with all rooms en-suite. Q🐕🍴🍴🕑🕛♿🅿️🚃(56)📶

Middlestone

Ship Inn Ⓛ

Low Road, DL14 8AB (between Coundon and Kirk Merrington)

☎ (01388) 810904

2 changing beers (sourced nationally; often Caps Off, Consett Ale Works, Maxim) Ⓗ

Regular drinkers come from far and wide to the Ship. It has a bar divided into three distinct areas with an open fire, and a large function room upstairs which is the location for occasional beer festivals. The rooftop patio has spectacular views. Various pieces of Vaux memorabilia are on display – one of the many subjects of conversation. At least two real ales available. A former local CAMRA Country Pub of the Year.

Q🐕🍴🕑🕛♿♣🅿️🚃(56) 🐕

Middleton-in-Teesdale

Teesdale Hotel Ⓛ

Market Place, DL12 0QG

☎ (01833) 640264 ⊕ teesdalehotel.co.uk

Black Sheep Best Bitter; 2 changing beers (sourced nationally) ⊞
A former coaching inn updated to provide excellent accommodation. This is a popular village local as well as a resting place for Pennine walkers (Middleton in Teesdale is often referred to as 'the capital of Upper Teesdale', with High Force and Cauldron Snout nearby). Up to two guest beers are served, often from local micros. Meals can be enjoyed in the main bar or the comfortable restaurant. A farmers' market is held on the last Sunday of the month. Q ☎ ✐ ◑ ▲ P ⊞ ⊟ (95,96) ✿

Newton Aycliffe

Turbinia 🅛

Parsons Centre, Sid Chaplin Drive, DL5 7PA (off Burnhill Way, next to Methodist church)
☎ (01325) 313034 ⊕ turbiniapub.co.uk
4 changing beers (sourced nationally; often Mithril, Three Brothers) ⊞
Named after the famous Tyneside ship, this friendly free house comprises a large lounge and function room in traditional pub decor, featuring a pictorial history of the Turbinia, and a woodchip fire. This local favourite serves an ever-changing variety of beers sourced locally and nationally, as well as craft gins. It hosts its own beer and cider festivals. Darts, dominoes and pool are played in he main bar during the week and live music at the weekend. Dogs are welcome. ☎ ⊛ ⅙ ♣ P ⊟ (7) ✿ ☎ ♪

No Place

Beamish Mary Inn 🅛

DH9 0QH (follow signs to No Place off A693 from Chester-le-Street to Stanley)
☎ (0191) 392 0543 ⊕ beamish-mary-inn.co.uk
3 changing beers (sourced nationally) ⊞
Characterful pub renowned for its warm welcome, generously portioned pub grub, and its selection of well-kept real ales. The location is handy for visitors to the famous Beamish open-air museum nearby. Consett Ale Works beers are usually included among the range of LocAles on offer. Accommodation is available, including twin, double and family rooms. A former CAMRA national Pub of the Year. ☎ ⊛ ✐ ◑ ⅙ P ⊟ (8,8A) ✿ ☎

North Bitchburn

Red Lion

North Bitchburn Terrace, DL15 8AL (½ mile up the hill from A689 in Howden le Wear)
☎ (01388) 767071
3 changing beers (sourced nationally; often Black Sheep, Timothy Taylor) ⊞
High above the Wear Valley, the exterior of this old building belies its clean-cut, spacious interior. The pub is famous for top-quality ale, with the guest beers changing regularly. A bright and comfortable bar area has a pool table, and there is a patio area to the rear of the building with views over the rooftops.
Q ☎ ⊛ ♣ P ⊟ (1B,X1) ✿

Norton

Highland Laddie ✔

59 High Street, TS20 1AQ
☎ (01642) 539570
Greene King Abbot; Ruddles Best Bitter; Sharp's Doom Bar; 7 changing beers ⊞
Named after the Scottish drovers who herded livestock to cattle markets south as far as London. During its conversion by Wetherspoon the pub was significantly

extended and now comprises two large open-plan areas, with the pub's original snug retained. It offers an excellent choice of seven guests, besides the chain's contracted beers. There is also a patio for those wishing to brave the north-easterlies. Served by local and express regional bus links. ☎ ⊛ ◑ ⅙ ⊟ (X7,X10) ☎

Ovington

Four Alls 🅛

The Green, DL11 7BP (2 miles S of Winston & A67)
☎ (01833) 627302 ⊕ thefouralls-ovington.co.uk
Mithril Kingdom of Ovingtonia; 2 changing beers (sourced locally) ⊞
Friendly, stone-built 18th-century inn opposite the village green in what is known as the 'maypole village'. A Victorian sign denotes the four alls: 'I govern all (queen), I fight for all (soldier), I pray for all (parson), I pay for all (farmer).' The single-roomed interior has an 'upstairs' snug serving excellent-value food cooked with local ingredients. Two real ales include a dark and a light from local Mithril Ales, and special house beer Kingdom of Ovingtonia. The rear beer garden is perfect on sunny days. A former local CAMRA Country Pub of the Year. Q ☎ ⊛ ◑ ⅙ ▲ P ✿ ☎

Romaldkirk

Kirk Inn

The Green, DL12 9EN
☎ (01833) 650260
Mithril Dere Street ⊞
Overlooking the large village green, surrounded by many fine houses, is this one-room, friendly inn, situated in a picturesque village. It's a warm and welcoming pub with a roaring fire, and the landlord is proud of his real ale. There is a lovely outside drinking area on the decking to the right of the door. Dogs are welcome. Q ⊛ P ✿

Running Waters

Three Horse Shoes 🅛

Sherburn House, DH1 2SR
☎ (0191) 372 0286 ⊕ threehorseshoesdurham.co.uk
2 changing beers (sourced nationally; often Consett Ale Works, Durham, Yard of Ale) ⊞
Country inn nicely situated a few miles from Durham city, offering good food and drink and comfortable accommodation. Two cask ales are served, usually at least one sourced locally, with alcohol available from noon. The interior was extensively refurbished in 2016, while the rear beer garden provides excellent views over open countryside. Q ☎ ⊛ ✐ ◑ ⅙ P ☎

Sadberge

Buck Inn 🅛

Middleton Road, DL2 1RR
☎ (01325) 335710
Maxim Samson; Mithril A66 ⊞
Friendly traditional English pub overlooking the village green. Named after George Buck, a benevolent 18th-century landowner. It has two bars, one mainly for dining, and there are outdoor benches and tables in front. It is a supporter of local micros and always has one beer from Mithril. A variety of good food is served lunchtimes and evenings; look out for their parmos. They have a monthly quiz and regular live music and race nights. The village sits atop a hill and is in a popular walking area. ☎ ⊛ ◑ ⅙ ⊟ (20) ☎

St John's Chapel

Blue Bell Inn L
Hood Street, DL13 1QJ
☎ (01388) 537256 ⊕ thebluebellinn.pub
2 changing beers (sourced regionally) ⊞
Originally a pair of terraced cottages, the Blue Bell is a friendly and cosy pub with a bar across the front of the building leading to a small pool room, and garden to the rear. Situated on the A689, it serves the local community and those who holiday in Upper Weardale. It is popular for pub games, and also doubles as a library.
Q❄☎❀▲♣➡(101)❀☎

Seaham

Coalhouse L
39 Church Street, SR7 7EJ
☎ (0191) 581 6235
4 changing beers (sourced locally; often Cullercoats, Yard of Ale) ⊞
A former bookmakers' and now a much-valued part of Seaham's licensed trade. The pub was refurbished in 2018 using 100-year-old timbers salvaged from the town's demolished Co-op building. The decor celebrates the area's coal-mining heritage, notably one wall's impressive mural depicting Seaham pits. Four changing cask beers are offered along with five keg taps.
❀≠♣➡(65,60)❀♪

Hat & Feathers L ✓
57-59 Church Street, SR7 7HF
☎ (0191) 513 3040
Greene King Abbot; Sharp's Doom Bar; 4 changing beers (sourced nationally; often Maxim) ⊞
This Wetherspoon pub gets its name from the Doggarts store that occupied the site from the 1920s to the 1980s and had a department selling hats and feathers. Upstairs are old photographs depicting the headgear of the best-dressed ladies of the time. Other interesting pictures show the past history of Seaham. The furnishings are a mix of modern and traditional styles, including comfortable settees. Outside is a plaque displaying a history of the building. ☎❀❶◑❺♣➡☎

Seaton

Dun Cow L
The Village, SR7 0NA
☎ (0191) 513 1133
4 changing beers (sourced nationally; often Jennings, Maxim, Wainwright) ⊞
Friendly and unspoilt inn on the village green, with a public bar and lounge areas. This is a pub for good conversation or a game of darts; the TV is only used for special events. The changing guest beer selection usually comprises two light and two dark ales. No meals are served but toasties are always available. The pub hosts regular busker and acoustic music nights. A former local CAMRA Country Pub of the Year. ☎❀❺♣P➡(71)❀☎♪

Seaton Carew

9 Anchors
2 The Front, TS25 1BS (on seafront at jct with Station Ln)
☎ (01429) 551343
2 changing beers (sourced regionally) ⊞
This former flower shop was converted into a micropub in 2017, and is now the pub of choice for the discerning drinker in this resort town. It is named after the rescue of nine crewmen from the Danish schooner Doris that floundered off the coast in 1930. The friendly locals,

sandstone walls, furniture made from driftwood and a bar constructed from a Welsh dresser all add to the ambience. Quiz night is Wednesday, while acoustic night is Thursday. There are views of the petrified forest at low tide. Q❺➡(1)❀☎♪

Sedgefield

Ceddesfeld Hall
Rectory Row, TS21 2AE
☎ (01740) 620341
2 changing beers (sourced nationally; often Theakston) ⊞
Built in 1791 as the local parsonage, the hall is set in extensive grounds and is ideal for a summer evening. There is a bar, comfortable lounge and large function room. This private club is run by volunteers from the Sedgefield Community Association, and is used by a wide variety of groups. CAMRA members are most welcome. An annual beer festival is held on the first weekend in July, with reasonably priced ale. Look out for the resident ghost, 'the Pickled Parson'. ☎❀❺P☎

Dun Cow
43 Front Street, TS21 3AT
☎ (01740) 620894 ⊕ duncow.wixsite.com
Black Sheep Best Bitter; Timothy Taylor Knowle Spring; 1 changing beer (sourced nationally) ⊞
Run by the same landlord for more than 40 years, this large and comfortable 18th-century inn has a countywide reputation for good food using locally sourced produce. Prime minister Tony Blair and US president George W Bush famously had lunch here in 2003. There are three bars, including a farmers' bar-cum-snug and restaurant. Three real ales are always available. The pub is open for breakfasts and non-alcoholic refreshment in the mornings. Q❄❀❻◑P➡(X12)❀☎

Shildon

Canteen Bar & Kitchen L
Norland House, Byerley Road, DL4 1HE
⊕ canteen-bar-kitchen.co.uk
George Samuel Locomotion No 1, Leaves on the Line, Harvey; 1 changing beer (sourced nationally; often George Samuel) ⊞
An ambitious conversion of the former canteen of the famous Shildon Wagon Works. The bar and brewery share a single space, and an entrance with other businesses in the building. There is a spacious drinking area with picnic-style tables, where you can sit within feet of the brewing vessels. The railway heritage is reflected in the decor. Open for breakfast.
Q◑❺≠P➡(X1)♪

Spennymoor

Frog & Ferret
Coulson Street, DL16 7RS
☎ (0191) 389 7246
6 changing beers (sourced nationally; often Camerons, Consett Ale Works, Hadrian Border) ⊞
Friendly family-run free house offering up to six constantly changing real ales, sourced from far and wide, with local and northern microbreweries well represented. The comfortably furnished lounge has a bar with brick, stone and wood cladding, and a solid fuel burner. Sports TV is featured. Children are welcome until 9pm. Live music is hosted each Saturday night and monthly on Thursday and Sunday. ☎❀❶◑❺♣☎♪

Little Tap L

King Street, DL16 6QQ
☎ (01388) 304001
5 changing beers (sourced regionally; often Daleside, Durham) ⊞

Clever remodelling of a former sandwich shop as a smart little bar. The plush carpet makes it unusually comfortable for a micropub. The 'cellar' is close to the pumps – beer is housed in cleverly converted fridges directly beneath the bar. Outside is a small yard in which to take advantage of any sunshine. It is handily located next door to a Chinese takeaway. Q✿&☐✿

Stanhope

Grey Bull

17 West Terrace, DL13 2PB
☎ 07885 676575
2 changing beers (sourced nationally) ⊞

A community-focused hostelry with a warm welcome, at the foot of Crawleyside Bank at the west end of town. It has a busy bar area across the front and a lounge to the rear with a pool table, served by a central bar that dispenses up to three cask beers. Tables to the front are popular in fine weather. Convenient for the coast to coast cycle route. Q✿☞♣☐(101)✿ 🔊

Stockton-on-Tees

Golden Smog ♀

1 Hambletonian Yard, TS18 1DS (in a ginnel between High St and West Row)
☎ (01642) 385022
5 changing beers ⊞

The town's original micropub, this local CAMRA Pub of the Year 2024, and a previous Regional Pub of the Year, is named after the environmental conditions that used to prevail on Teesside. Interesting decor, a small lending library and its friendly atmosphere make it well worth a visit. Five beers, real ciders and a range of craft beers are served alongside an impressive selection of Belgian and German beers, all served in their own matching glasses. Third-pints, served on bespoke Smog tasting tables, are also available. An extensive selection of free bar snacks is served on Sunday. The pub supports various charitable causes. Q●☐✿

Kopper Keg

27 Dovecot Street, TS18 1LH (just off High St in centre of town)
☎ 07984 624872
2 changing beers (sourced nationally) ⊞

A single-room micro run by an enthusiastic licensee, with two handpulls and a wide range of craft beers, bottles and cans. The cask ale is always fresh. Refectory-style tables add to the environment, while conversation flows freely. Two large screens feature sport at one end of the pub and bands at the other. The Facebook page keeps drinkers updated on which beers are available. &▲₹(Stockton) ♣☐☐✿🔊

Sun Inn

2 Knowles Street, TS18 1SU (off High St in centre of town)
☎ (01642) 329426 ⊕ craftunionpubs.com
Draught Bass ⊞

A popular a friendly traditional town-centre drinkers' pub, reputed to sell more 'banked' Draught Bass than any other pub in the country. Three distinct drinking areas include a large rear lounge. Numerous sports TVs are dotted around the pub and mainly devoted to horse racing and football. It also has a lovely, small beer garden. The pub is opposite the Stockton Flyer, a stylised depiction of Locomotive No. 1, which steams everyday at 1pm. ✿₹(Stockton)☐♣🔊

Thomas Sheraton L ✓

4 Bridge Road, TS18 3BW (at S end of High St)
☎ (01642) 606134
Greene King IPA, Abbot; Sharp's Doom Bar; 4 changing beers ⊞

This Grade II-listed Victorian building, now in its 16th year in the Guide, is a fine Wetherspoon's conversion of the law courts and named after one of the country's great Georgian cabinet makers, born in the town in 1751. The large, airy interior comprises several separate drinking and dining areas, plus a pleasant balcony and an upstairs outdoor terrace. The guest beers, usually from the area, are served alongside the chain's contracted beers, together with a range of real ciders.
Q🕏✿❶&₹(Thornaby) ♣●☐ 🔊

Tipsy Turtle L

5 Regency West Mall, West Row, TS18 1EF (100yds W of High St through any of the wynds)
☎ (01642) 670171
4 changing beers ⊞

Popular micropub in a mall containing several other licensed outlets, and now established on the town's micropub circuit. Four handpulls include at least one serving a rarer beer style, while a wide selection of craft beers, a dozen or more real and fruit ciders and an interesting selection of bottled continental beers are also available. When busy, drinkers overflow into the mall, while at weekends, the pub expands into the adjacent premises. Q🕏&₹(Stockton) ♣☐✿ 🔊🔊

Tanfield Lea

Tanfield Lea Working Mens Club

West Street, DH9 9NA
☎ (01207) 238783
2 changing beers (sourced nationally; often Consett Ale Works, Goff's, Play Brew) ⊞

The village has no pub, reflecting its strong Methodist history, but guests are most welcome in this CIU-affiliated club, which has become something of a flagship for real ale in the area. TV sport is shown in the bar, and there is also a quiet, comfortable lounge. Traditional club activities such as bingo take place and there is usually a live act on Sunday. Local CAMRA Club of the Year 2016-2019 and 2024. 🕏&♣P☐ 🔊🔊

Tanfield Village

Peacock

Front Street, DH9 9PX
☎ (01207) 232720
Black Sheep Best Bitter; 1 changing beer (sourced nationally; often Purity, Timothy Taylor) ⊞

A warm welcome is guaranteed in this friendly, traditional, two-bar pub in a pretty village. The Peacock is popular with locals and visitors alike, including bell-ringers from the church opposite. Black Sheep is always available alongside a changing guest beer. Lovely home-cooked meals are served Wednesday to Saturday evenings and Sunday lunchtime – the portions are generous and great value for money. There is a small beer garden and ample parking. Q🕏✿❶♣P☐(V8)🔊

Westgate

Hare & Hounds L

24 Front Street, DL13 1RX

☎ (01388) 517212
Weard'ALE Gold, Dark Nights Ⓗ
On the banks of the Wear, on the A689. The spacious, stone-flagged bar is partially fitted out with items salvaged from the former village chapel, and is a great place to catch up on local news. The restaurant's patio overlooks the river; here the beer is being brewed beneath your feet. Food, including the famous Sunday carvery, is locally sourced. **Q**☽❀ⅅ&Å♣P▯(101)

Witton-le-Wear

Dun Cow
19 High Street, DL14 0AY
☎ (01388) 488294
2 changing beers (sourced nationally; often Timothy Taylor, Wainwright) Ⓗ
A welcoming local set back from the road through the village, with a single L-shaped room warmed by open fires at both ends. Dating from 1799, the bar is guarded by a sleeping fox. There are benches to the left of the bar, and seating outside offering pleasant views over the Wear valley. **Q**❀♣P

Victoria Ⓛ
School Street, DL14 0AS
☎ (01388) 488058 ⊕ thevicwlw.co.uk

3 changing beers (sourced regionally; often Allendale, Maxim) Ⓗ
Traditional village pub with a central bar serving two distinct drinking areas, the larger of which is split level. The pub has great views over Wear Valley from the patio to the rear, and the church to the front. The bright interior has clean lines and pleasant decor. A wood-fired pizza oven in the garden is part of the occasional food offering. Close to the preserved Wear Valley Railway. B&B accommodation is available. ❀🛏ⅅ♣P🐾🛜

Wolsingham

Black Lion Ⓛ
21 Meadhope Street, DL13 3EN (50yds N of Market Place)
☎ (01388) 527772
4 changing beers (sourced nationally; often Firebrick, Rudgate, Timothy Taylor) Ⓗ
Hidden away only a minute from the Market Place, this welcoming, comfortable gem is a great place to relax. An open fire features in the single, open-plan room, with a pool table to the rear and TV sport to the front. Local charities benefit from the efforts of the pub. Opening hours may be longer in summer but it is best to check in advance. **Q**❀&♣▯(101)🐾🛜

Waiting Room, Durham (Photo: Stuart McMahon)

CASK MARQUE – WHO ARE WE?

Cask Marque was founded in 1998 by Paul Nunny, a former Director of Adnams, to improve the quality of cask ale in pubs and raise industry standards.

"We are a not-for-profit organisation set up to ensure that the cask ale you drink in pubs is in perfect condition. Today the Directors are made up of representatives from large and small breweries, pub companies and trade bodies, all engaged in continuing to drive beer quality."

In just over twenty years Cask Marque has:

- Accredited over 10,000 pubs for the quality of their beer
- Visited over 20,000 pubs each year
- Improved standards of cellarmanship through training, qualifications, and star ratings
- Ensured that your beer in the glass is cellar-cool by installing ale python cooling systems
- Communicated what Cask Marque stands for with 77% of consumers recognising the plaque (YouGov 2018)
- Launched the Cask Finder app to find Cask Marque pubs with over 60,000 users per month
- Championed cask ales through the annual Cask Seminar

Look out for our Marque in the Guide and you are guaranteed to find a great pint of cask ale ✅

Pubs who apply for a Cask Marque accreditation receive two unannounced visits per year from one of 60 assessors who are qualified brewers or senior technical services personnel. On a visit they sample up to six cask ales in the glass and check for temperature, aroma, appearance, and taste. In addition, new pubs must pass an 11-point check list to establish their beer cellar rating.

Use the free **Cask Finder** **app** and you are guaranteed to receive a great pint of cask ale

To find out more about Cask Marque visit www.cask-marque.co.uk and join us in championing beer quality in the glass

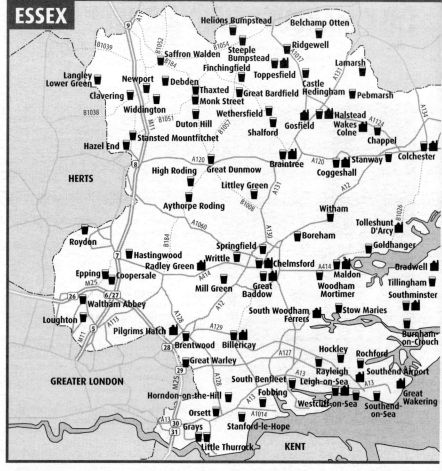

ESSEX

HERTS

GREATER LONDON

KENT

Aythorpe Roding

Axe & Compasses L

Dunmow Road, CM6 1PP (on B184 5 miles SW of Dunmow) TL594154

☎ (01279) 876648 ⊕ theaxeandcompasses.co.uk

3 changing beers (sourced locally; often Bishop Nick, Chelmsford) Ⓗ

The Axe is an 18th-century building surrounded by beautiful countryside. While drinkers are very welcome, it is know for its food and has won awards for being the best Essex pub restaurant. A mixed clientele of locals and farming folk enjoy the well-kept selection of beers and ciders. The food consists of pub classics with a modern twist, all locally sourced. Service is efficient and friendly. The pub hosts quizzes and themed food nights (see website). Open for breakfast 9-11.30 every day.
Q ☺ ❀ ❀ ⟲ ⓘ ♿ ⬤ P ⯈ (17,18) ♣ ☏

Belchamp Otten

Red Lion L

Fowes Lane, CO10 7BQ (on a small single-track lane, signed by the duck pond) TL799415

☎ (01787) 278301

Adnams Southwold Bitter; 2 changing beers (sourced nationally) Ⓗ

Lovely local inn, hidden away in the smallest of the Belchamps. The owner and his friendly dog provide a warm welcome, with an open fire in winter. The pub does not currently serve food, but has delivery arrangements with local takeaway restaurants. It has darts and a pool table, and occasional events are run. There are excellent views, good walks and cycle rides from here. ☺ ❀ ♣ P ♣ ☏

Billericay

Billericay Brewing Co. Shop & Micropub

52 Chapel Street, CM12 9LS

☎ (01277) 500121 ⊕ billericaybrewing.co.uk

Billericay Zeppelin, Blonde, Dickie; 1 changing beer (sourced locally; often Billericay) Ⓖ

The brewery tap serves up to four real ales on gravity, mostly from Billericay brewery plus two other beers on KeyKeg. Seating in the bar is on high stools next to solid wooden tables, or in the recently redecorated snug. Outdoor marquee seating is popular in the summer. The beer shop in the micropub sells bottles from Billericay and others, plus foreign beers. Beer festivals are held several times a year plus many other events; see social media for details. ☺ ❀ ❀ ♣ ♠ ⬤ ⟲ (100,222) ♣ ☏

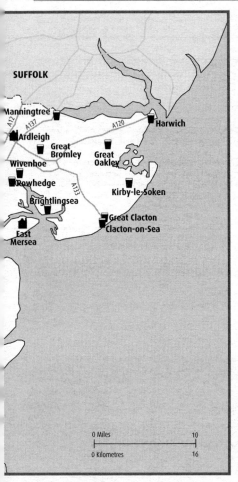

fire indoors during winter. A community oriented venue with traditional bar games including shove-ha'penny with real ha'pennies. There is live music two Sunday afternoons a month, and karaoke on the second Sunday of the month. ♿🏠👶🚯⚘P🚌(100,9)🐾🕸♪

Boreham

Queen's Head 🅛
Church Road, CM3 3EG
☎ (01245) 467298
Colchester Sweeney Todd; 3 changing beers (sourced nationally) 🅗
Dating from the 16th century and run by the same family for over 20 years, this friendly pub is tucked away just past the church. It has two contrasting bars – one with bench seating for darts, dominoes and crib, the other for dining. A wooden conservatory leads to the garden with picnic benches to enjoy food and drink in a tranquil setting. Home-cooked fare is served Thursday and Friday. Beer festivals are held at Easter and on the August bank holiday. Local CAMRA Pub of the Year 2022.
♿🏠🌶♣🍴P🚌(71,371) 🐾🕸♪

Braintree

King William IV 🅛
114 London Road, CM77 7PU
☎ 07595 911046
Mighty Oak Captain Bob 🅗; **4 changing beers (sourced nationally)** 🅖
Friendly traditional free house serving up to four real ales, usually featuring Essex microbreweries, and an interesting selection of ciders. There is a main bar and a small back bar. A large patio area with picnic tables is used to host events throughout the year including beer festivals and musical events. Primarily a drinking pub, it does not offer cooked meals. Moody Goose brewery is located in the pub grounds, at least one of their ales is usually available in warmer months. Q🏠⚘🍴P🚌(170)🐾♪

Picture Palace ●
Fairfield Road, CM7 3HA
☎ (01376) 550255

Coach & Horses 🅛
36 Chapel Street, CM12 9LU
☎ (01277) 622873 ⊕ thecoachandhorses.org
Fuller's London Pride; Mighty Oak Captain Bob; Oakham Citra; Wibblers Dengie IPA; 1 changing beer (sourced nationally) 🅗
Close to the High Street, this welcoming pub with an inviting atmosphere has appeared in this Guide for over 25 years. Five ales are served, with one always from Oakham (the pub is part of the Oakademy) plus one rotating craft beer and imported German lagers. Top quality, home-made food is available selected lunchtimes and evenings, with a curry night on Wednesdays. The bar service is efficient and friendly. There is a cosy and attractive courtyard garden.
🏠🍴♿🚯P🚌(100) 🕸

Railway
1 High Street, CM12 9BE
☎ (01277) 652173 ⊕ therailwaybillericay.co.uk
Dark Star Hophead; Wibblers Dengie IPA; 3 changing beers (sourced nationally) 🅗
A friendly pub which earns its tag line: No.1 in the High Street. It has served over 1,000 different real ales and won several local CAMRA awards. Guest beers are updated on social media. Regular events include a quiz, charity days and league darts. Welcoming in all seasons, it has a beer garden for warmer weather and an open

REAL ALE BREWERIES

Billericay 🍺 Billericay
Bishop Nick Braintree
Black Box ✦ Southend Airport
Brentwood ✦ Pilgrims Hatch
Brewhouse & Kitchen 🍺 Chelmsford
Chelmsford ✦ Great Baddow
Colchester Wakes Colne
Courtyard ✦ Gosfield
Crouch Vale ✦ South Woodham Ferrers
Datum Attitude Tolleshunt D'Arcy
George's Great Wakering
JackRabbit Ardleigh
Leigh on Sea ✦ Leigh-on-Sea
Mersea Island East Mersea
Mighty Oak Maldon
Moody Goose 🍺 Braintree
Neolithic Bradwell
Other Monkey ✦ Colchester
Pumphouse Community Toppesfield
Radio City Radley Green (NEW)
St Botolphs Colchester
Watson's Colchester
WHARF Coggeshall
White Hart 🍺 Halstead
Wibblers ✦ Southminster

Greene King Abbot; Ruddles Best Bitter; Sharp's Doom Bar; 4 changing beers (sourced nationally) ⊞
Originally a cinema, the Picture Palace was built in 1912, but replaced by the Embassy in 1930. This spacious Wetherspoon pub retains the character of a picture house. The floor slopes down to the long curved bar at the front where the stage used to be, with a very large TV screen above it and some eye-catching Art Deco installations. Additional TVs give a choice of channels. It serves four changing beers, and is close to the bus and train stations. 🏠🕪💺⟵🚪📶

Pub 🅛
East Street, CM7 3JJ
☎ (01376) 618033
6 changing beers (often Wibblers) 🅖
New permanent local brewery taproom which opened in spring 2023 with Wibblers beers. It now serves at least four local brewery ales from Colchester Brewery, with six to eight over the weekend. A large, open-plan, sports-orientated pub with spacious seating areas and a nightclub/function room at the rear. TV screens show live sporting events and there are regular live music acts. A front outside area has picnic tables. Has a strict over-25s only rule. ❀🕭⟵♣P🚪(21,38)❀📶♪

Brentwood

Rising Sun ✪
144 Ongar Road, CM15 9DJ (on A128, at Western Rd jct)
☎ (01277) 227400
Greene King IPA; Sharp's Atlantic; Timothy Taylor Landlord; 2 changing beers (sourced nationally) ⊞
Good community local with five real ales, that was extensively refurbished and extended in 2020. A charity quiz is held on Monday evenings. Five handpumps in the saloon bar dispense three regular ales plus two guests. Outside there is a covered heated smokers' area and a patio garden. Food service (pizzas) starts when the pub opens and finishes an hour before closing time. Children are not permitted in the bars, but well-behaved children are allowed in the outdoor covered, heated area. Major sporting events are shown on TV.
❀🕪♣P🚪(21,37)❀📶♪

Victoria Arms ⚑
50 Ongar Road, CM15 9AX (on A128)
☎ (01277) 201187
Crouch Vale Brewers Gold; Harvey's Sussex Best Bitter; St Austell Tribute; 3 changing beers (sourced nationally) ⊞
Pleasant and comfortable Gray & Sons pub with a friendly atmosphere. Unusually for the area, there is normally a Harvey's beer on tap, as well as Brewers Gold, Tribute and three changing beers. There are several TV screens which mostly show sports matches, and an outside smoking area. Cribbage and other card games are played. Local CAMRA Pub of the Year 2021, 2023 and 2024. ❀♣P🚪(498,21)♪

Brightlingsea

Railway Tavern 🅛
58 Station Road, CO7 0DT
🌐 alesattherails.co.uk
Crouch Vale Essex Boys Best Bitter; 2 changing beers (sourced nationally) ⊞
This traditional local pub has a number of bar areas and a covered garden area which is popular throughout the year. Regular events, including music and parties, are held in the garden, and details can be found on their Facebook page. Ales are kept in excellent condition

making it popular with visitors to the area as well as with locals. Local CAMRA Pub of the Year 2020 and 2023.
Q🏠❀●🚪(87)❀

Burnham-on-Crouch

Queen's Head
26 Providence, CM0 8JU
☎ (01621) 502422
Bishop Nick Ridley's Rite; Chelmsford Cool Bay; Oakham Citra; 2 changing beers (sourced nationally; often Chelmsford, Crouch Vale, Wantsum) ⊞
A truly locals' pub just off the High Street, owned by Gray & Sons. It is frequently busy, with a good and varied range of beers and ciders. The basic no-frills interior is warmed in winter by a log-burning stove. The pool table is a popular feature. The small sheltered garden to the rear of the pub provides a delightful outside space with a heated smoking area. A beer festival is hosted on the August bank holiday, and regular music nights and quiz nights are held. Burnham-on-Crouch railway station is a 15 minute walk away. 🏠❀♣●🚪(31)❀📶♪

Castle Hedingham

Bell ★ 🅛
10 St James Street, CO9 3EJ (on main road through village)
☎ (01787) 460350 🌐 hedinghambell.co.uk
3 changing beers (sourced locally) 🅖
Gray's-owned coaching inn dating from the 15th century, with small rooms for drinking and dining alongside two main bars, and a nice outside area for both dining and drinking. Beer is cask dispensed, and summer and winter beer festivals are held. Local musicians play on most Friday evenings and Sunday is quiz night. Locally sourced food includes Turkish specials prepared in a wood-fired stone oven, and a Wednesday evening barbecue fish menu is served in summer months.
Q🏠❀🕪♠♣P🚪(89)❀📶♪

Chappel

Swan Inn 🅛
The Street, CO6 2DD (near A1124)
☎ (01787) 222353 🌐 swaninn-chappel.com
Colchester No. 1; 2 changing beers (sourced nationally) ⊞
Situated in the Colne Valley, close to the awesome Chappel Viaduct which is comprised of seven million bricks and is one of the largest brick-built structures in England. The Swan Inn is a Grade II-listed building, 600 yards from Chappel & Wakes Colne station. The pub is food-orientated, with several dining areas, a courtyard and garden with a children's play area. It hosts regular live music. There is always at least one ale from Colchester brewery, which is under a mile away.
Q❀🕪⟵(Chappel & Wakes Colne) P🚪♪

Chelmsford

Ale House 🅛
24-26 Viaduct Road, CM1 1TS
☎ (01245) 260535 🌐 the-ale-house-chelmsford.co.uk
9 changing beers (sourced nationally) ⊞
A unique bar located under the railway station arches in Chelmsford. It boasts one of the widest ranges of continuously changing beers in Essex, always including dark and stronger beers. Nine ales, six real ciders and 15 craft keg beers sit alongside imported lagers on tap and a wide range of bottled beers from around the world. No food is served but customers are welcome to bring their

own, including takeaways. There is a quiz on the first and third Sunday of each month, and regular beer festivals are held. 为必&≠♣⊕吕◆令

Hop Beer Shop L
173 Moulsham Street, CM2 0LD
☎ (01245) 353570
4 changing beers (sourced nationally) Ⓖ
Essex's first micropub; four beers are served by gravity, usually a stout or porter and a golden beer, with local breweries always represented alongside interesting beers from around the country. There are also craft keg beers, many bottled beers from local and international breweries, and bottled ciders (not all real), which may be drunk there or purchased to take home. A frequent local CAMRA Pub of the Year and Cider Pub of the Year. Q♠吕(C1,351)❀令

Ivory Peg L ✿
7 New London Road, CM2 0NA
☎ (01245) 253130
Greene King Abbot; Ruddles Best Bitter; Sharp's Doom Bar; 5 changing beers (sourced nationally) Ⓗ
Town-centre pub with a single open-plan area at ground level, featuring large windows onto the street and a good collection of old photographs on the walls of the staircase to the toilets (accessible toilet on ground floor). Excavations prior to its building produced an ivory tuning peg from a medieval musical instrument (now in Chelmsford Museum). Food is served all day. As with other Wetherspoon pubs beer festivals are held twice a year with a cider festival in the summer. 为◑&≠吕令

Orange Tree L
6 Lower Anchor Street, CM2 0AS
☎ (01245) 262664
Chelmsford Cool Bay; Colchester Sweeney Todd; Mighty Oak Oscar Wilde, Captain Bob; 4 changing beers (sourced nationally) Ⓗ
The Orange Tree is one of the best real ale pubs in Chelmsford and is a former local CAMRA Pub of the Year. A second pub for Max and Jess, who also run the Queen's Head in Boreham, it is a place for conversation and meeting friends. It has two separate large bars – public and saloon – and also a lovely outside rear patio area. A great range of beer is served, always including something dark. Lunchtime food is served Wednesday to Friday. 为❀◑&♣♠P吕(C1,351)❀令

Railway Tavern L
63 Duke Street, CM1 1LW
☎ (01245) 280679
Mighty Oak Oscar Wilde; WHARF IPA; 6 changing beers (sourced nationally) Ⓗ
A Tardis-like corner pub directly opposite Chelmsford railway station. Unsurprisingly, a railway theme dominates. The interior is long and narrow with banks of handpumps at opposite ends of the central bar counter. There are also craft beers and over 50 different gins. This traditional pub has a small enclosed garden where you can listen to the station announcements and marvel at the ever-changing mural. May stay open later on summer Sundays. ❀≠♣❀令

Voodoo Keller Bar L
Basement, 59 New Street, CM1 1NE (entrance in Waterloo Ln)
☎ (01245) 476267 ⊕ chelmsfordbrewco.co.uk/voodookellerbar
4 changing beers (sourced locally) Ⓗ
Chelmsford Brew Co bar serving up to four changing cask ales and eight changing keg beers from the brewery. Originally the holding cells for the magistrates' court, it is

split into three areas. The back room has a cell door and bench seating, and two smaller areas have stools and barrel tables. Events include DJ nights and live music on some Fridays or Saturdays, and there is a quiz on the first Wednesday of the month. A bar snacks menu is available until 9pm. ≠吕♪

Clacton-on-Sea

Old Lifeboat House
39 Marine Parade East, CO15 6AD
☎ (01255) 476799
Greene King Abbot; St Austell Proper Job; 3 changing beers (sourced nationally; often Greene King, Colchester, St Austell) Ⓗ
A former local CAMRA Pub of the Year and Cider Pub of the Year, the Old Lifeboat House has been in this Guide regularly for more than a decade. This family-run pub is a favourite with locals, having up to five ales available and regularly featuring local brews. Food is available Wednesday evening, and occasionally at other times, although hours vary so check before travelling. Two darts teams play on Monday or Thursday. 为❀◑&≠♣吕令♪

Clavering

Cricketers ✿
Wicken Road, CB11 4QT
☎ (01799) 550442 ⊕ thecricketers.co.uk
3 changing beers (sourced nationally; often Adnams, Barsham) Ⓗ
Now part of the East Anglian-based Chestnut Group this is an upmarket establishment where, although food takes centre stage, drinkers are very welcome. Beware of the low beams! Formerly owned by the Oliver family, it is where Jamie first ventured into the kitchen. Booking for meals is advised for Friday and Saturday. It has a pleasant patio garden area at the front, and high-quality accommodation is available. Q为❀⇋◑P❀令

Coggeshall

Chapel Inn ✿
4 Market Hill, CO6 1TS
☎ (01376) 561655 ⊕ thechapelinn.com
4 changing beers (sourced nationally) Ⓗ
A welcoming second generation family-run pub overlooking the market square. The building is divided into four separate areas with wooden beams and is decorated in a traditional style with contemporary touches. It showcases vintage photos and pictures depicting the town's history. The Chapel Inn is known for hosting various events including live music, comedy nights, community gatherings and its locally famous weekly Sunday quiz. 为❀◑P吕(X20)❀令♪

Colchester

Ale House ♥ L
82 Butt Road, CO3 3DA
☎ (01206) 573464 ⊕ thealehousecolchester.co.uk/Ⓖ
8 changing beers (sourced nationally) Ⓗ/Ⓖ
A genuine free house just outside the city centre. A wide range of ales are on offer, including at least one dark, along with up to three ciders. Darts and TV sports are available, and regular quiz and folk nights are held. The pub has won many CAMRA awards under the friendly landlady and is current local Pub of Year. There is a large walled garden to the rear which includes an undercover area. ❀≠(Town)♣♠吕(S6,S7)令

British Grenadier
67 Military Road, CO1 2AP
☎ 07832 215118
4 changing beers (sourced nationally) Ⓗ
This welcoming local pub, run by a knowledgeable publican has featured in the Guide for over 15 years. This is a traditional Victorian two-bar pub with a pool table in the small rear bar and a dartboard in the main bar, which is heated by an open fire in the winter months. This venue stocks a changing range of local, regional and nationally sourced beers and ciders served via handpumps. ⛵☺&≉(Town)♣♠♿🚌♨🐾🕸

Fat Cat Ⓛ
65 Butt Road, CO3 3BZ
☎ (01206) 577990 ⊕ fatcatcolchester.co.uk
6 changing beers (sourced regionally) Ⓖ
Popular single-bar, split-level establishment with an open fire and an upstairs area and balcony. The pub is situated just outside of the city centre, and has Colchester's smallest beer garden. A variety of ales are sold on gravity from the tap room, with a selection of Belgian beers also available in bottles. Sunday roasts are available, with pizzas in the evenings.
⛵☺🕪&≉(Town)♣🚌♨🕸🎵

Magnet
134 North Station Road, CO1 1UZ
☎ 07707 399131 ⊕ themagnetpub.co.uk
3 changing beers (sourced nationally) Ⓗ
An independent micropub, 350 yards from Colchester (North) station, on the site of the old Norfolk pub. Its name honours Colchester-born physicist and natural philosopher, William Gilberd, the 'father of electricity and magnetism'. Three changing ales are on offer, with a selection of interesting craft beers, real ciders, spirits and quirky snacks. The pub has a relaxed atmosphere and a suntrap courtyard garden. ⛵☺≉♣♠P🚌♨🕸

New Inn Ⓛ
36 Chapel Street South, CO2 7AX
☎ (01206) 522422 ⊕ thenewinncolchester.com
4 changing beers (sourced regionally) Ⓗ
A rare example of a proper two-bar pub. With a quiet, comfortable saloon bar and an open public bar featuring music, TV sports, and friendly conversation, this is a venue of two halves. Both bars have log burners for the winter and the garden comes to life in the summer. A traditional roast is served on a Sunday with food also available Tuesday to Saturday. A function room out the back is available to hire. ⛵☺🕪&≉(Town)♣♠P🚌♨🕸

Odd One Out ★ Ⓛ
28 Mersea Road, CO2 7ET
☎ 07976 985083
Colchester Metropolis, No. 1; 3 changing beers (sourced nationally) Ⓗ
Run by Colchester brewery's head brewer and his wife, the multi award-winning Odd One Out features two bars and a back room and has been identified by CAMRA as having a regionally important historic pub interior. It offers at least two beers from Colchester brewery, changing guest ales and a range of ciders. Boasting a landscaped rear garden allowing for a quiet pint, open fires provide warmth in colder months. It hosts regular groups, impromptu music sessions and barbecues.
Q⛵☺☺≉(Town)♣♠🚌(8,S8) ♨🕸🎵

Purple Dog Ⓛ ✅
42 Eld Lane, CO1 1LS
☎ (01206) 564995 ⊕ thepurpledog.co.uk
Adnams Ghost Ship; Fuller's London Pride; Dark Star Hophead; 3 changing beers (sourced regionally) Ⓗ

One of the oldest pubs in Colchester, dating back to 1647, this corner pub in the town centre has an outdoor drinking area and wooden beams. Six handpumps provide mainly regional beers alongside the usual town-centre pub offerings. An extensive menu, which is complemented by changing special dishes, is available daily. The pub hosts occasional music (mainly DJ events) at weekends. ⛵☺🕪🍴≉(Town)🚌♨🕸

Victoria Inn Ⓛ
10 North Station Road, CO1 1RB
☎ (01206) 514510 ⊕ victoriainncolchester.co.uk
Colchester Metropolis, No. 1; 3 changing beers (sourced nationally) Ⓗ
This multi award-winning pub has three distinct seating areas, including a lively rear bar and a traditional pub area with low tables and a fire in winter. Two regular beers from Colchester brewery and three other constantly changing beers sourced nationally are available. Six to nine real ciders are on most of the time. A pleasant courtyard-style area outside is a suntrap in summer and leads to an open 'barn' with comfy conservatory-style seating. There is live music every other Sunday evening, often played outside in the warmer months. ☺≉♣♠🚌♨🕸🎵

Coopersale

Theydon Oak Ⓛ
9 Coopersale Street, CM16 7QJ (½ mile S of Coopersale, on the left at a jct)
☎ (01992) 572618 ⊕ thetheydonoak.co.uk
Fuller's London Pride; 4 changing beers (sourced regionally) Ⓗ
Located just east of Epping, this quaint pub has an open fire, comfortable seating and plenty of room to relax. The outside patio area has been constructed with easy access from the bar and is ideal for smoking customers, whilst inside good food is served in the seated area and good beer at the bar. Q⛵☺🕪♠P🚌(381)🕸🎵

Debden

Plough Ⓛ
High Street, CB11 3LE
☎ (01799) 541899 ⊕ theploughatdebden.co.uk
3 changing beers (sourced regionally) Ⓗ
The sole remaining village pub, with a restaurant and garden, it has been revitalised by a young, energetic couple and offers a warm and friendly welcome. An interesting and varied range of local beers is available alongside an extensive food menu. The pub is an important social centre for this village and the surrounding area, and a good base for walkers and cyclists. A monthly quiz night is normally held on the third Wednesday. Q⛵☺🕪P🚌(6,313)🎵

Duton Hill

Three Horseshoes Ⓛ
CM6 2DX (1 mile W of B184) TL606268
☎ (01371) 870681 ⊕ the-shoes.co.uk
Bishop Nick Heresy; 2 changing beers (sourced locally) Ⓗ
Outstanding village local with a garden, wildlife pond and terrace overlooking the Chelmer Valley and farmland. A millennium beacon in the garden, breweriana and a remarkable collection of Butlins memorabilia are features. A beer festival is usually held on the late spring bank holiday in the Duton Hill Den, and the landlord often hosts a weekend of open-air theatre in July. Look for the pub sign depicting a famous painting,

Our Blacksmith, by former local resident Sir George Clausen. Local and parish newspapers are available. ₴❀♿♣P🚌(313)🐾📶

Epping

Forest Gate Inn L

111 Bell Common, CM16 4DZ (turn off B1393 opp Bell Hotel)

☎ (01992) 572312 🌐 forestgateinnepping.co.uk

Adnams Southwold Bitter, Broadside; Bishop Nick Ridley's Rite H; 1 changing beer H/G

On the edge of Epping Forest, the pub is in a 17th-century building, with low ceilings and flagstone floors, run by the same family for 50 years. It is popular with locals, walkers and their dogs. Hot pub meals and soups are available in the bar, as well as in Haywards Restaurant next door, which also has a B&B. There is a large grassed seating area outside. It is about a mile from the town centre and its London Underground station. Q₴❀🛏◐P🚌🐾📶

Finchingfield

Finchingfield Lion L

6 Church Hill, CM7 4NN (on B1053, opp guildhall)

☎ (01371) 810400 🌐 thefinchingfieldlion.co.uk

3 changing beers (sourced regionally) H

A 15th-century coaching inn, just up the hill from the pond in a famously picturesque village. A friendly local with a warm atmosphere, it has a heavily-beamed bar area with an open fire, and a separate restaurant and function room. There is also a garden for better weather. Popular with cyclists, walkers and locals; families are also welcome. There are normally four beers on from different local breweries including Mauldons, Green Jack and Wibblers. The food menu features only pizzas, with old favourites and some interesting variations. Q₴❀🛏◐P🚌🐾📶♫

Fobbing

White Lion ✔

1 Lion Hill, SS17 9JR (near B1420)

☎ (01375) 673281 🌐 thewhitelionfobbing.co.uk

Greene King IPA; Sharp's Atlantic; St Austell Tribute; Wadworth 6X H

Attractive hilltop pub in a 14th-century building that was originally used as a chandlery, making sails for ships that used the nearby wharf. It was licensed to sell alcohol in 1605. This traditional village local has home-cooked food and a large beer garden which includes a small bar. The famous author Daniel Defoe and the Peasants' Revolt leader Jack Straw reputedly frequented the pub. ❀◐P🚌(201)📶

Goldhanger

Chequers ★ ✔

11 Church Street, CM9 8AS

☎ (01621) 788203 🌐 thechequersgoldhanger.co.uk

Adnams Ghost Ship; Bishop Nick 1555; Mauldons Silver Adder; St Austell Proper Job; Timothy Taylor Landlord; 2 changing beers (sourced nationally) H

Historic and characterful village inn with several timbered rooms including a snug, and a games room with a bar billiards table. There is an extensive menu offering quality locally sourced food. The rear courtyard is a suntrap in the summer, and open fires in the two bars provide a warm welcome in winter. Excellent walks along the River Blackwater are near by. Q₴❀◐♣P🚌(95)🐾📶

Grays

Theobald Arms

Kings Walk, RM17 6HR (7 mins' walk S down High St from Grays rail and bus stations; bear left just before Argent St)

☎ (01375) 372253

4 changing beers (sourced nationally) H

Genuine, traditional pub with a public bar that has an unusual hexagonal pool table. The changing selection of four guest beers features local independent breweries, and a range of British bottled beers is also stocked. Lunchtime meals are served Monday to Friday. There are old stables and an enclosed patio at the rear. Darts and cards are played. Local CAMRA Pub of the Year 2022. ❀◐♿⇌♣P🚌

Great Baddow

Chelmsford Brew Co Taproom L

Brewery Fields, Church Street, CM2 7LE

☎ (01245) 476267 🌐 chelmsfordbrewco.co.uk

3 changing beers (sourced locally; often Chelmsford) H

Located on a small industrial estate in Great Baddow, south of the city, the Tap Room is part of the brewery just behind the brewery shop, with comfortable seating and several benches to relax on. The seating layout lends itself to good conversation and a pleasant atmosphere. A selection of the brewery's own beers is always available, with the occasional cask guest beer. Q₴●P🚌(C7,31)📶

Great Bardfield

Bell Inn L

Dunmow Road, CM7 4SA

☎ 07506 661989

Bishop Nick Ridley's Rite; 1 changing beer (often Pumphouse Community) H

A friendly local with a warm welcome. The pub serves its own Bell Ale brewed by Pumphouse Community brewery at Toppesfield. It has a beamed bar and restaurant area with an open fire, and a separate public bar with TV and darts. There's a pool table, and an outside patio area. It is linked to the Great Bardfield artists, and a refreshment stop on the Dunwich Dynamo cycle trip. Closing time may vary. If the outside lights are on, then the pub is open. ₴❀◐♣🚌🐾📶♫

Great Bromley

Cross Inn

Ardleigh Road, CO7 7TL

☎ (01206) 621772 🌐 greatbromleycross.pub

2 changing beers (sourced nationally) H

Formerly the home of Frank Goddard, a British Heavyweight Boxing Champion, this pub was saved by the community in 2016 after much campaigning, fundraising and a share offer. It now also hosts the Post Office, a coffee shop and library on Wednesday mornings. The toilets have disabled access by radar key 24 hours per day. A remote country inn, which is an absolute gem, and well worth a visit. Hours vary so check before travelling. ❀♿●P🚌🐾♫

Great Clacton

Ship ✔

2 Valley Road, CO15 4AR

☎ (01255) 475889

St Austell Proper Job; Timothy Taylor Landlord; 1 changing beer (sourced nationally) H

The family at the helm of this local pub helped it return to the Guide after a few years' absence and have maintained the quality of their offering. The oldest building in Great Clacton after St John's church, the building dates back to the 16th century, becoming an alehouse in about 1709. Tales of smugglers' tunnels are numerous. Popular with diners, with about half the pub used for dining, those only visiting for a drink are made just as welcome. The large garden at the rear includes a secure children's play area. 🌲🏵🌕🚴P🚃🐾🛜

Great Dunmow

Angel & Harp ℒ
Church End, CM6 2AD (on B1057)
☎ (01371) 859259 ⊕ angelandharp.co.uk
Nethergate Augustinian Ale; 2 changing beers (sourced regionally) ⓗ
A refurbished pub and restaurant with a substantial garden area, a patio and a large car park. It runs occasional beer festivals, usually at Easter and in September. Local ales are regularly featured as guest beers. This pub is on the north east side of Great Dunmow and accommodates families and large parties, although the drinking area around the bar is small. Q🌲🏵🌕🚴P🏵🛜♫

Great Oakley

Maybush Inn 🎗 ℒ
Farm Road, CO12 5AL (near B1414)
☎ (01255) 880123 ⊕ maybushinn.co.uk
Courage Directors; house beer (by Eagle); 1 changing beer (sourced nationally) ⓗ
Voted local CAMRA Pub of the Year in 2022 and 2024 this community-owned pub has kept its ales in excellent condition since being saved by the community in 2016. Various weekly activities such as quizzes, bingo, crib and music are enjoyed and supported by the community. A beer festival to mark the anniversary of the pub's opening is held annually in early February. A quiet beer garden to the rear is a great location in summer. This is an extremely welcoming and friendly village local. Q🌲🏵♣🚃🐾🛜

Great Warley

Thatchers Arms
Warley Road, CM13 3HU (on B186)
☎ (01277) 233535 ⊕ thethatcherswarley.co.uk
Black Sheep Best Bitter; Fuller's London Pride; 1 changing beer (sourced regionally) ⓗ
An attractive family-run country pub that offers traditional food and drink. There are two bars, with plenty of seating both inside and outside. Two regular beers and a guest are served. Home-made food is available every day and booking is advisable. It is a friendly pub, with background music, and holds monthly events such as curry nights and Mother's Day. 🏵🌕P🚃(269)🐾

Halstead

Courtyard Tap ℒ
24 Trinity Street, CO9 1JA (on A131)
☎ 07710 230662
3 changing beers (sourced locally)
Halstead's first micropub, previously a converted shop, just down from the town centre. It has an L-shaped drinking area with cosy, comfortable seating, and a garden which is a suntrap in summer. As the Courtyard brewery tap, it specialises in its own beers, on a

changing basis, served direct from cask and in bottles, as well as occasional guests and two ciders. With a lively and enthusiastic staff, it attracts a wide range of customers. Q🌲🏵🌕🚴🐾🛜

Dog Inn ℒ
37 Hedingham Road, CO9 2DB
☎ (01787) 477774 ⊕ doginnhalstead.co.uk
5 changing beers (sourced regionally) ⓗ
Welcoming traditional local pub with two bars, close to the town centre. The public bar has TV with sports and the comfortable saloon has a real fire. Up to five changing beers are on tap, often with two to three from local microbreweries. A large beer garden at the rear is perfect for the summer. The pub has regular live music and B&B accommodation is available, with en-suite rooms. 🌲🏵🛏♣P🚃🐾🛜♫

Harwich

Alma Inn ℒ ✅
25 Kings Head Street, CO12 3EE
☎ (01255) 318681 ⊕ almaharwich.co.uk
~~Adnams Southwold Bitter, Broadside; 4 changing beers (sourced regionally)~~ ⓗ
A pub since 1859, this fascinating medieval building is the very embodiment of an ancient inn. Excellent food and drink is available as is accommodation with a distinctly modern twist. Take a seat in the main bar to be among the comings and goings, with plenty of history and artefacts to look at, or hide away in one of the plentiful nooks and crannies. Core ales from Adnams are complemented by ever-changing guests, including local brews. 🌲🏵🛏🌕➔(Town)🌕🐾🛜

Stingray
56 Church Street, CO12 3DS
☎ (01255) 503507
2 changing beers (sourced nationally) ⓗ
A long overdue appearance in the Guide for this pub built in 1921 by the Co-Op. Formerly known as the Wheatsheaf, it was sold in 1976 and the pub took its current name. A friendly pub, it participates in many community events such as the Shanty Festival and Harwich Ale Trail and is also popular with sports fans for its sport TV offering. There is a quiet patio area to rear. 🏵🛏➔(Town)🚃🛜

Hastingwood

Rainbow & Dove
Hastingwood Road, CM17 9JX (follow signs to Hastingwood from M11 jct 7 roundabout)
☎ (01279) 415419 ⊕ rainbowanddove.co.uk
3 changing beers (sourced locally; often Adnams) ⓗ
Originally a 16th-century farmhouse, the pub is Grade II-listed, with many original beams and a real fire in winter. It consists of small rooms, set up as a restaurant with limited seating for drinkers. There is a large barn in an extensive garden for outdoor seating. Dogs are welcome indoors at the landlord's discretion, though not in the evenings or on Sundays. At busy times tables may be reserved for food. Q🌲🏵🌕P🐾

Hazel End

Three Horseshoes
CM23 1HB
☎ (01279) 813429 ⊕ threehorseshoeshazelend.co.uk
Adnams Southwold Bitter; 1 changing beer (sourced regionally) ⓗ

A friendly pub opposite the cricket green at Hazel End. It has low ceilings, black wooden beams and two wood-burning stoves. It has been completely renovated, with a large extension creating more space to both eat and drink comfortably. Food includes an impressive fish menu. This is a good example of a once run-down premises transformed into a thriving, successful establishment. Under-14s are not allowed in the pub. ❀◑ ▲P❀

Helions Bumpstead

Three Horseshoes
Water Lane, CB9 7AL
☎ (01440) 730088 ⊕ threehorseshoeshelions.co.uk
Adnams Southwold Bitter; 3 changing beers (sourced regionally) ⊞
Village pub brought back to life by the Helions Bumpstead Community Benefit Society and reopened in 2021, having been closed for four years. Now managed by experienced local licensees, the pub is run on community principles with community events hosted. A mobile post office, refill provisions van and a fruit and veg stall visit the car park on Thursday mornings. The pub is gaining a reputation for its restaurant. Runner-up in CAMRA's National Pub Saving Award in 2022.
Q ❀ ❀◑◐ & ♣ P☐ (59) ❀

High Roding

Black Lion ⃞
3 The Street, CM6 1NT (on the B184 Dunmow to Ongar road)
☎ (01371) 872847 ⊕ theblacklionhighroding.co.uk
4 changing beers (sourced locally; often Colchester, New River) ⊞/⃝
A striking half-timbered 14th-century building that was a coaching inn on the London to Norwich road. It has low ceilings, oak beams and a huge fire in the winter. The restaurant serves good locally sourced food with a popular roast on Sundays. There is a TV in the end bar, usually showing rugby on Saturdays.
Q ❀ ❀◑◐ & P☐ (17,18) ❀

Hockley

White Hart
274 Main Road, SS5 4NS (by B1013)
☎ (01702) 203438 ⊕ whiteharthockley.co.uk
3 changing beers (sourced nationally) ⊞
Friendly village pub with a modern, comfortable interior. A popular quiz night is held on the first Monday of the month, on other Mondays in winter the pub is closed. This old coaching inn has been integral to village life for over 200 years. It retains original sash windows, central open fire and horse brasses. Three changing guest ales are served, and occasional beer festivals are held in the function room. There is a huge rear garden with seating, plus picnic tables at the front. ❀ ❀◑◐ & ⇌ ♣ P☐ (7,8) ☎

Horndon-on-the-Hill

Bell Inn
High Road, SS17 8LD (near centre of village, almost opp the Woolmarket and Orsett Rd)
☎ (01375) 642463 ⊕ bell-inn.co.uk
Crouch Vale Brewers Gold; Greene King IPA; Sharp's Doom Bar; 2 changing beers (sourced nationally) ⊞
Popular 15th-century coaching inn, where beamed bars feature wood panelling and carvings, run by the same family since 1938. Note the hot cross bun collection; a bun has been added every Good Friday for more than

100 years. Three regular beers are stocked plus two guests, which include ales from Essex breweries. The award-winning restaurant is open daily, lunchtimes and evenings (booking advisable). Gourmet nights are held – see website for details. Accommodation is available in 26 bedrooms. Q ❀ ❀ ⇐ ◑◐ & P❀ ☎ ☎

Kirby-le-Soken

Ship
35 Walton Road, CO13 0DT (on B1034)
☎ (01255) 679149 ⊕ theshipkirbylesoken.co.uk
Adnams Southwold Bitter, Ghost Ship, Broadside; 3 changing beers (sourced nationally) ⊞
This free house has an outside seating area to the front which is much used in fine weather. A marquee in the large beer garden to the rear is used for various events including beer festivals held in the spring, summer and autumn. Popular with drinkers and diners alike, trays of three thirds of cider are available and a wide selection of menus is offered in the restaurant. Well-behaved dogs are welcome. A former local CAMRA Pub of the Year and Cider Pub of the Year. Q ❀ ❀◑◐ ♣ P☐ ❀ ☎

Lamarsh

Lamarsh Lion
Bures Road, CO8 5EP (1 ¼ miles NW of Bures) TL892355
☎ (01787) 227007 ⊕ lamarshlion.co.uk
Woodforde's Wherry; 2 changing beers (sourced locally) ⊞
This wonderfully restored, community owned pub, largely staffed by volunteers, dates from the 14th century. Nicknamed the Painter's Pub, John Constable and Thomas Gainsborough, whose paintings portrayed the outstanding views of the Stour Valley, were former customers. It is close to the Stour Valley Footpath and good for walkers. The pub hosts several social events, including music, in its renovated interior. A daily food menu is available – check the website for serving times. Q ❀ ❀◑◐ & ▲ ♣ P❀ ☎ ♪

Langley Lower Green

Bull
Park Lane, CB11 4SB TL437345
☎ (01279) 777307 ⊕ thebullpub.co.uk
Adnams Southwold Bitter; Bishop Nick Heresy; 2 changing beers (sourced regionally) ⊞
Classic Victorian village local with original cast-iron lattice windows, in an isolated hamlet close to both Hertfordshire and Cambridgeshire. The pub has a band of local regulars. There is an aquarium in the lounge bar. Occasional quiz nights are held. An annual beer festival takes place in September. Parties can pre-book food at times when it is normally unavailable, and regular food vans are available at weekends. ❀ ❀◑ ♣ P❀ ☎ ♪

Leigh-on-Sea

Crafty Half
1376 London Road, SS9 2UH (on A13)
☎ 07879 438982
Changing beers (sourced locally)
Microbar and off-licence where a wide variety of bottled beers are sold, as well as eight beers on KeyKeg. Beers are available to drink on the premises or take away, either chilled or off the shelf. Real ale is served in bottles with a large number of the Essex breweries available. Cider is also served, and over 25 different gins can be tried. Seating is inside or on the decking in front of the bar. ❀ ⇌ ☐ (1,27)

137

Legra Tap & Kitchen

1517 London Road, SS9 2SF (on A13)
☎ (01702) 478954 ● legratapandkitchen.co.uk
Leigh on Sea Legra Pale; 3 changing beers (sourced nationally; often Leigh on Sea) Ⓗ
Joint venture between Leigh on Sea brewery and Black's Kitchen with a focus on beers from Leigh on Sea and other independent breweries. The food is fresh Asian inspired street food, with roasts on Sunday. Up to four real ales are available on handpump, with 12 keg lines and three ciders. Picnic tables in the front courtyard are popular on sunny days. Regular quiz nights and other events are held. Walkable from Leigh-on-Sea station, there is no customer parking except for a disabled space, by prior arrangement. ⬧❀◖●🖵(1,27)❀🛜

Leigh on Sea Brewery Tap Ⓛ

35 Progress Road, SS9 5PR (on Progress Rd Industrial Estate, N of A127, behind industrial unit; gravel and concrete path signposted to right of building)
☎ (01702) 817255 ● leighonseabrewery.co.uk
8 changing beers (sourced locally; often Leigh on Sea) Ⓗ
A wide range of Leigh on Sea brewery beers are served through two cask and six KeyKeg lines plus two handpumps, including one-off specials brewed on the pilot kit. The decor features a bar top of cockleshells. New covered and heated outdoor areas provide lots of seating. Occasional sporting events are shown on the TV, including international rugby. Regular music events and food pop-ups take place. Open Thursday to Saturday, and Sundays in the summer. Hours can change so check social media. ❀●🖵(20,9)❀🛜♪

Mayflower Ⓛ

5-6 High Street, Old Leigh, SS9 2EN (at far end of Old Leigh from railway station, behind chip shop)
☎ (01702) 478535 ● mayfloweroldleigh.com
Crouch Vale Brewers Gold; George's Cockleboats; Mauldons Silver Adder; St Austell Proper Job; 2 changing beers (sourced regionally) Ⓗ
Popular pub serving six real ales and one cider, most of which are locally brewed. One handpump is dedicated to a changing dark beer. The outdoor seating area has views across the Thames Estuary. Meals are served at lunchtime all week and in the evening on Friday, Saturday and Sunday, which is mainly fish & chips cooked in the adjoining restaurant. One wall lists the names of all who sailed on the Mayflower. Dogs and children are welcome. ⬧❀◖⑂➥P🖵(26)❀🛜

Little Thurrock

Traitors' Gate Ⓛ

40-42 Broadway, RM17 6EW (on A126)
☎ (01375) 372628
Greene King Abbot; 4 changing beers (sourced nationally) Ⓗ
This pub is independently owned and managed. It is now easier to find, since its name is displayed again after several years of absence, following a storm. The quieter, traditional end of the pub is to the right of the front bar. Four of the five handpumps dispense a varied selection of regional guest beers – look out for the chalk board at the end of the bar with the beers listed. A covered garden/outdoor drinking area is accessible through the pub. ⬧❀⑂♣🖵(66)❀🛜

Littley Green

Compasses Ⓛ

CM3 1BU
☎ (01245) 362308 ● compasseslittleygreen.co.uk
Bishop Nick Ridley's Rite; 5 changing beers Ⓖ
Formerly the Ridley's brewery tap, this is a picturesque Victorian country pub in a quiet hamlet. A wood-panelled bar has benches around the walls, and a tiled floor. Beers are drawn directly from casks with a changing range of boxed cider from popular producers, not all real. Filled huffers (giant baps) are available lunchtimes and evenings, plus other traditional dishes. Regular beer festivals are held. Accommodation is provided in five high-quality rooms. Local and Essex CAMRA Cider Pub of the Year 2022 and 2023. Q⬧❀➥◖♣●P▯❀🛜

Loughton

Victoria Tavern ✅

165 Smarts Lane, IG10 4BP
☎ (020) 8508 1779 ● thevictoriatavern.co.uk
Adnams Southwold Bitter; Sharp's Doom Bar; Timothy Taylor Landlord; 1 changing beer (sourced regionally) Ⓗ
This is an old-fashioned traditional pub that prides itself on real ale and inclusive conversation. It lies between Loughton and Epping Forest and is a 10 minute walk from Loughton tube station. It has a pleasant gated garden used by locals and walkers; well-behaved dogs are welcome. It serves generous portions of fresh seasonal food and has no TV, just good ale, good food and good company. Q⬧❀◖P🖵🛜

Maldon

Carpenters Arms

33 Gate Street, CM9 5QF
☎ (01621) 859896
Adnams Southwold Bitter; Crouch Vale Yakima Gold; Mighty Oak Oscar Wilde; Timothy Taylor Boltmaker; 3 changing beers (sourced nationally; often George's, Oakham) Ⓗ
A back-street gem at the top end of this historic town, this Gray's community pub offers a welcoming atmosphere. A pub since 1849, with ancient low wooden beams and parts dating to 1349, it was once the Gray's brewery tap. A wide range of ales and ciders are on offer, and an annual beer and cider festival is held. The pub supports thriving darts and dominoes teams. Q⬧❀⑂♣●P🖵❀🛜♪

Mighty Oak Tap Room

10 High Street, CM9 5PJ
☎ (01621) 853892 ● micropubmaldon.uk
Mighty Oak Oscar Wilde, Captain Bob, Maldon Gold, Old Man And The Sea; 2 changing beers (sourced locally) Ⓖ
A cosy welcoming micropub, housed in a 16th-century building, serving Mighty Oak's range of award-winning beers from a chilled cellar behind the bar. The seating arrangements and welcome lack of piped music, TVs or fruit machines encourages conversation. An upstairs room has oak beams and comfy seating for a dozen or so people and is available for private functions/meetings. Acoustic live music sessions are held most Sundays. Q●🖵❀🛜♪

Queen Victoria Ⓨ Ⓛ

Spital Road, CM9 6ED
☎ (01621) 852923 ● queenvictoriamaldon.co.uk
Adnams Southwold Bitter; Greene King Abbot; Mighty Oak Captain Bob; WHARF Pucks Folly; 3 changing beers (sourced nationally; often Lister's, Milestone, Portobello) Ⓗ

A warm and friendly welcome awaits everyone visiting this well-run Gray's pub. Extensive menus offer locally-sourced home-cooked meals, with gluten free, vegetarian and vegan options. Booking is recommended as it can get busy. Families are welcome throughout, and dogs in the beer garden and public bar. Seasonal events are celebrated, together with beer festivals. Darts, dominoes, bar skittles and board games are available. Local CAMRA Pub of the Year 2024.

♿❀◐&♣♠P⊟₩(5,31A) ❀🍴♫

Rose & Crown ✔

109 High Street, CM9 5EP

☎ (01621) 852255

Greene King Abbot; Ruddles Best Bitter; Sharp's Doom Bar; 3 changing beers (sourced nationally) Ⓗ

Wetherspoon revitalised this historic 16th-century High Street pub in 2015, adding an attractive airy extension to the rear, which houses a long marble bar with ample seating, and an outside courtyard. The pub is usually busy, with food being served all day. Children accompanied by an adult are welcome until 9pm. Sparklers are used on all beers. Q♿❀◐⊟₩🍴

Manningtree

Red Lion

42 South Street, CO11 1BG

☎ (01206) 391880 ⊕ redlionmanningtree.co.uk

Adnams Southwold Bitter; 2 changing beers (sourced regionally; often Colchester, Woodforde's, Mighty Oak) Ⓗ

This historic pub traces its origins back to 1603, and has seen many changes, although beer quality has been maintained in recent years. Large events such as the pub's annual Oktoberfest, and live music performances take place in the function room upstairs. A small function room is available downstairs. The pub has a pizza restaurant to the rear, and is takeaway friendly.

♿❀♣●⊟❀🍴

Mill Green

Viper ★ Ⓛ ✔

Mill Green Road, CM4 0PT

☎ (01277) 352010 ⊕ thevipermillgreen.co.uk

Mighty Oak Oscar Wilde; Oakham Citra; 2 changing beers (sourced nationally; often Nethergate) Ⓗ

This Grade II-listed country pub has been renovated to a high standard, in keeping with its character. The public bar and saloon are both split into two areas, including a wood-panelled snug with service via a hatch/door. The saloon bar area has exposed beams and cosy sitting areas. Food is available daily – the menu includes light bites, sandwiches, main meals and desserts. Large garden area with benches. It is a dog-friendly pub. Beer festivals are held every May and August.

Q♿❀◐♣●P❀🍴

Monk Street

Farmhouse Inn Ⓛ

CM6 2NR (off B184, 2 miles S of Thaxted) TL614288

☎ (01371) 830864 ⊕ farmhouseinn.org

Greene King IPA; 2 changing beers (sourced locally) Ⓗ

Built in the 16th century, this former Dunmow brewery establishment has been enlarged to incorporate a restaurant and accommodation. The bar is in the original part of the building. The quiet hamlet of Monk Street overlooks the Chelmer Valley, two miles from historic Thaxted. A disused well in the garden supplied Monk

Street with water during World War II. There is a rear patio, front garden and a top field.

♿❀🍴◐P⊟₩(313) ❀🍴♫

Newport

Coach & Horses ✔

Cambridge Road, CB11 3TR (on B1383)

☎ (01799) 540292

Adnams Southwold Bitter; Fuller's London Pride; 1 changing beer (sourced nationally) Ⓗ

An ex-coaching inn on the main road through Newport, on the north side of the village. This modernised pub has exposed beams and a welcoming and warm atmosphere. The pub can be used for functions and has an excellent kitchen serving great locally sourced food, both traditional British and continental dishes. There is a large garden suitable for families, with ample seating.

Q♿❀◐P⊟₩🍴🍴

Orsett

Foxhound

18 High Road, RM16 3ER (on B188)

☎ (01375) 891295 ⊕ foxhoundpuborsett.co.uk

Dark Star Hophead; Fuller's London Pride; 1 changing beer (sourced nationally) Ⓗ

A traditional two-bar village pub, taken on by new tenants in 2023, with a separate Fox's Den restaurant, which may be reserved for private functions. There is also a small seating area between the saloon bar and the outside rear patio which can double as a meeting room. Two regular beers are generally available and a changing guest. There is always a friendly welcome, whichever bar you choose to be in. Sunday roasts are served.

❀◐♣P⊟₩(200) 🍴

Pebmarsh

King's Head

The Street, CO9 2NH

☎ (01787) 267942 ⊕ kingsheadpebmarsh.co.uk

Greene King IPA; 3 changing beers (sourced nationally) Ⓗ

Dating back to 1450, this old pub was saved from closure, reopening as a community pub in 2017 after extensive refurbishment. A large plaque on the wall displays the names of its shareholders. A single bar serving three separate areas allows for a drinking area and dining space. A real fire makes the main bar a cosy area in the winter and a lovely garden plays host to a beer festival in the summer. ♿❀◐P⊟₩(F315)🍴🍴♫

Rayleigh

Crafty Casks

33 Eastwood Road, SS6 7JD

☎ (01268) 779516

5 changing beers (sourced locally) Ⓗ

Modern micropub with a constantly rotating line up of real ale – usually from local breweries - craft beer, wine, spirits, cider, cocktails and Prosecco. The bar has up to 25 taps with five real ales served, up to eight ciders, and many keg beers. The choice usually including a strong dark beer, and Brew York beers are often featured. Located just off Rayleigh High Street, regular events include live music. The owners also offer a mobile bar for events. ≈⊟₩(1,9)♫

Ridgewell

White Horse Inn L
Mill Road, CO9 4SG (on A1017) TL735408
☎ (01440) 785532 ⊕ ridgewellwhitehorse.com
3 changing beers (sourced locally) Ⓖ
Set in a pretty village, which was home to the American 381st Heavy Bomb Group during WWII, the White Horse is an attractive roadside pub. Annual beer festivals are held in summer on the patio behind the pub. As well as a choice of excellent real ale and food, the pub offers an interesting selection of good-quality wines to suit a variety of tastes, and 4-star accommodation.
🛇🏵🛏◑♣P🍴🚆🛜

Rochford

Golden Lion L
35 North Street, SS4 1AB
☎ (01702) 545487
Adnams Southwold Bitter; Greene King Abbot; 4 changing beers (sourced nationally) Ⓗ
This Grade II-listed weatherboarded free house is a long-standing Guide entry and has won many local CAMRA awards. In addition to the three regular ales, four are nationally sourced from Tring, Nethergate and Mighty Oak breweries, along with real cider. A beer festival is held in autumn in the attractive patio-style garden. Live sports are occasionally shown on largescreen TV. A wood-burning stove and a comprehensive jukebox add to the atmosphere. 🏵♿≉♣●P🚆🛜

Rowhedge

Olde Albion
High Street, CO5 7ES
☎ (01206) 728972
4 changing beers (sourced nationally) Ⓗ
The current local CAMRA Rural Pub of the Year, and overall winner for both 2022 and 2023, this free house on the waterfront plays a substantial role in local village life. The pub serves an interesting range of changing ales, sourced nationally. There is usually a cheese board on Sundays, and a warming fire in cold weather. In warmer weather there are tables and chairs on the greensward overlooking the Colne river. Occasional live music events are hosted. 🏵♣🚆(S9)🛜🛜♪

Roydon

New Inn ✔
90 High Street, CM19 5EE
☎ (01279) 792225 ⊕ thenewinnroydon.co.uk
Adnams Broadside; Greene King IPA; Sharp's Doom Bar; 1 changing beer (sourced nationally) Ⓗ
The New Inn was built in the 18th century in the charming village of Roydon and retains many period features. It is a short walk from Roydon station and the River Stort Navigation and welcomes walkers and boaters as well as a local clientele. It was nominated for 2020 Parliamentary Pub of the Year by the local MP. There is a large garden, with a children's play area. The pub runs a beer festival each September, barbecues on fine Friday evenings and a Wednesday senior citizens lunch. 🏵◑≉P🛜🛜♪

Saffron Walden

King's Arms L
10 Market Hill, CB10 1HQ
☎ (01799) 522768 ⊕ thekingsarmssaffronwalden.co.uk

Adnams Southwold Bitter; Otter Bitter; Timothy Taylor Landlord; 2 changing beers (sourced nationally) Ⓗ
Venerable wooden-beamed, multi-roomed pub, just off the market square (market days are Tue and Sat). It has welcoming log fires in cold weather and a pleasant patio for alfresco dining and drinking. A mild or dark beer is sometimes available in winter. There is live music at weekends, and a monthly quiz. Food is served at lunchtimes. Q🛇🏵◑🚆🛜🛜♪

Railway Arms 🍺 L ✔
Station Road, CB11 3HQ (300yds SE of war memorial)
☎ (01799) 619660 ⊕ railwayarms.co.uk
House beer (by Pumphouse Community); 5 changing beers (sourced regionally) Ⓗ
Victorian street-corner local opposite the former railway station, closed in 1964 as part of the Beeching cuts. Community-owned by over 500 shareholders, there has been significant renovation inside and out, much of it undertaken by volunteers. The pub has plenty of outside seating and tables in the garden and courtyard. Completely free of tie, it serves a range of beer styles exclusively from local breweries, including a dark ale, craft beers and a number of real ciders, some of which are produced on the premises. Local CAMRA Pub of the Year 2024. 🛇🏵♿●🚆🛜🛜♪

Shalford

George Inn L
The Street, CM7 5HH
☎ (01371) 850207 ⊕ thegeorgeinnshalford.com
3 changing beers (sourced locally) Ⓗ
Attractive, beamed 15th-century village pub, now re-established as the heart of the community after a period of closure. In summer it is pleasant to sit outside on the patio, while in winter the roaring log fire draws you in. A true local, the pub hosts a 'shed night' for men on the second Wednesday of every month and a ladies night on the last Tuesday of the month. Food is served every day with breakfast at the weekend from 8.30am to 11.30am. Q🛇🏵♿P🚆(9,10)🛜

South Benfleet

South Benfleet Social Club L
8 Vicarage Hill, SS7 1PB (on B1006 High Rd)
☎ (01268) 206159 ⊕ southbenfleetsocialclub.co.uk
3 changing beers Ⓗ/Ⓖ
A popular social club that is a huge asset to the community. A beer festival is held in May, and a good range of beers and ciders is always enjoyed. It was CAMRA East Anglia Regional Club of the Year in 2018 and has been the local CAMRA Club of the Year for 10 years and counting! Games include pool and poker, with quiz nights, sport on TV and live music at weekends all adding to the ambience. CAMRA members and Guide holders are always welcome.
🛇🏵◑♿≉(Benfleet) ♣●P🚆(1,27)🛜🛜

Southend-on-Sea

Mawson's L
781 Southchurch Road, SS1 2PP (on A13)
☎ (01702) 601781 ⊕ mawsonsmicro.com
George's Wallasea Wench, Cockleboats; 2 changing beers (sourced nationally) Ⓗ
Set in the Southchurch village area, this converted shop was Southend's first micropub and has up to four cask ales, with at least two from the local George's brewery. Five real ciders, three craft keg taps, one German pilsner

and two draught ciders, including Rocquette of Guernsey, are exclusively sold in Essex by Mawson's. Quiet music adds to happy conversation, with monthly open mic nights, including poetry, and monthly quiz nights. ♿♿⚐(East) ●⊟⊟(2,14) 🛜 ♪

Olde Trout Tavern

56 London Road, SS1 1NX (opp Sainsbury's)
☎ (01702) 337000
House beer (by Wantsum); 2 changing beers (sourced nationally) Ⓗ
Modern town-centre ale bar close to the High Street and both train and bus stations. It offers three real ales, one of which is a house beer, Trout Ale, and one changing cider. House beers also include Trout Smooth and Trout Lager on keg. The pub offers a loyalty card scheme. Open mic nights are held every other Thursday night with karaoke on the first Saturday of the month. A quiz night is held every Sunday night. Occasional beer festivals have been held. ⬤⚐(Victoria)♣⊟🛜♪

Southminster

Station Arms

39 Station Road, CM0 7EW
☎ (01621) 772225 ⊕ thestationarms.co.uk
Adnams Southwold Bitter; 4 changing beers (sourced regionally; often Colchester, George's, Mighty Oak) Ⓗ
A traditional Essex weatherboarded pub that has featured in this Guide for more than 30 years, which is testament to this welcoming and thriving community local. The comfortable bar area, with its open log fire, is decorated with railway and brewery memorabilia. An attractive courtyard is popular in fine weather and a barn with a wood-burning stove provides shelter if required. Live blues and folk music is hosted monthly. Various charity events take place during the year including a conker competition. Q❀⚐♣⊟♪

Wibblers Brewery Taproom & Kitchen

Goldsands Road, CM0 7JW
☎ (01621) 772044 ⊕ wibblers.co.uk
Wibblers Dengie IPA, Apprentice, Crafty Stoat Ⓗ**; 6 changing beers (sourced locally; often Wibblers)** Ⓗ/Ⓖ
The taproom is attached to a beautiful award-winning restored medieval tithe barn housing Wibblers brewery. The taproom extension is a dining area, for the extensive menu of home-cooked food using mostly local produce. The bar is simply furnished and, weather permitting, you can sit outside in the countryside. The brewery and taproom host open days and various other events throughout the year, including televised rugby and themed food evenings. Southminster railway station is only five minutes' walk away. Q♿❀⬤⚐♣⬤P⊟(31X) ❀🛜

Springfield

Endeavour 🍷 Ⓛ

351 Springfield Road, CM2 6AW (on B1137)
☎ (01245) 257717
Mighty Oak Captain Bob; 4 changing beers (sourced nationally) Ⓗ
Cosy and friendly community pub about 20 minutes' walk or a short bus ride from Chelmsford city centre. It has three separate rooms, with a quiet area on the left as you enter. Home-cooked meals are served on Thursday to Saturday. A regularly changing selection of cask ales are supplemented by mini beer festivals and tap takeovers, and the pub hosts regular charity events and theme nights. It picks a monthly 'special' beer, which is

something strong or different. Dog friendly, it has a suntrap garden. Local CAMRA Pub of the Year 2024 and regional Pub of the Year 2023. Q❀⬤♣⬤⊟(C8,73)❀🛜

Stanford-le-Hope

Rising Sun Ⓛ ✅

Church Hill, SS17 0EU (opp church and near A1014)
☎ (01375) 671097 ⊕ risingsunstanford.co.uk
5 changing beers (sourced nationally) Ⓗ
Much-improved two-bar traditional town pub in the shadow of the church. The five guest beers are mainly from independent breweries, including LocAle beers, and up to three ciders or perries are stocked. Regular monthly live music takes place, and beer festivals are held three times a year in spring, summer and winter, with the summer festival in the large rear garden. A cider festival is also held. The back bar is available for private functions. ❀⚐♣⬤P⊟(100,200)❀🛜♪

Stansted Mountfitchet

Rose & Crown Ⓛ

31 Bentfield Green, CM24 8HX (½ mile W of B1383)
TL505256
☎ (01279) 812107 ⊕ roseandcrownstansted.co.uk
2 changing beers (sourced regionally) Ⓗ
Family-run Victorian pub on the rural edge of a large village with the welcoming atmosphere of a local. This free house has been modernised to provide one large bar and a snug at the side. There is a covered outside drinking area and a garden. Home-cooked food is served at weekends and there are occasional food trucks. A large variety of gins is stocked. There is an interesting jukebox in the main bar. ♿❀⬤P⊟(7,7A)❀🛜

Stanway

Live & Let Live Ⓛ

12 Millers Lane, CO3 0PS (in a small lane 100yds from London Rd)
☎ (01206) 574071 ⊕ theliveandletlive.co.uk
4 changing beers (sourced regionally) Ⓗ
A traditional, welcoming local that continues to delight, with a homely saloon bar and a public bar. The publicans regularly support local breweries and take great pride in the condition and quality of their real ales. The beers are competitively priced, as is the traditional home-cooked food, served lunchtimes and most evenings. The pub is renowned for its beer, sausage and pie festivals. Local CAMRA Cider Pub of the Year 2024.
Q♿❀⬤♣⬤P⊟❀🛜♪

Steeple Bumpstead

Fox & Hounds Ⓛ

3 Chapel Street, CB9 7DQ (on B1057)
☎ (01440) 731810 ⊕ foxinsteeple.co.uk
Greene King IPA; 4 changing beers (sourced nationally) Ⓗ
A 17th-century coaching inn in a picturesque village on the Essex/Suffolk border, featuring an open fire in the main bar, a courtyard rear garden and further seating at the front. On Wednesday evening a complimentary cheese board is offered, with reduced-price real ale and wine all evening. Live bands perform, and quiz nights take place throughout the year. The outside barn has been converted into a games room.
Q♿❀♣⊟(18) ❀🛜♪

Stow Maries

Prince of Wales
Woodham Road, CM3 6SA
☎ (01621) 828971 ⊕ prince-stowmaries.net
6 changing beers (sourced nationally) Ⓗ
This classic weatherboarded pub boasts several
characterful drinking areas with open fires and an old
bread oven. The extensive garden and courtyards provide
plenty of options for outside drinking. Food is available,
made with local produce where possible. Many special
events are held including Burns Night, a firework display
on the last Saturday in October and live music. A free
comedy night with top West End acts takes place
monthly. Q⥥❀⚌ⓘ&♣P☷(503)☻🕏

Thaxted

Maypole ⊘
31 Mill End, CM6 2LT (by B184)
☎ (01371) 831599 ⊕ maypolethaxted.com
**Bishop Nick Ridley's Rite; Timothy Taylor Landlord; 3
changing beers (sourced nationally)** Ⓗ
A warm welcome awaits at this redecorated pub. The
current landlords took over in 2020 and are keen to
support community activities. Regular musical events
and quizzes are held along with occasional beer festivals.
Home-cooked food is available every day except
Tuesday. The pub sits back from the main road and there
is a rear car park and attractive garden with comfortable
outdoor seating. ⥥❀ⓘP☷(313,314)☻🕏♫

Tillingham

Cap & Feathers 🍸
8 South Street, CM0 7TJ
☎ (01621) 779212
**Greene King IPA; Mighty Oak Maldon Gold; Morland
Old Speckled Hen** Ⓗ; **Sharp's Doom Bar** Ⓗ/Ⓖ; **2
changing beers (sourced locally)** Ⓗ
A lovely 15th-century Grade II-listed weatherboarded
free house, situated in a picturesque village location, and
reportedly haunted. The pub has many exposed beams,
with a large open wood-burning fire. Food is available on
Fridays and Sundays with Sunday roasts being popular.
There are local pool and darts teams along with
entertainment on many themed nights. Local CAMRA
Rural Pub of the Year 2024. ⥥❀ⓘ♣P☷☻🕏♫

Toppesfield

Green Man Ⓛ
Church Lane, CO9 4DR
☎ (01787) 237418
**Greene King IPA; 2 changing beers (sourced locally;
often Pumphouse Community)** Ⓗ
A community-owned local which hosts beer festivals and
events throughout the year. It has two pool teams and
darts is played in the public bar. PumpHouse Community
brewery is next door. This village is the only place in the
UK to have a pub, brewery and shop all owned by the
community. Meals may need booking, and group pre-
booking at lunchtime is possible on weekdays. Fish &
chips (including to take away) is served on Friday, bacon
rolls on Saturday, and Sunday lunch. Events and private

> Give my people plenty of beer, good
> beer and cheap beer, and you will have
> no revolution among them.
> **Queen Victoria**

functions are catered for. Closing time depends on
whether there are customers, check if intending to arrive
late. ⥥❀ⓘ◐&♣P☻🕏♫

Waltham Abbey

Woodbine Inn Ⓛ ⊘
Honey Lane, EN9 3QT
☎ (01992) 713050 ⊕ thewoodbine.co.uk
Mighty Oak Oscar Wilde Ⓖ; **4 changing beers (sourced
locally; often Adnams, New River, WHARF)** Ⓗ/Ⓖ
A finalist for CAMRA National Cider Pub of the Year in
2019, and local CAMRA Pub of the Year 2023, this pub is
situated in Epping Forest and close to junction 26 of the
M25. It concentrates on real ales and over 40 small
producer ciders, and produces London Glider cider on
site. Food is home-made, with local sausages, ham and
steak as specialities. Dogs are welcome in main bar
where there is bar billiards. A monthly comedy club is
held. It may open later in the evening if there is demand.
⥥ⓘ♣♣P☷(66,66A) ☻♫

Westcliff-on-Sea

Mile & a Third 🍸
67 Hamlet Court Road, SS0 7EU
☎ (01702) 902120 ⊕ mileandathird.com
2 changing beers (sourced nationally) Ⓖ
Micropub run by two beer managers from the Rochford
Beer Festival. Two real ales are served on gravity, with three
real ciders, and eight keg lines offering beers from
independent breweries. The bottle shop has an
interesting selection including sours, stouts, German and
Belgian beers. Music is a feature and is mainly played on
vinyl. A pavement seating area offers additional space
and decorated trees give the interior a quirky look. Local
CAMRA Pub of the Year 2020-2024.
⥥❀&⇌(Westcliff)♣♣🜚☷(1,27) ☻🕏

West Road Tap
2 West Road, SS0 9DA
☎ (01702) 330647 ⊕ westroadtap.com
7 changing beers (sourced nationally) Ⓖ
Now under the management of a team that runs two
other bars in the area, this two-level micropub and bottle
shop is near the Palace Theatre in Westcliff. The main
bar, upstairs, serves one cask ale sourced nationally and
six KeyKeg beers. The Bunker bar downstairs serves six
taps. Both bars have an extensive fridge selection of craft
beer in bottles and cans, to drink in or take home. Two
real ciders in boxes are available. Children are welcome
until 7pm. Q⥥❀⇌(Westcliff)♣☷(1,27)☻

Wethersfield

Wethersfield Club Ⓛ
Old Mill Chase, CM7 4EB
☎ (01371) 850598 ⊕ wethersfield.club.co.uk
**2 changing beers (sourced locally; often Courtyard,
Nethergate, Pumphouse Community)** Ⓗ
Friendly and hospitable club in a village with no pubs.
Very spacious, it was dug out of the ground after the First
World War. It has one full-size snooker table, pool, darts, a
dance floor and plenty of seating. To find the club, take
the cul-de-sac to the right of the village hall, and the
entrance is down the alleyway at the end on the left. It is
worth finding the front door as the club now welcomes
the public too not just club members. ⥥♣☻🕏♫

Widddington

Fleur de Lys 🗓

High Street, CB11 3SG TL538316

☎ (01799) 543280 ⊕ thefleurdelys.co.uk

Timothy Taylor Landlord; Woodforde's Wherry; 2 changing beers (sourced nationally) Ⓗ

A welcoming 400-year-old village local which boasts a large open fireplace, beams and an attractive garden. This was the first pub to be saved from closure by the local branch of CAMRA after the branch's formation. A range of real ciders is available, and quality meals are offered, made with fresh local ingredients. The source of the River Cam and English Heritage site Prior's Hall Barn are both nearby. ⬢♿⛲🍴👶🚆🚶🅿️🚍(301)🐾

Witham

Battesford Court 🗓 ✅

100-102 Newland Street, CM8 1AH

☎ (01376) 504080

Greene King Abbot; Ruddles Best Bitter; Sharp's Doom Bar; 5 changing beers (sourced nationally) Ⓗ

Large Wetherspoon conversion of a former hotel of the same name. The 16th-century building was previously the courthouse of the manor of Battesford. It has distinct areas, with wood panelling and oak beams, and there is also a family area. Up to five regional beers are served including something local, usually from Bishop Nick or Wibblers. Q⬢♿⛲🍴👶🅿️🚍🛜

Woolpack Inn 🗓 ✅

7 Church Street, CM8 2JP

☎ (01376) 511195

Greene King IPA Ⓗ**; WHARF No Name** Ⓖ**; 2 changing beers (sourced locally)** Ⓗ/Ⓖ

A traditional local pub, this is the only regular outlet for the Witham No Name beer from WHARF brewery. Set in a conservation area, the building probably dates from the 15th century. It has two rooms with low wooden beams and a real log fire in winter. Up to two guest ales, usually from the local area, are served predominantly on gravity. An extensive collection of glass soda syphon bottles is a notable feature. 🚆🚶🚍🐾🛜

Wivenhoe

Black Buoy

Black Buoy Hill, CO7 9BS

☎ (01206) 822425 ⊕ blackbuoy.co.uk

5 changing beers (sourced nationally) Ⓗ

Friendly community pub that has won many local CAMRA awards. It has plenty of cosy areas for drinking or eating, and offers B&B accommodation. There is a pleasant outside area which is lit at night. The pub usually holds beer festivals throughout the year, which prove to be very popular, andalso hosts live music evenings and events.Current and upcoming beers are displayed on their website. ⬢♿⛲🍴👶🚆🚶🅿️🚍(S1)🐾🛜🎵

Station

27 Station Road, CO7 9DH (on B1028)

☎ (01206) 822991

2 changing beers (sourced nationally) Ⓗ

A corner pub with a pleasant atmosphere and an ever changing beer choice. It is opposite the railway station, with various railway artefacts displayed inside and seating outside. Live music often comes from local musicians, and there are occasional quiz nights. The pub is a favourite with rugby fans, and matches are shown on TV. On Friday evening there is a pizza van outside, which is popular and often sells out. ⛲🚆🚶🅿️🚍(S1)🐾🛜

Woodham Mortimer

Hurdlemakers Arms

Post Office Road, CM9 6ST

☎ (01245) 225169 ⊕ hurdlemakersarms.co.uk

6 changing beers (sourced locally; often Brentwood, Colchester, Wibblers) Ⓗ

A Gray's house, this 400-year-old former farmhouse seamlessly blends restaurant with pub, with good food complementing the beers. One area is dedicated to dining while a separate bar caters for drinkers. A huge beer garden is ideal for families, with a play area and shady trees. Barbecues feature on summer weekends and a popular beer festival is held in late June. Functions are catered for in a marquee or in Mortimer's barn. Q⬢♿⛲🍴👶🚶🅿️🚍🐾🛜

Writtle

Wheatsheaf 🗓

70 The Green, CM1 3DU

☎ (01245) 420672 ⊕ thewheatsheafwrittle.co.uk

Bishop Nick Ridley's Rite; Dark Star Hophead; Skinner's Betty Stogs; Timothy Taylor Landlord; Woodforde's Wherry; 2 changing beers (sourced nationally) Ⓖ

Traditional village pub, built in 1813, with a small public bar, an equally compact lounge and a covered patio by the road. Note the old Gray's sign in the public bar. The atmosphere is generally quiet, with the TV switched on only for occasional sporting events. Food is served Wednesday to Saturday, with light bites such as sandwiches and paninis at lunchtimes and home-made stonebaked pizza in the evenings. Q🍴🚶🚍(C4,32) 🐾🛜🎵

The Maypole

All bars are snug places, but the Maypole's was the very snuggest, cosiest and completest bar, that ever the wit of man devised. Such amazing bottles in old oaken pigeon-holes; such gleaming tankards dangling from pegs at about the same inclination as thirsty men would hold them to their lips; such sturdy little Dutch kegs ranged in rows on shelves ... such closets, such presses, such drawers full of pipes, such places for putting away in hollow window-seats, all crammed to the throat with eatables, drinkables, or savoury condiments; lastly, and to crown all, as typical of the immense resources of the establishment, and its defiance to all visitors to cut and come again, such a stupendous cheese.

Charles Dickens, Barnaby Rudge, 1841.

The model for the Maypole is the King's Head, Chigwell, Essex

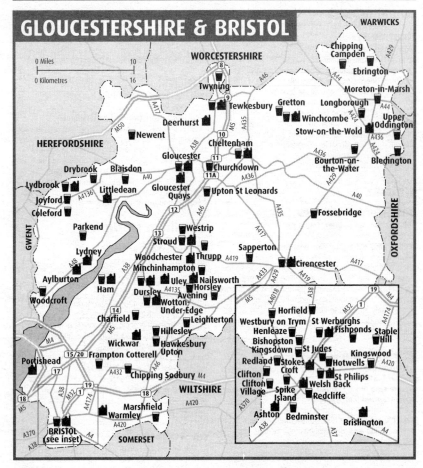

GLOUCESTERSHIRE & BRISTOL

Avening

Bell L

29 High Street, GL8 8NF (at bottom of the High St on B4014)

☎ (01453) 836422 ⊕ thebellavening.co.uk

Timothy Taylor Landlord; 1 changing beer (often Butcombe) Ⓗ

This pleasant village local is a a fine example of a community hub; being a friendly, confidently run old inn with exposed stone walls, two bay window seats and a roaring wood-burner. The jovial, amicable regulars are always chatty; enjoying the offerings from the attractive open bar, which features up to four different ales at busy times. The refurbished, comfortable dining area serves a competitively priced menu in collaboration with a local Indian restaurant. They show major sporting events in the lounge area. This pub can be quietly addictive and difficult to leave. Q❀❀❀◑♣▯◻☷

Blaisdon

Red Hart L

GL17 0AH (signed from A4136 E of Longhope, or from A48 at Westbury-on-Severn)

☎ (01452) 831717 ⊕ redhartinn.co.uk

Butcombe Original; Otter Bitter; 3 changing beers (sourced regionally; often Bespoke, Kingstone, Wye Valley) Ⓗ

Nestling in a picturesque village between the A40 and A48, the award-winning Red Hart is renowned for its excellent food and well-kept ales. Worn flagstone floors, photographs of bygone local scenes and display of paintings by local artists all add character. Charity quiz nights, occasional tractor runs, an annual soap box derby make the Red Hart a real community pub. Dog friendly, with warming log fires in the winter and a well-tendered garden. A former local CAMRA Pub of the Year. ❀❀❀◑❀♣♣◆P❀

Bledington

King's Head L

The Green, OX7 6XQ (off B4450 on village green)

☎ (01608) 658365 ⊕ kingsheadinn.net

Hook Norton Hooky; 3 changing beers (sourced regionally) Ⓗ

Delightful, 16th century stone-built inn overlooking the village green. The pub has original old beams an open inglenook log fire with high back settles and a convivial atmosphere. This free house, with 12 comfortable letting rooms, is renowned for its wide range of ale and food. Dining reservations are recommended, especially at weekends. Bledington is about four miles from Stow-on-the-Wold. There are good local walks to nearby villages, with Kingham station close by. The two guest beers are selected from local brewers in Gloucestershire and Oxfordshire. Q❀❀❀◑♣P❀☷

Bourton-on-the-Water

Mousetrap Inn L

Lansdowne, GL54 2AR (300yds W of village centre)
☎ (01451) 820579 ⊕ themousetrapinn.co.uk
4 changing beers (sourced locally) Ⓗ

Recently refurbished traditional Cotswold stone free house in the Lansdowne part of Bourton, close to the centre, with four changing beers on offer from local breweries including North Cotswold and Goffs. With friendly service, they welcome locals, tourists children and dogs. Nine letting rooms are available. A patio area in front of the pub with tables and hanging baskets provides a suntrap in the summer.
Q❀⊁⊯◗ё&P�(801,855) ✿🗢

Bristol

Bank Tavern L

8 John Street, BS1 2HR (take the lane next to the arcade on All Saints St)
☎ (0117) 930 4691 ⊕ banktavern.com
4 changing beers (sourced locally; often Arbor, Gloucester, Hop Union) Ⓗ

Popular, compact one-bar pub, hidden away near the old city wall. The four beers are often from microbreweries from the south-west or sometimes further afield, and can be of any style. There is a also real cider available. Bare floorboards feature throughout, with a slightly raised area to the rear. There are bespoke raised tables by the front windows, long green settles along the walls and covered seating in the courtyard outside. Quality food is served, with Sunday lunches booked up well in advance. Quiz night is Tuesday. ➣❀◗♣●➲✿🗢♪

Bridge Inn

16 Passage Street, BS2 0JF
☎ (0117) 929 0942
Quantock QPA; 3 changing beers (sourced locally; often Hop Union, Moor Beer, Redemption) Ⓗ

Conveniently located near Temple Meads station and Cabot Circus shopping centre, this small, friendly venue is a good place to start a visit to Bristol. It is close to many other good pubs, and an adventurous choice of ales is offered. Musical memorabilia adorn the walls and board games are available to play. Around 10 malt whiskies are also stocked, together with Belgian bottled beers. On Sundays from about 5pm complimentary cheese and biscuits are served. Outside tables increase capacity during good weather. Closed Mondays.
➣❀◗≠(Temple Meads) ♣●➲✿🗢

Cornubia

142 Temple Street, BS1 6EN
⊕ thecornubia.co.uk
House beer (by Twisted Oak); 6 changing beers Ⓗ

Originally built in 1775 this cosy traditional pub, tucked away off Victoria Street, is a short walk from Temple Meads railway station. It is a long term Guide entry with a good range of changing ales, usually including a dark ale, plus Cornubia house beer from Twisted Oak brewery. The attractive beer garden has an extended seating area to both the front and side of the pub, some of which is lit and covered. Bar snacks, including pies, sausage rolls and Scotch eggs are usually available. Closed on Sundays.
❀≠(Temple Meads) ●➲✿🗢

Gryphon

41 Colston Street, BS1 5AP
☎ 07894 239567
4 changing beers Ⓗ

A shrine to dark beer and rock/heavy metal music, posters, bespoke artwork and many pumpclips adorn the walls. Triangular in shape due to its corner plot and just a few yards up the hill from the Bristol Beacon, it has handpumps dispensing up to four rapidly changing and generally one-off brews, many dark and often strong. Children and dogs are admitted at the licensee's discretion. Closed on Mondays, and occasionally on Sundays. ➲✿🗢♪

LHG Brewpub

Compressor Building, Hawkins Lane, BS1 6EU
⊕ lhgbrewpub.com
2 changing beers (sourced locally; often Left Handed Giant) Ⓗ

Popular three-floor brewpub opened in 2019 on the old Courage brewery site which saw brewing return after a number of decades of inactivity. The wide range of beer is served from a number of dispense methods, including cask handpull, tank-conditioned, KeyKeg and keg. Beers are sold in all legal measures. Wood-fired pizzas are served. The second floor is open all day at weekends and on weekday evenings, with three dartboards and two pool tables. Card payment only. ➣❀◗&♣➲✿🗢

REAL ALE BREWERIES

Arbor Bristol
Ashley Down Bristol
Ashton Cheltenham
Basement Beer ✦ Bristol: Stokes Croft
Bath Ales Bristol: Warmley
Bespoke ✦ Littledean
Brewhouse & Kitchen ▤ Bristol
Brewhouse & Kitchen ▤ Cheltenham
Brewhouse & Kitchen ▤ Gloucester Quays
Bristol Beer Factory ✦ Bristol: Ashton
Bruhaha ▤ ✦ Bristol (NEW)
Clavell & Hind ✦ Cheltenham
Corinium ✦ Cirencester
Cotswold Lion Cheltenham
DEYA ✦ Cheltenham
Donnington Stow-on-the-Wold
Fierce & Noble ✦ Bristol: St Werburgh's
Forest, The ✦ Lydney
Fresh Standard ✦ Woodchester
Gloucester ✦ Gloucester
Goff's Winchcombe
Good Chemistry ✦ Bristol: St Philips
Hal's Dursley (brewing suspended)
Hop Union ✦ Bristol: Brislington
Incredible Bristol: Brislington
Inferno ✦ Tewkesbury
Keep ▤ Nailsworth
King Street ▤ Bristol: Welsh Back
Left Handed Giant ✦ Bristol: St Philips
Little Martha ✦ Bristol: St Philips
Lucifer Brewhouse Wotton-Under-Edge
Lydbrook Valley ▤ Lydbrook
Moor ✦ Bristol
New Bristol ✦ Bristol
New Street Bristol
On Point ✦ Bristol (NEW)
Portishead ▤ Portishead
Stroud ✦ Stroud
Tapestry By Props ✦ Bristol: St Philips
Tewkesbury Deerhurst
Tiley's ▤ Ham
Two Tinkers Aylburton
Uley ✦ Uley
Wiper & True ✦ Bristol
Zerodegrees (Bristol) Bristol

Lime Kiln

17 St Georges Road, BS1 5UU (behind City Hall)
☎ 07903 068256
6 changing beers ⊞
Named after nearby Lime Kiln Dock, covered over in 1903, this unpretentious free house directly behind the City Hall dispenses a constantly changing range of six beers in a variety of styles, more during the frequent beer festivals. Beers are often unusual for the area but local breweries also feature and there are two traditional ciders available. You are welcome to bring your own food. A recently added feature in the main room is a full-length mural painted by a local artist. There is a public car park directly opposite. ☼✿✦P🕮✿☂

Llandoger Trow

King Street, BS1 4ER
🌐 llandogertrow.co.uk
5 changing beers (often Bristol Beer Factory, Theakston, Timothy Taylor) ⊞
Architecturally important and impressive historic inn in which Daniel Defoe reputedly met Alexander Selkirk, who became the inspiration for Robinson Crusoe. It is also said to be the inspiration for the Admiral Benbow pub in Stephenson's Treasure Island. Reopened in 2021 after a closure of more than two years, it has been reinvented as an alehouse while retaining distinct drinking areas. The opening of several rooms on the first floor has increased capacity considerably. Up to five changing cask ales are served along with 28 keg lines from UK and overseas breweries. Card payments only. ✿✦🕮☂

Old Fish Market

59-63 Baldwin Street, BS1 1QZ (200yds from city centre)
☎ (0117) 921 1515 🌐 oldfishmarket.co.uk
Fuller's Oliver's Island, London Pride, ESB; 2 changing beers (sourced nationally; often Arbor, Siren) ⊞
This Fuller's pub has the style of a relaxed lounge. Sports events are televised, and multiple screens mean different events can be shown simultaneously. There is live jazz music every Sunday evening. The guest ales are often from small to medium-sized breweries, sometimes local and sometimes from farther afield. Between 20 and 30 gins are a great attraction for any gin fanatic. Food features a range of chowders, stone-baked pizzas and Sunday roasts. The pub is dog-friendly, with treats and water bowls provided. ☼🕀✿✦🕮☂♪

Shakespeare Tavern ✅

68 Prince Street, BS1 4QD
☎ (0117) 929 7695
Greene King IPA, Abbot; 5 changing beers (sourced locally; often Bristol Beer Factory, Gloucester, Hanlons) ⊞
By Bristol's historic docks, close to the city centre and Queen's Square, this converted Georgian town house claims to have the longest continuous ale licence in Bristol. Seven handpumps offer two regular ales plus four or five changing guests of varying styles from breweries near and far. There is a regular Wednesday night pub quiz and monthly Friday night live music. A large selection of classic meals is on offer. There are benches on the front terrace for watching the world pass by. Q☼✿🕀✦🕮✿☂♪

Volunteer Tavern 🄻

9 New Street, BS2 9DX (close to main Cabot Circus car park across carriageway from shops)
☎ (0117) 955 8498 🌐 volunteertavern.co.uk
4 changing beers ⊞

Tucked away in a quiet side street, close to the shopping centre and convenient for the Old Market bus interchange, this vibrant pub is over 300 years old. There is an interesting range of changing beers, as well as real ciders. The large, fully enclosed, paved and heated garden hosts beer festivals, live music and DJs. Sunday roasts are hugely popular (booking recommended), while the food offerings from Wednesday to Saturday include vegan options. Next to the pub is a brewery housed in a container. ☼✿🕀✦🕮✿☂♪

Bristol: Bedminster

Bristol Beer Factory Tap Room

291 North Street, BS3 1JP
☎ (0117) 902 6317 🌐 bristolbeerfactory.co.uk/taproom
Bristol Beer Factory Notorious, Fortitude; 3 changing beers (sourced locally; often Bristol Beer Factory) ⊞
This popular and comfortable brewery tap is a short walk from Ashton Gate stadium, and is busy on match days. Five Bristol Beer Factory cask ales are sold alongside six keg lines. The rear bar (keg only, but you can take beer through) is known as the Studio and has more of a sports bar feel, with darts and table football, and where major sporting events are shown on numerous large screens. Pavement tables and chairs at the front provide additional drinking space. ☼✿🕀🕀✦🚌(24)✿☂

Tobacco Factory Café Bar

Raleigh Road, BS3 1TF
☎ (0117) 902 0060 🌐 tobaccofactory.com/cafe-bar
Bristol Beer Factory Notorious, Fortitude; 3 changing beers (sourced locally; often Arbor, Good Chemistry, New Bristol) ⊞
Built in 1912, this was part of the vast Imperial Tobacco estate across Bedminster, Southville and Ashton. Saved from demolition in 1993, the café bar was transformed into a thriving, vibrant venue offering good-quality, locally produced vegetarian and vegan food and drink. The six handpumps usually feature several from near neighbours Bristol Beer Factory, plus other local brews and at least one real cider or perry. The outside yard has a covered area for year-round use, with a separate bar open in the warmer months. ☼✿🕀🕀✦🚌(24)☂♪

Bristol: Bishopston

Annexe

Seymour Road, BS7 9EQ (directly behind Sportsman pub near County Cricket Ground)
☎ (0117) 949 3931
Butcombe Original; Dark Star Hophead; Fuller's London Pride; St Austell Tribute; Timothy Taylor Landlord; Wye Valley HPA; 2 changing beers ⊞
Spacious community pub close to Gloucestershire County Cricket Ground and not far from the Memorial Stadium which means it can be busy on match days. At one side is a conservatory which is family friendly until evening. Several TVs, including one on the partially covered patio outside, show live sport. Pizzas are a specialty and are served until late every evening, and on Sundays roasts are available at lunchtimes. There is a quiz every Monday night. ☼✿🕀✦🕮✿☂

Bristol: Clifton

Port of Call ✅

3 York Street, BS8 2YE
☎ (0117) 973 0926 🌐 portofcallclifton.co.uk
Butcombe Original; Otter Ale; Timothy Taylor Landlord; 3 changing beers (often Gloucester, Hop Union) ⊞

Classic two-room pub at the top of the Whiteladies Road near the Downs. It has a country pub feel with exposed beams and two real fires. At the rear is a pleasant suntrap beer garden with some cover. Up to six real ales are served, some local and often including a dark ale. Food offerings include steak night on Tuesday, fish on Friday and Sunday roasts. Quiz night is Sunday. ⏚❀◗≢(Clifton Down)🚪❀🛜

Bristol: Clifton Village

Portcullis
3 Wellington Terrace, BS8 4LE (close to Clifton side of suspension bridge)
☎ (0117) 973 0270 ⊕ theportcullisclifton.com
Bristol Beer Factory Fortitude; 2 changing beers (sourced nationally; often Exmoor, Fine Tuned, Gloucester) 🅷
A pub since 1821, the building is part of a Georgian terrace close to Clifton Suspension Bridge. The pub combines the feel of a cosy 'proper pub' and Belgian beer bar, and has a downstairs bar and an upstairs lounge. A wide range of Belgian beers is stocked in bottles and on tap. A range of traditional pub fare is served Monday to Wednesday, with roasts on Sunday afternoon. There is a quiz on alternate Thursdays and Sunday film nights in winter. The rear garden is accessed from upstairs. ❀◗♣🚪(8,505)❀🛜

Bristol: Fishponds

Snuffy Jack's
800 Fishponds Road, BS16 3TE
☎ 07437 338496 ⊕ snuffyjacks.co.uk
4 changing beers 🅶
The name of this micropub relates to a former head miller at nearby Snuff Mills. There are usually four changing gravity-fed real ales plus three craft keg lines and several real ciders. Local breweries feature, plus some from further afield. Dog and child friendly, the pub has a community focus with a quiz every second Wednesday, and many other events featured on the noticeboard. A new beer garden to the rear opened in 2022. Conveniently located close to multiple bus routes with direct links to many areas. Closed on Monday and Tuesday. Q⏚❀●🚪❀

Bristol: Henleaze

Westbury Park 🄻
Northumbria Drive, BS9 4HP
☎ (0117) 962 4235 ⊕ westburyparkpub.co.uk
Butcombe Original; St Austell Tribute; Timothy Taylor Landlord; 2 changing beers (sourced locally; often Arbor, Bristol Beer Factory, Hop Union) 🅷
Featured as the Kebab & Calculator in the BBC series The Young Ones this circular pub is smartly decorated and furnished with dining tables and comfortable seating throughout the open-plan interior. Outside there are extensive seating areas and in front of the pub nine wooden booths with individual lighting and heating have been added. There are up to five cask ales on handpump, with one of them being substituted for real cider in the summer. Quality fresh, locally sourced food, from a regularly changing seasonal menu, is served. ⏚❀◗♿●P🚪❀🛜

Bristol: Horfield

Drapers Arms 🄻
447 Gloucester Road, BS7 8TZ
⊕ thedrapersarms.co.uk

7 changing beers 🅶
Bristol's first micropub, opened in 2015, prides itself on a changing selection of up to seven real ales on gravity, mostly from Bristol and the surrounding counties. Beer Miles are noted for each beer on the blackboard beer menu and at least one gluten-free and vegan beer is usually available. Wine and bar snacks are also served, but no keg or bottled beer, lager or cider. This popular and friendly place follows the micropub tradition of focusing on good beer and conversation, with no music or TV. Q❀🚪❀

Bristol: Hotwells

Bag of Nails
141 St Georges Road, BS1 5UW (5 mins' walk from cathedral towards Hotwells)
☎ 07941 521777 ⊕ catpub.co.uk
6 changing beers 🅷
Close to the floating harbour this small partially gas-lit terraced free house dates from the 1860s. It serves six changing cask ales from independent breweries both local and further afield. A dark ale is usually available, but no draught lager is served. The interior features terracotta colours, portholes in the floor, pub cats roaming free, and eclectic music from a popular record player. Board games and an extensive Lego collection are available for customers. Tuesday is quiz night. ●🚪

Grain Barge
Mardyke Wharf, Hotwell Road, BS8 4RU (moored by Hotwell Rd, opp Baltic Wharf Marina)
☎ (0117) 929 9347 ⊕ grainbarge.com
Bristol Beer Factory Notorious, Fortitude, Independence; 1 changing beer (sourced locally; often Arbor, Good Chemistry, New Bristol) 🅷
This moored 1930s barge, converted into a pub by the Bristol Beer Factory, boasts great views of the SS Great Britain, the floating harbour and passing boats. There is seating inside, with wooden tables at either end of the central bar and an extended shelf by the window overlooking the water. Outdoor seating is on the open top deck of the boat and on the dockside next to the boat. Themed food nights feature alongside a sustainable seafood and vegetarian menu. Payment by card only. ⏚❀◗●P❀🛜♪

Merchants Arms
5 Merchants Road, BS8 4PZ
☎ (0117) 927 3709 ⊕ themerchantsarms.co.uk
3 changing beers (often Ashley Down, Cheddar Ales, Nuttycombe) 🅷
A traditional free of tie community pub close to the Cumberland Basin waterfront selling mainly south-west cask ales, with a dark ale usually available. Two small rooms are furnished with dark wood seating and there is a real log fire and a television in the front room. A range of board games are available and occasional poetry nights feature. Its home-made rolls, pies and pasties are well known and are complemented by a Thirsty Thursday price promotion. There is a small free car park 50 yards away. Q⏚♣P🚪❀🛜♪

Bristol: Kingsdown

Hare on the Hill
41 Thomas Street North, BS2 8LX
☎ (0117) 987 8462
4 changing beers (sourced locally; often Arbor, Good Chemistry, Moor Beer) 🅷
Friendly and welcoming small street-corner local with an impressive traditional green-tiled frontage. The smartly

refurbished wooden interior is decorated with an eclectic range of prints and paintings. Four handpumps offer a range of beers, usually including a dark ale, with local breweries well represented. A real cider is also served. The pub hosts an array of live entertainment including sea shanty singing, jazz, folk and open mic sessions. At other times music comes from a collection of vinyl records. ♿🏠🚲≷(Montpelier)♠🚪🏃🌳🎵

Highbury Vaults ★

164 St Michael's Hill, BS2 8DE

☎ (0117) 973 3203 ⊕ highburyvaults.co.uk

St Austell Tribute, Proper Job; Young's London Original; 2 changing beers (often Goff's, Teignworthy, Young's) Ⓗ

Listed in CAMRA's Real Heritage Pubs of the South West and under the same management for many years, this popular local combines a traditional wood-panelled feel with its own brand of quirky charm. Seating areas range from a tiny snug at the front of the pub to a spacious garden with heating and covered sections at the rear. There is a bar billiards table, an impressive range of board games and a model railway running from room to room. Toilets are down steep and narrow stairs in the original vaults. Q🏠🌳≷(Clifton Down)♣🚪(72)🌳🎵

Hillgrove Porter Stores

53 Hillgrove Street North, BS2 8LT

☎ (0117) 924 9818

12 changing beers (sourced regionally) Ⓗ

A popular community pub serving a wide range of beer styles from the 12 handpumps, as well as a couple of real ciders. The interior of the pub is horseshoe-shaped, with a variety of furniture, a large array of pumpclips on the walls, and stained glass windows. To one side of the pub is a patio garden with a covered seating area. Japanese food is available in the evenings, with a reduced menu on Sundays and Mondays. There are occasional DJ sets. ♿🏠🌳≷(Montpelier)♠🚪🌳

Bristol: Redcliffe

Golden Guinea

19 Guinea Street, BS1 6SX

☎ 07940 026893 ⊕ thegoldenguinea.co.uk

House beer (by St Austell); 3 changing beers (sourced locally; often Arbor, Bristol Beer Factory, New Bristol) Ⓗ

Cosy back-street local, close to the waterside in the Redcliffe area, with wooden floors, contemporary flock wallpaper and urban art on the walls. Reclaimed furniture and French mirrors give the pub a modern but retro feel. There are three terraces and an eclectic music policy. Cask beers are usually from local breweries such as Arbor, Bristol Beer Factory and New Bristol. There are 11 craft keg lines and a range of local bottled and canned beers is also available. 🌳🚪🌳🏃🎵

King's Head ★

60 Victoria Street, BS1 6DE

4 changing beers (sourced locally; often Burnt Mill, Good Chemistry, Saltaire) Ⓗ

Close to Temple Meads station and Castle Park, this classic small pub, originally dating from around 1660, has been identified by CAMRA as having a nationally important historic pub interior; the magnificent mid-Victorian bar-back is the second oldest known in the UK. A narrow area around the bar leads to the Tramcar Bar at the rear. Now in the hands of Good Chemistry brewery, the pub serves four cask ales chosen from small independent breweries across the UK, with a dark beer usually available. Q🏠🌳≷(Temple Meads)♠🚪🌳🏃

Portwall Tavern

Portwall Lane, BS1 6NB

☎ (0117) 922 0442 ⊕ portwalltavern.co.uk

3 changing beers (sourced regionally; often Exmoor, Gloucester, Twisted) Ⓗ

Opposite the magnificent St Mary Redcliffe church, this comfortable one-bar Victorian pub has survived the redevelopment of almost everything around it. The flooring is partly wood and partly modern tiles, and there are some impressive ornate mirrors opposite the bar. Three changing cask beers are sourced from small to medium-sized breweries within a 15-mile radius of Bristol. Food is served at lunchtimes Monday to Friday, with a pizza menu available on weekday evenings. There is a seating area outside at the front of the pub. ♿🏠🕕≷(Temple Meads)🚪🌳🏃

Bristol: Redland

Good Measure Ⓛ

2B Chandos Road, BS6 6PE

☎ (0117) 903 9930

4 changing beers (sourced locally; often Arbor, Good Chemistry, Siren) Ⓗ

This small boutique bar is set in the heart of Redland, and is a short walk from both Clifton Down and Redland stations. Four handpumps dispense a selection of Good Chemistry beers and guest ales. A range of KeyKeg and keg beers, canned beers from Good Chemistry and organic wines are also sold. Takeaways can be brought in and quiz night is Monday. There is level access to the pub and an outside patio area at the side. Card payment only. ♿🏠🕕≷(Redland)🚪🌳🏃

Red Monkey

22 Chandos Road, BS6 6PF

Wye Valley HPA, Butty Bach; 3 changing beers (sourced locally; often Ashley Down, Bristol Beer Factory, Good Chemistry) Ⓗ

Reopening in 2023 under a new name, this was Bristol's second micropub when it originally opened in 2016 in a converted shop. Up to five real ales are served on handpump, with a dark ale usually available, as well as some traditional ciders. Food consists of simple bar snacks. There is a dog bar providing water and biscuits in aid of the Holly Hedge Dog Sanctuary. Wall space is available for monthly art exhibitions by local artists, and there is a book swap facility. Closed Mondays. Q♿🏠♣♠🚪🌳🏃🎵

Bristol: St Judes

Swan with Two Necks

12 Little Ann Street, BS2 9EB (off Wade St, near Old Market)

☎ (0117) 955 1837

3 changing beers (sourced locally; often Moor Beer, Timothy Taylor) Ⓗ

This small single-bar venue, tucked away in a side street near Old Market, has again become a destination beer pub as it was back in the 1990s. Three cask beers are served, mainly, but not always, from local breweries together with one changing real cider and up to 14 keg lines. The pub has bare floorboards, with long red settles around the walls and tall stools all along the bar. Music is from the vinyl collection behind the bar. ♿♣🚪🌳🏃🌳🎵

Wiper & True Old Market Taproom

Unit 11-15, City Business Park, Easton Road, BS5 0SP

☎ (0117) 941 2501

House beer (by Wiper & True); 1 changing beer (often Five Points, Thornbridge, Wiper & True) Ⓗ

Spacious new taproom opened in 2022 in a modern industrial unit at the eastern end of Old Market. Walk past the Royal Mail depot and around the outside of the brewery to the entrance at the rear. Many beers are served, mainly from the brewery, with two on cask – one from Wiper & True and a guest beer. There is bench seating inside where you can view the impressive brewery. Food trucks serve food outside, where there is also plenty of seating, some under cover. Closed on Monday and Tuesday.
&⌂❀&⌖(Lawrence Hill) P⛽❀🛜♪

Bristol: St Philips

Barley Mow
39 Barton Road, BS2 0LF (400yds from rear exit of Temple Meads station over footbridge)
☎ (0117) 930 4709 ⊕ bristolbeerfactory.co.uk
Bristol Beer Factory Notorious, Fortitude; 5 changing beers (often Bristol Beer Factory, Siren, Tapestry By Props) Ⓗ
A short walk from Temple Meads station, Bristol Beer Factory's pub has a traditional feel, with bare wood floors and half-panelled walls. Eight handpumps offer four beers from the brewery, plus three constantly changing guests of varying styles, mostly from local breweries, and one real cider. In addition there are 10 keg beer taps dedicated to changing brews, and a range of bottled and canned beers. There is a cosy walled beer garden, and benches at the front. A drop-down screen is used for selected major sporting events.
&⌂❀⊕⌖(Temple Meads) ●⛽(506) ❀🛜

Bristol: St Werburghs

Duke of York Ⓛ
2 Jubilee Road, BS2 9RS (S side of Mina Rd park)
☎ (0117) 279 5781
4 changing beers (sourced locally; often Ashley Down, Bristol Beer Factory, New Bristol) Ⓗ
Tucked away in a side street, this popular local has an eclectic clientele and decor. The wooden floors, coloured fairy lights, and intriguing range of memorabilia create a welcoming grotto-like atmosphere. Notable features include a skittle alley, carved wooden mirrors and window frames from a local artist, and the Grand Old Duke of York exterior mural, also by a local artist. The outside garden seating area has a retractable cover. Four changing beers are served, including a dark one, mostly from local breweries. Children are welcome until evening. &⌂❀⌖(Stapleton Road)●●⛽(25)🛜

Bristol: Spike Island

Orchard Inn
12 Hanover Place, BS1 6XT (off Cumberland Rd near the SS Great Britain)
☎ 07405 360994 ⊕ orchardinn.co.uk
Otter Bitter; St Austell Proper Job; 1 changing beer (sourced regionally; often Arbor, Bristol Beer Factory, Gloucester) Ⓖ
A frequent winner of CAMRA Cider Pub of the Year awards this unassuming friendly back-street local is close to the floating harbour and SS Great Britain. Around 20 ciders and perries are served, with real cider regularly supplied by Rich's, Hecks, Ashridge and others. Beer drinkers are welcome, with two regular cask ales and one guest, often from Bristol breweries, served from the casks behind the bar or fetched from the cellar. Locally sourced rolls, pasties and pork pies are available until they sell out for the day. &⌂❀●⛽(506,M2)❀♪

Bristol: Westbury on Trym

Post Office Tavern
17 Westbury Hill, BS9 3AG
☎ (0117) 940 1233 ⊕ post-office-tavern.co.uk
Butcombe Original Ⓗ; Draught Bass Ⓖ; Sharp's Doom Bar; 2 changing beers (often Fuller's, Wye Valley) Ⓗ
Originally a mail coach house, this impressive single-storey brickwork pub is situated at the top of Westbury Hill. Post Office memorabilia seems to adorn every available space including a traditional red telephone box. Some of the real ales are served straight from casks in a back room. There is a small library in one bar, and several TVs show sports. Families are welcome during the day.
&♣⛽(1)❀🛜

Charfield

Plough Inn
68 Wotton Road, GL12 8SR
☎ (01453) 845297
Fuller's London Pride; 3 changing beers Ⓗ
An attractive single-room micropub, it features two open fireplaces and a large covered outdoor seating area, heated in winter, which utilises the original off-sales hatch for serving real ale. It offers four real ales plus lagers and ciders. There is a piano in the bar and live music is a regular feature. One of the more unusual features in the bar is the large gnu head above the fireplace, which gives its name to the occasional house beer. Q&❀P⛽(60,85)❀🛜♪

Cheltenham

Bank House Ⓛ ✓
15-21 Clarence Street, GL50 3JL (by the main town-centre bus stops in Clarence St)
☎ (01242) 240940
Greene King Abbot; Ruddles Best Bitter; Sharp's Doom Bar; 7 changing beers Ⓗ
Large town-centre Wetherspoon pub on two floors in a former Bank. The building retains many fine architectural features, the upper floor taking the form of a gallery with a cosy library area and views to the floor below. Ten ales and two ciders are generally available, three of which are also available from the upper floor bar. As with many Wetherspoon pubs, the internal wall decor provides interesting facts about the building and other local history. Q&⌂&⛽🛜

Beehive Inn 🍴 Ⓛ ✓
1-3 Montpellier Villas, GL50 2XE
☎ (01242) 702270 ⊕ thebeehivemontpellier.com
Bristol Beer Factory Notorious; Timothy Taylor Landlord; 4 changing beers (often Ramsbury, Thornbridge) Ⓗ
A bustling popular local in the residential Suffolks area of town, close to Montpellier, with up to 6 ales and a cider. It has a separate first-floor function room. A good range of food is available, including a popular bar menu. A beer festival is generally held annually and there are regular live music evenings. The secluded courtyard garden to the rear is popular in summer. &⌂❀⌖●♣⛽❀🛜♪

Cheltenham Motor Club Ⓛ
Upper Park Street, GL52 6SA (first right off Hales Rd from London Rd lights, 100yds on right; pedestrian access from A40 via Crown Passage opp Sandford Mill Rd junction)
☎ (01242) 522590 ⊕ cheltmc.com
6 changing beers (often Tiley's) Ⓗ
This friendly club just off London Road is the three-time winner of CAMRA National Club of the Year, most

recently in 2020, and winner of multiple other awards. Six regularly-changing ales from across the country include a dark ale and a local ale. There is at least one keg beer, generally from Deya, and at least one real cider plus a range of bottled Belgian beers. Events include an annual beer festival plus meet the brewer and tap takeover evenings. Darts and pool teams play here. Non-members are welcome for occasional visits for nominal fee. Card payments only. Q ➳ ⊛ ♠ ♦ ⊟ ❀ ☂

Jolly Brewmaster ⓛ

39 Painswick Road, GL50 2EZ (off A40 Suffolk Rd, between Suffolks and Tivoli, 200yds S along Painswick Rd)
☎ (01242) 772261
7 changing beers (often Arbor, Bespoke, Moor Beer) Ⓗ

A frequent local CAMRA Pub of the Year, 13 handpumps feature a changing range of ales sourced nationally, including up to six ciders. This busy and friendly community hub features original etched windows, a horseshoe bar and an open fire. A traditional drinking pub, there is no food menu but hot bar snacks such as pasties and pies are generally available later in the week. The attractive courtyard garden is popular in summer, with regular Friday barbecues.
Q ➳ ⊛ ♦ ⊟ (10,94U) ❀ ☂

Moon Under Water ⓛ ⊘

16-28 Bath Road, GL53 7HA (from end of pedestrianised High St, take Bath Rd, pub is 100yds on left)
☎ (01242) 583945
Greene King Abbot; Ruddles Best Bitter; Sharp's Doom Bar; 5 changing beers Ⓗ

Open-plan Wetherspoon Lloyds bar just off the east end of the pedestrianised high street (Strand). A decked area at the back overlooks the River Chelt and Sandford Park. Some five changing guest ales from local to countrywide supplement the regular beers, plus a selection of real ciders. The dance floor is only used Friday and Saturday evenings, with a generally quiet atmosphere at other times. There is an interactive quiz night on Monday. Children are allowed until evening. ➳ ⊛ ⓘ ♦ ⊟ ☂

Railway Inn

New Street, GL50 3QL (400yds W from The Wilson museum, past St James Square)
☎ (01242) 522925 ⊕ therailwaycheltenham.co.uk
Stroud Tom Long; 2 changing beers Ⓗ

Smart local just west of the town centre, which has recently gone free of tie. It has two main rooms with large lounge with some comfy sofas at one end and a small cosy bar to the road frontage. The garden has a terrace for smokers. Thai food and smoky barbecue cuisine are now the main food focus, available every day until evening. Q ➳ ⊛ ⓘ P ❀

Sandford Park Alehouse ⓛ

20 High Street, GL50 1DZ (E end of High St, past Strand on right)
☎ (01242) 690242 ⊕ sandfordparkalehouse.co.uk
Oakham Citra; Wye Valley Butty Bach; 7 changing beers Ⓗ

Winner of CAMRA National Pub of the Year in 2015 and a frequent local winner in recent years, this contemporary alehouse has a U-shaped main bar area complete with bar billiards, a cosy front snug with wood-burning stove and a large south-facing patio/garden. A function room/ lounge is on the first floor. Ten handpumps feature constantly changing ales from microbreweries sourced nationally and locally, plus at least one cider and 16 speciality lagers and craft beers. Q ➳ ⊛ ⓘ ♦ ♦ ⊟ ❀ ☂

Strand ⓛ

40-42 High Street, GL50 1EE (E end of High St just past pedestrianised area)
☎ (01242) 373728 ⊕ thestrandcheltenham.co.uk
4 changing beers (sourced regionally; often Bristol Beer Factory) Ⓗ

Modern, wine bar-style pub, offering at least three ales mainly sourced from the region and often featuring a brewery of the month, plus up to six ciders and 10 craft keg beers. Good-value food is served daily. An upstairs function room is available for hire, along with a cellar bar, home to live comedy and music nights. The large south-facing patio/garden provides a pleasant outdoor drinking area for those summer days.
➳ ⊛ ⓘ ♿ ♦ ⊟ ❀ ☂ ♪

Chipping Campden

Eight Bells ⓛ

Church Street, GL55 6JG
☎ (01386) 840311 ⊕ eightbellsinn.co.uk
Hook Norton Hooky; North Cotswold Cotswold Best; Wye Valley HPA; 1 changing beer (sourced locally) Ⓗ

The Eight Bells was originally built in the 14th century to house the stonemasons that built St James' church and was later used to store the peel of eight bells. The inn was rebuilt using most of the original stone and timbers during the 17th century. What exists today is an outstanding example of a traditional Cotswolds inn with a cobbled courtyard. Four handpumps serve local and regional ales and two real ciders.
Q ➳ ⊛ ♿ ⓘ ♦ ♦ ⊟ (21) ☂

Chipping Sodbury

Horseshoe ♥ ⊘

2 High Street, BS37 6AH
☎ (01454) 537557 ⊕ horseshoepub.co.uk
Butcombe Original; Uley Pigs Ear; 5 changing beers (sourced regionally; often Palmers, Prescott, Quantock) Ⓗ

One of the oldest buildings in the town, this hub of the community was formerly a stationery shop, then briefly a wine bar, and was converted into a pub in 2013. It serves seven beers, often unusual but mostly from the West Country, including dark or strong choices, as well as many different gins. There are three linked rooms with assorted furniture and a pleasant rear garden with a marquee and heating. Freshly made rolls are available at all times. ➳ ⊛ ♦ ♦ ⊟ ❀ ☂ ♪

Churchdown

Old Elm Inn ⓛ

Church Road, GL3 2ER
☎ (01452) 530961 ⊕ theoldelminn.co.uk
Sharp's Atlantic; 4 changing beers (sourced locally; often Stroud) Ⓗ

Set in the heart of Churchdown village, this interesting, spacious hostelry is deservedly popular. A great mix of modern and traditional fittings gives a warm ambience throughout. They have gained a great reputation for their food, with good vegetarian options on the menu, and booking is highly advised. Serving five quality beers, mainly LocAles, they host lively quiz and music nights, plus occasional food and drink tasting evenings. Major sporting events are shown in the sports bar. Families are welcome and the garden hosts a children's play area. There are five well-appointed letting rooms.
➳ ⊛ ♿ ⓘ ♿ ♦ P ⊟ ❀ ☂

ENGLAND

Cirencester

Drillman's Arms

34 Gloucester Road, GL7 2JY (on old A417, 200yds from A435 jct)

☎ (01285) 653892

House beer (by Marston's); 3 changing beers (sourced nationally) Ⓗ

A proper locals drinking haunt, this lively Georgian inn, perched beside a busy road, has a warm, convivial lounge with wood-burner, a pub games-dominated public bar and a busy skittle alley. Run by the same family for over three decades, this lovely free house features low-beamed ceilings, horse brasses, brewery pictures and well-priced beer. Fresh flowers grace the frontage and the immaculate toilets. Sunday lunches are available, and the outside seating area is popular with the local dog walking fraternity. They host an annual summer bank holiday beer festival. ❀◖▲♣P🐾📶

Hop Kettle

4 The Woolmarket, GL7 2PR (in the Woolmarket between Dyer St and Waterloo) SP025020

🌐 hop-kettle.com

Hop Kettle Cricklade Ordinary Bitter, North Wall; 3 changing beers (often Hop Kettle) Ⓗ

A new micropub in a former toy shop in Cirencester's Woolmarket. Operated by local company Hop Kettle brewery it is a welcome addition to the real ale offering in the town. There are five handpumps, eight craft kegs and two cider taps. There is also a range of interesting local and brewery-based gins and other spirits. It is furnished in modern comfortable fashion with a range of seating options. The kitchen is operated on a pop-up street food basis with a variety of menus and styles. Local CAMRA Pub of the Year 2023. 🔥◖◗♿🚌📶♫

Marlborough Arms 𝕃

1 Sheep Street, GL7 1QW

☎ (01285) 651474

Goff's Jouster; North Cotswold Windrush Ale; 3 changing beers (sourced nationally; often Arbor, Corinium, Stroud) Ⓗ

A real ale haven, offering five beers sourced from regional and microbreweries and a fridge with an interesting range of cans and bottles. This lively, wooden floored pub lies opposite the old GWR station. A previous local CAMRA Pub of the Year, brewery memorabilia adorns the wood paneled walls, with pews and a deep-set fireplace adding character. The ceiling is disappearing behind the encroaching pumpclip collection. There is a small sheltered rear patio, which hosts barbecues during their beer festivals. Occasional live music events are popular. ❀♣🐾📶♫

Coleford

Dog House Micro Pub

13-15 St John Street, GL16 8AP

☎ 07442 787015

Bespoke Beware The Bear; 4 changing beers (sourced locally; often Bath Ales, Goff's) Ⓗ

A former local CAMRA Pub of the Year, and frequent winner of Cider Pub of the Year, the Dog House Micro Pub is a friendly and popular local with a constantly changing and varied selection of up to four real ales, box ciders and craft ales. There is also an impressive gin and rum range. As the name suggests it is dog friendly. There are fortnightly charity quiz nights, vinyl nights, live music at weekends, and even fishing and knitting groups. Outside to the rear is a small courtyard. Q🔥●🚌🐾♫

Drybrook

Hearts of Oak 🏆

The Cross, GL17 9EE (centre of village)

☎ (01594) 730783

Greene King Abbot; Wye Valley Bitter, Butty Bach; 1 changing beer (sourced locally; often Wye Valley) Ⓗ

Boarded-up and unloved just five years ago, this once failing pub is now firmly back into the heart of the community since reopening in 2022, thanks to the vision of the new owners. Wye Valley brewery are the main suppliers, but guest beers are served from the third handpump. Wholesome pub food is served all day Monday to Saturday with Sunday lunchtime roast dinners. There are real fires, charity quiz nights and live music most Saturdays. Local CAMRA Pub of the Year 2024. Q🔥❀◖◗▲♣P🚉🚌🐾♫

Dursley

New Inn 𝕃

82-84 Woodmancote, GL11 4AJ (on A4135 Tetbury Rd)

☎ (01453) 519288

5 changing beers (sourced regionally) Ⓗ

A dog friendly establishment, where the owners' dogs often help in providing the greeting. This is a welcoming, comfortable pub that features a large L-shaped public bar with tiled floor and a wood-burning fire during cold weather. It also has a smaller lounge. An eclectic selection of frequently changing guest beers come usually, but not exclusively, from smaller breweries, often at the request of regulars. There is a garden at the rear, which is popular on sunny days. 🔥❀♣●P🚌(61)🐾

Old Spot Inn 🏆 𝕃

2 Hill Road, GL11 4JQ (by bus station and free car park)

☎ (01453) 542870 🌐 oldspotinn.co.uk

Uley Old Ric; 7 changing beers (sourced nationally) Ⓗ

Excellent free house dating from 1776, serving up to eight ales, plus ciders and perrys. Named after the Gloucestershire Old Spot pig, a porcine theme blends with the extensive brewery memorabilia, low ceilings, wood-burning stove and welcoming staff to create a convivial atmosphere. There is an attractive garden and a heated outdoor covered area. Freshly prepared food is served at lunchtimes. On the Cotswold Way, it is popular with walkers, and hosts regular events in the evenings. Q🔥❀◖♿●🚌🐾📶

Ebrington

Ebrington Arms 𝕃

GL55 6NH (off B4035 in centre of village by the green)

☎ (01386) 593223 🌐 theebringtonarms.co.uk

North Cotswold Moreton Mild, Green Man IPA; Wye Valley Butty Bach; 1 changing beer (sourced regionally) Ⓗ

A 17th-century Cotswold stone-built village pub in a beautiful village with excellent walks. The cosy bar has a lovely open fireplace and three handpumps dispensing local North Cotswold and other local or national ales. The lovely well appointed beer garden has patio seating. Open seven days a week with accommodation available and a good food offering from local suppliers, served in large restaurant or the bar. Q🔥❀🛏◖◗♿▲♣●P

Fossebridge

Inn at Fossebridge 🏆 ✔

GL54 3JS (A429)

☎ (01285) 720721 🌐 innatfossebridge.co.uk

Butcombe Original, Gold; 3 changing beers (sourced locally) H

The Inn at Fossebridge is located in the pretty Cotswolds hamlet of Fossebridge, where the Fosse Way drops into the valley of the River Coln, an area of outstanding natural beauty. An attractive one-bar inn with old timbers, a fine flagstone floor and open fires the premises also benefits from an outstanding four-acre garden with a lake and river. A selection of regional ales and guests from local breweries can be enjoyed in these cosy surroundings. Q ⛲ ❀ ⇦ ◑ ♦ P ☀ ☏

Frampton Cotterell

Rising Sun
43 Ryecroft Road, BS36 2HN
☎ (01454) 772330 ⊕ hopunionbrewery.co.uk
Hop Union Bonville Pale, Maiden Voyage, Moose River; 3 changing beers (often Abbey, Hop Union) H
Village local and brewery tap for the Hop Union brewery in Brislington. The log-burning stove, archways and slate pillars add to the ambience. Additional seating can be found up the stairs to the left, and there is a restaurant in the warm conservatory. Lunchtime snacks and more substantial evening meals are served from an extensive menu, with all food made in-house. Up to six real ales are available, usually including a varying offering from Hop Union plus one or two guests. The skittle alley can be booked for private functions. Q ❀ ◑ ♣ P ⇦ (Y6) ☀ ☏ ♫

Gloucester

Brewhouse & Kitchen
Unit R1, St Anne Walk, Gloucester Quays, GL1 5SH
☎ (01452) 222965
Brewhouse & Kitchen Shed Head, Stevedore, SS Banner H
Situated by the side of the Gloucester and Sharpness Canal, this bar/restaurant brews its own range of beers on site, and is a delight to visit. Outdoor seating by the canal is great for a fine day, and swathes of the seating indoors allows customers to watch the brewing in progress. Beer tasting events, Meet the Brewer and brewing days are all regularly available. Regular beers plus a seasonal cask, and a range of keg beers are all brewed here. Please chat to the friendly, well informed staff to learn more about their products. ⛲ ◑ ⅄ ⇦ ☀ ☏

Drunken Duck
1 Bull Lane, GL1 2HG
☎ (01452) 757581
House beer (by Butcombe); 3 changing beers (sourced nationally) H
The city's smallest bar, tucked away just off Westgate Street. A friendly and welcoming venue where you can choose to join in with the conversation in the almost bijou bar, or tuck yourself away in the surprisingly spacious room upstairs, where you can dawdle on the retro games machines. Three regularly changing ales, plus a plethora of spirits and mixers, makes it popular with the weekend crowd; it may not the best place to visit for the shy and tongue-tied, but the banter here is inclusive and usually fun, although loud at times. ≠ ♣ ⇦ ☀ ♫

Fountain Inn L ✓
53 Westgate Street, GL1 2NW (down an alley between numbers 51 and 55)
☎ (01452) 522562 ⊕ thefountaininngloucester.com
Bristol Beer Factory Independence; Dartmoor Jail Ale; St Austell Tribute; Timothy Taylor Landlord; 2 changing beers H

Blessed with a well-deserved reputation for offering some cracking beers, coupled with a popular menu, especially busy on rugby match days, this fine establishment is conveniently located for events at the cathedral. This 17th-century inn was built on the site of an ale house, known to have existed in 1216. A passage leads from Westgate Street into a courtyard that is garlanded with flowers in warmer months. The Cathedral bar has a panelled ceiling and carved stone fireplace, the Orange Room serves as an overflow area, and is available for private functions. ❀ ◑ ⅍ ☀ ☏ ♫

Linden Tree
73-75 Bristol Road, GL1 5SN (on A430, S of docks)
☎ (01452) 527869 ⊕ lindentreepub.co.uk
Wadworth 6X; Wye Valley HPA, Butty Bach; 1 changing beer (sourced nationally) H
An intriguing property at the end of a Grade II-listed Georgian terrace, with a country feel inside; featuring an open log fire with unusual canopy, it has beamed ceilings and exposed stone walls. The front bar offers a variety of seating, and at the rear of the pub is a skittle alley, function room and sports bar. There is a patio in front and the bus from the city centre stops nearby. Substantial home-made meals are served (not Sat and Sun eve) with a Sunday carvery. Well-priced accommodation is available. Guest ales are from family brewers. ❀ ⇦ ◑ ♣ ⇦ (12,60) ☏

Pelican Inn L ✓
4 St Marys Street, GL1 2QR (WNW of cathedral)
☎ (01452) 582966 ⊕ pelicangloucester.co.uk
Wye Valley Bitter, The Hopfather, HPA, Butty Bach, Wholesome Stout; 3 changing beers (sourced nationally) H
Local CAMRA Pub of the Year again, this wonderfully run two-room establishment was rescued by Wye Valley brewery in 2012. Twice-yearly beer festivals and a tap takeover are still popular highlights of the year. The single bar is dominated by conversation and a large fire, with the beams rumoured to be from Drake's Golden Hind (originally the Pelican). Alongside regularly changing ciders and perries, a wide selection of cans showcases modern trends in small-batch brewing. The attractive patio area at the rear hosts a food wagon on rugby match days. Q ❀ ⅍ ♣ ♦ ⇦ ☀ ☏ ♫

Turks Head Inn
7-9 St Aldate Street, GL1 1RP
☎ 07771 982356
4 changing beers (sourced nationally) H/G
This was the first micropub in the city, successfully relocating from Southgate Street to St Aldate Street in 2022, while retaining its fan base. Selling four cask ales and a varied selection of ciders, for technophobes, this is the place, as mobile phones are really not encouraged, there is no WiFi, and no social media in any form. This is an adult pub with no children allowed, but is blessed with both a horseshoe bar and a spare staircase; the upstairs rooms are a lovely spot to sit and put the world to rights. A cash only hostelry. Q ≠ ♦ ⇦

Gretton

Royal Oak L
Gretton Road, GL54 5EP (E end of village, 1½ miles from Winchcombe)
☎ (01242) 604999 ⊕ royaloakgretton.co.uk
St Austell Proper Job; Wye Valley Bitter, Butty Bach; 2 changing beers (sourced regionally) H
A welcome is assured from the local owners of this popular Cotswold pub. All the regular beers are from St Austell and Wye Valley. Food can be eaten in the L-

shaped bar or the conservatory with its outstanding views across the Vale of Evesham. The Royal Oak dates from about 1830 and the large garden includes a children's play area and a tennis court. The Gloucestershire Warwickshire steam railway runs past the garden. ♿🚳🚬🍴🅿🐕♣🐾🚭❄

Ham

Salutation Inn 🅻

Ham Green, GL13 9QH (from Berkeley take the road signposted to Jenner Museum)
☎ (01453) 810284 ⊕ the-sally-at-ham.com
Dark Star Hophead; Tiley's Special Bitter; 4 changing beers (sourced nationally; often Bristol Beer Factory, Moor Beer, Tiley's) Ⓗ
Multi-award winning rural free house, popular with locals and visitors alike, offering up to six real ales and nine real ciders and perries plus an extensive bottled beer and cider menu. On-site microbrewery Tiley's Ales produces a range of traditional ales. There are three bars (two cosy ones share a central wood burner) and a skittles alley/ function room. Locally made hot pies are served on Friday evenings and weekend lunchtimes; there are also folk nights and singalongs. Q♿🚳🚬🍴🅟🐾♣🐕❄🎵

Hawkesbury Upton

Beaufort Arms 🅻

High Street, GL9 1AU (off A46, 6 miles N of M4 jct 18)
☎ (01454) 238217 ⊕ beaufortarms.com
Bristol Beer Factory Independence; Butcombe Original; 3 changing beers (sourced regionally) Ⓗ
An attractive Grade II-listed Cotswold stone free house, built in 1602, close to the historic Somerset Monument. It features separate public and lounge bars, a dining room and skittle alley/function room, which house a large collection of ancient brewery and local memorabilia. It serves up to five ales plus a traditional cider on handpump. There is an attractive garden with a barbecue used for local community activities. The friendly locals assure visitors a warm welcome.
Q♿🚳🍴🐕♣🅿🚭🐾❄

Hillesley

Fleece Inn 🅻

Chapel Lane, GL12 7RD (between Wotton-under-Edge and Hawkesbury Upton)
☎ (01453) 520003 ⊕ thefleecehillesley.com
Wye Valley Butty Bach; 5 changing beers (often Arbor, Church End, Oakham) Ⓗ
An attractive 17th-century village pub set in the heart of Hillesley. It has a single bar with a wood-burning stove, a separate lounge/dining room and a snug area. The pub has up to six real ales and also features guest craft keg and draft cider. Food is available at lunchtime and in the evening. There is a large attractive lawned garden with a safe play area for children and private car park. Dogs are welcome. Q♿🚳🍴🐕🅿🚭🐾❄🎵

Horsley

Hog

The Cross, GL6 0PR (take the A46 Bath Rd from Nailsworth centre; after ¼ mile turn right onto B4058 Old Bristol Rd; pub is on left after 1 mile)
☎ (01453) 833843 ⊕ hoghorsley.com
Stroud Tom Long; 3 changing beers (sourced locally; often Fresh Standard, Gloucester, Stroud) Ⓗ
Benefiting from a recent revamp of the interior, this well laid out, wonderful, friendly village local boasts a balanced, and carefully chosen, range of real ales and ciders. It has a single large bar area, with a snug at one end. There is plenty of seating and useful ledges for resting your glass when standing. They only do food Friday and Saturday evening; the latter usually a fantastic pop-up food night, although filled rolls are available at lunchtimes. The car park now features a marquee for sheltered seating when needed.
♿🚳🚬🍴🐕♣🐾🅿🚃(40) 🚭❄🎵

Joyford

Dog & Muffler

Wellmeadow Lane, GL16 7AS (at Globe Inn at Berry Hill take lane downhill to Joyford and follow pub signs; or use What Three Words driveways.staples.string)
SO5790013381
☎ (01594) 832444
Brains Rev James Original; Wye Valley HPA, Butty Bach; 1 changing beer (sourced regionally; often Hop Union, Wychwood) Ⓗ
Tucked away in a valley, the Dog & Muffler can be difficult to find for the first-time visitor. A deceptive modern exterior hides a genuine traditional pub with exposed stone walls and wooden beams bedecked with fairy lights. Making a welcome return to the Guide after 23 years, this renowned dining pub has a cosy snug bar with warming fires and one changing ale. There are extensive views from the picturesque garden. A dog friendly pub, be sure to say hello to the scarf-wearing Tibetan Mastiff pub dog. ♿🚳🚬🍴🚬🐕♣🅿

Kingswood

Lyons Den

121 Regent Street, BS15 8LJ
4 changing beers (often Arbor, Bristol Beer Factory, Tiny Rebel) Ⓖ
Micropub opened in 2019 in a former charity shop at the eastern end of the main shopping street. The bar area as you enter is simply furnished and there is a small snug space at the rear. The cask, keg beers and ciders for sale are displayed on a retro-style computer screen on the wall. There are regular tap takeovers from local breweries. Board games are available to play and there is low-volume background music. Dogs are made very welcome. Closed on Monday. Q♿🐕🚃🚭

Leighterton

Royal Oak 🅻

The Street, GL8 8UN (Leighterton is signposted off A46)
☎ (01666) 890250 ⊕ theroyaloakleighterton.co.uk
Arbor Shangri La; Uley Bitter, Old Spot Prize Strong Ale; 1 changing beer (sourced locally; often Wye Valley) Ⓗ
Attractive, sympathetically refurbished Grade II-listed Cotswold stone pub in the village centre. This cracking pub is split into a number of cosy areas for both drinking and dining. It has open fires, low ceilings, panelled rooms and exposed stone walls. Customers are served at a single bar dispensing up to four real ales, craft kegs and two ciders/perries. Some very pertinent wall decorations may give pause for thought. Delicious home-made bar snacks are available together with a popular food menu. The spacious car park can fill quickly. ♿🚳🚬🍴🐕♣🅿

Longborough

Coach & Horses

GL56 0QU (off A424 in village centre)
☎ (01451) 830325 ⊕ coachandhorseslongborough.co.uk

Donnington BB, Cotswold Gold, SBA H
Dating from the 18th century this village pub of Cotswold stone is perched on a bank overlooking a small green and war memorial. Located only one mile from the renowned Donnington brewery this friendly family-run, one-bar premises is the focal point of community activity in the village. Flagstone floors and open fire greet locals and visitors alike with the full range of the good-value Donnington Ales available along with home-cooked food. Q✿⟲❀◐♣🚲🐾🎧

Lydbrook

Forge Hammer L
Forge Row, GL17 9NP (B4234)
☎ (01594) 860310 ⊕ theforgehammer.co.uk
Lydbrook Valley IPA, Viaduct Pale Ale; 1 changing beer H
It is hard to believe that the Forge Hammer was once set in an industrial landscape of tin-plating works and furnaces in the shadow of the 80-foot-high Severn and Wye Railway viaduct. Now in a verdant valley setting close to the River Wye, the Forge Hammer is the home of the Lydbrook Valley Brewing Company, a nanobrewery just supplying the pub. Viaduct Pale Ale is a nod to the past. Fascinating photographs of bygone Lydrook are displayed. The popular Spice Garden Indian Resturant is incorporated into the premises. ✿⟲◐A♣P🎧

Marshfield

Catherine Wheel
39 High Street, SN14 8LR (If using postcode in sat nav check it is not showing Colerne)
☎ (01225) 892220 ⊕ thecatherinewheel.co.uk
Butcombe Adam Henson's Rare Breed; 1 changing beer (sourced locally; often Flying Monk) H
The Catherine Wheel is an impressive example of provincial baroque architecture. The façade and front rooms were built in 1680 as an addition to a much older house. By 1740 it was a coaching inn, changing its name to the Catherine Wheel about 40 years later. Simple, sympathetic decor complements the exposed stone walls and large open fireplaces. Inside it feels like a traditional Cotswold pub, with good ale, good food and a warm and welcoming interior. The large cosy bar area has rooms off and a courtyard-style garden with a covered area. Q✿⟲❀◐P🚲🐾🎧🎵

Minchinhampton

Old Lodge Inn L
Minchinhampton Common, GL6 9AQ (take The W from Nailsworth towards Minchinhampton Common; the Old Lodge is clearly signed down its own spur road)
☎ (01453) 832047 ⊕ food-club.com/pubs/the-old-lodge
4 changing beers (sourced nationally; often St Austell, Sharp's, Stroud) H
The Old Lodge is a large and welcoming 17th-century Cotswold stone inn set prominently on the Common. Unashamedly a food-led establishment, it does serve four real ales, two from Stroud brewery and two regional. On a warm, sunny day you will struggle to find a better location for alfresco drinking. The interior is decorated to a high standard (even the toilets) and this rambling, multi-roomed, premises is sprinkled liberally with individual statement art pieces. The large walled garden has delightful views over the Common. ✿❀◐⟲&P🚌(69)🐾🎧

Moreton-in-Marsh

Bell Inn L ✅
High Street, GL56 0AF (A429)
☎ (01608) 651688 ⊕ thebellinnmoreton.co.uk
Prescott Hill Climb; Purity Pure UBU; Timothy Taylor Landlord; 2 changing beers (sourced locally; often Hook Norton, North Cotswold) H
This old high street coaching inn dating from the 18th century has been pleasantly refurbished. The interior comprises of a mainly open-plan area which has been sympathetically divided into more intimate snug sections with a real fire. A large courtyard area is found through the old arched entrance with an enclosed garden at the rear. Famed for links with Lord of the Rings author J.R.R.Tolkien, a map of Middle Earth adorns the walls. Good food and local and national ales are available. Q✿❀⟲◐&A≠P🚌(801)🐾🎧🎵

Newent

Cobblers L
7 Church Street, GL18 1PU
☎ 07891 815654
4 changing beers (often Goff's, Not That California, Settle) H
Cobblers can claim to be Gloucestershire's first micropub, located in the centre of Newent. The pub is bigger than you might imagine with the cosy front bar leading on to two further rooms at the back converted from what was once local council offices. There are usually four gravity fed ales, sourced from all over the UK plus cider and a large selection of artisan gins. Thursday nights are generally live music nights. Q🐾🚌

King's Arms
Ross Road, GL18 1BD (on B4221)
☎ (01531) 820035 ⊕ kings-arms-newent.business.site
4 changing beers (often Brains SA, Shepherd Neame, Titanic) H
The pub has a comfortable refitted bar area with open fires, a large function room and skittle alley, and a big lower bar and dining room. There is also a spacious outdoor decked courtyard. With a good reputation for home-cooked food, the pub offers a wide menu including speciality pizzas, midweek offers and popular Sunday lunches. Four regularly changing ales are generally served. A former local CAMRA Pub of the Year. Q✿◐♣P

Parkend

Fountain Inn
Fountain Way, GL15 4JD (off B4234)
☎ (01594) 562189 ⊕ thefountaininn.info
Bespoke Forest Gold; Wye Valley HPA, Butty Bach; 2 changing beers H
Popular village inn, conveniently situated near to many Forest of Dean visitor attractions. The Dean Forest Steam Railway, and a bike hire centre are close by. A gate in the pub garden gives direct access to Whitemead Tourist Park. Many items of local interest are display in the pub, including railwayana. The landlord has written a fascinating book on the history of the Fountain Inn – ask behind the bar for more information. Accommodation is available at the inn itself, while an adjoining bunkhouse caters for groups. There are also spaces for motorhome stop-overs. Q✿❀⟲◐&A♣🐾P🐾🎧🎵

Sapperton

Bell 🄻

GL7 6LE

☎ (01285) 760298 ⊕ bellsapperton.co.uk

Stroud Tom Long, Budding; Uley Bitter 🄷

This 18th-century pub lies at the heart of the village, and has a couple of welcoming bars with log fires, a garden room for private functions and a courtyard garden. Freshly prepared dishes form the menu which changes daily, mainly using local produce, with fish a specialty. Horses and their riders are very welcome, and electric car charging is available. Opening times may vary – phone to check. The pub is usually closed on Mondays in winter. Q🕏✿🄽◑🕭♣P🌑

Staple Hill

Wooden Walls Micropub

30 Broad Street, BS16 5NU

☎ 07858 266596 ⊕ thewoodenwallsmicropub.com

5 changing beers 🄶

Micropub opened in 2018 in a former carpet shop on the main shopping street. The single room is pleasantly furnished with wooden booths and walls. Drinks currently available are displayed on a large blackboard surrounding the serving hatch. Five cask ales are on offer alongside real ciders, several craft keg beers, gin and wine, but no lager. There are a few steps up to the toilets and paved rear garden. Tap takeovers are a regular occurrence. Board games are available to play. Closed on Monday. Q🕏✿♣◑🖥🌑

Stroud

Ale House 🄻

9 John Street, GL5 2HA (opp Cornhill Farmers' Market)

☎ (01453) 755447 ⊕ thealehousestroud.com

Burning Sky Plateau; Tiley's Simcoe; 6 changing beers (sourced nationally; often Saltaire, Grey Trees, Wiper & True) 🄷

Built in 1837 for the Poor Law Guardians, this Grade II-listed building is a mecca for ale lovers. The bar occupies the double-height top-lit former boardroom, where an all-year-round beer festival showcases beers from By The Horns Hops, Mallinsons, Red Cat and many more – plus a cider and perry. Opposite is a blazing log fire and adjoining are two smaller rooms. Live music plays at weekends, with jazz once a month on Thursday. Sunday is quiz night. Food consists of home-made curries, chilli and other dishes. A restored 1932 bar billiards table is a popular recent addition. Local CAMRA Pub of the Year. 🌑◑🖫🕭⊟🌑🤶♣♠🖥🌑

Crown & Sceptre 🄻

98 Horns Road, GL5 1EG

☎ (01453) 762588 ⊕ crownandsceptrestroud.com

Stroud Budding; Uley Bitter, Pigs Ear; 1 changing beer (sourced regionally; often Blue Anchor, Butcombe, North Cotswold) 🄷

Lively back-street local at the heart of its community. The walls display an eclectic mix of framed prints, posters and clocks. There is even some stained glass. Local groups meet round a large table in a side room – including knit & natter on Tuesdays. The pub also has its own motorcycle society. It is famed for its Up the Workers good-value set meal on Wednesdays, and Sunday roasts. Sport is screened in the back bar. A terrace to the rear offers panoramic views across the valley to Rodborough Common. 🕏✿◑🕭♣P⊟(8)🌑🤶🌑

Lord John 🌑

15-17 Russell Street, GL5 3AB (from Stroud station, walk up Station Rd and then turn right onto Russell St; the Lord John is 50yds up on the right-hand side)

☎ (01453) 767610

Greene King Abbot; Ruddles Best Bitter; Sharp's Doom Bar; 3 changing beers (often Hook Norton, Hop Union, Theakston) 🄷

Behind a handsome red brick and Cotswold-stone façade, Wetherspoon's sympathetic conversion of the town's former post office has produced an L-shaped bar with a south-facing walled courtyard. The pub is dominated by the large greenhouse-style glazed skylight which used to light the sorting office. The bar counter runs down the right-hand side with booths and individual high tables opposite. There are more booths and tables to the rear, which has been designed to resemble an old-fashioned railway carriage, complete with overhead luggage racks and a curved, boarded ceiling. 🕏✿◑🕭🚻⊟(67,69)🌑

Prince Albert 🄻 🌑

Rodborough Hill, GL5 3SS (corner of Walkley Hill)

☎ (01453) 755600 ⊕ theprincealbertstroud.co.uk

Timothy Taylor Landlord; 4 changing beers (sourced nationally; often Bristol Beer Factory, Church End, Thornbridge) 🄷

This lively, cosmopolitan, Cotswold-stone inn below Rodborough Common has been run by the same family for 28 years. Simultaneously bohemian, homely and welcoming – with a big reputation for live music – the single L-shaped bar is full of local art, music and film posters, and an idiosyncratic mix of furniture, fittings and memorabilia. Stairs lead up from the large covered courtyard to a walled garden with an elegant cruck-framed shelter. Food consists of pizzas and burgers. Live music on Sunday and Monday evenings is ticketed. 🕏✿◑♣⊟(40,69)🌑🤶♫

Tewkesbury

Cross House Tavern 🏆 🄻

108 Church Street, GL20 5AB

☎ 07931 692227

10 changing beers (often Bristol Beer Factory, Goff's, Salopian) 🄶

Tewkesbury's first micropub was originally two houses in the early 16th century. It was extended in the 17th century, and extensively renovated throughout circa 1865. The Cross House Tavern's heritage has been restored with a great deal of dedication. It has again become a Victorian-style establishment serving real local ales (including vegan options), ciders, perries, wines and snacks – many sourced within 20 miles. Beer is served from tapped casks much as it was when the building was known as the Tolsey Inn and Coach House in the early 20th century. Q🛆◑⊟🌑🤶🌑

Inferno Brewery Tap 🄻

Bredon Road, GL20 5BU (off N end of High St)

☎ 07854 949731

Inferno Golden Embers, Tinder Box, Cinder Stout, Mental Martha, Prometheus, Vulcan; 6 changing beers (sourced locally; often Inferno) 🄷

In the grounds of the White Bear pub, which remains closed and is undergoing a change of use, Inferno brewery have taken over the old coaching buildings for a pop up venture serving up to five of their own brews on a regular basis. Renamed the Firepit, this brewery tap is well worth a visit to enjoy a great pint and some real cider. Inferno is a family-run business building a great reputation and following for the beers it produces. 🕏✿🛆♣P⊟🌑🤶🌑♫

Nottingham Arms 🅛 ✅

129 High Street, GL20 5JU (on A38 in town centre)
☎ (01684) 491514 ⊕ nottinghamarms-tewkesbury.co.uk
Sharp's Doom Bar; 4 changing beers (often Enville, Purity, Sharp's) Ⓗ

Dating from the 14th century, this town-centre hostelry has two welcoming rooms, a public bar at the front and the bar/restaurant behind, both with timber predominating. Framed photographs of old Tewkesbury adorn the walls, and knowledgeable staff will happily tell you about the resident ghosts. Four ales are generally served. The pub is getting a reputation for their excellent, well-priced food, served lunchtimes and evenings. Live music plays on most Friday and Sunday evenings and Thursday is quiz night. ⅚◐♿♣♠⬛🅟?♪

Olde Black Bear ★

68 High Street, GL20 5BJ (on A38 at top of High St near river bridge)
☎ (01684) 292202
Wye Valley Bitter, The Hopfather, Butty Bach; 8 changing beers (often Theakston, Uley) Ⓗ

The oldest inn in Gloucestershire, dating from 1308, it features many separate rambling bar areas, one boasting leatherwork on the ceiling dating from the 17th century. Resident ghosts are reported to include an old lady and a Cavalier. A pleasant terrace patio overlooks the garden and the river Avon (moorings available), where children (under supervision) can feed the ducks. The lower restaurant was once the stables, and was used as a hospital during the Wars of the Roses.
⅚❀🖷◐♿₹(Ashchurch)⬛♥

Royal Hop Pole 🅛 ✅

94 Church Street, GL20 5RS (in centre of town between the abbey and cross)
☎ (01684) 278670
Exmoor Beast; Greene King IPA; Hook Norton Old Hooky; Ruddles County; 6 changing beers (sourced locally) Ⓗ

This well-known landmark is an amalgamation of historic buildings from the 15th and 18th centuries. It has been known as the Royal Hop Pole Hotel since being visited in 1891 by Princess Mary of Teck (Queen Mary, royal consort of George V). The Hop Pole is mentioned in Dickens' Pickwick Papers. Purchased by JD Wetherspoon, it reopened in 2008. There is wood panelling on almost every wall of this spacious, multi-roomed drinking establishment, with a large patio and garden area at the rear. Q⅚❀🖷◐♿♣⬛(41,71)?

Thrupp

Stroud Brewery Tap 🅛

Kingfisher Business Park, London Road, GL5 2BY (take A419 from Stroud, turn right down Hope Mill Ln just before the painted bus shelter, immediate right turn and brewery is on your left over the bridge at the end)
☎ (01453) 887122 ⊕ stroudbrewery.co.uk
Stroud Tom Long, OPA, Budding; 1 changing beer (often Stroud) Ⓗ

Occupying a new purpose-designed building beside the Thames & Severn Canal, the brewery taproom opens directly onto a terrace beside the towpath. To one side is an open kitchen with an Italian wood-fired pizza oven. Seating consists mostly of wooden benches beside long tables – resembling at times a diminutive Bavarian beer hall. These benches are augmented by squishy leather sofas and large oak casks for vertical drinking. At the far end – and with windows allowing glimpses of the brewery – is a small stage with an upright piano.
⅚❀◐♿♣⬛(54A,69)♥?♪

Twyning

Village Inn 🅛 ✅

The Green, GL20 6DF
☎ (01684) 293500 ⊕ villageinntwyning.co.uk
4 changing beers (often Hobsons, Timothy Taylor, Wye Valley) Ⓗ

Busy village inn dating from the mid-15th century, popular with the locals. There is an attractive enclosed garden to the rear and the front patio overlooks the village green, with car parking on the green. There are pleasant walks to the river where the ferry runs daily to Tewkesbury and Bredon. The pub is used by local skittle and darts teams and as a meeting place for many local societies and clubs. It has low ceilings and a rambling bar area. Watch out for the low entrance doorway.
⅚❀◐♿♣

Upper Oddington

Horse & Groom 🅛 ✅

Upper Oddington, GL56 0XH (top of village signed off A436 E of Stow)
☎ (01451) 830584 ⊕ horseandgroom.uk.com
Goff's Jouster; Wye Valley Butty Bach; 1 changing beer (sourced locally) Ⓗ

Privately owned 16th-century inn situated in good walking country close to Stow and run by friendly licensees. The extended bar area, popular with locals, has its own sitting room linked by a real open log fire in an inglenook setting. A weekly changing guest is usually from a Gloucestershire brewer, and real cider from Dunkertons. Outside are a large car park and attractive garden and patio area. Eight letting bedrooms are available. Q⅚❀🖷◐♿⬛🅟🏠♥?

Upton St Leonards

BMI Club ✅

8 Bondend Road, GL4 8AG
☎ (01452) 616384 ⊕ bmiclub.co.uk
3 changing beers (sourced nationally; often Fuller's, Wye Valley) Ⓗ

The Birchall Memorial Institute is a members club, serving and connecting the local community since its foundation in 1898, and is the centre for many of the local sporting associations. Located next to the village hall, the entrance leads through to a pleasant, airy lounge bar on the left, and a smaller sports bar on the right, plus skittles, snooker and pool rooms. Blessed with an excellent cellar, a selection of freshly made rolls and toasties are available to complement their fine ales. They host regular entertainment nights alongside sports TV for major matches. Q♣⬛(02)♥♪

Westrip

Carpenters Arms

Redhouse Lane, GL6 6EY (approach Redhouse Ln from Stroud via Westrip Ln; do not come via the other end of Redhouse Ln as sharp left turn at junction is dangerous)
☎ (01453) 297728 ⊕ thecarpentersarmswestrip.co.uk
3 changing beers (sourced regionally; often Fresh Standard, Stroud) Ⓗ

This Gloucestershire CAMRA Cider Pub of the Year 2024 offers up to 12 local ciders as well as three well-kept real ales. A Cotswold stone building in a hillside location with impressive views from the pub's south-facing windows and garden, including Rodborough Fort, Selsley and down to the River Severn in the west. Inside there is a friendly public bar with a flagstone floor and mullioned windows, and a comfortable lounge, both with log

burners. The garden is sloping with terraced paved areas featuring circular picnic tables.
🐕🅰️🍽️🍴♿️P🚌(230,67) ❀ 📶 ♪

Winchcombe

Corner Cupboard
83 Gloucester Street, GL54 5LX (B4632)
☎ (01242) 602303 ⊕ cornercupboardwinchcombe.co.uk
Skinner's Betty Stogs; Timothy Taylor Landlord; Wye Valley Butty Bach; 1 changing beer (sourced locally) Ⓗ
Situated on the outskirts of Winchcombe, this traditional inn dating from the mid 16th century has several bars and rooms leaving the customer to choose their own style and company. A real ale bar with guest ales bosts flagstone floors, oak panelling and Cotswold stone walls. Good-value food is served daily in pleasant surroundings. There are reports the inn is haunted by the ghost of a 12 year old girl who runs across the floorboards above the bar. Q🐕🅰️🍽️🍴♿️🅿️🚌❀📶

Woodcroft

Rising Sun
Coleford Road, NP16 7HY (On B4228)
⊕ therisingsunwoodcroft.co.uk
Kingstone Llandogo Trow; Wye Valley HPA, Butty Bach; 2 changing beers (often Hive Mind) Ⓗ
Bought by a property developer in 2011 with the sole intention of converting the pub to residential use, the Save Our Sun group fought for a decade to get the Rising Sun back open. With support from the district council and a magnificent share-raising initiative the Rising Sun Community pub reopened in 2022. Their achievement was recognised by CAMRA, with the Rising Sun being the national winner of the Pub Saving Award 2024. This cosy

pub, set high above the River Wye near Wintour's Leap, is a great place for refreshment after exploring the local area. Dogs are welcome. Q🅰️🍽️🍴🅰️♿️P📶♪

Wotton-under-Edge

Falcon Steakhouse Ⓛ
20 Church Street, GL12 7HB (bottom of Long St shopping area)
☎ (01453) 521894 ⊕ falconsteakhouse.com
3 changing beers (sourced regionally; often Flying Monk, Hop Union, Lucifer Brewhouse) Ⓗ
A free house built in 1659, the quirky layout of the interior features rooms on differing levels. The cosy single bar has a wood-burning fire and leads to a snug with a flagstone floor. Their dining room specialises in steaks from the family farm (which can also be purchased in the pub) and locally sourced ingredients. Competitively priced beers are selected by customer vote from brewers within a 25 mile radius. A popular haunt with walkers on the Cotswold Way. Q🐕🍽️🍴♿️🚌❀📶

Star Inn Ⓛ ✅
21 Market Street, GL12 7AE (close to local museum and free car park at top of town)
☎ (01453) 844651 ⊕ starinnwotton.co.uk
Wickwar BOB; 2 changing beers (sourced locally; often Lucifer Brewhouse) Ⓗ
Situated at the top of this historic town on the Cotswold Way, this 16th-century comfortable two-bar pub has an exposed Cotswold stone interior. The pub contains memorabilia of the White Star Line famous for the ill-fated Titanic. John Cambridge, who started the company, was born in the pub in 1784. Major sporting events can be watched in the public bar or a quiet pint enjoyed in the lounge. There is a function room for community events. Q🅰️🍽️🍴♿️🚌🍴🚌

Olde Black Bear, Tewkesbury (Photo: Chris Amies / Flickr CC BY 2.0)

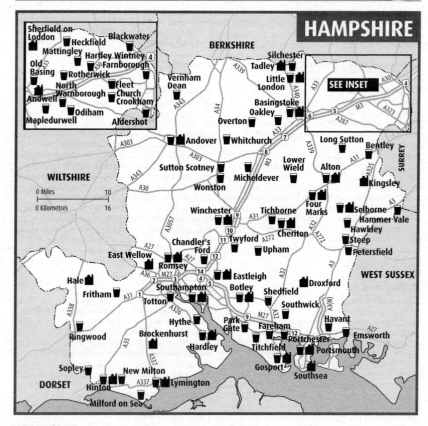

HAMPSHIRE

Aldershot

Garden Gate L ✅
2 Church Lane East, GU11 3BT
☎ 07396 721971
Surrey Hills Ranmore; 1 changing beer (sourced regionally; often Dark Star, Hogs Back, St Austell) H
Dating from the mid-19th century, this conversation-led pub is the heart of its local community. A popular stop-off for dog walkers, it is close to the railway station. A single bar serves two distinct drinking areas, and a separate back room leads to a small patio. Three beers are generally on tap, including a house beer, Wobbly Gate, whose origin is a closely guarded secret. The well-attended Thursday night charity quiz funds the community defibrillator, and CPR training is available.
❀≈P🖩❀🛜

Queen Hotel L ✅
1 High Street, GU11 1BH
☎ (01252) 361770
Greene King Abbot; Ruddles Best Bitter; Sharp's Doom Bar; 3 changing beers (sourced nationally; often Tillingbourne, Twickenham, Windsor & Eton) H
Grade II-listed hotel dating from 1857 and now fully restored and expanded by Wetherspoon, who have preserved its character while providing for modern needs. Pictures of old Aldershot abound, including postcards set into the tabletops. One long bar has two cosy rooms to the left, one with a real fire and an adjacent beamed open-plan area. The large, enclosed patio and smoking area is a summer suntrap.
Q🅱❀🛏🕪♿≈🖩🛜

Alton

Cassidy's
44 High Street, GU34 1BD
🌐 cassidysbar.co.uk
3 changing beers (sourced nationally; often Ascot, Castle Rock, Monkey Brewhouse) H
Independent real ale, craft beer and cocktail bar, opened in 2023. It has a long narrow drinking area and plentiful seating. Conversation is the main focus of the clientele, with no hot food just inventive bar snacks to accompany the three cask ales, six craft keg taps and a selection of cocktails, wines and spirits. Events hosted include a craft club with sessions ranging from pottery to flower arranging. Dogs are welcome and there is an active puppy club. Closed Monday and Tuesday. Card payment only. Q🅱≈●🛏🖩❀♩

Eight Bells ♟ L
33 Church Street, GU34 2DA
☎ (01420) 82417
Black Sheep Best Bitter; Flower Pots Perridge Pale, Pots Bitter H; 1 changing beer (sourced nationally; often Flower Pots, Longdog, Vale) G
This Grade II-listed building dating from the 1640s with English Civil War connections has been a pub since at least the 1840s. Now it is a privately owned free house where good beer and conversation rule. The guest beer is usually a stout or porter. The rear room TV is for major sporting events only. The rear patio with colourful shrubs in summer has a covered smoking area featuring a well. Local CAMRA Pub of the Year 2023 and 2024.
Q❀≈🖩(13)❀🛜

Railway Arms 🅛
26 Anstey Road, GU34 2RB
☎ (01420) 542316
Triple fff Alton's Pride, Moondance; 5 changing beers (sourced nationally; often Dark Star, Dorking, Triple fff) Ⓗ
Welcoming single-bar pub owned by Triple fff brewery and handy for both Alton mainline station and Mid-Hants on the Watercress Line. Two regular beers and up to five guests are accompanied by boxed cider from Seacider of Sussex. The rear room has occasional music sessions and is available for hire. The rear patio has bench seating and a covered smoking area and there are benches at the front under a steam locomotive emerging from the wall. Dogs are welcome. Q❀♣♿➤🚋(64,65)🐾🎵

Ten Tun Tap House 🅛
1 Westbrook Walk, GU34 1HZ
☎ 07971 076657 ⊕ tentuntaphouse.beer
4 changing beers (sourced nationally; often Steam Town, Verdant, Wylam) Ⓗ
One of Alton's newest pubs, which opened two days before the Covid lockdown of March 2020, featuring four pumps for rapidly-changing real ales and 11 taps for craft beers from the UK. There is a single bar with a back room featuring a viewing window into the Ten Tun Brewhouse which provides up to two constantly-changing craft keg beers for the bar. There are several benches on the patio facing on to Market Square. Card payment only.
🌰≈➤🚋❀🎵

Andover

Andover Tap at the Lamb 🍺 🅛
21 Winchester Street, SP10 2EA
☎ (01264) 323961 ⊕ theandovertap.co.uk
7 changing beers (often Longdog) Ⓗ
The Lamb, dating from the 17th century, now houses a joint venture between Wessex Spirits and the Andover Tap, each occupying half. The Tap serves six beers on handpump and four keg or membrane keg, plus real cider. It has a small front bar and a cosy back room. Families are welcome until 8pm and simple snacks are served. Special food and beer events are held regularly. Local CAMRA Pub of the Year and Cider Pub of the Year 2024. Q🌰➤🚋❀

Town Mills ✅
20 Bridge Street, SP10 1BL
☎ (01264) 332540 ⊕ thetownmills.co.uk
Wadworth Henry's IPA, 6X; 2 changing beers (sourced regionally; often Wadworth) Ⓗ
Located in the town centre by the River Anton, this friendly, family pub is in an historic mill with a working water wheel. The landscaped riverside garden is popular in summer. There are several separate areas for dining and drinking, including a comfy lounge upstairs. Pub games are played and a popular quiz is held weekly. The changing beers are from the Wadworth guest list.
🌰❀🌙&♣P🚋❀🎵

Basingstoke

Queen's Arms
Bunnian Place, RG21 7JE (E of station entrance)
☎ (01256) 465488 ⊕ thequeensarmspub.co.uk
4 changing beers (sourced nationally) Ⓗ
Located close to Basingstoke rail station, this cosy corner-sited pub is handy for commuters and locals alike and serves a wide-ranging clientele. The choice of up to four guest beers is imaginative and the turnaround can be swift. Good-value food is available. During warmer

weather the shady courtyard garden at the rear is a popular attraction. A beer festival is held annually and monthly quiz and weekly meat raffle feature.
Q❀≈P🚋🎵

Wheatsheaf
Winton Square, RG21 8EU
☎ (01256) 479601
Butcombe Original; Otter Ale; Sharp's Doom Bar, Atlantic Ⓗ
This is a lively corner local with the atmosphere you would expect at a busy town-centre pub with a good choice of cask beers and prices good for the area. Sport is regularly shown on largescreen TVs in this traditional no-frills pub with an interesting clientele and a warm welcome. ❀≈♣P🚋

Bentley

Star Inn 🅛
Main Road, GU10 5LW
☎ (01420) 23184 ⊕ thestarinnbentley.com
Crafty Brewing Loxhill Biscuit, Hop Tipple; Triple fff Moondance; 1 changing beer (sourced locally; often Triple fff) Ⓗ
Free house with emphasis on local produce, both for food and the selection of ales which consists of three permanent cask beers and a rotating guest. There is a lively pub atmosphere with quiz nights on first and third Wednesdays of the month and occasional music nights. Outside seating is to the front plus an attractive rear

REAL ALE BREWERIES	
Alfred's Winchester	
Andwell Andwell	
Bat Country East Wellow	
Botley Botley	
Bowman Droxford	
Breakbeat Southampton (NEW)	
Brew Forest ✦ Lymington	
Brewhouse & Kitchen 🍺 Portsmouth	
Brewhouse & Kitchen 🍺 Southampton	
Brewhouse & Kitchen 🍺 Southsea	
Brockenhurst Brockenhurst	
CrackleRock Botley	
Dancing Man 🍺 Southampton	
Dead Duck Hale (NEW)	
Drop The Anchor ✦ Hinton	
Dummer Down ✦ Basingstoke (NEW)	
Ewe Brew 🍺 Andover (NEW)	
Flack Manor ✦ Romsey	
Flower Pots Cheriton	
Gilbert White's Selborne	
Little London Little London	
Longdog ✦ Basingstoke	
Maverick ✦ Kingsley	
Monkey 🍺 Lymington	
Mysterious Tadley (NEW)	
Newtown Gosport	
Powder Monkey Gosport	
Queen Inn 🍺 Winchester	
Sherfield Village Sherfield on Loddon	
Southsea Portsmouth	
Staggeringly Good ✦ Southsea	
Steam Town 🍺 Eastleigh	
Tap It ✦ Southampton	
Ten Tun 🍺 Alton (NEW)	
Triple fff Four Marks	
Unity ✦ Southampton	
Urban Island ✦ Portsmouth	
Vibrant Forest ✦ Hardley	

garden with a vine-clad pergola and covered areas. The Guildford buses stop 100 yards away; the Alton-bound buses stop in Station Road. Q↘⚲❄◗♣P🍽(65)☻🛜♫

Blackwater

Mr Bumble 🅛

19 London Road, GU17 9AP

☎ (01276) 32691

Fuller's London Pride; 3 changing beers (sourced regionally; often Dark Star, Disruption Is Brewing, Windsor & Eton) Ⓗ

Firmly a community local, Mr Bumble is located near the station and bus stops. The regular London Pride is accompanied by up to three guest ales. It has a large L-shaped bar with comfortable seating, tables and chairs. A few steps around the corner is a sports bar with darts and three pool tables. Widescreen TVs show major sporting events, and live music is staged on Thursday and Saturday. ↘⚲❄♣P🍽(3)☻🛜♫

Botley

CrackleRock Tap Room 🅛

30A High Street, SO30 2EA (behind Turkish barber)

☎ 07565 553446 ⊕ cracklerock.co.uk

CrackleRock Verified, Fire Cracker, Gold Rush, Dark Destroyer, Crafty Shag, Crackatoa IPA; 3 changing beers (sourced locally; often Bowman, Steam Town, CrackleRock) Ⓗ

A popular, friendly, cosy brewery tap, hidden down an alley off the High Street. The pub comprises of a single L-shaped room split into several booths served by a single bar. Nine handpumps serve house beers and one guest, with cider boxes in the summer. One-third pint paddles of beers are available with four or six glasses, plus gin, vodka and wine options. The brewery is located across the road, where the tap room was until 2018. Open weekday evenings and all day Saturday and Sunday. ▲♣🍽(3,49)☻🛜♫

Chandler's Ford

Cleveland Bay ✅

1 Pilgrims Close, SO53 4ST

☎ (023) 8026 9814 ⊕ theclevelandbay.co.uk

Wadworth Horizon, 6X, Swordfish; 2 changing beers (sourced nationally; often Wadworth) Ⓗ

A modern and welcoming Wadworth pub at the edge of Chandler's Ford near the shops in Valley Park, one mile from Chandler's Ford railway station. Friendly and attentive staff serve good food and well-kept Wadworth beers, with some guest ales in summer and the occasional small beer festival. The pub is open-plan with a large U-shaped bar, and there are several different seating/eating areas. There is a large partly-covered garden and a children's play area. ↘⚲◗♿♣P🍽(5,46)☻🛜♫

Steel Tank Alehouse 🅛

1 The Central Precinct, Winchester Road, SO53 2GA

☎ 07895 584225 ⊕ thesteeltank.com

6 changing beers (sourced nationally; often Eight Arch, Flower Pots, Siren) Ⓗ

A former bank in a shopping precinct, the pub is handy for trains and buses. Its beer quality, knowledgeable staff and friendly atmosphere attract customers from a wide area. Handpumps serve six cask beers, with eight bag in box ciders served from the cool room, plus eight keg taps and a selection of canned and bottled beers. Benches and stools in semi-booth seating give a cosy and convivial feel, while the walls celebrate beer and

football. Over-18s only. Closed Tuesday and Wednesday. Local CAMRA Cider Pub of the Year 2024. Q♿❄♣◗🍽(1)☻🛜

Cheriton

Flower Pots Inn 🅛

Brandy Mount, SO24 0QQ (¾ mile N of A272 Cheriton/Beauworth crossroads) SU5812928293

☎ (01962) 771318 ⊕ theflowerpots.co.uk

Flower Pots Perridge Pale, Pots Bitter, Buster's Best, Goodens Gold, IPA; 1 changing beer (sourced locally; often Flower Pots) Ⓖ

A sensitively extended 19th-century pub in a pretty village. The original building contains the public bar (note the well), the more intimate locals' bar, and the new bar which was repurposed from domestic use. A covered walkway leads past the garden bar, used in summer and for special events, to the 'barn', a handsome function/overflow room. Customers may also enjoy two gardens and, in summer, the adjacent field. Food is available lunchtimes and Tuesday to Saturday evenings. Thai night is on Wednesday in autumn and winter. Q↘⚲◗♿♣P🍽(67)☻🛜♫

Church Crookham

Wyvern

75 Aldershot Road, GU52 8JY

☎ (01252) 624772 ⊕ thewyvernpub.co.uk

Wadworth 6X; 4 changing beers (sourced nationally; often Theakston) Ⓗ

This community local can become lively at times, especially during sporting events, but is always family friendly. Darts is played and there is a regular Thursday quiz night. Nine screens show Premier League football and other sporting events. A sunny garden features heated beach huts. The pub has live music, often tribute acts, and supports local charities with fundraising events. A changing beer range is from a variety of breweries and often includes Theakston Old Peculier. ↘⚲◗♿♣P🍽(10)☻♫

Eastleigh

Steam Town Brew Co. 🅛

1 Bishopstoke Road, SO50 6AD

☎ (023) 8235 9139 ⊕ steamtown.co.uk

Steam Town Stoke Pale, Barton; 4 changing beers (sourced locally; often Steam Town) Ⓗ

A popular microbrewery and taproom, serving its own ales in cask, keg and cans, and with a constantly changing range of guest kegs. The industrial-themed bar area hosts railway memorabilia, and a separate area, mainly for dining, features 1980s first class train seating. An upstairs room can be booked for groups and parties. The food concept is dirty burgers and fries with ever-changing specials. Regular music nights, plus monthly ticketed beer tasting and brewery tour evenings are available. ↘⚲◗❄◗🍽(2,3)☻🛜♫

Emsworth

Blue Bell ✅

29 South Street, PO10 7EG

☎ (01243) 373394 ⊕ bluebellinnemsworth.co.uk

Sharp's Doom Bar; 2 changing beers (sourced nationally) Ⓗ

The original Blue Bell was a short distance south but, along with its brewery, was demolished after WWII to give access to the buildings behind. This also saw the closure of the brewery. Internally, it is divided into two areas and the wooden beams give it the feel of a much older pub. Being close to the harbour, it is decorated in a maritime style with many plaques of Royal Navy ships' crests. To the front is a small patio. ❀❀◗≉🚮(700)🛜

Coal Exchange
21 South Street, PO10 7EG
☎ (01243) 375866 ⊕ thecoalexchange.co.uk
Dark Star Hophead; Fuller's London Pride; Gale's Seafarers Ale, HSB; 2 changing beers (sourced nationally; often Butcombe, Fuller's, Timothy Taylor) Ⓗ
This small, comfortable pub has a single L-shaped bar with open fires and wooden tables and chairs along with some pew-style seating and stools at the counter. It has a distinctive green tiled frontage which displays the name of its former owner, George Gale & Co. Originally it was a pork butchery and ale house. Its proximity to the harbour made it a place for local farmers to trade their produce for coal delivered by sea, hence the name.
❀❀◗≉🚮(700)❀

King's Arms
19 Havant Road, PO10 7JD
☎ (01243) 374941 ⊕ kingsarmsemsworth.co.uk
Fuller's London Pride; Gale's HSB Ⓗ
A somewhat unusual half-timbered building close to Emsworth mill pond, the exterior sports a number of buttresses on the ground floor level. The single L-shaped bar is carpeted and furnished with traditional tables and chairs as well as some bar stools. The left-hand section forms a small restaurant area. To the rear is a sizeable garden with a number of covered booths as well as open tables. ❀❀◗≉P🚮(700)❀🛜

Fareham

West Street Alehouse
164A West Street, PO16 0EH
☎ (023) 9435 0971 ⊕ weststreetalehouse.com
House beer (by Arundel); 2 changing beers (sourced regionally) Ⓗ
Fareham's first micropub is ideally situated close to the rail and bus stations on the main shopping street. Recently celebrating its fifth anniversary, the bar serves three ales on handpump, five craft beers from the tap wall and up to four ciders. With plenty of seating and no loud music, it is well placed for a quiet drink or socialising in the town centre. There is a bottle shop with local and foreign cans and bottles available for takeaway purchase.
Q❀❀≉❀🛢🚮❀

Farnborough

Goat in the Garden Ⓛ
21 Church Avenue, GU14 7AT
☎ 07920 153452
4 changing beers (sourced nationally; often Church End, Disruption Is Brewing, Rebellion) Ⓗ
Set in the elegant Farnborough Park area, this attractive bar is located in the grounds of a small hotel, Melford House, but accessed via its own entrance. The bar offering will usually include four guest cask ales, some supplied directly from local breweries. Brewery mirrors adorn the walls. A warm welcome is extended to hotel residents, CAMRA members and the local community. However, ring ahead, particularly in the early evening, as there is a capacity limit. ❀🛏♣P🚮(1)🛜♪

Prince of Wales Ⓛ ✓
184 Rectory Road, GU14 8AL
☎ (01252) 545578 ⊕ theprinceinfarnborough.co.uk

Bowman Swift One; Dark Star Hophead; Fuller's London Pride, ESB; Triple fff Pressed Rat & Warthog; 5 changing beers (sourced nationally; often Hop Back, Triple fff, Disruption is Brewing) Ⓗ
This cosy free house has featured in the Guide for over 40 years. There is a central bar around which are several distinct but interconnected areas, with a wonderful wood-burning stove between the snug and adjacent seating area. Five guest beers, invariably including both dark and local beers, are served from the lower snug with regular offerings found on the front bar. Trestle tables at the front and back are popular in fine weather, while the back patio is covered and heated.
❀❀≉(North) P❀♪

Thatched Cottage
122 Prospect Road, GU14 8NU
☎ (01252) 444180 ⊕ thatchedcottagefarnborough.co.uk
3 changing beers (sourced regionally; often Disruption Is Brewing, Hogs Back, Vale) Ⓗ
This thatched pub is situated in Cove, a western suburb of Farnborough. It has served its local community for over 50 years, being sympathetically refurbished, re-thatched and reopened as a free house in 2021. The pub prides itself on serving a wide range of locally-sourced food in a family-friendly setting. There are two distinct bar areas and a large garden. Three cask ales are generally on offer, with regular beers from Vale. Themed events are often held and advertised on the pub's Facebook page.
❀❀◗≉(Main) P🚮(10)❀🛜♪

Tilly Shilling ✓
Unit 2-5, Victoria Road, GU14 7PG
☎ (01252) 893560
Greene King Abbot; Ruddles Best Bitter; Sharp's Doom Bar; 7 changing beers (sourced nationally) Ⓗ
Modern town-centre pub named after Beatrice 'Tilly' Shilling, a celebrated engineer at the nearby former Royal Aircraft Establishment. Its aviation theme continues with a row of airline seats and Spitfire memorabilia. The large rectangular open-plan lounge features a glass frontage that can open onto the street and extra seating, in good weather. Twelve handpumps leave lots of space for three regular and generally up to seven guest beers. The toilets are all located on the ground floor. ❀◗❀≉(Main)🚮🛜

Fleet

Prince Arthur Ⓛ ✓
238 Fleet Road, GU51 4BX
☎ (01252) 622660
Greene King Abbot; Ruddles Best Bitter; Sharp's Doom Bar; 3 changing beers (sourced nationally) Ⓗ
A traditionally designed Wetherspoon pub housed in a former grocery shop, more than 100 years old, with alcoves and wood surrounds. It is named after Prince Arthur, Duke of Connaught, who lived in Fleet in the 1890s when he was commander of Aldershot Garrison. Four to six different guest ales are on tap, sourced nationally, usually including a dark beer. There are regular tap takeovers from breweries local and further afield. Q❀❀◗❀≉🚮(7,10)🛜

Four Marks

Offf the Rails Ⓛ
Unit 3 Magpie Works, Station Approach, GU34 5HN
☎ (01420) 561422 ⊕ triplefff.com
Triple fff Alton's Pride, Pressed Rat & Warthog, Moondance, Sundown; 2 changing beers (sourced locally; often Triple fff) Ⓗ

Offf the Rails was extended in late 2019 to create two distinct drinking areas, and in 2023 a new ground-floor cellar extended the range of cask ales to four regular plus two seasonal or more obscure ales from the adjoining Triple fff brewery. Mr Whitehead's ciders are also available. It adjoins the Triple fff off-licence which features bottled ales from microbreweries far and wide.
🅰🌝♿️≈(Medstead & Four Marks) P🖼(64) 🌝🛜♫

Fritham

Royal Oak 🅛
SO43 7HJ (W end of village down no through road)
SU2321614135
☎ (023) 8081 2606 🌐 royaloakfritham.co.uk
Flack Manor Flack's Double Drop; Hop Back Summer Lightning; house beer (by Bowman); 4 changing beers (sourced locally; often Dark Revolution, Monkey Brewhouse, Steam Town) 🅖
A welcoming, rustic pub standing near the end of a narrow, winding road. It has a public bar, a cosy room with an impressive fireplace, and a back room served via a hatchway. Outside is a large garden with seasonal ice-cream kiosk and marquee. Ploughman's lunches and salads favour local ingredients, including home-made pork pies, and on some evenings a pizza or fish & chip van visits. Accommodation is in shepherds' huts in the adjacent field. Closed Monday and Tuesday.
Q🌝🅰🔥◀🐾🌝♫

Gosport

Four-Ale Taproom 🅛
45 Stoke Road, PO12 1LS
☎ (023) 9258 4455 🌐 fouraletaproom.co.uk
4 changing beers (sourced regionally; often Portsmouth Brewing Co., Newtown) 🅖
Gosport's first micropub opened in 2018 on previously unlicensed premises. There is no bar and the four cask beers, from small and independent breweries, are on a gravity stillage along one wall. There is one dark beer usually served in a pin. Four ciders plus various keg beers are available, plus bottled and canned beers. Pumpclips are displayed on the walls, including several of former breweries. A free cheese board is available on Sunday lunchtimes. Q🌝♣🔴🖼🌝🛜

Junction Tavern 🍷
1 Leesland Road, Camden Town, PO12 3ND
☎ (023) 9258 5140
3 changing beers (sourced nationally; often Goldmark, Parkway, Portobello) 🅗
The venue is on the disused railway line between Gosport and Fareham which closed in 1953 and is now a cycle track and footpath. The three real ales usually include a dark beer, and the pub is a rare outlet for cask beers from Powder Monkey. The canopy over the bar is decorated with pumpclips of previous beers sold. A beer festival takes place over the Easter weekend.
🌝🌝♣🖼(E1) 🌝🛜

Queen's Hotel 🅛
143 Queens Road, Forton, PO12 1LG
☎ (023) 9229 2681 🌐 fouraletaproom.co.uk
Exmoor Fox; Flower Pots Goodens Gold; Oakham Citra; 2 changing beers (sourced nationally; often Newtown) 🅗
Established in 1896, in 2022 the upper floors of the building were sold to a builder for development, but the ground floor bar was declared an Asset of Community Value and saved as a pub. It reopened in 2023 with five cask conditioned ales available. In addition to real cider,

the pub is a rare outlet for real perry, with Mr Whiteheads Hampshire Perry sold. A meat raffle takes place on Sunday afternoons. ♣🖼🌝

Hammer Vale

Prince of Wales
Hammer Lane, GU27 1QH
☎ (01428) 652600 🌐 princeofwaleshaslemere.co.uk
Dark Star Hophead; Fuller's London Pride; Gale's HSB; 1 changing beer (sourced nationally; often Fuller's) 🅗
Although tucked away, this 1924-built pub is unmissable. Hosts Nick and Becky keep an historic house, located where Amey's of Petersfield believed that the A3 would pass. It has original stained-glass windows and period features, and a selection of historic photographs. Ales from the Fuller's portfolio are kept in superb order. There is a separate restaurant area and a large general seating area for drinkers. Outside there is more seating with access to walking and camping. Closed Monday.
Q🌝🌝◀🅿🖼🌝🛜♫

Hardley

Vibrant Forest Brewery Taproom 🅛
Unit 3, The Purlieu Centre, Hardley Industrial Estate, SO45 3AE
☎ (023) 8200 2200 🌐 vibrantforest.co.uk
2 changing beers (sourced locally; often Vibrant Forest) 🅗
The taproom has two handpumps serving cask ale, plus 12 membrane-keg lines serving the wide range of Vibrant Forest beers. Real cider is Mr Whitehead's. Wine, cans, bottles and soft drinks are also available. The ground floor accommodates 60 customers. The mezzanine, with its own bar, is available to hire for parties and events with room for another 60 people. A street food truck is on site every Saturday. Closed Monday to Wednesday; opening times vary with season.
🌝◀♿🖼(9) 🌝🛜♫

Hartley Wintney

Waggon & Horses ★
High Street, RG27 8NY
☎ (01252) 842119 🌐 thewagg.co.uk
Butcombe Original; Gale's HSB; 4 changing beers (sourced nationally; often Castle Rock, Flower Pots, Sharp's) 🅗
This award-winning local high street village pub has been identified by CAMRA as having a nationally important historic pub interior. The lively public bar with its original flagstone floor contrasts with the quiet lounge, both featuring real fires. Outside pavement tables enable guests to enjoy the atmosphere of the village, renowned for its unique shops. At the rear is a large pleasant courtyard garden and heated, covered marquee with smokers' area. Food is served but call for details. Q🌝◀🔴🖼(7)🌝🛜

Havant

Old House at Home
2 South Street, PO9 1DA
☎ (023) 9248 3464 🌐 oldhouseathomehavant.co.uk
Fuller's London Pride; Gale's Seafarers Ale, HSB; 1 changing beer (sourced nationally; often Fuller's, Dark Star) 🅗
Dating from the 17th century, the current building began its life as five cottages constructed from timber recovered from the Spanish Armada. It survived the 1760 fire and became a bakery. Finally becoming a pub, it is

famed for having held the last dancing bear in England. It retains two bars; the lounge bar is divided into two areas with traditional tables and chairs while the public bar has a part-tiled floor with some banquette seating and higher tables. ⏥❋◗≉♣◳◱♪

Robin Hood

6 Homewell, PO9 1EE
☎ (023) 9248 2779 ● robin-hood-havant.co.uk
Fuller's London Pride; Gale's Seafarers Ale, HSB; 1 changing beer (sourced nationally; often Fuller's) Ⓗ
Much-changed over the years, the pub was originally converted from two early 19th-century cottages. There are several drinking areas, with a large central fireplace. The bar counter is somewhat hidden behind pillars and low beams giving it a real homely feel. To the rear is a patio garden. It is just a short walk from the Homewell spring and the former parchment works which is understood to have produced the parchment used for the Magna Carta and the Treaty of Versailles. ❋◗≉◱❀♥

Hawkley

Hawkley Inn

Pococks Lane, GU33 6NE
☎ (01730) 827205 ● hawkleyinn.co.uk
Flower Pots Perridge Pale, Pots Bitter; 3 changing beers (sourced regionally; often Flower Pots, Triple fff) Ⓗ
A genuine free house set in the South Downs National Park, popular with locals and passers-by alike. It is divided into two drinking areas, one of which has a moose's head which gives rise to the pub's free hoose nickname. It has a good selection of guest ales. Great food is served and there are five rooms available for B&B. There is a large garden to the rear and a small patio under a veranda at the front. ⏥❋≉◗◖❀♥♪

Heckfield

New Inn

Odiham Road, RG27 0LE (on B3349)
☎ (0118) 932 6374 ● newinnheckfield.com
Longdog Basingstoke Pride; Triple fff Moondance; 1 changing beer (often Tilford) Ⓗ
This pub, restaurant and hotel has recently been refurbished by the owners after coming out of a tied lease, it is now a free house with rooms. Beamed ceilings and carpeted floor give the pub and restaurant area a comfy atmosphere. This is a popular lunch and dinner spot at the weekend and is priimarily food-led but there's a cosy snug with a real fire always awaiting those just wanting a drink. ⏥❋≉◗P❀♥

Hinton

Drop the Anchor Brewery

Building 9 East Close Farm, Lyndhurst Road, BH23 7EF
☎ 07806 789946 ● droptheanchorbrewery.co.uk
Drop The Anchor Misty Mountain Hop, Silent Stones, Black Dog Porter, Otakaro NZ Pale, The Phoenix IPA, Breaking Glass Hazelnut Latte Porter-Stout; 3 changing beers (sourced locally) Ⓖ
Pleasant brewery taproom in the New Forest with seating outside and inside, and car parking accessed directly from the A35. Beers are served on gravity from a side room off the bar and a new lounge with wood-burner has been opened across the courtyard. Summer live music sessions and comedy nights take place. The brewery hosts two beer festivals a year along with other events. Open on Friday and Saturday afternoons only. Q❋◐▲♣P❀♥♪

Hythe

Dusty Barrel Ⓛ

Unit 5, Pylewell Road, SO45 6AP
● thedustybarrel.co.uk
4 changing beers (sourced regionally; often Vibrant Forest, Steam Town, Flower Pots) Ⓗ
A busy two-floored micropub located in a small pedestrian precinct in the centre of Hythe, serving four ever-changing real ales, plus six membrane keg beers. Quiz night is on Wednesday and there is regular live music. No meals are served but customers may bring in takeaway meals to eat on the premises. Decor is industrial rustic mixed with record sleeves, and there is some outside seating. The upstairs room is available to hire for functions. Closed Monday. Q⏥❋◖♣◱(8,9)❀♥♪

Ebenezer's Ⓛ

18A Pylewell Road, SO45 6AR
☎ (023) 8020 7799
Greene King Abbot; Otter Bitter; 2 changing beers (sourced locally; often Hop Back, Draught Bass, Flower Pots) Ⓗ
This Hythe pub, a former Baptist chapel built 1845, delights beer-lovers with up to four real ales, and home-made meals on select days. A perfect blend of modernity and tradition, its cosy ambiance is enhanced with historical decor. There is a covered outdoor area. Food is a mix of traditional pub fare and Thai curries. It is near the Hythe Ferry terminal, with easy access to the world's oldest pier railway. Q❋◗◖◱(8,9)♥♪

Little London

Plough Inn

Silchester Road, RG26 5EP
☎ (01256) 850628
3 changing beers (sourced regionally; often Bowman, Flower Pots, Little London) Ⓖ
This cosy, rustic village local can rightly be called a gem. It is popular with visitors to Pamber Forest and nearby Silchester Roman site who can enjoy changing real ales, join in lively conversation, sit in front of a log fire or relax in the peaceful, spacious beer garden. Dogs and families are welcome. Baguettes are available at lunchtime. Q⏥❋◖P◱(14)❀

Long Sutton

Four Horseshoes

The Street, RG29 1TA (follow brown signs from B3349 Odiham to Alton Rd) SU748470
☎ (01256) 862488 ● fourhorseshoes.com
2 changing beers (sourced nationally; often Palmers) Ⓗ
Set in the rolling open countryside of the Hampshire Downs between Long Sutton village and the hamlet of Well this is a quintessential rural pub. Formerly a Gale's tied house, it has been free of tie for many years, offering two low-strength guest beers, one always from Palmers brewery. There is a monthly quiz and two jazz nights a month in the spacious but cosy bar, which has two real fires. Simple English dishes are served, with a popular roast on Sunday. Opening hours are limited. Q⏥❋◗◖P❀♪

Lower Wield

Yew Tree Ⓛ

SO24 9RX SU636398
☎ (01256) 389224 ● theyewtreelowerwield.co.uk

House beer (by Flower Pots); 2 changing beers (sourced locally; often Stonehenge, Triple fff) H
This popular, though isolated family-run pub is surrounded by picturesque rolling countryside, with an old yew tree at its door. A small one-bar, two-room pub, it is food-led with locally-sourced home-made fare. The outside space, partly covered, is extensive and the pub caters for cyclists, ramblers, horse riders and dogs. Live music events are run. A rural gem of a pub.
Q ⑤ ❀ ◑ P ❀ ✿ ♪

Lymington

Monkey Brewhouse L
167 Southampton Road, SO41 9HA
☎ (01590) 676754 ⊕ monkeybrewhouse.co.uk
Monkey Brewhouse Tollhouse, Sea Wall; 1 changing beer (sourced locally; often Monkey Brewhouse) H
A brewpub consisting of a small bar area, leading to a larger high-roofed lounge room with an impressive fireplace and a raised area to the side with huge windows looking into the brewery, which can also be viewed from a large outside patio area. Adjacent is a garden behind the recently renovated 18th-century toll house. The pub serves three real ales and four keg beers that are all brewed on site, plus a range of gastro pub food. ⑤ ❀ ⇔ ◑ & P ♠ (6) ❀ ✿ ♪

Six Bells L ✓
48 St Thomas Street, SO41 9ND
☎ (01590) 689990
Greene King Abbot; Ruddles Best Bitter; Sharp's Doom Bar; 3 changing beers (sourced nationally; often Bowman, Flack Manor, Stonehenge) H
Thriving Wetherspoon outlet with real ale-enthusiastic staff in a former furnishing store, and named after a previous Six Bells pub which was originally next door. Lymington-themed artwork is displayed including a fish sculpture and angled mirrors reflecting St Thomas Church belfry. Up to three frequently changing guest ales of differing styles and strengths are offered, both national and more local. Tap takeovers and beer festivals are featured and the premises caters admirably for disabled customers. Q ⑤ ❀ ◑ & ⇌ (Town) ♠ ♣ ✿

Mapledurwell

Gamekeepers L
Tunworth Road, RG25 2LU
☎ (01256) 322038 ⊕ thegamekeepers.co.uk
Andwell Resolute Bitter; 2 changing beers H
The Gamekeepers is a charming gastropub in a quaint thatched village. Run for the last 20 years by the same family, it features exposed beams and a flagstone floor, hinting at the building's long history. Outside are a patio and garden. A single bar serves the restaurant and a drinking area with settees and a real fire, and local ales are guaranteed. Locally produced food is served daily.
Q ❀ ◑ P ✿

Mattingley

Leather Bottle L
Reading Road, RG27 8JU
☎ (0118) 932 6371
Brunning & Price Original; 4 changing beers (sourced locally) H
The Leather Bottle is a Grade II-listed village pub dating from 1714 with period features including mellow Hampshire brick. Inside you'll find relaxed surroundings and a single bar with a changing range of ales, often local. Food is a major offering – booking is advised – and

can be enjoyed inside or out in the beautiful garden. Regular events include charity dog walks, food and drink tastings, coffee mornings and walks. Popular with cyclists and walkers, it welcomes dogs on a leash.
Q ⑤ ❀ ◑ & P ❀ ✿

Micheldever

Dove Inn
Andover Road, Micheldever Station, SO21 3AU
☎ (01962) 774288 ⊕ doveinn.co.uk
Flack Manor Flack's Double Drop; Flower Pots Goodens Gold; 1 changing beer (sourced locally) H
A free house set in the beautiful Hampshire countryside, this Georgian Grade II-listed building has retained a wealth of character and many of its original features including open fireplaces and oak-beamed ceilings. The pub consists of a general bar and a dining area, although customers can eat in either. Another room contains a pool table. Outside is a nice garden, ideal for summer days. ❀ ⇔ ◑ ⇌ ♠ P ✿

Milford on Sea

Wash House
27 High Street, SO41 0QF
☎ (01590) 644665 ⊕ thewashhousebar.co.uk
4 changing beers (sourced locally; often Hattie Brown's, Cerne Abbas, Goddards) H
Delightful, quirky, welcoming and well-lit gem of a micropub in a vibrant seaside village. Amusing wall features combine with launderette-themed decor. There are four handpumps with rapidly changing ales of all strengths and styles, sourced from many small independent brewers on the South Coast. Ales and ciders are described on a large blackboard and tasting paddles are available. A range of packet snacks is sold, and food from local outlets may be brought in. Children are welcome. Tables may be booked for busy times.
Q & ♣ ♠ ⊞ (X1) ❀ ♪

New Milton

Hourglass
8 Station Road, BH25 6JU
☎ (01425) 616074
4 changing beers (sourced nationally) G
Micropub close to New Milton station serving at least three ever-changing and widely sourced cask ales of different styles and strengths, real cider, plus many craft keg beers. New Milton's first micropub, opened in 2017, it is in a converted shop unit. Ample seating includes stools at the long bar to the rear of the pub. An ever increasing collection of beer mats is displayed on the ceiling and walls. Lighting is low and conversation abounds amongst the mixed clientele.
Q ⇌ ♣ ♠ ⊞ ⊟ (X1,X2) ❀ ✿ ♪

North Warnborough

Mill House L
Hook Road, RG29 1ET (from M3 jct 5 head towards Odiham and pub is on the right)
☎ (01256) 702953
Hogs Back TEA; house beer (by St Austell); 5 changing beers (sourced regionally; often Andwell, Longdog, Triple fff) H
This traditional Grade II-listed building on the River Whitewater was one of eight mills of Odiham mentioned in the Domesday Book. Last used as a corn mill in 1895, it became a pub restaurant in the 1980s. It has a pleasant central upstairs bar area and downstairs oak-panelled

dining areas, one of which has a view of the waterwheel. The extensive landscaped area around the millpond has outdoor seating. There is an old function barn and extensive parking. Q⤢❄◑P☏⏛(13)❀❖ ☎

Oakley

Barley Mow ⓛ ✔

19 Oakley Lane, RG23 7JZ

☎ (01256) 242906 ⊕ barleymowoakley.co.uk

2 changing beers (sourced locally; often Flower Pots) Ⓗ

A traditional, friendly local in the heart of a picturesque village, this free house serves well-kept traditional ales and a wide selection of gins from a varied drinks menu. Hearty pub lunches are served and evening meals feature on occasions. Warm, family-oriented and dog friendly, the pub is often used as a refreshment and meeting point for ramblers. Q⤢❄◑♣P☏(11)❀❖ ☎ ♪

Odiham

Red Lion

102 High Street, RG29 1LP

☎ (01256) 701145 ⊕ redlionodiham.co.uk

Hogs Back TEA; 2 changing beers (often Tilford) Ⓗ

The Red Lion stands on the site of a 17th-century High Street ale house of the same name in the village of Odiham. A small traditional pub with rustic beams, it has a modern design and atmosphere. The menu is fresh, local Hampshire fare. There are seven B&B rooms and a front pavement seating area. ⤢⇋◑⏛(13)☎

Old Basing

Crown

The Street, RG24 7BW

☎ (01256) 321424 ⊕ Thecrownoldbasing.co.uk

Fuller's London Pride; Otter Ale; Sharp's Doom Bar; 2 changing beers Ⓗ

The Crown is a pleasant pub/restaurant in the heart of Old Basing, offering classic, hearty pub food and a drinks range to suit everyone. All food is prepared and cooked in their kitchen and includes a children's menu. The pub has a large rear garden which is family-friendly with a play area for children, and a small patio to the front. Pool, darts and BT Sports are on offer as well as events including a regular quiz. Q⤢❄◑♣P❖ ♪

Overton

Old House at Home

Station Road, RG25 3DU

☎ (01256) 770335 ⊕ theoldhouseathome.com

Hogs Back TEA; St Austell Proper Job; 1 changing beer Ⓗ

The Old House at Home has a traditional local pub feel but with a daily Thai restaurant and takeaway service with a good vegetarian choice. It has five real ale pumps serving three regular and two changing beers. Outside is a conservatory and beer garden with a play area and decking. The pub hosts a fun pub quiz on Sunday and participates in local crib, pool, darts and quiz leagues. Sports TV is a feature. ⤢❄⇋◑♣P⏛(76)❀ ☎

Red Lion ⓛ

37 High Street, RG25 3HQ

☎ (01256) 212053 ⊕ theredlionoverton.co.uk

Bowman Swift One; Flower Pots Pots Bitter; Sharp's Doom Bar Ⓗ

This popular traditional village pub serves real ales from Hampshire. It has three areas, including a restaurant,

main bar and snug with wood-burning stove. Outside is an attractive beer garden with partially covered patio area and there is separate spacious function room with a skittle alley. Live music features on Friday and an extensive food menu is served Thursday to Saturday, as well as Sunday lunch. A famous gin distillery is nearby. Q⤢❄◑⤴♣P☏(76,86) ❀❖ ☎ ♪

Park Gate

Gate ⓛ

27-29 Middle Road, SO31 7GH

☎ (01489) 886677

Steam Town Barton; 2 changing beers (sourced regionally; often Steam Town, Bowman) Ⓗ

A good-sized micropub which opened in 2019 on the site of a former estate agent. The real estate map of the local area is displayed on one wall. Seating is available for about 40 customers, with additional outside tables and chairs in the summer. Alongside the three cask ales, there are four ciders and several keg beers. The pub hosts a monthly meeting of local home brewers. ⤢❄⇋(Swanwick) ♣●P⏛(X4) ❀ ☎

Petersfield

Square Brewery

7 The Square, GU32 3HJ

☎ (01730) 264291 ⊕ squarebrewery.co.uk

Fuller's London Pride; Gale's Seafarers Ale, HSB; 2 changing beers (sourced nationally; often Fuller's, Dark Star) Ⓗ

Dating from circa 1739, this substantial red tile-clad building is opposite the town square. It originally had its own brewery, but it was bought by George Gale & Co in 1907 and the brewery was closed. Internally the decor is modern and to the rear is a small covered courtyard with access to the upstairs function room. The single bar is divided into two distinct areas, one of which features a wood-burning stove. ⤢◑⇋⏛❀ ☎ ♪

Townhouse ⓛ

28 High Street, GU32 3JL

☎ (01730) 265630 ⊕ townhousepetersfield.co.uk

3 changing beers (sourced nationally; often Flower Pots, Langham, Bowman) Ⓗ

Set in the heart of Petersfield, this is a modern style micropub offering breakfast, lunch and dinner, a variety of keg beers and a good selection of both local real ales and those from further afield. The single L-shaped bar has tables and chairs as well as some bar stools. The pub has a family environment where children and dogs are welcome. A separate function room, upstairs, is available for hire. ⤢❄◑⤴⇋♣⏛❀ ☎ ♪

Portchester

Portcullis Taphouse ⓛ

6 New Parade, 38 West Street, PO16 9UY

☎ 07538 929204

3 changing beers (sourced nationally; often Newtown, Langham, Thornbridge) Ⓖ

Opened in 2021, this micropub has stillage for six casks and serves from three, with three others conditioning at any one time. Several ciders and craft membrane keg beers are also available. The landlord has planning permission for a microbrewery in the back yard and hopes to start brewing soon. ◑⤴⇋♣●⏛❀ ☎

Portsmouth

Barley Mow ★ ✓

39 Castle Road, Southsea, PO5 3DE

☎ (023) 9282 3492 ⊕ barleymowsouthsea.com

Fuller's London Pride; Gale's HSB; 6 changing beers (sourced nationally) ⊞

A sizeable two-bar community pub designed by A. E. Cogswell but not typical of his style. The lounge bar is wood panelled while the smaller public bar is more plainly decorated. The pub survived damage by a 500lb delayed-action bomb in 1941. It was defused and the bomb casing can be seen in the award-winning patio garden. The pub hosts many events including music, quizzes, raffles and a chess league. It also boasts bar billiards and shove ha'penny tables.

ॐ❀&♣⊟(3)✿🛜♬

Bridge Tavern

54 East Street, Old Portsmouth, PO1 2JJ

☎ (023) 9275 2992 ⊕ bridge-tavern-portsmouth.co.uk

Fuller's London Pride; Gale's Seafarers Ale, HSB; 1 changing beer (sourced nationally; often Fuller's, Dark Star) ⊞

The only surviving pub in East Street, this former fisherman's pub is set deep in the Camber Docks. The sign depicts the double swing bridge which used to cross the dock nearby and one wall is adorned with the cartoon Portsmouth Point by Thomas Rowlandson. Internally it is divided into several areas on two levels and there is an upstairs room which can be hired. Unsurprisingly it has a maritime feel and fish dishes are prominent on the menu. ॐ❀◑►⊟(25)✿🛜♬

George Inn 🄻

Portsdown Hill Road, Drayton, PO6 1BE

☎ (023) 9222 1079 ⊕ the-george-inn.co.uk

Flower Pots Goodens Gold; Fuller's London Pride; Gale's HSB; Harvey's Sussex Best Bitter; Timothy Taylor Landlord; 2 changing beers (sourced nationally) ⊞

On the old coaching route from London to Portsmouth, this pub offers extensive views over the city, Hayling Island and the Isle of Wight. The transport theme continues as it was once a tram stop on the Portsdown & Horndean Light Railway. Part of the building is the old Widley fire station. Internally, the single L-shaped bar with its unusual wood panelled front is surrounded by several carpeted drinking areas. Much of the decoration consists of local brewery memorabilia.

Q❀◑♣P⊟✿🛜♬

Hole in the Wall 🄻

36 Great Southsea Street, Southsea, PO5 3BY

☎ (023) 9229 8085 ⊕ theholeinthewallpub.co.uk

Flower Pots Goodens Gold; 6 changing beers (sourced nationally) ⊞

A multiple award-winning pub situated in the vibrant Castle Road area near Southsea Common, the Hole is a true free house with an ever-changing selection of cask beers. There is also an interesting selection of cans to take away and it has a sweet tuckshop. Extremely popular and often packed, it is a proper old local with wooden beams and a snug. Thursday is quiz night. On Friday last admission is one hour before closing.

Q♠⊟(3)✿🛜

Lawrence Arms ✓

63 Lawrence Road, Southsea, PO5 1NU

☎ 07522 495032

Harvey's Sussex Best Bitter; 5 changing beers (sourced nationally; often Langham, Vibrant Forest) ⊞

This large street-corner pub is a short walk from Albert Road. The L-shaped bar is divided into two drinking areas. It is comfortably and traditionally decorated and is one of the few pubs in town with a bar billiards table. In addition to the cask beers, there is a good range of cans and real ciders available. Good-value toasted sandwiches are available every day as well as roasts on Sunday afternoon. There is a patio garden to one side.

ॐ❀♣●⊟(18,25)✿🛜

Lord Palmerston ✓

84-90 Palmerston Road, Southsea, PO5 3PT

☎ (023) 9272 8000

Sharp's Doom Bar; Greene King IPA, Abbot; 3 changing beers (sourced nationally; often Langham) ⊞

Set in the heart of Southsea's shopping area, a short walk from Southsea Castle and the D-Day Museum, this Wetherspoon bar has strong military and historical connections, being named after the 3rd Viscount Palmerston who was responsible for building a series of forts to protect the city from invasion in the mid-19th century. As this never happened, they have been nicknamed Palmerston's Folly. Internally, it is divided into two drinking areas, the front one having a much higher ceiling. ॐ❀◑►&⊟🛜

Merchant House

9-11 Highland Road, Eastney, PO4 9DA

12 changing beers (sourced nationally)

A modern style street-corner pub that's bigger than it looks thanks to a basement seating area. The main ground floor bar is divided into two areas showing that it used to be two separate shops. The walls are bare brick and with the combination of large glass windows and bare floorboards it can be somewhat noisy when crowded. Popular with locals, it is dog-friendly. There is a stove to warm the cockles on winter days. ❀◑►⊟(1,2)✿

Northcote 🄻

35 Francis Avenue, Southsea, PO4 0HL

☎ (023) 9278 9888

Stonehenge Great Bustard; Timothy Taylor Landlord; 1 changing beer (sourced locally; often Langham, Flower Pots) ⊞

A former Pike Spicer pub, this substantial street-corner building close to Albert Road still retains two bars. The public bar, which is divided into several areas, has a dartboard on a raised area and a pool table. The comfortable lounge has booth style seating and the walls are adorned with memorabilia of comedians from the early days of cinema, and items relating to the great fictional detective Sherlock Holmes. To one side is a sizeable patio garden. ❀♣●⊟(2)♬

Old Customs House

Vernon Building, Gunwharf Quays, Gunwharf, PO1 3TY

☎ (023) 9283 2333 ⊕ theoldcustomshouse.com

Dark Star Hophead; Fuller's London Pride; Gale's Seafarers Ale, HSB; 2 changing beers (sourced nationally; often Dark Star, Fuller's) ⊞

Proclaiming itself the only traditional pub in the Gunwharf Quays retail complex this Grade II-listed building retains the layout of the former naval offices of HMS Vernon, one of the first purpose-built office buildings in the world. There is a heated rear patio area and seating at the front which is ideal for enjoying the sights during the summer. The menu includes breakfast, lunch and dinner with local ingredients to the fore.

ॐ❀◑►&⇌(Harbour)⊟✿🛜

Pembroke

20 Pembroke Road, Old Portsmouth, PO1 2NR
☎ (023) 9282 3961
Draught Bass; Fuller's London Pride; Greene King Abbot ⊞
Close to the Nelson Trail, which follows the great man's last walk before sailing to Trafalgar, this is a solidly traditional street-corner local in the oldest part of the city. Originally the Little Blue Line, it features in books by Frederick Marryat. The single U-shaped bar is traditionally decorated with a nautical theme. The nearby Royal Garrison Church dates back to 1212 and was partly destroyed in WWII. The city's oldest fortifications are also a short walk away. ♣🖳(25)🏵🎐♫

Phoenix

13 Duncan Road, Southsea, PO5 2QU
☎ (023) 9278 1055
Gale's HSB; Timothy Taylor Landlord; 1 changing beer (sourced nationally; often Urban Island, Vibrant Forest, Langham) ⊞
Just a short walk from Albert Road, this two-bar pub is a genuine community local. The public bar has bare boards and is decorated with memorabilia about Portsmouth's past. It also has a tabletop video games machine. The lounge is carpeted and has comfortable armchairs and a settee. The walls are adorned with photos of people who have appeared at the nearby Kings Theatre. Next to the lounge is a quirky patio garden which leads to a comfortable snug. 🏵🖳(2)🏵🎐

Rose in June ✅

102 Milton Road, Milton, PO3 6AR
☎ (023) 9282 4191
Gale's HSB; Goddards Wight Squirrel; Otter Amber; 8 changing beers (sourced nationally; often Arundel) ⊞
A friendly traditional community pub with two bars serving up to 10 cask ales, with additional beers on gravity when the outside bar is in use. Located close enough to Fratton Park to be popular on match days. Darts and a pool table feature along with a large garden at the rear which hosts twice yearly beer festivals. There is a regular quiz night as well as curry nights and charity events. Food is hearty pub grub and freshly-made pizza. Q🖢🏵🌓♣🖳🏵🎐

Sir Loin of Beef ⍗

152 Highland Road, Eastney, PO4 9NH
☎ (023) 9282 0115
Bowman Swift One; Gale's HSB; Hop Back Summer Lightning; 5 changing beers (sourced nationally; often Hop Back, Frome, Langham) ⊞
This street-corner local is a true free house, offering beers from breweries across the country. The main bar is divided into two drinking areas and has a bright, modern look. It is furnished with a mix of banquette, armchair and traditional pub type seating. A separate room to the rear which can be hired for private functions, has its own serving counter and gives access to a small patio area. 🖢🏵🖳(1,2)🏵

Still & West

2 Bath Square, Old Portsmouth, PO1 2JL
☎ (023) 9282 1567 ⊕ stillandwest.co.uk
Fuller's London Pride; Gale's Seafarers Ale, HSB; 1 changing beer (sourced nationally; often Fuller's, Gale's) ⊞
Situated alongside Portsmouth Harbour, the pub offers extensive views of ships heading to or from the Naval Base and the commercial port. The downstairs L-shaped bar is divided into two areas and is decorated with a nautical theme, and the upstairs bar can be hired. Outside is a patio seating area. On 4th August 1960,

when HMS Vanguard was being towed to be scrapped, she slewed across the harbour and the bow nearly ended up in the pub. 🖢🏵🌓🖢♿🖳(25)🏵🎐

Urban Tap ⍗

Unit 28, Limberline Spur, Hilsea, PO3 5DZ
☎ (023) 9266 8726 ⊕ urbanislandbrewing.uk
3 changing beers (sourced locally; often Urban Island) ⍾
Urban Island brewery tap room is set in the front of the brewery itself. Furnished with a number of tables and benches, as well as some empty casks used as stools, you are surrounded by the brewing equipment. Cask beers are served direct from the cask in the cold store and the keg offerings from taps behind the counter. Additional seating is provided outside the brewery in warmer weather. To the rear is Hilsea Lines, one of the city's old fortifications. Q🖢🏵≉(Hilsea)🖢P🖳(21)🏵

Ringwood

Railway

35 Hightown Road, BH24 1NQ
☎ (01425) 473701 ⊕ ringwoodrailway.com
Otter Bitter; Timothy Taylor Landlord; 2 changing beers (sourced nationally) ⊞
Traditional Victorian two-bar pub that serves four cask beers, two of a modern style, and three craft keg beers. The lounge bar has a recently created snug room behind with a modern log burner between them. This leads to a walled garden with a large fully covered patio area and outside bar open in the summer. The food menu features gourmet burgers and Korean inspired barbecue. Opens at 3pm Monday to Thursday and noon Friday to Sunday. 🖢🏵🌓🖢🖳(Ringo)🏵🎐

Romsey

Three Tuns ⍗

58 Middlebridge Street, SO51 8HL
☎ (01794) 512639 ⊕ the3tunsromsey.co.uk
Flack Manor Flack's Double Drop; Flower Pots Goodens Gold; 4 changing beers (sourced regionally) ⊞
Located in a quiet street, this pub consists of two areas – an agreeable bar and a more formal dining room. It has five handpumps and serves two regular and at least two guest beers. Outside there is a garden and a covered heated area. By car, the front of the pub, in Middlebridge Street, can only be reached from the town centre; walking is easier or use the rear car park accessible from the A27/A3090 bypass. 🖢🌓♣🖢P🖳🏵🎐

Rotherwick

Coach & Horses ⍗

The Street, RG27 9BG
☎ (01256) 768976 ⊕ coachandhorses-rotherwick.co.uk
Adnams Ghost Ship; Hogs Back TEA; 3 changing beers (sourced locally; often Longdog, Sherfield Village) ⊞
This unspoiled, traditional village pub with friendly staff and locals is situated in a lovely rural setting. It boasts a spacious landscaped south-facing rear garden overlooking farmland. A free house with a varied range of real ale from local breweries, it unpretentiously offers good old-fashioned hospitality. In cold weather, a large open fireplace and two wood-burning stoves guarantee a warm welcome. The menu mainly uses local suppliers' produce. Q🖢🏵🌓P🏵

Selborne

Selborne Arms Ⓛ
High Street, GU34 3JR
☎ (01420) 511247 ⊕ selbornearms.co.uk
Bowman Swift One; Courage Directors; 3 changing
beers (sourced regionally; often Crafty Brewing, Hogs
Back, Loddon) Ⓗ
Friendly village local where the needs of the drinker and
diner are well balanced. Up to five cask beers are
available, many from local microbreweries. The pub is an
enthusiastic participant in the village's October Zig Zag
Festival featuring beer and music. Three thirds of cask
beers for the price of a pint are available. The extensive
menu showcases local and home-made produce with
vegetarian and gluten free options. The safe play area in
the garden is popular with children.
Q ☎ ⊛ ◑ ♣ P ▱ (38) ♥ ♿ ≷

Shedfield

Wheatsheaf Inn Ⓛ
Botley Road, SO32 2JG (on A334)
☎ (01329) 833024
Flower Pots Perridge Pale, Pots Bitter, Goodens Gold;
1 changing beer (sourced locally; often Flower
Pots) Ⓖ
Friendly, popular, award-winning country pub, which is
always a pleasure to visit. The pub is split between two
rooms, warmed by a double-sided wood-burning stove.
Flower Pots beer is served direct from the cask behind
the bar. The side room has been extended to provide
more seating and easy access to the beautiful rear
garden. The garden's floral displays are delightful in
summer. Good home-cooked food is served daily at
lunchtimes (booking in advance is advised). Live music is
featured most Saturday evenings.
Q ⊛ ◑ & ♣ P ▱ (69) ♥ ≷ ♫

Silchester

Calleva Arms
The Common, RG7 2PH
☎ (0118) 970 0305 ⊕ callevaarms.co.uk
Dark Star Hophead; Fuller's London Pride; Gale's
Seafarers Ale, HSB; 1 changing beer Ⓗ
An attractive village pub opposite the common, named
after local Roman settlement Calleva Atrebatum. A
Fuller's pub with five handpumps serving four regular
Fuller's ales plus one guest ale, which is often a Fuller's
seasonal or a local real ale. There is a welcoming bar
with a separate comfortable dining area, and an
excellent choice of bar and restaurant food is also served
in the conservatory and the large garden in the summer
months. The front drinking area overlooks cricket and
football pitches. ☎ ⊛ ◑ ♣ P ▱ (14) ♥ ≷

Sopley

Woolpack Inn
Ringwood Road, BH23 7AX
☎ (01425) 672252 ⊕ thewoolpacksopley.co.uk
Flack Manor Flack's Double Drop; 2 changing beers
(sourced regionally; often Sandbanks, Exmoor,
Downton) Ⓗ
Picturesque 18th-century thatched pub with low beams,
a conservatory dining room, and split-level seating areas.
Outside are a patio and large garden with a historically
diverted brook. Real ales are selected predominantly
from local independent breweries, and the extensive,
imaginative menu is sourced from local ingredients. Well
established in, and supported by, the local community;

collections are arranged for local charities. Many
interesting and varied pictures adorn the walls.
☎ ⊛ ◑ ♣ P ⊛ ≷

Southampton

Beards & Boards
33 Bedford Place, SO15 2DG
⊕ beardsandboards.co.uk
4 changing beers (sourced nationally; often Vibrant
Forest, Flower Pots, Steam Town) Ⓗ
A popular and friendly micropub with a skateboard
theme and urban decor. Featuring four handpumps
serving regularly changing national and local real ales, 10
keg beers, canned beers and four draught ciders, all
complemented by frequent tap takeovers. A recently
opened back room adds to space inside the pub,
alongside an on-street seating area at the front. A retro
games console, a range of board games and background
punk music all adds to the welcoming buzz. Closed
Monday. ⊛ & ♣ ▱ ♥ ♿

Belgium & Blues Ⓛ
184 Above Bar Street, SO14 7DW
☎ (023) 8022 5411 ⊕ belgiumandblues.co.uk
4 changing beers (sourced nationally) Ⓗ
Located in Southampton's Cultural Quarter in an
attractive Tudor style building, it is popular with the
after-work crowd. The main cellar bar serves four real
ales and three real ciders, plus a selection of keg and
bottled beers from local breweries and from across
Europe (particularly Belgium) and the USA. Seating
includes a number of enclosed booths. Blues DJs and live
music feature on Thursday and Saturday with food theme
nights and quiz nights completing the scene.
◑ ≷ (Central) ● ▱ ♿ ♫

Bookshop Alehouse
21 Portswood Road, SO17 2ES
4 changing beers (sourced regionally) Ⓗ
A welcoming micropub with knowledgeable bar staff.
Situated within a former bookshop, this theme is
reflected with bookshelves throughout the pub. Four
handpumps serve ever-changing regional real ales, with
four keg lines and a fridge holding three to four bag in
box ciders and canned beers. Regular tap takeovers
complement the usual offerings. Community focused, it
holds quizzes and a basement room is used for events
including book clubs, poetry evenings, CAMRA meetings
and university societies. Well worth a visit. Closed
Monday. Q & ≷ (St Denys) ♣ ● ▱ ♿ ≷

Bottle & Stoat Ⓛ
45 Bedford Place, SO15 2DG
☎ (023) 8115 7210 ⊕ bottleandstoat.co.uk
6 changing beers (sourced nationally; often Dark
Revolution, Flower Pots, Vibrant Forest) Ⓗ
A small craft- and cask-oriented pub in the Bedford Place
area in the city centre, and the newest venture from the
owners of Olaf's Tun. It is tastefully furnished, with a
variety of seating including a sofa and armchairs. With six
front-facing cask handpumps, backed up by 12 keg beer
lines, it is a hotspot for cask and craft. Wines are also
available, and there are bar snacks, as well as the option
to order in food from local outlets. ● ▱ ♿

Brewhouse & Kitchen Ⓛ ⊘
47 Highfield Lane, SO17 1QD
☎ (023) 8055 5566
Brewhouse & Kitchen Speedwell, Walk The Line; 1
changing beer (sourced locally; often Brewhouse &
Kitchen (Southampton)) Ⓗ

Part of the Brewhouse & Kitchen chain, this brewpub opened in 2015. The 2½ barrel (720 pint) plant is situated in what was once the public bar and brews all four of the pub's ales. There is also a large selection of around 20 craft keg beers. Good quality food is served from noon every day. There is a large garden at the rear and a patio area to the front with tables and chairs. ᏪᏇᏠ◗ᏜᏺᏢᎁ(1,U2) ☻ 🛜

Butcher's Hook
7 Manor Farm Road, SO18 1NN
☎ (023) 8178 2280 ⊕ butchershookpub.com
3 changing beers (sourced nationally) 🅖
Positioned facing Bitterne Park Triangle clock tower, this compact micropub, the first in Southampton, opened in 2014. It was previously a butcher's shop, which is still evidenced with some original features – the tiling and butcher's rails have been left in situ. A large blackboard shows the range of cask, keg, bottles and cans on offer with two to three constantly changing cask beers. No food, but customers are welcome to purchase takeaways from local outlets. Closed Monday.
Q🕸&🚲(Bitterne) ♣🚃(20) ☻ 🛜 ♪

Dancing Man 🅛
Wool House, Town Quay, SO14 2AR
☎ (023) 8083 6666 ⊕ dancingmanbrewery.co.uk
Dancing Man Old Fashioned, Jesus Hairdo, Jack O'Diamonds; 2 changing beers (sourced nationally) 🅗
A popular, multi award-winning brewpub set in a historic stone built 14th-century wool house. Refurbished to a high standard complementing the history of the building, with the brew kit visible, it has a spectacular sweeping staircase and local memorabilia adorning the walls. Their own-brewed, often unfined, beer is served through six handpumps and 13 keg lines, while the home-made contemporary food is perfect to enjoy while soaking up the buzzing atmosphere. ᏪᏇᏠ◗Ꮛ&☻🛜♪

Fox & Hounds
106 Pound Street, SO18 6BP (off West End Rd, N of A3024 Bitterne bypass) SU4532613386
☎ (023) 8178 7304
Flower Pots Goodens Gold; 1 changing beer (sourced nationally) 🅗
A traditional back-street local, situated at the junction of five roads and converted from residential use around 1860. Games and pub sports take place Monday to Thursday evenings, Friday night is music night, with either live music, a DJ or karaoke. There is a meat draw Saturday early evening and a free jukebox until 5.30pm on Sunday. The monthly guest beer is from the Stonegate list or a local brewery. Filled rolls are available. The enclosed garden includes a covered area.
🕸♣🚃☻🛜♪

Freemantle Arms 🅛
31 Albany Road, SO15 3EF
☎ (023) 8077 2536 ⊕ thefreemantlearms.co.uk
Flower Pots Goodens Gold; 4 changing beers (sourced regionally; often Steam Town, Bowman, Triple fff) 🅗
Hidden urban oasis in a quiet cul-de-sac, which started life as a 19th-century cider house before becoming an ale house at the start of the 20th century. The single bar is tastefully decorated, with pictures of historical Southampton and interesting old tools adorning the walls. Five real ales are on the bar, four of which change regularly due to demand. A large conservatory to the rear leads to a beautiful enclosed summer garden, which hosts the annual beer festival. A short walk from Shirley Road's frequent buses. 🕸🚲(Millbrook)♣🚃☻♪

Guide Dog 🅛
38 Earl's Road, SO14 6SF
☎ (023) 8063 8947
Dark Star American Pale Ale; Flower Pots Goodens Gold; Steam Town Stoke Pale; 7 changing beers (sourced nationally; often Steam Town, Flower Pots, Dark Star) 🅗
Nestled in Bevois Valley, this authentic free house features a good array of real ales from both local and national sources across 11 handpumps. A refurbishment added the colourful Dog House back room, and a small patio. Hosting special events like Thai curry nights and pie sales on Southampton FC match days, it is a previous local CAMRA Pub of the Year, beloved for both its quality drinks and vibrant atmosphere. Q🚃(20,U6)☻ 🛜 ♪

Key & Anchor
90 Millbrook Road East, SO15 1JQ
☎ 07950 239067
St Austell Proper Job; Wadworth 6X; 1 changing beer (sourced nationally; often Caledonian, Flower Pots, Greene King) 🅗
A back-street Victorian pub built in 1862 and only a 10 minute walk from Central station. There is a small well-maintained garden at the rear, plus a small seating area at the front. The inside has a couple of different seating areas around the U-shaped bar supplemented by a small room at the back. The pub has three handpumps on the bar with one a changing beer. The jukebox offers a wide choice of music. 🕸🚲(Central)♣🚃☻🛜♪

Olaf's Tun
8 Portsmouth Road, SO19 9AA
☎ (023) 8044 7887 ⊕ olafstun.co.uk
6 changing beers (sourced regionally; often Flower Pots, Bowman) 🅗
A welcoming and inclusive micropub featuring up to six changing local and national real ales, eight keg craft beers, bag-in-box still ciders and a wide selection of bottled and canned beers, alongside freshly cooked food and bar snacks. With knowledgeable bar staff and friendly regulars, Olaf's Tun runs regular events including craft evenings and a running club. Definitely worth visiting, it was local CAMRA Pub of the Year 2022 and 2023 and Regional CAMRA Pub of the Year 2022.
Q🕸Ꮛ◗&🚲(Woolston) ♣🍴🚃☻🛜

Park Inn 🍸
37 Carlisle Road, SO16 4FN
☎ 07596 203702 ⊕ theparkinn.co.uk
Wadworth Henry's IPA, 6X, Swordfish; 3 changing beers (sourced nationally; often Ossett, Abbeydale, Timothy Taylor) 🅗
A proper street-corner local, fronting both Shirley Park and Carlisle Roads. Parking is difficult, however there are regular bus services to Shirley Precinct which is a short walk from the pub. The landlady's Scotch eggs, pies and sausage rolls are very popular. The pub serves three ales from Wadworth plus regular guest ales. Quizzes are held on Sunday and Wednesday. Local CAMRA Pub of the Year 2024. 🕸♣🚃☻🛜

Platform Tavern 🅛
Town Quay, SO14 2NY
☎ (023) 8251 7782 ⊕ platformtavern.com
Dark Star Hophead; Fuller's London Pride; 2 changing beers (sourced locally; often Vibrant Forest) 🅗
After a temporary closure following a fire in late 2023, the pub is now fully open with three handpumps in use. Being close to the cruise terminals and Isle of Wight ferries, the Platform is well situated for seafaring passengers. It is popular at weekends with live music on Friday and Saturday evenings, late Sunday afternoon,

and most Thursday evenings. Of historic interest is a small section of the old city wall and a plaque for the last victim of the Titanic to be recovered. ◑♣🖳😋🛜♪

South Western Arms
38-40 Adelaide Road, SO17 2HW
☎ (023) 8122 0817
9 changing beers (sourced nationally) Ⓗ
Adjoining St Denys railway station, this spacious Victorian era pub offers up to nine real ales. Set over two floors, with pub games in the upstairs area, there is also an enclosed paved back garden. The decor includes exposed brick walls and period bric-a-brac. No food is served but a pizza van operates on the front car park Wednesday to Friday. The pub has a popular jukebox and live bands typically play twice per month, usually on Sundays.
❀⇌(St Denys) ♣P🖳(20) 😋♪

Wellington Arms
56 Park Road, SO15 3DE
☎ (023) 8036 2364
Gale's HSB; 6 changing beers (sourced nationally; often Harvey's, Flower Pots, Butcombe) Ⓗ
Two-bar pub in the back-streets of Freemantle, dating from the 1860s and serving up to seven cask beers. Wellingtonian pictures found throughout celebrate its name. The front bar is adorned with pre-decimal copper coins and glassware hangs above. A real fire warms customers in winter and bands play in the rear bar every Saturday. Two dartboards and an extensive games collection offer additional entertainment for visitors. There is a paved garden to the rear. Several bus routes run nearby. ❀♣🖳◑🛜♪

Witch's Brew ⒧
220 Shirley Road, SO15 3FL
☎ 07403 871757
5 changing beers (sourced nationally; often Flower Pots, Steam Town, Wantsum) Ⓖ
A quirky witch-themed micropub on Southampton's busy Shirley Road. The Victorian building has two cosy rooms and a small serving bar at the back, which leads outside to a partially-covered, paved garden. The gated front yard is cyclist-friendly with parking stands. Up to six beers are served, and this is the only Southampton pub with gravity only dispense. Known for its friendly atmosphere, it is a frequent local CAMRA Pub of the Year finalist. Closed Monday to Wednesday. Q❀♣🖳🖳😋

Southwick

Golden Lion ⒧
High Street, PO17 6EB
☎ (023) 9221 0437 🌐 goldenlionsouthwick.co.uk
5 changing beers (sourced regionally; often Bowman, Langham, Palmers) Ⓗ
Nearby Southwick House was the centre of planning for Operation Overlord in the Second World War and the pub was visited by many of those involved, including Generals Eisenhower and Montgomery. The lounge bar was the unofficial Officers' Mess during that period. The village, apart from Church Lodge, is owned by Southwick Estates which is why the pub has a dark red front door in common with all the other properties so owned. Jazz music is played on Tuesday and folk on the last Thursday of the month. Q🖢❀◑▶♣🖝P😋🛜♪

Steep

Harrow ★ ⒧
Harrow Lane, GU32 2DA
☎ (01730) 262685 🌐 theharrowinnsteep.co.uk

2 changing beers (sourced locally; often Flack Manor, Bowman) Ⓖ
A genuinely unspoilt pub, it has two cosy rooms with serving hatches rather than counters. Beer is always 4% ABV or less, coming from a range of local breweries. Substantial meals are served. There are several benches at the front of the pub and a lovely well-kept garden. The toilets are across the road. It has been identified by CAMRA as having a nationally important historic pub interior. Card payments are not accepted. Q❀◑♣P😋

Sutton Scotney

Coach & Horses
Oxford Road, SO21 3JH
☎ (01962) 672207
Fuller's London Pride; Timothy Taylor Landlord; 1 changing beer (sourced locally) Ⓗ
Located in a rural village, this traditional, local pub, dating from the late 1700s, provides a friendly atmosphere for all. The main bar has a cosy atmosphere, and there are side rooms which give an even more intimate experience. Home-made food and three B&B rooms are available. The pub has a large beer garden and a pet-friendly attitude. 🖢❀◑▶♿P🖳(86)😋

Tichborne

Tichborne Arms ⒧
SO24 0NA (1¼ miles S of B3047 Alresford Rd jct) SU5719930412
☎ (01962) 588346 🌐 tichbornearms.com
Triple fff Moondance; 3 changing beers (sourced locally; often Bowman, Hogs Back, Langham) Ⓗ
Thatched pub built in 1939, matching the older buildings in the village and owned by the Tichborne estate. A wood-panelled bar at the front has an open fire and leads to a recently added comfortable dining area. Booking is recommended for meals. Outside is a large covered and enclosed patio that occasionally sees live sport, and a large garden with benches, a children's play area and pétanque pitch. In summer there is an outside bar and pizza oven. Card payment only. 🖢❀◑♿P😋🛜

Titchfield

Wheatsheaf ⒧
1 East Street, PO14 4AD
☎ (01329) 842965
🌐 thewheatsheaf-titchfield.foodanddrinksites.co.uk
Bowman Hop Hearted; Flower Pots Pots Bitter; 3 changing beers (sourced regionally) Ⓗ
A 17th-century free house, owned by the licensee since 2017, which has established a reputation for top-quality real ale. The premises comprise a main bar with real fire, garden, a cosy snug and a bistro restaurant. Separate bar and restaurant meals are available. Regular beer and cider festivals are held at the end of January and July each year. No food is served Sunday evening.
Q🖢❀◑♿🖝P🖳(X4)😋♪

Totton

6 Barrels
31 Salisbury Road, SO40 3HX
🌐 6barrels.co.uk
Steam Town Stoke Pale; 3 changing beers (sourced regionally; often Parkway, Twisted) Ⓗ
A mid-sized micropub near the town centre, furnished in a rustic style – long tables with stools and benches inside and out provide adequate seating. Handpumps serve Stoke Pale and potentially up to three more beers

depending on trade. Live music plays most weekends and there is a large screen showing major sports events (terrestrial TV only). Family-friendly, no food is served but customers are welcome to bring in pizza from next door. Buses stop outside and more bus routes and the railway station are nearby. ✲♿≠♣🚃(12,X7)🐾🛜♪

Twyford

Phoenix Inn Ⓛ
High Street, SO21 1RF
☎ (01962) 713322 🌐 thephoenixinn.co.uk
Flower Pots Pots Bitter, IPA; Morland Old Speckled Hen; Timothy Taylor Landlord; St Austell Tribute; 2 changing beers (sourced locally; often Hop Back, Flower Pots, Steam Town) Ⓗ
Friendly, family-run pub on the main road through the village. Although a Greene King pub, four of the eight handpumps serve local beers, usually from Flower Pots and Hop Back. A long bar serves a split-level room and there is a skittle alley which can be hired for catered events. Outside to the rear is a covered patio and beer garden with marquee. Home-cooked pub food is served lunchtimes and evenings. Closed Monday.
🛏✲🕙♣🚃(61,69)🐾🛜♪

Upham

Brushmakers Arms
2 Shoe Lane, SO32 1JJ (top of village near the pond)
SU5399620606
☎ (01489) 860231 🌐 thebrushmakersarms.com
Flower Pots Goodens Gold; Flack Manor Flack's Double Drop; Steam Town Stoke Pale; 1 changing beer (sourced regionally; often Hop Back, Bowman, Stonehenge) Ⓗ
Cosy and welcoming village pub, with an open fire, serving three regular ales and one guest ale – all local – and at least one real cider. The 600-year-old building was previously a school and a book makers, hence the name. Outside, there are benches at the front and a large pretty garden to the rear. The pub has an ever-changing menu and serves local and sustainably sourced produce (no food Mon or Tue). Q✲🕙🍴♣🐾🛜♪

Vernham Dean

George Inn
Back Lane, SP11 0JY
☎ (01264) 737279 🌐 thegeorgeatvernhamdean.co.uk
Bowman Swift One; Flack Manor Flack's Double Drop; Stonehenge Pigswill; 1 changing beer Ⓗ
This traditional village pub dates back to the 17th century and features eyebrow windows. It is situated in a pretty village with numerous foot and cycling paths, including to nearby Fosbury Hillfort. There is outside seating to front and at the rear is an enclosed beer garden. The interior features low oak-beamed ceilings and fireplaces. Locally produced food is served, and themed nights are regularly held. An annual beer festival is run in August.
Q🛏✲🕙P🐾🛜♪

Whitchurch

Bell Inn
26 Bell Street, RG28 7DD
☎ (01256) 893120 🌐 thebellwhitchurch.co.uk
Fuller's London Pride; Gale's Seafarers Ale; Sharp's Doom Bar Ⓗ
The 15th-century, half-timbered Bell oozes the character of a traditional pub. Look carefully for the wooden nail in the timber work. Conversation rules in both bars, while

an area off the lounge with exposed beams provides space for a quiet pint or a meeting. Local musicians feature regularly on Sunday afternoons. There is a pool table, and a small library raises funds for charity. A small patio is accessible through the pub.
Q✲🛏◑≠♣P🚃(76,86) 🐾♪

Prince Regent Ⓛ
104 London Road, RG28 7LT
☎ (01256) 892179
Hop Back Crop Circle; Summer Lightning Ⓗ
The Prince is a real traditional friendly local, 'up the hill' in this rural town. It has a single bar and small rear drinking area overlooking the Test Valley. A jukebox, pool table and sports TV screens feature, with an emphasis on football. Occasional quizzes and live music, including karaoke are held. The pub may open until 1am at weekends. ♣P🚃(76)🐾♪

Whitchurch Sports & Social Club
Winchester Road, RG28 7RB (S of town centre)
☎ (01256) 892493 🌐 whitchurchsport.co.uk/whitchurch-social-club
Flower Pots Perridge Pale; 2 changing beers (often Flower Pots) Ⓗ
Tucked away near the tranquil Millennium Meadow, this large Sports Club features two large bars serving local real ales. Home to Whitchurch United FC, a squash club and indoor and outdoor bowling clubs, the impressive green is visible from the comfortable lounge bar. Regular events include quizzes, discos, live bands, entertainment and functions. Normally open evenings and weekends and from 1pm on Saturdays when the football team is at home – call to check opening times. Local CAMRA Club of the Year 2024. 🛏✲P🚃(86)🛜♪

Winchester

Black Boy Ⓛ
1 Wharf Hill, SO23 9NQ
☎ (01962) 861754 🌐 theblackboypub.com
Alfred's Saxon Bronze; Flower Pots Pots Bitter; Hop Back Summer Lightning; 1 changing beer (sourced locally; often Bowman, Hop Back, Flack Manor) Ⓗ
Quirky free house on the eastern edge of the city near the River Itchen. A central bar serves a number of drinking areas with numerous nooks and crannies. Four real ales are served – three regular and one guest. There is a large outside patio with plenty of covered seating. Food is limited to pizzas (Thu and Fri eve) and tacos (Tue, Wed, Sat eve and Sun afternoon). The co-owned Black Hole next door has 10 en-suite rooms.
✲🛏♣🚃(4,WPR) 🐾🛜♪

Fulflood Arms Ⓛ
28 Cheriton Road, SO22 5EF
☎ (01962) 842996 🌐 thefulfloodarms.co.uk
Morland Old Speckled Hen; St Austell Tribute; 5 changing beers (sourced locally; often Flower Pots, Queen Inn, Electric Bear) Ⓗ
Traditional, back-street corner local, tucked away in a quiet residential area away from the city centre, but only a short walk west from the railway station. An original dark green tiled façade and frosted-glass windows remain as evidence of this 19th-century pub's former Winchester Brewery ownership. Inside, a capacious single bar is divided into differing areas, with a wood-burning stove, comfy chairs and a library. The walls have a photographic collection and posters showing historic reminders of Winchester. Outside, there are patios, front and rear. ✲♣≠♣🚃(3,4)🐾🛜

Hyde Tavern 🅛
57 Hyde Street, SO23 7DY
☎ (01962) 862592 ⊕ hydetavern.co.uk
Flower Pots Pots Bitter; 3 changing beers (sourced regionally; often Flower Pots, Steam Town, Harvey's) 🅗/🅖
This ancient pub with impressive twin gabled front has a cosy, unspoiled interior, split into two rooms with with low beams, and modern artwork on the walls. A small bar serves up to six, mostly local, real ales on both handpump and gravity. Down a narrow staircase is a small paved garden with plenty of seating and a cellar room used for live bands. The pub hosts various regular folk/community music evenings and a beer festival in June. Q❀❧≉♣🚐(67,Spring)🐾🤶♪

Queen Inn 🅛 ✅
28 Kingsgate Road, SO23 9PG
☎ (01962) 853898 ⊕ thequeeninnwinchester.com
Bowman Hop Hearted; Flack Manor Flack's Double Drop; Queen Inn A Long Way From Pillowcases, St Cross Ale; 5 changing beers (sourced locally; often Steam Town, Queen Inn, Electric Bear) 🅗/🅖
Attractive pub situated in the southern area of the city, close to Winchester College. The long single bar is well decorated with photographs of historic Winchester. Outside is a large beer garden to the rear and a sheltered front patio. The pub's own microbrewery produces a range of Queen Inn beers and can be viewed from the front bar. In addition, up to five ales are sourced from other local breweries. The comprehensive food menu is complemented by Sunday roasts. Q♿❀🍽️P🚐🤶🛜

Wykeham Arms 🅛
75 Kingsgate Street, SO23 9PE
☎ (01962) 853834 ⊕ wykehamarmswinchester.co.uk
Flower Pots Goodens Gold; Fuller's London Pride; Gale's Seafarers Ale, HSB; 1 changing beer (sourced regionally; often Fuller's, Dark Star) 🅗
Grade II-listed pub, located in the historic narrow streets near Winchester College, with distinctive curved glass entrance doors that lead straight into the busy main bar area where old school desks are used as bar tables. Various memorabilia, including beer tankards, walking sticks and antique naval pictures, adorn the pub's six interconnected rooms. Award-winning food is served in two restaurant areas to the left and rear of the main bar area. Q❀🛏️🍽️🚐🤶🛜

Wonston

Wonston Arms 🅛
Stoke Charity Road, SO21 3LS
☎ 07909 993388 ⊕ thewonston.co.uk
4 changing beers (sourced locally; often Bowman, Flower Pots, Oakham) 🅗
This community-focused pub is a real gem in a quaint village a 15-minute walk from Sutton Scotney and a bus stop. With a quirky exterior resembling a beach, the interior is homely and cosy in contrast. The pub only serves drinks but has regular pop-up food vendors plus a popular curry night which must be pre-booked. Regular activities include live music, quizzes and other events. Cyclists, walkers and dogs are welcome. It was CAMRA National Pub of the Year in 2018. Q❀♣P🤶🛜♪

Coal Exchange, Emsworth (Photo: Geoff Marsh)

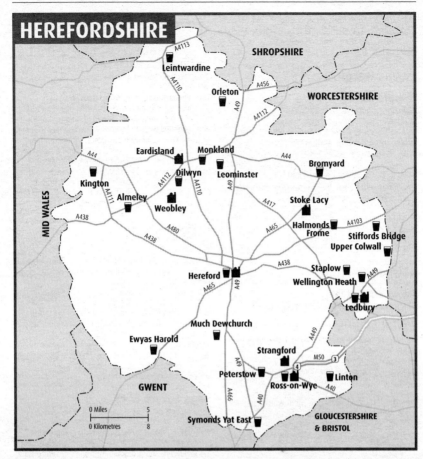

HEREFORDSHIRE

(map of Herefordshire showing surrounding areas SHROPSHIRE, WORCESTERSHIRE, MID WALES, GWENT, GLOUCESTERSHIRE & BRISTOL, and locations including Leintwardine, Orleton, Eardisland, Monkland, Bromyard, Kington, Dilwyn, Leominster, Almeley, Weobley, Stoke Lacy, Halmonds Frome, Stiffords Bridge, Upper Colwall, Hereford, Staplow, Wellington Heath, Ledbury, Much Dewchurch, Ewyas Harold, Strangford, Peterstow, Linton, Ross-on-Wye, Symonds Yat East)

Almeley

Bells Inn L

HR3 6LF (in village)
☎ (01544) 327216 ⊕ thebellsinnalmeley.com
**Goff's Lancer; Three Tuns XXX; 1 changing beer
(sourced locally; often Hobsons, Milestone)** Ⓗ
A genuine welcome is guaranteed at this enthusiastically
run, traditional country inn set in the heart of its rural
community, which incorporates an award-winning farm
shop and delicatessen. The low-ceilinged bar has an
alcove housing the dartboard. Home-prepared lunches
are served, and fish & chips every Friday evening
(booking required). The guest beer is typically from local
breweries. A former local CAMRA Pub of the Year runner-
up. ☆❀◐♣⬤🅿🚌❀🛜♫

Bromyard

Rose & Lion L ✔

5 New Road, HR7 4AJ
☎ (01885) 482381
Wye Valley Bitter, HPA, Butty Bach Ⓗ
A long-standing member of the Wye Valley pub estate,
the 'Rosie' is very much a town pub from the old school,
with a loyal local following. Two small, largely unaltered
rooms are complemented by a further bar area to the
rear, plus a more contemporary annexe and a pleasant
garden. Furnished throughout in a modern but
appropriate style, there is always a buzz about the place.

No food is served but pop up food events are held twice
a month. The car park is small, but there is free on-street
parking nearby. Q☆❀◐♣⬤🅿🚌(420)❀

Dilwyn

Crown Inn L

HR4 8HL (in village)
☎ (01544) 318063 ⊕ thecrowninndilwyn.co.uk
**Wye Valley HPA, Butty Bach; 2 changing beers (often
Hobsons, Otter, Three Tuns)** Ⓗ
Herefordshire's first community-owned pub was
originally a black-and-white coaching inn, before the
lovely village was bypassed. The 17th-century building
has been refronted and much altered, though many
beams remain visible in the two bars. Meals and bar
snacks are available, with roasts on Sunday and senior
citizens lunch on Wednesday. The pub fields several pub

REAL ALE BREWERIES

Corn 🍺 Ross-on-Wye
Hereford 🍺 Hereford
Ledbury Ledbury
Motley Hog 🍺 Ross-on-Wye
Simpsons 🍺 Eardisland
Weobley Weobley
Wobbly ⚡ Hereford
Woofy's Strangford
Wye Valley Stoke Lacy

game teams. An acoustic music session is held every third Thursday in the month (participation welcomed). The garden includes a children's play area.
Q❀☺❀◑P❖ ♪

Ewyas Harold

Temple Bar 🅛

HR2 0EU (just off B4347, in village)
☎ (01981) 240423 ∰ thetemplebarinn.co.uk
Wye Valley Butty Bach; 2 changing beers (sourced locally; often Hobsons, Ludlow) 🅗
First licensed in the 1850s, the Temple Bar Inn has also been used as a court house, corn exchange and stable. Located on the Golden Valley Pilgrim Way, it was extensively refurbished in 2011. It comprises a bar, games room, restaurant, outside seating area, function room and four en-suite rooms. Meals are served (except on Sun eve and Mon). The restaurant menu changes weekly and features locally sourced seasonal ingredients that are freshly prepared and cooked.
Q❀☺❀◑❀❖❀❀⊞(440) ❀❖ ♪

Halmonds Frome

Major's Arms 🅛

WR6 5AX (1 mile N of A4103 at Bishops Frome)
SO675481
☎ (01531) 640261
Purity Pure Gold; Wye Valley HPA; 1 changing beer (often Ledbury) 🅗
An isolated hillside pub that used to be a cider mill. The high-ceilinged main bar has stone walls and a large wood-burner, which is always lit in winter. An archway leads through to another drinking area. Outside is an extensive terrace on two levels, from which there are superb views, particularly sunsets, over west Herefordshire and into Wales. Complimentary bar snacks are often provided, and occasionally there is live music.
☺❀▲❀P❖❀ ♪

Hereford

Barrels 🅛 ✅

69 St Owen Street, HR1 2JQ
☎ (01432) 274968
Wye Valley Bitter, The Hopfather, HPA, Butty Bach, Wholesome Stout; 1 changing beer (sourced locally; often Wye Valley) 🅗
A must-visit Hereford institution that welcomes everyone. Local CAMRA Pub of the Year on seven occasions, it is a community pub of the highest order. There is no food and no gimmicks, just bags of character across five rooms, with a fantastic covered courtyard to the rear that hosts a charity beer and music festival each October. Events include jazz (first Mon eve of the month) and comedy (intermittent Wed eves). TVs feature throughout for major events, otherwise in one bar only.
☺❀≈❀❀⊟❖❀ ♪

Beer in Hand

136 Eign Street, HR4 0AP
☎ 07543 327548 ∰ bihhereford.co.uk
3 changing beers 🅖
Herefordshire's first micropub, this minimalist, single-bar establishment was converted from a launderette in 2013 and isn't actually that small! In recent years it has won local CAMRA Pub of the Year and Cider Pub of the Year. With an impressive chilled racking system, it typically sells up to five ales on cask, six keg beers and eight, mainly local, ciders and perries. Snacks are always available and artisan pizzas are made on-site on

Thursday evening. Quiz night is the first Wednesday and folk night the third Thursday of the month.
Q❀☺❀❀▲❀❀❀❀ ♪

Britannia 🅛 ✅

7 Cotterell Street, HR4 0HH
☎ (01432) 341780
Wye Valley Bitter, HPA, Butty Bach 🅗
A popular back-street venue with real pedigree, in an area of the city otherwise devoid of quality choices. It was reopened in 2010 by Wye Valley brewery following an impressive refurbishment, which included a new extension with an oak-vaulted ceiling and a landscaped rear garden/patio. The large central bar-servery is bookended by two distinct seating areas with modern decor. Snacks such as sandwiches and pork pies are always available, with barbecues in summer. A quiz is held monthly on Thursday. ☺❀❀❀⊟(71,72)❀❖ ♪

Orange Tree

16 King Street, HR4 9BX
☎ (01432) 800933
Black Country Bradley's Finest Golden, Pig on the Wall, Fireside; 6 changing beers (often Black Country) 🅗
Dating from the 17th century, this small, single-bar pub is a recent addition to the Black Country Inns estate. Grade II-listed for the original front part of the building, it has been slightly enlarged and thoroughly refurbished in a more cosy and traditional style than previously. Significantly increasing the choice of ales in the city, details of up to 10 ales plus two ciders are displayed on large screens. Snacks such as pork pies and cobs are served. ☺❀❀▲❀❀⊟(33)❀❖

Vaga Tavern 🅛 ✅

Vaga Street, HR2 7AT
☎ (01432) 509927
Wye Valley Bitter, Butty Bach; 1 changing beer 🅗
A friendly community pub in Hunderton, which is near the River Wye and accessible from the city centre via a pleasant riverside walk and cycleway. Owned by Wye Valley brewery, it consists of two spacious rooms and a skittle alley, with a large garden to the rear including a children's play area. Activities include regular live music, skittles and darts matches, plus events for the whole family. Filled rolls are normally available.
☺❀❀P⊟(75) ❀ ♪

Kington

Olde Tavern ★ 🅛

22 Victoria Road, HR5 3BX
☎ (01544) 231417
4 changing beers (often Hobsons, Ludlow, Three Tuns) 🅗
A living, breathing Victorian timewarp, once called the Railway Tavern (the railway closed in the 1950s) and before that the Tavern in the Fields. In the lobby there is an original serving hatch. To the left is a small bar with original timberwork, bench and alcove seating, and multifarious curios; to the right is the old smoke room with its fine flagstone floor and bench seating. The pub has a strong local following. Traditional pub grub is available Wednesday to Sunday (Wed curry night, Thu steak night, Sun lunches). Q❀☺❀◑▲❀⊟❖

Ledbury

Feathers Hotel

25 High Street, HR8 1DS
☎ (01531) 635266 ∰ feathersledbury.co.uk

3 changing beers (often Ledbury) ⊞
An elegant black-and-white Elizabethan coaching inn, one of the flagship hotels for the county, the Feathers has recently benefitted from a major refurbishment. Features inside this fine Grade II*-listed building include a function room that was once the town theatre, and hand-painted murals in the upstairs corridors. The smart, plush, quiet bar is complemented by a restaurant and separate coffee shop and eatery (open daytime). The toilets are fully accessible. Card payment only.
Q⌂♿️⏏️◑🅿️🐾🛜

Prince of Wales 🅛 ✅
Church Lane, HR8 1DL
☎ (01531) 632250
Hobsons Town Crier; Ledbury Dark, Ledbury Pale ale; Otter Amber; 2 changing beers (often New Bristol, Siren) ⊞
Tucked away down a picturesque cobbled alley leading to the church, this 16th-century timber-framed pub has two bars plus an alcove where folk jam sessions are held on Wednesday evening. A multi-award winner, it is a genuine community pub and always bustling with locals and visitors. Draught cider is available, as well as one rotating craft beer and an extensive range of foreign beers in bottles and cans. The bar meals are good value. Booking is advisable for Sunday roasts.
⌂🏮◑♣️🍴🖥️🐾🛜♪

Leintwardine

Sun Inn ★ 🅛
Rosemary Lane, SY7 0LP (off A4113, in village)
☎ (01547) 540705
Hobsons Mild, Best; Ludlow Stairway; Wye Valley Butty Bach ⊞
A national treasure and one of the last parlour pubs, the Sun was saved in 2009 following a CAMRA-led campaign. The redbrick-tiled public bar features bench furniture and a simple fireplace. Another room is the untouched parlour from where the landlady of 74 years, Flossie Lane, once held court. To the rear is a stylish pavilion-style extension overlooking the garden; venue for the August bank holiday Sunday beer festival. Light lunches are served daily. Fish & chips from next door may be eaten in the garden. Q⌂🏮◑♿️▲🍴🐾🛜♪

Leominster

Chequers ★ 🅛 ✅
63 Etnam Street, HR6 8AE
☎ (01568) 612473
Wye Valley Bitter, HPA, The Hopfather, Butty Bach, Wholesome Stout; 1 changing beer (often Wye Valley) ⊞
Probably the oldest pub in the town, with a fine timber-framed façade and interesting protruding gables. A wonderful front bar was at one time two bars, but still has much charm, with a fine tiled floor, original fireplace, timbers, and cosy window alcoves. To the rear is a more conventional lounge bar, a games room, and a patio with a feature oak-timbered shelter. Snack food is available. Children over 13 are admitted. A quiz is held monthly on Wednesday, and jazz on some Fridays in summer.
🏮♿️🚆♣️🍴🖥️🐾🛜♪

Linton

Alma Inn 🍽️ 🅛
HR9 7RY (off B4221, W of M50 jct 3) SO659255
☎ (01989) 720355 ⊕ almainnlinton.co.uk

Butcombe Original; Ludlow Gold; 3 changing beers (often Bristol Beer Factory, Hop Shed) ⊞
Hidden behind a rendered façade is this understated but multi-award winning pub of outstanding calibre. The convivial front bar, with wood-burner and original timber furniture, contrasts with the rear pool room and separate wood-panelled dining room. Hearty, freshly prepared pub classics are offered, with seasonal specials, light bites and bar snacks. Events include the nationally renowned Linton Music Festival in July, hosted in the extensive gardens, along with a beer festival. A quiz is held every last Sunday of the month. A former local CAMRA Pub of the Year. Q⌂🏮♣️🍴🐾♪

Monkland

Monkland Arms 🅛
HR6 9DE (on A44, W end of village)
☎ (01568) 720510 ⊕ themonklandarms.co.uk
Hobsons Best; Wye Valley Butty Bach; 2 changing beers (sourced locally; often Bewdley, Ludlow) ⊞
A single bar serves a drinking area, with dining areas to the side and back that drinkers are more than welcome to occupy. The beer garden to the rear, with covered seating, has views across open country. Home-cooked locally sourced food is served, including traditional Sunday lunches. Up to seven local draught ciders are available, plus a range of four real ales. There is a quiz on the last Wednesday of the month and live music on some Saturdays and Sundays. ⌂🏮◑♣️🍴🖥️(502)🐾🛜♪

Much Dewchurch

Black Swan
HR2 8DJ (on B4348, in village)
☎ (01981) 540295
Timothy Taylor Landlord; 2 changing beers (often Butcombe, Slater's) ⊞
One of the oldest pubs in Herefordshire, this delightful 15th-century beamed village inn comes complete with its own priest hole. A small lounge leads to a dining room with an open fire, while a separate public bar with flagstone floors leads to a pool and darts room. Home-prepared, mainly locally sourced food is available. Guest beers are typically from regional breweries, and draught Gwatkins perry is available, plus ciders from Cockyard, Colcombe House and other local makers. Folk night is on Thursday. A former local CAMRA Pub of the Year.
⌂🏮◑♣️🍴🖥️🐾🛜♪

Orleton

Boot Inn 🅛
Kitchen Hill Road, SY8 4HN (off B4361, in village)
☎ (01568) 780228 ⊕ bootinnorleton.co.uk
Hobsons Best, Twisted Spire; Ludlow Blonde; 1 changing beer ⊞
The Boot reopened under community ownership in 2019, following a period of closure. A major refurbishment of this distinguished Grade II-listed, 16th-century, half-timbered masterpiece has been achieved to good effect. It has been sympathetically opened out while maintaining a separate dining room, snug and original inglenook fireplace. High-quality seasonal food is served; booking is advised, especially at weekends. There is occasional live music. ⌂🏮◑▲♣️🅿️🖥️(490)♪

Peterstow

Yew Tree Inn
HR9 6JZ (on A49, in village)
☎ (01989) 562815 ⊕ rosscider.com

Hobsons Best; 1 changing beer (sourced locally) ⒣
The Yew Tree was taken over in 2014 by the Ross-on-Wye Cider & Perry Company. The four ales and two draught ciders are complemented by a large range of bottled cider and perry. Guest beers are often from distant microbreweries. The cider shop is open 12-6pm. A games night is held on Tuesday, and music on Friday. Meals consist of pop-up events advertised locally and on Facebook. A camping/caravan site is available with a toilet and shower block. Hereford to Ross bus service 33 stops in the village. ⏴⏵❀⏴⏵⏳Å⏳P🚲(33)❀🛜♪

Ross-on-Wye

King's Head Hotel ⓛ
8 High Street, HR9 5HL
☎ (01989) 763174 ⊕ kingshead.co.uk
Wye Valley Bitter, Butty Bach; 2 changing beers (sourced locally; often Corn Ales) ⒣
This large central hotel (a former coaching inn) is claimed to date from the 14th century, though the pine-panelled King's Bar is of Georgian origin. The library serves as the lounge bar, while the restaurant to the rear has a 60-foot well as its centrepiece. A varied menu of bar snacks and meals are served. Bottled Broome Farm cider is sold and beers are available from Corn Ales, a microbrewery based in the Corn Exchange to the rear of the pub, which has been transformed into a brewery tap and event space. ⏴⏵❀⏴⏵⏳P🚲❀🛜

Staplow

Oak Inn ⓛ
Bromyard Road, HR8 1NP (on B4214)
☎ (01531) 640954 ⊕ theoakinnstaplow.co.uk
Bathams Best Bitter; Ledbury Ledbury Pale ale; 2 changing beers (often Bathams, Three Tuns, Wye Valley) ⒣
A stylishly renovated and well-run roadside country inn offering exceptional food, good beer and quality accommodation. The contemporary public area neatly divides into three: a reception bar area with modern sofas and low tables; a snug; and a main dining area featuring an open kitchen. At the rear is a further room with scrubbed tables. Such is the reputation of the Oak that booking is essential for food and accommodation. Q⏴⏵❀⏴⏵⏳P🚲(417)❀🛜

Stiffords Bridge

Red Lion Inn ⓛ
WR13 5NN (on A4103)
☎ (01886) 880318 ⊕ redlioncradley.co.uk
RCH Pitchfork; Wye Valley Butty Bach; 4 changing beers (often Ledbury, Pitchfork) ⒣
This multi-roomed roadside pub is as popular with out-of-town diners as it is with locals and drinkers. A survivor of multiple floods, it is characterised by modern flagstone floors, wood panelling, bare brick walls, cosy window alcoves and a large fireplace with a wood-burner. There are pleasant and extensive gardens to the

rear where events are hosted. Traditional locally sourced food dominates the menu. The guest beers are from breweries far and near, many unusual for the area, supplemented by a craft keg beer and two real ciders. ⏴⏵❀⏴⏵⏳Å⏳P❀🛜♪

Symonds Yat East

Saracen's Head ⓛ
HR9 6JL
☎ (01600) 890435 ⊕ saracensheadinn.co.uk
Wye Valley HPA, Butty Bach; 4 changing beers (sourced locally; often Bespoke, Ledbury, Wye Valley) ⒣
A riverside inn that operates its own foot passenger ferry across the Wye when the pub is open. It has a large single bar with flagstone floor, pews, and scrubbed-wood tables, as well as a lounge/dining room and patio overlooking the river. A varied menu of locally sourced and freshly prepared bar snacks and full meals, including vegetarian options, is on offer. Bottled local cider is sold. Nine en-suite bedrooms are available and an adjacent (public) car park is free in the evening. ⏴⏵❀⏴⏵⏳Å❀🛜

Upper Colwall

Chase Inn ⓛ
Chase Road, WR13 6DJ (off B4218, turning at upper hairpin bend signed British Camp) SO766431
☎ (01684) 540276 ⊕ thechaseinnmalvern.co.uk
Holden's Golden Glow; 2 changing beers (often Purity, Three Tuns) ⒣
Small and cosy two-bar free house hidden away in a quiet wooded backwater on the western slopes of the Malvern Hills. With a genteel atmosphere, it is popular with walkers and locals alike. It comprises a small lounge for dining (booking advisable at weekends) and a long, narrow public bar, both adorned with many artefacts and curios. A delightful manicured rear beer garden commands panoramic views across Herefordshire to the Welsh hills. A quiz is held on the first Monday of the month. Q⏴⏵❀⏴⏵⏳P🚲(675)❀🛜

Wellington Heath

Farmers Arms ⓛ
Horse Road, HR8 1LS (in village, E of B4214)
☎ (01531) 634770 ⊕ farmersarmswellingtonheath.co.uk
Ledbury Bitter; Wye Valley Butty Bach; 2 changing beers (often Gloucester, Ledbury, Salopian) ⒣
Follow the signs carefully to find this pub in a scattered rural community. The bar and main dining area are in the original mid-19th century building, and on either side are more modern extensions housing a games room, with pool table, and a restaurant. The food ranges from burgers and pub classics to steaks and speciality dishes. Up to four local draught ciders are available in summer. A popular Beer & Beast festival is held in July. ⏴⏵❀⏴⏵⏳P🚲(675)❀🛜♪

Noted ales

At one time or another nearly every county town in England of any size has been noted for its beers or ales. Yorkshire claims not only stingo but also Hull and North Allerton ales whilst Nottingham, Lichfield, Derby, Oxford and Burton have almost branded their ales. During the eighteenth century the fame of Dorchester beer almost equalled the popularity of London porter. **Frank A. King, Beer has a History, 1947**

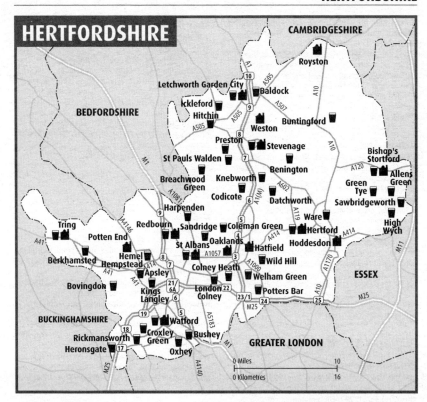

Allens Green

Queen's Head ▼ 🔲

CM21 0LS (turn up West Rd, Sawbridgeworth, at mini roundabout on main road, at T-jct turn right) TL455170
☎ (01279) 723393
Dark Star Hophead; Timothy Taylor Landlord; 2 changing beers (sourced locally) Ⓖ
All cask ale is dispensed by gravity from the cellar at this popular village inn. Four real ales are on offer, two national and two guest, with one always being dark. Extra beers are on stillage on bank holidays and the third weekend of the month. Hearty homemade food and snacks are served. There is a large garden and car park. Dogs are welcome. A frequent winner of local CAMRA Pub of the Year, and current regional Cider Pub of the Year. Q🕏🌣&◆P🍴🏧

Apsley

Oddfellows Arms

113 London Road, HP3 9SP
☎ (01442) 249338
Robinsons Trooper; St Austell Tribute; 1 changing beer (sourced nationally) Ⓗ
Lively, friendly free house with open mic and live music evenings most days. Two bars serve a good selection of well-kept beers, non-real ales, ciders, wines and spirits. There is a garden, which is partially covered, and a small car park at the rear. 🕏🌣🍴◆P🚃(508,501)🏧🏧♪

Baldock

Orange Tree ▼ 🔲 ⊘

Norton Road, SG7 5AW
☎ (01462) 892341 ⊕ theorangetreebaldock.com

Brewster's Hophead; Greene King IPA, Abbot; Titanic Plum Porter; Tring Mansion Mild; 4 changing beers (sourced nationally) Ⓗ
This 300-year-old multi-roomed pub is home to more than 10 local clubs and societies. The guest beers are all from small breweries and changed every weekend. Five local real ciders are also available. There is a huge malt whisky and vintage bottled beer collection on display. Good, home-cooked food is available. Quiz nights are held on Tuesday, folk music on Wednesday. Current local CAMRA Pub of the Year. 🕏🌣🍴&≋♣◆P🍴🏧♪

Benington

Lordship Arms

42 Whempstead Road, SG2 7BX
☎ (01438) 869665 ⊕ lordshiparms.com
Black Sheep Best Bitter; Crouch Vale Brewers Gold; Timothy Taylor Landlord; 6 changing beers (sourced nationally) Ⓗ
Under the same ownership since 1993, this pub is a frequent winner of CAMRA awards, including local and county Pub of the Year in 2023. The single bar is decorated with telephone memorabilia. The garden features floral displays to be enjoyed in the summer. Excellent fresh sandwiches and lunchtime snacks are served. There is a classic car gathering on the third Tuesday of each month from April to September. Winter Sunday hours can vary – call to check. Q🌣🍴◆P🍴🏧

Berkhamsted

Crown 🔲 ⊘

145 High Street, HP4 3HH
☎ (01442) 863993

Greene King IPA, Abbot; 4 changing beers (sourced nationally; often Sambrook's, Vale, Windsor & Eton) ⓗ
This historic establishment has served as a pub since the 1700s and is now owned and managed by JD Wetherspoon. A corridor layout offers snug areas at the front leading to the bar and main seated area, before opening out to a sizeable terraced patio garden. Guest ales feature from local brewers, with food served all day. Q ⓢ ⓧⓘⓓ ⓐⓡ ⓡ 및 (500) 중

Rising Sun Ⓛ
1 Canal Side, George Street, HP4 2EG (at lock 55 on Grand Union Canal; from station follow canal towards Hemel Hempstead)
☎ (01442) 864913
House beer (by Tring); 4 changing beers (sourced nationally; often Chiltern, Tring, Vale) ⓗ
This welcoming, traditional pub on the Grand Union Canal features snugs inside and a heated garden patio and scenic canalside seating area outside. Changing cask beers are sourced nationally, and are complemented by noted craft keg lines, well-chosen spirits, and an excellent real cider/perry range of up to 20 different boxes. They also host many events throughout the year such as beer festivals, quizzes, and a cheese club. Food is restricted to a renowned ploughman's.
ⓢ ⓧ ⓡ ⓐ ⓓ 및 (500,501) ⓕ 중

Bishop's Stortford

Belgian Brewer
Unit 11, Links Business Centre, Raynham Road, CM23 5NZ (off Raynham Rd, take first left)
☎ (01279) 507515 ⓦ thebelgianbrewer.co.uk
10 changing beers (sourced locally)
Brewery taproom serving a large selection of the brewery's Belgian-style beers. The draught beers are not real ale at present, but some cask beer may be available soon. They also stock 100% vegan, bottle-conditioned beers. The pizzas are made on-site. Closed Monday and Tuesday. Q ⓢ ⓓ 및 (508)

Bishop's Stortford Sports Trust Ⓛ ✓
Cricketfield Lane, CM23 2TD
☎ (01279) 654463 ⓦ bssportstrust.co.uk
4 changing beers (sourced locally) ⓗ
Everyone is welcome at this pub within a club – membership is not required. Beer quality is driven by high turnover from the thirsty sports-playing members. Conversation flows in the comfortable seating area as the TV sports screens are usually muted. Outside drinking in summer comes with an attractive view. The venue is easily reached from town via Chantry Road, turning left at the end to see the grounds on the right. Current local CAMRA Club of Year. ⓢ ⓧ ⓓ P

Castle Ⓛ
38 Castle Street, CM23 3TG (from South St, turn up Newton Rd then 1st left)
☎ (01279) 652578
2 changing beers (sourced regionally; often WHARF) ⓗ
This family-run, back-street local, established in 1840, is a real gem. The public bar adjoins a cosy snug with wooden settles, bookshelves, and Desmond, the famous pub dog. One handpump normally serves beers from WHARF (the former Red Fox brewery), while the other dispenses changing beers from large and small brewers. The pub is hidden away in the old town and well worth seeking out. Q ⓡ ⓐ 및 ⓕ

Star Ⓛ ✓
7 Bridge Street, CM23 2JU
☎ (01279) 654211
5 changing beers (sourced regionally) ⓗ
A 17th-century town-centre pub catering for all ages. It is busy on Friday and Saturday evenings with a young crowd, and at other times attracts a mixed clientele. Tuesday is quiz night. A quiet pint can be enjoyed on other evenings and at lunchtimes. Beers from local and regional breweries are offered on an ever-changing basis. Reasonably priced traditional pub food is freshly prepared throughout the day
ⓧ ⓘ ⓡ (Bishops Stortford) ⓕ 및 중 ♪

Bovingdon

Bell Ⓛ ✓
79 High Street, HP3 0HP
☎ (01442) 832800 ⓦ bellbovingdon.co.uk
Tring Side Pocket for a Toad; Young's London Original; 1 changing beer (sourced nationally; often Timothy Taylor, Tring) ⓗ
An 18th-century village pub which consists of a bar with TV, a snug, and a larger area to the rear, often used for dining. The pub feature low ceilings and log-burning fires, and there is a wooden terrace outside. It plays host to several events, including open mic sessions on alternate Sundays, food-themed evenings and a popular monthly quiz. Freshly prepared food uses local produce and includes gluten-free and vegetarian options. No food on Sunday evenings, Mondays or Tuesdays. There is a small car park to the rear. Q ⓢ ⓧ ⓘ ⓐ P 및 (1,352) ⓕ 중 ♪

Breachwood Green

Red Lion ✓
16 Chapel Road, SG4 8NU
☎ (01438) 833123 ⓦ redlionbreachwoodgreen.co.uk
Greene King Abbot; St Austell Tribute; Woodforde's Wherry; 1 changing beer (sourced nationally) ⓗ
The pub – the only one in the village – attracts many locals as well as visitors from further afield. There is a TV showing main sporting events as well as a quiet dining area. The garden provides views of the countryside and a good vantage point to view the aircraft approaching Luton Airport. It serves good, home-made food and the guest beers are unusual for this area. It has its own darts, dominoes, football and cricket teams. Letting accommodation is available. ⓢ ⓧ ⓘ ⓐ P 및 ⓕ 중

REAL ALE BREWERIES

3 Brewers of St Albans ✦ Hatfield
Belgian Brewer, The ✦ Bishop's Stortford
Bowtie Watford
Buntingford Royston
Crossover Blendery ✦ Weston
Farr Brew ✦ Redbourn
Garden City ▤ ✦ Letchworth Garden City
Hardline Watford (NEW)
Mad Squirrel ✦ Potten End
McMullen Hertford
New River Hoddesdon
Oxhey Village (OVB) Watford
Pope's Yard Watford
Six Hills ✦ Stevenage
Tring Tring
Two Bob Oaklands
White Hart Tap ▤ St Albans (brewing suspended)

Buntingford

Crown ★
17 High Street, SG9 9AB
☎ (01763) 271422
3 changing beers (sourced nationally; often Vale) Ⓗ
Town-centre pub with a large front bar, cosy back bar and large function room. Outside there is a covered patio and a secluded garden with a pétanque piste. Food is served on Friday evenings and there is an acoustic music night on the third Monday of the month. The pub has been identified by CAMRA as having a regionally important historic interior. Q🕏🏴‍☠️◗♣🖩(386,331)🐾♪

Bushey

Swan ★
25 Park Road, WD23 3EE
☎ (020) 8950 2256
Greene King Abbot; Timothy Taylor Landlord; Young's London Original; 1 changing beer (sourced nationally; often Black Sheep) Ⓗ
Located in a quiet side street in Bushey Village, this 150-year-old single-room Victorian local has bare floorboards and real fireplaces. The walls are adorned with old photos, paintings, and newspaper clippings of sporting events and life in Bushey. TV screens show sports and a dartboard complements the range of bar games available. The pub serves four real ales, and food consists of toasties, rolls and pies. There are picnic benches at the front. Access to the ladies' toilet is via the rear garden. 🏴‍☠️♣🖩(142,258)🐾🛜

Codicote

Goat ✔
77 High Street, SG4 8XE
☎ (01438) 820475 ⊕ thegoatinn.co.uk
Adnams Ghost Ship; Greene King Abbot; Sharp's Doom Bar; Timothy Taylor Landlord Ⓗ
This 16th-century farmhouse was converted into a pub in the 18th century. The cosy interior of this friendly locals' pub has retained its character and olde-worlde charm, and there is a large and comfortable beer garden. The pub is home to the annual Goatfest music festival as well as other community events. A former local CAMRA Community Pub of the Year. 🏴‍☠️◗♣P🐾

Coleman Green

John Bunyan
Coleman Green Lane, AL4 8ES (on country lane between B653 and B651) TL190126
☎ (01582) 832037 ⊕ johnbunyanpub.co.uk
3 Brewers of St. Albans Classic English Ale; Timothy Taylor Landlord; 2 changing beers (sourced nationally) Ⓗ
Fine, old-fashioned, family-run country pub dating back to 1932. It is named after the Baptist preacher (1628-1688) and author of The Pilgrim's Progress, who is believed to have stayed nearby on his travels. The walls and ceiling are festooned with china plates and jugs, with a roaring fire in winter. It is open all day from May to September, including bank holidays, and on Sunday evenings when the monthly quiz night held. Well-behaved dogs are welcome in both the pub and large garden. Q🏴‍☠️◗&♣P🐾🛜

Colney Heath

Crooked Billet Ⓛ
88 High Street, AL4 0NP
☎ (01727) 822128 ⊕ thecrookedbilletpub.com
Fuller's London Pride; Tring Side Pocket for a Toad; Young's London Special Ⓗ
Popular and friendly cottage-style village pub dating back over 200 years. A genuine free house, it stocks three beers from national, regional and microbreweries. A wide selection of good-value home-made food is served at lunchtimes and Friday and Saturday evenings. Summer barbeques and Saturday events are held occasionally. This is a favourite stop-off for walkers on the many local footpaths. Families are welcome in the bar until 9pm, and in the large garden, where there is play equipment. 🏴‍☠️◗♣P🖩(305)🐾

Croxley Green

Sportsman Ⓛ
2 Scots Hill, WD3 3AD (at A412 jct with the Green)
☎ (01923) 443360
6 changing beers (sourced nationally; often New River, Paradigm, Vale) Ⓗ
A family-run community pub with friendly, welcoming, service, providing a traditional pub atmosphere in a modern context. It serves up to six ever-changing guest ales, mostly from smaller breweries both local and from further afield. Two craft keg beers are sourced from the local Paradigm brewery. The dartboard and pool table are in frequent use. A rear patio offers comfortable outdoor seating. Croxley tube station is a short walk away. 🏴‍☠️♣P🖩(321)

Datchworth

Plough Ⓛ
5 Datchworth Green, SG3 6TL (on crossroads in centre of village)
☎ (01438) 813000
3 changing beers (sourced nationally) Ⓗ
Small, single-bar free house on the edge of Datchworth Green sporting an ever-changing selection of real ales including LocAle. This is a real locals' pub at the hub of the village and all are made to feel welcome. The 'secret' garden is a real suntrap in the summer months and features a well-used pétanque piste. Darts and pétanque teams meet here regularly. 🏴‍☠️♣◗P🖩(379)🐾🛜

Green Tye

Prince of Wales
Much Hadham, SG10 6JP (Green Tye is well signposted, but sat nav is recommended) TL444184
☎ (01279) 842139 ⊕ thepow.co.uk
Abbeydale Moonshine; Wadworth Henry's IPA; 1 changing beer (sourced locally) Ⓗ
A traditional rural local that is the centre of social life in the village. Opening hours are variable and the pub will stay open until 11pm if there is custom, or meetings and other events taking place. It is best to call in advance to make sure it is open. A beer festival is held over the May Day weekend. Q🕏🏴‍☠️&P🐾🛜

Harpenden

Cross Keys ★ Ⓛ ✔
39 High Street, AL5 2SD (opp war memorial)
☎ (01582) 763989
Timothy Taylor Landlord; Tring Side Pocket for a Toad; 1 changing beer (sourced nationally; often Tring) Ⓗ
A warm welcome awaits you at this two-bar pub, a regular entry in the Guide. The pub has retained its traditional charm, with a rare, fine pewter bar top, flagstone floors and oak-beamed ceiling. In spring and

summer you can enjoy a drink in the large, pleasantly secluded rear garden, and in autumn or winter savour your beer in front of the fire in the public bar.
Q❄☺❀≉♣⊟❀🐾❞

Marquis of Granby

31 Marquis Lane, AL5 5AE (at bottom of Crabtree Ln where it joins Marquis Ln)
☎ (01582) 713372 ⊕ omgmog.pub
Adnams Ghost Ship; Fuller's London Pride; Sharp's Doom Bar; 1 changing beer (sourced locally) Ⓗ
A pleasant neighbourhood local located by the River Lea. A guest changing beer from the Tring brewery range rotates with the regular beers served. The pub attracts many diners who come to enjoy the lunchtime meals and evening sharing tapas platters. A morning café serves breakfasts, pastries and coffees at the weekend.
Q❄☺♿≉♣P⊟❀🐾❞

Hemel Hempstead

Full House Ⓛ ✓

128 Marlowes, HP1 1EZ
☎ (01442) 265512
Greene King IPA; Sharp's Doom Bar; 6 changing beers (sourced nationally; often Mad Squirrel, Tring, Vale) Ⓗ
This Wetherspoon establishment was once an Odeon cinema and later a bingo hall, and the recent refurbishment pays homage to the building's history by showcasing the eye-catching art deco features. The 18 cask lines feature local ales alongside an extensive can and bottle range in fridges, and craft keg taps. There is a large food menu. Q❄☺❀◑♣⊟🐾❞

Heronsgate

Land of Liberty, Peace & Plenty Ⓛ

Long Lane, WD3 5BS (jct of M25, head W from Rickmansworth, ¾ mile on right) TQ023949
☎ (01923) 282226 ⊕ landoflibertypub.com
6 changing beers (sourced nationally; often Redemption, Tring, XT) Ⓗ
Welcoming pub just off the M25, popular with walkers, cyclists, locals and real ale enthusiasts. It has historic connections to the Chartists who had a short-lived rural community nearby. Up to six microbrewery beers are usually offered and cover a range of styles and strengths. Real ciders and a range of malt whiskies are stocked. Beer festivals, tastings and charity events are held throughout the year. Bar snacks are available all day. There is a large outside pavilion for families.
❀♣♠P⊟⊟(R2)🐾❞

Hertford

Black Horse Ⓛ ✓

29-31 West Street, SG13 8EZ
☎ (01992) 583630 ⊕ theblackhorse.biz
6 changing beers (sourced nationally) Ⓗ
A community-focused, timbered free house, dating from 1642 and situated in one of Hertford's most attractive streets, near the start of the Cole Green Way. Six real ales are available from around Britain, including one from Hertfordshire. The food menu features game and homemade curries, pies and daily specials. The well-kept garden includes a separate and safe children's area and a summer pizza oven. The pub has its own RFU-affiliated rugby team, and is handy for Hertford Town FC.
☺❀◑♣⊟🐾❞

Hertford Club

Lombard House, Bull Plain, SG14 1DT
☎ (01992) 421422 ⊕ hertford.club
3 changing beers (sourced nationally) Ⓗ
Dating from the 15th century but with later additions, Lombard House, on the River Lea, was built as an English hall house and is one of the oldest buildings in Hertford. It has been the home of this private members' club since 1897. CAMRA members are welcome and may be signed in on production of a membership card. You will find two or three changing beers and real cider, which can be enjoyed in the delightful walled garden and riverside terrace. Home-cooked food is served at lunchtimes and on Friday evenings. ☺❀◑≉(East)♣♠⊟⊟🐾❞♫

Old Barge

2 The Folly, SG14 1QD (ask for Folly Island and you'll find the Old Barge)
☎ (01992) 581871 ⊕ theoldbarge.com
Marston's 61 Deep; 3 changing beers (sourced nationally) Ⓗ
A free house on Folly Island, pleasantly situated canalside on the River Lea, offering a selection of ales – sometimes including a dark brew – and a range of ciders and perries. Locally sourced home-cooked food is served all day, with roasts on Sundays. There is a music quiz on the last Thursday of the month. The Spring Fling music festival takes place on the second May bank holiday Monday. Look out for the annual duck race on Easter Monday. ☺❀◑≉(East)♣🐾❞

Old Cross Tavern Ⓛ

8 St Andrew Street, SG14 1JA
☎ (01992) 381871 ⊕ oldcrosstavern.com
Timothy Taylor Landlord; 5 changing beers (sourced nationally) Ⓗ
Superb town free house offering a friendly welcome. Up to six real ales, including a dark beer of some distinction, come from brewers large and small, and there is a fine choice of bottle-conditioned Belgian beers. No TV or music here, just good old-fashioned conversation. Locally made pork pies and Scotch eggs are available.
Q≉(North)♣🐾❞

White Horse ★

33 Castle Street, SG14 1HH
☎ 07803 878821 ⊕ white-horse-hertford.co.uk
Dark Star Hophead; Fuller's London Pride, ESB; 1 changing beer (sourced nationally) Ⓗ
A charming, old, timber-framed building with two downstairs bars and additional rooms upstairs, one featuring bar billiards and darts, others where children are welcome. There is a small patio to the rear and benches at the front. This is a pub full of conversation and good beer, and has been identified by CAMRA as having a regionally important historic pub interior. Customers can bring their vinyl records to play in the upstairs 'Vinyl Room'. Dogs are welcome.
Q❄☺≉(East)♣♠⊟🐾❞

High Wych

Rising Sun

High Wych Road, CM21 0HZ
☎ (01279) 724099
4 changing beers (often Oakham, Tring) Ⓖ
Friendly village local, popular with locals and walkers. It has never used handpumps; the range of four or five beers are served on gravity, often featuring East Anglian breweries such as Tring, Adnams and Oakham. Although recently refurbished, the original character has been preserved, with a stone floor, attractive fireplace and

wood panelling. The pub holds an annual vegetable competition. Parking is in the village hall car park opposite. Q❀♣P🚽(347)❀

Hitchin

BB's Bar

12 Bridge Street, SG5 2DE
☎ (01462) 656084 ⊕ bbsbar.net
Fuller's London Pride; Oakham JHB, Citra; 3 changing beers (sourced nationally) Ⓗ
A sports and music bar with a friendly pub atmosphere, named after blues legend BB King. The bar counter with cask taps is at the rear of front room, separate from the main bar counter. A second room at the back is only open when busy, but is also available for private functions. The beer range usually includes two Oakham beers plus two others. ➤❀❀ ♪

Half Moon Ⓛ

57 Queen Street, SG4 9TZ
☎ (01462) 453010 ⊕ thehalfmoonhitchin.com
Timothy Taylor Landlord; 9 changing beers (sourced nationally) Ⓗ
Friendly and welcoming one-bar pub dating from the 18th century. Nine ever-changing guest ales ensure that a variety of beer styles is available from breweries around the country. A selection of traditional ciders is also available, and there are bar snacks. Twice yearly beer festivals are held, plus regular and popular quiz and music nights. A former local CAMRA Pub of the Year and current Cider Pub of the Year. ➤❀◐▮♣♠P🚽❀🛜♪

Victoria

1 Ickleford Road, SG5 1TJ (E of town centre towards railway station)
☎ (01462) 432682 ⊕ thevictoriahitchin.com
Greene King IPA; St Austell Tribute; 4 changing beers (sourced nationally) Ⓗ
This popular and busy community pub dating from 1865 hosts a range of events, from quiz nights and live music to comedy and cabaret. An annual beer and cider festival and the Vic Fest music festival are also held here. Two regular Greene King beers are available, plus four guest beers. Good-value home-made modern British food is served every day, including Sunday roasts and regular pie nights. The historic barn is available for community use and live events. ➤❀◐▮▲🚽🛜♪

Ickleford

Plume of Feathers ✅

Upper Green, SG5 3YD
☎ (01462) 455953
Greene King Abbot; Sharp's Doom Bar; Woodforde's Wherry; 1 changing beer (sourced nationally) Ⓗ
The recently refurbished Plume of Feathers has been a traditional village pub since around 1762 and continues to be closely involved in community events. It stands just off the Hitchin to Bedford bus route and is reported to be the only pub in Britain that has a stream running through the cellar. It has a secluded beer garden. ➤❀◐▮♣P🚽(9A) ❀

Kings Langley

Saracen's Head Ⓛ ✅

47 High Street, WD4 9HU (on main road through village)
☎ (01923) 400144 ⊕ saracensheadkingslangley.co.uk
Timothy Taylor Landlord; Tring Side Pocket for a Toad; 1 changing beer (sourced locally; often Tring) Ⓗ

Dating from 1619, this popular free house consists of a single bar with low ceilings and a large open fire. The bar has a good choice of beers and wines, and is noted for its gin and whisky offering. Food is served weekday lunchtimes; there are reductions for senior citizens and 'bottomless brunch' days. Darts are played on Tuesdays and there is a largescreen TV showing major sporting events. ➤❀◐●▮(501,508)❀🛜

Knebworth

Lytton Arms

Park Lane, SG3 6QB
☎ (01438) 812312 ⊕ thelyttonarms.co.uk
Abbeydale Daily Bread; Brancaster Brancaster Best; Woodforde's Wherry; 4 changing beers (sourced nationally) Ⓗ
A 19th-century pub adjacent to the Knebworth House estate. It was built for Hawkes & Company of Bishop's Stortford, whose original logo may still be seen in the pub sign's wrought ironwork. Four house beers are supplemented by a changing mix from regional and microbrewers. Home-made food is available every day. Live music features on Friday evenings. Outside is a decked patio and garden. ➤❀◐▮♣P🚽(44,45)❀♪

Station

1 Station Approach, SG3 6AT
☎ (01438) 579504 ⊕ stationpubknebworth.com
Shepherd Neame Spitfire; 3 changing beers (sourced nationally) Ⓗ
An attractively refurbished pub next to the railway station. Now owned by the local parish council, it was reopened after a lengthy campaign that saved it from residential development. Four cask ales are available, covering a range of styles, and delicious food is served every day. ➤❀◐▮⇌P❀🛜

Letchworth Garden City

Garden City Brewery & Bar Ⓛ

22 The Wynd, SG6 3EN (in a pedestrian street off Station Rd to the N and Leys Ave to the S)
☎ 07939 401359 ⊕ gardencitybrewery.co.uk
House beer (by Garden City Brewery); 8 changing beers (sourced nationally) Ⓖ
An award-winning, friendly, family-run brew-bar in a converted café on a charming pedestrianised street. All ales are served on gravity, normally four of the brewery's own brews, which are only available here and at local festivals, plus four guest beers. There is also a large selection of local and other UK ciders. Locally produced bar snacks are on offer. Outside is a paved beer garden with a weatherproof awning. The bar has a regular events programme. It is five minutes' walk from the station. Q➤❀❀⇌●P🚽❀🛜♪

London Colney

Bull Ⓛ

Barnet Road, AL2 1QU
☎ (01727) 823160 ⊕ thebullpublondoncolney.co.uk
St Austell Tribute; Timothy Taylor Landlord; 2 changing beers (sourced nationally) Ⓗ
A lovely 17th-century timbered building near the River Colne, offering a range of real ales. It has a cosy lounge featuring an original fireplace and a large public bar with a dartboard and TV. Evening events include live music sessions. Good value home-made meals are served Monday to Saturday lunchtimes and evenings, with breakfast on Saturday and a roast on Sunday. Outside is a children's play area. ❀◐▮♣P🚽❀🛜♪

Oxhey

Villiers Arms
108 Villiers Road, WD19 4AJ
☎ (01923) 448848
Timothy Taylor Landlord; 2 changing beers (sourced nationally; often Butcombe, Tring) ⊞
Traditional, family-run village pub, popular with the local community. The entrance leads straight into the single small bar, with a lounge area around the corner decorated with vintage advertising posters and other memorabilia. The pub is cosy in the evenings and has a light, airy feel in bright weather. The patio and beer garden provide extra space for the warmer months. Entertainment includes occasional live music and a regular quiz, normally on the first Monday of the month.
Q ॐ ❀ ≠(Bushey) ⊖(Bushey) ♣ ☐ ❀ 🤁

Potters Bar

Admiral Byng ✓
186-192 Darkes Lane, EN6 1AF (corner of Byng Drive)
☎ (01707) 645484
Greene King Abbot; Ruddles Best Bitter; Sharp's Doom Bar; 6 changing beers (sourced nationally) ⊞
A friendly community Wetherspoon pub with a display of two model sailing ships and other memorabilia celebrating the exploits and death of Admiral Byng who was executed for 'failing to do his utmost' to save Minorca from falling to the French in 1756 (the family estate is located nearby). In summer the frontage of the pub is opened onto the street, with additional seating provided. There is a good choice of real ciders.
ॐ❀◑&≠♣☐🤁

Cask & Stillage ✓
19 High Street, EN6 5AJ
☎ (01707) 656725
2 changing beers (sourced nationally) ⊞
This single-bar local is well supported by the local community. Inside is an inglenook fireplace and interesting display cabinets, as well as three TVs showing sport. There is a large beer garden with three TVs, also for watching sport. The pub can get busy at weekends. It specialises in Thai food, and there is karaoke every Saturday evening from 9pm. ॐ❀◑&♣P☐❀🤁♪

Preston

Red Lion ⃒
The Green, SG4 7UD (on the green at crossroads)
☎ (01462) 459585 ⊕ theredlionpreston.co.uk
Timothy Taylor Landlord; 4 changing beers (sourced nationally) ⊞
This attractive free house stands on the village green and was the first community-owned pub in Great Britain. There is an ever-changing list of beers, many of which are from small breweries. Fresh home-made food is prepared, with many of the ingredients sourced locally. The pub hosts the village cricket teams. A regular winner of local CAMRA Pub of the Year and a former regional Pub of the Year. It is also the holder of a CAMRA 50th anniversary golden award. Q ॐ ❀ ◑ ♣ ❀ P ☐ (88)❀🤁♪

Redbourn

Cricketers ⃒
East Common, AL3 7ND
☎ (01582) 620612 ⊕ thecricketersofredbourn.co.uk
Timothy Taylor Landlord; Tring Side Pocket for a Toad; 1 changing beer (sourced locally) ⊞

A gastropub serving three real ales from its tastefully modern small front bar. The back bar functions as a restaurant, serving modern pub classics. There are also three dining pods outside. The pub is opposite Redbourn Cricket Club and it is a delight to be able to watch cricket from there on a summer's day drinking a good pint. Next door is Redbourn Museum, which is open at weekends.
Q ॐ ❀ ◑ &P☐(46,307) ❀ 🤁

Rickmansworth

Wishful Drinking
124 High Street, WD3 1AB
☎ 07708 629862 ⊕ wishfuldrinking.co.uk
1 changing beer (sourced nationally) Ⓖ
A converted bottle shop-cum-bar in Rickmansworth High Street with real ale, craft keg and cider. The front part of the building is their bottle shop, with the back part having a small bar. One real ale is available on gravity from the cellar; takeaways are also available. It holds Meet the Brewer and open mic sessions.
Q ॐ ≠⊖(Rickmansworth) ❀❀🤁

St Albans

Boot Inn ⃒ ✓
4 Market Place, AL3 5DG
☎ (01727) 857533 ⊕ thebootstalbans.co.uk
Harvey's Sussex Best Bitter; St Austell Tribute; Timothy Taylor Landlord; 3 changing beers (sourced nationally) ⊞
Grade II-listed, city-centre, one-bar pub dating back to 1422. The historic clock tower stands outside the front door, and the abbey and Verulamium Park are nearby. Internal features include a low ceiling and a real fire. Five real ales are served, and still ciders are available on handpump. Home-made food is all locally sourced. Families are welcome until 6pm. ॐ◑&☐☐❀🤁♪

Garibaldi ✓
61 Albert Street, AL1 1RT
☎ (01727) 894745 ⊕ garibaldistalbans.co.uk
Fuller's Oliver's Island, London Pride, ESB; Gale's HSB; 1 changing beer (sourced nationally) ⊞
A fine example of a back-street local, situated in the heart of Sopwell. It is named after the 19th-century Italian patriot who allegedly lodged in St Albans while in exile. The friendly bar staff serve an extensive range of Fuller's ales (the landlord has previously won the Fuller's Master Cellarman award). Home-cooked roasts are served on Sunday (booking advised). This is a genuine community pub, hosting various charity events. Three TVs (one outside in the garden) show live sports events.
ॐ❀◑&≠(Abbey) ♣☐❀🤁

Great Northern ⃒ ✓
172 London Road, AL1 1PQ
☎ (01727) 730867 ⊕ greatnorthernpub.co.uk
Marston's Pedigree; 4 changing beers (sourced nationally) ⊞
This independent, Grade II-listed pub reopened in 2015 after significant renovation. A rotating range of cask beers includes at least one local Hertfordshire ale. It serves a menu of good-quality British classic dishes and Sunday roasts. There are occasional brewery tap takeovers. Quiz nights are held on Tuesday, and a music night on the first Wednesday of each month. There is a large garden with heated marquee. An annual summer beer festival is held in June/July with other ad hoc beer festivals hosted throughout the year.
ॐ❀◑&≠(City) ❀☐(357,602) ❀🤁

Lower Red Lion L

34-36 Fishpool Street, AL3 4RX
☎ (01727) 855669 ⊕ thelowerredlion.co.uk
**Tring Side Pocket for a Toad; 4 changing beers
(sourced nationally)** ⊞
Classic Grade II-listed pub located in a conservation area
between the city centre and the site of Roman
Verulamium in one of St Albans' most picturesque
streets. The Lower Red was an early champion of
CAMRA's values in the real ale revival movement and
continues to stock quality real ales, ciders and perries.
Home-cooked food is served at lunchtimes and weekday
evenings. Beer festivals are held in May/June and
August. Children are not admitted. ❀☎◖❶P🖫❀🛜♫

Mermaid

98 Hatfield Road, AL1 3RL
☎ (01727) 845700
**Nethergate Suffolk County Best Bitter; Oakham Citra;
4 changing beers (sourced nationally)** ⊞
Welcoming community pub with a diverse clientele, a
short walk from the city centre and railway station. It
serves an interesting and regularly changing choice of
ales, usually including a stout or porter, plus many ciders
and bottled foreign beers. Beer festivals are held on the
May and August bank holiday weekends, and a cider
festival over the spring bank holiday. Live music is
performed on Sunday evenings. The pub boasts an
impressive covered garden. Winner of several local
CAMRA awards. ❀◖➔≷(City)♣❶P🖫❀🛜♫

Portland Arms

63 Portland Street, AL3 4RA
☎ (01727) 851463 ⊕ portlandarmsstalbans.com
**Fuller's London Pride, ESB; Gale's Seafarers Ale; 2
changing beers (sourced nationally)** ⊞
Traditional back-street local, tucked away in a residential
area and at the heart of its community. An open fire,
wood panelling and pictures of old St Albans give the
pub a warm and cosy feel. It offers a variety of live
music, quiz and entertainment nights. Food is served and
the Sunday roasts are renowned. Along with the Lower
Red Lion, Farriers Arms and Verulam, it forms an
excellent short pub trail in the shadow of the cathedral.
Q❀❀◖♣P🖫(34,57) ❀🛜♫

Robin Hood ▼ ✅

126 Victoria Street, AL1 3TG
☎ (01727) 856459 ⊕ robin-hood-st-albans.co.uk
**Harvey's Sussex Best Bitter; 2 changing beers
(sourced nationally)** ⊞
A warm and friendly single-bar, community pub, handy
for St Albans City station and St Albans City FC. A wide
selection of real cider is always available to complement
the ever-changing beer range. Entertainment includes a
jukebox, dartboard, table skittles, a selection of board
games and daily newspapers. There is also folk music on
Wednesday evenings. It has a secluded garden at the
back. Current local CAMRA Pub of the Year and Cider Pub
of the Year. ❀❀≷(City)♣❶🖫❀🛜♫

Royston Social Club

12 College Road, AL1 5ND
☎ (01727) 853656
**Fuller's London Pride; 3 changing beers (sourced
nationally)** ⊞
A friendly, long-established social club serving a part of
St Albans that has few other real ale options. A warm
welcome awaits card-carrying CAMRA members who can
use the bar facilities as guests. The four well-kept cask
beers usually include offerings from smaller local
brewers. A large function room with a stage
complements a smaller drinking area with a traditional

public bar atmosphere. It boasts the only bar billiards
table in town. CIU affiliated. Current local CAMRA Club of
the Year. ❀❀❀♣🖫(S1)❀🛜♫

White Hart Tap L ✅

4 Keyfield Terrace, AL1 1QJ
☎ (01727) 860974 ⊕ whitetharttap.co.uk
**Timothy Taylor Landlord; Tring Side Pocket for a Toad;
St Austell Tribute; Wadworth 6X; 2 changing beers
(sourced nationally)** ⊞
One-bar, back-street local featuring two beers free of tie,
including some from microbreweries. Good-value, home-
cooked food is served at lunchtimes and Monday to
Sunday evenings, with roasts on Sunday (booking
recommended) and occasional themed food nights. Quiz
night is Wednesday and is very popular. Other attractions
include summer barbecues and occasional beer festivals.
There is a heated, covered smoking area outside, plus
gazebos. A public car park is opposite the pub.
❀❀◖♿≷(City)♣❶🖫❀🛜

St Pauls Walden

Strathmore Arms L

Whitwell Road, SG4 8BT TL193222
☎ (01438) 871654 ⊕ thestrathmorearms.co.uk
**Tring Side Pocket for a Toad; 4 changing beers
(sourced nationally)** ⊞
This pub on the Bowes-Lyon estate has been serving
drinkers since 1882. It offers a constantly changing list of
guest beers, featuring obscure breweries. Unusual
bottled beers are also sold, along with real cider and
perry. A regular in the Guide since 1981, the pub has a
collection of Guides since 1976. It has a separate snug.
The pub may stay open longer than advertised if there is
demand. Occasional Sunday roasts and barbecues also
feature. Q❀❀◖▲♣P🖫❀🛜♫

Sandridge

Green Man ✅

31 High Street, AL4 9DD
☎ (01727) 854845 ⊕ greenmansandridge.co.uk
**Greene King Abbot; Sharp's Atlantic; Tring Side Pocket
for a Toad** Ⓖ
This community pub located in the centre of the village
extends a warm welcome to beer drinkers, with all ales
served directly from casks in the cellar located a few
steps along from the bar. Traditional, freshly cooked food
using locally sourced ingredients is available at
lunchtimes. The pub holds a quiz every Monday night. A
rear conservatory caters for small groups. Dogs are
welcome. The courtyard garden behind the pub is lovely
place to enjoy a summer sunset with your pint.
Q❀❀◖♣P🖫❀🛜

Sawbridgeworth

George IV L

Knight Street, CM21 9AT
☎ (01279) 723527
McMullen AK Original Mild, Country Bitter, IPA ⊞
A friendly, community-led pub near the town centre and
railway station, with two bars and a pleasant, paved
garden. Food is not served but the landlady is happy for
you to bring your own, with a nearby bakers a popular
choice. The local beer group, darts teams and bellringers
meet here, and charity quizzes are run frequently.
Q❀❀❀≷🖫(509,510) ❀

Stevenage

Broken Seal Tap Room

29B High Street, SG1 3AU (entrance on Basils Rd, at N end of High St)

☎ 07973 673040 ⏣ sixhillsbrewing.co.uk

3 changing beers (sourced nationally) Ⓖ

Stevenage's first brewpub was opened in 2019 as the Tap Room for Bog Brew brewery, subsequently renamed as Six Hills brewery. Their beers are brewed on site and usually served via KeyKeg, but guest beers often include two or three cask beers. There is also large range of bottled and canned beers to drink in or take away. Q❀❀&◆🖵♫

Chequers ✅

164 High Street, SG1 3LL

☎ (01438) 510332

4 changing beers (sourced nationally) Ⓗ

Friendly locals' pub situated between the old and new towns. There is an interesting old map of Stevenage on the wall and a newly refurbished beer garden. The pub offers one of the best ranges of real ales and ciders in Stevenage. Food is available from a mobile van in the car park at peak times. Q🍽❀&≠◆P❀🖵

Tring

Bell 𝕃

36-37 High Street, HP23 5AA

☎ (01442) 890673 ⏣ thebelltring.com

Farr Our Best Bitter, Porter; house beer (by Farr); 2 changing beers (often Farr) Ⓗ

A 17th-century coaching inn in the centre of Tring with period features and a large courtyard garden. It was reopened in 2023 by local brewery Farr Brew following a sympathetic refurbishment that manages to balance plush aesthetics with respect for the building's history. The pub serves up to five rotating Farr Brew ales with a noted daily food offering sourced from local ingredients. There are quiz nights every Tuesday and an open mic night on the first Monday of each month. 🍽❀❀&◆🖵(500)❀🖵♫

King's Arms 🍴 𝕃

King Street, HP23 6BE (corner of Queen St and King St)

SP921111

☎ (01442) 823318 ⏣ kingsarmstring.co.uk

Tring Side Pocket for a Toad, Moongazing; 3 changing beers (sourced nationally; often Oakham, Shepherd Neame, St Austell) Ⓗ

Dating from 1830, the 'pink pub', as it is affectionately known, is a Grade II-listed and family-owned and -run free house. The bar in the single room serves well-kept real ales and excellent, freshly-made meals, all produced in-house. There is a courtyard garden with servery from the bar. The Coach House adjoining – with bar – is used as a dining and function room. Live music and quiz nights are held regularly, plus an annual beer festival. Q🍽❀❀❶🖵🖵(500,501)❀🖵

Robin Hood 𝕃 ✅

1 Brook Street, HP23 5ED (jct B4635/B486)

☎ (01442) 824912 ⏣ therobinhoodtring.co.uk

Fuller's London Pride, ESB; 2 changing beers (sourced regionally; often Dark Star, Fuller's, Gale's) Ⓗ

Dating from the 16th century, this busy, welcoming community pub is in the centre of the ancient market town of Tring. The warming stove gives the pub a cosy feel, and there is an outdoor patio area for better weather. Fuller's beers dominate the six handpumps, with one regular guest ale from the brewery's wider portfolio (e.g. Dark Star). Tasty food is a big draw for

locals, alongside weekly quizzes for charities, for which this pub has raised considerable sums.
Q❀❶◆🖵(61,500)❀🖵

Ware

Crooked Billet ✅

140 Musley Hill, SG12 7NL (via New Rd from High St)

☎ (01920) 462516 ⏣ thecrookedbilletware.co.uk

3 changing beers (sourced nationally) Ⓗ

Friendly gem of a traditional community pub, tastefully refurbished in 2021 and well worth the 15-minute walk up New Road and Musley Hill from the town centre. Its two small bars feature TV sport and darts. It serves a varying range of two to three ales, often including a mild, porter or stout at weekends. Outside there are tables to the front and rear of the pub.
❀◆🖵(395,M2)❀🖵

Watford

Two Trees Micro 🍴

18 Vicarage Road, WD18 0EH (in the pedestrian area at NE end of Vicarage Rd) ⏣ twotreesmicro.com

3 changing beers (sourced nationally) Ⓗ

A recently opened small micropub with four handpumps serving three real ales and a cider, plus four craft keg beers. Due to licensing restrictions, the bar has to close at 10.30pm during the week and 9.30pm on Sunday (though it may open until later if people arrive by 9.30pm). Closed Mondays and Tuesdays. Further restrictions may apply on Watford FC match days. There is a small outside drinking area at the front. Basic pub snacks are available. Q≠(High Street)◆🖵

Welham Green

North Mymms Social Club

38 Station Road, AL9 7PG

☎ (01707) 263275

2 changing beers (sourced nationally) Ⓗ

A warm and friendly village social club. It is members only but card-carrying CAMRA members are welcome on signing in. Knock on the door and wait for admittance. Two cask beers are usually available from a rotating list of 12. There are two full-size snooker tables upstairs, and pool and darts are popular in the main bar area, with teams competing in local leagues. The club hosts a monthly Saturday night quiz, and occasional live music on a Saturday evening. 🍽&≠◆P🖵🖵❀🖵♫

Wild Hill

Woodman

45 Wildhill Road, AL9 6EA (between A1000 and B158)

TL264068

☎ (01707) 642618 ⏣ thewoodman.uk

Greene King IPA, Abbot; 4 changing beers (sourced nationally) Ⓗ

A friendly and unpretentious rural village pub that is extremely community orientated. It is a staunch supporter of real ale, serving up to six ales including four guests. Lined, oversized glasses are available on request. The large garden is ideal in summer. Good pub grub is served at lunchtimes (Mon-Sat only). Look for God's Waiting Room – a good spot for a cosy drink. A multiple winner of local and county CAMRA Pub of the Year. 🍽❀◆P❀🖵

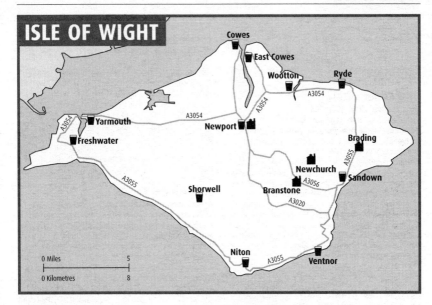

Cowes

Anchor Inn 🄛
1 High Street, PO31 7SA (opp Sainsbury's)
☎ (01983) 292823 ⊕ theanchorcowes.co.uk
Goddards Fuggle Dee-Dum; 1 changing beer (sourced nationally) 🄷
Originally the Three Trumpeters back in 1704, this pub is close to the Marina, tempting visiting yachtsman for their first pint ashore. A recent conversion has integrated the stables and added a pleasant beer garden. A good selection of beer is on offer, with one from the island and two or more guests ales available. The varied menu is served in prodigious quantities. Live entertainment features regularly. Accommodation is in seven comfortable rooms. ⍟⌂⊜⊕⊕⌂(1)⊛🛜♪

Duke of York 🄛 ✓
Mill Hill Road, PO31 7BT (towards floating bridge)
☎ (01983) 295171 ⊕ dukeofyorkcowes.co.uk
Timothy Taylor Landlord; 2 changing beers (sourced regionally; often Goddards, Yates') 🄷
Popular street-corner town pub with a reputation for interesting and appetising freshly prepared food. The charming interior features comfortable armchairs and memorabilia and signs celebrating Cowes and its association with yachting and the sea. There are more tables outside on the front terrace and a drinking area to the side. Well-priced accommodation is available for that cosy weekend away. Q⍟⌂⊜⊕⊕⌂(1)⊛🛜♪

Painters Arms 🄛 ✓
51 Cross Street, PO31 7TA
☎ (01983) 300977 ⊕ thepaintersarms.co.uk
Goddards Ale of Wight; Timothy Taylor Boltmaker; 1 changing beer (sourced nationally) 🄷
This superb building dates from 1903. With plenty of friendly banter at the bar, sport TV dominates and the beer garden also has TV. Additional outside tables can be found in Francki Place, named after the Polish captain whose destroyer ORP Blyskawica defended Cowes during air raids in 1942. The earlier Painters Arms stood at the head of Temperance Terrace, a renowned Cowes alleyway with its own community, now sadly a car park. ⍟⊜⌂(1) ⊛🛜♪

East Cowes

Ship & Castle 🄛
21 Castle Street, PO32 6RB
☎ (01983) 716230
3 changing beers (sourced regionally; often Adnams, Goddards, Island) 🄷
After several years this characterful, town-centre pub has returned as a free house, with three well-kept real ales on offer – even in winter. It is not overly large and you are assured a warm welcome and reasonable prices. Frequent and lively music sessions are hosted. It is handy for the ferry terminal and near the floating bridge to Cowes. ⍟⌂⊕⊕⌂(4,5)⊛♪

Freshwater

Red Lion 🄛
Church Place, PO40 9BP SZ34508738
☎ (01983) 754925 ⊕ redlion-freshwater.co.uk
St Austell Proper Job; 3 changing beers (sourced nationally; often Butcombe, Renegade, Timothy Taylor) 🄷
Former three-bar coaching inn dating back to the 11th century, now converted into one large bar but still retaining much of its character. It is situated in the most picture-postcard area of Freshwater, in the church square and by the Causeway, and enjoys views of the River Yar towards Yarmouth. The pub is noted for its fine food (diners are advised to book ahead). It may close earlier in winter. A guide for a walk to the Wheatsheaf in Yarmouth is available. Q⊛⊕P⌂(7,12)⊛🛜

Vine Inn
School Green Road, PO40 9UP
☎ (01983) 752959 ⊕ vineinnfreshwater.co.uk
Fuller's London Pride; Gale's Seafarers Ale; 1 changing beer (sourced nationally; often Fuller's, Gale's) 🄷
Close to Freshwater Bay and the Needles, this splendid former George Gale public house has an open fire and a separate dining area. There is a pleasant garden to the front with a patio under the actual vine. It stocks the full range of the Fuller's pint bottles. It has a good reputation for food, which is served all day in the summer, with an

interesting selection on the specials board and a Tuesday curry night. Also features occasional live music.
Q☎🏠🕽🍴👶♣P🚃(7,12) 🍺 🛜 ♫

Newport

Bargeman's Rest 🅻

Little London Quay, PO30 5BS

☎ (01983) 525828 🌐 bargemansrest.com

Goddards Fuggle Dee-Dum; Ringwood Razorback, Fortyniner; 3 changing beers (often Andwell, Marston's, Wychwood) 🄷

This locally owned pub has previously been an animal feed store, and a sail and rigging loft for the barge fleet that once used the river. The huge bar room provides intimate drinking areas and the nautical memorabilia, decor and ambience are what you would expect from a traditional, well-seasoned pub. The outdoor drinking area is only a few feet from the bustling River Medina. Beer and food are consistently good and the range varied. Live entertainment is hosted most nights.
☎🏠🕽👶P🚃🍺🛜♫

Man in the Moon 🅻 ✅

16-17 St James Street, PO30 5HB

☎ (01983) 530126

Greene King Abbot; Sharp's Doom Bar; 7 changing beers (often Goddards, Island) 🄷

Opened in 2014, this impressive Wetherspoon conversion of the former Congregational Church maintains the character of the original while adding sympathetic extensions. The drinking/dining areas include an upstairs gallery and an outdoor area where dogs and children are welcome. Although a food-led pub, the beers are well kept, with a good selection of local brews featuring among the large rotating selection. A cider is often available on handpump. ☎🏠🕽👶🚃🍺🛜

Newport Ale House 🍺 🅻

24A Holyrood Street, PO30 5AZ

☎ 07708 018051

3 changing beers (sourced nationally) 🄶

This listed building has previously traded as a hairdresser, undertakers and posting house and stables. It is the island's smallest pub, recalling the days when there were many such establishments in Newport. Hugely popular with all generations, conversation comes easy and it can get very crowded and noisy. Live music is often hosted, including on a Sunday afternoon. The beer choice is always interesting and varied. No meals, but snacks are high quality. Current local CAMRA Pub of the Year. Q☎🏠🚃🛜♫

Niton

No.7 🅻

High Street, PO38 2AZ

☎ (01983) 730280

Butcombe Original; Greene King Abbot; 1 changing beer (often Shepherd Neame, Yates') 🄷

No.7 opened when the village inn closed for a short time, and has since become the hub of village life, also serving as a post office, newsagent, confectioner and tea room. Titanic Plum Porter and local specialities are regular visitors. Pizzas from the wood-fired oven are popular. A unique establishment with an excellent garden and patio. Closing time is dependent on custom.
Q☎🏠🕽🚃(6)

Ryde

Castle Inn

164 High Street, PO33 2HT

☎ (01983) 613684 🌐 castleinnisleofwight.co.uk

Fuller's London Pride; Gale's HSB; 1 changing beer (often Fuller's) 🄷

Thomas Vanner, who operated the Ryde to Newport stagecoach, opened this large public house in 1850. The fine building stands proud at the junction with the High Street, and owing to its impressive etched windows is a Grade II-listed building, which may have saved it from demolition or conversion in the mid-1980s. It has enjoyed a long-standing reputation for its ales; HSB is a best seller. ☎🏠🛘(Esplanade)👶🚃(9,4)🍺🛜

S. Fowler & Co 🅻

41-43 Union Street, PO33 2LF

☎ (01983) 812112

10 changing beers (sourced nationally) 🄷

Although not the most charismatic pub in the Wetherspoon chain, this converted drapery store offers a constantly changing range of well-kept beers. Its name was suggested by the local CAMRA branch – not only is it the name of the former store, but also that of the first local CAMRA chairman and revered early campaigner. The family-friendly food area is upstairs. It is in the centre of town, with a bus stop conveniently outside.
Q☎🏠🕽👶🛘(Esplanade)🚃🛜

Solent Inn

7 Monkton Street, PO33 1JW

☎ (01983) 564265 🌐 solentinnryde.co.uk

Goddards Fuggle Dee-Dum; St Austell Proper Job; 1 changing beer (sourced nationally) 🄷

Excellent street-corner local with a warm, welcoming atmosphere. Parts of this handsome pub date back to medieval times. It originally fronted the sea before the reclamation of land (hence the name). Look out for the significantly sloping floor. Meal times can change depending on the season. There is live music at the weekend. Q☎🏠🕽👶🛘(Esplanade)👶🚃🍺♫

Star Coffee & Ale House

40 High Street, PO33 2HT

☎ (01983) 722658 🌐 ryde.cafe

2 changing beers (sourced regionally) 🄷

This handsome Victorian building on the corner of Star Street and the High Street dates back to 1873. It is a well-supported typical town local with a friendly, welcoming character, and is now established with new landlords and a bright outlook after a complete refurbishment during Covid lockdowns. There are up to four beers available in the busy season and a selection of craft beers. Live music features some evenings.
☎🕽🛘(St Johns Road)👶🚃🍺🛜♫

Sandown

Castle Inn 🅻

12-14 Fitzroy Street, PO36 8HY (off High St)

☎ (01983) 403169 🌐 sandowncastle.co.uk

Gale's HSB; Goddards Fuggle Dee-Dum; Wychwood Hobgoblin Gold; 3 changing beers (sourced regionally; often Andwell, Hop Back, St Austell) 🄷

REAL ALE BREWERIES

Goddards 🍂 Branstone
Island Newport
Wight Knuckle 🍂 Brading
Yates' Newchurch

An excellent town free house and locals' pub. Six real ales are offered, including the best from local breweries. There is a children's room at the back and a patio for warm weather. The TV is only turned on for special events. Happy hour is popular, as is the Sunday quiz. Beer festivals are held twice a year, usually featuring local ales and cider. Home to crib and darts teams. Q❂❄❅♣️🚐(3,8)🏵️🐕🛜🎵

Culver Haven Inn 🅛

Culver Down, PO36 8QT (by the Monument on Culver Down) SZ63258565

☎ (01983) 406107 ⊕ culverhaven.com

2 changing beers (sourced nationally; often Fuller's, Goddards, Ringwood) 🅗

Cosy restaurant and pub perched on Culver Down overlooking Sandown Bay and Bembridge Harbour. The view back down the hill is spectacular. Nearby is the Culver Battery, an impressive remnant of the Napoleonic Wars and built to protect Portsmouth (opened regularly by the National Trust). The pub has an excellent and varied menu. Closed Monday, Tuesday and all of February. Q❂❅◗🅿️🏵️🛜

Shorwell

Crown Inn 🅛

Walkers Lane, PO30 3JZ

☎ (01983) 740293

Gale's HSB; Timothy Taylor Landlord; house beer (by Yates'); 1 changing beer (sourced locally; often Fuller's, Yates') 🅗

In the picturesque village of Shorwell is this 300-year-old hostelry offering real ales, always including one from Yates', and good home-cooked pub food. It is the perfect stop-off point for walkers, cyclists and nature lovers. On a hot summers day the garden is a delight, and the trout stream running through it attracts ducks in abundance, keeping adults and children amused. Opening hours and food times are reduced in the winter. Plenty of parking. Q❂❅◗⚹♣️🅿️🚐(12)🏵️🛜🎵

Ventnor

Crab & Lobster Tap 🅛

Grove Road, PO38 1TH

☎ (01983) 852311

Timothy Taylor Landlord; 2 changing beers (sourced nationally; often Goddards, Yates') 🅗

This lively and welcoming town pub is a convenient stop on the coastal path. Local ale is available all year, with additional ales occasionally stillaged on the bar for a beer festival. There is a quiz on Thursday and live sports on five TVs. If you're lucky, you might be there when one of the rings league matches is taking place – Ventnor has one of the few leagues in the country. There is a large public car park nearby. ❂◖♣️🐕🚐(3,6)🏵️🛜🎵

Spyglass Inn 🅛

The Esplanade, PO38 1JX

☎ (01983) 855338 ⊕ thespyglass.com

Ringwood Razorback, Fortyniner; 3 changing beers (sourced locally; often Andwell, Goddards, Yates') 🅗

A 19th-century ex-guesthouse at the western end of Ventnor Esplanade in a superb location overlooking the English Channel. The temptation has been avoided to knock all the rooms into one; instead, they have been incorporated into the overall layout. The inn has considerable character and boasts a large collection of seafaring memorabilia. Food includes local seafood as a speciality. Entertainment features most evenings and Sunday lunchtime. Families are welcome. The beer range may reduce to four in winter. The pub is wheelchair accessible and an accessible toilet is nearby along the esplanade. ❂❅🚐◗🅿️🏵️🛜🎵

Volunteer ★ 🅛

30 Victoria Street, PO38 1ES

☎ 07592 262325

Goddards Fuggle Dee-Dum; 4 changing beers (sourced regionally; often Goddards, Wychwood, Yates')

Built in 1866, the Volunteer is one of the smallest pubs on the island. This former winner of local CAMRA Pub of the Year has been tastefully refurbished. Up to five beers are available, including a local brew. No fruit machines, no video games, no children – this is a pure adult drinking house, and one of the few places where you can still play rings and enjoy a traditional games night. Closing time varies. Q♣️🚐(3,6)🏵️🎵

Wootton

Cedars

2 Station Road, PO33 4QU

☎ (01983) 882593 ⊕ cedarsisleofwight.co.uk

Fuller's London Pride; Gale's Seafarers Ale, HSB 🅗

This late-Victorian two-bar village local enjoys a prominent location at the top of Wootton High Street. It is a large pub, though curiously has one of the smallest front doors on the island. There is a children's room and a large garden with kids play area. The outdoor smoking area is adapted from a beautiful Victorian outbuilding. The menu is extensive and the friendly bar staff ensure a good atmosphere. Close to the steam railway terminus. ❂❅◗❄♣️🅿️🚐(4,9)🏵️🛜

Yarmouth

Wheatsheaf Inn 🅛

Bridge Road, PO41 0PH

☎ (01983) 638359 ⊕ wheatsheafyarmouth.co.uk

St Austell Proper Job; 3 changing beers (often Courage, Flack Manor, Purity) 🅗

This large, spacious old coaching inn is twinned with the popular Red Lion in Freshwater and is well worth a visit. It was taken over in lockdown and revamped by a genial host with a wealth of experience in the trade. It offers a new experience for drinkers: from the takeaway hatch on the side for lunchtime or evening snacks to the craft ale tasting area, with a secret entrance and a list of many unusual ales to sample. ❂❅◗⚹▲♣️🚐(7)🏵️🛜

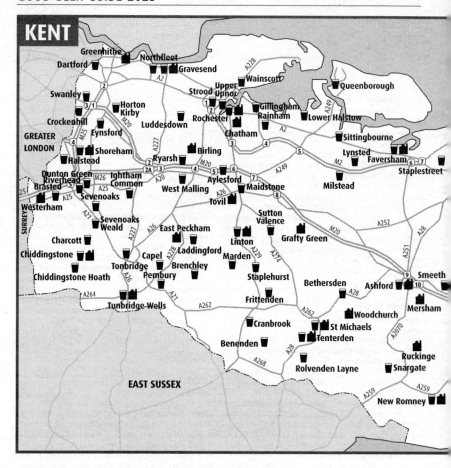

KENT

Greenhithe
Northfleet
Dartford
Gravesend
Swanley
Upper Upnor
Strood
Wainscott
Queenborough
Horton Kirby
Gillingham
Rainham
Crockenhill
Eynsford
Luddesdown
Rochester
Lower Halstow
GREATER LONDON
Shoreham
Chatham
Sittingbourne
Halstead
Birling
Lynsted
Faversham
Dunton Green
Riverhead
Brasted
Ryarsh
Ightham Common
Aylesford
Staplestreet
West Malling
Maidstone
Milstead
Sevenoaks
Tovil
SURREY
Westerham
Sevenoaks Weald
Sutton Valence
Charcott
East Peckham
Linton
Grafty Green
Chiddingstone
Capel
Laddingford
Marden
Chiddingstone Hoath
Tonbridge
Brenchley
Pembury
Staplehurst
Bethersden
Ashford
Smeeth
Mersham
Frittenden
Woodchurch
Tunbridge Wells
Cranbrook
St Michaels
Tenterden
Ruckinge
Snargate
Benenden
Rolvenden Layne
EAST SUSSEX
New Romney

Ashford

County Hotel ✓
10 High Street, TN24 8TD (at lower end of High St)
☎ (01233) 646891
Greene King Abbot; Ruddles Best Bitter; Sharp's Doom Bar; 4 changing beers (sourced nationally) Ⓗ
This pub was built around 1710, as a doctor's home and medical practice, becoming a hotel in the 19th century. It was acquired by Wetherspoons in 1988 and now has a spacious bar with three separate seating areas and a courtyard. Two real ciders are dispensed from polypins in the fridge. Food is available all day every day, and children are allowed in the dining area until 9pm. It holds summer and autumn national and international beer festivals. Q ➤ ❄ ◑ & ⇌ (International) 🖵 🛜

Matches Ⓛ
Unit 3, Elwick Place, Elwick Road, TN23 1AX
⊕ matchesashford.com
1 changing beer
This sports-themed bar opened in 2021 with many television screens showing domestic and international games. Darts, pool and shuffleboard can be played here. Self-pour taps are available at three of the tables, with cask beer available from the single handpump on the bar, while the fridge behing the bar is well stocked with a range of bottle and cans. A breakfast menu available on Saturday and Sunday from 10 to midday. ➤ ◑ & ⇌ (International) ♣ 🖵

Aylesford

Little Gem
19 High Street, ME20 7AX
☎ (01622) 715066
Goacher's Fine Light Ale Ⓖ, Gold Star Strong Ale Ⓗ; 2 changing beers (sourced locally; often Goacher's) Ⓖ
One of the smallest pubs in Kent, this Grade II-listed 12th-century building has been restored by local brewer Goacher's following a 10-year period of closure. As you enter beware the low doorway as well as the step down. A large inglenook fireplace provides winter warmth. The floor area is enhanced by a small mezzanine floor. Beer is dispensed from a handpump or by gravity feed from cooled casks above the bar. Snacks, cider and other drinks are also available. Q ❄ ● 🛏 ❄ 🛜 ♫

Benenden

Bull
The Street, TN17 4DE
☎ (01580) 240054 ⊕ thebullatbenenden.co.uk
Dark Star Hophead; Harvey's Sussex Best Bitter; Larkins Traditional Ale; 1 changing beer (sourced locally) Ⓗ
In one of the highest points of the Kent Weald, next to the picturesque village green stands a genuine 17th-century free house featuring fine chinoiserie windows. The bar area has wooden floors, exposed beams and a

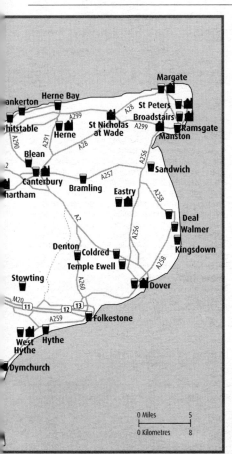

Timothy Taylor Boltmaker; 3 changing beers (sourced locally; often Musket, Ramsgate, Wantsum) 🍺
Traditional family pub, close to local bus routes, with an attractive newly renovated garden, conservatory dining area and a games room. The pub has pool, darts and bat and trap teams. The main bar has a log burner and a screen for sports. Four handpumps serve an excellent variety of ever-changing beers, often from local breweries. Good value food is served every day from noon to 8pm (4pm on Sun). 🛏️☆◐🅰️♣️Ⓟ🚌🐕🛜♪

Bramling

Haywain 🅛
Canterbury Road, CT3 1NB
☎ (01227) 720676 ⊕ thehaywainbramling.co.uk
Fuller's London Pride; Goacher's Real Mild Ale; 3 changing beers (sourced regionally; often Goacher's, Musket, Ramsgate) 🍺
Classic friendly country pub featuring hop bines, a cosy snug and a charity library where books are sold for 50p each. Traditional games include bat and trap, and there is a Wednesday crib night. Guest beers are usually from Kent breweries, and an annual beer festival is hosted in May in a marquee in the attractive garden. Excellent home-cooked food is served, made using local produce. Booking for meals is essential. The pub is closed on Mondays and Tuesdays. ☆◐♣️Ⓟ🚌(43,43A)🐕🛜

Brasted

Stanhope Arms 🅛 ✅
Church Road, TN16 1HZ
☎ (01959) 546829 ⊕ thestanhopearms.com
3 changing beers (sourced locally; often Bexley, Titsey, Westerham) 🍺
Tucked away from the village along a country lane leading to St Martin's church, the Stanhope offers a rotating range of three mostly local cask ales together with a Kentish cider from Charrington's. A good, locally-sourced, food range is available with Wednesday to Friday meal deals, a specials board and an extensive wine list. A large garden includes a well-equipped play area and a barn available for functions. Monthly jazz and blues jam sessions are held and quizzes organised on alternate Thursdays. 🛏️☆◐♿♣️Ⓟ🚌(1,401)🐕🛜♪

Brenchley

Halfway House 🍴 🅛 ✅
Horsmonden Road, TN12 7AX (½ mile SE of village)
☎ (01892) 722526 ⊕ halfwayhousebrenchley.co.uk
Goacher's Fine Light Ale, Gold Star Strong Ale; Kent Session Pale; Long Man Best Bitter; house beer (by Tonbridge); 4 changing beers (sourced locally; often Only With Love, Three Legs, Tonbridge) Ⓖ
Family-run since the landlord's parents acquired it in 2003 and approaching legendary status after 20 years in this Guide, this rustic and hop-strewn pub has something for everyone and attracts visitors from far and wide. The extensive gardens include a children's play area and outdoor bar which are perfect for hosting annual bank holiday beer festivals. Up to 12 beers are drawn direct from the cask along with three Kentish ciders. Hearty fare is served daily and campervans are welcome in the car park. Q🛏️☆◐♣️Ⓟ🚌(297)🐕🛜♪

large inglenook fireplace. There is a separate dining room but food is also served in the bar. Excellent food is produced using local suppliers where possible. The Sunday carvery is popular (booking advisable). Occasional live music and quiz nights are held. 🛏️☆◐♣️Ⓟ🚌(297)🐕🛜♪

Bethersden

George 🅛
The Street, TN26 3AG (off the A28 between Ashford and Tenterden, in the centre of the village)
☎ 07354 849122 ⊕ georgecommunity.com
Harvey's Sussex Best Bitter; 2 changing beers (sourced locally; often Long Man, Romney Marsh) 🍺
Following the pub's closure in 2020, local residents came together to form The George Community with the aim of saving it. After refurbishment, the pub reopened – initially as a wet pub with four handpumps – but food is now available. A proper village pub, it also opens as a café from 10.30 to 4 on Wednesday to Saturday. Buses from Ashford and Tenterden stop outside. 🛏️☆♣️Ⓟ🚌(2)🛜

Blean

Royal Oak 🅛 ✅
140 Blean Common, CT2 9JJ
☎ (01227) 760149 ⊕ theroyaloakblean.co.uk

Broadstairs

Magnet
37 Albion Street, CT10 1NE
☎ (01843) 600527
4 changing beers (sourced regionally; often Bexley, Iron Pier, Kent) Ⓗ
Just off the High Street, this alehouse features Kentish ales and ciders, with others from further afield, including craft beer. A large beer bottle chandelier sets the scene. The beer and cider-loving owners are also passionate about live music and hold monthly jam sessions. Corner picture windows flood light into all areas and the wood stove creates winter warmth and cosiness. An eclectic range of tables and seating provide comfortable spaces for friends, family, or couples. ❀❦♣♠🍴❀♪

Royston ▼
2 The Broadway, CT10 2AD
4 changing beers (often Kent, Pitchfork, Vocation) Ⓖ
An uber-stylish micropub with an eclectic mix of Victorian, steampunk and Art Deco themes – the toilet is boutique standard and photogenic. Three to five local and national cask ales include high-end brewers, while an extensive wines and spirits menu, alcohol-free choices and barista-quality espresso coffee ensure all are catered for. Outside seating is available in good weather. The pub is often open later than advertised if it is busy. Local CAMRA Pub of the Year winner 2023. ❀❦♣♠🍴❀

Canterbury

Bell & Crown ⓛ
10-11 Palace Street, CT1 2DZ
☎ (01227) 784639
Long Man Best Bitter; 3 changing beers (sourced locally; often Canterbury Ales, Hop Fuzz, Tonbridge) Ⓗ
Traditional city-centre wood-panelled pub with an ever-changing range of local beers. The seating in front of the pub gives a superb view of Canterbury Cathedral, and is enjoyed by locals and visitors alike. The flint walls of the ancient King's School are opposite. Palace Street is part of the King's Mile and has many small independent shops. The classic jukebox means the pub is lively at weekends and the cosy atmosphere makes it a lunchtime favourite. ❀◗⇌(West)🚆❀♪

Eight Bells
34 London Road, CT2 8LN
☎ (01227) 454794
Young's London Original Ⓗ
A small, traditional local dating from 1708 and rebuilt in 1902, retaining original embossed windows and outside toilets, and decorated with memorabilia. There is a quiz, usually on the third Wednesday of the month. Four darts teams play every week and their trophies are on display. The only food is a Sunday lunchtime roast, for which booking is advisable. There is an attractive small walled garden and a comfortable heated smoking area. ❦❀◗⇌(West)♣❀☀♪

Foundry Brew Pub ⓛ
77 Stour Street, CT1 2NR (just off High St)
☎ (01227) 455899 🌐 thefoundrycanterbury.co.uk
Canterbury Brewers & Distillers Foundryman's Gold, Foundry Torpedo, Streetlight Porter Ⓗ
Home to Canterbury Brewers & Distillers, four ales are usually on tap, and a wide range of keg-conditioned beers, all brewed on the premises. The taster palette of five third-pints is popular. Multi award winning whisky,

vodka, rum and gin are also made here, and two of the whiskies have won best in England recently. Double doors from the bar open into the attractive brewery and restaurant area, which is available for functions and brewery tours. Food is served every day. A former winner of Kent Tourism Pub of the Year. ❦❀◗⇌♿⇌(East)♣🚆❀

Monument
37 St Dunstan's Street, CT2 8BZ
☎ (01227) 451666 🌐 themonumentcanterbury.com
Dark Star Hophead; 2 changing beers (often Canterbury Ales, Cellar Head, Wantsum) Ⓗ
The pub was established in 1803 but the building itself is 400 years old. With St Dunstan's church just opposite, the street outside was the main route into Canterbury from London for over a millennium. The pub name comes from a large wooden crucifix which once stood outside, a landmark for pilgrims to Canterbury. The pub has three bars, including a cosy snug. Piano music plays on Thursday evenings and Sunday lunchtimes, and there is a quiz every Monday. A tempting food menu is served. ❦❀◗⇌(West)♣🚆❀♪

New Inn
19 Havelock Street, CT1 1NP (off ring road near St Augustine's Abbey)
☎ (01227) 464584 🌐 newinncanterbury.co.uk
7 changing beers (often Kent, Oakham, Ramsgate) Ⓗ
A Victorian back-street terraced pub a few minutes' walk from the cathedral, St Augustine's Abbey and the bus station. The welcoming main bar has a cosy wood-burner, a jukebox and a changing range of seven cask

REAL ALE BREWERIES

Breakwater ✦ Dover
Canterbury Ales Chartham
Canterbury Brewers 🍺 Canterbury
Chislet Canterbury (NEW)
Curious ✦ Ashford
Docker West Hythe
Farriers Arms 🍺 Mersham
Fonthill 🍺 Tunbridge Wells
Four Candles 🍺 St Peters
Goacher's Tovil
Goody ✦ Herne
Hinks Ruckinge (brewing suspended)
Hop Fuzz West Hythe
Iron Pier ✦ Gravesend
Isla Vale Margate (brewing suspended)
Kent Birling
Larkins Chiddingstone
Mad Cat Faversham
McCanns St Michaels
MootBrew ✦ Rochester
Musket ✦ Linton
No Frills Joe Greenhithe
Northdown ✦ Margate
Pig & Porter Tunbridge Wells
Ramsgate Broadstairs
Romney Marsh New Romney
Running Man Chatham
Shepherd Neame Faversham
Shivering Sands ✦ Manston
Stag Woodchurch
Stay Wild Shoreham (NEW)
Time & Tide ✦ Eastry
Tonbridge East Peckham
Twisted Wheel ✦ Tenterden
Wantsum ✦ St Nicholas at Wade
Westerham ✦ Westerham
Whitstable Grafty Green

beers. The floor is hand-stencilled by the landlady. At the back is a long, bright conservatory with board games. Beer festivals are held on the Whitsun and August bank holiday weekends indoors and in the attractive garden. There is an Airbnb self-catering apartment upstairs. Local CAMRA Pub of the Year 2022. Q☼⑩♿🅰♣♠🛒🐾🌐♪

Thomas Becket 🍷 ✿
21 Best Lane, CT1 2JB
☎ (01227) 938689 ⊕ thomas-becket.com
4 changing beers (sourced regionally; often Kent, Musket, Wantsum) Ⓗ
Snug 18th-century city-centre pub, close to the cathedral, theatre and shops, it is cosy, with an open-plan bar, wooden floors, a log burner and a small outside seating area. Traditional food is served daily and there are Sunday roasts. A dog-friendly pub, it displays over 400 photos of furry friends. Expect rotating guest ales from local breweries via four handpumps. There is intermittent Saturday night live music, monthly open mic sessions and epic Monday quizzes. Local CAMRA Pub of the Year 2024. ☼⑩♿(West)♣🛒🐾🌐♪

Thomas Tallis Alehouse Ⓛ
48 Northgate, CT1 1BE
⊕ thethomastallisalehouse.co.uk
3 changing beers (sourced locally; often Ramsgate, Tonbridge) Ⓖ
This alehouse opened in 2016, located in a lovely 15th-century half-timbered building, part of the historic Hospital of St John. Up to four different Kent cask beers are stocked, and many national and international beers in KeyKeg, bottles and cans, as well as several Kentish ciders. One of the two front rooms has a log-burning stove, the rear snug has armchairs and a sofa. Generally a seat/table service applies. Outside seating is available on the street. Q☼☼♿(West)♣🛒🐾🌐

Two Sawyers Ⓛ ✿
58 Ivy Lane, CT1 1TU
☎ (01227) 766293 ⊕ twosawyerscanterbury.com
Timothy Taylor Landlord; 2 changing beers (often Kent, Musket, Ramsgate) Ⓗ
Cosy inn with exposed beams and log-burning fires, situated over the ring road from the city walls and bus station, and a minute's walk from St Augustine's Abbey. The pub is open all day, serving three changing real ales and 50 gins. Dating back to 1796, it was originally a carpentry house, hence its name. It is now the last of seven pubs which would have graced this terraced lane in the 1900s. Ivy Lane also contains some historic houses. ☼⑩♿(East)🛒🐾🌐

Capel

Dovecote Inn Ⓛ ✿
Alders Road, TN12 6SU (½ mile W of A228 towards Tudeley)
☎ (01732) 798289 ⊕ dovecote-capel.co.uk
Harvey's Sussex Best Bitter; Larkins Traditional Ale; 3 changing beers (sourced locally; often Cellar Head, Tonbridge, Westerham) Ⓖ
An excellent country pub displaying interesting wall ornaments including hop pockets – a reminder of nearby surviving hop gardens. New owners since early 2023 have returned to tradition and promote unusual and seasonal ales such as green-hop and dark beers. Ales are served direct from the cask and four Kentish ciders are now similarly dispensed. Wholesome pub dishes are served and there is plenty of seating available in the large rear garden and covered terrace. Music nights are organised on alternate Tuesdays. ☼☼⑩♿♣🅿🐾🌐♪

Charcott

Greyhound Ⓛ
off Camp Hill, TN11 8LG (½ mile N of B2027 at Chiddingstone Causeway)
☎ (01892) 870275 ⊕ thegreyhoundcharcott.co.uk
Larkins Traditional Ale; 3 changing beers (sourced locally; often Canterbury Ales, Kent, Three Acre) Ⓗ
Located off the beaten track in a small hamlet, a warm welcome awaits customers, who are regarded as part of the family. Much attention is given to working with local producers including sourcing produce from the owners' nearby farm and this reflects in a regularly changing menu, complemented by cask ales from Kent and Sussex. Booking for Sunday lunch is particularly advised. Internally a relaxed atmosphere pervades, with flowers and candles on the tables, a real fire, and interesting toilet facilities with a rustic twist. ☼⑩♿(Penshurst)🚌(210)🐾🌐

Chiddingstone

Castle Inn ★ Ⓛ
TN8 7AH (turn off B2027 approx 1 mile W of Penshurst station)
☎ (01892) 870371 ⊕ thecastleinnchiddingstone.com
Harvey's Sussex Best Bitter; Larkins Traditional Ale; 1 changing beer (sourced locally; often Lakedown, Larkins) Ⓗ
An impressive 15th-century inn set in an impossibly picturesque Tudor village to which many visitors are drawn after visiting nearby Hever and Chiddingstone castles and Penshurst Place. The public bar has a cosy atmosphere with a tiled floor and quirky features while a secluded and comfortable snug room can be found to the right on entering. Adjacent to the pretty rear garden is a separate function room. Good homely fare ranges from light dishes through pub staples and home-made pies. Local Chiddingstone cider is served. ☼⑩♿♣🐾🌐

Chiddingstone Hoath

Rock Ⓛ ✿
Hoath Corner, Rywell Road, TN8 7BS (1½ miles S of Chiddingstone)
☎ (01892) 870296 ⊕ therockchiddingstone.com
Larkins Traditional Ale; 2 changing beers (sourced locally; often Lakedown, Larkins) Ⓗ
As a Grade II-listed building dating from 1520, the Rock features brick flooring, extensive wooden beams, and comfortable chairs surrounding a wood-burner within an inglenook, all overlooked by the ancient game of ring the bull. Investigate the naughty chair by the bar! Larkins Traditional is brewed just a couple of miles down the road and is often accompanied by one of their additional brews and a guest beer from further afield. Visitors arrive in cars, on cycles, on foot and even on horseback. Q☼☼⑩♣🅿🐾🌐

Coldred

Carpenters Arms ★ Ⓛ
The Green, CT15 5AJ
☎ (01304) 830190
2 changing beers (sourced locally; often Kent, Ramsgate, Romney Marsh) Ⓗ/Ⓖ
Overlooking the village green and duck pond, this two-roomed 18th-century pub has been identified by CAMRA as having a nationally important historic pub interior. It

has been family owned for over a century, remaining largely unchanged for 50 years. Two real ales are served, one from Kent, alongside three Kentish Pip ciders. As the community hub, it is a great place for conversation and for local societies to meet. A variety of events are held including themed food nights and a book club. A beer festival is held in the summer. Q ☆ ⑧ ▲ ♣ ♠ P ◐ ❖ ⬤ ♿ ☏

Cranbrook

Larkins' Alehouse ⬤

7 High Street, TN17 3EB
☎ 07786 707476 ⊕ larkins-alehouse.co.uk
4 changing beers (sourced locally; often Cellar Head, Goacher's, Larkins) G

A community focused micropub in a former florist shop, putting the heart back into the town. A simply furnished room with servery at the rear, beyond the cool room and toilet is the covered and heated courtyard garden. A chalkboard menu displays beers, ciders and other drinks. Homemade snacks and chutneys are available but customers are welcome to bring their own food. Voted the local CAMRA Cider Pub of the Year and Kent Pub of the Year in 2022. Q ☆ ⑧ ♣ ♠ ☷ (5,297) ❖ ⬤ ☏

Crockenhill

Chequers L ⬤

Cray Road, BR8 8LP
☎ (01322) 662132 ⊕ chequerscrockenhill.co.uk
Harvey's Sussex Best Bitter; 3 changing beers (sourced nationally) H

Friendly village local offering one permanent beer and three changing guest ales from a wide selection of breweries. Meals are served daily, with seniors discounts at the beginning of the week. There is a quiz on Monday evenings and various other events on regular occasions. Several pictures of old Crockenhill indicate that the pub has been a hub of village life for many years. This was an early outlet for local Stay Wild beers.
☆ ⑧ ◑ ♣ P ☷ (477) ❖ ☏ ♫

Dartford

Dartford Working Men's Club L

40 Essex Road, DA1 2AU
☎ (01322) 223646 ⊕ dartfordwm.club
Courage Best Bitter; 9 changing beers (sourced nationally; often Adnams, Marble, Thornbridge) H

A former CAMRA National Club of the Year, this CIU club serves up to seven real ales on handpump plus ciders on gravity. It hosts the BBC award-winning Dartford Folk Club every Tuesday night and has live music every Thursday and Saturday night and on the last Sunday afternoon of each month, with tribute acts on alternate Fridays. Quiz night is the first Wednesday of every month. CAMRA members are welcome as guests.
☆ ⑧ ◑ ≠ ♣ ♠ ☷ ☏ ♫

Foresters

15/16 Great Queen Street, DA1 1TJ
☎ (01322) 223087
Adnams Ghost Ship; Harvey's Sussex Best Bitter; 1 changing beer (sourced nationally; often Otter, Timothy Taylor) H

Traditional Victorian side-street local, just off East Hill, five minutes' walk from the town centre. Quiet at lunchtimes but often busy in the evenings with live sports on TV and darts, pool and crib teams. The U-shaped bar has a log burning fire at one end. The

graveyard opposite contains the unmarked pauper's grave of famed steam pioneer Richard Trevithick, its approximate location being indicated by a plaque on the north wall. ☆ ⑧ ♿ ≠ ♣ P ☷ ❖

Malt Shovel ★ ⬤

3 Darenth Road, DA1 1LP
☎ (01322) 224381 ⊕ maltshovelda1.co.uk
St Austell Tribute; Young's London Original; 2 changing beers (sourced nationally; often Fuller's, Young's) H

Traditional country-style pub, dating from 1673, five minutes' walk from the town centre. It has two separate bars: a small tap room with a low ceiling, featuring an 1880s Dartford Brewery mirror, and a larger saloon bar leading to a conservatory where meals are served Thursday to Sunday (booking advised for Sun roasts). The large beer garden is accessed from the conservatory. A quiz is held on Monday evenings, crib on Tuesdays, and a monthly jazz night. Two regular real ales and normally two guests are served. ⑧ ◑ ≠ ♣ ♠ P ☷ (B) ☏ ♫

Deal

Just Reproach L

14 King Street, CT14 6HX
4 changing beers (often Kent) G

This family-run micropub, with its high benches and table service, is located in Deal town centre. Its back-to-basics approach, with no keg, fruit machines or music, fosters a friendly atmosphere. Avoid using your mobile phone! Up to five real ales, often from Kent, are gravity dispensed from the cool room. Real ciders typically include one from Kent. There's a selection of craft beers, wines, gins, and soft drinks. Regular quiz nights are held to raise money for charity. Cheese Sunday occurs monthly.
Q ☆ ⑧ ≠ ♣ ♠ ☷ ❖

Ship Inn L

141 Middle Street, CT14 6JZ
☎ (01304) 372222
Ramsgate Gadds' Hoppy Pale, Gadds' No. 7 Bitter Ale, Gadds' No. 5 Best Bitter Ale; Timothy Taylor Landlord; 1 changing beer (often Young's) H

Situated in Deal's historic conservation area, and a short walk from the town centre, this traditional pub has a warm and comfortable atmosphere. Inside there are dark wooden floors, subdued lighting and a carpeted lounge. The wood-burning stove is welcome in winter. The décor has a nautical theme. A variety of drinkers enjoy a good selection of ales from five handpumps, featuring selections from Ramsgate and Dark Star. The small rear bar overlooks a large patio garden, accessible by staircase, with a covered smoking area. ☆ ⑧ ♣ ☷ ❖

Smugglers Record Shop L

9 King Street, CT14 6HX
☎ 07850 474296 ⊕ shop.smugglersrecords.com
Time & Tide Spratwaffler; 4 changing beers (sourced nationally; often Bristol Beer Factory, Oakham) G

This lively vinyl record shop and bar, situated just off Deal's seafront, has a large selection of vinyl for sale. The background music is an eclectic music mix, featuring local bands, world, folk, psych and roots. Two cask ales are served, sometimes three on busier weekends, which are gravity-fed from a cooler cabinet. These usually feature ales from a local brewery such as Time & Tide. Kentish Pip real cider is complemented by craft beer, canned and bottled beers, cider, and wines.
☆ ⑧ ≠ ♠ ☷ ☏ ♫

Denton

Jackdaw Inn

The Street, CT4 6QZ

☎ (01303) 844663 ⊕ jackdawdenton.co.uk

St Austell Tribute; 1 changing beer (sourced nationally; often Adnams, Harvey's) H

This friendly country inn featured in the 1969 film The Battle of Britain. RAF memorabilia and village photos adorn its walls. A log fire is lit in winter. St Austell's Tribute and another national ale feature on the bar. Homemade seasonal dishes are served, and afternoon teas are also available. The pub's annual beer and cider festival in September coincides with its Battle of Britain Weekend. There's a spacious, sunlit garden to the rear. A regular bus service runs throughout the day and evening. ⑤❀◖P🖵(16)❀❖♪

Dover

Breakwater Brewery Taproom and Pizzeria L

St Martin's Yard, Lorne Road, CT16 2AA

☎ 07427 304551

Breakwater Dover Pale Ale, Blue Ensign, Cowjuice Milk Stout; 6 changing beers (sourced locally; often Breakwater) G

The brewery and taproom sit on the site of the Harding's Wellington Brewery, which closed in 1890. The modern, well-lit bar boasts chunky wooden furniture, colourful table runners, and a stone breakwater-style counter. A spacious front patio with a pergola and a smaller side patio, overlooking the river, provide outdoor seating. Cask ales from the brewery are served on gravity, alongside the pub's house ciders. Stone-baked pizzas are available from their pizzeria. Events include live music, open mic nights and summer hog roasts. ⑤❀◖&♠🖵❀♪

Eight Bells L ✓

19 Cannon Street, CT16 1BZ

☎ (01304) 205030

Breakwater East Kent Gold G; Greene King Abbot; Ruddles Best Bitter; Sharp's Doom Bar; 6 changing beers (often Wantsum) H

This bustling Wetherspoon pub sits on the town's shopping precinct. The pub is named after the bells of the historic St Mary's Church opposite. Inside, there is a large open-plan room with a long bar, sofas and a raised restaurant area. An enclosed seating area at the front overlooks the precinct. Twelve handpumps dispense regular and guest ales, with at least two from a Kent microbrewery. There are real ale offers on Mondays and two beer festivals occur in spring and winter. Q⑤❀◖&⇌(Priory)🖵❖

Hoptimist Taproom & Bar L

3 Bench Street, CT16 1JH

☎ 07515 367802

6 changing beers (sourced locally; often Kent, Pig & Porter, Time & Tide)

This modern taproom provides a comfortable atmosphere for a drink and a chat. The pub serves a good variety of cask ale and real cider, served on gravity from the chilled rear cellar room. There's also modern craft beer, premium keg beers and a changing gin menu. Ales are mostly from Kent breweries with occasional guests, and ciders are from Biddenden and Kent Cider. There's a complimentary cheeseboard on Sundays, a selection of board games and occasional live music and food events. ⑤❀⇌(Priory)♠🖵(62,68)❖♪

Louis Armstrong L

58 Maison Dieu Road, CT16 1RA

☎ (01304) 204759

3 changing beers (sourced locally; often Canterbury Ales, Ramsgate, Romney Marsh) H

This renowned pub and local music venue has hosted live music events for over 50 years, featuring rock, folk, blues, jazz, and comedy nights. The large L-shaped bar and stage are adorned with music posters. Enjoy up to three real ales, mostly from Kent microbreweries, with occasional Kent cider. Good-value food is served on Wednesday evenings and fortnightly charity quizzes are held. At the back, there's a pleasant beer garden. Opening times may vary when events have been organised. ⊛◖♠♥🖵❀❖♪

Staggered Inn L

107 High Street, CT16 1EB

☎ 07921 573299

Chislet Brewery Island Road APA; 3 changing beers (sourced locally; often Hop Fuzz, Kent, Romney Marsh) G

This friendly, family-run micropub is situated on Dover's one-way system. There's a main bar room, with the bar situated on a mezzanine floor. Unsurprisingly, stags feature as part of the decor. Chislet's Island Road APA features alongside three guest ales from Kent breweries, served on gravity dispense from a rear chilled cellar room. Real ciders are from Biddenden and Dudda's Tun. There's a selection of wines and spirits, including a gin of the week. At the back there's a pleasant decked patio. ⑤❀♠♥🖵❀❖

Dunton Green

Miners Arms L ✓

22 London Road, TN13 2UF

☎ (01732) 462214

3 changing beers (sourced locally; often Kent, Ramsgate, Tonbridge) H

Originally built to cater for railway construction workers, this popular venue offers a warm welcome, serving up to three local cask ales, and recently won the local CAMRA Most Improved Pub award. The bar has a log fire and leads to a covered, heated terrace with sofas before opening onto a surprisingly large garden. Good-value meals are served weekday lunchtimes with a happy hour (Mon-Thu 12-3pm). A quiz night is held each month and it often hosts live music at weekends. ⑤❀◖⇌♠🖵(1,8)❀❖♪

Dymchurch

Hidden Treasure L

30 High Street, TN29 0NU

☎ (01303) 874049

2 changing beers (sourced locally) H

This is a friendly family-run micropub in the heart of Dymchurch close to the historic Martello Tower (which is open to the public by appointment), and the beach. Real ales, usually one from a Kentish brewer, are served through three handpumps with some extra beers occasionally dispensed from the fridge cabinet. Ciders on gravity are also dispensed from the fridge cabinet. There are several drinking areas with a corridor connecting them to the bar area. Check the pub's Facebook page for seasonal opening times. Q⑤❀▲⇌♠🖵(102)❀❖

Eastry

Five Bells ✓
The Cross, CT13 0HX
☎ (01304) 611188 ⊕ thefivebellseastry.com
2 changing beers (sourced nationally; often Fuller's, Harvey's, Timothy Taylor) Ⓗ
This local CAMRA Community Pub of the Year provides a traditional and welcoming atmosphere, with its comfortable lounge bar and dining room. The old fire station, with historic memorabilia, serves as a sports/function room. Two or three ales are served, with occasional beers from Kent. Home-made food is available all day, including breakfasts and a Sunday roast. The busy calendar features food events, live music, quiz nights and an Easter beer festival. The suntrap garden has a children's play area and pétanque pitch. B&B accommodation is available.
🛏️❀🅰🍽️◑🗚♣️🅿️🚃(81)❀🎵

Eynsford

Five Bells
High Street, DA4 0AB
☎ (01322) 863135
Harvey's Sussex Best Bitter; 2 changing beers (sourced nationally; often Fuller's) Ⓗ
Traditional community pub in the heart of this attractive village. The public bar retains a homely atmosphere with wooden tables and a wood-burning fire in winter. A comfortable separate saloon bar has a dartboard. There is a pleasant garden to the rear and a small car park. Dogs are welcome in the public bar. Food is not served here so diners may wish to try its larger sister pub, the Malt Shovel, nearby. 🛏️❀♣️🅿️🚃(421)❀🎵

Faversham

Bear Inn ★
3 Market Place, ME13 7AG
☎ (01795) 532668 ⊕ bearinnfaversham.co.uk
Shepherd Neame Master Brew; 1 changing beer (sourced locally; often Shepherd Neame) Ⓗ
Located in the historic market square this 16th-century pub has an impressive historic wood panelled interior. There are three separate bar areas off the corridor, which runs the length of the building. A quiz is held on the last Monday of the month. Popular with visitors to Faversham and locals alike, this is the place to try Shepherd Neame beers and they often serve a seasonal or guest beer. Tables out the front of the pub are popular in summer.
Q◑≒♣️🚃🎵

Creeker's Tap
37 Preston Street, ME13 8PE
2 changing beers (sourced nationally; often Track) Ⓗ
Popular, comfortable micropub converted from a former shop, it is now an established addition to the local drinking scene. There are two rooms with some solid and comfortable furniture: a lounge type area with a Chesterfield, and armchairs in the room at the rear. Cask beers and a range of keg products are dispensed from taps on the wall behind the bar in the front room, alongside a selection of cider, wines and gins. Q≒🚃❀

Elephant Ⓛ
31 The Mall, ME13 8JN
☎ (01795) 590157
5 changing beers (sourced regionally; often Canterbury Ales, Mighty Oak, Rother Valley) Ⓗ

Two-roomed traditional free house with separate function room out the back, the landlord takes pride in serving good real ale, occasionally including a beer matured in the cellar. Nautical memorabilia is displayed on the walls. The pub is host to local clubs and regular live music. A well-tended and attractive walled garden at the back, and a log fire within make this a good pub to visit at any time of year. The winner of multiple CAMRA awards, it was voted local Pub of the Year 2023.
🛏️❀≒♣️◑🗚❀🎵

Furlongs Ale House
6A Preston Street, ME13 8NS
☎ 07747 776200
5 changing beers (sourced locally; often Canterbury Ales, Kent, Ramsgate) Ⓗ
Often busy, this micropub has a heated and covered outside seating area at the rear. Beers are drawn by handpump from the cellar to the small bar, with many sourced from Kent microbreweries and others from across the UK, all with a shared emphasis on the hop. There is wooden bench style seating and solid tables within and, when required, air conditioning. Kent gins, selection of wines and ciders are also served. Snacks consist of various smoked nuts. Q🛏️❀≒●🚃❀

Quay
Conduit Street, ME13 7DF
☎ (01795) 530388 ⊕ thequayfaversham.co.uk
Ramsgate Gadds' No. 5 Best Bitter; 1 changing beer (sourced regionally; often Musket) Ⓗ
Just north of the Shepherd Neame brewery, sitting very close to Faversham Creek, this two-bar pub offers a friendly welcome to real ale drinkers, with competitive prices and a change in policy that saw an expansion of the range of ales to reflect customer choice. Beer is either dispensed on handpump or fetched from the adjacent cellar. Food is available on Sunday afternoons only. Sport is shown on a big screen and well-behaved dogs are welcome. Limited parking. 🛏️❀🍽️◑≒🅿️❀🎵

Shipwrights Arms Ⓛ
Hollowshore, ME13 7TU (situated over a mile N of Faversham at the confluence of Faversham and Oare creeks) TR017636
☎ (01795) 590088 ⊕ theshipwrightsathollowshore.co.uk
Harvey's Sussex Best Bitter; house beer (by Goacher's); 3 changing beers (sourced locally; often Goacher's, Kent) Ⓖ
Run by the same family for 25 years, this 300-year-old proper free house by the sea wall is well worth the 45-minute walk from Faversham. Wooden-clad, the cosy interior reflects the area's nautical heritage, with associated ornaments and pictures on display. Comfortable seating options surround the fireplaces. The large garden at the rear is open from spring to autumn, with outside seating at front is all seasons. Opening hours are extended in summer. In severe winter weather telephone to check opening times. Q🛏️❀◑♣️🅿️❀

Sun Inn
10 West Street, ME13 7JE
☎ (01795) 535098 ⊕ sunfaversham.co.uk
Shepherd Neame Master Brew, Spitfire; 1 changing beer (often Shepherd Neame) Ⓗ
The 14th-century Sun Inn, in Faversham's conservation area, is brimming with intriguing original features – with its inglenook fireplaces, oak beams and a lovely courtyard garden. Popular with diners in Faversham, breakfast, lunch and dinner are served (no food Sun eve). Eight comfortable and characterful bedrooms provide stylish accommodation. The early opening times do not allow the sale of alcohol. ❀🛏️◑≒🚃❀

Folkestone

Bouverie Tap 🅛
45 Bouverie Road West, CT20 2SZ
☎ (01303) 255977 ⊕ thebouverietap.co.uk
3 changing beers (sourced locally) Ⓗ
This alehouse was extended into the adjacent shop and courtyard in 2020 and is decorated with interesting old posters. The pub offers three changing local ales and cider. Food is prepared from locally sourced ingredients and wholesome roasts are available on Sundays. Breakfasts are available on Saturday and Sunday from 8.30, with alcohol served from 9 for those who prefer the 'hair of the dog' with their breakfast! Dogs are welcome and well-behaved children up to 7pm.
ॐ❀Ⓚ&≠(Central) ●🖳❀🛜

East Cliff Tavern 🅛
13-15 East Cliff, CT19 6BU (60m from Tram Rd via pedestrian crossing over disused tracks)
☎ (01303) 251132
2 changing beers (sourced locally; often Kent) Ⓗ
Traditional back-street pub and community hub since 1862. Family owned since 1967, under its current landlord it has earnt 18 Guide entries. Regulars, the Leaky Bladders, strum and pump nostalgic notes on Thursday evening and Sunday afternoon. Darts is played on Friday, with needlecraft on alternate Wednesdays. One pale beer from Kent Brewery is on pump, with Biddenden or Kingswood cider on gravity. Government surplus Bakelite tables support drinks and a traditional gas fire keeps the cold at bay. Dogs are welcome. Extended hours when busy. Cash only.
Q❀♣●🖳(74,102) ❀♪

Firkin Alehouse
21 Cheriton Place, CT20 2AY
☎ 07894 068432 ⊕ firkinalehouse.co.uk
4 changing beers (sourced nationally) Ⓖ
This welcoming micropub offers up to four cask beers, usually one from a Kent microbrewery, and up to six ciders served by gravity from a temperature-controlled room. The display fridge offers a selection of bottled and canned foreign and British beers with a limited wine selection. Bar snacks include pickled eggs, pickled onions, and other basic fare. No music or pub games, good company and conversation make the Firkin Alehouse a place to enjoy a good drink and relax.
Q&≠(Central) ●🖳❀🛜

Kipps' Alehouse
11-15 Old High Street, CT20 1RL
☎ (01303) 246766 ⊕ kippsalehouse.co.uk
3 changing beers (sourced regionally; often Mad Cat) Ⓖ
This alehouse serves real ale directly from the cask, usually including a Kentish ale, an award-winner and then another unusual beer from around the country, all sourced from small independent microbreweries. Several ciders are on sale from boxes, and a variety of bottled craft beers and draught international lagers complete the range. A range of international vegetarian food is available. Music some Sunday afternoons.
ॐ❀&♣●🖳❀🛜♪

Samuel Peto ✅
23 Rendezvous Street, Baptist Galleries, CT20 1EY
☎ (01303) 251154
Greene King Abbot; Ruddles Best Bitter; 3 changing beers Ⓗ
This unique Wetherspoon pub named after Samuel Morton Peto, a great railway engineer and builder of Nelson's Column, who funded this building as a Baptist church in 1874. The pub also features the original stained-glass windows, a façade of the organ pipes, original memorial plaques of local dignities, and a hand-painted ceiling of fluffy clouds across a blue sky. Cosily inviting booths wrap around both floors. There are even two pulpits upstairs where one can preach the Gospel of Real Ale. Qॐ◖Ⓚ🖳🛜

Frittenden

Bell & Jorrocks ✅
Biddenden Road, TN17 2EJ TQ815412
☎ (01580) 852415 ⊕ thebellandjorrocks.co.uk
Goacher's Fine Light Ale; Harvey's Sussex Best Bitter Ⓗ
Dating from the early 18th century and originally the Bell, it gained its current name when the other village pub, the John Jorrocks, closed in 1969. The pub sign celebrates both antecedents; one on each side. Once a coaching inn, its stables are used for an annual beer festival on the weekend closest to 13th April. The pub is the social centre of the village, serves excellent food and is a good base for circular walks in the local Low Weald countryside. Qॐ❀Ⓚ▲♣❀🛜♪

Gillingham

Frog & Toad
38 Burnt Oak Terrace, ME7 1DR
3 changing beers (sourced nationally; often Wantsum) Ⓗ
Traditional back-street local, just 10 minutes' walk from the town centre, where there are up to three cask ales sold. There is a TV for sports events, live music or karaoke most Saturdays, and a quiz night on the first Tuesday of every month. There is also a ladies' darts team. The patio garden at the rear has covered wooden tables and seating, along with an outdoor bar and stillage for the beer when the pub runs festivals.
ॐ❀≠♣●🖳(176,177) ❀🛜♪

Past & Present 🅛
15 Canterbury Street, ME7 5TP
☎ 07725 072293
4 changing beers (sourced nationally) Ⓖ
Winner of CAMRA Kent Regional Cider Pub of the Year 2023, this two level bar is popular with all ages. Along with ales and ciders it serves an extensive range of gins and rums and a large selection of bar snacks. It has a TV showing sports and a dartboard popular with regulars, both on the lower level. There's plenty of community spirit here with regular events held, including an annual cider festival with over 20 ciders available.
Qॐ≠♣●Ⓚ🖳(116,176) ❀

Will Adams
73 Saxton Street, ME7 5EG (on corner with Lock St)
☎ (01634) 575902
3 changing beers (sourced nationally; often Adnams, Oakham) Ⓗ
Inside this pub you will find murals of the life and times of Will Adams, who was the first Englishman to visit Japan. The pub offers up to three cask ales and five ciders (not all of which are real) in boxes and there is a large selection of single malt whiskies. It opens on Tuesdays at 5 when Gillingham FC are at home, and will close between 3-5 on afternoon match days. The pub runs four darts teams. ❀Ⓚ≠♣🖳❀🛜

Gravesend

Compass Alehouse ♀ 🗠

7 Manor Road, DA12 1AA
☎ 07951 550949 ⊕ thecompassalehouse.co.uk
4 changing beers (sourced nationally) 🄶
Micropub with a small front room with high bench seats and a smaller snug off a little courtyard to the rear. Four ever-changing real ales and three ciders are available, often from Kent producers. It has a convivial atmosphere where conversation is paramount but talking on mobile phones is discouraged and incurs a fine for charity. A water bowl is provided for dogs. Regular events include games nights, a monthly quiz on the third Wednesday and whisky tastings. Q ➰ ⊛ & ≷ ♠ ◉ 🖫 🗠 ❀

Jolly Drayman

1 Love Lane, Wellington Street, DA12 1JA (off Milton Rd, E of town centre)
☎ (01474) 352355 ⊕ jollydrayman.co.uk
Dark Star Hophead; Fuller's London Pride; 2 changing beers (sourced regionally; often Iron Pier, Kent) 🄷
This cosy pub on the eastern edge of the town, also known as the Coke Oven, is part of the former Walker's brewery. It features quirky low ceilings and a relaxed atmosphere and has been extended to provide a more spacious bar and some extra seating. Daddlums (Kentish skittles) is played many Sunday evenings and men's and ladies darts teams are hosted. Regular live music and fortnightly quizzes are held. Two changing beers often come from Kentish breweries and one is normally lighter and one darker. ➰ ⊛ ⇔ & ≷ ♠ P 🖫 ❀ ⦿ ♪

Three Daws 🗠

Town Pier, DA11 0BJ
☎ (01474) 566869 ⊕ threedaws.co.uk
4 changing beers (sourced nationally; often Bexley, Titsey, Tonbridge) 🄷
Historic riverside inn with stories of ghosts, press gangs, smugglers, secret tunnels and more, offering views of the Thames and passing river traffic. The bar is upstairs with a large function room below. Inside is divided into small rooms with photos and pictures of local or marine interest and very few right angles. One room features a bar billiards table. Substantial meals are served until 9pm every day. Many Fridays feature live music, there are quizzes on Sundays and beer festivals are held in August and October. ➰ ⊛ ◑ ≷ ♠ 🖫 ⦿ ♪

Three Pillars 🗠

25 Wrotham Road, DA11 0PA (on A227 opp Civic Centre)
☎ 07794 348529 ⊕ threepillarsgravesend.co.uk
Changing beers (sourced nationally; often Cellar Head, Kent, Mighty Oak) 🄶
Small cellar bar underneath the Masonic Hall, reached by steep steps to the right of the hall. Two carpeted front rooms lead to the brick-floored bar area. The ceilings are low throughout and on the walls are photos of Gravesend pubs past and present. There is a quiz on the third Thursday of the month and live music on some Sundays. Five or more real ales are dispensed from a cooled room together with some ciders. Patrons must not use the Masonic Hall car park. ➰ ≷ ♠ 🖫 ❀ ♪

Halstead

Rose & Crown 🗠

Otford Lane, TN14 7EA
☎ (01959) 533120

Larkins Traditional Ale; 5 changing beers (sourced regionally; often Cellar Head, Fuller's, Titsey) 🄷
Located close to the North Downs Way this attractive Grade II-listed flint-built pub can be reached using a regular bus service from Orpington. The two bars are differentiated only by the dartboard in the sports-oriented public bar and a real fire in the quieter lounge. The number of guest beers and the regularity of rotation indicates a local keenness to support real ale. The rear garden incorporates a children's play area, patio, barbecue and the summer game of bat and trap. ➰ ⊛ ◑ & ♠ 🖫 (R5,R10) ❀ ⦿ ♀

Herne

Butcher's Arms 🗠

29A Herne Street, CT6 7HL (opp church)
☎ 07908 370685 ⊕ micropub.co.uk
Ramsgate Gadds' No. 5 Best Bitter Ale; 2 changing beers (sourced regionally; often Iron Pier, Ramsgate) 🄶
Britain's first micropub, opened in 2005, is a real ale gem and the inspiration for others. Once a butcher's shop, it still has the original chopping tables. The compact drinking area ensures lively banter. Customers can buy beer to drink at home. The Butcher's Arms has won many CAMRA awards and landlord Martyn Hillier was voted one of CAMRA's top 40 campaigners and has recently been awarded the MBE for services to business and hospitality. Opening hours are now limited to 5.30-8pm, Tuesday to Friday, but groups can be accommodated on Saturday lunchtimes by arrangement. Q 🖫 ❀ ⦿

Herne Bay

Bouncing Barrel 🗠

20 Bank Street, CT6 5EA
☎ 07777 630685
5 changing beers (sourced nationally; often Musket, Oakham, Wantsum) 🄶
A welcoming micropub with bench seating for 20 customers around old workshop tables. The beer range changes regularly and comes from a wide selection of microbreweries countrywide, often including beers from Kent. Local snacks are available. The venue is named after the bombs used in the Dam Buster raids, which were tested off the coast nearby. The pub has a mural of a Lancaster flying past the Reculver Towers. Regular small beer festivals are held throughout the year. Q ➰ & ♠ ◉ 🖫 ❀

Parkerville

219 High Street, CT6 5AD
☎ 07939 106172
4 changing beers (sourced nationally; often Long Man, Mighty Oak, Oakham) 🄶
Lively micropub in a former music store. The spacious front seating area has a corner bar, and a small stage with a piano in the front window. The back bar has a TV screen for big events only. Beers are often from local microbreweries and there is a good selection of ciders, whiskies, rums, artisan gins and wines. Occasional live music is staged, and there are quiz nights on the last Tuesday of each month. Q ➰ & ◉ 🖫 ❀ ♪

Horton Kirby

Bull 🗠

Lombard Street, DA4 9DF
☎ (01322) 860341 ⊕ thebullhortonkirby.com

Dark Star Hophead; Hardys & Hansons Bitter; 2 changing beers (sourced nationally; often Kent, Oakham) ⊞

Friendly, comfortable one-bar village local with a large garden affording views across the Darent Valley. The pub has two regular and two rotating guest ales, of which one is often dark. Food includes pizzas on Tuesday nights. Booking is recommended for the Sunday roasts. There is an open mic night on the first Friday of each month and a quiz on the last Monday. Games include cribbage and board games. Parking can be difficult in the vicinity. ⏱❀◗◆🖵(414) ❀🛜🎵

Hythe

Potting Shed 🅛
160A High Street, CT21 5JR
☎ 07780 877226
3 changing beers (sourced regionally) ⊞
Hythe's only micro-alehouse at the Folkestone end of Hythe High Street serves an interesting range of ales from around the country, with one local Kentish beer typically on offer. A range of three chilled ciders is also usually available from boxes. Limited bar snacks are available. Small, convivial and welcoming, where chatter and laughter abound, this is a good place to enjoy a drink and interesting conversation after visiting the High Street. ❀●🖵❀🛜

Ightham Common

Old House ★ 🅛
Redwell Lane, TN15 9EE (½ mile SW of Ightham village, between A25 and A227) TQ590558
☎ (01732) 886077 ⊕ oldhouse.pub
6 changing beers (sourced locally; often Goacher's, Larkins, Long Man) 🅖
Kentish red-brick, tile-hung cottage located in an isolated narrow country lane. It has been identified by CAMRA as having a nationally important historic pub interior. The main bar features a Victorian wood-panelled counter, parquet flooring and an imposing inglenook fireplace. Up to six changing beers are dispensed by gravity, often from wooden casks, including at least one bitter, a golden ale and a dark beer. Ciders may include a local product also in a wooden cask. Local CAMRA Pub of the Year 2018-2021. It is only open in the evening during the week. Q❀🛆♣●P❀🛜

Kingsdown

King's Head 🅛
Upper Street, CT14 8BJ
☎ (01304) 373915 ⊕ kingsheadkingsdown.co.uk
3 changing beers (often Goacher's, Ramsgate) ⊞
This 18th-century village pub has three beamed rooms surrounding a central bar. The public bar has a welcoming log fire. The spacious dining/family room provides access to a quiet rear courtyard, skittle alley and heated smoking area. Historical photos adorn the walls. Three real ales (four during busier times), include beers from Goacher's and Ramsgate. Kentish Pip cider is served in summer. The home-made menu includes vegetarian and gluten-free options, and on Sunday there's a roast. Events include quiz nights and a guitar club. ⏱❀◗🛆♣❀🛜🎵

Laddingford

Chequers
The Street, ME18 6BP TQ689481
☎ (01622) 871266 ⊕ chequersladdingford.co.uk
Harvey's Sussex Best Bitter; 2 changing beers (sourced nationally) ⊞
An attractive oak-beamed pub dating from the 15th century. It is the heart of village life and the landlords have been at the pub for 30 years. A variety of events are held throughout the year, with the beer range increased to 10. A roaring log fire burns in winter, and the pub frontage is a sea of flowers in summer and has a covered seating area. Good food is served and a wide selection of sausage dishes is available on Thursdays. The large garden has children's play equipment. Q⏱❀◗P🖵(23,25) ❀🛜🎵

Linton

Armoury
Loddington Farm, Loddington Lane, ME17 4AG
☎ (01622) 749931 ⊕ musketbrewery.co.uk
Musket Trigger, Fife & Drum; 3 changing beers (sourced locally; often Musket) 🅖
The Musket brewery tap bar overlooks the brewhouse and has stillage for eight casks with four or more beers usually available for gravity dispense. Seating and tables are provided inside, and a large grassed area opposite the entrance has tables, umbrellas and cushioned casks with some shading under the many trees. A large tent has seating with heating and lighting. Pizzas are usually available and visiting vans offer other food varieties. Beer takeaways are available on weekdays from 11am. Q⏱❀◗&♣●P🖵❀🛜🎵

Lower Halstow

Three Tuns 🍷 🅛
The Street, ME9 7DY
☎ (01795) 842840 ⊕ thethreetunsrestaurant.co.uk
4 changing beers (sourced locally; often Wantsum, Goacher's) ⊞
A true, family-run, village pub with a friendly, bustling, cheerful atmosphere and lively chatter. The owners actively support real ale, offering mainly Kentish ales; third-pint flights are available for the indecisive. Several local ciders are offered including Dudda's Tun. The pub has a good reputation for high-quality locally sourced food and has won many awards. Events are held throughout the year including a beer festival during the summer bank holiday. A log fire, sofa seating, brick walls and beams add character. Local CAMRA Pub of the Year 2022 and 2024. ⏱❀🥘◗&♣●P🖵❀🛜🎵

Luddesdown

Cock Inn 🅛
Henley Street, DA13 0XB TQ664672
☎ (01474) 814208 ⊕ cockluddesdowne.com
Adnams Southwold Bitter, Broadside; Goacher's Real Mild Ale, Fine Light Ale; Harvey's Sussex Best Bitter; Shepherd Neame Master Brew ⊞
Proudly traditional rural free house dating from 1713, under the same ownership since 1984. Keen walkers can reach it by footpath from Sole Street station. It has two distinct bars, a large conservatory, a comfortable heated smoking area and separate function room where local clubs and societies meet. Traditional pub games are

played including bar billiards and darts with several different types of board. Children are not permitted. Q✿♣P✿

Golden Lion L ✅

Luddesdown Road, DA13 0XE

☎ (01474) 815644 ● thegoldenlionpub.uk

Iron Pier Perry St. Pale, Bitter; Young's London Original; 1 changing beer (sourced nationally; often Adnams) Ⓗ

Large rural pub, now owned by a local vineyard. It has a comfortable bar area with a log fire, and offers good-value meals. It hosts several groups including a custom car club and an investment group, and regular quiz evenings and other events. The pub is both family and dog-friendly and popular with walkers. Beer festivals are held on Whitsun Saturday and August Bank holiday Saturday. Plans include the provision of a wine and farm shop and a separate restaurant area. ♿✿◑♣Pᵈ✿🎵

Lynsted

Black Lion L

The Street, ME9 0RJ

☎ (01795) 521229 ● blacklionlynsted.co.uk

Goacher's Fine Light Ale, Best Dark Ale; Mad Cat Pow Wow Session Pale Ale Ⓗ

Welcoming free house with two Goacher's beers available plus occasional guest ales well known for their quality. A true village local, it has a homely atmosphere and usually offers good conversation. Meals are prepared on the premises. Open fires and large lawned gardens make this a pub for all seasons. A function room is available on the first floor for up to approximately 45 people. The pub is a brisk 30 minute walk from Teynham railway station. ♿✿🚪◑♣P✿🔊

Maidstone

Cellars Alehouse

The Old Brewery, Buckland Road, ME16 0DZ (if front gates in Rocky Hill closed, use rear entry to old Style & Winch brewery via alley alongside railway; access is by steps down from yard)

☎ (01622) 761045 ● thecellarsalehouse.co.uk

House beer (by Kent); 14 changing beers (sourced nationally; often Drop Project, Iron Pier, Kent) Ⓖ

Step down into the barley wine cellar of the former Style & Winch brewery where flagstone flooring and a collection of old brewery signs await. Comfortable seating and oil lamps provide a cosy atmosphere and pumpclips line the vaulted ceiling. Six cask and eight keg ales as well as 10 local and 10 fruited ciders are all perfectly kept in a temperature-controlled cool room. Bar snacks are available and a selection of wines, spirits, canned and bottled beers is maintained. Q♿✿≈(West)♣●P🔊✿🎶

Flower Pot

96 Sandling Road, ME14 2RJ

☎ (01622) 757705 ● flowerpotpub.com

Goacher's Gold Star Strong Ale; 5 changing beers (sourced nationally; often Kent, Oakham, Thornbridge) Ⓗ

A street-corner alehouse with split-level bars. The upper bar has handpumps serving ales from microbreweries, and a log fire in the winter. The lower bar has a pool table and is used for Tuesday jam nights and music nights on some Saturdays. Up to four ciders and perries are usually available and a small selection of KeyKeg

beers. An outdoor covered seating area is open most of the year. Food is served Wednesdays to Saturdays with pizzas being popular. ✿🌒≈(East)♣●P🖵(101)✿🔊🎶

Olde Thirsty Pig

4A Knightrider Street, ME15 6LP

☎ 07762 279907 ● thethirstypig.co.uk

3 changing beers (sourced locally; often Bexley, Musket, Tonbridge)

Reputedly the third-oldest building in the town, dating from around 1430, it was originally a farmhouse in the Archbishop's Palace estate. It has massive timber beams, sloping floors and nooks and crannies to explore on two floors. Handpumps dispense up to four constantly-changing ales, mainly from Kent microbreweries. Draught cider is stocked, alongside many bottled beers including some foreign ones. Two small meeting rooms may be booked, and there is a heated and covered courtyard area. The bus station is a short walk away. ✿♣●🖵✿

Rifle Volunteers ★

28 Wyatt Street, ME14 1EU

☎ (01622) 750540 ● theriflevolunteers.co.uk

Goacher's Real Mild Ale, Fine Light Ale, Crown Imperial Stout, Gold Star Strong Ale; 1 changing beer (sourced locally; often Goacher's) Ⓗ

A short stroll from Maidstone town centre finds a Victorian stone-built pub that is one of only three Goacher's tied houses. The single bar retains some of the fittings from the early 20th century and the four handpumps are constantly busy. Having no jukebox or gaming machines allows conversation to flow or quiet time to enjoy a drink. The courtyard garden provides a place to relax in the summer sunshine. A fun quiz alternates with a winter league quiz on Tuesdays. Q✿≈(East)♣●🖵✿🎶

Society Rooms ✅

Brenchley House, Week Street, ME14 1RF

☎ (01622) 350910

Greene King Abbot; Ruddles Best Bitter; Sharp's Doom Bar; 4 changing beers (sourced nationally; often Southwark, Tonbridge, Wantsum) Ⓗ

Known locally as the Glass House, this large Wetherspoon house is a well-lit building with glass walls. A large enclosed patio at the rear is for smokers and anyone requiring a quieter area or fresh air. Meals may be taken in all areas but the raised section looking out towards the station and street is favourite. Main sporting fixtures are shown on the large cinema screen (sound off). At least four handpumps are kept for guest beers and two for cider. Q♿✿◑&≈(East)🖵(101)✿

Walnut Tree

234 Tonbridge Road, ME16 8SR

☎ (01622) 727260

Goacher's Fine Light Ale; Harvey's Sussex Best Bitter Ⓗ

A cosy L-shaped local warmed by a central fire. The interior displays various sayings and quotes, and comfortable furnishings are used throughout. Regular live music is played on Friday evenings, there is a popular comedy night on the third Thursday of the month and a live band music quiz on the first Thursday. A jukebox is provided. The locally brewed Goacher's Fine Light Ale is a regular as is Harvey's Sussex Best. Private functions may be catered for on request. ✿✿♣P🖵(3,7)✿🎶

Marden

Marden Village Club
Albion Road, TN12 9DT
☎ (01622) 831427 🌐 mardenvillageclub.co.uk
Shepherd Neame Master Brew; 5 changing beers (sourced regionally; often Goacher's, Kent, Pig & Porter) Ⓗ
This Grade II-listed club and community hub offers six real ales. Five change regularly and are generally from local Kent microbreweries, with one dark beer always available. Many members are involved in the club's snooker teams; others simply enjoy the friendly ambience. Bingo and music evenings are held. Card-carrying CAMRA members are welcome but regular visitors will be required to join. CAMRA National Club of the Year 2022 and 2023. ♿✺♣●🖵(23)✿🛜♪

Margate

Ales of the Unexpected
105 Canterbury Road, CT9 5AX
☎ 07720 442892
4 changing beers Ⓖ
This micropub is located in a former fishmonger's in a row of shops in the Westbrook district of town. The pub has a front seating area with various tables and chairs and is decorated with maps of the UK and the world. A serving counter is found in a rear room, decorated with pumpclips of the various ales served since the pub opened in 2013, beyond which is a separate temperature-controlled cold room where the beers are served direct from the cask. Q🌅✺✳🚆●🖵✿

Mechanical Elephant ✅
Marine Terrace, CT9 1XJ
☎ (01843) 234100
Greene King Abbot; Ruddles Best Bitter; Sharp's Doom Bar; 2 changing beers Ⓗ
Ideally located opposite the main beach, with a flower-bedecked summer balcony offering the famous sunset views. This Wetherspoon is a quiet daytime pub, while on Friday and Saturday evenings recorded music is played. Good-value food and a good selection of well-kept ales is on sale, including Kent and regional guest beers. The staff are friendly and helpful. Its name derives from a large roving mechanical elephant that gave rides along the seafront in the 1950s. 🌅🕩♿✺🖵🛜

Two Halves
2 Marine Drive, CT9 1DH
☎ 07538 771904
5 changing beers Ⓖ
This small, friendly, welcoming micropub has an incredible location on Margate's seafront. The landlord knows his beer and sources them from all around the country. No matter what the weather this micropub has a great aspect, enjoy the sunsets out of the window or just watch the world go by. The beer and cider is kept in great condition in a large stillage room. Look out for the old-fashioned postcards in the loo! Q✺●🖵✿

Milstead

Red Lion
Rawling Street, ME9 0RT
☎ (01795) 830279 🌐 theredlionmilstead.co.uk
Goacher's Fine Light Ale, Special/House Ale, Best Dark Ale Ⓗ
Traditional family-run country pub with a well-kept range of permanent Goacher's ales. Set in the village of Milstead, three miles from Sittingbourne it is a welcoming venue and various groups meet in the pub on an ad hoc basis. There is a large patio and garden, and a car park to side of pub. The pub's aim is to provide food of good quality at a reasonable price, including Sunday lunches. Q🌅✺🕩P✿

New Romney

Smugglers' Alehouse Ⓛ
10 St Lawrence Court, High Street, TN28 8BU
☎ 07919 156336
3 changing beers (sourced locally) Ⓗ
Micropub located at the south end of the High Street. You can relax or join in with the varied conversations between customers and staff. Well behaved dogs on leads are welcome. In addition to the ever-changing real ales and ciders on offer, there is a selection of wines and spirits, with tea and coffee usually available on request. Various snacks (including pickled eggs) are also available. Please note, the pub accepts cash only. Q♿●P🖵✿

Northfleet

Earl Grey
177 Vale Road, DA11 8BP
🌐 earlgreynorthfleet.co.uk
Shepherd Neame Master Brew, Bishops Finger Ⓗ
An old-fashioned local in a distinctive late-18th century cottage-style building with a Kentish red brick and flint exterior. Internally there is an L-shaped bar with a raised seating area at the rear. The pub hosts two darts teams, euchre is played on Thursdays and there is a light-hearted quiz on the fourth Friday of the month. There is a large garden where children and dogs are welcome. A seasonal ale or a special brew from the Shepherd Neame range may also be available. ✺♣P🖵(483,489)

Iron Pier Taproom Ⓛ
Units 6 & 7 May Industrial Estate, May Avenue, DA11 8RU
☎ (01474) 569460 🌐 ironpier.beer
Iron Pier Perry St. Pale, Bitter, Wealdway Ⓖ
Brewery taproom opened in 2018 with plenty of seated accommodation with an excellent view of the brewery itself, and a large TV for sports fans. The Iron Pier brewery is only the second to operate in the Gravesend area since Russell's closed in the 1930s. Three regular Iron Pier beers are available, often with others depending on production at the time. A selection of KeyKeg and bottled beers, gins, wines and soft drinks are also available. Closed on Monday, weekday afternoons and Sunday evening. 🌅P🖵(483,489)✿🛜

Pembury

King William IV
87 Hastings Road, TN2 4JS
☎ (01892) 458241 🌐 kingwilliampembury.com
Greene King IPA; St Austell Proper Job; 4 changing beers (sourced regionally; often Fuller's, Lakedown, Thornbridge) Ⓗ
The King Will serves a wide range of rotating beers sourced from local and regional breweries along with a Kentish cider from Biddenden in a bright and spacious setting with plenty of comfortable seating. A flower-bedecked front garden and large garden to the rear

provide attractive facilities and are ideal for families. Traditional pub games in the form of darts, crib and bar billiards are prominent for the keen regulars who are also supportive of community initiatives promoted by the pub. Q✿⭐♣♠♦P🚲(6,297)🌮🍴♪

Queenborough

Admiral's Arm ⓛ

West Street, ME11 5AD (in Trafalgar Court, 30yds left from crossroads of High St and Park Rd)
☎ (01795) 668598 ⊕ admiralsarm.co.uk
4 changing beers (sourced nationally; often Lancaster, Ramsgate, Settle) Ⓗ/Ⓖ
A three-room micropub which opened on Trafalgar Day in 2016. Four real ales are sold through handpumps, along with a large range of 12 or more ciders/perries on gravity dispense, all from a temperature-controlled room. Ale can be served on gravity dispense from the cellar and an extensive range of gins and pub snacks from an extensive menu. The décor is mainly lifeboat and nautical themed. Kent CAMRA Regional Pub of the Year 2019. Q✿⭐♦⊕≠♣♠P🚲(334)🌮🍴♪

Rainham

Mackland Arms ⓛ

213 Station Road, ME8 7PS (5 minute walk N of railway station)
☎ (01634) 232178 ⊕ macklandarms.co.uk
Shepherd Neame Master Brew, Bishops Finger; 1 changing beer (sourced regionally; often Shepherd Neame) Ⓗ
On entering the wood-panelled L-shaped one-room bar, the drinker will find two or three cask ales on handpump. There is a fireplace to the left with a display of books and a television showing mainly football updates, and at the end of the bar the rear drinking area opens up into a large area with two dartboards then to a covered patio area for smokers and a large garden. ✿⭐≠♣♠🚲(327)🌮

Prince of Ales ⓛ

121 High Street, ME8 8AN (near centre of Rainham, adjacent to Post Office)
☎ 07982 756412 ⊕ princeofales.co.uk
4 changing beers (sourced nationally; often Kent, Tonbridge) Ⓖ
A minimum of three cask ales are always available served by gravity dispense from a chiller room in this micropub, supplemented by a craft KeyKeg dispensed beer and up to 10 ciders. A celebratory ale festival is held every March. A compact rear paved yard can be a suntrap in the warmer months. The walls are adorned with brewery paraphernalia including pumpclips, bottle labels and bar towels. Q⭐≠♣♠🚲(132)

Railway ✪

113 Station Road, ME8 7SF (opp railway station)
☎ (01634) 365396
Greene King Abbot; Ruddles Best Bitter; Sharp's Doom Bar; 3 changing beers (sourced nationally) Ⓗ
Originally called the Railway Hotel it was previously owned by Style & Winch and later Courage. It closed in 2012 and was reopened seven years later by Wetherspoon. Conveniently next door to the railway station, there is a screen at the end of the bar counter showing train departures times. The pub offers six ales, three of which are guests. There is an outdoor seating area. ✿⭐⊕&≠♣🚲(132)🍴

Ramsgate

Artillery Arms

36 West Cliff Road, CT11 9JS
☎ (01843) 853202
Oakham Citra; Ramsgate Gadds' No. 5 Best Bitter Ale; 4 changing beers (often Ramsgate, Wantsum) Ⓗ
One of the most authentic of all the Ramsgate pubs, it's unashamedly a no-frills real ale boozer with a wide selection of beers on draught. The tables and seats are different, varying from traditional bar stools through to aircraft seating, which gives the pub an interesting feel. There is a military theme throughout this multi-level pub which is packed full of character – from the stunning stained-glass windows to the mix of memorabilia adorning the walls. There are popular open mic and food nights. ⊕♦♠🚲🌮♪

Honeysuckle Inn

31 Honeysuckle Road, CT11 8AA
☎ 07800 545305
4 changing beers (often Tonbridge, Wantsum) Ⓗ
The pub seems to have had few changes in the last 200 years, not least its interior, which has been spared the modern trend of retro-fitting various exposed timbers as structural decoration, so it has real authenticity. Uniquely, it also contains a men's hairdressing business, which operates from Monday to Thursday and is called Salt Barbers. Q✿⭐≠(Dumpton Pk)🚲(Loop)🌮🍴♪

Hovelling Boat Inn

12 York Street, CT11 9DS
☎ 07968 800960
5 changing beers Ⓖ
A welcoming, dog friendly micropub that serves a good range of cask ale and ciders/perries. Drinks are brought to your table by the friendly and well-informed staff from a rear cellar where they are kept in a temperature-controlled environment and dispensed on gravity. The chalkboard names up to six beers that are available. Good chat and putting the world to rights is a common pastime in this superb micro. A pleasant outdoor pétanque area at the rear of the establishment offers somewhere to enjoy the warmer days. Q✿⭐♦🚲🌮

Montefiore Arms

1 Trinity Place, CT11 7HJ
⊕ montefiorearms.co.uk
Ramsgate Gadds' Hoppy Pale, Gadds' No. 7 Bitter Ale; 3 changing beers (often Ramsgate) Ⓗ
This award-winning traditional snug backstreet local enjoys a good reputation with real ale drinkers in the Thanet area. The pub's name and sign are unique, honouring the great Jewish financier and philanthropist Sir Moses Montefiore who lived locally for many years and was a benefactor to the town's poor. The pub showcases the beers of the Ramsgate brewery along with changing guest ales and Biddenden cider. ⭐♣♠🚲(Loop)🍴

Pub Ramsgate

87 High Street, CT11 9RJ
☎ (01843) 585404 ⊕ thepubramsgate.com
3 changing beers (sourced nationally; often Brew York, Kent, Mighty Oak) Ⓗ
A small, welcoming micropub in a chic, minimalist style, offering a good selection of cask and craft beers alongside cider and the occasional Bavarian beer. It can be found hidden away on the way down the High Street from Ramsgate station. Take-outs are available. Special draught Bavarian beers are sourced directly for the pub's Springfest and Oktoberfest events. ✿♣♠🚲🌮

Red Lion

1 King Street, CT11 8NN
☎ (01843) 586713
3 changing beers (often Ramsgate) Ⓗ

Busy pub in the heart of the town centre, probably the oldest surviving pub in the town. It has a mixed lunchtime clientele, while in the evening it is predominantly used by younger people, especially when loud rock music is played. There is a raised area towards the rear with a pool table. Beers from the Ramsgate brewery (Gadds') are normally available on handpump along with beers from further afield. ♣🚃(38,39)🛜♪

Riverhead

Bullfinch

London Road, TN13 2DR (on the corner of London Rd and Bullfinch Ln)
☎ (01732) 455107 ⊕ destinationinns.co.uk/pubs/bullfinch
McMullen Country Bitter, IPA; 1 changing beer (sourced nationally; often McMullen)

The only McMullen's pub in Kent. Although popular for food which is served all day every day, three well-kept real ales from the McMullen range are served. A weekly pub quiz and a number of other food or music-themed events are held. Although extensively opened up in smart modern style with an attractive exposed wood beam construction, many old pub features remain. There is a large log fire and an extensive garden with outside table service for warmer times.
🛏️❀🕪♿🅿🚃(1,8) 🌸🛜♪

Rochester

12 Degrees Ⓛ

352 High Street, ME1 1DJ
☎ 07512 040453 ⊕ rams-micropub-12degrees.business.site
6 changing beers (sourced locally; often Kent, Tonbridge, Wantsum) Ⓖ

Up to six cask ales are served by gravity disperse from glass doors behind the bar of this micropub. A seventh glass door houses a choice of bag in box ciders. This outlet is full of quirky signs and historical photos of the local area. Look out for the beer o'clock on the wall. There is a basement giving extra seating for music performances, a pool table and dartboard. The drinks are keenly priced for the area. No children and no dogs are admitted. Q⇌(Chatham)♣♿🚃♪

Coopers Arms 🏆

10 St Margaret's Street, ME1 1TL (behind cathedral)
☎ (01634) 404298 ⊕ thecoopersarms.co.uk
Timothy Taylor Landlord; 5 changing beers (sourced regionally; often Canterbury Ales, Mad Cat, Tonbridge) Ⓗ

Situated behind both the cathedral and castle, a short stroll from the busy High Street, this charming building dates from 1199 and was previously the home of monks, becoming a pub in 1543. The front bar is of particular interest, with an impressive beamed ceiling and fireplace. A short passageway leads to a more modern rear bar and pleasant garden which is busy in summer. Lunchtime meals are available Friday to Sunday and there is a fortnightly quiz night. ❀🕪⇌🅿🌸🛜

Man of Kent Ale House Ⓛ

6-8 John Street, ME1 1YN (200yds off A2 from bottom of Star Hill)
☎ 0871 951 1000
8 changing beers (sourced locally; often Canterbury Ales, Ramsgate, Tonbridge) Ⓗ

Traditional back-street pub with an impressive tiled sign of long-closed Style & Winch brewery, just a short uphill stroll from the High Street. All eight cask ales are from Kent breweries and there is an extensive range of ciders and German and Belgian beers. There is an open fire for the colder months and an enclosed garden that gets busy in the evening. Live music acts perform on a Thursday evening and on Sunday there's a jam session.
❀🛜♣♿🖤🚃(155) 🌸♪

Who'd Ha' Thought It

9 Baker Street, ME1 3DN (off Rochester's Maidstone Rd)
☎ (01634) 830144 ⊕ whodha.com
3 changing beers (sourced nationally) Ⓗ

Friendly backstreet local with a spacious wood-panelled bar that has two TVs showing sports. The three ever-changing cask ales are served with one usually from a Kent brewery. Various filled rolls are available at lunchtimes. To the rear is a snug area ideal for small groups. There is a log fire for the winter months. Outside there is a raised garden with a covered stillage area used for beer festivals. 🛏️❀♣🚃(155)🌸🛜♪

Rolvenden Layne

Ewe & Lamb ✅

26 Maytham Road, TN17 4NP (a mile off A28 in centre of Rolvenden towards Wittersham)
☎ (01580) 241429 ⊕ theeweandlamb.co.uk
Harvey's Sussex Best Bitter; Long Man Long Blonde; 2 changing beers (sourced nationally; often Timothy Taylor, Wantsum) Ⓗ

A friendly and relaxing village pub, reopened in March 2023 after a lengthy closure. Four real ales are normally available. A patio area for drinking is in the front and a small courtyard at the rear. Dogs are welcome and there are some beautiful local walks in the area. If you come by train, the pub is a 30-minute walk from Wittersham Road station on the Kent & East Sussex Railway, please note that some trains do not stop at this station.
Q🛏️❀🕪♣🚃(294) 🌸🛜

Ryarsh

Duke of Wellington

Birling Road, ME19 5LS
☎ (01732) 842318 ⊕ dukeofwellingtonryarsh.com
Harvey's Sussex Best Bitter; St Austell Proper Job; Timothy Taylor Landlord; 1 changing beer (sourced nationally) Ⓗ

A 16th-century pub with inglenook fireplaces in each of its two bars. The restaurant to the right displays part of an original wattle and daub wall behind glass. A covered and heated patio and a garden with pétanque pitchesare accessed through bifold doors. Some tables are provided at the front of the pub. Good food is available daily plus the popular Sunday roasts. A jazz evening is held on the first Thursday in month. Ramblers are welcome.
Q🛏️❀🕪🅿🌸🛜♪

St Michaels

Hop House Ⓛ

McCanns Brewery Ltd, Haffenden Farm, Bugglesden Road, TN30 6TG
☎ (01303) 760957 ⊕ mccanns.beer
4 changing beers (sourced locally) Ⓗ

The McCanns brewery tap room moved its operation from Caple-le-Ferne and is now located at Haffenden Farm, the home of Hukins Hops. Twenty taps on the back

wall and four handpumps on the bar serve a range of McCanns beers, guest ales and cider. A restaurant will open in the near future, meanwhile pizzas are available from the outside area and food trucks visit regularly (times vary). Brewery tours are planned.
🏃😋🍴P🚃(12) 🌼

St Peter's

Four Candles Alehouse
1 Sowell Street, CT10 2AT
☎ 07947 062063 ⊕ thefourcandles.co.uk
4 changing beers (sourced locally; often Four Candles) 🄶
This former shop is now firmly established on the local micropub scene and is renowned for its friendly atmosphere. Seating is provided at high bench tables, while the beer is served from a cooled cabinet in an adjacent room. The pub has its own microbrewery in the cellar which supplies excellent one-off beers to complement the offerings from other brewers. In the warmer weather benches outside provide a superb suntrap. **Q**⇌(Broadstairs)🍴🚃(Loop)🌼

Sandwich

New Inn 🄻
2 Harnet Street, CT13 9ES
☎ (01304) 612335 ⊕ newinn-sandwich.co.uk
Sharp's Doom Bar, Sea Fury; 1 changing beer (sourced locally; often Ramsgate) 🄷
This impressive pub, located in the medieval Cinque Port, is perfect for exploring the historic market town. Inside, the wood panelling and carpeted bar provide a traditional, comfortable feel. Roadside seating allow you to watch Sandwich life go by. The bar offers one guest ale from the Ramsgate brewery, with a second when local events are held. Home-made food, from local produce, is available all day. Weekly live music and occasional charity events are hosted. Step-free access is from the rear car park. 🏃😋🛏🍺🅰⇌♣P🚃🌼🛜🎵

Sevenoaks

Anchor
32 London Road, TN13 1AS
☎ (01732) 454898
House beer (by Wantsum); 2 changing beers (sourced regionally; often Harvey's, Ramsgate) 🄷
The Anchor is a friendly town-centre pub run for over 40 years by effervescent landlords Barry and Phil. A Guide regular of over 20 years standing, great pride is taken over the quality and range of the cask ales with Wantsum Imperial always available alongside two other independent regional brews. Good-value meals are served at lunchtimes with roasts proving very popular. Darts and poker evenings feature and regular live music evenings, usually on Wednesday and Sunday, are listed on the pub's Facebook page. 😋🍺🚃🌼🛜🎵

Sevenoaks Weald

Windmill 🄻 ✅
1 Windmill Road, TN14 6PN
☎ (01732) 463330 ⊕ windmillsevenoaksweald.com
Larkins Traditional Ale; 4 changing beers (sourced regionally; often Titsey, Tonbridge, Wantsum) 🄷
Situated at the heart of the village by the green, the Windmill provides a real community focus, hosting local

cricket and football teams. Nearby Larkins brewery supplies the permanent ale which is supplemented by four rotating cask beers from Kent and the south-east together with local Chiddingstone cider. Recently refurbished in a stylish retro feel, a well-used wood-burning stove has been retained to add cosiness. The pleasant, flower-adorned garden has plenty of covered seating, ideal for the summer months.
🏃😋🍺🅰♣🍴🚃(5,401) 🌼🛜

Shoreham

Samuel Palmer 🄻
Church Street, TN14 7RY
☎ (01959) 525442 ⊕ thesamuelpalmer.com
Larkins Traditional Ale; house beer (by Three Acre); 2 changing beers (sourced locally; often Stay Wild, Three Acre) 🄷
Since its refurbishment and change of ownership in 2022 this smart village pub has continued to thrive. It makes the most of its namesake, displaying many paintings by the artist who named the area as the 'Valley of Vision'. Four handpumps dispense an interesting selection of real ales with particular support being given to local micro Stay Wild. Quality food is served every day but the menus and times vary so check the website beforehand. The Darent Valley Path runs nearby.
🏃😋🍺🛏⇌P🚃(2) 🌼🛜

Sittingbourne

Paper Mill 🄻
2 Charlotte Street, ME10 2JN (N of Sittingbourne railway station, almost in Milton Regis at the corner of Church St and Charlotte St)
☎ 07927 073584 ⊕ thepapermillmicropub.co.uk
3 changing beers (sourced regionally; often Goacher's, Vocation) 🄶
Popular one-room micropub, located close to Sittingbourne town centre and railway station, with bench seating around four large wood tables. Local beers feature alongside national brwers such as Blue Monkey and Cloudwater. A range of real ciders are available. Blackboards displaying the beer list include a number of interesting KeyKeg offerings. Occasional events such as Meet the Brewer and pub quizzes take place. Opening hours can be flexible with advance notice.
Q🏃😋⇌♣🍴🚃(334,347) 🌼

Yellow Stocks
22A High Street, ME10 4PD
☎ 07572 180627
4 changing beers (sourced locally; often Canterbury Ales, Iron Pier, Ramsgate) 🄶
Micropub which opened in 2018 in a former clothes shop, it is named after a type of handmade building brick once made in large quantities in the surrounding countryside. Real ales and ciders/perries are sold on gravity dispense from a temperature controlled cellar room behind the small bar counter. They mainly have a Kentish provenance but some unusual other regional beers are offered. The unisex toilet is spotlessly kept. A garden and outside smoking area are at the rear.
🏃😋⇌♣🍴🚃🌼🛜

Smeeth

Dog House Pub 🍺 🄻
Evegate Business Park, Station Road, TN25 6SX (S of the A20 at Smeeth crossroads, towards the rear of the

Business Park)
☎ 07340 985064 ⊕ thedoghousepub.co.uk
2 changing beers (sourced locally) Ⓖ
A small pub/restaurant with recently extended dining area, it serves an ever-changing range of ales from local microbreweries, and local ciders. Local craft lagers, ales on draught keg and a range of spirits and soft drinks complete the offering. Home-cooked food served is lunchtimes daily and evenings Thursday to Saturday, often locally sourced. Pizzas on Friday and Saturday evenings use locally milled flour. There is a small patio smoking area, and outdoor covered and heated seating. Live music at weekends, typically acoustic blues and folk.
🅑❀◑&♠P♣📶🎵

Snargate

Red Lion ★ Ⓛ
TN29 9UQ (on B2080, 1 mile NW of Brenzett) TQ990285
☎ (01797) 344648
Goacher's Real Mild Ale; 3 changing beers (often Canterbury Ales, Goacher's, Rother Valley) Ⓖ
A regular Guide entry since 1981 this superb, unspoilt, multi-room 16th-century smugglers' pub has been in the same family for over 100 years. Passing to the next generation in 2016, but still universally known as Doris's, it is decorated with posters from the 1940s and the Women's Land Army. Identified by CAMRA as having a nationally important historic pub interior, it is well worth a visit. A beer festival is held in June near to the summer solstice, with a mini festival in October.
Q❀♣●P🚌(11B)♣

Staplehurst

Lord Raglan
Chart Hill Road, TN12 0DE (½ mile N of A229 at Cross at Hand) TQ786472
☎ (01622) 843747 ⊕ lord-raglan.co.uk
Goacher's Fine Light Ale; Harvey's Sussex Best Bitter Ⓗ
A 15 minute walk from the bus stop on the main road brings you to this family-owned country pub. Two log fires and a stove provide a welcome in the colder months. The bar is decorated with hops and the excellent food and drink is welcomed by the frequently returning customers. Sunny evenings may be spent in adjacent orchard garden. Well-behaved children and dogs are welcome. Local perry and Double Vision cider are both stocked alongside the beer. Q❀◑●P♣

Staplestreet

Three Horseshoes
46 Staple Street, ME13 9UA (follow the signs from the A299 for Mount Ephraim Gardens)
☎ (01227) 750842 ⊕ threehorseshoesfaversham.co.uk
Shepherd Neame Spitfire, Master Brew; 1 changing beer (sourced locally) Ⓗ
Dating from 1690, this is a traditional community pub at the heart of village life. It is popular with walkers, cyclists and locals alike. It has an attractive, weather-boarded exterior with a traditional Kent peg tile roof. Inside it has exposed brickwork, old oak beams and a large open fireplace. A small outdoor suntrap patio is sheltered by an ancient walnut tree. The pub serves good quality food and has regular music nights and an annual charity wheelie-bin race. ❀◑&♣P🚌(638)♣📶🎵

Stowting

Tiger Inn ✓
TN25 6BA (village signposted off the B2068, 2 ½ miles N of jct 11 of M20)
☎ (01303) 862130 ⊕ tigerinn.co.uk
Fuller's London Pride; Harvey's Sussex Best Bitter; 1 changing beer (sourced locally) Ⓗ
Reopened in 2021 after major internal improvements, the Tiger is in the scattered hamlet of Stowting, nestled in beautiful countryside at the foot of the North Downs. The pub has upmarket and contemporary decor yet has retained a cosy and traditional feel. Parts of the inn date back to the 16th century and it still displays the 'Mackeson of Hythe Ales' on its frontage (it was one of the first pubs that the Mackeson Brothers purchased). Food is available daily, often using local and seasonal produce. 🅑❀◑&●P♣📶

Strood

10:50 From Victoria Ⓛ
Rear of 37-39 North Street, ME2 4SJ (in a railway arch opp Asda car park)
☎ 07941 449137
6 changing beers (sourced regionally) Ⓗ/Ⓖ
Situated opposite ASDA's car park, and approached through a side gate from the entrance, the path leads to a spacious garden with a stage for live music. There are three brightly painted beach huts with bench seating and tables. This micropub's bar area in the railway arch is wood panelled throughout, with wall mounted bench seats and tables with railway memorabilia and pictures on the wall. There is a log fire for the colder months. Q❀&⇌●P🚌(191)♣📶🎵

Sutton Valence

Queen's Head
High Street, ME17 3AG
☎ (01622) 843225 ⊕ thequeenshead-pub.co.uk
Goacher's Fine Light Ale; Timothy Taylor Landlord; Young's London Original; 1 changing beer (sourced nationally; often Musket) Ⓗ
Glorious views across the Weald may be seen from this village pub. Hops decorate the central bar and in winter a log fire blazes in the inglenook fireplace. On the right is a large dining area and two snug areas to the left. A raised garden is above the small car park at rear and the barn is used for events. See social media for Tuesday quiz night dates. Darts and various games are played and there are occasional live music evenings.
🅑❀◑P🚌(12)♣📶

Swanley

Cotton Mill Ⓛ ✓
10 Station Road, BR8 8ET
☎ (01322) 669619 ⊕ thecottonmillpub.com
4 changing beers (sourced regionally; often Iron Pier, Kent) Ⓗ
Micropub opened in 2018 in a former public WC and extended by taking over the next-door taxi office in 2023. It serves four changing real ales on handpump, several ciders in boxes, and six KeyKeg beers. The pleasantly renovated building, with comfortable seating has recently been fitted with a new bar and beer store. Regular events include darts Tuesday, crib night Wednesday and seasonal quizzes. There is pleasant

outside drinking area with live music, street food and beer festivals in summer. Closed on Monday and weekday afternoons. ᗉ✿❀♣♠⬤🖶🌳🎵

Tankerton

Tankerton Arms 🅛
135 Tankerton Road, CT5 2AW
☎ 07897 741811
4 changing beers (sourced regionally; often Iron Pier, Kent, Westerham) Ⓖ
This friendly micropub, with a firm policy of supporting Kent microbreweries, is situated among Tankerton's small shops. The range of four cask beers changes frequently. There are some KeyKeg beers and occasional beer swaps with regional breweries. The pleasant, airy room is lined with high wooden tables and stools, and is adorned with pictures of Thames sailing barges and the sea forts. The cosy snug holds up to 12 people and can be pre-booked for meetings. There is a patio in front for outdoor drinking. Q ᗉ✿♣♠⬤🖶🌳🎵

Temple Ewell

Fox
14 High Street, CT16 3DU
☎ (01304) 823598
3 changing beers (sourced nationally; often Courage, Marston's, Timothy Taylor) Ⓗ
This traditional village pub, with wooden beams, local photos and fox ornaments, warmly welcomes locals and visitors alike. A good range of styles and strengths of real ales are on offer, which can be enjoyed in the main bar, one of the smaller rooms, or in the suntrap garden. Events include quiz nights, curry nights, and occasional music evenings. Outside, there is an attractive stream-side garden with a skittle alley. The pub is a short walk from Kearsney Abbey gardens and public transport. ᗉ✿◑➤≷(Kearsney) ♣P🖶🌳🎵

Tenterden

Old Dairy Tap Room
Tenterden Station Yard, Station Road, TN30 6HE
☎ (01580) 456007 ⊕ olddairytaproom.com
3 changing beers (sourced locally) Ⓗ
The Tap Room is located at the front of the brewery and offers the range of Old Dairy and Cow Shed beers along with a selection of bottled beers. There is also a range of local ciders from the local Nightingale Cider Company. Kentish gin, whisky, vodka, and local wines and soft drinks including a variety of teas and coffees are also available. ✿≷(Town)⬤P🎵

This Ancient Boro'
3 East Cross, TN30 6AD
☎ (01580) 388815 ⊕ thisancientboro.com
9 changing beers (sourced nationally) Ⓖ
A Whitbread pub which closed in 1968 and reopened as an ale house and tapas bar in 2018 and became local CAMRA Pub of the Year in 2020 and 2023. The pub is a hybrid of the original and a micropub, with no live music or gaming machines. An ever-changing variety of beers are available by gravity dispensed from cooled casks on stillage behind the bar, together with various ciders which are served from a fridge. There is an interesting snack/tapas menu. Q ᗉ◑➤≷(Town)♣⬤🖶🌳🎶🎵

Tonbridge

Fuggles Beer Café 🅛
165 High Street, TN9 1BX (N end of High St near parish church)
☎ (01732) 666071 ⊕ fugglesbeercafe.co.uk/locations
Tonbridge Coppernob; 3 changing beers (sourced nationally; often Downlands, Kent, Vocation) Ⓗ
Reflecting the relaxed mood of its original sister pub in Tunbridge Wells with subdued lighting, candlelit tables and colourful wall-mounted brewery nameplates from across Europe, this establishment will delight customers with eclectic beer tastes. Care is taken to advertise the daily beer menu both online and within the pub and this, together with prominent advertising of frequent special beer promotion events, demonstrates the continued commitment to supplying a whole range of beer styles from respected breweries in cask, keg and bottle. ᗉ◑🍴♿≷♣⬤🖶🌳🎵

Humphrey Bean 🅛 ✔
94 High Street, TN9 1AP (near castle and river)
☎ (01732) 773850
Greene King Abbot; Ruddles Best Bitter; Sharp's Doom Bar; 3 changing beers (sourced nationally; often By The Horns, Hook Norton, Tonbridge) Ⓗ
Occupying an enviable position with views towards the river Medway and Tonbridge castle, this town-centre Wetherspoon house continues as a reliable real ale outlet. The open-plan interior is deceptively large with a broad range of seating, and ceiling windows provide an airy feel. An attractive, verdant and spacious garden extends through to the rear. Brewery tap takeovers and occasional Meet the Brewer events are organised to supplement the spring and autumn festivals. Easy Street Pale from Tonbridge brewery has been adopted as a regular. ᗉ✿◑♿≷P🖶🌳🎵

Nelson Arms 🍷
19 Cromer Street, TN9 1UP
☎ (01732) 358284 ⊕ thenelsonarms.com
8 changing beers (sourced nationally; often Kent, Rother Valley, Surrey Hills) Ⓗ
In 2024 the accolades of local CAMRA, overall Kent and CAMRA National Pub of the Year finalist were deservedly bestowed on this back-street community pub, located close to the High Street and railway station. The pub's interior has a nautical theme with decorations including a ship's wheel, naval brasses and a Nelson painting. A selection of at least six beers of different styles and strengths are served along with an extensive selection of ciders and keg beer. Themed beer events, food evenings, Sunday quiz nights, and weekend live music and singalongs feature regularly. Convenient Airbnb accommodation is available above the pub. ᗉ✿◑➤≷♣⬤🖶🌳🎵🎶

Tunbridge Wells

Fuggles Beer Café 🅛
28 Grosvenor Road, TN1 2AP (opp Tesco bus stop)
☎ (01892) 457739 ⊕ fugglesbeercafe.co.uk/locations
Tonbridge Coppernob; 3 changing beers (sourced nationally; often Burning Sky, Downlands, Iron Pier) Ⓗ
One of Kent's most special bars for beer-lovers, boasting 28 taps dispensing beer styles from across the UK, Europe and around the world, all to be enjoyed in an atmosphere combining the best elements of a British pub and a continental café-style establishment. A huge choice of craft keg and bottled beers along with real

cider from Ascension, and regular special beer promotion events make this a destination pub, deservedly celebrating its 10th consecutive appearance in the Guide. ⬢◑🐕⬥≈♠♿🖿♣☼🐾🛜

George 🄻
29 Mount Ephraim, TN4 8AA
☎ (01892) 539492 ⊕ thegeorgepubtunbridgewells.co.uk
Fonthill Good Morning Captain; Creedence; Where's Me Jumper; Gun Zamzama IPA; Long Man Best Bitter; 3 changing beers (sourced locally; often 360 Degree, Only With Love, Pig & Porter) Ⓗ
A warm and welcoming atmosphere pervades in this stylish former coaching inn which features much wooden flooring, panelling and furniture, log burners and sofas. The old stables have been converted into the home of the Fonthill brewery, brewing three core cask ales available in the pub and in the Tap Room which is open Friday evenings and all day Saturday. A partly-covered secluded rear garden provides a pleasant alfresco space. A range of traditional board games are available to play.
Q⬢❀◑≈♠♿🖿🐾🛜♪

Grove Tavern ✔
19 Berkeley Road, TN1 1YR
☎ (01892) 526549 ⊕ grovetavern.co.uk
Harvey's Sussex Best Bitter; Timothy Taylor Landlord; 2 changing beers (sourced nationally; often Harvey's, Marston's) Ⓗ
Tucked away in the old town, only five minutes' walk from the railway station, the Grove has been a reliable real ale outlet for more than a quarter of a century. Loyal locals encircle the traditional bar layout and engage in friendly chat and banter while sharing a few snacks, readily welcoming any newcomers. A cosy pub where customers' conversation happily coexists alongside darts and pool players and those escaping the bustle of the town centre while enjoying their refreshment.
⬢≈♠🖿🐾🛜

Royal Oak
92 Prospect Road, TN2 4SY
☎ (01892) 542546 ⊕ theroyaloaktw.co.uk
Harvey's Sussex Best Bitter; 5 changing beers (sourced regionally; often Cellar Head, Five Points, Iron Pier) Ⓗ
The Oak is a family-owned, spacious and well-kept free house is a short walk from the town centre and railway station. With up to seven handpumps, the focus is on providing a choice of ever-changing beers mainly from Kent and Sussex breweries together with real ciders from Turners and Charrington's. Entertainment is promoted with live bands performing most Saturday evenings and festival weekends. A chalkboard advertises forthcoming music, events and quizzes. A pizza van serves on Friday evenings. ⬢❀≈♠♿P🖿(6,285)🐾🛜♪

Sussex Arms 🄻
Sussex Mews, TN2 5TE (off the Pantiles)
☎ (01892) 549579 ⊕ thesussextw.co.uk
Fonthill Good Morning Captain; Long Man Best Bitter; 2 changing beers (sourced nationally; often Only With Love, Tiny Rebel) Ⓗ
Tucked away behind the historic, bustling Pantiles the Sussex provides a welcome place to drink or dine on its front and rear outdoor terracing in a sheltered and traffic-free environment. The cosy main bar has an open fire and log burners at either end and TV screens show major sporting events. The excellent on-site Forum Basement hosts numerous and regular live musical and comedy performances. Tunbridge Wells-brewed Fonthill beers are sold along with Ascension cider and pop-up food vendors operate from the kitchen. ❀≈♠🖿🐾🛜♪

Upper Upnor

King's Arms ★
2 High Street, ME2 4XG
☎ (01634) 717490 ⊕ kingsarmsupnor.co.uk
3 changing beers (sourced regionally) Ⓗ
This pub is just a short walk from the River Medway and the historic Upnor Castle. The main bar leads to a smaller drinking area with access to a large garden and restaurant. The garden, with roped areas, contains tables and bench seats plus a large statue and children's play furniture, all ideal for those warm summer days. Usually three or four guest cask ales are on offer, plus ciders and a range of foreign bottled beers. Food is available in the restaurant, with a bar menu for drinkers.
⬢❀🖾◑🐕♿P🖿(197)🐾🛜

Wainscott

Crafty Fox
1 Hollywood Lane, ME3 8AG
☎ (01634) 921088
Grainstore Ten Fifty; Kent Session Pale Ⓗ**; 1 changing beer (sourced regionally)** Ⓗ/Ⓖ
Inviting pub, greeting the visitor with its warm welcome and friendly locals. Two separate connected rooms each have a bar, the second of which is carpeted and has a dartboard. Three cask ales are on offer, from Kentish and regional breweries, plus ciders from Kentish cider makers. There is a small unheated smoking area to one side of the entrance. Q⬢❀🐕♠🖿(191)🛜

Walmer

Berry 🍷 🄻
23 Canada Road, CT14 7EQ
☎ (01304) 362411
Harvey's Sussex Best Bitter; Oakham Citra; Time & Tide Spratwaffler; 12 changing beers (often Arbor, Cloudwater, Thornbridge) Ⓗ
This multi-CAMRA award-winning alehouse is one of the top real ale pubs in the area. The welcome, service, and quality of real ales and ciders reflect the landlord's enthusiasm, making every day a beer festival. The main bar is light and airy, with a pleasant, shaded courtyard at the back. Up to 11 cask ales, seven KeyKeg ales and 10 ciders/perries are on offer. Two festivals are held each year. Events include live music and quiz nights. Burgers and wraps are served on Thursday and Friday.
⬢❀◑♠🖿🐾🛜♪

Freed Man 🄻
329 Dover Road, CT14 7NX
☎ 07793 321126 ⊕ thefreed-man.co.uk
4 changing beers Ⓗ
The unremarkable exterior belies this pub's offerings for discerning drinkers. Inside, there's a cosy micropub atmosphere, with reclaimed wood walls decorated with nautical memorabilia. Up to four real ales, mainly from local breweries, are served from a Victorian beer engine. Real ciders (some from Kent), European lagers, wines and spirits are available. Events include Ladies' night, monthly quizzes, and Sunday cheese platters. Guests can bring in food from local eateries. The bar accommodates wheelchair users with a low bar. Q⬢🅰≈♠🖿🐾🛜

West Hythe

Unit1 🄻

Unit 1, Riverside Craft Centre, CT21 4NB TR125342
☎ (01303) 265000 ⊕ unit1riverside.co.uk
3 changing beers (sourced locally; often Hop Fuzz, Romney Marsh) Ⓗ

Located adjacent to the Royal Military Canal at the base of Lympne Hill and close to Stutfall Castle. Three Hop Fuzz beers are usually available as well as a cider served on gravity. Boomers, a lager brewed by Hop Fuzz, and Kronbacher, a German imported lager, are also served. Food is available every day and includes pop up kitchens with a new menu each weekend (Fri-Sun) and homemade pizzas on a Thursday. Q🚫❄️🕭◑🌿🐾

West Malling

Bull Inn

1 High Street, ME19 6QH
☎ (01732) 842753 ⊕ thebullwestmalling.com
Goacher's Gold Star Strong Ale; Young's London Original; 4 changing beers (sourced nationally; often Goacher's, Musket) Ⓗ

This welcoming free house sits at the north end of the historic High Street. Following a recent makeover it now has a brighter look with predominantly high tables while preserving the wood panelling and floors. Changing beers are usually sourced locally and the Bull's Malling Special is often a rebadged beer from Musket. There is a terraced garden to the rear. A number of local groups meet at the pub, and a quiz is held on Monday evenings. Q🚫❄️◑🖳(72,151) 🐾☂♪

Malling Jug

52 High Street, ME19 6LU (in a narrow alley opp Swan St between a funeral directors and a charity shop)
☎ (01732) 667832
Kent Session Pale; 6 changing beers (sourced nationally) Ⓖ

Hidden down an alleyway off the High Street this micropub announces itself by the presence of an A-board on the pavement. A former residential property, now converted to a pub, with its own courtyard garden at the rear. Available and coming soon casks are listed on a chalkboard and on clipboard menus dotted around the pub. Beers may be ordered as pints, halves or third-pint samplers on beer bats. Various hot and cold snacks are available. Q🚫❄️♿≒🕭◑🖳(72,151)🐾☂

Whitstable

Handsome Sam 🄻

3 Canterbury Road, CT5 4HJ
☎ 07947 984991
7 changing beers (sourced regionally; often Long Man, Wantsum, Bexley) Ⓖ

Popular micropub just outside the town centre, 10 minutes' walk from the railway station. Named after the original owner's late cat, the high-ceilinged pub has original exposed beams and a cat motif is apparent throughout. Catman murals adorn the walls – the Catman artist lives locally. The beers are usually, but not always, from Kent breweries, and the draught cider is from Biddenden. Check the Facebook page to see if major sporting events are being televised, and also if there is a quiz night. Sister pub to the Brickfield in Swalecliffe. Q🚫❄️≒🕭◑🖳🐾

Ship Centurion 🄻 ✅

111 High Street, CT5 1AY
☎ (01227) 264740 ⊕ theshipcenturion.com
Adnams Southwold Bitter; 3 changing beers (sourced regionally; often Canterbury Ales, Goacher's, Ramsgate) Ⓗ

A friendly and traditional town-centre pub. Colourful hanging baskets add to its charm in summer, and pictures of Whitstable are displayed. A Kentish beer is always served. Home-cooked bar food includes authentic German dishes. A roast is served on Sundays, booking advised. Live music plays on Thursday evenings in March to December. There is a meat raffle on Sundays, and a music quiz on the first Wednesday of each month. A good place to watch sport on Sky and TNT. 🚫◑≒🕭◑🖳🐾☂♪

Artillery Arms, Ramsgate (Photo: Julian Stone)

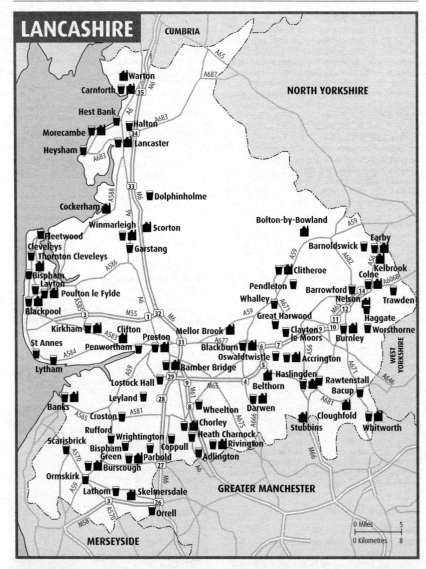

Accrington

Arden Inn
81 Abbey Street, BB5 1EH
☎ 07518 563663 ⊕ ardeninn.co.uk
4 changing beers (sourced nationally; often Bradfield, Timothy Taylor) ⊞

A traditional pub situated at the gateway to Accrington's historic town centre. Though essentially open-plan there are a number of separate drinking areas. It has a pool table and dartboard, a pleasant atmosphere and everything you'd expect from a town-centre pub. Live bands feature Fridays and Saturdays and live vocalists on Sundays. Buses to the Rossendale Valley and Manchester stop close by. ⇌🖳(464,X41)♪

Canine Club 🅛
45-47 Abbey Street, BB5 1EN
☎ (01254) 233999

Tetley Bitter; 3 changing beers (sourced nationally; often Moorhouse's, Reedley Hallows) ⊞

An award-winning social club on a busy street in an area of the town centre known for its many independent retailers. The central bar serves a comfortable lounge to the front and a games room to the rear where snooker, pool and darts are played. There is a large upstairs function room. This traditional club is always busy but is welcoming to all. Alongside the Tetley Bitter the changing beer range features local breweries such as Reedley Hallows and Moorhouse's. Buses to the Rossendale Valley and Manchester stop close by. ⇌♣🖳(464,X41) 🛜♪

Adlington

Old Post Office 🅛
161 Chorley Road, PR6 9LP
☎ (01204) 228969 ⊕ escapebrewery.co.uk
4 changing beers (sourced locally; often Escape) ⊞

The Old Post Office opened in 2021 and is brought to you by Bolton's Escape brewery, in partnership with MV Pub Group. It is the brewery's tap bar, located in the old post office building near the Ridgway Arms (now Tesco). There are four cask ales on handpumps serving Escape brewery ales and the occasional guest, with additional keg lines for craft ales from smaller North-West breweries such as Rivington, Chain House and Pomona Island, and quality lagers and ciders. ▷❀≠P🖳(125)❀🛈

Spinners Arms 🅛
23 Church Street, PR7 4EX
☎ (01257) 483331 ⊕ thespinners.pub
Timothy Taylor Landlord; 5 changing beers (sourced regionally; often Abbeydale, Oakham, Salopian) 🄷
Known as the Bottom Spinners to differentiate it from the other Spinners Arms in the village this pub celebrated 20 consecutive years in the Guide in 2022. Built in 1838, it is welcoming and friendly, with a single bar serving three seating areas with no pool table or gaming machines, just an open log fire. A pleasant outdoor drinking area is to the front. The bar menu offers a range of light bites and hot and cold sandwiches. One regular beer and up to five alternating guest beers are served on handpump. ▷❀◖≠P🖳(8A)❀🛈♪

Bacup

Crown Inn 🅛
19 Greave Road, OL13 9HQ (off Todmorden Rd)
☎ (01706) 873982
Pictish Brewers Gold; 3 changing beers 🄷
Cosy, traditional country pub, just off the road out to Todmorden, with a large L-shaped bar and stone-flagged floors throughout. It was built in 1865 and was once owned by Baxter's of Glentop brewery. A welcoming coal fire warms the atmosphere in the cooler months. There are always three beers available, usually sourced locally. Food is available most evenings. Quiz nights are held on Wednesday and Sunday. On the second floor is a function room accommodating up to 35 guests. There is a large patio beer garden to the front of the pub. ▷❀◖♣P🖳(465,7) ❀

Bamber Bridge

Beer Box 🅛
Unit 3, 143 Station Road, PR5 6LA
☎ (01772) 339619
5 changing beers (sourced locally; often Fell, MBH Beer) 🄷
Bamber Bridge's longest-established micropub, which opened in 2018, is located on the main road running through the northern end of the town. There is one relatively large room with plenty of seating and some standing room, and an outside seating area to the front. Up to five real ales are available, mainly from local breweries and including one dark beer, alongside a selection of real ciders, Bavarian lager, gins and wines. Live music is on Sunday. Q&≠❀🖳(125)❀🛈♪

Banks

Ralph's Wife's 🍺
4 Hoole Lane, PR9 8BD
☎ (01704) 214678
Fell Crag; 1 changing beer (sourced locally) 🄷
A coffee shop and bar with two changing real ales, it is now the only real ale outlet in Banks, and a welcome addition to the real ale scene in Southport and West Lancashire. It has the usual friendly, welcoming

attributes of micropubs, and there is some seating outside. Tapas nights and cheese and wine events are held. Tea and coffee are also served, including a range of speciality teas. Q❀P🖳❀🛈

Barnoldswick

Barlick Tap Ale House 🅛
8 Newtown, BB18 5UQ
☎ 07739 088846
5 changing beers (sourced nationally) 🄷
This dog-friendly one-room micropub was the first in the town and is situated just off the town square, two minutes from the main bus stop. A choice of five constantly-changing cask beers is offered, one of which will be a dark beer and one a LocAle. There is a large selection of continental bottled beers and always two ciders available. The pub hosts occasional events and tastings. There is no background music. Q❀🖳(M1)❀

Barrowford

Banker's Draft
143 Gisburn Road, BB9 6HQ
☎ 07739 870880

REAL ALE BREWERIES	
4 Mice 🍺 Bolton-by-Bowland	
Accidental Morecambe	
Avid Lancaster	
BB18 🍺 Earby	
Beer Shack 🍺 Clitheroe	
Ben's ✦ Chorley	
Big Clock 🍺 Accrington	
Bowland Clitheroe	
Brewhouse Kirkham	
Brewsmith Stubbins	
Chain House ✦ Preston	
Clay Brow Skelmersdale	
Farm Yard ✦ Cockerham	
Fuzzy Duck Poulton le Fylde	
Hop Vine 🍺 Burscough	
Hopstar Darwen	
Hopworks ✦ Bamber Bridge	
Jimbrew ✦ Clifton	
Lancaster Lancaster	
Lune ✦ Lancaster (NEW)	
Moorhouse's Burnley	
Northern Whisper Cloughfold	
Old School ✦ Warton	
Oscars Nelson	
Parker Banks	
Patrons Tap 🍺 Blackburn (NEW)	
Patten 🍺 Winmarleigh (brewing suspended)	
Peregrine Accrington	
Problem Child 🍺 Parbold	
Q Brew Carnforth	
Red Rose Darwen	
Reedley Hallows Burnley	
Rivington ✦ Rivington	
Rossendale 🍺 Haslingden	
Shed Thornton Cleveleys	
Snowhill Scorton	
Spring Hill Farm Belthorn (NEW)	
Tangled Web Preston (NEW)	
Three B's Blackburn	
Three Peaks Kelbrook	
Thwaites Mellor Brook	
Unbound ✦ Colne	
West Coast Rock 🍺 Blackpool	
Whitworth Valley ✦ Whitworth (NEW)	

4 changing beers (sourced nationally) Ⓗ
This imposing detached former bank is now a small and friendly micropub specialising in real ale and conversation, with no loud music or TVs. The five handpumps dispense continually rotating cask ales from national small brewers, and offer a great variety of beer styles – from hoppy blondes and traditional bitters to dark beers. There is also a good selection of wines and bottled craft lagers and wheat beers, with at least one real cider normally on draft. Q✤🐸♿️P🚲(2)🌸

Bispham Green

Eagle & Child
Maltkiln Lane, L40 3SG
☎ (01257) 462297 ∰ eagleandchildbispham.co.uk
Moorhouse's White Witch; 7 changing beers (sourced regionally) Ⓗ
An 18th-century pub with eight handpumps, seven showcasing real ales. Moorhouse's White Witch, Wainwright and Bowland brewery beers are usually available alongside a variety of guest ales. This busy country pub has been Lancashire Dining Pub of the year and is noted for its food, with its meat sourced from the Ainscough family farm. The huge front and back beer gardens, with their wildlife area and great views, host a beer festival on the first May bank holiday. Quiz night is every Monday. 🐸✤🍴♣️P🚲(337)🌸🛜

Blackburn

Black Bull Ⓛ
Brokenstone Road, BB3 0LL (corner of Brokenstone Rd and Heys Ln) SD666247
☎ (01254) 581381 ∰ threebsbrewery.co.uk
Three B's Stoker's Slake, Bobbin's Bitter, Oatmeal Stout, Black Bull, Weavers Brew, Knocker Up; 2 changing beers (sourced locally; often Three B's) Ⓗ
In the heart of rural Lancashire, this is an independent award-winning family-run pub with brewery and beer shop attached. There are eight handpumps serving a fine selection of Three B's ales including the exclusive Black Bull bitter. The three-beer wedges are very popular. It was built on a farmhouse in the 18th century, purchased by Robert Bell from Thwaites and now transformed into a place for those who appreciate fine beer and friendly conversation. No jukebox, fruit-machines or food, just a friendly relaxing atmosphere. Q✤🐸✤♿️♣️P🌸

Drummer's Arms Ⓛ
65 King William Street, BB1 7DT
☎ (01254) 941075
Lancaster Red; Three B's Stoker's Slake; 4 changing beers (sourced locally; often Big Clock, Deeply Vale, Hopstar) Ⓗ
Single-roomed bar opposite the Town Hall on the edge of the main shopping area run by a mother and daughter team. The walls are adorned with breweriana and old pub signs. The bar always offers a range of styles from stouts through to hoppy bitters, with Stoker's Slake mild a regular. There is a pleasant terrace at front featuring upcycled drum tables. Live music is on the first and third Sunday of every month. At other times expect a range of unobtrusive background music. ✤🍴🌸🎵

Hare & Hounds Ⓛ
78 Lammack Road, BB1 8LA
☎ (01254) 676724
4 changing beers (sourced regionally; often Bowland, Reedley Hallows, Worsthorne) Ⓗ
Former Whitbread estate pub rescued by the current landlord and backed by a passionate local community. It is adjacent to Old Blackburnians FC, and to Pleckgate and Lammack playing fields. Local breweries such as Three Bs, Bowland, Reedley Hallows, Moorhouse's and Worsthorne feature regularly. The large, comfortable open-plan lounge is served from a bar with five handpumps. There is a variety of quality live entertainment at weekends when the pub can get very busy. 🐸✤♿️♣️P🚲(25,10)🌸🎵

Blackpool

Blackpool Cricket Club
Barlow Crescent, West Park Drive, FY3 9EQ (follow signs to Stanley Park)
☎ (01253) 393347 ∰ blackpoolcricket.co.uk
5 changing beers (sourced regionally; often Cumbrian Ales, Moorhouse's) Ⓗ
On the western edge of Stanley Park, around 20 minutes' walk from the town centre, this club, housed in the impressive pavilion, is a vibrant, local social centre. A range of five changing beers is available to the visitor. Quizzes and entertainment nights are regularly held. Several TVs show various sports events. Upstairs functions rooms are available for social events. Free entry to the club and all cricket games except when Lancashire come to town. Multiple local CAMRA Club of the Year winner. 🐸✤🍴♿️P🚲(18)🛜🎵

Cask & Tap
82 Topping Street, FY1 3AD
∰ caskandtap.co.uk
8 changing beers (sourced nationally) Ⓗ
A friendly welcome is always guaranteed at this quirky micropub, tucked just off Blackpool's main central square a little over five minutes' stroll from the Tower. An ever-changing range of up to eight real ales from near and far normally includes a dark beer, with a selection of craft beers and real ciders and perries also available. Some of lighting is made from recycled electrical test gear and even an old handpull. Dogs are welcomed with tame owners. Q🐸🚲(North)🚉(North Station)🌭🚲(18,6)🌸🛜

JD Drinkwater's Alehouse
75 Highfield Road, FY4 2JE
4 changing beers (sourced nationally; often Bowness Bay, Cross Bay, Lancaster) Ⓗ
One of a number of micropubs opened locally during Covid restrictions, this is a great asset to the local real ale scene and an instant success. The landlord has previously been the licencee of several local pubs and this venture is named after his father JD. Situated on a busy South Shore thoroughfare, it is frequented by locals and visitors alike. The four ever-changing beers come from near and far. Note the unusual bar built from beer barrels, along with its many quirky features. 🐸♿️🚉(Pleasure Beach)♣️🚲🌸

No.10 Ale House & Kitchen
258 Whitegate Drive, FY3 9JW
☎ (01253) 694913 ∰ no10alehouseandthai.co.uk
3 changing beers (sourced nationally; often Pennine) Ⓗ
Blackpool's first micropub underwent a refurbishment in 2024 including a larger downstairs room and a new upstairs sports room. A range of three beers, usually including a dark beer, regularly change. Pre-bookings are recommended for their ever popular Thai-themed food. Outdoor drinking at the front of pub is courtesy of canteen-style metal benches and seats. It occasionally hosts private functions, so it is worth checking before setting off. ✤🚲🌸🛜

Blackpool: Bispham

Cask
103 Red Bank Road, FY2 9HZ
4 changing beers (sourced regionally; often Bank Top, Moorhouse's, Pennine) Ⓗ
Situated between the Prom and Bispham village, this micropub conversion opened in 2022 serving four frequently-changing cask ales and craft beers, with real cider often available. The lower level is a restored brick area and is family and dog-friendly. The front area has a spacious seated patio for relaxing in the warmer months. Upstairs is kitted out with plenty of seating and there is artwork of the local area. The pub is a great asset to the local community and compliments the many restaurants and shops. Q✿❀♿(Bispham)🚌(3,3A)❀

Blackpool: Layton

Cask
9 Layton Road, FY3 8EA
☎ (01253) 396321
4 changing beers (sourced nationally) Ⓗ
Situated about a mile or so from Blackpool town centre, en-route to Poulton le Fylde, no fewer that six bus routes pass close by. Four ever-changing cask beers are always available, normally including a dark beer. This compact, dog-friendly, micropub has a pleasant suntrap drinking area to the front and a walled area at the rear. The Layton Cemetery opposite contains the grave of the last known survivor of the Charge of the Light Brigade. ☭✿♿🚌❀

Burnley

Bridge Bier Huis Ⓛ
2 Bank Parade, BB11 1UH
☎ (01282) 411304
Moorhouse's Premier; 4 changing beers (sourced regionally) Ⓗ
Award-winning freehouse serving home made-food with a large open-plan bar area and a small snug to one side. It offers two Moorhouse's beers and three from smaller nationally sourced breweries plus one cider/perry. Over 50 foreign bottled beers are stocked together with seven beers on tap. Quiz night is Wednesday and occasional live music events are held on Sundays. The owners celebrated 20 years in charge in 2023. Closed Monday and Tuesday unless Burnley FC are at home. Q◖≋(Central)●🅿🚌❀♪

Commercial ✪
446 Briercliffe Road, BB10 2HA
☎ 07811 343834
Hydes Original; 1 changing beer Ⓗ
A popular traditional locals' pub located on the border between Burnley and Harle Syke and often known as the last pub in Burnley. The pub serves a varying selection of beers from the Hydes brewery range. Live bands and karaoke feature every weekend, while during the week darts and bingo are hosted. The regular Hydes quiz night is popular. Buses stop close by. ♣🚌♪

Lane Ends Hotel
Kiddow Lane, BB12 6LL
☎ (01282) 456814
Moorhouse's Blonde Witch; Timothy Taylor Landlord Ⓗ
A large roadhouse-style establishment in red brick with some mock-Tudor features. The large single room features a pool table at one end and offers comfortable seating all round. Live bands feature on Saturday evenings – see social media for details. There are a lot of old Massey's Burnley Brewery windows (MBB) around the building. The pub is handy for Lowerhouse cricket club. ♿≋(Rose Grove)♣🚌❀♪

New Brew-m Ⓛ
11 St James Row, BB11 1DR
☎ 07902 961426
Reedley Hallows Pendleside; 5 changing beers (sourced regionally)
Smart micropub, hidden behind Barclays bank, in the centre of town. It is run as the brewery tap for Reedley Hallows brewery but also serves guest beers sourced by brewer/owner Pete Goldsbrough. There are a limited number of bottled beers and ciders together with a small wine and spirit selection and packet snacks. Closed on Tuesdays unless Burnley FC are at home. Q≋(Manchester Road)🚌❀🛜

Burscough

Hop Vine
Liverpool Road North, L40 4BY (in village centre on A59)
☎ (01704) 893799
Timothy Taylor Landlord; 4 changing beers (sourced regionally; often Hop Vine, Salopian) Ⓗ
This spacious former coaching house is now a thriving community brewpub renowned for its friendly atmosphere and popular for its exceptional ale and food. The classic country pub interior has wood panelling and characterful wood flooring throughout and is decorated with historic local maps, photographs and vintage bottled ales. The Hop Vine brewery operate from the attractive floral courtyard at the rear. Catering for all age groups, it offers great value meals, live music and twice-yearly beer festivals. ☭✿◖♿≋(Bridge)🅿🚌❀🛜♪

Thirsty Duck Ⓛ
Unit 9 & 10 Burscough Wharf, L40 5RZ
☎ (01695) 816116
Hawkshead Thirsty Duck Bitter; 4 changing beers Ⓗ
This bar and bottle shop opened in 2020 in the Burscough Wharf complex, making a welcome addition to the thriving real ale scene. A tastefully decorated modern bar with five cask lines, 10 keg lines and real cider, as well as a full range of wine and spirits. The bottle and can stock that was previously housed and sold from Beer Haul is now within the bar. It has a rotating stock of Belgian ales, ciders, pale ales, dark beers, sour, gluten free and alcohol free drinks. Q✿♿≋(Bridge)♣●🅿🚌❀🛜

Carnforth

Royal Station
Market Street, LA5 9BT
☎ (01524) 733636 🌐 royalstation.co.uk
4 changing beers Ⓗ
Traditional Victorian station hotel which has now benefited from a facelift. In 1900, it became the Royal Station Hotel in recognition of the fact that the Duke of York, later to become George V, availed himself of the hotel's hospitality during a shooting trip. A grand entrance and foyer lead to a tapas bar, while round the back is the larger and more basic Junction Bar, where the games, real ale and live music on Friday and Saturday are. A microbrewery is planned. ✿◖≋♣🚌❀🛜♪

Snug
Unit 6, Carnforth Gateway Building, LA5 9TR (at N end of former mainline platform)
🌐 thesnugmicropub.blogspot.co.uk
5 changing beers Ⓗ

The area's first micropub: the only drinks are ale, cider, wine, a few soft drinks and at least 10 good-quality gins; the only food is a few light snacks; the only sounds are conversation and the roar of the passing trains. Decor is similarly stripped-back: painted walls, bare floorboards and chunky tall tables. The eye is naturally drawn to a beautiful glazed wooden cabinet where all the drinks are stored. Paid parking is in the station car park. Q✿&≠♣🚽🖵✿

Taps on the Green
77 Kellet Road, LA5 9LR
☎ 07305 800648
5 changing beers (sourced locally) Ⓗ
An old suburban local reinvented as the Q Brew flagship. Comprehensively revamped in 2016 in contemporary neutral tones, and carpeted throughout, it has two distinct areas, the back one having the bar counter. It is usually the only outlet for Q Brew beers brewed nearby – experimentation is to be expected from them but not weirdness. There is a car park to the rear and an adjoining bowling club. Q✿P🖵(49)✿🛜

Chorley

Ben's Tap ⓛ
2 Market Place, PR7 1DA
☎ (01257) 367890 ⊕ bensbrewery.co.uk/bens-tap-and-bottle-shop
6 changing beers (often Ben's) Ⓗ
Brewery tap for Ben's brewery, which opened in 2022 in a former café premises. The interior has a rustic feel with recycled wooden pallets lining the walls. Six cask ales from Ben's own range are served, with third of a pints available. There is also a range of craft ales, up to six real ciders and an excellent selection of bottles and cans at good prices, which may be drunk on the premises or taken away. No food is served, but you are welcome to bring your own. Local and Regional CAMRA Cider Pub of the Year 2023. 🚶✿≠♣🖵(125,362)✿🛜

Bob Inn
24 Market Place, PR7 1DA
☎ 07767 238410
3 changing beers (sourced nationally; often Red Rose) Ⓗ
A tiny bar housed in a market stall, this is certainly the smallest pub in the local area. Outside seating is available, as well as seating within the market hall. This is a pub where conversation and banter are an important part of the experience. An adjacent unit now forms a lounge area separate from the main bar. There are three ever-changing cask beers, sourced from smaller breweries and usually including a mix of styles including a dark beer. No food is served, but you are welcome to bring your own. Q🚶&≠🖵✿

Flat Iron ⓛ ✅
21 Cleveland Street, PR7 1BH
⊕ flatironchorley.co.uk
Ossett White Rat; 4 changing beers (sourced locally; often Blackedge, Cross Bay, Titanic) Ⓗ
This is a smart town-centre pub and part of the growing real ale scene in Chorley. It featured in the very first CAMRA Guide in 1974 when it was described as a 'true drinker's pub' and served beers from Tetley Walker in Warrington. These days, expect to find up to five cask ales with one regular beer, White Rat, plus four changing beers sourced within a 50-mile radius. Real cider on handpump and beer tasting paddles are also available. With multiple TVs around the pub, expect to see regular televised sport. 🚶✿≠♣🖵✿🛜♪

Malt 'n' Hops ⓛ
50-52 Friday Street, PR6 0AA
☎ (01257) 260074
Bank Top Dark Mild; Ossett White Rat; 7 changing beers (sourced nationally; often Blackedge, Moorhouse's, Wily Fox) Ⓗ
Converted from an old shop in 1989, the pub is close to the town's railway and bus stations. Seating is on two levels, with a bright yet traditional feel and a pleasant beer garden. A genuine free house with up to nine guest ales (including a regular mild) served from a single L-shaped bar, usually from Lancashire and Yorkshire micros including Rat, Wily Fox, Ossett, Elland, Lancaster, Fernandes, Goose Eye and Blackedge. Good-value filled rolls and pork pies are available. A former local and regional CAMRA Pub of the Year. 🚶✿🖵✿🛜♪

Mason's Arms ⓛ
98 Harpers Lane, PR6 0HU
☎ (01257) 367038
5 changing beers (sourced locally; often Blackedge, Pictish) Ⓗ
A light and airy, yet cosy pub, with a reputation for good beer, a mile from the town centre. The taproom has five changing ales available at any one time, sourced mainly from north-west micros, but beers from further afield are also sold. The taproom and two distinctive lounges, both with wood-burning stoves, are markedly different drinking areas, and there is a partly covered beer garden to the rear. Pizzas are served 5-8pm Wednesday-Sunday. 🚶✿🍴🖵(2,125)✿🛜♪

Riley's Taproom & Wine Bar ⓛ
Victoria Buildings, 4 Cleveland Street, PR7 1BH
☎ 07889 496720 ⊕ rileystaproomchorley.com
2 changing beers (sourced regionally; often Nightjar, Rivington, Vocation) Ⓗ
Riley's opened in 2021 in premises previously used as a greengrocer's. They specialise in craft ales and fine wines and there is a comfortable atmosphere with plenty of seating inside. Ten keg lines serve a range of craft beers sourced mainly from local breweries, which include some real ales and real cider, which are dispensed through membrane keg, along with three handpumps for cask ale enthusiasts. A full beer menu is provided on a screen behind the bar. Cold platters are available at all times, subject to availability. 🚶🍴&≠🖵✿🛜

Shepherds' Hall Ale House & Victoria Rooms ⓛ
63-67 Chapel Street, PR7 1BS
☎ (01257) 270619
Vocation Bread & Butter; 5 changing beers (sourced nationally) Ⓗ
This friendly and welcoming bar next door to the bus station opened in 2014 and was the first micropub in Chorley. It was refurbished in 2020 and extended into adjoining premises in 2021. Up to six cask ales are now served from microbreweries all over the country, including regular beers from Vocation. You should find a wide range of beer styles, always including a dark beer. Third of a pint beer paddles are available, three real ciders, six craft keg lines often featuring Rivington beers, and a variety of other drinks to suit all tastes. Q🚶≠♣🖵✿🛜♪

Sir Henry Tate ⓛ ✅
New Market Street, PR7 1DB
☎ (01257) 248470
Bank Top Dark Mild; Greene King Abbot; Ruddles Best Bitter; Sharp's Doom Bar; house beer (by

Moorhouse's); 5 changing beers (sourced nationally) 🅷

A purpose-built pub trading under the Lloyds banner situated next to Booths supermarket in the centre of town. This Wetherspoon pub is on three levels and has an outside drinking area to the front. The main bar features five regular cask ales served on handpump plus five guests, with beers from Moorhouse's and Phoenix often featuring. Reflecting local tastes, the beers tend to be of lower gravity than is often found in Wetherspoon pubs. The two changing real ciders are served from boxes behind the bar and food is served seven days a week. ⓢ🏵️⏸️⬤🚲⮕⬤🚃⬤🛜

Clayton le Moors

Old England Forever ♈ 🅛 ✅
13 Church Street, BB5 5HT
☎ (01254) 383332
Bank Top Bad to the Bone, Dark Mild, Flat Cap, Port O Call; 2 changing beers (sourced locally; often Bank Top) 🅷

Comfortable Edwardian terraced pub serving a large range of Bank Top beers. A single-roomed establishment, there are defined bar and lounge areas. It sits just off Barnes Square and is easily reached from the towpath of the Leeds-Liverpool Canal. An unusual feature is the section of glass flooring in front of the bar from where the cellar can be viewed. The pub is wheelchair friendly and has fully accessible toilets. Q🏵️⬤♣️⬤🚃(6,7)♫

Cleveleys

Jolly Tars ✅
154-158 Victoria Road West, FY5 3NE
☎ (01253) 856042
Greene King Abbot; Ruddles Best Bitter; Sharp's Doom Bar; 7 changing beers (sourced nationally; often Hawkshead, Moorhouse's, Phoenix) 🅷

Named after a nine-strong, highly popular family of concert party entertainers who visited Celveleys on a regular basis between the wars and whose open-air shows attracted large audiences during summer months. This lively, friendly and welcoming pub attracts visitors and locals alike. It has a great reputation for its ales and food and can get busy, although you can enjoy a quiet drink in one the three secluded booths. Six ever-changing guest beers are always available. The outdoor drinking area at the front is popular in summer. ⓢ🏵️⏸️⬤🚃🛜

Shipwreck Brewhouse 🅛
53 Victoria Road West, FY5 1AJ
☎ (01253) 540597 ⊕ theshipwreckbrewhouse.co.uk
5 changing beers (sourced locally) 🅷

Looking small from the outside, this micropub and café in the heart of Cleveleys' main street is a real Tardis, with two indoor seating areas, covered and heated outdoor areas to the front and rear, and meeting rooms. There is an emphasis on Lancashire ales, of which five are normally available, including a dark beer. There is also a menu of local snacks and pub food. The modern, seaside-themed decor includes photographs of historic local shipwrecks and well-known landmarks. May close early during winter months. 🏵️⏸️⬤🚃⬤

Clitheroe

Ale House
12-14 Market Place, BB7 2DA
☎ 07530 045365

5 changing beers (sourced nationally; often Deeply Vale, Lakeland Brewhouse, Wishbone) 🅷

A quirky, popular pub right in the centre of town. There is a slightly unfinished feel here but the beer range is excellent, varied and constantly changing. Dark beers, including a strong one, often feature. The bar area is quite snug but the other areas are fairly spacious. Most of the walls are covered in a riot of beer memorabilia. There are spectacular views of Pendle Hill from the upstairs windows. ⚍⮕⬤🚃⬤♫

Beer Shack ✅
22-24 King Street, BB7 2EP
☎ (01200) 411967 ⊕ thebeershack.uk
4 changing beers (sourced locally; often Carnival, Moorhouse's, Pentrich) 🅷

First opened in 2021, this new bar has added four handpulls. Beers come mainly from well-known microbreweries and larger ones such as Lancaster. There is nearly always a dark cask beer available. Robb and Sam, the licensees, have even begun brewing on the premises. Food is limited in choice but is well thought out. The large outdoor area at the rear is a real suntrap. Convenient for both railway and bus stations. ⮕🚃⬤🛜

Bowland Beer Hall 🅛 ✅
Greenacre Street, BB7 1EB
☎ (01200) 401035 ⊕ jamesplaces.com/holmes-mill/bowland-beer-hall
Bowland Pheasant Plucker, Gold, Boxer Blonde, Hen Harrier, Buster IPA, Deer Stalker; changing beers (sourced nationally) 🅷

The enormously popular beer hall is now a major part of Clitheroe's thriving beer scene. It opened in 2016, in a former mill dating back to the 19th century. It has the second longest bar in Britain at 106ft with more than 40 handpulls on the bar. You can expect to find all of Bowland's beers on, as well as another dozen or more beers from around the UK. The complex hosts a hotel, cinema, coffee shop and delicatessen and is a short walk from Clitheroe Castle and the town centre. ⓢ🏵️⏸️⬤⮕⬤P🚃⬤♫

New Inn 🅛
20 Parson Lane, BB7 2JN
Coach House Gunpowder Premium Mild, Farriers Best Bitter, Blueberry Classic Bitter; Moorhouse's Premier, Pride of Pendle, Blonde Witch; 5 changing beers (sourced regionally; often Prospect, Saltaire) 🅷

The bar at the New Inn is a welcome sight, with at least 10 beers on offer. The bar itself is central, with a number of smaller rooms clustered around it. In addition to the regular beers from Coach House and Moorehouse's you may also find the likes of Saltaire, Ilkley, Prospect or Wharfedale breweries represented. The pub dates from the early 1800s and faces Clitheroe Castle. It is just a short walk from the bus and railway stations. Q🏵️⬤A⮕🚃⬤♫

Colne

Admiral Lord Rodney 🅛
Mill Green, BB8 0TA
☎ (01282) 219759
9 changing beers (sourced regionally; often Goose Eye, Ilkley, Reedley Hallows) 🅷

A much loved community pub in Colne's old South Valley area, the old industrial heart of the town. The stone-flagged floor includes mosaics and there are beautiful tiles up the inner staircase. Set out over three rooms, the pub has become the meeting place for a number of clubs. There is regular live entertainment during the evening, and local history and art displays. There has been a recent refurbishment with open fires and flagged floors, plus a much improved outdoor seating area and a separate smokers' area. All are made welcome. Q🐎❀🍴♣🐾📶♫

Boyce's Barrel

7 New Market Street, BB8 9BJ

5 changing beers (sourced nationally) [H]

The first micropub in Colne, this member of the Micropub Association offers five high-quality real ales with no music, no lager, just a great atmosphere and plenty of banter. Tastefully styled, with tall polished wooden sleeper tables, it is reminiscent of a rail staging post. Ales are rotated often, with new beers put on the bar almost as soon as a barrel runs dry. All ales are sourced from non-local breweries and always include one mild and one porter or stout. Q♿🚆🍎📺🚌🐾♫

Coppull

Wheatsheaf [L]

1 Westerton Court, Spendmore Lane, PR7 4NY

☎ (01257) 470666

3 changing beers (sourced locally; often Bank Top, Blackedge, Coach House) [H]

The Wheatsheaf has been at the centre of the local community since the 1700s and remains so today, hosting weekly quiz nights and welcoming regular live musicians. It underwent an extensively refurbishment a few years ago and has a smart modern interior including a log-burning stove for those winter evenings, a new outdoor drinking area and Italian street food available on Friday evenings. There are three handpumps serving a changing selection of real ales, with a focus on supporting local microbreweries. Q🐎❀♿♣P🚌🐾📶♫

Croston

Wheatsheaf

Town Road, PR26 9RA

☎ (01772) 600370 🌐 wheatsheaf-croston.com

Goose Eye Chinook Blonde; 4 changing beers (sourced nationally; often Bowland, Titanic) [H]

On the main road and overlooking the village green, this tastefully refurbished pub has a contemporary feel. It has a distinct area for dining as well as a comfortable drinking area with sofas and chairs and a large patio area to the front. There's a wide choice of beers, generally sourced locally, with one regular and four ever-changing ales which invariably include one dark beer. Food is served lunchtimes and evenings during the week and all day, including breakfast, at weekends. 🐎❀🍴♿🚆P🚌(112,337)🐾📶♫

Darwen

Bird in th'hand [L]

225 Duckworth Street, BB3 1AU

☎ 07926 115292

4 changing beers (sourced regionally; often 12 Steps, Blackedge) [H]

Home to 12 Steps brewery, named after the number down to the cellar, this is a brewpub and bottle shop with four handpumps, 10 craft lines and three for ciders. The shelves are full of Belgian, international and UK bottled beers and craft ciders which can be consumed on or off the premises. Three rooms include one with a with a log-burner, and there is a covered back yard. Smoking is permitted out back or the front pavement. Toilets are upstairs. The name comes from the pub which stood here over 100 years ago. ❀🚆🚌(1)🐾♫

Loom & Shuttle [L]

165 Duckworth Street, BB3 1AT

☎ (01942) 259071

4 changing beers (sourced regionally) [H]

A single-roomed bar with beer garden at the rear, this is the first pub venture for Mayflower brewery of Wigan. It is a sustainability-conscious cocktail, cask and craft ale bar with a large hand-picked selection of world beer, gins, rums and whiskies. A number of Mayflower traditional cask ales are served, alongside guest beers. Situated on the busy A666, regular buses connecting Blackburn with Darwen and Bolton pass the door. 🐎🚆P🚌🐾

Dolphinholme

Fleece

Bay Horse, LA2 9AQ

☎ (01524) 791233 🌐 fleeceinn.co.uk

4 changing beers (often Bowland, Farm Yard) [H]

At first sight this former farmhouse is in the middle of nowhere, but as the nearby village and the country beyond have no pubs, it is the default local for quite a lot of people. It clearly relies, however, on diners from further afield. The main entrance gives onto an old-fashioned hall with lots of old prints. The main bar, oak-beamed and with pews and usually a roaring fire is to the right, the dining-room is to the left. There are two rooms off the bar, one designated a family room. 🐎❀🛏🍴♿⛺♣P📶

Earby

Red Lion [L]

70 Red Lion Street, BB18 6RD

☎ (01282) 843395

4 changing beers (sourced locally; often Settle) [H]

A warm and friendly welcome awaits you from both host and regulars at this a traditional country local, owned by local people. Both rooms have been renovated with taste, the lounge being heated with a wood burner. A extensive menu is served in the lounge both lunchtime and evenings. It is situated close to the youth hostel and is a drinker's delight. 🐎🍎P🚌🐾📶♫

Fleetwood

Beer Shed

20 Poulton Street, FY7 6LP

☎ (01253) 867290 🌐 shedbeer.co.uk

4 changing beers (sourced nationally; often Ben's, Copper Dragon, Three B's) [H]

An ambitious conversion of a previous bistro in a quiet town-centre side street, this unique micropub provides quality cask ale within a relaxed, friendly, single room. Pub games and brewing memorabilia enhance the experience for local clientele and visitors alike. There are four handpumps serving a changing range of regional beers, with real cider and Shed Beer, brewed by the owner, usually available. An outside seating area is a popular place to chat and unwind in summer. Q❀🚋(Fisherman's Walk) ♣🍎🚌🐾

Steamer

1-2 Queens Terrace, FY7 6BT

☎ (01253) 681001

🌐 thesteamerfleetwood.foodanddrinksites.co.uk

Reedley Hallows Pendleside; 3 changing beers (sourced nationally) [H]

Fleetwood's oldest surviving pub, the Steamer is situated across from the famous market. It offers a varying selection of up to four real ales in a traditional pub setting. The decor is complemented with pictures of the local area and historic fishing vessels, reflecting its close association with the fishing industry and history of the town. Good food is available daily from noon, with regular theme nights and live entertainment at weekends. Fleetwood Museum is only 60 yards away and is worth a visit to find out about local history. ﾐ❀◑▮占ﾞ(Victoria Street) ♣ﾛ❀ﾗ♪

Garstang

Farmers Arms
18 Church Street, PR3 1PA
☎ (01995) 603350
2 changing beers Ⓗ
Early 19th-century inn just outside the town centre, comprehensively modernised in 2014 in a contemporary uncluttered style with white walls, grey carpet and a little pine. There is a bar counter in the middle surrounded by several distinct spaces. It is popular with families for daytime meals. Occasional theme nights and live music events are hosted. ❀◑占♣Pﾛ♪

Great Harwood

1B Tap House Ⓛ
1B Glebe Street, BB6 7AA
5 changing beers (sourced nationally) Ⓗ
Welcoming two-roomed bar in historic former co-operative society building close to Towngate square and preservation area, on a side street opposite the post office. The main room, featuring plenty of beer and brewery-related items, sells a skillfully selected range of cask beers which always includes a stout or porter. Note the collection of old beer guides. There is a large comfortable lounge and a small outdoor seating area by the door. Many buses stop close by and there is a large free car park across the road. Pﾛ(6,7)ﾗ♪

Royal Ⓛ ✓
2 Station Road, BB6 7BA
☎ (01254) 876237
4 changing beers (sourced regionally; often Pictish) Ⓗ
One of East Lancashire's premier ales houses, the Royal is a large pub offering a varying range of real ales. It is a regular outlet for beers from the Pictish brewery. There is a separate concert room, and large beer gardens to the rear and side which are ideal for families. The pub once served as the hotel for the long-gone railway station. The disused railway, now a pleasant walking and cycling track passes close by. There is regular entertainment on Sundays. ﾐ❀◑ﾛ(6,7)♪

Haggate

Hare & Hounds ✓
1 Halifax Road, BB10 3QH
☎ (01282) 424612
4 changing beers (sourced regionally) Ⓗ
A traditional country pub in the Briercliffe area of Burnley. There are superb open views over the Pennine moorland from the rear patio area. Food is served Wednesday to Sunday and there are distinct rooms to the front of the pub, with a large restaurant/function room to the rear. Live music events are held at weekends. The bus from Burnley terminates 200 yards before the pub. ﾐ❀◑♣Pﾛ(5) ❀ﾗ♪

Halton

Greyhound
10 Low Road, LA2 6LZ
☎ 07869 837732 ⊕ thegreyhoundhalton.co.uk
Timothy Taylor Knowle Spring, Landlord; house beer (by Theakston); 1 changing beer (sourced nationally; often Lancaster) Ⓗ
The local for a large and growing village. The single large room with modern decor is dominated by a long counter, but divided up so that there are some intimate and cosy areas. The pub is handy for walks alongside the River Lune, accessed via an old railway toll bridge. ❀◑占▮♣Pﾛ(49)

Haslingden

Griffin Inn Ⓛ
86 Hud Rake, BB4 5AF
☎ (01706) 214021 ⊕ rossendalebrewery.co.uk
Rossendale Floral Dance, Glen Top Bitter, Ale, Halo Pale, Pitch Porter, Sunshine; 1 changing beer Ⓗ
Situated on Hud Rake this is a traditional community pub and also the home of the Rossendale brewery, housed on the lower floor below the pub. The large bar area has a separate area for pub games, and the spacious lounge has picture windows overlooking the local hills and valleys. On the hill facing the front sits the Halo panopticon. The pub is easily accessible, but there is a steep uphill walk from main road bus stops. Cuban food is served. Q◑占♣❀ﾛ(464,X41)❀ﾗ♪

Heath Charnock

Bay Horse Ⓛ ✓
Babylon Lane, PR6 9ER
☎ (01257) 485849
Timothy Taylor Golden Best, Boltmaker; 2 changing beers (often Moorhouse's, Wily Fox) Ⓗ
Dating from the 1750s, this attractive stone-built inn overlooks open countryside and the Rivington Hills. Originally a farm and smithy, it became a coaching inn in the 1830s, and is now a multi-roomed pub with exposed stonework and beams and several open fires. To the rear is a bowling green and outdoor seating. Up to four cask ales are served on handpump, featuring regular beers from Timothy Taylor. A strong community-focused pub with a loyal following, excellent home-cooked food with a modern twist is served seven days a week. Walkers and dogs are always welcome. ﾐ❀🚃◑占♣Pﾛ(8,8A) ❀ﾗ♪

Yew Tree Ⓛ
Dill Hall Brow, PR6 9HA
☎ (01257) 480344 ⊕ yewtreeinnanglezarke.co.uk
2 changing beers (sourced locally; often Blackedge, Bowland) Ⓗ
Attractive, isolated stone-built pub with flagged floors and great views over open countryside. The pub is essentially open plan but walls and partitions divide this into separate cosy areas. It has long had a reputation for quality food with a full range of meals available, made from locally sourced produce wherever possible. Dogs are welcome in the bar area but not the restaurant. The pub showcases regular ales from the nearby Blackedge brewery and the occasional guest from other independent local breweries. Closing times may vary. ﾐ❀◑占▮P❀ﾗ

Hest Bank

Crossing
6 Coastal Road, LA2 6HN
☎ 07584 660075
5 changing beers ⊞
This former café opened as a micropub in 2018. An old stone building, it has a timber extension and a plate-glass window from its café days. The U-shaped layout contains a bar counter near the entrance in one arm, a wood-burning stove in the middle, and a back room with games, bound copies of Railway magazine and photos of Hest Bank station, closed in 1969. The pub's name refers to the fact that the pub is close to both one of the last level crossings on the West Coast Main Line and the ancient route over the sands. Q♣️🚃(5,55A)❀🛜

Heysham

Bookmakers ✓
364 Heysham Road, LA3 2BJ
☎ 07785 257648
5 changing beers ⊞
Micropub opened in 2019 in a former betting shop, amongst other shops in a suburban neighbourhood, a most welcome addition to the micropub scene in this area. The single wedge-shaped room is done out in industrial chic with a few comfy chairs and bar stools, and an arrangement of standing and seated areas. It attracts large numbers of locals. ♿♣️🚃❀

Kirkham

Kirkham Bierhaus
36 Poulton Street, PR4 2AH
☎ (01772) 417792 ⊕ kirkhambierhaus.co.uk
6 changing beers (sourced regionally; often Brightside) ⊞
Based in the former Santander bank this pub, which opened in 2022, is already a favourite with locals. It has a bright interior and there is always a good conversational vibe in the air. A range of regularly changing beers, mostly from local brewers, is offered along with a range of German draught and bottled beers and UK craft cans. A suntrap garden is to the rear. ❀♿🚃❀

Tap & Vent Brewhouse Ⓛ
26 Poulton Street, PR4 2AB
☎ (01772) 382019 ⊕ tapandventbrewhouse.co.uk
5 changing beers (sourced regionally; often Brewhouse, Fuzzy Duck) ⊞
This smart pub is located in a row of shops in the centre of Kirkham, just up from the market square and bus stops. This is the home of the Brewhouse brewery, located at the rear, although their beers do not dominate choice, with a good range of guest ales and continental lagers and bottled beers also available. A quieter snug is hidden behind the bar and there is a sunny pavement area to the front. Q🐾❀🌀♿♣️🚃❀🛜

Lancaster

Bobbin ✓
36 Cable Street, LA1 1HH
☎ (01524) 32606
5 changing beers (often Anarchy, Tiny Rebel) ⊞
Large mainly-Victorian pub, with parts dating back to the 18th century, it is entirely open plan but still divided up by raised areas and pillars. It is frequented by a goth/metal crowd, but they are by no means the only customers. The decor includes 70s-style flock wallpaper and laminate floor, and the pub has an extremely

eclectic jukebox. Live music is on Friday and Saturday, with pool night Wednesday. Handy for the bus station. ❀♿🚆♣️🚃🛜♫

Tite & Locke
Lancaster Railway Station, Meeting House Lane, LA1 5NW (on platform 3)
☎ (01524) 66737
Lancaster Amber, Blonde, IPA, Black, Red; 1 changing beer (often Lancaster) ⊞
A large part of the old station buildings now lies empty, but here a few rooms have been joined together and given a new use in a modern style without wallpaper or carpets. Curiously, although on the outside the station is built of the local gritstone, inside it can be seen to be mostly brickwork. It has four rooms: one with the bar, the others called first-, second- and third-class lounges. The first can be hired for functions, the beer store is visible from the third. ❀🚆P🚃❀

White Cross Ⓛ ✓
Quarry Road, LA1 4XT (behind town hall, on canal towpath)
☎ (01524) 33999 ⊕ thewhitecross.co.uk
Timothy Taylor Landlord; Wye Valley HPA; 8 changing beers (sourced regionally; often Allendale, Titanic, Tirril) ⊞
An 80s renovation of an old canalside warehouse with an open-plan interior and a light, airy feel. French windows open on to extensive canalside seating. There is a Tuesday quiz, and a beer and pie festival each April. Situated in the corner of an extensive complex of Victorian textile mills, now converted to other uses. The wide open spaces and general style makes it look like a circuit pub, but in fact much of the custom comes either from the residential areas up the hill or from the nearby workplaces. ❀🌀◗♿♣️P🚃🛜

Lathom

Ship Inn
4 Wheat Lane, L40 4BX (take School Ln from Burscough, turn right after hump-backed bridge) SD452116
☎ (01704) 893117 ⊕ shipatlathom.co.uk
House beer (by Moorhouse's); changing beers (sourced regionally; often Black Sheep, Sharp's) ⊞
A traditional country pub set in an idyllic canalside location. The cosy central bar features a real fire and separates the two dining areas which serve a menu ranging from pub classics through to interesting and changing specials. There is a dog-friendly boot room complete with log burner. The pub is popular all year but especially in summer with its large beer garden. A highlight is the September Beer, Pie and Sausage festival with over 40 handpulled ales. 🐾❀◗♿🚆(Hoscar) P🚃(337,3A)❀🛜

Leyland

Golden Tap Ale House Ⓛ
1 Chapel Brow, PR25 3NH
☎ (01772) 431859
6 changing beers (sourced nationally) ⊞
Located in a former shop, the Golden Tap is a cosy one-roomed micropub which opened its doors to the public in 2016. Up to six changing cask ales are served, usually including two dark beers, sourced from microbreweries far and wide, but usually with at least one from the local region. No food is served other than a few snacks, but the pub is right in the heart of the town's fast food and takeaway area. 🐾🚆♣️🖤🚃(111)❀🛜

Market Ale House 🅛

33 Hough Lane, PR25 2SB
☎ (01772) 623363
6 changing beers (sourced nationally) Ⓗ
Opened in 2013 this was the area's first micropub, located at the entrance to the former Leyland Motors North Works, which now serves as the town's market hall. With an extension into the adjoining premises added in 2021 and an upstairs lounge, there is plenty of seating. Six changing real ales come from local and national breweries. Changing ciders, wine and a few spirits are also served. There's no TV but there is live acoustic music from early evening on Sunday. An outside drinking area to the front has ample tables and seating.
🏵🚲🏵🦽🚹(109,111) 🏵🛜♪

Lostock Hall

Lostock Ale 🅛

7 Hope Terrace, PR5 5RU
6 changing beers (sourced locally; often Blackedge, Wily Fox) Ⓗ
Located within the pedestrianised Tardy Gate shopping area, this micropub opened in 2020 in former gift shop premises, quickly becoming popular. Six changing cask ales often include beers from local breweries such as Pennine and Wily Fox, while there are also eight keg lines in place. This community-focused pub has a relaxed friendly atmosphere and, with the acquisition of the adjoining charity shop premises in late 2021, its floor space has more than doubled in size.
🛏🚲🚹(109,111) 🏵🛜♪

Lytham

Craft House Beer Café

5 Clifton Street, FY8 5EP
☎ (01253) 730512
4 changing beers (sourced regionally) Ⓗ
This cosy micropub, now in its seventh year, guarantees a warm welcome. It has fast developed into a popular destination for real ale drinkers and can get busy. Four ever-changing beers are served, sourced far and wide and always including a dark beer. These are supplemented by a selection of British and world craft beers in bottle and can. This small bar is dog friendly and offers pavement seating, weather permitting. A small food menu is served daily. Q🏵🕙🚲🏵🚹🛜🛜

Railway Hotel ✓

Station Road, FY8 5DH (next to fire station on B5259)
☎ (01253) 797250
Greene King Abbot; Moorhouse's White Witch, Blonde Witch, Pendle Witches Brew; Ruddles Best Bitter; Sharp's Doom Bar; 4 changing beers (sourced nationally; often Coach House, Peerless, Phoenix) Ⓗ
This two-story building was purpose built next to Lytham's first railway station in 1847 and named appropriately. After several incarnations it reopened in 2012 as a Wetherspoon pub, reverting to its original name. The bright interior is split across three areas on different levels, depicting golf, railways and Lytham's halcyon days. There are pleasant outdoor drinking areas to the front and rear with disabled access at the rear.
🛏🏵🕙🦽🚹🛜

Taps ✓

12 Henry Street, FY8 5LE
☎ (01253) 736226
Greene King IPA; Robinsons Dizzy Blonde; 6 changing beers (sourced nationally; often Acorn) Ⓗ

Several times local CAMRA Pub of the Year, and national Pub of the Year runner-up in 2011, this pub has been in the Guide for over 30 consecutive years during which time it has had only two landlords. A range of rapidly changing beers is available, always including a mild. Though this can be a busy pub, service is usually prompt. The pub has an outside drinking area which is heated. There is a quiz every Monday night. 🛏🏵🕙🦽🚲🏵🚹🛜

Morecambe

Eric Bartholomew ✓

10-18 Euston Road, LA4 5DD
☎ (01524) 405860
Greene King Abbot; Ruddles Best Bitter; Sharp's Doom Bar; 5 changing beers (often Cross Bay) Ⓗ
Opened in 2004, this Wetherspoon pub near the seafront is dedicated to Eric Morecambe (nee Bartholomew). The pub functions on two levels, with an upstairs lounge and dinner area. The long bar services an open-plan area with pictures of 19th-century Morecambe and some artwork with a Morecambe and Wise theme. There is outside seating at front for smokers, but no drinking allowed. It is close to shops and a public car park.
Q🏵🕙🦽🚲🚹🛜

Little Bare 🍸

23 Princes Crescent, LA4 6BY
☎ 07817 892370
5 changing beers Ⓗ
Micropub opened in 2017 in a former off-licence and retaining the shop window. Following the micropub formula with no food, no music and no machines it features grey paint, bare floorboards and candles after dark. There's a second room down a corridor with extra seating. A small beer garden to the rear of the premises is accessed through the back room.
🏵🚲(Bare Lane) 🏵🚹(100,5) 🏵

Torrisholme Taps ✓

312 Lancaster Road, LA4 6LY
☎ 07786 073626
6 changing beers Ⓗ
Micropub opened in 2021 amongst shops in an old village which is now a suburb. Located in a former bridal shop, it has a picture window and is light and spacious for a micro, with a wide range of beverages. Pies are on sale. There is a bike rack at the front, but nearly all the customers walk. Q🚹(1,1A)🏵

Ormskirk

Kicking Donkey

Narrow Moss Lane, L40 8HY
☎ (01695) 227273 🌐 thekickingdonkey.co.uk
Lancaster Blonde; 3 changing beers (sourced regionally) Ⓗ
Elegant country pub that has recently been refurbished. Three handpulls offer a rotating selection of local ales which usually include one pale, one amber and one dark beer. Due to its popularity, Lancaster Blonde is a semi-regular. The pub is a collection point for the Ormskirk Food Bank and run a monthly prize draw to support it. Hand a donation for the food bank in at the bar to receive an entry. Opens bank holiday Mondays. 🛏🕙P🚹

Prince Albert

109 Wigan Road, L40 6HY
☎ (01695) 573656
Moorhouse's Pendle Witches Brew; Tetley Tetley Bitter; 3 changing beers Ⓗ

A country community local on the main road between Ormskirk and Skelmersdale. With its warm atmosphere it is well worth the walk or the bus journey from the real ale desert of Skelmersdale. The fresh cooked food and real ale are good value for money and there are always some interesting guest ales from North-West breweries. The small central bar serves three distinct areas with real fires in the winter, and there are also a good selection of pub games such as darts and dominoes. The 310, 375 and 385 buses all stop outside. Q♣🛇🖚🕭🅿🚲🛜

Tap Room No 12 🅛
12 Burscough Street, L39 2ER
☎ (01695) 581928
3 changing beers (sourced regionally) 🅗
This former shop has been custom converted into a Belgian-style single-room bar with wooden panels. It features four changing cask ales sourced regionally and aims to offer a porter or stout, an amber bitter and two pale beers of different strength. It has an extensive range of foreign bottled beers, and authentic foreign lagers on draught. There is a monthly quiz on a Wednesday and live music Friday and Saturday with background music during the rest of the week. 🍴♣🖚🛜🛜♪

Orrell

Delph Tavern
Tontine, WN5 8UJ
☎ (01695) 622239
5 changing beers 🅗
Free house, popular with locals and visitors, serving five ever-changing ales with an emphasis on local breweries. Bar snacks are provided on a Friday evening. Live sports are shown on a number of unobtrusive screens while a vault area offers pool and darts. The outside area has tables and chairs to relax and enjoy the good weather and offers a small play area for children. Weekly quiz nights are popular. 🛇🕭🖚♣🅿🖚(352)🚲🛜

Oswaldtwistle

Vault 🅛
343 Union Road, BB5 3HS
☎ (01254) 872279
Moorhouse's White Witch; 4 changing beers (sourced regionally) 🅗
A popular single-roomed bar on the busy main road through Oswaldtwistle. It is easy to reach by public transport as buses from Accrington and Blackburn pass the door every few minutes. There is high bench seating around the walls and a standing area at the bar. The six handpumps dispense four changing beers and two ciders. Keen Rugby League supporters, the Vault sponsor one of the junior teams at Accrington Wildcats – note the framed team photo in the bar. Q🍴🖚(6,7)🚲

Parbold

Wayfarer 🅛
1-3 Alder Lane, WN8 7NL
☎ (01257) 464600 ⊕ wayfarerparbold.co.uk
6 changing beers (often Problem Child) 🅗
A country pub with a focus on dining, offering six handpulls and a range of craft keg beers. Landlord and brewer Jonny Birkett is happy to show you around his on-site microbrewery, Problem Child brewing. The pub has low beamed ceilings with cosy nooks and crannies. It is popular with walkers as it is close to the Leeds-Liverpool Canal and Parbold Hill – suitable walks are shown on the website. The countryside beer garden has pleasant views. Q🛇🕭🖚🛜🖚🅿🖚(313,337)🚲🛜♪

Pendleton

Swan with Two Necks 🅛
Main Street, BB7 1PT
☎ (01200) 423112 ⊕ swanwithtwonecks.co.uk
5 changing beers (sourced regionally; often Goose Eye, Phoenix) 🅗
A plethora of awards acknowledge that this has been one of the best pubs in the area for the past decade. It has been run by the same owners for over 30 years and it is rumoured that the beer is so good because the landlord talks to it. The five handpulls offer an ever-changing range that may feature beers from Blackedge, Fernandes, Rat and Goose Eye. Real cider is available. Food is high quality yet reasonably priced. There are real fires during winter months and a large beer garden with amazing views. Q🕭🕭♣🅿🚲

Penwortham

Tap & Vine
69 Liverpool Road, PR1 9XD
☎ (01772) 751116 ⊕ tapandvine.co.uk
4 changing beers (sourced locally) 🅗
Penwortham's first micropub, this is an upmarket wine bar-type establishment housed in a former arts and craft shop. It has limited seating, and can get quite busy at times. To the rear is a small secluded room with a wood-burning stove, while there is also a covered outdoor seating area for use in the warmer weather. Four changing beers are always available, often including some from lesser-known microbreweries. The food consists of snacks, pies and serving platters. Q🛇🖚♣🖚🚲🛜♪

Poulton le Fylde

Old Town Hall
5 Church Street, FY6 7AP
☎ (01253) 892257
Moorhouse's Pride of Pendle; 5 changing beers (sourced locally; often Bowland, Reedley Hallows, Titanic) 🅗
Located in the old market place in Poulton, facing the churchyard, the pub was built in 1869 and originally called the Bay Horse. Later used as council offices, it returned to its original purpose in 1988. The now open-plan layout retains some of its heritage features. Six real ales are available to whet the appetite. Live music plays every Saturday. Live sports are screened on many TVs and a dedicated area is provided for horse racing enthusiasts. 🛇🖚🍴♣🖚🚲🛜♪

Poulton Elk 🕭
22 Hardhorn Road, FY6 7SR
☎ (01253) 899667
Greene King Abbot; Ruddles Best Bitter; Sharp's Doom Bar; 7 changing beers (sourced nationally; often Bradfield, Kirkby Lonsdale, Moorhouse's) 🅗
This highly popular Wetherspoon pub has been in the Guide for the last 10 years and was the 900th to be opened by them. It has gained a reputation for serving quality real ale and food. The name relates to the finding of a 13,000-year-old elk skeleton nearby. Converted from the former telephone exchange in 2013 it is always busy, especially in summer with two outdoor drinking areas. 🛇🕭🖚🖚🍴🖚🛜

Thatched House 🕭
30 Ball Street, FY6 7BG
☎ (01253) 891063

Bank Top Flat Cap; Bradfield Farmers Blonde; Timothy Taylor Landlord; 6 changing beers (sourced regionally; often Saltaire) ⓗ
This unmissable mock-Tudor pub is located in the corner of St Chad's churchyard. Pictures of sports and local history decorate many walls and there are two open fires and a log-burning stove. A range of up to nine beers is available. It gets busy at weekends when many TVs show sports. There is space for outdoor drinking and smoking in a small yard between the pub and former brew house and on a roof terrace. Q✿&♿🚲🚃🚌☻🏵

Preston

Black Horse 🍷 ★
166 Friargate, PR1 2EJ
☎ (01772) 204855
Robinsons Dizzy Blonde, Old Tom; 6 changing beers (sourced nationally) ⓗ
Victorian Grade II-listed pub close to the historic open market; it has been identified by CAMRA as having a nationally important historic pub interior, with its tiled bar, walls and mosaic floor. Two front rooms are adorned with Robinsons memorabilia and photos of old Preston; the famous 'hall of mirrors' seating area is to the rear. Robinsons beers are available with an additional four ever-changing guest beers coming from far and wide. The pub is away-supporter football-friendly. Local CAMRA Pub of the Year 2023 and 2024, and Lancashire Pub of the Year 2024. Q🐂🚃♣♠🏵☻♪

Chain House Brewing Co Taproom Ⓛ
139-141 Market Street West, PR1 2HB
☎ 07707 511578 ⊕ chainhousebrewing.com
2 changing beers (sourced locally; often Chain House) ⓗ
The Chain House Brewing Company started life in 2017 in a garage in Longton and opened its taproom in 2022; located in the city centre just off Friargate on Market Street West. There are two cask ales on handpump and 12 keg lines showcasing the brewery's own beers together with various guest ales. There is also a selection of local gins and a variety of other drinks to suit all tastes. 🐂🚃🚌☻♪

Crafty Beggars Ale House
284B Garstang Road, Fulwood, PR2 9RX
☎ (01772) 370780 ⊕ craftybeggars.co.uk
4 changing beers (sourced nationally) ⓗ
Appearing in the Guide for a third consecutive year, Crafty Beggars opened in 2020. It is a large micro with a traditional small pub atmosphere, selling four cask ales on handpump sourced mainly from the North-West area. There are five changing keg lines, some of which are likely to be serving live beer from a membrane keg, fine wines and boxes of real cider. Homemade pizzas, paninis, breads and pies are served Monday to Saturday teatimes and Crafty Cask Club is on Tuesdays. ✿&♠🚌(125,23)☻♪

Fulwood & Broughton Cricket Club
Garstang Road, Fulwood, PR3 5JE
☎ (01772) 863003 ⊕ fulwoodandbroughtoncc.weebly.com
3 changing beers (sourced nationally) ⓗ
This welcoming club first opened in 1909 and has a fully licensed members' clubhouse open weekday evenings and from lunchtime on Saturday and Sunday. It is open to non-members. There are two lounges, serving a full range of beers, wines, spirits and soft drinks with Sky Sports and BT Sports available. Three free of tie cask ales are available on handpump, with a variety of interesting ales often sourced locally. Local CAMRA Club of the Year 2023. 🐂&♣🚌(40)☻🏵

Guild Ale House Ⓛ ✅
56 Lancaster Road, PR1 1DD
☎ 07932 517444
7 changing beers (sourced regionally) ⓗ
Preston's first micropub opened in 2016 just a few doors away from Preston's Guild Hall complex. The main room has high- and low-level seating and the high ceilings give a light and airy feel. A small lounge is tucked away to the rear and there is a comfortable lounge upstairs. Seven changing beers are mainly local or from Yorkshire, with at least one dark beer. A range of continental beers in keg and bottle is served. No jukebox, TV, or food, but there is live acoustic on Sunday afternoons. Q🐂✿&🚃♣♠🚌☻🏵♪

Moorbrook
370 North Road, PR1 1RU
☎ (01772) 823302 ⊕ themoorbrook.co.uk
8 changing beers (sourced nationally) ⓗ
This place is where the local CAMRA branch was formed in 1973. It has a traditional-style wood-panelled bar with two rooms off the main bar area, and an enclosed beer garden to the side and rear. Food features authentic wood-fired pizzas and home-made shortcrust pies. The eight guest beers come from all over the country, providing a wide choice of regional beer types while retaining a strong emphasis on microbreweries from the area. The venue gets busy on Preston North End match days. 🐂✿🕦&♣🚌🏵♪

New Continental
South Meadow Lane, PR1 8JP
☎ (01772) 499425 ⊕ newcontinental.net
House beer (by Marble); 6 changing beers (sourced nationally) ⓗ
Out-of-town pub alongside the River Ribble, Miller Park, and the large railway bridge. It has a main bar area, a lounge with a real fire in winter, plus a conservatory overlooking a sizeable beer garden. Live music and theatre is hosted regularly in the Boatyard events space, which has also been used for beer festivals. Eight handpumps serve one cider plus up to seven microbrewery beers, including the house beer from Marble and a dark brew. A beer menu is produced and updated each day. Freshly cooked meals are available Wednesday to Sunday. Q🐂✿🕦&🚃♠🅿🚌(119)🏵🎸♪

Old Vic Ⓛ
79 Fishergate, PR1 2UH
☎ (01772) 828519
⊕ theoldvic-preston.foodanddrinksites.co.uk
Wainwright Amber; 6 changing beers (sourced regionally) ⓗ
Opposite the railway station and on bus routes into the city this popular pub helpfully provides travellers with a TV screen showing live updates of train departures. This is a pub that can get busy, particularly at weekends, with a quiz every Sunday evening. To the rear of the building is a separate area for pool and darts. Seven handpumps offer a good range of mainly Yorkshire breweries including Ossett and Rat being popular. The car park is only available on a Sunday and in the evenings. ✿🕦🚃♣🅿🚌(2,3)🏵

Orchard
Earl Street, PR1 2LA (on Preston covered market)
☎ 07756 583621 ⊕ the-orchard-bar.business.site
3 changing beers (sourced nationally) ⓗ
The Orchard was opened in 2018, a sister pub to the Guild Ale House. Located within the Grade II-listed covered market the decor/framework is of wood recycled from the old market trestle boards plus lots of modern glass. No food but there is plenty on the

neighbouring market, which can be ordered and taken in. Three cask ales and 10 craft beers are always available alongside real cider. Q ⛱ ♿ ⊛ ≒ ♣ ● 🖵 ❀ 🛜 ♫

Plug & Taps

32 Lune Street, PR1 2NN
4 changing beers 🅗
This is a craft beer bar featuring 10 keg lines and four handpumps, as well as a large can and bottle fridge. Expect to find changing beers from anywhere in the country and internationally, with a permanent Rivington brewery line. There are also occasional tap takeovers from various breweries. There is a large function room upstairs with a jukebox, and an outside seating area for use in summer or in warm weather. Located just 300 metres from the railway station, the pub is an away-supporter football-friendly venue. ⛱ ≒ ♣ ❀ 🛜

Tap End

450 Blackpool Road, Ashton-on-Ribble, PR2 1HX
☎ 07947 246022
4 changing beers (sourced nationally) 🅗
Opened in 2021 in a former card and gift shop, this is a high-end micropub specializing in cask and craft ales generally sourced from microbreweries. It has a fairly low-key atmosphere conducive to conversation, with dark wood and subdued lighting. Four handpumps dispense cask ales with a variety of styles, usually including a dark beer. Keg lines, bottles and cans provide alternatives. Changes to all beers are uploaded to the Untapped and Real Ale Finder apps and beer menus are available providing full descriptions of current and future beers for your perusal. Q ♿ 🖵 ❀ 🛜

Vinyl Tap

28 Adelphi Street, PR1 7BE
☎ (01772) 555995
Oakham Citra; 4 changing beers (sourced nationally) 🅗
Single room bar adjacent to the university that opened in 2018 with up to five real ale pumps on the bar. People can select from an ever-growing 'pick and choose' vinyl selection or bring their own to be played while enjoying a drink and a bite to eat; authentic German hotdogs are served. Fridays and Saturdays feature live music with a rock and roots theme. There is a quiz every Tuesday and open mic on Thursdays. ▶ ≒ 🖵 🛜 ♫

Winckley Street Ale House

8B Winckley Street, PR1 2AA
☎ (01772) 962017 ⊕ winckleyale.co.uk
4 changing beers (sourced regionally) 🅗
This premises initially opened in 2018 as the Otter's Pocket and was a single-room bar and restaurant occupying the whole ground floor of a former shop. March 2020 saw the pub closed undergoing renovation and it has since reopened as the Winckley Street Ale House, offering a wider menu and great range of beers with up to four regularly changing cask ales as well as a range of 10 keg lines with a strong focus on local and regional breweries. An away-supporter football-friendly venue. ⛱ ⊛ ◑ ♿ ≒ 🖵 ❀ 🛜

Rawtenstall

Buffer Stops

Bury Road, BB4 6AG
☎ (0161) 764 7790 ⊕ eastlancsrailway.org.uk/plan-your-day-out/buffer-stops/
8 changing beers (sourced nationally; often Northern Whisper, Oscars, Reedley Hallows) 🅗
Located on the platform at the northern terminus of the East Lancs Railway, this unique one-roomed bar, once

the station café, is small but further seating is available in the ticket hall and waiting room and on benches and at tables on the platform. It is busy with both railway visitors and locals. Close to Ski Rossendale, Whitaker park and museum and the Weavers cottage. Snacks are available. Q ⛱ ⊛ ♿ ≒ ● P 🖵 ❀ ♫

Hop Micro Pub 🅛

70 Bank Street, BB4 8EG
☎ 07753 775150 ⊕ hopmicropubs.com
Deeply Vale Hop; 5 changing beers 🅗
Situated at the top end of Rawtenstall's cobbled Bank Street, close to the market, Hop is a pleasant and congenial venue with the atmosphere of a traditional local pub. In addition to the bar there is a pleasant first-floor lounge and a heated outside drinking area. With six hand-pulled cask ales, including the permanent Hop from Deeply Vale, as well as keg craft beers and ciders available, there is always a fantastic choice. A short walk from the bus station and from the northern terminus of the East Lancashire Heritage Railway. ⊛ ≒ ● P 🖵 ❀

Rivington

Rivington Brewery Co. Tap 🅛

Home Farm, Horobin Lane, PR6 9HE
☎ 07859 248779 ⊕ rivingtonbrewing.co.uk
Rivington Beach House 🅗; 11 changing beers (sourced locally; often Rivington) 🅗 /🅚
Opened in 2019, housed in a converted stable block at the farm by the brewery, this taproom showcases their extensive range of ales, with up to three on handpump and 15 on keg, with cider and guest craft ales also available. Walkers and their dogs are welcome with outdoor seating providing beautiful views across the reservoir towards Winter Hill. The bar is lofty with bare stone walls and a large stone-topped bar counter. It was recently extended into the adjoining stable block providing a family-friendly zone. ⛱ ⊛ ♿ ◑ ♠ ● P ❀

Rufford

Hesketh Arms

81 Liverpool Road, L40 1SB (on A59 at jct with B5246)
☎ (01704) 821009 ⊕ theheskethharmsrufford.co.uk
Moorhouse's White Witch, Pride of Pendle; 7 changing beers (sourced regionally; often Cross Bay, Phoenix, Reedley Hallows) 🅗
A spacious former Greenall's inn on the A59, the Hesketh is now a free house serving up to six ales mostly from local microbreweries. Set in the charming village of Rufford, it is near the National Trust property of Rufford Old Hall, the delightful St Mary's Marina, and the popular Mere Sands nature reserve. A large split-level pub with several dining areas, the pub serves good quality food throughout the day. Monthly live entertainment and a Tuesday quiz attract a mixed clientele. Q ⛱ ⊛ ◑ ♿ ≒ P 🖵 (2A,347) ❀ ♫

St Annes

Fifteens of St Annes 🍷

42 St Annes Road West, FY8 1RF
☎ (01253) 725852 ⊕ fifteensstannes.com
9 changing beers (sourced nationally; often Bank Top, Ossett) 🅗
A popular and lively community pub that has won many awards and has featured in every edition of the Guide since it opened. Converted from a former bank, the old vault still provides a haven of peace and calm, while a state-of-the-art cellar helps maintain the beer in excellent condition. A real cider and a dark beer are

always available. There is live music every Saturday, with a unique quiz on Sundays. Sport is shown at other times. ⇌(St Annes-on-the-Sea) ♣🍴P🖵☕♫

Hop Shoppe
2-2A Wood Street, FY8 1QS
☎ 07593 222535 ⊕ thehopshoppe.co.uk
4 changing beers (sourced nationally; often DEYA, Verdant, Vocation) Ⓗ
Now an established venue, The Hop Shoppe is a fresh and modern take on the micropub, managing to be open and inviting while still being cosy and intimate. The four cask ales and one cider are supplemented by 16 craft keg lines (with always at least one sour) and a generous selection of cans, all with an absolute commitment to small, independent UK producers. Q🕸♿&⇌(-on-Sea) ♣🍴🖵☕🛜

Keg n Cask
17 St Andrews Road South, FY8 1SX
☎ 07743 502711
5 changing beers (sourced locally; often Copper Dragon, Lancaster, Reedley Hallows) Ⓗ
A friendly and distinctive micropub with a loyal clientele, set in what is said to be the oldest brick building in the town. The background music is soft and there are otherwise no electronic distractions, just good beer and conversation in calm and civilised surroundings. A pavement drinking area outside provides an excellent spot for people-watching. Opening hours can vary, especially in winter. Q🕸&⇌(St Annes-on-the-Sea)🖵☕

Victoria ✅
Church Road, FY8 3NE
☎ (01253) 721041
Caledonian Deuchars IPA; Morland Old Speckled Hen; Timothy Taylor Landlord; 2 changing beers (sourced nationally; often Big Bog, Kirkby Lonsdale, Moorhouse's) Ⓗ
Originally multi-roomed, this thriving community pub retains a number of discrete areas which give it an intimate quality which belies its size. There is a separate vault for sports on a large screen, as well as a room for the full-sized snooker table. Family and dog-friendly, the Victoria hosts social groups, men's and women's darts teams, and has a quiz on Thursday nights. Other events are listed on the active Facebook and Instagram pages. 🕭🕸🌂◗&⇌(St Annes-on-the-Sea)♣P🖵☕🛜♫

Scarisbrick

Heatons Bridge Inn ✅
2 Heatons Bridge Road, L40 8JG (on B5242 road by Leeds-Liverpool Canal)
☎ (01704) 840549
2 changing beers (sourced regionally; often Moorhouse's, Tetley) Ⓗ
Great canalside pub dating from 1837, when it served as offices for the Leeds and Liverpool freight services. It iis a traditional pub with separate areas and home-cooked food. Pillbox beer is often served in reference to the WWII defensive structure outside. Twice-yearly military displays and annual classic bus services are hosted, with themed beers for the occasion. This is a popular pub with families, walkers and cyclists, in an excellent rural setting, with a garden and outside eating area. 🕭🕸◗&🅰♣🖵(375)☕🛜

> I never drink water. I'm afraid it will become habit-forming.
> **W C Fields**

Trawden

Trawden Arms
Church Street, BB8 8RU
☎ (01282) 337055 ⊕ trawden-arms.mydirectstay.com
4 changing beers (sourced regionally) Ⓗ
Refurbished tastefully decorated contemporary village pub, now community-owned, serving a classic modern menu of delicious homemade food. It offers three changing cask ales, a regular cask pale ale, a fruit cider on draft and three craft ales. A variety of events are hosted, including a Sunday quiz night and live music. There are four stunning B&B rooms. 🕭🕸🛏◗P🖵☕♫

Whalley

Dog Inn Ⓛ
55 King Street, BB7 9SP
☎ (01254) 823009
6 changing beers (sourced regionally) Ⓗ
Deservedly popular and usually crowded, especially at weekends, the Dog has been run by the same family since the early 1990s. Six handpumps serve a range of beers, changed continually, from breweries such as Acorn, Hetton, Moorhouse's, Peerless and Wishbone. Food is served only at lunchtimes and is always excellent. This traditional, historic pub is close to the ruins of Whalley Abbey and is handy for exploring the picturesque Ribble Valley. With trains to Bolton and Manchester and buses to virtually everywhere in East Lancashire, Whalley is extremely well served by public transport. 🕭🕸◗⇌🖵☕🛜

Wheelton

Red Lion
196 Blackburn Road, PR6 8EU (in centre of village opp clock tower)
☎ (01254) 659890
Hawkshead Lakeland Gold; Timothy Taylor Landlord; 6 changing beers (sourced nationally; often Acorn, Fyne, Oakham) Ⓗ
Built around 1826, this former Matthew Brown house retains many original features including a large stone lion at roof level above the door. Close to the West Pennine Moors, many local walks pass by, dogs are welcome and food is served seven days a week. It features a comfortable lounge with an open fire and a second room up a few steps. There are eight handpumps showcasing two regular beers and six changing real ales from local independents, usually including a stout and a strong ale. Local CAMRA Pub of the Year 2022. Q🕭🕸◗P🖵(24)☕🛜♫

Whitworth

Whitworth Vale & Healey Band Club Ⓛ
498 Market Street, OL12 8QW
☎ (01706) 852484
Wainwright Gold; 2 changing beers (sourced regionally) Ⓗ
Popular social club, notable for being the home of the local brass band of the same name. The Club is part of a terrace on the main road through the town, with the regular 464 bus service passing by the door. It is quite spacious despite the low ceiling. There is an outside seating area. Winner of local and regional CAMRA Club of the Year awards. 🕸🖶🖵(464)☕🛜♫

Winmarleigh

Patten Arms

Park Lane, PR3 0JU (on B5272 3 miles N of Garstang)
☎ (01524) 791484 ⊕ thepattenarms.co.uk
Wainwright Gold; 3 changing beers (sourced nationally) ⊞

Genuine, isolated free house situated away from villages on a B-road, yet enjoying regular local custom. This early 19th-century Grade II-listed building has a single bar with a country pub feel, high-backed bench seats, cream-painted walls and open fires. There is a separate restaurant, and terraced seating overlooking a bowling green. Since 2019 there has been a tiny brewery in the cellar, but it is currently mothballed. ⌖ ◑ Å ♣ P ❀ 🛜 ♪

Worsthorne

Crooked Billet ★ 🅛 ✅

1-3 Smith Street, BB10 3NQ
☎ 07766 230175 ⊕ crookedbilletworsthorne.co.uk
Timothy Taylor Landlord; Tetley Bitter; 2 changing beers (sourced regionally; often Lancaster) ⊞

An award-winning true free house, this well-presented village pub has a beautiful wood and glass horseshoe bar serving both the main lounge area and snug. Quiz nights are popular as are Thai nights and soul nights. Its position in the hills close to Burnley makes it popular with walkers and cyclists. It is dog friendly and has a large covered outdoor drinking area where you can enjoy the flower-bedecked exterior. Q ⌖ ❀ ◑ & ♣ P ➐ (2) ❀ 🛜 ♪

Wrightington

Rigbye Arms

2 Whittle Lane, WN6 9QB
☎ (01257) 462354 ⊕ therigbyearms.co.uk
Ossett White Rat; Timothy Taylor Landlord; Tetley Bitter ⊞

This award-winning pub/restaurant situated in a rural setting near to Wrightington is popular with ramblers. Recently refurbished, it has a real fire and an upstairs function room for up to 35 people. Outstanding food is available Wednesday to Sunday. Three handpumps serve the regular ales. Outside are a bowling green and beer garden. Q ⌖ ❀ ◑ P ❀

White Lion

117 Mossy Lea Road, WN6 9RE
☎ (01257) 425977 ⊕ thewhitelionwrightington.co.uk
Bowland Hen Harrier; Moorhouse's White Witch; 6 changing beers ⊞

This popular country pub has a good offering for diners and drinkers with eight handpumps and a good range of food. The pub runs a Monday Club with drinks offers and a quiz on Tuesdays. It is highly community orientated, running the village scarecrow festival, and offering themed evenings throughout the year. It is family-friendly, with a large beach hut-themed outside garden area and board games inside the pub. Q ⌖ ❀ ◑ & P ➐ (111) ❀

Fifteens of St Annes, St Annes (Photo: Stuart McMahon)

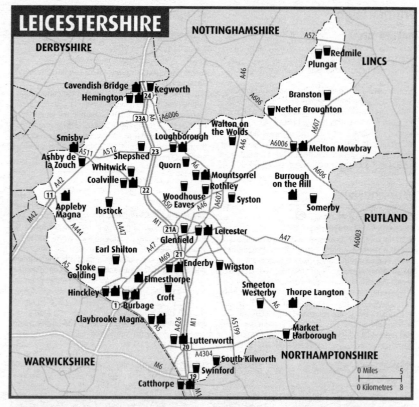

LEICESTERSHIRE

Ashby De La Zouch

Tap at No.76

76 Market Street, LE65 1AP
⊕ tollgatebrewery.co.uk
Tollgate Ashby Pale; 5 changing beers (often Tollgate) Ⓗ
This micropub on the high street was originally a medieval farmhouse. Grade II listed, it is one of the oldest buildings in town. Now a Tollgate brewery house and a relatively recent addition to the Ashby beer scene, it offers a warm and friendly welcome and serves five real ales and up to four real ciders. Three third-pint tasting trays are available for those wishing to try the whole range of beers. A large selection of bottle-conditioned Tollgate beers is available to take away. Snacks include pork pies. Closed Monday. Q&♣🚐🌼

Brânston

Wheel Inn Ⓛ ✓

Main Street, NG32 1RU
☎ (01476) 248165 ⊕ thewheelinn.uk
3 changing beers Ⓗ
This attractive stone-built 18th-century village pub houses a cosy bar with seating plus a larger restaurant with rustic tables and a real fire. The attractive outdoor area is quiet and relaxing in the summer months, and boasts a barbecue table. Traditional outbuildings are used for beer festivals and live music, and weddings are hosted in a large marquee. The Wheel boasts an extensive food menu using locally sourced ingredients where possible, including produce from the Belvoir Estate. A former local CAMRA Pub of the Year.
Q🛏🕸🕮🌼&♣P🌼🅿🛜♪

Burbage

Red Lion

14 Windsor Street, LE10 2EF
☎ (01455) 636108
Draught Bass; Eagle Bombardier; Sharp's Doom Bar; Theakston XB; Timothy Taylor Landlord Ⓗ
Burbage Church Warden's records show the name of the Red Lion going back over 200 years. This one-room, traditional village pub with a cosy fire was updated and refurbished by new landlords in 2022. The newly furnished garden has a children's play area, and there is a separate covered smoking area and patio. A large function room is available. There is live entertainment at weekends, and sports events are shown on TV.
🛏🕸&P🚐(7,8) 🌼🛜♪

Catthorpe

Cherry Tree Ⓛ

Main Street, LE17 6DB (on main road through village ½ mile from A5)
☎ (0116) 482 7042 ⊕ cherrytreecatthorpe.co.uk
3 changing beers (sourced locally; often Dow Bridge, Langton, Phipps NBC) Ⓗ
Welcoming, two-roomed village local with a modern twist, which has been sympathetically renovated by the new owners. Ales from Catthorpe's Dow Bridge brewery take pride of place on the bar alongside English red and white wines, local gins and whiskies. Locally sourced home-cooked food includes vegetarian, vegan and children's options. The south-facing terrace and garden overlook the Avon Valley. A former local CAMRA Country Pub of the Year. Closed Monday to Thursday.
Q🛏🕸🕮AP🌼🛜♪

Claybrooke Magna

Pig in Muck 𝕃

Manor Road, LE17 5AY

☎ (01455) 202859 ⊕ piginmuck.co.uk

Pig Pub Chinook Pale Ale, Pigs Best Bitter; Sharp's Doom Bar; 1 changing beer (sourced regionally) ℍ

The only pub in the village increased in popularity after a change of ownership in 2012. The current licensee brews his Pig Pub beers in a small brewery behind the pub and also cooks the increasingly popular food. The pub runs a Real Ale Club loyalty scheme on the brewery's beers. Hinckley Bus service eight runs hourly between Hinckley and Lutterworth, Monday to Saturday daytimes.

❀◑♣P🖵(8) 🛜

Coalville

Rock Café & Bar

97 Meadow Lane, LE67 4DQ

☎ 07710 532970 ⊕ rockales.beer

House beer (by Rock Ales); 6 changing beers (sourced nationally) ℍ

Located in a leafy suburb but on a main bus route, the Rock continues to be a welcome addition to Coalville's beer scene. Deservedly popular, with the largest selection of real ales in the area, plus a craft 'beer wall', it also has an extensive selection of gins and wines. The café serves a wide range of dishes, sourced and prepared locally, and at very competitive prices. Cobs are available at the bar for those with a big appetite.

Q❀❀◑◖♣●🖵(29) 🐾🛜

Croft

Heathcote Arms

Hill Street, LE9 3EG

☎ (01455) 699107

Everards Sunchaser, Tiger, Old Original; 1 changing beer ℍ

The pub consists of a public bar, lounge bar and a games room. Out the back is the former stable/pig-sty/cattle-shed, which was converted in 1926 into a skittles long alley and now also doubles as a function room. Next to the car park is a covered, decked area furnished with leather settees, and a tarmacked area with picnic tables. There is also a lawn with children's play equipment and a secluded paved patio with garden furniture. No meals are served, but filled cobs are prepared daily.

Q❀❀◖♣P🖵(X84) 🐾🛜♪

Earl Shilton

Shilton Vaults

3 The Hollow, LE9 7NA

☎ 07715 106876

Draught Bass; 8 changing beers ℍ

Previously a bank, this welcoming pub with friendly staff opened in 2018. There are three rooms – the main bar, a centre room, and the original vault – and a small outdoor space. The air-conditioned ground-floor cellar has racking for 12 casks, and three or four real ales are available, along with eight traditional ciders, craft lagers, and speciality gins. Toilets are upstairs. Sister pub to the Pestle & Mortar in Hinckley. Cobs and pork pies are available. Local CAMRA Cider Pub of the Year runner-up 2024. Q❀❀◖♣●🖵(148,158)🐾🛜♪

Enderby

Everards Beer Hall 𝕃

Cooper Way, LE19 2AN

☎ (0116) 201 4100 ⊕ everardsmeadows.co.uk

Everards Sunchaser, Tiger, Old Original; house beer (by Everards); changing beers (sourced locally) ℍ

The new home of Everards brewery incorporates the Beer Hall, a large pub and restaurant. The full range of Everards' regular beers is available, plus seasonal short-run specials, and three unique beers brewed on site and served from copper tanks behind the bar. The site of the old brewery opposite is now a large shopping area. Extensive grounds with walks connect up with the canal towpath and the Great Central Way footpath.

❀❀◑◖♣P🖵(50,X84) 🐾🛜

Mill Hill Cask & Coffee

12-14 Mill Hill, LE19 4AL

⊕ millhillcaskandcoffee.com

4 changing beers (often Mill Hill Brew Co) 🄶

Micropub with modern decor, a relaxed atmosphere and a growing clientele of locals and passing trade. The owners have established a reputation for well-conditioned ales from top UK breweries, with up to four cask ales and up to 10 KeyKegs to choose from. Food includes home-made sandwiches, cakes, locally sourced pies and Scotch eggs. An outside seating area with heaters and a retractable roof is a popular addition.

Q❀❀◑◖♣●P🖵(50) 🐾🛜♪

New Inn

51 High Street, LE19 4AG

☎ (0116) 286 3126

Everards Tiger; 2 changing beers (often Everards) ℍ

Friendly thatched village local dating from 1549, tucked away at the top of the High Street. Everards' first tied house, the pub is well-known locally for the quality of its beer and is frequented by Everards brewery staff. Three rooms are served by a central bar, all modernised in traditional style with some wall panelling. Long-alley skittles and a function room are off a covered walkway to the rear. Outside there is a patio area. Lunches are served Wednesday to Saturday. Q❀❀◑♣P🖵(50)🐾🛜

Glenfield

Railway ⊘

152 Station Road, LE3 8BR

☎ (0116) 216 1575

4 changing beers (sourced nationally; often Draught Bass) ℍ

This comfortably modernised pub has been extended to create a large lounge bar with dining room at the rear, and a bar area at the front. It also has a completely separate snug bar with TV (for sport) and a pool table. The pub has a constantly changing range of beers, and serves food throughout. There are TVs around the pub, often showing different programmes, as well as broadcasting the quiz. There is an outdoor smoking area and a patio to the rear, plus three dining pods. ➸❀◑&♣P➸❀♠☀♪

Hemington

Jolly Sailor
21 Main Street, DE74 2RB
☎ (01332) 812665
Draught Bass; 4 changing beers (sourced regionally) Ⓗ
This 17th-century building is thought to have originally been a weaver's cottage. It has been a pub since the 19th century, and is now the only one in the village. It retains many original features, including old timbers, open fires and beamed ceiling. There is a large outside seating area for warmer weather. Filled rolls are available until 6pm and home-made pizzas are served all day. Q➸❀&P➸☀

Hinckley

Elbow Room Cask & Craft
26 Station Road, LE10 1AW (below Cineworld at The Crescent)
☎ 07900 191388
Shiny 4 Wood; 6 changing beers Ⓖ
This family-run micropub, decorated in an industrial style, offers a warm welcome and great atmosphere. The ales and ciders are served by gravity directly from the cellar behind sliding glass doors. High-quality wines, over 40 gins, whiskies, vodkas, world craft beers, lagers plus cocktails and soft drinks are also available. Food is limited to pork pies and Scotch eggs. There is no TV or gaming machine as conversation is king. Children are welcome until 8pm. Q➸❀&♣●➸(7,7A)❀☀♪

Greyhound Ⓛ ✔
9 New Buildings, LE10 1HN
☎ (01455) 697575 ⊕ thegreyhoundhinckley.co.uk
Courage Directors; Draught Bass; Marston's Pedigree; 2 changing beers (sourced locally; often New Buildings) Ⓗ
A three-roomed town-centre public house since at least 1815, the Greenhound features a traditional interior. It was reopened in 2013, under the management of the landlady of the nearby New Plough Inn, and became a free house in 2014. The bars were refurbished in 2022. It offers a popular Sunday carvery. A spacious function room hosts many community clubs, and it is the base of Castlemead Community Radio. On the exterior a blue plaque commemorates William Butler of Mitchells & Butlers. Q◑➸♣➸(8)❀☀♪🏆

New Plough Inn ⛾ ✔
Leicester Road, LE10 1LS
☎ (01455) 615037 ⊕ thenewploughinn.co.uk
Courage Directors; Marston's Pedigree; Tetley Bitter; 5 changing beers (sourced nationally) Ⓗ
Opened at the beginning of the last century, it was called the New Plough because a pub called the Plough was already in existence in Hinckley. This welcoming and friendly local pub features old settles, log-burners, skittles alley, over 50 gins, and rugby memorabilia that reflects its sponsorship of the local team. The landlady is

a CAMRA member and the pub has raised over £150,000 for charity via the monthly quiz. Local CAMRA Pub of the Year in 2022, 2023 and 2024. ➸❀➸♣●➸(8)❀☀

Pestle & Mortar Ⓛ
81 Castle Street, LE10 1DA
☎ 07715 106876 ⊕ thepestlehinckley.co.uk
Draught Bass; 8 changing beers (sourced nationally) Ⓗ
Opened in 2015, Hinckley's first micropub is a frequent winner of both the local CAMRA Cider Pub of the Year and Cider Pub of the Year awards. This friendly, comfortable, and pleasantly quirky micropub satisfies a wide range of drinking tastes. Up to 22 changing real ciders are available, and handpumps deliver up to eight changing real ales from casks behind the bar. Cobs and pork pies are available. Q➸➸♣●➸(8)❀☀

Queen's Head
Upper Bond Street, LE10 1RJ
☎ 07951 063484
Draught Bass; 3 changing beers Ⓗ
A warm welcome awaits at this multi award-winning, family-run Victorian free house serving Bass alongside three changing real ales. The original building dates back to 1809 and has been sympathetically refurbished. It features open fires and a Victorian range, and a new snug was created in 2020, helping to create a cosy atmosphere. There is a large, pleasant beer garden to the rear, which is a suntrap during the summer months. A four-time local CAMRA Pub of the Year. Q❀&➸♣➸(158,148)

Ibstock

Waggon & Horses ★
71 Curzon Street, LE67 6LA
☎ (01530) 262123
Draught Bass; 2 changing beers Ⓗ
A 300-year-old traditional village local, unscathed by the passing of time, with quarry-tiled floors, open fireplaces and a solid fuel heating stove with stovepipe rising to join the chimney just below first floor level. It has been identified by CAMRA as having a regionally important historic pub interior. To the rear is a partially covered courtyard with timber garden furniture. Q➸❀♣P❀☀

Kegworth

Red Lion ★ ✔
24 High Street, DE74 2DA
☎ (01509) 672466 ⊕ redlionkegworth.co.uk
Charnwood Salvation, Vixen; Courage Directors; Marston's Pedigree; 3 changing beers (sourced nationally; often Dancing Duck) Ⓗ
An impressive, refurbished Georgian building on the historic A6 route, with six public rooms, including a restaurant and the new lodge. Seven cask beers are available, along with a large selection of gins, whiskies and fine wines. Bar snacks are available. Outside is a large beer garden with ample seating, and there is a large car park. It is on the bus route from Derby and Leicester to nearby East Midlands Airport. Q➸❀◰&♣P➸❀☀♪

Leicester

Ale Stone
660 Aylestone Road, Aylestone Village, LE2 8PR
Leatherbritches Ashbourne Ale, Hairy Helmet; 3 changing beers Ⓗ

Micropub in a converted shop unit, featuring a nicely furnished interior that has wooden benches and dados all round. A large barrel with a millstone top forms a table in the centre. Up to three real ales, plus two ciders, are stillaged in a temperature-controlled glass-fronted cellar which is visible from the bar. Ham and cheese cobs are available. Q ♿ ♠ ☗ ❁

Ale Wagon L
27 Rutland Street, LE1 1RE
☎ (0116) 262 3330 ⊕ thealewagon.co.uk
Hoskins Hob Bitter, IPA; 5 changing beers (often Hoskins) H

City-centre pub whose 1930s interior features an original oak staircase. It has two rooms with tiled and parquet floors and a central bar. On the walls are photos of the former Queen's Hotel, which was across the road from this pub in the 1930s, and the former Hoskins brewery. It is handy for the Curve Theatre. The pub still serves Hoskins family recipe beers. ≒ ♠ ☗ ❁

Black Horse L
1 Foxon Street, LE3 5LT
☎ (0116) 254 0446
Everards Sunchaser, Tiger, Old Original; 2 changing beers (sourced nationally) H

A traditional community pub in a street that caters mostly for younger revellers. The two rooms are separated by a central bar, and the wood-panelled walls and practical furniture provide a comfortable setting for any event. The pub sources its guest beers through Everards. There is live music four nights a week. A roof terrace for open-air drinking accommodates up to 40. ❀ ♣ ☗ ❁ ☂ ♫

Black Horse
65 Narrow Lane, Aylestone Village, LE2 8NA
☎ (0116) 283 7225 ⊕ blackhorseaylestone.co.uk
Everards Tiger; 3 changing beers (often Titanic, Everards) H

Welcoming traditional Victorian pub with a distinctive bar servery in a village conservation area on the edge of the city. Up to eight real ales are available, as well as a changing range of four real ciders, and home-cooked food. The skittle alley and function room can be hired and comedy features regularly. Beer festivals and community events are regularly hosted. Quiz night is Sunday. There is a large beer garden. Coaches are welcome by prior arrangement. Q ♿ ❀ ◑ ♣ ♠ ☗ ❁ ☂ ♫

Blue Boar ⛊ L
16 Millstone Lane, LE1 5JN
☎ (0116) 319 6230 ⊕ blueboarleicester.co.uk
Beowulf Finn's Hall Porter; house beer (by Shiny) H/G; **7 changing beers** H/G

This single-roomed micropub is named after the Blue Boar Inn where Richard III stayed before the Battle of Bosworth Field. The cellar is visible through a glass partition behind the bar. Guest beers are from microbreweries around the country and include many rare beers. Local pork pies and filled cheese or ham cobs are sold. Board games and reading material may be found on shelves, and there are displays of old maps of Leicester. Q ♿ ❀ ♣ ♠ ☗ ❁ ☂ ♫

Castle
8-9 Castle View, City Centre, LE1 5WH
Charnwood Salvation; Timothy Taylor Landlord; Titanic Plum Porter H

This micropub was converted from two tiny historic cottages close to the site of Leicester Castle. The building, which had been unused since it was an antiques shop in the 1990s, is next door to a former pub on Castle View

which closed many years ago. The pub aims to support local businesses and is completely plastic free. Last orders are 30 minutes before closing time. Q ❀ ☗ ❁

King's Head
36 King Street, LE1 6RL
☎ (0116) 254 8240
Black Country Bradley's Finest Golden, Chain Ale, Pig on the Wall, Fireside; Sharp's Atlantic; 6 changing beers H

A traditional one-room city-centre local owned by Black Country Ales. Twelve handpulls serve seven regularly changing guest ales and a cider, plus a range of bottles. Its open fire and covered roof terrace make it popular throughout the year with real ale enthusiasts. Filled cobs are often available. Live sport is shown on TV and it gets very busy on match days for football and rugby. ❀ ≒ ♠ ☗ ❁ ☂

Old Horse ✅
198 London Road, LE2 1NE
☎ (0116) 254 8384 ⊕ oldhorseleicester.co.uk
Everards Sunchaser, Tiger, Old Original; 3 changing beers (sourced nationally; often Everards) H

Recently refurbished 19th-century coaching inn, handy for dog walkers, students and sports fans. There are four monthly changing guest beers, and a cider bar serving eight handpulled options. Tasty, good-value food is served, including Sunday carveries. Behind the pub is the largest pub garden in Leicester complete with children's play equipment. Regular quiz nights, karaoke and special events take place. A former local CAMRA Cider Pub of the Year. ♿ ❀ ◑ ♿ ♣ ♠ P ☗ ❁ ☂ ♫

Queens Road Tap
109 Queens Road, Clarendon Park, LE2 1TT
5 changing beers (often Tollgate) H

A micropub opened in a former shop in 2017 by the Tollgate brewery, which is based at the Calke Estate in south-east Derbyshire. The modern, single room interior has rustic furniture. The pub sells a constantly varying range of up to five real ales, including three or four from Tollgate. There is no music or TV. The bus stop to Leicester is right outside, but evening services are limited. Q ♠ ☗ (44,83) ❁

Real Ale Classroom L
22 Allandale Road, Stoneygate, LE2 2DA
☎ (0116) 319 6998 ⊕ therealaleclassroom.com
4 changing beers (often Pentrich, Polly's, Two by Two) G

Classroom-themed micropub run by former teachers in a converted suburban shop. The furniture includes reclaimed desks with original graffiti and the beers are written up on a blackboard. Cask and KeyKeg ales and ciders are served from a home-made chiller cabinet behind the high bar. Seating around large tables encourages conversation in both rooms, and a log-burner warms the rear room. Crisps, nuts and scratchings are available and the pub sells takeaway cans. Q ♿ ❀ ♣ ♠ ☗ ❁ ☂ ♫

Salmon
19 Butt Close Lane, LE1 4QA (from Clock Tower walk down Churchgate, Butt Close Ln is 2nd left)
☎ (0116) 253 2301
Black Country Bradley's Finest Golden, Chain Ale, Pig on the Wall, Fireside; Sharp's Atlantic; 5 changing beers H

A small corner local whose single, U-shaped room is decorated in as bright, traditional style. A Black Country Ales pub since 2016, it has a friendly, welcoming atmosphere, and a strong sports following. The 12

handpumps serve beers from Black Country Ales, alongside those from guest breweries, plus two real ciders. Cobs, pork pies and Scotch eggs are available throughout the day. Bus stations are nearby.
ॐ&◕♣▤◨◻️❓🎵

Two-Tailed Lion
22 Millstone Lane, LE1 5JN
☎ (0116) 224 4769 ⊕ thetwotailedlion.com
3 changing beers Ⓗ
A modern, beer-orientated pub, which was originally a Victorian dwelling, featuring three handpumps and six keg taps serving beers in a wide variety of styles. There is also a well-stocked bottle and can fridge. Unobtrusive music is played in the bar. As well as the small downstairs bar with a range of comfortable seating there are two upstairs rooms that can be hired. The food offering is samosas. ॐ▤◻️❓

Loughborough

Moonface Brewery & Tap
13 Moira Street, LE11 1AU (Moira St is accessed from Barrow St)
☎ (01509) 700171
4 changing beers (sourced nationally; often Moonface) Ⓖ
Popular micropub offering a constantly changing range of three to five real ales served direct from casks stillaged behind the counter. Two changing KeyKeg brews are also served, and there is a range of bottled Belgian beers. The Moonface microbrewery is visible in a room directly behind the bar. Live music, craft evenings and fish & chips evenings feature in this local hub. It serves a good selection of bar snacks. Local CAMRA Micropub of the Year 2024. Closed Monday and Tuesday.
Q❀&◕▥(2,127)◻️❓

Needle & Pin
15 The Rushes, LE11 5BE
☎ 07973 754236
4 changing beers (sourced nationally) Ⓗ
Loughborough's first genuine micropub, created from an old electronics shop in 2016, continues to serve an impressive, ever-changing range of handpulled and gravity-fed real ales, plus a choice of several ciders and perries. More than 80 types of foreign and craft bottled beers are also available. There is more extensive seating available upstairs. Pizzas can be ordered from a local supplier and delivered to your table. It hosts occasional evening music events. Card payment only. Closed Monday. Qॐ◕▥◻️🎵

Organ Grinder 🏆
4 Woodgate, LE11 2TY
☎ (01509) 264008
Blue Monkey BG Sips, Primate Best Bitter, Guerrilla; 4 changing beers (sourced locally; often Blue Monkey) Ⓗ
Close to the town centre, this popular Blue Monkey brewery pub offers eight cask ales. The stable bar at the back reflects the pub's past life as a coaching inn. There is a selection of four real ciders, sometimes including a perry, as well as Belgian bottled beers. Bar snacks include sausage rolls and an interesting range of pork pies. Live music played most weekends. Current local CAMRA Pub of the Year. ॐ❀◕▤▥◻️❓🎵

Swan in the Rushes ★
21 The Rushes, LE11 5BE
☎ (01509) 217014
Castle Rock Harvest Pale, Preservation, Elsie Mo; 7 changing beers (often Castle Rock, Charnwood) Ⓗ

A welcome return for this traditional three-room Castle Rock pub comprising a quiet, traditionally styled lounge and a lively bar with a jukebox. A constantly changing range of guest beers usually includes one dark brew, and it also serves up to 20 varieties of real cider, perry, a wide range of continental bottled and draft beers and a good choice of malt whiskies. Country wines are also available. Upstairs is the Hop Loft function room and first floor outside terrace. Current local CAMRA Cider Pub of the Year. Qॐ❀◑&◕▤◻️❓🎵

Wheeltapper
60 Wood Gate, LE11 2TZ
☎ (01509) 230829 ⊕ wheeltapper.co.uk
5 changing beers (sourced regionally; often Nene Valley, Shiny, Shipstone's)
A modern pub on the ground floor of a modern building. The decor has a railway theme, with reproduction posters and a board with photos of the Great Central Heritage Railway, which is not far away. The furniture is basic. Five handpulls dispense a wide range of real ales. At least one gluten-free beer is always served, and popular gluten-free beer festivals are held twice a year. Regularly changing craft beers and real ciders are also available. Excellent disabled access. Dogs welcome.
❀&≈♣◕▥◻️❓

White Hart
27 Churchgate, LE11 1UD
☎ (01509) 236976
Charnwood Salvation, Vixen; Timothy Taylor Landlord; 3 changing beers (sourced locally; often Leatherbritches) Ⓗ
Large, single-roomed pub situated close to the Market Place and All Saints Church. The secluded patio and beer garden to rear are very popular in sunny weather. Regularly changing guest beers are from local breweries such as Leatherbritches and Charnwood. Bar snacks and tapas are available until early evening. Live music and other entertainment is hosted on Friday and Saturday evenings on occasional weekends. Over-21s only.
ॐ❀◑♣▤◻️❓🎵

Lutterworth

Greyhound
9 Market Street, LE17 4EJ (on main road)
☎ (01455) 553307 ⊕ greyhoundinn.co.uk
Oakham Bishops Farewell; St Austell Proper Job; Sharp's Doom Bar; Timothy Taylor Landlord Ⓗ
This Grade II-listed coach house hotel offers a warm welcome. It dates from 1758 and was renovated by the current owner. The lounge has period style furnishings, nautical pictures, old clocks and original features. The bar has a wood-block floor and stocks over 100 whiskies. There is an outside paved courtyard for summer drinks. It is a popular venue for private parties and weddings.
Q❀⌂◑▥◻️❓

Real Ale Classroom
4 Station Road, LE17 4AP
☎ 07824 515334 ⊕ therealaleclassroom.com
4 changing beers (sourced nationally; often Shiny, Two by Two) Ⓖ
A spacious micropub with a schoolroom theme owned by former teachers. It offers a constantly changing line-up of four cask and four craft keg ales, plus a wide range of bottled and canned beers and five ciders. The back room has a log-burner for winter and the fantastic beer garden can be enjoyed in the summer months. Friendly staff are knowledgeable about the drinks on offer, including excellent gin and spirits from local distillers. Pub snacks are locally sourced. Qॐ❀♣◕▤◻️❓🎵

Market Harborough

Admiral Nelson

49 Nelson Street, LE16 9AX
☎ (01858) 433173
Brewpoint DNA Amber Ale; Draught Bass; 1 changing beer (often Brewpoint) ⊞
A friendly and welcoming locals' pub in a quiet street to the west of the centre of this historic market town. It has been fully refurbished, inside and out, with a new outside courtyard. There is a lounge with TV (rugby is popular) and a bar with darts, pool, jukebox and another TV. A function room is available. A beer festival is held over the second weekend in June each year. Outside is a heated and covered smoking area with seating. Dogs are welcome. ⊛♣PⰃ❀ ⧉ ♫

Beerhouse

76 St Mary's Road, LE16 7DX (directly behind St Mary's chippy)
☎ (01858) 440105 ⊕ beerhousemh.square.site
6 changing beers ℗
Market Harborough's first micropub is in a converted furniture shop. The focus is very much on beer, so there is no food, gaming machines, or loud music. There are 20 taps for draught products – the first eight are used for cask ales, the rest for KeyKegs and ciders. Monday night is quiz night, with occasional comedy nights and live music. A book club, vinyl nights and cider festival are also hosted. ➽⊛♧♦PⰃ❀ ⧉ ♫

Sugar Loaf ✅

18 High Street, LE16 7NJ
☎ (01858) 469231
Greene King IPA, Abbot; Sharp's Doom Bar; 3 changing beers (sourced nationally) ⊞
A JD Wetherspoon conversion of a traditional grocery store in the centre of Market Harborough close to the Old Grammar School. Prints on the walls describe the history of the building and of the town in general. There is a small garden at the rear. Children are welcome until 9pm. Q➽⊛◑᛭Ⰲ⧉

Melton Mowbray

Anne of Cleves ⓛ

12, Burton Street,, LE13 1AE
☎ (01664) 481336 ⊕ theanneofcleves.com
Everards Sunchaser, Tiger, Old Original; 2 changing beers (sourced nationally) ⊞
One of Melton Mowbray and Everards' most historic pubs and an icon for the town. Part of the property dates back to 1327 when it was home to monks. The house was gifted to Anne of Cleves by Henry VIII as part of her divorce settlement. It is now a popular hostelry following a sympathetic restoration, with stone-flagged floors, exposed timber beams, and tapestries throughout. ➽⊛◑≈PⰃ❀ ⧉

Charlie's Bar

7 King Street, LE13 1XA
☎ 07852 232937
2 changing beers (sourced nationally) Ⓚ
Located in a former 14th-century manor house, this is one of Melton Mowbray's oldest buildings, with a timber frame dating back to 1301. In the 1500s it was known as the manor of John Mowbray. A more contemporary use of the building was as Manchester and Son Clothiers, and their signage still appears to the front of the pub. It sells a wide range of beer styles and cider from new and innovative breweries. ⊛≈◨Ⰲ(5,19)❀

Kettleby Cross ⓛ ✅

Wilton Road, LE13 0UJ
☎ (01664) 485310
Greene King IPA, Abbot; Sharp's Doom Bar; 6 changing beers (sourced nationally) ⊞
The Kettleby Cross is a JD Wetherspoon newbuild opened in 2007 as a 'flagship' eco pub, complete with a prominent wind turbine on the roof. The pub stands close to the bridge over the nearby river Eye and is named after the cross that once directed travellers in the direction of Ab Kettleby. The interior consists of a large single room on two levels. As with most Wetherspoon pubs, the Kettleby Cross is usually busy with a good atmosphere. ➽◑᛭≈PⰃ ⧉

Round Corner Brewing Taproom ⓛ

Melton Mowbray Market, Scalford Road, LE13 1JY
⊕ roundcornerbrewing.com
1 changing beer (sourced locally; often Round Corner) ⊞
Opened in 2018 in a former sheep shed in the heart of Melton Cattle Market, Round Corner has quickly established its popularity in the town due to the quality of its award-winning beers. Their principle of 'bringing beer back to its agricultural roots' are reflected in the location of the brewery, and the name, which is based on the 'round corners' of locally produced Stilton cheese. The taproom is housed within the brewery and there is plenty of seating outside where the beers can be enjoyed. Q➽◑≈♦PⰃ(5,19)❀

Mountsorrel

Sorrel Fox

75 Leicester Road, LE12 7AJ
☎ (0116) 230 3777
Charnwood Salvation, Vixen; 2 changing beers (sourced locally; often Charnwood) ⊞
Charnwood brewery's first micropub is a cosy, single-roomed bar serving their popular cask ales and craft beers as well as an imported Austrian lager. Bottled ciders, quality wines, a selection of gins, plus a couple of rums are also available. It is close to the A6, with a stop for buses to Leicester, Loughborough and Shepshed. Freshly made sausage rolls and a selection of bar snacks are available, with added cobs at the weekend. Closed Monday. Q♦Ⰲ(127)❀ ⧉

Swan Inn

10 Loughborough Road, LE12 7AT
☎ (0116) 230 2340
Black Sheep Best Bitter; Castle Rock Harvest Pale; Grainstore Ten Fifty; 2 changing beers (often Soar) ⊞
A traditional 17th-century, Grade II-listed coaching inn, entered via a narrow arch into a courtyard. The split-level interior has open fires, stone floors and low ceilings, and includes a small dining area. Good-quality, interesting food is cooked to order, with the menu changing weekly and featuring regular themed menus. Outside is a long secluded riverside garden. The attached Soar microbrewery is visible in an adjacent building. A former local CAMRA Pub of the Year. Q➽⊛◑♦Ⰲ❀ ♫

Nether Broughton

Anchor

Main Road, LE14 3HB
☎ (01664) 822461
Ringwood Razorback; 1 changing beer ⊞
A cosy village roadside pub on the A606, reopened in 2015. The main bar has a real fire and a dartboard, and a separate dining area offers a quieter space. The pub has

a large car park, and pleasant outside seating. Traditional pub food is served regularly, with occasional themed nights. The pub hosts regular charity events, and welcomes families and dogs. ⏃🕸🌙◖♣P🖳🌑♪

Plungar

Anchor ☗ 🖳

Granby Lane, NG13 0JJ
☎ (01949) 860589
3 changing beers Ⓗ
This brick building in the heart of this small Leicestershire village dates from 1774, having previously served as the local courtroom. The pub houses a large bar, cosy lounge and a separate pool room. Outside is an attractive beer garden and seating area. Up to three cask ales are served, featuring at least one local beer. There is a generous car park, making the pub popular with horse riders and cyclists. Local CAMRA Pub of the Year 2022 and 2024. Q⏃🌑🕸&♣P🖳(24)🌑☗

Quorn

Royal Oak

2 High Street, LE12 8DT
☎ (01509) 415816 ⊕ TheRoyaloakquorn.co.uk
Charnwood Vixen; St Austell Tribute; Timothy Taylor Landlord; 1 changing beer Ⓗ
Traditional 160-year-old inn situated in the centre of the village, formerly three terraced cottages. The old internal walls were removed to open up the building, while retaining many original features, including beamed ceilings, tiled floors and an open log fire. Draught cider is occasionally available as the guest. A sheltered covered courtyard is to the side. Q⏃🕸🌑🚲🛇▲◖🌑☗

Redmile

Windmill

4 Main Street, NG13 0GA
☎ (01949) 842281 ⊕ thewindmillinnredmile.co.uk
2 changing beers (sourced locally; often Castle Rock, Shipstone's) Ⓗ
A privately owned and run restaurant and bar in Redmile, a mile down the hill from Belvoir Castle. It has two rooms: a stone-floored bar complete with log fire and a lounge, as well as a generous terrace. It enjoys a cult status among fans of the popular TV series Auf Wiedersehen Pet, in which the Windmill appeared as the Barley Mow. Photos taken during filming are on display. Q⏃🕸◖AP🖳🌑☗

Rothley

Woodman's Stroke

1 Church Street, LE7 7PD
☎ (0116) 230 2785 ⊕ thewoodies.co.uk
Charnwood Vixen; Draught Bass; Woodforde's Wherry; 1 changing beer Ⓗ
The Woodies is a quintessentially English village pub, with thatched roof and traditional interior of exposed ceiling joists and stone floors. Out the back is a paved terrace with enormous heated parasols, beyond which is a pétanque piste set in the large garden rolling down to Rothley brook. It has up to four different guest beers and a fine selection of wines. A selection of good home-cooked food is available weekday lunchtimes only. The large amount of rugby, cricket and golf memorabilia on display reflects the enthusiasm for sport. Q⏃🕸🌑🚲P🖳(126,127) 🌑☗

Shepshed

Black Swan

21 Loughborough Road, LE12 9DL
☎ (01509) 458929
Draught Bass; Greene King Abbot; Timothy Taylor Landlord; 2 changing beers (sourced nationally) Ⓗ
An imposing, multi-roomed pub in a prominent position close to the town centre, offering two guest beers alongside the regulars. The main room has two drinking areas, both with comfortable seating. A further small room can be used by families, and is available for hire. Shepshed Dynamo football ground is nearby, and the pub can get very busy on match days. Wednesday is the popular quiz night. Q⏃🌑🕸♣P🖳🌑☗

Hall Croft Tap

20-22 Hall Croft, LE12 9AN
☎ (01509) 729920 ⊕ charnwoodbrewery.co.uk/micropubs
Charnwood Salvation, Vixen; 2 changing beers (sourced locally; often Charnwood) Ⓟ
Charnwood brewery's second micropub features a central courtyard with bar/lounge on one side and on the other side a large snug, where families with children are welcome until 7pm (at weekends only). A flight of steps leads up from the courtyard to a large garden with seating at the rear of the pub. The pub and courtyard are wheelchair accessible, but not the garden. Snacks include pork pies. Closed Monday. ⏃🕸&♣🖳(126,127)🌑

Smeeton Westerby

King's Head 🖳

23 Main Street, LE8 0QJ
☎ (0116) 279 2676
Langton Inclined Plane Bitter; 2 changing beers (sourced locally; often Church End, Grainstore, Nene Valley) Ⓗ
This 18th-century building was originally three cottages, with a lean-to barn on the end. The new owners, who were locals, bought the pub in 2023 when the previous owner retired. Three local cask ales are available, including a dark beer. There is a large outside seating area. ⏃🕸♣P🖳(44)🌑☗♪

Somerby

Stilton Cheese ☗ 🖳

High Street, LE14 2QB
☎ (01664) 454394 ⊕ stiltoncheeseinn.co.uk
Marston's Pedigree; Grainstore Ten Fifty; 3 changing beers (sourced nationally) Ⓗ
Welcoming family-run pub built in local ironstone in the late 16th century. It has a cosy bar with adjoining room featuring an eclectic mix of copper pots and pans, horse brasses, pictures of hunting scenes and a stuffed pike and badger. At least four real ales are always available, often from local breweries. Local CAMRA Pub of the Year and former County Pub of the Year. Q⏃🌑🕸♣P🖳🌑☗

South Kilworth

White Hart 🖳

Rugby Road, LE17 6DN (on main road)
☎ (01858) 575416
Langton Inclined Plane Bitter; 2 changing beers (sourced locally; often Charnwood, Dow Bridge) Ⓗ
A traditional, family-run village pub with low ceilings, exposed beams and a large fireplace with a wood-burning stove. Outside is a large grassed drinking area. The three ales are all sourced from Leicestershire breweries. Sport is shown on TV. Good-value cheese cobs

are available, and there is a pizza van on Wednesday evenings. Nearby attractions include Stanford Reservoir, and Stanford Hall, dating from 1697, which has a museum dedicated to aviator pioneer Percy Pilcher.
🛇🏵▲♣🅿🚆(58) ♿ 🛜 ♪

Stoke Golding

George & Dragon L
Station Road, CV13 6EZ
☎ (01455) 213268
Church End Goat's Milk, Gravediggers Ale, What the Fox's Hat, Stout Coffin, Fallen Angel; 3 changing beers (sourced locally; often Church End) Ⓗ
Renowned village local serving eight real ales from Church End brewery and a real cider. Good home-cooked lunches featuring local produce are available, and home-made bar snacks. The second Tuesday of the month is steak night, and lunch is served on the last Sunday. The pub supports a number of clubs and societies and an annual charity event takes place in summer. It is close to the historic Bosworth Battlefield, and is a popular destination for walkers, cyclists and boaters from the nearby Ashby Canal. Q🛇🏵🐕▲♣🅿🚆(7A)♿🛜

Swinford

Chequers ✔
High Street, LE17 6BL (near church)
☎ (01788) 860318 ⊕ chequersswinford.co.uk
St Austell Tribute; Timothy Taylor Landlord; 2 changing beers (sourced nationally) Ⓗ
A warm welcome is assured at this family-run community local, whose landlord has been in place for over 37 years. The menu caters for all and includes vegetarian and children's options. The large garden and play area are popular with families in good weather. A marquee provides the venue for the annual music festival and is available for hire. Pub games include table skittles. The 18th-century Stamford Hall, with a caravan park and museum, is less than a mile away.
🛇🏵🐕▲♣🅿♿🛜♪

Syston

Pharmacie Arms L
3 High Street, LE7 1GP
☎ (0116) 269 6933 ⊕ pharmarms.co.uk
Shipstone's Mild, Original; 3 changing beers (often Oakham) Ⓗ
Syston's first micropub opened in 2018 with a 1950s pharmacy theme, including medical artefacts, equipment, adverts and a friendly skeleton sitting on a dentist's chair. There is an upstairs seating area with a 1950s movie theme, and a board room and kitchen available for private hire. Apart from a varying selection of real ales, it has up to six craft kegs. No meals are served but cheese cobs and other snacks are available.
Q🛇🐕♣●🚻🚆♿🛜♪

Queen Victoria L
76 High Street, LE7 1GQ
☎ (0116) 260 5750
Everards Tiger, Old Original; 3 changing beers (often Everards) Ⓗ
This 200-year-old building, formerly a coach house, has been run by Everards since 1922. Guest beers are sourced through Everards, and can include ones from regional breweries and microbreweries. The bar across the front consists of three rooms knocked together and a smaller room at the rear. At the back is a courtyard drinking area, a large garden (including pétanque court) and a carvery

restaurant. The pub hosts regular entertainment, and beer and cider festivals are held during the year.
🛇🏵🍴🐕&≠♣🅿🚆♿🛜♪

Walton on the Wolds

Anchor
2 Loughborough Road, LE12 8HT
☎ (01509) 880018
Charnwood Salvation; Draught Bass; Timothy Taylor Landlord; 1 changing beer (sourced regionally) Ⓗ
The Anchor is in the centre of a small village within easy reach of Leicester and Nottingham via the A46. It is a popular venue for locals as well as the many walkers, with or without their dogs, who stop for a well-earned rest. Outside is an elevated seating area to the front and a garden and large car park to the rear.
Q🛇🏵🍴🐕🅿🚆(27)♿

Whitwick

Three Horseshoes ★
11 Leicester Road, LE67 5GN
☎ 07736 677855
Draught Bass; Marston's Pedigree; 1 changing beer (sourced nationally) Ⓗ
Nicknamed Polly's after a former landlady, the Thee Horseshoes was originally two separate buildings but now has two rooms. To the left is a long bar with a quarry-tiled floor and open fires, wooden bench seating and pre-war fittings; to the right is a similarly furnished small snug. It has been identified by CAMRA as having a nationally important historic pub interior. Closed Monday.
Q🛇🏵♣🚆♿

Wigston

Tap & Barrel
58 Leicester Road, LE18 1DR
☎ 07734 480280
5 changing beers Ⓖ
An unpretentious ambience in this pub is enhanced by bare timber floorboards, exposed ceiling joists braced with traditional timber herringbone strutting, a freestanding log-burning stove, and ornamental turned spindles in the balustrade to the open staircase leading to an extra seating area. The bar is built of rustic timber, with a thick slab of waney edge beech as the counter. Beer is dispensed behind he bar straight from casks kept in a perspex-fronted cooler cabinet with only taps poking through. 🛇&♣●🅿🚆♿🛜♪

Woodhouse Eaves

Wheatsheaf
90 Brand Hill, LE12 8SS
☎ (01509) 890320 ⊕ wheatsheafinn.net
Adnams Broadside; Charnwood Vixen; Timothy Taylor Landlord; 2 changing beers (sourced nationally; often Charnwood) Ⓗ
Built around 1800 as a meeting place for miners from the Swithland quarry, this popular pub, on the outskirts of the village, is traditionally furnished with wood-beamed ceilings, open fires and comfortable seating. Upstairs is a more formal restaurant. Meals are served at lunchtime and evenings from the main menu and daily specials board. The pub is close to the National Forest Way long distance walking trail, Cropston Reservoir, and the Beacon Hill and Bradgate Country Parks.
Q🛇🏵🍴🅿🚆(154)♿🛜

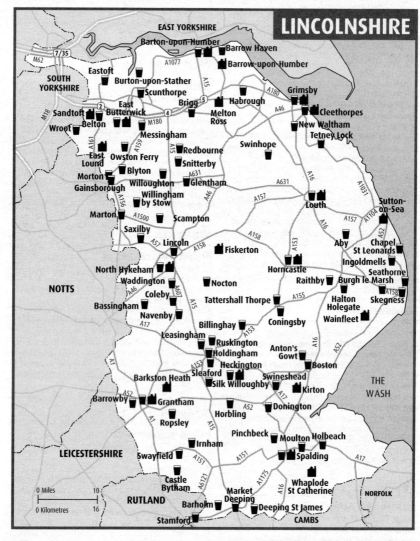

LINCOLNSHIRE

Aby

Railway Tavern ☕

Main Road, LN13 0DR (off A16 via South Thoresby)
☎ (01507) 480676 ⊕ railwaytavern-aby.co.uk
2 changing beers (sourced nationally) Ⓗ

Keith and Dawn took on this closed rural pub 19 years ago and have grown it to what it is now. Winner of numerous awards including local CAMRA Pub of the Year four times, this is also a community venue that raises money for charity. Changing real ales and a menu serving local produce are available. Two recently built holiday cottages can be booked for short breaks.
Q🌣🏠🛏️🍴🚲♣️P🌣

Anton's Gowt

Malcolm Arms

Frith Bank, PE22 7BE
☎ (01205) 839924
2 changing beers Ⓗ

The pub, located next to the lock by River Witham, was taken over in 2016. It has been refurbished and has extensive floral displays in summer. The large conservatory acts as a restaurant and attracts many diners. There is also an enclosed garden area. The landlord is a CAMRA member and keen gardener. Closed Monday and Tuesday outside of boating season. During the summer there are Wednesday and Sunday boat trips to the pub from Boston for lunch.
🌣🏠🍴🚲♣️P🚍(IC5) 🌣♫

Barholm

Five Horseshoes Ⓛ

PE9 4RA
☎ (01778) 560238
Adnams Southwold Bitter; Draught Bass; Oakham JHB; 3 changing beers (often Bowler's, Church End, Ossett) Ⓗ

A classic 18th-century country pub, built from local Barnack stone. It is comprised of two bars, two cosy side rooms and a pool room. A wood fire burns throughout the winter. Three permanent and three changing real ales are served. Pizzas are available on Friday and street food on Saturday evenings, while barbecues and live music events in the large garden are a feature of the summer months. Local CAMRA Rural Pub of the Year 2023, it is well known for its support of local charities. Q❄🕮♿🍴☕P🅿🤵✦♪

Barrow Haven

Haven Inn
Ferry Road, DN19 7EX (approx 1½ miles E of Barrow-upon-Humber)
☎ (01469) 530247
Timothy Taylor Landlord; 2 changing beers (sourced regionally; often Batemans) 🅗
Built in 1730 as a coaching inn in the quiet North Lincolnshire countryside for travellers using the former ferry, the Haven has been renowned for hospitality, good food and drink and comfortable lodgings ever since. Full of character, a warm welcome awaits, with a bar, lounge and large comfortable conservatory. Perfect for walkers from the Humber bank to call in for a well-kept pint. Timothy Taylor Landlord is ever-present and there are two rotating guest beers, often from Batemans. ❄🕮🍴🛏♿≹P✦

Barrowby

White Swan ✅
Main Street, NG32 1BH
☎ (01476) 562375
2 changing beers (sourced nationally) 🅗
Run by the same landlord for over 30 years this Grade II-listed village pub just off the A1 and A52 is a must visit. The comfortable lounge and separate bar area, pool table, dartboard makes this village pub the heart of the area. Cribbage teams play in the local leagues. Outside are a heated smoking area and secluded garden. Locally sourced home-made food is available Wednesday to Sunday, with regularly changing real ales. Q❄🕮🍴♣P🅿✦🤵♪

Barton-upon-Humber

Sloop Inn
81 Waterside Road, DN18 5BA (follow Humber Bridge viewing signs)
☎ (01652) 637287
Pennine Millie George; Timothy Taylor Boltmaker; Theakston Best Bitter; 1 changing beer (sourced regionally; often Camerons, Theakston) 🅗
This welcoming 19th-century multi-roomed pub, popular with both locals and walkers, has been refurbished throughout to a high standard, but original features such as the Delft fireplace tiles and stained glass windows remain. It gets busy with traditional pub food trade. Three real ales are normally available, plus a changing guest beer. The Far Ings Nature Reserve, Waters' Edge Visitor Centre, Ropewalk, Ropery Hall and the Humber Bridge are all nearby attractions. ❄🕮🍴♿A♣≹(Barton-on-Humber) ♣P🖃🅿(350,250) ✦

White Swan 🅛
66 Fleetgate, DN18 5QD (follow signs for railway station)
☎ (01652) 661222
4 changing beers (sourced regionally; often Great Newsome, Horncastle, Yorkshire Heart) 🅗
Multi award-winning 17th-century coaching inn opposite the bus/train interchange. The Swan offers a warm welcome to all, hosting community groups, traditional pub games and a monthly vinyl night. Four ever-changing cask ales are complemented by a rotating craft keg beer and traditional ciders. Regular beer and cider

festivals are held in the characterful, renovated coaching outbuildings. Popular weekend brunches are available. Winner of several local CAMRA awards. Q❄🕮♿≹(Barton-on-Humber) ♣🤵P🅿(250,350)🤵🤵♪

Bassingham

Bugle Horn Inn
19 Lincoln Road, LN5 9HQ
☎ (01522) 789773 ⊕ bassinghambuglehorn.co.uk
3 changing beers (sourced nationally; often Beermats, Greene King, Welbeck Abbey) 🅗
Built in the 17th century as an inn, the Bugle Horn is a locals' pub retaining many of its original features, including beamed ceilings and open fires. The lounge bar has an open fire and the bar has two sports TV screens. Food is available in a separate dining room, with steak nights on a Wednesday and Thursday plus Sunday lunch. Three constantly-changing beers are available. The pub hosts two darts teams plus football and cricket teams. A regular quiz takes place on the last Friday of the month. ❄🕮🍴♣P🅿(47) ✦

Belton

Crown Inn 🅛
Church Lane, DN9 1PA (turn off A161 at All Saints Church and follow the road behind)
☎ (01427) 872834
Bradfield Farmers Blonde; Great Newsome Frothingham Best; Oakham Citra; Wainwright Gold; 2 changing beers (sourced regionally; often Tetley, Wychwood) 🅗
Situated behind All Saints church, this pub is difficult to find but well worth the effort. For many years it has been a haven for the discerning drinker and a winner of many CAMRA awards. At least four, and often six cask ales are available, with light beers and pale ales especially popular. The Crown does not offer meals, but bases its appeal on consistently good quality real ales. Beer festivals are held in the summer months. ❄🕮A♣P🅿(399) ✦🤵♪

REAL ALE BREWERIES

8 Sail ✦ Heckington
Austendyke Spalding
Bacchus 🍺 Sutton-on-Sea
Batemans ✦ Wainfleet
Blue Bell 🍺 Whaplode St Catherine
Brewster's Grantham
Consortium ✦ Louth
Dark Tribe 🍺 East Butterwick
Docks ✦ Grimsby
Don Valley ✦ Sandtoft
Ferry Ales Fiskerton
Firehouse 🍺 Louth
Fuddy Duck Kirton
Horncastle 🍺 Horncastle
Lincolnshire Craft Melton Ross
Little Big Dog Barrow-Upon-Humber
Luda ✦ Louth (NEW)
Munyard ✦ Louth (NEW)
Newby Wyke Grantham
Pig Barn East Lound
Poachers ✦ North Hykeham
Shadow Bridge ✦ Barton-upon-Humber
Wickham House Louth
Willy's 🍺 Cleethorpes
Zest Barkston Heath

Billinghay

Ship Inn
20 High Street, LN4 4AU (near Co-op)
☎ (01526) 268118
Batemans XB; Timothy Taylor Landlord; 1 changing beer (sourced nationally) Ⓗ
Village-centre pub run by a husband and wife team with an open-plan main bar and separate dining room. The car park is located at the side of the property adjacent to the outside seating area which also has a designated smoking area. There are a wide variety of live music events held at the venue throughout the year, which are promoted on Facebook. The pub supports the local football team, Billinghay FC. 🕭🕪♣🅿🖵☂🛜♪

Blyton

Black Horse
93 High Street, DN21 3JX
☎ (01427) 628277
Batemans XB, Gold, XXXB; 1 changing beer Ⓗ
Recently refurbished, the Black Horse Inn is one of two pubs in the village and is sited at the northern end. The interior is divided into five distinct areas; three for dining and two drinking areas. All dining areas are dog-friendly and one features depictions of the owners' dogs. There are usually beers from Batemans and occasional changing guests, sometimes from local brewers. Self-contained accommodation is available and there is generous parking and outside drinking space.
Q🛏🕭🛌🕪🕭♣🅿🖵☂🛜

Boston

Carpenters Arms
20 Witham Street, PE21 6PU
☎ (01205) 362840 🌐 carpentersarmsboston.com
Batemans XB, Gold, XXXB; 1 changing beer (often Batemans) Ⓗ
This is a multi-roomed low-ceilinged traditional local, hidden in the maze of side streets off the medieval Wormgate and overlooked by the magnificent Boston Stump. There is a patio area outside for sunny days. The pub is close to the town centre but you may need to ask for directions more than once to find it. Occasional one-off food nights are held. 🛌🕭🛌🚆♣🖵☂🛜♪

Eagle
144 West Street, PE21 8RE
☎ (01205) 361116
Castle Rock Harvest Pale, Preservation, Screech Owl; 5 changing beers (often Castle Rock) Ⓗ
Part of the Castle Rock chain, the Eagle is known as the real ale pub of Boston. This two-roomed, friendly hostelry has an L-shaped bar with a large TV screen for big sports events. The smaller lounge has a cosy feel. The pub stocks a wide range of guest ales, and at least one cider. A function room upstairs is home to Boston Folk Club. Q🕭🛌🚆♣🖶🖵☂🛜♪

Brigg

White Horse ✪
Wrawby Street, DN20 8JR (close to station at E end of Wrawby St)
☎ (01652) 659344
Greene King Abbot; Ruddles Best Bitter; Sharp's Doom Bar; 3 changing beers (sourced regionally; often Brains, Oakham, Rooster's) Ⓗ
Town-centre Wetherspoon outlet, a conversion of an historic public house and brewery. Large, airy and open plan, it opens onto a large, secure, well-appointed beer garden. The pub has many framed photographs and pictures of local interest reflecting historic Brigg. There are always a varied selection of beers and ciders, with beer festivals in spring and autumn. Food is served throughout the day. Close to the market and bus and train transport hubs. Q🛏🕭🛌🕪🛌🚆🖶🖵(4)🛜

Yarborough Hunt Ⓛ
49 Bridge Street, DN20 8NS (across bridge from market place)
☎ (01652) 658333
Lincolnshire Craft Best Bitter, Lincoln Gold, Bomber County; 4 changing beers (sourced regionally; often Acorn, Adnams, Castle Rock) Ⓗ
Formerly Sargeants brewery tap, it was originally built in the 1700s. This is a traditional pub which retains its original features following refurbishment and extension. Simply furnished with welcoming open fires, it has an outdoor courtyard with separate cabins. No food is available but cold food can be brought in and consumed on the premises. The main outlet for Lincolnshire Craft Beers, it also offers four changing guest beers and a real cider, plus an extensive range of craft beers.
Q🛏🕭🛌🚆🖵(4,X4) ☂🛜

Burgh le Marsh

Bell Hotel
45 High Street, PE24 5JP
☎ (01754) 228400 🌐 bellhotelburgh.co.uk
3 changing beers (sourced locally; often Batemans) Ⓗ
The pub lives up to its name with a large bell above the entrance doorway. Inside is an L-shaped bar with a substantial bar area, which is popular with local groups. Regular live music evenings are held, and for those wanting something different, there is a fishing lake nearby. One of the beers is always Batemans XB or Gold; the third handpump is only available in summer. The pub offers nine en-suite hotel rooms, with three self-catering cottages located in the hotel grounds.
🛏🕭🛌🕪♣🅿🖵☂🛜♪

Burton-upon-Stather

Ferry House Inn Ⓛ
Stather Road, DN15 9DJ (follow campsite signs through village; down hill at church)
☎ (01724) 721783 🌐 ferryhousepub.co.uk
2 changing beers (sourced regionally; often Great Newsome, Wold Top) Ⓗ
Popular village freehouse on the banks of the River Trent, run by the same family for over 60 years. Two changing guest beers and real cider are joined on the bar by beers from its own microbrewery. Food is served Thursday to Saturday evenings and lunchtime on Sunday. An annual beer festival held on the first weekend in September. There is a large outdoor seating area and children's play area with occasional live music and barbecue events. A popular meeting place for local heritage groups, with monthly quizzes and music jam sessions.
Q🛏🕭🛌🕪🛌♣🖶🅿🖶🖵(60) ☂🛜♪

Castle Bytham

Castle Inn Ⓛ
High Sreet, NG33 4RZ
☎ (01780) 411223 🌐 castleinnbytham.co.uk
Abbeydale Absolution; Grainstore Ten Fifty; Ossett White Rat; 1 changing beer (sourced nationally) Ⓗ
One of the original public houses in the village, this 17th-century gem is a memorable place to visit. With oak-

beamed ceilings, period furnishings, walls hung with antique prints and artifacts and a warm welcome from the staff and locals this country pub is not to be missed. Three regular ales and one guest are served. An excellent menu of home-cooked foods cooked on a wood-fired stove is available lunchtimes and evenings. Q☺⛅🕮◗♣♠❀♪

Fox & Hounds

6 High Street, NG33 4RZ
☎ (01780) 410336 🌐 thefoxcastlebytham.co.uk
Abbeydale Deception, Absolution; Timothy Taylor Landlord; 1 changing beer (often Oakham) Ⓗ
This traditional country pub in the beautiful Lincolnshire village of Castle Bytham offers a warm and friendly welcome. With a roaring open fire in the winter and beautiful beer garden in the summer this pub is a great place to stop. Serving English pub food, Sunday roasts, Friday night pizzas and three regular and one changing beer this pub caters for all tastes and appetites. The large sports TV and surround sound make it the perfect place for watching major sporting events. ❀◗◆♣P

Chapel St Leonards

Admiral Benbow

The Promenade, PE24 5BQ
☎ (01754) 871847 🌐 admiralbenbowbeachbar.co.uk
Black Sheep Best Bitter; 2 changing beers Ⓗ
Located on the promenade, the opening times and facilities of this beach bar are dependent on the weather and are limited in winter. Please see the website for current times, but if the flag is flying they are open. Bar snacks are available. There is an outside seating area on the Hispaniola boat deck, or plastic glasses to take your favourite ale on to the beach. Dogs on leads are very welcome, with blankets and dog treats available. Hot drinks are also served. ☺❀❀♠♥

Cleethorpes

Message in a Bottle

91-97 Cambridge Street, DN35 8HD
☎ (01472) 453131 🌐 miabcleethorpes.net
3 changing beers Ⓗ
This bottle shop with weekend bar is open Wednesday to Sunday. Three cask ales are offered each weekend. The original seating area, fondly known as the Cage, is outside but boasts heat lamps. A beer lounge inside the shop gives a unique atmosphere, complete with octopus mural. Throughout the year, pop-up food and music events showcasing local talent are held, these can get busy, but a seat is usually found for passers by, and a warm welcome assured. ☺♣🔄(4)♠♪

No.1 Pub

Railway Station Approach, DN35 8AX
☎ (01472) 696221
Draught Bass; 4 changing beers (sourced regionally; often Batemans, Great Newsome, Horncastle) Ⓗ
A large railway bar on Cleethorpes station. This popular local has a main bar and a smaller back room overlooking the station platforms. Local railway memorabilia adorn the walls. An outdoor seating area is at the front. The pub is renowned for its imaginative, home-cooked and locally sourced food. There is live music most weekends and an annual music festival in the summer.
❀◗🔄♣♠♥📶♥♪

No.2 Refreshment Room

Station Approach, DN35 8AX
☎ (01472) 691707

Hancocks HB; Rudgate Ruby Mild; 5 changing beers (sourced regionally) Ⓗ
Local CAMRA award winning pub set on the railway station. Known locally as Under the Clock, this small-roomed bar has been a regular feature in the Guide over the years. There is always an excellent selection, usually including one dark beer as well as a range of ciders. Smokers may use a covered and heated area on the station concourse. ❀♿🔄♣♠♥📶♥

Nottingham House ★ ❂

7 Seaview Street, DN35 8EU
☎ (01472) 597181
Oakham Citra; Ossett Yorkshire Blonde; Timothy Taylor Landlord; Tetley Bitter; 2 changing beers (sourced regionally; often Titanic, Thwaites) Ⓗ
A popular traditionally-styled pub, converted from two cottages built in 1856, with three rooms all accessible from the front of the bar – a cosy snug can be found at the rear. All bars and toilets are on the ground floor. The public bar shows sports matches on TV and games are available to play. Children and dogs are welcome in this old coaching house. Q☺🛏▲🔄♣♠♥📶♥♪

Willy's

17 High Cliff Road, DN35 8RQ
☎ (01472) 602145
Willy's Original; 2 changing beers (sourced nationally) Ⓗ
Willy's overlooks Cleethorpes beach and the estuary of the River Humber. The new lifeboat station is close by. Spurn Point lighthouse can be seen on a clear day. Willy's brew their own beer on the premises and the brewery is visible from the far end of the bar. Food is served, with Sunday roasts being particularly popular. Dogs are not permitted in the bar during meal times.
☺❀◗▲🔄♣♠♥📶♥♪

Coleby

Tempest Arms

High Street, LN5 0AG
☎ (01522) 810258 🌐 thetempestarms.co.uk
Batemans XXXB; Timothy Taylor Landlord; 2 changing beers (sourced nationally; often Thornbridge, York) Ⓗ
Perched on the edge of an escarpment south of Lincoln, the pub is close to the Viking Way long-distance path. At its heart is a three-sided bar. Picture windows along one side provide panoramic views towards the River Trent. Outside is a patio and a beer garden. In winter, two log burners add to the cosy feel. Meals from an extensive menu can be enjoyed in the bar or the restaurant. Monthly quiz and open mic nights are held.
☺❀◗P🔄(1) ♥♥

Coningsby

Leagate Inn

Leagate Road, LN4 4RS
☎ 07957 756495 🌐 theleagateinn.co.uk
Timothy Taylor Landlord; 2 changing beers (often Adnams, Vocation) Ⓗ
Very much a food venue with hotel accommodation, this pub dates from the mid 16th century when it was on the edge of the scrub and fen land. Until 1824 a light was hung outside to guide travellers across the fen. The name refers to a toll gate which stood here for many years. One of the changing beers is a best bitter from Adnams or Black Sheep, the other tends to be a lighter type from Vocation or Tiny Rebel. ☺❀🛏◗♿▲P♥♥📶♥♪

Deeping St James

Thirsty Giraffe ▼ 🄻
65 Manor Way, PE6 8PX (only the rear of the pub and shops are visible from the road)
☎ 07756 066503 ⊕ thirstygiraffe.co.uk
8 changing beers (sourced regionally; often Bowler's, Church End, Froth Blowers) 🄶
Created from a former bistro, this is the first micropub in the Deepings. Expect interesting beers and lively banter. All the ales are presently served from the cellar and the range usually includes a dark beer and something from local breweries Hopshackle or Bowler's. There is always a large range of bag in box ciders, including fruit ciders, and a small range of continental lagers available. Food may be ordered from the adjacent takeaways, with plates and cutlery provided. The nearest bus stop is a 10-minute walk. Q&♿P🚋(102)🌂

Donington

Black Bull
7 Market Place, PE11 4ST
☎ (01775) 822228 ⊕ theblackbulldonington.co.uk
Batemans XB; Sharp's Doom Bar; 2 changing beers (often Batemans) 🄷
This busy local has five handpumps featuring three regular beers and occasionally two guest beers from small brewers as well as large regionals. The comfortable bar has low-beamed ceilings, wooden settles and a cosy fire in winter. Due to the return in 2024 of the remains of Captain Matthew Flinders, navigator and cartographer, born 1774, to his birthplace, Donington, the pub intends to have an exclusive beer named in his honour, brewed by Batemans. ⏾❀◑♣P🚋🌂♿

East Butterwick

Dog & Gun 🄻
High Street, DN17 3AJ (off A18 at Keadby Bridge, E bank)
☎ (01724) 782324 ⊕ doggunpub.com
3 changing beers (sourced locally; often Dark Tribe) 🄷
Riverside country pub flanking the River Trent which is especially popular locally for the on-site brewed Dark Tribe beers. It comprises three rooms, one heated by a real fire, with wooden floors and rustic wooden furniture. Two or three Dark Tribe beers are available. Renowned Sunday lunches are served two days a month, with booking essential. Picnic benches are available on the river bank across the road, where you can enjoy views of the Trent with your drink. Q⏾❀◑♣P🚋(12)🌂

Eastoft

River Don Tavern
Sampson Street, DN17 4PQ (on A161 Goole to Gainsborough road)
☎ (01724) 798040
2 changing beers (sourced regionally; often First and Last, Great Newsome, Tyne Bank) 🄷
Traditionally-styled village pub which offers accommodation in four external lodges and three rooms in the pub. Open-plan in design, it has an L-shaped bar which serves two distinct areas, one of which is used for dining. The light and airy interior is enhanced by historic pictures of the village. Evening meals are available Tuesday to Saturday. A separate restaurant is used for the renowned Sunday carvery. Two changing real ales are offered, often from the north-east region. ⏾❀🛏◑&♣P🚋(361)🌂🛜

Gainsborough

Blues Club
Northolme, North Street, DN21 2QW
☎ (01427) 613688
Horncastle Angel of Light; 2 changing beers (sourced locally) 🄷
The club has a bar area with several TVs showing sport, a quieter lounge and a large function room which hosts regular live entertainment (admission charges may apply). Two or three changing real ales are usually available and details of forthcoming beers can be emailed to customers on request. CAMRA guests are always welcome on production of a membership card. ⏾≉(Central)♣🚋🛜♪

Sweyn Forkbeard ⊘
22-24 Silver Street, DN21 2DP
☎ (01427) 675000
Greene King Abbot; Ruddles Best Bitter; Sharp's Doom Bar; 4 changing beers 🄷
This town-centre Wetherspoon, the local CAMRA Pub of the Year 2019 and 2023, is one of the must-do pubs in town. Three or four rotating guest beers often feature some oddities for this part of the country. Customers can ask for their favourite beer and it often appears. The pub is named after the Danish King of England in 1013, whose son Canute is rumoured to have stopped the Aegir. Food is available all day. ⏾◑&≉(Central)🚋🛜

Glentham

Crown Inn
High Street, LN8 2EQ
☎ (01673) 847867
Timothy Taylor Landlord; 3 changing beers (sourced locally; often Batemans, Horncastle, Milestone) 🄷
Traditional local with a large car park, and beer garden with seating and children's play area. The pub is open plan but has specific areas for food, pub games – including pool and darts – and a lounge area with comfy sofas around a log burner. Sports TV is available. Pumpclips and local history photographs are displayed. The pub holds quiz nights and also has pork scratchings cooking on the bar. ⏾❀◑♣P🌂🛜♪

Grantham

Blue Pig
9 Vine Street, NG31 6RQ
☎ (01476) 574502 ⊕ bluepiggrantham.co.uk
Fuller's London Pride; St Austell Proper Job; Timothy Taylor Landlord; 1 changing beer 🄷
One of only a few half-timbered buildings remaining in town this award-winning pub is situated just off the main high street. Once inside you are met with an open fire, beamed ceilings and a bar with six handpulls – one with Weston's Old Rosie and five for real ale. There is seating spread all around the bar that you can be served from both sides of, and an impressively-sized beer garden winding its way through the space out back with views of the stunning St Wulfram's Church. ❀♣🚋

Grantham Railway Club 🄻
Huntingtower Road, NG31 7AU
☎ (01476) 564860
2 changing beers 🄷
Voted local CAMRA Club of the Year for the last four years, this recently refurbished community-run club is just a short walk from the station. A former British Rail Staff Association club hosting weekly entertainment, darts, cribbage and domino teams, and supporting various social and community organisations. A spacious

back room is available to hire and open to all CAMRA members. Call during opening hours for the most up-to-date entertainment information, or check the noticeboards inside the front door. ♿⚲♣P♠🅿️🛜♪

Lord Harrowby 🍺 Ⓛ
65 Dudley Road, NG31 9AB
☎ (01476) 563515
Brewster's Hophead; 4 changing beers (sourced nationally) Ⓗ

This award-winning back-street local is not to be missed. A proper community pub run by the landlady and her son, both real ale enthusiasts and CAMRA members who always ensure a LocAle is available among four changing guest beers. The traditional Victorian layout boasts a central bar and open fire in the lounge with comfy seats. The other side has a TV for sports and pool table. Holding at least two beer festivals a year and now serving food, with regular weeknight events and live entertainment, this truly is what a pub should be. Q⚲🕽⚲♣♠♠🛜♪

White Lion
53 Bridge End Road, NG31 6JJ
☎ (01476) 562084
1 changing beer (sourced nationally) Ⓗ

Split over two rooms this traditional family pub, with five guest bedrooms available, is a great place to stop when visiting Grantham. A monthly quiz for charity, hosted by the landlord who has over 20 years trade experience, always raises a smile and plenty of money for charity. The pub has its own pool and darts team, is dog friendly and has its own enclosed beer garden. With weekly events you will be assured of a warm and friendly welcome by all. ♿⚲⚲♣P♠🛜♪

Grimsby

Barge
Victoria Street, DN31 1NH
☎ (01472) 340911 ⊕ thebargegrimsby.co.uk
2 changing beers Ⓗ

As its name implies, this is an old converted grain barge that is berthed in the town centre near all bus routes. It has a slight list to starboard, but do not worry, it has had this for over 20 years. Usually quieter during the day, but still attracting a mixed crowd, it is livelier from the evening onwards once the jukebox is turned on. On Monday nights there is a quiz with a free supper. An outdoor seating area is to the front. ♿⚲⚲(Town)🚌

Docks Beers
The Church, King Edward Street, DN31 3JD
☎ (01472) 289795 ⊕ docksbeers.com
3 changing beers (sourced locally; often Dock Beers) Ⓗ

Docks brewery taproom opened in 2018. There are three real ales on handpull and a tap wall with a variety of craft beers and ciders. Many of the beers are brewed in-house, and cans, bottles and merchandise are available to take away. Food is served daily. Brewery tours take place every Sunday and can be booked in advance on their website. Docks Academy, above the brewery, is a 300-capacity live music and comedy venue, with event tickets from their website. ♿⚲🕽♿⚲(Docks)🚌(10)♠🛜♪

Yarborough Hotel 🍺 ⊘
29 Bethlehem Street, DN31 1JN
☎ (01472) 268283
Batemans XXXB; Greene King Abbot; Ruddles Best Bitter; Sharp's Doom Bar; 8 changing beers (sourced regionally) Ⓗ

Large open-plan pub serving 12 real ales from national and local breweries. It has regular quiz nights and Meet the brewer events. The pub can get busy at times due to its central location next to Grimsby Town railway station. There is a lovely restored hotel on the upper floors. Local CAMRA Pub of the Year 2024. ♿⚲🍴🕽♿⚲(Town)♦🚌🛜

Habrough

Station Inn
Station Road, DN40 3AP
☎ (01964) 630262
3 changing beers (sourced regionally; often Butcombe, Exmoor) Ⓗ

This lively village community pub is found across from the railway station. As you enter the pub, an open fire greets you and gives the spacious room a cosy feel in winter. The pubs games area is to the right of the bar. Three handpumps feature local and regional beers. Live bands play monthly and there is a large outside area to enjoy in better weather. ♿♿⚲♣P♠♪

Halton Holegate

Bell Inn
Spilsby Road, PE23 5PA
☎ (01790) 753242 ⊕ thebell.me.uk
2 changing beers (sourced locally; often Batemans, Horncastle) Ⓗ

This 16th-century country inn is situated in a quiet village. Pictures of the Dambusters adorn the small cosy lounge. The friendly welcoming landlord has a keen interest in beers and the guests are often from small breweries within the county. There is usually an annual beer festival on the first weekend in October. During the winter a chip van provides food on Wednesday nights. The sign was redone in 2023, referencing the RAF squadrons based at RAF Spilsby that drank here during WWII. ♿⚲♣P♠♪

Heckington

8 Sail Brewery Bar
Heckington Mill, Hale Road, NG34 9JW
☎ (01529) 469308 ⊕ 8sailbrewery.com
8 Sail Ploughmans Lunch, Windmill Bitter, Froglet, Fenman, Rolling Stone, King John's Jewels; 3 changing beers (sourced locally; often 8 Sail) Ⓗ

Situated in part of the Heckington Windmill complex, this single-room brewery bar features a restored Victorian bar, some church pew seating and Britannia style tables. A bank of handpulls offers changing 8 Sail brewery beers and two German-style 8 Sail brewed lagers. Ciders, bottled wine and bottled Belgian and German beers are usually available. Beer festivals are held over Easter, on the last weekend in July when Heckington Show is on, and in the autumn. Check the website for current hours and the full range of beers. Q♿⚲♿⚲♦P🚌♠♪

Holbeach

Crown Hotel
5 West End, PE12 7LW
☎ (01406) 423941 ⊕ the-crown.co.uk
Sharp's Doom Bar; 2 changing beers (sourced locally; often Tydd Steam) Ⓗ

Traditional pub, serving the town for over 300 years. The pub retains its beamed ceiling and other woodwork, and a brick-fronted bar. Home-cooked meals are available at lunchtime when there is a relaxed atmosphere. Younger and noisier customers are more prevalent in the evenings. There is a beer garden to the side of the pub. A pool table and dartboard are located in the upstairs room. ♿✿🚃◗♣P🖵❀🛜♪

Holdingham

Jolly Scotchman
18 Lincoln Road, NG34 8NP
☎ (01529) 304864
Greene King IPA, Abbot; 2 changing beers (sourced locally; often 8 Sail) Ⓗ
Located at the northern end of Sleaford, near the A17 Holdingham roundabout, this pub boasts a modern open-plan interior with a mix of seating styles. A multicoloured tile floor surrounds the wooden bar front. The restaurant area is of garden room format, with large picture windows. Very much food-orientated, it can be busy at times, so advance booking for meals is advisable. On the site of a coaching inn, the name refers to the person who 'scotched' the wheels of carriages. ♿✿◗♠P🖵🛜♪

Horbling

Plough Inn
4 Spring Lane, NG34 0PF
☎ (01529) 241500
Batemans XB; Greene King Abbot; 2 changing beers (often Batemans) Ⓗ
A community pub owned by the parish of Horbling, built in 1832 and set just off the main road. In addition to its lounge/bar, its snug is surely one of the smallest and most intimate of its kind. In 2023 it changed licensee and is now managed by Batemans on behalf of the parish. The Spring Wells, a feature worth seeing, are just a few yards down the lane. ♿♣P❀🛜♪

Horncastle

King's Head
16 Bull Ring, LN9 5HU
☎ (01507) 523360
Batemans XB, Gold, XXXB Ⓗ
A comfortable, cosy and friendly pub. Unusually for this locality the building has a thatched roof, hence its local name the Thatch. Three beers from Batemans are generally available plus a guest. Reputedly the pub inspired an OO gauge Hornby model, an example of which is displayed behind the bar. Summertime sees the pub resplendent with hanging baskets and it has been the winner of Bateman's Floral Display competition. Try spotting the pub cat, Rufus. ♿✿◗🖵❀🛜♪

Ingoldmells

Countryman Ⓛ
Chapel Road, PE25 1ND
☎ (01754) 872268
House beer (by 8 Sail) Ⓗ
The privately-owned Countryman appears to be a modern building but it incorporates the early 19th-century Leila Cottage. A notorious smuggler, James Waite, used to reside here when Ingoldmells was a wild and lonely place, but he certainly would not recognise the current holiday coast, with Skegness, Butlins and Fantasy Island all nearby. The pub is on northern bus routes from Skegness. Previously the pub was supplied by its own on-site brewery, but this has now closed and house beers are brewed by 8-Sail brewery in Heckington. ♿✿◗♿♣P🖵

Irnham

Griffin Inn Ⓛ
15 Bulby Road, NG33 4JG
☎ (01476) 550201 ⊕ thegriffininrnham.co.uk
Timothy Taylor Landlord; 1 changing beer (often Grainstore, Oakham) Ⓗ
A recently refurbished 200-year-old stone-built property with a bar area serving Timothy Taylor Landlord and an ever-changing guest beer. Two separate dining rooms serve a wide selection of food from traditional to innovative. This is a good place for walking, including a countryside walk around the Irnham Estate. The pub hosts a beer and sausage festival in August.
Q♿✿🚃◗P❀🛜♪

Leasingham

Duke of Wellington
19 Lincoln Road, NG34 8JS
☎ (01529) 419000 ⊕ thedukeofwellington-leasingham.com
Marston's Pedigree; Wainwright Gold; 2 changing beers (often Ringwood, Woodforde's) Ⓗ
A community-owned pub in every sense with games days and nights, quizzes in daytime and evenings, food-themed nights, as well as open mic once a month. The two guest ales are often Wherry and sometimes Boondoggle or Bass. Originally a thatched pub named the Sun, the pub was renamed when it was bought by a local officer following the Battle of Waterloo. The pub is now in its 6th year as community run. It has a cosy, comfortable, lounge and a spacious garden with plenty of outdoor seating. Q♿✿◗♣P🖵❀🛜♪

Lincoln

Adam & Eve Tavern
25 Lindum Road, LN2 1NT
☎ (01522) 537108 ⊕ adamandevelincoln.co.uk
Castle Rock Harvest Pale; Sharp's Doom Bar; Timothy Taylor Landlord; 1 changing beer (sourced nationally) Ⓗ
Dating from 1701, this listed building is in a prominent position opposite Pottergate Arch, one of only two remaining medieval gates that gave access to the cathedral close. The surprisingly large interior has many historic features and is divided into a number of separate areas, including one for pool. A beer garden is built into the hillside. Quizzes and live music events take place regularly. Two screens show sporting events. Home-cooked pub grub is served. ♿✿◗♣P🖵❀🛜♪

BeerHeadZ
4 Eastgate, LN2 1QA
☎ (01522) 255430 ⊕ beerheadz.biz
3 changing beers (sourced nationally) Ⓗ
A bright, colourful pub with an industrial feel situated in the uphill city area serving up to four cask ales, craft keg beers, two ciders and a range of bottled and canned beers, always including at least one gluten-free offering. Oversized glasses are used. Customers are welcome to bring in their own food or order in from outside suppliers. Regular events include a quiz and open mic night alternating on Wednesdays. Dogs are welcome. ●◗🖵❀🛜♪

Birdcage ✔
54 Baggholme Road, LN2 5BQ
☎ (01522) 274478 ⊕ birdcagelincoln.com
Sharp's Doom Bar; 3 changing beers (sourced nationally; often Ferry Ales, Milestone, Zest) Ⓗ
Situated on a street corner of the city's east end, this dog-friendly pub has a strong community behind it which

is evident from their busy events calendar which ranges from craft group Yarned and Dangerous, to quiz nights, spoken word, karaoke, live bands, open mic nights, vinyl nights and even their own Ukulele group. Be you a regular or infrequent visitor you are sure to be made to feel welcome as you enjoy their regularly changing range of real ales. ✿⊒♿❀?♪

Cardinal's Hat
268 High Street, LN2 1HW
☎ (01522) 527084
Adnams Mosaic; Ossett White Rat; Timothy Taylor Landlord; house beer (by Lincolnshire Craft); 4 changing beers (sourced nationally) Ⓗ
Refurbished as a pub in 2015, 500 years after its namesake Cardinal Wolsey was Bishop of Lincoln from 1514 to 1515. Housed in a Grade II-listed building dating back to the 15th century, the refurb showcases some original features. It has an extensive drinks menu complimented by bar snacks, cheese and charcuterie boards. This multi-roomed building makes it ideal for a quiet drink for couples, friends or larger groups, including its regular art class sessions. ⛄✿◐&⇌(Central)●?♪

Golden Eagle
21 High Street, LN5 8BD
☎ (01522) 521058
Castle Rock Harvest Pale; 7 changing beers (sourced nationally; often Castle Rock, Pheasantry, Welbeck Abbey) Ⓗ
A popular local at the southern end of High Street, it is close to Lincoln City's football ground and is very busy on match days. The building dates from the 1700s. Up to nine real ales are served from two bars. The large garden has covered and heated seating. The pub is dog-friendly and the cosy front lounge has a log-burner. Two beer festivals are held annually and, in summer, the barbecue may be fired up. ⛄♣●P⊒❀?♪

Joiners Arms ✓
4 Victoria Street, LN1 1HU
☎ 07871 887459
4 changing beers (sourced nationally) Ⓗ
Nestled among the Victorian terraces, this traditional back-street boozer has two open fires. Three steps lead to the bar. The back room has a pool table, dartboard and a retro Space Invaders machine. The quirky beer garden features funky sculptures which extend to the steampunk inspired bike racks located in the car park. Tuesday is quiz night with an open mic night every other Saturday and a monthly air rifle target shooting night. Four-legged friends are warmly welcomed. ⛄✿♣❀?

Morning Star ✓
11 Greetwell Gate, LN2 4AW
☎ (01522) 514269 ⏚ morningstarlincoln.co.uk
Milestone Shine On; St Austell Proper Job; Sharp's Doom Bar; Timothy Taylor Boltmaker; 2 changing beers (sourced nationally) Ⓗ
A cosy locals' pub in the city's uphill area. Each end of the front bar has a seating area, with one featuring a real fire in winter months. There is a small back room. The large, outside seating area is partly covered and affords a stunning view of the Gothic-style cathedral. An occasional vinyl night is held but conversation is the main entertainment. There is usually at least one guest ale from a local brewer. Q✿⊒❀?

Ritz Ⓛ ✓
143-147 High Street, LN5 7PJ
☎ (01522) 512103
Sharp's Doom Bar; Ruddles Best Bitter; Greene King Abbot; 5 changing beers (sourced nationally) Ⓗ

Situated on the city's high street, previously a cinema and live entertainment venue, JD Wetherspoon refurbished the Ritz, retaining its Art Deco design and external neon lighting reflecting its past. Inside, the walls are decorated with pictures/autographs of past acts and performers that appeared there in its previous life. Unusually for a Wetherspoon you won't have to walk far to visit the restrooms! The venue hosts monthly Meet the Brewer/tap takeover evenings. Very popular on football match days. Q⛄✿◐&⇌(Central)⊒?

Strugglers Inn Ⓛ ✓
83 Westgate, LN1 3BG (use What Three Words below.feel.escape)
☎ (01522) 535023
Greene King Abbot; Timothy Taylor Landlord; 7 changing beers (sourced nationally; often Brewster's Brewing Company Limited, Pheasantry, Welbeck Abbey) Ⓗ
The multi-award-winning Struggs stands in the shadow of Lincoln Castle and is popular with locals and visitors alike. The walls of the two rooms are festooned with old photographs and the ceilings are covered with pumpclips. The sunken garden is a suntrap. The numerous guest beers offer a range of styles and strengths, and local brews always feature. There is live music most weekends and the Practice Christmas in September is always great fun. Q✿♣●⊒❀♪

Tiny Tavern ♟
107 High Street, LN5 7PY
☎ 07761 123697
6 changing beers (sourced nationally) Ⓗ
What better way is there to preserve two Grade II-listed 17th-century cottages than to turn them into a small pub? A cosy interior includes a window seat, fireplace, counter, and access to an unexpected garden area at the rear. Ring the doorbell on the right to be admitted, and leave by the other! A separate room may be used for community purposes. The beers are from all over the country; real cider is sometimes available. Local CAMRA Pub of the Year 2024. ✿⇌(Central)♣●⊒

Louth

Brown Cow ✓
133 Newmarket, LN11 9EG (top of Newmarket on jct with Church St)
☎ (01507) 605146
Black Sheep Best Bitter; Castle Rock Harvest Pale; Fuller's London Pride; 1 changing beer Ⓗ
Owners Nigel and Victoria Hopper are celebrating 10 years behind the bar of this friendly freehouse. With a great atmosphere and, most important, great beer it is a must when visiting Louth. A free quiz is held on the first Sunday of the month. The kitchen serves traditional, home-cooked food, made with locally sourced products. The pub is a popular community meeting place. ⛄✿◐&▲⊒❀?♪

Cobbles Bar
2 New Street, LN11 9PU (off Cornmarket)
1 changing beer (often Ossett) Ⓗ
Traditional pub-style bar based in the centre of town, with friendly staff at all times. This small but accommodating venue has multiple personalities, from a bustling coffee shop serving light lunches to a busy pre-club local with DJ and live music at weekends. It has a good beer trade, with one changing cask ale, as well as a huge selection of exotic spirits. Disabled access is right through the front doors. ◐&⊒?

Consortium Micropub 🅛

13C Cornmarket, LN11 9PY
☎ (01507) 600754 ⏥ theconsortiumlouth.co.uk
Consortium ZigZag, Black Frog, Best Bitter, Obliging Blonde, Thanks Pa Ⓗ

This micropub, in a small courtyard 50 yards from the Market Place next to the Masons Arms Hotel, opened in 2017 to give people a chance to taste various ales, ciders and lagers from around the UK. The pub has its own microbrewery and distillery located on the industrial estate which produces a massive range of diverse real ales and gins. Six ales are supplied to the bar, as well as a well-stocked gin shelf and a local market stall selling bottled ales ciders and lagers.
Q♂&⅄♣🖦P🖳(51) ❀🛜

Gas Lamp Lounge 🅛

13 Thames Street, LN11 7AD (bottom of Thames St by factories)
☎ (01507) 607661
5 changing beers Ⓗ

This unique pub is one of only 22 pubs in the UK still lit by gas lamps. There is no music or games machines, just good pub traditions. Four beers from the upstairs brewery are served, plus a guest beer. Benches are set along the canalside where you can enjoy a drink during the summer, and inside there is a roaring log-burner to sit beside in the winter months. Dogs are welcome.
Q♂&♣🖦P🖳❀🛜♪

Olde Whyte Swanne ✅

45 Eastgate, LN11 9NP
☎ (01507) 824141 ⏥ whyteswannelouth.co.uk
Timothy Taylor Landlord; house beer (by Marston's); 2 changing beers Ⓗ
The oldest pub in a pretty market town of Louth. Established in the early 1600s, upon entering this Grade II-listed building you are met by traditional ceilings with low beams and a real fire. Beyond this is another modern room which is used for dining and meetings. The bar offers a good variety of beers and cider on handpump.
Q♂❀◖&🖳❀🛜

Tap on the Line

29 Upgate, LN11 9HD
☎ (01507) 311646 ⏥ theludabrewco.com
LUDA Black Mass Stout, Funky Slice East Coast IPA, Stingray IPA, Tropic Thunder Ⓟ
The Luda brewery tap room, located in the heart of town, is a popular destination for locals or visiters alike. There is a warm friendly welcome and the staff are always willing to chat and to help with recommendations with the beer menu which features a wide range of beers and other drinks, with craft beers grouped by brewery and guest beers on the bar regularly. There is a large seating area inside and out, with dartboard and pool tables.
❀&❀❀

Woolpack 🅛

14 Riverhead Road, LN11 0DA
☎ (01507) 606568 ⏥ woolpacklouth.com
Batemans XB, Gold, XXXB; 3 changing beers Ⓗ
The Woolpack is situated close to the theatre and the canal and is popular for drinkers and diners alike. It usually offer four or five real ales on handpull. The Grade II-listed building is dog-friendly and has disabled access and baby changing facilities. There is an outside beer garden and ample parking. ♂❀◖&P🖳❀🛜

Market Deeping

Vine Inn 🅛

19 Church Street, PE6 8AN
☎ (01778) 348741
Butcombe Original; Sharp's Doom Bar; 3 changing beers (often Abbeydale, Blue Monkey, Skinner's) Ⓗ
Formerly a Charles Wells pub, now a free house, this small, friendly local features oak beams and stone floors, with many 20th-century prints on the walls. There is a large patio at the rear. Five handpumps dispense an ever-changing range of interesting ales from near and far. Boxed real cider is available. Free nibbles are provided Sunday lunchtime and early evenings during the week. The television is only used for major sporting events. The pub celebrated 10 years in this Guide in 2022. ❀🖦P🖳(101)❀🛜♪

Marton

Ingleby Arms

42 High Street, DN21 5AH
☎ (01427) 718707 ⏥ inglebyarmsmarton.com
Bradfield Farmers Blonde Ⓗ
This village pub/restaurant is celebrating its first entry in the Guide. It has recently been taken over and there has been substantial renovation and redecoration to make the pub as inviting and welcoming as possible. There is a new and extensive menu of delicious home-cooked meals. It is Grade II-listed by English Heritage for its architecture. The real ale has been chosen by the regular customers. ♂❀◖♣P🖳❀🛜

Messingham

Pooley's

46 High Street, DN17 3NT
☎ 07860 799178
5 changing beers (sourced regionally; often Batemans, Ossett, Salopian) Ⓗ
Popular village local decorated in rustic style, open in the evenings from Wednesday to Sunday. A bar at one end serves three distinct drinking areas, all with wooden or flagstone floors and real fires, where conversation is encouraged. Vintage pictures and signs displayed throughout add to the charm. Five changing real ales are normally available, plus an extensive range of wines and spirits. Winner of several local CAMRA awards and always welcoming to regulars and visitors alike.
Q&🖳(100,103)❀🛜

Morton

Ship Inn

34 Front Street, DN21 3AE
☎ (01427) 613298
Wainwright Gold; 1 changing beer Ⓗ
Situated in the village of Morton, to the north of Gainsborough, this is a quaint typical-style village pub. There are weekly darts, dominoes and pool matches and regular quiz evenings. Two rotating cask ales are sold. Food is available four days a week, with Sunday lunches proving to be very popular. Q♂❀◖&♣🖳❀🛜

Moulton

Swan

13 High Street, PE12 6QB
☎ (01406) 478773 ⏥ theswanmoulton.com
Fuller's London Pride; 4 changing beers (often Bombardier) Ⓗ

Family-run pub in the centre of an attractive village which enjoys a good daytime bus service; Norfolk Green buses stop just across the road. Two regular real ales and three changing guest ales are available as well as Westons cider on handpump. The pub has an excellent reputation for food, with an interesting and varied menu. It is family and dog friendly, with a pleasant and popular garden. ⌂ 🛏️ ❄️ ◑ ♣ P 🚫 ❀

Navenby

Lion & Royal
57 High Street, LN5 0DZ
☎ (01522) 810368
Greene King IPA, Abbot; 3 changing beers (sourced nationally; often Parkway, Welbeck Abbey) Ⓗ
Formerly the Lion, the name changed after a visit by the Prince of Wales in 1870. Guy Gibson of 617 Squadron fame spent his wedding night in this imposing, Grade II-listed building. The bar has a flagged floor and an impressive fireplace. There is an enclosed beer garden and a large car park. The pub is on the Lincoln to Grantham bus route. There is a weekly quiz and regular live music. Bar food is served. ⌂ 🛏️ ❄️ ◑ ♿ ♣ P 🚫 (1) ❀ 🐾 ☂ ♪

New Waltham

Farmhouse ✅
Station Road, DN36 4PF
☎ (01472) 827472
St Austell Proper Job; Sharp's Doom Bar; 3 changing beers Ⓗ
Attractive looking pub set back from the road by the beer garden. Catering for all ages, it is open plan, with several secluded areas. There is a welcoming fire located at each end. Well behaved dogs are allowed in both the beer garden and the bar area and even have their own menu. A comprehensive food menu available all day, including award-winning pies. Live music plays at weekends and there is a weekly quiz. ⌂ 🛏️ ❄️ ◑ ♣ P 🚫 (8) ❀ 🐾 ☂ ♪

Nocton

Ripon Arms 🅛
Main Street, LN4 2BH
☎ 07989 449353
3 changing beers (sourced nationally) Ⓗ
Centrally located, this community run pub is based in the village Hub. There is ample car parking on site with a wooden ramp providing wheelchair access to the bar, lounge and outside seating area. A monthly quiz night is held on the first Saturday of the month. Traditional pub games are available. A popular beer festival is held in early May and an Oktoberfest is included in the pubs events calendar. The pub is family and dog friendly. ⌂ 🛏️ ♿ ♣ P 🚫 (31,IC5) ❀ 🐾 ☂ ♪

North Hykeham

Centurion
Newark Road, LN6 8LB
☎ (01522) 509814
Sharp's Doom Bar; 2 changing beers (sourced nationally; often Adnams, Fuller's, Purity) Ⓗ
A spacious community pub, popular with diners and drinkers alike. Whether dining or drinking, a warm welcome awaits, especially in the colder months when the fire is lit. The large beer garden is great for sunny days. Popular quiz nights are held on Mondays and Thursdays. Ideally located next to a large supermarket so a post-shopping pint can be enjoyed. Booking is advised if dining. ⌂ 🛏️ ❄️ ◑ ♿ ♣ P 🚫 ☂

Owston Ferry

White Hart
North Street, DN9 1RT
☎ (01427) 728206
2 changing beers (often Black Sheep) Ⓗ
A hidden gem down by the river, the White Hart is a lovely local pub serving traditional pub meals. They have four main areas which are the bar, lounge, dining room and the White Hard Landing, recreating the historic river port that once stood there. It is a great spot to sit and relax in the summer overlooking the River Trent. Three real ales are constantly rotating with beers from Black Sheep, Marston's and others. Q ⌂ 🛏️ ❄️ ◑ P 🚫 ❀ ☂

Pinchbeck

Ship
Northgate, PE11 3SE
☎ (01775) 711746
Adnams Ghost Ship; Black Sheep Best Bitter; Greene King Abbot; 1 changing beer Ⓗ
Thatched pub on the banks of the River Glen by the railway bridge at the western end of Knight Street. The pub has been given a sympathetic update and is smart, neat and tidy but retains a warm and cosy appeal. Food is farm to fork, locally sourced, fresh quality produce. Events through the year range from beer, wine and spirit tasting evenings to an annual garden party with car shows and live music. Card payments only. ⌂ 🛏️ ❄️ ◑ P 🚫 ❀ ☂ ♪

Raithby

Red Lion
Raithby Road, PE23 4DS
☎ (01790) 753727 ⊕ redlionraithby.co.uk
Batemans XB; 2 changing beers (often Ferry Ales) Ⓗ
Cosy village pub built around 1650, with beamed low ceilings in the many small rooms that surround the bar. Pictures of outdoor pursuits, and old photographs adorn the walls. The pub sits in an attractive quiet village in the Wolds and is excellent for walking and cycling. The various small rooms are now popular dining areas. Closed on Mondays, including bank holidays. A discount available for those arriving by bus and presenting their ticket. Q ⌂ 🛏️ ❄️ ◑ ♿ ♣ P 🚫 (56) ❀ ☂

Redbourne

Red Lion
Main Road, DN21 4QR
☎ (01652) 408292 ⊕ redlionredbourne.co.uk
Timothy Taylor Landlord; 3 changing beers (sourced nationally; often Morland, Sharp's, Timothy Taylor) Ⓗ
Attractive village inn with white walls and a timber façade. The modern open-plan interior has a central bar serving two drinking/dining areas and a separate dining room. There is a strong emphasis on food with daily specials and offers on meals throughout the week. There are four real ales, three of which are rotated as guest ales. Accommodation is in seven en-suite rooms. Occasional live music is featured. ❄️ 🛌 ◑ P 🚫 ❀ ☂ ♪

Ropsley

Green Man
24 High Street, NG33 4BE
☎ (01476) 585897
Wainwright Gold; 3 changing beers (sourced nationally) Ⓗ

This 17th-century multi award-winning traditional English village pub is nestled in the heart of Ropsley. A warm and friendly welcome always awaits. Knowledgeable staff will help you choose the perfect ale from the four available. The innovative food choice, including exotic meats, locally sourced game and seafood, served in generous portion sizes, will have you coming back for more. Visitors arriving via local walking and cycle routes are welcome. It is clear to see why this pub has won so many awards. ♿✿❶❀☂

Ruskington

Shoulder of Mutton
11 Church Street, NG34 9DU
☎ (01526) 832220
St Austell Cornish Best Bitter; Sharp's Doom Bar; 2 changing beers (sourced regionally) Ⓗ
A popular and thriving pub in the heart of the village attracting customers of all ages. It is one of the oldest buildings in the village and was once a butcher's shop, hence the name. A few old meat-hooks can still be seen in the wooden ceiling in the bar. Changes have been made in recent years but have not spoiled the essential character. Standing guard outside is Knight and Day, a sculpture from Lincoln's 2017 Knight's Trail.
✿≒♣P🚃(31)❀☂

Saxilby

Anglers ✅
65 High Street, LN1 2HA
☎ (01522) 702200 ⊕ anglerspublichouse.com
Theakston Best Bitter; 3 changing beers (sourced nationally; often Beermats, Pheasantry, Milestone) Ⓗ
Family-run community local built around 1850, it is home to various sports and pub games teams and U3A group meetings. Conveniently close to bus stops, the railway station and visitor moorings on the Fossdyke, the country's oldest canal. The lounge bar (no dogs) features old photographs of the village. The extensive outside area, part-covered, includes a boules court and hosts street food at least weekly. Guest beers are often from local breweries. Q✿▲≒♣P🚃❀☂♫

Scampton

Dambusters Inn Ⓛ
23 High Street, LN1 2SD
☎ (01522) 731333 ⊕ dambustersinn.co.uk
Beermats Dambusters Ale; 8 changing beers (sourced nationally; often Beermats, Brewster's, Pheasantry) Ⓗ
This thriving village pub/restaurant is packed with memorabilia and prints relating to the famous bombing raid. Murals add to the wartime feel. The front extension has a roof terrace and, at the rear, bifold doors open onto a patio. The eight handpumps offer an ever-changing selection of ales, many from local breweries. An annual beer festival is held around the anniversary of the Dambusters mission. Local CAMRA Pub of the Year on numerous occasions. Closed Mondays.
Q✿❶●P🚃(103)❀☂

Scunthorpe

Berkeley Hotel ★
Doncaster Road, DN15 7DS (½ mile from end of M181)
☎ (01724) 842333 ⊕ theberkeleyscunthorpe.co.uk
Samuel Smith Old Brewery Bitter Ⓗ
Large, ornate 1930s Samuel Smith's pub at one end of town, open again after a long period of closure. Grade II-

listed, with art deco stylings, it has been identified by CAMRA as having a nationally important historic pub interior. Three separate rooms lead from the front reception area, two with real fires. Meals and accommodation will be offered once the refurbishment of the kitchen and bedrooms is completed. This is the only Sam Smith's pub in town offering real ale. Located close to the football ground, so it can be busy on match days. Q✿&P🚃☂

Blue Bell Inn ✅
1-7 Oswald Road, DN15 7PU (at town-centre crossroads)
☎ (01724) 863921
Greene King Abbot; Ruddles Best Bitter; 6 changing beers (sourced regionally; often Bradfield, Milestone, Saltaire) Ⓗ
Busy Wetherspoon pub in the town centre on two levels. It has a large open area on first floor with access by stairs and a lift. Photos and details of local personalities adorn the walls. Food is served all day. Wetherspoon beer festivals are supported along with special days such as Burns Night, St George's Day and St Patrick's Day. Occasional Meet the Brewer events are arranged and special fundraising days for local charities also held. A large council-run car park is at the rear of the pub.
♿✿❶&P🚃☂

Honest Lawyer
70 Oswald Road, DN15 7PG (on main road between railway station and town centre)
☎ (01724) 276652
Sharp's Solar Wave; 2 changing beers (sourced nationally) Ⓗ
This refurbished legal-themed pub is long and narrow. There is a small, heated outdoor drinking area at the front of the pub. The upstairs restaurant is now closed, but the room is available for private functions. Sky Sports are shown on several screens. Midweek trivia nights are held, with live music at weekends. It opens at 4pm Monday to Thursday. Sharp's Solar Wave is the regular real ale available, with two others regularly featured.
✿&●🚃☂♫

Malt Shovel
219 Ashby High Street, DN16 2JP (in Ashby Broadway shopping area)
☎ (01724) 843318
Ossett White Rat; 5 changing beers (sourced regionally; often Abbeydale, Acorn, Titanic) Ⓗ
This self-styled country pub in the town comprises a main open-plan bar area and a conservatory extension leading off the main room. It is comfortably furnished throughout. A beer garden at the front overlooks the High Street. It is popular at mealtimes, especially for Thursday market day and for the Sunday carvery. One permanent real ale is joined by up to five rotating guests, plus ciders drawn straight from the cellar. Quiz night is Thursday with live music most Saturdays. Public car parks are nearby. ♿✿❶●&●🚃♫

Seathorne

Seathorne Arms
40-42 Seathorne Crescent, PE25 1RP
☎ (01754) 767797
2 changing beers (often Batemans, Greene King) Ⓗ
Set back from Roman Bank, 15 minutes' walk from Butlins, the pub has a large outside seating area and a spacious interior. The inside is one large area with partitioned areas for eating, pub games, drinking and TV watching. With very seasonal trade due to the local caravan sites, the pub is closed in January and closing

time may vary in February and March. The landlord operates a constantly rotating two beer selection. 🛇🏵️&♿♣🏠♻️🛜

Silk Willoughby

Horseshoes
London Road, NG34 8NZ
☎ (01529) 414092 🌐 horseshoessilkwilloughby.co.uk
Sharp's Doom Bar; Timothy Taylor Landlord; 2 changing beers (sourced locally; often Batemans) 🅷
Situated in a quiet village just south of Sleaford, this is a welcoming free house. As well as the regular beers, there is always one Batemans beer available. The landlord holds regular quiz nights with proceeds going to local charities. There are regular acoustic music events and occasional bands; see the Facebook page for details. Special meal deals are often available on Thursday lunchtime, with takeaway meals also available. There is an attractive outdoor area with seating and a large car park. 🛇🏵️◑P♻️🛜🎵

Skegness

Crafty Local Ale House
7 Lumley Avenue, PE25 2AH
3 changing beers 🅷
Based in an old college building that was previously an office for the blind society, this micropub was opened in October 2023 by Donna and Jason. Their aim is to bring more choice of real ales and still ciders to Skegness while promoting Lincolnshire's breweries and products. Beers regularly change and suggestions are accepted on what beers customers would like to see coming on the bar. 🛇🏵️≈♣🏠♻️

Vine Hotel ★
Vine Road, PE25 3DB
☎ (01754) 763018 🌐 thevinehotel.com
Batemans XB, XXXB; 1 changing beer (often Batemans) 🅷
A delightful building, one of the oldest in Skegness, dating from the 18th century and set in two acres of pleasant grounds. Inside are comfortable wood-panelled bars in which to enjoy a quiet pint or two after experiencing some of the noisier attractions and bustle of Skegness. Within striking distance of the Gibraltar Point National Nature Reserve, walking trails, beach and golf links, the inn has reputed Tennyson connections. 🛇🏵️🛌◑&P♻️🛜

Sleaford

White Horse
45 Boston Road, NG34 7HD (located on the left corner of the one-way system at the bottom of Carre St)
☎ (01529) 968003
Milestone Cromwell Best; 1 changing beer (often Greene King, Horncastle, Morland) 🅷
Located on the junction of Carre Street and Boston Road, the pub serves the housing area along the Boston Road. It is one of the few remaining traditional locals' pubs in Sleaford, with wet sales only. The interior has been opened out into a single L-shaped room, but which still retains a cosy feel. Photos of old Sleaford that adorn the walls. Do not be fooled by the clock above the fireplace – it displays an anticlockwise face. Sports predominate, with both darts and pool teams. Occasional charity events are held. 🛇🏵️≈♣P♻️🛜🎵

Snitterby

Royal Oak
High Street, DN21 4TP (1.5 miles from A15)
☎ (01673) 818273 🌐 royaloaksnitterby.co.uk
Rooster's Buckeye; Stancill Barnsley Bitter 🅷**; 3 changing beers (sourced nationally; often Caledonian, Morland)** 🅷/🅶
Traditional family-run community pub in a village setting focusing on good company, conversation and good beer. The comfortable and spacious interior is light and airy with wooden floors and real fires. It comprises three rooms, one with sports TV. The outside seating area overlooks a stream and a ford. The pub is very child and dog friendly. Traditional pub games are available. There is also a good selection of alcohol-free beers. Q🛇🏵️&♣●P♻️

Spalding

Prior's Oven 🅛
1 Sheep Market, PE11 1BH
☎ 07866 045778
3 changing beers (sourced locally; often Digfield, Tydd Steam, Austendyke) 🅶
The first micropub to be opened in Lincolnshire. The building was part of the Priory of Spalding and is believed almost 800 years old. Because of its shape it has always been known as the Oven or the Prior's Oven and has been used as Spalding Monastic Prison. Its more recent use was as a bakery and it became a pub in 2013. The ground-floor bar has a vaulted ceiling. Beer is also available in one-third pint measures. Q≈●🏠♻️

Red Lion Hotel ✅
Market Place, PE11 1SU
☎ (01775) 722869 🌐 redlionhotel.co.uk
Draught Bass; St Austell Cornish Best Bitter; 3 changing beers (sourced nationally; often St Austell) 🅷
The Red Lion is a carefully refurbished 18th-century family-run hotel. The cosy, comfortable and welcoming bar overlooks the marketplace. It is popular owing to its consistently well-kept range of cask ales, which the bar staff take great pride in serving in top condition. It is a rare outlet for Bass in the locality. On fine sunny days the experience is enhanced with tables and chairs outside. A blue plaque boasts that Jimi Hendrix stayed at the pub on 29th May 1967 when he played at a nearby gig with Pink Floyd and Cream. 🛇🛌◑&≈🏠♻️🛜🎵

Stamford

Green Man 🅛
29 Scotgate, PE9 2YQ
☎ (01780) 753598
Castle Rock Harvest Pale; 6 changing beers (sourced locally; often Grainstore, Oakham) 🅷
Dating from 1796, this stone-built former coaching inn stands on what was once the Great North Road. It comprises a large L-shaped split-level bar, with a real fire. Up to eight real ales, many from local micros, are complemented by a good range of European bottled beers with some ciders and perries, often from Broad Oak, on offer. The secluded patio boasts a mounting block from the days of horse riding. 🏵️🛌≈♣●🏠(201)♻️🛜🎵

King's Head
19 Maiden Lane, PE9 2AZ
☎ (01780) 753510 🌐 kingsheadstamford.co.uk

Black Sheep Best Bitter; 3 changing beers (sourced locally; often Bakers Dozen, Drum and Monkey, Nene Valley) ⊞
A 19th-century family-run free house of small stature, but with a big reputation for excellent food and beer. This one-roomed, stone-built pub features a wooden-beamed ceiling and has a quaint suntrap garden to the rear, with cover and heating for inclement weather. The pub serves four constantly-changing ales from the length and breadth of the country with a further eight craft taps offering all manner of beer styles. It is popular with diners at lunchtime. Local CAMRA Pub of the Year 2022.
Q❀❁●≒🏠

Millstone
All Saints Street, PE9 2PA
☎ (01780) 592357 🌐 millstoneinnpub.co.uk
Timothy Taylor Landlord; 3 changing beers (often Grainstore, Oakham, St Austell) ⊞
Late 17th-century pub with a beamed ceiling, which used to be an important station for carriers in the area. It has a lively bar with several TVs, popular with younger clientele. There is a large beer garden, patio and stage at the rear. A pizza menu is available throughout the day. The real ale range has increased with the appointment of an enthusiastic new landlord, who has increased the real ale line-up to four handpumps. ❀●≒🏠(201,204)❀♪

Tobie Norris
12 St Pauls Street, PE9 2BE
☎ (01780) 753800
Bowler's Special Bitter; Oakham Citra ⊞; 3 changing beers (sourced regionally; often Abbeydale, Nene Valley) ⊞/Ⓖ
This ancient stone building, parts of which date back to 1280, was bought by Tobie Norris in 1617 and used as a bell foundry. Formerly a RAFA club, a major refurbishment gained it CAMRA's Conversion to Pub Use Award in 2007. It now has many small rooms with real fires, stone floors and low beams. Five handpumps serve beers from local and country-wide breweries, with other ales sometimes available directly from the cask. A former local CAMRA Pub of the Year. Card payments only.
Q❀❀●≒♣🏠(202,203) ❀🗢

Swayfield

Royal Oak
27 High Street, NG33 4LL
☎ (01476) 550415 🌐 royaloakswayfield.co.uk
Fuller's London Pride; Timothy Taylor Landlord Dark; 1 changing beer (sourced nationally) ⊞
Located in the pleasant surroundings of rural Lincolnshire, this family-friendly stone-built pub dates from around 1650. The pub's name the Royal Oak is derived from the English oak tree in which the future King Charles II hid to escape the Roundheads following the Battle of Worcester. The pub's other claim to fame is that Dick Turpin once stayed there. Opening hours may vary during winter months, so check ahead.
Q❀❀🏠●♣P❀🗢♪

Swineshead

Green Dragon
Market Place, PE20 3LJ
☎ (01205) 821381
Batemans XB; Theakston Traditional Mild; 3 changing beers (sourced regionally) ⊞
Originally called the Green Dragon, its fortunes gradually declined until new owners brought it back to life with a new name. A change of ownership has now seen the

pub revert to its original name, and it is now a vibrant and thriving village local, successfully blending old and new to recreate a genuine community pub with an emphasis on beer and traditional pub games. Pizza and bar snacks to eat in or take away are available Thursday to Saturday. ❀❀●♣🏠(K59)❀🗢

Swinhope

Clickem Inn ♀
Binbrook Road, LN8 6BS (2 miles N of Binbrook on B1203)
☎ (01472) 398253
Theakston Old Peculier; Timothy Taylor Landlord; house beer (by Pheasantry); 3 changing beers (sourced nationally; often Batemans, Horncastle, Ossett) ⊞
Set in the picturesque Lincolnshire Wolds this is a popular stopping place for walkers and cyclists. The pub's name eminates from the counting of sheep passing through a nearby clicking gate. Renowned for its home-cooked food served in the bar and conservatory, it offers a choice of drinks, including six real ales and a traditional cider. The house beer is Terry's Tipple. There is pool, darts and a jukebox. A covered but unheated area is provided for smokers. Q❀❀❀●♣🏠P🗢

Tattershall Thorpe

Blue Bell Inn
Thorpe Road, LN4 4PE
☎ (01526) 342206 🌐 bluebell-inn.com
Greene King IPA, Abbot; 2 changing beers (sourced locally) ⊞
This ancient building, in a delightful location, has 13th-century origins and is one of Lincolnshire's oldest inns. It has a large open fire and beamed ceilings that are covered in signatures and photographs of airmen from World War II RAF squadrons who used the pub, including the 617 Dambusters and 627 Pathfinders. King Henry VIII reputedly visited the Blue Bell and there is a ghost in residence. Q❀❀❀●♣🏠P🏠♪

Tetney Lock

Crown & Anchor
Lock Road, DN36 5UW TA342021
☎ (01472) 388291
5 changing beers (sourced nationally; often Morland, Otter, Woodforde's) ⊞
Overlooking the historic but now defunct Louth Navigation Canal, this is a popular call for walkers, anglers and tourists including those from Cleethorpes. Home-cooked food is a major draw, along with constantly changing ales. The highly experienced hosts very much focus on these two core aspects. Dogs welcomed in the front public bar (with its welcoming open fire) and garden. An external area is available for smokers. Q❀❀❀●♣P❀🗢

Waddington

Three Horseshoes
High Street, LN5 9RF
☎ (01522) 720448
Theakston Best Bitter; 2 changing beers (sourced nationally; often Timothy Taylor) ⊞
A real community pub in the heart of the village. A warm welcome awaits in this dog-friendly, two-roomed local. The main bar has a log-burner and both rooms are used for a wide variety of social events, including live music, bingo, poker and darts. The back room has a pool table. A

beer garden provides additional space. Large TV screens show sports events alongside traditional pub games. Regular beers include a couple from Pheasantry brewery just across the border in Nottinghamshire.
ᗡ❀♣🖳(1,13) ❀ 🛜

Willingham by Stow

Half Moon 🄻
23 High Street, DN21 5JZ
☎ (01427) 788340
Batemans XB, Gold; Sharp's Doom Bar; 1 changing beer 🄷
Traditional-style village pub in a building dating back to 1850 with a public bar, lounge bar, an open fire and a beer garden. There are sometimes four beers available; three regular and one changing. Food is available from Thursday to Sunday and the fish & chips are very popular with locals and visitors. There are entertainment nights on a relatively regular basis and themed charity nights. Opening times may vary, always check ahead.
Q ᗡ❀🕽 & ♣ 🖳 ❀

Willoughton

Stirrup Inn 🄻
1 Templefield Road, DN21 5RZ
☎ (01427) 668270
Black Sheep Best Bitter; 1 changing beer 🄷

Built from local Lincolnshire limestone, this hidden gem is over 350 years old and is well worth seeking out – you can be sure of a warm welcome. The pub oozes character with a roaring log fire in winter and is popular with locals and folk from further afield. A choice of ales is usually available; Black Sheep and one changing guest. Lincolnshire bell target shooting, doubles darts and dominoes are regularly played and a regular quiz is hosted. No food is served but pop-up vendors regularly visit. Q ᗡ❀ & ♣ P ❀

Wroot

Cross Keys
High Street, DN9 2BT (on the main street in centre of village)
☎ (01302) 770231
Black Sheep Best Bitter; Theakston Best Bitter; 2 changing beers (sourced regionally; often Pheasantry, Welbeck Abbey, Westgate) 🄷
The pub was built in 1909 in the small village of Wroot. Off the beaten track, but popular, and well supported by locals, this is a genuine village pub. There are four separate rooms, two bars, a games room and a snug. It is home to the local football team and regular quizzes are hosted. Now with one or two rotating and two regular real ales. This is a drinker's pub, but meals, with monthly specials, are available four days a week, including Sundays. ᗡ❀🕽 Å ♣ P ❀ 🛜

Blue Pig, Grantham (Photo: Matt Brown / Flickr CC BY 2.0)

The Devil's in the Draught Lines
1,000 Years of Women in Britain's Beer History

Dr Christina Wade

Once our ancient ancestors discovered that by settling and cultivating grains they would have a regular and plentiful food source, it was only a matter of time before beer became a part of everyday life. And that beer was mainly made by women. For centuries, women brewers remained key participants in our beer trade, up to the Industrial Revolution when increased mechanisation, alongside Victorian societal constraints, conspired to push a lot of them out. From then on, commercial brewing was generally considered a male-led profession.

But things are changing. With the increase in new breweries, and a growing enthusiasm for beer, women are back at the helm at an ever-growing number of British brewers, large and small, reasserting their dominance in the industry.

This important book, meticulously researched by beer historian Dr Christina Wade, charts the rise and fall – and rise – of women in Britain's brewing trade, and includes interviews with women working in today's beer industries. It tells us the whole story, explaining the real reasons why women brewers became marginalised, while also debunking some tired old myths along the way.

RRP: £16.99   **ISBN**: 978-1-85249-386-8

For this and other books on beer and pubs, visit CAMRA's online bookshop at **shop1.camra.org.uk** or call 01727 867201.

Discounts are available for CAMRA members.

London index

*shown on Inner London map

GREATER LONDON

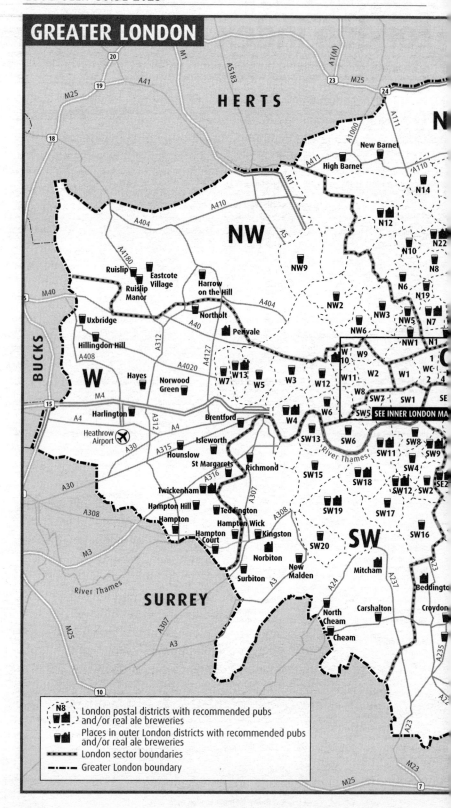

HERTS

NW

W

SW

BUCKS

SURREY

New Barnet
High Barnet

N14
N12
N10
N22
N6
N8
N19
NW9
NW2
NW3
NW5
N7
NW6
NW1
NW10
W9
W10
W2
W1
WC2
W11
W8
SW7
SW1
SW5
W13
W7
W5
W3
W12
SE
SW13
SW6
SW8
SW11
SW9
SW15
SW18
SW4
SW12
SW2
SE2
SW19
SW17
SW16
SW20

SEE INNER LONDON MA

Ruislip
Eastcote Village
Ruislip Manor
Harrow on the Hill
Northolt
Uxbridge
Perivale
Hillingdon Hill
Hayes
Norwood Green
Harlington
Heathrow Airport
Brentford
Isleworth
Hounslow
St Margarets
Richmond
Twickenham
Hampton Hill
Teddington
Hampton
Hampton Wick
Hampton Court
Kingston
Norbiton
Surbiton
New Malden
Mitcham
Beddingto
North Cheam
Carshalton
Croydon
Cheam

River Thames

W4
W6

Legend

N8 — London postal districts with recommended pubs and/or real ale breweries

Places in outer London districts with recommended pubs and/or real ale breweries

•••••• London sector boundaries

–•–•– Greater London boundary

ENGLAND

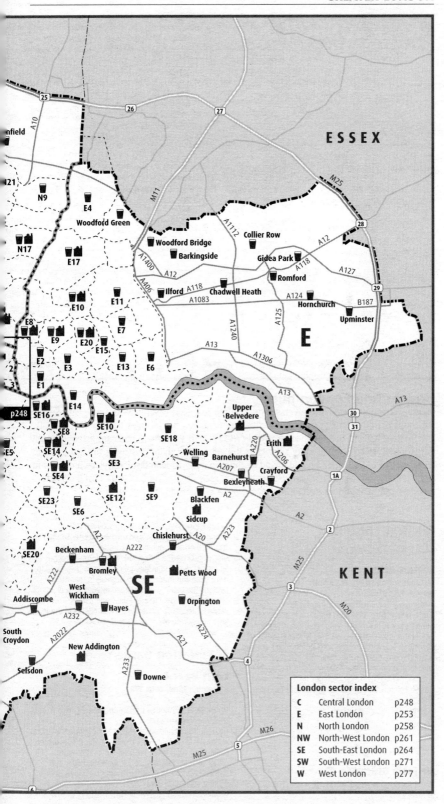

ESSEX

 nfield

N9

E4

Woodford Green

Woodford Bridge

N17

E17

Barkingside

Collier Row

Gidea Park

Romford

Ilford

Chadwell Heath

Hornchurch

E10

E11

Upminster

E8

E9

E20

E7

E

E2

E15

E3

E13

E6

E1

E14

SE16

p248

Upper
Belvedere

SE8

SE10

SE18

Erith

SE5

SE14

Welling

Barnehurst

Crayford

SE4

SE3

Bexleyheath

SE23

SE12

SE9

Blackfen

SE6

Sidcup

Chislehurst

SE20

Beckenham

Petts Wood

Bromley

SE

Addiscombe

West
Wickham

Orpington

South
Croydon

Hayes

New Addington

Selsdon

Downe

KENT

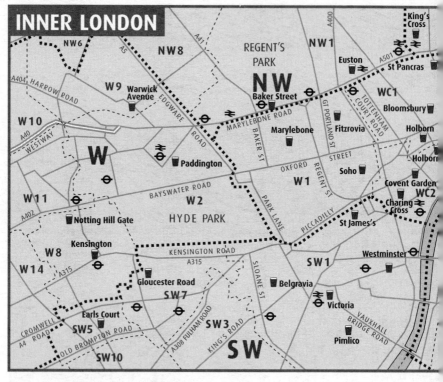

How to find London pubs

Greater London is divided into seven sectors: Central, East, North, North-West, South-East, South-West and West, reflecting postal boundaries. The Central sector includes the City (EC1 to EC4) and Holborn, Covent Garden and the Strand (WC1/2) plus W1, where pubs are listed in postal district order. In each of the other six sectors the pubs with London postcodes are listed first in postal district order (E1, E2 etc), followed by those in outer London districts, which are listed in alphabetical order (Barking, Chadwell Heath, etc) – see Greater London map. Postal district numbers can be found on every street name plate in the London postcode area.

CENTRAL LONDON
EC1: Clerkenwell

Sutton Arms
16 Great Sutton Street, EC1V 0DH
☎ (020) 7253 2462
3 changing beers (often Five Points) Ⓗ
A free house since 1991, this former Whitbread pub is named after 17th-century plutocrat Thomas Sutton who founded nearby Charterhouse. This is your traditional after-work bar, a corner pub with side bar and upstairs function room. Besides the three cask beers and KeyKeg from local breweries, there is a range of foreign bottled beers. A tap takeover is sometimes held for breweries outside London. Pies and sausage rolls are available. There is some outside seating.
ॐ❀≠⊖(Barbican) ●🚆❀ 🛜

EC1: Farringdon

Sir John Oldcastle ✔
29-35 Farringdon Road, EC1M 3JF
☎ (020) 7242 1013

Greene King IPA, Abbot; Sharp's Doom Bar; 3 changing beers (often Adnams, Rooster's, Titanic) Ⓗ
This Wetherspoon pub is named after the Sir John Oldcastle Tavern, which stood in the former grounds of Sir John's nearby mansion. John Oldcastle is thought to have been the model for Shakespeare's character, Falstaff. The pub has an L-shaped interior with plenty of seating in the usual mix of tables and booths. There are various interesting framed prints and photos of the local area around the premises. Q🏃🛇⊕≠⊖🚆🛜

EC1: Hatton Garden

Craft Beer Co. ★
82 Leather Lane, EC1N 7TR
☎ (020) 7404 7049
House beer (by Kent); 8 changing beers (often Exale, Redemption, Siren) Ⓗ
Grade II-listed building identified by CAMRA as having a nationally important historic pub interior. Below a glass ceiling and chandelier, the long bar of this popular pub offers several cask ales, 20 keg fonts and over 100 bottled beers, as well as bag in box real ciders. Most seating is on high stools and it can get busy in the evenings with an after-work crowd. Snacks comprise

crisps, nuts, olives and pork pies. Alternatively, pizza can be ordered from nearby to be delivered. Closed Sunday.
☺✿⇄(Farringdon) ⊖(Chancery Lane/Farringdon)
🚿📶🐾📶

Olde Mitre ★ 🅛

1 Ely Court, Ely Place, EC1N 6SJ
☎ (020) 7405 4751 ⊕ yeoldemitreholborn.co.uk
Fuller's London Pride; 5 changing beers (often Brentwood, Kent, Windsor & Eton) ⊞
This ancient pub is located down an alley off Hatton Garden and can be hard to find the first time. The current building dates from the 18th century and has been identified by CAMRA as having a nationally important historic pub interior, with two bars and an upstairs function room, reached by a narrow staircase. A beer from the wood is often available: check the website for details. Snacks include toasties and sausage rolls. Closed at weekends.
Q✿⇄(City Thameslink) ⊖(Chancery Lane/Farringdon)
♣🚿🐾📶

EC1: Old Street

Old Fountain 🅛

3 Baldwin Street, EC1V 9NU
☎ (020) 7253 2970 ⊕ oldfountain.co.uk
4 changing beers (sourced nationally) ⊞
A privately owned free house, in the same family since 1964, and popular with workers from the nearby Silicon Roundabout. Adorned with stained glass windows at front and back, the split-level bar serves real ale as well as real cider, and 20 keg lines including Belgian and German beers. The roof terrace, with parasols and outdoor heaters, is an oasis in the city. A small menu, focused on pub classics and burgers, is served daily.
☺✿⇄⊖♣🚿🐾📶

EC1: Smithfield

Bishop's Finger

9-10 West Smithfield, EC1A 9JR
☎ (020) 7248 2341 ⊕ thebishopsfinger.co.uk
Shepherd Neame Spitfire, Bishops Finger; 1 changing beer (often Shepherd Neame) ⊞
The pub is named after direction signposts in Kent which pointed pilgrims on their way. Downstairs is a single bar, upstairs a function/dining room along with the toilets. The pub is traditional in feel with wooden furniture and an array of pictures on the walls. There are a couple of tables outside at the front. Food is available from a classic pub menu, with the meat from nearby Smithfield Market. Closed at weekends. ✿⇄⊖(Farringdon)📶🐾📶

Viaduct Tavern ★

126 Newgate Street, EC1A 7AA
☎ (020) 7600 1863 ⊕ viaducttavern.co.uk
Fuller's London Pride, ESB; Gale's Seafarers Ale; 1 changing beer (often Green Duck, St Austell) ⊞
Identified by CAMRA as having a nationally important historic interior, this Grade II-listed Victorian gin palace was built on the site of the old Newgate Prison; its reputedly haunted cellars include remains of the cells. Surrounding the single horseshoe bar is a mixture of tables and booths, with extra seating on the pavement outside and on the roof. A wide choice of gins is available. Although closed on Sundays, the pub can be hired at weekends.
☺✿⇄(City Thameslink) ⊖(St Paul's)📶🐾📶

EC2: Liverpool Street

Hamilton Hall ⊘

Unit 32, Street-level Concourse, Liverpool Street Station, EC2M 7PY
☎ (020) 7247 3579
Greene King IPA, Abbot; Sharp's Doom Bar; 7 changing beers (sourced nationally) ⊞
Once a ballroom, now a Wetherspoon pub that has retained a lavish interior. Real ale is dispensed from 10 handpumps on the entrance-level bar and five on the upstairs bar. An extensive food menu is served all day. There is an outside seating area and children are welcome during the day. The pub can sometimes be very busy. TV screens show train departure and arrival times.
Q☺✿⇄♿⇄⊖🐾📶

Lord Aberconway

72 Old Broad Street, EC2M 1QT
☎ (020) 7929 1743
Fuller's London Pride; St Austell Nicholson's Pale Ale; Sharp's Doom Bar; 2 changing beers (often Harvey's, Timothy Taylor, Titanic) ⊞
A dark panelled, Victorian M&B Nicholson's house named after a chairman of the Metropolitan Railway. Steeped in railwayana, it includes a departure screen for adjacent Liverpool Street Station. A beer library houses a collection of interesting books. Leather bench seats are available in the numerous booths and a gallery provides extra seating. The food menu is traditional. Wheelchair users can access the main bar but a stairway leads to the toilets. Closed Sundays. ⇄⇄⊖🐾📶📶

EC3: Aldgate

Craft Beer Co.

29-31 Mitre Street, EC3A 5BZ
☎ (020) 7929 5112
House beer (by Kent); 2 changing beers (sourced nationally) ⊞

A city pub with wooden floorboards and bare brick walls adorned with mirrors from Bass and Burton breweries. There are high tables and stools in the upstairs bar and more seating downstairs. The 18 keg lines include cider, and a range of bottled beers is available. Scotch eggs are offered as bar snacks. Toilets are downstairs. The pub is closed at weekends but available for private hire.
≥(Fenchurch Street) ⊖(Aldgate/Aldgate East) ●🚋🕮🌐🛜

EC3: Gracechurch Street

Counting House
50 Cornhill, EC3V 3PD
☎ (020) 7283 7123 ⊕ the-counting-house.com
Fuller's Oliver's Island, London Pride, ESB; Gale's Seafarers Ale; 1 changing beer (often Dark Star, Fuller's) ⊞
Hotel, restaurant and pub converted from a bank in 1997 and refurbished in 2023. Opulent furnishings and fittings include leather seating, an impressive mural, marble wall tiles and large mirrors. Note the mosaic flooring leading from the entrance. A glass dome above the oval island bar complements the stylish lighting. Curved wooden stairs lead to mezzanine level seating and upstairs toilets. Four side rooms are open and available for hire.
🌑🍴🕮🛜≥(Cannon St/Liverpool St) ⊖(Bank/Monument) 🚋🕮🛜

Crosse Keys 🅛 ⊘
7-12 Gracechurch Street, EC3V 0DR
☎ (020) 7623 4824
Fuller's London Pride; Greene King IPA, Abbot; Sharp's Doom Bar; 8 changing beers (often Green Jack, Orkney, Sambrook's) ⊞
Housed in a grandiose building that used to be the headquarters of a banking corporation, this Wetherspoon pub is named after an old coaching inn. Handpumps dispense up to 12 rotating guest ales and two ciders. The ales are listed on TV screens above the bar and are ordered by pump number. There are function rooms to the rear. A spiral staircase leads down to the toilets.
Q🌑🍴🕮≥(Cannon St/Fenchurch St) ⊖(Bank/Monument) 🚋🛜

EC3: Tower Hill

Ship ⊘
3 Hart Street, EC3R 7NB
☎ (020) 7702 4422 ⊕ shipec3.co.uk
Fuller's London Pride; St Austell Tribute; Timothy Taylor Landlord; 1 changing beer (often Adnams) ⊞
A cosy bar with a nautical theme. Seating is provided by tall bar stools alongside round tables and barrels. Look up to see the multitude of sailors' hats, each with a ship's name on its brim. The pub, with its opulent upstairs function room, is closed at weekends but available for private hire. Bar snacks such as filled rolls are usually available. The Gents toilet is down a tightly spiralled staircase while the Ladies is upstairs.
≥(Fenchurch St) ⊖(Tower Gateway/Tower Hill) ♣🚋🕮🛜

EC4: Blackfriars

Cockpit
7 St Andrew's Hill, EC4V 5BY
☎ (020) 7248 7315
St Austell Tribute, Proper Job; Shepherd Neame Whitstable Bay Pale Ale; Timothy Taylor Landlord ⊞
Small pub on an old corner site, adapted from one of the Blackfriars monastery's gateways and most recently rebuilt circa 1865. Its shape recreates that of a cockpit and fighting cock prints adorn the walls. By the time cockfighting was prohibited in 1849, the pub had been renamed the Three Castles; it reverted in 1970. Enter by the corner door to a drinking area with a curved bar up a few stairs. Galleries above are inaccessible. ≥⊖⊖

EC4: Cannon Street

Bell ⊘
29 Bush Lane, EC4R 0AN
☎ (020) 7283 0029
Harvey's Sussex Best Bitter; Timothy Taylor Landlord; 1 changing beer (often Adnams) ⊞
No-nonsense, one-bar drinking house near Cannon Street station. Copper pots and pans hang from the ceiling. On the back wall is a list of former licensees going back

REAL ALE BREWERIES

40FT ✦ E8: Dalston
Affinity ✦ SW9: Stockwell (brewing suspended)
Anspach & Hobday Beddington
Battersea ✦ SE16: South Bermondsey
Battersea ✦ SW11: Battersea Power Station
Beerblefish ✦ E17: Walthamstow
Belleville SW12: Wandsworth Common
Bexley Erith
Brewhouse & Kitchen 🍺 E2: Hoxton
Brewhouse & Kitchen 🍺 N5: Highbury
Brixton SE24: Loughborough Junction
Brixton ✦ SW9: Brixton
Brockley ✦ SE4: Brockley
Brockley ✦ SE12: Hither Green
Broken Drum Upper Belvedere
Clarkshaws ✦ SW9: Loughborough Junction
Cronx New Addington
Drop Project ✦ Mitcham
East London E10: Leyton
Five Points ✦ E8: Hackney
Forest Road ✦ SE14: South Bermondsey
Fuller's ✦ W4: Chiswick
Goodness ✦ N22: Wood Green
Hammerton ✦ N7: Barnsbury
Howling Hops ✦ E9: Hackney Wick

Kernel SE16: Bermondsey
Libertalia ✦ E10: Leyton (NEW)
London Beer Lab SW9: Loughborough Junction
London Brewing 🍺 N12: North Finchley
Marko Paulo 🍺 W13: Northfields
Marlix Petts Wood
Mutineers Bromley
Park ✦ Norbiton
Perivale ✦ Perivale
Portobello W10: North Kensington
Redemption ✦ N17: Tottenham
Sambrook's ✦ SW18: Wandsworth
Signal ✦ Beddington
Signature ✦ E17: Walthamstow
Small Beer ✦ SE16: South Bermondsey
Southey ✦ SE20: Penge
Southwark ✦ SE1: Bermondsey
Tankleys Sidcup
Tap East 🍺 E20: Stratford Westfield
Temple Brew House 🍺 🍺 WC2: Temple
Twickenham ✦ Twickenham
Up The Creek 🍺 SE10: Greenwich
Villages ✦ SE8: Deptford
Wild Card ✦ E17: Walthamstow
Wimbledon ✦ SW19: Colliers Wood

centuries. Televised sports are quietly shown with tasteful background music gently playing. Pie and mash dominates the menu. A small upstairs eating area doubles up as a function room that is available for hire. Closed at weekends. ⏰◑≠⊖🚃❀🏵

Pelt Trader
Arch 3, Dowgate Hill, EC4N 6AP
☎ (020) 7160 0253 ⊕ pelttrader.com
3 changing beers (often Burning Sky, Iron Pier, Redemption) Ⓐ
Nestled under an archway on the west side of Cannon Street station, this independent venue offers a variety of ales and a cider on cask, and up to 14 keg taps showcasing modern craft beer and cider. Decorative mirrors and pictures portray pelt traders, and a canoe hangs from the ceiling. Pizzas are available. Family and dog friendly, the pub can get very busy in the evenings with the city trade. Closed at weekends.
⏰❀◑≠⊖🚃❀🏵

EC4: Temple
Old Bank of England Ⓛ
194 Fleet Street, EC4A 2LT
☎ (020) 7430 2255
McMullen AK Original Mild, Country Bitter; 1 changing beer (often McMullen) Ⓗ
A Grade II-listed building belonging to the Bank of England until 1975 and then the Bristol & West Building Society. After a period as a Fuller's pub, their lease reverted in 2019 to owners McMullens, who refurbished it in early 2020. The ornate high ceiling and gallery now contrast with a modern metalwork island bar. There are two function areas but the whole pub may sometimes be booked, so do check before any special visit. Closed Sundays. ⏰❀◑≠(City Thameslink)⊖🚃❀🏵

WC1: Bloomsbury
Perseverance Ⓛ ✅
63 Lambs Conduit Street, WC1N 3NB
☎ (020) 7405 8278 ⊕ theperseverance.co.uk
Timothy Taylor Landlord; 2 changing beers (often Portobello, Sambrook's, Southwark) Ⓗ
This Grade II-listed building, a free house owned by Market Taverns since 2016, was once the legendary real ale house the Sun. In summer, three of the handpumps may be used for real cider. There is an outside seating area and a quieter dining/function room upstairs. Try their famous thin-based pizzas (not served Sun).
⏰❀◑👶⊖(Russell Square)●🚃❀

Swan ✅
7 Cosmo Place, WC1N 3AP
☎ (020) 7837 6223
Greene King IPA; Morland Old Speckled Hen; Timothy Taylor Landlord; Theakston Old Peculier; 2 changing beers (often Black Sheep, Greene King, St Austell) Ⓗ
Popular, lively family-oriented venue among the tourist hotels on Southampton Row, close to Great Ormond Street Children's Hospital and the lovely Queen Square constructed between 1716 and 1725. It has a single long room and tables at the front on the pedestrianised passage. Seven handpumps offer three to four regular real ales and up to three guest beers. An extensive menu of pub grub and snacks is served all day. A largescreen TV shows live sports events.
Q⏰❀◑👶⊖(Russell Square)🚃❀🏵

WC1: Holborn
Craft Beer Co.
168 High Holborn, WC1V 7AA
☎ (020) 7836 5485
Kent Pale, Kent Golding Bitter; 8 changing beers (sourced nationally) Ⓗ
Though in the ancient parish of St Giles, whose church featured in several of Hogarth's etchings including Gin Lane, this pub on the north-eastern edge of Covent Garden has a modern resonance. Over two levels, the sixth Craft Beer Co outlet would be more at home in Beer Street, with its many handpumps dispensing a changing range of ales from across the UK. There are frequent tap takeovers and Meet the Brewer events.
❀⊖(Covent Garden/Holborn)●🚃

WC1: St Pancras
Queen's Head ★ Ⓛ
66 Acton Street, WC1X 9NB
☎ (020) 7713 8328 ⊕ queensheadlondon.com
Redemption Trinity; 2 changing beers (sourced nationally) Ⓗ
Narrow, late-Georgian premises off Gray's Inn Road, identified by CAMRA as having a nationally important historic pub interior. It has a smoking patio at the rear and benches in front. A piano is used for jazz and blues on Thursday and late Sunday afternoon. One handpump serves cider, with three more real ciders and a range of draught and bottled beers in stock. Sharing snack platters are on offer at this comfortable pub frequented by locals and the occasional tourist. Local CAMRA Pub of the Year 2022. ❀◑≠⊖(King's Cross St Pancras)●🚃🏵♪

WC2: Chancery Lane
Seven Stars ★
51-54 Carey Street, WC2A 2JB
☎ (020) 7242 8521 ⊕ thesevenstars1602.co.uk
Adnams Ghost Ship, Broadside; 1 changing beer (often Dark Star, Greene King) Ⓗ
Dating from 1602 as the League of Seven Stars, signifying the seven provinces of the Netherlands, this pub has been identified by CAMRA as having a nationally important historic pub interior. With its decorative Victorian bar-back, the narrow bar separates two distinctive drinking areas, one named the Wig Box (the Royal Courts of Justice are nearby). Legendary landlady Roxy Beaujolais serves gastronomic food. Resident cat, General often wears a legal ruffle. The toilets are accessible only via steep stairs.
Q◑≠(City Thameslink) ⊖(Chancery Lane/Temple)🚃🏵

WC2: Charing Cross
Harp Ⓛ
47 Chandos Place, WC2N 4HS
☎ (020) 7836 0291 ⊕ harpcoventgarden.com
Dark Star Hophead; Fuller's London Pride; Harvey's Sussex Best Bitter; 5 changing beers (sourced nationally) Ⓗ
Small, friendly, Fuller's pub where ciders and perries complement the fine beer range. Local CAMRA Pub of the Year in 2023, during its time as a free house run by the late, legendary Binnie Walsh it was CAMRA National Pub of the Year 2010, Greater London's only ever winner of this award. The narrow bar is adorned with mirrors and portraits. There is no intrusive music or TV and a cosy upstairs room provides a refuge from the throng.
Q≠⊖●🚃🏵

Lemon Tree ⊘
4 Bedfordbury, WC2N 4BP
☎ (020) 7831 1391 ⊕ lemontreecoventgarden.com
Harvey's Sussex Best Bitter; 2 changing beers (often St Austell, Sambrook's, Timothy Taylor) ⓗ
A one-bar pub next to the stage door of the Coliseum that is a favourite among locals, musicians and theatregoers. There is a large wall map of London from the 1700s. The Thai restaurant upstairs doubles as a function room. Look out for the pub entrance, slightly set back. In the choice of guest beers there is an emphasis on London brews, by popular demand. It is operated by All Our Bars, a small chain based in Edenbridge.
⓪▬≉⊖🖵🛜

Ship & Shovell
1-3 Craven Passage, WC2N 5PH
☎ (020) 7839 1311 ⊕ shipandshovell.co.uk
Hall & Woodhouse Badger Best Bitter, Fursty Ferret, Tanglefoot; 1 changing beer (often Hall and Woodhouse) ⓗ
Almost beneath Charing Cross station, the two uniquely divided halves of this pub face each other across Craven Passage alleyway between Villiers Street and Craven Street. Acquired by Hall & Woodhouse in 1997, it is named after Admiral Sir Cloudesley Shovell whose fleet was grounded off the Scilly Isles in 1707, drowning him and 2,000 men. That catastrophe is believed to have inspired the Admiralty to offer the Longitude Prize for an accurate nautical timepiece. Closed Sundays.
Q🏠🕭⊕≉⊖🖵🐾🛜

WC2: Covent Garden

Lamb & Flag ★
33 Rose Street, WC2E 9EB
☎ (020) 7497 9504 ⊕ lambandflagcoventgarden.co.uk
Dark Star Hophead; Fuller's Oliver's Island, London Pride, ESB; Gale's Seafarers Ale; 2 changing beers (sourced nationally) ⓗ
Owned by Fuller's since 2013, this Grade II-listed pub remains pleasant and traditional, without piped music or games machines. Tucked away up Rose Street from Garrick Street, it has been identified by CAMRA as having a nationally important historic pub interior, with two dark wood-panelled rooms, the rear one with an attractive fireplace and a connecting passage from the main bar on the ground floor. The upstairs bar and restaurant has table service only. Charles Dickens and Karl Marx were both regulars.
🏠🕭⓪≉(Charing Cross) ⊖(Covent Garden/Leicester Sq) 🖵🐾🛜♪

WC2: Holborn

Shakespeare's Head ⓛ
Africa House, 64-68 Kingsway, WC2B 6BG
☎ (020) 7404 8846
Greene King IPA, Abbot; Sharp's Doom Bar; 6 changing beers (often East London, Twickenham, Windsor & Eton) ⓗ
Large Wetherspoon bank conversion from 1998, named after a famous local pub (until the demolition of Wych Street over 100 years ago). It is usually busy with shoppers, tourists, local office workers and students from the nearby LSE. A convenient place for a couple of pints after your cultural sojourn at the nearby Sir John Soane's Museum. Q🏠🕭⓪🕭⊖🖵🛜

WC2: Temple

Devereux
20 Devereux Court, WC2R 3JJ
☎ (020) 7583 4530 ⊕ thedevereux.co.uk
Fuller's London Pride; 3 changing beers (often Adnams, St Austell, Timothy Taylor) ⓗ
An attractive Grade II-listed pub built in 1844; part of the site was once the Grecian Coffee House. The comfortable lounge with wood panelling has a bar with five handpumps. Prints on the walls show local places of interest and historic figures – the judges and wigs reflecting proximity to the law courts. Upstairs is a restaurant, available for hire. Closed at weekends.
♿🏠🕭≉(City Thameslink) ⊖🖵🛜

Edgar Wallace
40 Essex Street, WC2R 3JF
☎ (020) 7353 3120 ⊕ edgarwallacelondon.co.uk
3 changing beers (often Redemption, St Austell, Southwark) ⓗ
Just off Fleet Street near the Royal Courts of Justice, this is a real gem of a one-room pub, with additional seating upstairs. The comfortable downstairs room, its walls and ceiling covered with beer mats and old advertising signs, has a fine wooden bar offering a range of rotating ales. This quiet pub allows no music, laptops, mobiles or electronic devices. Good-value food is served all day (no food Fri eve). Closed at weekends. Q🏠🕭⓪⊖🖵🐾🛜

W1: Fitzrovia

Stag's Head ★ ⓛ
102 New Cavendish Street, W1W 6XW
☎ (020) 7580 8313
Tring Side Pocket for a Toad; 1 changing beer (often Tring) ⓗ
A smart, oak-panelled pub identified by CAMRA as having a nationally important historic pub interior, offering a friendly welcome to regulars and visitors alike. Rebuilt in the late 1930s by brewers William Younger, it has a marvellous Art Deco exterior, sporting a curved corner profile. Vertical drinking is assisted by unusual peninsular shelf projections to the bar and elsewhere. Sun lovers and smokers can relax on shaded benches outside. Traditional pub food is served at lunchtimes, extending to early evening on Sunday.
🏠🕭⓪⊖(Great Portland St) 🖵

W1: Marylebone

Barley Mow ★
8 Dorset Street, W1U 6QW
☎ (020) 7487 4773 ⊕ barleymowlondon.co.uk
Fuller's London Pride; 4 changing beers (sourced nationally) ⓗ
A Grade II-listed pub dating from 1791, identified by CAMRA as having a nationally important historic interior, most notably retaining two small drinking compartments fronting the main bar counter. Both bars, with their partly bare wood, partly carpeted floors, are furnished with upholstered pews, benches and stools. Original matchboard panelling displays prints of 18th-century Marylebone. Pieminister pies are served on weekday lunchtimes and until evening on Monday and Tuesday.
🏠🕭⓪👫≉⊖(Baker St) ♣🖵🛜

Golden Eagle ★
59 Marylebone Lane, W1U 2NY
☎ (020) 7935 3228
Fuller's London Pride; 2 changing beers (often Elgood's, Otter, Twickenham) ⓗ

First licensed in 1842 and rebuilt in 1890, this single-bar pub is traditional in every way: small and cosy, with smart decor, a fine etched bar-back mirror and leaded windows. It has been identified by CAMRA as having a nationally important historic pub interior. Landlady Gina Vernon and her family celebrated 30 years here in 2021. Piano singalongs on Tuesday, Thursday and Friday evenings maintain the timeless atmosphere. Real ales are quality, not quantity. Closed Sundays.
&⊖(Bond St)🚌♪

Jackalope ★
43 Weymouth Mews, W1G 7EQ
☎ (020) 3455 2871 ⊕ jackalopelondon.com
4 changing beers (often Iron Pier, Redemption, Thornbridge) Ⓗ
One of Marylebone's two remaining mews pubs. Built in 1777 and Grade II-listed, it has been identified by CAMRA as having a nationally important historic pub interior. The mirrors underneath the dividing beam allowed coachmen to observe when their passengers wanted to depart. A sister operation of the Euston Tap, it has London's first Xiao Mian noodle kitchen downstairs, specialising in ramen dishes. A Jackalope is a cross between a jackrabbit and an antelope, a mythical creature of North American folklore. Closed Sundays.
🏳◐⊖(Great Portland St/Regent's Park)🚌❀🛜

W1: Soho

Coach & Horses ★
29 Greek Street, W1D 5DH
☎ (020) 7437 5920 ⊕ coachandhorsessoho.pub
Fuller's London Pride; Gale's Seafarers Ale; 3 changing beers (often Almasty, Burning Sky, Dark Star) Ⓗ
First licensed in 1724, this Grade II-listed pub was most recently rebuilt in 1889. It is thought that a type of shuttle service ran from here to the Smithfield Market area, the main starting-point for horse-drawn coaches going north. The pub has been identifiedby CAMRA as having a nationally important historic pub interior because of its 1930s interior. Following cessation of a previous tenancy, it became a Fuller's managed house. Bar snacks are on offer but no substantial food.
🏳&&⊖(Leicester Sq)🚌❀🛜♪

Dog & Duck ★
18 Bateman Street, W1D 3AJ
☎ (020) 7494 0697
St Austell Nicholson's Pale Ale; Sharp's Doom Bar; 5 changing beers (often St Austell, Sharp's) Ⓗ
In the heart of Soho, this Grade II-listed M&B Nicholson's outlet, built in 1897, has been identified by CAMRA as having a nationally important historic interior. An elaborate mosaic depicts dogs and ducks, and wonderful advertising mirrors adorn the walls. The upstairs Orwell Bar can be hired for functions. The pub is small and so popular, especially with media people, that it is not just smokers who have to drink outside. The bar extends towards the Frith Street door.
◐⊖(Tottenham Court Rd)🚌🛜

Lyric Ⓛ
37 Great Windmill Street, W1D 7LT
☎ (020) 7434 0604 ⊕ lyricsoho.co.uk
Harvey's Sussex Best Bitter; 8 changing beers (often Oakham, Southwark, Tring) Ⓗ
A small, independently owned bar just off Shaftesbury Avenue, bay-fronted with a tiled, panelled interior, popular with local trade. Once two adjacent taverns, the Windmill and the Ham, it merged in the mid-18th century to form the Windmill & Ham, renamed in 1890

and rebuilt 16 years later. Alongside other draught beers, including London specialities, the cask ales come from a wide range of mainly small breweries nationwide, including Big Smoke. 🏳◐⊖(Piccadilly Circus)🚌❀🛜

Old Coffee House Ⓛ
49 Beak Street, W1F 9SF
☎ (020) 7437 2197
3 changing beers (sourced locally) Ⓗ
A large but cosy pub, close to the buzz of Carnaby Street. First licensed as the Silver Street Coffee House, it was rebuilt in 1894 and is now Grade II-listed. The long bar and dark panelling are adorned with Watneys Red Barrel signage, brewery mirrors and sundry prints, posters, pictures and brassware. At lunchtimes you will find good-sized and reasonably-priced portions of pub grub.
🏳❀◐⊖(Piccadilly Circus)🚌❀

Queen's Head Ⓛ
15 Denman Street, W1D 7HN
☎ (020) 7437 1540 ⊕ queensheadpiccadilly.com
Fuller's London Pride; 2 changing beers (often Dark Star, Harvey's, Sambrook's) Ⓗ
A rare West End free house with plenty of vertical drinking space below and a restaurant upstairs. The traditional feel is enhanced by an attractive bar-back and wall mirroring downstairs and an unusual leather-fronted bar in the restaurant. With its real ales, good-value pies and other pub food, including snacks and cheeseboards at the bar, this is a popular pub for both before and after theatre visits. ⊖(Piccadilly Circus)🚌❀🛜

EAST LONDON
E1: Spitalfields

Pride of Spitalfields Ⓛ
3 Heneage Street, E1 5LJ
☎ (020) 7247 8933
Crouch Vale Brewers Gold; Fuller's London Pride, ESB; Sharp's Doom Bar; 1 changing beer (sourced locally; often Five Points) Ⓗ
This back-street local is on a cobbled side street just off Brick Lane. A traditional pub, it is fairly small and can get quite busy in the evenings with standing room only. It has an excellent atmosphere and there is a piano that customers sometimes play. Food is available weekday lunchtimes. The landlady has been here for a number of years and there is always a warm welcome.
🏳⊖(Aldgate East/Shoreditch High St)🚌❀

E1: Wapping

Prospect of Whitby ✅
57 Wapping Wall, E1W 3SH
☎ (020) 7481 1095
Greene King Abbot; 5 changing beers (often St Austell, Southwark, Twickenham) Ⓗ
Grade II-listed Thames-side pub named after a coal boat. The current building is a 1777 rebuild of a 16th-century one all but destroyed by fire. The interior has a flagstone floor and an unusual pewter bar top supported by wooden barrels. There are three more rooms upstairs and a riverside beer garden. Popular with locals and tourists, it is often busy. The pub claims connections with Samuel Pepys and Charles Dickens.
🏳❀◐&⊖(100,D3)❀🛜

Town of Ramsgate ★ Ⓛ
62 Wapping High Street, E1W 2PN
☎ (020) 7481 8000 ⊕ townoframsgate.pub

Harvey's Sussex Best Bitter; Sharp's Doom Bar; Young's London Original; 1 changing beer (often Portobello) Ⓗ

This Grade II-listed pub with a long narrow bar area, comfortable seating and tables throughout has been identified by CAMRA as having a nationally important historic pub interior. A riverside terrace can be found at the rear. The many references to Ramsgate include a magnificent large etched mirror to the left of the entrance, depicting the harbour. Weather watchers can check out the ornate barometer hanging on the wall. Food is served, with a short break between lunch and dinner service. A quiz is held on Monday evening.

🏠🍴🌓👤🚆(100,D3) 🐾

Turner's Old Star
14 Watts Street, E1W 2QG
☎ (020) 3726 5371 ⊕ turnersoldstar.co.uk
3 changing beers (often Brockley, Redemption, Southwark) Ⓗ

A family-run, street-corner free house, named in honour of JMW Turner, the famous landscape artist who once owned the building. The red leather bench seats that abut the walls benefit from light shining through the multi-coloured stained glass windows. A pool table and dartboard complement the two large TVs that show sporting events. Pie and chips comprise the food offering. A covered garden provides the location for occasional small beer festivals.

🏠🍴🌓👤🚆(100,D3) 📶

E2: Bethnal Green

Carpenter's Arms Ⓛ
73 Cheshire Street, E2 6EG
⊕ thecarpentersarms.net
Five Points Best; 1 changing beer (sourced locally; often Orbit) Ⓗ

Small back-street corner pub of a type becoming rare in East London, reputedly once belonging to the notorious Kray twins in the 1960s. Independently owned, it is comfortably furnished and tastefully decorated. Background music is just that and there are no TVs. The two real ales are served alongside kegs and a range of UK and imported bottles. There is a small garden to the rear. Card payments only.

🏠🍴🌓(Bethnal Green/Shoreditch High St) 🚆🐾📶

King's Arms
11A Buckfast Street, E2 6EY
☎ (020) 7729 2627 ⊕ thekingsarmspub.com
4 changing beers (often Iron Pier, Siren, Thornbridge) Ⓗ

A stylish back-street local serving four cask ales regularly, with five at the weekend, together with a dozen keg beers, a large range of bottles and a cider. Pumpclips are not displayed; the beer menu is on the tables and on the wall. The food offering is Scotch eggs and tortillas with cheese or meat. There is some seating outside.

🏠🍴👤🚆(Bethnal Green/Shoreditch High St) 🍴🐾📶

E3: Bow

Coborn
8 Coborn Road, E3 2DA
☎ (020) 8980 3793 ⊕ thecoborn.co.uk
Young's London Original, London Special Ⓗ

Once a Lacons brewery pub, acquired by Young's from Whitbread in 1984 along with the property next door and now a diners' destination. Spacious inside, with a segregated restaurant area to the rear and cosy snug rooms either side of the entrance, it also provides heated

and sheltered seating on a pavement patio outside at the front. There is a quiz night on Sunday.

🏠🍴👤🌓(Bow Rd/Mile End) 🚆🐾📶

E4: Highams Park

Stag & Lantern
11-12 The Broadway, E4 9LQ
☎ (020) 7998 8930 ⊕ thestagandlantern.co.uk
2 changing beers Ⓗ

A welcoming and inclusive community-focused micropub, converted from shops in 2020. The inside is fairly small, with stools made from beer casks. There is also seating outside at the front. Craft beer, cider, bottles and cans are also served, including from the online shop. See the website for opening hours, current beer list and events, including quizzes. Closed Monday and Tuesday. Local CAMRA Pub of the Year 2023. Q🍴🚆🐾

E6: Upton Park

Boleyn Tavern ★
1 Barking Road, E6 1PW
☎ (020) 8472 2182 ⊕ boleyntavern.co.uk
4 changing beers (often Five Points, Purity, Shepherd Neame) Ⓗ

Built by Cannon Brewery in 1899, this former local to West Ham United football club's Boleyn ground closed after the team moved to the London Stadium but reopened in 2021 after a spectacular £1.5m restoration by Remarkable Pubs with the aim of making the interior look like it was when it first opened. Hand-crafted wooden screens with acid-etched cut glass have been recreated to restore the original seven-bar layout, and the pub has been identified by CAMRA as having a nationally important historic pub interior. The highlight is a massive coloured skylight in the rear dining area. The Grade II-listed building is floodlit at night, making it visible from a distance. 🏠🍴🌓👤🚆🐾📶

E7: Forest Gate

Holly Tree
141 Dames Road, E7 0DZ
☎ (020) 8221 9830 ⊕ thehollytreepub.co.uk
Shepherd Neame Whitstable Bay Pale Ale, Spitfire; 2 changing beers (often Five Points) Ⓗ

A large community pub refurbished in 2019 by Remarkable Pubs in a traditional style, with an outside conservatory and spacious garden. Besides the beer and food menu, the single bar offers a real cider from Oliver's on handpump. A miniature train runs round the garden at weekends – see website for times – provided the weather is good, and accommodates riders of all ages, but note that some areas of this family-friendly pub are off-limits to children.

🏠🍴👤(Wanstead Park) 🍴🚆(58,308) 🐾📶

E8: Hackney

Cock Tavern Ⓛ
315 Mare Street, E8 1EJ
⊕ thecocktavern.co.uk
8 changing beers (sourced locally; often Howling Hops) Ⓗ

A bustling, friendly town-centre single-roomed pub with a small beer garden. There has been a pub called the Cock Tavern in Hackney since the 1650s. This one was built by Truman's in the 1930s. Eight of the 16 handpumps dispense a changing range of real ciders. A wide KeyKeg beer selection is also available. Food can be brought in from outside, supplementing the range of

pickled eggs available as snacks. Local CAMRA Cider Pub of the Year 2024.
♿❀⇘(Downs) ⊖(Central/Downs) ●🅿❀🛜

Five Points Brewery Taproom L
61 Mare Street, E8 4RG
☎ (020) 8533 7746 ● fivepointsbrewing.co.uk
2 changing beers (often Five Points)
Based at the brewery warehouse on Mare Street, this taproom has a vibrant atmosphere, with seating downstairs and on the mezzanine level as well as outside in the yard in the summer. There are 18 beers available from Five Points, mostly in keg format. The food offering is from ACE pizzas. You can also prebook a brewery tour, hosted weekly – see the website for dates and times. Closed Monday to Wednesday.
♿❶♿⊖(Cambridge Heath) 🅿🛜

Hackney Tap
354 Mare Street, E8 1HR
☎ (020) 3026 4373 ● hackneytap.com
3 changing beers (often Five Points, Hammerton, Rooster's) 🅷
This interesting building has been a town hall, a bank and a bookmakers. Original features are still in place: the panelling on the bar is from when it was a bank. On the outside you can see the logos from the previous incarnations. Besides the variety of changing cask beers, up to 20 keg choices are on offer, plus gyoza dumplings. Plenty of outside seating is available.
♿❀❶⇘(Downs) ⊖(Central/Downs) ●🅿🛜

Old Ship Inn
2 Sylvester Path, E8 1EN
☎ (020) 8986 2732 ● oldshiphackney.com
3 changing beers (often Five Points, Redemption, Twickenham) 🅷
A pub and kitchen, combined with a hotel and helpfully accessible via an alleyway from Mare Street opposite Morning Lane. Two skylights generate a light and airy atmosphere. The walls are decorated with an eclectic mix of pictures, mirrors and artwork. Tables and chairs are plentiful alongside leather wall-benches. One of the three handpumps dispenses a real cider. Food is served all day, with a short break in service on weekday afternoons.
🛏❶⇘(Downs) ⊖(Central/Downs) ♣●🅿❀🛜

Pembury Tavern L
90 Amhurst Road, E8 1JH
☎ (020) 8986 8597 ● pemburytavern.co.uk
Five Points Pale, Railway Porter; 3 changing beers (sourced nationally; often Five Points) 🅷
A large corner pub with a friendly vibe, run by Five Points brewery. The spacious interior with wooden floors is comfortably furnished. Apart from cask beers, there are also 16 keg lines. Pizzas are available, with meat, vegetarian and vegan options. The pub is famous locally for its bar billiards table. There are quiz nights on Monday and occasional comedy nights. Check the website for upcoming events. Card payments only.
♿❶♿⇘(Downs) ⊖(Central/Downs) ♣●🅿❀🛜

E9: Homerton

Chesham Arms
15 Mehetabel Road, E9 6DU
☎ (020) 8986 6717 ● cheshamarms.com
4 changing beers (sourced nationally) 🅷
A lovely and friendly traditional back-street local that was saved from closure. It now sits at the heart of the community, with book swaps and occasional singalongs at the piano. The cosy atmosphere inside is enhanced by

two real fires. There is a large and attractive garden at the back. Four changing ales and one cider are on offer in winter; three and two respectively in the summer. Food can be ordered in from Yard Sale Pizzas.
♿❀❶⊖(Hackney Central) ♣●🅿❀🛜

E10: Leyton

Coach & Horses
391 High Road, E10 5NA
☎ (020) 8194 0332 ● thecoachleyton.com
Crouch Vale Brewers Gold; Mighty Oak Captain Bob; 4 changing beers (often East London, Purity) 🅷
A recently refurbished pub with a horseshoe bar. Some beers from London breweries are among those on the handpumps and 20 keg fonts. There is ample seating in the two rooms and rear beer garden. The menu includes speciality burgers, pies and Sunday roasts. Sport is shown on multiple screens. The pub gets busy on Leyton Orient match days, when it is for home fans only.
♿❀❶⊖●🅿❀🛜♪

Leyton Orient Supporters Club L
Breyer Group Stadium, Oliver Road, E10 5NF
☎ (020) 8988 8288 ● orientsupporters.org
Mighty Oak Oscar Wilde G; 10 changing beers 🅷
Multi award-winning club, previously a CAMRA national finalist, and local CAMRA Club of the Year 2024. It is open on home match days (not during the matches) and for some England football fixtures, but also hosts four brewery ale nights every year. It can get extremely busy but the volunteer staff are efficient. On match days CAMRA members may need to show their membership card; other events are open to all. Q♿❀⊖●🅿

E11: Leytonstone

North Star ♈ ★ L
24 Browning Road, E11 3AR
☎ 07747 010013 ● northstar.pub
East London Foundation Bitter; Oakham JHB; 4 changing beers (often Harvey's, Timothy Taylor) 🅷
A traditional glass-fronted pub in the Leytonstone Village Conservation Area, it has been identified by CAMRA as having a nationally important historic pub interior. The various cask ales, keg and other drinks are dispensed in the smaller saloon bar and can be ordered from the public bar hatch. There is ample seating in the public bar, outside in front and in the walled garden at the rear. Food is traditional Thai and stonebaked pizza. Local CAMRA Pub of the Year 2024. Closed on Mondays in winter. ♿❀❶⊖♣🅿

E13: Plaistow

Black Lion ★ ✅
59-61 High Street, E13 0AD
☎ (020) 8472 2351 ● blacklionplaistow.co.uk
Mighty Oak Captain Bob; 3 changing beers (often Adnams, Sharp's, Timothy Taylor) 🅷
Former coaching inn, rebuilt in 1747, it has been identified by CAMRA as having a nationally important historic pub interior, comprising a split-level main bar and small back bar, both with beams and wood panelling. The back bar has its own door or can be accessed via the serving area. The cobbled courtyard leads to converted stables and outbuildings that house a function room, available for hire. The pub has had the same landlord for over 35 years and is still busy for West Ham United home games. ♿❀❶⊖♣🅿🅿🛜

E14: Limehouse

Grapes ★
76 Narrow Street, E14 8BP
☎ (020) 7987 4396 ⊕ thegrapes.co.uk
Timothy Taylor Landlord; 4 changing beers (often Otter, Theakston) ⊞
Backing on to the River Thames near Limehouse basin, this small, narrow, Grade II-listed building has been identified by CAMRA as having a nationally important historic pub interior. There has been a pub here for nearly 500 years. It makes a (barely disguised) appearance in Our Mutual Friend; Charles Dickens, whose portrait is on the wall, knew the area well. There are two floors, a heated riverside deck and an extensive bar food menu. Under-18s are not admitted.
Q⚭✿◐≠(Limehouse) ⊖(Westferry) ◻✿

E15: Stratford

Olde Black Bull
13 Broadway, E15 4BQ
☎ (020) 8519 6720
2 changing beers (often St Austell, Timothy Taylor) ⊞
A friendly welcome awaits in this East End landmark, popular with shoppers thanks to its location opposite Stratford Mall. Ceiling-height etched windows illuminate the wood and glass-panelled bar. Most of the floorspace is furnished with tables and chairs. Images of old Stratford complement Irish drink adverts. At the back is a small canopied garden with six picnic benches. Sports is shown on multiple TV screens. It gets busy when West Ham United are at home. ✿≠⊖(Stratford/High St)◻

E17: Blackhorse Lane

Beerblefish Brewing Taproom ⅃
Unit 2A-4, Uplands Business Park, E17 5QJ
☎ 07594 383195 ⊕ beerblefish.co.uk/taproom
4 changing beers (often Beerblefish)
A spacious bar, sharing the space with the brewery in part of an old factory building, where you are sure to be welcomed. The range of beers varies but often includes heritage beers from 19th-century recipes. Community events include sip sip knit craft sessions on the first Sunday of every month. Shuffleboard and a wide variety of board games are available. Closed on Monday and Tuesday. ⏁✿♿⊖(Blackhorse Rd)♣●P◻◻(158)✿✿

E17: Higham Hill

Tavern on the Hill ⅃
318 Higham Hill Road, E17 5RG
☎ (020) 3524 0747 ⊕ tavernonthehill.co.uk
Wild Card Best, Pale; 1 changing beer ⊞
Perched atop Higham Hill, overlooking Walthamstow, this is a large, essentially one-room pub with pillars breaking up the space. There is a traditional red brick fireplace and the Warrant Officer sign (its previous name) occupies pride of place. Reopened after renovation during lockdown, the Tavern is now operated by Wild Card brewery. There is a huge outside seating area to the side, back and front. Various events take place – see Instagram for details. ✿◐♣●◻(W15)✿✿♫

E17: Walthamstow

Nag's Head ⅃
9 Orford Road, E17 9LP
☎ (020) 8520 9709 ⊕ nagsheadwalthamstow.co.uk
Timothy Taylor Landlord; 2 changing beers (sourced locally; often East London) ⊞

A cat-friendly pub with a pleasant, relaxed atmosphere, in the heart of Walthamstow Village Conservation Area. It has a courtyard garden at the rear and outside seating at the front. Food consists mainly of burgers during the week, with pizzas at the weekend and a roast on Sundays. Bottled beers include gluten-free options. There is live jazz on Sundays. Children are allowed in the garden until evening and there are bike racks by the side entrance. ⏁✿◐●(Central)◻(W12)✿♫

Olde Rose & Crown ⅃ ✅
53-55 Hoe Street, E17 4SA
☎ (020) 8509 3880 ⊕ yeolderoseandcrowntheatrepub.co.uk
5 changing beers (sourced nationally; often East London) ⊞
A large, welcoming community pub, free of tie. A theatre upstairs and a function room downstairs host a range of community activities. There is live music at weekends and sometimes mid-week. Freshly cooked Grenadian cuisine is available on Tuesday, Thursday and Saturday evenings, with roasts on Sunday afternoons. Regular beer festivals are held. The pub offers so much to enjoy, and its popularity is a tribute to the management and staff. ⏁✿◐⊖(Central)♣●◻✿♫

Queen's Arms
42 Orford Road, E17 9NJ
☎ (020) 8520 9184 ⊕ queensarms-e17.co.uk
2 changing beers (often Five Points, New River, Redemption) ⊞
A friendly back-street gastropub with rear restaurant and front pub areas. Tables and chairs cover the floorspace, with some stools at the bar. Outside seating is available on the front pavement with further bench tables in the paved summer garden at the back. Note the collection of beer mats and pumpclips above the bar. The art prints hanging in the back room are for sale. Two predominantly local ales are complemented by a real cider in summer. ⏁✿◐⊖(Central)●◻✿

E20: Stratford Westfield

Tap East ⅃
7 International Square, Montfichet Road, E20 1EE
☎ (020) 8555 4467 ⊕ tapeast.co.uk
3 changing beers (often Tap East)
Opposite the Stratford International station entrance, this brewpub is furnished with sofas, high tables and chairs, with the brewery visible from the bar. Having the West Ham United stadium nearby, it gets busy on match days, usually the only time for guest cask ales. Many keg and bottled beers are available. There is no food but there are numerous eating places nearby. Major sporting events are shown on TV. Children are admitted but not dogs. Card payments only.
⏁✿♿≠⊖(Stratford/Stratford Intl)●P◻✿

Barkingside

New Fairlop Oak ✅
Fencepiece Road, Fulwell Cross, IG6 2JP
☎ (020) 8500 2217
Greene King Abbot; Ruddles Best Bitter; Sharp's Doom Bar; 7 changing beers (sourced nationally) ⊞
A Wetherspoon pub that puts customers and real ale first, with six handpulled guests waiting for eager patrons ready to quench their thirst. It is named after an oak tree that was replanted in 1909; the original was one of Britain's largest trees and is thought to have been named by Queen Anne on a 1704 visit to the Fairlop Fair.
⏁✿◐♿⊖(Fairlop) P◻✿

Chadwell Heath

Eva Hart ✅
1128 High Road, RM6 4AH
☎ (020) 8597 1069
Greene King Abbot; Ruddles Best Bitter; Sharp's Doom Bar; 4 changing beers (often Adnams, Fuller's) Ⓗ
Large and comfortable split-level Wetherspoon pub, divided into several distinct drinking areas. The building dates from 1892 and used to be the local police station. It is named after a local musical personality who was one of the longest-living survivors of the 1912 Titanic disaster; photographs and memorabilia are on display around the pub. Alcoholic drinks are served from 9am, food all day. Toilets (except accessible) are upstairs. Muted TVs show subtitles. Q ➰ ⚘ ◑ ♿ ⊖ P 🖵 🛜

Collier Row

Colley Rowe Inn ✅
54-56 Collier Row Road, RM5 3PA
☎ (01708) 760633
Greene King Abbot; Ruddles Best Bitter; Sharp's Doom Bar; 3 changing beers (sourced nationally) Ⓗ
Converted by Wetherspoon from two shops, the pub is close to bus routes, giving easy access to and from Romford. It has a changing selection of guest ales and is often lively around the bar, but there are quieter alcoves at the rear. Alcoholic drinks are served from 9am. Food is served all day, every day and steak night is particularly popular. ◑ ♿ 🖵 🛜

Gidea Park

Gidea Park Micropub 🏆
236 Main Road, RM2 5HA
Wibblers Apprentice; 6 changing beers (sourced nationally) Ⓖ
Havering Borough and East London's second micropub opened in 2017 after winning a planning appeal for the change of use. Five to eight cask ales from microbreweries are served (in all legal measures) from the ground-floor cellar, alongside Keykeg beers, real ciders, wines and gins. There are high and low tables and chairs, unusual spider lighting and an ever-growing display of pumpclips from beers sold here. Mobile phones should be silent. Local CAMRA Pub of the Year 2024. Q ➰ ⚘ ♿ ⊖ ● 🖵 (174,498) ❀ 🛜

Ship ✅
93 Main Road, RM2 5EL
☎ (01708) 741571 ⊕ theshipgideapark.co.uk
Greene King IPA; Sharp's Doom Bar; Timothy Taylor Landlord; 1 changing beer (sourced nationally) Ⓗ
More than 260 years old, this Grade II-listed split-level pub has extensive dark wood panelling, timber beams and huge fireplaces. The building is largely unchanged and has low ceilings in places. It is a family-run business with home-cooked food. Quiz nights are held on Thursday and live music is hosted on Saturday. ➰ ⚘ ◑ ⊖ P 🖵 (174,498) ❀ 🛜 ♪

Hornchurch

Hop Inn Ⓛ
122-124 North Street, RM11 1SU
☎ 07888 622532 ⊕ hopinnhornchurch.co.uk
5 changing beers (sourced nationally) Ⓖ
Havering Borough's third micropub, opened in 2019, now has a snug room in the former Hop Shop off licence. Cask ales are dispensed from cooled cabinets behind the bar,

KeyKeg beers, ciders and perry are served in all legal measures, plus craft beer cans and bottles, wines, gins and malt whiskies. No under-18s are admitted and mobile phones must be on silent! A recent local CAMRA Pub of the Year winner, twice regional winner and 2022 National Cider Pub of the Year. Closed Mondays. Q ⊖ (Emerson Park) ♣ ● P 🖵 🛜 ❀

J.J. Moon's
48-52 High Street, RM12 4UN
☎ (01708) 478410
Greene King IPA, Abbot; Sharp's Doom Bar; 5 changing beers (sourced nationally) Ⓗ
A busy Wetherspoon pub, opened in 1993 and popular with all age groups, featuring a good variety of ales with an emphasis on breweries from London and the South East. Watercolour paintings of local scenes provide the main decoration, with the usual local interest panels to the rear. Families are welcome until early evening. Alcoholic drinks are served from 9am. Silent TVs show subtitles. Q ➰ ◑ ♿ ⊖ (Emerson Park) 🖵 🛜

Ilford

Jono's ✅
37 Cranbrook Road, IG1 4PA
☎ (020) 8514 6676
St Austell Tribute; 1 changing beer (sourced nationally) Ⓗ
A converted shop with an unusual style, just a minute's walk from the station. The front of the bar is in dark wood and the rear is half-timbered with a patch of thatch over the seating. Largescreen TVs and a projector show sports fixtures and it can be noisy at times. There is live music on Friday and Saturday evenings. The bar staff are friendly and efficient. The second handpump sometimes dispenses Banks's Wainwright. ⊖ 🖵 🛜 ♪

Romford

Moon & Stars ✅
99-103 South Street, RM1 1NX
☎ (01708) 730117
Greene King Abbot; Ruddles Best Bitter; Sharp's Doom Bar; 3 changing beers (sourced nationally) Ⓗ
Reopened in 2019 with a new roof terrace and lift after a £1.1 million refurbishment, this Wetherspoon pub is close to the station and buses. Children are allowed in the raised rear area until early evening Friday and Saturday, but later for the rest of the week. Food is served all day. There are displays of local history on the walls. Toilets are upstairs (except accessible, which requires a key). It gets quite busy on Thursday and Friday evening. ➰ ⚘ ◑ ♿ ⇌ ⊖ 🖵 🛜

Upminster

Upminster TapRoom Ⓛ
1B Sunnyside Gardens, RM14 3DT
☎ 07801 413540 ⊕ aftervi.co.uk
7 changing beers (sourced locally) Ⓖ
Upminster and East London's first micropub, opened in a converted office in 2015 as a snack bar selling real ale before obtaining change of use on appeal. Its ownership changed in 2022. There are high tables, comfortable new chairs and benches. Up to eight cask ales, four KeyKeg beers, ciders and perry are served from the cool cellar, visible through the large window. Silence mobile phones or pay a fee for charity. Closed Mondays except bank holidays. ➰ ⚘ ♿ ⇌ ⊖ ● 🖪 ❀ ♪

Woodford Bridge

Crown & Crooked Billet ✔
13 Cross Road, IG8 8BN
☎ (020) 8502 9192
Adnams Broadside; Fuller's London Pride; 3 changing beers (sourced nationally) Ⓗ
Spacious multi-room pub overlooking the village green with its church spire, duckpond and large weeping willow tree. Refurbished, the pub is clean and stylish, with wood beams and a conservatory as well as plenty of outdoor seating, making for a pleasant venue in which to enjoy drinks and meals from an inviting menu. Q♨❀◑♿P🚌(275,W14)🐾📶♫

Woodford Green

Cricketers 𝕃
299-301 High Road, IG8 9HQ
☎ (020) 8504 2734
McMullen AK Original Mild, Country Bitter; 1 changing beer (sourced locally) Ⓗ
Warm and friendly, this two-bar local has a dartboard in the public bar and plaques in the saloon for all 18 first-class cricket counties, together with photographs of former MP Sir Winston Churchill, whose statue stands on the green almost opposite. Good-value food is served. There are tables on the rear patio and a covered seating area for smokers. Boules is sometimes played on a pitch at the back. Q❀◑♿♣P🚌(179,W13)🐾📶♫

NORTH LONDON

N1: Hoxton

Wenlock Arms ★ 𝕃
26 Wenlock Road, N1 7TA
☎ (020) 7608 3406 🌐 wenlockarms.com
Mighty Oak Oscar Wilde; 10 changing beers (sourced nationally) Ⓗ
Free house saved from closure by a vigorous local campaign. It features beers from small and medium-sized breweries across the UK, usually including a mild and subject to regular change. With one traditional cider, and a small snacks menu of toasties, Pieminister pies, baked Camembert and vegan sausage rolls, this is a truly welcoming street-corner local with an international reputation. A former local CAMRA Pub of the Year. Closed Mondays. ♨◑♿⇌⊖(Old St)♣🍎🚌🐾📶♫

N1: Islington

Earl of Essex
25 Danbury Street, N1 8LE
☎ (020) 7424 5828 🌐 earlofessex.net
4 changing beers (sourced nationally) Ⓗ
A craft beer house with an ever-changing list of cask beers from local and national breweries. Its own on-site brewery ceased operations some time ago. There is an impressive list of bottled and canned beers from the UK and abroad. A tasty food selection is served all day and, as with an increasing number of pubs, the use of pumpclips has been dropped and the beers on sale are listed on a large board. ❀◑♿⊖(Angel)🍎🚌📶

N1: King's Cross

Parcel Yard
King's Cross Railway Station, Euston Road, N1C 4AH
☎ (020) 7713 7258 🌐 parcelyard.co.uk
Dark Star Hophead; Fuller's London Pride, ESB; 4 changing beers (often Fuller's, Gale's, Verdant) Ⓗ
A large pub, up the stairs at the rear of the concourse, converted from the former station parcel office. It is used by local workers and commuters, and to host meetings. As well as bars on two levels, there are semi-private rooms converted from offices (available to book) and an indoor balcony. The decor is minimal and features rescued furniture. No music is played. Food is served throughout the day. Wheelchair access is by lift.
♨❀◑♿⇌⊖(King's Cross St Pancras) ♣🚌📶

Scottish Stores ★ 𝕃
2-4 Caledonian Road, N1 9DU
☎ 07920 196603 🌐 thescottishstores.co.uk
House beer (by Wantsum); 3 changing beers (often Hammerton, The Horns) Ⓗ
Identified by CAMRA as having a nationally important historic pub interior, this Grade II-listed pub, built in 1901, was the 2016 winner in the conservation category of the CAMRA National Pub Design Awards. Retaining an incredibly intact partitioned interior consisting of three separate bars, it is one of London's very few such survivals. Four handpumps offer a rotating selection of beers, some rarely seen in London.
❀◑⇌⊖(King's Cross St Pancras) 🚌📶

N1: Newington Green

Lady Mildmay 𝕃
92 Mildmay Park, N1 4PR
☎ (020) 7241 6238 🌐 ladymildmay.com
Five Points Best; 2 changing beers (often Five Points, Redemption) Ⓗ
A large corner bar facing Newington Green, refurbished in 2015 when ownership moved to the current operator. That internal redecoration brought back the pub's original features. With its open kitchen, cosy fireplaces, sofas to lounge on and large windows to watch the world go by, this is a pleasant place to visit. The beers listed may change, but Five Points Best is close to being a regular, and others come mostly from London breweries.
♨◑♿⊖(Canonbury) 🚌🐾📶

N1: Pentonville

King Charles I ★
55-57 Northdown Street, N1 9BL
☎ (020) 7837 7758 🌐 kingcharles1st.co.uk
4 changing beers (sourced nationally; often Kent) Ⓗ
Identified by CAMRA as having a nationally important historic interior dating from the 1930s, this Georgian building is small and cosy, containing knick-knacks and homely artefacts, and warmed by real fires in the winter. Food can be ordered from local restaurants (menus on bar) including the Blue River café opposite. Firmly established in the London music scene with live blues, folk and indie music, which can be impromptu or planned. Since 2015 the pub has been community-owned, with a 20-year lease shared by local residents and regulars. Outside seating is partly covered.
❀⇌⊖(King's Cross St Pancras) 🍎🚌🐾📶♫

N5: Canonbury

Snooty Fox 𝕃
75 Grosvenor Avenue, N5 2NN
☎ (020) 7354 9532 🌐 snootyfoxlondon.co.uk
Otter Ale; 2 changing beers (sourced nationally) Ⓗ
A vibrant community establishment with 1960s icons depicted throughout, serving up to three real ales. The airy bar features a 45 rpm jukebox. A function room accommodates local groups and private dining, and outside there is a pleasant patio with seating. The

kitchen serves quality modern British food and an excellent Sunday roast. A former local CAMRA Pub of the Year. 🐴❀◑⊖🚌♫

N6: Highgate

Crown

86 Highgate High Street, N6 5HX
☎ (020) 4553 3068
Harvey's Sussex Best Bitter; 3 changing beers (sourced nationally) [H]
Reopened as a pub in June 2023 after a long period as a posh bakery, prior to which it had been the Rose & Crown. It is part of the Northern Union company chain of previously closed and now reinvigorated pubs. Up to four cask ales come from across the country. Food can be brought in from nearby cafés/bakeries. The rear garden is a lovely place to sit and relax until 9pm. There is occasional live music and a Wednesday quiz.
🐴❀⊖♣🚌🐾📶♫

Wrestlers ★

98 North Road, N6 4AA
☎ (020) 8340 4297 🌐 thewrestlershighgate.com
Fuller's London Pride; St Austell Tribute; Timothy Taylor Boltmaker [H]
Near the top of North Hill, this pub, identified by CAMRA as having a nationally important historic pub interior, was first built in 1547 and last rebuilt in 1921. It features stained glass windows, wooden furniture and panelling throughout. The ancient ceremony of 'swearing on the horns', which dates back to 1623, takes place twice yearly in March and August; details are shown above the impressive original fireplace. There is a large front terrace and a little heated rear beer garden.
🐴❀◑⊖♣🚌🐾

N7: Holloway

Lamb [L]

54 Holloway Road, N7 8JL
☎ (020) 7619 9187 🌐 thelambn7.co.uk
3 changing beers (often East London, Five Points, Howling Hops) [H]
Highbury brewery's tap, taken over by Taylor Walker in 1912, later becoming the Flounder & Firkin before the demise of that chain. Three cask beers rotate, typically a best bitter and a pale ale alongside an amber, rye beer or porter from Redemption, Howling Hops, Five Points, Signature and many more local breweries. The beautiful interior has handsome wood panelling and skylights; the façade parades its painstakingly stripped back original green tiles. Live music is a speciality.
❀♿⇌⊖(Highbury & Islington)🚌🐾📶♫

N8: Crouch End

Small Beer

22 Topsfield Parade, Tottenham Lane, N8 8PT
☎ (020) 8350 0032 🌐 smallbeern8.co.uk
4 changing beers (often Almasty, Two by Two, Vibrant Forest) [H]
Occupying a converted shopfront in the middle of a busy high street, this is a cross between a brewery tap house and a rustic cocktail bar, with brick walls, wood floor, rustic tables and chairs and techno background music that is not overly intrusive. It has a comfortable, vibrant and inviting atmosphere and for a while was named after Henry Reader Williams (1822-97) in whose honour the nearby clock tower was built. Food comprises a variety of pizzas and desserts. ◑🍎🚌

N9: Lower Edmonton

Beehive

24 Little Bury Street, N9 9JZ
☎ (020) 8360 4358 🌐 thebeehivebhp.co.uk
Greene King IPA; 4 changing beers (often Beerblefish, Goff's, Vale) [H]
Tucked away in semi-detached suburbia, this 1929 rebuild is now an imposing gastropub. A wide selection of food is on offer, including excellent Sunday roasts. The bar runs along most of the back wall and has an aquarium. There is live entertainment on Friday or Saturday and a weekly quiz on Tuesdays. The garden houses an interesting selection of animals including pigs, goats, ducks and also an iguana only visible from the Gents. 🐴❀◑♣P🚌(329,W8)🐾📶♫

Rising Sun ✔

240 Winchester Road, N9 9EF
☎ (020) 8807 1512 🌐 therisingsunlondon.co.uk
3 changing beers (often Adnams, Dark Star, Vale) [H]
A large, traditional back-street local with four Taylor Walker signs still fixed to the outside walls. It has a cosy bar on one side and a larger games room where pool and darts can be played. Darts league matches take place every week: men on Monday; women on Tuesday. You can choose your music from a jukebox. For outside drinking there is an enclosed area to the side of the pub and additional pavement seating at the front.
🐴❀♣P🚌🐾📶

N10: Muswell Hill

Mossy Well ✔

258 Muswell Hill Broadway, N10 3SH
☎ (020) 8444 2914
Greene King IPA, Abbot; Sharp's Doom Bar; 4 changing beers (often Twickenham) [H]
A former Express Dairies tearoom and milk depot but a pub since 1984, reopened by Wetherspoon in 2015. Its name derives from the etymology of Muswell. Many internal features reflect its milky history. It is spacious inside, with a mezzanine floor and outdoor drinking areas at both front and back. Despite the size, it can be packed. Q🐴❀◑♿🚌📶

N12: North Finchley

Bohemia [L]

762-764 High Road, N12 9QH
☎ (020) 8446 0294 🌐 thebohemia.co.uk
London Brewing Flying The Mags, London Lush, Beer Street, 100 Oysters Stout; 1 changing beer (often East London) [H]
A lively, spacious brewpub on two levels with large comfortable sofas in the front area and the brewery to view at the rear. Usually four cask ales, plus five real ciders, are served in a variety of measures. Table football and pinball complement a selection of board games. Quiz night is Tuesday, monthly comedy night the second Thursday and live jazz-funk-blues usually two Sundays a month. A Meet the Brewer social is held on the last Thursday of each month.
🐴❀◑♿⊖(Woodside Park)♣🍎🚌🐾📶♫

Elephant Inn ★

283 Ballards Lane, N12 8NR
☎ (020) 8343 6110 🌐 elephantinnfinchley.co.uk
Fuller's London Pride, ESB; 2 changing beers (often Dark Star, Fuller's) [H]
This fine wood-panelled pub has been identified by CAMRA as having a nationally important historic pub interior, with three distinct areas round a U-shaped bar.

The right-hand bar has a pool table and shows sports TV; major events may be screened throughout the pub. The two guest ales are usually from the Fuller's portfolio. Bar food is served from the upstairs Thai restaurant. Outdoor spaces include a large wooden pergola on the front patio and a courtyard at the rear. Monday is quiz night. ♿🏠🍴🕓🚻⊖(West Finchley) ♣🚃🛏🐾☕️🎵

N14: Southgate

New Crown ✅
80-84 Chase Side, N14 5PH
☎ (020) 8882 8758
Greene King Abbot; Ruddles Best Bitter; Sharp's Doom Bar; 7 changing beers (often Exmoor, Redemption, Wimbledon) Ⓗ
There was an Old Crown on Chase Side until its demolition in the 1960s, hence the name. This large, well established Wetherspoon pub is convenient for the tube, and four bus routes stop outside. Converted from a Sainsbury's store more than 20 years ago, it has a single open-plan seating area. Up to two guest ales come from breweries across the country, but with an emphasis on London brews whenever possible. Now celebrating 16 consecutive years in this Guide. Q♿🏠🍴🕓&⊖🚃☕️

N17: Tottenham

Antwerp Arms Ⓛ
168-170 Church Road, N17 8AS (500yds from Sports Centre bus stop on High Rd)
☎ (020) 8216 9289 ⊕ antwerparms.co.uk
Redemption Pale Ale, Hopspur; 2 changing beers (often Redemption) Ⓗ
Tucked away in the historic and atmospheric Bruce Castle Park area, this Georgian building with beer garden is Tottenham's oldest working pub, serving the neighbourhood since 1822. Facing demolition in 2013, it was saved by the local community and CAMRA campaigners. Now owned as a community collective, it is in effect a permanent outlet for Redemption brewery beers. Food is served at limited times, so do check the pub website. Closed Mondays.
♿🏠🍴🕓⊖(White Hart Lane) ♣P🚃🐾☕️🎵

N19: Upper Holloway

Landseer Arms Ⓛ
37 Landseer Road, N19 4JU
☎ (020) 7281 2569 ⊕ landseerarms.com
Hammerton N1; 3 changing beers (often Twickenham) Ⓗ
A Victorian pub, quite different from most of the places on nearby Holloway Road, and one that has been through many incarnations, eventually renamed after the artist whose works included the Trafalgar Square lions and the painting Monarch of the Glen. The spacious interior includes a conservatory-style area on the other side of the bar, sometimes used for dining. There is plenty of pavement seating, with heaters and retractable awnings. ♿🏠🍴🕓&🐾🚃🛏☕️🎵

St John's Tavern
91 Junction Road, N19 5QU
☎ (020) 7272 1587 ⊕ stjohnstavern.com
Black Sheep Best Bitter; Hammerton N1; Thornbridge Jaipur IPA Ⓗ
Another piece of the real ale renaissance taking place in this part of London. Although the emphasis here is undeniably on food (hams hanging in the food preparation area are visible from the bar), this gastropub usually has three real ales on at any one time and has

room for those who just want to relax with a drink. The whole impression is one of space, helped by a large bar area and high ceilings. Closed Mondays.
♿🏠🍴⊖(Archway) ♣🚃☕️

N21: Winchmore Hill

Little Green Dragon 🍺
928 Green Lanes, N21 2AD
☎ (020) 8351 3530 ⊕ littlegreendragonenfield.com
4 changing beers (often Beerblefish, Five Points, New River) Ⓖ
Local CAMRA Pub of the Year again in 2024, this adventurous and exciting micropub won the Greater London regional award in 2018. Meet the Brewer events are often held as well as regular music nights. Eclectic furniture, including a church pew, bus seats and padded kegs, contributes to the friendly community atmosphere, with pavement seating or a small courtyard at the back for alfresco drinking. No excuses for missing your bus – live times are displayed. Closed Mondays.
Q♿🏠🚆♣🐾🚃(125,329) 🐾☕️🎵

N22: Wood Green

Prince
1 Finsbury Road, N22 8PA
☎ (020) 8888 6698 ⊕ theprincen22.co.uk
6 changing beers (often Five Points, Hammerton) Ⓗ
A handsome two-roomed venue occupying a prominent corner site opposite the pleasant Finsbury Gardens and the New River Path, brought back to life in 2016. Up to six cask ales and 12 keg beers come from small breweries across the UK and are listed on the website as they change regularly. For the varied food offering, also see their website. 🏠🍴🚆(Alexandra Palace)⊖🐾🚃🎵

Spouter's Corner ✅
Unit 5, Spouter's Corner, 180 High Road, N22 6EJ
☎ (020) 8881 3891
Greene King Abbot; Ruddles Best Bitter; Sharp's Doom Bar; 4 changing beers Ⓗ
Part of the Hollywood Green leisure complex, that corner of the High Road was called Spouter's Corner in the past for its popularity for free speech, or 'spouting', in a similar style to Speaker's Corner at Hyde Park. Open-air meetings were held until the 1950s. You enter through an outside, covered terrace into a modern Wetherspoon pub. Some striking and large murals and wall art adorn the place, together with a large sculpture from a local artist. Q♿🏠🍴🕓&⊖🚃☕️

Westbury
57 Westbury Avenue, N22 6SA
☎ (020) 8889 2059 ⊕ westburyn22.co.uk
Timothy Taylor Landlord; 3 changing beers (often Goodness, Hammerton, Redemption) Ⓗ
Large, impressive corner pub taken over in 2014 by London Village Inns and extensively renovated as a pub and kitchen with lots of space, big windows throughout and heated outside seating. The wide range of beers includes a number from London breweries. Quiz night is Tuesday and there is live music on a Saturday. Card payments only. ♿🏠🍴🕓&⊖(Turnpike Lane)🐾🚃☕️🎵

Enfield

Jolly Butchers Ⓛ
168 Baker Street, EN1 3JS
☎ (020) 8363 7879
McMullen AK Original Mild, Country Bitter; 1 changing beer (often McMullen) Ⓗ

Friendly community local, acquired by McMullen in 1922. A pub first opened on the site in 1841 and the current building dates from 1905. There is one large bar area with some seating to the front and rear and an interesting range of pop and rock images. Quiz nights are held on the second and fourth Thursdays of the month and there are frequent live music events.
❀◑⊖(Town) ♣P🚌(191,W8) ᯤ ♫

Moon Under Water 🄻 ✔

115-117 Chase Side, EN2 6NN
☎ (020) 8366 9855
Greene King Abbot; Ruddles Best Bitter; Sharp's Doom Bar; 3 changing beers (often New River, Redemption, Twickenham) Ⓗ
An early Wetherspoon pub from 1988 in what had been the British School, which opened in 1838 and closed in 1901, and later a public hall, a dairy and then a restaurant. Popular with all age groups, it has a dedicated area for families and a patio garden space that used to be a car park. Local beers are sourced when possible. ❀◑♿⇌(Chase)🚌(191,W9)ᯤ

High Barnet

Lord Nelson ✔

14 West End Lane, EN5 2SA
☎ (020) 8449 7249
Young's London Original, London Special; 1 changing beer (often Timothy Taylor, Young's) Ⓗ
A friendly and comfortable one-bar locals' pub hidden away off Wood Street. Full of bric-a-brac, it has a fabulous collection of novelty salt and pepper pots donated by customers returning from holiday. A guest beer may be available from the Marston's list. Tuesday night alternates between bingo and a quiz. Dogs are welcome provided they are on leads and off chairs. A lunchtime meal service has recently been introduced. The pub gained Asset of Community Value status in 2022.
Q❀◐♣🚌🐾ᯤ

Olde Mitre Inne ★ ✔

58 High Street, EN5 5SJ
☎ (020) 8449 5701
Greene King IPA, Abbot; Timothy Taylor Landlord; house beer (by Greene King); 3 changing beers (often Oakham, Tring, Wantsum) Ⓗ
The oldest coaching inn in Barnet, there has been a pub here since 1553 and this Grade II-listed building oozes character and charm. It has been identified by CAMRA as having a nationally important historic pub interior, and has beams, exposed brickwork, wood panelling and open fires. There are three separate drinking areas in the original building, then behind is a converted old stables and a large courtyard that has a retractable roof and a brick-built chimenea. Quiz night is Thursday.
❀◑⊖🍎🚌🐾ᯤ♫

Olde Monken Holt ✔

193 High Street, EN5 5SU
☎ (020) 3674 3145
Greene King IPA, Abbot; Timothy Taylor Landlord Ⓗ
Close to the site of the 1471 Battle of Barnet, this traditional Greene King tenanted house dates from 1863. Locals mix with walkers dropping in after a stroll over the vast Hadley Common. Granted Asset of Community Value status in 2017, the pub offers four separate areas within an open-plan layout. Many TVs at the rear show sport or news. Well behaved dogs are welcome inside, in the beer garden at the back or within the additional seating area to the front. ❀♣🚌(84B,399)🐾ᯤ♫

New Barnet

Railway Bell ✔

13 East Barnet Road, EN4 8RR
☎ (020) 8449 1369
Courage Directors; Greene King Abbot; Ruddles Best Bitter; Sharp's Doom Bar; 6 changing beers (often East London, Oakham, Twickenham) Ⓗ
A rarity for Wetherspoon's, this was not a conversion but had been a pub since the late 19th century. A massive refit, including a conservatory at the rear, gives it an airy and bright feeling, and families are welcome until late evening. The car park has gone, replaced by a larger garden that is now segregated between smoking and non-smoking, the latter having the benefit of astroturf.
Q❀◑♿⇌🚌ᯤ

NORTH-WEST LONDON

NW1: Baker Steet

Metropolitan Bar ✔

7 Station Approach, Marylebone Road, NW1 5LD
☎ (020) 7486 3489
Fuller's London Pride; Greene King IPA, Abbot; Sharp's Doom Bar; 4 changing beers (sourced nationally) Ⓗ
Between two exits from Baker Street tube station, a cinema-style flight of stairs leads to a foyer with seating and then into the main bar of this Wetherspoon pub. Look out for the tableaux detailing local history and personalities. The restaurant here featured in John Betjeman's nostalgic 1973 Metro-Land film. Part of the world's first underground railway, Baker Street station opened in 1865. The high ceilings in the bar have heraldic crests that reflect the transport links.
Q◑♿⇌⊖(Baker St) 🚌ᯤ

NW1: Camden Town

Golden Lion ★ 🄻

88 Royal College Street, NW1 0TH
☎ (020) 3915 3852 🌐 goldenlioncamden.com
Sambrook's Junction; 2 changing beers (often Butcombe, St Austell, Sambrook's) Ⓗ
A real back-street community boozer, saved from closure in 2013. The licensee and the local community, supported by Camden Council, waged a long campaign to prevent its conversion into flats. This came to its satisfying conclusion with the sitting tenant buying the building, which he now leases out. It has been identified by CAMRA as having a nationally important historic pub interior. The tasteful decor complements the original features, notably the mirrored bar-back.
❀◑♿⊖(Camden Rd) ♣🚌🐾ᯤ♫

Tapping the Admiral 🄻

77 Castle Road, NW1 8SU
☎ (020) 7267 6118 🌐 tappingtheadmiral.com
Redemption Trinity; 7 changing beers (sourced regionally) Ⓗ
A lively and enjoyable community venue where friendly, knowledgeable staff offer a warm welcome. Guest ales come mainly from local breweries. Great British food includes speciality home-made pies. Outside at the back is a well-designed, heated and covered beer garden. There is a popular Wednesday quiz and live traditional music on Thursday evening. Look out for tap takeovers every couple of months and pop-up events, and also Nelson, the pub's cat. Local CAMRA Pub of the Year 2023.
Q❀◑♿⊖(Kentish Town West) 🍎🚌🐾ᯤ♫

NW1: Euston

Doric Arch 🄻

Euston Station Colonnade, 1 Eversholt Street, NW1 2DN

☎ (020) 7383 3359 ⊕ doric-arch.co.uk

Dark Star Hophead; Fuller's London Pride, ESB; 3 changing beers (sourced nationally; often Fuller's) Ⓗ

Right next to Euston Station, celebrating the arch wantonly demolished as part of its 'development', the pub is up a flight of stairs, with large picture windows below. It is used extensively by commuters, aided by the train times screen. Excellent staff are helpful and informative about the ales, including up to three guest beers. Railway memorabilia adorn the walls. Toilets are at basement level. ⏱🏵️🅾️⚤⊖(Euston/Euston Sq)🚌🐾🎵

Euston Tap 🄻

West & East Lodges, 190 Euston Road, NW1 2EF

☎ (020) 3137 8837 ⊕ eustontap.com

7 changing beers (sourced nationally; often Redemption) Ⓟ

Fronting the main station building, these impressive Grade II-listed Portland stone lodges, separated by a bus lane, are relics from the original 1830s station. The beers, mostly from smaller breweries, are pumped up to taps behind the bar. The small ground-floor spaces are augmented by seating above the wrought iron spiral staircases, where the toilets are also located, and large heated drinking areas outside. The East Lodge opens later and its offering can vary – it was formerly the Cider Tap. ⏱🏵️⚤⊖(Euston/Euston Sq) ●🚌🐾🎵

NW2: Cricklewood

Beaten Docket ✅

50-56 Cricklewood Broadway, NW2 3ET

☎ (020) 8450 2972

Greene King Abbot; Ruddles Best Bitter; 3 changing beers (sourced nationally) Ⓗ

A Wetherspoon pub named after a losing betting ticket; framed prints reflect the racing link, a feature of this area in the late 19th century. Booths provide more intimate drinking areas while two TVs on silent mode offer either sport or rolling news. In summer, some of the doors and windows open more fully to create a pleasant atmosphere around the outside seating area to the front, which is open all year round.
Q⏱🏵️🅾️&⚤🚌🎵

NW3: Hampstead

Holly Bush ★

22 Holly Mount, NW3 6SG

☎ (020) 7435 2892 ⊕ hollybushhampstead.co.uk

Dark Star Hophead; Fuller's London Pride; Gale's HSB Ⓗ

A marvellous multi-roomed gem, this Grade II-listed Fuller's pub at the top of steep steps from Heath Street has been identified by CAMRA as having a nationally important historic pub interior. Sensitive refurbishment some years ago opened up the rooms at the back and there is another dining room upstairs. However, the jewels of this pub are the main bar and, off to the left as you enter, the room with the traditional open fire (now reserved for diners). ⏱🏵️🅾️⊖♣🚌(46,268)🐾🎵

Magdala ★ 🄻

2A South Hill Park, NW3 2SB

☎ (020) 7433 8322 ⊕ themagdala.co.uk

Big Smoke Solaris Session Pale Ale; Five Points Best; Harvey's Sussex Best Bitter; 4 changing beers (often By The Horns, Hammerton, Southwark) Ⓗ

Reopened as an independent pub after years under threat of permanent closure, the carefully restored historic interior of this typical Charrington inter-war rebuild with its wood panelling and green stained glass has been identified by CAMRA as nationally important. Dating back to 1885, the pub commemorates Lord Napier of Magdala. Outside was where Ruth Ellis, the last woman hanged in England, shot her lover to death on Easter Sunday 1955, though alleged bullet marks on the façade are not authentic.
🏵️🅾️⊖(Hampstead Heath) ●🚌🐾

Old White Bear 🄻

1 Well Road, NW3 1LJ

☎ (020) 4553 0602 ⊕ theoldwhitebearhampstead.co.uk

Five Points XPA; Harvey's Sussex Best Bitter; Leeds Pale; 1 changing beer (sourced nationally) Ⓗ

Now run by Northern Union Pubs, this pub had been closed for nearly eight years until it was saved after prolonged campaign by locals and CAMRA alike. The interior will be familiar to returning customers. The bar remains in a central position, with bar stools in front available for drinkers. The side rooms both have fireplaces, large wooden bench-style tables and banquette seating. A parquet floor extends throughout.
🅾️⊖🚌(46,268)

Spaniards Inn ★

Spaniards Road, NW3 7JJ

☎ (020) 8731 8406 ⊕ thespaniardshampstead.co.uk

Fuller's London Pride; Timothy Taylor Landlord; 2 changing beers (often Dark Star, St Austell, Titanic) Ⓗ

A large, rambling inn identified by CAMRA as having a nationally important historic pub interior. Several rooms, some featuring wooden beams and low ceilings, make for a cosy atmosphere. Grade II-listed, the building dates back to 1585 although it may not originally have been a pub. It is popular with walkers from the heath and weekends can be extremely busy; booking is recommended for meals. Drinkers may be directed to the large heated garden if inside tables are booked for food.
Q⏱🏵️🅾️Ⓟ🚌(210,H3) 🐾

NW5: Gospel Oak

Gipsy Queen 🄻

166 Malden Road, NW5 4BS

☎ (020) 3092 0598 ⊕ thegipsyqueennw5.co.uk

3 changing beers (often Hammerton, Timothy Taylor) Ⓗ

Since reopening in 2015 after a period of closure, considerable effort has been successfully made to transform this pub and engage with its customers. Local cask beers can alternate between ELB, Hammerton and Southwark and a large selection of keg beers can also rotate. There is a take-away bottle/jug shop service. The garden at the rear offers booth seating, is heated and also has a big TV screen. The kitchen rotates its food residencies every four months.
⏱🏵️🅾️&⊖🚌(24,46) 🐾🎵♪

NW5: Kentish Town

Pineapple ★ 🄻

51 Leverton Street, NW5 2NX

☎ (020) 7284 4631 ⊕ thepineapplepubnw5.com

4 changing beers (sourced nationally) Ⓗ

An authentic and friendly community venue, saved from closure by the locals, it is Grade II listed and identified by CAMRA as having a nationally important historic pub interior, notable for its mirrors and splendid bar-back. The front bar, with comfortable seating around tables, leads through to an informal conservatory overlooking the patio garden. The menu is Thai kitchen cuisine. Some of the beers come from across London and the range changes regularly as the pub is free of tie. Q♿☆🕮➔➰🚍♣❄

Southampton Arms 🍺 ★
139 Highgate Road, NW5 1LE
🌐 thesouthamptonarms.co.uk
8 changing beers (sourced nationally) 🅗
The pub does what it says on the sign outside: Ale, Cider, Meat. The 14 handpumps serve almost equal numbers of ciders and beers from microbreweries across the UK. Snacks include roast pork, cheese or meat baps, pork pies and veggie options. Music is played on vinyl and the piano is in regular use. It has been identified by CAMRA as having a nationally important historic pub interior. At the back is a secluded patio. Local CAMRA Pub and Cider Pub of the Year 2024.
☆🕮➔➍(Gospel Oak/Kentish Town) ♣🚍🎵

NW6: Kilburn

Black Lion ★ 🅛
274 Kilburn High Road, NW6 2BY
☎ (020) 3876 8204 🌐 blacklionkilburn.co.uk
Five Points Pale; 2 changing beers (sourced nationally) 🅗
A Grade II*-listed building, identified by CAMRA as having a nationally important historic interior, this pub is worth a visit for its fantastic interior decor alone, with a rich ceiling, original bar counter, island back bar, screen partition, etched and cut glass, and decorative cornice. There is a separate dining area, which may have been the former billiards room. Cask beer and cider returned in 2022, after many years' absence, when London Village Inns, who already operated seven thriving and diverse pubs across London, took over and installed three handpumps. Opposite the Kiln Theatre.
♿☆🖼🕮➔(Brondesbury/Kilburn) ♣🚍♣

NW6: Kilburn Park

Carlton Tavern 🅛
33 Carlton Vale, NW6 5EU
☎ (020) 7625 4760 🌐 carltontavern.co.uk
House beer (by Anspach & Hobday); 3 changing beers (often Big Smoke, Five Points, London Brewing) 🅗
A pub famous nationally since the developer who demolished it illegally was forced by Westminster Council to rebuild it brick by brick from original plans. Much was salvaged from the wreckage, including tiles, reusable bricks, the original bar and fireplaces and some of the decorative ceilings. The new pub showcases mostly London ales. Outside is a garden/patio area also used for dining in summer. Local CAMRA Pub of the Year 2022. ♿☆🕮➔➰🚍♣❄🎵

NW9: Colindale

Moon Under Water ✅
10 Varley Parade, Edgware Road, NW9 6RR
☎ (020) 8200 7611
Greene King IPA, Abbot; Ruddles Best Bitter; 3 changing beers (often Sambrook's, Twickenham, Windsor & Eton) 🅗
A large Wetherspoon pub converted from a Woolworth store in 1990. The rear is mainly for food and where well behaved children can sit with their parents, while the front is the more traditional drinking and chatting area. Some of the three changing beers will be from London breweries, and the manager occasionally arranges Meet

the London Brewer events. Many of the craft beers on keg or in bottles are similarly sourced. The silent TVs show either news or racing. Q♿🕮➔♿🚍(32,142)❄

NW9: Kingsbury

J.J. Moon's 🅛
553 Kingsbury Road, NW9 9EL
☎ (020) 8204 9675
Greene King IPA, Abbot; Sharp's Doom Bar; 3 changing beers (sourced regionally; often Redemption, Twickenham) 🅗
A Wetherspoon shop conversion dating from 1988, with silent TV screens majoring on horse racing, and admitting children until 8pm. A large, one-room establishment with low ceilings, lots of wood panelling, subdued lighting and a raised section at the rear, it is a rare outlet for real ale in this part of outer London. The name plays on the George Orwell Moon Under Water theme of some of the company's earliest pubs. Q♿🕮➔♿🚍❄

Eastcote Village

Woodman ✅
Joel Street, HA5 2PR
☎ (020) 8868 0833 🌐 thewoodmanpinner.com
Rebellion IPA; Timothy Taylor Boltmaker; 1 changing beer (often Brains, Butcombe, Otter) 🅗
A Grade II-listed, two-bar former Harman's pub dating from the 1640s, extended in 2005 and refurbished in 2021. Overlooking the Eastcote cricket club, it features a large function room with bar at the rear and a patio-style covered garden. On Sunday traditional roasts are available. Saturday evening meals are usually available from a changing food vendor in the pub garden.
♿☆🕮🖼🅿🚍(282) ♣🎵

Harrow on the Hill

Castle ★
30 West Street, HA1 3EF
☎ (020) 8422 3155 🌐 castle-harrow.co.uk
Dark Star Hophead; Fuller's London Pride, ESB; 1 changing beer (often Dark Star, Fuller's, Thornbridge) 🅗
A lively and friendly Fuller's house in the heart of Harrow on the Hill. Built in 1901 and Grade II listed, it has been identified by CAMRA as having a nationally important historic pub interior. Reservations are recommended for Sunday lunchtimes. Three real coal fires help to keep the pub warm and cosy in the colder months, and a secluded beer garden is popular during the summer. Local CAMRA Pub of the Year 2022. ♿☆🕮➔🚍(258,H17)♣❄🎵

Ruislip

Hop & Vine
18 High Street, HA4 7AN
🌐 hopandvinebar.com
4 changing beers (sourced nationally) 🅖
A micropub converted from a café, with seating at low tables with chairs and benches. The small bar counter in the right-hand corner dispenses four real ales, four keg beers and two ciders from a temperature-controlled cellar room behind it. Bottled and canned beers, wines and spirits are also sold. Snacks are enhanced by cheeseboard and pork pie options. Table service is often provided. Closed Mondays. Q☆🖼➔♣🚍♣

Woodman ★ ✅
Breakspear Road, HA4 7SE
☎ (01895) 635763 🌐 thewoodmanruislip.com

Fuller's London Pride; Rebellion IPA; Timothy Taylor Boltmaker; 1 changing beer (sourced nationally) H
This cheerful and welcoming two-bar local close to Ruislip Lido and woods has been identified by CAMRA as having a nationally important historic pub interior. The cosy lounge bar is open-plan with a dartboard and games machine. The public bar is friendly and comfortable. Some of the outside seating is covered. A street food truck changes weekly, serving food on Friday evenings. Winner of the Stars of Stonegate Pub of the Year 2022 award. Q ✿ ✿ ◑ & ▦ (331) ✿ ♠ ♪

Ruislip Manor

J.J. Moon's
12 Victoria Road, HA4 0AA
☎ (01895) 622373
Courage Directors; Greene King Abbot; Ruddles Best Bitter; Sharp's Doom Bar; Vale Gravitas; 7 changing beers (often Twickenham) H
A large Wetherspoon pub conveniently located opposite the tube station. It is popular and often busy in the evening and at weekends. Food and beer alike are of good value, with the usual promotions and also tap takeovers from local breweries. At the rear is an elevated section, leading to a small garden patio, while the front has a partitioned-off smoking area on the street. Local CAMRA Pub of the Year 2022. Q ✿ ✿ ◑ & ▦ ✿ ♠

SOUTH-EAST LONDON
SE1: Bermondsey

Southwark Brewing Co Tap Room L
46 Druid Street, SE1 2EZ
☎ (020) 3302 4190 ⊕ southwarkbrewing.co.uk
Southwark London Pale Ale, Bermondsey Best, Harvard; 3 changing beers (often Southwark) H
This addition to the Bermondsey Beer Mile opened in 2014 in a railway arch. Six handpumps offer the brewery's regular real ales plus seasonal and one-off brews. Some beers may also be sold on gravity dispense behind the bar, together with a number of membrane keg dispensed beers from taps on the rear wall. Closed Mondays and Wednesdays.
✿ & ⇌ ❂ (London Bridge) ▦ ✿ ♪

SE1: Borough

King's Arms
65 Newcomen Street, SE1 1YT
☎ (020) 7407 1132 ⊕ kingsarmsborough.co.uk
Harvey's Sussex Best Bitter; Purity Mad Goose; Timothy Taylor Landlord; 2 changing beers (often Five Points, Sambrook's, Twickenham) H
A Grade II-listed, single-room pub with a traditional and comfortable interior, just off the busy Borough High Street but easily missed. The striking plaque above the entrance originally stood at the southern end of Old London Bridge and was rescued when all the buildings on the bridge were demolished in the mid-18th century. Five cask beers are usually available and traditional, mainly British, meals are served lunchtimes daily and evenings Monday to Saturday. An upstairs function room is available for hire. ✿ ✿ ◑ ⇌ (London Bridge) ❂ ▦

Roebuck L
50 Great Dover Street, SE1 4YG
☎ (020) 7357 7324 ⊕ theroebuck.net
3 changing beers (often By The Horns, Five Points, Southwark) H
Spacious, cosy and airy Victorian wedge-shaped corner pub a little off the beaten track and operated by the local

Parched Pub Company. The large oval central bar usually offers three real ales plus a real cider, mainly locally sourced. The food menu is varied; the pub is a member of the Sustainable Restaurant Association. There is pavement bench seating outside. Quiz, comedy, karaoke and film nights feature monthly, along with other events. ✿ ◑ ❂ ♣ ◐ ▦ (21) ✿

Royal Oak ✓
44 Tabard Street, SE1 4JU
☎ (020) 7357 7173 ⊕ royaloaklondon.co.uk
Harvey's Dark Mild, IPA, Sussex Best Bitter; 2 changing beers (often Harvey's) H
A charming, back-to-basics drinkers' pub separated into two sections by the bar counter and an off-sales hatch. This was the first London tied house of Sussex-based Harvey's brewery, and is renowned for friendly and attentive service. The ales include seasonal brews, a dark mild, which is unusual for London, and Harvey's bottled beers. The pub is something of a local institution with regulars coming from miles around to spend time here. There is a popular Wednesday quiz. Local CAMRA Pub of the Year 2023. ✿ ✿ ◑ ⇌ (London Bridge) ❂ ▦ ✿ ✿ ♪

SE1: Borough Market

Market Porter ✓
9 Stoney Street, SE1 9AA
☎ (020) 7407 2495 ⊕ themarketporter.co.uk
Harvey's Sussex Best Bitter; 5 changing beers (often Brew York, Portobello, Timothy Taylor) H
This classic, rustic, Victorian market pub next to the famous Borough Market has a licence to open from 6am to 9am during the week, to accommodate the market workers from whom it gets its name. Popular with locals and visitors alike, it can get busy, with drinkers spilling out onto the street. An upstairs wood-panelled restaurant serves a changing seasonal menu, mainly focused on British classic dishes. Card payments only. ✿ ✿ ◑ & ⇌ ❂ (London Bridge) ▦ ✿

Old King's Head
King's Head Yard, 45-49 Borough High Street, SE1 1NA
☎ (020) 7407 1550 ⊕ theoldkingshead.uk.com
Harvey's Sussex Best Bitter; St Austell Proper Job; 2 changing beers (sourced nationally) H
A traditional hostelry down a narrow, cobbled lane off Borough High Street. Stained glass windows hint at a bygone era and the pictures adorning the walls tell the story of a pub, and an area, that has a rich history. The layout inside is simple, with an L-shaped bar in one corner usually offering four cask ales on handpump. The clientele is a mix of tourists, office workers and visitors to the nearby Borough Market.
◑ & ⇌ ❂ (London Bridge) ▦ ✿

Rake
14 Winchester Walk, SE1 9AG
☎ (020) 7407 0557 ⊕ utobeer.co.uk
4 changing beers (sourced nationally) H
On the edge of Borough Market, this small speciality beer bar prides itself on offering a high-quality, varied beer selection, and over the years has become a real global destination for beer aficionados and brewers. The ever-changing cask ales are complemented by a comprehensive range of keg and bottled beers, mainly from North America and Europe, plus a small range of wines and spirits. Beer festivals, brewery tap takeovers and other themed beer selections all feature.
Q ✿ & ⇌ ❂ (London Bridge) ▦ ✿

SE1: Lambeth North

Hercules
2 Kennington Road, SE1 7BL
☎ (020) 7920 9092 ⊕ thehercules.co.uk
Dark Star Hophead; Fuller's London Pride; 2 changing beers (sourced nationally) Ⓗ
Having operated as a variety of restaurants over the preceding years, the Hercules reverted back to a pub in 2019 under the ownership of Fuller's. The decor is contemporary, including exposed brickwork and large, modern chandeliers. There are bars on both the ground and first floors, the former serving cask beer and the latter featuring a large shuffleboard table. A separate meeting room is also available. Food is served all day.
🏠◑⭢≷(Waterloo) ⊖♣🚗

SE1: London Bridge

Shipwrights Arms ★ ✅
88 Tooley Street, SE1 2TF
☎ (020) 7378 1486 ⊕ shipwrightsarms.co.uk
Sharp's Doom Bar; 5 changing beers (sourced nationally) Ⓗ
Built in 1884, this Grade II-listed pub has been identified by CAMRA as having a nationally important historic pub interior that includes an original tiled mural of shipwrights at work and the rare central island bar. An impressive six real ales are on offer. It is well served by London Bridge public transport links and numerous buses. The river, Tower Bridge and City are also close by, making it popular with commuters, tourists and locals alike. There is good home-made food lunchtimes and evenings. 🏠◑⭢≷⊖🚗

SE1: Southwark

Ring
72 Blackfriars Road, SE1 8HA
☎ (020) 7620 0811 ⊕ theringbarlondon.co.uk
Sharp's Doom Bar; 3 changing beers (often Southwark) Ⓗ
One-bar corner pub named after a famous boxing arena that stood across Blackfriars Road from 1910 until destroyed by bombs in WWII. Pictures of the rich local boxing history adorn the walls, including one of a former professional boxer who ran the pub until 2001. Terrestrial TV sporting events and YouTube boxing bouts are shown. Outside seating is available under awnings on the pavement/patio. Thai food is served weekday lunchtimes and evenings and all day Saturday. Card payments only.
🚶🏠◑⭢🚻≷(Waterloo/Waterloo East) ⊖🚗🐾📶

SE1: Waterloo

Hole in the Wall
5 Mepham Street, SE1 8SQ
☎ (020) 7928 6196
7 changing beers (often Brew York, By The Horns, Southwark) Ⓗ
In a railway arch opposite Waterloo railway station's main entrance, this independent family-owned free house enjoys the comforting rumble of trains overhead. It offers a small rugby-themed front bar, a larger more basic bar to the rear showing sport on TV and a small heated patio at the back. A long time real ale stalwart, it has four handpumps for beer in the front bar and seven at the rear. Irish folk music is played on Sunday evening.
🚶🏠⭢≷(Waterloo/Waterloo East) ⊖🚗🐾📶🎵

King's Arms ★ 🄻
25 Roupell Street, SE1 8TB
☎ (020) 7207 0784 ⊕ thekingsarmslondon.co.uk
Adnams Southwold Bitter; house beer (by Sharp's); 6 changing beers (often Portobello, Redemption, Siren) Ⓗ
Tucked away in a street of Victorian terraced cottages often used for filming, this Grade II-listed pub has been identified by CAMRA as having a nationally important historic pub interior. The narrow public bar and small saloon share a horseshoe-shaped bar with four different cask ales in each. The rear conservatory, packed with bric-a-brac, serves Thai food lunchtimes and evenings on weekdays and all day at weekends. Drinking is allowed outside on the pavement. A quiz is held on Sunday evenings. Card payments only.
🚶◑⭢≷(Waterloo/Waterloo East) ⊖🚗🐾

Waterloo Tap
Arch 147, Sutton Walk, SE1 7ES
☎ (020) 3455 7436 ⊕ waterlootap.com
5 changing beers (often Iron Pier, Redemption, Thornbridge) 🄰
Under a railway arch on the pedestrian route between the South Bank attractions and Waterloo rail and tube stations, this small bar, one of the Tap chain, is often crowded but has additional covered seating outside at the front and a narrow patio area at the rear. The cask ales and a real cider, dispensed from taps centrally mounted on the copper bar-back, are flanked by up to 20 keg lines, all listed on the blackboard above. Card payments only. 🚶🏠&⭢≷⊖🚗🐾📶

SE3: Blackheath

Hare & Billet ✅
1A Eliot Cottages, Hare & Billet Road, SE3 0QJ
☎ (020) 8852 2352 ⊕ hareandbillet.com
House beer (by Greene King); 6 changing beers (often Five Points, Siren, Thornbridge) Ⓗ
Overlooking Blackheath's open expanse, on the site of an 18th-century coaching inn, the pub is operated by Greene King's ale and food-focused Metropolitan brand, with a restaurant to the rear. The decor is contemporary, with bare wooden floorboards and pictures of dogs on the walls. Outside drinking on the heath, close to the pond with its aquatic avian wildlife, is allowed using plastic glasses. A quiz is held on Wednesday and there is live music on Friday evenings. Card payments only.
🚶◑&≷🚌(380) 🐾📶🎵

SE4: Brockley

Brockley Barge ✅
184 Brockley Road, SE4 2RR
☎ (020) 8694 7690
Greene King IPA, Abbot; Sharp's Doom Bar; 2 changing beers (often Portobello, Sambrook's, Twickenham) Ⓗ
A former Courage house, part of the Wetherspoon chain since 2000, close to the railway station, this popular, thriving hub attracts a clientele reflecting the vibrant local area. Laid out in a semi-horseshoe shape with a variety of seating spaces, it has all facilities on the same level. A small courtyard to the south side is well used in the summer. The name recalls the former Croydon Canal, where the railway line now runs. Alcoholic drinks are served from 9am. Q🚶🏠◑&⭢≷⊖🚗📶

SE4: Crofton Park

London Beer Dispensary 🅛
389 Brockley Road, SE4 2PH
☎ (020) 7018 3740
3 changing beers (often Five Points, Southey) 🄷
This former wine bar is run by Penge-based Southey brewery and conveniently sited for travel by rail and local buses. The beers were previously gravity-dispensed but the counter now sports a set of handpumps. Alongside a Southey beer are two changing guest beers, usually from microbreweries, and a real cider. The bar is popular with families; children are welcome until the evening. Food is available to order, in partnership with the pizzeria next door. Card payments only.
🌢🏵🍴⭢🌭🚗🐾🛜

SE5: Camberwell

Grove House
26 Camberwell Grove, SE5 8RE
☎ (020) 7703 8910 ⊕ grovehousetavern.co.uk
3 changing beers (sourced nationally) 🄷
An impressive interwar pub reminiscent of a French villa, taken over by the small Parched London Group in 2021. The exterior is rich with architectural flourishes and sports a distinctive mansard roof. Its columned entrance leads to the high-ceilinged space of the L-shaped public bar. The focus is on beer from small independent breweries and constantly changing cocktails. Entertainment includes comedy nights, jazz and quiz nights. 🌢🏵🍴⭢⊖(Denmark Hill)🚗🐾🛜

Hermit's Cave
28 Camberwell Church Street, SE5 8QU
☎ (020) 7703 3188
4 changing beers (sourced nationally) 🄷
An imposing curve-fronted corner pub run by the same family for 25 years and popular with a cross-section of local residents and art college students. The premises have remained essentially unchanged, with etched windows and wooden floors adding to the traditional feel. A corner TV provides the only distraction to convivial conversation. Guest beers come from independent breweries. An impressive range of whiskies includes examples from Wales and Japan.
♿⭢⊖(Denmark Hill) 🚗🐾

Sun of Camberwell 🅛
61-63 Coldharbour Lane, SE5 9NS
☎ (020) 7737 5861 ⊕ suncamberwell.com
Timothy Taylor Landlord; Volden Session Ale; 1 changing beer (often Wye Valley) 🄷
A spacious and friendly pub operated by Antic. The tasteful decoration includes retro items such as suitcases, a radio and interesting pictures that add to the pleasant atmosphere. Children and dogs are welcome. Quality meals are available all day and the large floorspace with plentiful tables makes for comfortable dining.
🌢🏵🍴⭢(Denmark Hill/Loughborough Jct) ⊖(Denmark Hill) 🚗🐾🛜♪

SE5: Denmark Hill

Fox on the Hill ✅
149 Denmark Hill, SE5 8EH
☎ (020) 7738 4756
Greene King Abbot; Ruddles Best Bitter; Sharp's Doom Bar; 4 changing beers (often Southwark, Surrey Hills, Twickenham) 🄷
An attractive and imposing brick-built Wetherspoon pub opposite Ruskin Park. Rooms with quiet alcoves and screened booths surround a central bar area. Framed

prints celebrate the numerous historic figures and notable thinkers who lived nearby, often lending their names to the streets. A lawn at the front affords views across to central London and there are large gardens at the rear. The pub is particularly popular when Dulwich Hamlet FC is playing at home. Alcoholic drinks are served from 9am. 🌢🏵🍴♿⭢⊖🚗🛜

SE6: Catford

Catford Constitutional 🅛
108 Rushey Green, SE6 4HW
☎ (020) 3848 9078 ⊕ catfordconstitutionalclub.com
Volden Session Ale, Pale Ale; 3 changing beers (often Oakham, Sharp's, Thornbridge) 🄷
An expansive former Argos shop conversion opened by Antic in 2022. Furniture and decorations follow the company's eclectic style and some is reminiscent of the now closed namesake pub round the corner. Five cask ales are on offer and the food menu is extensive and concentrates on British style classics. Sunday roasts are bookable. Stairs inside lead up to the Fairytop roof garden, albeit with more limited opening days and times. 🌢🏵🍴♿⭢(Catford/Catford Bridge)🚗🛜♪

SE8: Deptford

Dog & Bell 🅛 ✅
116 Prince Street, SE8 3JD
☎ (020) 8692 5664
Fuller's London Pride; 4 changing beers (often Brockley, Drop Project, Redemption) 🄷
A Guide stalwart for over 30 years, this sensitively extended traditional pub is rather hidden on a pedestrianised side street. A lively bar and real fire in winter attract a broad mix of clientele including locals and those strolling along the nearby Thames Path. The cask ales are complemented by a selection of Belgian bottled beers, malt whiskies and simple, tasty meals. Regular beer festivals are always themed. Real ciders include Biddenden. A bar billiards table is available.
🌢🏵🍴♿🍴🍴🚗🛜♪

SE9: Eltham

Long Pond
110 Westmount Road, SE9 1UT
☎ (020) 8331 6767 ⊕ thelongpond.co.uk
House beer (by Tonbridge); 4 changing beers (often Goacher's, Musket, Tonbridge) 🄶
Archetypal micropub in an area previously without a pub at all, named after the pond in nearby Eltham Park North. Mainly Kentish cask ales, served from a chilled stillage room, are kept in exceptional condition. Wine, gins, malt whiskies and Dudda's Tun real cider or perry are also available, along with limited bar snacks. Seating is mainly high benches and tables, though the rear snug features low tables and chairs. Children and dogs are not admitted. Card payments strongly preferred.
Q♿⭢🍴🚗(B16)♪

Park Tavern
45 Passey Place, SE9 5DA
☎ (020) 8850 3216 ⊕ parktaverneltham.co.uk
6 changing beers (often Butcombe, St Austell) 🄷
A free house since 2022, this traditional Victorian pub retains original Truman's brewery tiled frontage and signage. The compact interior has an L-shaped bar with stylish lamps and chandeliers. Etched windows feature elegant drapes; decorative plates and pictures line the walls. Light background music is played. Plenty of outdoor seating includes a covered and heated rear

garden. There is an impressive selection of craft keg beers and lagers, whiskies and wine. Lunchtime meals are served except on Sunday. Q❀✧❂≅♣♠🍴🐾

Rusty Bucket
11 Court Yard, SE9 5PR
☎ (020) 8859 5500 ⊕ therustybucket.pub
3 changing beers (often Harvey's, Kent, Siren) Ⓖ
Opened along micropub lines in 2018, the pub retains the original frontage of the redeveloped Crown. Inside, the walls are half-panelled and brightly painted. The place is run by a couple of friends who are enthusiastic and knowledgeable about beers. The cask ales and some real ciders are dispensed from a walk-in chilled cellar cupboard. A large range of keg draught, bottled and canned beers is on offer. Live music sessions are held on Sunday. Card payments only. ➳♿≅♣♠🍴🐾🎵

SE10: East Greenwich

River Ale House 🍷
131 Woolwich Road, SE10 0RJ
☎ 07963 127595 ⊕ theriveralehouse.com
6 changing beers (often Goacher's, Iron Pier, Oakham) Ⓖ
A multi-award winning micropub: two drinking areas are linked by a ramp, with cask ales and ciders dispensed from a chilled room behind the bar counter. Wines and spirits are also available and pizzas may be ordered in. Very much part of the local community, this friendly, family-run house also has a much wider following. The cask ale range changes constantly, with today's list shown on blackboards above the bar and printed lists. Not all ciders are real. Local CAMRA Pub of the Year 2024. ❀♿≅(Westcombe Park) ♣🍴🐾🎵

SE10: Greenwich

Morden Arms
1 Brand Street, SE10 8SP
☎ (020) 8858 2189
Sharp's Doom Bar; 3 changing beers (often Brockley, Iron Pier) Ⓗ
An ex-Courage corner house, now an eclectic independent pub with a strong orientation to recorded music, plus live music most weekends. Unpretentious, with no external pub sign or even name, this is one of a dying breed of back-street boozers in the area. It has a clientele of locals and music lovers. Cribbage night is Monday. The beer range is mainly from London breweries, with guest ales from further afield appearing occasionally. Cash payments only. ➳❀≅❂♣🍴🐾🎵

Plume of Feathers ✓
19 Park Vista, SE10 9LZ
☎ (020) 8858 1661 ⊕ plumegreenwich.com
Harvey's Sussex Best Bitter; 3 changing beers (often Bexley, By The Horns, Wantsum) Ⓗ
With parts dating from the late 17th century, this cosy and quiet historic pub sits opposite the northern wall of Greenwich Park in a quiet residential street, close to the National Maritime Museum. The maritime association is reflected inside with numerous interesting historical paintings and memorabilia. Outside is a pleasant back garden area. Meals are served daily in both the bar and the separate rear restaurant. It has a loyal local following and is also popular with tourists and visitors. ➳❀✧❂≅(Maze Hill) ❂(Cutty Sark) 🍴🐾🎵

SE11: Kennington

Dog House Ⓛ ✓
293 Kennington Road, SE11 6BY
☎ (020) 3643 8982 ⊕ doghouse.pub
Fuller's London Pride; 4 changing beers (often Big Smoke, East London, Southwark) Ⓗ
Quirky twin bar pub situated in a prominent position in Kennington and handy for those visiting the Oval cricket ground. Plenty of outdoor seating is available at the front. As it says of itself, it not a sports pub but it does love sport. Food is a mixture of British classics and modern bistro fare. It positively encourages dogs (and their owners) to visit. ➳❂♿❂♣🍴🐾🎵

SE14: New Cross

Royal Albert
460 New Cross Road, SE14 6TJ
☎ (020) 8692 3737 ⊕ royalalbertpub.co.uk
4 changing beers (often Five Points, Portobello, Southwark) Ⓗ
Now run by Portobello brewery, this Grade II-listed Victorian pub retains the original etched-glass windows and bar-back. The recently extended, spacious interior is furnished with wood panelling, ornate lamps and a mix of seating including Chesterfield sofas. The open kitchen at the rear serves a selection of distinctive and enticing dishes. Monday is quiz night, comedy features every third Wednesday of the month and there is a live jazz session on Sunday evening. ➳❀❂≅❂❂♣🍴🐾🎵

Shirker's Rest
9 Lewisham Way, SE14 6PP
☎ (020) 8091 4584 ⊕ theshirkersrest.co.uk
House beer (by Anspach & Hobday); 3 changing beers (often Brockley, Burning Sky, Thornbridge) Ⓗ
A micropub opened in 2022, opposite Goldsmiths university, as a joint venture between local bloggers Deserter and pop-up pub specialists Camberwell Shark. Above the main ground-floor bar, an upstairs drinking area also hosts exhibitions and events showcasing local talent. There is limited outdoor seating. It offers four cask ales, seven craft keg taps, bag in box cider, wine and spirits. Bar snacks are augmented by a free delivery arrangement with a local pizzeria. Regular tap takeovers feature. Card payments only. ❀❂♿❂(New Cross/New Cross Gate) ♣🍴🐾🎵

SE16: Rotherhithe

Mayflower ★
117 Rotherhithe Street, SE16 4NF
☎ (020) 7237 4088 ⊕ mayflowerpub.co.uk
House beer (by Greene King); 5 changing beers (often Kent, Park, Southwark) Ⓗ
A nautical-themed pub celebrating the Mayflower's historic journey to New England. Those with a family connection may sign its Descendants' Book. The 17th-century tavern-style interior actually dates from 1957 but has been identified by CAMRA as nationally important. To the rear is a covered, wooden jetty over the River Thames. A popular place for tourists, this is the only pub licensed to sell UK and US postage stamps. The house beer is the appropriately named Scurvy Ale. ❀❂❂🍴(381,C10)

SE18: Plumstead Common

Plum Tree
154 Plumstead Common Road, SE18 2UL
☎ (020) 3556 0277

3 changing beers (often Arbor, Brew York, Bristol Beer Factory) Ⓖ
A micropub located in Birds Nest Hollow, as the area is locally known. Opened in 2019, the venue is now well settled into the local pub scene and conversation between locals and visitors is almost inevitable. The three changing cask ales and up to eight real ciders or perries are served on gravity dispense from a chilled cellar room. There are also seven craft beers on tap. To the rear is an outdoor drinking area. ▓❀♣●🚌❀♫

SE23: Forest Hill

Blythe Hill Tavern ★
319 Stanstead Road, SE23 1JB
☎ (020) 8690 5176 ⊕ blythehilltavern.org.uk
Dark Star Hophead; Harvey's Sussex Best Bitter; Sharp's Doom Bar; 1 changing beer (often Adnams, Brockley, Timothy Taylor) Ⓗ
A multiple award-winning suburban pub with a longstanding licensee. This friendly Grade II-listed Victorian local has an unusual three-bar layout that has been identified by CAMRA as a nationally important historic interior. Alongside the cask beers are up to 13 ciders, many of them real. In two of the bars TV screens show sporting events, especially horse racing. Live traditional Irish music is played on Thursday evening. There is a spacious outdoor seating area at the rear.
Q▓❀≉(Catford/Catford Bridge) ●🚌❀🛜♫

Sylvan Post Ⓛ
24-28 Dartmouth Road, SE23 3XU
☎ (020) 8291 5712 ⊕ sylvanpost.co.uk
3 changing beers (sourced locally; often Portobello) Ⓗ
Various types of ambient lighting add to the quirky feel of this ex-Antic pub, set out like a utilitarian café with shabby-chic furnishings. Now operated by Portobello, it is a former post office, retaining many original features. The two strongrooms have been converted into intimate booths and postal memorabilia decorate the walls. Regular community events are held and a Wednesday quiz. Guest beers are usually available to supplement Portobello's own ales. ▓❀◑👤≉⊖♣🚌❀🛜

SE24: Herne Hill

Commercial ★
212 Railton Road, SE24 0JT
☎ (020) 7733 8783 ⊕ thecommercialhernehill.co.uk
Timothy Taylor Landlord; 2 changing beers (sourced nationally) Ⓗ
An imposing, curve-fronted hostelry opposite the station. It has been identified by CAMRA as having a nationally important historic pub interior. The spacious, wood panelled, larger room contains the bar. It runs the full length of the pub and is furnished with a mix of low tables and comfy chairs. A lighter, airier section is towards the rear. The smaller second room is laid out for dining but without feeling like a restaurant. There is outdoor seating at the front and in a small back yard.
▓❀◑👤≉♣🚌❀🛜

Addiscombe

Claret & Ale ♆
5 Bingham Corner, Lower Addiscombe Road, CR0 7AA
☎ (020) 8656 7452
Palmers IPA; 5 changing beers (often Palmers, Sambrook's, Twickenham) Ⓗ
This small, privately owned and friendly free house is making its 37th continuous appearance in this Guide. It is

a community pub where conversation is king, although sports are shown on usually silent screens. As well as pictures of local scenes, the walls carry several award certificates now including local CAMRA Pub of the Year 2024. Five changing beers come from local and national breweries, and a board indicates those being served or waiting in the cellar. ♆🚌❀♫

Barnehurst

Bird & Barrel Ⓛ
100 Barnehurst Road, DA7 6HG
House beer (by Bexley); 2 changing beers (sourced nationally; often Bexley) Ⓗ
A micropub in a former tropical fish emporium, opened in 2018 by Cliff and Jane of Bexley brewery and in effect their brewery tap. A small one-roomer with a handful of standard-height tables, it has a covered, secluded beer garden at the back. House beer Hills & Holes commemorates the old name of the lane serving the station nearby. Some keg beers, wines and spirits are available. Last orders are 30 minutes before closing time. Closed Monday and Tuesday. ▓❀≉●🚌❀🛜♆

Beckenham

Bricklayers Arms
237 High Street, BR3 1BN
☎ (020) 8402 0007 ⊕ bricklayersarmsbeckenham.co.uk
St Austell Tribute, Proper Job; 2 changing beers (sourced nationally) Ⓗ
A traditional high-street pub providing a popular venue for a clientele of all ages. The interior decor is basic yet smart with wooden flooring around the bar. There is also a covered outdoor seating area at the side. The guest ales often reflect customers' recommendations. Occasional beer festivals are held. Live music is popular; both local and visiting bands play here. Live sports fixtures are also shown. Sunday hours apply on most bank holidays. Card payments only.
▓❀≉(Junction/Clock House) ♆(Junction) ♣🚌❀🛜♫

Three Hounds Ⓛ
57 Beckenham Road, BR3 4PR
☎ (020) 3976 0028 ⊕ threehoundsbeerco.com
Anspach & Hobday The Ordinary Bitter; 2 changing beers (often Drop Project, Three Hounds) Ⓗ
Opened in 2020, this self-styled beer café quickly established itself as a community-focused venue. The modern interior has plenty of seating, including in the basement and benches outside on the pavement. Up to three cask beers are available from local and national microbreweries, sometimes including their own from the Three Hounds brewery. At least 12 keg beers are also served, along with several real ciders and over 100 beers in the fridges for takeaway.
▓≉(Clock House) ♆(Beckenham Rd) ●🚌❀♫

Bexleyheath

Furze Wren ✪
6 Market Place, Broadway Square, DA6 7DY
☎ (020) 8298 2590
Greene King Abbot; Ruddles Best Bitter; Sharp's Doom Bar; 7 changing beers (often Oakham, Portobello, Twickenham) Ⓗ
Spacious Wetherspoon pub named after a local bird, better known as the Dartford Warbler. It is at the heart of the shopping area, with buses serving every route through town. Plenty of seating and large windows make it a great place to eat, drink and people-watch. It attracts a full mix of clientele. Local history panels are

displayed around the walls. Alcoholic drinks are served from 9am. No new admittance after 11pm.
Q🍺❀◑♿♣🚌📶

Kentish Belle

8 Pickford Lane, DA7 4QW
☎ (020) 3417 2050 🌐 thekentishbelle.com
4 changing beers (often Arbor, No Frills Joe, Thornbridge) Ⓗ
Located next to the station, Bexleyheath's first micropub, now under new ownership, has been furnished with a flexible mixture of tables and chairs. Outdoor seating is provided during the summer. Regular events include tap takeovers, quiz nights and mini-festivals. Various unusual beers, plus real cider and perry, are served by gravity from a chilled cellar room. A former regional CAMRA Cider Pub of the Year. Q🍺≹♣●P🚆🚌🐾📶

Long Haul

149 Long Lane, DA7 5AE
☎ 07753 617874 🌐 thelonghaul.co.uk
3 changing beers Ⓖ
Opened in 2020 in what had been a tattoo parlour, this micropub is handy for the nearby Indian restaurant. The bar counter is towards the back, with bench seating and standard tables. Usually there is also seating on the forecourt. Predominantly Kentish real ales and ciders are served from a rear chilled cellar room. Last orders are requested 30 minutes before closing time. Local CAMRA Pub of the Year 2022 and 2023. Closed Mondays.
Q❀●🚆🚌(301,401) 🐾

Robin Hood & Little John 🏆 Ⓛ

78 Lion Road, DA6 8PF
☎ (020) 8303 1128 🌐 robinhoodbexleyheath.co.uk
Adnams Southwold Bitter; Bexley Bexley's Own Beer; Fuller's London Pride; Harvey's Sussex Best Bitter; 2 changing beers (often Bexley, Shepherd Neame, Westerham) Ⓗ
A back-street local pub dating from the 1830s, when it was surrounded by fields. Ray and Katerina have been running it for 44 years. Real ales come mostly from independent breweries. It has a good reputation for its home-cooked food at lunchtimes (no food Sun) with Italian specials, which can be eaten at tables made from old Singer sewing machines. Local CAMRA Pub of the Year again in 2024 and three-time regional winner. Over-21s only. Closed Mondays. Q❀◑🚌(B13)🐾♫

Blackfen

Broken Drum Ⓛ

308 Westwood Lane, DA15 9PT
☎ 07803 131678 🌐 thebrokendrum.co.uk
3 changing beers (sourced nationally) Ⓖ
Micropub named after an inn from Terry Pratchett's Discworld series – you can't beat it! Seating is a settle in each of the bay windows and at a variety of tables and chairs, plus pavement tables and chairs for fair-weather drinking (up to 8pm). With Cheesy Thursday the first Thursday of each month, occasional quizzes and excursions, this is a real community pub. It has won awards from both CAMRA and the Society for the Preservation of Beers from the Wood.
Q🍺♣●P🚆🚌(51,132) 🐾📶

Bromley

Partridge

194 High Street, BR1 1HE
☎ (020) 8464 7656 🌐 partridgebromley.co.uk
Dark Star Hophead; Fuller's London Pride, ESB; Gale's HSB; 2 changing beers (often Butcombe, Fuller's) Ⓗ
Built in 1927, this imposing Grade II-listed former bank is now a spacious pub retaining many original features including the high ceilings and chandeliers. There are two snug rooms off the long main bar, plus a small back patio. Six cask ales are offered along with an upmarket food menu. Located by the Market Square, the pub is popular with shoppers and theatregoers for the nearby Churchill Theatre, as well as those drawn by its live music on Saturday evenings.
🍺❀◑♿≹(North/South) 🚌🐾📶♫

Red Lion ✔

10 North Road, BR1 3LG
☎ (020) 8460 2691 🌐 redlionbromley.co.uk
Greene King IPA, Abbot; Harvey's Sussex Best Bitter; 2 changing beers (often Black Sheep, Oakham) Ⓗ
Traditional, well-kept Victorian pub tucked away in the quiet back streets just north of Bromley town centre. Friendly and welcoming, it attracts a wide range of customers of all ages. Now in its 28th consecutive year in the Guide, up to five cask ales are available, with two that change on a regular basis. It retains many original features, including tiling and ornate dark wood, while an extensive library of books dominates one wall. Bar food consists of artisan pizzas. ❀◑≹(North)♣🚌📶

Star & Garter

227 High Street, BR1 1NZ
🌐 starandgarterbromley.com
7 changing beers (often Fyne Ales, Siren, Thornbridge) Ⓗ
Rebuilt 1898 in the Arts and Crafts 'Old English' style, this Grade II-listed pub has been completely refurbished to be more open plan around the U-shaped bar. Real ales are usually from outside the mainstream, with local and regional microbreweries strongly represented. Up to 16 keg beers are also on offer. Customers are welcome to order in food from nearby takeaways. Local CAMRA Pub of the Year 2018-2020. 🍺❀♿≹(North/South)🚌🐾📶

Chislehurst

Cockpit 🏆 Ⓛ

4 Royal Parade, BR7 6NR
☎ 07946 100018 🌐 thecockpitchislehurst.co.uk
7 changing beers (sourced nationally) Ⓖ
Opened in 2020 in premises shared with a florist, this micropub has quickly proved to be a popular addition to the local community. A choice of real ales comes from small breweries from around the country. The deceptively spacious interior has wooden panelling and exposed brickwork. There is plenty of seating inside, plus more benches at the front. The pub name comes from the ancient cockpit situated nearby on Chislehurst Common. Local CAMRA Pub of the Year 2023 and 2024.
Q🍺❀♣●🚌🐾

Crayford

Penny Farthing Ⓛ

3 Waterside, DA1 4JJ
☎ 07368 448446 🌐 pennyfarthingcrayford.co.uk
4 changing beers (often Old Dairy, Wantsum, Whitstable) Ⓖ
Bexley's second micropub, opened in 2014. Ale and cider are served from a cold room with a viewing window. A charity fine is levied should your mobile phone ring. Kentish brewers feature mostly, with an increasing cider range supplementing Dudda's Tun and Westons. Summer pavement seating overlooks a small riverside park.

Usually open on bank holidays, it is a good venue to watch local public events. A former local CAMRA Pub of the Year and regional runner-up. Closed Mondays.
Q✿☸≉♠♦🚇🚃❀

Croydon

Builders Arms
65 Leslie Park Road, CRO 6TP
☎ (020) 8654 1803 ⊕ buildersarmscroydon.co.uk
Dark Star Hophead; Fuller's London Pride, ESB; 1 changing beer (sourced locally) Ⓗ
A back-street community local opened in the 19th century, and now a Fuller's tenancy serving beers from the brewery's range. The two bars each have their own character. The smaller public-style bar has a dartboard, and the larger saloon bar has a mix of comfortable seating types. Both have large TV screens showing sport. There is a pleasant garden at the rear. Events include family fun days and occasional live music.
🌞✿◖♿≉(East) 🚌(Lebanon Rd) ♦🚃❀🛜♪

Cronx Tap
71 High Street, CRO 1QE
⊕ thecronx.com
2 changing beers (often Cronx)
A friendly and welcoming new outlet for the Cronx brewery, opened in 2023 and replacing a former unit in Boxpark. Two handpumps dispense Cronx beers, with an occasional guest such as Titsey. A wide range of craft beers plus five or six ciders are served from 20 taps. A regular quiz is held, and music and comedy nights feature occasionally. It opens mid-afternoon during the week. Food is available Thursday to Saturday evenings from a Venezuelan pop-up kitchen.
◖♿≉(East/West) 🚌(George St/Reeves Corner) ⊖(West) 🚃❀🛜

George Ⓛ ✅
17-21 George Street, CRO 1LA
☎ (020) 8649 9077
Fuller's London Pride; Greene King IPA, Abbot; Sharp's Doom Bar; Thornbridge Jaipur; 6 changing beers (often Oakham, Twickenham) Ⓗ
The only remaining Wetherspoon pub in the town centre, the George was named after a former coaching inn, the George & Dragon. There are two bars, with ramp access to the upper one (which may close early). The changing beers often include ones from local brewers, and the pub partakes in a London beer festival as well as the national chain ones in spring and autumn. Alcoholic drinks are served from 9am.
🌞◖♿≉(East/West) 🚌(George St/Reeves Corner) ⊖(West) 🚃🛜

Green Dragon Ⓛ ✅
58-60 High Street, CRO 1NA
☎ (020) 8667 0684
7 changing beers (often Brentwood, Southwark, Wantsum) Ⓗ
Housed in a former bank building near Croydon's historic market, the Dragon appeals to people of all ages. The pub serves up to seven cask ales and eight other draught beers from local and national breweries. The food menu includes vegetarian and vegan options. Upstairs, the function room is available for hire and hosts weekly events such as quizzes, poker and live music including jam sessions. The bag in box ciders may include one that is not from concentrate.
🌞◖♿≉(East/West) 🚌(George St/Reeves Corner) ⊖(West) ♦🚃🛜♪

Royal Standard Ⓛ
1 Sheldon Street, CRO 1SS
☎ (020) 8680 3106 ⊕ royalstandardcroydon.co.uk
Fuller's London Pride, ESB; Gale's HSB Ⓗ
A friendly street-corner local in the shadow of the Croydon flyover, making its 36th appearance in this Guide. This quiet retreat south of the town centre has a single bar with four different drinking areas, including one with a dartboard. Etched windows, wood panelling and owls feature throughout the pub. There are a couple of tables outside at the front and a small, secluded garden area across the road. It opens mid-afternoon most days. 🌞✿🚌(Church St/George St)♦🚃❀

Spread Eagle
39-41 Katharine Street, CRO 1NX
☎ (020) 8781 1135
Dark Star Hophead; Fuller's London Pride, ESB; Gale's HSB; 1 changing beer Ⓗ
Large street-corner pub built in 1893 as a bank and now operated by Whelan Inns as a Fuller's tenancy. The spacious interior boasts wood panelling, high ceilings, chandelier lighting and an imposing staircase leading up to a function room, occasionally used for events. As well as the Fuller's range of cask ale, a good range of other draught and bottled beers is on offer. Sport is shown on the TV screens and quiz night is Sunday.
✿◖♿≉(East/West) 🚌(George St/Reeves Corner) ⊖(West) ♦🚃🛜

Downe

Queen's Head Ⓛ
25 High Street, BR6 7US TQ432616
☎ (01689) 852145 ⊕ queensheaddowne.com
Harvey's Sussex Best Bitter; 3 changing beers (often Bexley, Northdown, Westerham) Ⓗ
Attractive, traditional venue with open fireplaces, dating from 1565 and named following a visit to Downe by Queen Elizabeth I. There are several dining areas that offer a daily menu including home-made specials. The pretty walled garden is popular in warmer weather. In the centre of this quiet historic country village but accessible by bus from Bromley and Orpington, it is frequented all year round by walkers, cyclists and visitors to nearby Down House, the former home of Charles Darwin. 🌞✿◖♦P🚌(146,R8)❀🛜♪

Hayes

Real Ale Way Ⓛ
55 Station Approach, BR2 7EB
☎ 07446 897885
House beer (by Tonbridge); 8 changing beers (often Kent, Larkins, Ramsgate) Ⓖ
Originally built in the 1930s within a shopping parade, this former bank and accountancy office opened as a spacious micropub in 2018. Handy for Hayes station, it quickly became a popular venue for local drinkers and rail commuters alike. Up to nine cask ales, mostly sourced from smaller breweries in Kent, are dispensed by gravity from a cold room. Wooden flooring, framed prints and mirrors are complemented by subdued lighting with plenty of assorted seating. Q≉♦🚃❀♪

Orpington

Orpington Liberal Club Ⓛ
7 Station Road, BR6 0RZ
☎ (01689) 820882 ⊕ orpingtonliberalclub.co.uk
5 changing beers Ⓗ

Friendly club serving over 200 different cask ales every year, mainly from smaller breweries, across a range of beer styles. Up to five cask ales are available along with real cider. Two real ale festivals are held annually. The club is a hub of the community, hosting many events in its spacious hall and supporting local charities. Regularly voted local CAMRA Club of the Year and a national finalist in 2020. A CAMRA or NULC card is required for entry. Q⏳☺✿≉♣♠P⛽🚃❀🎵

Selsdon

Golden Ark
186 Addington Road, CR2 8LB
☎ (020) 8651 0700 ⊕ thegoldenark.co.uk
4 changing beers (sourced locally) Ⓗ
Croydon borough's first micropub, situated in Selsdon's main street, offering four cask ales plus keg taps and cider. Small-pack beers and cider are available for off-sales. Boards detailing the current beers and ciders are hung on the ceiling beam above the corner bar. There is also an unusual selection of gins and whiskies. Some of the wooden tabletops have been artistically finished, and artworks adorn the walls. The pub has won local CAMRA awards and has strong links with the community. ⏳♿♠🚃❀🎵

South Croydon

Crown & Sceptre
32 Junction Road, CR2 6RB
☎ (020) 8688 8037 ⊕ crownandsceptresouthcroydon.co.uk
Dark Star Hophead; Fuller's London Pride, ESB Ⓗ
A traditional side-street pub, with its name etched into one of the front windows. The single L-shaped bar has been extended towards a patio at the rear. The interior has a mix of seating styles, mostly in leather, and there is a large seating area outside. The walls carry pictures of old local scenes or with a royalty theme, and there is a large brewery mirror. Food served is mainly pizzas, although other dishes are available. Tuesday is quiz night. ⏳✿🕐♿≉♣♠P🚃❀

Welling

Door Hinge Ⓛ
11 Welling High Street, DA16 1TR
☎ 07305 809066 ⊕ thedoorhinge.co.uk
3 changing beers (often Kent, Mighty Oak, Old Dairy) Ⓖ
A breath of fresh air on the local pub scene and handy for the football ground, London's first permanent micropub opened in 2013 in part of a former electrical wholesaler's. Normally at least three beers are dispensed by gravity from a glass-fronted cold room. The cosy bar encourages conversation among previous strangers and there is an even smaller quiet room to the rear. Cider comes from various sources. Closed Mondays. Q♣♠⛽🚃❀

West Wickham

Real Ale Way Ⓛ
75 Station Road, BR4 0PX
Larkins Pale; Tonbridge Traditional Ale; 6 changing beers Ⓖ
A former soft furnishings shop, this micropub opened in 2021 as the second Real Ale Way within Bromley borough and operates in a similar manner to its sister in Hayes. Up to eight cask ales, mostly sourced from smaller breweries in Kent, are dispensed by gravity from a cold room. The premises have plenty of assorted seating,

large double-aspect windows and exposed floorboards. Pictures by local artists complement the light and bright contemporary interior. Q≉●🚃(119,194)❀🛜

SOUTH-WEST LONDON
SW1: Belgravia

Antelope
22-24 Eaton Terrace, SW1W 8EZ
☎ (020) 7824 8512 ⊕ antelope-eaton-terrace.co.uk
Fuller's London Pride, Day Dreamer; Gale's HSB; 2 changing beers (often Dark Star, Fuller's) Ⓗ
Dating back to 1827, this Fuller's venue spent several years as an M&B Nicholson's pub until 2005. Original preserved features include etched-glass windows, a side room used as a snug, and the central bar. The upstairs bar and side room can be hired for functions. This is an upmarket house and the clientele consists mainly of local professionals. The pub plays cricket matches against the Churchill Arms in Notting Hill. Q⏳🕐●⊖(Sloane Sq)🚃🛜

Fox & Hounds ✓
29 Passmore Street, SW1W 8HR
☎ (020) 7730 6367 ⊕ foxandhoundssw1.co.uk
Young's London Original; 2 changing beers (often St Austell, Timothy Taylor) Ⓗ
Until 1998 this was the only remaining beer house (pub without a spirit licence) in London, if not the country. The Beer Act 1830 allowed any ratepayer to set one up in their home on payment of a small fee and the estate landlord who granted the licence here in 1869, the future Duke of Westminster, was a temperance campaigner opposed to spirits. There is no music and no TVs. It is rumoured to be the pub where Coronation Street was devised. Q⊖(Sloane Sq)🚃❀🛜

Star Tavern ★
6 Belgrave Mews West, SW1X 8HT
☎ (020) 7235 3019 ⊕ star-tavern-belgravia.co.uk
Fuller's London Pride, ESB; 2 changing beers (often Butcombe, Dark Star, Wimbledon) Ⓗ
Down a mews, near embassies, and rich in the history of the powerful and famous, this is rumoured to be where the Great Train Robbery was planned. A popular Fuller's pub where local residents, business people and embassy staff rub shoulders with casual visitors, it has featured in all 52 editions of this Guide. Sometimes a special Fuller's beer can be found here. Upstairs is a function room. ⏳🕐⊖(Hyde Park Corner/Knightsbridge)♣🚃❀🛜

SW1: Pimlico

Cask Pub & Kitchen
6 Charlwood Street, SW1V 2EE
☎ (020) 7630 7225 ⊕ caskpubandkitchen.com
10 changing beers Ⓗ
Formerly the Pimlico Tram, the Cask was converted to a beer destination 13 years ago by owners who have since also found renown for the Craft Beer Co chain. Ten handpumps serve an ever-changing selection of real ales from microbreweries, and a vast range of bottled beers from the UK and around the world complements some unusual draught choices. Burgers feature on the weekday menu, with roasts on Sundays until late afternoon. ⏳✿🕐≉(Victoria)⊖🚃❀🛜🎵

SW1: St James's

Red Lion ★
2 Duke of York Street, SW1Y 6JP
☎ (020) 7321 0782 ⊕ redlionmayfair.co.uk

Fuller's London Pride, Day Dreamer; Gale's Seafarers Ale; 2 changing beers (often Fuller's) ⊞
Close to the upmarket shops in Jermyn Street, this celebrated little gem is worth visiting just for its historic interior, identified by CAMRA as nationally important, and, in particular, its spectacular Victorian etched and cut mirrors and glass. The Grade II-listed building dates from 1821 and was given a new frontage in 1871. When busy, customers often spill out onto the pavement. Beware of the steep steps down to the toilets.
ᏰᏪⱺ(Green Park/Piccadilly Circus) 🚆♿🐾🛜

SW1: Victoria

Wetherspoons ✅
Unit 5, Upper Concourse, Victoria Station, Terminus Place, SW1V 1JT
☎ (020) 7931 0445
Greene King IPA, Abbot; Sharp's Doom Bar; 5 changing beers (often Windsor & Eton, Adnams, Sambrook's) ⊞
Above WHSmith, overlooking the station concourse and accessed mainly by escalators, this pub has a bright café bar atmosphere and was refurbished in 2024, adding extra seating. Features include blue and cream tiling, two curved bars with marble-style tops and banquettes along the opposite side. TV screens show times of train departures. Note that British Transport Police sometimes close the bar when football fans are due.
Q ᏰᏪ♿≠⊖🚆🛜

Willow Walk ⓛ ✅
25 Wilton Road, SW1V 1LW
☎ (020) 7828 2953
Greene King IPA, Abbot; Sharp's Doom Bar; 6 changing beers (often Portobello, Sambrook's) ⊞
Ground-floor Wetherspoon pub converted from a Woolworths in 1999, extending from opposite the eastern side entrance to Victoria Station back to Vauxhall Bridge Road, with entrances on both streets. Some wood panelling, a fairly low ceiling and subdued lighting create a warm atmosphere. Friendly and attentive staff look after a mixed clientele, including families. Some London-brewed guest beers are usually available. Alcoholic drinks are served from 9am. Q ᏰᏪ♿≠⊖🚆🛜

SW1: Westminster

Buckingham Arms
62 Petty France, SW1H 9EU
☎ (020) 7222 3386 ⊕ buckinghamarms.com
Young's London Original, London Special; 3 changing beers (often Adnams, Twickenham, Wimbledon) ⊞
Said to have once been a hat shop, the Bell opened here in the 1720s and was renamed the Black Horse in the 1740s. Rebuilt in 1898, renamed again in 1901 and substantially renovated in recent years, it is another pub that has appeared in all 52 editions of this Guide. A mix of modern and traditional seats and tables draws civil servants, visitors and the occasional MP. Open Sunday afternoons from the end of March through the summer.
ᏰᏪ⊖(St James's Park) 🚆

Speaker ✅
46 Great Peter Street, SW1P 2HA
☎ (020) 7222 4589
Sharp's Doom Bar; Timothy Taylor Landlord; 3 changing beers (often London Brewing, Portobello, Sambrook's) ⊞
A friendly pine-panelled one-bar local decorated with parliamentary caricatures. Dating from 1729 or earlier, the Castle, renamed the Elephant & Castle around 1800

and the Speaker from 1999, was part of the Devil's Acre slum next to the world's first public gas works. The pub now welcomes local estate residents, office workers and the occasional MP, all of whom enjoy the attractive range of beers. No music, TV or children.
⊖(St James's Park) 🚆🛜

SW2: Brixton

Elm Park Tavern
76 Elm Park, SW2 2UB
☎ (020) 8674 0023 ⊕ elm-park-tavern.co.uk
1 changing beer (often Anspach & Hobday, Gipsy Hill, Timothy Taylor) ⊞
A sister pub to King & Co in Clapham, with a single bar serving separate front and back rooms, each with a cosy atmosphere. There are three handpumps serving two beers at a time with another 16 draught beers on tap. Monday and Tuesday evening Ale Club sees lower prices for cask beers. A popular quiz night is held on Sundays. Note the unique portrait of 18th-century stage mimic Samuel Foote. ᏰᏪ♦🚆♿🛜♫

SW4: Clapham

Apollo Arms
13-19 Old Town, SW4 0JT
☎ (020) 3827 1213 ⊕ apolloarms.co.uk
Wye Valley HPA, Butty Bach; 1 changing beer (sourced nationally) ⊞
Following its reopening and latest renaming, real ale has returned to this Clapham Old Town venue in the form of two regular beers that are unusual for London plus an ever-changing guest ale. The main drinking area in this modern pub offers a mixture of high stools and tables plus more conventional furniture. Dining areas can be found at either side. At the rear is a paved outside area which is heated and covered.
ᏰᏪ♿⊖(Common) 🚆♿🛜

King & Co
100 Clapham Park Road, SW4 7BZ
☎ (020) 7498 1971 ⊕ thekingandco.uk
3 changing beers (often Adnams, Portobello, Twickenham) ⊞
Popular with the after-work crowd, this Portobello brewery outlet ticks all the boxes. Two real ciders and two or three real ales, often from London breweries, are served by genial staff in a buzzy atmosphere. Pop-up food enterprises are in charge of the kitchen, changing every six weeks. There are tables outside on the heated front terrace for alfresco drinking and eating when the weather is favourable. All available beers are listed on blackboards near the bar. ᏰᏪ⊖(Common)♦🚆♿🛜

Prince of Wales ✅
38 Old Town, SW4 0LB
☎ (020) 7622 4964 ⊕ powsw4.com
Harvey's Sussex Best Bitter; Timothy Taylor Landlord; 1 changing beer (often Sambrook's) ⊞
This is one of the very few remaining drinkers' pubs in the Old Town area of Clapham and its interior has similarly ignored passing trends. Bric-a-brac adorns the ceiling and old prints and pictures line the walls. The falcon emblem of the pub's previous owners, the original Lacons brewery of Great Yarmouth, features on the charming tiled fireplaces and on an exterior plaque. Bench tables outside the front are provided for alfresco drinking. ᏰᏪ⊖(Common)🚆♿🛜

SW5: Earls Court

King's Head
17 Hogarth Place, SW5 0QT
☎ (020) 7373 5239 ⊕ kingsheadearlscourt.co.uk
Fuller's Oliver's Island, London Pride; 2 changing beers (often Fuller's, Robinsons) Ⓗ
A comfortable, friendly corner pub with a modernised interior, hidden away off the busy Earls Court Road; the building is a 1937 rebuild of the oldest (circa 17th century) licensed premises in the area. Seating is a mixture of high stools around tall tables. Three Fuller's cask ales are supplemented by a guest, usually from another local brewery. Upstairs is a separate dining room. On Monday evenings there is a quiz.
⧗◑&⮯(West Brompton)⊖🚐🐾🌳

SW6: Fulham

Lillie Langtry ✅
19 Lillie Road, SW6 1UE
☎ (020) 3637 6690 ⊕ thelillielangtry.co.uk
4 changing beers (sourced nationally; often Park, Timothy Taylor, Twickenham) Ⓗ
Fulham's oldest surviving 19th-century pub, built in 1835 as the Lillie Arms and named after owner Sir John Scott Lillie. Originally a watering hole for the nearby Kensington Canal, later to become the West London Railway, it was renamed in 1979 after the famous actress and socialite who reputedly entertained many noblemen including Bertie, Prince of Wales. Real ales were introduced with the extensive 2016 refurbishment by Hippo Inns. 🏮◑&⮯(West Brompton)⊖🚐🐾🌳♫

SW6: Parsons Green

White Horse Ⓛ
1-3 Parsons Green, SW6 4UL
☎ (020) 7736 2115 ⊕ whitehorsesw6.com
6 changing beers (sourced nationally) Ⓗ
Destination Mitchells & Butlers pub that normally boasts five guest beers on handpump and an international selection of bottled beers. Regular beer and food matching events take place as well as beer festivals; the Old Ale Festival in late November has run for 40 years, with a stillage in the Coach House, normally reserved for dining. The pub can get busy when Chelsea FC are playing at home, but upstairs there is room to escape the crowds. A Sunday evening quiz is held.
Q⧗🏮◑&⊖🚐(22,424)🐾🌳

SW7: Gloucester Road

Queen's Arms
30 Queen's Gate Mews, SW7 5QL
☎ (020) 7823 9293 ⊕ thequeensarmskensington.co.uk
Harvey's Sussex Best Bitter; Timothy Taylor Landlord; 2 changing beers (often Hogs Back) Ⓗ
Lovely corner mews Mitchells & Butlers pub, discreetly tucked away off Queen's Gate, well worth seeking out for its real ales and its large range of interesting draught and bottled beers, malt whiskies and other spirits. Note the unusual curved doors. The L-shaped room has wooden floors and panelling. The clientele reflects the location: affluent locals, students from Imperial College and musicians from, and visitors to, the nearby Royal Albert Hall. It is wise to reserve a table. ◑&⊖🚐🐾🌳

SW8: South Lambeth

Surprise
16 Southville, SW8 2PP
☎ (020) 7622 4623
2 changing beers (often Morland, Purity, Wadworth) Ⓗ
Tucked away next to Larkhall Park, this small, down-to-earth, L-shaped local with conservatory extension is the only building remaining from streets that were replaced by the park after WWII bomb damage. The back room walls display caricatures of former and regular customers, while the middle section has old photographs of Battersea Power Station. The adjacent pétanque pitch is due to reopen. There is an all-day pizza menu.
⧗🏮◑⊖(Nine Elms/Wandsworth Rd)♣🚐🐾🌳

SW9: Brixton

Crown & Anchor
246 Brixton Road, SW9 6AQ
☎ (020) 7737 0060 ⊕ crownandanchorbrixton.co.uk
3 changing beers (often Hophurst, Sambrook's, Siren) Ⓗ
Now the south London outpost of the small London Village Inns chain, this stripped-back yet stylish corner pub reopened in 2012, offering an enterprising range of beers from cask, keg, bottle and can, as well as at least one cider on handpump, usually from Seacider. The long, single bar has large windows, bare brick back walls and a high ceiling, with plenty of seating. Burgers and German sausages feature on the menu, with vegan alternatives. Cashless payments only. ⧗◑♣🚐🐾

SW11: Battersea Power Station

Battersea Brewery Tap Room Ⓛ
12-14 Arches Lane, SW11 8AB
☎ (020) 8161 2366 ⊕ batterseabrew.co.uk
Battersea Admiral Best Bitter; 1 changing beer (often Brodie's) Ⓗ
A must for the cask ale drinker visiting the Power Station complex, this taproom is located in a railway arch adjacent to its brewery. The decor on the ground and mezzanine floors has a suitably industrial feel with bare brick, exposed pipework and copper-topped tables. Food is limited to bar snacks such as chicken wings and toasties. In fine weather bench seating outside provides a good vantage point on Arches Lane, home to restaurants, a cinema and a theatre.
⧗🏮◑&⮯(Battersea Park)⊖♣🚐🐾🌳

SW11: Clapham Junction

Eagle Ale House Ⓛ
104 Chatham Road, SW11 6HG
☎ (020) 7228 2328 ⊕ eaglealehouse.wordpress.com
Changing beers (often Downton, East London, Surrey Hills) Ⓗ
A charming, cosy local, just off the busy Northcote Road, the Eagle is a bastion for microbrewery cask and KeyKeg beers from near and far. One handpump is kept for ciders and bottle coolers now feature continental classics including several Lambics. The garden benefits from a large heated shelter. Several TV screens come to life for major sporting events, with rugby dominating. Occasionally there is live music. Local CAMRA Pub of the Year 2022. Cash payments preferred.
⧗🏮🚐(319,G1)🐾🌳♫

SW12: Balham

Nightingale
97 Nightingale Lane, SW12 8NX
☎ (020) 8673 1637 ⊕ thenightingalebalham.co.uk

Young's London Original, London Special; 3 changing beers (often By The Horns, St Austell, Sambrook's) H
Dating from the mid-19th century, this pub has the feel of a country pub in town. It has two distinct areas: a public bar at the front and a saloon area at the rear. It also has an attractive back garden and outside seating to the front. The 40-year-old annual summer walk raises large funds for charity. The food offering is very popular, and there is a quiz on Wednesdays.
&(Wandsworth Common) ⊖(Clapham South) ♣🚌(G1) 🌸 ?

SW13: Barnes

Red Lion
2 Castelnau, SW13 9RU
☎ (020) 8748 2984 ⊕ red-lion-barnes.co.uk
Fuller's London Pride, ESB; 2 changing beers (often Dark Star, Fuller's, Twickenham) H
Large Victorian landmark establishment at the entrance to the Wetland Centre, comprising a front bar area and a spacious rear dining room with a mosaic domed ceiling light and an impressive fireplace. Outside is a covered patio, a large artificial grass garden, play area, two four-seater heated cabins and outside bar in summer. Well-behaved dogs are welcome inside, children under 10 until early evening. Occasional beers come from Wimbledon and Park breweries. The pub has a Fuller's Master Cellarman award. Q &🌸 P🚌 🌸 ?

SW15: Putney

Bricklayer's Arms ★
32 Waterman Street, SW15 1DD
☎ (020) 8246 5544
Timothy Taylor Boltmaker, Landlord; 8 changing beers (often Five Points, Surrey Hills, Wimbledon) H
A back-street local dating from 1826 identified by CAMRA as having a nationally important historic pub interior. Besides offering an interesting selection of real ales that are unusual for the area, often from microbreweries in London and the South East, it runs a cricket team. The pub is favoured by Fulham FC supporters and so the beer range may be depleted following home matches. Recently refurbished, it is also increasingly popular with families and younger drinkers.
&⊖(Bridge) ♣🚌 🌸 ?

Spencer Arms L
237 Lower Richmond Road, SW15 1HJ
☎ (020) 8788 0640 ⊕ thespencerarms.com
Surrey Hills Shere Drop; Wimbledon Common Pale Ale; 2 changing beers (often Dark Star, Sambrook's) H
Overlooking Putney Common and at the end of the number 22 bus route from Piccadilly Circus, this former hotel is a popular pub with a large restaurant area and heated patio. It is dog and family-friendly with no time restriction for children. Background music is quiet and the television often silent. The four real ales served are mostly from local breweries. Monday is quiz night. Card payments only. &🌸 🚌 ♪

SW15: Putney Heath

Telegraph L
Putney Heath, SW15 3TU
☎ (020) 8194 2808
Timothy Taylor Landlord; house beer (by St Austell); 9 changing beers (often Sambrook's, Twickenham) H
On the edge of Putney Heath, this impressive pub has many separate drinking and dining areas and offers a

generous choice of real ales, some always locally brewed. The smart decor includes many prints and old London Underground posters, vintage maps and photographs. There is an extensive beer garden to enjoy in fine weather. It is on the site of the Putney Telegraph, part of the Admiralty Telegraph between London and Portsmouth, which operated from 1796 to 1848.
&🌸 P🚌 🌸 ?

SW16: Streatham

Railway L ✓
2 Greyhound Lane, SW16 5SD
☎ (020) 8769 9448 ⊕ therailwaysw16.co.uk
Sambrook's Wandle; 4 changing beers (often Portobello, Southwark, Twickenham) H
This busy two-bar community pub is close to Streatham Common station. Now free of tie, it showcases London-brewed beers in cask, keg, bottles and cans. The back bar, available for hire, is open on weekday afternoons as a popular tearoom. There is outside seating at the front and in the spacious rear enclosure. There is a quiz on Tuesdays, a popular monthly Sunday comedy night and occasional live music performances. Two-time local CAMRA Pub of the Year.
&⊖(Common) ♣🚌(60,118) 🌸 ?

SW17: Tooting

Antelope ★ L
76 Mitcham Road, SW17 9NG
☎ (020) 8672 3888 ⊕ theantelopepub.com
Sambrook's Wandle; Thornbridge Jaipur; Volden Session Ale, Pale Ale; 3 changing beers (often Twickenham, Wimbledon) H
A large, lively Victorian community pub identified by CAMRA as having a nationally important historic pub interior, preserved and cherished by operators, Antic. The main bar area, retaining some Barclay's signage, leads back to dining tables and the spacious Rankin Room that shows big-screen sports. Seating in the large back yard is part-covered and heated in winter. Regular events include live music and a quiz night. Sundays feature popular roasts and folk music in the afternoon. Children are welcome until mid-evening.
&⊖(Broadway) 🚌 🌸 ? ♪

J.J. Moon's
56A Tooting High Street, SW17 0RN
☎ (020) 8672 4726
Greene King Abbot; Ruddles Best Bitter; Sharp's Doom Bar; 3 changing beers (often Twickenham, Windsor & Eton) H
A busy Wetherspoon pub that reflects its location at the heart of multicultural Tooting. Its long and narrow, wood-panelled interior stretches back from the High Street and is decorated in the chain's typical style, with local history panels featuring famous Tooting residents, including actor George Cole and snooker player Jimmy White. Guest beers often include choices from independent breweries in London and the South East.
&⊖(Broadway) 🚌 ?

SW18: Southfields

Pig & Whistle L ✓
481 Merton Road, SW18 5LD
☎ (020) 8874 1061 ⊕ pigandwhistlesw18.co.uk
Sharp's Doom Bar; Timothy Taylor Landlord; 1 changing beer (often Sambrook's, Wimbledon) H
A busy, family-friendly pub, refurbished in contemporary Young's style featuring stripped wood, high tables and

picture windows. A collection of miniature pigs is on display near the bar. Chairs and tables in front of the pub and seating on astroturf and in hutlets at the rear offer an alternative to being indoors. The food menu has a South African influence, and there is also a menu for dogs 👪❀◐♿🚆(Earlsfield) ⊖(Wimbledon Park) 🚌(156) 🐾📶

SW18: Wandsworth

Cat's Back

86-88 Point Pleasant, SW18 1PP

☎ 07523 047335 🌐 thecatsback.co.uk

Harvey's IPA, Sussex Best Bitter, Old Ale; 1 changing beer (often Harvey's) [H]

In an area dominated by new riverside residential developments, the Cat's Back downstairs has the feel of a back-street local, as befits a pub owned by one of Britain's most traditional breweries. The upstairs room has been artistically remodelled. Outdoors is a single bench on the pavement in front, and a back garden with tables and chairs. In winter a real fire adds to the cosy atmosphere. Closed Mondays. 👪❀♿♣🚌🐾📶♫

Sambrook's Brewery Tap [L]

40 Ram Street, SW18 1UD

☎ (020) 7228 0598 🌐 sambrooksbrewery.co.uk

Sambrook's Wandle, Pumphouse Pale, Junction; 2 changing beers (often Sambrook's) [H]

Opened in 2021 within the historic site of the former Young's Ram brewery, the taproom here has outside seating in Bubbling Well Square and two inside bars, downstairs and upstairs, each with tall tables and stools as well as comfortable bench seating. Both bars have great views of large fermenting and conditioning tanks. Delicious pizzas and other savoury snacks are served. The old Young's brewery coppers now form the centrepiece of a heritage centre and museum. Closed Mondays. 👪❀◐♿🚆(Town) 🚌🐾📶

Spread Eagle ★

71 Wandsworth High Street, SW18 2PT

☎ (020) 8161 0038 🌐 spreadeaglewandsworth.co.uk

Young's London Original, London Special; 1 changing beer (often St Austell, Young's) [H]

With an historic pub interior identified by CAMRA as being of national importance, this opulent drinkers' establishment sits at the heart of Wandsworth opposite the former Young's brewery. Fine glass and woodwork include a full-height partition separating the ornate saloon bar from the public bar to the left. Since the pub's recent award-winning refurbishment and extension to include hotel facilities, the food service now includes Sunday roasts. The public bar can be hired for private functions. 👪🛏◐♿🚆(Town)🚌🐾📶

SW19: South Wimbledon

Sultan ★

78 Norman Road, SW19 1BT

☎ (020) 8544 9323

Hop Back GFB, Citra, Taiphoon, Entire Stout, Summer Lightning; 2 changing beers (often Downton, Hop Back) [H]

Hop Back's only London tied house is an attractive two-bar 1950s brick building identified by CAMRA as having a nationally important historic interior. Mostly carpeted, it has dark wood walls, large tables with chairs, some fixed seating, settees in the conservatory and benches in the patio and outside. An upstairs room is available for hire. Beer festivals in spring, summer and Christmas. The pub opens at 11am on Saturdays when AFC Wimbledon are at home; visiting supporters welcome. 👪❀♿🚆(Haydons Rd) ⊖(Colliers Wood/South Wimbledon) ♣🚌🐾📶♫

Trafalgar 🏆 [L]

23 High Path, SW19 2JY

☎ 07872 957662

Surrey Hills Shere Drop; 4 changing beers (often Downton, Lacons, Redemption) [H]

A small, street-corner house conversion dating from the 1860s with a 1906 extension. This narrow, one-bar pub was reopened and refurbished in September 2023, with a variety of tables, chairs and settles and illustrations of the battle of Trafalgar. Alongside the excellent cask choice is an interesting range of bottled beers, canned beers, keg craft beers and lagers. Three guest real ciders may be local. The pub has its own cricket team. Live folk music is played some Saturdays – check the pub's Facebook page for details. Local CAMRA Pub of the Year 2024. 🚊(Morden Rd)⊖🍏🚌🐾📶♫

SW19: Wimbledon

Hand in Hand [L]

7 Crooked Billet, SW19 4RQ

☎ (020) 8946 5720 🌐 thehandinhandwimbledon.co.uk

Courage Directors; St Austell Proper Job; Young's London Original, London Special [H]**; 3 changing beers (often Adnams, Young's)** [H]/[G]

Popular, dog-friendly establishment on the edge of Wimbledon Common with separate drinking areas and a variety of seating. At least three guest beers are regularly sold, usually from local breweries. Children are welcome in the family room. This is a great place to eat, inside or on the front patio, with beer included in several recipes. There is a quiz on Tuesday and occasional beer tastings and cellar tours. Q👪❀◐♿♣🚌(200)🐾📶

SW20: Raynes Park

Cavern

100 Coombe Lane, SW20 0AY

☎ (020) 8946 7980 🌐 thecavernfreehouse.co.uk

Sharp's Doom Bar; Wimbledon Common; 1 changing beer (often Wimbledon) [H]

Opened in 1991 but with a 1960s rock'n'roll atmosphere successfully created by many photographs and posters, matched by the landlord's record selection and regular live music sessions. The floor is tiled but with carpeted seating corner areas. An original Gilbert Scott red telephone kiosk stands next to the door. A small room at the back has a pool table. The pub does not serve food but customers are welcome to bring in their own. ❀🚆♣🚌♫

Carshalton

Cryer Arts Centre [L]

39 High Street, SM5 3BB

☎ (020) 8773 9390 🌐 cryerarts.co.uk

Surrey Hills Shere Drop; 2 changing beers (sourced nationally) [H]

Formerly the Charles Cryer Theatre, the Cryer Arts Centre now hosts arts events. The large, separate, Spotlight Bar and restaurant has three handpumps and a selection of bottled and KeyKeg beers; it is a popular place for lunch. There is a small outdoor drinking area at the front. A large outdoor and marquee space at the rear is sometimes in use. A function room is available for hire. 👪◐♿🚆🍏🚌🐾📶♫

Hope ⓛ

48 West Street, SM5 2PR

☎ (020) 8240 1255 ⊕ hopecarshalton.co.uk

Downton New Forest Ale; Windsor & Eton Knight of the Garter; 5 changing beers Ⓗ

A traditional pub in the heart of the Carshalton Conservation Area, owned by its regulars. Seven handpumps dispense cask ale in various styles, and up to four real ciders and a range of craft keg beers are served. Third-pint measures are available and a good range of bottled beer is stocked. A permanent marquee, available for hire, is where regular beer festivals are held. Children are not admitted. Regular winner of local and regional CAMRA awards. Q❀◐&≒♣♠P🖪🖵❀🥂♫

Railway Tavern ⊘

47 North Street, SM5 2HG

☎ 07710 476437 ⊕ railwaytaverncarshalton.co.uk

Fuller's London Pride; 2 changing beers (sourced regionally; often Dark Star) Ⓗ

Street-corner community local close to the railway station, adorned with hanging baskets and with window boxes beneath the fine etched windows. Inside are a small U-shaped drinking area around a central bar and a comfortable side area. The walls display various items of railway and brewery memorabilia. The pub opens early afternoon during the week. ❀≒♣🖵❀🥂♫

Cheam

Railway

32 Station Way, SM3 8SQ

☎ (020) 8395 5393

Courage Best Bitter; Timothy Taylor Landlord; 4 changing beers (often Banks's, Lister's) Ⓗ

A small, traditional pub conveniently close to Cheam Station, and a local landmark for more than 150 years. A charming and warm ambience dominates and the pub provides a home to several community groups. The two regular beers are supplemented by up to three changing ales from a range of breweries. Well-behaved dogs are welcome. Rugby and horse racing are screened and there are regular quiz nights and occasional live music evenings. ≒♣🖵❀🥂♫

Kingston

Albion ⓛ

45 Fairfield Road, KT1 2PY

☎ (020) 8439 7787 ⊕ thealbionkingston.com

Big Smoke Solaris Session Pale Ale; Harvey's Sussex Best Bitter; 8 changing beers (often 360 Degree, Big Smoke) Ⓗ

Part of the Big Smoke brewery chain, serving ales mostly from small breweries nationwide and up to four changing ciders. Varnished wooden floors and comfortable wood-panelled seating areas extend back to a rear patio garden with heaters, gin distillery and a glazed garden room (available for hire). Music is from an extensive collection of vinyl LPs. Home-cooked food is served lunchtime and evenings (all day Fri-Sun). Board games are available and a Sunday night quiz. A former local CAMRA Pub of the Year. ☾❀◐&≒♠🖵❀🥂

Park Tavern

19 New Road, KT2 6AP

☎ (020) 8549 0361 ⊕ perfectpub.co.uk

Fuller's London Pride; Young's London Original; 4 changing beers (often Adnams, Ascot) Ⓗ

Near the Kingston gate into Richmond Park, this 150-year-old pub has been owned by the same family for over 30 years. The ceiling displays an impressive

collection of pumpclips. Cards and dominoes are available, with children welcome until evening. As well as the front outside seating, which is available all year round, the rear garden is open in summer months. Up to four changing guest beers are usually available. ☾❀♣🖵(371)🥂

Willoughby Arms ⓛ

47 Willoughby Road, KT2 6LN

☎ (020) 8546 4236 ⊕ thewilloughbyarms.com

4 changing beers (often Exeter, Twickenham) Ⓗ

Friendly Victorian back-street local, with a games and TV sports bar and a quieter lounge area. Upstairs is a soundproofed function room. Free of tie, it sources beers from smaller breweries. Pizzas and pies are cooked to order. The spacious garden includes heated beach huts and a covered, heated and lit smoking area with a large TV screen. Quiz night is Sunday; folk music plays on Monday nights. A former local CAMRA Pub of the Year. Q☾❀&♣🖵(371,K5)🥂🥂

Wych Elm ⓛ ⊘

93 Elm Road, KT2 6HT

☎ (020) 8546 3271 ⊕ thewych.co.uk

Dark Star Hophead; Fuller's London Pride, ESB; 2 changing beers (sourced locally) Ⓗ

Tucked away in a residential area, this is a delightfully warm and welcoming local pub. The guest ales are supplied by Asahi but one is often from another brewery; a Master Cellarman takes care of the beers. The food is traditional pub staples with a vegetarian option. There is a secluded garden and log-burners in winter. Some major sporting events are shown; parties and celebrations can be hosted. Charity quizzes, piano and wine evenings are also held. ☾❀◐≒♣🖵(K5)🥂🥂

New Malden

Watchman ⓛ ⊘

184 High Street, KT3 4ES

☎ (020) 8329 0450

Greene King IPA, Abbot; Sharp's Doom Bar; 5 changing beers (sourced nationally; often Twickenham) Ⓗ

A warm and friendly Wetherspoon pub in a former police station dating from the 1890s. The bright interior has a variety of seating, including booths and a dining area. The cask cellar is visible through a window in the passageway behind the bar. At least one guest beer is usually from a local brewery. The name comes from an air raid siren operated by a member of the Royal Observer Corps who was stationed on the roof during WWII. Q☾❀◐&≒🖵🥂

North Cheam

Nonsuch Inn ⊘

552-556 London Road, SM3 9AA

☎ (020) 8644 1808

Greene King IPA, Abbot; Ruddles Best Bitter; Sharp's Doom Bar; 6 changing beers (sourced nationally) Ⓗ

This compact Wetherspoon pub opened in 1995 and stands in the shopping area on the site of the Granada cinema. The pub is named after what was probably the greatest of Henry VIII's palaces, which stood on the west side of today's Nonsuch Park. Its history is featured in texts and illustrations on the walls, along with a three-quarter life-sized statue of Henry VIII. Q☾◐&🖵🥂

Richmond

Mitre
20 St Mary's Grove, TW9 1UY
☎ (020) 8940 1336 ⊕ themitretw9.co.uk
Timothy Taylor Landlord; 6 changing beers (often Bristol Beer Factory, Saltaire, Siren) ⊞
Small traditional community free house, originally built as a coach house in 1865 as part of the Church Estates. Church mitres feature in the leaded stained glass windows. There is a decked area at the front and covered patio at the rear. Cask beers rotate from independent brewers outside the M25, with three handpumps dispensing cider or perry. Neapolitan-style pizzas are cooked to order to eat in or take away (Wed-Sun).
১৫৫ (North Sheen) ⊖⊕P🖵🏵♪

Roebuck
130 Richmond Hill, TW10 6RN
☎ (020) 8948 2329
Greene King IPA, Abbot; house beer (by Greene King); 3 changing beers (often Exeter, Oakham, Sambrook's) ⊞
Dating from Georgian times, this pub commands the famous vista over Petersham Meadows and the Thames painted by JMW Turner. Reopened in 2024 after a comprehensive renovation, it offers a number of comfortable secluded areas including a cosy corner with a log fire. Guest beers are on constant rotation. Upstairs is the Turner Room for private dining and a function room with bar. The bus stop and Richmond Park are a short walk away. ১৫◑&🖵(371)🏵🛜

Surbiton

Antelope ⓛ
87 Maple Road, KT6 4AW
☎ (020) 8399 5565 ⊕ theantelope.co.uk
Big Smoke Solaris Session Pale Ale; 8 changing beers (often 360 Degree, Big Smoke) ⊞
The original home of the Big Smoke brewery, with two of its cask beers and a wide range of changing guest beers available. The spacious split-level interior has a real fire in winter and a covered, heated and lit courtyard behind, beyond which the old brewhouse serves as a dining or function room. Four changing ciders are usually sold. Home-cooked food includes Sunday roasts. Three beer festivals are held annually. A former local CAMRA Pub of the Year. ১৫🏵◑�⊕🖵🏵🛜

Coronation Hall ⓛ ✅
St Marks Hill, KT6 4LQ
☎ (020) 8390 6164
Fuller's London Pride; Greene King Abbot; Ruddles Best Bitter; Sharp's Doom Bar; 4 changing beers (often Adnams, Oakham, Sambrook's) ⊞
A Wetherspoon pub in a large and impressive building dating from 1911. Various former uses included a lecture hall, cinema, bingo hall and nudist club. The decor within the split-level interior is a mix of movie stars, film artefacts, the coronation of George V and the planets. Guest beers change regularly, many from local breweries. Occasionally the pub hosts local beer festivals. Wheelchair access is via a side entrance. Children are welcome until evening. Q১৫◑&🖵🛜

Lamb 🍷 ⓛ
73 Brighton Road, KT6 5NF
☎ (020) 8390 9229 ⊕ lambsurbiton.co.uk
Hop Back Summer Lightning; Surrey Hills Shere Drop; 2 changing beers (sourced nationally) ⊞
This small, family-run free house hosts many community events, especially those bringing people together

through creativity. Live music often plays. Built in 1850 and formerly comprising four separate rooms and a small brewery, it retains the original horseshoe-shaped bar. Changing beers are usually from a microbrewery, sometimes local. Visiting local caterers serve evening food from the outdoor kitchen (Wed-Sun). Children are welcome until evening. Behind is an extensive, covered outside area. Local CAMRA Pub of the Year 2024.
১৫🏵◑�⊕🖵🛜♪

WEST LONDON
W2: Paddington

Bear
27 Spring Street, W2 1JA
☎ (020) 7262 3907 ⊕ thebearpaddington.com
House beer (by Kent); 5 changing beers (often Park, Siren, Titanic) ⊞
The newest pub from the Craft Beer Co, the independent pub company owned by Martin Hayes and Peter Slezak, was a welcome addition to the Paddington beer scene in 2022. This former wine bar has been refurbished in an elegant spring green colour. Alongside the six real ales from small breweries, 29 craft keg offerings are available and an extensive range of Belgian bottled beers, alcohol-free beers and whiskies. The Den in the basement can seat about 25 people. ১৫◑�⊕🖵🏵🛜

Mad Bishop & Bear
Upper Level, The Lawn, Paddington Station Concourse, W2 1HB
☎ (020) 7402 2441 ⊕ madbishopandbear.co.uk
Dark Star Hophead; Fuller's Oliver's Island, London Pride, ESB; Gale's Seafarers Ale, HSB ⊞
Above the shopping complex just behind the station concourse, the modern pub interior features one long bar, railway memorabilia and train information screens. The raised areas can be hired for events and there are café-style seats outside. It can be quiet even in the rush hour, but the bar could close early if football crowds are passing through. A former local CAMRA Pub of the Year and shortlisted several times. ১৫◑&�⊖⊕🖵🏵🛜

Monkey Puzzle
30 Southwick Street, W2 1JQ
☎ (020) 7723 0143 ⊕ themonkeypuzzlepub.co.uk
Hall & Woodhouse Fursty Ferret, Tanglefoot ⊞
A modern pub with a partially heated beer garden on its Sussex Gardens side. It was built in 1969 on the ground floor of a residential high-rise development. The one long bar room has a raised eating area at the rear. Trade is mainly local, supplemented by some tourists from the numerous hotels nearby.
🏵◑�⊖(Edgware Rd/Paddington) 🖵🏵🛜

Victoria 🍷 ★
10A Strathearn Place, W2 2NH
☎ (020) 7724 1191 ⊕ victoriapaddington.co.uk
Dark Star Hophead ⊞/Ⓟ**; Fuller's London Pride, ESB; 3 changing beers (often Fuller's, People's Captain, Twickenham)** ⊞
Grade II-listed, mid-Victorian inn, popular with tourists and locals alike. Identified by CAMRA as having a nationally important historic pub interior, it has ornately gilded mirrors above a crescent-shaped bar, painted tiles in wall niches, numerous portraits of Queen Victoria, displays of cartoons and paperweights and a Silver Jubilee plate. Upstairs, via a spiral staircase, the Library and Theatre Bar provide extra space. Tuesday is quiz night. Local CAMRA Pub of the Year 2024.
Q১৫🏵◑�⊖(Lancaster Gate/Paddington) 🖵🏵🛜

W3: Acton

Red Lion & Pineapple ✪
281 High Street, W3 9BP
☎ (020) 8896 2248
Greene King IPA, Abbot; Sharp's Doom Bar; 6 changing beers (often Oakham, Twickenham) ⊞
A Wetherspoon pub at the top of Acton Hill, formerly owned by Fuller's. It was originally two pubs that then combined in 1906 – hence the name. The larger room is home to the circular bar, surrounded by red and black tiles. The windows are large, with etched and stained tops, and the walls are decorated with historical photographs of Acton. The smaller room is mainly used by diners and families. The rear patio was recently refurbished. Alcoholic drinks are served from 9am.
Q❄🐕🏠🍴🛗➲(Town) 🚃♿🚻

West London Trades Union Club
33-35 High Street, W3 6ND
☎ (020) 8992 4557 ⊕ wltuc.com
2 changing beers (often Portobello) ⊞
A small, friendly club, run as a co-operative, that combines excellent beer with a busy cultural and social life. Two real ales are served from a variety of independent breweries, and particularly from the wide Nelson range. The Acton Community Theatre is upstairs and regular film shows are also held. The local CAMRA branch is an associate member; show a CAMRA membership card or this Guide for entry. Closed on most Saturdays – check website for exceptions.
Q❄🐕🏠➲(Central) ♣🚃♿🚻

W4: Chiswick

George IV
185 Chiswick High Road, W4 2DR
☎ (020) 8994 4624 ⊕ georgeiv.co.uk
Fuller's London Pride, ESB; 3 changing beers (often Brew By Numbers, Sambrook's, Windsor & Eton) ⊞
There has been an inn here in the heart of Chiswick since 1777, and the present inter-war pub is still reputed to have its own ghost, George. Inside, the different areas include the board game-themed mezzanine, while the Boston Room across the rear courtyard hosts activities including a comedy club. Regular music events are held on Friday and Saturday. Fuller's small-batch brews are often available, including a good variety of craft beers. Monday is quiz night.
❄🐕🏠🍴🛗➲(Turnham Green) ♦🚃♿🚻🎵

W5: Ealing

Questors Grapevine Bar 🅛
12 Mattock Lane, W5 5BQ
☎ (020) 8567 0011 ⊕ questors.org.uk/grapevine
Fuller's London Pride; 2 changing beers ⊞
A friendly theatre club bar near the centre of Ealing and Walpole Park, run by enthusiastic volunteers. CAMRA members and Questors theatre ticket holders are also welcome. Guest beers include some from local breweries, beer festivals are held twice-yearly and there are malt whisky tastings. Some books and the odd board game are available. Local CAMRA Club of the Year 2022, it won the CAMRA national award in 2012.
Q❄🐕🏠♿➲(Broadway) ♣🅿♿🚻

Sir Michael Balcon ✪
46-47 The Mall, W5 3TJ
☎ (020) 8799 2850
Greene King IPA, Abbot; Sharp's Doom Bar; 4 changing beers (sourced nationally) ⊞

Located on the Uxbridge Road east of Ealing town centre, this became a Wetherspoon pub in 2008, converted from Bryant's furniture shop. It is named after the legendary producer of films such as The Ladykillers and The Lavender Hill Mob, whose life and work form the basis of many of the wall displays. Split level, there is a raised area at the rear and a glass-covered enclosed area at the front. Alcoholic drinks are served from 9am.
Q❄🐕🏠🛗➲(Broadway) 🚃♿🚻

W6: Hammersmith

Andover Arms
57 Aldensley Road, W6 0DL
☎ (020) 8748 2155 ⊕ theandoverarmsw6.com
Fuller's London Pride; 2 changing beers (often Dark Star, Fuller's, Gales) ⊞
A popular, welcoming local, hidden away in the back streets and with a rural feel about it. The attractive panelled bar counter, with its elaborate bar-back, separates two areas furnished with an assortment of dining tables and chairs. The pub is closed on Monday and until 5pm on Tuesday and Wednesday.
❄🏠🍴➲(Ravenscourt Park) 🚃🐾🚻

Crabtree ✪
Rainville Road, W6 9HA
☎ (020) 7385 3929 ⊕ thecrabtreew6.co.uk
Greene King IPA; 4 changing beers (sourced nationally) ⊞
Large Thames-side pub in the back streets half a mile from Fulham football ground, rebuilt in 1898 by Sich's Lamb brewery of Chiswick. The split-level bar, with restaurant at rear, has a high-vaulted ceiling. Some plush furniture includes leather banquettes. A large patio/ garden area overlooks the river and affords a view of the annual Varsity Boat Race; weeping willows and parasols provide shade. Occasional events include Meet the Brewer – see website and social media for details. Quiz night is Tuesday. ❄🏠🍴🚃🎵

Craft Beer Co.
17-18 Broadway Shopping Centre, W6 9YD
☎ (020) 8748 7033
3 changing beers (sourced regionally) ⊞
A welcome addition to the local scene when opened in 2019 after transformational refurbishment. Inside is an L-shaped room around the bar counter and outside a good-sized, heated terrace. Up to six real ales on handpump are complemented by 20 keg lines and more than 50 bottled and canned beers, including some rarities at appropriate prices. The Broadway Shopping Mall location makes it convenient for the Apollo music venue; it can be busy before concerts there. ❄🏠🍴🛗➲🚃🐾🚻

Dove ★
19 Upper Mall, W6 9TA
☎ (020) 8748 9474 ⊕ dovehammersmith.co.uk
Fuller's London Pride, ESB; 2 changing beers (often Dark Star, Fuller's) ⊞
A Grade II-listed pub dating from the 1740s, identified by CAMRA as having a nationally important historic pub interior, overlooking the Thames and hence often crowded in summer. The likes of Dylan Thomas, Ernest Hemingway and Alec Guinness have enjoyed a pint or two here. Down off the main bar area, a tiny public bar holds the Guinness world record for the smallest bar area. ❄🏠🍴➲(Ravenscourt Park)🚃🐾🚻

William Morris 🅛 ✪
2-4 King Street, W6 0QA
☎ (020) 8741 7175

Greene King Abbot; Ruddles Best Bitter; Sharp's Doom Bar; 7 changing beers [H]
Close to Hammersmith's underground station, this popular, modern Wetherspoon pub commemorates the Arts & Crafts designer who lived nearby. With entrances on both King Street and the pedestrianised Lyric Square, where there is terrace seating, the interior stretches in an L-shape, with the bar in the middle. Frequently changing interesting ales are usually on offer, often from smaller breweries. Alcoholic drinks are served from 9am. 🐴❀◑♿⊖🚌📶

W7: Hanwell

Dodo Micropub [L]
52 Boston Road, W7 3TR
☎ (020) 8567 5959 🌐 thedodomicropub.com
5 changing beers (sourced nationally) [G]
A classic micropub shop conversion, opened in 2017. Up to five cask beers, almost always including some from local breweries, are served from a temperature-controlled cellar room at the rear, along with cider and wine. There is a small bar counter by the front door but table service is the order of the day. It hosts regular tap takeovers for local breweries and has arrangements with nearby street food vendors. Local CAMRA Pub of the Year 2023. Closed Monday and Tuesday. Q🐴❀⊖🚆🚌🐾📶

Fox ★ [L]
Green Lane, W7 2PJ
☎ (020) 8567 0060 🌐 thefoxpub.co.uk
Fuller's London Pride; St Austell Proper Job; Timothy Taylor Landlord; 1 changing beer (sourced locally) [H]
This wonderful free house in Hanwell has been identified by CAMRA as having a nationally interior historic pub interior. It is as popular with walkers, cyclists and other users of nearby canal as it is with locals. Refurbishment in 2020 extended the pub into the garden, creating a large, partly covered outdoor seating area. It has a Thursday evening quiz and runs Easter and autumn beer festivals. Local CAMRA Pub of the Year on many occasions. 🐴❀◑♿🚌(195,E8)🐾📶♫

Grosvenor ★ [L]
127 Oaklands Road, W7 2DT
☎ (020) 8840 0007
Fuller's London Pride; 3 changing beers (often Twickenham, Windsor & Eton) [H]
A traditional local dating back to 1904, refurbished in 2014 without losing the features and charm of its historic interior which has been identified by CAMRA as nationally important. There is a main bar and a dining room section. A wide range of locally produced beers is available. Family-friendly, it has a congenial atmosphere and promotes local events. Jazz night is the second Tuesday and open mic night the fourth Tuesday of every month. A former local CAMRA Pub of the Year.
🐴❀🛏◑♿♣🚌🐾📶♫

Viaduct
221 Uxbridge Road, W7 3TD
☎ (020) 8567 5866 🌐 viaduct-hanwell.co.uk
Dark Star Hophead; Fuller's London Pride, ESB; Gale's Seafarers Ale; 1 changing beer [H]
A friendly Fuller's pub, much larger on the inside than it looks from the outside. A separate function room is available for hire when it is not being used for the Friday comedy nights. The pub was renamed around 1838 after the Wharncliffe Viaduct behind it, which was made famous as the first viaduct to carry a commercial electric telegraph. Ealing Hospital is also close by.
Q🐴❀◑♿⊖P🚌🐾📶♫

W8: Kensington

Elephant & Castle ★
40 Holland Street, W8 4LT
☎ (020) 7937 6382
Fuller's London Pride; St Austell Nicholson's Pale Ale; Sharp's Doom Bar; 3 changing beers (often Banks's, Oakham, Timothy Taylor) [H]
Tucked away north-east of Kensington Town Hall, this busy, cosy, wood-panelled M&B Nicholson's pub was first licensed in 1865 as a beer house in what were originally two adjacent houses. Note the fine Charrington's bar-back. It has been identified by CAMRA as having a nationally important historic pub interior. With its rural feel, it is a welcome refuge from the hurly-burly of Kensington High Street. Food, especially pies and sausages, is available all day, with a short afternoon break. 🐴❀◑⊖(High St)🚌🐾📶

W8: Notting Hill Gate

Churchill Arms ★
119 Kensington Church Street, W8 7LN
☎ (020) 7727 4242 🌐 churchillarmskensington.co.uk
Fuller's Oliver's Island, London Pride, ESB; 2 changing beers (often Fuller's) [H]
A multi award-winning and deservedly popular pub, identified by CAMRA as having a nationally important historic pub interior that includes snob screens, now rare. Churchillian and Irish memorabilia are among the bric-a-brac suspended from the panelled ceiling. The Thai restaurant in the conservatory was one of the first in a London pub. At busy times, drinkers stand on the pavement outside. At Christmas, the tree decorations are something to behold. Q🐴◑⊖🚌🐾📶

Windsor Castle ★
114 Campden Hill Road, W8 7AR
☎ (020) 7243 8797 🌐 thewindsorcastlekensington.co.uk
Timothy Taylor Landlord; 3 changing beers (often Banks's, St Austell, Sharp's) [H]
A back-street, Grade II-listed pub dating from 1830 and identified by CAMRA as having a nationally important historic interior. Sited on a corner, it contrasts an olde-worlde rural feel with a modern upmarket service and menu style. The bar room is divided into four drinking areas separated by partitions that date from a 1933 refurbishment. The beer garden to the rear boasts its own bar. Q🐴❀◑⊖🚌🐾📶

W9: Warwick Avenue

Prince Alfred ★
5A Formosa Street, W9 1EE
☎ (020) 7286 3287 🌐 theprincealfred.com
Young's London Original; 2 changing beers (often Redemption, St Austell) [H]
A Grade II*-listed mid-Victorian pub with a nationally important historic interior dating from 1896 when many London pubs had small drinking compartments. The ornate bar-back draws the eye up to a highly decorated ceiling. Together with the intricate carving on the partitions, these impart a rococo feel to the place. The passageway and bar area to the side sport some delightful wall tiling and floor mosaics as well as a fireplace. Beyond is the open kitchen and separate restaurant. 🐴❀◑♿⊖🚌🐾📶

Warwick Castle ★ ✔
6 Warwick Place, W9 2PX
☎ (020) 7266 0921 🌐 warwickcastlemaidavale.com
Greene King IPA; house beer (by Greene King); 2 changing beers (often Timothy Taylor) [H]

With a dark green frontage blending with the rest of the terrace, this 1846 pub, featured in a 1927 painting by artist and illustrator Edward Ardizzone, is recognised by CAMRA as having a nationally important historic interior. Note the leaded windows with varied shades of coloured glass inserts. An interesting food menu offers a variety of dishes, including pub classics and roasts on Sundays. The clientele reflects the broad social mix of the area.
ⓈꙶⒹⒺꝀ❀

W12: Shepherds Bush

Central Bar ✅
Unit 1, West 12 Centre, Shepherds Bush Green, W12 8PH
☎ (020) 8746 4290
Greene King IPA, Abbot; Sharp's Doom Bar; 4 changing beers (often Theakston, Thornbridge, Twickenham) Ⓗ
A Wetherspoon pub opened in 2002 on the upper floor of the shopping centre. Access from the ground floor is via an escalator or lift and through a wide entrance into a long bar area with large windows to the side overlooking the Green. It is named after the Central London Railway (or Tuppenny Tube), now the Central Line, which reached Shepherds Bush in 1900 when the Prince of Wales (later Edward VII) opened the station opposite.
QꙶⒹꝂ⬌⊖(Shepherds Bush/Market) Ꝁ?

Crown & Sceptre
57 Melina Road, W12 9HY
☎ (020) 8746 0060 ⊕ crownandsceptreshepherdsbush.co.uk
Fuller's London Pride; 2 changing beers (often Dark Star, Fuller's, Gale's) Ⓗ
Well off the beaten track, this large 1866 corner pub is now an upmarket but welcoming Fuller's house, usually offering two real ales from their range and a third that may be a guest. Well-reputed Thai food is available and the comfortable garden is equipped with shelters and heaters. Weekly events include a Monday quiz night.
ꙶꝀⒹꝂꝀ❀?♪

W13: Northfields

Owl & the Pussycat ♈ Ⓛ
106 Northfield Avenue, W13 9RT
⊕ markopaulo.co.uk
6 changing beers (often Ealing, Marko Paulo) Ⓗ
Unique to West London, the combination of microbrewery and pub based in a former bookshop has retained the atmosphere of its previous incarnation. All beers, cask and keg, are brewed on site and mostly branded as Marko Paulo, although some are Ealing Brewing. There is a wide selection of real ciders available, along with wine, soft drinks and snacks. In this small, friendly environment, conversation is all-important. Local CAMRA Pub of the Year 2024.
Q⊖♣Ꝁ(E2,E3) ❀?

Brentford

Black Dog Beer House
17 Albany Road, TW8 0NF
☎ (020) 8568 5688 ⊕ blackdogbeerhouse.co.uk
4 changing beers (often Oakham, Ramsbury, Windsor & Eton) Ⓗ
This former Royal brewery (Brentford) pub, rebuilt in its present form in 1901, has become a neighbourhood favourite since opening in 2018 as a free house. The open L-shaped room has plenty of seating and no TV screens. For table reservations, see the website. Chalkboards list the currently available real ales, ciders

and 14 keg beers on tap. At the rear is an attractive beer garden on artificial turf. A former local CAMRA Pub of the Year. Closed on Tuesday. ꙶⒹⒺ⬌♣Ꝁ❀?

Express Tavern ★
56 Kew Bridge Road, TW8 0EW
☎ (020) 8560 8484 ⊕ expresstavern.co.uk
Big Smoke Solaris Session Pale Ale; Draught Bass; Harvey's Sussex Best Bitter; 7 changing beers (often Bristol Beer Factory, Rudgate, Thornbridge) Ⓗ
A local landmark since the 1860s, still featuring its illuminated external Bass signage. Draught Bass remains a fixture on the bar. It has been identified by CAMRA as having a nationally important historic pub interior. The small Chiswick Bar has 10 handpumps and the saloon/lounge bar has up to five ciders and perries on handpump and 10 craft keg taps. Has a large, heated conservatory with TV screens and a spacious beer garden. A short walk from Kew Gardens.
ꙶꙷⒹꝂ⬌(Kew Bridge) ♣Ꝁ❀?

Hampton

Jolly Coopers ★
16 High Street, TW12 2SJ
☎ (020) 8979 3384 ⊕ thejollycoopers.co.uk
Courage Best Bitter; Hop Back Summer Lightning; 3 changing beers (often Exeter, Park) Ⓗ
Traditional community pub which has been identified by CAMRA as having a nationally important historic pub interior. A wall panel lists its landlords since 1726; the present incumbent took over in 1986. The small horseshoe bar has five handpumps, always including a local guest beer. Water jugs, pictures and local memorabilia adorn the walls. Squiffy's restaurant behind serves excellent tapas and traditional food; booking is essential for Sunday lunch. Outside is a covered patio. Local CAMRA Pub of the Year 2022 and 2023.
ꙶꙷⒹꝂ⬌♣Ꝁ❀?

Hampton Court

Mute Swan
3 Palace Gate, Hampton Court Road, KT8 9BN
☎ (020) 8941 5959 ⊕ muteswan.co.uk
House beer (by St Austell); 3 changing beers (often Ilkley, Surrey Hills, Twickenham) Ⓗ
A popular and friendly Brunning & Price pub opposite the palace gates, drawing locals and tourists alike. The main feature as you enter is the wrought iron spiral staircase to the restaurant area (also accessible via normal stairs). Food is also served downstairs, with bar snacks listed on a chalkboard. Cask beers change frequently. There is a log fire in winter and no distracting TV screens or music. Outside seating includes a side courtyard. No prams are allowed inside. QⒹ⬌♣Ꝁ❀?♪

Hampton Hill

Roebuck
72 Hampton Road, TW12 1JN
☎ (020) 8255 8133
St Austell Tribute; Young's London Original; 2 changing beers (often Elgood's, Portobello, Vale of Glamorgan) Ⓗ
Comfortable Victorian free house with partitioned seating areas and carpeted throughout. It is owned by an inveterate collector, something that is obvious from the decor. Look beyond the wickerwork Harley Davidson, fishing rods, flying boats and miniature steam locomotive for the collections of smaller items. Also worth noticing are the four hand-made wooden

handpumps on the bar with nicely polished brasswork. There is a real fire that never goes out in winter. ✿≠(Fulwell)🖵❀🛜

Hampton Wick

Foresters Arms 🅛
45 High Street, KT1 4DG
☎ (020) 8943 5379 ⊕ the-foresters.com
Sharp's Doom Bar; 2 changing beers (sourced locally; often Surrey Hills, Twickenham) 🖽
With a reputation for good food, this traditional pub is part carpeted, with a wooden floor in the centre bar area and a small cosy side room with side door access. A separate restaurant room can be curtained off. The corner TV in the bar area shows old films silently but with subtitles. Outside is seating on the front corner pavement and to the side. The pub provides accommodation with four ensuite rooms. Quiz night is every other Monday. 🛏🍴🕽≠♣🖵❀🛜♪

Harlington

White Hart
158 High Street, UB3 5DP
☎ (020) 8759 9608 ⊕ whitehartharlington.co.uk
Fuller's London Pride, ESB; 1 changing beer (often Dark Star, Fuller's, Gale's) 🖽
Large, Grade II-listed Fuller's pub at the north end of the village. It was refurbished in 2009 to improve facilities and create the welcoming feel now enjoyed by regulars and passengers from the nearby Heathrow Airport. The bar provides access to an open-plan space with soft seating, leading to an area favoured by diners. Local history is the theme of the wall displays. Fuller's or Gale's seasonal ales are sometimes on the bar. 🛏✿🕽♣🅿🖵❀🛜

Hayes

Botwell Inn ✅
25-29 Coldharbour Lane, UB3 3EB
☎ (020) 8848 3112
Greene King Abbot; Ruddles Best Bitter; Sharp's Doom Bar; 3 changing beers (often Adnams, Windsor & Eton) 🖽
Named after the hamlet of Botwell, now the location of Hayes town centre, this large Wetherspoon pub with several areas for dining and drinking opened in 2000 following a shop conversion from furnishers S Moore & Son. There is a fenced paved area to the front and a patio at the rear with large market-type parasols with heaters. Several beer festivals are held annually. Q🛏✿🕽♣≠⊖(Hayes & Harlington)🖵🛜

Hillingdon Hill

Red Lion Hotel
Royal Lane, UB8 3QP
☎ (01895) 236860 ⊕ redlionhotelhillingdon.co.uk
Fuller's London Pride; Gale's HSB; 1 changing beer (often Fuller's) 🖽
A Grade II-listed pub more than 400 years old, although it was refronted in 1800, with wood panelling, low ceilings and exposed beams. Part of the London Wall is claimed to be visible in the car park and it is believed that Charles I stayed here in 1646. The second handpump offers ESB or HSB; the third is often used to showcase Dark Star and other brewery ales. Major sporting events such as the Six Nations are shown. Q🛏✿🍴🕽♣🅿🖵❀🛜

Hounslow

Moon Under Water ✅
84-86 Staines Road, TW3 3LF
☎ (020) 8572 7506
Greene King Abbot; Ruddles Best Bitter; Sharp's Doom Bar; 6 changing beers (often Portobello, Twickenham) 🖽
Licensed from 9am, this is a 1991 Wetherspoon shop conversion still in original style, displaying many local history panels and photographs. A real ale oasis for beer fans from the surrounding area, it has been in the Guide for 23 consecutive years. Up to six guest ales come from across the country, with more at festival times when 11 handpumps are put to work. The regular cider is usually Weston's Old Rosie. Families are welcome during the day. Q🛏✿🕽♣⊖(Central)🖵🛜♪

Isleworth

Royal Oak
128 Worton Road, TW7 6EP
☎ (020) 8560 2906 ⊕ royaloakisleworth.co.uk
Fuller's London Pride; Gale's HSB 🖽
Dating from 1843, this is a classic, traditional pub in a residential area with a waterside location alongside the Duke of Northumberland's River. It has a normally tranquil riverside patio. Locally sourced food is served all day. Table bookings are strongly recommended, particularly on major Twickenham rugby days; the pub is only seven minutes' walk from the Stadium by a public footpath opposite through Mogden Water Works. Quiz night is on Sundays from 8pm in the dining room. 🛏✿🕽♣🖵(H20,H22)❀🛜♪

Northolt

Greenwood Hotel ★ 🅛 ✅
674 Whitton Avenue West, Wood End, UB5 4LA
☎ (020) 8423 6169
Greene King Abbot; Ruddles Best Bitter; Sharp's Doom Bar; 5 changing beers (often Redemption, Sambrook's, Twickenham) 🖽
This 1930s former Courage road house, identified by CAMRA as having a nationally important historic pub interior, was reopened by Wetherspoon's in 2016 after six years of closure. The pub has been sympathetically refurbished, honouring the Grade II-listed heritage features, including the original flooring, bar tops and light fittings. The old ballroom has been converted into a dining area. Twelve hotel rooms have also been added. Alcoholic drinks are served from 9am. Q🛏✿🍴🕽♣≠(Park)♣🖵🛜

Norwood Green

Plough
Tentelow Lane, UB2 4LG
☎ (020) 8574 7473 ⊕ ploughnorwoodgreen.com
Fuller's London Pride; 1 changing beer (often Dark Star, Twickenham) 🖽
Dating back to circa 1650, this Grade II-listed building is Fuller's oldest tied house, with a superb landlord who takes pride in both friendly service and a well kept range of real ales and ciders. With low, exposed beams and two real fires, it offers traditional roasts alongside other dishes every day. Musicians entertain from time to time inside the pub as well as in the garden during the summer. There is patio seating at the front. 🛏✿🕽♣♣🖵(120)❀🛜♪

St Margarets

Turk's Head ★

28 Winchester Road, TW1 1LF

☎ (020) 8892 1972 ⊕ turksheadtwickenham.co.uk

Dark Star Hophead; Fuller's London Pride, ESB; 2 changing beers (often Fuller's, Twickenham) ⊞

A corner pub built in 1902 and identified by CAMRA as having a nationally important historic pub interior. Ringo played darts here in the Beatles' film, A Hard Day's Night. The Bearcat Comedy Club meets on Saturday nights in the Winchester Hall (except in summer) and there is regular live music. The Jazz Sanctuary operates every other Thursday and the pub is included in London's Festival of Jazz. There is a covered garden area with plenty of seating and a children's playground.

Q❄️☺️◑◐♿️⇌�🐾🐕🎵

Teddington

Anglers

3 Broom Road, TW11 9NR

☎ (020) 8977 7475 ⊕ anglers-teddington.co.uk

Dark Star Hophead; Fuller's London Pride; 2 changing beers (often Castle Rock, Fuller's, Park) ⊞

Popular riverside pub near Teddington Lock footbridge, featuring a conservatory and large garden with a variety of seating styles. It has its own mooring for customer use. Popular in the summer, it offers a pizza shack, barbecues and hog roasts, and a children's play area. Inside are sectioned areas for privacy and intimate parties and a seated library. Awarded Fuller's Master Cellarman status, the pub hosts many groups and events during the year: a quiz, choir, Shakespeare in the Garden and talks. A loyalty card operates. ☺️◑◐♿️♣️P🚽🐾🐕

Masons Arms 🍷

41 Walpole Road, TW11 8PJ

☎ (020) 8977 6521 ⊕ the-masons-arms.co.uk

Hop Back Summer Lightning; Sambrook's Junction; Vale Best IPA; 1 changing beer (often Buntingford, Hop Back, Portobello) ⊞

A small, friendly, back-street community free house built in 1860. A beer-drinkers' haven, with bottles, pictures and pub memorabilia on display. Carpeting and comfortable seating create a cosy atmosphere. There is a log-burning stove, a dartboard and a small secluded rear patio. Music evenings include a bring-your-own-vinyl night on the third Tuesday of the month. The guest beer, from a wide range of independent brewers, changes frequently. Local CAMRA Pub of the Year 2024.

🐾♿️♣️🐕🚽🐾🎵

Twickenham

Rifleman

7 Fourth Cross Road, TW2 5EL

☎ (020) 8255 0205

Harvey's Sussex Best Bitter; Twickenham Grandstand Bitter, Naked Ladies; 2 changing beers (often Hook Norton, Otter, Twickenham) ⊞

A traditional late-Victorian pub whose name commemorates rifleman Frank Edwards, a local resident, who dribbled a football across No Man's Land towards the German trench in WW1. A Twickenham Fine Ales house since 2019 and a community hub, it has a small beer garden, front patio, board games, TV sport and, on Thursdays, an open mic evening. Twickenham Stadium and Harlequins rugby clubs are a short walk away. Several bus routes are close.

Q🐾⇌(Strawberry Hill) ♣️🚽🐾🎵

White Swan

Riverside, TW1 3DN

☎ (020) 8744 2951 ⊕ whiteswantwickenham.co.uk

Otter Bitter; Twickenham Naked Ladies; 1 changing beer (often Dark Star, Gale's, St Austell) ⊞

A Grade II-listed building and traditional award-winning pub, built around 1690. Entry is via steps up to the first floor, where the bar has real fires and walls covered with memorabilia. A small veranda and a triclinium (a three-sided room with window seats) afford views of the river and Eel Pie Island. Directly opposite is a beer garden, tides permitting, right on the water's edge. Quiz night is every Wednesday (Sep-Apr). Q☺️❄️☺️◑◐⇌♣️🚽🐾🎵

William Webb Ellis

24 London Road, TW1 3RR

☎ (020) 8744 4300

Greene King IPA, Abbot; Sharp's Doom Bar; Twickenham Naked Ladies; changing beers (often Oakham, Twickenham, Windsor & Eton) ⊞

Twickenham is the home of rugby and William Webb Ellis is said to have invented the game. Wetherspoon converted this historic town centre building which for 100 years had been Twickenham's post office. The pub is large and spacious, with live news and sport on silent screens. The frequent beer festivals are well supported. On match days only two beers, served in plastic glasses, are generally available. Q☺️❄️☺️◑◐♿️⇌🚽🐾

Uxbridge

General Eliott

1 St Johns Road, UB8 2UR

☎ (01895) 237385 ⊕ generaleliottuxbridge.co.uk

Fuller's London Pride; St Austell Tribute; 1 changing beer (often Butcombe, St Austell, Tring) ⊞

One of six pubs in the country named after the teetotaller who defended Gibraltar from the Spanish in the late 18th century, this attractive, comfortable canalside pub dating from 1820 has a warm and friendly atmosphere. Refurbishment prior to lockdown included a new covered seating area next to the canal. A vegan menu is available. There is a Tuesday quiz, open mic on Thursdays, karaoke on Fridays and live music on Saturday nights. ☺️❄️◑P🚽(3)🐾🐕🎵

Good Yarn ✅

132 High Street, UB8 1JX

☎ (01895) 239852

Greene King Abbot; Ruddles Best Bitter; Sharp's Doom Bar; 4 changing beers ⊞

Wetherspoon pub opened in 1994 in a former menswear shop in the town centre. Behind the narrow frontage is a long, narrow bar, with a raised far end surrounded with shelves of old books. The front section boasts old framed advertisements for local businesses on the walls and old local photographs can be found throughout. Alcoholic drinks are served from 9am. Q☺️◑♿️❤️🚽🐾

Three Tuns ✅

24 High Street, UB8 1JN

☎ (01895) 233960

Greene King IPA, Abbot; Timothy Taylor Landlord; house beer (by Greene King) ⊞

A traditional high-street pub in a 350-year-old, Grade II-listed building. There is a small front bar and, down a few steps to the rear, a stone-flagged bar area, with a conservatory to one side. Outside are a small, covered back patio and tables at the front on the pedestrianised high street. Good quality food is served at lunchtimes and evenings, with the bar and food service attentive and friendly. ☺️❄️◑◐❤️🚽🐾🎵

GREATER MANCHESTER

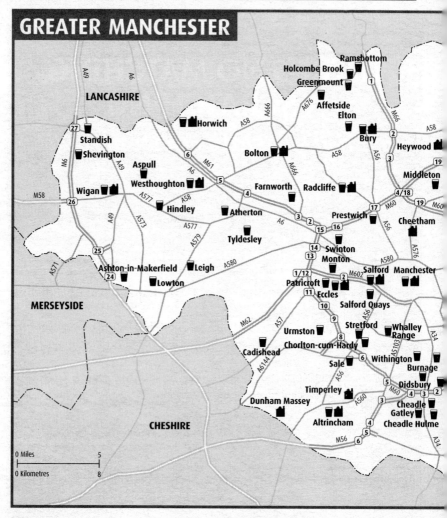

Affetside

Pack Horse

52 Watling Street, BL8 3QW (2 miles NW of Walshaw)
☎ (01204) 884584 ⊕ packhorseataffetside.co.uk
**Hydes Hopster, Original, Lowry; 1 changing beer
(often Hydes)** ℍ
Cosy, traditional pub dating back to the 16th/17th
century, on the old Roman Road between Manchester
and Ribchester. Owned by local brewery Hydes, it has
four handpumps on the bar serving three regular beers
and one seasonal. Most of the rooms have wood-burning
stoves and there is a restaurant at the rear. A pub quiz is
held on Tuesday evenings and there is also occasional
live music. Standing in an elevated position between
Bury and Bolton, it commands fabulous 360-degree
views. ⚲❀❄️⏾♿A P❀☀

Altrincham

Beacon

18 Shaws Road, WA14 1QU
☎ (0161) 929 9098
3 changing beers (sourced regionally) ℍ

Formerly Pi, this unassuming bar is opposite the popular
Altrincham Market Hall alongside various eateries and
takeaways. Three handpumps serve the relatively
compact ground-floor bar area which is supplemented by
additional space upstairs. There is also a small beer
garden to the rear, with chairs and tables also placed on
the Shaws Road frontage when the weather is fine. A
variety of table-top games are available.
⚲❀♿❄️♠️🚆❀☀

Costello's Bar 🅛

18 Goose Green, WA14 1DW (alleyway from Stamford
New Road/opp Regent Road, adjacent to the new
hospital)
☎ (0161) 929 0903 ⊕ costellosbar.co.uk
**Dunham Massey Big Tree Bitter, Dunham Dark; 5
changing beers (sourced locally; often Dunham
Massey)** ℍ
Sitting on Altrincham's historic Goose Green, in a
pedestrianised area of mainly cafés, bars and
restaurants, Costello's serves as the Dunham Massey
brewery tap. There is always a wide range of the
brewery's various beers across seven handpumps, often
including a stout, porter or dark mild. The bar has a
modern feel with smart, clean decor, and a vibrant

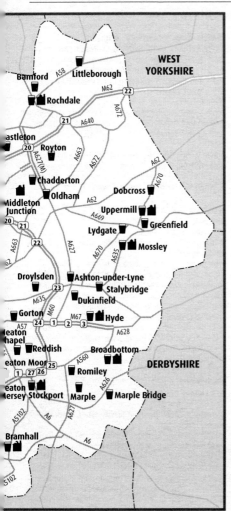

WEST YORKSHIRE

Bamford · A58 · Littleborough
M62 · 22
Rochdale
21 · A640
astleton
20 · Royton
Chadderton
Oldham · Dobcross
Middleton Junction · A62 · Uppermill
20 · 21 · Lydgate · Greenfield
22 · Mossley
Droylsden · Ashton-under-Lyne
23 · Stalybridge
Dukinfield
Gorton · M67 · Hyde
24 · 1 · 2 · 3 · A628
eaton hapel · Reddish · Broadbottom
eaton Moor · 25 · DERBYSHIRE
1 · 27 · 26 · Romiley
eaton ersey Stockport · Marple · Marple Bridge
Bramhall

the handpumps on the bar dispense beers from well-known Manchester breweries Brightside and Marble, with a rotating guest on the third. These are complemented by a wide range of keg beers and cocktails. The function room upstairs hosts salsa lessons and comedy evenings.

Ashton-in-Makerfield

Hingemakers Arms
34 Heath Road, WN4 9DY
☎ 07968 531613 ⊕ hingemakers.pub
Wainwright Gold; 1 changing beer ⊞
Traditional pub which was transformed eight years ago following a community purchase. The refurbishment has given it a welcoming, airy feel with the clever use of lighting and mirrors. The bar area is adorned with pictures of racehorses while the separate games room has modern decor and features pool and darts. There are two TVs in each room. Outside is a covered smoking shelter leading to a secure beer garden with a barbecue area.

Ashton-under-Lyne

Half Way House ⓛ
123 Whiteacre Road, OL6 9PJ
☎ (0161) 343 1344
3 changing beers (sourced locally; often Bridge Beers, Millstone, We Are Wolf Brewing) ⊞
This large, popular open-plan locals' pub was first licensed in 1860. A good-sized beer garden at the rear can be enjoyed during pleasant weather. There is also an upstairs function room with capacity for 50 people. Up to three cask beers are available, all at reasonable prices, plus a cider during the summer months. Live entertainment takes place every Saturday, plus open-mic nights on Sundays. Live Premier League football from Sky and BT Sports is shown on TV.
(38,39)

Tapsters ⓛ
31 Old Street, OL6 6LA (100yds from SE corner of Market Hall)
☎ (0161) 465 0205
3 changing beers (sourced locally; often Bridge Beers, Lancaster, Millstone) ⊞
Previously a high-street shop in the town centre, Tapsters is close to the indoor market and the bus and rail stations. Opened in 2018, it has been fitted out to a high standard, creating a relaxing, comfortable, spacious place. There is a small courtyard beer garden to the rear. Up to three mainly local beers, normally of differing styles, feature at any time. Functions for up to 20 people are catered for. Background music plays and the TV is muted when on.

Aspull

Colliers Arms ⓛ
192 Wigan Road, WN2 1DU
Escape Moonlight Flit; 3 changing beers (often Escape) ⊞
A popular local pub dating from 1700, known locally as 'The Stone'. It has been totally refurbished, and reopened in 2023 as an Escape brewery tap, with four of their cask beers served alongside seven craft beers. It has attractive stone-flag style flooring on one side and a carpeted lounge area with a real fire on the other, making for a comfortable and cosy pub. Wednesday is quiz night. It is close to the canal and Haigh Hall Country Park. Q

atmosphere at weekends and evenings. A haven for those searching for traditional English styles.

Old Roebuck
42 Victoria Street, WA14 1ET
☎ (0161) 928 2755 ⊕ theroebuckaltrincham.co.uk
Timothy Taylor Landlord; house beer (by MBH Beer); 1 changing beer (sourced nationally; often Wainwright) ⊞
The Old Roebuck has a very traditional feel, with a bar to the right and a snug/lounge to the left. It also has a large heated outside seating area to the side, and a back room suitable for meetings. Lunchtime and evening meals are served from a varied menu. The pub holds a regular quiz every Tuesday and dogs are welcome in the bar area.

Rustic
41 Stamford New Road, WA14 1EB
☎ (0161) 928 9190 ⊕ rusticalty.com
Brightside Odin Blonde; 1 changing beer (sourced nationally; often Marble) ⊞
A long, thin bar set out like an American diner, with booth seating to the left and the bar to the right. Two of

Atherton

Atherton Arms
6 Tyldesley Road, M46 9DD
☎ (01942) 875996
Joseph Holt Bitter, Two Hoots Ⓗ
Traditional public house with a great atmosphere and facilities, including a full-sized snooker table and function room. It is known for its superb beer garden, which has TV screens and heaters. The beer is competitively priced and promotions change on a monthly basis. The pub offers a wide range of events, with live entertainment at the weekends, and most sports are shown throughout the week. ❧❀&♣🖵(V2)🛜♫

Mechanics Rest at the Taphouse
119 Market Street, M46 0DF
☎ (01942) 367519
5 changing beers (sourced regionally) Ⓗ
Family-friendly micropub in the centre of Atherton. This comfortable, welcoming one-room bar is decorated in a mechanics theme. There is additional seating upstairs, along with table football, and a beer garden outside. Beers are sourced from regional microbreweries, with a live beer list online. Beers are competitively priced, with gluten-free options and a dark beer, and real cider is always available. The pub is dog friendly, and even has treats, blankets and beds. ❧❀&🖵(V2)🐾🛜

Bamford

Hare & Hounds
865 Bury Road, OL11 4AA
☎ (01706) 369189
Thwaites IPA; 2 changing beers Ⓗ
A traditional stone-built pub on the main Rochdale to Bury road. The comfortable and welcoming interior of this Thwaites house consists of upper and lower bars in an L-shaped layout. The well-kept beers are dispensed from three handpumps, and sometimes a guest beer features. The pub also serves good pub food at reasonable prices. A beer garden to the rear has views across the fields. ❧❀🌑♣🖵🐾🛜

Bolton

Bank Top Brewery Tap Ⓛ
68-70 Belmont Road, Astley Bridge, BL1 7AN
☎ (01204) 302837 ⊕ banktopbrewery.com
Bank Top Dark Mild, Flat Cap, Pavilion Pale Ale, Palomino Rising; 5 changing beers (sourced locally; often Bank Top) Ⓗ
The original tap house for the multi-award winning Bank Top brewery, which is based less than a mile away. This two-roomed street-corner community local has a large outdoor area complete with smoking shelter. There are nine handpumps showcasing ales from Bank Top brewery, including the regular Flat Cap, Pavilion Pale and Dark Mild, plus others from the brewery stable, the current seasonal or special, and a guest beer. A real cider is sometimes available. ❧❀&♣🖵(1,534)🐾🛜

Bolton Ukrainian Social Club Ⓛ
99 Castle Street, BL2 1JP
☎ (01204) 526038
3 changing beers (sourced locally; often Bank Top, Blackedge) Ⓗ
Welcoming club that is home to several societies, including brass band, choir, chess and Scottish pipers. The comfortable two-room bar has three handpumps serving mostly local beers from the likes of Bank Top and Blackedge, alongside guests from further afield. A selection of Ukrainian beers are often available in bottled or keg format. To gain entry press the intercom button and have your CAMRA membership card or Guide ready. Local CAMRA Club of the Year from 2011 to 2023. Q❧❀❄♣🖵(471,544)🛜

Bunbury's
397 Chorley Old Road, BL1 6AH
☎ 07952 344838 ⊕ bunburys.co.uk
3 changing beers (sourced locally; often Blackedge, Marble, Siren) Ⓗ
One of a growing number of micropubs based in former retail outlets, this cosy bottleshop with a bar serves a range of the more unusual beers and beer styles. This includes three constantly changing beers on handpump from local breweries such as Torrside, Siren, Marble and Blackedge, plus offerings from similar breweries further afield. They also stock a wide range of often rare bottled beers from around the world, as well as a choice of interesting modern keg beers. Q❧♣🖵(125)🐾🛜

King's Head 🄻

52-54 Junction Road, Deane, BL3 4NA
☎ 07947 532741
Bank Top Dark Mild, Flat Cap; 1 changing beer (sourced locally; often Blackedge) 🄷
Located near Deane Parish Church in the Deane Village conservation area, this pub is a late 18th-century Grade II-listed building, which was extended in the mid 19th century. The pub has three rooms, one with a cast-iron range and the other two with low, wooden ceiling beams. Crown Green bowls and a children's play area are available. The pub is set back from the road with a two-tier car park that is partially surrounded by woodland.
Q🛇🟟🛇🕭🌲🄿🆒(520,573) 😺🛜🎵

Northern Monkey Bar 🄻

Nelson Square, BL1 1AQ
☎ 07825 814631 ⊕ northernmonkeybrew.co.uk
4 changing beers (sourced locally; often Northern Monkey) 🄷
This pub was set up and renovated from what was previously a restaurant, though originally it was the dining room of the Pack Horse Hotel, which dominated this side of Nelson Square before being converted to student accommodation. The four real ales include Northern Monkey beers and sometimes a couple of guests. At least one dark ale is normally available. Eight fonts serve modern keg beers from Northern Monkey and elsewhere. Basic pub food is offered at weekends.
🛇🌒🛬🌲🆒😺🛜🎵

One For the Road 🄻

Stalls F14 to F15 Ashburner Street Lifestyle Hall, BL1 1TJ
☎ 07725 338773
House beer (by Deeply Vale); 2 changing beers (sourced locally; often Deeply Vale) 🄷
This microbar is located in the Lifestyle Hall of Bolton's award-winning indoor market, and has a choice of three beers from a wide range of smaller breweries. Sharing the same large seating area at the front of the bar is a choice of takeaway food stalls, with dishes from Malaysia to Cameroon alongside the more standard sandwiches and pasties. Opening days and hours are restricted to those of the main market. Q🛇🛇🌲🄿🆒🛜

Bramhall

Mounting Stone

8 Woodford Road, SK7 1JJ (at jct Bramhall Ln South)
☎ (0161) 439 7563 ⊕ themountingstone.co.uk
Bollington Long Hop, Best; 4 changing beers (sourced locally) 🄷
Sister pub to Cheadle Hulme's Chiverton Tap, this is a cosy, friendly micropub right in the village centre. The former blacksmith's has two floors – ground and basement – with a small beer garden to the rear. The name derives from a local large stone that allowed riders to mount their horses. Alongside the Bollington ales are up to four beers, often from microbrewers – one usually a dark brew – and eight keg lines. The pub has an on-site one-barrel brewery named Made of Stone.
Q🛇🟟🛇🌲🛬😺🛜

Broadbottom

Harewood Arms 🄻 ✅

2 Market Street, SK14 6AX
☎ (01457) 762500 ⊕ theharewoodarms.co.uk
Green Mill Gold, Northern Lights; 4 changing beers (sourced locally; often Green Mill) 🄷
A large pub catering for all the community in this quiet village on the edge of the Peak District. Home to the Green Mill brewery, which moved here from its origins in Rochdale, the pub serves several Green Mill ales, plus occasional seasonal and guest beers. Its partially open-plan layout consists of various seating areas and features two real fires. A beer garden at the rear is popular in summer. The pub is about a five-minute walk from Broadbottom railway station.
🛇🟟🛇🕭🌲🆒(341) 😺🛜

Burnage

Reasons to be Cheerful

228 Fog Lane, M20 6EL (jct of Elmsmere Rd, near Burnage station and Parrs Wood Rd)
☎ (0161) 425 9678 ⊕ reasonsbeercafe.co.uk
3 changing beers (sourced locally)
Small, two-room modern beer-café near Burnage railway station. The L-shaped bar has three handpulls dispensing changing cask beers, and there are also eight craft beer taps and a good selection of cans and bottles to take out. There is some bench seating, and stools at the bar. The room to the rear can accommodate up to 20 people and there are two small tables outside at the front. Occasional quizzes and wine-tastings are held. Card payment only. 🛇🟟🌲🛬🆒😺🛜

Bury

Art Picture House 🄻 ✅

36 Haymarket Street, BL9 0AY (opp Metro/Bus Station interchange)
☎ (0161) 705 4040
Bank Top Flat Cap; Brightside Odin Blonde; Phoenix Phoenix; 7 changing beers (often Peerless) 🄷
Wetherspoon pub in a beautifully restored former 1920s cinema, and a regular entry in the Guide. The large seating area is on two levels, with several private booths facing the back bar. Seven handpumps dispense regular and constantly changing beers from near and far. It gets busy at lunchtimes on market days (Wed and Fri). Food is available all day. The team of experienced bar staff are able to advise on ales and help with your choice.
🛇🌒🛇🌲(Bolton Street) 🆒🆒😺🛜

Broad Street Social 🄻

9 Broad Street, BL9 0DA
☎ (0161) 204 7387 ⊕ broadstreetsocial.co.uk
Brewsmith Bitter, New Zealand Pale, Pale, Oatmeal Stout; 1 changing beer (often Mallinsons, Marble, RedWillow) 🄷
This bar in the centre of Bury is the Brewsmith Brewing Co tap. There are six handpumps on the bar dispensing a selection of cask ales from the Brewsmith range plus one guest beer. There is nearly always a stout or porter on offer. The pub operates a loyalty discount scheme every night except Monday (closed) and Friday and Saturday. Live music and other events are occasionally held.
🛇🌲(Bolton Street) 🆒🆒😺🎵

Cadishead

Grocers

152A Liverpool Road, M44 5DD (close to Moss Ln)
☎ 07950 522468
3 changing beers (sourced regionally; often Blackedge, Brewsmith, Coach House) 🄷/🄶
This microbar is a frequent local CAMRA Pub of the Year and was regional Cider Pub of the Year in 2023. There is no bar in the single room; beers are brought to you by the proprietor from a separate air-chilled room, served

on handpull and gravity. Three ciders or perries are also usually available. The lack of TV, music or other electronic entertainment means that conversation rules here. There is a yard to the rear for outside drinking. May close early if quiet. Q🐴❀♿🍎🚌(67,100)🐾

Castleton

Blue Pits Inn

842 Manchester Road, OL11 2SP
☎ (01706) 632151
JW Lees Manchester Pale Ale, Boilerhouse Craft Pale, Bitter Ⓗ; 1 changing beer (sourced locally; often JW Lees) Ⓗ/Ⓟ
Nestled in the heart of Castleton is this traditional local gem. It boasts a distinctive red brick and tiled exterior and showcases an original John Willie Lees mosaic on the outside wall. Inside are three distinct rooms providing separate drinking areas. The tap room is lively and the sports TV corner adds excitement to the atmosphere. With a trio of JW Lees beers flowing from handpumps, quiz nights, and karaoke sessions, this JW Lees pub is a lively community haven. ≉♣🚌(17)🐾📶♫

Old Post Office Ale House 𝕃

858 Manchester Road, OL11 2SP
☎ (01706) 645464
House beer (by Pictish); 4 changing beers (sourced locally; often Phoenix, Wilde Child) Ⓗ
This family-run pub is welcoming to first-time visitors and their dogs. A house beer, Old Postie, is served alongside four other handpumps with changing beers. There are two real, full-juice ciders from Sheppeys, keg Czech and German lagers, as well as bottles cans, gins and cocktails. The pub retains features such as the sign, safe and postbox from its previous existence. There is also a pool table, and a beer garden overlooking the canal. Q❀♿≉♣🍎🚌(17)🐾📶

Chadderton

Crown Inn 𝕃

72 Walsh Street, OL9 9LR (off Middleton Rd via Peel St)
☎ 07880 038876
2 changing beers (sourced locally; often Leatherbritches, Millstone) Ⓗ
Known locally as the 'Sump Hole', this large, open-plan, family-run free house is within reasonable walking distance of Chadderton town centre and the Freehold tram stop. It serves two changing beers, usually from Leatherbritches, plus a variety of regional and local breweries. Live sports are shown on TV and there are also traditional pub games. It is a cash only pub.
🐴❀◗♿🚊(Freehold)♣🚌(415,159)🐾📶♫

Rose of Lancaster ✔

7 Haigh Lane, OL1 2TQ
☎ (0161) 624 3031 🌐 roseoflancaster.co.uk
JW Lees Manchester Pale Ale, Bitter; 3 changing beers (sourced locally; often JW Lees) Ⓗ
This attractive pub by the Rochdale Canal boasts a conservatory restaurant, lounge bar, and a separate vault showing sporting events. Service is swift and cheerful, and the discerning management ensure a pleasant visit. Drinkers and diners mix comfortably in the busy lounge. The covered patio, with views of the canal, is popular in fine weather. Handy bus and train links make for easy travel to this well-run, popular pub. Seasonal and Lees Boilerhouse beers are always available.
❀◖◗♿≉(Mills Hill)♣P🚌(59)🐾📶♫

Cheadle

Wobbly Stamp

130 Stockport Road, SK8 2DP (jct Park Rd)
☎ (0161) 523 0188
House beer (by Stancill); 3 changing beers (sourced nationally) Ⓗ
Opened in 2020 in a former post office by two local businessmen. The deceptively long main room has plenty of seating, with two seating booths towards the back of the pub. The interior is a mix of rough-planed timber, plasterboard and bare brick, all variously adorned with local artwork, breweriana and mirrors. Outside drinking areas are at the front and side of the building with views over a local park. Three rotating guests always include a dark beer. Q🐴❀♿🍎🚌(11,370)🐾📶♫

Cheadle Hulme

Chiverton Tap

8 Mellor Road, SK8 5AU (off Station Rd)
☎ (0161) 485 4149 🌐 thechivertontap.co.uk
Bollington Long Hop, Bollington Best; 4 changing beers (sourced locally) Ⓗ
Friendly micropub in what was once Arthur Chiverton's draper's shop. Note the mosaic in the doorway. This vibrant pub offers a diverse beer selection. Alongside the Bollington beers are four cask lines and six keg taps with an ever-changing selection, all from UK micros. In addition, there is an extensive range of bottles and cans. In 2019 it added a first-floor room and an outside area at the rear with tables. Local CAMRA Pub of the Year 2022.
Q🐴❀♿≉🍎🚌🐾📶

Chorlton-cum-Hardy

Beer House 🏆 𝕃

57 Manchester Road, M21 9PW
☎ (0161) 881 9206
Marble Pint, Manchester Bitter; 4 changing beers (sourced regionally; often Cloudwater, RedWillow, Saltaire) Ⓗ
Standing on a main road next to Chorlton public library, this long, narrow pub has an excellent, friendly atmosphere, and knowledgeable and attentive staff. It serves two regular Marble beers, plus a range of keg beers, cans and bottles, including some continental choices. Real cider is also available. Outdoor seating is available to the front and rear. A selection of board and card games are available for use, and there is a free library of books. 🐴❀🚊(Chorlton)♣🚌(86)🐾📶

Fell

518 Wilbraham Road, M21 9AW
🌐 fellbrewery.co.uk
4 changing beers (often Fell) Ⓗ
Opened in 2020 near the centre of Chorlton, this is the only Fell brewery bar outside of Cumbria. Though occupying a relatively small premises, the interior is spacious, decorated in green tiles and dark wood. Four handpumps dispense beers from Fell, and 11 keg fonts have guests from near and far, often Manchester Union, Track and Kernel. Outdoor seating is at the front. Live music plays every fourth Sunday, and retro videos are shown on the large TV screen. Card payment only. Dogs are welcome. 🚊(Chorlton)♣🚌

Didsbury

Fletcher Moss ✔

1 William Street, M20 6RQ (off Wilmslow Rd, via Albert Hill St)

☎ (0161) 438 0073
Hydes Dark Ruby, Hopster, Original, Lowry; 2 changing beers (sourced regionally) Ⓗ
This gem of a pub is named after the alderman who donated the nearby botanical gardens to the city. The buzz of conversation is audible before opening the door, and though a drinks-only operation, this does not detract from its popularity. Look for the assortment of porcelain teapots; this is part of the late landlady's 100-piece collection now under the care of her husband who took on the role of manager. There is a large, mostly covered outdoor area to the rear. Q❀&Ɽ(Village)🚌🚲🎵

Gateway ✔

882 Wilmslow Road, M20 5PG (jct Kingsway and Manchester Rd)
☎ (0161) 438 1700
Greene King Abbot; Ruddles Best Bitter; house beer (by Brightside); 5 changing beers (sourced nationally) Ⓗ
This comfortable and popular 1930s roadhouse is conveniently located opposite the public transport interchange for bus, tram and rail. It stands out due to its welcoming atmosphere, enthusiastic staff and excellent beer. This large Wetherspoon pub's central island bar is surrounded by distinct seating areas, ensuring that you can always have a quiet drink somewhere, no matter how busy to gets. Extensive outside seating is available, including under cover.
Q🏷❀⏺&➾(East)Ɽ(East Didsbury)P🚲🛜

Dobcross

Dobcross Band Social Club Ⓛ

Platt Lane, OL3 5AD
☎ (01457) 873741 🌐 dobcross.club
JW Lees Bitter; Joseph Holt Bitter; 2 changing beers (sourced locally; often Millstone, Phoenix) Ⓗ
Located in the charming village of Dobcross in the Pennine foothills, with spectacular views over Saddleworth. The club serves five handpulled beers from local breweries. Its large function room is available for hire and hosts concerts, kids theatre groups, pilates, coffee mornings and community events, and is home to three brass bands, bowling and snooker teams. There is a full-size snooker table in the games room, with live sport on the big screen. Current runner-up in the National CAMRA Club of the Year Awards. 🏷&♣P🚌(356)❀🛜🎵

Swan Inn (Top House) ✔

The Square, OL3 5AA
☎ (01457) 238690 🌐 swaninndobcross.com
Banks's Sunbeam; Courage Directors; Jennings Cumberland Ale; Marston's Pedigree; Wainwright Gold Ⓗ
Traditional stone-built Grade II-listed pub and restaurant dating back to 1765, overlooking the picturesque square in the centre of Dobcross. It offers a good selection of home-cooked food with regularly changing menus and hosts events in the function room upstairs. Real open fires feature in all three rooms, and the bar area is stone-paved. A popular quiz night is held on Thursday evenings.
Q🏷❀⏺🚌(X356) ❀🛜🎵

Droylsden

Silly Country Bar & Bottle Shop Ⓛ

121 Market Street, M43 7AR
4 changing beers (sourced locally; often Bridge Beers) Ⓗ
Open-plan bar and bottle shop with outside drinking area. Four cask conditioned beers are served from local

and regional breweries. Cider and perry are also available (usually one boxed and one on handpump) plus an enterprising selection of bottled/canned beers. Various board and card games are available, and open-mic nights are held every first Sunday of the month. Customers can bring in their own food. Treats for dogs are available behind the bar. Q🏷&♣Ɽ♣🚌❀🛜🎵

Snug

122 Market Street, M43 7AA
☎ (0161) 370 1925
3 changing beers (sourced locally; often Bridge Beers, Millstone, Purple Moose) Ⓗ
A smart new micropub opened in 2023 by Kyle, Danielle and Darren, who also own the Jam Works next door. Three handpumps serve one locally sourced beer and two nationally sourced, in addition to several craft/keg beers. This deceptively large venue is furnished to a high standard, with comfortable traditional seating. A similarly furnished function room with its own bar (keg only) is available upstairs and has capacity for 40 to 50 people. 🏷&Ɽ🚌❀🛜

Dukinfield

Angel Ⓛ

197 King Street, SK16 4TH
☎ 07399 662974
Sharp's Doom Bar; 2 changing beers (sourced locally; often Bridge Beers, Millstone) Ⓗ
Friendly, family-run community pub on the main road close to the centre of Dukinfield. There is a pleasant, well-furnished lounge where entertainment and quizzes take place, and a taproom with pub games. the pub also features live music and karaoke on Fridays and Saturdays. Comedy club nights take place regularly in the upstairs function room. A full food menu is served daily until 8pm, with pizzas and snacks available after 8pm. At weekends the pub opens at 9am for breakfast.
🏷❀⏺♣●P🚌(330) ❀🛜🎵

Wheatsheaf

41 Birch Lane, SK16 4AJ
☎ (0161) 523 1979
Wainwright Gold; Banks's Mild Ⓗ
A traditional street-corner locals' pub with a large lounge and a separate smaller vault. The pub welcomes families and is dog-friendly, and the beers are competitively priced, making it a popular venue. A large well-appointed beer garden is a suntrap in the warmer summer months. Regular live entertainment and karaoke are hosted in the lounge area. 🏷❀♣Ɽ❀🛜🎵

Eccles

Lamb Hotel ★

33 Regent Street, M30 0BP (opp Eccles Metrolink station)
☎ (0161) 789 3882
Joseph Holt Mild, Bitter; 1 changing beer (sourced nationally) Ⓗ
Large red-brick building opposite the Eccles bus and tram interchange. From the porch go right for the vault or straight on for any of the other three rooms. All four surround the the bar which is carved oak and etched glass in a traditional Manchester style from the early 20th century. This award-winning pub is relatively quiet, despite the music channels being shown on the TV. The large back room can be reserved for functions.
Q➾Ɽ♣P🚌❀🛜

Elton

Elton Liberal Club ⃝
New George Street, BL8 1NW
☎ (0161) 764 1776 ⊕ eltonliberalclub.co.uk
Brightside Odin Blonde; Moorhouse's White Witch; Reedley Hallows Filly Close Blonde; 2 changing beers ⊞
Friendly social club where you can enjoy a warm welcome and a drink. Non-members can be signed for £1 per visit. Facilities include two function rooms, three snooker tables, sports TV and three bars. There are two changing real ales served through handpumps. A bowling green is surrounded by a seating area for the summer months. A wide variety of quality entertainment is available, with live music every Saturday and Sunday.
Q➣❀&♣P➡(480,469) ●🕏♪

Farnworth

King's Arms Hotel ⃝
2 Mossfield Road, BL4 0AB
☎ (01204) 577357
Ossett White Rat; 3 changing beers (sourced locally; often Beartown, Mallinsons) ⊞
A popular local with a modern, friendly feel that offers something for everyone. The pub usually serves beers from various well-regarded breweries such as Ossett, Blackedge, Small World, Titanic, Beartown and Mallinsons. There is always a dark beer among the selection. There is a pool table, a free (but not too loud) jukebox, unobtrusive TV, a quiet corner, and a comfortable beer garden/smoking area. It also provides accommodation, room only. Q❀🛏♣➡(129,36)🕏

Gatley

Horse & Farrier ●
144 Gatley Road, SK8 4AB (jct Church Rd)
☎ (0161) 428 2080
Hydes Dark Ruby, Hopster, Original, Lowry; house beer (by Hydes); 1 changing beer (often Hydes) ⊞
This Hydes house in the village centre was originally three cottages. Bay windows were added and the elevations later rendered to mimic stone. It has a traditional feel inside, with a large, centrally situated bar serving six rooms, plus a food servery at the rear. It can get busy when live sports are on TV. A pair of seats are set cosily under the stairs leading up to the function room. There is a good-sized, enclosed and partially covered beer garden to the side.
➣❀🛏&⇋♣P➡(11,370) ●🕏♪

Gorton

Vale Cottage
Kirk Street, M18 8UE (off Hyde Rd, E of jct Chapman St)
☎ (0161) 223 4568 ⊕ thevalecottage.co.uk
Timothy Taylor Landlord; 2 changing beers (sourced nationally; often Timothy Taylor) ⊞
Hidden away off busy Hyde Road and sited in the Gore Brook conservation area, the Vale Cottage feels like a country local transplanted to the inner city. The low-beamed ceilings, wood-burning stove and multiple drinking areas all add to the cosy, out-of-town feel. The atmosphere is relaxed and friendly, with conversation to the fore. Events include a music quiz, a folk music night on occasional Sundays, a general knowledge quiz on Tuesday night, and steak night on the last Thursday of each month. Q➣❀🛏&⇋(Ryder Brow)P➡🕏♪

Greenfield

Railway Inn ⃝ ✓
11 Shaw Hall Bank Road, OL3 7JZ (opp station)
☎ (0161) 300 3380
Millstone Tiger Rut; 5 changing beers (often Acorn, Ossett, Thornbridge) ⊞
Unspoilt pub comprising a central bar, lounge, games area and taproom which boasts a log fire and old pictures of Saddleworth. It is a popular venue for many live music acts at weekends, and has six real ales available. It is also a stop-off point on the famous Transpennine Real Ale Trail which links many pubs between Stalybridge and West Yorkshire. The pub affords great views over Chew Valley towards Dove Stone reservoir, and is a good base for walkers. ➣❀Å⇋♣P➡(180,350)●🕏♪

Wellington Inn ⃝
29 Chew Valley Road, OL3 7AF (100yds past Tesco)
Eagles Crag Golden Eagle; Millstone Citra, Tiger Rut, Ibex; Wainwright Amber; 2 changing beers (sourced locally; often Eagles Crag, Phoenix) ⊞
Run by the same family for over a decade, this end-of-terrace free house comprises a small bar area, a main room popular with diners, and a side room with TV, dartboard, cribbage and dominoes. Six handpumps dispense LocAle selections. Home-cooked food from The Stockpot has daily specials available on Wednesdays, Fridays and Sundays. Real chips, pies and puddings are popular, along with Friday fish dishes. Some pavement seating fronts the stone-built pub.
➣🛏Å⇋♣➡(180,350)●🕏

Greenmount

Greenmount Cricket Club
Brandlesholme Road, BL8 4DX
☎ (01204) 883667 ⊕ greenmountcricketclub.com
Brewsmith Bitter; 2 changing beers (often Bowland, Moorhouse's) ⊞
Friendly and welcoming club which is open all year round. In summer you can sit outside on a warm weekend watching cricket and supping fine ales. It regularly offers up to three cask lines. A catering service operates from Thursday to Sunday. The club has had a major refurbishment of the lounge bar area and large function room, with new toilets that include a separate accessible toilet. Well-behaved dogs are welcome. ➣❀🛏&P➡(474)●🕏

Heaton Chapel

Heaton Hops ♕
7 School Lane, SK4 5DE (jct Manchester Road)
⊕ heatonhops.co.uk
3 changing beers (sourced regionally; often Timothy Taylor) ⊞
Since opening in 2015, this cosy, highly popular micropub has won many awards, including local CAMRA Pub of the Year 2024. It is an intimate and hospitable place to have a drink, with two modestly sized rooms (including one downstairs). There is also a sizeable drinking area on the pavement outside, with heaters for the winter. As well as three cask beers it sells a range of bottle-conditioned and membrane keg beers. Heaton Chapel railway station and 192 bus stop are a short walk away. ➣❀⇋●➡●🕏

Heaton Mersey

Crown
6 Vale Close, SK4 3DS (jct Didsbury Rd)

☎ (0161) 442 4531
Robinsons Cumbria Way, Dizzy Blonde, Unicorn, Trooper Ⓗ

A suburban pub with a country feel situated in a conservation area. Exposed brickwork and old beams reflect the heritage of the building, part of which was once the village bakery. The room to the left has a small bar at one end; to the right, two interconnected rooms are served by the main bar, which has four handpulls for cask beer. Seating consists of wooden tables and chairs, and bar stools. There is outside seating at the front, plus a detached beer garden to one side. ⬧✿♣P🅿❁☀🛜

Heaton Moor

Beer Shop

13 Kingsleigh Road, SK4 3QF (jct Mauldeth Rd)
3 changing beers (sourced regionally) Ⓗ

Despite its name, this is very much a pub (albeit with a range of bottles and cans to take away), and a welcome oasis in an area where pubs are thin on the ground. Old film posters, mixed furniture and sixties-influenced fabrics create a Bohemian feel. The three cask beers, usually from local brewers, always include a dark one. There are also two live beers on keg. Payment is by card only. Closed on Mondays. Q⬧⬧✿♣P🅿(25,197)❁☀

Hindley

Hare & Hounds Ⓛ

31 Ladies Lane, WN2 2QA
☎ 07305 640675
3 changing beers Ⓗ

This small but traditional pub is located between Hindley railway station and the town centre. There is a large, comfortable lounge, a distinct bar/vault area and a charming beer garden to the rear, renovated to a high standard in 2020. The lounge displays pictures from bygone Hindley and has a largescreen TV for sports. The pub is home to darts and dominoes teams playing in the local leagues. Beers are from Wigan Brewhouse along with other breweries both local and further afield. ⬧✿⬧♣🅿(7)❁☀

Holcombe Brook

Hare & Hounds Ⓛ ✅

400 Bolton Road West, BL0 9RY (on A676 at jct with Longsight Rd)
☎ (01706) 822107
Bank Top Flat Cap; Brightside Odin Blonde; Greene King IPA; Morland Old Speckled Hen; Timothy Taylor Landlord; 3 changing beers (often Bowland, Hawkshead, Ossett) Ⓗ

A popular community pub where families and dogs are welcome. Six handpumps serve two Greene King beers and four varied, often local, ales. Food is served daily until 8pm. Live sports are shown on TV in the bar area, but there is a quiet room where patrons can sit and chat. There is also a secluded beer garden. A function room is available and is used by various community groups. The pub has its own quiz team and sponsors a local football team. ⬧✿🌗⬧♣P🅿(472,474)❁☀♪

Horwich

B33R@33

33 Lee Lane, BL6 7AX
🌐 b33r33.com
2 changing beers (sourced locally) Ⓗ

A bar created in the centre of Horwich by four local beer enthusiasts. It has a bright, airy, contemporary feel with

background music complementing convivial chat. Two cask ales from some of the best local breweries are available alongside keg fonts dispensing beers from independent breweries, including one from nearby Rivington. A range of real ciders are served from handpump, keg font, bag in box and bottle. ⬧✿⬧🖥(125)❁🛜♪

Bank Top Brewery Ale House 🍷 Ⓛ ✅

36 Church Street, BL6 6AD
☎ (01204) 693793 🌐 banktopbrewery.com
Bank Top Bad to the Bone, Dark Mild, Flat Cap, Pavilion Pale Ale; 5 changing beers (sourced locally; often Bank Top) Ⓗ

Immaculate pub with a modern feel showcasing Bolton's award-winning Bank Top brewery. It is situated in a conservation area opposite Horwich Parish Church and next to cottages associated with the area's history of textiles and bleaching. Choose from eight Bank Top cask beers, including Dark Mild, a former Champion Mild of Britain, plus one changing guest. A popular pub to meet and chat, it attracts a mixed crowd of locals and visitors. Frequent buses stop outside the door, making it a good place to start your visit to the town, or finish a walk in the nearby countryside. ⬧✿♣⬧🖥(125)❁♪

Brewery Bar Ⓛ

Moreton Mill, Hampson Street, BL6 7JH (just behind Old Original Bay Horse)
☎ (01204) 692976 🌐 thebrewerybar.co.uk
Blackedge Hop, Black, Pike; 4 changing beers (sourced locally; often Blackedge) Ⓗ

This bar is on the first floor above the award-winning Blackedge brewery, which is visible through glass windows at the entrance. Converted from industrial premises and retaining some original features, it has bench tables with comfortable upholstered seating. Choose from seven cask beers plus an extensive keg offering, all brewed on the premises, supplemented with occasional guests. There is usually at least one real cider available. Note the toilets are on the ground floor and there is no lift. ⬧✿♣⬧🖥(125,516)❁🛜♪

Crown Ⓛ

1 Chorley New Road, BL6 7QJ
☎ (01204) 693109
Joseph Holt Mild, IPA, Bitter, Two Hoots; 4 changing beers (sourced locally; often Bank Top, Blackedge) Ⓗ

A historic landmark pub close to the beautiful countryside around Lever Park and Rivington. It serves a range of Joseph Holt's beers and up to four guest ales from local breweries. The multi-room layout provides home to many community activities including darts, pool and chess. Elsewhere are quiet drinking areas and a large sports TV. Home-cooked food is served every day. Winner of a CAMRA 50th anniversary Golden Award in recognition of its long-term contribution to cask ale. ⬧✿🌗⬧♣P🅿(125,575)❁🛜♪

Hyde

3 Drinks Behind Ⓛ

285 Stockport Road, Gee Cross, SK14 5RF
☎ (0161) 368 6827
House beer (by Beartown); **3 changing beers** (sourced locally) Ⓗ

Opposite Hyde Chapel cemetery, this microbar was bought out by four locals in 2021 and is named after the famous quote by Humphrey Bogart. House ale is from Beartown and there are three guests, which always include a stout or porter. Though space is limited, the bar can seat 30 people comfortably, and the layout inevitably encourages conversation. A huge mirror also creates a more spacious feel. Jam sessions feature every fortnight and live music monthly. It can be booked for private functions. Q ⛲🖵(202)❀❦🎵

Cheshire Ring Hotel 🅛
72-74 Manchester Road, SK14 2BJ
☎ 07917 055629
6 changing beers (often Beartown) 🄷
One of the oldest pubs in Hyde, this one-time Beartown brewery pub is now a cash-only free house. Up to six guest beers are available from microbreweries near and far (including Beartown), as well as ciders, perries and continental beers, plus a selection of bottled beers. Home-made curries are available on Thursday evenings, and Sunday is quiz night. Opening hours vary with the season and the pub may also close early on Monday and Tuesday. ⛲❀≠(Central)🖵(201,202)❦

Jack's Bar
3 Hamnett Street, SK14 2EX
☎ 07962 367676
3 changing beers (sourced locally; often Bradfield, Thornbridge) 🄷
Smart, cosy and friendly micropub just off Hyde Market Place. Formerly named Tweed Tap, it was tastefully refurbished before reopening under new management in 2021. It is surprisingly spacious and decked out with comfortable seating, creating a light, fresh and modern look. It serves three weekly changing cask beers, often including a stout or porter. It is close to the bus station and only 10 minutes from Hyde Central railway station. Q♿≠(Central) 🖵

Sportsman Inn ★ 🅛
57 Mottram Road, SK14 2NN (next to exit from Morrisons car park)
☎ (0161) 368 5000
Rossendale Floral Dance, Glen Top Bitter, Halo Pale, Pitch Porter, Sunshine; house beer (by Rossendale) 🄷
This former regional CAMRA Pub of the Year is popular with locals and retains its character. It offers a full range of Rossendale brewery ales. The upstairs restaurant offers Cuban tapas and vegetarian options, and on Sundays there is a traditional roast from noon until it has gone. The choice of food varies with day and time. The rear patio includes a covered and heated smoking area. Closed on Tuesdays in winter. It is on the main road, close to Hyde United football ground. ⛲❀◑≠(Newton for Hyde)♣🖵❦🛜

Leigh

Bobbin
38A Leigh Road, WN7 1QR
☎ (01942) 581242
4 changing beers (sourced locally) 🄷
On the northern edge of the town centre, this one-room micropub offers a warm welcome and has comfortable seating. The bar is decorated with pumpclips and there are pictures on sale for charity. Prices are competitive, and a dark beer and real cider are always available. Beers are sourced from regional microbreweries with current and forthcoming selections on their website. Open from 1pm on Sundays when Leigh RLFC is playing at home. Q♿◑🖵❦🛜🎵

Thomas Burke 🅛 ✅
20A Leigh Road, WN7 1QR
☎ (01942) 685640
Greene King Abbot; Moorhouse's Blonde Witch; changing beers 🄷
Popular with all ages, this Wetherspoon pub is named after a renowned Leigh tenor, known as the Lancashire

Caruso. The pub divides into three areas: the main long bar, a raised dining area and, in what was once a cinema foyer, lounge-style seating. There is also a small courtyard at the back for outside drinking. A changing range of beers is sourced from breweries near and far, including a house beer called Leigh Leopards Blond Ale. Q⛲❀◑♿🖵(V1)🛜

Littleborough

Hare on the Hill
132 Hare Hill Road, OL15 9HG (588 bus stops nearby)
☎ (01706) 375220 ⊕ beerbreadpork.pub
Vocation Bread & Butter 🄷**; 4 changing beers (often Pictish, Saltaire, Tiny Rebel)** 🄰
This little gem of a pub, in the grounds of a former pub just outside the centre of Littleborough, has become the go-to place for locals. It is highly rated for its food, beers and wines, as well as the friendly staff and welcoming atmosphere. Five cask ales always available, one regular and four changing. Cask cider is often on tap. ⛲❀◑♿♣♠🖵(455,457)❀🛜🎵

Red Lion 🅛
6 Halifax Road, OL15 0HB
☎ (01706) 378195
House beer (by Coach House); 2 changing beers (often Little Valley) 🄷
Close to the village centre, just behind the railway arches, is this traditional, welcoming local. The detached stone-built pub comprises four distinct rooms, three of which have a bar face, including a large lounge area and a cosy snug with high-backed chairs. Free of tie, it serves three cask ales, one of which is Red Lion Bitter, a house beer brewed by Coach House. The other beers vary, but are usually from microbreweries. Q♿≠♣🖵❦🛜

White House 🅛
Blackstone Edge, Halifax Road, OL15 0LG
☎ (01706) 378456 ⊕ thewhitehousepub.co.uk
Timothy Taylor Landlord; Theakston Best Bitter; 2 changing beers (often Goose Eye, Phoenix) 🄷
Dating from 1671, this old coaching inn is situated high up on the moors, where the Pennine Way crosses the road, and commands stunning views. Family-run for 40 years (it has appeared in this Guide for 21 consecutive years), it always offers a warm and friendly welcome. Inside are separate rooms, including a cosy snug. Four handpumps serve immaculately kept cask ales. There is ample car parking, and the 587 bus conveniently stops outside the front door. Q⛲❀◑♿🅰🖵(587)🛜

Lowton

Ram's Head Inn
248 Slag Lane, WA3 2ED
☎ 07459 912911
2 changing beers (sourced regionally) 🄷
Standing opposite St Luke's Church, this traditional pub attracts a good local following of all ages, who come for conversation or to watch sport on TV. A central bar serves a number of separate areas with many wooden features and a large brick fireplace. There is ample outside seating in the garden at the side, which also has a play area for children. Quiz nights are held every Thursday and live bands play on Saturday nights. ⛲❀♣🖵(10)🎵

Travellers Rest 🍺
443 Newton Road, WA3 1NZ
☎ (01925) 293222
2 changing beers (sourced regionally)

Traditional country pub and restaurant, dating back to the 19th century, between Lowton and Newton-le-Willows, popular with locals, walkers and cyclists. There are a number of seating areas and a separate restaurant, with a bar area to the right for drinkers. Outside is a large garden and car park. A private room is available to hire for special occasions. Haydock Park racecourse is only a mile away. Q✿❄◗⚫⑃க▣(34)❀🕏

Lydgate

White Hart Inn ⓛ
51 Stockport Road, OL4 4JJ
☎ (01457) 872566 ⊕ thewhitehart.co.uk
JW Lees Bitter; Millstone Tiger Rut; Timothy Taylor Golden Best; 1 changing beer (often JW Lees) Ⓗ
Dating from 1788, this former police station is now a free house, with a smart, multi-room layout. There are log-burning stoves in the bar and brasserie, and quality food is served daily from an award-winning kitchen. There is also a separate restaurant, function rooms, and guest accommodation, and fine views over the surrounding countryside. A number of events are run throughout the year, including themed dinners and wine tastings. The pub also hosts the Whit Friday Brass Band Contests. Q✿❄⚫◗⑃க▣(84,184) 🕏

Manchester

Café Beermoth
Brown Street, M2 1DA (entrance is on Brown St)
☎ (0161) 835 2049 ⊕ beermoth.co.uk
7 changing beers (sourced nationally; often Runaway) Ⓗ
Modern pub with a Belgian theme and a welcoming, homely feel. The long bar is backed by windows into the adjacent cellar, and upstairs is a small mezzanine. There are seven cask beers on draught, including a house beer from Runaway, plus 10 keg lines and an extensive bottle menu, with many imported from Germany and Belgium. There are regular tap takeovers and tastings, often supporting new artisanal producers. Rolls and pies, artisanal cheese and cured meat plates are available. There is some outdoor seating. ✿❄க⚡(Market Street) ●❀♪

Cask
29 Liverpool Road, M3 4NQ
☎ (0161) 819 2527
4 changing beers (sourced regionally; often Mallinsons, Pictish) Ⓗ
Entering this ex-motorbike workshop via the listed saloon-style doors, the first view is of the four handpumps, which feature a good range of styles. There is a traditional feel about the bar, while further in are bench seated booths and access to the garden. A closer look will reveal an impressive selection of specialist beers, both local and imported. Real cider is also available in bottles and draught. Customers can bring their own food, if they dispose of rubbish responsibly. ❄⚡(Deansgate) ⚡(Deansgate-Castlefield) ●▣❀🕏

City Arms 🍷 ★ ✅
46-48 Kennedy Street, M2 4BQ (near town hall, next door to Waterhouse pub)
☎ (0161) 236 4610
Brightside Odin Blonde; 7 changing beers (sourced regionally; often Neptune, Thornbridge, Titanic) Ⓗ
A fine, Grade-II listed traditional pub with two standard rooms and numerous original features. The bar and a few chairs are in the area overlooking the street, which is fairly basic. To the back is a cosier area where you can

relax in good company. Eight handpulls give a wide variety of beer types in great shape; Titanic Plum Porter is a popular and reliable choice. The bar is frequently packed. ⚫◗❄(Oxford Rd)⚡(St Peters Sq)♣▣❀

Gas Lamp
50A Bridge Street, M3 3BW
☎ (0161) 478 1224 ⊕ thegaslampmanchester.co.uk
4 changing beers (sourced nationally; often Pomona Island) Ⓗ
Opened in 2010 and housed in the basement of the former Manchester and Salford Children's Mission, this pub features an impressive frontage with a discreet entrance leading to the subterranean bar. The main bar boasts Victorian glazed-brick walls and wooden flooring, while a narrow passageway leads to a charming back room adorned with photos of the building's rich history. A selection of four cask beers are offered, one or two of which are from the pub's own brewery, Pomona Island, in Salford. ❄⚡(Salford Central) ⚡(St Peters Square) ●▣❀🕏

Grey Horse ✅
80 Portland Street, M1 4QX (jct Princess St)
☎ (0161) 228 2595
Hydes Original; 3 changing beers (sourced locally; often Hydes) Ⓗ
This compact city-centre bar – which vies with its neighbour, the Circus Tavern, for the title of 'smallest pub' – has been serving beer since 1851. The small, semi-circular bar serves the single-room layout, and there is a small backyard for smokers. This Hydes pub always has up to four beers from the brewery's range, often including the mild, Dark Ruby. ❄(Piccadilly) ⚡(St Peters Square) ▣(1) ❀🕏

Hare & Hounds ★
46 Shudehill, M4 4AA (opp Shudehill bus station)
☎ (0161) 832 4737
Joseph Holt Bitter; 1 changing beer (sourced regionally) Ⓗ
This busy, Grade II-listed busy pub has been identified by CAMRA as having a nationally important historic pub interior, which dates from 1925, though the pub itself is from the early 1800s. Take time to admire the mottled tile frontage before entering. The central bar serves all three rooms, front vault, central vault and lounge bar, where the superbly kept Holts Bitter is a big seller. 'Free and Easy' music sessions on a Wednesday afternoon are popular with its more mature clientele. ❄(Victoria) ⚡(Shudehill) ▣❀🕏♪

Jack in the Box
1 Eagle Street, M4 5BU
8 changing beers (sourced nationally) Ⓗ
Located inside the historic, Grade II-listed Mackie Mayor Building, is this lively bar which serves a good selection of quality cask and keg beers. There are eight handpumps and 10 keg lines offering a changing range from Blackjack brewery, as well guest ales, in a relaxed atmosphere. Food can be bought from vendors within the building and customers can sit anywhere in the hall. Real cider is available in bottles. Payment by card only. Closed Mondays. Dogs and children welcome. ✿க❄(Victoria) ⚡(Shudehill) ●▣❀🕏

Lower Turks Head
36 Shudehill, Manchester, M4 1EZ (opp Shudehill bus and metrolink interchange)
☎ (0161) 834 2910
Joseph Holt Mild, IPA, Bitter, Two Hoots; 2 changing beers (sourced locally; often Bootleg) Ⓗ

After lying empty for 22 years, this pub reopened in 2013 and was acquired by Joseph Holt in 2021. There are several drinking areas on the split-level ground floor, as well as an upstairs lounge that leads to a roof terrace. An interesting feature are the six raised drinking pews opposite the bar. The pub sits in a terrace opposite Shudehill tram shop. It offers a full range of Holts beers, including specials, all kept in excellent condition. May close early if quiet.

Q ✿ ⊛ ⚑ ≠ (Victoria) 묘 (Shudehill) 🚍 ✿ 🛜

Marble Arch ★
73 Rochdale Road, Collyhurst, M4 4HY (corner Gould St)
☎ (0161) 832 5914 ⊕ marblebeers.com
Marble Metric, Manchester Bitter; 4 changing beers (sourced nationally; often Marble) Ⓗ
The Marble Arch, birthplace of the city's iconic Marble brewery (now moved to Salford), is an impressive Grade II-listed building. A striking pillared entrance porch leads to an equally impressive interior with a famously sloping mosaic floor approaching an ornate bar. A good range of cask beer is served, and keg lines dispense both Marble and guest beers. There is a small range of carefully selected artisanal real and live ciders. At the rear is a dining area and a yard with well-designed kiosk shelters.
✿ ⊛ ⏰ ≠ (Victoria) 묘 (Shudehill) ● 🚍 ✿ 🛜

Molly House
26 Richmond Street, M1 3NB (jct Sackville St)
☎ (0161) 237 9329 ⊕ themollyhouse.com
4 changing beers (sourced regionally) Ⓗ
Tucked away just behind the main Canal Street section of the gay village, Molly House has the look of a traditional pub at first glance. Set on two floors, the ground floor has four handpumps, always with a range of choice from Manchester and North-West breweries. The adjacent kitchen serves tapas. There are further handpumps in the more glamorous first-floor room, though not all may be available. Local CAMRA Pub of the Year 2023.
✿ ⊛ ⏰ ≠ (Piccadilly) 묘 (Piccadilly Gardens) ♣ ● ✿ 🛜 ♫

Peveril of the Peak ★
127 Great Bridgewater Street, M1 5JQ (jct Great Bridgewater St and Chepstow St)
☎ (0161) 236 6364
Millstone Tiger Rut; Timothy Taylor Landlord; Titanic Plum Porter; 1 changing beer (often Brightside) Ⓗ
This impressive Grade II-listed building stands alone, with an outdoor drinking area created by a road diversion. The bar is an island between a pool room, cosy snug and a traditional bar. Dark wood and stained glass predominate. The four handpumps serve a selection of regular beers, which are prominently displayed on a board next to the snug.
Q ⊛ ≠ (Oxford Road) 묘 (St Peters Square) ♣ 🚍 ✿ ♫

Piccadilly Tap
8 Gateway House, Piccadilly Station Approach, M1 2GH (up station approach, off London Rd)
☎ (0161) 393 4168 ⊕ piccadillytap.com
5 changing beers (sourced nationally; often Adnams, Lakes) Ⓗ
Conveniently located on the approach to Manchester Piccadilly station, this bar is a popular meeting point, and with commuters coming and going. The ground floor features a standing room area and a mixture of tall and low tables. Upstairs is a seating area with outdoor terrace, pool table and toilets. There is also seating outside at the front. Free buses around the city centre leave from near the pub.
✿ ⊛ ⏰ ≠ (Piccadilly) 묘 (Piccadilly) ♣ ● 🚍 (1,2) ✿ 🛜

Port Street Beer House
39-41 Port Street, M1 2EQ (opp Brewer St)
☎ (0161) 237 9949 ⊕ portstreetbeerhouse.co.uk
7 changing beers (sourced nationally) Ⓗ
Vibrant pub split over two floors of a former shop in the Northern Quarter. The bar is on the ground floor, with outdoor pavement seating and an outdoor yard, and an additional room upstairs. An accessible toilet is on the ground floor. Seven handpumps and a number of keg lines provide an interesting range of beers. Real cider from Hogans and Pulp is available in bottles and can. The pub holds group beer tastings. Its associated festival, IndyManBeerCon, made an important contribution to the growth of the city's beer scene.
✿ ⊛ & ≠ (Piccadilly) 묘 (Piccadilly Gardens) ♣ ● 🚍 ✿ 🛜

Sadler's Cat
Sadler's Yard, M4 4AH
☎ (0161) 834 4989 ⊕ sadlers-cat.pub
3 changing beers (sourced locally; often Cloudwater) Ⓗ
Now firmly established under its new name (previously Pilcrow), Sadler's Cat is a modern, one-storey building off Hanover Street by Sadler's Yard within the NOMA complex. The pub serves three cask beers from Cloudwater brewery and also has 14 keg lines. A team of community volunteers and makers provided the interior fittings. Notice the terracotta bar edge, a new take on an architectural feature and a material much used in Manchester in the past to protect buildings from grime and pollution during its industrial past.
✿ ⊛ ⏰ & ≠ (Victoria) 묘 (Victoria) ♣ 🚍 🛜

Salisbury Ale House ✓
2 Wakefield Street, M1 5NE
☎ (0161) 236 5590
4 changing beers (sourced nationally; often Robinsons, Timothy Taylor, Theakstons) Ⓗ
Hidden away in the historic 'Little Ireland' area between Oxford Road Station and Oxford Road, this friendly, brown-tiled pub has long been a favourite with rock fans. The interior has lost a lot of its original features, but the bar has some areas of interest. There are usually four real ales on, including often the rare Old Peculier. Pizzas are served from 3pm. The beer garden is out the back of the pub, past the jukebox.
✿ ⊛ ≠ (Oxford Road) 묘 (St Peters Square) ♣ 🚍 ✿ 🛜

Smithfield Market Tavern
37 Swan Street, M4 5JZ (corner of Coop St and Swan St)
⊕ the-smithfield-market-tavern.business.site
6 changing beers (sourced nationally; often Blackjack) Ⓗ
Refurbished in 2020 and again in 2023, the Smithfield is a lively, modern take on a traditional pub. It is the flagship venue for Blackjack brewery and serves six cask ales – four from Blackjack and two guests – as well as 10 keg beers, a cider and an interesting selection of bottled brews. A traditional bar billiards table, dartboard and a small selection of board games provide entertainment. It was voted local CAMRA Pub of the Year in 2022.
✿ ⊛ ≠ (Victoria) 묘 (Shudehill) ♣ ● 🚍 ✿ 🛜

Track Brewery Tap
Unit 18, Piccadilly Trading Estate, M1 2NP
☎ (0161) 536 3975
Track Sonoma; 2 changing beers (sourced locally) Ⓗ
After being located in a number of other venues, the Tap joined the brewery in its US-inspired, all-in-one facility on the Piccadilly Trading estate in 2021. There are 20 keg and three cask lines serving the freshest Track beer, plus some occasional guests. The seating is largely canteen style, with the tanks within touching distance in the

open-plan layout. There is a dedicated space for a food residency (currently pizza). Dogs are welcome. Card payment only. Closed on Monday.
👁🅿🚺👐♿🚲(Piccadilly) ♫(New Islington) 🚃♣

Marple

Samuel Oldknow
22 Market Street, SK6 7AD
☎ (0161) 425 9530 ⊕ samueloldknow.co.uk
6 changing beers (sourced regionally; often Brightside, Northern Monkey) Ⓗ
Named after a local mill owner who was responsible for much of the development of Marple and Mellor some 200 years ago. This is a welcoming and slightly quirky two-level bar in a converted shop. Six vintage-style handpulls dispense changing real ales, often including ones from Brightside and Northern Monkey, plus real ciders from Biddenden. There is always a dark beer. A range of canned and bottled beers is also available to take away. Food consists of snacks and locally made pies.
Q🚃♣🕮🍴🚃🛜♫

Traders
111-113 Stockport Road, SK6 6AF
3 changing beers (sourced nationally) Ⓗ
Originally a shop conversion, this micropub expanded into the next-door premises in 2019, and a further extension has followed since. The industrial chic interior is brightened up by colourful wall paintings, posters and plants. Three handpumps serve regularly changing ales, and 12 keg lines serve a mix of beers. Live music often features on Tuesday evenings and some weekends, a quiz night is held on Wednesday, and occasional international sports games are shown.
🚃👁🅿🚲(Rose Hill Marple) 🚃♣♫

Marple Bridge

Norfolk Arms
2 Town Street, SK6 5DS
☎ (0161) 427 8090 ⊕ thenorfolkarms.co.uk
5 changing beers (sourced regionally; often Seven Bro7hers, Storm) Ⓗ
A recently refurbished stone-built pub sitting in an attractive setting in the centre of Marple Bridge and close to the River Goyt. Five locally/regionally sourced real ales are usually on offer, which is a welcome addition to the choice in the area. This warm and friendly pub is comfortably furnished and attracts a wide-ranging clientele by catering for all tastes. It also serves good-value food and is well-served by public transport.
🚃👁🅿♿🚲(Marple) 🚃♣🛜♫

Northumberland Arms 🍸
64 Compstall Road, SK6 5HD
⊕ thenorthumberlandarms.com
Robinsons Unicorn; Track Sonoma; 2 changing beers (sourced locally; often Beartown, Brightside) Ⓗ
A community-owned pub run by a group of enthusiastic local people who have worked hard to restore this cosy welcoming pub to its former glory. A varied range of well-kept beers is always available, often including a mild or a dark beer. There is also a thriving scene of local events and varied activities. Thursday is quiz night. Street food vendors are outside every Thursday evening and alternate Saturdays. Bus stops (in both directions) are outside. 🚃👁♣🅿🚃(383,384)♣🛜

Middleton

Harbord Harbord Ⓛ ✅
17-21 Long Street, M24 6TE
☎ (0161) 654 6226
Greene King Abbot; Ruddles Best Bitter; Sharp's Doom Bar; 3 changing beers Ⓗ
This town-centre pub, formerly a Woolworth's, is named after the last Lord of the Manor. The pub has a single long bar and a raised drinking and eating area. It is popular throughout the day with locals and shoppers, and the varied beer selection makes it well worth a visit. It hosts twice-yearly beer festivals and occasional Meet the Brewer nights. The interesting local history is depicted on the walls. 🚃👁♿🚃🛜

Ring o' Bells
St. Leonards Square, M24 6DJ
☎ (0161) 654 9245
JW Lees Manchester Pale Ale, Bitter; 2 changing beers (sourced locally; often JW Lees) Ⓗ
The Ringers has been a pub since 1831. The community-focused local stands opposite the medieval parish church and enjoys stunning views across to Oldham and beyond, especially at night. It has a fabulous beer garden to the rear. It serves Boilerhouse beers and JW Lees seasonal ones. The pub hosts an annual Maypole event on May bank holiday Monday and a unique Pace Egg play on Easter Monday. Its attraction is further enhanced by occasional live music and quizzes. 👁♣🅿🚃(17)♣🛜♫

Monton

Monton Tap
165 Monton Road, M30 9GS
☎ 07413 487560
3 changing beers (sourced locally; often Brightside, Marble, Strange Times) Ⓗ
A converted shop premises in an up-and-coming area. Opened in 2018, the Monton Tap has quickly become a popular venue, with three handpumps and an ever-changing variety of ales, often locally sourced. There is a good range of KeyKeg and bottles. It also champions local gins and rums. There are some tables at the front of this small pub. 👁🚃♣🛜

Mossley

Butchers Arms
7 Stockport Road, OL5 0QX
☎ (01457) 831111
Millstone Tiger Rut; 3 changing beers (often Timothy Taylor, Theakston, Titanic) Ⓗ
Near the traffic lights in Top Mossley, this privately owned and run town-centre pub caters for a younger clientele while enthusiastically promoting cask ale to all in a lively and friendly atmosphere. The four handpumps serve local and regional ales and a busy pool table is located in the bar area. Thursday is quiz night, on Saturdays there is a DJ disco and karaoke, and on Sundays a gameshow. ♿🚲♣🚃♫

Gillery Ⓛ
1-3 Old Brow, OL5 0AD (Stamford Rd, immediately above the railway station)
☎ (01457) 237007
Millstone Tiger Rut, Stout, True Grit; 1 changing beer (sourced locally; often Millstone, We Are Wolf Brewing) Ⓗ
This pub was converted from the last remaining bank in Mossley and opened in 2019. The stone building towers over Stamford Road immediately behind the railway station. Four handpumps dispense beers from the town's

Millstone brewery and occasionally another local brewer, We Are Wolf Brewing. The pub welcomes all, including runners, walkers and cyclists. Light meals and snacks are available until 9pm. Live music features most weekends, often from local musicians. There is also work from local artists on display. ➠❀❅⬜❀❄♪

Rising Sun ⓛ

235 Stockport Road, OL5 0RQ
☎ (01457) 238236 ⊕ risingsunmossley.co.uk
Millstone Tiger Rut, Stout, True Grit; 4 changing beers (sourced locally; often Saltaire, Thornbridge) ⓗ
A former Wilsons pub that has been a free house for many years. The current owner added a small brewery in 2016 to augment the range of regular beers (usually from nearby Millstone), plus guest beers. The pub has an open-plan layout, with log-burning fires in winter, and enjoys views across the Tame valley towards the Pennines beyond. Several large screens show mainly City and United matches, and with bands playing some nights there is frequently a boisterous atmosphere in the pub. ➠❀◑P⬜(353,356) ❀❄♪

Oldham

Ashton Arms ⓛ

28-30 Clegg Street, OL1 1PL (opp Odeon cinema complex)
☎ (0161) 630 9709
6 changing beers (sourced locally; often Millstone, Ossett, Pictish) ⓗ
Traditional town-centre pub on two levels. Six handpumps serve mainly locally sourced microbrewery beers which are always well kept, and there is usually one real cider on handpump. A range of bottled Belgian and German beers are also on offer. Good-value home-cooked food is served daily. Live sport is often shown on the TV. Payment is cash only. The Ashton has been in this Guide for over 20 consecutive years.
Q❀◑⬜(Central) ❀⬜❄❄

Cob & Coal Tap ⓛ

12-14 units, Tommyfield Market, Albion Street, OL1 3BG
☎ (0161) 624 0446
6 changing beers (often Pictish, Thirst Class, Wishbone) ⓗ
Cosy micropub in the market hall, with plenty of extra seating available in the hall itself opposite the bar. Six handpumps serve a changing menu of beers that are well looked-after and always in good condition. At least two real ciders are also on offer. A variety of food is available from the market stalls and can be eaten in the bar. A former CAMRA regional Pub of the Year and local cider Pub of the Year. Q⬜(Central)❀⬜❄❄

Fox & Pine ⚐

18 Greaves Street, OL1 1AD (halfway along Greaves St between Union St and Yorkshire St)
☎ (0161) 628 2475
Draught Bass; 9 changing beers (sourced regionally; often Durham, Mallinsons, Pictish) ⓗ
The Fox is a real community pub with a welcoming atmosphere. This former (and current) local CAMRA Pub of the Year has not rested on its laurels and continues to serve top-quality beer through 10 handpumps. Draught Bass is a constant, and there are always three dark beers on offer. Downstairs is a busy bar area, while upstairs are two linked rooms. There are also outside seating areas to the front and rear. Food is available. It is a five-minute walk from Oldham bus station.
Q❀◑❀⬜(Central)❀⬜❄❄

Patricroft

Bird in Hand

304 Liverpool Road, M30 0RY (next to Eccles fire station)
☎ (0161) 511 9275
Joseph Holt Mild, Bitter, Two Hoots ⓗ
Large, recently refurbished four-roomed pub on the old Manchester to Liverpool road. Inside are a large TV room, darts room, pool room and a quiet snug surrounding a spacious bar area. There is a large garden and smoking area to the rear. Tunnels reputedly lead to the old police station but there is little evidence. Quiz night is Friday and there is occasional live entertainment. The pub has pool and darts teams and there is free pool on Thursdays. ➠❀❅❄P⬜❀❄♪

Prestwich

Ostrich

163 Bury Old Road, M25 1JF
☎ 07827 850269
Joseph Holt Bitter ⓗ
Built over 300 years ago, this genuine community pub has five separate rooms off the bar area. A Joseph Holt's house, the Ostrich has three handpulls, though at the time of writing was serving only Holt's Bitter. The outside beer garden is popular with families, and children are welcome until 7pm. Camera and computer clubs are held on weekday nights, and functions are bookable with catering by arrangement.
Q➠❀⬜(Heaton Park) ❄P⬜(135) ❀❄♪

Radcliffe

New Inn

387 Ainsworth Road, M26 4HF
☎ (0161) 723 0583
Ossett White Rat; Sharp's Doom Bar; 1 changing beer ⓗ
A traditional, friendly, red-brick pub, free of tie, with three real ales on offer. It has a clean and pleasant interior, with comfortable seating. There is a large beer garden to the rear, with barbecues in summer. It has a real community feel, with various activities taking place, including free pool, karaoke, a quiz night, a weekly raffle and live music on Saturday nights. There is limited car parking on the unmade rear lane.
➠❀❅❄P⬜(98,471) ❀❄♪

Ramsbottom

Casked ⓛ

2-4 Prince Street, BL0 9FN
House beer (by Reedley Hallows); 4 changing beers (sourced locally; often Brewsmith, Red Rose) ⓗ
Now well established on the Ramsbottom's vibrant real ale scene, this bright and modern looking, single-floor pub is a welcoming and pleasant place to visit. Five handpumps serve ales sourced predominantly from local breweries, with two changng real ciders on gravity. There are also 15 keg lines. The pub is extremely dog friendly, and if you take your hound in, its picture may appear on the pub's Facebook page. ❀❅❄❅⬜❀❄

Irwell Works Brewery Tap ⓛ

Irwell Street, BL0 9YQ
☎ (01706) 825019 ⊕ irwellworksbrewery.co.uk
Irwell Works Breadcrumbs, Costa Del Salford, Marshmallow Unicorn, Mad Dogs & Englishmen; 8 changing beers (often Irwell Works, Pictish) ⓗ

Recently refurbished and back under its original ownership, this snug, comfortable brewery tap is above the brewery itself on the first floor. The old coppersmiths building oozes character and fits in well with the heritage of Ramsbottom. The full range of Irwell Works beers are usually on offer on the eight handpumps, plus a guest ale. Snack food is available Friday to Sunday afternoons. The pub is a worthwhile stop on the nearby East Lancashire Railways Rail Ale Tours.
🖼️🚲🕭♿🚪🚍(472,474) ♣🕸️🛜♪

Ramsbottom Royal British Legion
Central Street, BL0 9AF
☎ (01706) 822483
Ossett White Rat; 1 changing beer (sourced locally; often Brightside, Ossett) ⊞
A small, quiet, traditional club at the back of Bolton Street in the centre of Ramsbottom. Non-members are always welcome (no entry fee) but regulars would be expected to join the club. The two handpumps on the bar and usually dispense Fyne Ales Jarl and Ossett White Rat. The main bar is on the ground floor, with a largescreen TV for sports, while upstairs is a function room.
🚲🚲♿🚪🚍(472,474) 🛜♪

Reddish

Reddish Ale
14 Broadstone Road, SK5 7AE (opp jct Stanhope St)
3 changing beers (sourced locally; often Pomona Island, RedWillow, Thornbridge) ⊞
Small, one-room pub, opened in 2022 in former restaurant premises. The interior consists of refectory-style seating supplemented by narrow counters and stools around the perimeter and at the bar. There are several small tables outside at the front for sunnier days. Mirrors, framed beer mats and some football-related photos decorate the walls. Three handpulls dispense changing cask beers, plus there are several keg lines. There's a fridge also with bottled and canned beers for off-sales. Various home-made snacks and small plates are available. 🚲🖼️🍴🚲(South)♣♠🚪🛜🕸️

Rochdale

Baum 🅛
35 Toad Lane, OL12 0NU
☎ (01706) 352186 ⊕ thebaum.co.uk
6 changing beers (sourced nationally; often Pictish, Vocation) ⊞
The Baum is a tastefully decorated, traditional-style pub in the Toad Lane conservation area, next door to the Co-op museum. It has six handpumps serving a changing range of beers, plus usually a guest cider. The well-trained staff are very knowledgeable about real ale, and the beers are always in immaculate condition. The food menu offers high-quality food at reasonable prices. A former CAMRA National Pub of the Year.
Q🚲🖼️🍴🚪(Town Centre) ♣🚍🕸️🛜

D'Ale House
18 Drake Street, OL16 1NT
Brightside Odin Blonde; house beer (by Pictish); 4 changing beers (often Brightside, Pictish) ⊞
Close to the tram and bus interchange, this popular town centre micropub opened in 2021. Tastefully refurbished, it is perfect for convivial drinking. It has five handpumps on the bar selling mainly local ales, including a house beer, D'ale, brewed by Pictish, and often a beer from further afield. There are also two German beer fonts and eight keg taps. The staff are knowledgeable about real ale, and the beer is always in good condition. The bar is

on an elevated platform in the rear of the pub with two lower seating areas on either side.
Q🚲🚲(Town Centre) 🚍🕸️🛜

Flying Horse Hotel 🅛
37 Packer Street, OL16 1NJ
☎ (01706) 646412 ⊕ theflyinghorsehotel.co.uk
House beer (by Pictish); 9 changing beers (sourced locally; often Phoenix, Pictish, Serious) ⊞
The Flyer is an impressive Edwardian stone-built free house, opposite the magnificent, recently renovated, gothic Town Hall. There are 12 very well kept and quality cask ales, 11 constantly changing, sold alongside three real ciders. There is usually one house beer on, Lancashire Bitter, brewed by Pictish. It has an extensive menu of high-standard, value-for-money food. An upstairs function room is often used for comedy nights, and there is live music at weekends.
🚲🏠🚲🖼️🚲🚪(Town Centre) ♣🅿️🚍🕸️🛜♪

Oxford
662 Whitworth Road, OL12 0TB
☎ (01706) 345709
Wainwright Gold; 2 changing beers (sourced nationally; often Serious) ⊞
A family-run pub at the foot of the Pennines on the A671 (Rochdale to Bacup road), two miles out of Rochdale centre. In addition to excellent beers and food, it is well-known for its open fires in winter, its large beer garden in summer, and its warm welcome all year round. Live music features occasionally in the beer garden. Opening hours change from winter to summer, so check before visiting. Q🚲🖼️🍴♿🅿️🚍(486)🛜

Romiley

Hop Haus
27 Compstall Road, SK6 4BT
☎ 07927 076941
5 changing beers (sourced locally; often Abbeydale, Magic Rock, RedWillow) ⊞
This micropub, opened a few years ago in a former shoe and clothes shop, has become a popular part of the Romiley pub scene. The double front provides the cosy, relaxed bar area with a light and airy feel, and there is a small room to the rear. The five real ales always include a dark beer, and there are craft beers on font and boxed ciders. It is near the railway station and bus routes, and the Peak Forest Canal is a short walk away.
🚲🖼️🚲♿🚪🚍🕸️

Royton

Puckersley Inn 🅞
22 Narrowgate Brow, OL2 6YD (off A671, via Dogford Rd and Fir Ln)
☎ (0161) 652 2834
JW Lees Dark, Manchester Pale Ale, Bitter; 1 changing beer (sourced locally; often JW Lees) ⊞
A stone-fronted, detached pub in a green belt location, with panoramic views over Royton, Shaw and Oldham from the dining room and large beer garden. This popular pub serves three or four ales from the JW Lees range and is a Lees pub of the year. It has a small vault, an open-plan lounge, and dining extension where children are welcome. An excellent range of meals is served daily. The 402 bus stops outside. 🚲🖼️🍴♿🅿️🚍(402)🛜♪

Sale

JP Joule 🅛
2A Northenden Road, M33 3BR

☎ (0161) 962 9889
Greene King Abbot; Ruddles Best Bitter; Sharp's Doom Bar; house beer (by Brightside); 6 changing beers (sourced nationally; often Beartown, Exmoor, Thornbridge) Ⓗ
Wetherspoon pub on the main road in Sale, named – and themed – after the famous physicist who lived locally. Two floors are connected by a grand staircase: the main bar is downstairs, while the upstairs bar has more handpumps, and a separate toilet. There are several keg lines serving lagers, cider (not real) and Guinness. An extensive food menu is available until 11pm. Pub-based beer festivals are held several times a year.
🚫❀⬤🕭🛇🚪🐾🛜

Railway
35 Chapel Road, M33 7FD (behind town hall)
☎ 07526 365835
Robinsons Dizzy Blonde, Unicorn Ⓗ
Traditional Robinsons public house that is community-oriented, friendly and welcoming. The interior is spacious, with a side room that is use for meetings and local clubs, and outdoor seating to the front and back. Live music features every weekend. The pub sits close to the Bridgewater Canal, and the Metrolink is less than five minutes' walk away. 🚫❀🚪🐾♣P🚪🐾🛜🎵

Salford

Eagle Inn ★
18-19 Collier Street, M3 7DW (off Queen St)
☎ (0161) 819 5002 ⊕ eagleinn.co.uk
Joseph Holt Bitter, Two Hoots; 1 changing beer (sourced locally) Ⓗ
This Grade II-listed, award-winning pub, also known as the Lamp Oil, is hard to find but worth the effort. It has three rooms running off a central corridor, with an extension into the next-door property to accommodate regular music performances. The surrounding roads have been cut off and sequestered for outdoor seating. Two regular Holt's beers and usually one from Bootleg are served, plus non-real Old Rosie cider on handpull.
Q🚫❀⬤≹(Central) 🚪(Victoria) ♣🚪🛜🎵

King's Arms
11 Bloom Street, M3 6AN (corner William St)
☎ (0161) 832 3605 ⊕ kingsarmssalford.com
House beer (by Strange Times); 4 changing beers (often Beartown, Stockport) Ⓗ
There is always something happening at the King's. Quiz night is Wednesday, Monday is needlecraft, while films and theatre productions are shown upstairs. The entry corridor passes the snug to the left, and, in a racetrack-shaped room, the main lounge and bar are to the right, with bench seating stretching three-quarters of the way around the wall. Another corridor leads out to the garden. Q❀⬤≹(Central)🚪🎵

New Oxford ♆ Ⓛ
11 Bexley Square, M3 6DB (off A6 Chapel St, close to Magistrates Court)
☎ (0161) 832 7082 ⊕ thenewoxford.com
House beer (by Phoenix); 11 changing beers (sourced regionally; often Empire, Moorhouse's, Phoenix) Ⓗ
A two-roomed Victorian corner-house that has benefitted from a recent refurbishment, restoring the pub to something resembling its former glory. The central bar boasts 11 handpumps and over 20 fonts. The cask ales are sourced regionally, in a variety of styles, and there is usually at least one dark beer on offer. They also have over 50 Belgian beers. An outdoor area has been fenced off in Bexley Square for drinking. The pub is a winner of many CAMRA awards. 🚫❀⬤≹(Central)🚪🐾🛜

Salford Quays

Dockyard
Dockhouse, Media City, M50 2EQ (to right of Media City Metrolink stop)
☎ (0161) 713 3810 ⊕ dockyard.pub/media-city
House beer (by Strange Times); 3 changing beers (sourced nationally; often Marston's, Sharp's, Strange Times) Ⓗ
Large, warehouse-style premises in Media City, often used by personalities from the nearby BBC and ITV studios. A house beer and three other changing beers are complemented by local and international craft offerings. An open-plan kitchen and see-through cellar are either side of the bar. Outside seating areas include greenhouses; plastic glasses only. Card payment only.
⬤🕭🚪(Mediacityuk) ♣🚪(50,53) 🐾🛜

Shevington

Plough & Harrow ✅
Broad o'th Lane, WN6 8EA
☎ (01257) 456361 ⊕ ploughandharrowshevington.co.uk
Wainwright Gold Ⓗ
A real community village pub with a large open-plan lounge, a separate bar/games room where pool, darts and dominoes are played, and an outside covered area. A function room is available on the first floor for private events. Live music features every Saturday and karaoke (or an acoustic singer) some Sundays. A car park is located to the rear. Q🚫🕭♣🚪🐾🎵

Stalybridge

Bridge Beers Ⓛ
55 Melbourne Street, SK15 2JJ
☎ 07948 617145 ⊕ bridgebeers.co.uk
4 changing beers (sourced locally; often Bridge Beers) Ⓖ
A combined micropub and bottle shop on the main pedestrianised shopping street. There is a small entrance area with table games leading into the bar, which sits in front of a row of stillaged casks. Four beers, mainly from Bridge brewery, are generally available, plus occasional locally sourced guest ales, all served by gravity dispense. The bottle display is opposite. Upstairs is a comfortable, Victorian-styled lounge featuring an eclectic mix of local heritage items. Q🚫≹♣🚪🐾

Cracking Pint
41 Melbourne Street, SK15 2JJ
☎ 07512 753544
3 changing beers (sourced locally; often Phoenix, RedWillow, Vocation) Ⓗ
Spacious microbar opened in 2017 by a local CAMRA member and located next to the canal in the main pedestrianised shopping street. It usually serves three changing real ales, sourced mainly from local breweries and some from further afield. There is also a good selection of bottled beers, many from Germany. This is a bar where conversation dominates in the absence of piped music, TV screens or fruit machines. Dogs and their well-behaved owners are welcome, as are children until 6pm. Q🚫≹🚪🐾🛜

Ol's Bier & More
93 Market Street, SK15 2AA
☎ (0161) 303 1887
1 changing beer (sourced locally; often Bridge Beers, Buxton, Marble) Ⓗ
A micropub and bottle shop which opened in 2021 and was subsequently extended into a former storeroom in 2022. This enabled them to serve a single real ale,

mostly sourced locally. Two keg beers are also available: a German Pils and an IPA. There is an extensive range of bottled beers, including many from Belgium and Germany, in addition to ciders. Pies are available on Fridays. Q ☕ 🍴 ➡ 🖥 ☻ 🌐 ♿

Society Rooms ✓
49-51 Grosvenor Street, SK15 2JN
☎ (0161) 338 9740
Greene King Abbot; Phoenix Wobbly Bob; Ruddles Best Bitter; Sharp's Doom Bar; 6 changing beers (sourced nationally; often Moorhouse's, Phoenix) ⃝
Popular split-level Wetherspoon in the town centre, named after the former Co-op store it now occupies. It was extended into the next-door premises in 2018, which also created a spacious beer garden, making it one of the largest Wetherspoons in the UK. Enthusiastic management and a strong focus on cask beers make this a favourite with local drinkers, with 10 real ales and two ciders usually available. Two beer festivals a year are held. Q ☕ ☻ ① ♿ ⬅ 🖥 🌐

Station Buffet Bar ★
Platform 4 Stalybridge Railway Station, Rassbottom Street, SK15 1RF (access from Platform 4)
☎ (0161) 303 0007
4 changing beers (sourced nationally; often Millstone, Thornbridge, Timothy Taylor) ⃝
One of the very few remaining Victorian station buffet bars and well worth missing a train for. This well-loved gem has 10 handpumps, with a minimum of four dispensing a variety of local and regionally sourced beers, plus at least one real cider or perry. A good range of bottled beers is also available. Sunday is quiz night, with Spanish classes on Mondays and folk music on Tuesdays. As part of the Transpennine Real Ale Trail, it can be busy on Saturdays. Hours may vary.
Q ☕ ① ♿ ⬅ ● P 🖥 ☻ 🌐

Standish

Albion Ale House Ⓛ ✓
12 High Street, WN6 0HL
☎ (01257) 367897 🌐 albionalehouse.co.uk
8 changing beers ⃝
The first micropub in Standish, located in a former shop on the High Street, it is now well established, with a loyal clientele, and was local CAMRA Community Pub of the Year in 2022. Five cask-conditioned ales are usually on offer, sometimes more, and always include one dark beer. Snacks are usually available. There is occasional live music and beer festivals are held. Q ☕ ☻ ♿ 🖥 ☻ 🌐 ♪

Hoot Ⓛ
34A High Street, WN6 0HL
☎ (01257) 806262 🌐 thehoot.bar
4 changing beers (sourced regionally; often Coniston, Cumbrian Ales, Lancaster) ⃝
A modern bar that is popular with customers of all ages. The large, single-room bar (which features novelty owls) is lit by interesting accent lighting and has a tiled slate floor and a wood-burning stove. The bar boasts four handpumps serving a good choice of cask ales, alongside spirits, cocktails and prosecco. There is a lovely covered area outside. Q ☕ ☻ ♿ P 🖥 ☻ 🌐

Standish Unity Club Ⓛ
Cross Street, WN6 0HQ
☎ (01257) 424007 🌐 standishunityclub.com
Sharp's Doom Bar; 4 changing beers (sourced regionally) ⃝
In the centre of Standish but tucked away so a little tricky to find, this popular club offers five real ales including

one dark beer – often Titanic Plum Porter. The club is split into two sides, a large function room and a bar area including the games room and a quieter drinking area. A frequent winner of local CAMRA Club of the Year and previous runner-up for regional Club of the Year.
Q ☕ ☻ ♿ ♣ P 🖥 🌐 ♪

Stockport

Angel Inn
20 Market Place, SK1 1EY (opp Market Hall)
☎ (0161) 429 0251
6 changing beers (sourced regionally; often Beartown) ⃝
After a 67-year closure, the Angel reopened in 2018. It has since gone from strength to strength and is now a regular in this Guide. While the interior is largely open-plan, it is nicely broken up, with a particularly attractive snug to the rear. In addition, there is a large outdoor drinking area at the back which is well-used in the summer. Live music features some evenings and Sunday afternoons when the pub can get very busy.
☕ ☻ ♿ ⬅ 🖥 ☻ 🌐

Arden Arms ★ ✓
23 Millgate, SK1 2LX (jct Corporation St)
☎ (0161) 480 2185
Robinsons Dizzy Blonde, Unicorn, Trooper ⃝**, Old Tom; 1 changing beer (often Robinsons)** Ⓖ
Grade II listed and recognised by CAMRA as having a nationally important historic pub interior, this multi-room pub is just down the hill from Stockport's Market Place. Note the superb curved, glazed bar, the grandfather clock, and particularly the snug, which can only be accessed through the bar area itself (one of only four such in the UK). The building alone warrants a visit, and the food is also recommended. The large, attractive courtyard hosts live music on winter Saturday nights. A true gem. ☕ ☻ ① ♿ 🖥 (384,383) ☻ 🌐 ♪

Bakers Vaults
Market Place, SK1 1EU (jct Vernon St)
Robinsons Dizzy Blonde, Unicorn, Trooper, Old Tom; Titanic Plum Porter; 3 changing beers (sourced nationally) ⃝
Opposite the town's historic market hall, this lively and vibrant pub has a spacious interior with a comfortable arrangement of seating to the front of and behind the centrally sited bar. High ceilings and arched windows accentuate the gin-palace style in which the pub was built. It is one of the few Robinsons brewery houses to serve guest beers from other brewers. Live music features on Sunday afternoons. A former local CAMRA Pub of the Year. ☕ ☻ ① ♿ ⬅ 🖥 ☻ 🌐 ♪

Blossoms ★
2 Buxton Road, Heaviley, SK2 6NU (jct Bramhall Ln)
☎ (0161) 222 4150
Robinsons Dizzy Blonde, Unicorn ⃝**, Old Tom** Ⓖ
Landmark street-corner local whose three rooms radiate off a traditional drinking lobby, served by the central bar. Many old features remain, particularly in the rear Smoke Room. The full Robinsons range is often available and includes a seasonal beer. Popular quizzes are held on a Thursday night, and the upstairs function room hosts live music at the weekend. An outside drinking has been created from a cobbled section of street and the former toilets are now a smoking area. Q ☕ ① ♣ P 🖥 ☻ 🌐 ♪

Magnet
51 Wellington Road North, Heaton Norris, SK4 1HJ (jct Duke St)
☎ (0161) 429 6287 🌐 themagnetfreehouse.co.uk

Salopian Oracle; 13 changing beers (sourced nationally; often RedWillow, Track) ⊞
Popular, family-run pub that has been a free house for over a dozen years. It offers 14 cask ales, alongside 12 craft keg beers; the digital display boards show the available selection. Occasional specials are served from the in-house Mount Crescent microbrewery. On entry, the left side is a bustling vault leading to a lower pool room. The right side leads to a series of other rooms. Outside is a two-storey beer terrace. A pizza vendor operates on Friday evenings. ♘❀◗⇌♣P🚌🐾ᯤ

Olde Vic

1 Chatham Street, Edgeley, SK3 9ED (jct Shaw Heath)
🌐 yeoldevic.pub
6 changing beers (sourced nationally) ⊞
Now owned by its regulars, Ye Olde Vic has undergone a continuous programme of improvements in recent years, all done without compromising its unique atmosphere. There is bric-a-brac at every turn, while the ceiling and wall displays of pumpclips are testimony to the array of guest beers sold over the years, as well as a reminder of numerous defunct beers and breweries. The ever-changing guest beers come from small breweries around the UK. The beer garden at the back is a summer suntrap. Q❀⇌♣●🚌🐾ᯤ♫

Petersgate Tap

19A St Petersgate, SK1 1EB (jct Etchells St)
☎ (0161) 938 4444 🌐 petersgatetap.com
6 changing beers (sourced regionally)
This family-run bar on two floors is a dark beer specialist and was local CAMRA Pub of the Year 2023 and Cider Pub of the Year for the last six years. Downstairs, recycled oak-topped tables and a mix of seating is arrayed beneath interesting wall posters and breweriana. Upstairs there is a well-stocked bottle shop, with an additional drinking area that hosts live music, various events, and regular tastings. Food from local takeaways can be eaten inside. Well worth a visit.
♘❀♿⇌●🚌🐾ᯤ♫

Runaway Brewery Tap

9-11 Astley Street, SK4 1AW (jct Heaton Ln, overlooking River Mersey)
☎ (0161) 480 1359 🌐 therunawaybrewery.com
2 changing beers (sourced locally; often Runaway) ⊞
Large, sparsely decorated room on the ground floor of a former metalworks factory. The bar is to the right, while a dividing wall with a glazed area showcases the brewery to the left. The rustic decor echoes the building's industrial past. The furniture is eclectic and comprises large, refectory-style tables and benches. The bar features handpulls for the cask beers, plus a bank of taps on an adjacent wall for the keg/membrane options. A door leads to the yard and garden.
Q♘❀◖◗♿⇌●🚌🐾ᯤ

Swan with Two Necks ★

36 Princes Street, SK1 1RY (jct Hatton St)
☎ (0161) 480 2185
Robinsons Dizzy Blonde, Unicorn, Old Tom; 1 changing beer (often Robinsons) ⊞
This pub was rebuilt in the 1920s and the interior remains pretty much unchanged since then. Of particular note are the classic, light-oak panelled drinking lobby, and the top-lit middle room with mock-Tudor fireplace. Further back is a small lounge-cum-diner, where a pie-and-mash menu is served at lunchtimes. The rear outside area was stylishly reworked a few years ago and is now a lovely spot for a pint in the warmer months. It is close to the Red Rock entertainment complex.
Q♘❀◖⇌♣🚌(325,330)🐾ᯤ

Stretford

Longford Tap 🄻

Unit 107 Stretford Mall, M32 9BA
☎ (0161) 865 7007
Marble Manchester Bitter; 3 changing beers (sourced regionally; often Blackjack, Dunham Massey, Runaway) ⊞
A former retail unit on the outside of Stretford Mall. The inside is decorated with pictures of old Stretford, and there is a small outside seating area to the front which is also used for smoking. The bar prides itself on its dedication to local brewers, with four handpumps and five keg lines all serving local ales. They host quiz nights, live music and karaoke, and also support local charity and community groups. ♘❀♿🚊🚌🐾ᯤ

Swinton

Park Inn

135-137 Worsley Road (A572), M27 5SP (corner Shaftesbury Rd, 200yds from A580)
☎ (0161) 793 1568
Joseph Holt Mild, Bitter ⊞
A good, traditional local, which has been a Joseph Holt's pub since 1878. There is a vault to the left as you enter, and a large lounge to the right with a snug tucked away behind the central bar. Karaoke, disco and guest singers are often a weekend feature in the main room, while the other two rooms are reasonably quiet. Disabled access is via the car park to the rear. Q❀♿♣P🚌(2,73)🐾ᯤ

White Horse Hotel ✔

384 Worsley Road, M27 0FH (opp Lime Ave)
☎ (0161) 794 2404
Greene King IPA; 5 changing beers (sourced nationally; often Big Bog, Brightside) ⊞
Swinton's oldest pub, dating back to the mid-1700s. Once a Boddington's house, the old building has been refurbished inside, with several separate areas clustered around the one bar. The pub features regular DJ nights on Friday, and quiz nights. Food is popular and served until well into the evening, and there is also a special menu for coeliacs. ♘❀◖◗♿♣P🚌🐾ᯤ

Wobbly Stool

233 Manchester Road, M27 4TT
☎ 07764 621471
3 changing beers (sourced locally; often Beartown, Brightside) ⊞
Opened in 2019, this former flower shop quickly became a popular little bar. It has three handpumps and an ever-changing selection of ales, which are usually sourced locally. There is also a fine selection of craft beers on KeyKeg, bottled Belgian beers and cider from Westons. Bar games are available. Quiz night is Wednesday and there is a fortnightly open-mic session during the summer. There are a few tables at the front. ❀♣🚌🐾ᯤ

Tyldesley

Mort Arms ★

235-237 Elliott Street, M29 8DG
☎ 07584 341099
Joseph Holt Bitter ⊞
The Mort Arms is an atmospheric, community-based pub in Tyldesley town centre. It was purchased by Edward Holt 2nd in 1932 and rebuilt the following year. Inside, the pub still retains many historic features, including engraved wood-panelling, etched glass and beautiful tiled fireplaces. This is a good place to watch live sports on one of the many TVs. The pub participates in both the local darts and dominoes leagues. ❀♿♣P🚌(V2)🐾ᯤ

Union Arms

83 Castle Street, M29 8EW
☎ (01942) 870645 ● unionarmstyldesley.co.uk
Thwaites Gold; 2 changing beers (sourced regionally; often Wigan Brewhouse) Ⓗ
This family-friendly pub is part of the local community. It is divided into several separate connected rooms, and there is also a large outside patio area. On the left side is the vault and on the right a lounge used at mealtimes. The guest beers are from Wigan Brewhouse. Fresh home-cooked food is served until early evening and Sunday lunches are avaiable. Most sporting events are shown on TV. Once a month they host a lunch for dementia sufferers and carers, featuring music and dance. ☺⊛◑♠🚐(V2)♪

Uppermill

Cross Keys Inn ✅

Running Hill Gate, OL3 6LW (off A670, up Church Rd)
☎ (01457) 874626 ● crosskeysinn.pub
JW Lees Dark, Manchester Pale Ale, Bitter; 3 changing beers (sourced locally; often JW Lees) Ⓗ
A charming 18th-century stone pub in a popular walking area near the moors. There are exposed beams everywhere and the public bar (Buckley's Kitchen) has a Yorkshire range and a stone-paved floor. Outside is a garden and children's play area, as well as an extensive flagged patio. Home-cooked food includes pies and daily specials. Walkers and dogs are welcome. The pub is packed during the Rushcart Festival in August.
☺⊛◑♿P🔥♪

Urmston

Barking Dog

9A Higher Road, M41 9AB
☎ (0161) 215 0858 ● the-barking-dog.co.uk
House beer (by Banks's); 3 changing beers (sourced locally; often Dunham Massey) Ⓗ
Converted from a post office, this popular local venue has an L-shaped room, with the bar covering half the length on one side. Five handpumps serve four cask ales, usually sourced locally, and one cider. Through a small corridor, the origins of the building are evident, with a strongroom and, further on, the quiet snug, which is available for meetings (free of charge). On Tuesday and Thursday two-for-one deals are available on food, with a 25% discount for key workers. ☺⊛◑♿⇄♠🚐🐾♪

Flixton Conservative Club

Abbotsfield, 193 Flixton Road, M41 5DF
☎ (0161) 748 2846 ● flixtonconservativeclub.co.uk
5 changing beers (sourced regionally; often Bank Top, Dunham Massey, Pictish) Ⓗ
A multi CAMRA award-winning club with five handpumps offering an ever-changing range of ales from mainly local breweries. The club facilities include a bowling green, snooker tables, darts room and Sky/BT TV showing major sports events. It is a meeting place for guitar and cycle clubs, and also hosts regular events, including pensioners' afternoons, live music, quiz nights, bingo, race nights and charity fundraisers. Visitors are warmly welcomed but must apply for membership if using on a regular basis.
☺⊛⇄(Chassen Road)♠P🚐(255,256) 📶

Lord Nelson

49 Stretford Road, M41 9LG
☎ 07827 850255
Joseph Holt Mild, Bitter; 1 changing beer (sourced locally; often Joseph Holt) Ⓗ

An iconic Urmston landmark, the Nelly, as it is known locally, is about as traditional as you can get. Inside, two small, comfortable side rooms of the main vault, and a larger room to the rear are served by the island bar. Beers are all from the Holts brewery; usually Mild, Bitter and Two Hoots. Quiz night is Tuesday and there is a disco on Saturdays. ⊛⇄♠P🚐🐾 📶♪

The Schooner Ⓛ

33 Flixton Road, M41 5AW
● prairie-schooner-taphouse.co.uk
4 changing beers (sourced locally; often Brewsmith, Brightside, Track) Ⓗ
This relatively large micropub opened in 2014 and is a favourite with local real ale drinkers and those from further afield. The four ever-changing, mainly locally sourced cask ales are supplemented by eight craft beers on tap, including US independents, and an extensive range of bottled and canned beers from the UK and the continent. Hogan's and bottled ciders are available. Two weekly quiz nights are held (music and general knowledge), and a monthly board games night, plus occasional live music or DJ. ☺⊛♿⇄♠●🚐(255)🐾 📶

Westhoughton

Beer School Ⓛ

88 Market Street, BL5 3AZ
☎ (01942) 396280 ● thebeerschool.co.uk
4 changing beers (sourced locally) Ⓗ
This micropub, decked out like a school, has developed into a lively and popular part of the local community. Four handpumps serve beers of varied style and strength, often from local suppliers. Up to four bag in box real ciders and perries are available. Drinks can be sampled before ordering. Note that the toilets are upstairs. Local CAMRA Pub of the Year 2022, Cider Pub of the Year 2020-23, and a Highly Commended Regional Cider award in 2023. ☺⊛⇄♠●🚐(7,521)🐾 📶♪

Brewery Tap Ⓛ

55 Market Street, BL5 3AG
☎ 07464 150029 ● blackedgebrewerytap.co.uk
7 changing beers (sourced locally; often Blackedge) Ⓗ
Opened in 2019, this is the second outlet for award-winning local Blackedge brewery. It has the friendly, community feel of a micropub. The timber and brick decor is complemented by the subdued and artistic lighting to give a homely atmosphere. Seven handpumps serve the core range of Blackedge beers, supplemented by their seasonal and one-off beers. There are also 10 modern keg fonts with beers from Blackedge and sometimes one from Rivington. Note that the toilets are upstairs. ☺⇄●🚐(7,521)🐾 📶♪

Whalley Range

Carlton Social & Bowling Club

Rowan Lodge, 113 Carlton Road, M16 8BE
☎ (0161) 881 3042 ● carltonclub.org.uk
3 changing beers (sourced regionally; often RedWillow, Saltaire) Ⓗ
Housed in a former Victorian villa, the Carlton Social and Bowling Club is a private members' club that is open to the public. It hosts a wide variety of community events, gigs and regular blues and jazz evenings. There are regular real ales from Saltaire and RedWillow, along with keg beer from Manchester Union Lager, Brightside, Redwillow and Shindigger. There is a pool table in the main room. A food vendor caters on Friday and Saturday evenings. ☺⊛🚉(Firswood)P🐾 📶♪

Wigan

Anvil L
Dorning Street, WN1 1ND
☎ (01942) 239444
6 changing beers (sourced nationally; often Phoenix, Wainwright, Wigan Brewhouse) ⊞
Popular town-centre pub, close to the bus station, with seven handpumps offering various guest beers, two boxed ciders, six draught continental ales and a range of bottled beers. Several TV screens show sports action and the small snug has the wall of fame displaying numerous award certificates. There is a garden at the rear. Over-18s only. ❀≠(Wallgate)⎙

Crooke Hall Inn L
92 Crooke Road, WN6 8LR
☎ (01942) 236088
4 changing beers (often Moorhouse's, Wigan Brewhouse) ⊞
Large, multi-roomed canalside pub in picturesque Crooke village, just outside Wigan. Popular with locals and visitors, dogs and children are welcome until 9pm. Home-made food features locally sourced ingredients where possible. There is a separate cellar bar, ideal for functions, and a large beer garden. The pub is very much the hub of the village and has won the local CAMRA Community Pub of the Year five times since 2014.
⌂❀⑴P⎙(635,635) ❀♿♪

John Bull Chophouse
2 Coopers Row, Market Place, WN1 1PQ
⊕ johnbullchophousewigan.co.uk
House beer (by Thwaites); 5 changing beers ⊞
A vibrant and lively pub in a building over 300 years old, previously cottages, stables and a slaughterhouse. This popular town-centre venue has been run by the same family for over 40 years. The six handpumps serve Thwaites beers. This quirky pub is spread over two floors, with the toilets upstairs, and has seating outside. It is reputed to have the best pub jukebox in the North-West. ❀≠(Wallgate) ⎙♿♪

Real Crafty L
9 Upper Dicconson Street, WN1 2AD
☎ (01942) 200364 ⊕ realcraftywigan.co.uk
Ossett White Rat; 4 changing beers ⊞
A real ale and craft beer emporium in Wigan town centre, five minutes' walk from the bus station and 10 minutes from both railway stations. Up to five real ales are dispensed via handpull, alongside craft beer, cider and perry served from 30 keg fonts. The Beer Atlas offers a collection of bottled and canned beers from around the world. Draught beer can be canned on site for takeaway. A popular weekly quiz is hosted on Tuesdays. Winner of CAMRA Regional Pub of the Year in 2022.
⌂❀♿≠(Wallgate) ♣●P⎙♿♪

Sherrington's L
57 Kenyon Road, WN1 2DU
☎ 07500 171114 ⊕ sherringtonsbar.com
Wily Fox Crafty Fox; 5 changing beers (sourced regionally) ⊞
An industrial-themed bar with six real ales on handpump, always including three from the Wily Fox stable, and three varying guests. There are also 10 craft/lager/continental beer taps offering Peroni, Moretti and a Wily Fox, along with seven varying guests. A selection of UK and continental bottled beers is also stocked, and there is an upper-floor gin bar. Tea, coffee and hot chocolate are available. A former local CAMRA Pub of the Year. ⌂❀♿●⎙♿♪

Swan & Railway L ✓
80 Wallgate, WN1 1BA
☎ (01942) 375817 ⊕ swanandrailwayhotelwigan.co.uk
Bank Top Dark Mild; Draught Bass; 5 changing beers (sourced nationally) ⊞
Winner of a Historic England Conservation Award in 2021, the pub was built in 1898 by WEV Crompton. This beautiful classic period inn features an impressive stained-glass window, and a collection of historical photos of the old town, the railway and rugby league. It has seven handpumps celebrating Draught Bass and also featuring local breweries such as Hophurst, Wily Fox and Wigan Brewhouse. Directly opposite Wigan North Western railway station.
❀⌂⑴≠(North Western) ♣⎙♿♀♪

Tap 'n' Barrel
16 Jaxon's Court, WN1 1LR
☎ (01942) 386966 ⊕ tapnbarrelwigan.co.uk
Hawkshead Windermere Pale; 2 changing beers (sourced regionally) ⊞
This former local CAMRA Cider Pub of the Year is located in Wigan's Victorian Quarter, conveniently next to the bus station. The friendly staff are happy to provide advice on the good selection of drinks available. The bar is split over three areas: the main bar, an upstairs seating area, and a heated undercover back room where live music is hosted on Sunday afternoons. There are six handpulls on the bar, usually serving three cask ales and three boxed ciders, alongside one or two draft craft beers.
Q⌂≠(Wallgate) ⎙♿♀♪

Wigan Central ▼ L
Arch No. 1 & 2, Queen Street, WN3 4DY
☎ (01942) 246425 ⊕ wigancentral.bar
House beer (by Bank Top); 6 changing beers (sourced nationally) ⊞
This two-roomed pub has a railway-themed interior with a live feed displaying arrival and departure times from both Wigan railway stations. It sources real ales from all over, alongside a wide range of continental bottled beers. Live music plays on Sunday. Bar snacks are available. Voted local CAMRA Pub of the Year 2024, it is a four-times previous winner, and is also a former local Cider Pub of the Year, Regional Pub of the Year and runner-up National Pub of the Year.
Q♿≠(North Western) ●⎙♿♀♪

Withington

Victoria ✓
438 Wilmslow Road, M20 3BW (jct Davenport Ave)
☎ (0161) 434 2600
Hydes Dark Ruby, Hopster, Original, Lowry; 2 changing beers (sourced nationally; often Hydes) ⊞
This friendly Hydes community pub attracts a convivial cross-section of Withington life. It is usually busy all day, and especially in the evenings. Its late 19th-century exterior features etched windows, while the large interior was refurbished and opened out some years ago to create distinct drinking areas, each with its own atmosphere. A beer patio at the rear provides a useful escape from the bustle. Attractions include a poker school, twice-weekly quizzes, TV sport, and weekend live entertainment. ⌂❀♣⎙♿♀♪

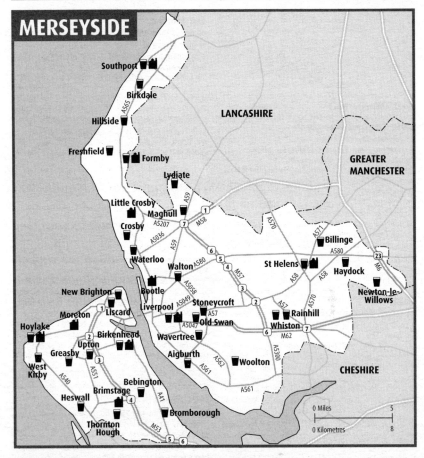

MERSEYSIDE

Southport
Birkdale
LANCASHIRE
Hillside
Freshfield
Formby
GREATER
MANCHESTER
Lydiate
Little Crosby
Maghull
Crosby
A5207
Waterloo
Billinge
A580
Walton
St Helens
Haydock
New Brighton
Bootle
Newton-le-Willows
Moreton Liscard
Liverpool Stoneycroft
Hoylake
Birkenhead
Old Swan
Rainhill
Upton
Wavertree
Whiston
Greasby
Aigburth
Woolton
West Kirby
Bebington
Heswall Brimstage
CHESHIRE
Thornton Hough
Bromborough

0 Miles 5
0 Kilometres 8

Bebington

Rose & Crown L ✓

57 The Village, CH63 7PL

☎ (0151) 644 5829 ⊕ roseandcrownbebington.co.uk

Thwaites Original, IPA, Gold; 4 changing beers (sourced locally; often Brimstage, Neptune, Thwaites) Ⓗ

This old coaching inn, built in 1732, is a thriving, vibrant and friendly community local. It has a lounge, small bar and games room, with traditional decor and old photos of the area. Live music features on Saturday night and quiz night is Sunday. The nearby Port Sunlight Village was founded by Lever in 1888 to house his soap factory workers, and is home to the Lady Lever Art Gallery, one of the most beautiful collections of art in the country.
Q ☺ ≠ (Port Sunlight) ♣P�# (410,487) 🌸 🤶 ♪

Traveller's Rest

169 Mount Road, CH63 8PJ

☎ (0151) 608 2988 ⊕ thetravsbebington.co.uk

Ossett White Rat; Timothy Taylor Landlord; 3 changing beers (sourced regionally; often Brimstage, Facer's, Spitting Feathers) Ⓗ

A popular and traditional former coaching inn by the edge of Storeton Woods. It has a cosy country pub feel and is decorated throughout with brasses and bric-a-brac. The main area has a central bar and there are two side rooms. The guest ales are sometimes from local microbreweries, and real cider is sometimes available. There is a quiz night on Monday and live music on

Saturday, and it serves good home-cooked pub food (no evening meals Mon and Tue).
Q ☺ ◑ & �# (464,487) 🌸 🤶 ♪

Billinge

Masons Arms

99 Carr Mill Road, WN5 7TY

☎ (01744) 603572

5 changing beers (sourced regionally) Ⓗ

Friendly, traditional, community-based pub on the edge of open countryside, run by the same family for over 200 years. The warm and welcoming bar allows the opportunity to chat without loud music and is adorned with rugby memorabilia. There is also a quiet side lounge. All areas are dog and child friendly. Outside is a large landscaped beer garden with an interesting smoking shelter. 🌸 & ♣P🚦# (137)🌸 🤶 ♪

Birkenhead

Gallaghers Traditional Pub L

20 Chester Street, CH41 5DQ

☎ (0151) 649 9095 ⊕ gallaghers-pub.business.site

Brimstage Trapper's Hat Bitter; Ossett White Rat; 4 changing beers (sourced nationally; often Brimstage, Hawkshead, Ossett) Ⓗ

Multiple-award winning free house, rescued after closure and refurbished in 2010. It is decorated with a fascinating range of military memorabilia and a collection of

303

shipping images. Meals are served daily except Monday evening and Sunday lunchtime. There is usually live music on Sunday evening. The outside area at the rear has a retractable roof. The mural on the side wall of the pub commemorates the sinking of HMS Birkenhead and the Birkenhead Drill, 'women and children first'.
✿◑➤(Hamilton Square) ♣🚭✿ ♪

Bromborough

Bow-Legged Beagle 𝕃

11 Allport Lane, CH62 7HH
4 changing beers (sourced regionally; often Beartown, Brimstage, Neptune) ℍ
This friendly, comfortable micropub, the third of the local Bow-Legged Beagle chain, is located in a former shop in the main street, near the ancient market cross in the town centre. The selection of cask ales usually includes a session pale and a stronger IPA, plus a bitter or amber brew and a stout or porter. It was winner of a local CAMRA Cellarmanship Award in 2023. Convenient for buses and a 10-minute walk from Bromborough Rake station. Q🐾🚭🚪(1,38)✿ 🛜

Crosby

Coop

84 College Road, L23 0RP
5 changing beers (sourced nationally; often Ossett, Salopian) ℍ
Opened in 2023, the Coop (as in pigeon coop), has two main areas. The entrance opens into to a long, narrow room, with a bar in the top left corner. One side of the main room has bookshelves with a wide range of reading matter and board games. Opposite the bar, a doorway leads to a conservatory-style side room. Up to five cask beers are available, the choice often including a dark beer. Wines, spirits, keg and bottled beers are also available.
Q✿⏥➤(Blundellsands & Crosby) 🍴🚪(63,53) ✿

Corner Post 𝕃

25 Bridge Road, L23 6SA
5 changing beers (sourced locally; often Peerless, Rock the Boat) ℍ
This micropub is located in a former post office (hence the name), and is easily spotted by the postbox outside. As well as real ales and cider, bottled continental beers, wine and soft drinks are available. Interesting pictures depicting the history of the building and the local area adorn the walls. It is close to the 53 bus route and a short walk from Blundellsands & Crosby railway station. Also handy for visiting Antony Gormley's famous iron men on Crosby beach. Well-behaved dogs welcome.
Q➤(Blundellsands & Crosby) ♣🐕🚪(53) ✿

Formby

Sparrowhawk

Southport Old Road, L37 0AB (next to Formby bypass opp Woodvale airfield)
☎ (01704) 882350
Salopian Oracle; Titanic Plum Porter; 3 changing beers (sourced regionally) ℍ
The Sparrowhawk is a Brunning & Price pub on the original road between Southport and Formby. It was built as the Dower House to the nearby Formby Hall and is situated in five acres of woodlands and gardens. The open-plan pub places an emphasis on food, but always has up to six real ales in excellent condition. The bus stop at Woodpile traffic lights is less than five minutes' walk away. Q🐾✿◑♿♣P🚪(47,49)✿ 🛜

Tin Shed 𝕃

60 Brows Lane, L37 4ED
☎ (01704) 808220
5 changing beers (sourced locally; often Parker) ℍ
New micropub on the main street in Formby, handy for the local shops and the leisure centre. There is ample seating inside for such a small pub, and the owners are starting a collection of pumpclips for the real ales on sale. The pub is also keen to support local breweries including Parker and Southport. It is less than 10 minutes' walk from Formby station, with trains normally every 15 minutes to Liverpool or Southport.
Q🐾♿➤(Formby) ♣🐕✿ 🛜

Freshfield

Beer Station

3 Victoria Buildings, L37 7DB (opp Freshfield railway station)
☎ (01704) 807450
3 changing beers (sourced locally; often Neptune, Rock the Boat) ℍ
Freshfield's first micropub strongly favours all things local. Beers are sourced to promote local brewers, with the exception of one beer a month from outside the region. The few spirits available also have their provenance checked. A fridge with bottled beers adds to the variety. Food comes in the form of local pies and nuts. The walls are decorated with work by local artists. Dogs are welcome on a lead. Q🐾♿➤♣🚪(F1)✿ 🛜

Freshfield 𝕃 ✅

1 Massams Lane, L37 7BD (from station turn inland into Victoria Rd and then left into Gores Ln)
☎ (01704) 874871
Greene King IPA, Abbot; Oakham Citra; 4 changing beers (sourced regionally) ℍ
A community pub at its heart with three distinct areas: a dining room serving quality food, a bar area dominated by a bar full of handpumps, and 'the flags', where well-behaved dogs are allowed. Sport is shown on three large TVs and a real fire adds warmth in winter. The pub occasionally has real cider in for festivals. This is a place to meet, talk and be with friends old or new. A former CAMRA National Pub of the Year finalist and multi-award winner. 🐾✿◑♿➤♣P🚪(F2,F6)✿ 🛜

REAL ALE BREWERIES

Beer Station 🍺 Formby
Black Lodge ✦ Liverpool
Brimstage Brimstage
Brooks Hoylake
Carnival ✦ Liverpool
Colbier Bootle (NEW)
Glen Affric Birkenhead
Handyman 🍺 Liverpool
Hex Southport
Howzat 🍺 St Helens
Liverpool Brewing Liverpool
Love Lane 🍺 Liverpool
Neptune Liverpool
Peerless ✦ Birkenhead
Rock the Boat Little Crosby
Southport Southport
Stamps Bootle
Sun Bear Moreton (NEW)
Top Rope ✦ Liverpool

Greasby

Coach & Horses ★ ✅
Greasby Road, CH49 3NG
☎ (0151) 677 4509
Brains Rev James Original; Butcombe Original; 2 changing beers (sourced nationally; often Black Sheep, Ossett) Ⓗ
In a whitewashed building dating back nearly 300 years is this charming street-corner pub. Tastefully redecorated in 2021, it has retained its character and has the atmosphere of a traditional country local. The compact central bar serves several discrete areas including two small cosy rooms with real warming fires for the winter. There is a small garden to the side. Live music usually features on Sunday and a folk/acoustic jam session every Monday. Q▷ゐ❀❶♣P🚆(22,437)❀♪

Haydock

Haydock Reading Room Ⓛ ✅
86 Church Road, WA11 0TH
☎ (01942) 728307
3 changing beers Ⓗ
Since 1884 the Haydock Reading Room has provided a warm and welcoming place for all who like a drink in good company. The club allows CAMRA members in as guests on production of a valid CAMRA membership card. Three real ales are available with at least one from a local brewery. A 'coming soon' board highlights what beers to look forward to. The club was awarded CAMRA Merseyside Club of the Year 2023. Live music and other events for the community often take place over the weekend. ♿♣🚆🛜♪

Heswall

Beer Lab Ⓛ
53 Telegraph Road, CH60 0AD
☎ (0151) 342 5475 ⊕ thebeerlab.co.uk
Peerless Triple Blond; 2 changing beers (sourced locally; often Beartown, MBH Beer, Neptune) Ⓗ
Heswall's first micropub opened in 2018 in a former cycle shop. The relaxed, minimalist single-room bar is bright and airy, making the most of the available space. A good range of real ciders are always on the bar, together with Belgian bottled beers. Beer is served in pint, one-third and two-third measures. The pub is an easy five-minute walk from the main shopping area and the bus station. Local CAMRA Cider Pub of the Year 2020-22. Q▷ゐ❶🚆(22,471)❀🛜

Dee View Inn
2 Dee View Road, CH60 0DH
☎ (0151) 345 9165
Black Sheep Best Bitter; Fuller's London Pride; 2 changing beers (sourced nationally; often Purity, Timothy Taylor, Wadworth) Ⓗ
Dating from the late 1800s, this homely, welcoming traditional local has retained its character and friendly atmosphere. It sits on a hairpin bend by the war memorial and famous mirror, with views over the Dee Estuary and close to the Wirral Way path. There is live music on the last Saturday of the month. No food is served but customers can bring their own or get takeaways delivered. There is a Cask Club on Tuesday with discount on cask beers. ▷❀P🚆(471,472)❀🛜♪

Jug & Bottle Ⓛ
13 Mount Avenue, CH60 4RH
☎ (0151) 342 5535 ⊕ the-jugandbottle.co.uk
Brains Rev James Original; Brimstage Trapper's Hat Bitter; Timothy Taylor Boltmaker; 3 changing beers
(sourced regionally; often Beartown, Brimstage, Titanic) Ⓗ
Built as a private house in the 1870s, before being converted to offices and then a pub, the Jug & Bottle has been in its present incarnation since 1993. Hidden behind the village hall and library, it is a short distance from the the main shopping street. It has a strong emphasis on food, and the open fires and different cosy areas inside create a warm and friendly atmosphere. The decking outside gives fine views towards the the River Dee and North Wales. Accommodation is in nine boutique bedrooms that sit above the pub.
Q▷ゐ❀❷❶◔⑃&P🚆(471,472)❀🛜

Hoylake

Black Toad Ⓛ
32 Market Street, CH47 2AF
☎ 07835 360691 ⊕ theblacktoad.co.uk
4 changing beers (sourced regionally; often Chapter, Neptune, Peerless) Ⓗ
Micropub opened in 2019 in an abandoned unit on the shopping street. The narrow main room and bar is attractively decorated with simple furniture and has been expanded into the adjacent shop to create a new lounge area. The small room beyond the bar is now a well-stocked bottle shop. At the rear is a pleasant beer garden. A balanced selection of cask beers at all times. Local CAMRA Pub of the Year runner-up in 2023 and 2024. Q▷ゐ❀♯❶🚆(38,407)❀🛜

Liscard

Lazy Landlord Ale House Ⓛ
56 Mill Lane, CH44 5UG
☎ 07583 135616
Oakham Citra; 4 changing beers (sourced nationally; often Brimstage, Joseph Holt, Ossett) Ⓗ
Wirral's first micropub opened in 2014 in a former shop premises. Two small, cosy rooms decorated with breweriana, local art works and a small library, are served from the front bar. Mostly frequented by a more mature clientele, the pub is a venue for meetings of many local societies. Cider is often from Seacider. Closed Monday and Tuesday. A multiple CAMRA award winner. Q▷ゐ♣❶🚆(410,432)❀🛜

Twelve-Sixty Bar & Lounge
45-51 St Albans Road, CH44 5XH
Draught Bass; 4 changing beers (sourced regionally) Ⓗ
Opened in 2022, this comfortable micropub lounge bar in the centre of Liscard is popular with locals of all ages. The bright, airy interior is tastefully decorated with old photos of Liscard centre. The pub serves Draught Bass and four changing cask beers of different styles, sourced mainly from small local and regional breweries. Convenient for the shopping area and bus stops. Q▷ゐ♿🚆❀🛜

Liverpool: Aigburth

Little Taproom on Aigburth Road Ⓛ
278 Aigburth Road, L17 9PJ
⊕ aigburthtap.co.uk
5 changing beers (sourced locally; often Chapter, Neptune) Ⓗ
A friendly two-roomed micropub that opened in 2020 near Sefton Park, on a main road with excellent bus and Merseyrail services close by. The front bar has a number of handpulls serving beer and cider. Bottled and canned beers are also stocked, and there are spirits available,

including their own Sefton Park gin. Entertainment includes board games and a book club – there is no TV, jukebox or background music. Q⌂✥♠⊟(82)🌻🦇🎵

Liverpool: City Centre

Augustus John ⓛ
Peach Street, L3 5TX (off Brownlow Hill)
☎ (0151) 794 5507
5 changing beers (sourced nationally; often Peerless, Rock the Boat) Ⓗ
Opened in 1968 and run by the University of Liverpool, the Augustus John is an open-plan pub popular with students, lecturers and locals. The cask ales always include a range of styes, light, dark, plus a large number of ciders, two on handpump and many more from the cellar. Pizza is served at all times. Opening times may vary during university holidays; it is closed over Christmas and New Year. A former local CAMRA Pub of the Year. Card payment only. 🦇◑&♣♠⊟(79)

Baltic Fleet ⓛ
33A Wapping, L1 8DQ
☎ (0151) 709 3116 ⊕ balticfleet.co.uk
Brimstage Trapper's Hat Bitter; 3 changing beers (sourced locally) Ⓗ
Grade II-listed building near the Albert Dock. It has a distinctive flatiron shape and the interior is decorated on a nautical theme. The existence of tunnels in the cellar has led to speculation that the pub's history may involve smuggling and press gangs (it originally had multiple doors to allow customers to escape when press gangs entered). There is an extensive outside drinking area. It can get busy when events are on at the nearby arena. 🦇◑≋(James Street)♠P⊟🌻🎵

Belvedere ★ ⓛ
8 Sugnall Street, L7 7EB (off Falkner St)
4 changing beers (sourced regionally) Ⓗ
Tucked away in the Georgian area of the city, close to the famous Philharmonic Hall, and frequented by its orchestra members, this small two-roomed pub is a free house serving four rotating beers from mainly local microbreweries. Redeemed in 2006 from closure for housing development, the Grade II-listed building retains original fixtures and interesting etched glass features. It is a pub with a mixed local clientele, where various small cultural groups meet and good conversation thrives. Q🦇⊟(86,80A)🌻🎵

Bridewell ⓛ
1 Campbell Square, L1 5FB
☎ (0151) 707 2372 ⊕ thebridewellpub.co.uk
Kirkstall Bitter, Three Swords; 2 changing beers (sourced nationally) Ⓗ
An imposing, Grade II-listed building that dates from the mid-19th century when it was a police bridewell, or jail. The cells are used as seating areas and provide an unusual focus for the downstairs bar. There is a outdoor patio area inside the wall at the front. The pub is close to the Liverpool One shopping area, the Albert Dock and the riverfront. Local CAMRA Pub of the Year 2022 and 2023. ✥🦇&≋(Central)🌻🎵

Caledonia ⓛ
22 Caledonia Street, L7 7DX (on corner of Catherine St behind Philharmonic Hall)
☎ (0151) 306 2496 ⊕ thecaledonialiverpool.com
4 changing beers (sourced locally; often Carnival, Stamps) Ⓗ
Located in the Georgian quarter of the city, this street-corner pub, popular with students, comprises one room on two levels and has a small function room upstairs. The

enterprising licensee has developed a programme of live music events and on these occasions this normally quiet pub buzzes with energy. Food is vegan only and all beers are unfined. ◑●♠⊟(86)🌻🎵

Denbigh Castle
10 Hackins Hey, L2 2AW (off Dale St)
☎ (0151) 236 8558 ⊕ thedenbighcastle.co.uk
Kirkstall Bitter; 3 changing beers (sourced nationally) Ⓗ
After various guises, this pub was refurbished and opened in 2020 as the Denbigh Castle, its original name from over 200 years ago. Run by the same couple as the Bridewell. Located on a side street off Dale Street, it has an open-plan ground floor with rooms both upstairs and downstairs for functions and events. Cask, craft beers and German lagers are available. Liverpool city tourism Pub of the Year 2021. ≋(Moorfields)●♠🌻🎵

Dispensary
87 Renshaw Street, L1 2SP
☎ 07472 291403 ⊕ dockleafbar.co.uk/thedispensary
Oakham Citra; Ossett White Rat; Titanic Plum Porter; 4 changing beers (often Liverpool Brewing Company, Ossett) Ⓗ
This lively city pub is a haven for real ale drinkers of all ages. The attractive bar area has Victorian features, with a raised wood panelled area to the rear. Originally called the Grapes (the old sign is behind the bar), it was completely redesigned as a Cains tied pub, but now is leased out as a free house. It can be busy if football matches are shown on the big screens. An outside food stall is available. 🦇◑≋(Central)⊟🌻🎵

Doctor Duncan's ⓛ ✅
St Johns Lane, L1 1HF
☎ (0151) 709 5100 ⊕ doctorduncansliverpool.com
5 changing beers (sourced nationally) Ⓗ
This former Cains brewery flagship pub has an impressive Victorian interior consisting of four distinct drinking areas; the green tiled room is particularly handsome. Medical memorabilia can be found throughout, reflecting the fact that the pub's name commemorates William Henry Duncan, the city's first chief medical officer and a ruthless campaigner against poor living conditions in Victorian times. 🦇◑≋(Lime Street)♣⊟🌻🎵

Excelsior ⓛ ✅
121-123 Dale Street, L2 2JH (close to Birkenhead Tunnel entrance)
☎ (0151) 352 9544 ⊕ excelsiorliverpool.co.uk
Timothy Taylor Landlord; 4 changing beers (sourced locally; often Liverpool Brewing Company, Ossett, Rock the Boat) Ⓗ
Named after a sailing ship, this large corner pub is adjacent to what were Higsons brewery offices in 1962. A tastefully decorated and comfortable pub, appealing to both a business and leisure clientele. The main room has a three-sided bar with a series of distinct seating areas. A large room off the main bar area includes a raised seating area. Largescreen TVs show sports events, particularly football, but are generally silent otherwise. ≋(Moorfields) P⊟🌻🎵

Globe ✅
17 Cases Street, L1 1HW (opp Central Station)
☎ (0151) 707 0067 ⊕ theglobe.pub
Sharp's Doom Bar; Timothy Taylor Landlord; Wainwright Gold; 1 changing beer (sourced nationally) Ⓗ
This small traditional pub is a former local CAMRA Best Community Pub. The pub attracts people from all over the city. A buzz of lively conversation prevails, and

visitors are equally welcomed. In the small back room a brass plaque commemorates the inaugural meeting of CAMRA Merseyside and 50th anniversary celebrations were held here in 2024. The sloping floor in the bar area is legendary. ≈(Central)🖸

Head of Steam
85-89 Hanover Street, L1 3DZ
☎ (0151) 708 6096 ⊕ theheadofsteam.co.uk
Camerons Strongarm; 6 changing beers (sourced locally; often Camerons, Neptune, Tiny Rebel) Ⓗ
This large pub – previously the Abbey – opened in 2017 (it has no connection to the Head of Steam previously on Lime Street). It has plenty of seating but can get busy, especially on evenings when major sporting events are shown live on TV. It stocks a large selection of foreign bottled and keg beers, such as Chimay. A private function area is available for bookings. Handy for Liverpool One shops. ◑&≈(Central)●🖸(86,82)🔊♪

Lion Tavern ★ 𝕃
67 Moorfields, L2 2BP
⊕ theliontavernliverpool.co.uk
Peerless Triple Blond; Wily Fox Crafty Fox; 3 changing beers (sourced nationally) Ⓗ
Named after the locomotive that worked the Liverpool to Manchester Railway (and is on display at the Musuem of Liverpool), the Lion features mosaic floors, a tiled corridor, plus intricately etched and stained glass. Refurbished in 2017, it retains Grade II-listed status and has been recognised by CAMRA as having a nationally important historic pub interior. Cider is regularly available, and local gins are kept. Local CAMRA Pub of the Year 2020. ◑≈(Moorfields)●🖸🌸🔊

Liverpool Brewing Company Tap 𝕃
72 Lime Street, L1 1JN
☎ (0151) 703 0116
4 changing beers (sourced locally; often Liverpool Brewing Company) Ⓗ
Opened in 2017, this pub, close to Lime Street station, is themed like a run-down hotel, with art deco lighting and long abandoned suitcases high up on the fine, well-stocked wooden beer cabinet. There are further rooms upstairs and downstairs, which can be used as function rooms. The five cask pumps and craft keg on offer concentrate on locally brewed beers mostly from Liverpool Brewing Company who run the pub. ◑&≈(Central)♣🖸🌸🔊

Ma Boyle's Alehouse & Eatery 𝕃
The Tower Building, The Strand, L3 1BH
☎ (0151) 236 0070 ⊕ maboyles.co.uk
1 changing beer (sourced locally; often Rock the Boat) Ⓗ
Named after the first landlady from Victorian times, Boyle's was originally a coffee bar, then an oyster bar. It is set over two floors, with a side room and seating outside. Although right in the city centre, it has the atmosphere of a more rural pub due to its setting in a quiet street overlooked by St Nicholas' church. It is across the road from the Pier Head and the iconic Three Graces and therefore convenient for visiting the city's sights. ➳🌸◑≈(James Street) 🖸🔊♪

Peter Kavanagh's ★ ✪
2-6 Egerton Street, L8 7LY (off Catharine St)
☎ (0151) 709 3443
Greene King Abbot; 4 changing beers (sourced nationally; often Castle Rock) Ⓗ
A Grade II-listed stuccoed pub in the Georgian area, which has been identified by CAMRA as having a nationally important historic pub interior. The snugs have

murals by Eric Robinson on the walls and there are fine stained-glass windows with wooden shutters. The benches have carved armrests thought to be caricatures of Peter Kavanagh, the licensee for 53 years until 1950. These features were not adversely affected when the pub was expanded, firstly in 1964 into next door, then in 1977 into next door but one. A former local CAMRA Pub of the Year. Q🖸(86,80)🌸🔊♪

Red Lion ✪
36 Slater Street, L1 4BX
⊕ redlionpubliverpool.com
Ossett White Rat; 4 changing beers (sourced nationally; often Ossett, Salopian) Ⓗ
This traditional pub was converted from a terraced house in 2022 by the same owner as the Green Man in Lark Lane and the Vines (aka Big House) on Lime Street. Hanging knick-knacks, low lighting, bare walls and wooden panels create the atmosphere. There is a games room and interior courtyard. It is located in a busy late-night drinking area popular with clubbers, but by day it provides refuge from the city bustle. 🌸◑≈(Central)♣🖸♪

Roscoe Head 🏆 ★
24 Roscoe Street, L1 2SX
☎ (0151) 709 4365 ⊕ roscoehead.co.uk
Timothy Taylor Landlord; Tetley Bitter; 4 changing beers (sourced locally; often Fyne) Ⓗ
One of the 'famous five' pubs that have appeared in every edition of this Guide. The freehold of Roscoe Head was sold to the tenant in 2020, following a five-year campaign against the previous owners. This is a cosy, four-roomed pub where conversation and the appreciation of real ale rules. Six handpumps feature national and local breweries. It has been run by members of the same family for over 30 years, and commemorates William Roscoe, a leading campaigner against the slave trade. Q◑&≈(Central)♣🖸(86,80)🔊

Ship & Mitre 𝕃
133 Dale Street, L2 2JH (by Birkenhead Tunnel)
☎ (0151) 236 0859 ⊕ theshipandmitre.uk
8 changing beers (sourced nationally; often Liverpool Brewing Company, Ossett) Ⓗ
This 1930s Art Deco pub is partly hidden by the Queensway tunnel entrance. The name derives from two previous incarnations, the Flagship and the Mitre. It retains the original Art Deco bar and function room upstairs, but downstairs has had a nautical-themed makeover. Some 15 handpulls serve an ever-changing array of beers, plus an impressive range of world beers, as well as real cider, and the friendly and knowledgeable staff are always willing to make a recommendation. ◑&≈(Moorfields)♣●🖸🌸🔊

Vernon Arms 𝕃
69 Dale Street, L2 2HJ
☎ (0151) 236 6132
Brains Rev James Original; Ossett White Rat; 4 changing beers (often Brimstage, Coach House) Ⓗ
Situated close to the business district, the Vernon retains the feel of a street-corner local. The single, long-roomed bar serves three drinking areas that include a back room with frosted glass windows advertising the Liverpool Brewing Company, which once again serves the pub. The main bar has wood panelling, several large columns, and a small snug area. As well as the house beers, there is real cider on handpull, which is unusual for the city centre. ◑≈(Moorfields)●🖸🔊♪

Vines ★ ✅

81 Lime Street, L1 1JQ

☎ 07902 052003 ⊕ vinesbighouse.co.uk

Brains Rev James Original; Ossett Silver King; Salopian Shropshire Gold; Timothy Taylor Landlord; Titanic Plum Porter; 4 changing beers (sourced nationally; often Ossett, Salopian, Timothy Taylor) Ⓗ

Rebuilt in 1907 as a Cains pub, the Vines, like its sister pub the Philharmonic, is one of the great show pubs of the country, and has been identified by CAMRA as having a nationally important historic pub interior. The harvest-themed plasterwork in the smoke-room was created by sculptor Walter Gilbert in 1908. The plasterwork and glass in the other room are the work of Henry Gustave Hiller. Refurbished in 2023 after a period of decline, it is now run by the owner of the Red Lion, who has reintroduced cask beer. ▷❀◑≢(Lime Street)🖵❀🛜

Liverpool: Old Swan

Navigator Ⓛ ✅

694 Queens Drive, L13 5UH

☎ (0151) 220 2713

Greene King Abbot; Ruddles Best Bitter; Sharp's Doom Bar; 3 changing beers Ⓗ

This branch of Wetherspoon, named after the patron saint of navigators St Brendan, occupies a former showroom. The open-plan layout is punctuated with alcoves along one side. It is a welcome oasis on the edge of a busy shopping area, with the raised area being set aside for families. Children are not allowed after 9pm. ▷❀◑⛽🖵(10A,81) 🛜

Liverpool: Stoneycroft

Cask Ⓛ

438 Queens Drive, West Derby, L13 0AR (near jct Queens Dr and Derby Ln)

☎ 07562 713967

5 changing beers (sourced nationally) Ⓗ

A comfortable one-roomed micropub that opened in 2015. Normally four beers are served on Tuesday and Wednesday, with more on offer at weekends. Cider and perry are dispensed direct from the taps at the rear of bar, and there are occasional special beers in wooden pins. There is also a selection of bottled beers. The pub is on Queens Drive, which acts like a Liverpool circular road, near the turning to West Derby. Some roadside parking is available. A former local CAMRA Pub of the Year. Q♣❀🖵(60,81) ♪

Liverpool: Walton

Raven Ⓛ ✅

72-74 Walton Vale, L9 2BU

☎ (0151) 524 1255

Fuller's London Pride; Greene King Abbot; Ruddles Best Bitter; Sharp's Doom Bar; 5 changing beers Ⓗ

An open-plan Wetherspoon's that is popular with locals, particularly at weekends. It is themed on Edgar Allan Poe's The Raven – local pavement artist, James William Carling, created illustrations for the famous poem in the late 19th century. He later went to America and is buried in Walton Cemetery. Aintree, the home of the world-famous Grand National, is less than a mile away. No children allowed after 9pm. ▷◑⛽≢(Orrell Park) 🖵(310) 🛜

Liverpool: Wavertree

Black Cat Ⓛ

174 Smithdown Road, L15 3JR

⊕ crafttaproom.myshopify.com

2 changing beers (sourced nationally) Ⓗ

Lively bar, in a busy shopping street lined with many other bars and cafés. It is popular with students, and can get busy during the various events such as quizzes and live music. It serves a wide selection of craft beers, ciders and spirits, and also has a bottle shop. Bottomless coffee is available from 8.30am. ▷◑🖵(86)❀🛜♪

Liverpool: Woolton

Cobden

89 Quarry Street, L25 6HA

☎ 07708 231796

Ossett White Rat; Timothy Taylor Landlord; Wainwright Gold; 1 changing beer (sourced locally) Ⓗ

A classic and popular community pub. There is a main room and a smaller back room for more convivial conversation. The pub hosts a quiz on Monday night, plus live music on Friday, Saturday and Sunday evenings, as well as many other community events. Nearby is the quarry from which a famous local band got the name the Quarrymen, before late changing it to the Beatles. ▷🖵(76) ❀🛜♪

Lydiate

Scotch Piper ★ ✅

Southport Road, L31 4HD (800yds N from A5147/Moss Ln jct)

☎ (0151) 345 6399 ⊕ scotchpiper.com

3 changing beers (sourced nationally; often Titanic) Ⓗ

This Grade*II-listed, thatched, medieval building, just north of Lydgate, takes its name from an incident in 1745 when a highland piper, injured in the Jacobite rebellion, took refuge here. The entrance opens into a traditional bar with a servery on the left. A passage to the right leads to a further two rooms, the middle one with old, basic woodwork. The end room, added later, is less rustic but still retains some upholstered bench seating. Q▷❀◑🅰♣P🖵(300) ❀🛜♪

Maghull

Maghull Cask Café Ⓛ

43 Liverpool Road South, L31 7BN

☎ (0151) 526 3877

5 changing beers (sourced locally; often Neptune, Oakham) Ⓗ

This micropub is a hidden gem. Opened in 2018, it now serves a good range of changing cask ales, bottled continental beers, and gin. The cask ales are from good regional brewers such as Oakham, Titanic and Salopian. Friendly, knowledgeable staff help create a great atmosphere where conversation prevails. The Leeds-Liverpool Canal runs through Maghull and makes the ideal base of a nice walk towards Burscough. Q♿❀🖵(300,310) ❀🛜

Neptune Beerhouse Ⓛ

25-27 Liverpool Road North, L31 2HB

☎ (0151) 522 1722 ⊕ neptunebrewery.com

4 changing beers (sourced locally; often Neptune) Ⓗ

Neptune brewery taproom opened in 2023, mainly serving the brewery's beers, on cask and keg, plus new or collab beers. The taproom is close to the Leeds-Liverpool Canal and the towpath makes a very pleasant walk from Maghull station or towards pubs in the countryside. Pizza is served on the last Friday and Saturday of the month. ⛄🍴♿🏠🚪🚍(300 310)🌟

New Brighton

James Atherton 🆕
117-119 Victoria Road, CH45 2JD
☎ (0151) 638 8022
Brimstage Trapper's Hat Bitter; Ossett White Rat; 1 changing beer (sourced regionally; often Hawkshead) 🅗

Refurbished and reopened in 2019 as part of the regeneration of the Victoria Quarter of New Brighton, this lively pub was renamed after one of the founders of the town. The single-room pub is split into three areas served from one bar, and is bright and airy, with comfortable seating and local photos adorning the walls. The pub is on the main shopping street, with outside seating on the pavement, and is close to the seafront attractions and the Floral Pavilion Theatre.
⛄🏵♿⚘🚍🌟🏠🎵

Magazine Hotel 🍴 ★ 🆕 ✅
7 Magazine Brow, CH45 1HP (above Egremont Promenade)
☎ (0151) 630 3169 🌐 the-magazine-hotel.co.uk
Brimstage Trapper's Hat Bitter; Draught Bass; 3 changing beers (sourced regionally; often , Beartown, Brimstage) 🅗

Unspoilt multi-roomed pub dating from 1759. It has three rooms leading off the main central bar area with an open fireplace. It is renowned for its Draught Bass, and other beers are often from local microbreweries. One real cider is sometimes available. The pub overlooks Egremont Promenade, with fine views over the River Mersey to Liverpool. Live music plays on Saturday evening and there is a folk night on Tuesday. Good-value home-cooked food is served. Local CAMRA Pub of the Year 2024. Q⛄🏵🍴⚘♿🚪(106,107)🌟🏠🎵

Stanley's Cask ✅
212 Rake Lane, CH45 1JP
☎ (0151) 691 1093
Ossett White Rat; 4 changing beers (sourced nationally; often Purple Moose, Robinsons, Theakston) 🅗

This ever-popular friendly local continues to thrive, due in no small part to the landlady who has a track record of serving good beer. The guest ales on offer often include seasonal beers from regional breweries and usually include a beer from a local brewery. The traditional, single-roomed community local hosts various sports teams, quiz nights and regular very popular live music including rock, blues and folk. Local CAMRA Community Pub 2022. ⛄🏵♿⚘🚪(410,433)🌟🏠🎵

Newton-le-Willows

Firkin
65 High Street, WA12 9SL
☎ (01925) 225700 🌐 thefirkin.co.uk
8 changing beers 🅗

A former shop, this small friendly establishment dispenses a selection of eight real ales, including at least one dark as well as a range of keg/craft beers. There are regular tap takeovers from small independent breweries (details on social media). Two traditional ciders are also available. Small seating areas are to the front and the rear. With no music this is somewhere to engage in conversation and to make new friends.
Q🍴⚘🚪(34,22) 🌟🏠

Rainhill

Commercial Hotel ★ 🆕
12 Station Road, L35 0LP
☎ (0151) 431 0984
3 changing beers (sourced nationally) 🅗

Located next to Rainhill railway station, this pub first opened in the 19th century, offering rooms to commuters. After an extensive refurbishment, many original features have been retained, including stained-glass windows and the original bar. In the beer garden to the rear is a cast iron gas lamp (converted to electric) made in Rainhill circa 1850 and used to light the platform at the railway station. 🏵🚆⚘🅿🚪(10A)🌟🏠🎵

Skew Bridge Alehouse 🆕
5 Dane Court, L35 4LU
☎ (0151) 792 7906 🌐 skewbridge.co.uk
5 changing beers (sourced nationally) 🅗

This micropub in the centre of Rainhill offers a selection of high-quality cask ales, real ciders and two craft lagers. Locally sourced ales are complimented by beers from all over the UK. A good range of gins and single malt whiskies are also stocked. With no TVs or music to distract customers, conversation is very much encouraged. A wide selection of board games is available for use. Q⛄🏵♿🚆⚘🅿🌟

St Helens

Cricketers Arms 🆕 ✅
64 Peter Street, WA10 2EB
☎ (01744) 361846
13 changing beers (sourced locally) 🅗

A former CAMRA National Pub of the Year, this family-run community establishment has 13 handpulls, real cider, and a range of spirits. An outside bar increases the number of handpulls for special events. Freshly prepared stonebaked pizzas and cheese boards are available. In 2020 the on-site Howzat brewery started producing their own house beers for the Cricketers Arms and other pubs within the local area. ⛄🏵🍴⚘🅿🏠🌟🎵

Lamb Inn 🆕 ✅
113 Corporation Street, WA10 1SX
6 changing beers (sourced nationally) 🅗

Built in 1854, this friendly town-centre pub was tastefully renovated in 2022, highlighting many of its historical features. It has a traditional two-room layout, with a bar and lounge. There is a small but comfortable beer garden to the rear. The pub hosts a weekly quiz and relaxed music nights. It is a three-minute walk from St Helens main bus station, and a five minutes from St Helens Central railway station. ⛄🏵🚆(Central)🚪🎵

News Room 🆕
89 Duke Street, WA10 2JG
☎ (01744) 322129
3 changing beers (sourced nationally) 🅗

A small, stylish, modern bar with a warm, friendly, laid-back atmosphere. The three handpulls always include a local ales, and there are craft beers and a range of bottled continental beers, as well as gins, rums and malt whiskies. Conversation is encouraged here, and not hindered by background music playing on large screens. It is within walking distance of the town centre, main bus station and railway station. ⛄♿🚪🌟

Royal Alfred 🆕
Bickerstaff Street, WA10 1DH
5 changing beers 🅗

Large, traditional pub with a friendly welcome. It is opposite the railway station, close to the town's main

bus stop and town centre, and screens show live train times, so you always know when your train leaves. The pub offers comfortable seating by an open fire and air conditioning in the summer. There are two pool tables and a dartboard at the far end of the pub.
🕭♿➳(Central) ♣🍴🐾🛜🎵

Turk's Head 🍷 🅻
49 Morley Street, WA10 2DQ
☎ (01744) 751289
14 changing beers 🅗
Attractive Tudor-style 1870s pub near the town centre. Real ales and ciders on 14 handpulls, and there is a large whisky and gin bar. The upstairs Tower Lounge serves cocktails, craft and continental beers, and hosts live music on Saturday evening. High-quality home-cooked food is available every day. A large beer garden to the side and rear has an outside bar, and the adjacent Cowley Grill serves food until 11pm Wednesday-Sunday. Local CAMRA Pub of the Year. 🕭♿🕦🍴🍽🐾🛜🎵

Southport

Guest House ★ ⊘
16 Union Street, PR9 0QE
☎ (01704) 537660 ⊕ guesthouse-southport.blogspot.com
Butcombe Adam Henson's Rare Breed; Ruddles Best Bitter; Theakston Best Bitter; house beer (by Caledonian); 11 changing beers (sourced nationally; often Phoenix, Salopian, Southport) 🅗
Close to the station and Lord Street, this listed building has an impressive frontage and interior, with three separate wood-panelled drinking areas. There are 11 handpumps, one of which serves a local microbrewery beer, and there is a wide range of malt whiskies. This quiet, traditional pub attracts a mixed clientèle. It has outside seating at the front and a courtyard area to the rear. A quiz night is held on Thursday, and acoustic folk club nights on the first and third Mondays of each month.
Q♿🕦➳🍽🛜

Masons Arms
4 Anchor Street, PR9 0UT
☎ (01704) 534123
Robinsons Dizzy Blonde, Unicorn; 3 changing beers (sourced nationally) 🅗
Small pub tucked away behind the town's former main post office and close to the railway station. The only Robinson's pub in Southport, it has new tenants, replacing one of the longest-serving licensees in the town. The interior has been revamped, with wood-panelled walls, and its roaring fire makes it an ideal winter haunt. Q🕭➳🍽🐾

Tap & Bottles
19A Cambridge Walk, PR8 1EN
☎ (01704) 544322
4 changing beers 🅗
A micropub in the arcade between Chapel Street and Lord Street, next to the Atkinson Centre. It has a choice of four real ales from virtually any brewery, with a preference for North West breweries, plus a huge bottle selection, not all of which are real ale. It has taken over the adjacent unit to make more lounge space with benches and tables. there are also benches and table in the arcade outside. Q🕭➳♣🍽🐾🛜

Southport: Birkdale

Fishermens Rest
2 Weld Road, Birkdale, PR8 2AZ
☎ (01704) 569986

Timothy Taylor Landlord; Theakston Best Bitter; Wychwood Hobgoblin Gold 🅗
The pub gets its name from the infamous Mexico disaster of 1886, which is still commemorated every 10th December by crews from the local Southport lifeboat station. The pub was originally part of the Palace Hotel and was renamed after the bodies of the brave sailors and lifeboat crews were laid out in the building. The pub is also close to the Sefton Coastal footpath. A quiz night is held every Thursday night from 9pm. 🕦♿🍽

Southport: Hillside

Grasshopper 🍷
70 Sandon Road, PR8 4QD
☎ (01704) 569794
8 changing beers (sourced regionally; often Heritage, Peerless, Salopian) 🅗
This micropub opened in 2016 in a former Martins Bank branch (the logo of Martins bank was a grasshopper). It is situated in the row of shops close to Hillside railway station. There is outdoor seating at the front and a secluded beer garden to the rear. Eight changing real ales and six real ciders are served. Oversized pint glasses are available on request. Local CAMRA Pub of the year 2024 and Cider Pub of the Year 2023.
Q♿➳(Hillside) ♣🍽(47) 🐾

Pines
3 Hillside Road, PR8 4QB
☎ 07454 453090
2 changing beers (sourced regionally) 🅗
Housed in a former hairdressers, this tastefully decorated bar is in a part of town that was once devoid of drinking establishments. Two handpumps offer a variety of beers, and a selection of bottled beers is also available. Sandwiches are delivered daily. Doggy treats are available (for well-behaved dogs). An outside seating area at the front is very popular in the warmer months. It can get noisy at busy times, but the atmosphere is generally calm and relaxing.
🕭♿➳(Hillside) 🍽(47) 🐾🛜🎵

Thornton Hough

Red Fox 🅻
Neston Road, CH64 7TL
☎ (0151) 353 2920
Brightside Odin Blonde; house beer (by Brightside); 7 changing beers (sourced locally; often Brimstage, Neptune, Weetwood) 🅗
An impressive sandstone building dating from the 1860s and set in extensive grounds. Refurbished in 2014, it is now a smart gastropub. The front bar area retains a pub feel, with the restaurant areas to either side. At the rear is a terrace and large garden. Changing beers are usually from local microbreweries, and the house beer by Brightside is Brunning & Price Original Bitter. Up to 10 ciders are also available. Local CAMRA Pub of the Year 2023. Q🕭♿🕦♿🍽(487)🐾🛜

Upton

Bow-Legged Beagle 🅻
19 Arrowe Park Road, CH49 0UB
4 changing beers (sourced regionally; often Brimstage, Neptune, Ossett) 🅗
A micropub opened in 2018 in a former bank on a busy row of shops near the centre of the village. The light, airy one-room bar has a friendly ambience, with wood-panelled walls and floors and basic furnishings. Some of the old bank safes have been retained at the back of the

pub. The selection of cask ales usually includes a session pale and a stronger IPA, plus a bitter or amber brew and a stout or porter. Q❀☙🚃(437)❀📶

Waterloo

Four Ashes 🅛
23 Crosby Road North, L22 0LD
6 changing beers (often Neptune, Wily Fox) Ⓗ
A family-run micropub owned by the Ashe family – hence the name. On the site of a former restaurant, it is a great addition to the vibrant real ale scene in and around Waterloo station. Beers are ordered directly from local microbreweries or through a wholesaler, which allows them to offer a varied and interesting selection. They try to always have at least one dark beer on sale. Beers conditioning in the cellar are displayed on the wall.
Q👶🚆♣🍴☙🚃(53,47)❀

Trap & Hatch
135 South Road, L22 0LT
☎ (0151) 928 5837
3 changing beers (sourced regionally) Ⓗ
A micropub on a busy suburban street, with a stylish, modern interior, low lighting and long tables. The bar has three handpulls and the pub goes out of its way to source interesting beers that are rarely seen in this area. Real cider is also served. In addition there is also a good range of bottled beers. Music is played but does not distract from conversation.
❀👶🚆🍴🚃(47,53)❀📶♫

Volunteer Canteen ★ 🅛
45 East Street, L22 8QR
☎ 07891 407464
3 changing beers (sourced nationally; often Black Lodge, Liverpool Brewing Company, Salopian) Ⓗ
Nestling in the back streets of Waterloo, this cosy, traditional pub dates back to 1871 and is housed in a Grade II-listed terraced building. The Volly, as it is known

locally, still provides table service. Until the 1980s, it was owned by Higsons, evidence of which can be seen etched into the windows. It is now managed by Liverpool Brewing Company. Small breweries around Merseyside and North Wales often supply guest ales.
Q❀🚆♣🚃(53)❀📶

West Kirby

White Lion 🅛 ✔
51 Grange Road, CH48 4EE
☎ (0151) 625 9037 ⊕ whitelionwestkirby.co.uk
Brains Rev James Original; Theakston Best Bitter; 3 changing beers (sourced regionally) Ⓗ
A traditional pub in a 200-year-old sandstone building close to the centre of West Kirby. The pub is a little quirky, laid out over several different levels, with lots of cosy nooks to sit in and a real fire to keep you warm in winter. During warmer months you can enjoy the lovely beer garden to the rear. There is a quiz on Monday night. Food serving hours can vary so check in advance.
☙❀◑🚆🚃(80)❀📶♫

Whiston

Beer EnGin 🅛
9 Greenes Road, L35 3RE
☎ 07496 616132
6 changing beers Ⓗ
Set in a row of shops, this cosy, single-room microbar is a delight as soon as you walk in. It serves six real ales, plus real cider, craft beers, wines and a selection of unusual gins. A warm welcome is assured for all, including dogs. Check opening hours before visiting on bank holidays. Local CAMRA Pub of the Year 2022.
Q☙👶🚆🍴P🚃(61)❀

Skew Bridge Alehouse, Rainhill (Photo: Stuart McMahon)

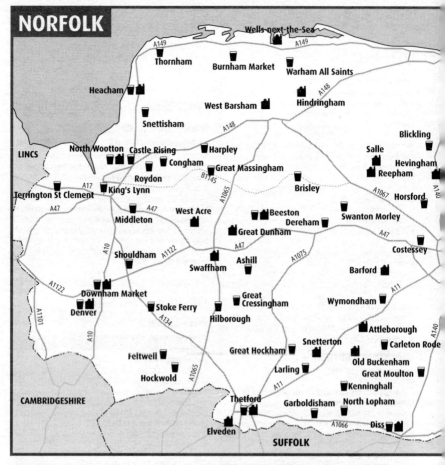

NORFOLK

Map showing Norfolk with locations including Wells-next-the-Sea, Thornham, Burnham Market, Warham All Saints, Heacham, West Barsham, Hindringham, Blickling, Snettisham, Salle, Hevingham, North Wootton, Castle Rising, Harpley, Reepham, LINCS, Congham, Great Massingham, Roydon, Brisley, Horsford, King's Lynn, Terrington St Clement, West Acre, Beeston, Swanton Morley, Middleton, Dereham, Great Dunham, Costessey, Shouldham, Ashill, Barford, Swaffham, Downham Market, Great Cressingham, Wymondham, Denver, Stoke Ferry, Hilborough, Attleborough, Carleton Rode, Feltwell, Great Hockham, Snetterton, Old Buckenham, Hockwold, Larling, Great Moulton, Kenninghall, Thetford, Garboldisham, North Lopham, Diss, Elveden, CAMBRIDGESHIRE, SUFFOLK.

Ashill

White Hart Free House L ✓

Church Street, IP25 7AW (100yds from St Nicholas' Church)
☎ (01760) 622190 ⊕ ashillwhitehart.co.uk
6 changing beers (sourced regionally) Ⓗ
Voted local CAMRA Pub of the Year for 2022 despite only re-opening in 2020, this pub is a hub for the local community as well as a good place for visitors to stay to enjoy the local area. Four en-suite rooms are available. There is a warm and friendly atmosphere with a great choice of draught beers and home-cooked foods. Take a look at the impressive beer menu on the pub's website. There is an EV charger in the car park. The pub operates a loyalty card scheme. ⛟❀🛏🍴🅿❀🎵

Banningham

Banningham Crown L ✓

Colby Road, NR11 7DY (N of B1145, 1 mile E of A140)
☎ (01263) 733534 ⊕ banninghamcrown.co.uk
Greene King IPA, Abbot; 4 changing beers (sourced regionally) Ⓗ
Welcoming, traditional, family-friendly, 17th-century village inn with original timbers in the bar area. The warm atmosphere is enhanced by a log fire in winter. There are two permanent ales plus up to four guest beers, usually two from regional brewers. The pub is popular for its extensive menu of quality home-cooked food using local produce. It has a patio and garden areas for outdoor dining in summer. Regular events include the annual Banneroo music festival.
Q❀❀🛏♣🅿(18)❀🎵

Beeston

Ploughshare ✓

The Street, PE32 2NF
☎ (01328) 598995 ⊕ beestonploughshare.com
Beeston Worth the Wait; Greene King Abbot; 2 changing beers (sourced regionally; often Beeston) Ⓗ
This popular community-owned pub reopened in 2019 after extensive refurbishment. It has a comfortable bar with an inglenook fireplace and a log-burner, and a separate dining room with a small area off the bar that doubles as a café during the day. Traditional English meals are served in the bar and dining room. Outside is a large patio and car park. Closed Mondays.
Q⛟❀🅿❀🎵

Blickling

Bucks Arms ★

Blickling Road, NR11 6NF (next to Blickling Hall)
☎ (01263) 732133 ⊕ bucksarms.co.uk
Grain ThreeOneSix; Woodforde's Wherry; 3 changing beers (sourced regionally) Ⓗ

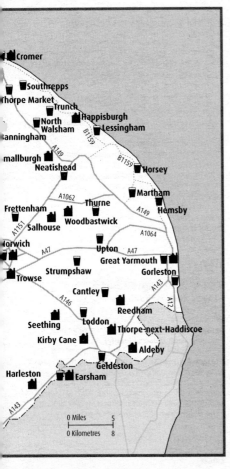

☎ (01328) 738777 ⊕ thehostearms.com
Adnams Ghost Ship; 3 changing beers (sourced nationally) ⊞
This historic hotel, overlooking the village green, blends luxury with a friendly pub feel. The one-room bar is original and the main building dates from the 17th century and is brimming with history. There are four ales from Adnam's and Barsham breweries, which can be enjoyed in the seating area at the front of the pub. The beer garden and large modern terrace have received several design awards. Tucked away on the lower ground floor is a 20 seat cinema. ✿🏠🌙⏻P🖵✿🌐

Cantley

Cock Tavern ⃝
Manor Road, NR13 3JQ (1½ miles N of the village centre)
☎ (01493) 700895
Fuller's London Pride; Morland Old Speckled Hen; 3 changing beers (sourced locally; often Humpty Dumpty, Moon Gazer) ⊞
A characterful roadside pub serving a large rural catchment area. The original bar area dates from 1789, and is complemented by an airy conservatory for diners and a pleasant outside decked area. Although a popular food venue, it retains the feel and atmosphere of a proper pub, helped by the traditional decor. There are themed food nights weekly. Its range of cask ales, often

REAL ALE BREWERIES

All Day ◆ Salle
Ampersand ◆ Diss
Barsham West Barsham
Beeston Beeston
Birdhouse Downham Market
Blackfriars Tavern 🍺 Great Yarmouth (NEW)
Bull of the Woods Kirby Cane
Chalk Hill 🍺 Norwich
Dancing Men 🍺 Happisburgh
Drenchfoot Thetford
Duration ◆ West Acre
Elmtree Snetterton
Fat Cat Norwich
Fengate Hevingham
Fox 🍺 Heacham
Golden Triangle Barford
Grain ◆ Harleston
Humpty Dumpty Reedham
Iceni Elveden
Lacons Great Yarmouth
Lynn North Wootton
Malt Coast Wells-next-the-Sea
Moon Gazer Hindringham
Mr Winter's Norwich
Opa Hay's Aldeby
Panther Reepham
People's Thorpe-next-Haddiscoe
Poppyland ◆ Cromer
Redwell ◆ Norwich: Trowse
St Andrews Brewhouse 🍺 Norwich
Steam-Shed Swaffham
Stumptail Great Dunham
Tindall Seething
Tipple's Salhouse
Tombstone 🍺 Great Yarmouth
Two Rivers Denver
Wagtail Old Buckenham
Waveney 🍺 Earsham
Wildcraft ◆ Smallburgh
Wolf Attleborough
Woodforde's ◆ Woodbastwick

Unspoiled, 17th-century, former coaching inn, a few steps from Blickling Hall, birthplace of Anne Boleyn. There's a delightful snug and a bar with a real fire inside, and plenty of outside tables at the front and rear, with views over the surrounding parkland. It serves good food from a varied menu, and four B&B rooms are available. The Weavers' Way footpath and Bure Valley Railway are also nearby. Q✿🏠⏻♣P✿

Brisley

Brisley Bell ⃝ ✓
The Green, NR20 5DW
☎ (01362) 705024 ⊕ thebrisleybell.co.uk
Adnams Ghost Ship; Woodforde's Wherry; 4 changing beers (sourced nationally) ⊞
A country pub with excellent views across a large open common. The pub has been much expanded, particularly at the rear, with a large patio and garden, but has retained its beams and brick interiors, with two large inglenook fireplaces. The impression is one of space, with a warm welcome for diners, casual drinkers and dogs. An award-winning menu is locally sourced, as are most of the cask beers. Q🐕✿🏠⏻&♣P🖵✿🌐

Burnham Market

Hoste Arms ✓
14 Market Place, PE31 8HD

from local breweries, make the pub well worth the detour off the usual Broads tourist trail.
⏰❀◑♣●P☺✦

Carleton Rode

Carleton Rode Social Club

Jubilee Hall, Mill Road, NR16 1NQ
☎ (01953) 788219
Adnams Southwold Bitter; 3 changing beers (sourced locally; often Moon Gazer) Ⓗ
Large club on the outskirts of the village, serving three well-kept ales. It was extensively refurbished in 2020, and has active pool and darts teams, as well as a large garden. Beer festivals are planned. No food is served, but a pizza van visits. ❀Ⓐ♣P

Castle Rising

Black Horse Inn ✅

Lynn Road, PE31 6AG (on old Hunstanton Rd)
☎ (01553) 631594 ● blackhorsecastlerising.co.uk
Timothy Taylor Landlord; 2 changing beers (sourced regionally) Ⓗ
A picturesque village pub close to the Norman St Lawrence church and the 12th-century castle. Plenty of exposed beams and plaster walls, alongside a friendly atmosphere and a good choice of ales give a traditional pub experience. There are plenty of casual dining tables in the bar areas, and a separate restaurant. Classic dishes are available using locally sourced produce. Bingo and quiz nights are held regularly. ⏰❀◑P🏠☺✦

Congham

Anvil Inn

St Andrews Lane, PE32 1DU (off the B1153)
☎ (01485) 600625 ● anvilcongham.co.uk
Greene King Abbot; 2 changing beers (sourced nationally) Ⓗ
Tucked away a short distance off the A148, this pub is well worth finding. The large, open-plan bar area has three handpumps for continuously changing beers. The focus is on beer from local breweries with varying strengths and styles. Food is served in the bar area, and separate restaurant that also doubles as a function room. There are regular pub quizzes, charity bingo nights and live music. A small campsite at the rear of the pub has a static van for hire. ⏰❀◑Ⓐ♣P✦♫

Costessey

Crown

79 Norwich Road, NR5 0EU
☎ (01603) 742849 ● thecrownpub.business.site
6 changing beers (sourced locally) Ⓗ
Traditional two-bar pub with plush lounge and unspoiled public bar. There are car parks to the front and rear, as well as a large, well-maintained beer garden to the rear. The pub has a good community feel, with darts, pool and bowls teams. The current owners took over in 2021, and have introduced six real ale pumps from breweries around Norfolk and Suffolk. Expect a warm and welcoming atmosphere from proprietors enthused by, and knowledgeable about, real ales. ❀♣🏠☺

Cromer

Albion

32 Church Street, NR27 9ES
☎ (01263) 515398
5 changing beers (sourced locally) Ⓗ

Well placed in the town centre with a bus stop 20 yards away and the train station just a ten-minute walk, this traditional single-bar pub features up to five real ales from the likes of Lacons, Woodforde's and Green Jack breweries. Popular with locals and holidaymakers alike, it has Sky TV, karaoke and live music and is just two minutes from the beach. No food is served.
🚆🚲(CH1,X44) ☺♪

Red Lion Hotel ★ Ⓛ

Brook Street, NR27 9HD (S of church on cliff top)
☎ (01263) 514964 ● redlion-cromer.co.uk
8 changing beers (sourced locally) Ⓗ
The 19th-century Red Lion has retained many original features including panelling, tiled floors and open wood fires. The work of local artists is displayed in the two bar areas. Up to eight guest ales are served, from local breweries such as Green Jack, Mr Winter's and Lacons. The restaurant offers an extensive menu and a bar menu is also available daily. Accommodation is available, and the bar is open all day every day.
Q⏰❀🛏◑Ⓐ♣🚆●P🏠(CH1,X44) ☺✦

Denver

Blackstone Engine Bar Ⓛ

95 Sluice Road, PE38 0DZ
☎ 07518 099868
Two Rivers Miners Mild, Hares Hopping, Kiwi Kick, Denver Diamond, Happy Hopper, Porters Pride; 3 changing beers (sourced locally) Ⓗ
The bar is in the old workshop of the Denver Mill complex and you can see some of the machinery which gives the bar its name. The mighty Blackstone diesel engine that powered the mill is in its original engine house and still in working condition. There is no food available but you can take beer into the café next door, or food from the café into the bar. Q●P

Dereham

Cock

28 Norwich Street, NR19 1BX
☎ (01362) 693393 ● the-cock.co.uk
4 changing beers (sourced nationally) Ⓗ
A cosy front bar area with low beams and a large inglenook fireplace with a wood burner opens into a larger bar area with soft furnishings. To the rear is another room with additional seating and a dartboard. Outside to the rear is an attractive courtyard area with several tables and chairs. There is a separate room available to hire for functions. Four changing beers from local and national breweries feature alongside a range of snacks such as rolls and panini. There is live music every Sunday afternoon. ⏰❀🛏Ⓐ♣🚆♣P🏠☺✦♪

Diss

Ampersand Brew Tap Ⓛ

27-31 Sawmills Road, IP22 4GG
☎ (01379) 643944 ● ampersandbrew.co
Ampersand The Cap Bitter; 4 changing beers (often Ampersand) Ⓗ
The brewery tap for Ampersand Brew Co, it serves three cask ales and up to 12 keg Ampersand ales and lagers. Food is in-house by Burger Jam. Sunday roasts are served and a monthly Saturday brunch must be prebooked. There are regular live music and DJ nights and a weekly bottle share night. Several special beer festival weekends are organised throughout the year, including Oktoberfest. Brewery tours and tastings can be booked, and the brewery shop opens at 10am. ◑Ⓐ🚆☺✦

Downham Market

Crown Hotel ★
12 Bridge Street, PE38 9DH
☎ (01366) 382322 ⊕ crowncoachinginn.com
Greene King IPA, Abbot; 2 changing beers (sourced nationally) ⊞
A 17th-century, Grade II-listed, traditional coaching inn full of original features and character. A room with a lovely staircase leads to the bar with a beamed ceiling, panelled walls and large fireplaces. A good selection of ales is served. There is a restaurant, plenty of outside seating, and a separate function room that caters for parties and weddings. Accommodation in 18 rooms, including family suites. Q❀✿◗▶P🖵🛜

Whalebone 🛒 ✅
58 Bridge Street, PE38 9DJ
☎ (01366) 381600
Adnams Ghost Ship; Greene King Abbot; Ruddles Best Bitter; Sharp's Doom Bar; 3 changing beers (sourced nationally) ⊞
This listed building is now part of the Wetherspoon chain. The pub has been extensively modified but retains the original façade. A large bar area leads to the gardens at the rear and side. Heritage displays on the walls include whaling, drainage of the Fens, Horatio Nelson and replica whalebones. There are regular beer and cider festivals plus occasional tap takeovers. Wheelchair access throughout. ➳❀◗▶🖣🖵🛜

Earsham

Queen's Head 🛒
Station Road, NR35 2TS (Just W of Bungay)
☎ (01986) 892623
Waveney Lightweight, Welterweight; 2 changing beers (often Ampersand, Cloudwater) ⊞
This busy 17th-century locals' brewpub has a large front garden overlooking the village green. The main bar has flagstone floor, wooden beams and a large fireplace with a roaring fire in winter. There is a separate dining area serving food at lunchtimes (not Mon and Tue). The landlord has owned the pub since 1998. Home to the Waveney Brewing Co., four ales and at least one real cider are usually available. A former local CAMRA Pub of the Year. Q➳❀&♣🖣P🖵(580)🌸🛜

Feltwell

Wellington 🛒
27-29 High Street, IP26 4AF
☎ (01842) 828224 ⊕ feltwellington.co.uk
3 changing beers (sourced nationally) ⊞
Landlords Chris and Chris celebrated their 10th anniversary at this pub in 2024. There is a cosy lounge bar with a separate games room featuring pool and darts. One real cider is always on handpump. There is plenty of interesting memorabilia relating to the pub's namesake bomber. The pub is heavily involved with the local community and participates in the Meet Up Mondays initiative. On alternate weeks movies are screened for free to provide a way for people to meet others and find companionship. ➳❀&♣🖣P🌸🛜♫

Frettenham

Rose & Crown
50 Buxton Road, NR12 7NJ
☎ (01603) 898341
Greene King IPA; 4 changing beers (sourced nationally) ⊞

Large and friendly single-bar traditional wet-led pub with wood panelling throughout and a wood-burning stove, serving four real ales from local breweries, usually including a dark beer. There's plenty of seating outside at the front and rear, some of it covered. Light lunches are served from Wednesday to Friday, Thai food is available Thursday to Saturday evenings, with breakfast at weekends from 10am. ➳❀◗▶🖣P🌸

Garboldisham

Fox Inn 🛒
The Street, IP22 2RZ
☎ (01953) 688538 ⊕ garboldishamfox.co.uk
6 changing beers (sourced locally; often Lacons, Moon Gazer, Mr Winter's) ⊞
17th-century coaching inn near Bressingham Gardens and Banham Zoo. Bought by the local community to operate as a community pub, it has a welcoming feel, with ales from breweries such as Mr Winter's, Lacons, Norfolk Brewhouse and Wolf. Various Adnams ales from keg and local ice cream in tubs are also served. Food from various street food vendors is available on Friday and Saturday evening, with updates posted on social media. Also serves Sunday roasts. Rumour has it that one of the pub ghosts is a black labrador. Q➳❀&♣🖣P🌸🛜

Geldeston

Locks Inn 🛒
Locks Lane, NR34 0HS (around 800yds along track from Station Rd)
☎ (01508) 830033 ⊕ thelocksinn.com
4 changing beers (sourced locally; often Lacons, People's, Wolf) ⊞
The Locks Inn, community owned with over 1,400 shareholders, is on the River Waveney with large gardens and overnight moorings for boats. It is reached at the end of a long track off Station Road in Geldeston. The original small main bar has low ceiling beams and a clay floor and is still lit by candlelight at night. A regular and extremely varied programme of events feature all year round at this outstanding community focused venue. Winter hours vary. Q➳❀◗&🅰♣P🖵🌸🛜♫

Gorleston

Dock Tavern 🛒
Dock Tavern Lane, NR31 6PY (opp north side of Morrisons)
☎ (01493) 442255 ⊕ thedocktavern.com
4 changing beers (sourced nationally; often Tombstone, Woodforde's) ⊞
As the pub's name suggests, the Dock Tavern is close to the river, and not far from the main shopping area. Subject to flood damage many times, the various flood levels can be seen by the front door. The outside drinking area at the front, a suntrap in summer, has views of the river and docks. A welcoming pub with a friendly lively atmosphere, it has live music most weekends, plus an annual charity music day. ❀&♣P🖵🌸🛜♫

New Entertainer 🛒
80 Pier Plain, NR31 6PG
☎ (01493) 300022
9 changing beers (sourced regionally; often Green Jack, St Austell, Woodforde's) ⊞
Traditional pub with a unique curved frontage including original Lacons windows, and an interesting design and layout. A varied choice of beers including a dark, are always on offer. This is a proper pub, where people go for a beer and a chat, with a loyal following. Pool, darts

and sports TV are available, and there is a monthly quiz. Note that the main entrance is on Back Pier Plain. Local CAMRA Pub of the Year 2023. ♣♠🖥♨♥🛜♪

Oddfellows Arms 🅛

43 Cliff Hill, NR31 6DG (entrance is on Drudge Rd)
☎ 07876 545982 ⊕ dorbiere.co.uk/oddfellows-arms
4 changing beers (sourced locally; often Adnams, Grain) Ⓗ

Cosy two-bar back-street pub on Cliff Hill, a short distance from the harbour. Music and jam sessions are held most Fridays, especially in summer and there is plenty of music-themed memorabilia inside the pub. There are always three cask ales on offer, often from Norfolk breweries. A west-facing outdoor seating area is at the front of the pub and limited parking at the rear. This is its eighth consecutive year in this Guide, reflecting the high standard of the ales on offer. 🛞❀P♥🛜♪

Great Cressingham

Olde Windmill Inn

Water End, IP25 6NN (off A1065 S of Swaffham)
☎ (01760) 756232 ⊕ oldewindmillinn.co.uk
Adnams Southwold Bitter, Broadside; Greene King IPA; 2 changing beers (sourced nationally) Ⓗ

Dating back to circa 1650, this large rural pub and hotel has been run by the Halls family for three generations. Despite its size it has a cosy feel to it. There is a changing range of beers, many of which are sourced locally, and real cider is also available. A popular food menu has something for everyone. The dining areas vary in size from a large conservatory to smaller, intimate rooms. Modern hotel accommodation with 14 en-suite bedrooms is found in separate buildings behind the pub. Q🛞❀🖾🕽ᴦ&▲♣♠P♥

Great Hockham

Eagle 🅛 ✅

Harling Road, IP24 1NP
☎ (01953) 498893
Greene King IPA, Abbot; Morland Old Speckled Hen; 2 changing beers (sourced nationally) Ⓗ

Run by the same landlord since 2009, this large, family-friendly pub is set in a lovely village close to Thetford Forest. The main bar is separated from a games area by an open fire. Five real ales are available on handpump. Outdoor seating is provided at the front of the pub. Quiz nights are held on alternate Wednesdays and numerous other events are held regularly. 🛞🕽&♣♥♪

Great Massingham

Dabbling Duck

11 Abbey Road, PE32 2HN
☎ (01485) 520827 ⊕ thedabblingduck.co.uk
Adnams Ghost Ship; Woodforde's Wherry; 2 changing beers (sourced nationally) Ⓗ

A classic pub with views across the village green and two tree-fringed ponds. Inside there are cosy fireplaces, stone floors and flint walls. Known locally as the Mucky Duck, the pub has developed a reputation for its excellent food. There is accommodation in eight rooms plus an adjacent cottage. It was included in the Sunday Times list of the best 80 places to stay in Britain in 2020. 🛞❀🖾🕽♣P♥🛜

Great Moulton

Fox & Hounds

Frith Way, NR15 2HE (on NE outskirts of village)

☎ (01379) 677506
4 changing beers Ⓗ

Lovely village pub, parts of which date from the 15th century. The main bar has a low ceiling, with copped beams, and comfortable sofa seating. A large inglenook fireplace holds a roaring log fire in winter. There is a separate restaurant and food is served Wednesday to Saturday lunchtimes and evenings, and Sunday breakfast and lunch; booking recommended at the weekend. The large beer garden has four pods with lighting, heating and an intercom to the bar, plus children's play area and a large field with a marquee for events. Q🛞❀🕽ᴦ&▲♣♠P🖥♥🛜♪

Great Yarmouth

Blackfriars Tavern 🏆 🅛

94 Blackfriars Road, NR30 3BZ
☎ (01493) 859853 ⊕ blackfriarstavern.co.uk
Blackfriars Tavern Herring Bridge Pale Ale, Pilgrims Porter; 8 changing beers (sourced locally; often Drenchfoot, Mr Winter's, Wolf) Ⓗ

Friendly, welcoming village-style pub set in an urban conservation area, opposite the best-preserved sections of the town wall. Eight ever-changing cask ales complement the two permanent offerings from on-site Blackfriars Tavern brewery, more than 20 real ciders, sourced locally, plus over 100 bottled Belgian beers. The pub is family, dog and cyclist friendly and is known for its home-cooked pies and hearty meals. The pub has two separate bars, with traditional games on tables, plus two planted courtyards for outside drinking. Local CAMRA Pub of the Year and Regional Cider Pub of the Year 2024. Q🛞❀🕽♣♠P🖾🖥(2) ♥🛜♪

Red Herring 🅛

24-25 Havelock Road, NR30 3HQ (Havelock Rd is off St Peters St and is at the back of the Time & Tide museum)
☎ 07876 644742
4 changing beers (sourced nationally; often Green Jack, Lacons, Mighty Oak) Ⓗ

Named after the fish that were smoked in the nearby but now-closed smoke houses, the pub is close to the impressive medieval walls and the award-winning Time & Tide museum. The Herring has a dartboard, pool table and hosts pool and darts teams. This is its 11th consecutive year in this Guide, reflecting the landlord's passion for serving well-kept ales, often from the nearby Lacons brewery, in a relaxing community focused pub environment. No children or dogs allowed. Q❀🕽ᴦ♣♠🖾🖥

Tombstone Saloon Bar 🅛

6 George Street, NR30 1HR (on the north east corner of Hall Quay)
☎ 07584 504444 ⊕ tombstonebrewery.co.uk
Tombstone Arizona, Gunslinger Ⓗ**; 6 changing beers (sourced regionally; often Green Jack, Milestone, Moon Gazer)** Ⓖ

Well established as the tap for the on-site Tombstone brewery, this small Wild West-themed bar always showcases a wide range of mainly regional ales across various beer styles. A winner of numerous CAMRA awards, this is its ninth consecutive year in this Guide. The impressive range of ciders always includes real cider. Conversation rules, but there is unobtrusive TV and music. Frequent bus services stop outside and the bar is close to Great Yarmouth Market Place. An annual Easter beer festival is held. Q🛞🕽≒♣♠P🖾🖥♥♪

Troll Cart 🅛 ✅

7 Regent Road, NR30 2AF (adjacent to the Market Gates bus station)
☎ (01493) 332932

Greene King Abbot; Ruddles Best Bitter; Sharp's Doom Bar; 3 changing beers (sourced nationally; often Green Jack, Wolf, Woodforde's) Ⓗ
Opened in 1996, this new-build Wetherspoon pub is unusual in not being a conversion of an existing building. The comfortable interior has various seating areas and the usual JDW offerings, which makes it appealing to all age groups. There is also outside seating front and rear, and accommodation in their hotel. Guest cask ales are often local. Centrally located and handy for shops, bus routes and a taxi rank. ⮿⧖⊄⍾⚷⎅⧠🞄

Harpley

Rose & Crown

Nethergate Street, PE31 6TW
☎ (01485) 521807 ⊕ roseandcrownharpley.co.uk
Woodforde's Wherry; 4 changing beers (sourced regionally) Ⓗ
Family run pub and a former local CAMRA Pub of the Year, this attractive 17th-century pub offers guest ales from local breweries. It features open bar areas with a stylish and comfortable feel and has log fires in winter. Outside is an enclosed beer garden for summer drinking. In recent years the pub has developed an excellent reputation for top quality food – the Late Lunch Club is particularly popular. The unspoilt village provides pleasant walks and is close to Houghton Hall.
Q⮿⧖⊄⍾P⎅(X29) 🞄🞂

Heacham

Fox & Hounds Ⓛ

22 Station Road, PE31 7EX
☎ (01485) 570345
Fox Heacham Gold, Nelson's Blood, IPA; 1 changing beer (sourced nationally) Ⓗ
A friendly pub in the heart of this village near the coast. The eight beers on offer include a selection from neighbouring Fox brewery. Bottled beers are also sold, plus a range of imported beers. The restaurant offers beer recommendations to match the food. There is live music on Tuesday evenings (mainly blues) and a quiz on Thursdays. Beer festivals are hosted throughout the year.
⮿⧖⊄⍾⚷P⎅🞄🞂

Hemsby

King's Head

North Road, NR29 4LR
☎ (01493) 731026
3 changing beers (sourced nationally; often Woodforde's) Ⓗ
This is a traditional village pub, recently refurbished to a high standard. Well supported by the locals who live nearby and popular with visitors who choose to explore away from the bustling seafront area. Competitively priced food is available both lunchtime and evenings and there is a separate dining area along with a secluded garden for the warmer months. There is a bus stop and parking nearby. Sports TV and a dog friendly bar area add to this pub's attraction. ⮿⧖⊄P⎅(1)🞄🞂🎜

Hilborough

Swan

Brandon Road, IP26 5BW
☎ (01760) 756380 ⊕ hilboroughswan.co.uk
4 changing beers (sourced nationally) Ⓗ
A smart 17th-century building on the A1065 south of Swaffham. It opens early for breakfast every day except Sunday, and good value food is served throughout the

day. On a Sunday there is a popular carvery. There are up to four beers on the bar, mostly from local breweries. Outside there is a pleasant seating area and a non-smoking tent. Q🞄⧖⊄⍾⚵P🞄🞂

Hockwold

Red Lion

114 Main Street, IP26 4NB
☎ (01842) 829728 ⊕ redlionhockwold.com
3 changing beers (sourced nationally) Ⓗ
Set on the village green this traditional, friendly village pub had a new landlord in August 2023. It has a smart, but comfortable interior with a sizeable collection of toby jugs. A good selection of home-made food is served all week, with a carvery on Sunday. There are regular, well-supported quizzes and darts matches. Outside is a spacious garden with plenty of seating, a smoking shelter and a children's play area. ⮿⧖⊄⚵P🞄🞂

Horsey

Nelson Head Ⓛ

The Street, NR29 4AD (just off B1159; down lane ½ mile N of Horsey Mill)
☎ (01493) 393378 ⊕ thenelsonhead.com
Woodforde's Wherry, Albion Stout, Nelson's; 8 changing beers (sourced regionally; often Milestone, Moon Gazer, Tombstone) Ⓗ
This traditional, National Trust-owned country pub consists of a bar area with a large open fire and separate dining area. The pub is decorated with various memorabilia and paintings relating to Nelson. It offers quality food prepared using locally sourced ingredients. The extensive beer garden is host to festivals and events in summer. The pub is on the route of popular walks to access the Broads, beach and local seal colony. The cider range includes real ciders. Q⮿⧖⊄Å⚵P⎅🞄🞂

Horsford

Horsford Social Club

Holt Road, NR10 3DN
⊕ horsfordvillagehall.org.uk/social-club
2 changing beers (sourced nationally) Ⓗ
Social club with darts on Monday and Wednesdays, poker on selected Tuesdays, pool Thursdays and Bingo Fridays. There is live entertainment most weekends. Families are welcome, with no age restriction. There's a large bar area serving two or three ales, and the manager is a keen real ale enthusiast – pins are used to extend the range and ensure quality. CAMRA members are admitted on production of a valid membership card or current Guide. ⮿⧖⍾⚵P🞄🎜

Kenninghall

Red Lion 🍷 ★ ⦰

East Church Street, NR16 2EP (opp parish church)
☎ (01953) 887849 ⊕ redlionkenninghall.co.uk
4 changing beers (sourced locally; often Black Sheep, Shortts, Timothy Taylor) Ⓗ
A beautifully restored pub dating from the early 16th century with a traditional bar and pine panelled snug (one of only two of its kind in East Anglia) adjacent to the 40 seater restaurant in the style of old stables. It has been identified by CAMRA as having a nationally important historic pub interior. Good wholesome home-cooked food includes fresh fish Fridays. Regular live music and other community events are held. Sunday roasts and special boards all locally sourced where possible. ⮿⊄⍾🞄🎜

King's Lynn

Ferry Lane Social Club
Ferry Lane, PE30 1HN (off King St)
☎ (01553) 772239
4 changing beers (sourced nationally) G
Known locally as the Ouse Booze, this local CAMRA Club of the Year for 2020 and 2022-2024 can be found at the end of a narrow lane next to the departure point for the West Lynn Ferry. The bar overlooks the river and there is a balcony where you can sit and enjoy the view. Five beers are on offer from breweries near and far, as well as local cider from Sandringham. CAMRA members and visitors using this Guide are welcome, with a limit on the number of visits before being asked to join.
✤◀≠(Kings Lynn) ●❀🌐♪

Live & Let Live 🄻
18 Windsor Road, PE30 5PL (off London Rd near Catholic church)
☎ (01553) 764990
5 changing beers (sourced regionally) H
Popular back-street local with two bars; a small cosy lounge and a larger public bar with TV. Five beers are available, including a mild (rare for the area). The range of ciders usually includes something from local producers. Local CAMRA Cider Pub of the Year 2020-2024, and contender for Pub of the Year 2024. Live music is sometimes played in the public bar. ●❀♪

Larling

Angel 🍺 ★
NR16 2QU (1 mile SW from Snetterton racetrack, just off A11)
☎ (01953) 717963 ⊕ angel-larling.co.uk
Adnams Southwold Bitter; 4 changing beers (sourced nationally) H
Winner of local CAMRA Pub of the Year in 2023 and 2024, this 17th-century coaching inn has been in the same family for several generations. Five real ales plus a real cider are on handpump (always including a mild). Over 100 whiskies are stocked, as well as 50 gins. The lounge and bar have real open fires, and there is a dining room which serves home-made fare. There is a campsite in the field opposite where a long-running beer festival is held in August with 80 real ales and live music.
Q❀✤🚗◀◑Ġ♣⋏●P☐

Lessingham

Star Inn 🄻
Star Hill, NR12 0DN (just off B1159 coast road; corner of High Rd and Star Hill)
☎ (01692) 531829
Green Jack Trawlerboys Best Bitter; Lacons Encore; 1 changing beer (sourced regionally) G
A friendly country pub just outside the village. The two regular cask beers are local, guests may be national. There are two ciders. Food is prepared to order using locally sourced ingredients – booking is essential. Meals may be taken in the bar, the separate restaurant or the garden in summer. There is a log fire in winter. A pool room is separate from the bar. Two ensuite B&B rooms are available. Closed Mondays.
Q❀🚗◑⋏♣P☐(34) ●🌐

Loddon

Angel Inn Loddon ✔
15 High Street, NR14 6ET
☎ (01508) 520417 ⊕ theangelinnloddon.co.uk

5 changing beers (sourced regionally) H
This family-run, artisan free house is already famous for its breakfasts, ploughman's and evening platters (booking only please), as well as a range of interesting indoor and outside pub games. However, it is its wide and ever-changing offering of local ales that really sets it apart. Over 170 regional ales have gone through the five handpumps in its first year alone, with a different line up of Norfolk and Suffolk cask ales every week. Closed Tuesday and Wednesday. May close early.
Q❀✤◑Ġ♣●🚗(X22,X21) ●🌐♪

Martham

King's Arms 🄻
15 The Green, NR29 4PL
☎ (01493) 749156
3 changing beers (sourced nationally; often Adnams, Lacons, St Peter's) H
Traditional two-bar village pub located opposite the picturesque pond. The pub has a separate dining area and good value food is available. The landlord is also the chef. A welcoming fire awaits in the winter months and a garden with children's play area for the warmer days. With three or more ales on offer and a friendly welcome for visitors, the pub is very much a part of the social scene in the village. Q❀✤◑ĠP☐●🌐

Middleton

Gate
Hill Road, Fair Green, PE32 1RW (N of A47; follow Fair Green signs)
☎ (01553) 840518
Greene King Abbot; Woodforde's Wherry; 1 changing beer (sourced nationally) H
A traditional village local, close to the A47. The bar and snug are used mainly by drinkers, but eating is also an option, in the pleasantly decorated dining room. The excellent food features seasonal produce and ingredients are sourced from local suppliers. The pretty garden is popular in summer. Bingo is held twice each month with other events held periodically. Look out for the terracotta warriors guarding the loos! Q❀✤◑Ġ⋏♣P●🌐

Neatishead

White Horse 🄻
The Street, NR12 8AD
☎ (01692) 630828 ⊕ thewhitehorseinnneatishead.com
Fat Cat Tom Cat; Woodforde's Wherry; 4 changing beers (sourced locally) H
Traditional village pub near the Radar museum. It has two bar areas, with a log fire and cosy dining area in the main pub, and a courtyard garden and split-level restaurant to the rear. House beers include Miss-E-Malt (Fat Cat) and Somebody Called Chris (Mr Winter's). Humpty Dumpty Farriers is also a regular guest beer. An annual beer festival is held, plus OctoberFest in September. Good home-prepared meals are served, with local produce a priority. The pub sells its own spirit range.
Q❀✤◑Ġ♣●P☐(3) ●🌐

North Lopham

King's Head
16 The Street, IP22 2NE (2 miles N of A1066)
☎ (01379) 688007 ⊕ kingsheadnl.com
3 changing beers (sourced nationally; often Drenchfoot, Elmtree, Woodforde's) H
Two-bar timber-framed and thatched 16th-century pub set back from the main road through the village. The

public bar has pool table and inglenook fireplace while the comfortable saloon/dining room has woodburner. The guest ale varies but is usually above 4% ABV. Food is served Wednesday to Saturday lunch and evening plus Sunday lunch. The pub has a crazy golf course with free club and ball hire. Q७॰♿🛏🌞◑♣P❀🐶🤶♪

North Walsham

Hop In ⃝L

2 Market Street, NR28 9BZ
☎ 07714 688386 ⊕ thehopin.co.uk
6 changing beers (sourced nationally) Ⓖ
Around the corner from the marketplace, and owned and run by keen CAMRA members, this was Norfolk's first micropub. Six changing ales are served on gravity dispense plus a real cider, and there is usually one dark beer available. There is no Wi-Fi, music or machines, just good conversation. There is a small seating area downstairs and more upstairs, plus a patio area outside. Plates and cutlery are provided for takeaway food if required. Closed Monday. Q❀🚲◑🐶🖼�*🐶*

North Wootton

Red Cat Hotel

Station Road, PE30 3QH (Station Rd is opp All Saints church, where Nursery Ln meets Manor Rd)
☎ (01553) 631244 ⊕ redcathotel.com
Adnams Southwold Bitter; 1 changing beer (sourced nationally) Ⓗ
No longer offering accommodation or restaurant meals, the Red Cat now concentrates solely on well-kept real ales. Built in 1898 and constructed in local gingerbread carrstone, this traditional village local offers two real ales. It is nicely decorated and in a quiet location close to the Wash marshes. Ask about the history of the namesake red cat – if you can believe it. The pub is near National Cycle Route 1, the Sandringham Estate and the West Norfolk coast. Q七❀P🖼(3)🐶🤶

Norwich

Alexandra Tavern

16 Stafford Street, NR2 3BB
☎ (01603) 627772 ⊕ alexandratavern.co.uk
5 changing beers (sourced locally) Ⓗ
Popular, bustling and friendly, this traditional pub sited just outside the city centre is a real gem. The pub serves up to five changing beers from local breweries, and two real ciders. Freshly prepared food, sourced locally, is served daily, with a good variety, including a soup menu. There is a dartboard and plenty of board games to choose from, with children also welcome until early evening. The interior is brightly decorated, with the walls featuring nautical pictures and articles. Open all day every day. Q七❀◑🐶♣🖼🐶🤶

Artichoke

1 Magdalen Road, NR3 4LW
☎ (01603) 662807
5 changing beers (sourced nationally; often Golden Triangle) Ⓗ
A 1930s flint building, originally decorated in the Brewers' Tudor style, original Young's, Crawshay & Young's windows, parquet flooring and a long solid wood bar. The bar has five handpumps offering a changing selection of real ales, and a great selection of craft beers. In-house catering provides meals and occasional wine and food tasting events. Outdoor seating in front and at the side (part covered). Opens 2pm Monday and Tuesday. 🐶♣🖼🐶🤶

Beehive ⃝L

30 Leopold Road, NR4 7PJ (between Unthank Rd and Newmarket Rd)
☎ (01603) 451628 ⊕ beehivepubnorwich.co.uk
Green Jack Golden Best; 5 changing beers (sourced nationally; often Oakham) Ⓗ
A friendly two-bar local with knowledgeable staff, featuring a comfortable lounge bar with sofas. A beer festival is held in late June with around 25 ales and ciders. The popular beer garden is used all year round, with charity barbecues during the summer months. There is a function room upstairs (available to hire) with a pool table. The pub has a fortnightly quiz on Wednesdays as well as regular themed food nights. A book swap library was established in 2021. Opens at 3pm Monday to Thursday. Q七❀♣🐶P🐶🤶

Bell Hotel ⊘

5 Orford Hill, NR1 3QB
☎ (01603) 630017
Greene King Abbot; Sharp's Doom Bar; 7 changing beers (sourced nationally) Ⓗ
Large two-bar city-centre pub over three floors serving traditional real ales and food, at reasonable prices. The building is said to date from 1485 and was one of the city's leading coaching inns. The ground floor bar has a tree-shaded terrace outside with plenty of seating and views along Castle Meadow and Orford Place. The pub was home to the American Women's Army Air Corp during WW2, and there is memorabilia throughout the pub celebrating this. 七❀◑🖼🐶🤶

Brewery Tap ⃝L

98-100 Lawson Road, NR3 4LF
☎ (01603) 413153 ⊕ fatcattap.co.uk
Fat Cat Norwich Bitter, Tom Cat Ⓗ; Oakham Bishops Farewell; 15 changing beers (sourced nationally) Ⓖ
Serving a huge range of real ales, ciders and quality keg beers from across the country, the Brewery Tap is a large single-bar pub in a 1970s building. Live music on Sundays complements a variety of events including tap takeovers, themed beer evenings and festivals, beer launches and community events. Loaded chips and other snacks are available. There is lots of outside seating at front and rear (mostly covered). The Fat Cat brewery is located in the same building. Q❀◑🐶♣🖼P🖼(11,12)🐶🤶♪

Champion

101 Chapel Field Road, NR2 1SE
☎ (01603) 628148 ⊕ thechampionpub.com
Batemans XB, XXXB; 1 changing beer (sourced nationally) Ⓗ
Friendly L-shaped Bateman's corner pub, situated immediately adjacent to the main shopping street. A substantial section of the original city wall can be seen from all aspects of the pub. Sporting photographs adorn the walls of the larger of the two drinking areas. There is a small outdoor area adjacent to the pub and a small function room is available. An acoustic music 'round' is hosted on Mondays, with the pub open until 11.30. Closes 8pm Tuesdays. 🐶◑♣🖼🐶🤶♪

Coach & Horses

82 Thorpe Road, NR1 1BA
☎ (01603) 496152 ⊕ thecoachthorperoad.co.uk
Chalk Hill Tap Bitter, Black Anna, CHB, Gold, Dreadnought; 2 changing beers (sourced nationally) Ⓗ
Close to the station this coaching inn, with its iconic balcony, is the home of the Chalk Hill brewery, and serves its full range of beers. A tour of the brewery is available by appointment. Excellent-value food is served

along with Sandford cider. Sport, especially rugby, is shown on big screens, and the large fire is welcome in winter. Not far from the football ground, it gets busy before matches. There is lots of outside covered seating at the front. ✹❍◗⇒♣♠⊟❀☎♪

Coach & Horses
51 Bethel Street, NR2 1NR
☎ (01603) 618522 ⊕ thecoachandhorsesbethelstreet.co.uk
7 changing beers (sourced regionally) ⊞
Historic city-centre local near the Theatre Royal, Market Place and City Hall. The pub has a bright, welcoming bar with several separate seating areas, including cosy alcoves, and a long part-covered patio garden area to one side. At least one dark ale is always available. Good value tapas-style food is served every day. A bar billiards table is in regular use in the right-hand bar, and the pub participates in the local league. ☎✹❍◗♣♠⊟❀☎

Cottage
9 Silver Road, NR3 4TB
⊕ norwichcottage.com
4 changing beers (sourced nationally) ⊞
A large single-room pub with a lovely enclosed patio garden at the rear. Refurbished to a high standard, with solid oak flooring, wood panelling, exposed brickwork and a copper bar-top. Four beers sourced nationally, often previous award winners, are served, plus a selection of quality spirits and craft beers. Sunday roasts are served, plus burgers and sandwiches. Opens at 4pm during the week, 2pm on Saturday. ✹❍◗♣♠⊟❀☎

Duke of Wellington ⬡
91-93 Waterloo Road, NR3 1EG
☎ (01603) 441182 ⊕ dukeofwellingtonnorwich.co.uk
Oakham JHB, Bishops Farewell ⒼⒼ; **Wolf Golden Jackal** ⊞**, Wolf in Sheep's Clothing** Ⓖ**, Wolf Ale** ⊞**; 8 changing beers (sourced nationally)** Ⓖ
Friendly pub with a changing range of guest ales to complement the permanent beers (mainly from Wolf brewery), the majority of which are served on gravity from a taproom behind the bar. The attractive enclosed rear garden/patio area hosts a beer festival in late August, and regular barbecues at weekends in summer. Events include monthly quiz evenings. Customers can bring in their own food; crockery, cutlery and sauces are provided. ✹⇒♣●P⊟❀☎

Fat Cat ⬡
49 West End Street, NR2 4NA
☎ (01603) 624364 ⊕ fatcatpub.co.uk
Crouch Vale Yakima Gold; Fat Cat Norwich Bitter ⊞**, Marmalade; Greene King Abbot; Oakham Bishops Farewell, Green Devil** Ⓖ**; 12 changing beers (sourced nationally)** ⊞/Ⓖ
Comfortable traditional street-corner pub with an outstanding and extensive range of ales, sourced from all over the UK. Ales from the Fat Cat range are served, plus real ciders and perries. Food is limited to pork pies. The interior is tiled, and has plenty of seating in two areas each side of the bar, and a small room at the rear. This is a superb example of what a real ale outlet should be, with excellent, friendly service. Twice CAMRA's National Pub of the Year. Q✹●⊟❀☎

Fat Cat & Canary ⬡
101 Thorpe Road, NR1 1TR
☎ (01603) 436925
13 changing beers (sourced regionally; often Fat Cat, Oakham, Crouch Vale) ⊞/Ⓖ
About a mile and a half from the city centre, this sister pub to the original Fat Cat serves most of the Fat Cat brewery's ales, plus guests from around the UK,

continental beers and real ciders. There is a small TV to the rear of the main bar, a large car park and terraces to the front and rear, the latter being heated. Home-made rolls are available and there are regular pop-up food vendors. It gets busy on Norwich City match days. ☎✹❍◗♿●P⊟❀☎

Garden House
1 Pembroke Road, NR2 3HD
☎ (01603) 628059
Brains SA; Oakham JHB ⊞**; 6 changing beers (sourced nationally)** ⊞/Ⓖ
This pub has two bar areas with extensive and comfortable seating and a separate pool room. There is a large garden at rear with tables and seating, both covered and uncovered, plus a TV for hardy sports addicts. There are always three ales on handpump – SA, JHB and Rev James – and at least six on gravity, sometimes increasing to 10 for special sporting events. A extensive range of ciders and keg and bottled beers is available. The landlord is always on the door to extend a personal welcome. ☎✹♿♣P❀☎♪

Golden Star ★
57 Colegate, NR3 1DD
☎ (01603) 632447 ⊕ goldenstarnorwich.co.uk
Greene King IPA, Abbot; 3 changing beers (sourced nationally) ⊞
A welcoming and relaxing pub with a main bar area and a second room to the left and behind the bar which hosts the bar billiards table and occasional live music sessions. A quiz is held on Sunday evenings and a specials menu is served daily, along with Sunday roasts. A wide selection of music is played, but unobtrusively. There is a small patio at the rear, and tables outside the front in summer. Open all day every day. ✹❍◗♣●⊟❀☎♪

Jubilee ⬡
26 St Leonards Road, NR1 4BL
☎ (01603) 618734
Oakham Citra ⊞**; 4 changing beers (sourced regionally)** ⊞
Attractive Victorian corner pub with a warm welcome. There are two bars, a comfortable conservatory and an enclosed patio garden. Many of the well-kept ales and craft beers are local, often from Mr Winter's or Ampersand, with Beartown Ales usually stocked too. This popular venue, within easy reach of the city centre, is at the heart of the community and caters for all tastes, from sports fans to those who enjoy local history talks. Customers are welcome to bring in takeaway food, and occasional pop-up street-food fairs are held in the summer. ☎✹❍⇒♣❀☎

King's Arms
22 Hall Road, NR1 3HQ
☎ (01603) 477888 ⊕ kingsarmsnorwich.co.uk
Batemans XB, Gold, XXXB; 5 changing beers (sourced regionally; often Tindall) ⊞
A friendly Batemans house close to the city centre, serving a wide range of guest ales to complement the Batemans beers, usually including a stout or porter and a mild. The guest brewery changes monthly. Sausage rolls, pork pies and filled rolls are on the bar but customers can bring in food from various nearby takeaways, with plates and condiments provided. Monthly quiz nights, poker evenings and live music take place. It gets busy on football match days. ✹♣⊟❀☎♪

King's Head ⬡
42 Magdalen Street, NR3 1JE
⊕ kingsheadnorwich.com

8 changing beers (sourced regionally; often Elmtree, Mr Winter's, Tindall) ⊞
A traditional-style two-bar pub which offers up to eight quality real ales, mostly from local breweries but also selected guests from further away, plus two ciders. A mild or stout is usually available. No food is served except snacks, pork pies and pickled eggs, but customers can bring or order in their own, with plates and cutlery supplied. Bar billiards is well supported, with two teams in the local league. Finalist for CAMRA National Pub of the Year 2022. Open all day every day. Q❀♣🏠🗓🚃🐾🛜

Leopard ⑂

98-100 Bull Close Road, NR3 1NQ
☎ (01603) 631111 ⊕ theleopardpub.co.uk
6 changing beers (sourced nationally) ⊞
Welcoming, traditional, single-bar local with a variety of changing regional and national ales and craft beers. The pub has a clean and bright bar area which gives a spacious feel, and a pleasant and quiet enclosed courtyard garden at the rear which is popular in the summer months. Luca Pizza pop-up is available most Thursday evenings, along with sausages from the Archers served Friday to Tuesday. Fortnightly quiz nights are on Wednesdays. ❀🕪👦♣🗓🚃(10,10A)🐾🛜

Lollards Pit ⑂

69-71 Riverside Road, NR1 1SR
☎ (01603) 624675 ⊕ lollardspit.com
Woodforde's Wherry; 5 changing beers (sourced nationally) ⊞
An attractive 17th-century inn, one of the first built outside the city walls, on the site of Lollards Pit, a place of execution for heretics for over 200 years. Guest ales are from local breweries, with interesting offerings from further afield. The pub is close to the river and yacht station moorings. It has a large patio garden at the rear, and a real fire, and hosts local community groups and weekly quiz and bingo nights. Closed Monday. 🌄❀👦🚲≈♣🗓🐾🛜

Malt & Mardle

163 Magdalen Street, NR3 1NF
⊕ maltandmardle.co.uk
3 changing beers (sourced locally) ⊞
Norwich's first micropub was converted from a shop in 2021 by three friends, who now run it. It seats 25 in a single room, and serves three ales and four keg beers. The ales are served on handpump inside the cooler on the right-hand side of the room, and there's a small bar at the front. 'Mardle' is a Norfolk word for a relaxed conversation! Closed Monday and Tuesday, and restricted hours when open. Q❀♣🗓🐾🛜

Marlborough Arms

43 Spencer Street, NR3 4PB
4 changing beers (sourced regionally; often Mr Winter's, Shortts) ⊞
The Marlborough is a large corner pub, built in the 1890s at the same time as the surrounding rows of terraced houses, and typical of its time. Inside there are two bars, with a pool table at the rear and a bar billiards table to one side. The walls are exposed brickwork decorated with signage from well-known and local businesses such as Colman's. Comfortable seating, including at the bar, a jukebox and sports on TV complement four real ales and a selection of real ciders. Opens 3pm Monday to Wednesday. 🌄❀🕪♣🗓🐾🛜🎵

Murderers

2-8 Timber Hill, NR1 3LB
☎ (01603) 621447 ⊕ themurderers.co.uk

Wolf Edith Cavell; 8 changing beers (sourced nationally) ⊞
A busy city-centre pub with a wide appeal. Up to 10 real ales are served, including two permanent beers, one of which is the house Murderer's Ale (brewed by Wolf). Beer festivals feature in summer and autumn, with over 50 beers available, including many from local brewers. The upper area has a large-screen TV and there is a bar available for private hire and an outside terrace. Traditional British food is served in generous portions. ❀🕪🏠🐾🛜

Plasterers Arms ⑂

43 Cowgate, NR3 1SZ
☎ (01603) 440992 ⊕ theplasterersarms.co.uk
Moon Gazer Pintail; 2 changing beers (sourced nationally; often Moon Gazer) ⊞
A friendly corner local with a range of cask, keg, bottled and canned beers from around the country. Its motto is 'Drink less, drink better' and prices are by the half-pint to encourage sampling a variety of beers rather than drinking quantity. It offers tap takeovers, sport (with a big screen for more important events), excellent pizzas and a Monday evening quiz. Opens 4pm Monday to Thursday. 🏠❀♣🏠🐾🛜🎵

Plough

58 St Benedict Street, NR2 4AR
☎ (01603) 661384 ⊕ linktr.ee/Ploughnorwich
5 changing beers (sourced nationally; often Grain) ⊞
A popular pub in one of the city's oldest areas. One of two Grain brewery-owned outlets, it sells five ales, usually all from the brewery. The two-bar interior is fairly small, with wooden chairs and tables, and has an open fire in winter. The large Mediterranean-style courtyard garden is a fine place to spend a summer's evening. Grain lager and craft beers are also served and there are barbecues in the summer. ❀♣🗓(30)🐾🛜

Ribs of Beef ⑂ ✔

24 Wensum Street, NR3 1HY
☎ (01603) 619517 ⊕ ribsofbeef.co.uk
Lacons Encore; Oakham Citra; Woodforde's Wherry; 4 changing beers (sourced nationally) ⊞
Relaxed and friendly traditional pub overlooking the River Wensum. The nine handpumps dispense three regular ales and a selection from quality microbreweries, with two ciders and a variety of craft beers on draught and in cans also available. Food is provided by a pop-up kitchen. There is a room downstairs, a small riverside balcony, several tables outside at the rear, and tables on the street at the front. There is a regular Monday quiz, live music most Sunday evenings (until it closed at 8pm) and live sport on TV. ❀🕪🗓🚃🐾🛜🎵

Rose Inn

235 Queens Road, NR1 3AE
☎ (01603) 623942 ⊕ therosepubanddeli.co.uk
4 changing beers (sourced nationally) ⊞
Popular pub, close to the football ground and city centre. The owner's passion for beer shows in the selection of four regularly changing real ales and six keg beers from some of the most exciting microbreweries around the country. Stone-baked pizzas plus savoury pastries and cheeseboards are available from the in-house deli. There is also a bar billiards table (and team), regular quizzes, DJ nights, and a monthly curry night. Closed Sunday and Monday. ❀🎁🕪👦🗓🅰♣🚃🐾🛜

Rosebery

94 Rosebery Road, NR3 3AB
⊕ theroseberypubnorwich.co.uk
6 changing beers (sourced regionally) ⊞

A popular Victorian corner pub with large windows and high ceilings, decorated in modern tones. Further seating is outside at the front and in a gravelled and part-covered beer garden at the rear. Up to six real ales are available, mostly sourced from local brewers, as well as occasional real ciders. Food is served daily and there is an excellent Sunday roast. The Tuesday quiz night is popular. B&B accommodation is available.
✿⌂◗&♣●P☐(21)✿☞

Trafford Arms 🅛 ✅
61 Grove Road, NR1 3RL
☎ (01603) 628466 ⊕ traffordarms.co.uk
Adnams Ghost Ship; Lacons Encore; 8 changing beers (sourced regionally; often Barsham, Mr Winter's, Woodforde's) 🄷
This friendly local has a strong community feel and is open all day, every day. The pub offers a changing guest beer list including beers from Lacons, Oakham and Moon-Gazer, and usually including a dark beer. The February Valentine's beer festival is a major attraction, as is the regular quiz on the last Sunday of the month. Regular pop-up food is available. The pub is popular when Norwich City are at home. Q⌕✿◗P☐(38,39)✿☞

Vine 🅛
7 Dove Street, NR2 1DE
☎ (01603) 627362 ⊕ vinethai.co.uk
Fat Cat Tom Cat; Oakham JHB; 2 changing beers (sourced regionally) 🄷
Just off the marketplace, this pub has been serving up to four quality ales, alongside traditional Thai cuisine in the upstairs restaurant, for over 15 years, although customers often eat downstairs in the bar area. Quiz nights are every first Thursday of the month. Two permanent ales and two guests from local providers are complemented by a good range of bottled cider, Belgian and world beers. Extra tables and chairs are set outside in the pedestrianised street. Closed Sunday. Q✿◗●✿

Warwick Arms
2 Warwick Street, NR2 3LD
☎ (01603) 627687 ⊕ warwickarmsnorwich.co.uk
4 changing beers (sourced nationally) 🄷
Large, prominently-situated pub with a relaxed vibe and comfortable seating. There is a large main bar, a smaller snug room to one side and a spacious event space upstairs that can be boked at no charge for all manner of get-togethers. Ales are sourced from across the country and draught lagers include favourites as well as interesting craft beers. Wine and selection of cocktails are also available, with pizza from a pop-up kitchen on Tuesday, Friday and Saturday evenings. ⌕✿◗&

Weavers Arms
2 Muspole Street, NR3 1DJ
☎ (01603) 952336 ⊕ theweaversarms.com
4 changing beers (sourced nationally) 🄷
Single-bar pub in the heart of 'Norwich-over-the-water', with a large gravelled terrace area with plenty of seating and views of St George's Church, which is pleasant in summer. A high-quality, extensive menu is served all day. Four ales from local breweries are always available. ✿◗✿☞

White Lion 🏆
73 Oak Street, NR3 3AQ
☎ (01603) 632333
7 changing beers (sourced nationally; often Bull of the Woods, Mr Winter's, Tindall) 🄷
Runner-up in the CAMRA National Cider Pub of the Year competition in 2023, with eight to ten real ciders and perries always available. A good changing range of real

ales come from local and select national breweries, often from Mr Winter's, Tindall's, Bull of the Woods and Nene Valley. Food is varied and excellent value, mainly using local produce. The traditional interior is split into three rooms at the front, rear and right, with a small enclosed garden with further seating to the side. Closed Monday; opens 5pm Tuesday. Q✿◗♣●☐✿☞

Wig & Pen 🅛
6 St Martin at Palace Plain, NR3 1RN
☎ (01603) 625891 ⊕ thewigandpen.com
5 changing beers (sourced locally) 🄷
Friendly and attractive 17th-century free house opposite the Bishop's Palace, with an impressive view of the cathedral spire. Five ales are always available, all from local breweries. Good-quality food is served lunchtimes and evenings. It is a short walk from Tombland, where there are bus stops for several bus routes, and is an ideal starting or stopping place for a walk along the river or in the Cathedral Close. Closed Monday and by 10pm latest. Q✿✿⌂&●✿☞

Roydon

Union Jack
30 Station Road, PE32 1AW (off A148)
☎ 07771 660439
Greene King Abbot; 3 changing beers (sourced nationally) 🄷
This traditional village pub has twice been local CAMRA Pub of the Year. The same landlord has been here since 2002. Four handpumps dispense one regular and three changing ales, and beer festivals are held over the Easter and August bank holidays, usually featuring local breweries. There are occasional food nights, live music each month, regular bingo and quizzes, and weekly support for darts, crib and dominoes. Outdoor seating is at the front. Q✿🅰♣●☐(48)✿☞

Shouldham

King's Arms 🅛
The Green, PE33 0BY
☎ (01366) 347410 ⊕ kingsarmsshouldham.co.uk
2 changing beers (sourced nationally) 🄶
West Norfolk's first community-owned pub and a repeat local CAMRA Pub of the Year. Beer is served in lined glasses straight from the cask and two or three choices are usually available. Cider is also often on offer. Many community activities take place, from poetry evenings and live music to quiz nights. There is a large child-friendly garden. ⌕✿◗●P☐✿☞

Snettisham

Queen Victoria ✅
19 Lynn Road, PE31 7LW (on B1440)
☎ (01485) 779961 ⊕ thequeenvictoriasnettisham.com
Greene King IPA; Sharp's Doom Bar; 1 changing beer (sourced nationally) 🄷
Located just a few miles from the Sandringham Estate, this dog-friendly pub is just a short distance from the Norfolk coast and the Snettisham RSPB Reserve. The updated interior has a traditional bar and separate dining area. All food is freshly prepared and sourced locally – the Sunday roast is particularly popular. Food service times are extended in the summer and there are regular live music sessions. Next to the extensive garden is a small Caravan Club certified site.
✿⌂◗&🅰P☐(34, 35, 36)✿☞♪

Southrepps

Vernon Arms ✓
2 Church Street, NR11 8NP (NE of Thorpe Market off A149 Cromer-North Walsham road)
☎ (01263) 833355 🌐 vernonarms.com
Adnams Southwold Bitter; Fat Cat Norwich Bitter; Greene King Abbot; 1 changing beer (sourced nationally) Ⓗ
A lively and welcoming village-centre local. The bar has a games area at one end and a winter log fire at the other. The front terrace includes a heated, covered, smoking area and there is a garden at the rear. There are three regular ales and a guest sourced from mainly national breweries. Three separate dining areas serving meals prepared with locally-sourced ingredients where possible – booking is advisable. Acoustic music sessions are held occasionally. Closed Monday. ❀◖ᐖᗱ♣Pᗇ(33)❀☂♪

Stoke Ferry

Blue Bell
Lynn Road, PE33 9SW
☎ (01366) 502204 🌐 bluebellstokeferry.org
Greene King IPA; 1 changing beer (sourced regionally) Ⓗ
The Blue Bell officially reopened in July 2022 after a campaign by the local community to resurrect the village's only pub. A deal to buy the pub was completed in 2021 after a major fundraising and share option campaign. Much of the renovation work was completed by locals. The campaign was awarded CAMRA's National Pub Saving Award. There is also a licensed café operating from 10-3 Wednesday to Saturday. ᗱ❀◖ᐖPᑎ☂

Strumpshaw

Shoulder of Mutton ᳐
9 Norwich Road, NR13 4NT (on Brundall-Lingwood road)
☎ (01603) 926530 🌐 themuttonstrumpshaw.co.uk
Adnams Southwold Bitter, Ghost Ship; Moon Gazer Hare Today; 3 changing beers (sourced nationally) Ⓗ
Traditional cosy Broadland village pub with a friendly welcome and a woodburning stove. Beers from Mr Winter's, Lacons and Tindall are regular guests, and three local ciders including Burnard's are also available. Food is served all day, and there is separate dining room with a heated marquee extension. Patios at the rear overlook the courtyard, which has a pétanque court. There is regular live music and events. Close to RSPB Buckenham and Strumpshaw Steam Museum. ❀◖ᐖᗱ(Lingwood) ♣♠Pᗇ(15A) ☂☎♪

Swanton Morley

Darbys
1 Elsing Road, NR20 4NY
☎ (01362) 637346 🌐 darbys-pub.co.uk
3 changing beers (sourced locally; often Lacons, Timothy Taylor) Ⓗ
This pub was originally a row of cottages which were converted to a public house around 30 years ago. There is one long bar plus a dining area and a function/dining room upstairs. Outside a covered patio area leads to a large garden with fully-enclosed children's play area. To the side is a large car park. Beers are mainly sourced locally, with three regularly changing offerings. A wood-fired pizza oven adds to the attractive food offering. Closed Monday. Q ᗱ❀◖ᐖᗱ♣♠Pᗇ(4)☂☎♪

Terrington St Clement

Wildfowler
28 Sutton Road, PE34 4PQ
☎ (01553) 828260
Greene King IPA, Abbot; 2 changing beers (sourced regionally) Ⓗ
This family-friendly pub sits in the heart of the village on the old A17. The large spacious bar has a dining area for those wishing to partake of the excellent cuisine, but there is still plenty of room for those just wishing to pop in for a drink. In addition to the two regular beers there are always two guest beers on offer from local breweries. Theme nights and musical entertainment are held on a regular basis. ᗱ❀◖ᐖPᗇ(505)☂☎♪

Thetford

Black Horse ᳐
64 Magdalen Street, IP24 2BP
☎ (01842) 762717
Greene King IPA; Nethergate Venture; 3 changing beers (sourced nationally) Ⓗ
A warm and friendly town pub offering a varying range of ales on five handpumps. Good-value and -quality home-made food is served in a small, pleasant eating area, with a covered pergola for outside dining. In the garden are several wooden huts that can be booked for special occasions. It stages a popular St George's Day beer festival. ❀◖ᐖP

Red Lion ᳐ ✓
Market Place, IP24 2AL
☎ (01842) 757210
Adnams Broadside; Greene King Abbot, IPA; 3 changing beers (sourced nationally) Ⓗ
On the market square, the Red Lion has had a varied history. It was opened by Lacons and the wall outside still retains its plaque, then it became a Portuguese restaurant, before becoming a Wetherspoon establishment. The decor features information about local history and attractions. There is often a dark ale on the bar. The pub has a variety of eating and drinking areas plus an outdoor space. ᗱ❀◖≠♠☂

Thornham

Lifeboat Inn ✓
Ship Lane, PE36 6LT (signed from A149 Coast Rd)
☎ (01485) 512236 🌐 lifeboatinnthornham.com
Greene King Abbot; Woodforde's Wherry; 3 changing beers (sourced nationally) Ⓗ
A busy pub just off the Norfolk Coastal Path on the edge of unspoilt expanses of salt marshes. There are timber beams, large fireplaces and plenty of nooks and crannies to explore with an enclosed garden at the rear. The interior has been tastefully renovated while retaining the atmosphere of the smugglers' inn it undoubtedly once was. Food is served throughout and there is also a large separate restaurant. A more recent addition is an outdoor restaurant, The Sail, for alfresco dining. Accommodation is available in 16 rooms. Q ᗱ❀⇴◖P☂☎

Thorpe Market

Gunton Arms ᳐ ✓
Cromer Road, NR11 8TZ (signposted on W of A149 Cromer-North Walsham road SE of Thorpe Market)
☎ (01263) 832010 🌐 theguntonarms.co.uk
Lacons Falcon Ale, Legacy; Woodforde's Wherry; 1 changing beer (sourced regionally) Ⓗ

A fine inn set in the grounds of Gunton Park with its deer herd. The decor is English country house. The bar includes pub games, and two other areas have log fires. There are three Norfolk ales, the guest may be national. First-class cuisine is provided in three restaurant areas; the vaulted Elk Room hosts dishes cooked on an open range (not Sun) and booking is advised. A large beer garden provides alfresco dining. Sixteen luxurious rooms, suites and a lodge complete this welcoming gem.
✿🏛◗❀ὐ占★≠(Gunton) ♣P🚃(4) ❀🌢 ❧

Suffield Arms

Station Road, NR11 8UE (signpost on main road S of Thorpe Market; head E on Station Rd)
☎ (01263) 586858 🌐 suffieldarms.com
Grain ThreeOneSix; Lacons Encore, Falcon Ale; Woodforde's Wherry; 1 changing beer (sourced locally) ⊞
A country pub with an outstanding wood-panelled interior. The large front bar has a log fire and traditional games. There are four regular ales and one guest plus a high-quality bar menu. Upstairs is a comfortable saloon bar serving cocktails, and an outside seating area overlooking the rear gardens. The stylish restaurant extension at the rear has a tapas bar and is popular for its fine Mediterranean cuisine. Gunton train station is opposite. Q✿◗ὐ占★≠(Gunton)♣P🌢 ❧

Thurne

Lion Inn ⎣

The Street, NR29 3AP (at the end of Thurne Dyke, off A149 via Mill Ln and Repps Rd)
☎ (01692) 671806 🌐 thelionatthurne.com
5 changing beers (sourced regionally; often Fat Cat, Humpty Dumpty, Pell & Co) Ⓖ
Large country pub in a remote village near the River Ant at the end of Thurne Dyke. Plenty of moorings are available nearby for passing broads cruisers with free daytime mooring. The pub has a large garden area with outside dining pods. Good value meals are available in the spacious restaurant or bar area. Up to five cask ales are on handpump including two under the Pell & Co badge brewed locally. Various craft cans along with 14 taps cater for craft ale fans. Q🐾✿◗ὐ占P🌢 ❧

Trunch

Trunch Social Club

18 Gimingham Road, NR28 0PS
☎ (01263) 720463
Greene King Abbot; Wolf Wolf Ale; 2 changing beers (sourced locally) ⊞
Friendly social club two miles from the coast, open from 5pm on weekdays, or lunchtime at the weekend. Three or four ales are available, and two beer festivals are held each year, usually on the end of May and August bank holidays. A guest day membership is available to non-members up to three times per year. There is plenty of outside space and parking. ✿P

Upton

White Horse ⎣

17 Chapel Road, NR13 6BT (about 10 mins walk from moorings at Upton Dyke)

☎ (01493) 750696 🌐 whitehorseupton.com
3 changing beers (sourced locally) ⊞
Traditional community-owned Broadland pub dating from 1798, a 10-minute walk from Upton Dyke Staithe and moorings. A community shop caters for locals and holidaymakers alike. Beers are usually from local breweries, and genuine pub food features strongly, with noted Sunday roasts, while fish & chip night is Friday. An annual beer, cider and perry festival takes place over the first full weekend in July when motorhomes are welcome to park on the car park. Closed Monday.
Q🐾✿◗ὐ占★♣P🌢 ❧ ♫

Warham All Saints

Three Horseshoes

69 The Street, NR23 1NL (2 miles SE of Wells)
☎ (01328) 710547 🌐 warhamhorseshoes.co.uk
2 changing beers (sourced locally) ⊞
A traditional brick and flint village pub with a unique serving hatch and log fires in winter. Meals are prepared with local ingredients where possible, pies being a speciality. Bottled and a draft cider is available. There is a separate dining room and a barn provides a games room, preserving the tranquillity of the pub itself. The large garden is perfect for alfresco dining, with a covered area and its own bar in summer. There are 10 excellent en-suite rooms. Q✿🏛◗ὐ占★P🌢 ❧

Wymondham

Feathers

13 Town Green, NR18 0PN
☎ (01953) 605675
Adnams Southwold Bitter, Ghost Ship; Fuller's London Pride; St Austell Tribute; 2 changing beers (sourced locally) ⊞
Local community free house run by the same family for many decades, a short walk from the Market Cross, Abbey and the Mid-Norfolk Railway terminus. It has an L-shaped interior with an open-plan main bar and seating. To the side are cosy alcoves and bar access. Good-value meals are served. The patio garden has a large covered seating area and serving hatch for garden customers. In winter months Adnams Tally Ho (on gravity) is available. Town Green car park (paying) is behind the pub. Closed Monday. Q🐾✿◗ὐ≠(Abbey)♣🚃🌢 ❧

Wymondham & District Ex-Services Club

9 Friars Croft, NR18 0AT
☎ (01953) 602261
Sharp's Doom Bar; 2 changing beers (sourced nationally; often Oakham) ⊞
Club with over 1,000 members, located in the centre of the town. Three real ales are always available and there's an annual beer festival. There's a dartboard, sports TV, pool table and separate function room, plus a beer garden. CAMRA members are admitted up to six times a year, and must sign in. Guests pay a small premium on prices, but even so these are comparable to local pub prices. 🐾✿占≠♣🚃🌢 ❧ ♫

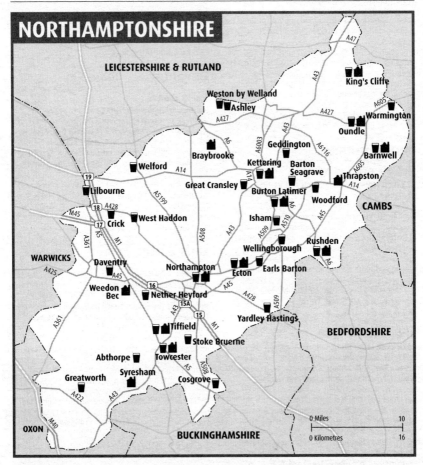

NORTHAMPTONSHIRE

Abthorpe

New Inn Ⓛ
Silver Street, NN12 8QR (off Main St, left at church)
☎ (01327) 857306 ⊕ newinnabthorpe.uk
Hook Norton Hooky, Off The Hook, Old Hooky; 1 changing beer (often Hook Norton) Ⓗ
A tranquil country hostelry tucked away, close to the village green and church. It is a quintessentially English village pub built of local mellow sandstone, complete with an inglenook fireplace with seating and low ceilings. It is welcoming to visitors and locals, and serves good food with meats sourced from the owner's farm, plus ales that are still brewed in the traditional way by Hook Norton whose seasonal beers feature as guests. Fresh fish from Billingsgate Market is a speciality.
🌂🕭🕪ⓓ♣ᴾ🌣☏♪

Ashley

George Ⓛ
21 Main Street, LE16 8HF (off B664)
☎ (01858) 565900 ⊕ thegeorgeatashley.com
St Austell Tribute; 2 changing beers (sourced locally; often Grainstore, Langton, Oakham) Ⓗ
Traditional, 17th-century ironstone village pub that was saved from being converted into houses. It stands proud above a patch of grass at the roadside. Inside has been opened out, although there are still two separate areas for dining and drinking. Good-quality home-cooked food

varies, with Tuesday night pie (winter) or fish & chips (summer), and Wednesday steak nights. The Coach House to the rear has been redecorated to a high standard and offers six individual rooms.
🌂🕭🕪ⓓ🕪ᴾ🌣☏

Barnwell

Montagu Arms Ⓛ
PE8 5PH
☎ (01832) 273726 ⊕ montaguarmsbarnwell.co.uk
Adnams Ghost Ship; Digfield Fools Nook, Barnwell Bitter; 1 changing beer (sourced locally) Ⓗ
Overlooking the local river and bridge, this 16th-century stone-built inn has a public bar at the front, large restaurant to the rear and a new drinking area to the side. There is a large play and camping area at the rear. The traditionally decorated bar area has original exposed ceiling and wall beams. Recent alterations have enlarged the bar area. There is disabled access from the rear to the restaurant. The car park is behind the inn and accessed via the village hall entrance. Q🕭🕪ⓓ🕪ᴾ🚌🌣

Barton Seagrave

Stirrup Cup Ⓛ ✅
Woodland Avenue, NN15 6QR (off A14 jct 10)
☎ (01536) 722841 ⊕ thestirrupcupbartonseagrave.co.uk

Adnams Southwold Bitter; Morland Old Speckled Hen; 2 changing beers (sourced locally; often Nene Valley, Potbelly) ⊞

A popular, welcoming community-focused estate pub featuring a sports bar with darts, pool and Northants skittles, along with large sports TVs. The coffee lounge offers breakfast, lunches and afternoon teas Monday to Friday. There is an emphasis on beer choice, with regular guests often from Potbelly. Regular events involve a quiz (Wed) and jazz (Thu) plus live bands once a month. Ideal for a break off the A14. ⵣ❀◑Ⴇ♣P🖵(16,48)❀🛜♪

Burton Latimer

Duke's Arms ᴸ ✓

123 High Street, NN15 5RL (off A14 jct 10)
☎ (01536) 390874
3 changing beers (sourced regionally; often Avalanche, Potbelly, Roman Way) ⊞

A community pub with four handpumps after many years of being keg only. It supports the local micros when pumps allow. The central U-shaped bar serves the opened-out rooms, which feature comfortable leather seating and more traditional seating in the small bay windows. The walls are adorned with vinyl LPs and there is a collection of books. No parking, but local amenity free car park is just across the road. ⵣ❀♣⬤🖵(X1,X4) ❀🛜

Olde Victoria ᴸ ✓

Bakehouse Lane, NN15 5NJ (off A6 at 2nd roundabout)
☎ (01536) 721286 ⊕ theoldevic.co.uk
Greene King IPA, Abbot; 2 changing beers (sourced regionally; often Greene King, Potbelly) ⊞

Originally called the Jockey and renamed 60 years ago, this stone-built pub has a small frontage with outdoor seating. The traditional, U-shaped bar has exposed beams, high chairs and seating to the left, with an interior stone-walled area to the right. There is a raised dining area to the rear. The car park opposite is council owned. It is the sister pub to the Old Cobbler in Northampton. ⵣ❀◑⬤P🖵(X1,X4)❀🛜♪

Cosgrove

Barley Mow ✓

7 The Stocks, MK19 7JD
☎ (01908) 562957 ⊕ thebarleymowcosgrove.co.uk
Everards Sunchaser, Tiger, Old Original; 1 changing beer (sourced regionally) ⊞

A beautiful countryside pub which backs onto the Grand Union Canal by Bridge 65. Located in a lovely 17th-century building, the main bar and adjoining segregated areas provide a charming environment, especially when the log fire is ablaze. Outside is a patio leading onto a lovely garden. The home-cooked food is suitable for all dietary requirements. Events are staged throughout the year, and may include murder mystery evenings and the monthly quiz. Q❀❀◑Ⴇ♣AP🖵(90,90A)❀🛜♪

Crick

Wheatsheaf ᴸ

15 Main Road, NN6 7TU (on main road through village)
☎ (01788) 823824 ⊕ wheatsheafcrick.com
4 changing beers (sourced nationally; often Oakham, Phipps NBC, Roman Way) ⊞

Village free house built out of local ironstone. To the front, a comfortable bar has tables and settees, while to the rear is a large restaurant catering for up to 80 diners. Food, much of it sourced locally, ranges from pub favourites to restaurant specials, with a variety of vegetarian options and regular theme nights. Breakfast is served 9-11am at weekends. Occasional live music is played. Good-value accommodation is available. Q❀🛏◑Ⴇ♣P🖵(96) ❀♪

Daventry

Early Doors ᴸ

3 Prince William Walk, NN11 4AB
☎ 07976 247312 ⊕ earlydoorsdaventry.com
House beer (by Potbelly); 4 changing beers (sourced locally; often Towcester Mill, Vale, XT) Ꮐ

The first Northamptonshire micropub is run by a father-and-daughter team who took over from the founders. Tucked away down a narrow alley, this is a warm and welcoming oasis in the heart of Daventry, with a real community feel. The bar is simply decorated and is made from reclaimed doors and weathered scaffolding planks. A good range of beers is always available, served straight from the barrel. QႶ⬤P🖵❀

Earls Barton

Saxon Tavern ᴸ

25B The Square, NN6 0NA
☎ 07956 462352
House beer (by Phipps NBC); 3 changing beers (sourced regionally; often Grainstore, Parkway, Tring) Ꮐ

A large, comfortable and relaxed single-roomed micropub with welcoming hosts. It stands in the centre of a village between the famous Barkers Shoes and Earls Barton's historic Saxon Tower, in premises that had previously been the local headquarters of the Magic Circle. Up to six casks with cooling jackets are stilled behind the bar. It has an extensive range of gins and rums, and box ciders from the fridge. Local CAMRA Rural Pub of the Season autumn 2023. Q❀♣⬤P🖵❀♪

Ecton

Three Horseshoes ♟ ᴸ

23 High Street, NN6 0QA (off A4500)
☎ (01604) 407446
Benjamin Franklin Dougal's Thumper; St Austell Proper Job; house beer (by Benjamin Franklin); 1 changing beer (sourced locally; often Oakham) ⊞

A whitewashed ironstone pub which has been extended over many years, although the original pub is said to date from 1757. The name is taken from the forge that was originally on the site and where Benjamin Franklin's uncle, Thomas, was the last of the family to work. The Franklin name is now being used for the brewery that

REAL ALE BREWERIES

Avalanche Burton Latimer
Benjamin Franklin 🍺 Ecton
Braybrooke Braybrooke (NEW)
Digfield Barnwell
Great Oakley Tiffield
King's Cliffe King's Cliffe
Maule Northampton
Nene Valley ✦ Oundle
Phipps NBC ✦ Northampton
Potbelly Kettering
Rockingham King's Cliffe
Roman Way ✦ Weedon Bec
Silverstone Syresham
Three Hills ✦ Thrapston
Towcester Mill ✦ Towcester
Weldon Rushden

was established three years ago in outbuildings. The traditional multi-room layout has been retained, with a separate bar and games area. Local CAMRA Pub of the Year 2024. ➷❀♣P☴❀☂♪

Geddington

Star Inn L
2 Bridge Street, NN14 1AD (from A43 turn onto West St and follow to village square)
☎ (01536) 745990 ⊕ thegeddingtonstar.co.uk
Greene King Abbot; 3 changing beers (sourced locally; often Digfield, Nene Valley) ⊞
Attractive 17th-century pub situated directly opposite what is considered to be the finest of the surviving Eleanor Crosses. The main entrance contains the former off-sales window, with doors leading to a traditional bar and lounge. A restaurant leads off the lounge bar, which has a further raised area towards the rear, next to the back entrance. Three guests beers are from local breweries. This great community pub serves good-quality food. ➷❀◑P☴(15)❀☂♪

Great Cransley

Three Cranes L
1 Loddington Road, NN14 1PY
☎ (01536) 790287
Phipps NBC Phipps IPA; 2 changing beers (sourced locally; often Phipps NBC, Timothy Taylor) ⊞
A village pub/restaurant constructed in the 17th century from local ironstone. Inside is a large open-plan room with an open fire at one end. The pub was refurbished in 2019 following a campaign fought by the locals. A two-roomed guest house is in the grounds along with a large beer garden and car park. Q➷❀◑&♣P❀☂♪

Greatworth

Greatworth Inn
Chapel Road, OX17 2DT (off B4525)
☎ (01295) 521426 ⊕ thegreatworthinn.co.uk
Fuller's London Pride; St Austell Tribute; Wadworth 6X; 1 changing beer (sourced regionally; often Dancing Duck) ⊞
A 16th-century stone-built pub in the centre of an attractive village. Following the return of its owners to the village, the pub has been returned to its former glory and is now a free house. Numerous improvements have been made, while still retaining the cosy and traditional atmosphere. The bar area features an inglenook fireplace and log-burning stove. There is also a dining area. A soapbox derby is held in June and a music/beer festival in August. An outside bar is open in the summer. ➷❀◑&♣P❀☂♪

Isham

Lilacs L
39 Church Street, NN14 1HD (off A509 at church)
☎ (01536) 722348 ⊕ thelilacsisham.co.uk
Greene King IPA; Hardys & Hansons Bitter; 2 changing beers (sourced locally; often Oakham, Potbelly, Roman Way) ⊞
A welcoming village pub owned by the community since 2019 and popular with locals, diners and drinkers. It has a small lounge – the former snug with a dartboard – and a large room at the rear, which is often set out for meals. Food is available lunch and evenings, and a carvery is provided on Sunday. Guest beers from local breweries feature. The pub name is derived from a local breed of rabbit. Q➷❀◑&♣P☴(X4)❀☂♪

Kettering

Alexandra Arms L
39 Victoria Street, NN16 0BU
☎ (01536) 522730
Hop Back Summer Lightning; Marston's 61 Deep; Wychwood Hobgoblin Gold; 11 changing beers (sourced nationally) ⊞
Traditional street-corner local in the town centre. The landlord searches out new beers all the time, served through 14 handpumps. There is always an interesting choice of beer from around the country, often including one from nearby Potbelly. Two opened-out rooms contain a settee and walls covered in breweriana and pumpclips. The rear bar has a TV and Northants skittles. A patio to the rear is a real suntrap. Q❀&♣●P❀☂

Earl of Dalkeith ⊘
13-15 Dalkeith Place, NN16 0BS
☎ (01536) 312589
Greene King Abbot; Ruddles Best Bitter; Sharp's Doom Bar; 2 changing beers (sourced nationally) ⊞
Formerly a furniture shop, this pub opened in 1996 and is named after the Earl of Dalkeith. It is on two levels downstairs, while an upstairs area has a gallery and is surrounded by bookcases. Historic photographs of local buildings adorn the walls. An adjacent yard has been turned into a pleasant drinking courtyard outside. Two beer festivals are held every year. Q➷❀◑&☴❀☂

Kettering Midland Band Social Club L
2 Hallwood Road, NN16 9RG
☎ (01536) 512929
Ruddles Best Bitter, County; Sharp's Doom Bar; house beer (by Potbelly); 5 changing beers (sourced regionally; often Titanic) ⊞
A popular club tucked away close to Rockingham Road Pleasure Park. In addition to the long public bar, it has a small, sunken lounge area, a separate games area, and a large concert room. The five guest ales are from established micros and will always contain a dark beer. Regular entertainment and trips are laid on. Local CAMRA Club of the Year 2023, and the bar manager won the Club Mirror Bar Manager of the Year Award. ➷❀◑&♣P☴❀☂♪

King's Cliffe

Cross Keys L
2 West Street, PE8 6XA
☎ (01780) 470030 ⊕ thecrosskeysinnkingscliffe.co.uk
Digfield Barnwell Bitter; house beer (by King's Cliffe); 1 changing beer (sourced locally; often Grainstore) ⊞
Independently owned, family-run free house in the heart of the village. The main bar has a TV, dartboard and jukebox, with photos of old King's Cliffe adorning the walls. There is also a small snug room at the front, with a bar, which is used as a dining room. At the rear is a lounge room with a rare Northants Hood skittles table, which leads into a large restaurant. All rooms have open fireplaces, two of which are stone inglenooks. Local CAMRA Gold Award winner in 2023. ❀≠◑♣●P❀☂

Lilbourne

Head of Steam L
10 Station Road, CV23 0SX (1 mile from A5; just off Rugby Rd)
☎ 07933 100850
Dow Bridge Ratae'd; St Austell Tribute; Wye Valley Butty Bach ⊞

Converted from a house in 2013, this railway-themed, thriving community free house regularly wins the local CAMRA Country Pub of the Year. Friendly conversation dominates in this welcoming pub, creating a comfortable atmosphere. The large garden, with its new barn, has an outside bar during the warmer months, making this a great summer venue. Sunday lunches are served, and there are steak and cheese nights once a month on a Thursday. Q ⚲ ❁ ◑ ⅃ 🕭 ♣ ● P ❀ 🛜 ♫

Nether Heyford

Foresters Arms 🗓

22 The Green, NN7 3LE
☎ (01327) 340729
2 changing beers (sourced locally; often Phipps NBC) 🖽

The father-and-daughter owners have made many improvements since buying this attractive ironstone pub in 2012, not least the introduction of their enlightened choice of two rotating beers, one of which is always sourced locally. Real cider is available on gravity dispense behind the bar. The pub remains the hub of village life, and though predominantly wet-led, simple bar meals and snacks are often available. On Thursday and Friday evenings pizza is sold from a van parked outside. ❁ ◑ ♣ ● P 🖳 (D3) ❀ 🛜 ♫

Northampton

Albion Brewery Bar 🗓

54 Kingswell Street, NN1 1PR
☎ (01604) 946606 ⊕ phipps-nbc.co.uk
Phipps NBC Diamond Ale, Red Star, Cobbler's Ale, India Pale Ale, Ratliffe's Celebrated Stout, Bison Brown; 1 changing beer (sourced locally) 🖽
Phipps NBC returned to its roots in 2014 to this Victorian brewery in the heart of Northampton. The brewery bar subsequently opened and features an added oak and glass partition between the bar and brewery, enabling the brewing process to be viewed. Almost all of the bar fittings are reclaimed, with many coming from closed Phipps pubs. Eight handpumps serve six ales from the brewery, plus a rotating guest. Q ⚲ ⅃ 🕭 & ≒ ♣ ● 🖳🚍 (7,X6) ❀ 🛜 ♫

Bold Dragoon 🗓 ✪

48 High Street Weston Favell, NN3 3JW (off A4500 at traffic lights)
☎ (01604) 401221
Adnams Ghost Ship; Fuller's London Pride; St Austell Proper Job; Timothy Taylor Landlord; Wychwood Hobgoblin Ruby; 2 changing beers (sourced locally; often Roman Way, Towcester Mill) 🖽
A popular, large village pub which has been completely refurbished. It has three distinct drinking areas: a front bar showing TV sports, a lounge bar in the middle has a real fire, and a new restaurant is at the rear. The pub always has at least six different real ales on, including LocAle. There is a wood-fired pizza oven in the garden is always on in the spring/summer months. ⚲ ❁ ◑ & ♣ ● P 🖳 (1,X46) ❀ 🛜 ♫

Cordwainer 🗓 ✪

The Ridings, NN1 2AQ (near jct with Fish St)
☎ (01604) 609000
Fuller's London Pride; Greene King Abbot; Phipps NBC Gold Star; Ruddles Best Bitter; Sharp's Doom Bar; 7 changing beers (sourced regionally; often Oakham) 🖽
Large, popular, town-centre Wetherspoon pub with two floors and a roof terrace with a ground floor garden area.

There is a large bar on each floor with two sets of handpumps. A wide choice of 12 real ales includes local and regional, as well as nationally sourced brews, with dark ales always available. Many pictures in the building depict the history of the town and local people of note. ⚲ ❁ ◑ & ● 🖳 🛜

Garibaldi Hotel 🗓

19 Bailiff Street, NN1 3DX (near police station on The Mounts)
☎ (01604) 622202
Roman Way Senate Gold; 2 changing beers (sourced locally; often Phipps NBC, Roman Way) 🖽
A popular local pub described as the best-back street boozer in town. The three-storey Victorian building may once have operated as a hotel, and the former two-roomed pub is now open plan with the bar at the centre. Three handpumps usually serve two ales from local breweries. The refurbishment work included adding a new kitchen, and there is a nice courtyard-style outdoor area which is busy in summer. ⚲ ❁ ◑ ♣ ● ❀ 🛜 ♫

Malt Shovel Tavern

121 Bridge Street, NN1 0QF
☎ (01604) 234212 ⊕ maltshoveltavern.com
Nethergate Melford Mild, Suffolk County Best Bitter; Oakham JHB; 4 changing beers (sourced regionally; often Nethergate, Purity, Roman Way) 🖽
The former NBC brewery tap is a popular, award-winning pub near the town centre, opposite the Carlsberg brewery. The pub serves real cider, local ales, and Belgian draught and bottled beers. At least one dark beer is always available. A fantastic exhibition of breweriana features everywhere inside the pub. Live blues bands play on the first Wednesday of every month. The pub has a strong rugby following. ⚲ ❁ & ≒ ♣ ● 🖳 (3,11) ❀ 🛜 ♫

Olde Cobbler 🗓

Acre Lane, NN2 8BN
☎ (01604) 844016 ⊕ oldecobbler.co.uk
Phipps NBC Phipps IPA; 4 changing beers (sourced locally; often Greene King, Phipps NBC, Potbelly) 🖽
A family pub and restaurant in the residential area of Kingsthorpe. It has three distinct areas – bar, restaurant and function room – alongside a good-sized garden which is an ideal space for families and friends to meet. There are always four ales available, with the emphasis on LocAle. A varied menu is available with pie night on Monday, steak night on Wednesday and breakfast at weekends. ⚲ ❁ ◑ & P 🖳 (14) ❀ 🛜 ♫

Olde England 🗓

199 Kettering Road, NN1 4BP (near racecourse)
☎ (01604) 619285
Potbelly Best, Hedonism, Olde England Black Prince; Wainwright Gold; 3 changing beers (sourced regionally; often Hop Back, Marston's, Phipps NBC) 🖽
Converted end-of-terrace Victorian building on three floors: the ground and first floors are medieval themed, with solid fuel burners, while the cellar has a contemporary style and is more intimate. There are usually seven beers served on handpump, four of them from local breweries, plus various ciders. Board games, cards and dominoes are provided, and there is live folk music on Thursdays. A former local CAMRA Cider Pub of the Year. Q ⚲ ♣ 🖳 (2,X10) ❀ 🛜 ♫

Road to Morocco 🗓

Bridgwater Drive, NN3 3AG (can be walked from Abington Park)
☎ (01604) 632899

Greene King IPA; Phipps NBC India Pale Ale; St Austell Tribute; Theakston Old Peculier; 1 changing beer (sourced nationally) ⊞

A popular 1960's brick-built estate pub with two connected but distinctly different rooms. The bar is quite lively with its pool table, darts and and sports TVs. The homely lounge is quieter, though it still has two large TV screens showing sports. Quiz nights are held every Tuesday. There are up to five handpumps serving real ale, one of which is usually saved for the popular Old Peculier. Local CAMRA Town Pub of the Year 2023. ⏩✿♿♣♠P🚋(5)✿🛜

Wheatsheaf

126 Dallington Road, NN5 7HN

☎ (01604) 240382 ⊕ wheatsheafdallington.co.uk

Everards Tiger; 2 changing beers ⊞

An attractive, thatched, two-roomed pub with an unspoilt frontage, tucked away in the conservation area of Dallington, opposite the 13th-century village church. The bar has a partly flagstoned floor. It hosts live music on Saturday nights and open mic alternate Sundays. The lounge/dining room is a large, quiet area with many photos of old Dallington on the walls. Up to three guest ales and two real ciders are available. ⏩✿◑♿♣♠P🚋(7)✿🛜♪

Oundle

Ship Inn Ⓛ

18 West Street, PE8 4EF

☎ (01832) 273918 ⊕ theshipinnoundle.co.uk

Brewster's Hophead; St Austell Tribute; 1 changing beer ⊞

This Grade II-listed, 16th-century building is welcoming and full of character, with low-beamed ceilings and a cosy, open fire. It is said to be haunted by a former landlord who met his demise by throwing himself out of a bedroom window. The pub consists of two bars, with many small rooms adjoining. Wednesday is steak night, with generous discounts applied. Accommodation can be found in two stone annexes and a small cottage to the rear. Q✿🛏◑♿♣♠P🚋(X4)✿🛜♪

Tap & Kitchen

Oundle Wharf, Station Road, PE8 4DE

☎ (01832) 275069 ⊕ tapandkitchen.com

Nene Valley Australian Pale, Release the Chimps, Egyptian Cream; 5 changing beers (sourced locally) ⊞

The main outlet for the Nene Valley brewery, this pub has spacious eating and drinking areas. Built in a revamped wharfside warehouse, the industrial revolution ethos has been retained, with chrome and wood, cogs and rails. An extensive menu of home-cooked and locally sourced food is available. There is a outdoor seating area and live music. Up to eight real ales from Nene Valley brewery are available, plus a selection of craft beers and ciders. ⏩◑♠P🚋✿🛜♪

Rushden

Rushden Historical Transport Society Ⓛ

Station Approach, NN10 0AW

☎ (01933) 213066 ⊕ rhts.co.uk

Phipps NBC India Pale Ale; 5 changing beers (sourced regionally; often Tring) ⊞

This award-winning club occupies the former Midland Railway station. The former ladies' waiting room is now the bar, with gas lighting and walls adorned with enamel advertising panels, railway photos and many CAMRA awards. The carriages on the platform provide a meeting room, Northants skittles, and a buffet for the numerous open days held during the year when steam and diesel train rides are provided. A beer festival is held in September. Q⏩✿♿♣♠P🚋✿🛜♪

Stoke Bruerne

Boat Inn ✅

Bridge Road, NN12 7SB

☎ (01604) 862428 ⊕ boatinn.co.uk

Banks's Amber Ale; Marston's 61 Deep, Old Empire; Ringwood Razorback; Wainwright Amber; 1 changing beer (sourced nationally; often St Austell) ⊞

Situated on the Grand Union Canal, the Boat Inn has been owned and operated by the Woodward family since 1877. Popular with walkers and boaters, the delightful tap bar's interconnecting rooms have canal views, open fires, original stone floors and window seats, while an adjoining room has Northants skittles. There is a lounge, restaurant and bistro. Additional beers are sold in the summer. A canal boat is available for hire to individuals and parties. Breakfast is served. ⏩✿◑♿♣P✿🛜♪

Tiffield

George at Tiffield Ⓛ

21 High Street North, NN12 8AD (in centre of village)

☎ (01327) 350587 ⊕ thegeorgeattiffield.co.uk

Great Oakley Wot's Occurring; 1 changing beer (sourced locally; often Great Oakley) ⊞

The brewery tap for Great Oakley is housed in this 16th-century building with Victorian additions. The welcoming bar has been opened up to include a cosy sitting area, while the back room hosts Northants skittles and darts. The large garden has gazebos with retractable awnings. The pub holds regular music events, quizzes and various village activities. The pub was recognised by CAMRA for its role in 'pub is the hub'. Q⏩✿◑♿♣♠P🚋✿🛜♪

Towcester

Towcester Mill Brewery Tap Ⓛ

Chantry Lane, NN12 6YY

☎ (01327) 437060 ⊕ towcestermillbrewery.co.uk

Towcester Mill Mill Race, Bell Ringer, Steam Ale, Black Fire; 2 changing beers (sourced regionally) ⊞

Popular and welcoming brewery tap in a Grade II-listed mill dating from 1794, straddling the old mill race, and adjacent to Bury Mount on which the town's fort once stood. The bar has been moved but retains many original features including beams, stonework, and a wooden floor, with a second room to cope with demand. Two upstairs rooms are also available. Outside is a large garden alongside the mill. Two guest ales and six ciders are available. Q⏩✿♿♣P🚋(87,X91)✿🛜♪

Warmington

Red Lion

Peterborough Road, PE8 6TN

☎ (01832) 280362 ⊕ theredlionwarmington.com

Dark Star Hophead; Timothy Taylor Landlord ⊞

Built of local stone around the turn of the 18th century, this popular, family-run village pub has a small, olde-worlde bar and an inglenook fireplace, with an adjacent restaurant. The bar serving area stretches across to a separate lounge dining room. Home-cooked food is available Wednesday to Sunday. The large beer garden has Roman-influenced seating. Guests are advised to book a table, especially on Sundays, as food is popular. Opening times and days may vary. Q✿◑P🚋(24,X4)✿

Welford

Wharf Inn ⓛ

NN6 6JQ (on A5199 by canal basin)
☎ (01858) 575075
Grainstore Ten Fifty; Marston's Pedigree; Oakham Bishops Farewell; 3 changing beers (sourced regionally) Ⓗ
Dating from 1814, this friendly pub stands at the end of the Welford arm of the Grand Union Canal. Inside, the main room is segregated by an open fireplace between the two rooms. A smaller snug is to the back of the bar. Good-value food is served. The guest beers are often sourced locally. Beer and cider festivals are held in June and over the August bank holiday. The pub is popular with walkers and a leaflet with suggested routes is available. Local CAMRA Rural Pub of the Year 2023.
Q❄❀⇄◑↹⚲P🚗(60) ❀ 🎵

Wellingborough

Coach & Horses ⓛ

17 Oxford Street, NN8 4HY (800yds from Market Square)
☎ (01933) 441848
⊕ thecoachandhorseswellingborough.co.uk
8 changing beers (sourced regionally; often Hop Back, Oakham, Salopian) Ⓗ
A regular CAMRA award-winner and long-standing Guide entry, this popular town-centre local serves a constantly changing choice of eight real ales and seven ciders. The central bar serves three drinking areas which are adorned with breweriana. Traditional home-cooked food is served (not Sun eve, Mon and Tue), with a wide choice of pies being a feature. It hosts regular live music and quiz nights. Q❄❀⇄◑↹♣⚲🚗❀ 🎵

Little R'Ale House ⓛ

Midland Road, NN8 1NQ (on station platform)
☎ 07366 996505 ⊕ thelittleralehouse-bar.business.site
5 changing beers (sourced locally; often Nene Valley, Potbelly) Ⓖ
A charming micropub on the station platform, occupying the former munitions building and filled with memorabilia. Five ales are served straight from the barrel, as well as 40 ciders and an interesting range of bottled beers and craft tins. The outside patio area allows outdoor summer drinking. The pub is dog friendly and popular with locals and commuters. Opening times may vary according to season. East Midlands Cider Pub of the Year 2024 runner-up, and local CAMRA Town Pub of the Season in autumn 2023. Q❄❀⇄☀⇄⚲P🚗❀ 🎵

Locomotive ★ ⓛ

Finedon Road, NN8 4AL
☎ (01933) 276600 ⊕ the-locomotive.edan.io
3 changing beers (sourced regionally; often Adnams, Phipps NBC)
This roadside pub is close to the railway on the outskirts of the town, not far from the site of the old locomotive sheds. A strong railway theme prevails with an extensive collection of railway memorabilia, a display of classic '00' gauge locomotives and a railway running above the servery. Consisting of three separate rooms, the front bar has comfortable seating while the rear games area features bar billiards, darts and Northants skittles.
❀♣P🚗(48) ❀ 🎵

West Haddon

Sheaf ⓛ

7 West End, NN6 7AY
☎ (01788) 511693 ⊕ thesheafinn.co.uk

Purity Pure Gold; 3 changing beers (sourced locally; often Church End, Digfield, Purity) Ⓗ
Reopened in 2018 following a lengthy closure and extensive refurbishment, this charming Grade II-listed building has an attractive, low-beamed bar with various nooks and crannies in which to enjoy a pint. There is also a pleasant garden and outside drinking area, and a separate dining area to the rear. Recently there has been a strong emphasis on beers sourced from independent microbreweries such as Purity, Church End, Digfield Roman Way, and Langton's. The pub has an excellent reputation for its food. ◑🍴(96)🎵

Weston by Welland

Wheel & Compass

Valley Road, LE16 8HZ (off B664)
☎ (01858) 565864 ⊕ thewheelandcompass.co.uk
Banks's Amber Ale; Greene King Abbot; Marston's Pedigree Ⓗ
A rural pub in the picturesque Welland Valley which has been refurbished by opening up the entrance lobby and incorporating part of the former dining area with flagstone floors, a wood burner, and sofas. An outside drinking area offers good views across the Welland Valley and is an ideal playground for children. This is an ideal stopping-off place for walkers of the Jurassic Way which runs close by. Good-value food is served, with lunchtime specials. ❄❀◑↹⚲P❀ 🎵

Woodford

Dukes ⓛ

83 High Street, NN14 4HE (off A510)
☎ (01832) 732224
Greene King Abbot; Sharp's Doom Bar; 4 changing beers (sourced nationally; often Digfield, Elgood's, Hop Back) Ⓗ
A popular, community-focused pub overlooking the village green, renamed in honour of the Duke of Wellington who was a frequent visitor to the area. Inside are multiple rooms, including a lounge restaurant and upstairs games room. Excellent, reasonably-priced home-cooked food is available. Regular music nights are held, along with a May bank holiday beer festival and August bank holiday music festival. Local CAMRA Rural Pub of the Year 2022. Q❄❀◑♣⚲P🚗(16X)❀ 🎵

Yardley Hastings

Rose & Crown ⓛ

4 Northampton Road, NN7 1EX
☎ (01604) 696276 ⊕ roseandcrownbistro.co.uk
Greene King IPA, Abbot; Phipps NBC Phipps IPA; 2 changing beers (sourced regionally; often Nene Valley) Ⓗ
An extensively refurbished, award-winning ironstone pub, with a single large room in olde-worlde style. It retains stone-flagged floors and beamed ceilings throughout, and has a small drinking area in the bay window. The emphasis is on traditional home cooking, with a daily changing menu and light meals served all day. Board games and monthly music events are held. The landscaped gardens are wonderful in summer. A previous Northamptonshire Food and Drink Award winner. Q❀◑↹♣P🚗(41)❀ 🎵

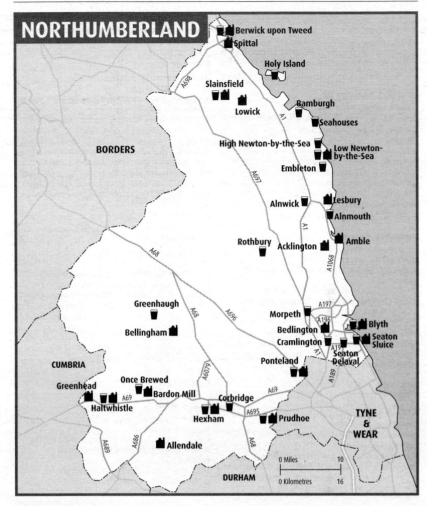

NORTHUMBERLAND

Berwick upon Tweed
Spittal
Holy Island
Slainsfield
Lowick
Bamburgh
Seahouses
High Newton-by-the-Sea
Low Newton-by-the-Sea
Embleton
Alnwick
Lesbury
Alnmouth
Rothbury
Acklington
Amble

BORDERS

Greenhaugh
Bellingham

Morpeth
Bedlington
Cramlington
Blyth
Seaton Sluice
Ponteland
Seaton Delaval

CUMBRIA

Greenhead
Once Brewed
Bardon Mill
Corbridge
Haltwhistle
Hexham
Prudhoe

TYNE & WEAR

Allendale

DURHAM

0 Miles 10
0 Kilometres 16

Alnmouth

Red Lion Inn ★ 🅛 ✅
22 Northumberland Street, NE66 2RJ
☎ (01665) 830584 🌐 redlionalnmouth.com
2 changing beers (sourced regionally) Ⓗ
Charming, family-run, 18th-century coaching inn with a cosy lounge bar featuring attractive woodwork. The decked area at the bottom of the garden enjoys panoramic views across the Aln Estuary. Occasional live music plays in the open air in summer. Guest beers usually include one local ale and two interesting brews from further afield. An annual beer festival is held in October. It opens early for breakfast. Excellent en-suite accommodation in seven rooms is available.
Q ☆ ⊛ ⇦ ◑ 🅟 🚍 (X18) ❁ 🗇

Alnwick

Ale Gate 🅛
25 Bondgate Without, NE66 1PR
☎ 07979 101332
6 changing beers (sourced locally) Ⓗ
Sited in a former shop unit, latterly an insurance office, Alnwick's first micropub opened in 2019. It has a single main room to the front and a raised area to the rear. Six

handpumps on the traditionally styled, dark, wooden bar offer a regularly changing range of beers from local breweries and those further afield. 🚍 ❁

Black Swan Pub & Kitchen
26 Narrowgate, NE66 1JG
☎ (01665) 798228
3 changing beers (sourced regionally) Ⓗ
A long, thin pub in three parts: the comfortable front area is for dining; the bar is on a raised area, with a TV screen, mirrors and two gaming machines; this leads to mezzanine seating, then into a sunken area with a very large TV screen, which in turn leads through to an outdoor patio. The origin of the pub is unknown, but it is claimed that Robert Burns slept here. The pub was reopened under new ownership in 2022 after refurbishment. Card payment only. 🏠 ◑ 🚍 ❁ ♪

Harry's Bar
20 Narrowgate, NE66 1JG
☎ 07821 505028
Timothy Taylor Landlord; 3 changing beers (sourced regionally) Ⓗ
Located on historic Narrowgate, in the heart of Alnwick, this vibrant micropub opened in 2021 following conversion from a former haberdashery shop. The door

opens into a cosy main bar with stone-flagged flooring and ample seating. There is also window seating where you can gaze at passers-by as you enjoy one of the four real ales on offer from the small corner servery. There is another small seating area down steps at the rear of the premises. ♿

Market Tavern ✔
7 Fenkle Street, NE66 1HW
☎ (01665) 602759 ● alnwickpub.co.uk
2 changing beers (sourced nationally; often Alnwick) Ⓗ

Welcoming, family-run pub near the market place, with a bare brick- and stone-style public bar, and a separate restaurant. It was recently, and tastefully, refurbished, and is handy for the bus station and Alnwick Castle. Note that opening hours and availability of food may vary. Dogs are welcome. It has en-suite accommodation.
&⊛⇦◑♿♣🖵❀📶♪

Tanners Arms 🅛
2-4 Hotspur Place, NE66 1QF
☎ (01665) 601628
Tempest Armadillo; 5 changing beers (sourced nationally) Ⓗ

Ivy-covered stone-built pub just off Bondgate, a short distance from Alnwick Garden. The rustic single room has a flagstone floor and a unique tree beer shelf. A large fireplace provides added warmth in winter. Acoustic music nights feature regularly, with open mic on the last Friday of the month. The varied real ales frequently come from North East and Scottish Borders microbreweries.
&♿♣🖵❀📶♪

Bamburgh

Castle Inn
Front Street, NE69 7BW
☎ (01668) 214616 ● castleinnbamburgh.co.uk
Born Blonde, Amber Ⓗ

Pub with a U-shaped bar with wood panelling throughout and adorned with old photos, including some of the fishing trade. Note the cornices on the left-hand side. There are two fires; the one to the right is a traditional-style range. An extension to the back provides an airy restaurant, through which a large terrace and garden can be found. &⊛◑🖵(418,X18)❀📶

Berwick upon Tweed

Atelier 🅛
41-43 Bridge Street, TD15 1ES
☎ (01289) 298180
3 changing beers (sourced regionally; often Hadrian Border) Ⓗ

A welcoming café bar with a shabby-chic interior. Three real ales are available, usually from Hadrian Border or other local breweries, and also kegged craft beers. The food on offer is all locally sourced and a real highlight. The specialities are hot shortcrust pies (with a variety of exciting fillings) and an excellent, locally sourced meat and cheese platter. &⇌(Berwick-upon-Tweed)🖵❀📶

Curfew 🅛
46A Bridge Street, TD15 1AQ
☎ 07842 912268
4 changing beers (sourced nationally) Ⓗ

Berwick's first micropub is located up a small lane which opens out into a large courtyard off Bridge Street. It has a small bar area, with a bottle fridge to one side, offering interesting local keg beers and bottled foreign beers. The courtyard makes a pleasant outdoor drinking area in

summer. Excellent pork pies are available. A regular CAMRA award winner. Q&⊛⇌(Berwick-upon-Tweed)♣●❀

Pilot ★ 🅛
31 Low Greens, TD15 1LZ
☎ (01289) 304214
3 changing beers (sourced nationally; often Hadrian Border, Firebrick) Ⓗ

This friendly and welcoming, 19th-century, stone-built pub is a real gem and popular with locals and train travellers. It has been recognised by CAMRA as having a regionally important historic pub interior. It has retained its original small room layout and boasts several nautical artefacts over 100 years old. The pub has a darts team and hosts music nights. Check Tuesday opening hours in winter. &⊛⇦♿⇌(Berwick-upon-Tweed)♣❀

Blyth

Lounge
5-7 Simpson Street, NE24 1AX
☎ 07732 533976
House beer (by Metalhead); 4 changing beers (sourced locally; often Metalhead) Ⓗ

Friendly and welcoming micropub in the centre of Blyth. The tap for the Metalhead brewery, it offers a range of over 20 ciders. There is live music in the small, L-shaped bar once a month on Sunday afternoons. Toasted sandwiches and snacks are available. It is handily placed for bus services into Blyth town centre as it is a five-minute walk from the station. Q🖵❀♪

Corbridge

Black Bull 🅛
Middle Street, NE45 5AT
☎ (01434) 632261
Hadrian Border Tyneside Blonde; house beer (by Greene King); 4 changing beers (sourced nationally) Ⓗ

Traditional, stone-built pub in the heart of a town with strong links to the Romans. It retains several original features, and has a separate dining area. The pub has been under new management since 2022 and now has more focus on cask beers. Breakfast is served at the weekend. The town is well served by good transport links to Hadrian's Wall and Tyne Valley Railway. Q&◑⇌P🖵(685,684)❀

REAL ALE BREWERIES

Allendale 🡒 Allendale
Alnwick 🡒 Lesbury
Backlash Prudhoe
Bear Claw 🡒 Spittal
Brewis 🡒 Amble
Chasing Everest Blyth (brewing suspended)
Cheviot 🡒 Slainsfield
First & Last 🡒 Bellingham
Flying Gang 🡒 Ponteland
Grounding Angels Hexham (brewing suspended)
Hetton Law Lowick (brewing suspended)
Hexhamshire Hexham
King Aelle 🍺 Seaton Sluice (brewing suspended)
Metalhead Bedlington
Monkey House 🡒 Berwick upon Tweed
Muckle Haltwhistle
Rigg & Furrow 🡒 Acklington
Ship Inn 🍺 Low Newton-by-the-Sea
Twice Brewed 🍺 🡒 Bardon Mill
Wrytree Greenhead

Pele Corbridge

Market Place, NE45 5AW

☎ (01434) 632905 ⊕ thepele.co.uk

2 changing beers (sourced locally; often First & Last, Allendale) Ⓗ

Standing next to Corbridge Parish Church, this privately owned and run micropub occupies the old Pele Tower, built in 1300 for the Vicar of Corbridge. It is spread over the ground and first-floor levels, and also has a balcony in the roof space. The newly relocated bar has two handpumps dispensing local beers, often from First & Last brewery. Bottles from Allendale, including the house Pele Ale, and First & Last brewery, are available. Card payment only. ❀✿◆☐♣

Wheatsheaf Hotel Ⓛ

St Helens Street, NE45 5HE

☎ 07519 202542

Timothy Taylor Landlord Ⓗ

Reopened in 2018 after an extended closure and comprehensive refurbishment, this imposing, Grade II-listed, stone-built pub stands near the centre of Corbridge, at the heart of Hadrian's Wall country. A Roman statue is housed on the exterior of the barn. There is a small bar area to the left of the door where the two handpumps are sited. To the right is an informal seating area with a large restaurant to the rear.
ॐ❀✿◑₾♣♠P☐♣◆♥

Cramlington

Plough Ⓛ

Middle Farm Buildings, NE23 1DN

☎ (01670) 737633

Cullercoats Shuggy Boat Blonde; Anarchy Blonde Star; 5 changing beers (sourced nationally) Ⓗ

Converted farm buildings in the old village make up this Sir John Fitzgerald outlet, which is arranged in the style of a traditional pub with separate bar and lounge areas. There is a function room upstairs, where children are always welcome; under-18s are only permitted in the bar areas during the daytime. An excellent range of local micros are on continual rotation, in addition to the local core range, with a commitment to bringing in the best ales from across the UK. Q ॐ❀♠P☐♣♥ ♪

Embleton

Greys Inn Ⓛ

Stanley Terrace, NE66 3UZ

☎ (01665) 576983

5 changing beers (sourced locally; often Alnwick) Ⓗ

Pleasant, traditional inn in a lovely seaside hamlet, just a short walk from some of the best beaches in the country, and Dunstanburgh Castle across the bay. It has three open fires, and is home to a ladies' darts team, clay pigeon club and golf club. Note the rare McLennan & Urquhart's Edinburgh Ales mirror on the chimney breast. Winter hours may vary. ॐ❀◑♣☐♥(418,X18)♣♪

Greenhaugh

Holly Bush Inn Ⓛ ✓

NE48 1PW

☎ (01434) 240391 ⊕ hollybushinn.net

Hadrian Border Grainger Ale; Twice Brewed Sycamore Gap; 3 changing beers (sourced locally; often Hexhamshire) Ⓗ

Independently owned pub, over 300 years old and set in the heart of the Northumberland National Park and the Dark Sky Park, making it ideal for those with an interest in real ale and real stars. No TV and no mobile reception

make for a peaceful drinking experience. The pub hosts informal jam sessions – bring your instrument if you like. A 10% happy hour discount applies Monday to Thursday 4-6pm. Q ॐ❀✿₾♣P☐♥ ♥

Haltwhistle

Black Bull ✓

Black Bull Lane, Market Square, NE49 0BL

☎ (01434) 320463 ⊕ theblackbullhaltwhistle.co.uk

Allendale Golden Plover; 3 changing beers (sourced nationally) Ⓗ

A warm and friendly two-roomed pub close to Hadrian's Wall, popular with locals and ramblers. Six handpulls adorn the wooden bar. An open fire, with a low-beamed timber ceiling and horse brasses add to the traditional ambience. It is located down a cobbled lane, just off the Market Place in the centre of the town. Check winter hours; meal times can vary too. It hosts regular themed nights. Q ॐ❀✿◑₾≩☐♥

Haltwhistle Comrades Club Ⓛ

2 Central Place, NE49 0DF

☎ (01434) 320666

3 changing beers (sourced nationally) Ⓗ

Traditional private club at the top of the main street, with comfortable surroundings. Card-carrying CAMRA members are welcome. It hosts leek-growing, pigeon, wildlife, gardening and angling clubs, and is also popular with visitors to the nearby Hadrian's Wall heritage site. The club hosts an egg-jarping competition every Easter Sunday, which CAMRA members replicate on trips. The bar features several photographs of yesteryear, including military and sport themes. ॐ♣≩♠☐♥

Manor House Inn

Main Street, NE49 0BS

☎ (01434) 322588 ⊕ manorhousehaltwhistle.com

Allendale Golden Plover; 3 changing beers (sourced nationally) Ⓗ

A large, stone-built hotel on the main street in the centre of Haltwhistle, just two miles south of Hadrian's Wall. An L-shaped bar is to the left, and a dining room to the right of the main entrance. A large patio garden is to the rear. Fewer beers may be offered in winter.
ॐ❀✿₾◑≩♠☐♥ ♥

Hexham

County Hotel Ⓛ ✓

Priestpopple, NE46 1PS

☎ (01434) 608444 ⊕ countyhotelhexham.co.uk

Hadrian Border Tyneside Blonde; Timothy Taylor Landlord; 1 changing beer (sourced nationally) Ⓗ

The plush public bar of the modernised County Hotel has replaced the former, and much smaller, Argyles Bar, which was down a side street. The bright and comfortable bar has several distinct areas. Beers are served are from local and regional brewers. It is popular for food and has an extensive and varied menu supplemented with specials. Handy for the bus station.
ॐ₾◑♣≩☐♥ ♥

Dipton Mill Inn Ⓛ

Dipton Mill Road, NE46 1YA (take B6306 Eastgate out of Hexham and fork right towards Whitley Chapel)

☎ (01434) 606577 ⊕ diptonmill.co.uk

Hexhamshire Devil's Elbow, Shire Bitter, Blackhall English Stout, Devil's Water, Whapweasel, Old Humbug Ⓗ

The tap for Hexhamshire brewery, which is now located in the beer garden, is run by real ale enthusiasts who brew their own excellent beers. Blackhall English Stout has proved so popular with drinkers that it has ousted Guinness. To complement the ales there is great home-cooked food – Saturday is curry night. A cosy atmosphere and warm welcome make this pub well worth seeking out. A former local CAMRA Pub of the Year. Q❀◐P

Heart of Northumberland ⓛ

5 Market Street, NE46 3NS
☎ (01434) 608013 ⊕ thehearthexham.com
Timothy Taylor Landlord; 4 changing beers (sourced locally) ⊞

Five handpumps, four selling local ales including Allendale and Wylam, adorn the bar in this independent free house, just off the Market Square. It has wooden floors throughout the single large room, which is almost divided in two near the end of the bar. A huge open fireplace warms things nicely in the back room. It serves excellent food using local produce. Dogs are welcome.
🍽❀◐🗟♣🚌🅿♫

Platform Bar ⓛ

Platform 2 Hexham Railway Station, Station Road, NE46 1EZ
☎ 07909 046698
3 changing beers (sourced locally) ⊞

This single-room micropub was opened in 2019 in the former waiting room on the westbound platform of Hexham station. It has perimeter seating round three walls, with free-standing tables, and railway memorabilia adorning the walls. Teas, coffees and light snacks are available from breakfast time. The pub may stay open later than advertised, if busy. Note that the toilets are at the other end of the platform.
Q🗟🚌(684,AD122) 🛜

High Newton-by-the-Sea

Joiners Arms ⓛ

Town Square, NE66 3EA
☎ (0191) 833 7409 ⊕ Joiners-arms.com
4 changing beers (sourced locally; often Alnwick, Anarchy) ⊞

This 18th-century former manor house is now a tastefully restored and refurbished gastropub after being closed for two years. Set in a pleasant hamlet on the B1340, the pub has outdoor seating overlooking the small, picturesque green. The house ale, St Mary's, is named after the local church and for every pint sold a donation is made towards its upkeep. The pub also offers a takeaway menu. Five en-suite bedrooms are fitted out to a high standard. 🍽❀🛏◐♿🅿🚌(418)❀

Holy Island

Crown & Anchor Hotel ⓛ

Market Place, TD15 2RX (check tide table for causeway crossing times)
☎ (01289) 389215 ⊕ holyislandcrown.co.uk
3 changing beers (sourced locally; often Cheviot, Rigg & Furrow) ⊞

Exposed floorboards and wooden tables and benches provide comfortable seating in the cosy bar – note the Gothic carving of a local monk in the corner. There is a comfortable sitting room to the rear. The large beer garden provides scenic views to Lindisfarne Castle and the ruined priory to the rear of the pub. Beers are mainly from local breweries. ❀🛏◐🚌(477)❀🛜

Ship Inn ⓛ

Marygate, TD15 2SJ (check tide table before crossing causeway)

☎ (01289) 389311 ⊕ theshipinn-holyisland.co.uk
House beer (by Hadrian Border); 2 changing beers (sourced nationally) ⊞

The Ship Inn lives up to its name, with wood-panelled walls adorned with artefacts of life at sea in days of yore. In addition, various photographs and paintings portray a history of island life past and present. The house beer is brewed by Hadrian Border. Food is served, and there is accommodation in four en-suite bedrooms.
❀🛏◐🚌(477)❀

Low Newton-by-the-Sea

Ship Inn ⓛ

Newton Square, NE66 3EL
☎ (01665) 576262 ⊕ shipinnnewton.co.uk
Ship Inn Sea Coal, Sea Wheat; 4 changing beers (sourced locally; often Hadrian Border) ⊞

This small pub nestles in the corner of three sides of a square of former fishermen's cottages around a green, a few yards from the beach and close to a nature reserve. It attracts drinkers seeking ales from the in-house microbrewery, diners enjoying an excellent menu featuring fresh local ingredients, and walkers exploring the local scenery. A public car park is close by at the top of the hill. Opening times may vary in winter; phone ahead if travelling. Q🍽❀◐❀♫

Morpeth

Joiners Arms ⓛ

3 Wansbeck Street, NE61 1XZ
☎ (01670) 511457
Black Sheep Best Bitter; Draught Bass; 2 changing beers (sourced nationally; often Anarchy) ⊞

This unusual former Sir John Fitzgerald outlet is located just over the footbridge from the town centre. There is a roomy public bar to the front, and a large, comfortable, family-friendly lounge to the rear, with a view of the river and access to the delightful, planter-decorated beer terrace overlooking the weir. Beer selection includes beers from local and regional brewers. Dogs are welcome in the bar. ❀🗟🐾❀

Office ⓛ

Chantry Place, NE61 1PJ
☎ 07957 721066
Rigg & Furrow Run Hop Run; 5 changing beers (sourced locally) ⊞

The Office is a micropub that has no music or games machines. It features eight handpumps and three craft keg beers, all of local origin, and three real ciders served on gravity from the glass-fronted fridge opposite the bar. No food is served. Dogs are welcome. Local CAMRA Pub of the Year 2022. Q🗟♣🚌❀

Pleased to Meet You ⓛ

Bridge Street, NE61 1NB
☎ (01670) 333970
House beer (by Almasty); 3 changing beers (sourced nationally) ⊞

Reopened in late 2021 after a lengthy closure and extensive redevelopment. The layout offers several discrete drinking areas on various levels, with the bar towards the rear. The walls have been taken back to bare brick and the various areas tastefully furnished. Work continues on the hotel accommodation. It also incorporates Emily's tearoom (named after famous suffragette, Emily Davison) which is open from 8am.
◐🗟🚌❀

Tap & Spile L

23 Manchester Street, NE61 1BH

☎ (01670) 513894

Greene King Abbot; Hadrian Border Tyneside Blonde; Timothy Taylor Landlord; 5 changing beers (sourced nationally) ⊞

All are welcome at this popular locals' pub near the town's bus station. Seven handpulls offer a good choice of ales, with local brews from Northumbrian breweries often available. The bar area at the front of the building is usually busy, though there is a cosy lounge to the rear, which is accessible from either side of the room. A traditional folk group plays on Sunday lunchtimes. Q🕮◖♣🖵😊��

Once Brewed

Twice Brewed Inn L ✓

Miltary Road, Bardon Mill, NE47 7AN

☎ (01434) 344534 ⊕ twicebrewedinn.co.uk

6 changing beers (sourced locally; often Twice Brewed) ⊞

An excellent remote inn on the Military Road, with Hadrian's Wall, Steel Rigg and Vindolanda nearby, attracting walkers and tourists. It has a fully refurbished bar area and offers a wide range of bottled beers from around the world. It has full wheelchair access and welcomes dogs. Accommodation is offered in 18 en-suite bedrooms. The Twice Brewed Brew House started producing its own beers in 2017, using water from its own well. Q🕮😊🛏◖🕭♣AP🖵😊🞜

Ponteland

Pont Tap L

10 West Road, NE20 9SU

☎ 07446 098501

4 changing beers (sourced nationally) ⊞

The Pont Tap opened in 2020 in what was previously an interior design shop. It servea a good range of mostly local cask and craft keg, beers together with wine and spirits. The friendly welcome and comfortable surroundings make this a must visit if you're in the area. Monthly quiz and music nights are held. Dogs are welcome. Q🖵

Prudhoe

Wor Local L

Front Street, NE42 5HJ

☎ 07447 702265

4 changing beers (sourced nationally) ⊞

Located on Prudhoe's Front Street, Wor Local (or Our Local if you're not a Geordie) is a micropub with room for around 40 customers. The layout of the bar, with its comfy seats and carpet, encourages conversation. There are lots of traditional pub and board games for customers' use. Three beers are offered from the North East and Cumbria, in a variety of styles, and real ciders are always available. Snacks include pork pies, cheese, crisps and nuts. ●🖵😊

Rothbury

Narrow Nick L

High Street, NE65 7TB

☎ 07707 703182

4 changing beers (sourced locally) ⊞

Opened in 2016, this micropub was previously a clothes shop. The front windows feature Art Deco-style stained glass. The single room has the bar at one side sporting six

handpumps that offer a range of local brewery beers. A large range of gins is also stocked. Wooden bar-back fittings have recently been added. Winter opening times may vary. Q🖵😊

Seahouses

Olde Ship Inn ★ L

7-9 Main Street, NE68 7RD

☎ (01665) 720200 ⊕ theoldeship.co.uk

Black Sheep Best Bitter; Hadrian Border Farne Island Pale Ale; Ruddles County; Theakston Best Bitter; 4 changing beers (sourced locally) ⊞

This former farmhouse, built in 1745, was converted to the licensed trade in 1812 and has been identified by CAMRA as having a regionally important historic pub interior. The pub has three quality bars adorned with a veritable treasure trove of 19th- and 20th-century maritime memorabilia. It offers an interesting menu of fish, seafood and snacks. A great base for exploring the beautiful Northumberland coast. Q🕮😊🍴◖🕭&♣P🖵(418,X18)

Seaton Delaval

Crafty Lodge L

30 Astley Road, NE25 0DG

☎ 07811 108362

3 changing beers (sourced nationally; often Almasty, Two by Two) ⊞

Located just north of the roundabout in the centre of the village, this micropub, converted from a former shop, recently reopened with a change of name. The small bar has four handpumps serving local and regional beers. There is also a large range of bottled beers and cider. Dogs are welcome. Q&♣🖵

Seaton Sluice

Melton Constable ✓

Beresford Road, NE26 4QL

☎ (0191) 237 7741 ⊕ themeltonconstable.co.uk

Adnams Southwold Bitter, Broadside; Ossett Yorkshire Blonde; 2 changing beers (sourced nationally) ⊞

Large roadside pub a few minutes walk from the beach and local history sights. It is named after the southern seat of Lord Hastings, a member of the Delaval family – Delaval Hall is close by. Tuesday is steak night, Wednesday is quiz night, and Sunday evening features live music. A fishing club meets here late at night, and the BSA owners' club gets together on the first and third Thursdays of the month. 🕮😊◖&P🖵😊🞜♫

Slainsfield

Cheviot Tap L

TD12 4TP (turn right opp small bus stop just before Etal, signposted faintly for Letham Hill and Slainsfield)

NT948393 ⊕ cheviotbrewery.co.uk

4 changing beers (sourced locally; often Cheviot) ⊞

Set on the Ford and Etal estate, the Cheviot brewery tap opened in 2021. It was converted from former hunting hound kennels, with the addition of rustic wooden gazebos and cask stools, and plenty of wooden panelling. Glamping and camping are available on-site, with a small shop open to residents. Brewery tours (charged for) are available. Designated drivers are welcome to free tea and coffee while onsite. 🕮😊Å♣P😊

NOTTINGHAMSHIRE

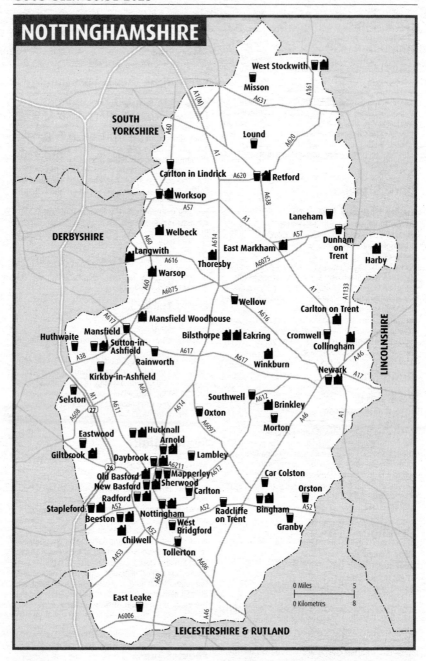

Arnold

Robin Hood & Little John 🅛

1 Church Street, NG5 8FD (on corner of Cross St)
☎ (0115) 920 1054 ⊕ lincolngreenbrewing.co.uk
Lincoln Green Archer, Hood, Tuck; 16 changing beers 🅷

Former Home Brewery pub, now operated by Lincoln Green under the Everards Project William scheme. The bar features Home Ales memorabilia, while the lounge has details of the pub's history and the local area, along with a piano. A new snug is near the rear courtyard, with outdoor seating, a raised sun terrace, and a covered skittle alley. Along with the 10 real ale pumps in each bar showcasing Lincoln Green beers, guests from microbreweries also feature, alongside real ciders.
🅂🅰🅱♣🛏🖼♿🛜♪

Beeston

Crown Inn ★ 🅛

Church Street, NG9 1FY
☎ (0115) 967 8623

Blue Monkey BG Sips; Brewster's Hophead; Dancing Duck 22; Everards Tiger; 7 changing beers ⊞

A 19th-century Grade II-listed alehouse refurbished by Everards. It offers 11 cask ales, nine craft beers and six real ciders. Five distinct drinking areas include a snug and a three-seat 'confessional', once used as a hideaway by the local vicar! Although busy, the pub retains its community feel, with a cosy atmosphere throughout. Regular events are held in the beer garden and an outside bar offers further cask ales and craft beers during the summer. Traditional pub snacks, cobs, Scotch eggs, pork pies and cheeseboards are available every day. Q►ở☺ở&⧆♠(Beeston Centre) ♣●P➡☺ᯤ♪

Pottle ℒ

1 Stoney Street, NG9 2LA
6 changing beers (sourced nationally) Ⓖ

A friendly little micropub devoted to real ale and ciders. Five or six rotating beers are served by gravity from a small, temperature-controlled room to the rear. Two craft keg dispensers and four traditional ciders are also available. Tables and chairs offer seating on both sides of the room and there is also seating outside. Toilets are upstairs. A wide range of bottled and canned craft beers are available to drink in or take away. Closed Monday. Q☺&⧆(Middle Street) ●➡☺

Star Inn ℒ

22 Middle Street, NG9 1FX
☎ (0115) 854 5320 ⊕ starbeeston.co.uk
House beer (by Lenton Lane); 9 changing beers ⊞

This former Shipstones pub, still with branded windows, has been restored to its former glory. It offers 10 cask ales, four traditional ciders, and a wide selection of whiskies, gins, rums and wines. The decor is tasteful and minimal. Outside is a permanent marquee, sports room and spacious garden. Families are welcome during the day. Meals are served, alongside an extensive range of bar snacks. Eight en-suite rooms are available. Visitors may recognise the bar as having featured in Auf Wiedersehen, Pet and Boon.
►☺⇆⑈&⧆♠(Beeston Centre) ♣●P➡☺ᯤ♪

Victoria Hotel ★ ℒ

85 Dovecote Lane, NG9 1JG
☎ (0115) 925 4049 ⊕ vichotelbeeston.co.uk
Black Sheep Best Bitter; Castle Rock Harvest Pale; Full Mash Séance; 8 changing beers (sourced regionally) ⊞

Located alongside the platform of Beeston railway station, this restored Victorian masterpiece has mass appeal. Eleven real ales are joined by six continental draught beers, two craft beers and three ciders/perries, plus an extensive whisky and wine menu, and a renowned food menu. Taster trays of three third-pints are also offered. Two distinct bars are complemented by a dining room, and outside is a covered, smoke-free seating area. VicFest is hosted in July and beer festivals feature throughout the year.
Q☺⑈&⧆♠(Beeston Centre) ♣●P➡☺ᯤ♪

Bingham

Horse & Plough ℒ

Long Acre, NG13 8AF
☎ (01949) 839313
Castle Rock Harvest Pale, Preservation; 7 changing beers ⊞

A former Methodist chapel in the heart of a busy market town, this small pub has a traditional interior and flagstone floor, with a terrace added in 2019 and a pool room in 2022. Up to nine cask ales and four ciders are served. Four times local CAMRA Pub of the Year, the

Horse & Plough always offers a wide range of styles and strengths of real ale and cider, showcasing smaller producers alongside Castle Rock and other established favourites. ☺&⇆♣●P➡☺ᯤ♪

Wheatsheaf ⦚

Long Acre, NG13 8BG
☎ (01949) 837430 ⊕ thewheatsheafbingham.co.uk
6 changing beers ⊞

The Wheatsheaf reverted to its traditional name when it reopened in 2016 under new ownership. Ten handpumps offer a range of changing cask ales and ciders. Food is served lunchtimes and evenings in the bar and in the separate restaurant. The pub has a real fire in the bar, a fantastic outdoor terrace and hosts live music every week. A former local and regional CAMRA Cider Pub of the Year. ►☺⇨⑈&⧆♠P➡☺ᯤ♪

Car Colston

Royal Oak ✅

The Green, NG13 8JE
☎ (01949) 20247 ⊕ royaloakcarcolston.co.uk
Eagle Bombardier; Wainwright Gold; 2 changing beers ⊞

This country inn – a former hosiery factory – is situated on one of England's largest village greens. The pub has a cosy bar with comfortable seating and a real fire. In addition there is a generously sized restaurant and a

REAL ALE BREWERIES

Aither Mansfield Woodhouse
Angel ⦚ Nottingham
Beermats ✦ Winkburn
Beeston Hop Nottingham: Beeston
Black Iris ✦ Nottingham: New Basford
Black Market ⦚ Warsop
Blue Monkey Nottingham: Giltbrook
Brewhouse & Kitchen ⦚ Nottingham
Castle Rock ✦ Nottingham
Cat Asylum ✦ Collingham
Dolomite Langwith (NEW)
Dukeries ⦚ ✦ Worksop
FireRock ✦ Sutton-in-Ashfield
Full Mash Stapleford
Good Stuff ⦚ Daybrook
Grumpy Fish Arnold (NEW)
Harby ⦚ Harby
Harrison's Retford
Idle ⦚ West Stockwith
Jacaranda Brinkley
Lenton Lane Nottingham
Lincoln Green Nottingham: Hucknall
Linear Bingham
Liquid Light ✦ Nottingham
Lord Randalls Newark
Magpie ✦ Nottingham
Maypole Eakring
Milestone ✦ Newark
Neon Raptor ✦ Nottingham
Nottingham ✦ Nottingham: Radford
Pheasantry East Markham
Reality Nottingham: Chilwell
Reckless Dweeb Bilsthorpe
Scruffy Dog ⦚ Sutton-in-Ashfield
Shipstone's Nottingham: Old Basford
Tom Herrick's Carlton on Trent
Tucks ✦ Thoresby (NEW)
Two Matts Sutton-in-Ashfield (NEW)
Vaguely Bingham
Welbeck Abbey Welbeck

function room. Four beers, all from the Marston's range but often featuring less-heralded varieties, are available in the bar, and food is served lunchtimes and evenings. There is a skittle alley to the rear, plus a beer garden and camping facilities. ♿☕❶♿♣⚑Ⓟ❀☂

Carlton in Lindrick

Grey Horses Inn 🅛
The Cross, S81 9EW (in centre of old village) SK592845
☎ (01909) 730252
6 changing beers (sourced locally; often Chantry, Welbeck Abbey) Ⓗ
This welcoming pub is situated in the conservation area in the heart of the village. It has a front bar accessible from the street, a large lounge area where excellent food is served, and a large beer garden. The pub offers six real ales: two or three beers usually from Welbeck Abbey, and three or four guest beers from local breweries. A former winner of local CAMRA Pub of the Season. Q♿☕❶♿♣Ⓟ⚑(21,22)❀☂♪

Cromwell

Milestone Brewery Tap
Great North Road, NG23 6JE
☎ (01636) 822255 ● milestonebrewery.co.uk
6 changing beers (often Milestone) Ⓗ
The taproom of the Milestone brewery, which can be viewed through the large windows down one side of the bar. There is a large beer garden with heated, sheltered seating areas to the rear. Five handpumps dispense Milestone beers, and there are traditional cider and craft beers also on offer. A wide selection of bottles is available to purchase. Food is provided by a variety of food vans – check in advance for times. ♿☕Ⓟ❀

Daybrook

Abdication 🅛
89 Mansfield Road, NG5 6BH (opp gates of former Home Brewery) ● theabdication.co.uk
4 changing beers Ⓗ
This friendly micropub is based in the Home Brewery Coronation Buildings (built in 1936/37), opposite the former brewery. The four ever-changing cask ales, four craft lines and three ciders are sourced from microbreweries, small producers or the on-site nanobrewery, Good Stuff Brewing, and include a mix of styles. An archway splits the single room, giving an appearance of a much larger area. Dogs are welcome. It is closed on Mondays and Tuesdays and during the first two weeks in January. Q♿☕♣♥⚑❀♪

Dunham on Trent

White Swan
Main Street, NG22 0TY (on A57, as you enter from Markham Moor) SK813745
☎ (01777) 228307
Pheasantry Pale Ale; 2 changing beers (sourced locally) Ⓗ
An attractive village pub at the side of the A57, close to the River Trent. The pub has a separate bar, a reasonably sized dining room, and a function room. Pheasantry PA is the regular beer and there are two changing real ales, usually from local breweries. Outside there is ample seating, and a large children's play area. The pub has its own fishing lake and camping and caravan park. ♿☕✍❶♿♣Ⓟ⚑❀♪

East Leake

Round RobINN 🅛
54 Main Street, LE12 6PG
☎ 07301 288651
6 changing beers (sourced locally) Ⓖ
Micropub opened in 2015, serving six local beers on gravity, cooled on racks behind the bar. A range of local ciders and continental bottled beers are also available. Seating is a mixture of chairs, cushioned benches and high stools, with the single room accommodating up to 45 patrons. A small outdoor area to the front offers alfresco drinking. Food is restricted to light bar snacks. Closed on Monday. Q♿☕♣♥⚑(1)❀♪

Eastwood

Pick & Davy 🅛
237A Nottingham Road, Hill Top, NG16 3GS
Castle Rock Elsie Mo; Oakham Bishops Farewell; 4 changing beers Ⓗ
Opened in 2018, this micropub is dedicated to the mining industry. The rear wall has been designed to look like a coal face, complete with Davy lamp lighting, and a history of the local mining industry is highlighted on one wall. The interior is smart and modern, but with a rustic feel. At the front, a covered patio area has been created. Up to six real ales are served, four of which change frequently. Q♿☕♣♥⚑❀☂

Tap & Growler 🅛
209 Nottingham Road, Hill Top, NG16 3GS
● tapandgrowler.co.uk
Acorn Barnsley Bitter; Oakham Bishops Farewell Ⓗ**; 8 changing beers (sourced locally)** Ⓗ/Ⓖ
Micropub selling up to 10 real ales, five on handpump with up to a further five on gravity. Local ciders are also available, and there are nine craft beer taps. Though the name is partially derived from the US word for a take-out container (Growler), when the building was being renovated a ceramic lion was found, now proudly on display as 'The Growler'. A patio garden to the rear seats around 50. Closed Monday to Wednesday.
Q♿☕♥♣♥⚑❀☂♪

Granby

Marquis of Granby
Dragon Street, NG13 9PN
☎ (01949) 859517 ● brewstersbrewery.co.uk
Brewster's Hophead, Marquis; 4 changing beers Ⓗ
Believed to be the original Marquis of Granby, dating back to 1760 or earlier, this small two-roomed pub is the brewery tap for Brewster's brewery. York stone floors complement the yew bar tops and wood-beamed rooms, and the lounge has a welcoming open fire in winter months. No food is served, but the regular visits from street food vans are popular. The pub also houses a small village store. Guest beers are served alongside the Brewster's range and usually come from micros. Q♿☕♣♥Ⓟ⚑❀☂

Hucknall

Byron's Rest 🅛
8 Baker Street, NG15 7AS
Titanic Plum Porter; 5 changing beers (often Lenton Lane, Magpie, Shipstone's) Ⓗ
A former local CAMRA Cider and LocAle Pub of the Year. A narrow establishment with a recently refurbished snug off the entrance, it extends considerably to the rear where the bar is located, along with comfortable bench

seating, creating a convivial atmosphere. It serves six real ales and up to 12 real ciders, many sourced locally. Outside is the largely covered secret garden, providing a tranquil oasis in the heart of Hucknall.
Q❀❀①☀❦♣❀❀♪

Huthwaite

Market Inn

15 Main Street, NG17 2QW

☎ (01623) 556711

Titanic Plum Porter; 1 changing beer ℍ

This former private club is now a pub and open to everyone. There are two handpulls on the bar serving locally sourced and regularly rotated ales, with guests from further afield. A selection of beers and ciders are stocked in the bottle fridge, for consuming in-house or to take away. A beer garden with a separate smoker's area is popular with ramblers. Well-behaved children and dogs are welcome at all times. ☎❀❦♣❀❀❀♪

Kirkby-in-Ashfield

Dandy Cock Ale House

184a Victoria Road, NG17 8AT

☎ 07854 054060 ⊕ thedandycock.co.uk

4 changing beers (sourced locally; often Dancing Duck) ℍ

Micropub offering four real ales and up to 18 ciders served directly from the cellar which is visible behind the bar. A range of wines and spirits is also available, with a choice of over 200 different gins. It hosts acoustic nights; check for details. The pub is dog friendly. There is on-street parking only, but a bus stop is directly outside the front door. Only open Friday and Saturday.
Q☎❦☀❀❀♪

Lambley

Woodlark Inn Ⓛ

Church Street, NG4 4QB

☎ (0115) 931 2535 ⊕ woodlarkinn.co.uk

Theakston Best Bitter; Timothy Taylor Landlord; 3 changing beers (often Lenton Lane) ℍ

Located in the quaint-sounding Upper Dumbles area of Lambley village, this traditional pub dates back to the 19th century is popular with locals and visitors from afar. Cask ales (usually LocAles) are served from the bare red-brick bar with exposed beams, and excellent home-cooked food is served in the lounge/restaurant. The landlord holds three well-attended weekend beer festivals each year. Q☎❀①♣❀❀(46,47)❀❀

Laneham

Bees Knees Ⓛ

Main Street, DN22 0NA (centre of village) SK803762

☎ (01777) 228090

Don Valley Atomic Blonde; Ossett Silver King; Pheasantry Dancing Dragonfly; 3 changing beers (sourced nationally) ℍ

A quirky country pub, converted from a former shop, with three small rooms and some outside seating. Well supported by locals, it serves three regular real ales, three rotating guest beers, including a stout or porter, over 180 gins, and excellent food (booking recommended). Quiz night is Wednesdays and jazz features on the first Sunday of the month. A former local CAMRA Pub of the Season. Q☎❀①❦♣❀❀❀♪

Lound

Bluebell Inn

Town Street, DN22 8RN (on main street through village) SK691864

☎ (01777) 818457 ⊕ bluebellinnlound.co.uk

3 changing beers (sourced locally; often Abbeydale, Bradfield, Welbeck Abbey) ℍ

A traditional village pub with a lounge bar where food is served, and a taproom with a pool table. Three changing real ales, usually from local breweries, are served. The pub has gained a good reputation for the quality of its food and beers. Outside is a large car park and a partly covered seating area. Wednesday night is quiz night. Accommodation is available in three rooms.
Q☎❀❦①❦♣❀❀❀❀

Mansfield

Brown Cow

31 Ratcliffe Gate, NG18 2JA

☎ (01623) 645854 ⊕ browncow-mansfield.co.uk

Everards Tiger; 9 changing beers ℍ

Owned by Everards brewery and run as a Project William business. A range of up to 12 real ales is offered alongside ciders and craft keg beers. There are two separate bar areas, with a function room upstairs and a popular rear courtyard beer garden. The pub is a short walk from the town centre. Recently awarded best pub on the local CAMRA Ale Trail. Q☎❀☀♣❀❀❀❀♪

Garrison

Leeming Street, NG18 1NA

☎ 07702 253235

6 changing beers ℍ

Inspired by the TV show Peaky Blinders, and with some beer names reflecting the theme, this pub serves six real ales and a range of ciders along with six craft ales. Located in the pedestrianised area of the town centre, it is a five-minute walk from public car parks. Live music usually features on Thursday evenings. Closed Monday and Tuesday. Q☎❀☀❀❀❀♪

Pavilion

Racecourse Park, Epsom Street, NG18 3AL

☎ 07790 190020

4 changing beers ℍ

A family- and dog-friendly pub on the park. It has five handpulls on the bar offering a regularly changing range of styles of beers, as well as up to six real ciders. Live music and quiz nights both feature each week. A function room is available. A beer loyalty scheme is in operation, and a beer and cider festival is held each year. Closed Monday and Tuesday. Q☎❀❦♣❀❀❀♪

Railway Inn Ⓛ

9 Station Street, NG18 1EF

☎ 07898 518539

4 changing beers (often Dancing Duck, Full Mash, Pheasantry) ℍ

Close to the bus and train stations in the town centre, this community pub serves popular home-cooked meals, with daily specials and offers available. As well as the main bar area there are two separate rooms for diners or those looking for a quieter space. Up to four real ales and up to two real ciders are offered. The walled rear garden is busy in the summer. Q☎❀①☀❀❀❀♪

Stag & Pheasant ✅

4 Clumber Street, NG18 1NU

☎ (01623) 412890

Greene King Abbot; Ruddles Best Bitter; Sharp's Doom Bar; 5 changing beers ℍ

A spacious Lloyds No. 1 bar not far from the town centre. It gets busy at weekends, with a DJ after 10pm on Saturday nights. Up to eight real ales are usually available, plus two real ciders from the large bar. Food is served until 11pm every day. There is a large covered smoking area to the front. ♿🍴❤️♿🚲🚍🛜

Stella Taps

Stella Street, NG18 4AN (Just behind Miller's Made2Fade barber shop)
☎ 07835 401515
3 changing beers (sourced nationally) Ⓗ
Micropub, opened in summer 2021 in a former takeaway premises. It serves three varying real ales and a regular selection of three craft kegs from Joseph Holt: Crystal Gold lager, Bootleg American IPA and Trailblazer stout, plus Appleshed cider. The modern interior has mostly high seating in the main bar area on entry, with some lower seating to the rear, and a capacity of around 50 occupants. Closed Monday to Wednesday. Q🚲🚍

Mapperley

Blues Dawg Ⓛ

960 Woodborough Road, NG3 5QS
☎ 07923 517390
4 changing beers Ⓗ
The bar of this little micropub, opened in 2018, has four handpumps serving beers from local breweries, plus Beartown and including a stout. Furniture consists of circular tables made from large cable drums, wooden benches and a variety of seating, and guitars adorn the walls. Live music is featured. Dogs are welcome. Open Thursday to Sunday. 🌿🐾🐕🚍🐕‍🦺🎵

Misson

White Horse Inn

High Street, DN10 6ED
☎ (01302) 710211 ⊕ thewhitehorseinnmisson.co.uk
2 changing beers (sourced nationally) Ⓗ
A traditional country inn full of character and charm, in the lovely village of Misson. Two changing real ales are available, as well as a good selection of beers, lagers, ciders, spirits and fine wines. Excellent food is served (booking highly recommended). There is a quiz every Sunday evening, and occasional themed nights are held throughout the year. ♿🍴P🚍(27)🎵

Morton

Full Moon Inn ✔

Main Street, NG25 0UT
☎ (01636) 830251 ⊕ thefullmoonmorton.co.uk
Acorn Barnsley Bitter; Timothy Taylor Landlord; 2 changing beers (often Jacaranda) Ⓗ
Welcoming village pub serving up to four real ales, with at least one from a local or regional brewery, often including Jacaranda. Low ceilings with natural oak beams and brickwork, and two open log fires, give the pub a cosy, rustic-yet-modern feel. There is a restaurant area where food is served daily, including a popular Sunday lunch. There is a large car park, a play area for children, and an outside drinking area. Q♿🌿🍴♿🐾P🌿🛜🎵

Newark

Flying Circus Ⓛ

53 Castle Gate, NG24 1BE
☎ (01636) 611844 ⊕ flyingcircuspub.co.uk
Brains Rev James Original; 4 changing beers (sourced nationally) Ⓗ

Reopened in its present incarnation in 2014, this pub features Monty Python quotes and brewery logos decorating the walls, and old model aircraft suspended from the ceiling. The four changing cask ales are complemented by a wide range of keg, bottled and canned craft beers. There is regular live music, and a quiz night. The large outdoor courtyard is popular in the summer. ♿🌿🚍(Castle)🚍🐾🛜🎵

Just Beer Micropub 🍺

32A Castle Gate, NG24 1BG (in Swan & Salmon Yard, off Castle Gate)
☎ (01636) 312047 ⊕ justbeermicropub.biz
4 changing beers (sourced nationally) Ⓗ
Friendly micropub offering a varied range of cask ale, craft beer on tap, cider and perry, plus international and rare UK craft ales from the fridge. Several beer festivals are held throughout the year, and there is a popular quiz night once a week. Traditional pub games are played such as cribbage and darts. Twice regional CAMRA Pub of the Year and local Pub of the Year 2024. Since opening in 2010 they have served over 6,000 different cask ales. Q♿🅰🚍(Castle) ♣🐾🛢🚍🐾🛜

Organ Grinder

21 Portland Street, NG24 4XF
☎ (01636) 671768
Blue Monkey BG Sips, Primate Best Bitter, Infinity IPA, Guerrilla, Ape Ale, Infinity Plus 1; 1 changing beer (sourced regionally) Ⓗ
Opened in 2014, this no-nonsense beer-drinking pub offers six or seven real ales from Blue Monkey and often a guest ale. Real cider, a range of bottled beers and a selection of spirits are also available. The Monkey Room has a dartboard and a large TV screen, and books, games and a piano are available for customer use. Bar snacks are served. It hosts a popular quiz every other Wednesday. Local CAMRA Cider Pub of the Year 2024. ♿🚍(Castle) ♣🐾🚍🐾🛜🎵

Nottingham: Carlton

Brickyard Ⓛ ✔

Standhill Road, NG4 1JL
☎ (0115) 987 8707 ⊕ brickyardcarlton.co.uk
Lincoln Green Archer, Hood; 3 changing beers Ⓗ
This former social club was renovated by Lincoln Green and reopened in 2018. The pub contains a number of items of Hardys & Hansons memorabilia, complete with a scale model of the former brewery cleverly built into a table. Although fairly small overall, a snug is located at the back of the pub to the right of the bar. It serves mainly Lincoln Green beers, plus occasional guests. Craft keg beers are also sold, and there is a basic food offering. 🌿🚍🐾🛜🎵

Nottingham: Central

Barrel Drop Ⓛ

7 Hurts Yard, NG1 6JD (in passageway off Upper Parliament St)
☎ (0115) 924 3018
5 changing beers (often Magpie) Ⓗ
Tucked away on Hurts Yard between Angel Row and Upper Parliament Street, this city-centre micropub opened in 2014 and is now operated in conjunction with Magpie brewery. Beers are regularly available from Magpie, and other microbreweries around the country. Several taps dispense keg beers and real ciders. There is a small sitting area to the right with steps leading down to the bar, with further seating available. Q♿🅰🚍(Royal Centre) ♣🐾🚍🐾🛜

Cock & Hoop 🄻

25 High Pavement, NG1 1HF
☎ (0115) 948 4414 ⊕ lacemarkethotel.co.uk/dining
5 changing beers (sourced locally) ⊞
A former Home Ales pub, now part of the Lace Market
Hotel, opposite the National Justice Museum. There is a
welcoming gas fire and comfortable seating in the front
bar, and a quieter lounge area has access to an outdoor
non-smoking courtyard. Downstairs is the restaurant,
which is used for breakfasts and afternoon teas during
the day. Pizzas are available all day up to 9pm. It serves
an interesting selection of LocAles.
Q✍◀♦★Q(Lace Market) ♦Q❀☎♪

Dragon 🄻 ✅

67 Long Row, NG1 6JE
☎ (0115) 941 7080 ⊕ the-dragon.co.uk
**Castle Rock Harvest Pale; Oakham Citra; 2 changing
beers** ⊞
Small and welcoming unspoilt pub with a laid-back
ambience, serving up to four real ales. Seating in the
split-level interior is a combination of bar stools and
comfortable benches. There is a delightful enclosed beer
garden at the back with seating. Hambleton Bakery cobs
are available throughout the day. Check out the Scalextric
room which has a scale model of Market Square to drive
round. Phone for opening times.
❀Q(Market Square) ❀☎♪

Falcon Inn 🄻

1 Alfreton Road, Canning Circus, NG7 3JE
☎ (0115) 924 4635 ⊕ thefalconinn.co.uk
**Oakham Citra; Titanic Plum Porter; 4 changing
beers** ⊞
Established in 1853, this prominently positioned pub in
the centre of Canning Circus was acquired and
extensively refurbished in 2013. There are two small
rooms, with a function room/restaurant area upstairs. Six
handpumps serve mainly local beers, always including a
dark beer. Meals are served on Sundays only, although
parties can be catered for at other times (by prior
arrangement). Bar snacks are available, including cheese
cobs. Closed Monday and Tuesday. ❀◀♣♦Q❀

King William IV 🄻

6 Eyre Street, Sneinton, NG2 4RG
☎ (0115) 958 9864 ⊕ new.thekingbilly.co.uk
**Black Iris Snake Eyes; Oakham Citra; 6 changing beers
(often Lenton Lane)** ⊞
Known widely as the King Billy, this cosy pre-Victorian
gem on the edge of the city centre is close to the
Motorpoint Arena. The family-run free house oozes
charm and character, and is a haven for real ale drinkers,
with a choice of up to eight microbrewery ales from near
and far, as well as real cider. Folk music is popular on
Thursdays and the second Tuesday of the month. It
features a function room and rooftop terrace. The pub
sign won a national award in 2015.
Q☺❀◀♣♦Q(43,44) ❀☎♪

Navigation 🄻 ✅

6 Wilford Street, NG2 1AA
☎ 07735 490816 ⊕ navigationnottingham.uk
4 changing beers (often Timothy Taylor) ⊞
Friendly canalside pub with a single open-plan room.
Outside, there is a decked area to the rear, and a patio
down some steps to the side of the canal lock. Four
changing real ales, at least one from Timothy Taylor, and
a dark beer are always available. Reasonably priced,
good-quality food is available daily. Live music is
performed regularly on the stage.
❀◀♦★Q(Nottingham Station) Q❀☎♪

Newshouse 🄻

123 Canal Street, NG1 7HB
☎ (0115) 681 6800
**5 changing beers (sourced locally; often Castle
Rock)** ⊞
Now part of the Castle Rock managed estate and only a
four-minute walk from Nottingham rail/tram station, this
1960s, blue tile-fronted pub, stands on a site occupied by
public houses for nearly 200 years. The name derives
from the time when newspapers would be read publicly
to inform the masses of elections at home as well as
military victories overseas. The walls are covered with
framed front pages of local newspapers showing
headlines stretching back over many years.
☺❀✍▲♦★Q(Nottingham Station) ♣♦Q❀☎

Olde Trip to Jerusalem ★ 🄻 ✅

Brewhouse Yard, NG1 6AD (off Castle Rd)
☎ (0115) 947 3171 ⊕ triptojerusalem.com
**Greene King IPA; Hardys & Hansons Olde Trip;
Nottingham Extra Pale Ale; 6 changing beers** ⊞
This famously historic pub built into the rock beneath
Nottingham Castle is popular with tourists. Previously
known as the Pilgrim, no one knows for sure ho wlong
an inn has stood on this site. There are several rooms at
ground floor level; in the Ward Room bar you can play
ring the bull. The Museum Room and Rock Lounge are
upstairs, the latter featuring their 'Cursed Galleon'.
Occasional beer festivals are held in the covered
courtyard. A cobblestone area outside gets busy on warm
days. The pub sells a selection of souvenir merchandise.
Q❀◀♦★Q(Old Market Square) ♣Q❀☎

Partizan Tavern

13-15 Manvers Street, NG2 4PB
☎ 07974 361645
4 changing beers (sourced regionally) ⊞
Opened in 2021, this micropub adds to the growing beer
scene in the Sneinton Market area. It serves four varying
real ales, four real ciders/perries, four craft beers, and an
extensive selection of bottles and cans (which are listed
in 'The Book of Doom'). The name is taken from the
Serbian football club that the landlord visits regularly. A
collection of Partizan Belgrade memorabilia are hung on
the walls. ☺♣♦Q(24,43)❀☎

Sir John Borlase Warren 🄻 ✅

1 Ilkeston Road, Canning Circus, NG7 3GD
☎ (0115) 988 1889
**Everards Tiger; 11 changing beers (often Lincoln
Green)** ⊞
An Everards Project William pub run by Lincoln Green
brewery, in the most prominent building in Canning
Circus. The lower bar area can be hired for private parties
and there is a small snug at the far end of the bar.
Outside is a secluded, enclosed pub garden and a large
rooftop patio, a quiet haven in the centre of a busy area.
Twelve handpulls serve real ales and ciders, and feature
Lincoln Green ales as well as guests from breweries near
and far. ☺❀◀♣♦Q❀☎♪

Nottingham: New Basford

Lion Inn 🄻

44 Mosley Street, New Basford, NG7 7FQ
☎ (0115) 970 3506 ⊕ thelionatbasford.co.uk
Draught Bass; 9 changing beers ⊞
A large, traditional free house with a horseshoe central
bar and a rustic, bare-brick decor. The well featured in
the centre of the pub is the old barrel drop. The focus is
on an ever-changing range of cask ales and traditional
ciders from near and far. Outside are extensive heated

covered decking areas and a large seated garden. An eclectic range of live music features every weekend. The pub is dog friendly.
ਠ⊛ⅅ◐ᕪ♬(Shipstone Street) ♣●P🖫❀🛜♪

Nottingham: Radford

Plough Inn 🅛
17 St Peter's Street, NG7 3EN
☎ 07815 073447
Nottingham Rock Bitter, Rock Mild, Legend, Extra Pale Ale; 4 changing beers Ⓗ
This traditional two-roomed public house is the brewery tap for the adjoining Nottingham brewery and features a number of their ales, with some changing guests. It attracts a diverse clientele, including students from the nearby university accommodation. The cosy interior has two wood-burning stoves. It hosts a very popular Thursday night quiz and a couple of live music evenings every month. Q ਠ⊛♣P🖫❀🛜♪

Nottingham: Sherwood

Samuel Hall 🅛 ✅
Old Bus Depot, Mansfield Road, NG5 2JN
☎ (0115) 924 6230
Greene King Abbot; Ruddles Best Bitter; Sharp's Doom Bar; 5 changing beers (sourced nationally) Ⓗ
A large Wetherspoon pub in the centre of Sherwood. This former tram and bus garage has been tastefully converted, with a raised seating area opposite the bar, and, to the rear, an area with booths and settees. Eight real ales, including five guests and a traditional cider, are available. Two staircases lead to further seating upstairs with views over Mansfield Road. Various local photographs and commissioned artwork hang on the walls. The pub was named after a local lacemaker.
ⅅ & 🖫🛜

Orston

Durham Ox ✅
Church Street, NG13 9NS
☎ (01949) 850059 ⊕ thedurhamoxorston.co.uk
Black Sheep Best Bitter; Castle Rock Harvest Pale; Theakston Best Bitter; 2 changing beers Ⓗ
A traditional country pub in the village of Orston, in the picturesque Vale of Belvoir. It serves a range of real ales across five handpumps, plus wines, and quality home-cooked food at the bar and in the separate restaurant. There is a pretty beer garden to the rear of the pub, and a function room. This is a lovely village pub, popular both with locals and visitors to the area. ਠ⊛ⅅ&P🖫❀🛜♪

Oxton

Old Green Dragon 🅛 ✅
Blind Lane, NG25 0SS
☎ (0115) 965 2243
6 changing beers Ⓗ
This former local CAMRA Village Pub of the Year retains its traditional village pub charm while incorporating a contemporary, popular eating venue. There is an ever-changing selection of six real ales, usually with two from local breweries, alongside offerings from further afield and at least two real ciders. Outside at the front there is a patio area, and at the rear is an enclosed garden. The car park has three electric car charging points.
ਠ⊛ⅅ&●P🖫❀🛜♪

Radcliffe on Trent

Chestnut 🅛 ✅
Main Road, NG12 2BE
☎ (0115) 933 1994
Brewster's Hophead; Timothy Taylor Boltmaker; 5 changing beers Ⓗ
Popular cask beer-led village pub. Originally the Cliffe Inn, following a major refurbishment in 2006 it became the Horse Chestnut, then in 2015 simply the Chestnut. Seven real ales are served, including ever-changing guests, and always including a locally brewed ale. Quality home-made food is served in a relaxed, casual atmosphere, and ranges from stonebaked pizzas to classic British dishes. ਠ⊛ⅅ&⇌(Radcliffe-on-Trent) P🖫❀🛜♪

Yard of Ale 🅛
1 Walkers Yard, NG12 2FF (off Main Rd, between Costa and public car park)
☎ (0115) 933 4888 ⊕ yard-of-ale.business.site
6 changing beers Ⓗ
Small, friendly micropub in a former café and chocolate shop in the centre of the village. The premises are narrow, with access via steps at the side leading up to a small room with basic seating and tables. A smaller second room to the left offers further space. It serves up to six ever-changing guest ales, always including at least one locally brewed beer and a dark ale. Open Wednesday to Saturday. Q⇌(Radcliffe-on-Trent)P🖫❀

Rainworth

Inkpot 🅛
Kirklington Road, NG21 0JY
☎ (01623) 230500
4 changing beers (often Batemans, Bradfield, Leatherbritches) Ⓗ
This friendly micropub, converted from a former betting shop, usually serves a range of up to four real ales and 11 real ciders. It is named after the octagonal building that used to stand nearby, now demolished, which was the toll house for the road to Mansfield. There is an outside seating area in front of the building. A former local CAMRA Cider Pub of the Year. Closed Monday to Wednesday. Q ਠ●🖫(28)❀♪

Retford

Beer Under the Clock
3 Town Hall Yard, DN22 6DU (off Market Square, through arch at side of town hall, opp Butter Market)
SK705811
☎ 07985 102192 ⊕ beerundertheclock.com
5 changing beers (sourced nationally) Ⓗ
This small, friendly pub – formerly known as BeerHeadZ – serves five rotating beers, including a dark beer and a bitter, plus three ciders, a range of bottled and canned beers and a limited range of wines and spirits. The beers are often one-offs from near and far, and are kept in excellent condition and served in oversized glasses. Local CAMRA Pub of the Year 2022 and 2023.
Q⊛&●P🖫❀🛜♪

Black Boy Inn 🅛
14 Moorgate, DN22 6RH
☎ (01777) 7099 ⊕ the-black-boy.edan.io
2 changing beers (sourced locally; often Little Critters, Pheasantry) Ⓗ
A traditional pub just off the town centre with a good regular trade. Recently refurbished, this cosy, open-plan pub has a dartboard, live sport on TV, a comfortable smoking area and outside seating. Two or three changing

real ales are normally available, sourced from local breweries, and are reasonably priced. Visitors are always made welcome. Q🖤🍴🅿🐾♿🛜

Brew Shed
104-106 Carolgate, DN22 6AS (on Carolgate bridge opp the Masonic Hall) SK706807
☎ (01777) 948485 🌐 harrisonsbrewery.com/the-brew-shed
Harrison's Vacant Gesture, Best Bitter, Porter, Proof of Concept; 2 changing beers (sourced locally; often Harrison's) Ⓗ
The Brew Shed is the tap for Harrison's brewery. The pub consists of an open-plan room at street level and a smaller downstairs room that leads onto the large canalside patio. Five or six Harrison's beers are on offer, plus the occasional guest beer, a variety of kegs, and a good selection of gins, spirits, wines and cider. A former Nottinghamshire CAMRA Pub of the Year and East Midlands runner-up. Q🖤♿🍴🅿🐾♿🛜

Idle Valley Tap Ⓛ
Carolgate, DN22 6EF (at S end of main shopping area)
☎ (01777) 948586
House beer (by Welbeck Abbey); 6 changing beers (sourced nationally; often Abbeydale, Ilkley, Welbeck Abbey) Ⓗ
A welcoming pub, initially the tap for the Idle Valley brewery, but since the brewery's closure beers are sourced elsewhere. Up to eight real ales are available, with a midweek teatime 50p discount. The one-room pub has a pool table and dartboard, and the outside space, which has plenty of seating, gets busy in fine weather. 🖤♿🍴🅿🐾♿🛜🎵

Selston

Horse & Jockey
Church Lane, NG16 6FB
☎ (01773) 781012
Blue Monkey Infinity IPA; Greene King Abbot; 4 changing beers Ⓗ
A drinkers' gem dating from 1664, with wooden bench seating, large open fires and flagstone floors. Up to six real ales are available, two served under gravity from stone trestles. A real cider or perry is always available. A quiz is held on Sunday evening and a folk night every Wednesday. Look out for Selstock Beer and Music Festival in the summer. A winner of many CAMRA awards. Q🖤♿♿🍴🅿🐾♿

Southwell

Final Whistle 🍺
Station Road, NG25 0ET
☎ (01636) 814953
Brewster's Hophead; Draught Bass; Everards Tiger; Salopian Oracle; 6 changing beers (sourced nationally; often Oakham) Ⓗ
Located at the end of the Southwell Trail, a disused railway line, this comfortable, multi-roomed pub has a railway theme and is teeming with memorabilia. The courtyard garden is laid out like a mock station and has a separate bar and function room called The Locomotion. The main bar has 10 handpumps which always offer Bass and a stout or porter. Real cider is also served. Quiz nights are Sunday and Tuesday. Various quality bar snacks are available. Local CAMRA Pub of the Year 2024. Q🖤♿♿🍴🅿(28,100)🐾🛜🎵

Old Coach House Ⓛ
69 Easthorpe, NG25 0HY
☎ (01636) 813289 🌐 pubpeople.com

Oakham JHB; 6 changing beers (sourced nationally) Ⓗ
Traditional, cosy, open-plan pub with five different drinking areas, oak beams and a large range fire. Six regularly changing real ales are on handpump from local and national breweries, often including Oakham JHB and Timothy Taylor Landlord. Live music features regularly on Saturday night, and an open mic session is held on the last Sunday of the month. Outside to the rear is a well-kept patio garden. Local CAMRA Pub of the Year 2020 and 2023. Q🖤♿♿🍴🐾♿🛜🎵

Stapleford

Horse & Jockey 🍺 Ⓛ
20 Nottingham Road, NG9 8AA
☎ (0115) 875 9655 🌐 horseandjockeystapleford.co.uk
Full Mash Horse & Jockey; 12 changing beers Ⓗ
This pub offers 13 ales, including a house beer from local Full Mash brewery, plus a craft beer and four real ciders. The main bar features open-plan seating. A larger seating area, up a couple of steps, can serve as a function room. Food includes bar snacks (filled cobs, pork pies and sausage rolls), pies (available all day) and pizzas on Thursdays. Accommodation is also available. Twice national CAMRA Pub of the Year finalist. Q🖤♿🛏♿♿🍴🅿🐾🛜🎵

Sutton-in-Ashfield

Duke of Sussex
Alfreton Road, NG17 1JN
☎ (01623) 511469 🌐 duke-of-sussex.co.uk
6 changing beers (often Dancing Duck, Pheasantry, Welbeck Abbey) Ⓗ
Large open-plan pub serving up to six real ales from a central bar connecting the bar and restaurant. It is owned by the local Pub People Company of South Normanton. Food is served every day, with daily offers available. It hosts live music and quiz nights, and most live football matches are shown. Closed Monday. Q🖤♿♿🅿(9.1)🐾🛜🎵

FireRock Ⓛ
24 Outram Street, NG17 4FS
☎ 07875 331898
3 changing beers (often FireRock) Ⓗ
Opened in 2018, this large open-plan bar is the tap for FireRock Brewing. Up to three real ales are on offer, and ales from other local breweries are regularly available, alongside a good range of (often rare) spirits. Regular live music is hosted on the stage, and there are also occasional tap takeovers/Meet the Brewers, quizzes and charity events. Closed Monday to Wednesday. 🖤♿🅿🐾♿🎵

Picture House ✅
Forest Street, NG17 1DA
☎ (01623) 554627
Greene King Abbot; Ruddles Best Bitter; Sharp's Doom Bar; 4 changing beers (sourced nationally) Ⓗ
A popular Wetherspoon pub near the bus station. Art Deco in style, and open plan with a high ceiling, it was originally built as the King's cinema in 1932, then closed and reopened in 1967 as the Star Bingo and Social Club. The bingo hall survived into the 1990s, and was used as the Picture House Night Club. It features up to eight real ales. 🖤♿♿🛜

Scruffy Dog
Station Road, NG17 5HF
☎ (01623) 550826 🌐 thescruffydog.co.uk
4 changing beers (often Scruffy Dog) Ⓗ

Comfy sofas and a real fire on colder days welcome visitors to this dog-friendly pub. Refurbished by the current owners, it has is own on-site Scruffy Dog microbrewery, which can be seen working at weekends. Four real ales are available on the bar. It also has a pizzeria where all pizzas are made fresh to order. There is a large beer garden outside and a car park at the rear. Closed Monday to Wednesday and bank holidays. Q🕏🏶🌓⏷🚶👜P🖵🌼

Tollerton

Air Hostess
Stanstead Avenue, NG12 4EA (corner of Burnside Grove)
☎ (0115) 648 0439 ⊕ theairhostesstollerton.co.uk
Timothy Taylor Landlord; 5 changing beers (sourced regionally) 🅗
The Air Hostess is a community-owned pub that was remodelled following its purchase from a local brewery. It offers up to six real ales – one regular and five from a mix of both local and regional independent breweries – and home-cooked food is available daily. The pub is comfortably furnished and its beer garden is popular in the summer, with a pizza kitchen at weekends. Many community events are hosted and a summer beer festival is staged. Q🕏🏶🌓⏷🚶♣P🖵🌼🛜♪

Wellow

Olde Red Lion 🅛
Eakring Road, NG22 0EG (opp maypole on village green) SK669660
☎ (01623) 861000
House beer (by Maypole); 2 changing beers (sourced regionally; often Castle Rock, Eagle) 🅗
Situated on the village green, with its maypole, this 400-year-old village pub participates in a large event on May Day. The traditional wood-beamed interior includes a restaurant, lounge and bar areas. Photographs and maps depicting the history of the village are on the walls. Three real ales are available – Olde Lion Ale and two rotating guest beers. Rufford Park, Sherwood Forest and Clumber Park are all nearby. Q🕏🏶🌓♣P🛜

West Bridgford

Poppy & Pint 🅛
Pierrepont Road, NG2 5DX
☎ (0115) 981 9995
Castle Rock Harvest Pale, Preservation, Screech Owl; 9 changing beers 🅗
Former British Legion Club converted in 2011, it has a large main bar with a raised area and a family area with a café bar (children welcome until 9pm). An upstairs function room hosts a folk club, and the beer garden overlooks a former bowling green. Twelve handpumps dispense Castle Rock beers, plus guests, often from new breweries. There are usually two real ciders and excellent food is served. The car park now has two EV charging points. 🕏🏶🌓⏷🚶👜P🖵🌼🛜♪

Stratford Haven 🅛
2 Stratford Road, NG2 6BA
☎ (0115) 982 5981
Castle Rock Our House, Harvest Pale, Preservation, Elsie Mo, Screech Owl; 9 changing beers 🅗
A former pet shop, the 'Strat' has a single central bar with extended seating at the back and a secluded snug

to the right. Up to nine cask ales plus a cider are available on handpump at any one time, and include at least four from owner Castle Rock's portfolio. Guest ales are predominantly from microbreweries near and far. There is a burger night on Wednesday and a traditional Sunday roast. Q🕏🏶🌓⏷🚶👜P🖵🌼🛜♪

West Stockwith

White Hart 🅛
Main Street, DN10 4EY (opp church and car park)
SK790947
☎ (01427) 892672 ⊕ idlewhitehart.co.uk
House beer (by Idle); 1 changing beer (sourced locally; often Idle) 🅗
A popular country pub close to the River Trent, Chesterfield Canal and West Stockwith Marina. A single bar serves the bar, lounge and dining areas. The range of four or five changing real ales are usually from the Idle brewery, which is housed in outbuildings at the side of the pub. The pub is especially busy during the summer with canal and river traffic. 🕏🏶🌓⏷🚶♣P🖵(97)🌼♪

Worksop

Fuggle's Chapter One
20 Park Street, S80 1HB (50yds past Eyres, going away from Market Square)
☎ 07813 763347
3 changing beers (sourced locally; often Fuggle Bunny) 🅗
This modern and tastefully refurbished little alehouse opened in 2017 and is now firmly established on the local scene. The L-shaped single room serves three rotating quality real ales from the Fuggle Bunny Brew House, plus speciality gins, spirits and wine. The pub is close to the cinema. Closed Monday to Wednesday. Q👜P🖵🌼♪

Liquorice Gardens 🅛 ✅
1A Newcastle Street, S80 2AS (just off town centre)
☎ (01909) 512220
Greene King IPA, Abbot; Sharp's Doom Bar; 4 changing beers (sourced nationally; often Bradfield, Milestone, Pheasantry) 🅗
This friendly and popular Wetherspoon pub, located just outside the town centre, has gained a good reputation for its real ales. There are usually seven real ales on at all times, often including a dark beer, plus a vast selection of ciders and craft beers. Several beer festivals are held each year. The pub attracts an older clientele at lunchtime and a younger crowd in the evenings. 🕏🏶🌓⏷🚶⇌P🖵🛜

Mallard 🏆
Station Approach, S81 7AG (on Platform 1)
☎ 07973 521824
4 changing beers (sourced nationally) 🅗
Formerly the station buffet, this small, cosy pub offers a warm welcome. The four changing real ales usually include a dark beer and a bitter, and there are two ciders, a selection of foreign bottled beers, country fruit wines and specialist gins. There is a downstairs room for special occasions, where four beer festivals are hosted each year. CAMRA regional Pub of the Year 2024 and the recipient of many local CAMRA awards. Q🏶⇌♣👜P🖵🌼

Beer: a high and mighty liquor. **Julius Caesar**

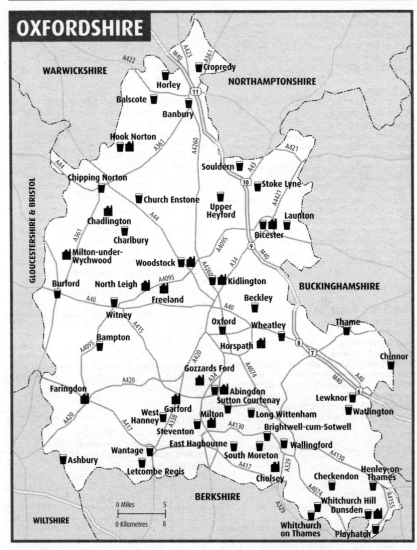

Abingdon

Brewery Tap ♀ ▯
40-42 Ock Street, OX14 5BZ
☎ (01235) 521655 ⊕ thebrewerytap.net
Loose Cannon Gunners Gold; LoveBeer Bonnie Hops; Renegade Good Old Boy; 2 changing beers (sourced locally; often LoveBeer, Oxford, XT) Ⓗ
Morland created a tap for its brewery in 1993 from three Grade II-listed town houses. The brewery is no more but the pub, run by the same family since it opened, has thrived. It offers a diverse range of beers, all sourced locally, and hosts two or three beer festivals each year featuring ales from further afield. The pub has three rooms, two of them away from the bar, and a courtyard outside. A local CAMRA Pub of the Year 2024. Closes at 9pm on Sunday. Q ⩔ ❀ ⩐ ◑ ᗕ P ♟ ❀ ☎ ♫

Broad Face ▯
30-32 Bridge Street, OX14 3HR
☎ (01235) 538612 ⊕ thebroadface.com

Dark Star Hophead; 7 changing beers (sourced nationally) Ⓗ
Deceptively large, two-roomed, Grade II-listed pub near the river, with a small outside seating area on Thames Street. The building was erected in 1840 but there are records of a pub on the site dating back to 1734, and possibly before that under a different name. Mystery surrounds the origin of pub's unique name – theories are displayed on the outside wall, but omit the most likely explanation – that it was originally called the Saracen's Head and the sign was overpainted. Q ⩔ ❀ ◑ ᗕ ⊟ ☎ ♫

Nag's Head on the Thames ▯
The Bridge, OX14 3HX
☎ (01235) 639023 ⊕ thenagsheadonthethames.co.uk
Brakspear Gravity, Oxford Gold; Loose Cannon Abingdon Bridge; Timothy Taylor Landlord; 2 changing beers (sourced locally; often Animal, Loddon) Ⓗ
The bridge dates from 1416, and there has been a building here on an island in the Thames since the 17th century. Licensed since the 18th century, this Grade II-

listed pub is split over two levels, with a large garden area next to the river and lovely views of the countryside and the town's historic buildings. The beer offering is bit seasonal and the full range may not be available in the winter. Card payment only. Closes at 9pm on Sunday. Q☺🕭🍴🕿◑🛇&♿🅿🚪🌞🛜♪

Ashbury

Rose & Crown 🅛

3 High Street, SN6 8NA
☎ (01793) 378354 ⊕ roseandcrownatashbury.co.uk
Arkell's 3B; 1 changing beer (sourced locally; often Arkell's) 🅗
This welcoming 16th-century coaching inn nestles at the foot of the White Horse Downs, within a mile of The Ridgeway, in the centre of the scenic village of Ashbury. It is a comfortable village pub offering a range of beers sourced locally from Arkell's brewery, with 3Bs being especially popular. Food is sourced from local suppliers, and traditional pub fare and à la carte menus are available. Accommodation is available in seven sympathetically refurbished en-suite rooms.
Q☺🕭🍴◑🛇&♿🅿🚪(47)🌞🛜♪

Balscote

Butcher's Arms ✅

Shutford Road, OX15 6JQ
☎ (01295) 730750 ⊕ thebutchersarmsbalscote.co.uk
Hook Norton Hooky; 3 changing beers (sourced nationally; often Hook Norton) 🅖
A friendly welcome awaits in this cosy parlour pub where Hook Norton beers and a monthly guest are served straight from the cask behind the bar. Bar snacks can also be enjoyed in the bar, with a roaring fire in winter, or outside in the lovely beer garden. There is a monthly quiz and occasional live music, with Aunt Sally played in summer. Local CAMRA Pub of the Year and Regional Pub of the Year 2023. Closed weekday afternoons and Monday to Wednesday at 8.30pm. Q☺🕭♿🅿🌞♪

Bampton

Morris Clown 🅛

High Street, OX18 2JW
☎ (01993) 850217
2 changing beers (sourced locally; often Chadlington, Hop Kettle (Swindon), North Cotswold) 🅗
This simply furnished, single-bar free house, run by the same family for two generations, has a log fire in the winter and some unusual murals on the wall, painted by one of the family and depicting other members of the family. The name change by former owners Courage (in 1975 from New Inn) proved controversial as morris dancing teams have a fool, not a clown, and this led to a boycott for 25 years. Closed every lunchtime and weekday afternoons. Q☺🕭♣🛇🍴🅿🚪(19)🌞🛜

Banbury

Coach & Horses ✅

Butchers Row, OX16 5JH
☎ (01295) 266993 ⊕ thecoachandhorsesbanbury.com
Hook Norton Hooky, Off The Hook, Old Hooky; 1 changing beer (sourced locally; often Hook Norton) 🅗
This popular town-centre pub is a great place to relax in comfort, or for socialising. Three or four Hook Norton beers are available on tap, along with ciders and home-made-to-order cocktails. The Coach holds regular live events, with live music, karaoke and a monthly disco with DJ Birch. Sunday lunch is served from 12-4pm. There

is a small enclosed beer garden to the rear of the pub to enjoy alfresco drinking. Closed Monday, and weekday lunchtimes. 🌞&≈🛇🍴🚪♪

Exchange ✅

49-50 High Street, OX16 5LA
☎ (01295) 259035
Greene King Abbot; Ruddles Best Bitter; Sharp's Doom Bar; 9 changing beers (sourced nationally) 🅗
This imposing, split-level pub on the High Street near Banbury Cross was once the home of Banbury's main post office and telephone exchange. The town's history is celebrated by photos of the town and surrounding areas. Two banks of handpumps offer a variety of ales, usually including at least one local beer, plus two regulars. Beer festivals are held in March and October. Good-value food is served all day. ☺🕭◑&≈🚪🛜

Olde Reine Deer Inn ★ ✅

47 Parsons Street, OX16 5NA
☎ (01295) 270972 ⊕ yeoldereinedeerinn.co.uk
Hook Norton Hooky Mild, Hooky, Off The Hook, Old Hooky; 3 changing beers (sourced locally; often Hook Norton) 🅗
Welcoming and historic traditional town-centre pub that dates back to 1570 and played a role in the Civil War. A wide range of Hook Norton beers are available, along with a varied menu. The oak-panelled Globe Room is thought to be where Cromwell's soldiers planned the siege of Banbury Castle. The panelling itself was sold in 1912 but returned to Banbury in 1981. There is an outside seating area with some cover. Identified by CAMRA as having an interior of some regional interest. Q☺🕭◑≈♣🛇🅿🌞♪

White Horse 🍷

50-52 North Bar Street, OX16 0TH
☎ (01295) 277484 ⊕ whitehorsebanbury.com
Everards Tiger; 3 changing beers (sourced nationally) 🅗
This friendly community pub offers a warm welcome and at least four real ales on handpump, along with several ciders and a regularly changing guest ale. Friday nights are busy, often featuring local bands or DJ, while Sunday attractions include popular lunches and an entertaining monthly quiz. The sheltered courtyard garden is a lovely space for a drink. Beer festivals take place on St George's Day and at Easter. Local CAMRA Pub of the Year 2024. Closed on Monday. Q☺🕭🍴◑&≈♣🛇🚪🌞🛜♪

REAL ALE BREWERIES	
Amwell Springs 🍺 Cholsey	
Barn Owl Gozzards Ford	
Bicester 🍺 Bicester (brewing suspended)	
Chadlington Chadlington	
Church Hanbrewery 🍺 North Leigh	
Craftsman Abingdon	
Faringdon 🍺 Faringdon	
Hook Norton 🍺 Hook Norton	
Little Ox Freeland	
Loddon 🍺 Dunsden	
Loose Cannon 🍺 Abingdon	
LoveBeer Milton	
Oxford 🍺 Horspath	
Parlour Garford	
Tap Social Movement 🍺 Kidlington	
Turpin Hook Norton (brewing suspended)	
Virtue 🍺 Milton-under-Wychwood	
Woodstock Woodstock	

Beckley

Abingdon Arms L
High Street, OX3 9UU
☎ (01865) 655667 ⊕ theabingdonarms.co.uk
Little Ox Yabba Dabba Doo; Oxford Prospect; 2 changing beers (sourced locally; often Chadlington, Loose Cannon, Vale) ⊞
A lovely old pub with a fine garden affording great views across Otmoor. There is a small bar and separate dining area. The arms in question are of James Bertie (1653-1699) who was created 1st Earl of Abingdon in 1682. The Bertie family owned the village until 1919 when it was broken up and sold off in lots. The pub was put up for sale in 2016 and bought by a local community group after a community share offer. It closes at 3pm on Monday and Tuesday and at 6pm on Sunday.
Q❀❄●◐&♣P❀?

Bicester

Angel ✓
102 Sheep Street, OX26 6LP
☎ (01869) 360410 ⊕ theangelbicester.co.uk
6 changing beers (sourced regionally; often Chiltern, Rebellion, Vale) ⊞
Five minutes from the centre of the town, this friendly pub has a good range of local guest ales on its six handpumps. The bar area has a welcoming atmosphere, and on wintry days the log fire will keep you warm. Outside there is a large seating area, a permanent marquee, an outdoor snug and a barn that is home to The Pizza boys pop-up restaurant Wednesday to Friday 5-9pm. Perfect for all sorts of occasions. Closed Monday to Friday lunchtimes. Q❀❄❀&≈(North)P🕮❀?♫

Penny Black ✓
58 Sheep Street, OX26 6JW
☎ (01869) 321535
Greene King Abbot; Hook Norton Old Hooky; Ruddles Best Bitter; 8 changing beers (sourced nationally) ⊞
Formerly the post office, this pub, with its elegant façade, comprises one large room with a long crescent-shaped bar serving up to 12 real ales. In its post office days Anthony Trollope worked as clerk before he was a famous novelist. The suntrap garden at the rear is very popular in good weather. Usually two beer festivals take place each year, in March and October.
Q❀❄●◐&≈(North) 🕮?

Brightwell-cum-Sotwell

Red Lion L
Brightwell Street, OX10 0RT (S off A4130)
☎ (01491) 837373 ⊕ redlionbcs.co.uk
Amwell Springs Stay Jammy; Loddon Hullabaloo; Timothy Taylor Landlord; 1 changing beer (sourced nationally; often Loddon, Loose Cannon) ⊞
A traditional, Grade II-listed thatched inn dating from the 16th century in a quiet village. Its cosy bar features exposed beams and an inglenook fireplace with log-burner, and leads to the restaurant area. The beers are usually from local breweries and a good-quality seasonal menu is served (no food Sun eve, or Mon and Tue). The rear courtyard garden, which was renovated and repaved in spring 2024, is a summer suntrap. The pub hosts weekly meat raffles and regular live music. Closed Monday, Tuesday lunchtimes and weekday afternoons.
❄❀◐&♣●P🕮(33,33A)❀?♫

Burford

Angel Inn ✓
14 Witney Street, OX18 4SN
☎ (01993) 822714 ⊕ theangelatburford.co.uk
Hook Norton Hooky, Old Hooky; 2 changing beers (sourced locally; often Hook Norton) ⊞
A small, cosy, welcoming 16th-century inn, hidden away from the bustling main street. Four draught ales are available from Hook Norton brewery, which can be sampled by the real fire or the comfortable bar area seating. Locally sourced meals are served in the bar or the cosy restaurant, and outside is an attractive courtyard and walled garden with some covered seating. Families and dogs are welcome. Three guest rooms are available.
Q❄☕●◐&●🕮❀?♫

Charlbury

Rose & Crown
Market Street, OX7 3PL
☎ (01608) 810103 ⊕ roseandcrown.charlbury.com
Hop Kettle Cricklade Ordinary Bitter; Salopian Oracle; 6 changing beers (sourced nationally; often Oakham, XT) ⊞
A popular wet sales pub that has been in this Guide for an amazing 38 years. Step inside the traditional front bar, then make your way to the back bar, ideal for gatherings and meetings, or the traditional outside space for a summer pint. Two regular and up to six ever-changing ales and six traditional ciders and perries give a fantastic choice, and pop-up food is available most Saturdays. There is regular live music. A former local and county CAMRA Pub of the Year. Opens at 2pm on weekdays.
❄❀♠≈♣●🕮(S3,X9) ❀?♫

Checkendon

Black Horse ★ L
Burncote Lane, RG8 0TE (500yds along narrow lane NE from the Checkendon-Stoke Row road) SU666841
☎ (01491) 680418
Loddon Hoppit; Rebellion IPA; Renegade Good Old Boy; Timothy Taylor Landlord ⒢
Hidden in the woods of the Chiltern Hills AONB is this 350-year-old pub, run by the same family since 1905. It welcomes an eclectic mix of locals, cyclists, walkers and horse riders. Beer is served by gravity dispense from the cellar. Filled rolls, baguettes and chips are available at lunchtime. Well-behaved dogs on a lead are welcome. It has been identified by CAMRA as having a nationally important historic pub interior. Closed Monday, weekday afternoons and at 7pm on Sunday.
Q❄❀◐&♠●P❀♫

Chinnor

Red Lion L ✓
3 High Street, OX39 4DL
☎ (01844) 353468 ⊕ theredlionchinnor.co.uk
XT Three; 3 changing beers (sourced nationally) ⊞
Over 300 years old and originally a set of three cottages, this multi-roomed pub has a bustling bar and separate public bar. A lounge area has an inglenook fireplace with seats recessed into the wall next to a wood-burning stove. The rear of the pub has ample outdoor seating. Food trucks visit on busy nights. A varied range of ales is served, often from microbreweries both local and national. Regular events are hosted, such as weekly quiz nights and occasional comedy nights. Local CAMRA Pub of the Year runner-up 2024. Closed weekday lunchtimes.
❄❀◐P🕮❀?♫

Chipping Norton

Fox L ✓

Market Place, OX7 5DD
☎ (01608) 638535 ⊕ foxchippingnorton.co.uk
Hook Norton Hooky, Off The Hook, Old Hooky; 1 changing beer (sourced locally; often Hook Norton) Ⓗ
This traditional 16th-century inn sits in the centre of Chipping Norton marketplace, ideally placed for bus stops for all routes and the taxi rank. Four handpumps serve ales from the Hook Norton range in the contemporary and light, open-style bar. Outside there is a courtyard seating area. There is also a separate restaurant, upstairs snug and meeting room, alongside 10 individually themed letting rooms, making it a good base to explore the area. There is occasional live music on Friday nights. Q📶🕏🍴🕭🌳♿🅟🚃🏳🎵

Church Enstone

Crown Inn L

Mill Lane, OX7 4NN (off A44, on B4030)
☎ (01608) 677262 ⊕ crowninnenstone.co.uk
Hook Norton Hooky; 2 changing beers (sourced nationally) Ⓗ
A 17th-century Cotswold stone pub set back off the road, featuring an inglenook fireplace, wooden beams, and a flagstone bar, ideal for a pint of local Hook Norton beer or one of two guest ales. Food is locally sourced, with daily specials and Sunday roasts. This is a pub for conversation as there is no jukebox, gaming machines or TV. Families and well-behaved dogs are welcome in this gem of a pub. Rooms available to let. Closes at 9pm on Sunday. Q📶🕏🕭🍴🕭🅟🚃(S3)🌳

Cropredy

Brasenose Arms

Station Road, OX17 1PW
☎ (01295) 750244 ⊕ thebrasenose.co.uk
Fuller's London Pride; 2 changing beers (sourced nationally) Ⓗ
Welcoming 17th-century pub in the heart of the village. Well-kept ales can be sampled in the bar, and a menu, changed every two months, is available in the bar and restaurant. There is a large beer garden to the rear, with covered pods for rainy days. Live music and other events are held, such as Oktoberfest. It is here that the founding members of Fairport Convention met in the 1970s to plan their annual music festival held in August. Closes at 8pm on Sunday. 🕏🕭🍴🕭♣🅟🚃(497,502)🌳🏳🎵

Dunsden

Loddon Tap Yard L

Dunsden Green Farm, Church Lane, RG4 9QD
☎ (0118) 948 1111 ⊕ loddonbrewery.com
Loddon Hullaboloo; 2 changing beers (sourced locally; often Loddon) Ⓗ
A popular tap yard next to the main Loddon brewhouse, serving a selection of the brewery's ales on handpump. It is the perfect place to enjoy a pint in the beautiful countryside whatever the weather. Food is provided from a permanent kitchen in the courtyard. The farm shop sells local produce, as well as Loddon beers and local ciders, wines, spirits and liqueurs. Closed on Monday (except bank holidays), and closes at 8pm (6pm in the winter) on Sunday and Tuesday to Thursday. 🕏🕭🍴🕭♣🅟🚃(800) 🌳🏳🎵

East Hagbourne

Fleur de Lys L

30 Main Road, OX11 9LN (400yds W of war memorial)
☎ (01235) 813247 ⊕ thefleurdelyspub.co.uk
Morland Original Bitter; house beer (by LoveBeer); 4 changing beers (sourced nationally) Ⓗ
This 17th-century village pub offers two regular ales – one a house beer, Wibbly Wobbly Whippet, from nearby LoveBeer – alongside up to four guests. The spacious bar and dining area are warmed by an open fire. The pub hosts regular live music evenings and holds two weekend summer music festivals. Aunt Sally is played in the garden, which features a large semi-enclosed beer hall. A former local CAMRA Pub of the Year. Closed Monday, Tuesday lunchtime, and Wednesday and Thursday afternoons. 🕏🕭🍴♣🅟🚃(94,94A)🌳🏳🎵

Henley-on-Thames

Bird in Hand

61 Greys Road, RG9 1SB
☎ (01491) 575775
Brakspear Gravity; Fuller's London Pride; 3 changing beers (sourced nationally; often Butcombe, Rebellion, Timothy Taylor) Ⓗ
Celebrating 30 consecutive years in the Guide, the Bird has flourished under the stewardship of the same family throughout. Three guest beers complement the two regulars. TVs show sporting events, and the pub is home to darts and cribbage teams and hosts regular quiz nights. The family room leads to a delightful garden boasting a pond and aviary. Dogs on leads are welcome. Closed weekday afternoons and at 9pm on Sunday. Q📶🕏🕭🅰🚲♣🍴🚃🌳🏳🎵

Hook Norton

Malthouse Kitchen (Hook Norton Brewery Visitor Centre)

Brewery Lane, OX15 5NU (follow the brown tourist signs to Hook Norton brewery)
☎ (01608) 730384 ⊕ hooky.co.uk
Hook Norton Hooky Mild, Hooky, Off The Hook, Old Hooky; 3 changing beers (sourced locally; often Hook Norton) Ⓗ
The licensed Malthouse Kitchen restaurant, within the brewery visitor centre, serves a good selection of Hook Norton beers. Themed evening events and the monthly open tap beer nights (second Wed 5-8pm) are held here. There are brewery tours daily, and the visitor centre also includes a well-stocked shop selling merchandise, and a museum area. Shire horses and steam engine are added attractions. Open daily for breakfast and lunch. Closed evenings. 🕏🕭🍴🅟🚃(488)🌳🏳

Pear Tree Inn L ✓

Scotland End, OX15 5NU (follow the brown tourist signs to Hook Norton brewery)
☎ (01608) 737482 ⊕ peartreehooknorton.com
Hook Norton Hooky Mild, Hooky, Off The Hook, Old Hooky; 2 changing beers (sourced locally; often Hook Norton) Ⓗ
This friendly village pub, driven mainly by wet sales, is an excellent place to sample Hooky Ales. Hook Norton brewery is only 200 yards away, and the pub's accommodation makes it ideal for staying over after a brewery tour. A good range of Hooky beers, including the Mild, may be enjoyed in the cosy bar or large family-friendly beer garden. Delivery is made by horse-drawn dray on Friday lunchtimes, and food trucks often visit on Saturdays. Q📶🕏🕭🍴♣🅟🚃(488)🌳🏳🎵

Horley

Red Lion ⌊

Hornton Lane, OX15 6BQ

☎ (01295) 730427

Hook Norton Hooky; Wye Valley Butty Bach; 1 changing beer (sourced nationally) Ⓗ

Friendly and welcoming village pub, with a warming fire and a lovely garden for all year round tipples. There are three handpumped ales available, with a fourth for special occasions such as the St George's Day annual beer festival. Aunt Sally, darts and dominoes are played here. Closed Monday, lunchtimes Tuesday to Saturday and at 6pm on Sunday. ❀🅰♣🅿🌢🛜♪

Kidlington

King's Arms

4 The Moors, OX5 2AJ (near jct of High St and Church Rd)

☎ (01865) 579287

Wainwright Gold; 2 changing beers (sourced nationally; often Little Ox, Vale, XT) Ⓗ

This double-fronted limestone pub was built in around 1815 and still retains some old thatched outbuildings which were most likely barns or stables. For a long time it belonged to Halls Oxford brewery but was put up for sale by Punch Taverns in 2011 and was bought by a near neighbour who wanted to make sure it stayed a pub. The long-standing two-room layout has been altered to make one large room. ❀&🅿🌢🛜

Launton

Bull Inn

Bicester Road, OX26 5DQ

☎ (01869) 248158 ⊕ bullinnbicester.co.uk

Greene King IPA; 2 changing beers (sourced nationally) Ⓗ

A partially thatched building, with a garden to the rear and a large car park, situated on the crossroads at the heart of the village. The decor is modern yet retains original features including beams and a real fire. Historical photos of the village adorn the walls of this family-run pub. One regular and two changing guest beers are served, and there is a separate dining area. Outside is an attractive beer garden. Regular games nights and a Sunday night quiz are held. ☎❀🅓&♣🅿(17)🌢🛜

Letcombe Regis

Greyhound Inn ⌊

Main Street, OX12 9JL

☎ (01235) 771969 ⊕ thegreyhoundletcombe.co.uk

4 changing beers (sourced nationally; often Oakham, Salopian, Thornbridge) Ⓗ

Large, welcoming pub in the centre of the village. Inside is a single bar, with dining areas and an original inglenook fireplace. Locally sourced home-cooked food and four constantly changing handpumped beers are available. The garden hosts outdoor dining during the summer months. It is a couple of miles from The Ridgeway, and provides an ideal resting place for wayfarers. Local CAMRA Pub of the Year 2022. Parking is available at the side of the pub, and there is secure bicycle storage. Eight boutique en-suite bedrooms are available. Q☎❀🏠🅓&🅰🅿(68)🌢🛜♪

Lewknor

Leathern Bottle

1 High Street, OX49 5TW (N off B4009 near M40 jct 6)

☎ (01844) 351482 ⊕ theleathernbottle.co.uk

Brakspear Gravity; Young's London Special; 2 changing beers (sourced nationally) Ⓗ

Featuring in all but one edition of the Guide, this welcoming, CAMRA award-winning Grade II-listed country pub has been run by the same family since 1980. It has three rooms, separated by a large inglenook fireplace. It serves excellent home-cooked pub food, and has a family-friendly garden. It is popular with walkers from the nearby Ridgeway; some of the best trails start and finish here. Closed Monday (except bank holidays), Tuesday to Saturday afternoons and at 4.30pm on Sunday. ☎❀🅓&♣🅿🌢🛜

Long Wittenham

Plough ⌊

24 High Street, OX14 4QH

☎ (01865) 407738 ⊕ theploughinnlw.co.uk

Butcombe Original; 2 changing beers (sourced locally; often Amwell Springs, Loose Cannon) Ⓗ

A traditional Grade II-listed family-friendly pub built in the 17th century. Its large garden stretches down to the River Thames and has ample outdoor seating and a children's play area. There are two bar areas and a separate restaurant. One regular and two changing beers from local breweries and microbreweries are served. The pub hosts many community events, notably Wittfest, a summer music festival that raises money for local charities. Closed Monday, and at 9pm on Sunday. ☎❀🅓🅰♣🅿(95,D1)🌢🛜♪

Oxford

Bear Inn ★

6 Alfred Street, OX1 4EH

☎ (01865) 728164 ⊕ bearoxford.co.uk

Fuller's London Pride, ESB; Gale's HSB; 2 changing beers (sourced regionally; often Dark Star, Fuller's, Oxford) Ⓗ

Tucked away behind the town hall, this small pub is popular with students and visitors. It gets crowded at times but there is more seating in a paved area to the rear. It is a tied house in more ways than one, and is renowned for its collection of tie remnants taken from customers. The precise age of the pub is open to debate; the present building dates back to 1606. It has recognised by CAMRA as having a nationally important historic pub interior. Q☎❀🅓≋♣🅿🌢🛜♪

Chequers

131 High Street, OX1 4DH (down a narrow passageway off High St, 50yds from Carfax)

☎ (01865) 727463

St Austell Nicholson's Pale Ale; 4 changing beers (sourced nationally) Ⓗ

Much of this Grade II-listed pub dates back to the early 16th century when it was converted from a moneylender's tenement to a tavern, hence the name. Note the fine carvings and windows, and the ceiling in the lower bar. There is ample seating, including an upstairs bar, and the passageway ends in a cobbled courtyard which has plenty of benches and tables. Worth searching out. ☎❀🅓&≋♣🅿🌢🛜

Gardener's Arms ⌊

39 Plantation Road, Walton Manor, OX2 6JE

☎ (01865) 559814 ⊕ thegardenersarms.com

3 changing beers (sourced regionally; often Little Ox, Loose Cannon, XT) Ⓗ

Established in the 1830s, this cosy pub is down a narrow street off Woodstock Road. A popular and relaxing place to eat and drink, the small bar opens up to a spacious dining area, once two rooms, serving some of the finest vegetarian and vegan food in the city. At the rear is a large and pleasant garden, as well as the outside toilets. The famous weekly quiz is on Sunday evening. Closed Monday and Tuesday lunchtimes and Monday to Friday afternoons. Q🛏️❄️●◗♣🚪😺🛜

Grapes 🄻

7 George Street, OX1 2AT

☎ (01865) 793380 ⊕ thegrapesoxford.co.uk

Harvey's Sussex Best Bitter; 5 changing beers (sourced nationally) 🄷

First built in 1820 and rebuilt in 1879, this is a rare Victorian pub in the city centre and is now the oldest building on George Street. There is a single, narrow, panelled room, with the bar on one side and seating on the other. It has been in the hands of an independent pub company since 2023 and boasts 40 keg lines, six casks, and two ciders. Handy for the New Theatre across the road. 🛏️◗&❄️♣🚪😺🛜

Jolly Farmers 🄻

20 Paradise Street, OX1 1LD

⊕ jollyfarmers-oxford.co.uk

Otter Bitter; 1 changing beer (sourced regionally; often Chadlington, LoveBeer, Oxford) 🄷

Oxford's oldest established LGBTQ+ venue, the Jolly Farmers is housed in a 17th-century building, which rests against remains of the city wall, though the first record of it being a pub is in 1829. There are two small, low-beamed rooms, a raised area to the rear with the bar, and a short flight of stairs that lead to a terrace and small garden. The pub is welcoming to all. You can order your own takeaway food and get it delivered. Q🛏️❄️♣🚪😺🛜🎵

Lamb & Flag

12 St Giles, OX1 3JS

☎ (01865) 515787

Oxford Prospect; XT Hop Kitty; 3 changing beers (sourced locally; often Hook Norton, North Cotswold, XT) 🄷

Grade II-listed building owned by the adjacent St John's College since 1695 when it became an alehouse, which was possibly called the Lamb. It was run by various pubcos over the years, then taken back by St John's before being leased to a Community Interest Company in 2023. Some of the profits support student scholarships. It has many literary links, but is not the pub of the same name described in Thomas Hardy's novel Jude the Obscure (that was actually the Turf Tavern). It also has 12 keg lines. Q🛏️❄️●🚪😺🛜

Mason's Arms 🄻

2 Quarry School Place, Headington Quarry, OX3 8LH

☎ (01865) 764579 ⊕ themasonsarmshq.co.uk

Harvey's Sussex Best Bitter; Rebellion Smuggler; Vocation Bread & Butter; 2 changing beers (sourced nationally) 🄷

Family-run community pub hosting many games leagues, including bar billiards and Aunt Sally. The guest ales are varied and turn over quickly, and a wide range of bottled beers is also stocked. The venue is home to the Headington beer festival in September. A heated decking area and garden lead to the function room which hosts music and comedy nights. A regular local CAMRA City Pub of the Year. Closed Monday, Tuesday to Saturday lunchtimes, Tuesday to Friday afternoons, and at 7pm on Sunday. Q🛏️❄️&♣P😺🛜🎵

Rose & Crown ★ 🄻

14 North Parade Avenue, North Oxford, OX2 6LX (½ mile N of city centre, off Banbury Rd)

☎ (01865) 510551 ⊕ roseandcrownoxford.com

Hook Norton Old Hooky; Oxford Trinity; Vale Best IPA; 1 changing beer (sourced locally; often Little Ox, Loose Cannon, XT) 🄷

This characterful free house on a vibrant north Oxford street is a time capsule, with two small rooms and many original features. There is a large, covered patio to the rear giving access to the outside Gents'. The friendly community pub has been run by the same landlords for 40 years. There is no intrusive music and mobile phone use is not permitted. It has been identified by CAMRA as having a regionally important historic pub interior. Closed Monday to Thursday afternoons in August and September. Q🛏️❄️●◗♣🚪🛜🎵

Royal Blenheim 🍺 🄻

13 St Ebbes Street, OX1 1PT

☎ (01865) 242355

Everards Tiger; Titanic Plum Porter; 8 changing beers (sourced nationally; often Lister's, Loose Cannon, Titanic) 🄷

Single-room Victorian pub next to the back of Modern Art Oxford (the building is all that is left of Hanley & Co Ltd, City Brewery). It was built in 1889 for Hanley's on the site of two alehouses in what was then a very rough part of the city. The pub is owned by Everards but run by Titanic brewery. Ten handpumps dispense a choice of Titanic beers, one from Everards, plus interesting guests. Local CAMRA City Pub of the Year 2023 and 2024. 🛏️&❄️♣🚪😺🛜

St Aldates Tavern 🄻 ✅

108 St Aldate's, OX1 1BU

☎ (01865) 241185 ⊕ staldatestavernoxford.co.uk

Oakham Citra; Timothy Taylor Landlord; 4 changing beers (sourced nationally; often Animal, Hook Norton, Ringwood) 🄷

Not the original St Aldates Tavern – that was at No 61, which still has its Morland 'Artist' plaque – but there was an inn recorded at this site in 1397. The pub has been rebuilt at least once since then and renamed several times. It was a coaching inn in the 18th century, with stables and a yard. A taxi service is run from the same yard today. The toilets are down a flight of stairs and at least 30ft below street level. Q🛏️◗❄️♣🚪😺🛜

Teardrop 🄻

Unit 21, Covered Market, High Street, OX1 3DU (on Avenue 1 towards Market St)

☎ (01865) 244407 ⊕ teardropbar.co.uk

Oxford Porter; 1 changing beer (sourced locally; often Animal, Church Hanbrewery, Little Ox) 🄶

This nanopub was opened by Church Hanbrewery in a tiny retail unit in the Grade II-listed Covered Market. Beer is served directly from a cask on stillage or from kegs. It sells its own, somewhat unusual, beers, and others from local small breweries, in ⅓ and ⅔ pint measures. Local wine, spirits and upmarket snacks are also available. It is not open in the evening. Customers have to use the public toilets in Market Street. Q🛏️❄️🚪

White Hart 🄻

12 St Andrew's Road, Headington, OX3 9DL (opp church in Old Headington village)

☎ (01865) 761737 ⊕ thewhitehartheadington.com

Everards Tiger; 4 changing beers (sourced nationally; often Castle Rock, Everards, Oakham) 🄷

Terraced, stone-built pub offering a good selection of Everards ales and guests. The interior is divided into three, with two small bars, and it has a large garden.

Note the framed extract from a play 'The Tragi-Comedy of Joan of Hedington' by Dr William King of Christ Church, written in 1712 about the proprietor of a dishonourable alehouse; thankfully the pub now has a much better reputation. Traditional home-made food is served, with pies a speciality. Closes at 6pm on Sunday.
Q🔥❀◑P🚌🐾📶

White Hart [L]

126 Godstow Road, Wolvercote, OX2 8PQ
☎ (01865) 511978 🌐 thewhitehartwolvercote.co.uk
3 changing beers (sourced locally; often Amwell Springs, Loose Cannon, XT) [H]
A former bakery, this small, open-plan local facing the green at Lower Wolvercote has been a community-run pub since 2014, with a welcoming and family-friendly feel. It serves three or four regularly changing local ales. Food is available on Wednesday to Friday evenings and Sunday brunch is offered. The pub hosts regular music nights featuring jazz, sea-shanties, and Irish folk. Closed Monday to Friday lunchtimes, Monday and Tuesday afternoons and at 8pm on Sundays.
🔥❀◑♿♣P🚌(6,ST2) 🐾📶♫

White Rabbit [L]

21 Friars Entry, OX1 2BY (alley between Magdalen St and Gloucester Green)
☎ (01865) 241177 🌐 whiterabbitoxford.co.uk
5 changing beers (sourced locally; often Amwell Springs, Loose Cannon, Oxford) [H]
Before being renamed the White Rabbit in 2012, this was the Gloucester Arms, which described itself as Oxford's 'premier rock pub'. It has a small bar surrounded by three separate areas. Five local real ales are usually on offer, with one often swapped for cider in the summer. Hand-made pizzas are a speciality, with gluten-free bases available. Outside is a covered paved space with heated seating. ❀◑🚆♣●🚌📶

Playhatch

Flowing Spring

Henley Road, RG4 9RB (on A4155)
☎ (0118) 969 9878 🌐 theflowingspringpub.co.uk
Tring Ridgeway, Colley's Dog; 2 changing beers (sourced nationally; often Arkell's, Palmers, Vale) [H]
Sociable 18th-century country pub on the edge of the Chilterns. This free house features two regular and two varying beers. It serves home-made meals to suit all dietary needs, with award-winning gluten-free, dairy-free, vegetarian and vegan options. Events include monthly unplugged nights, classic car and bike meets, and summer concerts in the large garden. The pleasant covered balcony and large riverside garden are ideal for summer. Standalone motorhomes or campervans are welcome when pre-booked. Closed Monday, Tuesday to Friday afternoons and at 5pm on Sunday.
🔥❀◑♣●P🐾📶♫

Souldern

Fox Inn

Fox Lane, OX27 7JW
☎ (01869) 345284 🌐 thefoxatsouldern.co.uk
St Austell Tribute; 2 changing beers (sourced nationally; often Hook Norton, Loose Cannon, Timothy Taylor) [H]
Licensed in 1784, this former coaching inn in the centre of the village provides a warm welcome and three ales to sample. Tribute is always on tap, along with two regular guests, and there is a menu featuring locally sourced ingredients. Inside is a cosy log-burner, and there is seating outside for enjoying the well-kept ales in the sunshine. Accommodation is available. Closed Monday, weekday afternoons and at 5pm on Sunday.
❀🛏◑♣P🚌(81) 🐾

South Moreton

Crown [L]

High Street, OX11 9AG (in centre of village)
☎ (01235) 810005 🌐 thecrown-southmoreton.co.uk
Loose Cannon Abingdon Bridge; house beer (by Amwell Springs); 1 changing beer (sourced nationally; often Hook Norton, Loddon, North Cotswold) [H]
Community-owned village pub that showcases local ales, including a collaboration with Amwell Springs for the regular house beer, Ye Olde Dash & Tipple, a session IPA. Freshly prepared food is sourced locally and the menu changes regularly to reflect this. There is a large sunny patio for summertime. Local CAMRA Pub of the Year and Cider Pub of the Year 2022. Opens Monday evening for the quiz, then closes all day Tuesday and Wednesday lunchtime, closes at 5pm on Sunday.
Q🔥❀◑⛺♣●P🚌(94A) 🐾📶♫

Steventon

North Star ★ [L]

2 Stocks Lane, OX13 6SG (at the end of The Causeway off B4017)
3 changing beers (sourced regionally; often Amwell Springs, Loose Cannon) [G]
Identified by CAMRA as having a nationally important historic pub interior, this Grade II-listed pub is next to The Causeway, and is a listed ancient monument. Popular with locals and visitors, it hosts many village clubs and social events. Inside are two bars, one with three settles around an open fireplace, and a separate function room. Three beers are served by gravity and presented through a stable door or hatch. Not to be missed. Closed Monday, weekday lunchtimes and Tuesday to Thursday afternoons. 🔥❀♣P🚌(X2)🐾📶

Stoke Lyne

Peyton Arms ★

School Lane, OX27 8SD
☎ 07546 066160
Hook Norton Hooky, Old Hooky [G]
An unspoilt village gem. Two Hook Norton ales are poured directly from the cask, from a small room behind the bar. This is a place for conversation around the small bar or by the fire, and memorabilia is all around. The bar is for adults only; children are welcome in the garden (no dogs allowed). Identified by CAMRA as having a nationally important historic pub interior. Closed Monday to Wednesday, lunchtimes Thursday and Friday, and at 7pm on Saturday and Sunday. Q❀P🚌(81)

Sutton Courtenay

George [L] ✔

4 Church Street, OX14 4NJ (on B4016)
☎ (01235) 848142 🌐 georgesuttoncourtenay.co.uk
Amwell Springs Rude Not To; Loose Cannon Abingdon Bridge; 1 changing beer (sourced locally; often Chiltern) [H]
An imposing, Grade II-listed, 17th-century half-timbered building with two main bar areas, one with a traditional beamed ceiling and real fire. A small meeting room lies beyond the right-hand bar. There is an attractive enclosed garden at the rear with a large covered paved

area. No food is served, though items purchased at the small deli counter in the entrance can be eaten in the pub (or taken away) and there are occasional pop-up street food vendors on some Fridays or Saturdays. Local CAMRA Pub of the Year 2023. Closed Monday to Thursday afternoons. Q☺♿❄)P🚐(33)❀🐕🛜

Thame

Cross Keys 🍷 Ⓛ ✅
East Street, OX9 3JS
☎ (01844) 218202 ⊕ crosskeysthame.co.uk
XT Four; 7 changing beers (sourced nationally; often Thame) Ⓗ
A cosy, friendly and popular drinkers' local. It serves an ever-changing range of ales and ciders, and local breweries often feature alongside unusual ales from small and microbreweries from around the country. On busy evenings, it is not uncommon for several beers to be changed. It hosts many community events, such as comedy nights, live music and local clubs. Local CAMRA Pub of the Year 2024. Closed lunchtimes on Monday, Thursday and Friday, and early afternoons Monday to Thursday. Q☺♣♿🚐❀🛜

Falcon Ⓛ ✅
1 Thame Park Road, OX9 3JA
☎ (01844) 212118
Hook Norton Off The Hook, Old Hooky; 1 changing beer (sourced regionally; often Hook Norton) Ⓗ
Hook Norton's only pub in Thame is a Victorian brick-built establishment about half a mile out of the town centre. It has a large L-shaped bar, and has some seating outside at the front, which is useful for cyclists using the nearby Phoenix Trail, the disused railway between Thame and Princes Risborough. Dominoes, shut the box and shove ha'penny are played by the locals. Closed Monday, weekday lunchtimes and early afternoons, and at 7.30pm on Sunday. ☺◑)♿🚐(121)🛜

Upper Heyford

Barley Mow
Somerton Road, OX25 5LB
☎ (01869) 232300 ⊕ barley-mow-upper-heyford.co.uk
Fuller's London Pride; 2 changing beers (sourced nationally; often Fuller's) Ⓗ
A traditional, community-focused local, on the main road through the village. This is a hub of the community, where a warm welcome is assured. Two Fuller's beers are always available, with a regular guest. There is a large open bar area, refurbished in 2024, with a dartboard and log-burner, and a separate dining room. Outside is a lovely beer garden, with a play area. Regular events include live music and quizzes. Closed Monday lunchtime and afternoon, Tuesday, and Wednesday and Thursday lunchtimes. Q☺♿◑♣P🚐(25)❀🛜

Wallingford

Cross Keys 🍷 Ⓛ ✅
48 High Street, OX10 0DB
☎ (01491) 915888 ⊕ thecrosskeyswallingford.com
House beer (by XT); 3 changing beers (sourced nationally; often Rebellion, Vale, XT) Ⓗ
A 17th-century pub in a Grade II-listed building retaining many original features such as exposed low beams, large fireplaces and an internal cellar. The house beer is Keys Amber from XT, and it offers up to five bag in box real ciders. The large, fenced garden sits on probable Saxon-age town ramparts. There are pop-up food stalls at the rear of the pub (Wed to Sun eve). There is wheelchair to

the pub, but no disabled toilet facilities. Local CAMRA Pub of the Year 2024 and Cider Pub of the Year 2023 and 2024. Closed Monday to Thursday lunchtimes. ☺♿Å⇌(Cholsey & Wallingford)♣♿P🚐❀🛜♪

Wantage

Blue Boar
4 Newbury Street, OX12 8BS
☎ (01235) 760344 ⊕ blueboarwantage.com
2 changing beers (sourced nationally; often St Austell, Timothy Taylor) Ⓗ
Extensively refurbished by the new owner, this spacious town-centre pub has two changing real ales and four changing craft ales. A friendly, pleasant pub with a convivial atmosphere. There is a well-furnished bar with a large selection of gins. Customers can also spend sunny days in the seated area outside. Winner of local CAMRA award for Most Improved Pub 2023. Closed Monday to Thursday lunchtimes. ☺♿♣♿🚐❀🛜♪

King's Arms 🍷 Ⓛ
39 Wallingford Street, OX12 8AU (E of Market Square)
☎ (01235) 765465 ⊕ kingsarmswantage.co.uk
6 changing beers (sourced nationally) Ⓗ
A friendly, open-plan pub with polished wooden floors and panelling. It was given a new lease of life when refurbished by owners Oak Taverns in 2020. Six handpumps adorn the bar, serving constantly changing beers, with six ciders also available. There is a large, sloping garden at the rear, with tables and chairs for drinkers. Local CAMRA Pub of the Year and Cider Pub of the Year 2023 and 2024. Closed Monday to Thursday lunchtimes. Q☺♿♣♿🚐❀🛜♪

Royal Oak Ⓛ
Newbury Street, OX12 8DF (S of Market Square)
☎ (01235) 763129 ⊕ royaloakwantage.co.uk
Wadworth 6X; 8 changing beers (sourced nationally) Ⓖ
This multi award-winning street-corner pub is a mecca for the discerning drinker. All beers are served by gravity, along with 30-plus ciders and perries. Photographs of ships bearing the pub's name are displayed on the walls. The lounge features wrought-iron trelliswork covered in pumpclips. Table football is available in the public bar. Multiple local CAMRA Pub of the Year winner, and local Cider Pub of the Year in 2022. Closed weekday lunchtimes and every afternoon. Q☺♣🚐❀🛜

Shoulder of Mutton Ⓛ
38 Wallingford Street, OX12 8AX (E of Market Square)
☎ (01235) 767158
5 changing beers (sourced nationally) Ⓗ
Friendly and popular Victorian corner pub, colloquially known as the Shoulder, just a short walk from the town centre, serving five constantly changing beers on handpump to suit all tastes. The interior was redesigned in late 2022 to allow greater space for customers. There is an open mic night every Tuesday evening. It has featured in this Guide many times and is a former local, county and regional CAMRA Pub of the Year. Q☺♿♣❀🛜♪

Watlington

Spire & Spoke Ⓛ
21 Hill Road, OX49 5AD (E off B4009)
☎ (01491) 614956 ⊕ thespireandspoke.co.uk
Timothy Taylor Landlord; 4 changing beers (sourced regionally; often Oxford, XT) Ⓗ

A pub with a distinct continental café bar feel serving guest beers sourced mainly from local breweries, as well as coffee, home-made cakes and savoury snacks, and pizzas from their wood-fired oven. It is popular with cyclists and walkers using the nearby Ridgeway route. The pub garden gives a good view of the White Mark chalk triangle on Watlington Hill, originally cut to look like a spire on the parish church. Alcoholic drinks are served from 11am. ♿️🅿️⏰🚲♿️🅰️🅿️🅿️🐕🌳🎵

West Hanney

Plough 🅛
Church Street, OX12 0LN
☎ (01235) 868987 ⊕ theploughathanney.co.uk
4 changing beers (sourced nationally; often Butcombe, Loose Cannon, Timothy Taylor) 🄷
Friendly, 16th-century thatched pub that is the hub of the community. Sold in 2015 by Punch Taverns to a local community group, it has been refurbished and serves four changing beers. It has a cosy, beamed and alcoved split-level bar with an open fire, and there is a separate dining room serving traditional British food. Most of the local clubs meet here from time to time. In summer Aunt Sally is played in the local league. Closed Monday, and at 6pm on Sunday. ♿️🅿️⏰♿️🅰️🅿️🐕🌳🎵

Wheatley

Sun ✅
5 Church Road, OX33 1NB
☎ (01865) 876226 ⊕ sunwheatley.co.uk
XT Four; 3 changing beers (sourced nationally; often Oxford, XT) 🄷
A two-roomed pub with a small front bar, large fireplace, and a low-beamed ceiling. The back room is bigger and brighter, and there is a smart terrace garden. It operated as café for a while, but has been a pub under Oak Taverns since late 2022. Street food pop-ups provide a rotating food option, normally Thursday-Saturday evening and Sunday afternoon. Closed Monday to Thursday lunchtimes. Q♿️🅿️⏰♿️🅿️🐕🌳🎵

Whitchurch Hill

Sun 🅛
Hill Bottom, RG8 7PU
☎ (0118) 984 3909 ⊕ thesunwhitchurchhill.co.uk
Loddon Hoppit; Renegade Good Old Boy; 1 changing beer (sourced locally; often Windsor & Eton) 🄷
A traditional village local, rebuilt in 1910, the Sun was bought from Brakspear in 2013 by a local businessman and became a free house. It serves three local real ales and excellent-value home-cooked pub food lunchtime and evenings Wednesday to Saturday, including a popular roast on Sunday lunchtimes. A log fire warms the bar on cold winter days and benches at the front and on the rear patio are ideal for warmer weather. The pub hosts many events, such as classic car shows, informal chess games and morris dancing. Closes at 8pm on Sunday and Monday. ♿️🅿️⏰♣️🐕🅿️🅿️(146)🌳🎵

Whitchurch on Thames

Greyhound 🅛 ✅
High Street, RG8 7EL (on B471)
☎ (0118) 984 1485
⊕ thegreyhoundwhitchurchonthames.co.uk
XT Four; 2 changing beers (sourced nationally) 🄷
A former ferryman's cottage, the Greyhound has a main L-shaped bar with a low ceiling and plenty of beams and wood panelling, all decorated in a contemporary,

minimalist style. A small meeting/function room has been opened up to the right of the entrance, which can be booked by groups. It has an attractive, partially covered, garden to the rear with plenty of seating. Pop-up hot food is available Friday and Saturday evenings, and either Tuesday or Thursday evening and all day Sunday. Closed Monday to Thursday lunchtimes. Q♿️🅿️⏰🅰️🚉(Pangbourne)♣️🐕🅿️🅿️(143,146)🌳🌳🎵

Witney

Angel Inn 🅛 ✅
42 Market Square, OX28 6AL
☎ (01993) 703238
Brakspear Oxford Gold; Wychwood Hobgoblin Gold, Hobgoblin Ruby; house beer (by Marston's) 🄷
A Grade II-listed free house at one time owned by Joseph Early of the blanket manufacturing dynasty and a brewer. It has a fine front bar with low beams and a bay window, with plenty of space for drinkers and diners to the rear. Outside is a small paved and walled courtyard. The beer range is mostly from Marston's, though its Wychwood brewery, which was just around the corner, has closed. 🅿️⏰♣️🐕🅿️🌳🌳🎵

Crafty Pint 🅛
8 Langdale Court, OX28 6FG (walk down passageway directly opp Blue Boar in town centre)
☎ 07973 693972 ⊕ craftypintbar.co.uk
2 changing beers (sourced locally; often Little Ox, LoveBeer, Oxford) 🄷
Witney's first micropub was opened by a father-and-son team who started a nearby brewery, Oxbrew, which merged with Little Ox brewery in 2019. It has since changed hands and is now run by the former managers. The pub has two handpulls from casks and six taps from kegs, serving a selection of beers from small local breweries. No food but you can bring your own. Closed Monday and Tuesday, Wednesday and Thursday afternoons, and at 8pm on Sunday. Q🌳🅿️🅿️🌳🎵

Eagle Tavern 🅛 ✅
22 Corn Street, OX28 6BL
☎ (01993) 700121 ⊕ eagletavernwitney.co.uk
Hook Norton Hooky, Hooky Gold, Old Hooky; 1 changing beer (sourced locally; often Hook Norton) 🄷
This Grade II-listed building has been an inn from the early 19th century, when it was the Coach & Horses. Owned by Hook Norton for over 20 years, it serves a range of the brewery's ales alongside malt whiskies, bourbons, gins and rums. The interior has three seating areas and lots of dark wood. You can see the cellar through the window next to the bar. Closed Monday and Tuesday, lunchtimes except Friday and Saturday, and Wednesday and Thursday afternoons. Q🌳♿️♣️🐕🅿️🌳🌳🎵

Woodstock

Punch Bowl
12 Oxford Street, OX20 1TR
☎ (01993) 811218 ⊕ punchbowlwoodstock.co.uk
Arkell's Wiltshire Gold, 3B 🄷
This attractive, recently refurbished town-centre pub provides a calm and relaxing atmosphere. Inside you can either sit by the fire and try the two Arkell's beers on tap, or the occasional Donnington brewery guest, or try the locally sourced menu in the back area. There is a pleasant courtyard at the back and seating outside at the front. There are nine en-suite rooms available. Closes at 9pm Mondays and Tuesdays, at 9.30pm Wednesdays and Thursdays, and at 6pm on Sundays. Q♿️🅿️⏰♿️🅰️🅿️🌳🌳

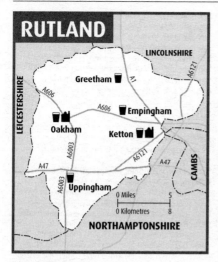

Empingham

Empingham Cricket & Social Club
Exton Road, LE15 8QB
☎ 07813 177293 ⊕ empinghamcsc.org
2 changing beers Ⓗ
The Cricket & Social Club is noted for the quality and variety of its ales, which are all from microbreweries. It is run and staffed by volunteers and therefore has limited hours, often extended on Saturdays by sporting and other functions. An annual beer festival is held to coincide with the final matches of the Six Nations rugby in March. A regular local CAMRA award winner.
Q ➳ ⑳ ♿ P 🖵 ♬ 🌳 🎵

Greetham

Plough
23 Main Street, LE15 7NJ
☎ (01572) 813613 ⊕ theploughgreetham.co.uk
Timothy Taylor Boltmaker, Knowle Spring, Landlord; 1 changing beer Ⓗ
A former Mann's pub, with a decent beer range. The new owners have made many changes, including an ice cream parlour and tea room in the garden, both of which are open from Easter. Good-value pub food is served daily using local suppliers and food from the pub's own allotment. This community-focused pub has undergone extensive work to enlarge the outdoor seating area. Live music at weekends and regular quiz nights are held. A former local CAMRA Pub of the Year.
Q ➳ ⑳ ⑪ Å P 🖵 ♬ 🎵

Ketton

Railway 🍷
Church Street, PE9 3TA
☎ (01780) 721050
Bakers Dozen Electric Landlady; Grainstore Ten Fifty; Oakham Citra Ⓗ
A traditional village local situated in the shadow of the impressive church, serving good beer and wine in a welcoming and friendly atmosphere. The Grade II-listed building is several hundred years old, with much character and more than a little charm. Food is not normally served, but functions can be catered for. A fourth beer can be added at busy times. A former local and regional CAMRA Pub of the Year. Q ➳ ⑳ P 🖵 ♬

Oakham

Captain Noel Newton ✅
55 High Street, LE15 6AJ
☎ (01572) 725490
Greene King Abbot; Ruddles Best Bitter; Sharp's Doom Bar; changing beers Ⓗ
Rutland's only JD Wetherspoon outlet, this town-centre pub features regularly in the local CAMRA shortlists for the quality of ales served. It has an excellent range of frequently changing ales and several real ciders are usually available. With friendly and knowledgeable staff, it is well worth a visit. The premises was previously the Royal British Legion having been acquired from Captain Noel Newton who served in WWI and was awarded the Military Cross. ➳ ⑳ ⑪ ♿ ≠ 🖵 🛜

Grainstore Brewery Tap
Station Approach, LE15 6RE
☎ (01572) 770065 ⊕ grainstorebrewery.com
Grainstore Cooking, Rutland Osprey, Triple B, Ten Fifty; 3 changing beers (often Grainstore) Ⓗ
A pub and brewery in a cleverly converted small warehouse, retaining some original features. Brewery tours are available but must be booked in advance. Ten handpumps offer a range of beers, always including a mild. Home-made food is served, with breakfasts at weekends. Live bands feature regularly. Walkers and their dogs are welcome. Regular beer and cider festivals are held, the main one being over the August bank holiday. A regular local CAMRA award winner.
➳ ⑪ ♿ ≠ ♣ ⑪ P 🖵 ⑳ 🛜 🎵

Wheatsheaf
2-4 Northgate, LE15 6QS
☎ (01572) 756124 ⊕ wheatsheafoakham.com
Everards Sunchaser, Old Original, Tiger; 1 changing beer (sourced locally) Ⓗ
Attractive, traditional pub in the heart of Oakham village, opposite the church. It has plenty of olde-worlde character and a good range of Everards beers, with changing seasonal options. The pub has a strong local following, but is welcoming to all. It serves good food. A popular monthly quiz is held on the third Thursday of the month. ⑳ ⑪ ≠ ♠ ⑳ 🛜

Uppingham

Exeter Arms
3 Leicester Road, LE15 9SB (follow High St W past the school and turn right)
☎ (01572) 822900
Langton Inclined Plane Bitter; 2 changing beers (often Thornbridge) Ⓗ
A friendly, old-fashioned drinking establishment to the west of the town centre. Though recently refurbished, the Ex is a real survivor, featuring fixtures and fittings from a previous era in several different seating areas and the separate pool table area. The pub has a largescreen TV and can be busy when major rugby and football matches are shown. Inclined Plane from nearby Langton brewery is the regular ale, supplemented by two frequently changing guests. ➳ ♿ ♣ ⑳ 🛜 🎵

REAL ALE BREWERIES

Bakers Dozen Ketton
Grainstore 🍺 ♦ Oakham

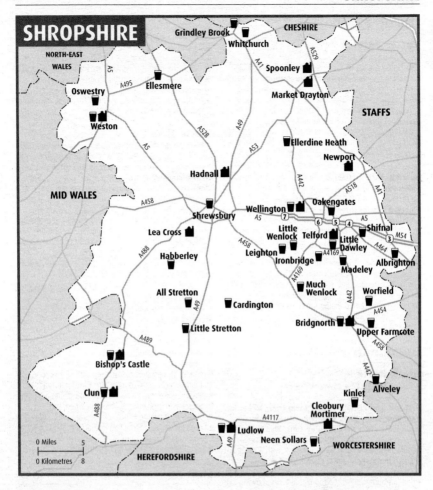

Albrighton

Harp Hotel L

40 High Street, WV7 3JF

☎ (01902) 271754

Black Country Bradley's Finest Golden, Pig on the Wall, Fireside; 7 changing beers ⊞

This traditional village local has a large U-shaped room served by a central bar. There is a sheltered outdoor seating area and covered smoking shelter. Three regular beers are available, often with monthly specials from Black Country Ales and changing beers from around the UK. Snacks including pies and cobs are usually on the bar. Quizzes are held on the first Tuesday of the month and a darts team plays on Monday. Children are welcome until 7pm. ⍟❀❅✇♣🚪(891)❀🛜

All Stretton

Yew Tree Inn L

Shrewsbury Road, SY6 6HG

☎ (01694) 328953

Wye Valley HPA, Butty Bach; 2 changing beers (sourced locally) ⊞

A three-roomed Grade II listed local situated in a pretty village surrounded by the Shropshire Hills. The pub consists of a bar, a separate lounge, and a dining room, each with its own character, but with an overall atmosphere of comfort, permanence and tradition. There are exposed low beams, log fires and masses of photographs, paintings and other ornaments adorning the walls. Traditional pub meals are offered, with roast dinners available on Sundays. There is a large pleasant outdoor area by the main door. Dogs are welcome in the bar. Q⍟❀⍟♣🚪(435)❀

Alveley

Three Horseshoes Inn 🏆 L

Main Street, WV15 6NB (turn from A442 to village, pub is opp end of Daddlebrook Rd) SO760845

☎ (01746) 780923 ⊕ thethreehorseshoesalveley.co.uk

Bathams Best Bitter; Wye Valley HPA; 3 changing beers (sourced locally; often Enville, Hobsons, Three Tuns) ⊞

Set in the picturesque village of Alveley, the pub has stood on the site since 1406, making it the oldest in Shropshire. The tastefully restored interior combines original features while still being cosy and comfortable. The spacious beer garden offers views of the Severn Valley and the Clee Hills beyond, and has a play area for children. Traditional bar food is available as well as a fine dining menu in the restaurant.
⍟❀⍟▲♣♦P🚪(297) ❀🛜♪

Bishop's Castle

Castle Hotel ★
The Square, SY9 5BN
☎ (01588) 638403 ⊕ thecastlehotelbishopscastle.co.uk
Clun Pale Ale; Salopian Oracle; Three Tuns Best, XXX Ⓗ
A welcome return to the Guide for the 18th-century
Grade II-listed Castle Hotel at the top of the town. Its
three character-filled rooms feature real fires in winter,
and serve three beers from local breweries, plus one
from regional brewer Salopian. It also boasts a wonderful
beer garden with great vistas. Traditional pub games are
played. Q ➔ ✿ 🛏 🌙 ⅃ & ♿ P ☐ (553) ✿ 🌐 ♫

Three Tuns Inn Ⓛ
Salop Street, SY9 5BW
☎ (01588) 638797 ⊕ thethreetunsinn.co.uk
**Salopian Oracle; Three Tuns XXX; Timothy Taylor
Landlord; Wye Valley HPA, Butty Bach** Ⓗ
A truly historic pub that was once linked to one of the
Famous Four brewpubs still brewing in the early 1970s
when CAMRA was formed, but now separately owned.
This means that sometimes no Three Tuns beers are
served, although usually there is at least one. The pub
has been extended into four rooms: a public bar, a
lounge and snug in the original building, and the
extended oak-framed dining room. Function and
meeting rooms are available for hire.
Q ➔ ✿ 🌙 Ⓐ ♣ ☐ (553) ✿ 🌐 ♫

Bridgnorth

Black Horse Ⓛ
4 Bridge Street, Low Town, WV15 6AF
☎ (01746) 762415 ⊕ theblackhorsebridgnorth.co.uk
**Bathams Best Bitter; Hobsons Town Crier; Three Tuns
XXX; Wye Valley HPA; 3 changing beers (sourced
regionally; often Enville, Three Tuns, Wye Valley)** Ⓗ
First licensed in 1810, this Low Town free house is
popular with all ages. It has a front bar with a rustic but
modern atmosphere and a double-sided log-burner, a
panelled lounge and a conservatory, also with a double-
sided log-burner. All three rooms have TVs showing live
sport. There is karaoke every Thursday and regular live
entertainment on Saturday. There are two external
drinking areas, one of which is mostly covered. En-suite
B&B accommodation is available. Many bus routes stop
outside. ➔ ✿ 🛏 ♿ ♣ P ☐ ✿ 🌐 ♫

Golden Lion Ⓛ
83 High Street, High Town, WV16 4DS
☎ (01746) 762016 ⊕ goldenlionbridgnorth.co.uk
**Holden's Black Country Mild, Black Country Bitter,
Golden Glow, Special; 1 changing beer (sourced
locally)** Ⓗ
A traditional town-centre pub with three bars. Regulars
congregate in the main public bar for a communal quiz
on Mondays. Historic pictures of the pub are displayed in
the two lounges. A corridor to the rear leads to a covered
smoking area, a patio garden and a car park. Filled rolls
are generally available, with free bar snacks on Friday
evening and Sunday daytime. It has B&B
accommodation. Q ➔ ✿ 🛏 ♣ P ☐ ✿ 🌐

Railwayman's Arms Ⓛ
**Severn Valley Railway Station, Hollybush Road,
WV16 5DT** (follow signs for SVR)
☎ (01746) 760920 ⊕ svr.co.uk
**Bathams Best Bitter; Bewdley Worcestershire Way;
Hobsons Mild, Best, Town Crier; house beer (by
Bewdley); 2 changing beers (sourced nationally;
often Bewdley)** Ⓗ

The Severn Valley Railway's popular pub on platform 1 of
Bridgnorth Station has been licensed continuously since
1861 and is full of railway memorabilia. The eight
handpumps serve local and national ales, plus one cider
or perry. The platform drinking area is incredibly popular
at weekends and holidays for absorbing the atmosphere
of a steam railway. Opening times vary in winter when
the railway is not operating; check Facebook for details.
Q ➔ ✿ ♿ ≠ ♣ P ☐ (9,297) ✿ 🌐

White Lion Ⓛ
3 West Castle Street, WV16 4AB (between town centre
and Severn Valley Railway) ⊕ whitelion-bridgnorth.co.uk
**7 changing beers (sourced nationally; often Hobsons,
Thornbridge)** Ⓗ
Reopened in 2023, this popular town-centre pub
comprises two seating areas with a central bar. It has
seven cask beers on handpump, most of which are
sourced from micro and regional brewers beers and are
not available elsewhere in Bridgnorth. Street food is
available during kitchen hours, and cobs or baguettes are
available all day. A large outside area has an
entertainment stage. It is said to be the most haunted
pub in town! Q ➔ ✿ 🛏 ♿ ≠ ☐ (297,890) ✿ 🌐 ♫

Cardington

Royal Oak
SY6 7JZ
☎ (01694) 771266 ⊕ at-the-oak.com
Ludlow Best; 2 changing beers Ⓗ
The Royal Oak, dating back to the 15th century, is
reputedly Shropshire's oldest continually licensed pub,
and is the archetypal country inn. The single room is
multi-functional, with a bar, lounge and dining area, and
has a relaxed ambience. It is low-beamed and
dominated by a large inglenook fireplace which provides
a home for various interesting artefacts. A good choice of
beers includes a mix of local and regional brews and a
draught cider. Q ✿ 🌙 Ⓐ ♣ ♣ P ☐ (540) ✿ 🌐

Clun

White Horse Inn Ⓛ ✅
The Square, SY7 8JA
☎ (01588) 418151 ⊕ whitehorseclun.com
**Clun Loophole, Pale Ale, Citadel; Ludlow Gold; Wye
Valley Butty Bach** Ⓗ
16th-century inn and posthouse standing in the old
market square of a timeless town, described by AE
Housman as one of the quietest places under the sun.
Inside is an L-shaped bar with low beams, and the pub
has extended into the properties on either side to form a
dining room and quiet room. Excellent, reasonably-priced
food is served. The pub is linked to the Clun brewery and

REAL ALE BREWERIES	
All Nations 🍺	Telford
Clun 🍺	Clun
Finney's Telford:	Wellington (brewing suspended)
Hobsons ✦	Cleobury Mortimer
Joule's	Market Drayton
Ludlow ✦	Ludlow
Noble Craft	Spoonley (NEW)
Plan B	Newport
Rowton 🍺 Telford:	Wellington
Salopian	Hadnall
Severn Valley	Bridgnorth (brewing suspended)
St Annes	Lea Cross
Stonehouse ✦	Weston
Three Tuns 🍺	Bishop's Castle

stocks its products. Rotating real ciders are available. There is a secluded garden outside.
🚴🏵️✇🌓🅰️🐾🐕🤵🛜🎵

Ellerdine Heath

Royal Oak 🅛 ✅
Hazles Road, TF6 6RL (midway between A442 and A53) SJ603226
☎ (01939) 250300
Hobsons Best; Wye Valley HPA, Butty Bach; 3 changing beers (sourced locally; often Rowton, Salopian) 🅗
A long-standing Guide entry, known locally as the Tiddly, at the heart of the local community. It features a real fire, three regular beers and up to three guests, plus real cider. Substantial cobs and snacks are available. Dominoes is played on Monday, poker on the last Tuesday of the month, and bike night is hosted on Wednesdays from April to October. Disabled access is at the rear. This gem welcomes locals, visitors, families and dogs. Camping is possible at the rear and there is a large car park outside. Q🚴🏵️♿🅰️🐾🐕🅿️🤵🛜🎵

Ellesmere

White Hart 🅛
Birch Road, SY12 0ET
☎ (01691) 624653
House beer (by Plan B); 2 changing beers (sourced locally) 🅗
A Grade II-listed building of the early Jacobean period, with a wealth of exposed timber, but also some later alterations. The interior comprises a public bar and a lounge. The drinking area to the rear has a tented gazebo. Three guest beers include offerings from local breweries. It is convenient for the Llangollen Canal as the marina is close by. The pub was once owned by the Border Brewery of Wrexham. 🏵️🐕🅿️🚗🤵🛜🎵

Grindley Brook

Horse & Jockey 🅛
SY13 4QJ
☎ (01948) 662723 ⊕ thehorseandjockey.pub
House beer (by Merlin); 7 changing beers 🅗
The 19th-century core of the pub is quite small, but over time it has been extended considerably, and is now a welcoming and attractive place. There are various nooks and crannies serving different purposes, all tastefully done, with extensive use of reclaimed timber and quality furnishing. While the emphasis is on dining, there is ample provision for drinkers. Outside is a lawned area with children's play equipment. The pub is close to the Llangollen Canal and Cheshire's Sandstone Trail.
🚴🏵️🌓♿🅰️🐕🅿️🚗(41)🤵🛜

Habberley

Mytton Arms 🅛
SY5 0TP
☎ (01743) 792490
Three Tuns XXX; Wye Valley HPA 🅗
Situated in a small village on the edge of the South Shropshire Hills, somewhat off the beaten track, this popular, rustic pub is worth seeking out. There are four low-beamed rooms and a friendly atmosphere where beer and conversation dominate. Outside there are seats to the front, and a paved area with a vine-covered pergola to the side. A well-known local character and pub regular features on the inn sign. Q🏵️🐕🅿️🤵

Kinlet

Eagle & Serpent 🅛
DY12 3BE SO717802
☎ (01299) 841227
Hobsons Town Crier; Wye Valley HPA; house beer (by Hobsons) 🅗
A welcoming, family-run, 17th-century pub in a rural village. It has a roomy bar and a large dining area to the rear, with other, separate drinking areas surrounding a log fire. There are four handpulls dispensing at least three cask ales from local breweries. Bar snacks as well as lunchtime and evening menus are available. It is popular with walkers and cyclists as it is on the Geopark Way Trail and close to the Wyre Forest. The hourly Bridgnorth to Kidderminster bus stops outside. 🚴🏵️🌓♿🐕🅿️🚗(125)🤵🛜

Leighton

Mill at Leighton 🅛 ✅
Main Road, SY5 6RN (on the B4380, about 4 miles W of Ironbridge)
☎ (01952) 443559 ⊕ themillatleighton.com
Wye Valley HPA; 4 changing beers (sourced locally; often Hobsons, Rowton, Three Tuns) 🅗
This vibrant, friendly pub is on a site mentioned in the Domesday Book. It retains an ancient corn mill wheel and was featured in the archaeological TV programme Time Team. It is now community owned and has been sympathetically refurbished. Photographs of the beautiful local area are on the walls, and local produce is used whenever possible in the wholesome food available. Carefully chosen, well-kept ales make this pub a most welcome new entry to this Guide. Closed on Monday during the winter.
Q🚴🏵️🌓🅰️🐕🅿️🚗(96,96A)🤵🛜🎵

Little Stretton

Green Dragon
Ludlow Road, SY6 6RE
☎ (01694) 722925 ⊕ thegreendragonpub.co.uk
Ludlow Gold; Wye Valley HPA, Butty Bach; 1 changing beer (often Ludlow, Monty's) 🅗
A pub set in a picturesque location in the Shropshire Hills Area of Outstanding Natural Beauty, with an abundance of walks in the district. The L-shaped bar has a comfortable and welcoming feel and the pleasant dining areas are well used. A collection of wonderfully shaped clay pipes on the bar wall may well be of interest. The beer is mostly from local breweries, as is the cider. Popular with walkers. 🚴🏵️🌓🐕🅿️🚗(435)🤵🛜

Little Wenlock

Huntsman of Little Wenlock 🅛
Wellington Road, TF6 5BH
☎ (01952) 503300 ⊕ thehuntsmanoflittlewenlock.co.uk
Wye Valley HPA, Butty Bach; house beer (by Greene King); 4 changing beers (sourced locally; often Hobsons, Rowton, Three Tuns) 🅗
Nestling below the prominent Wrekin hill, this award-winning pub is popular with locals, walkers, and visitors to this scenic area near Telford, and is the focus of village life. Food is served all day in the restaurant and cosy bar from a varied menu, including Sunday lunch and bar nibbles. B&B rooms, a holiday cottage, and motor caravan hook-up are available. Dogs are allowed in the bar only. Q🚴🏵️✇🌓♿🅰️🅿️🤵🛜

Ludlow

Blood Bay
13 High Street, SY8 1BS
Uley Taverner, Pale; 1 changing beer Ⓗ
This small pub is a gem, with many 19th-century features surviving from when the building was a Victorian shop. The public bar serves three beers, usually an amber bitter, a pale ale and a dark beer, and a limited range of other drinks. The snug behind the main bar can also be accessed from Market Street. A further room and toilets are upstairs. Dogs are welcome but mobile phones and young children are not permitted. Q➺♦🌳🏠🐾

Blue Boar ✅
52 Mill Street, SY8 1BB (opp Assembly Rooms)
☎ (01584) 878989 ⊕ blueboarludlow.co.uk
Black Sheep Best Bitter; Hobsons Town Crier; Three Tuns XXX; Wye Valley HPA Ⓗ
This popular hostelry, just off the local square, has a long history, including an alleged ghost. It is a one-bar pub with three distinct areas; the front area is wood panelled with a real fire while the others have their own character. There is an outdoor drinking area and a separate function room upstairs. The pub serves mainly local beers but can stock an occasional surprising guest. ➺🏯🌳◑➺🏠🐾🎵

Church Inn
The Buttercross, SY8 1AW
☎ (01584) 874034 ⊕ thechurchinn.com
Hobsons Best; Ludlow Gold; Wye Valley HPA, Butty Bach Ⓗ
Popular 14th-century town-centre pub which has undergone a comprehensive refurbishment. The ground-floor drinking area has a contemporary feel, with a range of seating. There is also an upstairs seating area with spectacular views of the Church of St Laurence, from which the pub takes its name. Local beers and gins are served. Traditional pub fare and gastro-style meals are available. The pub has accommodation.
➺🏯🏠◑➺🌳🐾🛜

Ludlow Brewing Co Ⓛ
Station Drive, SY8 2PQ
☎ (01584) 873291 ⊕ theludlowbrewingcompany.co.uk
Ludlow Best, Blonde, Gold, Black Knight, Red Dawn, Stairway; 1 changing beer (sourced locally; often Ludlow) Ⓗ
The Ludlow Brewing Co tap was once a railway shed beside Ludlow Station. Now it showcases the brewery's beers as well as other local produce. It comprises a two-level bar area, a balcony, shop and brewery, with many brewing operations visible from the bar. The company has green credentials, harvesting rain water and using solar panels. Although normal opening hours end late afternoon, there are many after-hours events, including live music, charity events and a beer festival in February.
Q➺🌳🏯♿🌳♦P🏠🛜🎵

Much Wenlock

George & Dragon Ⓛ ✅
2 High Street, TF13 6AA
☎ (01952) 727009 ⊕ thebestpubintheworld.com
Wye Valley HPA; 4 changing beers (sourced nationally; often Exmoor, Salopian, Timothy Taylor) Ⓗ
A lively, friendly pub in a beautiful small market town. The attractive frontage opens to the front bar, with timber-backed settles and original flooring and beams. The rear bar, dominated by a large fireplace, is cosy and intimate, with an abundance of old timbers. Effort is

made to accommodate wheelchairs here. A wide variety of meals, mostly home-made, is available, including pub favourites, vegetarian options, and smaller meals. A public Pay & Display car park is behind the pub.
Q➺🌳🏯◑♿♦🌳🚌(8A,436) 🐾🛜🎵

Neen Sollars

Live & Let Live Ⓛ
DY14 9AB (1 mile off A456 W of Mamble) SO668720
☎ (01299) 832391
Hobsons Best; Wye Valley HPA; 1 changing beer (sourced locally; often Bewdley) Ⓗ
Partly dating from the 13th century, this out of the way rural gem is awash with elaborate reclaimed woodwork. The main bar leads to a number of rooms, including the smaller original bar and a large dining area. Locally sourced home-cooked food includes seasonal specials. A range of malt whiskies and gins complements the local ales (those from Hobsons may vary). There are extensive views towards Clee Hill and Ludlow from the elevated beer garden. A holiday let is available and motorhomes may be parked overnight. May close early if quiet.
Q➺🏯🏠◑♦P🐾🛜

Oswestry

Bailey Head 🍷 Ⓛ
Bailey Head, SY11 1PZ (in Market Square opp Guildhall)
☎ (01691) 570418 ⊕ baileyhead.co.uk
Stonehouse Station Bitter; 6 changing beers (sourced nationally) Ⓗ
Award-winning free house in the market square near the old castle. The pub offers one permanent and five changing real ales – including vegan-friendly options – KeyKeg beers, four draught real ciders and a perry. Beers are sourced locally, regionally and nationally, usually from microbreweries, and served in thirds if requested. Food can be ordered in. Events include tap takeovers, Meet the Brewer and music or quiz nights. Dogs are especially welcome. The market car park is nearby.
➺🏯♿♦🌳🚌🐾🛜

Shifnal

Anvil Inn Ⓛ
22 Aston Road, TF11 8DU
☎ (01952) 462686
Black Country Bradley's Finest Golden, Pig on the Wall, Fireside; 5 changing beers (sourced regionally) Ⓗ
Popular family-run Black Country Ales pub with a real fire and 10 handpulls, supporting many local pastimes including darts and domino teams, curry evenings and coach trips to other pubs. Substantial fresh bar snacks are always available. A garden area at the rear sports a large gazebo. Beer festivals are held three times a year and feature foot-long hot dogs. Dogs are welcome. Free parking is 150 yards away, and the train station is 100 yards on foot. Q➺🏯♿➺♦P🌳🐾🛜

King's Yard Ⓛ
2 Cheapside, Bradford Street, TF11 8BN
☎ (01952) 453553 ⊕ kingsyardpub.com
Wye Valley Butty Bach, HPA; 2 changing beers (sourced regionally) Ⓗ
A popular micropub in the centre of town. Four handpulls include two dedicated to Wye Valley, one to a dark beer and one to a guest. Six craft beers, a craft lager and a cider are on tap and numerous bottles and cans are available from fridges. Upstairs seating adds to the available drinking area, and the pub is conducive to

drinking and conversation. Fresh filled cobs, pork pies and sausage rolls are made to order if needed. Parking is available nearby. Q❄️❄️♿️♣️♠️🅿️🚃🔊

Plough Inn L
26 Broadway, TF11 8AZ
☎ (01952) 411507 ⊕ theploughinnshifnal.co.uk
Hobsons Best; 3 changing beers (sourced regionally) 🅷
Traditional free house dating back to the 17th century, with tiled floors and exposed beams. Up to four cask ales and two ciders are available. Home-cooked meals are served Tuesday to Saturday with a popular roast on Sunday. A huge beer garden is a suntrap in warm weather, and also has a large outdoor covered heating area. A large function room is available for hire. Wednesday afternoon bingo and a Sunday night quiz are hosted weekly. Dogs are welcome.
Q❄️❄️◐♣️♠️♣️🅿️🚃🔊

Shrewsbury

Abbey L ✅
83 Monkmoor Road, Monkmoor, SY2 5AZ
☎ (01743) 236788
Sharp's Doom Bar; 4 changing beers 🅷
A large pub with several alcoves, plus a beer garden with heated and covered areas. Up to five ales are offered, from a range of breweries and across a variety of styles, as well as a number of sparkling and still ciders (not all of which are real), plus craft keg beers. Food is served until 10pm every evening. There are regular community events including quizzes and a Monday Club with discounted real ales. ❄️❄️◐♿️♣️♠️♣️🅿️🚃(1)🔊♪

Cromwell's Tap House
11 Dogpole, SY1 1EN (in town centre, just past St Mary's Church)
☎ (01743) 365158 ⊕ cromwellstaphouse.co.uk
3 changing beers 🅷
Making its first appearance in the Guide is this free house, with three handpulls serving beers sourced widely, but usually from microbreweries; craft beers and local spirits are also available. The bar frontage is Grade II-listed though much of the rest was refurbished in 2010. A separate room is used for functions and dining. Outside is a secluded, ivy-clad garden terrace, with a smoking area and patio heaters. The garden offers unrivalled views of medieval Shrewsbury's rooftops. Beer festivals are planned for 2024.
❄️❄️♿️◐🚃♠️🔊♪

Cross Foxes
27 Longden Coleham, SY3 7DE (close to River Severn in suburb of Longden Coleham)
☎ (01743) 355050
Draught Bass; Three Tuns XXX; Wye Valley HPA; Butty Bach 🅷
The pub has been a free house since its purchase from Mitchells & Butlers in the late 1980s, and run by the same family since 1985. It has one large L-shaped room, with the bar and major drinking area on the long side, the shorter side occupied by the dartboard and another drinking area. The main part has an efficient wood-burner and the walls are adorned with sports trophies and a fine Bass mirror. Q♿️♣️♠️🚃🔊

Nag's Head L
22 Wyle Cop, SY1 1XB
☎ (01743) 362455
Timothy Taylor Landlord; Wye Valley HPA; 3 changing beers (often Titanic) 🅷

Situated on the historic Wyle Cop, the main architectural features of this popular Grade II-listed timber-framed building are best appreciated externally. To the front there is notable upper-storey jettying and in the pleasant beer garden to the rear are the timber remnants of a 14th-century hall house. The old-style interior has remained unaltered for many years. The pub is said to be haunted and features on the Shrewsbury Ghost Trail.
❄️≋🚃♠️

Prince of Wales L
30 Bynner Street, Belle Vue, SY3 7NZ
☎ (01743) 343301 ⊕ theprince.pub
Hobsons Mild, Twisted Spire; Salopian Golden Thread; St Austell Tribute; 2 changing beers (sourced locally) 🅷
Welcoming two-roomed community pub with a heated smoking shelter and large suntrap deck, adjoining a bowling green overlooked by a 19th-century maltings. Darts, dominoes and bowls teams are hosted. Beer festivals are held in February and May. Shrewsbury Town FC memorabilia adorn the building, with some of the seating from the old Gay Meadow ground skirting the bowling green. Westons Rosie's Pig is served on handpull. In 2019 the pub deservedly reached the last 16 of the CAMRA National Pub of the Year.
❄️❄️♿️♣️♠️🅿️🚃♠️🔊♪

Salopian Bar L ✅
29-31 Smithfield Road, SY1 1PW
☎ (01743) 351505
Oakham Citra; Salopian Oracle; Wye Valley Butty Bach; 2 changing beers (sourced nationally) 🅷
A multi-room pub, expanded and refurbished in 2020, now with an added separate lounge and function room. The bar's management strives to vary the beer, cider and perry range to satisfy demand for variety (though some ciders are not real), and an increasing range of bottled beers, including gluten-free, can also be bought. Largescreen TVs show coverage of major sports events. It is popular with all age groups, and there is regular live music on Friday and Saturday evenings.
❄️♿️≋♣️🚃♠️🔊♪

Shrewsbury Hotel ✅
Mardol, SY1 1PU (by Welsh Bridge, best access from bottom of Mardol)
☎ (01743) 236203
Greene King Abbot; Ruddles Best Bitter; Sharp's Doom Bar; 3 changing beers (sourced nationally; often Ludlow, Salopian, Titanic) 🅷
Situated close to Welsh Bridge and the River Severn, this hotel was Wetherspoon's first. The two linked bar areas are distinct from each other; one has an open fire and a library while at the other end of the bar is an area with alcoves and a large window with a view of the newly-built cellar. There is a large outdoor drinking area.
❄️❄️≋◐♿️≋🚃🔊

Tap & Can
13 Castle Gates, SY1 2AB
☎ 07837 490495
4 changing beers 🅷
Opened in 2019, this single-room bar close to the town railway station has its counter at the far end. Four handpumps offer a changing range of real ales, plus live KeyKeg and craft keg beers. Real ciders and perries are served from the cellar, while cans are served from vast fridges near the bar, available to drink in or take away. The rear wall of the Gents is the exposed castle foundations and is over 900 years old. Dogs are welcome. ◐≋♠️🚃♠️

Three Fishes L

4 Fish Street, SY1 1UR
☎ (01743) 344793
4 changing beers (sourced regionally; often Salopian) Ⓗ

15th-century building of historic character standing in the shadow of two churches, St Alkmund's and St Julian's, within the maze of streets and passageways in the town's medieval quarter. Freshly prepared food is available at lunchtimes Tuesday to Saturday. The pub offers up to five local and national ales, often including a dark beer, and still cider. It is a friendly pub with no TV screens and good conversation. Dogs are welcome. Q❶♣♠🚃♿🐾🌭

Woodman ★ L

32 Coton Hill, SY1 2DZ
☎ (01743) 351007
Ossett White Rat; Salopian Shropshire Gold; Wye Valley Butty Bach; 2 changing beers (sourced regionally) Ⓗ

Part-brick and part half-timbered black and white corner pub, rebuilt in 1925 following a fire, and reputedly haunted by the ex-landlady who died in the fire. The wonderful oak-panelled lounge has two real log fires and traditional settles, and the separate bar has the original stone-tiled flooring, wooden seating, fire and listed leaded windows. The courtyard has a heated smoking area and seating, and a coach house has been converted to a meeting/function room. The pub specialises in pale, hoppy beers. Q❄🌭♣♠🚃🐾🌭♫

Telford: Ironbridge

Coracle Micropub & Beer Shop

27 High Street, TF8 7AD
☎ (01952) 432664
Salopian Shropshire Gold; 4 changing beers (sourced nationally; often Glasshouse, Salopian, Verdant) Ⓗ

A popular micropub just yards from the historic Iron Bridge. Its name reflects the local production and operation of coracles on the River Severn. The choice of cask ale (four in winter) is supplemented by an ever-changing selection of 11 KeyKeg dispensed beers, plus 60 bottled and canned beers. The pub hosts regular tap takeovers. Locally made bar snacks are available and customers may bring in their own food. Children are welcome until 7pm. Q❄🚃♣🚃(8,18)🐾🌭

Telford: Little Dawley

Unicorn Inn

Holly Road, TF4 3HZ
☎ 0800 246 5173
Salopian Lemon Dream; Three Tuns XXX; 2 changing beers (sourced regionally; often Enville, Purple Moose, Rowton) Ⓗ

This large free house has four handpulls supplying two regular beers and two guests, including a stout, plus a real cider. An extensive range of craft beers is also available, including low- and no-alcohol beers. A long room with a couple of steps leads to the bar and access to the large garden and smoking area. Generously sized cobs, pies and bar food are always available. Live music is hosted at weekends and a quiz on the last Thursday of the month. Dogs are welcome. 🌭❶♣🌭♠P🚃🐾🌭♫

Telford: Madeley

All Nations L

20 Coalport Road, TF7 5DP (signed off Legges Way, opp Blists Hill Museum)

☎ (01952) 585747 ⊕ allnationsinn.co.uk
All Nations Bitter; Wye Valley HPA; 3 changing beers (sourced regionally; often Ludlow, Wye Valley) Ⓗ

One of the last four historic brewhouses in the country at the start of the 1970s, near Blists Hill museum and the World Heritage Area. Now a CAMRA Golden Award winner, the pub is well known for its friendly clientele. Five handpumps serve two own-brewed beers plus three guest ales. It has a small, cosy interior, with a wood-burner in winter. Substantial fresh baps are served. Dogs are welcome. Glamping pods are located in the field at the rear of the pub. Q🌭❄♿🏕️♠P🌭🐾🌭♫

Telford: Oakengates

Crown Inn L ✓

Market Street, TF2 6EA
☎ (01952) 610888
Hobsons Best, Twisted Spire; 10 changing beers (sourced nationally; often Big Hand, Burton Bridge, Goff's) Ⓗ

Cosy, traditional three-room town pub with real fires in front and rear bars. It offers real cider, mild and stout/porter. There are 14 cooled handpulls, with more for festivals in May, and an extensive range of overseas bottled beers is sold. A regular comedy club is hosted, as well as live music, quiz and games nights (details on Facebook). There is level access via a suntrap courtyard at the rear from the bus station and car park. Quality bar snacks are available. CAMRA Golden Award winner. 🌭🌭♿🚃(Oakengates)♣🌭🚃🐾🌭♫

Old Fighting Cocks L

48 Market Street, TF2 6DU
☎ (01952) 615607
Everards Old Original; Oakham Citra; Rowton Area 51; Ironbridge Gold, Meteorite; 4 changing beers (sourced nationally) Ⓗ

Popular and cosy family-run pub in the town's busy high street, close to good transport links. The front entrance bar leads to a rear area and snug, with a larger drinking area at the back. Twelve handpulls dispense three from Rowton's own brewery, one from Everards, and a selection of ever-changing beers on the others. A function room is available upstairs. A covered courtyard has some seating outside. Bar snacks are usually available. Car park nearby. 🌭♿🚃(Oakengates)♣🌭🚃🐾🌭

Telford: Wellington

Boot Micropub

2 Market Square, TF1 1BP
☎ (01952) 240118
Hobsons Town Crier; 3 changing beers (sourced nationally) Ⓗ

Micropub in the centre of Wellington, near the Market Hall entrance. Six handpulls serve at least one dark ale, one from Salopian brewery and two real ciders, plus a large range of keg beers. Bar food is available. Dogs are allowed; and children up to 7pm. The car parks in Wellington are free, but with restricted hours; check at the ticket point for details. Wellington bus station is nearby. 🌭🌭♿🚃(Wellington)🌭P🚃🐾🌭♫

Pheasant Inn ♥ L

54 Market Street, TF1 1DT
☎ (01952) 260683
Everards Tiger; Rowton Ironbridge Gold, Area 51; 4 changing beers (sourced nationally; often Rowton) Ⓗ

Rowton's brewery tap is one of their three family-run traditional pubs, and was local CAMRA County Pub of The

Year 2022. Nine handpulls dispense three Rowton's ales, four changing beers (at least one of which is dark), plus two changing ciders. A large beer garden with a covered area is next to the brewery. Home-made food is served Tuesday to Saturday noon to 4pm; bar snacks are available at any time. Public car parks are nearby. Disabled access is via the rear door. Dogs are welcome. Q☆✿◖◗↺≥(Wellington) ●🚷🚍🐕🦮🛜

Wrekin Inn 🅛

26 Wrekin Road, TF1 1RH (just off ring road by the leisure centre on the edge of town)
☎ (01952) 263375 🌐 rowtonbrewery.com
Rowton Area 51, Ironbridge Gold, Meteorite; 4 changing beers (sourced nationally; often Rowton) Ⓗ
A recently refurbished traditional real ale pub run by Rowton brewery. There are two comfortable bar areas with log-burners and a pool room. Three Rowton beers are on handpull, plus three guests, one of which will normally be below 4% ABV, and a dark beer. An extensive craft beer range is available from the fridge. Live music regularly features at weekends, but is quiet at other times. There are good public transport links and and is less than half a mile from the brewery and its tap house, the Pheasant Inn.
☆✿◖≥(Wellington) ♣●🚍🐕🦮🛜♪

Upper Farmcote

Lion O'Morfe 🅛

WV15 5PS (½ mile from A458 signposted Claverley) SO770919
☎ (01746) 389935
Hobsons Town Crier; Wye Valley HPA; 2 changing beers (sourced locally; often Enville, Ludlow, Three Tuns) Ⓗ
A popular locals' pub dating back to the 1850s, this former Georgian farmhouse serves a good range of ales and cider on handpump. There are several rooms: a bar with an open fire, snug, lounge, and conservatory, as well as a large garden that is popular with walkers and cyclists. Home-cooked meals are served every lunchtime except Monday, and Wednesday to Saturday evenings.
Q☆✿◖◗▲♣●P🐕🦮♪

Weston

Stonehouse Brewery 🅛

Stonehouse, Weston Road, SY10 9ES (just off A483 Oswestry bypass)

☎ (01691) 676457 🌐 stonehousebrewery.co.uk
Stonehouse Station Bitter, Cambrian Gold; 1 changing beer (often Stonehouse) Ⓗ
The Stonehouse Brewery Visitor Centre bar is part of the family-run brewery and distillery next to the preserved Cambrian Railway. The rustic-styled Centre sells only Stonehouse products – at least four cask beers, their own keg beers, Sweeney Mountain Cider, and Henstone spirits. Stonehouse spirits will appear during 2024, starting with gin. Bottles, gift packs and fill-your-own facilities are available. Brewery tours are by appointment. Food is served Wednesday to Sunday in summer, and Thursday to Sunday in winter
Q☆✿◖◗♿♣●P🚍🐕🦮🛜

Whitchurch

Black Bear 🅛

49 High Street, SY13 1AZ

☎ (01948) 663800 🌐 blackbearwhitchurch.co.uk
Stonehouse Station Bitter; 4 changing beers (sourced regionally; often Hobsons, Plan B, Weetwood) Ⓗ
A tastefully renovated black and white pub with a welcoming beer garden to the rear. It lies opposite the historic St Alkmund's church at the top of High Street. The ornate bar has five handpulls serving an ever-changing range of guest beers from both local and lesser-known national microbreweries, with pumpclips adorning the walls, ceiling and bar area. Cider is served on gravity. There are two separate dining areas, and an upstairs meeting room. ✿◖◗🚍🐕🦮🛜♪

Worfield

Dog & Davenport Arms 🅛

Main Street, WV15 5LF (from A454 towards village, then turn towards church and pub is opp school) SO758956
☎ (01746) 716020
Hobsons Town Crier; Wye Valley HPA; 1 changing beer (sourced locally) Ⓗ
Known locally as the Dog, this 19th-century, Grade II-listed village inn was first licensed in 1800 and was originally called the Greyhound. It has a separate bar with a low ceiling, a lounge with a wood-burning stove, restaurant areas, and a small patio area at the rear. The hourly Wolverhampton to Bridgnorth bus (Arriva route 9) stops nearby in Wyken. Q☆✿◖◗♿♣●P🚍(114)🐕🦮🛜

Kitchen of an inn

In the evening we reached a village where I had determined to pass the night. As we drove into the great gateway of the inn, I saw on one side the light of a rousing kitchen fire beaming through a window. I entered, and admired for the hundredth time that picture of convenience, neatness, and broad honest enjoyment, the kitchen of an English inn.

It was of spacious dimension, hung around by copper and tin vessels, highly polished, and decorated here and there with a Christmas green. Hams, tongues, and flitches of bacon were suspended from the ceiling; a smoke-jack made its ceaseless clanking behind the fireplace, and a clock ticked in one corner. A well-scoured deal table extended along one side of the kitchen, with a cold round of beef, and other hearty viands upon it, over which two foaming tankards of ale seemed mounting guard. Travellers of inferior order were preparing to attack this stout repast, while others sat smoking or gossiping over their ale, on two high-backed oaken settles beside the fire.

Washington Irving, Travelling at Christmas, 1884

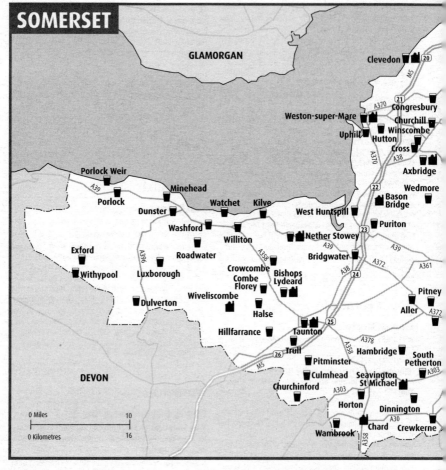

SOMERSET

Map showing: GLAMORGAN, Clevedon (20), Congresbury (21), Churchill, Winscombe, Weston-super-Mare, Uphill, Hutton, Cross, Axbridge, Wedmore, Bason Bridge (22), Puriton, Porlock Weir, Minehead, Watchet, Kilve, West Huntspill, Porlock, Dunster, Washford, Williton, Nether Stowey (23), Exford, Roadwater, Crowcombe, Bishops Lydeard, Bridgwater (24), Withypool, Luxborough, Combe Florey, Wiveliscombe, Halse, Pitney, Dulverton, Aller, Hillfarrance, Taunton (25), Trull, Hambridge, South Petherton, Pitminster, Culmhead, Seavington St Michael, Churchinford, Horton, Dinnington, Wambrook, Chard, Crewkerne, DEVON

0 Miles 10
0 Kilometres 16

Aller

Old Pound Inn

1 High Street, TA10 0RA (centre of village)
☎ (01458) 250469 ⊕ oldpoundinn.com
Butcombe Original; Teignworthy Reel Ale; 1 changing beer (sourced regionally; often Exmoor, Otter) ⊞
This lovely 16th-century inn stands on the ground of the old village pound. A varying selection of three regional ales and a local cider is on handpump. A wonderful open Dutch fire is a feature in the centre of the bar. There is a separate restaurant/function room, public lounge and a delightful snug. Excellent food, including a Sunday carvery is served in the bar or restaurant.
⅌❀❄◐&▲♣♠P☷⊟(16)❀☎♪

Axbridge

Lamb ⊘

The Square, BS26 2AP
☎ (01934) 732253 ⊕ butcombe.com/the-lamb
Butcombe Original; 1 changing beer (sourced locally; often Butcombe) ⊞
Lovely Butcombe-owned Grade II-listed coaching house in the village square. Inside is a large low-beamed bar area with several smaller, quieter areas leading off it, where traditional pub games can be played. There are outside drinking spaces to the front, and to the rear via the courtyard. The interesting food menu includes bar

snacks. Directly opposite is the National Trust's medieval King John's Hunting Lodge, where Hanging Judge Jeffreys held court. Q⅌❀◐♣⊟(26,126)❀☎♪

Bath

Bath Brew House ⊘

14 James Street West, BA1 2BX
☎ (01225) 805609 ⊕ thebathbrewhouse.com
Bath Brew House Gladiator, Emperor; 3 changing beers (sourced locally; often Bath Brew House) ⊞
A 2013 refurbishment turned the Midland Hotel into a busy and popular town-centre brewpub. The on-site brewery, Bath Brew House, produces two regular beers, the malty Gladiator (3.9% ABV) and the hoppy, citrussy Emperor (4.4% ABV) and up to four additional real ales. The large bar leads to a dining area and a large beer garden (covered in winter) which shows major free-to-air sporting events. The upstairs Tank room hosts quizzes, comedy, and other events. ⅌❀◐&⩥(Spa)❀☎♪

Bell

103 Walcot Street, BA1 5BW
☎ (01225) 460426 ⊕ thebellinnbath.co.uk
Bath Ales Gem; Bristol Beer Factory Independence; Butcombe Adam Henson's Rare Breed; Hop Back Summer Lightning; Otter Ale; 2 changing beers (sourced locally) ⊞

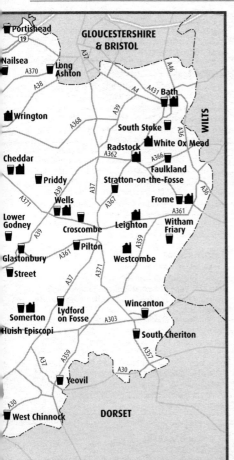

Fuller's London Pride, ESB; 2 changing beers (sourced regionally) 🅷
A handsome old building set on the pretty Abbey Green. Dating from 1654 it was originally known as the Three Tuns Lodging House and is where Admiral Nelson is believed to have stayed. The cosy interior consists of a bar and separate lounge with a conservatory and enclosed courtyard to the rear. There are usually two Fuller's beers on offer, plus one or two often interesting guest ales from local or regional brewers.
꩜❀◑🕭⇌(Spa)🚌❀🛜

Curfew

11 Cleveland Place West, BA1 5DG
☎ (01225) 251505
Fuller's London Pride; Timothy Taylor Landlord; 3 changing beers (often Butcombe, St Austell) 🅷
A busy and popular rugby-oriented pub on the outskirts of the city centre. Previously a Wadworth pub it reopened in 2023 under the management of a well-known local publican and usually features two regular ales and up to three guests. An upstairs dining room is decorated in the modern wine bar style. Food offerings may vary, so check with pub. Opening hours may also change with the seasons. ❀◑🕭❀♪

Huntsman

1 Terrace Walk, BA1 1LJ
☎ (01225) 482900 ⊕ huntsmanbathpub.co.uk
Fuller's London Pride, ESB; 3 changing beers (sourced regionally) 🅷
A smart gastro-pub run by Fuller's since 2012 and popular with visitors, especially when Bath rugby club plays at home. The historic Grade-II listed building near the Abbey dates back to between 1748 and 1750 and has a large à la carte style restaurant and function room with its own bar upstairs. Up to three guest beers are usually on offer alongside the Fuller's beers.
꩜◑⇌(Spa)🚌❀🛜

The Bell was purchased by 536 of its regulars, fans, and staff, through a community buy-out in 2013. It has five regular ales plus two or three ever-changing guests from local micros. Live music is a mainstay with bands playing Monday and Wednesday evenings and Sunday lunchtimes. Open-mic nights on Thursday evenings are held in the separate back bar to the rear. Features include bar billiards, board games and even a tiny launderette. At the rear is a walled garden with covered seating. ꩜❀◑♣🚌❀🛜♪

Coeur de Lion ✅

17 Northumberland Place, BA1 5AR
☎ (01225) 463568
Abbey Bath Best, Bath Pale Ale; 2 changing beers (sourced nationally; often Abbey, Millstone) 🅷
Situated in a narrow passageway in the centre of town, this pub claims to be the smallest in Bath; with just four tables in the small bar this may well be true. Operated by local Abbey Ales brewery, it features a range of their beers. An upstairs room is used mainly for food, and seating capacity is increased in summer by tables outside the pub. The pub's most unique feature is the fine stained-glass window that forms the pub's frontage.
Q꩜❀◑⇌(Spa)♣🚌❀🛜

Crystal Palace

10-11 Abbey Green, BA1 1NW
☎ (01225) 482666 ⊕ crystalpalacepub.co.uk

REAL ALE BREWERIES

Abbey Bath
Badgworth 🍺 Axbridge (NEW)
Bason Bridge 🍺 Bason Bridge
Bath Brew House 🍾 Bath
Black Bear 🍾 Wiveliscombe (brewing suspended)
Blindmans Leighton
Butcombe Wrington
Cheddar 🍺 Cheddar
Clevedon 🍺 Clevedon
Electric Bear 🍾 Bath
Exmoor Wiveliscombe
Fat Head 🍾 Weston-super-Mare (NEW)
Fine Tuned Somerton
Frome Frome
Golden River Bath
Nuttycombe 🍺 Wiveliscombe
On The Level Taunton (NEW)
Parkway Somerton
Pinkers Weston-Super-Mare
Quantock 🍺 Bishops Lydeard
Ralph's Ruin 🍾 Bath
Somer Valley White Ox Mead (NEW)
Stowey Nether Stowey
Tapstone 🍺 Chard
Twisted Oak Wrington
Windy 🍾 Seavington St Michael
Woodshedding Westcombe (NEW)
Wookey Wells
Yonder Radstock

New Inn

23-24 Monmouth Place, BA1 2AY
☎ (01225) 442944 ● newinnbath.co.uk
**Uley Old Spot Prize Strong Ale; 3 changing beers
(sourced regionally; often Butcombe, Exeter)** Ⓗ
A small and friendly venue with a modern tiled bar area
serving a range of local cask and craft ales. Further
seating can be found upstairs in a small room and a roof
terrace with its own bar. A popular spot on Bath's music
scene, with regular sessions held in the main bar. It is
part of a small local pub group, Banwell House, that
operates pubs in and around Bath.
❀❀◑⇌(Spa) ●🅿️❀🛜🎵

Old Green Tree 🍷 ★

12 Green Street, BA1 2JZ
☎ (01225) 448259
**Butcombe Original; RCH Pitchfork; house beer (by
Blindmans); 3 changing beers (sourced locally)** Ⓗ
A classic, unspoilt pub in a 300-year-old building. The
oak-panelled rooms include a superb northern-style
drinking lobby. Though often crowded, there can be
space in the cosy back room. Guest beers are generally
sourced from local microbreweries, with a stout or porter
usually on offer during the winter. A local farmhouse
cider is also available, along with a range of fine wines
and malt whiskies. Local CAMRA Pub of the Year 2024.
Closed on a Sunday evening. **Q**⇌(Spa)●🅿️

Pulteney Arms ✅

37 Daniel Street, BA2 6ND (on corner of Daniel St and
Sutton St)
☎ (01225) 463923 ● thepulteneyarms.co.uk
**Timothy Taylor Landlord; Wye Valley HPA; 3 changing
beers (sourced nationally; often Exmoor, Fuller's,
Otter)** Ⓗ
Tucked away near the end of Great Pulteney Street, this
pub dates back to 1792. The decor shows an emphasis on
sport, particularly rugby, and the cat symbol on the pub
sign refers to the Pulteney coat of arms. The guest beers
are usually from a national brewery. There are five gas
light fittings (now sadly condemned) above the bar. The
pub is likely to be closed Mondays and Tuesdays, and
midweek afternoons in winter; check before travelling.
❀❀◑♣🅿️❀🛜

Raven

6-7 Queen Street, BA1 1HE
☎ (01225) 425045 ● theravenofbath.co.uk
**Cheddar Ales Potholer; Exeter Darkness; Frome The
Usual; Hop Back Summer Lightning; house beer (by
Blindmans); 4 changing beers (sourced regionally;
often Branscombe, New Bristol)** Ⓗ
A popular and busy 18th-century free house in the heart
of Bath. Significantly extended in 2022 it now has four
bars across three floors serving up to nine ales, with the
guests coming from far and wide. The two house beers
are brewed exclusively by local brewery Blindmans. Real
cider from local producers is always available, and there
are occasional mini beer festivals. Pieminister pies are
served. Local CAMRA Pub of the Year 2023.
Q❀◑⇌(Spa)♣●🅿️🛜🎵

Ring o'Bells

10 Widcombe Parade, BA2 4JT
☎ (01225) 727599 ● ringobellsbath.com
**4 changing beers (often Butcombe, Exeter, Timothy
Taylor)** Ⓗ
A friendly and lively Widcombe pub with a village pub
feel yet only a stone's throw from the city centre. Rugby
is often shown on one of several TV screens and the pub
is especially popular on match days when the large
upstairs function room is brought into use. The main bar

is a single long room with a range of wooden tables
overlooking the street and along one wall facing the bar
counter. Four changing ales are served, along with well-
regarded food. ❀❀◑⇌(Spa)🅿️❀🛜🎵

Royal Oak

Lower Bristol Road, Twerton, BA2 3BW (on A36 at
intersection with the road to Windsor Bridge)
☎ (01225) 481409 ● theroyaloakbath.co.uk
**Ralph's Ruin Ivory Tower, Sirius, Dark Side of the
Ralph; 5 changing beers (sourced nationally; often
Bristol Beer Factory, Fine Tuned)** Ⓗ
A pub since 1840, it closed in 1999, but has now turned
its fortunes around. Eight real ales include three or four
from its own brewery, Ralph's Ruin, and up to five guest
beers from microbreweries near and far, alongside an
interesting range of real ciders, perries and bottled
Belgian beers. There is live music up to five nights per
week, regular quiz nights and Meet the Brewer events.
Outside is a secluded garden and a small car park.
❀⇌(Oldfield Park)●🅿️🚌(5,15)❀🎵

Salamander

3 John Street, BA1 2JL
☎ (01225) 428889 ● salamanderbath.co.uk
**Bath Ales Gem; St Austell Anthem, Proper Job; 2
changing beers (sourced locally; often Bath Ales, St
Austell)** Ⓗ
An 18th-century building, tucked away in a side street,
that opened as a coffee house in 1957 and got a pub licence
five years later. Taken over by St Austell in 2017 it looks
and feels like a pub that's been there for a century or
more, with wooden floorboards, wood panelling and
subdued lighting adding to the ambience of the ground-
floor bar, created from several small rooms. A popular
restaurant upstairs uses local ales in cooking.
◑⇌(Spa)♣🅿️❀🛜

Star Inn ★ ✅

23 Vineyards, BA1 5NA
☎ (01225) 425072
Abbey Bellringer Ⓗ**; Draught Bass** Ⓖ**; 3 changing
beers (sourced nationally; often Abbey, Adnams,
Titanic)** Ⓗ
A main outlet for Abbey Ales, this classic town pub dating
from 1760 was fitted out by Gaskell and Chambers in
1928. Its four small rooms have benches around the
walls, wood panelling and roaring fires. The smallest
room has a single bench, called Death Row. Bass is
served from the cask and complimentary snuff is
available. Cheese night is every Thursday and live music
features on Fridays evenings. Local CAMRA Pub of the
Year 2022. **Q**♣🅿️❀🛜🎵

Bishops Lydeard

Quantock Brewery Tap Ⓛ

Westridge Way, Broadgauge Business Park, TA4 3RU
(follow signs to West Somerset Railway, and shop is on
left just before station)
☎ (01823) 433812 ● quantockbrewery.co.uk
**Quantock QPA, Wills Neck, Radicle; 4 changing beers
(sourced locally; often Quantock)** Ⓗ
Brewery tap room with up to six of the brewery's cask
beers on handpump and two on KeyKeg plus a monthly
small batch KeyKeg, subject to availability. One or two
guest KeyKeg beers are available, typically from
Northern Monk, Salopian, Thornbridge or Weird Beard. A
brewery shop supplies takeaway bottles and other
merchandise. There is an annual beer festival in July and
regular live band, comedy and quiz nights. Street food is
available Friday and most Saturday evenings.
❀❀♿⇌🅿️🚌(28)❀🛜🎵

Bridgwater

West India House

101 Durleigh Road, TA6 7JE (top of Durleigh Rd Hill)
☎ (01278) 452533
Butcombe Original; Sharp's Doom Bar; 2 changing beers (sourced locally; often Cheddar Ales, St Austell, Twisted Oak) Ⓗ
Constructed in 1936, there has been a pub on site for many years with the name derived from the days when Bridgwater was a bustling port. For a quiet drink in cosy surroundings there is the lounge bar complete with open log fire and for a more vibrant atmosphere try the saloon bar which has been extended and refurbished with modern decor and has three good ales from Butcombe, Sharp's and occasionally Cheddar Ales, Twisted Oak, St Austell and Quantock. Q❀◑♣P🚌(14)📶♫

Cheddar

Bath Arms

Bath Street, BS27 3AA
☎ (01934) 742425 🌐 batharms.com
Cheddar Ales Gorge Best, Potholer; 1 changing beer (often Cheddar Ales) Ⓗ
Large friendly pub close to Cheddar village centre, set back from the road, with an impressive creeper-clad exterior giving way to a thriving L-shaped bar area, and a separate dining room. The outdoor seating area is where the old stagecoaches would have parked at an older inn called the George which stood on the roadside in front of the present pub. There is a pleasant garden and a car park to the rear. Freshly-cooked meals are served throughout the pub. ❀🛏◑♿ΔP🚌🐾📶

Cheddar Ales Tap Room

Unit 5, Winchester Farm, Draycott Road, BS27 3RP
☎ (01934) 744193 🌐 cheddarales.co.uk
Cheddar Ales Gorge Best, Piney Sleight, Potholer, Crown & Glory; 2 changing beers (often Cheddar Ales) Ⓗ
Taproom for Cheddar Ales brewery, situated just outside the world-famous village. The venue is a pleasant diversion from the tourist hotspot and serves up to six cask ales brewed on site. A takeaway service is also available. Cider, gins and wines are served, along with wood-fired pizzas at weekends, except during the winter months. There is indoor and outdoor seating, and occasional live music events take place on Saturdays. Check the website for seasonal opening times as they can be changeable. ❀◑♿Δ♣●P🐾♫

Churchill

Crown Inn 𝕃

The Batch, Skinners Lane, BS25 5PP (off A38, 400yds S of A368 junction)
☎ (01934) 852995 🌐 crowninnchurchill.co.uk
Butcombe Original; Otter Bitter; Palmers IPA; St Austell Tribute; 1 changing beer (often Bristol Beer Factory, Exmoor, Otter) Ⓖ
Long-time Guide regular and winner of many CAMRA awards, this unchanged classic old pub is tucked away down a small lane close to the village centre. Several cosy rooms with stone-flagged floors are warmed by two log fires, and offer an assortment of seating. Excellent food made using local ingredients is available at lunchtimes. Five ales from local and regional breweries are served on gravity. Outside drinking areas are to the front and rear. Families are welcome away from the bar itself. Q❀◐Δ●P🚌(125,FAL)🐾📶♫

Churchinford

York Inn ✔

Honiton Road, TA3 7RF
☎ (01823) 601333 🌐 yorkinn.co.uk
Otter Bitter, Amber; Sharp's Sea Fury; 1 changing beer (sourced regionally) Ⓗ
The York Inn, situated in the Blackdown Hills, is a traditional hostelry dating back, in some parts, to the 16th century. It has an open fireplace and oak beams and offers contemporary facilities and a good range of four cask ales and one real cider. Good, traditional home-cooked food includes a specialist range of pies. ❀◑♣●P🐾📶♫

Clevedon

Fallen Tree Micropub 𝕃

43 Hill Road, BS21 7PD
☎ 07493 924386
6 changing beers (sourced locally; often Cheddar Ales, Frome, Twisted Oak) Ⓖ
Situated close to the Grade I-listed pier, this was the first micropub in North Somerset when it opened in 2018. Ales are dispensed straight from casks located in the wooden stillage behind the bar. Up to six beers are served, mainly from local breweries but with occasional guests from further afield. A real cider, local gins, wines, prosecco and soft drinks are also sold. Additional seating is available on the pavement outside. Closed on Monday and Tuesday. Q♿♣●🚌🐾

Old Inn ✔

9 Walton Road, BS21 6AE
☎ (01275) 340440 🌐 theoldinn.pub
Butcombe Original; Sharp's Doom Bar; 2 changing beers (often Cheddar Ales) Ⓗ
This traditional, award-winning pub is one of Clevedon's oldest pubs, dating to about 1754. There is an ever-changing array of real ales, with up to four served. The hosts pride themselves on their locally sourced home-cooked food. There is decked area and a garden at the rear of the pub. Wednesday quiz nights are popular and live music features as well as other events. ❀🛏◑P🚌🐾📶♫

Combe Florey

Farmers Arms 𝕃

TA4 3HZ (on A358 between Bishops Lydeard and Williton)
☎ (01823) 432267 🌐 farmersarmsatcombeflorey.co.uk
Exmoor Ale, Gold; Timothy Taylor Landlord; 1 changing beer Ⓗ
A beautiful thatched 14th-century Grade II-listed pub with cob walls, a medieval chimney, fireplace and restored staircase. The bar serves three cask ales and three real ciders plus some unusual keg beers, bottled beers and a large selection of gin and malt whisky. Thre is a large pizza oven in the attractive garden, which has covered and heated seating. If travelling by car, access is on the south side of second bridge from Taunton under the West Somerset Railway; beware the tricky turn. ❀◑♿●P🐾📶♫

Congresbury

Plough 𝕃

High Street, BS49 5JA (off A370 at B3133 jct)
☎ (01934) 877402 🌐 the-plough-inn.net

Butcombe Original Ⓗ; St Austell Tribute; 3 changing beers (sourced locally; often Cheddar Ales, Nuttycombe, Twisted Oak) Ⓗ/Ⓖ
Characterful village inn with flagstone floors and many original features, decorated with interesting old artefacts. Three guest ales, mainly from local and regional breweries such as Cheddar, Twisted Oak and Nuttycombe, are delivered from a row of old cask heads behind the bar, and one handpump. The pub has a well-deserved reputation for the quality of its food, which is served lunchtimes and evenings, except Sunday evening, which is quiz night. Real fires and a large garden make this a year-round destination. Q❤️🛏🏠🍴🚆🍽🅿🚌☀️🐾🎵

Crewkerne

King William Inn

Barn Street, TA18 8BP (take A30 towards Chard; at fringe of town, the uphill Barn St is on left)
☎ (01460) 73692 🌐 kingwilliamcrewkerne.com
3 changing beers (sourced nationally; often Bristol Beer Factory, Cerne Abbas, Quantock) Ⓗ
A short walk from the town centre towards Chard takes you to this well hidden traditional pub. There are three changing ales and two ciders and the array of pumpclips adorning the beams indicates the huge range of beers that have been served over the years. X (formerly Twitter) shows the beers that are being added. There is a happy hour during the early evening every Monday and Wednesday. For music lovers there is an acoustic night the last Wednesday of each month. Its spacious beer garden features a children's play area.
🛏🏠🐾🍴🅿🚌(6,96)☀️🎵

Croscombe

George Inn

Long Street, BA5 3QH (on A371 between Wells and Shepton Mallet)
☎ (01749) 342306 🌐 thegeorgeinn.co.uk
House beer (by Blindmans); 2 changing beers (often Cheddar Ales, St Austell) Ⓗ
Attractive 17th-century inn, refurbished by the owner, serving at least four guest ales from West Country independents and hosting two beer festivals a year. Blindmans King George and George & Dragon are exclusively brewed for the pub. Two real ciders are available, with Hecks Kingston Black and Thatchers ciders regulars. There is a large main bar, snug with fireplace, family room and a separate dining room. The food is home-cooked using locally sourced ingredients in modern theatre kitchen. A skittle alley/meeting room is to the rear and outside is a large garden with a covered terrace. Q🛏🏠🚐🍴🚆🍴🅿🚌☀️🎵

Cross

New Inn

Old Coach Road, BS26 2EE (on the A38/A361 junction)
☎ (01934) 732455 🌐 newinncross.co.uk
Otter Bitter, Ale; 3 changing beers (often Bristol Beer Factory, Cheddar Ales, Twisted Oak) Ⓗ
A 17th-century roadside inn on the A38, close to the historic medieval town of Axbridge. Up to three guest beers, often rare for the area, are usually available as well as two regular ales from Otter. The pub is popular for its extensive food menu, using quality local produce, served all day. Families and dogs are welcome. The large hillside garden with children's play facilities offers a fine view of the Mendip Hills and Somerset Levels. There is a small car park opposite. 🛏🏠🍴🅿🚌(48)☀️🎵

White Hart

Old Coach Road, BS26 2EE
☎ (01934) 733108 🌐 whitehartcross.co.uk
2 changing beers (often Dartmoor, St Austell) Ⓗ
This 17th-century inn reopened in 2019 after refurbishment. It is reputed to be haunted by one of Hanging Judge Jeffreys' victims. Inside there is a games bar with pool and darts, and a door leading to a lounge-style area. Beers come from St Austell or sometimes another regional brewery. Lunches are served, as well as evening meals on Friday. There is a large car park opposite. Closed Monday and Tuesday.
🛏🏠🍴🗡🚆🅿🚌(48)☀️🍴🎵

Crowcombe

Carew Arms ★ Ⓛ

TA4 4AD (village signed off A358)
☎ (01984) 618631 🌐 thecarewarms.co.uk
Exmoor Ale, Gold; house beer (by Marston's); 1 changing beer (sourced locally; often Nuttycombe, Quantock) Ⓗ
A 17th-century rural pub at the foot of the beautiful Quantock Hills. The flagstone public bar has a historic inglenook, and the large garden looking towards the Brendon Hills makes this popular with locals, walkers and dogs. The bar/restaurant serves locally sourced food with some restaurant tables set within the old stables area. The skittle alley doubles as a function room. The pub serves up to four ales, including one changing guest ale, and two real ciders. Q🛏🏠🚐🍴🗡🚆🅿🚌(28)☀️🍴🎵

Culmhead

Holman Clavel Inn

TA3 7EA (¼ mile off B3170)
☎ (01823) 421070 🌐 theholmanclavelinn.co.uk
Hanlons Yellow Hammer; Otter Bitter; 1 changing beer (sourced regionally; often Otter) Ⓗ
This is a real country pub set in the Blackdown Hills area of outstanding natural beauty, with three good ales straight from the barrel, Harry's cider, wine, food and company. Children, dogs, walkers, cyclists and muddy boots are welcome. Food is sourced from local farmers, suppliers and local businesses and gluten free diners and vegetarians are catered for. Local musicians play Irish style sessions every first Thursday of the month. Q🛏🏠🚐🍴🗡🚆🅿☀️🎵

Dinnington

Dinnington Docks Inn ✅

TA17 8SX (approx 3 miles E of Ilminster off B3168)
☎ (01460) 52397 🌐 dinningtondocks.com
Butcombe Original; Hanlons Yellow Hammer; Teignworthy Gun Dog; 2 changing beers (sourced locally; often Bristol Beer Factory, Exmoor, Fine Tuned) Ⓗ
A quirky gem, this traditional Somerset country pub has beautiful views from the large garden. A pub that wears its heart on its sleeve, it supports the local community and offers a warm welcome to locals and visitors alike. It has a good selection of three permanent and two guest ales to suit all tastes along with a good selection of wines and spirits. This, combined with its renowned hearty meal menu, makes it a must-visit pub.
Q🛏🏠🍴🚆🅿☀️

Dulverton

Bridge Inn 𝕃

20 Bridge Street, TA22 9HJ
☎ (01398) 310161 ⊕ thebridgeinndulverton.com
Dartmoor Jail Ale; Exmoor Ale; St Austell Tribute; 1 changing beer (sourced regionally; often St Austell) 🅷

A warm, welcoming pub dating from 1845. As the name implies it is close to a bridge crossing the River Barle upstream from its confluence with the River Exe. Situated in the delightful small town of Dulverton, the pub has a cosy single-room bar with a wood-burning stove and an extended restaurant area. There is always an interesting selection of national cask ales. Check the website for restricted opening hours in winter.
Q♿🛏️❄️◑🅰️♣️●🚆(25,198) 🐾 🛜

Dunster

Luttrell Arms Hotel ★

36 High Street, TA24 6SG
☎ (01643) 821555 ⊕ luttrellarms.co.uk
Exmoor Ale; Otter Amber; 1 changing beer (sourced locally; often Quantock) 🅷

The hotel with 28 unique bedrooms is on the site of three ancient houses dating back to 1443. The back bar with an open log fire features some of the oldest glass windows in Somerset and there is fine plasterwork on the lounge ceiling. You can dine in the fine restaurant or, if you prefer, order a bar snack. The view of Dunster Castle from the back garden is spectacular. Mini beer and cider festivals are held.
Q♿🛏️❄️🛌◑🅰️♣️●🚆(28,198) 🐾 🛜

Exford

White Horse Inn

TA24 7PY (on the B3224 W of Wheddon Cross)
☎ (01643) 831229 ⊕ exmoor-whitehorse.co.uk
Exmoor Ale, Gold; 2 changing beers (sourced locally) 🅷

Set in the pretty village of Exford, within Exmoor National Park, this is an ideal base for walking, fishing and various country pursuits. The long bar features fine ales and a choice of 200 malt whiskies in the separate whisky bar. There are 28 en-suite rooms and a honeymoon suite. The outside tables are set on the bank of the River Exe. Food, featuring locally sourced produce, ranges from fine dining to bar snacks. Q♿🛏️❄️🛌◑🅰️●P🐾 🛜

Faulkland

Tucker's Grave ★

BA3 5XF
☎ (01373) 834230 ⊕ tuckersgraveinn.co.uk
Butcombe Original 🅶

A gem from a bygone age, with a nationally important historic pub interior, this pub was built in the 17th century and has changed little since. Tucker hanged himself nearby and is buried at the crossroads outside. There is no bar in the original inn, the beers and ciders are served from an alcove. Shove-ha'penny is played and there is a skittle alley. Behind the pub, the old milking parlour was converted into a modern function room and bar in 2021. Q♿🛏️❄️🅰️♣️●P🐾 🎵

Frome

Griffin

Milk Street, BA11 3DB
☎ (01373) 466299 ⊕ griffinfrome.co

Frome Funky Monkey, Zig-Zag Stout; 1 changing beer (often Frome) 🅷

Situated in the part of Frome known as Trinity, the Griffin was formerly the brewery tap for Milk Street (now Frome) brewery, Up to three Frome ales and guests are served, as well as a range of craft beers and ciders. The single bar retains some original features such as etched windows and wooden floor. Food from a Thai menu is available daily except Tuesday. ♿❄️P🚆(184)🐾

Just Ales

10 Stony Street, BA11 1BU
☎ (01373) 462493 ⊕ Justalespart2.com
3 changing beers (sourced nationally; often Magpie, Slaughterhouse, Tollgate) 🅷

Frome's first micropub opened in 2018, serving up to three real ales on handpump as well as a large range of local real ciders. Simply furnished, in what was previously a small café, it is in the heart of Frome's vibrant St Catherine's District. Extremely dog friendly, the pub's hound is a constant and noticeable presence. Snacks including cheese and biltong are available. Watch out for the steep stairs to very basic toilet in the cellar. Closed Monday. Q●🚆🐾 🛜

Three Swans

16-17 King Street, BA11 1BH
☎ (01373) 452009 ⊕ thethreeswans.com
Abbey Bellringer; Butcombe Original; 1 changing beer (sourced nationally) 🅷

A quirky yet traditional 17th century, Grade II-listed two-bar pub in the centre of Frome. Extensively refurbished, it has an eccentric but inviting and comfortable feel. Paintings and various ornaments adorn the walls. The back door leads out to a beautiful secluded courtyard. It has a function room upstairs. The two regular beers are often supplemented by a single guest, which can be from all over the country. ❄️◑🚆🐾 🛜

Glastonbury

George & Pilgrims

1 High Street, BA6 9DP (near the Market Cross)
☎ (01458) 831146 ⊕ georgeandpilgrims.com
Bristol Beer Factory Fortitude; Otter Bitter; 2 changing beers (sourced nationally; often Bristol Beer Factory, Quantock) 🅷

This three-storied Grade I-listed stone-built gatehouse inn boasts a panelled embattled frontage with mullion windows. Walking through the stout doorway there is a corridor leading to the rear patio and several tabled alcoves on the right. The Pilgrims Bar on the left oozes olde worlde charm and displays medieval artefacts. It is worthwhile reading about the history of the inn over a pint. There are four well-kept real ales and a choice of ciders. Q♿🛏️❄️🛌◑♣️●P🚆🐾 🛜 🎵

King Arthur 𝕃

31-33 Benedict Street, BA6 9NB
☎ (01458) 830338 ⊕ thekingarthurglastonbury.com
2 changing beers (sourced locally; often Bristol Beer Factory, Fine Tuned) 🅶

Lively free house hidden just off the High Street. The pub concentrates on beer, a good range of ciders and music, and is supported by an interesting mix of people. There is a garden and a music venue with regular live music most nights. Parking is available on-street only or in the town's car parks, but bus routes are within easy walking distance. ♿🅰️●🚆🐾 🛜 🎵

Halse

New Inn

TA4 3AF

☎ (01823) 432352 ⊕ newinnhalse.com

Exmoor Ale; Quantock QPA; 1 changing beer Ⓗ

Nestling between the Quantock Hills and Exmoor National Park the New Inn is an 18th-century former coaching inn situated in the quaint village of Halse, five miles from Taunton and only 40 minutes' walk from the West Somerset Railway. Regular ales come from Quantock and Exmoor plus one changing local ale. Facilities include B&B rooms and the pub hosts a quiz, folk music and themed menu evenings. Local CAMRA Pub of the Year runner-up 2022. Q⧖ㅎ綦齒◑も✦P❀❅♪

Hambridge

Lamb & Lion

The Green, TA10 0AT (on B3168 in village)

☎ (01460) 281774 ⊕ lambandlionhambridge.co.uk

St Austell Tribute, Proper Job; 1 changing beer (often Quantock) Ⓗ

A splendidly refurbished 17th-century village inn with some parts dating from the 16th century. The pub has hamstone mullion windows and flagstone floors and a wealth of beams throughout. A fireplace sits at each end of the pub which has a bar area for drinkers and a restaurant area for diners. There is a splendid upstairs terrace with lovely views of the surrounding countryside. Unusually, there is a Port and Cheese room for private dining. ⧖綦◑も✦P❅♪

Hillfarrance

Anchor Inn Ⓛ

TA4 1AW

☎ (01823) 461334 ⊕ theanchorinn.net

Exmoor Ale; Otter Ale; St Austell Tribute Ⓗ

Large 300-year-old family-run village free house that caters for drinkers in a cosy bar and diners in the large restaurant. A two-sided log burner separates the bar from a smaller dining area. There is also a large function room. Food is locally produced and home cooked and includes a Sunday carvery. Accommodation is available in five en-suite rooms. Outside is a large car park and garden with a children's play area. Q⧖ㅎ綦◑✦P❀❅

Horton

Five Dials Inn

Goose Lane, TA19 9QQ

☎ (01460) 55359 ⊕ thefivedials.co.uk

Otter Bitter; Sharp's Doom Bar; 1 changing beer (often Otter) Ⓗ

This old coaching inn has been given a contemporary face-lift. Three real ales are joined by traditional local ciders from Perry's and Burrow Hill, including the famous Somerset Cider Brandy. Food is fresh and seasonal, with a daily changing specials board. The Inn offers six guest rooms with en-suite shower rooms and has been awarded four stars by Enjoy England. There is also a self-contained studio apartment which includes kitchen and dining facilities. ⧖綦◑✦P❀❅

Huish Episcopi

Rose & Crown ★ Ⓛ

TA10 9QT (on A372 in village)

☎ (01458) 250494 ⊕ elisroseandcrown.co.uk

Teignworthy Reel Ale; 2 changing beers (sourced regionally; often Hop Back, Otter) Ⓗ

Thatched 17th-century inn known as Eli's after the former owner Eli Scott who took over the pub in 1920. The pub is still in the same family. The hub of the pub is the rare counterless flagstoned taproom which usually serves four cask ales and leads out to four cosy parlours, West room, Piano room, Mens kitchen and Fire room. It hosts regular music, quiz nights and a weekly food co-op. Q⧖ㅎ綦✦◑P❀❅♪

Hutton

Old Inn

Main Road, BS24 9QQ

☎ (01934) 812336

Fuller's London Pride; Otter Head; St Austell Tribute; 1 changing beer (often Palmers) Ⓗ

Genuine free house and thriving local, right at the heart of the community. The pub is popular for its excellent and good-value food, particularly the Sunday carvery, for which booking is advised. Food is served every lunchtime and evening except Sunday evening, which is quiz night. Dogs are welcome in the bar and there is a heated marquee outside during the winter months. The rear car park is accessed by narrow one-way lanes either side. ⧖綦◑も✦P⛽🚍(126) ❀♪

Kilve

Hood Arms Ⓛ

TA5 1EA (on A39)

☎ (01278) 741114 ⊕ thehoodarms.co.uk

Exmoor Gold; St Austell Tribute; 1 changing beer (often Quantock) Ⓗ

Former 17th-century coaching inn set beside the main road, near a beach frequented by fossil hunters. Inside you will find oak beams, an open fireplace, a comfortable bar and separate restaurant. The pub offers good food and wines, and welcomes dogs. Outside is a walled garden where boules is played in the summer. There are nine en-suite rooms and is an ideal base for walkers with easy access to the Quantock Hills and the Coleridge Way. Q⧖ㅎ綦◑も▲✦P❀❅♪

Long Ashton

Angel Inn ◉

172 Long Ashton Road, BS41 9LT

☎ (01275) 392244 ⊕ theangelinn-longashton.co.uk

Draught Bass; Otter Bitter; St Austell Tribute; Sharp's Doom Bar; 1 changing beer (sourced nationally; often Butcombe, Timothy Taylor) Ⓗ

This late 15th-century roadside inn retains a real rural charm despite being less than a mile from Bristol. The Smoke Room acts as a snug; while diners enjoy the Parlour branched off the main bar area, with a lovely old fireplace. The rear courtyard has traditionally been a haven for swallows in summertime. Although owned by Stonegate, the pub is run as an independent business. Quiz night is every third Wednesday of the month, and there is monthly live music. ⧖綦◑▲🚍❀❅♪

Lower Godney

Sheppey Inn

BA5 1RZ

☎ (01458) 831594 ⊕ thesheppey.co.uk

4 changing beers (sourced locally; often Frome, Pitchfork, Wookey Brewing Company) Ⓗ

A many-roomed pub with lots of contemporary paintings on the walls, set in the wilds of the Somerset levels, west of Wells. It has a good range of ever-changing real ales, plus six or more craft beers from home and overseas, and up to six ciders on gravity. Outside the barnlike interior is a lovely terrace overlooking the eponymous River Sheppey, where otters have been spotted. The food is highly recommended. Often closed Mondays, ring to check. ⬥🌟🏠🍴◐♿🅰♣🅿🐾🎵

Luxborough

Royal Oak Inn 🅛 ✅
TA23 0SH (2½ miles from B3224 between Wheddon Cross and Raleghs Cross)
☎ (01984) 641498 ⬥ royaloakinnluxborough.co.uk
Butcombe Original; Exmoor Ale; 2 changing beers (sourced regionally; often Nuttycombe, Pitchfork) 🅗
Set within Exmoor, this ancient village pub has an original flagstone floor in the main bar and a large inglenook fireplace. It serves a range of four cask ales. A second bar has a pool table and a radiogram where you can play some vinyl. Freshly cooked meals using seasonal produce are served in three intimate dining areas. Dog friendly, the pub is popular with ramblers and shooting parties. If you wish to sit outside there is a sunny river garden. Q⬥🌟🏠◐♣🅿🐾🎵

Lydford on Fosse

Cross Keys Inn 🅛
TA11 7HA (next to the A37 between Yeovil and Shepton Mallet, at traffic lights in village)
☎ (01963) 240473 ⬥ crosskeysinn.info
Church End Goat's Milk; Otter Bitter; 2 changing beers (sourced regionally; often Fine Tuned, Hanlons, Hop Back) 🅖
An 16th-century traditional pub with flagstone floors, blue lias stonework and a wealth of beams. The open-plan bar area has two fireplaces at each end and a snug area. This is a community pub with many events organised such as live music, a beer festival, comedy nights and charitable events. Camping is available on-site with 29 pitches, a shower block and toilets. There are up to four gravity poured ales available, including the house beer and farmhouse ciders.
Q⬥🌟🏠◐♿🅰♣🅿(667)🐾🎵

Minehead

Kildare Lodge ✅
Townend Road, TA24 5RQ (2 mins from town centre)
☎ (01643) 702009 ⬥ kildarelodge.com
St Austell Tribute; 3 changing beers (sourced regionally) 🅗
This cracking locals' pub is close to Minehead town centre and is a Grade II-listed building in the Arts and Crafts style. It has a bar, two lounges and a dining room. Two beer festivals are held every year with up to 20 beers available. The pub is in the local boules and quiz leagues. There are 12 en-suite rooms including a bridal suite with a four-poster bed, and it is a great base for exploring Exmoor National Park, Dunster and the coast. Q🌟♿🅰≈♣🅿(28,198)🐾

Old Ship Aground
Quay Street, TA24 5UL (beside Minehead harbour)
☎ (01643) 703516 ⬥ theoldshipaground.com
Hall & Woodhouse Badger Best Bitter, Fursty Ferret; 1 changing beer (sourced nationally; often Hall & Woodhouse) 🅗
Built in 1906 between the harbour and the lifeboat station, the pub has 12 letting rooms with fantastic views over the Bristol Channel. Exmoor National Park is only a 20 minute drive away and it is within walking distance to the town centre and the West Somerset Railway. The pub

holds themed food nights through the week and a Sunday carvery. Beer festivals are held and there is live music on a Friday night. ⬥🌟🏠◐♿🅰≈♣🅿(28,198)🐾

Quay Inn
Quay Street, TA24 5UJ
☎ (01643) 702839 ⬥ thequayinnminehead.co.uk
3 changing beers (sourced regionally; often Dartmoor, Exmoor, Nuttycombe) 🅗
The Quay Inn serves a good range of three changing cask ales, usually from local and regional breweries. Recently refurbished, it offers excellent views of the Bristol Channel. Good pub food is served at reasonable prices, with pork and award-winning sausages from Little Oak Farm. Regular live music evenings are held, with open mic nights on the first and third Wednesday of each month. It featured on and won Channel 4's Four in a Bed competition in 2001. ⬥🌟🏠◐🅰≈♣🅿(28,198)🐾🎵

Nailsea

Nailsea MicroPub
Unit 4, Ivy Court, 63A High Street, BS48 1AW
☎ 07496 428350
3 changing beers (sourced locally) 🅖
Nailsea's first micropub, which opened in 2019, serves up to four ales straight from the cask, along with a real cider. Beers of all styles come from around the country, but more often they are sourced from local breweries. Bottles and cans of beer and cider are sold along with gins, wines, alcohol-free beers and soft drinks. Reasonably priced bar snacks are also available. There is no dedicated parking but there are ample public car parks nearby. Closed on Mondays. Q🌟♣🅿🐾

Nether Stowey

George 🅛
1 St Mary Street, TA5 1LJ
☎ (01278) 732248 ⬥ georgestowey.com
Exmoor Ale; 1 changing beer (often Bays, Dartmoor, Exmoor) 🅗
The George is the oldest pub in the village and can trace its history back to 1616, although the original building dates back another century. It is a friendly multi-roomed pub with a real fire, dark wood interior and Tiffany lamps. Historical photographs of the village adorn the walls. A function room is available upstairs. No food is served but you are welcome to bring your own, or the post office/cafe across the road will deliver. Weekday afternoons are happy hour. ⬥🌟🏠🍴♣🐾🎵

Pilton

Crown
Conduit Square, BA4 4EA
☎ (01749) 890300 ⬥ thecrowninnpilton.co.uk
Bristol Beer Factory Fortitude; 2 changing beers (sourced locally; often Bristol Beer Factory, Quantock) 🅗
Taken over by a local couple, this 18th-century coaching inn reopened in 2022 after refurbishment and has a new restaurant, traditional bar area and function room. The main bar and side room have been decorated in a dark theme with much wood panelling and Victorian style ornaments, and feature the contributions of many local artists. The large garden has a children's play area and stage for live music. The pub is closed during the Glastonbury festival which is held nearby.
⬥🌟◐♣🅿(669)🐾🎵

Pitminster

Queen's Arms

TA3 7AZ
☎ (01823) 587940 ⊕ queensarmspitminster.co.uk
Otter Bitter, Bright; Quantock Wills Neck; St Austell Tribute ⊞
A clean and friendly pub in a small village south of Taunton. Well worth the effort to find with four cask ales from Otter, Quantock and St Austell breweries along with excellent and reasonably priced food cooked to order. Homemade snacks are also available. There is a great beer garden for the summer and warming log burners in the winter. A good range of tradional pub games are available, including pool, darts and skittles.
ﾐ✿◖◗▲♣♠🅿️🌸🛜

Pitney

Halfway House ⓛ

Pitney Hill, TA10 9AB (on B3153 between Langport and Somerton)
☎ (01458) 252513 ⊕ thehalfwayhouse.co.uk
Hop Back Summer Lightning; Otter Bright; Teignworthy Reel Ale; 6 changing beers (sourced regionally; often Fine Tuned, Parkway, Quantock) Ⓖ
An outstanding pub serving eight to ten regional ales on gravity alongside many bottled beers and four real ciders. The inside is traditional, with flagstone flooring, three real fires and old solid wooden tables and benches. Superb home-cooked food is served. This basic but busy pub deserves its many accolades including being in this Guide for over 30 years, CAMRA local and Regional Pub of the Year 2023 and gaining the ultimate award of National Pub of the Year in 1996.
Q ﾐ✿🚲◖◗♣🅿️🚃(54)🌸🛜

Porlock

Ship Inn ★ ⓛ

High Street, TA24 8QD
☎ (01643) 862507 ⊕ shipinnporlock.co.uk
Exmoor Ale, Beast; Otter Amber, Ale; St Austell Tribute, Proper Job; 2 changing beers (sourced regionally; often Quantock) ⊞
Appearing in this Guide for 15 years and known locally as the Top Ship, the bar is a gem with its flagstone floor, open fire and settle seating. The pub dates from the 13th century and sits at the bottom of the notorious Porlock Hill that takes you up to Exmoor. It has changed little since featuring in R.D. Blackmore's novel Lorna Doone. Up to eight ales and a local cider are available, and good food can be enjoyed in its restaurant or delightful three-tiered garden in summer.
Q ﾐ✿🚲◖◗🚿▲♣♠🅿️🚃(10,EXMO)🌸♪

Porlock Weir

Ship Inn ⓛ

TA24 8PB (take the B3225 from Porlock)
☎ (01643) 863288 ⊕ shipinnporlockweir.co.uk
Exmoor Ale, Stag; Otter Amber; St Austell Tribute, Proper Job; 2 changing beers (sourced regionally) ⊞
This 400-year-old pub pub offers fantastic views of the Bristol Channel and South Wales coast. It is situated in Exmoor National Park, set next to the small harbour and pebbled beach, and is ideal for walkers on the South West Coast Path. It is busy in the summer but has a Pay & Display car park opposite. A beer festival is held in early July with up to 50 ales available. Dog friendly accommodation is available.
Q ✿🚲◖◗▲♣♠🅿️🚃(10)🌸🛜♪

Portishead

Ship

310 Down Road, BS20 8JT
☎ (01275) 848400
Draught Bass; Otter Bitter; Sharp's Doom Bar ⊞
A large pub on the coast road between Clevedon and Portishead with extensive views over the Severn estuary. The landlord has been in charge at the pub that he built since 1973. Meals are served lunchtime only, but pasties are available in the evening. It has a small library of books with a particularly good selection on local history. There is a rarely found bar billiards table board. Outside are a generous car park and an award-winning pub garden, with a covered outdoor area where extensive estuary views can be enjoyed. 🌸◖♣🅿️🚃(X4)🌸

Siren's Calling ⓛ

315 Newfoundland Way, Portishead Marina, BS20 7QH
☎ (01275) 268278 ⊕ sirenscalling.co.uk
Bristol Beer Factory Fortitude; 4 changing beers (often Bristol Beer Factory, Ilkley) ⊞
A modern single-room waterside bar serving up to five cask ales and nine craft keg beers in a variety of styles. Beers from the north of England often feature, reflecting the landlord's heritage. Real ciders are also sold. The pub is simply furnished, with large front windows overlooking the many boats moored in the marina. Only basic bar snacks are served but customers are welcome to bring in fish & chips from next door. Regular beer festivals are held. ﾐ✿🚲🚿♣🚃🌸🛜♪

Windmill Inn ⓛ

58 Nore Road, BS20 6JZ (next to former municipal golf course above coastal path)
☎ (01275) 818483 ⊕ thewindmillinn.org
Butcombe Original; Fuller's London Pride; 1 changing beer (often Fuller's) ⊞
Large split-level pub with a spacious patio to the rear, plus an extension enjoying panoramic views. It is above the coastal path on the edge of town; the Severn Estuary and both Severn bridges can be seen on clear days. Renowned for its food, a varied menu is served all day with table bookings available. The surrounding fields are a popular dog-walking area and dogs are welcomed in the main bar area by a treats jar and a plentiful supply of water bowls. Q ﾐ✿◖◗🚿🅿️🚃(X4)🌸🛜

Priddy

Hunters' Lodge ★

Old Bristol Road, BA5 3AR (isolated crossroads 1 mile from A39; close to TV mast) ST549500
☎ (01749) 672275
Butcombe Original; Cheddar Ales Potholer Ⓖ
The landlord of this timeless classic roadside inn has been in charge for 54 years. Priddy is the highest village in Somerset, and is popular with cavers and walkers. The pub's three rooms include one with a flagged floor. All beer is served direct from casks behind the bar; local cider is also on offer. Simple home-cooked food is excellent and exceptional value. A folk musicians' drop-in session is held on Tuesday evening. The garden is pleasant and secluded. Mobile phones aren't welcome but dogs are. Cash payments only. Closed on Mondays.
Q ﾐ✿◖◗🚿♣🅿️🚃(683)🌸♪

Queen Victoria Inn ✅

Pelting Drove, BA5 3BA
☎ (01749) 676385 ⊕ thequeenvicpriddy.co.uk
Butcombe Adam Henson's Rare Breed, Original; 1 changing beer (sourced locally) ⊞

This creeper-clad inn, which has been a pub since 1851, has four rooms featuring low ceilings, flagged floors and two log fires. It is a wonderfully warm and relaxing haven on cold winter nights, and is particularly popular during the Priddy Folk Festival in July. Reasonably priced home-cooked food is a speciality. There is a lovely beer garden with six sheds named after royal palaces. Children are welcome and there is a play area by the car park. Q👶❀🍴⛺🍎P🐾📶♫

Puriton

37 Club [L]

1 West Approach Road, Woolavington Road, TA7 8AD (5 mins from M5 jct 23; between Bridgwater and Wells)
☎ (01278) 685190 🌐 37club.co.uk
St Austell Tribute; 2 changing beers (sourced regionally; often Nuttycombe, Quantock) [H]
On the site of the former Royal Ordnance Factory which was allocated the number 37, this large club offers a great many facilities to members and visitors. It has two bars and its multi-roomed layout incorporates a concert room, two skittle alleys, dining room and a snooker room with five tables. Outside is a beer garden, fishing lake and football pitch. CAMRA members are welcome with a membership card. 👶❀🍴⛺♣P🚌(75)🐾♫

Roadwater

Valiant Soldier [L] ✔

TA23 0QZ (off A39 at Washford)
☎ (01984) 640223 🌐 thevaliantsoldier.co.uk
Dartmoor Jail Ale; Exmoor Ale [H]
The pub dates back to 1720 and is ideal for country walks and exploring nearby Exmoor, the Brendan and Quantock Hills, the coast and Dunster. This vibrant locals' pub has a quiz, pool, darts and nine skittles teams to see it through the winter months. It is set by a small river where you can relax and watch the ducks and, if you are lucky, kingfishers. It offers good quality locally sourced food and has been run by Mike the landlord for over 30 years. 👶❀🛏🍴♣🍎P🐾📶♫

Somerton

Etsome Arms

6 West Street, TA11 7PS
☎ (01458) 762352
8 changing beers (sourced locally; often Arbor, Bristol Beer Factory, Fine Tuned) [G]
This micropub, a winner of a local CAMRA award, is among first of its breed in Somerset and well worth a visit. A cosy, friendly venue, it serves between six and eight reguarly-changing ales on gravity, from Bristol and Somerset breweries. Seating is comfortable sofas or traditional tables and chairs. Quality cold bar snacks are sourced locally and include a range of Scotch eggs and pies. Children and dogs are welcome. 👶❀♣🍎🚌(54,77)🐾📶

South Cheriton

White Horse

Cabbage Lane, BA8 0BL
☎ (01963) 370394 🌐 thewhitehorsesc.co.uk
Cheddar Ales Potholer; Dartmoor Jail Ale; Gritchie Moon Lore; 1 changing beer (sourced regionally) [H]
A 17th-century public house with a definite traditional country pub feel that has strong local support. There is a variety of seating areas to suit all needs, with casual seating in the bar and snug plus a restaurant. High quality freshly cooked meals are served from a varied and reasonably priced menu. Well-behaved dogs and children are welcome. It has a car park and attractive well-fenced beer garden. Q👶❀🍴♣P🚌(58)🐾📶♫

South Petherton

Brewers Arms [L]

18-20 St James Street, TA13 5BW (½ mile off A303 in centre of village)
☎ (01460) 241887 🌐 the-brewersarms.com
Otter Bitter; 3 changing beers (sourced nationally; often Bristol Beer Factory, Fine Tuned, Hop Back) [H]
This pub is just ½ mile from the A303 and has appeared in 25 consecutive editions of this Guide. During this time around 3,000 different ales have been served and documented. The Brewers is a hub of village life, a true community pub that keenly supports local events and charities. Beer festivals are held over both spring and summer bank holiday weekends. Regular live music and quiz nights feature. The adjoining Old Bakehouse provides excellent quality food. 👶❀🛏🍴⛺♣🍎🚌(81)🐾📶♫

South Stoke

Packhorse

Old School Hill, BA2 7DU
☎ (01225) 830300 🌐 packhorsebath.co.uk
Butcombe Original; 1 changing beer (sourced locally) [H]
A historic community pub renowned for the high-profile campaign to save it from developers, which has become an exemplar for other communities faced with similar threats. Built in 1618 and a pub since at least 1847, the Packhorse has been superbly and sympathetically refurbished. To the rear is a gorgeous garden overlooked by the church. There are two traditional taprooms downstairs, with a central hallway with bar counter, that echo the original pub layout, plus two new rooms upstairs for drinking and eating. High quality food is served and booking is recommended. 👶❀🍴♣🍎P🚌(4A,D2)🐾📶♫

Stratton-on-the-Fosse

King's Arms

South Street, BA3 4RA
☎ (01761) 210165
House beer (by Bason Bridge); 1 changing beer (sourced regionally) [H]
A characterful pub in the village of Stratton on the Fosse, offering usually two or three ales, mainly from West Country breweries, including their house beer from Bason Bridge brewery near Highbridge. The pub has a strong tradition of supporting live music, encouraging open-mic sessions and even providing instruments. A wide range of ciders is on sale and they run up to four cider festivals per year. The village is set in beautiful countryside, with the pub directly opposite Downside Abbey. 👶❀🛏🍴♿♣🍎P🚌🐾📶♫

Street

Lantokay [L] ✔

111-113 High Street, BA16 0EY
☎ (01458) 444940
Greene King IPA; Ruddles Best Bitter; Sharp's Doom Bar; 3 changing beers (sourced locally) [H]
The name of this Wetherspoon pub recalls the town's origin as an ancient settlement, called Lantokay. In time, the name was forgotten, and the settlement was called Leigh and then Street. The pub has a large and recently

extended bar area with varied seating options as well as a partially covered garden/patio area. Immediately inside the entrance there is a stand featuring CAMRA information. 🐴❀🍴♿🚌📶

Taunton

Ale House ✔

78 Station Road, TA1 1PD

☎ (01823) 617408 🌐 thealehousetaunton.pub

3 changing beers (sourced nationally; often Greene King, Marston's, Otter) [H]

A new addition to the Guide and a pleasant locals' pub on a main road junction. It was originally called the Royal Mail before becoming the Cricketers Arms and now Ale House. There is a central bar with five handpumps usually serving at least three cask ales at any one time from a huge range of 60 in the SIBA local beer catalogue. The menu has a good range of reasonably priced and good quality food. 🐴❀🍴♿🚆♣🚌🐾♫

Perkin Warbeck [L] ✔

22-23 East Street, TA1 3LP

☎ (01823) 335830

Greene King Abbot; Ruddles Best Bitter; Sharp's Doom Bar; 3 changing beers (sourced nationally; often Butcombe, Exmoor, Otter) [H]

This Wetherspoon pub is named after the man who claimed to be the rightful heir to the throne of England in 1497. Recently refurbished, the pub has one of the longest bars in the county and at the rear is a splendid outside terrace. Somerset cricket memorabilia adorn the walls as befits the fact that the pub is a stone's throw from the cricket ground. An excellent range of ales and ciders kept. Q🐴❀🍴♿🍎🚌📶

Ring of Bells [L]

16-17 St James Street, TA1 1JS

☎ (01823) 259480 🌐 theringofbellstaunton.com

5 changing beers (sourced nationally; often Bristol Beer Factory, Otter, Quantock) [H]

Being close to Somerset cricket ground, this pub is a favourite haunt of cricket fans. Wooden floored, there are two bar areas with open fires, a downstairs eating area, upstairs restaurant and large outside courtyard. The five cask beers are from local, regional and national breweries and you may find some interesting keg beers. Excellent locally produced food is served, and booking is recommended. Sporting events are shown on a TV in the bar area. 🐴❀🍴🚆🚌🐾📶

Wyvern Social Club [L]

Mountfields Road, TA1 3BJ (off South Rd, approx 1 mile from town centre)

☎ (01823) 284591 🌐 wyvernclub.co.uk

4 changing beers (sourced regionally; often Exmoor, St Austell) [H]

For over 35 years this club has been a great venue to drink real ales and cider. A members-only club with a visitors licence, a CAMRA membership card can be produced to be signed in as a guest. The club is the hub for rugby, cricket and squash clubs who use the adjoining playing fields. It has been local CAMRA Club of the Year on many occasions over the last 20 years.
🐴❀🍴♿♣🍎P🚌(99)📶♫

Trull

Winchester Arms

Church Road, TA3 7LG

☎ (01823) 284723 🌐 winchesterarmstrull.co.uk

4 changing beers (sourced regionally; often Dartmoor, Exmoor, Otter) [H]

Thriving community free house on the outskirts of Taunton and near to the Blackdown Hills. A comfortable bar area, usually with a range of four cask ales, is separated from the long dining area by a fireplace. The locally sourced home-cooked food is excellent. The streamside gardens are perfect for families and dogs, and become the venue for entertainment and barbecues. Sunday nights are popular for quizzes and there is occasional live music. The pub offers good-value accommodation. Q🐴❀🛏🍴♣🍎P🚌(97)🐾📶♫

Uphill

Ship

56 Uphill Way, BS23 4TN

☎ (01934) 253120 🌐 theshipinnuphill.com

Otter Ale; 1 changing beer (often Adnams, Fuller's) [H]

This spacious family-friendly pub, where customers of all ages mix harmoniously, is real hub of the community, with its own skittles teams and a pool table. One regular cask beer and one changing beer is served. Food is available at lunchtimes and in the evenings, both in the main pub and upstairs restaurant area. Most of the pub is easily accessible and there is a covered and heated smoking area in the rear garden. Dogs are welcome, there is a quiz on Thursdays and occasional live music features. 🐴❀🍴♿♣🍎P🚌(20 Coaster, 126)🐾📶♫

Wambrook

Cotley Inn

TA20 3EN (from A30 W out of Chard, take left fork by toll house and almost immediately left again; continue for just over 1 mile on narrow lane following signs for pub)

☎ (01460) 62348 🌐 cotleyinnwambrook.co.uk

Otter Bitter; 2 changing beers (sourced regionally; often Exeter, Teignworthy) [G]

A traditional country pub that is well worth finding. It makes the most of its wonderful rural setting, with its raised patio area and beer garden. Excellent food is served and, due to the popularity, booking is advised. There are usually two or three well kept beers available straight from the cask, typically from the Otter, Teignworthy and Exeter breweries, with others on an occasional basis, sharing stillage space with a choice of local ciders from Sheppy's, Perry's and others.
🐴❀🛏🍴♣🍎P🐾📶♫

Washford

White Horse Inn [L]

Abbey Road, TA23 0JZ (take road towards Cleeve Abbey off the A39)

☎ (01984) 640415 🌐 exmoorpubs.co.uk

3 changing beers (sourced regionally; often Sharp's, St Austell) [H]

The pub dates from 1709 and is near to the ruins of Cleeve Abbey and close to the Torre cider farm. This riverside free house is an ideal base for visits to the coast, Exmoor National Park, the Quantock Hills and the West Somerset Steam Railway. A good range of locally sourced food is available. Various charity events are held, including the famous bike pub run. B&B accommodation is available in the pub and in a separate lodge.
Q🐴❀🛏🍴♣🍎P🚌(28)🐾📶

Watchet

Esplanade Club Ⓛ

5 The Esplanade, TA23 0AJ (opp the marina)
☎ 07876 353819 ⊕ esplanadeclub.net
Sharp's Doom Bar; 2 changing beers (sourced regionally; often Exmoor, St Austell) Ⓗ
Built in the 1860's as a sail making factory and now home to the Boat Owners Association, the club is an archive of local history and memorabilia with unique murals and even its own Tardis. There are great views over the Marina and Bristol Channel. This a busy music venue with live acts every weekend and regular open mic and folk nights. Six-time winner of local CAMRA Club of the Year, it has been in the Guide for 15 years.
➤❀♿🅰♿♣🅿🚃(28) ❀ 🕏 ♪

Pebbles Tavern

24 Market Street, TA23 0AN (in the heart of Watchet, near the museum)
☎ (01984) 634903 ⊕ pebblestavern.co.uk
3 changing beers (sourced nationally; often Nuttycombe, Pitchfork, Timothy Taylor) Ⓗ/Ⓖ
This small, unique, tavern has won numerous CAMRA awards and was the runner-up National Cider Pub of the Year in both 2015 and 2022. As well as the ales there can be up to 30 ciders, 60 gins, 24 rums and 64 whiskies. You may bring in food to eat from various shops in Watchet. Poetry night is the first Tuesday of the month and regular music nights include folk, sea shanty, acoustic and jazz.
➤🅰♣♣♿🚃(28) ❀ 🕏 ♪

Star Inn Ⓛ

Mill Lane, TA23 0BZ
☎ (01984) 631367 ⊕ starinnwatchet.co.uk
4 changing beers (sourced regionally; often Dartmoor, Exmoor, Nuttycombe) Ⓗ
This two-time local CAMRA Pub of the Year has been in the Guide for 21 consecutive years. It is also the brewery tap for Nuttycombe brewery. It is renowned for friendly staff and its congenial atmosphere. The pub hosts dart, quiz and boules teams and holds music nights in the summer. Is home to the Sunday night 'bad boys club'. Mick's beer tours have run over 100 trips from the pub.
➤❀🕪♿🅰♿♣♣❀ 🕏 ♪

Wedmore

New Inn Ⓛ

Combe Batch, BS28 4DU
☎ (01934) 712099
Butcombe Adam Henson's Rare Breed, Original; 1 changing beer (sourced nationally) Ⓗ
This classic village inn is the centre for many local events including the famous annual turnip prize, spoof and penny chuffin. The public bar, lounge and dining areas are complemented by a beer garden to the rear. A chalkboard lists forthcoming ales, mainly from the West Country, served from two handpumps with two on gravity. Traditional, good-value home cooked food is served. There is a skittle alley/function room and in winter skittles and darts provide a hive of activity.
Q➤❀♿🅰♣♿🅿🚃(67) ❀ 🕏 ♪

Wells

Crown Inn

Town Hall Square, BA5 2RP
☎ (01749) 673457 ⊕ crownatwells.co.uk/pub
Butcombe Original; Cheddar Ales Potholer; Sharp's Doom Bar Ⓗ
The Crown is a lovely old building overlooking the main square and marketplace. Although a hotel and bistro, the separate bar is run as a pub with a range of well-kept ales and is entered via the door on the left of the main entrance. William Penn, the Quaker, preached to a large crowd outside the building in 1685. The cathedral is a few minutes' walk away. ➤❀♿🚃❀ 🕏 🕏

West Chinnock

Muddled Man Ⓛ ✔

Lower Street, TA18 7PT
☎ (01935) 881235 ⊕ themuddledmaninn.co.uk
3 changing beers (often Bays, Hop Back, Otter) Ⓗ
A popular traditional free house in a picturesque village. The large beer garden has exceptional flower boxes, troughs and baskets, which are a sight to be seen. A warm welcome is extended to locals and visitors alike, with good home-cooked food served in a happy and jovial way by the family team who specialises in a variety of steaks, and Sunday lunch so popular it must be pre-booked. There is always a good range of three well kept ales and a real cider. Q➤❀🕪♿🕪♣❀ 🕏

West Huntspill

Crossways Inn ♟ Ⓛ

Withy Road, TA9 3RA (on the A38)
☎ (01278) 783756 ⊕ thecrosswaysinn.com
8 changing beers (sourced nationally; often Bristol Beer Factory, Dartmoor, Exmoor) Ⓗ
This fabulous 17th-century character inn is the well-deserved winner of local CAMRA Pub of the Year on 10 occasions over the last 12 years! It has several charming bar areas, a dining room, and two log fires during winter. A range of eight cask, three keg, 20 craft canned ales and a selection of real ciders ensure a wide selection of drinks for all tastes. Good local pub food is served.
➤❀🕪♿🅰🅿🚃(21) ❀ 🕏 ♪

Weston-super-Mare

Black Cat Ⓛ

135 High Street, BS23 1HN
☎ (01934) 620153
4 changing beers (often Cheddar Ales, Glastonbury, Verdant) Ⓖ
Popular micropub in a former clothes shop opposite the Playhouse Theatre and next to the main entrance of picturesque Grove Park, featuring a wonderful black cat mural reminiscent of Edgar Allan Poe. Up to four cask ales, usually from local breweries, are served, as well as many quality craft keg beers and a large selection of boxed real ciders. There is reasonable access for those of limited mobility, and children are welcome until early evening. Occasional live music and quizzes feature. Payment by card only. Closed Mondays and Tuesdays.
Q➤♣♿🚃❀ 🕏 ♪

Brit Bar Ⓛ ✔

118 High Street, BS23 1HP
☎ (01934) 632629
5 changing beers (often Bristol Beer Factory, New Bristol, Quantock) Ⓗ
Established town-centre pub in which quality real ale and live music are the key ingredients. Five changing ales of varying styles and strengths are served, always including some dark brews. Bag in box real cider is usually sold too. Live music features every weekend, as well as on Thursdays during the summer, in the covered courtyard, which is heated in cold weather. Families are welcome, but only until 9pm if live music is on. The pub hosts its own version of the Brit Awards each February.
➤❀♿🕪♿🚃❀ 🕏 ♪

Duke of Oxford L

27 Oxford Street, BS23 1TF

☎ (01934) 417762 ⊕ dukeofoxford.co.uk

4 changing beers (sourced locally; often Exmoor, Quantock, Twisted Oak) Ⓗ

Reopened in 2016 after a long period of closure, this pub is just outside the main shopping area and near the seafront. It is fitted out in the style of a café bar, with a grand piano and with jazz music sometimes featuring. The beers served are usually from local breweries. A small outdoor space is accessible via stairs and accommodation is also available upstairs. Note that the pub may close early during the off season.
ᵠ❄️🏠🍺🌳♿🚶♣🛇🅿🚳🎵

Fork n' Ale Taproom & Kitchen

18 Walliscote Road, BS23 1UG

☎ (01934) 627937 ⊕ forknale.com

5 changing beers (sourced locally; often Good Chemistry, Pinkers, VOG/Vale of Glamorgan) Ⓖ

Conveniently located in the town centre near the seafront and railway station, this pub has a modern look and feel, with an interior of wood, metal and brick, as well as a few comfy sofas. There is a big focus on beer with up to five cask ales served at any one time. The food offering is well regarded, with Sunday lunches popular. Regular live music is featured on Thursdays, and quizzes once a month. Toilets are upstairs, so not ideal for those with limited mobility. ⊕≉♣🛇🅿🚳🎵

Regency

22-24 Lower Church Road, BS23 2AG

☎ (01934) 633406

St Austell Tribute; Timothy Taylor Landlord; 1 changing beer (sourced nationally; often Dark Star) Ⓗ

Comfortable, friendly town-centre local serving a good range of regular beers plus one guest. It has pool, skittles and crib teams, and also offers a quiet refuge for conversation. There is a games room to the left as you enter, with TV and jukebox, separate from the main bar area; children are welcome here and it can be used for parties and functions. Outside are front and rear patios. Live music often features on Sundays and filled rolls are available at all times every day. ᵠ❄️♿♣🛇🅿🚳🎵

Williton

Mason's Arms L

2 North Road, TA4 4SN

☎ (01984) 639200 ⊕ themasonsarms.com

3 changing beers (sourced regionally; often Dartmoor, Exmoor, St Austell) Ⓗ

This beautiful thatched 16th-century inn has oak beams throughout and offers five en-suite rooms in the adjoining annexe. The pub hosts quiz teams in the local league. There is a pleasant beer garden where locals and visitors alike can sit and relax. It serves three quality cask ales and has a good reputation for its food. Rich's cider is always available. Close to the Quantock Hills and West Somerset Railway it is a short drive to Exmoor National Park. Q ᵠ❄️🏠🍺🌳♿🛏♣🅿🚳 (28)🚳🎵

Wincanton

Nog Inn

South Street, BA9 9DL

☎ (01963) 32998 ⊕ thenoginn.com

Sharp's Sea Fury; 1 changing beer (sourced regionally) Ⓗ

This attractive listed pub with a striking Georgian façade fronts a long, narrow building with parts dating back to the 16th century. A secluded sunny garden with covered seating can be found at the far end of the property. The guest ales are often seasonal and an extensive range of continental beers is always available. Home-cooked pub classics use locally sourced and seasonal ingredients where possible. ᵠ❄️🏠🍺🌳♣🅿🚳 (58,667)🚳🎵

Winscombe

Woodborough Inn

2 Sandford Road, BS25 1HD

☎ (01934) 844167 ⊕ woodborough-inn.co.uk

Butcombe Original; 2 changing beers (sourced locally; often Glastonbury, Twisted Oak) Ⓗ

This large village-centre pub has a black and white Tudor style exterior and pleasant front patio area for alfresco drinking. There are two bars, one of which is mainly for dining, as well as a separate restaurant area. A large skittle alley doubles as a function room. Guest beers are sourced from local breweries. Breakfast, lunchtime and evening meals are served as well as bar snacks. Quiz night is the first Sunday of every month. ᵠ❄️🏠🍺🌳♿♣🅿🚳 (126)🚳🎵

Witham Friary

Seymour Arms ★

BA11 5HF

☎ (01749) 684280

Cheddar Ales Potholer Ⓗ

A hidden rural gem, this pub has probably changed very little over the last 50 or so years – apart from new loos! Built in the 1860s as a hotel to serve the nearby Mid-Somerset Great Western Railway branch railway station, it was part of the Duke of Somerset's estate. Sadly, in the 1960s, Mr Beeching closed the station, and the hotel became a quiet country pub. One, locally sourced beer, and cider are served from a glass panelled hatch in the central hallway. Q ᵠ❄️🏠♣🅿🚳

Withypool

Royal Oak Inn L

TA24 7QP (W of B3223 between Dulverton and Exford at Comers Cross) SS847356

☎ (01643) 831506 ⊕ royaloakwithypool.co.uk

Dartmoor Jail Ale; Exmoor Ale, Gold; 1 changing beer (sourced locally; often Exmoor) Ⓗ

Set in a remote village, the pub has been providing great ale and food for over 300 years. It is larger than first appears, with two bars and a dining room, which are decorated with an array of historic country pursuits memorabilia. It also has eight en-suite rooms. The pub will arrange shooting, riding and fishing locally. Although remote, it is easily accessible to beauty spots such as Tarr Steps. ᵠ❄️🏠🍺🛏🅿🚳🚳🎵

Yeovil

Quicksilver Mail ✅

168 Hendford Hill, BA20 2RG (at jct of A30 and A37)

☎ (01935) 424721 ⊕ quicksilvermail.com

Butcombe Original; 2 changing beers (sourced nationally; often St Austell, Timothy Taylor) Ⓗ

Roadside pub with a unique name commemorating a high speed mail coach. The pub has been run by the same landlord since 2002 and it has been virtually ever-present in the Guide. There is a large single bar and separate dining area serving excellent food and a well priced range of wine. The pub is a well-known live music destination and also holds comedy, bingo and quiz nights in the bar or function room. ᵠ❄️🏠🍺🛏♣🅿🚳 (6,96)🚳🎵

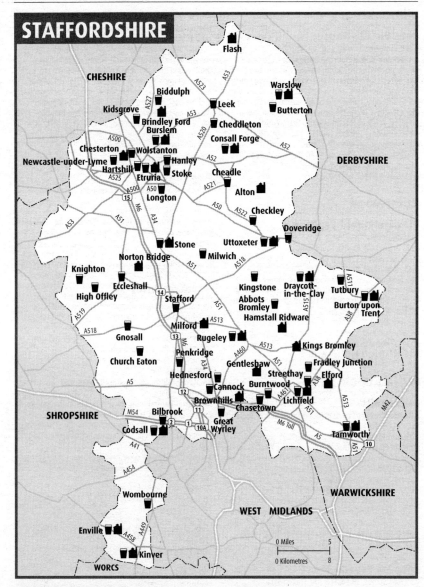

Abbots Bromley

Crown Inn

Market Place, WS15 3BS (centre of village, opposite the Butter Cross; on B5014)

☎ (01283) 840227 ⊕ thecrownatabbotsbromley.co.uk

Draught Bass; Timothy Taylor Landlord; Wye Valley HPA 田

Imposing mock-Tudor style village pub overlooking the Butter Cross. The building is thought to have originally been a series of cottages. The public bar features pictures of the world-famous annual Abbots Bromley Horn Dance which is held in September. The former lounge, comprising two rooms connected through an archway, is now used primarily for dining. No meals are served Monday, Saturday lunchtime or Sunday evening.
Q ☺ ❀ ◑ ♣ P ➡ (402A,403) ● 🛜

Biddulph

Crafty Flanker

35 High Street, ST8 6AW

☎ 07973 764298

5 changing beers (often Front Row) 田

This tiny micropub is owned and run by the small, independent, locally based Front Row brewery, with all house beers having rugby-themed names. A range of six cask ales are sold, with four more on keg taps, plus some unusual lagers and real ciders. A large range of locally-produced specialist gins are on the top shelf. Major sporting events are shown in the smaller back room, and an even smaller upstairs function room is available to hire. A former local CAMRA Cider Pub of the Year.
Q ● ➡ ❀ ♪

Bilbrook

Olde Vic Ale House

9 Bilbrook Road, WV8 1EU

6 changing beers (sourced nationally) ⊞

Newly-opened in 2023, this micro-style pub has been sympathetically converted in keeping with its origins. A short hallway opens into an L-shaped main room with a bar to the right and a seating area extending round to the left into a snug-style room with a piano and fireplace. Additional seating and a dartboard are upstairs, while outside there is a courtyard beer garden. Six handpumps (one supporting small brewers) offering cask ale and a cider are supported by three craft keg lines. Live music is usually held at weekends.

Q🌣☺🖙🌳🍽🚍(5,10B) 🌸♪

Burntwood

Vintage Liquid Taphouse

1 Bridge Cross Road, WS7 2BX

☎ 07592 074069 ⊕ vltaphouse.co.uk

4 changing beers (often Bristol Beer Factory, Dancing Duck, Oakham) ⊞

This pleasant one-room micropub is a family-owned establishment with a warm and friendly atmosphere. They have four ever-changing local and national beers as well as ciders, with bar snacks and cobs available during the day. On Tuesday there is a discount on drinks, a weekly pub quiz is held on Wednesday, and live entertainment at the weekend. Closed Monday except bank holidays. &🍽🅿🚍(60,61)🌸🛜♪

Burton upon Trent

Beeropolis

81 High Street, DE14 1LD (at northern end of High St)

☎ 07715 097797

2 changing beers (sourced nationally) ⊞

Refreshed and renamed in 2021, this micropub is on the ground floor of a Grade II-listed end-terrace building. The comfortable single room features upholstered bench seating around the periphery, with a raised area under the shop-style windows. There is a small bar counter to the side towards the rear, with the stillage room behind. The Gents incorporates an unusual 'keg' urinal! Beers and other drinks are listed on a TV screen near the bar. There is no pub car park, but public car parks are nearby.

Q🌣☺🍽🚍🌸🛜

Coopers Tavern ★

43 Cross Street, DE14 1EG (off Station St)

☎ (01283) 567246

Draught Bass; Joule's Pale Ale Ⓖ**, Slumbering Monk** ⊞**; 6 changing beers (sourced regionally)** ⊞/Ⓖ

Classic 19th-century ale house, once the Bass brewery tap but currently part of the Joule's estate. Following a sympathetic refurbishment and expansion in 2017, the pub incorporates five linked rooms. The intimate inner tap room has retained its barrel tables and bench seating, with the beer served from a small counter by the cask stillage. Fruit wines, plus up to six ciders/perries (choice varies) are also available. Impromptu folk music regularly features on Tuesday evening, live music most Sunday afternoons, and open mic on the last Wednesday of the month. 🌣☺🎅≷(Burton on Trent)🍽🚍🌸🛜♪

Devonshire Arms ☗

86 Station Street, DE14 1BT (on corner of jct with Milton St)

☎ (01283) 480022

Burton Bridge Bridge Bitter; Draught Bass; Gates Burton Reservoir; 4 changing beers (sourced regionally) ⊞

Popular old pub, now a free house, dating from the 19th century and Grade II listed. Brewery memorabilia is displayed in the refurbished public bar at the front; to the rear is a larger, more comfortable, split-level lounge featuring an 1853 map of Burton, old local photographs, and unusual arched wooden ceilings. An extended rear patio is adorned with flower borders and hanging baskets. Tuesday and Thursday food evenings have a theme, such as fish, pies, or steak. Football fans are welcome, including away supporters.

🌸🍽≷(Burton on Trent)🍼🅿🚍🌸🛜

Dog Inn

5 Lichfield Street, DE14 3QZ (opp Burton College; near jct with High St/New St)

☎ (01283) 517060

Black Country Pig on the Wall, Fireside; house beer (by Black Country); 7 changing beers (sourced regionally) ⊞

An attractive half-timbered terrace pub near the town centre, dating back to the early 19th century. Radically revitalised by Black Country Ales in 2015, an impressive selection of cask ales and ciders is offered. Internally, a large, comfortable, square single room surrounds a central bar and features a wood-framed ceiling and wood panelling on the walls, plus three real fires and numerous framed old photographs of Burton. Available beers and other drinks are listed on a wall-mounted screen near the bar. 🌣🍼🍽🚍🌸🛜♪

Elms Inn ⦿

36 Stapenhill Road, Stapenhill, DE15 9AE (on A444)

☎ (01283) 535505

Draught Bass; Oakham Citra; Timothy Taylor Landlord; 2 changing beers (sourced nationally) ⊞

Lively local on the opposite bank of the River Trent from the town centre. Built as a private house in the late 19th

REAL ALE BREWERIES

Beowulf Brownhills
Blythe Hamstall Ridware
Brewhouse & Kitchen 🍽 Lichfield
Burton Bridge Burton upon Trent
Consall Forge Consall Forge
Crown Brewhouse 🍽 Elford (brewing suspended)
Enville Enville
Firs 🍽 Codsall
Flash Flash
Front Row Brindley Ford
Gates Burton Burton upon Trent
Gentlewood Gentleshaw
Inadequate 🍽 Stoke-on-Trent: Etruria
Izaak Walton 🍽 Norton Bridge
Kinver Kinver
Lymestone Stone
Marston's Burton upon Trent
Outwoods 🍽 Burton upon Trent (NEW)
Peakstones Rock Alton
Quartz Kings Bromley
Roebuck Draycott-in-the-Clay
Shugborough Milford (brewing suspended)
Tamworth ⬧ Tamworth
Titanic Stoke-on-Trent: Burslem
Tower ⬧ Burton upon Trent
Trinity ⬧ Lichfield
Uttoxeter ⬧ Uttoxeter
Vine Inn 🍽 Rugeley
Weal ⬧ Chesterton
Wilsons of Warslow 🍽 Warslow

century, this is one of Burton's original parlour pubs. Sensitively renovated, the small public bar, snug and a side room at the front of the pub are largely unchanged. In contrast, the lounge to the rear has been extended and refurbished in a modern style. Food is normally limited to light snacks, but themed food evenings are sometimes held, and there is occasional live entertainment. ☺❀♿♣🚌(18)🐾📶♫

Roebuck Inn ✔

101 Station Street, DE14 1BT (on corner of jct with Mosley St)

☎ (01283) 511213 🌐 roe-buck-inn.co.uk

Draught Bass; Gates Burton Reservoir; Marston's Pedigree; Theakston Old Peculier; 3 changing beers (sourced regionally; often Brains, Fuller's) H

Friendly Victorian corner-terrace pub near the railway station, once the Ind Coope brewery tap, opposite the former brewery. The original classic Draught Burton Ale was launched here in 1976. Inside, there is a long narrow single room with dark wood panelling and the bar counter down one side. A small patio at the rear is available for outdoor drinking, plus a few tables and chairs outside at the front in summer. Live music is played early Sunday evening. It is an unofficial Gates brewery tap. ❀⇌⇌(Burton on Trent)♣🚌🐾📶♫

Weighbridge Inn

Grain Warehouse Yard, Derby Street, DE14 2JJ (off S end of Derby St, A5121, one-way section)

☎ 07758 546922

Muirhouse Tick Tock Boom H**; 3 changing beers (sourced nationally)** H/G

Two-room micropub created in a late-Victorian former coal yard office in 2015 and now operated by the Muirhouse brewery. It is close to the railway station and en route to Burton Albion's Pirelli Stadium, nearly a mile distant. The bar counter is in the main room, with the available beers and other offerings listed on a TV screen. A cosy smaller room is located through a doorway at the far end; both rooms feature fireplaces. Meals are limited to pre-booked Sunday lunches. Children are welcome until 8pm. ☺❀◐⇌(Burton on Trent)♣●P🚌🐾

Butterton

Black Lion Inn L

ST13 7SP (in centre of the village next to church)

☎ (01538) 304232 🌐 blacklioninn.co.uk

Draught Bass; 2 changing beers (often Whim, Wincle) H

A charming pub with plenty of olde-worlde charm set in the heart of the village, next to the church. Butterton is within the Peak District National Park and close to the Manifold Way. There is a single bar, separate restaurant, and a good-sized car park. The old range is very warming on cold winter days. The husband and wife team source their guest beers from local independents. The beers are diverse for a country pub and something unusual for the area can frequently be found. Q☺❀⇌◐◑♿▲♣P🐾📶

Cannock

Arcade

49 Mill Street, WS11 0DR (opp Morrisons car park)

☎ (01543) 462920 🌐 thearcadecannock.co.uk

3 changing beers (sourced locally; often Green Duck, Hobsons, Salopian) H

This gem of a pub on the outskirts of the town centre has a post-industrial feel with pop culture references throughout the bar. The back room is a comfortable lounge with period furniture and local historic photography, leading to an outside area with wooden decking. The pub currently serves up to three real ales with bar snacks available. A weekly quiz night is hosted on Wednesday, an open-mic evening once a month on Sunday, and local street food every Friday. ☺❀♿🐾📶♫

Linford Arms ✔

79 High Green, WS11 1BN

☎ (01543) 469360

Greene King Abbot; Ruddles Best Bitter; Sharp's Doom Bar; 5 changing beers (sourced nationally; often Beowulf, Salopian, Titanic) H

Established town-centre Wetherspoon pub serving up to eight real ales and ciders. The pub name originates from the builders' merchant that formerly occupied the premises in the 19th century. The Tudor inspired timber frame runs through this two floored building, with quiet alcoves and snug areas giving it a homely feel. Two ale festivals are held each year, and local breweries feature regularly. There are good bus and rail links. Not to be missed if you are visiting Cannock. ☺❀◐◑♿🚌📶

Newhall Arms 🏆

81 High Green, WS11 1BN

Oakham Citra; Wye Valley HPA; 6 changing beers (often Green Duck, Shiny, Wye Valley) H

Opened in 2016, Cannock's first micropub is family owned and a must-visit pub with great beers and fantastic staff. Serving local and national cask ales alongside craft kegs and cans, you're guaranteed to find a beer to make you want another. No-nonsense snacks and fresh cheese and onion cobs go hand-in-hand with the beers to make this a true gem. Q❀♿P🚌🐾📶

Chasetown

Uxbridge Arms

2 Church Street, WS7 3QL SK045080

☎ (01543) 221568

Black Country Bradley's Finest Golden, Pig on the Wall, Fireside; 13 changing beers (sourced nationally; often Church End, Green Duck, Titanic) H

This building was formerly a mine foreman's house, and also a mortuary, before Black Country Ales took over in 2021 and fully refurbished it. This open-plan pub has 16 handpulls with 13 for real ale and three serving cider. Bar snacks and cobs are available, with the friendly staff always happy to help. Children are allowed until 7pm. It is a short walk from Chasewater Country Park and railway. ☺❀♿♣●P🚌(60)🐾📶

Cheadle

Bakers Arms

21 High Street, ST10 1AA (100yds from Leek Rd roundabout)

☎ (01538) 756237

Draught Bass; 5 changing beers (often Dancing Duck, MBH Beer) H

Now a regular in the Guide the Bakers Arms, opened in 2017, is named after its former use as a local bakery. Three separate areas and a superbly set out rear yard contrive to make the most of the small space. A real fire, comfortable seating and suntrap outdoor area make visiting the Bakers a real pleasure. Jenga, Wednesday crib, and weekend evening live music combine to make this place a lovely little boozer for both locals and visitors. Q❀♿♣●P🚌(32,32X)🐾📶♫

Bird in Hand L

117 Tape Street, ST10 1ER

☎ (01538) 421126

Burton Bridge Bridge Bitter; Dancing Duck #Wet
February; 2 changing beers (often Brunswick, Burton
Bridge) Ⓗ
A well-deserved entry into the Guide, this small,
traditional, terraced street-corner pub occupies a main
road position just outside the town centre. Two rooms
have lovely coal fires. A large screen shows major
sporting events, another room houses a dartboard, and a
pool table is found in the anteroom. The cosy snug is
quieter and also has a real fire. There is a patio outside
for smokers. The licensees always give a warm welcome,
as do the bar staff. Q♣●🖵(32,32X)❀

Checkley

Red Lion
28 Church Lane, ST10 4NJ
☎ (01538) 423792
Brains Rev James Original; Draught Bass; Timothy
Taylor Landlord; 1 changing beer (sourced locally;
often Uttoxeter) Ⓗ
This traditional, comfortable old village pub by the
church, is welcoming and friendly. The main bar area is
elongated, with a real fire to the right of the entrance.
There is an outside seating area at the front of the pub
and a small car park can be found at the rear. Breakfast is
served Saturday and Sunday, with a grill night on
Wednesday and lunch on Sunday.
Q🕏❀🅓👵🅰♣🖵❀ ⚲ ♪

Cheddleton

Black Lion ♇ Ⓛ
12 Hollow Lane, ST13 7HP (turn off the A520 into
Hollow Ln, opp Red lion; pub is 100yds up the hill on right
next to the church)
☎ (01538) 360620
Draught Bass; Timothy Taylor Landlord; 4 changing
beers (often Salopian, Wincle) Ⓗ
The Black Lion is a comfortable village pub, with two real
fires in winter. It is close to the Flint Mill Museum and the
Cauldon Canal, and beside the Grade II-listed St Edward's
Church, which has a Wardle family connection and Arts
and Crafts features. Recently extended with a
continuation of the modern rustic style theme, there is a
patio area outside to the front and an enclosed beer
garden at the rear. An excellent range of well-kept beers
is offered from this former local CAMRA Pub of the Year.
Q🕏❀🅓≠♣🖵(16) ❀ ⚲

Church Eaton

Royal Oak
High Street, ST20 0AJ (centre of the village; signposted
from A518 at Haughton and Gnosall)
☎ (01785) 823078 ⊕ royaloakchurcheaton.co.uk
Wye Valley Bitter, HPA, Butty Bach Ⓗ
Once threatened by closure but saved by a village
consortium, the Royal Oak is now run by Lanvar Ltd, a
group of 34 villagers. A thriving pub at the centre of the
community, it is the hub of charity fundraising in the
village. The pub has Sky Sports, a pool table and holds a
quiz one night a month. It also has a music night on the
last Sunday of the month – check the pub website for
artists and dates. 🕏❀🅰♣🖵(877)❀ ⚲ ♪

Codsall

Codsall Station Ⓛ
Chapel Lane, WV8 2EJ
☎ (01902) 847061

Holden's Black Country Bitter, Golden Glow, Special; 2
changing beers (sourced nationally; often
Holden's) Ⓗ
Sensitively converted in 1997 from the waiting room,
offices and stationmaster's house, the Grade II-listed
building comprises a bar, lounge, snug with log fires and
a conservatory; all display collections of worldwide
railway memorabilia. Steps lead from the conservatory
up to the outside drinking terrace with tables and
benches overlooking the working station platforms. Bar
meals are served, except Monday, with cobs and locally-
made pork pies available all week.
Q🕏❀🅓≠P🖵(5,10B) ❀ ⚲

Firs Club Ⓛ
Station Road, WV8 1BX (entrance from shared Co-op car
park off Station Rd)
☎ (01902) 844674 ⊕ thefirscodsall.com
5 changing beers (sourced locally) Ⓗ
Frequent local award winner and CAMRA Regional Club
of the Year 2023. It contains a bar area, quiet lounge and
separate sports lounge with a pool table and dartboard.
Five changing ales, usually including a mild, are mainly
local, and often feature a beer from the in-house
brewery. A beer festival is held in November. The Firs
Suite, a dedicated function area, is available to hire for
weddings and other events.
Q🕏❀👵≠♣P🖵(5,10B) ⚲ ♪

Love & Liquor
1-3 Church Road, WV8 1EA
☎ (01902) 843277
Wye Valley HPA, Butty Bach; 3 changing beers
(sourced nationally; often Abbeydale, Oakham,
Salopian) Ⓗ
This converted shop in the centre of Codsall is always
popular and a mainstay of the local real ale scene. An
upstairs room with bench seating has a large TV showing
sport. Downstairs is a bar area with comfortable seating,
a wood-burning stove and another TV. Pavement tables
provide an outdoor drinking area. Five ales are served
with three changing guests which usually include a stout
or porter. ❀≠🖵(5,10B)❀ ♪

Consall Forge

Black Lion Ⓛ
ST9 0AJ (off A522 follow signs to Consall Gardens, then
Nature Reserve on hairpin bend; go straight on, ignore
No Vehicular Access sign; at bottom of hill go left along
track to car park)
☎ (01782) 550294
Peakstones Rock Black Hole; 3 changing beers
(sourced regionally; often Consall Forge, Falstaff) Ⓗ
A welcome return for a regular in the Guide. Walk, drive
or travel by boat or train to visit this destination pub with
its changing beer and cider selections. Regular beer
festivals are held, normally to coincide with a steam gala
on the neighbouring Churnet Valley Railway. Typical pub
food is served; arrive hungry as the portions are large.
Set in an Area of Outstanding Natural Beauty, the pub is
not easy to find by car but is well worth the effort. Seek it
out! Q🕏❀🅓🅰≠(Consall)♣●P❀ ⚲ ♪

Doveridge

Cavendish Arms ✔
Derby Road, DE6 5JR
☎ (01889) 358586 ⊕ cavendisharms.com
Greene King Abbot; Marston's Pedigree; Timothy
Taylor Landlord; 1 changing beer (often Wye
Valley) Ⓗ

Large Grade II-listed corner building, slightly away from the village high street on the old route of the A50. It changed hands in 2021, and has a good selection of handpulled ales along with a choice of lagers, ciders and IPAs in keg, plus a gin bar. With friendly service, the good food menu includes vegetarian, vegan and gluten-free options. Regular functions are held, there is a large garden area, and families and larger parties are welcomed. Q ⏦ ❀ ◑ ㊉ ♣ P ⊟ (1) ❀ ♫

Draycott-in-the-Clay

Roebuck

Toby's Hill, DE6 5BT (at Toby's Hill/A515 junction, 600yds N of village)
☎ (01283) 821135 ⊕ theroebuckdraycott.co.uk
Roebuck Blonde, Bitter, IPA; 1 changing beer (sourced locally; often Roebuck) ⊞
Welcoming early 19th-century family-owned free house, close to the A50/A515 junction and Staffordshire/Derbyshire border. The pub showcases beers from the associated Roebuck brewery, which is in a splendid English oak-framed building to the rear of the large car park. Traditional home-cooked food is served in the restaurant and cosy bar (no meals Sun eve). The Klondike Mill Steam Preservation Centre is nearby and the National Trust's Sudbury Hall and Museum of Childhood are within easy reach, as is the national football centre at St George's Park. ⏦ ❀ ◑ P ⊟ ❀ ♠

Eccleshall

Ecclian ⏺

27 High Street, ST21 6BW
☎ 07812 033618
Draught Bass; 4 changing beers (sourced nationally; often Lymestone, Three Tuns) ⊞
Small, family-friendly, comfortable and welcoming one-room pub with a friendly atmosphere. It is well fitted out in a traditional style, with brass handpumps and dark wood surround. The beer range varies – see the pub's Facebook page for updates – and more than 100 whiskies, over 100 gins and 10 brandies are stocked. Tea and coffee are also available. Bar snacks include fresh rolls. Bingo sessions are held one Wednesday a month, and there is occasional live music. A pavement seating area is outside. Q ⏦ ❀ ㊉ ⊟ (423) ❀ ♠ ♫

Enville

Cat Inn ⏺

Bridgnorth Road, DY7 5HA (on A458)
☎ (01384) 872209 ⊕ thecatinn.com
Enville Ale; Wye Valley HPA, Butty Bach; 3 changing beers (sourced regionally; often Enville, Hobsons, Holden's) ⊞
This idyllic country pub, which serves as the taphouse for Enville, guarantees a warm welcome. The interior is reminiscent of a country cottage, and has multiple rooms in which to dine and imbibe, with several having their own real fires. Home-made food is served. The majority of the cask offering is made up of staple and seasonal Enville beers, but you will also find a small number of guest beers and up to two real ciders. Q ⏦ ❀ ◑ P ❀ ♠

Fradley Junction

Swan Inn

DE13 7DN (by Trent & Mersey Canal, about 1 mile W of Fradley village) SK140140
☎ (01283) 790330 ⊕ swaninnfradley.co.uk

Everards Sunchaser, Tiger, Old Original; 1 changing beer (sourced regionally) ⊞
Known locally as the Mucky Duck, this late 18th-century, Grade II-listed, mid-terrace pub overlooks the junction of the Trent & Mersey and Coventry canals. The cosy public bar, which retains an old-fashioned charm, and the smaller lounge are on opposite sides of a central serving area. There is also a cellar room, with a vaulted brick ceiling. Guest beers are usually from Midlands microbreweries. No meals are served on Sunday evening. Boaters, walkers and gongoozlers are welcome. Q ⏦ ❀ ◑ ㊉ ♣ P ❀ ♠

Gnosall

George & the Dragon ⏺

46 High Street, ST20 0EX
☎ 07779 327551 ⊕ georgeandthedragongnosall.com
Holden's Black Country Mild, Golden Glow; Parkway Cheeky Monkey; 2 changing beers (sourced nationally; often Glastonbury, Parkway, Salopian) ⊞
This lovely little pub, comprising two rooms served by one bar, opened in 2015 and has won multiple local CAMRA awards. The building dates from 1736 and has seen many changes of use. With no TVs, no music and no games machines it has a good old-fashioned appeal. At the bar there is always a choice of a light, medium and dark ale. Tasty home-made snacks are available at the bar, but they do sell out quickly. Only cash is accepted. Q ⏦ ♣ ❀ ⊟ ❀

Great Wyrley

Andys' Ale House ⏺

Unit 8 Quinton Court, Hilton Lane, WS6 6DZ (in the Quinton Court Precinct)
☎ 07311 661688
5 changing beers (often Bristol Beer Factory, Green Duck, Sarah Hughes) ⊞
A welcoming one-room micropub with a traditional feel and friendly staff, located in the Quinton Court shopping centre. This pub has no music or TVs, just good conversation. A quiz is held on the first Monday of the month, there is a monthly poker night, and pub games are played. Bar snacks are available including cobs, pork pies and Scotch eggs. Q ⏦ ❀ ➤ (Landywood) ♣ ❀ P ⊟ (x51) ❀ ♠

Hednesford

Cross Keys Hotel ⏺

42 Hill Street, WS12 2DN
☎ (01543) 879534
Draught Bass; Salopian Oracle; Wye Valley HPA, Butty Bach; 5 changing beers (sourced nationally; often Fuller's, Oakham, Ossett) ⊞
A former coaching inn dating back to 1746 with historic photographs decorating the walls of this traditionally styled pub. A separate bar and lounge serves up to eight real ales. This is the closest pub to the local football team Hednesford Town FC so it can be busy on match days. It is rumoured that the infamous highwayman Dick Turpin stopped here on his famous ride to York. ❀ ♣ P ⊟ (3,60)

High Offley

Anchor Inn ★

Peggs Lane, Old Lea, ST20 0NG (from A519 at Woodseaves turn W on High Offley Rd by chapel, then left on Peggs Ln) SJ775256
☎ (01785) 284569
Wadworth 6X ⊞

On the banks of the Shropshire Union Canal by bridge 42, the pub has changed little since the 19th century, and is recognised by CAMRA as having a nationally important historic interior. There are two rooms, each with a coal fire. Beer is bought up from the cellar. A gorgeous garden, with seating, is between the pub and the towpath, where moorings are available. The pub is normally open Friday to Sunday, but may open weekday evenings in summer – check before visiting. It is well worth searching out. Q✿☺♿🅰♣🅿✿

Kidsgrove

Blue Bell
25 Hardingswood, ST7 1EG (off A50 near Tesco, by canal bridge)
☎ (01782) 774052 ⊕ bluebellinnkidsgrove.com
Whim Arbor Light; 5 changing beers (sourced nationally) Ⓗ
Traditional canalside pub offering six real ales and a good range of ciders, plus a warm welcome from the hosts. It has two separate areas off the main bar and a smaller room at the back. The well-kept beer range features different styles, always including one dark ale. There is a beer garden to the rear. The pub holds an annual beer festival as well as seasonal and charity events. It is popular with locals, walkers and canal users.
Q✿☺♿🅰≢♣🅿🖵(3,4A) ✿🛜

Crown & Thistle
143 Liverpool Road, ST7 4EY
☎ (01782) 786971
Burton Bridge Bridge Bitter, Stairway to Heaven; 5 changing beers (sourced regionally) Ⓗ
Large roadside pub on the road into Kidsgrove, refurbished in grand style by Caldmore Taverns. Five separate areas lead off from the bar room, so there is plenty of room for a quiet drink. Seven handpulls serve two regular beers from Burton Bridge plus five guests from local and regional breweries. A good range of ciders and spirits plus craft ales, ensures something for everyone. There is a pleasant beer garden on two terraces to the rear. Note that doors close at 10.30pm on Friday and Saturday. Q✿☺♿≢♣🅿🖵(3,4)✿

Kingstone

Shrewsbury Arms Ⓛ
Uttoxeter Road, ST14 8QH
☎ (01889) 500181 ⊕ shrewsburyarmskingstone.co.uk
Marston's Pedigree; Uttoxeter Paddock Porter; 1 changing beer (sourced regionally; often Uttoxeter) Ⓗ
A delightful community-owned country inn, run by dedicated tenants, it is the perfect place to enjoy excellent fine ales and traditional home-cooked food. Situated in the centre of the small village of Kingstone, a warm and friendly atmosphere awaits in both bar and restaurant. Several permanent and changing handpulled ales from local independent brewers adorn the bar. Facilities include a beer garden and large outside seating area. The pub is family-friendly and dogs are allowed in the bar area. Q✿☺🕪♿🅰♣🅿✿🛜

Kinver

Cross Inn 🏆 Ⓛ
Church Hill, DY7 6HZ
☎ (01384) 878481
Black Country Bradley's Finest Golden, Pig on the Wall, Fireside; 4 changing beers (sourced nationally; often Fixed Wheel, Oakham, Salopian) Ⓗ

A popular destination Black Country Ales outlet, with a real fire, serving up to six guest beers. Tasty and tempting food is served at the weekend including hot pork sandwiches. A small number of flatscreen TVs show live football. There is a large adjacent car park and Stourbridge buses stop nearby, but there is no service after 6pm or on Sunday. ✿♿♣🅿🖵(228)✿🛜♪

Knighton

Haberdashers Arms Ⓛ
Newport Road, ST20 0QH (between Adbaston and Knighton) SJ753275
☎ (01785) 280650
Wye Valley Butty Bach; 1 changing beer (sourced locally; often Rowton, Salopian) Ⓗ
This Victorian era pub, with the same licensee for over 25 years, offers a warm welcome. The interior is reminiscent of country pubs in the middle of the last century. A central bar with handpump dispense serves two rooms, one with a pool table and dartboard. There is an adjacent camping field with toilet block. Various theme nights are held, including a Lamp Night when the collection of oil lamps is lit and the electric lights are turned off, creating a relaxed atmosphere. Q✿☺🕪🅰🅿✿🛜♪

Leek

Benks
39 Stockwell Street, ST13 6DH
☎ (01538) 382783
Draught Bass; 2 changing beers (often MBH Beer) Ⓗ
Friendly, unassuming, street-corner free house run by same family for over 50 years. The very much hands-on landlady owner is passionate about beer quality and attention to detail. The 100-year-old mechanical till complements four antique handpumps, serving regular Bass plus rotating guests from both local and national breweries. It is well patronised by league sports teams, having several dartboards and two pool tables. There is occasional live music plus a great jukebox. A suntrap rear yard contains an original well which is illuminated on request. Small functions are catered for. 🕪♣🖵✿🛜♪

Blue Mugge Ⓛ
17 Osbourne Street, ST13 6LJ (off A53 Buxton Rd)
☎ (01538) 384450
Draught Bass; 4 changing beers (sourced nationally; often Coach House) Ⓗ
Just outside the town centre, this unassuming terraced street-corner local is now an established Guide entry. Owned and run by the same family for over 40 years, the building has several distinctive themed rooms, a result of three adjoining properties being knocked into one. The unique layout has bar service from a central octagonal pillar, with the beer pumps and taps behind the staff. Two handpulls are believed to be 120 years old. Constantly changing guest ales are listed on a blackboard. Good-value food is available lunchtimes. The bus station is nearby. Q✿☺🕪♣🖵✿🛜♪

Fountain Inn Ⓛ
14 Fountain Street, ST13 6JR
☎ (01538) 382060
Draught Bass; Exmoor Gold; Wye Valley Butty Bach; 5 changing beers (sourced nationally; often Exmoor, Front Row, Wincle) Ⓗ
A magnificent bank of 10 handpulls greets the eye on entering this smart town-centre local, a former CAMRA Regional Pub of the Year. Eight real ales change regularly and always include a darker, stronger brew. Real ciders are also on sale. Live music on Sunday plus a beer raffle

help make this friendly community pub a real gem. Four smart rooms upstairs offer accommodation, with plenty of places to eat nearby. Q⛴♿🅿♣♠🅿☕🛜♪

Roebuck L
18 Derby Street, ST13 5AB (on main shopping street)
☎ (01538) 385602
Everards Tiger; Titanic Steerage, Iceberg, White Star, Plum Porter, Captain Smith's Strong Ale; 4 changing beers (sourced regionally; often Magic Rock, Salopian, Tiny Rebel) Ⓗ
With its distinctive black-and-white wooden-framed frontage, this Titanic brewery owned former coaching inn in the town centre dates back to 1626. Up to 13 ales at busier times are mainly from the Titanic range, including the award-winning Plum Porter, plus four guest ales, a range of craft beers and sometimes real cider too. Award-winning food is served all day, including breakfast. Regular live music and outdoor events take place in the large rear beer garden. It is close to the bus station and is a well-deserved entry in the Guide.
Q⛴🅴🅸♣♠🅿☕🛜♪

Lichfield

Beerbohm
19 Tamworth Street, WS13 6JP
☎ (01543) 898252 ⊕ beerbohm.bar
4 changing beers (sourced nationally) Ⓗ
A cosy Belgian-accented café-bar, featuring continental draught and bottled beers alongside the four real ales. A large, comfortable upstairs room offers views of the busy pedestrian street below, while the downstairs bar room is decorated with beer enamels, gilded mirrors and globular chandeliers. There is occasional live music. Simple snacks are served, but you can bring your own food, with plates and cutlery provided. The unisex toilets are upstairs. Q⛴🚆(City)🅿☕🛜♪

BitterSuite L
55 Upper St John Street, WS14 9DT
☎ 07852 179340 ⊕ bittersuite.co.uk
5 changing beers (sourced nationally) Ⓖ
Close to Lichfield City rail station, this pub has three comfortable rooms but no bar counter, so service is to your table. The five real ales and five ciders are complemented by gins, wines and bottled beers. Simple snacks are offered, or you can bring your own food. There is a large beer terrace to the rear, with occasional live music. Children are welcome until 7pm. Monday is quiz night, which finishes with a fish & chip supper.
Q⛴♿🚆(City)🅿☕♪

Horse & Jockey L
8-10 Sandford Street, WS13 6QA
☎ (01543) 410033
Holden's Golden Glow; Marston's Pedigree; Wye Valley HPA, Butty Bach; 4 changing beers (sourced nationally) Ⓗ
Busy city-centre outlet with various comfortable areas surrounding the central bar, and a large suntrap beer terrace to the rear and side. The house beers are big sellers but this does not detract from the quality and diversity of guest beers sourced. Sports screenings are popular. Freshly-made rolls and a pork pie/cheeseboard selection are always available. A 21-plus age policy is applied. ♿🍴🚆(City)♣🅿☕

Whippet Inn
21 Tamworth Street, WS13 6JP
☎ 07590 543024 ⊕ thewhippetinn-lichfield.co.uk
5 changing beers (sourced nationally) Ⓗ

Former dress shop in the heart of the city which features up to five diverse, varying ales and a good selection of canned craft beers. This intimate venue has seating for around 25 people and a maximum capacity of around 40. Given the name, it is unsurprising that the pub welcomes dogs. The seating comprises various benches and pews with additional stools and a small standing zone.
⛴🚆(City)🅿☕🛜

Milwich

Green Man L ✓
Sandon Lane, ST18 0EG (on B5027 in the centre of the village)
☎ (01889) 505310 ⊕ greenmanmilwich.com
Draught Bass; Greene King IPA; Ruddles Best Bitter; 3 changing beers (sourced nationally) Ⓗ
Free house at the heart of the village which has been under the same management since 1990 and is a long-standing entry in the Guide. It has a wooden-floored bar area with a smaller eating and drinking area to the rear. A free music festival is hosted in the huge lush green garden in summer. The jukebox and TV are rarely used. This is a true and lively village community pub with an open fire and lots of craic. Q⛴♿🍴♣🅿☕🛜♪

Newcastle-under-Lyme

Boat & Horses
2 Stubbs Gate, ST5 1LU (opp Morrisons, 500yds from bus station)
☎ (01782) 911528
Draught Bass; Oakham Citra; Thornbridge Jaipur; 3 changing beers (sourced nationally) Ⓗ
This friendly and pleasant pub on the edge of the town centre (less than a five minute walk from the bus station) offers six real ales (four permanent and two guests) alongside four or more real ciders and a selection of craft beers in cans and bottles. The elongated open-plan layout has the feel of three separate areas, with the main bar area plus two slightly raised areas at each end. Q⛴♿♠🅿☕♪

Bridge Street Ale House L
31 Bridge Street, ST5 2RY
☎ (01782) 499394
5 changing beers (sourced nationally; often Beartown, Facer's, Three Tuns) Ⓗ/Ⓖ
The first micropub in the area, the capable hands of Grum and his hospitable staff make this is a special place for regulars and newcomers alike. The pub oozes charm and appeal, enhanced by the quirky decor. Five changing guest beers are on handpull from various breweries, with more occasionally available straight from the barrel. Nine real ciders and an extensive range of speciality rums add to the individuality of this fantastic pub. A Newcastle real ale institution. Q♿♣♠🅿☕♪

Cask Bar
1-2 Andrew Place, ST5 1DL
☎ (01782) 870560
Sarah Hughes Dark Ruby Mild; 4 changing beers (sourced nationally) Ⓗ
Award-winning microbar which opened in 2017, located just outside of Newcastle-under-Lyme town centre. One room houses a variety of different seating, from ordinary tables and chairs to the higher 'posing'-style tables. Sarah Hughes Dark Ruby Mild is the permanent cask beer along with four changing guests, a rotating craft keg selection, and one of the best gin selections in the area. Meals are served Wednesday to Sunday (times vary).
Q⛴🍴♠🅿☕🛜♪

Castle Mona

4 Victoria Street, ST5 1NT
☎ 07502 562207
Draught Bass; 3 changing beers (sourced nationally; often Brains, Salopian) ⊞
A gem of a corner pub located in a residential area close to the A34, a five minute walk from Newcastle bus station and on a number of bus routes. It has a splendid panelled lounge and traditional bar where pool and table skittles are played. There is a large, pleasant beer garden and the pub has a genuine community spirit. Major sports fixtures are shown on TV, and regular live music events and quiz nights are held. Q❄✿♣♠◻(25)🌐🎵

Crossways (Bottlecraft)

Nelson Place, ST5 1RW (large building at the end of the Ironmarket by Fountain Roundabout, opp Queens Gardens)
☎ (01782) 405280 ⊕ bottlecraft.beer
5 changing beers (sourced nationally) ⊞
The Crossways is a welcome addition to the fantastic ale scene in Newcastle-under-Lyme from the team at Bottlecraft in Hanley. A warm welcome is assured from the friendly and enthusiastic bar staff. It offers a range of unusual and interesting traditional and craft beers across five cask and 12 keg taps, plus bottles and cans, all in a classic pub environment. Beers are served in pint, two-thirds and one-third measures. A pool table is available. Q♦◻✿🌐🎵

Hopinn ⃝

102 Albert Street, ST5 1JR
☎ (01782) 711121
Black Sheep Best Bitter; Draught Bass; Oakham Citra; 5 changing beers (sourced nationally; often Mallinsons, Northern Monk, Oakham) ⊞
Comfortable, friendly pub on the edge of Newcastle-under-Lyme offering an outstanding range of eight cask ales from both local and national breweries, supplemented up to five KeyKeg beers. There are three comfortably furnished rooms. The staff are friendly and attentive, and there is a true community feel to the pub. Sports events are screened, and newspapers are provided. Q❄♣♠◻(4,4A)✿

Mellards

Mellard's Warehouse, Market Lane, ST5 1AA
☎ (01782) 610497
3 changing beers (sourced nationally) ⊞
Smart modern bar which is housed in an old warehouse building. The pub is split-level with the bar on the ground floor containing high tables and chairs, while settees and armchairs can be found on the upper level. The bar prides itself on the four handpulls, including a draught cider, plus a great range of keg beers. A large selection of bottled beers and cans are also available. The large outside seating area is to the front of the bar. Card payments only. ✿♦◻✿🌐

Penkridge

Horse & Jockey

24 Market Street, ST19 5DH
☎ (01785) 716299
Black Country Bradley's Finest Golden, Pig on the Wall, Fireside; 6 changing beers (sourced nationally) ⊞
A warm, friendly pub in a large village completely renovated to a high standard by Black Country Inns in 2021. There is a single bar which rambles around several distinct drinking areas. Rolls from a local source, plus sausage rolls and pork pies from a local butcher, hot

sandwiches and jacket potatoes are available. Two of the 12 handpumps are reserved for cider but these might not always be real. ❄✿&♣♠◻✿🌐🎵

Star Inn ⃝ ⊘

Market Place, ST19 5DJ
☎ (01785) 712513
Banks's Amber Ale; Holden's Golden Glow; Wainwright Gold; 2 changing beers (sourced nationally; often Holden's, Peakstones Rock, Thornbridge) ⊞
A one-room pub with several distinct areas and a cosy welcoming feel. The pub is situated in the old Market Place and first traded as an inn in 1830. It became a shop in 1908, then a private residence. It was restored and converted back into a pub in 1981. Outside there is a covered and heated patio area where dogs are welcome. Pub snacks such as Scotch eggs are available. Weekly Sunday music sessions feature local acts and a free cheese board, and an open mic night is hosted the last Tuesday of every month. ❄✿▲≈♣♠P◻(878)🌐🎵

Rugeley

Rusty Barrel

Fernwood Shopping Centre, 103 Fernwood Drive, WS15 2GS
⊕ rustybarrel.co.uk
4 changing beers (sourced locally; often Blythe, Shiny, Silhill) ⊞
The pub takes its name from the owner's love of classic VW vehicles. This one-room micropub has simple painted brick walls and the ceiling is adorned with pumpclips showing the vast array of beers that have been sold. Four handpumps offer different choices of beers, and there are at least five real ciders. The atmosphere is friendly and it is popular with locals. Q❄&♠P◻(826,828)✿

Vine Inn

Sheepfair, WS15 2AT
☎ (01889) 574443
Vine Inn Session Ale, Vanilla Porter, Grapefruit IPA ⊞
An old-styled pub on a quiet street owned by the same family for two generations. The pub retains a traditional multi-room layout with a spacious bar to the front incorporating an open fire and quarry tiles, a small snug behind the bar, plus a room to the rear. There is also a large function room upstairs which can hold live music events. The pub has its own brewery on site and holds regular food events and monthly quiz nights. ✿&♣✿🌐🎵

Stafford

Olde Rose & Crown ⃝

10 Market Street, ST16 2JZ
☎ (01785) 249631
Joule's Pure Blonde, Pale Ale, Slumbering Monk; 1 changing beer (sourced locally; often Joule's) ⊞
Situated next to the Gatehouse Theatre in the heart of Stafford, the familiar Joule's style of log fires, wood panels, oak beams, and old signs create a traditional atmosphere. The central bar, offering four Joule's beers on handpump, serves a cosy front bar and larger rear lounge. Music is a big feature of the pub with live rock, blues and folk acts most Fridays and Saturdays, and there are lively quiz nights on Thursday. Dogs are welcome but must be kept on a lead at all times ❄✿≈◻✿🎵

Spittal Brook ⊘

106 Lichfield Road, ST17 4LP (1 mile SE of centre off A34 at Queensville Bridge)

☎ (01785) 251343 ⊕ thespittalbrookstafford.co.uk
St Austell Tribute; Timothy Taylor Boltmaker, Landlord; Wye Valley Butty Bach; 2 changing beers (sourced nationally) 🅷
Traditional, friendly two-roomed local within walking distance of the town centre. Thriving after refurbishment and a change of management in 2018, the front room offers TV sports and darts. Dogs are welcome here and in the spacious garden. The rear room is both the lounge and a restaurant where fresh home-cooked food is served daily. Two ever-changing guest beers are on the bar. The popular quiz night is on Wednesday, live entertainment most Saturdays, and a popular acoustic jam on the last Tuesday of each month.
🌣🕏🖾🕽🍴🅿🖵🌣🛜♪

Sun 🅻
7 Lichfield Road, ST17 4JX
☎ (01785) 248361
Everards Tiger; Titanic Steerage, Iceberg, White Star; house beer (by Titanic); 3 changing beers (sourced nationally; often Beartown, Ossett, Thornbridge) 🅷
A Titanic brewery pub since 2010, food is served throughout the day from a varied menu, with daily specials; Sunday roasts include a vegan option. An outdoor drinking area with its own bar is great on warmer summer days. Music festivals are held two or three times a year with additional beers available. Wheelchair access is from the car park and the pub has accessible toilets, but the interior is on several levels. A number of bus routes serve the nearby stop.
Q🌣🕏🕽🚰🍴🅿🖵🌣♪

Stoke-on-Trent: Burslem

Bull's Head 🅻
14 St John's Square, ST6 3AJ
☎ (01782) 834153
Titanic Steerage, Iceberg, White Star, Plum Porter; 6 changing beers (sourced nationally) 🅷
The Titanic brewery tap offers 10 real ales, 10 ciders and perries served from the cellar, and a selection of draught and bottled Belgian beers. It has a large central bar where bar billiards, a skittle table and jukebox can be found. Customers can also opt for the intimacy of the snug. A beer garden to the rear has many covered tables. The pub is close to Port Vale FC, opening early for home supporters on match days, and is involved with community events in the area. Q🌣🕏🟤🍴🖵🅿(3)🌣🛜

Johny's Micro Pub
9 St John's Square, ST6 3AH
4 changing beers (sourced nationally) 🅷
This comfortable micropub on St John's Square opened in 2016. On the ground floor, its small square room with chairs and tables ensures that conversation is never far away. The four, well-kept, real ales change regularly and will be from anywhere in the country. There are several real ciders in the fridge, alongside a good selection of bottles and cans. The toilets are on the first floor, as is the Harold Harper suite which is available for meetings and small parties. Q🚰(Longport)🍴🖵(3,98)🌣

Olde Crown
10A Westport Road, ST6 4AW
Greene King Abbot; Newby Wyke Bear Island; 3 changing beers (sourced nationally) 🅷
Small community local on a side street, just off the centre of Burslem. A central bar divides the single room into separate areas and there is a small smoking shelter to the rear. Very much a Port Vale supporters pub, only home fans are allowed on match days. There is a spacious patio to the rear and a pool table around the

bar. The three changing beers can be varied and interesting, and from just about anywhere.
🌣🕏🖵(3,98)🌣♪

Stoke-on-Trent: Etruria

Holy Inadequate 🍺 🅻
67 Etruria Old Road, ST1 5PE
☎ (01782) 911393
Inadequate Roundhouse Stout, Tickety Boo; Joule's Pale Ale; 6 changing beers (sourced nationally; often Inadequate) 🅷
A regular winner of the local CAMRA Pub of the Year, this fantastic pub showcases a huge range of beers from across the UK plus beers from its on-site Inadequate brewery. Bottled beers are also available. Three seating areas with log-burners, plus a large beer garden, provide plenty of space, and the traditional decor in the main bar gives a cosy feel. Friendly and welcoming to everyone, this is perfect place to spend time drinking excellent beer. Q🕏🟤🅿🖵(4)🌣🛜

Stoke-on-Trent: Hanley

Coachmakers Arms ★
65 Lichfield Street, ST1 3EA (opp Hanley bus station)
☎ 07876 144818 ⊕ coachmakersarms.co.uk
Draught Bass; 4 changing beers (sourced nationally) 🅷
The Coachmakers is the first pub you will encounter on leaving the bus station. It is one of the few remaining pubs of its type left in the city, comprised of four small rooms, with a dividing passage and serving hatch. The passage has been recognised by CAMRA as historically important. An extremely friendly atmosphere always pervades, driven by the main source of entertainment, conversation. As for the beers, Bass is king, accompanied by three ever-changing quality ales, plus up to five real ciders. It is also handy when visiting the Victoria Hall. Q🌣🟤🅿🖵🌣

Irish Woodman 🅻
3 Goodson Street, ST1 2AT
☎ (01782) 213996
House beer (by Facer's); 5 changing beers (sourced nationally) 🅷
Situated in Hanley Town centre, and part of the respected Caldmore Taverns chain, the recently renamed Irish Woodman has a large split-level bar that features a snug to the rear. It has garnered quite a reputation for the outstanding range and the quality of its beers, with six handpumps on display including the unique house beer Woodman Pale. Two real ciders are also served. Q🟤🅿🖵🛜♪

Unicorn Inn ★ ✅
40 Piccadilly, ST1 1EG
Draught Bass; Fuller's London Pride; 2 changing beers 🅷
One-roomed city-centre pub, opposite the Regent Theatre, comprised of a comfortably furnished lounge and a snug at the rear. Popular with theatre goers, both before and after the show, interval drinks can be pre-ordered. In the alley alongside is a narrow-gauge tram track, along which draymen used to deliver barrels. Watch out for the resident ghost! 🖵🛜

Victoria Lounge Bar 🅻
5 Adventure Place, ST1 3AF (next to Hanley bus station, opp Victoria Hall entrance)
☎ (01782) 273530 ⊕ victorialoungebar.co.uk

Draught Bass; Ossett White Rat; Salopian Oracle; 3 changing beers (sourced nationally) Ⓗ
To have been run for over 40 years by the same family that created it says a lot about the standards that have been set and maintained by this extremely popular hostelry. The large split-level room is furnished to a high quality, with the addition of Chesterfield settees adding to the cosy atmosphere. Six handpulls are available with Bass, Oracle and White Rat plus three ever-rotating ales. It is situated close to the Victoria Hall and bus station. Q🕮◑&🖨🛜

Stoke-on-Trent: Hartshill

Artisan Tap
552 Hartshill Road, ST4 6AF
☎ (01782) 618378
4 changing beers (sourced nationally) Ⓗ
Part of the 'Hartshill Mile' since 2017, this popular pub is a converted workshop with real character, bigger than it looks from the outside. The large main bar has a stage for its many live music events, and a separate quieter lounge area to the rear has gorgeous decor and comfortable seating. A generous outdoor area for sunny evenings completes the picture. A great range of four rotating ales from across the UK is offered plus bottled beers and up to three real ciders. Dogs are welcome. Q❀♣●🖨(11)❀🛜♪

Greyhound Ⓛ
67 George Street, ST5 1JT
☎ (01782) 635814
Titanic Iceberg, White Star, Plum Porter, Captain Smith's Strong Ale; 5 changing beers (sourced nationally; often Titanic) Ⓗ
A warm welcome awaits at this dog-friendly pub on the outskirts of Newcastle-under-Lyme. The second pub in the Titanic fleet, the Greyhound boasts nine handpumps showcasing Titanic ales as well as a fantastic, ever-changing range of beers from across the UK. A great selection of bottled beers as well as country wines and real cider make this an excellent choice for a quality drink. Bar snacks are available. There is occasional live music, and open mic nights, plus a regular pub quiz on Sunday night. Q🕮❀●🖨(11)❀🛜♪

Sanctuary Ⓛ
493-495 Hartshill Road, ST4 6AA
☎ (01782) 437523 ⊕ sanctuaryhartshill.co.uk
4 changing beers (sourced locally) Ⓗ
A true sanctuary in every sense, this wonderfully cosy pub features four constantly rotating real ales, up to four varied real ciders and a choice of bottled beers plus wines and gins. Ales are sourced from both local brewers and from further afield. Decorated in a cosy and eclectic style, including quirky features such as leather car seats and a rocking chair, this one-room pub feels like a home from home where all are made welcome. There are monthly open mic nights. Q🕮♣●🖨(11)❀🛜♪

Stoke-on-Trent: Longton

Congress Inn
14 Sutherland Road, ST3 1HJ (near Longton Police Station)
☎ (01782) 763667
Draught Bass; 3 changing beers (sourced nationally) Ⓗ
A convivial, multi award-winning, two-roomed pub, just outside the centre of Longton, dedicated to the dispense of good-quality real ale from a host of microbreweries. The left-hand room contains the bar where the three

permanent beers are joined by up to six guest beers. The right-hand room houses the dartboard, and is used for meetings and the annual beer festival, held every May. It's hard for the real ale fan to go wrong in a place like this – four ciders and a good selection of beer in bottles are also available. 🕮≠(Longton)♣●🖨❀♪

Stoke-on-Trent: Stoke

Glebe Ⓛ
35 Glebe Street, ST4 1HG
☎ (01782) 860670
Joule's Pure Blonde, Pale Ale, Slumbering Monk; 1 changing beer (sourced nationally; often Joule's) Ⓗ
Situated between the railway station and Stoke town centre, this superb Joule's establishment has one of the most stunning interiors in the area with its stained-glass windows, tiled flooring, and wood-panelled walls. The addition of candles on all tables creates the perfect environment for both drinking and dining. The three Joule's mainstay beers are always accompanied by a seasonal beer, and alongside the quality kitchen menu, a tasty and extensive cheese board is offered. ◑≠(Stoke-on-Trent)🖨❀♪

Stone

Borehole ⦿
Unit 5, Mount Road Industrial Estate, Mount Road, ST15 8LL
☎ (01785) 813581 ⊕ lymestonebrewery.net
Lymestone Stone Cutter, Stone Faced, Foundation Stone, Ein Stein, Stone the Crows; 1 changing beer (sourced nationally) Ⓗ
The Lymestone brewery tap, a few metres from the brewery itself, it is effectively two rooms with a log-burner in each, and a lovely enclosed suntrap garden to the rear. Snacks are available at all times and dogs are especially welcome. Children are welcome until 8pm. The full range of Lymestone beers are served, plus their seasonal beer and maybe a regional guest ale too. Real cider is available. An open mic night is held on Wednesday, with occasional live entertainment – check Facebook for details. Local CAMRA Pub of the Year 2023. Q🕮❀≠♣●P❀🛜♪

Royal Exchange Ⓛ
26 Radford Street, ST15 8DA (on corner of Northesk St and Radford St)
☎ (01785) 812685
Everards Tiger; Titanic Steerage, Iceberg, White Star, Plum Porter; 2 changing beers (sourced regionally) Ⓗ
A comfortable, welcoming Titanic pub, full of character, that serves all the brewery's regular beers. Two distinct bay-windowed, seating areas are to the left and right of the entrance, one of which has a solid fuel fire during winter. The interior extends beyond the bar to a lounge-style area. Children and dogs are welcome. There are no TVs or musak here, but plenty of good conversation! Occasional live entertainment is hosted – visit the pub's Facebook page for details. Q🕮❀≠♣🖨❀🛜♪

Swan Inn
18 Stafford Street, ST15 8QW (on A520 near Trent & Mersey Canal)
☎ (01785) 815570
House beer (by Coach House); 8 changing beers (sourced nationally) Ⓗ
A truly independent free house, close to the Trent & Mersey Canal, with nine handpulls, eight of which vary almost daily. It is a two-room pub with open fires at each end and a pleasant outside walled, semi-covered area to

the rear. The Swan is strictly 18+ with free live music Thursday, Friday and Saturday evenings. There is a cask beer loyalty card (buy 10 pints, get one free), and it regularly wins CAMRA accolades including several local Pub Of The Year awards. 🏴‍☠️🚫♿🍴🚃(101)🌟📶♫

Streethay

bod Lichfield
Unit 2 Yoxall Way, WS13 8FT
☎ (01543) 761517
Titanic Steerage, Iceberg, Plum Porter; 3 changing beers (often Everards, Titanic) Ⓗ
Large new-build café-bar serving a large housing development near Lichfield Trent Valley railway station. It is part of the growing chain of bod bars operated by Titanic. Food is served all day, starting with breakfast at 8.30am; alcohol is served from 11am. Additional seating is available upstairs in a mezzanine area. One of the guest handpulls will usually carry a local ale, and there are also 10 keg taps. Outside is a small set of benches around the perimeter of the premises for warmer days. 🏴‍☠️🚫🍴♿🚃(Lichfield Trent Valley) P🚗📶

Tamworth

King's Ditch Ⓛ
51 Lower Gungate, B79 7AS
☎ 07989 805828 ⊕ kingsditch.co.uk
4 changing beers (sourced nationally; often Leatherbritches, Pentrich, Shiny) Ⓖ
Tamworth's first micropub, offering four predominantly local ales. Formerly a cycle shop, it opened as a licensed premises in 2014. A well-chosen range of around 20 ciders and perries has led to the pub being a finalist in CAMRA's National Cider Pub of the Year competition several times. With a modern bare brick and wood interior, the single ground-floor room is a sociable environment, and there is an additional small overspill drinking area upstairs, which is generally quieter and more private. Simple snacks are served. Q🏴‍☠️🚫🚃♿🍴🚗🌟

Old Bank House
9 Ladybank, B79 7NB
☎ 07907 097935
5 changing beers Ⓗ
This attractive Victorian building was formerly home to Sir Robert Peel's Tamworth Savings Bank. It dates from 1845 and bears a blue plaque marking its history. A small bar area serves four well-appointed comfortable rooms. A pleasant beer terrace is to the rear, and in fine weather there's also seating to the front. Five varied and interesting ales typically showcase an ever-changing range of national breweries. Board games are available to play. 🏴‍☠️🍴🚗🌟📶♫

Sir Robert Peel Ⓛ
13-15 Lower Gungate, B79 7BA
☎ (01827) 300910
5 changing beers (often Church End, Little Critters, Sharp's) Ⓗ
Featuring in every issue of the Guide since 2005, the Peel was recognised in CAMRA's national 50th anniversary Golden Awards. It is named after the former prime minister, known for his role in the creation of the police force and the Tamworth pig. Up to five changing ales are complemented by a good selection of continental bottled beers. Occasional live music is hosted. A large beer garden is to the rear, with ancient stone walls, overlooked by the historic St Editha's Church. 🏴‍☠️🚃🚗🌟♫

Tamworth Tap 🍴 Ⓛ ✅
29 Market Street, B79 7LR
⊕ tamworthbrewing.co.uk
8 changing beers (sourced nationally) Ⓗ
CAMRA's National Pub of the Year 2023 occupies an elegant building which is also home to Tamworth Brewing Company. The cosy upstairs rooms have Tudor features and the historic courtyard beer terrace to the rear offers striking views of Tamworth Castle. Eight handpulls feature one Tamworth ale; the rest from near and far. Various snacks are offered, plus a wide range of ciders, gins, wines and bottled beers. Regular live music features plus a broad range of community activities. 🏴‍☠️🚃🍴🚗🌟📶♫

Tutbury

Cross Keys
39 Burton Street, DE13 9NR (E side of village, 300yds from A511)
☎ (01283) 813677
Burton Bridge Draught Burton Ale; 3 changing beers (sourced regionally) Ⓗ
Privately owned 19th-century free house, overlooking the Dove Valley and providing a fine view of Tutbury Castle from the extended patio. The two split-level rooms – public bar and lounge – have a homely feel and are served from a similarly split-level bar. A separate large dining room to the rear serves evening meals Wednesday to Saturday, and Sunday lunches (pre-booking advised). This is the only pub in the area which has offered Draught Burton Ale from its launch by Ind Coope in 1976 through its 2015 reincarnation by Burton Bridge. 🏴‍☠️🚫🍴♿P🚗🌟📶♫

Uttoxeter

Night Inn 🍴 Ⓛ
Lion Building, 8 Market Place, ST14 8HP (in courtyard to the side of Domino's pizza)
☎ 07426 191886 ⊕ nightinn.co.uk
Uttoxeter Bartley Bitter, Paddock Porter, American IPA; 1 changing beer (sourced regionally) Ⓗ
Established in 2020 by the Uttoxeter Brewing Company, their tap serves three of the brewery ales on a rotating basis, with one guest ale often available. There are also craft beers, lagers and locally-distilled spirits, with snacks also available. A loyalty card scheme is in operation plus discounted ales for all on Sunday. A function room is available to hire. A winner of multiple local CAMRA awards including Pub of the Year. Closed on Wednesdays. Q🏴‍☠️🚫♿🚃♣🍴P🚗🌟📶♫

Warslow

Greyhound Inn Ⓛ
Leek Road, SK17 0JN
☎ (01298) 84782 ⊕ thegreyhoundinnwarslow.co.uk
Marston's Pedigree; Sharp's Doom Bar; 6 changing beers (sourced locally; often Beartown, Wincle, Wilsons of Warslow) Ⓗ
A welcome return to the Guide for this attractive village pub in the Peak District National Park owned and run by a local family. Recently renovated throughout, the venue now includes six double en-suite bedrooms, all new toilet facilities and outside has been given a fresh look with flower beds and a seating area. Eight handpulls adorn the bar, of which two are permanent popular brands and the other six changing beers will be sourced locally from around the Peak District or from the on-site brewery. 🏴‍☠️🚫🛏️🍴♿P(442)🌟📶

Wolstanton

Archer

21 Church Lane, ST5 0EH

☎ (01782) 740467

Hop Back Citra, Summer Lightning; 4 changing beers (sourced nationally) Ⓗ

Traditional village pub with six guest ales including a dedicated dark beer pump. This single-room pub has three distinct drinking areas, and an outdoor area which proves popular in the summer months. The pub remains Wiltshire brewer Hop Back's most northern outpost and carries two of its beers among its impressive offerings. While not a sports pub, the landlord always goes the extra mile for showing large sporting events. The pub hosts a popular quiz night on Sunday.

Q ☞ ֎ ♣ P ➡ (98,99) ❀ 🛜 ♪

Wombourne

Old Bush

High Street, WV5 9DT

☎ (01902) 271752

Black Country Bradley's Finest Golden, Pig on the Wall, Fireside; 7 changing beers (often Fixed Wheel, Oakham, Salopian) Ⓗ

This large pub sits next door to the Vine in historic Wombourne. The pub was extensively refurbished by Black Country Ales and reopened in 2023 with a plentiful supply of real ales on tap. It offers the brewery's own beers and a changing menu of ales from other breweries. Traditional bar snacks are available including cobs. The pub has seen a large increase in customers since its refurbishment. Children are welcome until 7pm.

Q ☞ ֎ & ♣ ⬤ P ➡ (15,16) ❀ 🛜

Dog Inn, Burton upon Trent (Photo: The Roaming Picture Taker / Flickr CC BY 2.0)

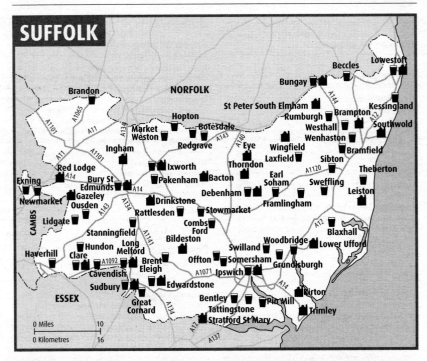

SUFFOLK

(Map showing locations including: Lowestoft, Beccles, Brandon, NORFOLK, Bungay, Kessingland, St Peter South Elmham, Brampton, Rumburgh, Hopton, Southwold, Botesdale, Westhall, Market Weston, Wenhaston, Redgrave, Eye, Wingfield, Bramfield, Ingham, Laxfield, Sibton, Red Lodge, Ixworth, Thorndon, Theberton, Exning, Bury St Edmunds, Pakenham, Bacton, Earl Soham, Sweffling, Leiston, Newmarket, Gazeley, Debenham, Framlingham, Ousden, Drinkstone, Stowmarket, Lidgate, Rattlesden, Blaxhall, Haverhill, Stanningfield, Combs Ford, Bildeston, Swilland, Woodbridge, Lower Ufford, Hundred, Long Melford, Offton, Somersham, Grundisburgh, Clare, Brent Eleigh, Ipswich, Cavendish, Edwardstone, Kirton, Sudbury, Bentley, Pin Mill, Trimley, Great Cornard, Tattingstone, Stratford St Mary, CAMBS, ESSEX)

0 Miles 10
0 Kilometres 16

Beccles

Butchers Arms ⒧
51 London Road, NR34 9YT
☎ (01502) 712243
6 changing beers (sourced regionally; often Barsham, Mr Winter's, Wolf) Ⓗ
Standing opposite the cemetery, a 10-minute walk from the town centre, this friendly pub serves up to six real ales from local breweries. Quiz nights, community events and occasional food nights are hosted. The interior, formerly with separate lounge and public bars, is now open plan. The bar and real fire remain, with a dartboard and pool tables in an extension. There is a garden to the rear and a patio with seating at the front.
🏠❀♣P🖵(522,524) ❀🛜

Caxton Club
Gaol Lane, NR34 9SJ
☎ (01502) 712829 ⊕ becc022caxtonclub.co.uk
4 changing beers (sourced nationally; often Greene King, Mauldons, Parkway) Ⓗ
Spacious club conveniently situated a short walk from bus and train stations and the town centre. All members and guests are warmly welcomed (a small charge is made to cover entertainment on Sat eve). Four constantly changing real ales are offered. To one side of the main bar is a lounge with a TV screen and dartboard and a separate snooker room. There is also a large function room available for hire. CAMRA Regional Club of the Year 2023. Assistance dogs only are allowed.
🏠❀&♣🖵🛜♪

Ingate ⒧
108 Grove Road, NR34 9RE
☎ 07503 969220
3 changing beers (sourced locally; often Green Jack, Lacons, Wolf) Ⓗ
Privately owned and popular two-bar free house serving the local community, a short walk from the town centre

and railway station. The lounge bar serves three real ales on handpump, with tables, bar stools and sofas for seating. The sports bar contains the dartboard and pool table – the pub's teams play in local leagues. Sports events are shown on large screens. The former car park is now a partially covered outdoor seating area.
🏠&🞥♣🖵❀🛜♪

Bentley

Case is Altered ⒧ ✅
Capel Rd, IP9 2DW
☎ (01473) 805575 ⊕ thecasepubbentley.co.uk
Adnams Southwold Bitter; 3 changing beers (sourced locally) Ⓗ
Owned and run by the local community, this pub has a single bar serving two drinking areas, a restaurant area with a wood-burning stove, and a pretty beer garden with plenty of seating. Various music evenings and themed food nights are hosted. Traditional pub games are played, including darts, cards and dominoes. A quiz is held on the last Saturday of the month. Local artists' work is on display. Some produce used in the kitchen is grown by the local community. 🏠❀&♣P🖵❀🛜♪

Blaxhall

Ship ⒧
School Road, IP12 2DY
☎ (01728) 688316 ⊕ blaxhallshipinn.co.uk
Adnams Southwold Bitter; Woodforde's Wherry; 3 changing beers Ⓗ
Cosy, two-roomed, 16th-century pub with a reputation for traditional singing in the bar. The menu offers a wide choice of home-made dishes and daily specials using locally sourced ingredients. A variety of live entertainment features, including folk sessions (Mon afternoons), local bands, and story tellings. The pub is used as a stage during Folk East festival weekend. Letting chalets are available beside the pub and there is

camping by arrangement. Open all day, but book for breakfast (from 10.30am) in summer. Dogs welcome.
ॐ✿❀◑ё⅄⚘♣♠P⊞✿🐾♪

Botesdale

Greyhound
The Street, IP22 1BS
☎ (01379) 898003 ⊕ greyhoundbotesdale.co.uk
Woodforde's Wherry ⊞; 2 changing beers (often Elmtree, Nethergate) ⊞/Ⓖ
Once a coaching in on the London to Norwich road, this characterful, no-frills pub has a loyal following of regulars. Bare floorboards, old furniture, old photos and taxidermy exhibits add to the atmosphere of the busy bar. There's also a quieter lounge and a pool room. Home-made burger nights, curry nights and steak nights are popular, while on Sunday food is hog rolls and wedges only. Some of their beers are served under CO2. Parking is very limited. ॐ✿❀◑♣P⊞(304)✿♪

Bramfield

Queen's Head Ⓛ
The Street, IP19 9HT (on A144)
☎ (01986) 784214 ⊕ queensheadbramfield.co.uk
4 changing beers (sourced locally) ⊞
The refurbishment of this 16th-century pub shows off the original beams, large open fireplaces and vaulted ceiling. Some examples of wattle and daub have been retained, along with the original ale serving hatch. The walled garden is particularly popular in warmer months. A single bar serves local ales, and food, including gluten-free options, is available throughout the day. There is also a takeaway food menu. The restaurant is available for private hire. ॐ✿◑P⊞(522)✿🐾♪

Brandon

Ram Ⓛ ✅
High Street, IP27 0AX
☎ (01842) 810275
Greene King Abbot; 6 changing beers (sourced nationally) ⊞
Said to be one of the oldest surviving buildings in town, this attractive, Grade II-listed building has some parts dating back 500 years. A wonderful log-burner greets you as enter this friendly, family-owned and run free house. It hosts regular club nights for the Iceni Car Club, Classic Vehicle Club, Model Engineering Club, Brandon Speakers Club and the Champions Poker League.
ॐ✿❀◑ё⅄≒♣P⊞(86)

Brent Eleigh

Cock ★ Ⓛ
Lavenham Road, CO10 9PB (on A1141)
☎ (01787) 247371
Adnams Southwold Bitter; Greene King Abbot; 2 changing beers (sourced locally; often Bishop Nick, Mauldons) ⊞
An unspoilt gem, deservedly recognised by CAMRA as having a nationally important historic pub interior. The two bars are small and guarantee a conversation with the pub regulars. The public bar has a 'pinch penny' cut into the settle beside the main table which has been deeply etched with shove halfpenny grooves. The snug bar is ideal for families. Home-cooked food is available.
Q✿❀◑♣⚘P✿🐾♪

Bungay

Green Dragon ★ Ⓛ
29 Broad Street, NR35 1EF
☎ (01986) 892681 ⊕ greendragonbungay.co.uk
Green Dragon Chaucer Ale, Gold, Bridge Street Bitter, Strong Mild; 1 changing beer (sourced locally; often Green Dragon) ⊞
On the northern edge of town, this is Bungay's only brewpub and the home of the Green Dragon brewery, with ales brewed in the outbuildings adjacent to the car park at the rear. The pub is popular and a regular in the Guide. It has a public bar, and a spacious lounge with a side room where families are welcome, leading to an enclosed garden. In addition to the full range of Green Dragon ales, KeyKeg and canned craft ales are also available. ॐ✿❀◑♣P⊞✿🐾♪

Bury St Edmunds

Beerhouse Ⓛ
1 Tayfen Road, IP32 6BH
☎ (01284) 766415 ⊕ burybeerhouse.co.uk
Brewshed Best Bitter; 7 changing beers (sourced nationally) ⊞
Traditional beer house in an unusual semi-circular Victorian building, refurbished with a modern feel and handy for the nearby railway station. It serves beers from their own Brewshed brewery, which also supplies four other local pubs owned by same company. Seven beer engines provide an ever-changing selection of well-kept real ales, plus three real ciders. Regular beer festivals and an annual cider festival are held. Major sporting events are shown on a large screen, and there is an open fire in winter. ॐ✿≒⚘P⊞✿🐾

REAL ALE BREWERIES	
Adnams	Southwold
Artefact	Ixworth
Beccles	Brampton
Biochemist	Red Lodge
Brewshed	Ingham
Briarbank 🍴	Ipswich
Bruha 🌾	Eye
Cabin	Bildeston
Dove Street	Ipswich
Drinkstone	Drinkstone
Earl Soham	Debenham
Green Dragon 🍴	Bungay
Green Jack	Lowestoft
Greene King	Bury St Edmunds
Gruff	Stratford St Mary (NEW)
Humber Doucy	Bacton
Krafty Braumeister	Leiston
Little Earth Project	Edwardstone
Mauldons 🌾	Sudbury
Mr Bees	Trimley
Munson's 🍴	Gazeley
Nethergate 🌾	Long Melford
Old Cannon 🍴	Bury St Edmunds
Old Felixstowe	Kirton
Old Goat 🍴	Sudbury (NEW)
Rascality 🍴	Bury St Edmunds (NEW)
Roughacre 🌾	Clare
Shortts	Thorndon
St Judes 🍴	Ipswich
St Peter's 🌾	St Peter South Elmham
Stow Fen	Bungay
Turnstone	Wingfield
Uffa 🍴	Lower Ufford
Watts & Co	Debenham

Constitutional Club ✓

12 Guildhall Street, IP33 1PR

☎ (01284) 754113 ⊕ conclubbse.com

4 changing beers (sourced nationally; often Marston's, Shortts, St Austell) ⌂

This club has been in existence since 1888. It lies close to the historic Guildhall, in the historic medieval centre of the town. It boasts an impressive beer garden, and hosts many local events, including beer festivals in spring and autumn. The function room is for hire and is used for a variety of events, including live music sessions. Real ales are sourced from Marstons, and supplemented by beers from local brewers. ⊛♣♪

Dove ♥ ⌶

68 Hospital Road, IP33 3JU (5 mins' walk from town centre)

☎ (01284) 702787 ⊕ thedovepub.co.uk

Changing beers (sourced regionally; often Mauldons, Mighty Oak, Nethergate) ⌂/ⓖ

An early-Victorian back-street free house, just five minutes from the town centre. It has six handpumps, plus jugged ales brought up direct from the cellar. It also offers a selection of ciders. This is a genuinely traditional and basic pub with no TV, pool or gaming machines, and the knowledgeable staff can advise on their ever-changing range of local ales. It has twice been winner of CAMRA Regional Pub of the Year and was local CAMRA Pub of the Year in 2023. Q⊛♣♠P🖵⊛♪

Oakes Barn ⌶ ✓

St Andrews Street South, IP33 3PH (opp Waitrose car park)

☎ (01284) 761592 ⊕ oakesbarnfreehouse.co.uk

Oakham JHB; 5 changing beers (sourced nationally; often Greene King, Nethergate, Shortts) ⌂

A real ale free house near the town centre with some period features and historic links to the medieval town. Six real ales are always available, including one dark beer, alongside craft cider. Home-made food comprises lunchtime specials and snacks served all day. There is an outside covered smoking area and open courtyard with seating. Regular events are held in the bar, and the upstairs function room is also available to hire. ⌸⊛⌚&♣🖵⊛⊛♪

Old Cannon Brewery ⌶

86 Cannon Street, IP33 1JR

☎ (01284) 768769 ⊕ oldcannonbrewery.co.uk

Old Cannon Best Bitter, Blonde Bombshell, Black Pig, Gunner's Daughter; 2 changing beers (sourced nationally; often Old Cannon) ⌂

This excellent brewpub is on the site of the original Cannon brewery. Both the brewpub and stable block date from mid-19th century and are Grade II listed. Now in private hands, it is a true free house. Beers are brewed on site and tours of the microbrewery are available (book ahead). Brewing in two copper vessels in the bar happens every Monday and Wednesday. The pub also serves good-quality food and offers comfortable accommodation. ⊛⌸⌚≯P🖵⊛⊛

Cavendish

Five Bells

The Green, CO10 8BA

☎ (01787) 280070

3 changing beers (sourced nationally) ⌂

The Five Bells is a thatched, single-bar pub with fine views across the picturesque green in one of the prettiest villages in Suffolk. Up to three real ales are sourced nationally. Food is supplied by a variety of food vans on a regular basis (see Facebook for details). It was winner of local CAMRA Pub of the Season award in autumn 2023. ⌸⊛⌚&♣P🖵(236,374) ⊛⊛

Clare

Globe

10 Callis Street, CO10 8PX

☎ (01787) 278122 ⊕ globeclare.co.uk

4 changing beers (sourced nationally; often Colchester, St Austell, Woodforde's) ⌂

Beer and conversation dominate at this 18th-century alehouse. The current owners have run the Globe for over 10 years and enjoy enthusiastic support for their wide range of local and nationally acclaimed real ales, served on up to four handpumps. Live music plays every Sunday afternoon (2-5pm). There is a dedicated pool room and large beer garden for summer drinking and outdoor music on Sunday, weather permitting. No food is served. Q⌸⊛♣P🖵⊛⊛

Roughacre Taproom

Clare Hall Barns, Cavendish Road, CO10 8PJ

☎ 07801 930091 ⊕ roughacre.com

6 changing beers (sourced locally; often Roughacre) ⓖ

This cosy brewery taproom, located on the outskirts of Clare village, opened in October 2021. Many of the house beers are available in bottles when not available on draught. It regularly hosts a wide variety of events, plus food trucks (check website for details). It is only open on Fridays and Saturdays. ⊛&P

Combs Ford

Gladstone Arms ⌶

2 Combs Ford, IP14 2AP

☎ (01449) 771608 ⊕ gladstonearms.co.uk

Adnams Southwold Bitter, Broadside; Crouch Vale Brewers Gold; Fuller's London Pride; Sharp's Doom Bar; Woodforde's Wherry ⌂**; 4 changing beers** ⌂/ⓖ

Large open-plan pub owned by the same people who run the Dove Street Inn in Ipswich. Both pubs offer a similar beer range, with at least 12 real ales, including house beers brewed in Ipswich and a wide range of craft lagers, ciders and specialist foreign beers. Good-value snacks and meals are served, with vegetarian options. There are board games, sports TV and regular live music. A beer festival is held over the Easter weekend. There is a large patio and riverside garden to the rear. Q⌸⊛⌚&♣♠P🖵(87,88) ⊛⊛♪

Debenham

Woolpack

49 High Street, IP14 6QN

☎ (01728) 860516

Earl Soham Victoria Bitter ⌂**; Sir Roger's Porter** ⓖ**; Fuller's London Pride; 1 changing beer (often Earl Soham)** ⌂

Small one-bar pub with a wooden floor, accessed via steps from the road. Until recently it was still licensed as a beer house. Lots of horse brasses, village photographs and miniature bottles are on display in the bar area. Two TVs show sport on terrestrial TV. Keenly-priced home-cooked food is available. The pub is home to darts, and hosts occasional live music, karaoke and quiz nights. There is a splendid view of the church from the patio to the rear – bell ringers meet here after practice sessions on Tuesdays. ⌸⊛⌚♣🖵(116)⊛⊛♪

Earl Soham

Victoria 🅛

The Street, IP13 7RL (on A1120)

☎ (01728) 685758

Earl Soham Victoria Bitter; 2 changing beers (often Cliff Quay, Earl Soham) 🅗

A former traditional beer house that has changed very little, despite refurbishment a few years ago. The two small bars are still separated by a large fireplace, which is now fitted with a wood-burner. The popular menu includes many home-cooked daily specials. Weekends can be very busy, when even a seat in the garden can be hard to find. Dogs and children are welcome. The Gents toilet is located outside. Earl Soham brewery was originally behind the pub. Q➳❀❶♣P🖵🌢❄🕏♪

Edwardstone

White Horse Inn 🅛

Mill Green, CO10 5PX

☎ (01787) 211211 ⊕ edwardstonewhitehorse.co.uk

5 changing beers (sourced regionally; often Ampersand, Artefact, Burnt Mill) 🅗/🅖

This traditional Suffolk free house is off the beaten track and hard to find, but is well worth seeking out. A selection of cask beers are available from local breweries including Burnt Mill, Ampersand, Artefact, and Crouch Vale, plus real ciders and up to 16 craft beer taps, including six from on-site brewery Little Earth Project. Two small holiday cottages and a campsite are within the grounds. Pizzas (Thu-Sun) and bar snacks are available. Beer festivals and other events are held. Q➳❀✍❶Å♣♠P🖵🌢❄♪

Exning

White Horse ✅

23 Church Street, CB8 7EH

☎ (01638) 577323 ⊕ whitehorseexning.co.uk

3 changing beers (sourced nationally) 🅗

Mentioned in the Domesday Book, this fine, 300-year-old free house has been run by the same family since 1935. The pub retains much of its original character, with a public bar, cosy lounge and separate restaurant offering a good choice of home-cooked food. At least 10 real ales are rotated each week, and there is often cider on draught. A private room is available for hire. Q❀❶♣P🖵(11)🌢

Framlingham

Station Hotel 🅛

Station Road, IP13 9EE

☎ (01728) 723455 ⊕ thestationframlingham.com

Earl Soham Gannet Mild, Victoria Bitter, Brandeston Gold; 1 changing beer (often Earl Soham) 🅗

Two-bar pub set in a former station buffet (although the branch line closed in 1963). A selection of Earl Soham beers and a guest cider are served from a set of Edwardian German silver handpumps. The pub has a long-standing reputation for good food, made with locally sourced ingredients and all prepared on the premises. The ever-changing menu is displayed on chalkboards. The garden bar also has a wood-fired pizza oven. Children and dogs are welcome. Q➳❀❶♠P🖵🌢❄🕏

Great Cornard

Brook Inn

241 Bures Road, CO10 0JQ

☎ 07759 960051

5 changing beers (sourced nationally) 🅗

Friendly, welcoming country locals' pub near the Suffolk/Essex border, with a beer garden and a good sized car park. Formerly owned by Greene King but now independent, it offers a good range of up to five real ales on handpump. It has two bars, one with low-key TV for sports events, and also has bar billiards and pool tables, with teams in local leagues. Open mic music sessions are held on the third Sunday of each month. ➳❀❅♣P🖵🌢🕏

Grundisburgh

Dog

The Green, IP13 6TA

☎ (01473) 735267 ⊕ grundisburghdog.co.uk

Adnams Southwold Bitter; Earl Soham Victoria Bitter; Woodforde's Wherry; 2 changing beers 🅗

Traditional two-room pub serving good beer and good food. The public bar has a fine beamed ceiling, flagstone flooring and comfortable seating, and offers a selection of pub games including darts and dominoes. The lounge bar is mostly used for dining, with a varied menu of home-cooked meals and snacks made with locally sourced ingredients and including gluten-free options. Monthly themed food evenings are held. There are outside seating areas to the front and rear, and a children's play area. Q➳❀❶♣P🖵(70)🌢🕏

Haverhill

Royal Exchange 🅛 ✅

69 High Street, CB9 8AH

☎ (01440) 702155

Greene King IPA; Nethergate Suffolk County Best Bitter; 3 changing beers (sourced nationally; often Nethergate) 🅗

Friendly town-centre local with a classic street-corner situation. The Greene King-managed house has been fully refurbished, with scrubbed floors and traditional furniture. It can be boisterous when live sport is shown on the five TVs – one of which is 3D (free goggles provided). A swift turnover on beer helps sustain the good quality. There is a large public car park behind the Arts Centre opposite. ➳❅♣🖵🌢

Hopton

Vine

High Street, IP22 2QX

☎ (01953) 688581

Adnams Southwold Bitter; Greene King IPA, Abbot; Timothy Taylor Landlord; 5 changing beers (sourced locally; often Colchester, Lacons, Mauldons) 🅗

On the main road near the church, this village local has been revitalised since being taken over by the current landlord in 2013. Nine ales are available, including a selection of local and regional guests offered at reasonable prices, plus a variety of ciders. This welcoming pub is popular with locals and visitors, and is a regular local CAMRA Pub of the Year. ➳❀❅♣♠P🖵(100)🌢🕏

Hundon

Rose & Crown

20 North Street, CO10 8ED (centre of village)

☎ (01440) 786261
Sharp's Doom Bar; 3 changing beers (sourced nationally; often Fuller's, Mauldons, St Austell) Ⓗ
Traditional country pub comprising two bars with open fires. Home-cooked food is available Thursday to Sunday, including a popular Sunday lunchtime roast. The large beer garden has a patio to the side for alfresco dining, leading to a lawned area with a stage. An outside bar is used for weddings, parties, an annual community music festival (August bank holiday) and other events. The morris men gathering on St George's Day is enjoyed by all. Proud former winner of local CAMRA Community Pub of the Year. ⌂✿⓪♿♣P✿🅿 ☂

Ipswich

Arbor House
43 High Street, IP1 3QL
☎ (01473) 219660 ⊕ thearborhouse.co.uk
Lacons Encore; Mauldons Suffolk Pride; 2 changing beers (often Lacons) Ⓗ
A cosy and stylish single-bar pub close to Ipswich Museum and a short walk from the town centre. Originally called the Arboretum, it was renamed in 2016 (the name derives from a nearby arboretum in Christchurch Park). Three well-kept real ales are available, at least one of which is from a local brewer. The pub also has an enclosed patio to the rear of the bar and a function room upstairs. ⌂✿⓪♣🚃(116)✿ ☂

Arcade Street Tavern
Arcade Street, IP1 1EX (behind the Corn Exchange)
☎ (01473) 805454 ⊕ arcadetavern.co.uk
2 changing beers (sourced regionally) Ⓗ
A stylish and highly popular multi-roomed café bar with a traditional wooden interior. Though the emphasis is on craft and imported beers, there are two handpumps dispensing a variety of ever-changing local real ales. There is a heated seating area outside and two function rooms, one of which is often used for product launches and tasting evenings. Street-food traders are hosted on Friday evenings, and artisan coffee is available. It can be very busy on match days when most tables are pre-booked. ✿🚃 ☂

Briarbank Ⓛ
70 Fore Street, IP4 1LB
☎ (01473) 284004 ⊕ briarbank.org
Briarbank Perpendicular, Old Spiteful; 3 changing beers (sourced locally; often Briarbank) Ⓗ
A smart and modern first-floor drinking bar that opened in 2013 in a former bank above a small brewery. House beers are available as draught beers, craft ales or in bottles. A large outside seating area includes a marquee that provides additional seating. Monthly quiz nights are held, and live music – usually jazz – features twice monthly, either in the bar or outside. TVs show various sporting events. Easter and summer beer festivals are held. ✿⓪P🚃 ☂ ♫

Dove Street Inn Ⓛ ✅
76 St Helen's Street, IP4 2LA
☎ (01473) 211270 ⊕ dovestreetinn.co.uk
Adnams Broadside; Crouch Vale Brewers Gold; Fuller's London Pride; Greene King Abbot; Ruddles County Ⓗ; **7 changing beers (often Dove Street)** Ⓗ/Ⓖ
Popular multi-roomed pub with a wide selection of draught ales, continental beers, craft beers and ciders. Some of the beers are brewed in pub's own microbrewery. Home-cooked food and bar snacks are served at all times. Sports TV is frequently shown in the conservatory. The large, patio-style outdoor seating area includes a covered smoking space. Well-behaved dogs

and children are welcome. A sister pub to the Gladstone Arms in Combs Ford. Accommodation is available. Last admission is 10.45pm. ⌂✿🚐⓪♿♣🔌🚃(66)✿ ☂

Fat Cat ☏
288 Spring Road, IP4 5NL
☎ (01473) 726524 ⊕ fatcatipswich.co.uk
Adnams Southwold Bitter Ⓗ; **Woodforde's Wherry; 14 changing beers** Ⓖ
A highly popular multi-roomed drinking bar, free from intrusive background music and games machines. Up to 14 beers and five ciders are available, most served on gravity from the taproom. An airy conservatory behind the main bar leads to a pretty garden that provides lots of extra space, especially on sunny afternoons. A monthly quiz is very popular. Occasional pop-up food vendors appear on Saturday evenings. Frequently voted best pub in town by local CAMRA members. No under-16s. Q✿⓪🔌🚃✿ ☂

Lord Nelson
81 Fore Street, IP4 1JZ
☎ (01473) 407510 ⊕ thenelsonipswich.co.uk
Adnams Southwold Bitter, Ghost Ship Ⓖ; **3 changing beers (often Adnams)** Ⓗ
Timber-framed building dating from 17th century, just a short walk from the historic waterfront. An unusual gravity-dispense system used here incorporates old wooden casks to good effect and guarantees temperature-controlled real ales. Freshly prepared food is served daily including specials. A small enclosed patio area to the rear is popular most of the year. Families and dogs are welcome. Quiz nights are held twice a month. A sister pub to the Red Lion in Manningtree and the Marlborough in Dedham. ⌂✿⓪♿♣ ☂

Spread Eagle Ⓛ
1-3 Fore Street, IP4 1JW
☎ (01473) 421858
Grain ThreeOneSix, Best Bitter, Slate, Lignum Vitae; 2 changing beers (often Grain) Ⓗ
A distinctive Grade II-listed building – the sole survivor of four pubs that once dominated this busy road junction – restored to a high standard a few years ago by Grain. It now offers up to six real ales on handpump, plus a selection of craft beers and some imported ones, and locally roasted coffee. The various events include occasional music sessions, regular quiz nights and an annual Octoberfest. There is a secluded outside seating area, and the pub is candlelit on Tuesday evenings. Q✿🚃✿ ☂ ♫

Steamboat Tavern ✅
78 New Cut West, IP2 8HW
☎ (01473) 601902 ⊕ thesteamboattavern.co.uk
4 changing beers Ⓗ
A popular historic riverside tavern which regularly features live music and offers good food prepared on the premises. The L-shaped bar has various drinking areas, including a nicely maintained beer garden. Music includes jazz (alternate Sun) and folk sessions (third Thu), plus occasional blues and punk nights and an annual acoustic folk weekend. Local songwriters also play here monthly. ⌂✿⓪♣✿☂ ♫

Woolpack ★ ✅
1 Tuddenham Road, IP4 2SH
☎ (01473) 215862 ⊕ woolpack-ipswich.co.uk
Adnams Southwold Bitter, Ghost Ship; 2 changing beers Ⓗ
Popular three-bar tavern with a tiny snug at the front, flanked by a larger lounge and public bars. The more spacious back room is mostly used for dining. An

interesting selection of high-quality home-cooked food is served all week (including weekend breakfasts). The menu includes specials, bar snacks and vegetarian options. The pub hosts a regular Sunday night quiz and traditional music sessions. The patio area outside at the front is often busy, and another patio to the rear has a pizza counter. Q✿◑♣P🅿️❀☮♪

Ixworth

Greyhound 🍷 ⓛ ✅
49 High Street, IP31 2HJ
☎ (01359) 230887
Greene King IPA, Abbot; 3 changing beers (sourced nationally) Ⓗ
Situated on the village's attractive high street, this welcoming traditional inn has three bars, one of which is a lovely central snug. The heart of the building dates back to Tudor times. Good-value lunches and early evening meals are served in the restaurant and include a bargain daily special. Dominoes, crib, darts and pool are all played in leagues and for charity fundraising. Dogs and children are welcome. Local CAMRA Rural Pub of the Year 2024. Q☕✿◑Å♣P🖰(304,338)❀

Kessingland

Sailors Home ⓛ
302 Church Road, NR33 7SB
☎ (01502) 740245 ⊕ sailorshome.co.uk
Green Jack Golden Best, Gone Fishing ESB; 5 changing beers (sourced locally; often Green Jack, Lacons, Wolf) Ⓖ
Situated on the seafront, within easy reach of the shingle beach, this pub is popular all year with locals, walkers and holidaymakers. The interior has a mock-Tudor design, with four adjoining rooms, one serving good-value food, a large central bar area with a TV screen, a games room, and a side room. Up to seven ales and a regularly changing cider are served by gravity dispense. ☕✿◑Å♣P🖰(99,146)❀☮♪

Laxfield

King's Head ★ ⓛ
Gorams Mill Lane, IP13 8DW (walk through churchyard and exit via lower street gate, pub is on right)
☎ (01986) 798395 ⊕ lowhouselaxfield.com
Earl Soham Albert Ale; Green Jack Golden Best; 2 changing beers (sourced locally; often Shortts) Ⓖ
Nestled behind All Saints Church and popularly known as the 'Low House', this timeless, multi-roomed thatched building is a classic pub which is always worth a visit. The main room features listed high-back settles set around a small fireplace, with beers served on gravity direct from a small tap room to the rear. A separate dining room offers an interesting menu of locally sourced food, including a Sunday roast at lunchtime. It has an enclosed garden patio to the rear. Accommodation is available in an outside building. Q☕✿╬◑♣P🖰❀

Royal Oak
High Street, IP13 8DH
☎ (01986) 798666
4 changing beers (often Adnams, Crouch Vale, Earl Soham) Ⓗ
A warm welcome is always assured at this multi-roomed pub where the main part of the building dates back to the 16th century. It has a large inglenook fireplace in the main bar and a small patio seating area to the front of the pub. Four handpumps dispense a range of ales, with one serving a regularly changing guest ale. Food is

available every day (not after 6pm on Sun). The pub has occasional live music, a monthly quiz and an annual beer festival. Q✿◑♣P🅿️❀☮♪

Lidgate

Star
The Street, CB8 9PP
☎ (01638) 500275 ⊕ lidgatestar.co.uk
4 changing beers (sourced locally) Ⓗ
Grade II listed, the Star Inn is the quintessential 16th-century English pub, with its large log fires, oak beams, real ales and a warm, welcoming atmosphere. The four real ales are supplemented by a range of craft keg beers, bottled beers and real cider. Charcuterie boards are available at lunchtimes and home-made pizzas are served in the evening every day. Frequent events are held such as history talks, tap takeovers and beer festivals. A classic pub, currently run by two CAMRA members, and not to be missed. Q☕✿╬♣P🖰(312)❀

Long Melford

Nethergate Brewery Tap ⓛ
Rodbridge Corner, CO10 9HJ
☎ (01787) 377087 ⊕ nethergate.co.uk
8 changing beers (sourced locally; often Nethergate) Ⓗ
Nethergate brewery was originally founded in 1986 in Clare. The custom-built visitor centre and taproom opened in early 2017 and is the third location they have operated from. The taproom has a bar with a range of Nethergate ales on draught, and a shop selling bottled beers, wines, and spirits. There is a window to view the brewery and tours can be booked. The members' club hosts regular club events including beer festivals. Q✿♿P☮

Lowestoft

Oak Tavern ⓛ
73 Crown Street West, NR32 1SQ
☎ (01502) 537246
Adnams Southwold Bitter; Greene King Abbot; 2 changing beers (sourced locally; often Greene King, Woodforde's) Ⓗ
Well-run, lively, drinkers' back-street local with an open plan interior. At one end is a pool table and TV for sporting events, while the other side has a larger seating area, which is decorated with memorabilia from Belgium. Its four handpumps serve local real ales and usually include a dark beer in winter months. Outside at the rear is a small patio and a car park. The pub is popular with all ages. ✿♣P🖰(102)❀

Plough & Sail
212 London Road South, NR33 0BB
☎ (01502) 566695
Greene King IPA; Sharp's Doom Bar; 4 changing beers (sourced nationally; often Green Jack, Mauldons, Mr Winter's) Ⓗ
Set back off the street, with a small frontage, this friendly local is close to Lowestoft south beach and amenities. Inside is a long bar with wooden flooring and wood panelling throughout. TV screens show sporting events. A secluded enclosed courtyard with a canvas covered smoking area leads to a private function room. Live music and quiz evenings are regular attractions. Two permanent beers are available, plus up to four regularly changing beers from other breweries. ✿♣🖰❀☮♪

Stanford Arms 🅛

Stanford Street, NR32 2DD

☎ (01502) 574505 ● stanfordarmslowestoft.co.uk

6 changing beers (sourced nationally; often Mr Winter's, Nene Valley, Three Blind Mice) ⊞

This quality free house is within easy reach of Lowestoft rail and bus stations and close to the football ground. The open-plan L-shaped bar, with TV screen showing sporting events, leads to an enclosed courtyard garden. The pub offers an exceptional range of cask and craft beers sourced from around the UK, plus bottled and canned beers from across Europe. There are regular quiz and food nights and live music most weekends. Closed on Mondays. ≈❀◑●🚪❀ 🎵

Triangle Tavern 🅛

29 St Peters Street, NR32 1QA

☎ (01502) 582711

Green Jack Golden Best, Trawlerboys Best Bitter, Lurcher Stout, Gone Fishing ESB, Mahseer IPA, Ripper Tripel; 2 changing beers (sourced locally; often Green Jack) ⊞/🅖

This lively town-centre tavern is the brewery tap for Green Jack brewery. The cosy, parlour-style front bar is heated with a wood-burner in winter months and hosts live music most Friday evenings, plus occasional quiz nights. A corridor leads to the back bar with a central pool table and a jukebox. Alongside the full Green Jack range are real ciders and continental craft beers. Customers are welcome to bring in their own food. The pub is family- and dog-friendly. ❀≈♣●🚪❀ 🎵

Market Weston

Mill 🅛

Bury Road, IP22 2PD (on B1111)

☎ (01359) 221018

Adnams Southwold Bitter; 2 changing beers (sourced nationally; often Greene King, Lacons, St Austell) ⊞

The Mill is a striking white brick- and flint-faced inn standing at a crossroads on the B1111. It used to be the unofficial tap for Old Chimneys brewery and old pumpclips can still be seen behind the bar. It offers an excellent choice of beers, complemented by a good menu of home-cooked meals. Q≈❀◑&♣P🚪❀🎵

Newmarket

Bull ❂

62 High Street, CB8 8LB

☎ (01638) 662534

Greene King IPA, Abbot; 1 changing beer (sourced nationally) ⊞

Located at the top end of Newmarket's high street, this Greene King house serves well-kept Abbot and IPA and is friendly and welcoming to drinkers and diners. It is popular with younger drinkers in evening, and hosts quiz nights on Mondays and occasional live music. It is open from 10am every day and serves food all day. ❀◑&≈♣P🚪🎵

Offton

Limeburners 🅛

Willisham Road, IP8 4SF

☎ 07949 466111

Greene King IPA, XX Mild; 2 changing beers ⊞

Friendly split-level bar with a fish & chip shop (eat in or takeaway) attached. The pub is named after a chalk pit opposite which used to contain historic lime kilns (some photos are on display in the pub). Outside is a large garden and car park. Guest ales change regularly.

Buskers play every Sunday night, and a quiz is held on the first Thursday of every month. No food on Sunday evenings or Tuesdays (but there is a Sun lunchtime roast). ≈❀◑&♣P🚪(111)❀ 🎵

Ousden

Fox

Front Street, CB8 8TR

☎ (01638) 500740

Timothy Taylor Boltmaker, Landlord; 2 changing beers (sourced nationally) ⊞

Popular traditional 17th-century local pub. There are steps between the two bars: the main bar has a double-sided wood-burner, several bar stools, and tables, and there is a pool table in the second bar. There are four handpull pumps, with at least two beers always available. Bar snacks and locally made honey are for sale. A regular quiz night takes place. The pub is popular with locals and has a large car park at the rear. Q≈❀◑&♣P(312)❀

Pakenham

Fox 🅛

The Street, IP31 2JU

☎ (01359) 230194 ● pakenhamfox.co.uk

4 changing beers (sourced regionally; often Earl Soham, Mighty Oak, Shortts) ⊞

A traditional 18th-century pub set in a picturesque village. This free house has been restored beautifully and now has a handcrafted central bar. It serves four well-chosen ales that are sourced from local breweries, and several real ciders. The spacious beer garden has been extended and special events are held there throughout the year. There are also regular quiz and music nights. All in all, a great village pub. Q≈❀◑&♣P🚪(304,338)❀

Pin Mill

Butt & Oyster ★ ❂

Pin Mill Road, IP9 1JW

☎ (01473) 780764 ● debeninns.co.uk/buttandoyster

Adnams Southwold Bitter, Ghost Ship, Broadside; 1 changing beer (often Adnams) 🅖

Dating from the 17th century, this riverside inn enjoys a famous setting, and magnificent views of the Orwell estuary with its quay and historic coastal barges. Inside, three small rooms are connected via a flagstoned corridor. High-backed settles and a wood-burner dominate the main tap room to recreate some olde-worlde charm, especially on cold winter days. Renowned for its traditional food menu with a number of fish dishes, the pub gets busy during lunchtime and dinner so it's best to book if you want to eat. Breakfast is served at weekends. Q≈❀◑&♣P🚪(97)❀

Rattlesden

Five Bells 🅛

High Street, IP30 0RA

☎ (01449) 737373

3 changing beers (sourced locally; often Earl Soham, Elgood's, Woodforde's) ⊞

Set on the high road through a picturesque village, this is a fine traditional Suffolk drinking house – sadly few of its kind still survive. Three well-chosen ales on the bar are usually sourced direct from the breweries, and often include a mild. The cosy single-room interior has a games area on a lower level and there is occasional live music. Regular community events are hosted. Pub games

include shut-the-box and shove-ha'penny, and there's pétanque in the garden in summer. Dogs are welcome.
Q❀♣🕿🍴♫

Redgrave

Cross Keys
The Street, IP22 1RW (on B1113)
🕿 (01379) 779822 ⊕ crosskeysredgrave.co.uk
4 changing beers (sourced locally; often Lacons, Nene Valley, Oakham) H
The building dates from the late 16th or early 17th century, with later extensions and refronting. It was bought by the local community and reopened in 2018, and is now leased to a private landlord. It has a bar, a restaurant/lounge and a snug area. The pleasant garden has mature walnut trees, and seating and tables at the front, leading on to the Knoll (village green).
🛏❀🕯🕨♿♣🍴P🚲(304)🐾🐕📶

Rumburgh

Buck ♟ ★ L
Mill Road, IP19 0NT
🕿 (01986) 785257 ⊕ rumburghbuck.co.uk
Adnams Southwold Bitter; 4 changing beers (sourced regionally; often Earl Soham, Greene King, Mighty Oak) H
Charming, characterful and popular local inn at the heart of village life. Interlinked rooms have been added to the original timber-framed core, with its flagstone floor. There are also dining areas and a games room, and outside is a covered garden. Guest beers and ciders are often locally sourced, and the pub serves good food. Mini beer festivals are held twice yearly, alongside regular folk music and craft events. Local CAMRA Pub of the Year in 2023. Q🛏❀🕯🕨♣A♣🍴P🐕📶♫

Sibton

White Horse
Halesworth Road, IP17 2JJ
🕿 (01728) 660337 ⊕ sibtonwhitehorseinn.co.uk
Adnams Southwold Bitter; 2 changing beers H
A charming and characterful 16th-century inn with lots of exposed timbers and a large fireplace fitted with a wood-burner. There is a raised galley on one side of the main bar area. The large garden to the rear has a barbecue in the summer and a children's play area, and most of the kitchen's produce is grown here. There are various themed food evenings. There is a separate annex for accommodation, and the pub is a registered Caravan Club campsite. 🛏❀🛏🕯🕨A♣P🐕📶♫

Somersham

Duke of Marlborough
Main Road, IP8 4QA
🕿 (01473) 831283 ⊕ thedukeofmarlborough.com
Earl Soham Victoria Bitter; 3 changing beers (often Adnams) G
Saved by the local community and reopened in 2017, this 15th-century timber-framed inn has been restored to a high standard and now features several seating areas for drinking or eating. Special event nights are held on Monday or Wednesday evenings. Food is served Wednesday to Sunday, and there are also occasional street-food nights. A beer festival is held from over the August bank holiday weekend.
Q🛏❀🕯🕨♣P🚲(111)🐕📶

Stanningfield

Red House L
Bury Road, IP29 4RR
🕿 (01284) 828330 ⊕ theredhousesuffolk.co.uk
Greene King IPA; 2 changing beers H
This red-brick family-run free house is at the centre of the village in every sense. Its sign displays the red dress uniform of the Suffolk regiment. Good-value lunches and early evening meals are all home cooked. The pub supports teams for darts, cribbage and bar billiards, as well as hosting regular entertainment nights. There is a lovely garden at the rear. Car parking is available, plus a 10-bike parking space. 🛏❀♣P🚲(750,753)🐕📶

Stowmarket

Royal William L
53 Union Street East, IP14 1HP
🕿 (01449) 674553
Greene King IPA; 10 changing beers G
An end-of-terrace back-street bar, tucked away down a narrow side street, just a short walk from the town centre and the nearby railway station. All ales are served by gravity dispense from the cellar behind the bar, with up to 10 beers and five ciders always available. Regular dominoes, darts and crib matches are played, and there's an outside smoking area and games room. Sport is shown on TV and traditional music is hosted monthly. Home-made bar snacks are often available. A winner of many local CAMRA awards. 🛏❀🕯🕨♿🍴♣🍴🚲🐕📶

Walnut
39 Violet Hill Road, IP14 1NE
🕿 (01449) 401 6769
6 changing beers H
Refurbished by the current landlord and landlady in 2019, this much-improved back-street pub now offers an ever-changing selection of real ales on handpump, along with ciders and craft beers. The beer menu regularly features some unusual choices for the town. Good-value snacks are available. The pub holds regular quiz and vinyl nights, and its own Octoberfest. There are two beer gardens, where children are allowed until 8pm. A former local CAMRA Pub of the Year. 🛏❀♿🍴♣🍴🚲🐕📶

Sudbury

Brewery Tap L
21-23 East Street, CO10 2TP (200yds from market place)
🕿 (01787) 370876 ⊕ thebrewerytapsudbury.co.uk
Mauldons Moletrap Bitter, Suffolk Pride, Black Adder H**; 7 changing beers (sourced nationally)** H/G
The Mauldons brewery tap is a haven for ale lovers. A good selection of Mauldons beers are always available, and these are complemented by a selection of national and locally sourced ales, with up to 10 at any one time on both handpump and gravity. Hearty snacks are available at lunchtimes, including pies and sandwiches. Beer festivals are held in April and October, and quiz, music and comedy nights are a regular feature in this traditional pub where conversation dominates.
Q❀🕯♿🍴♣🍴🚲🐕

Swefling

White Horse L
Low Road, IP17 2BB (on B1119)
🕿 (01728) 664178 ⊕ swefflingwhitehorse.co.uk
3 changing beers G

A cosy two-room pub with a wood-burner and wood-fired range. Beers from local brewers are dispensed on gravity, served through a taproom door. Cider is also available, as well as Fairtrade, organic, locally produced bottled beers. Pub games include bar billiards, darts, crib and board games. Live music features twice a month. Local horse and trap rides may be available in summer. A former CAMRA East Anglian Pub of the Year, with a garden and a popular, award-winning campsite.
Q ► ✿ ✍ ♪ ▲ ♣ ● P ● 🐱 🎵

Swilland

Moon & Mushroom
High Road, IP6 9LR
☎ (01473) 785320 ⊕ themoonandmushroom.co.uk
4 changing beers (sourced locally) Ⓗ
Comfortable, cosy single-bar pub and café that is nicely decorated throughout with local pictures, a tiled floor and scrubbed tables. A good selection of beers on gravity is always available from the taproom. Home-cooked meals are served in the bar and in the adjoining dining room, while the café menu offers breakfasts or afternoon tea and cake if you prefer something else. Outdoor seating is available to the front. There are occasional live music and special themed nights. Dogs are welcome.
► ✿ ◑ ♿ P 🐱 🎵

Tattingstone

Wheatsheaf Ⓛ
Church Road, IP9 2LY
☎ (01473) 805470 ⊕ wheatsheaftattingstone.com
3 changing beers (sourced locally) Ⓖ
Recently refurbished and extended, this pub is on the outskirts of a small village that is divided by the Alton Water Park reservoir. An ever-changing beer selection includes many from local brewers. The large garden to the rear hosts a popular charity Beer and Beetroot festival every June, and also holds popular live music and quiz nights, plus themed food evenings and Sunday roasts. The pub hosts local cribbage league matches, and caters for private parties. Camping is possible by arrangement. ► ✿ ◑ ▲ ♣ P 🚍 (94,96) 🐱 🎵

Theberton

Lion Ⓛ
The Street, IP16 4RU
☎ (01728) 830185 ⊕ thebertonlion.co.uk
Earl Soham Victoria Bitter; 2 changing beers (sourced locally) Ⓗ
A lively village bar with patio seating outside at the front, various seating areas inside and a large central fireplace. Many local pictures decorate the walls. The beer range is varied and a local beer club regularly meets in the bar. Real ciders in bottle are available all year round, including Giggler and Thistly Cross Traditional. It still has traditional outdoor toilets. The pub is quite close to popular coastal attractions, and log cabins are available to let. Opening hours may be extended during the summer. ► ✿ ✍ ◑ ♿ ♣ ● P 🐱 🎵

Wenhaston

Star Inn Ⓛ
Hall Road, IP19 9HF
☎ (01502) 478240 ⊕ wenhastonstar.co.uk
Green Jack Golden Best, Trawlerboys Best Bitter; 3 changing beers (sourced locally; often Harvey's, Humpty Dumpty, Oakham) Ⓗ
Free house on the outskirts of the village, with a large garden and fine views of the Blyth valley. The pub has three small public rooms; the front bar is full of character, with old enamel advertising signs. Good home-cooked food uses local produce where possible (no food on Sun or Mon). Beer festivals are held over the late May and August bank holiday weekends. The pub is popular with walkers and cyclists, and camping is available by prior arrangement. Q ► ✿ ◑ ▲ ♣ ● P 🚍 (99A) 🐱 🎵

Westhall

Racehorse Inn Ⓛ
Mill Common, IP19 8RQ
☎ (01502) 575665 ⊕ westhallpub.com
5 changing beers (sourced locally; often Ampersand, Green Jack, Mr Winter's) Ⓗ / Ⓖ
This village free house, deep in rural Suffolk, is community owned and has a central bar with three interlinked rooms and a restaurant area. Up to five real ales and two real ciders are usually available. The pub is well supported by locals, with food available daily (when open). There are patio seating areas at the front and rear. A marked route from Brampton rail station emerges close to the pub (check the relevant OS map).
Q ► ✿ ◑ ♿ ▲ ♣ ● P 🚍 (524) 🐱 🎵

Woodbridge

Angel Ⓛ
2 Theatre Street, IP12 4NE
☎ (01394) 382660 ⊕ theangelwoodbridge.co.uk
Adnams Southwold Bitter; 5 changing beers Ⓗ
A lively, traditional two-bar drinking pub with beams and tiled floors. The regularly changing range of real ales is complemented by a massive selection of craft gins, with gin-tasting sessions by arrangement. There is seating outside and a former stables to the rear. No regular meals are served, but there is a wood-fired pizza oven in the garden. An open mic night is held on the second and fourth Wednesday of the month, plus a DJ every Saturday evening and other live music sessions.
► ✿ ≷ ♣ ● P 🚍 🐱 🎵

Cherry Tree
73 Cumberland Street, IP12 4AG
☎ (01394) 384627 ⊕ thecherrytreepub.co.uk
Adnams Southwold Bitter, Ghost Ship, Broadside; 1 changing beer (often Adnams) Ⓗ
A deceptively spacious family-friendly lounge bar/diner with a central servery and several distinct seating areas. The new kitchen provides popular, home-cooked food all day every day, starting with breakfast and including vegetarian and gluten-free options. Board games and cards are available to play and a quiz is often held on Thursday evenings. The large garden has children's play equipment. Accommodation is available in a converted barn. ► ✿ ✍ ◑ ≷ ♣ ● P 🐱 🎵

Where village statesmen talked with looks profound
And news much older than the ale went round.
Alfred, Lord Tennyson

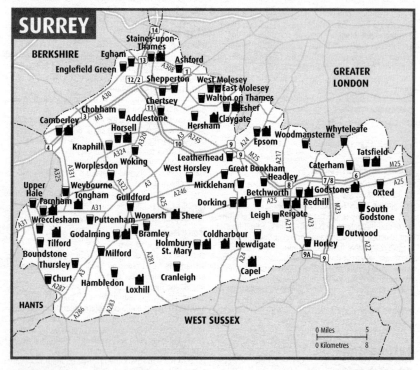

SURREY

BERKSHIRE
Egham
Englefield Green
Staines-upon-Thames
14
13
Ashford
A308
1
Shepperton
West Molesey
12/2
East Molesey
Walton on Thames
Chertsey
Esher
GREATER
LONDON
Chobham
11
Addlestone
Claygate
Camberley
M3
Horsell
Hersham
Knaphill
Woodmansterne
Whyteleafe
Worplesdon
Woking
A320
Leatherhead
A3 A245
Epsom
9
A24
Tatsfield
Upper
Hale
Weybourne
Tongham
Guildford
West Horsley
Great Bookham
Headley
Caterham
M25
6
Farnham
Micklam
Betchworth
8
Godstone
Oxted
Wrecclesham
Puttenham
Wonersh
Shere
Dorking
A25
Redhill
South
Godstone
Leigh
Reigate
Tilford
Godalming
Bramley
Coldharbour
Newdigate
Horley
Outwood
Boundstone
Milford
Holmbury
St. Mary
9A
9
Thursley
Capel
Churt
Hambledon
Cranleigh
HANTS
Loxhill
WEST SUSSEX

0 Miles 5
0 Kilometres 8

Addlestone

RAOB Club
136 Church Road, KT15 1SQ
☎ (01932) 883335
Shepherd Neame Spitfire; 1 changing beer (sourced regionally; often Shepherd Neame) Ⓗ
The principal aims of the Royal Antediluvian Order of Buffaloes are friendship, charitable works, social activity, and mutual support. This community social club also prides itself on its two real ales, and even held its first beer festival in 2023. Inside is a TV showing sports and a games room with pool and darts. There is live music some Saturday nights, and a monthly quiz. CAMRA members can be signed in as guests on production of their membership card. ★❀🅿️🚃(461,557)❀🛜♪

Ashford

Freeman Arms ✅
77 Feltham Road, TW15 1BS
☎ (01784) 252115
Greene King IPA, Abbot; 2 changing beers (sourced nationally; often Caledonian, Hardys & Hansons) Ⓗ
First year in the Guide for this Greene King eating house and community local. The extensive food menu including pizzas, burgers and Sunday roasts. Two regular and usually two changing ales from the Greene King portfolio are available. There are several seating areas, and pool tables are at one end of the pub, together with a sports TV. Outside is a garden at the rear. The pub is family- and dog-friendly. ★❀🅿️🚃(117)❀🛜

Betchworth

Dolphin ★
The Street, RH3 7DW
☎ (01737) 842288 🌐 dolphinbetchworth.com

Young's London Original, London Special; 1 changing beer (sourced locally; often By The Horns, Surrey Hills) Ⓗ
The Dolphin is in an attractive spot opposite the village church that featured in the film Four Weddings and a Funeral. Dating from the 18th century, there are three distinct areas served from a single bar, plus a separate restaurant, all of which serve good food. There are two real fires, old flagstone floors and comfortable old furniture. A pleasant seated area is in front of the pub and there is a garden to the rear. Q❀🅿️🚃(32)❀

Boundstone

Bat & Ball 🅛
15 Bat & Ball Lane, GU10 4SA (by road off Sandrock Hill Rd via Upper Bourne Ln) SU833444
☎ (01252) 792108 🌐 thebatandball.co.uk
Dark Star Hophead; Hop Back Summer Lightning; Triple fff Moondance; 3 changing beers (sourced nationally; often Triple fff, Young's) Ⓗ
A traditional country free house dating back 150 years, set in the Bourne Valley near Farnham. It has been run by the same family for two generations. The pub has several different rooms, with an open log fire, panelled walls, and oak beams. The attractive garden has a children's play area and is popular with families on warm days. There is an annual beer festival, a weekly quiz on Tuesday, and live music once a month. An afternoon menu is served on Friday and Saturday.
Q★❀🅿️🚃(16,17)❀🛜♪

Bramley

Jolly Farmer 🅛
High Street, GU5 0HB
☎ (01483) 893355 🌐 jollyfarmer.co.uk

Crafty Brewing Hop Tipple; house beer (by Crafty Brewing); 6 changing beers (sourced nationally; often Crafty Brewing, Firebird) Ⓗ
Originally a stagecoach inn, this is now a privately owned free house serving eight real ales. It has a cosy, welcoming atmosphere, with dark wood beams and decor that celebrates the countryside and beer, featuring historic beer mats and pumpclips. The L-shaped bar offers a diverse range of real ales, keg beers, plus real ciders in summer. There is accommodation available in four en-suite rooms. Bramley is served by buses from Guildford and Horsham. ♣P🚌🐾📶

Camberley

Claude du Vall Ⓛ ✔

77-81 High Street, GU15 3RB
☎ (01276) 672910
Greene King Abbot; Ruddles Best Bitter; Sharp's Doom Bar; 2 changing beers (sourced nationally; often Dorking, Tillingbourne, Windsor & Eton) Ⓗ
The Claude du Vall is conveniently close to the station and bus stops, at the end of the High Street. The large, modern interior is divided into a number of different seating areas. The long bar offers three regular beers and between two and four guests. Wetherspoon's reputation for good-value food and drinks attracts customers throughout the day. Muted TV screens generally show news programmes and occasional sports events. ♿🚌📶

Caterham

King & Queen Ⓛ

34 High Street, CR3 5UA (on B2030)
☎ (01883) 345303 🌐 kingandqueencaterham.co.uk
Dark Star Hophead; Fuller's London Pride, ESB; 1 changing beer (sourced nationally) Ⓗ
Dating back to the 1840s and converted from three former cottages, the pub retains three distinct areas. The front section is a public bar, the high-ceilinged middle section is a games room with a dartboard, and there is a smaller, cosier section at the back. There are patios front and back and a covered smoking section at the rear. There are occasional theatrical and operatic performances. The pub is named after the joint monarchy of William and Mary and displays their portraits. ♣P🚌🐾📶

Chertsey

Coach & Horses Ⓛ

14 St Ann's Road, KT16 9DG (on B375)
☎ (01932) 563085 🌐 thecoachandhorseschertsey.co.uk
Fuller's London Pride, ESB Ⓗ
This attractive, tile-hung Fuller's community local was built in 1860 as a school. This is a proper pub for beer and conversation, with linked drinking areas. League darts is played, and a TV shows sports at one end of the pub. There is a garden at the rear and a seating area outside at the front. It is a short walk to the local cricket and football grounds, and Abbeyfields, and a short bus or car journey to Thorpe Park. ♣P🚌(446,456)📶♫

Olde Swan Hotel

27 Windsor Street, KT16 8AY
☎ (01932) 562129 🌐 theoldeswanhotel.co.uk
Sharp's Doom Bar; Tring Side Pocket for a Toad; 2 changing beers (sourced nationally; often Dorking, Timothy Taylor) Ⓗ
Refurbished without spoiling its historic charm, the Olde Swan has a mellow ambience with its shabby-chic decor. Four ales are usually on offer, as well as real cider. The menu features stonebaked pizza, home-made burgers, and sizzling steaks, with Mexican night on Friday. There is a covered patio at the rear for alfresco drinking. Accommodation includes double, twin, and family rooms. The pub is handy for the M25/M3 and Thorpe Park. P🚌(446,456)📶♫

Chobham

Horse & Groom Ⓛ

30 High Street, GU24 8AA
☎ 07709 658066 horseandgroommicropub.com
3 changing beers (sourced locally) Ⓗ
The first micropub locally, the Horse & Groom was previously a hairdresser's, but before that it was part of the original Horse & Groom pub that closed in 1960. Describing itself as 'a village pub but smaller', it has a locals' pub feel, with social chat a key part of the atmosphere. Beers are from local breweries and a local traditional cider is also available. Cheese plates are available to accompany your beer, or you can bring your own food. Closed Monday. Q🚌(39A,73)

White Hart Ⓛ

58 High Street, GU24 8AA
☎ (01276) 857580
House beer (by St Austell); 4 changing beers (sourced locally) Ⓗ
A lovely rambling old building next to the village church on the historic High Street. It serves five ales in a variety of strengths and styles, mostly from local breweries, with the distance from the pub displayed. There are two restaurant areas and a less formal space as you enter. Log fires keep the pub warm in winter and in summer you can watch cricket from the garden at the rear. No dogs in the restaurant. Q♿P🚌(39A,73)🐾📶

Churt

Crossways Inn ★ Ⓛ

Churt Road, GU10 2JS
☎ (01428) 714323 🌐 thecrosswaysinn.co.uk
Hop Back Crop Circle; 3 changing beers (sourced regionally) Ⓗ
A traditional village inn with a warm welcome, the Crossways is the centre of village life and has had the

REAL ALE BREWERIES

Big Smoke ✎ Esher
Brightwater Claygate
By the Horns Redhill
Crafty Loxhill
Disruption Is Brewing ✎ Camberley
Dorking ✎ Capel
Drop Kick ✎ Dorking (NEW)
Farnham ✎ Farnham
Felday 🛢 Holmbury St. Mary
Fuzzchat 🛢 Epsom
Godalming Beerworks 🛢 ✎ Godalming
Godstone ✎ Godstone
Hogs Back ✎ Tongham
Leith Hill 🛢 Coldharbour
Pilgrim ✎ Reigate
Surrey Hills ✎ Dorking
Terra Tempo Tongham
Thames Side ✎ Staines-upon-Thames
Thurstons Horsell
Tilford Tilford
Tillingbourne Shere
Titsey ✎ Tatsfield

same owners for 30 years. The comfortable saloon bar is complimented by a small, old-fashioned, quarry-tiled public bar. One regular ale and three changing guest beers, sometimes including a stout or porter, are served. Four ciders are also available and may be from any independent cider maker. The large garden is ideal for the warm weather. Close to countryside walks.
Q✿♣P🏠(19) ✿

Cranleigh

Three Horseshoes ♥ 🅛 ✅
4 High Street, GU6 8AE (on B2128)
☎ (01483) 276978 ● threehorseshoescranleigh.co.uk
Dorking DB One; Harvey's Sussex Best Bitter; 4 changing beers (sourced nationally) 🄶
Pub run as a traditional local with the emphasis on cask ale and home-made pub food. There is a small snug bar at one end, separated from the main bar, which features an inglenook fireplace. The dining room is to the rear, linking to the veranda, outside seating and play area. The guest beers are ever-changing with local and regional offerings and are listed on the website.
🌀✿🕪&♣P🏠✿ 🎵

Dorking

Cobbett's 🅛
23 West Street, RH4 1BY (on A25 one-way system eastbound)
☎ (01306) 879877 ● cobbettsdorking.co.uk
3 changing beers (sourced nationally; often Surrey Hills) 🄶
This excellent micropub and bottleshop was once a shop selling dolls' houses. Early in the week there might only be one cask beer available, often from Surrey Hills, but this rises to two or three by the end of the week. Three ciders plus six keg beers and around 200 different canned and bottled beers are also available. The pub has a limited amount of seating, but there is also a small, heated patio garden. Q🌀✿≠(West)●🏠✿🛜

White Hart 🅛
5 Dene Street, RH4 2DR (just off A25)
☎ (01306) 882655
Surrey Hills Ranmore, Shere Drop 🄷
Known locally as 'the Snakepit', this small but lively drinker's pub is just off the High Street. There are two distinct areas on either side of a horseshoe shaped bar, one of which houses a pool table (the pub has a pool team). The three TVs show different sporting events, and there is a jukebox. The walls are decorated with old adverts, including one from 1849 that describes the pub as having a good bar, tap room and parlour and a well of fine spring water. No food is served, but customers can bring their own, on request. The gent's toilet is accessed through a police telephone box. ≠(Deepdene)♣🏠✿🛜

East Molesey

Bell 🅛 ✅
4 Bell Road, KT8 0SS (off B369)
☎ (020) 8941 0400
Greene King IPA; Morland Old Speckled Hen; 4 changing beers (often St Austell, Timothy Taylor, Twickenham) 🄷
A quirky, welcoming back-street inn, close to the main shopping street. The pub is claimed to date from 1460, although the building itself is 16th century with later additions. It was once East Molesey's first post office. The 18th-century highwayman Claude Duvalier hid from the Bow Street Runners here. Several separate drinking areas

make it ideal for a quiet pint or larger gathering. The generous garden contains a children's play area. The changing beers include at least one local one.
🌀✿🕪♣P🏠(411) ✿🛜

Egham

Egham United Services Club 🅛
111 Spring Rise, TW20 9PE (close to A30 Egham Hill)
☎ (01784) 435120 ● eusc.club
Rebellion IPA; Surrey Hills Ranmore; 3 changing beers (sourced nationally; often Kent, Oakham, Titanic) 🄷
A comfortably furnished club featuring two regular and five ever-changing real ales, including something dark, plus a real cider. it holds three beer festivals a year which showcase an eclectic range of ales, mostly from the newest micros around. It has a TV showing sport and hosts live music some Saturday evenings. As well as bar snacks, chips and samosas are usually available. CAMRA members can be signed in as guests on production of their membership card. 🌀✿&≠♣P🏠(8,441)🛜 🎵

Englefield Green

Barley Mow 🅛 ✅
Barley Mow Road, Egham, TW20 0NX
☎ (01784) 480210 ● barleymowenglefield.com
St Austell Tribute; Sharp's Doom Bar; Timothy Taylor Landlord; Windsor & Eton Guardsman; 1 changing beer (sourced nationally; often Windsor & Eton) 🄷
A spacious, family-friendly Heartwood Inn. The gastropub menu is supported by bar snacks, plus there is a traditional Sunday roast. A proper bar area is retained, with several real ales available, and a full range of barista teas and coffees. The pub has a pretty rear garden, and a front patio overlooking the village green, where cricket is played in summer. Dogs are welcome in the bar and outside areas, with water and biscuits provided. Card payment only. Q🌀✿🕪P🏠(8,441)✿

Happy Man ✅
12 Harvest Road, TW20 0QS (off A30)
☎ (01784) 433265 ● happymanenglefieldgreen.co.uk
4 changing beers (sourced nationally; often Goff's, Tring, Woodforde's) 🄷
In Victorian times two houses were converted to this pub serving workers building the nearby Royal Holloway College. Refurbished but virtually unchanged, with several snug spaces, this former local CAMRA Pub of the Year is a popular haunt for students and locals. Up to four rotating ales, local and national, are available. Occasional beer festivals are held on the heated and covered rear patio. Pub games include darts and there are quiz nights. Food is usually available daily. ✿🕪♣🏠(8,441)✿🛜

Epsom

Jolly Coopers 🅛
84 Wheelers Lane, KT18 7SD (off B280 via Stamford Green Rd)
☎ (01372) 723222 ● jollycoopers.co.uk
Surrey Hills Ranmore; 4 changing beers (sourced regionally; often Dark Star, Fuzzchat) 🄷
Close to Epsom Common, this pub is more than 200 years old. The interior consists of a carpeted bar area to the left, and another larger area with polished parquet flooring to the right, which is used mainly for dining. The decor is modern, with painted walls. There is a large, paved garden at the rear and bench seating at the front. Fuzzchat brewery is in an outbuilding at the back. A changing real cider is sold.
Q🌀✿🕪♣●P🏠(E9,E10) ✿🛜

Rifleman 🄻

5 East Street, KT17 1BB (on A24)
☎ (01372) 721244
Greene King London Glory; Surrey Hills Ranmore; house beer (by Hardys & Hansons); 2 changing beers (sourced locally; often Hogs Back, Twickenham, Windsor & Eton) Ⓗ

Small corner pub in the shadow of a bridge carrying the railway to and from London. It is decorated in a traditional style featuring two fireplaces and dark-green wood panelling, but also has some modern features such as bare brickwork and high tables at the front. There is a pleasant garden to the rear, which is an oasis of calm close to central Epsom. The name comes from the 8th Corps of the Surrey Rifle Volunteers who trained nearby. ⌂🏵🌓➰🚌🐾🛜

Rising Sun 🄻

14 Heathcote Road, KT18 5DX (off B290)
☎ (01372) 940015 🌐 risingsun-pub.co.uk
Big Smoke Solaris Session Pale Ale; 3 changing beers (sourced nationally; often Anspach & Hobday, Big Smoke) Ⓗ

Famous as the birthplace of the Society for Preservation of Beers from the Wood in 1963, this back-street pub is only a few minutes' walk from the town centre. Though food focused, it retains a traditional bar area at the front, with a wood floor, polished brasses, and a small Victorian fireplace. To the rear is a covered atrium and large garden. Guest beers can be from local brewers. Parking is available nearby in Church Street.
Q⌂🏵🌓♿➰🚗🚌🐾🛜

Esher

Wheatsheaf 🄻

40 Esher Green, KT10 8AG
☎ (01372) 464014 🌐 wheatsheafesher.co.uk
Surrey Hills Shere Drop; Young's London Original; 1 changing beer (often Dorking, Hogs Back) Ⓗ

Imposing inn, about 200 years old, opposite Esher Green. The smart, popular local has a vibrant atmosphere, and is comfortably furnished throughout in a modern style. Its spacious interior comprises a large central bar and several seating areas, with original oak flooring in the main area and open fire in the bar. Drinkers and diners are equally welcome, with high-quality food available all day. A bicycle rack is provided at the rear.
⌂🏵🌓♿🅿🚌(K3,515)🐾🛜

Farnham

Borough Beer House

6 Town Hall Buildings, GU9 7ND
🌐 boroughbeerhouse.co.uk
6 changing beers (sourced nationally) Ⓗ

Independent beer house in a characterful building dating from 1674. Six handpumps serve a variety of cask ale styles from around the UK, with 18 keg lines providing changing beers from UK, Belgium and beyond. There are also four real ciders from bag in box containers and two from keg. It has a small downstairs seating area and large upstairs room. Sandwiches and ploughmans are served until 5pm, with pork pies, cheese boards and vegan boards available all day. Children aged eight and over are admitted. ⌂🌓➰🚗🚌🐾🛜

Hop Blossom

50 Long Garden Walk, GU9 7HX (between Waitrose and Castle St)
☎ (01252) 710770 🌐 hopblossom.co.uk

Dark Star Hophead; Fuller's London Pride; Gale's Seafarers Ale; 1 changing beer (sourced nationally; often Fuller's) Ⓗ

A traditional, friendly and welcoming pub tucked away in the centre of Farnham. The original wooden floor adds character, as does the subdued lighting, and the furniture is comfortable. In winter a log fire and the recently added antique grate adds further individuality to the pub. Dogs are welcome. ⌂➰🚗🚌🐾🛜♪

Godalming

Richmond Arms ✅

149 High Street, GU7 1AF
☎ (01483) 921561 🌐 therichmondarmsgodalming.co.uk
St Austell Tribute; Young's London Original; 1 changing beer (sourced regionally) Ⓗ

A traditional and unspoilt locals' pub at the south-western end of Godalming High Street, handy for buses and the railway station. The main bar at the front of the pub has maroon half-panelling and a fireplace at each end. The public bar at the rear has a separate entrance. Behind the pub there is a raised garden with plenty of seating. ⌂🏵🌓➰⚓🚗🐾🛜

Star Inn 🍷 ✅

17 Church Street, GU7 1EL
☎ (01483) 417717 🌐 staringodalming.co.uk
St Austell Tribute Ⓗ**; 13 changing beers (sourced nationally; often Godalming Beerworks)** Ⓗ/Ⓖ

Dating from around 1830, the Star has a small public bar at the front and a main room to the side leading to a patio garden and separate lounge. Up to 14 real ales are served, plus 10 ciders and perries, and also mead. Beer festivals are held at Easter and Halloween. The pub is a regular winner of CAMRA cider awards and is home to Godalming Beerworks whose beers can be regularly found on the bar. Local CAMRA Pub of the Year 2024. ⌂🏵🌓➰⚓🚗🚌🐾🛜♪

Great Bookham

Anchor

161 Lower Road, KT23 4AH (off A246 via Eastwick Rd)
☎ (01372) 452429
Fuller's London Pride; Surrey Hills Ranmore Ⓗ

Historic Grade II-listed inn dating from the 15th century. Low-beamed ceilings, wooden floors, exposed brickwork, and an inglenook with a real fire in winter give the pub a traditional and homely feel. A charity quiz night is held every Tuesday (book ahead) and a meat raffle every Sunday. There is a patio garden with a pond and heated smoking area at the front. Children under 14 are allowed in the bar during eating times.
Q⌂🏵🌓⚓🅿🚌(479)🐾🛜

Guildford

Rodboro Buildings 🄻 ✅

1-10 Bridge Street, GU1 4SB (opp Friary Centre)
☎ (01483) 306366
Greene King IPA, Abbot; Sharp's Doom Bar; 7 changing beers (sourced nationally; often Hogs Back, Surrey Hills, Tillingbourne) Ⓗ

This Wetherspoon pub is spread over three levels in a Grade II-listed former industrial building that was the original home of the Dennis car (later truck) company. It serves a range of up to 10 real ales, often from local breweries. The community noticeboard publicises a range of local events. The pub also hosts occasional Meet the Brewer nights and brewery battles. ⌂🌓♿➰🚗🚌🐾🛜

Royal Oak

15 Trinity Churchyard, GU1 3RR (behind Trinity Church)
☎ (01483) 457144 🌐 royaloakguildford.co.uk
Fuller's London Pride; Gale's HSB; 3 changing beers (sourced nationally; often Dark Star, Fuller's) Ⓗ
This former Gale's pub has been serving real ale since 1870. It was built as an extension to the rectory next door, with a hall upstairs and rooms at ground level. These rooms now comprise the bar area and show the building's heavily beamed structure. Three brewery supplied guest beers are available. Outside there is a patio area on one side and a couple of tables overlooking Trinity churchyard are on the other.
♉❀≋(London Road) ♣P🚌🐾📶♫

Hambledon

Merry Harriers Ⓛ ✔

Hambledon Road, GU8 4DR SU967391
☎ (01428) 682883 🌐 merryharriers.com
Crafty Brewing Crafty One; Surrey Hills Shere Drop; 2 changing beers (sourced locally; often Hogs Back, Langham) Ⓗ
This impressive 16th-century country inn, popular with walkers and cyclists, takes you back in time. It stands on a quiet country lane set against the backdrop of the Surrey Hills in a designated Area of Outstanding Natural Beauty. There is an inglenook fireplace in the bar and benches on the forecourt, with a garden to the rear. It is now under new ownership so opening times are under review. ♉❀🛏◐♣P🚌(503)🐾📶♫

Headley

Cock Inn

Church Lane, KT18 6LE
☎ (01372) 377258 🌐 cockinnheadley.co.uk
Tilford Hankley Gold, Punchbowl; 1 changing beer (sourced regionally; often Fuller's) Ⓗ
The interior of this 250-year-old building is split into the bar and dining areas. The decor is modern, with painted walls and varnished wood floors, and there are real log fires in the main bar and function room. Despite the emphasis on food, drinkers are made welcome. There are wonderful views from the pub and garden across the valley opposite. ♉❀◐♿P🚌(21)🐾📶♫

Hersham

Bricklayers Arms

6-8 Queens Road, KT12 5LS (off A317)
☎ (01932) 220936
Hogs Back TEA; Hop Back Crop Circle; Shepherd Neame Spitfire Ⓗ
This two-bar Victorian pub, just off the green, has built up a fine reputation and has been run by the same landlord for the past 42 years. It is divided into a spacious public bar with a real fire and a comfortable saloon, where excellent food is served, including daily specials. Features include wonderful external floral displays and a secluded rear garden. Accommodation is in two rooms. Parking can be difficult. Q❀🛏◐♿♣🚌(458,515)🐾📶

Holmbury St Mary

Royal Oak Ⓛ

The Glade, Felday Road, RH5 6PF
☎ (01306) 898010 🌐 theroyaloakholmbury.co.uk
Felday Legacy; Firebird Parody; Harvey's Sussex Best Bitter; 1 changing beer (sourced locally; often Surrey Hills) Ⓗ
In a picturesque setting beside the village green and church, this pub is an excellent destination for walkers and cyclists. Dating back to the 17th century, the bar has a real fire and serves a bitter brewed at the next-door Felday brewery. Home-made food is a feature and is available in the bar, the upstairs dining room, or in the front garden and rear patio in summer. Closed Monday.
♉❀◐P🚌(22)🐾📶

Horley

Jack Fairman Ⓛ ✔

30 Victoria Road, RH6 7PZ (main shopping street near Waitrose)
☎ (01293) 827910
Greene King Abbot; Ruddles Best Bitter; Sharp's Doom Bar; 3 changing beers (sourced nationally; often By The Horns, Titanic) Ⓗ
This distinctive Art Deco-style building in the town centre was formerly a garage used by Jack Fairman, a local motor racing driver. After use as a tyre centre, it reopened as a Wetherspoon pub, conveniently close the station and bus stops. Of the three guest ales, one is normally LocAle, two are from national brewers, and one of these three will usually be a dark beer. Food is available all day. News or sport is shown on muted TV screens. Q♉❀◐♿≋🚌📶

Horsell

Crown Ⓛ

104 High Street, GU21 4ST
☎ (01483) 771719
Surrey Hills Shere Drop; Thurstons Horsell Gold; 4 changing beers (sourced regionally; often Thurstons) Ⓗ
Welcoming two-bar community local with six real ales in the saloon bar. Normally three beers are from Thurstons, who started brewing in pub and are now located next door. This wet pub with no food is a rarity for the area. The large garden has two pétanque piste, and is used for at least one beer festival a year. Regular motorcycle and scooter club meets are held in the summer. A former CAMRA Surrey Pub of the Year, and local Pub of the Year in 2022 and 2023. ♉❀♣P🚌(48)🐾📶♫

Knaphill

Garibaldi Ⓛ

134 High Street, GU21 2QH
☎ (01483) 473374 🌐 thegaribaldiknaphill.co.uk
2 changing beers (sourced regionally) Ⓗ
On the edge of Knaphill, this pub has a compact interior, exposed beams and wooden floors. Two or three changing cask ales are served, with regional beers favoured. Monday is real ale club night, with beers sold at reduced prices, and a beer festival is held at Easter. The pub hosts a Sunday evening quiz and raises a lot for local charities through a wide range of events including an annual cycle ride. Closed lunchtimes on Monday and Tuesday. ♉❀◐P🚌🐾📶♫

Leatherhead

Running Horse Ⓛ

38 Bridge Street, KT22 8BZ (off B2122)
☎ (01372) 372081 🌐 running-horse.co.uk
Shepherd Neame Spitfire; Surrey Hills Ranmore Ⓗ
Overlooking the River Mole, this Grade II*-listed two-room pub, dating from 1403, features a real log fire, home-made food, a courtyard seating area, and a large back garden. The public bar has a TV, pool table and

dartboard, and the cosy lounge bar features low ceilings and exposed beams. Elizabeth I apparently spent the night here. Quiz night is Tuesday and live bands play monthly. A former local CAMRA Pub of the Year. Closed Monday and Tuesday lunchtime. Q➎❀❶➤➍P➜❀ 🛜

Leigh

Plough at Leigh 🅛

Church Road, RH2 8NJ

☎ (01306) 611348 ∰ theploughatleigh.co.uk

Harvey's Sussex Best Bitter; Pilgrim Progress; 3 changing beers (sourced nationally; often Surrey Hills, Timothy Taylor) 🅷

Overlooking the village green is this traditional, friendly local, parts of which date from the 15th century. The weatherboarded exterior to the right contains a low-beamed lounge bar, leading to a cosy restaurant which serves a good variety of home-cooked food. The public bar offers darts and other bar games, along with the daily papers. Children and dogs are welcome here; the latter have their own water bowl and biscuit jar. Q➎❀❶➍P➜(22,433) ❀ 🛜

Mickleham

King William IV 🅛

4 Byttom Hill, RH5 6EL (off A24 southbound behind 51 Degrees North café)

☎ (01372) 372590 ∰ thekingwilliamiv.com

Hogs Back TEA; Surrey Hills Shere Drop; 1 changing beer (sourced locally; often Crafty Brewing, Dorking, Tillingbourne) 🅷

A quaint, welcoming country pub, dating from 1790, nestled on a hillside. The cosy main bar has a log fire, and there is a smaller bar to the front. The outside terrace, which has some tables under cover, enjoys stunning views over the Mole Valley. Good home-made food is served – book ahead for lunch, especially on summer weekends. Steep steps can make access difficult. A public car park is on the A24 southbound. Opening hours are seasonal. Q➎❀❶P➜(465)❀ 🛜

Milford

Refectory 🅛

Old Portsmouth Road, GU8 5HJ

☎ (01483) 413820

House beer (by St Austell); 4 changing beers (sourced regionally; often Firebird, Gun, Surrey Hills) 🅷

A large, open-plan pub with exposed beams and several distinct areas, all set in a fascinating building dating from the 1950s, though it feels much older. Farming paraphernalia adorn the walls, with roaring log fires in the pretty fireplaces warming the pub in winter. There is an extensive courtyard garden to the rear. The four or five guest beers are generally from local independent microbreweries, supplemented by four or five varying ciders, predominantly from small producers. ➎❀❶♿➍P➜(70,71) ❀ 🛜

Newdigate

Surrey Oaks 🅛

Parkgate Road, Parkgate, RH5 5DZ (between Newdigate and Leigh) TQ20524363

☎ (01306) 631200 ∰ thesurreyoaks.com

Surrey Hills Ranmore, Shere Drop; 4 changing beers (sourced nationally) 🅷

This 16th-century free house serves a changing range of up to six cask beers, 12 craft keg beers and 15 ciders. There are a number of distinct areas, with low beams,

flagstones and an inglenook fireplace with log-burning stove. The excellent large garden includes a heated and covered area and a children's play area. The pub garden hosts popular beer festivals on the late May and August bank holidays. Good food is sold daily and breakfast at weekends. Q➎❀❶♣➍P➜(21)❀ 🛜

Outwood

Bell Inn ✅

Outwood Lane, RH1 5PN

☎ (01342) 891835 ∰ belloutwood.co.uk

Fuller's London Pride, ESB; Gale's Seafarers Ale, HSB; 2 changing beers (sourced nationally) 🅷

Dating from 1635, this former coaching house is now a characterful country pub, with low ceilings and nooks and corners to hide away in. There is a large bell by the entrance, reputedly made from melted down ships' cannon, which originally came from a London church. Regular community events are hosted, including a summer beer festival. ➎❀❶P➜(315)❀ 🛜

Oxted

Oxted Inn ✅

Units 1-4 Hoskins Walk, Station Road West, RH8 9HR

☎ (01883) 723440

Greene King Abbot; Ruddles Best Bitter; Sharp's Doom Bar; 4 changing beers (sourced nationally; often Twickenham, Wantsum) 🅷

Next to the railway station this Wetherspoon pub dates from 1996, and is the only remaining pub in New Oxted. The town is on the Greenwich Meridian and the interior is decorated with more than 20 clocks showing the time in various parts of the world. Local historians will find the many photos on display of interest. Q➎❀❶♿➤➜ 🛜

Puttenham

Good Intent 🅛

60-62 The Street, GU3 1AR

☎ (01483) 923434 ∰ goodintentputtenham.co.uk

Sharp's Doom Bar; Timothy Taylor Landlord; house beer (by Crafty Brewing) 🅷

Attractive, welcoming village pub. Classic red carpets and contrasting dark varnished woodwork contribute to a warm, comfortable ambience, and an inglenook fireplace adds warmth in winter. Partitions create separate areas. The house beer is brewed for the pub by Crafty Brewing. Food is served at lunchtime and dinner, except on Monday, and there is a traditional roast until 6pm on Sunday. The North Downs Way passes the door and one of Surrey's few remaining hop growers is at the other end of the village. Q➎❀❶♣P❀ 🛜 🎵

Redhill

Garibaldi 🅛

29 Mill Street, RH1 6PA

☎ (01737) 773094 ∰ thegaribaldiredhill.co.uk

5 changing beers (sourced nationally) 🅷

This not-for-profit, community-run pub has stood here for over 150 years opposite Redhill Common. There is a single room with a small side area that contains a dartboard. Two TV screens show live sport at a discrete volume. Many social and charitable events are run by the pub, including at least three beer festivals. The large garden, with views across Redhill, is well tended. The beer range changes frequently and usually includes at least two LocAles. ➎❀➍➜❀ 🛜

Hatch �Ⓛ

44 Hatchlands Road, RH1 6AT (on A25 W of town)
☎ (01737) 222651
Pilgrim Surrey, Progress; 3 changing beers (sourced regionally) ⓗ
This comfortable and deceptively spacious 17th-century pub was once a workhouse with a hayloft for horses. It became Pilgrim brewery's first pub in 2022. The L-shaped bar offers up to five cask beers and nine craft keg lines, including some from other brewers. There are two more secluded rooms to the left plus a cosy fire to the right. Food is provided by a local pizza company. Closed Monday. Q🕏🏠🌂◑🌳🚲🐾🛜

Reigate

Bell Inn Ⓛ

21 Bell Street, RH2 7AD (on A217)
☎ (01737) 244438
6 changing beers (sourced nationally; often By The Horns, Surrey Hills, Titsey) ⓗ
This town-centre pub is packed with character and its friendly, bohemian ambience attracts a varied clientele. The long, narrow low-ceilinged room has a bar running down one side and a bay window looking onto the passing shoppers on Bell Street. No food is served, but customers can bring their own. The beer selection changes regularly and usually include a couple from local breweries. Children are welcome until 5pm.
🕏🏠🚲🐾🛜

Hop Stop Bar

73 Bell Street, RH2 7AN (on A217 S of town centre)
☎ (01737) 221781 ⊕ hopstopbeers.co.uk
Surrey Hills Shere Drop; 1 changing beer (sourced nationally) ⓗ
Opened in 2019, this former restaurant is now a modern, continental-style style bar. It usually serves one or two cask beers and has an additional nine lines that are used for an eclectic array of keg beers and cider, details of which are shown on an electronic board. There is also a chiller cabinet with an assortment of international bottles and cans, which are available to drink in-house or for take-away. Beers can also be ordered online for collection. Closed Sunday to Tuesday. 🕏🚲🐾🛜

Pilgrim Brewery Taproom Ⓛ

11 West Street, RH2 9BL (off A25 towards Dorking)
☎ (01737) 222651 ⊕ pilgrimbrewery.co.uk/taproom
Pilgrim Progress, Surrey; 3 changing beers Ⓖ
The oldest brewery in Surrey, founded in 1982, has been on the present site since 1984, and the taproom is next door. There will usually be five cask and up to nine keg beers available, all brewed on-site. No food is served but you can bring your own. An external food provider is usually there on Saturday. Dominoes, shove-ha'penny and board games are available. Additional seating outside offers views of Reigate Priory Cricket Ground. Closed Monday and Tuesday. Q🕏🏠🚲♣🅿🐾🛜

Shepperton

Barley Mow Ⓛ

67 Watersplash Road, TW17 0EE (off B376 in Shepperton Green)
☎ (01932) 225326 ⊕ thebarleymowshepperton.co.uk
Hogs Back TEA; Hop Back Summer Lightning; 3 changing beers (sourced regionally; often Crafty Brewing, Twickenham, Windsor & Eton) ⓗ
Friendly community local in Shepperton Green, to the west of the main village centre. Five handpumps serve two regular and three changing guests. Pumpclips adorn

the bar and beams, along with CAMRA certificates, including a 50th anniversary Gold Award and a local Pub of the Year. Entertainment includes jazz on Wednesday, a quiz night on Thursday, live rock or blues on Friday or Saturday night, and a charity raffle on Sunday. There is a heated patio at the rear. 🕏🏠♣🅿🚍(400,458)🐾🛜🎵

South Godstone

Fox & Hounds Ⓛ ✔

Tilburstow Hill Road, RH9 8LY
☎ (01342) 893474 ⊕ foxandhounds.org.uk
Fuller's London Pride; Pilgrim Progress, Surrey; 2 changing beers (sourced regionally; often Tonbridge) ⓗ
This delightful building, parts of which date back to 1368, first became a pub in 1601. There are many original features, including a large inglenook in the restaurant. The cosy low-ceilinged bar area has high-backed settles and a fireplace. The garden features a children's play area with a wooden pirate ship. The pub has a deserved reputation for good food and an ever-changing menu of home-cooked, locally sourced food, plus specials is available (booking advised). Closed Tuesday.
🕏🏠◑♣🅿🐾🛜🎵

Staines-upon-Thames

George ✔

2-8 High Street, TW18 4EE (on A308, opp town hall)
☎ (01784) 462181
Greene King Abbot; Ruddles Best Bitter; Sharp's Doom Bar; 4 changing beers (sourced nationally) ⓗ
Family-friendly Wetherspoon pub in the town centre. The spacious downstairs bar, with its mixture of tables and booths, is always busy, and there is a quieter bar upstairs. It offers three regular and up to six guest ales, occasionally from local brewers, as well as national brands. A varied selection of foreign bottled beers and ciders are also stocked. Value-for-money pub food, coffees and tea are served all day every day.
Q🕏🏠◑♿🌂🚍🛜

Last Hop

Unit 2 Thames Edge Court, Clarence Street, TW18 4SU (on towpath, on downstream side of Staines Bridge)
☎ (020) 3637 5756 ⊕ lasthop.co.uk
6 changing beers (sourced nationally; often Stardust, Windsor & Eton) ⓗ
A large family- and dog-friendly bar overlooking the River Thames by Staines Bridge, with some seating outside by the towpath. Up to six ales from local and national breweries are served, alongside a range of craft keg beers. Occasional live music, quiz and other events are held. There is a coffee bar, and food includes pizzas. The venue is also available for exclusive use as an event space for up to 250 people. 🕏♿🅿🐾🎵

Thames Side Brewery ⛾

1 Hale Street, TW18 4UW (next to Travelodge near entrance to Two Rivers car parks)
⊕ thamessidebrewery.co.uk
Thames Side Heron Ale, White Swan Pale Ale, Egyptian Goose India Pale Ale, Black Swan Porter; 4 changing beers (sourced locally; often Five Points, Thames Side) ⓗ
The home and taproom of Thames Side brewery, with up to 12 real ales from regular and occasional ranges, real ciders from Thirsty Farmer, as well as craft keg and a full range of other drinks. There is plenty of seating, including comfy sofas in one corner. Regular live music features, including open mic, and there are quiz and

curry nights. Food sometimes available, see Facebook or website for details. Closed Monday and Tuesday.
🌫🕸🕩♿➍🅿🖳🐾♪

Tatsfield

Titsey Brewing Co Taproom
Clarks Lane Farm, Clarks Lane, TN16 2JU (off B2024)
☎ (01959) 528535 ⊕ titseybrewingco.com
Titsey Gresham Hopper, Leveson Buck, Gower Wolf; 3 changing beers Ⓗ
Popular with walkers and cyclists, the taproom for Titsey brewery opened in 2023 on the top of the North Downs. The full range of Titsey beers is sold along with all their seasonal offerings. Good food is served, including breakfast, burgers and rotisserie chicken. Sport is shown on a large screen and there is occasional live music. Closed Monday to Wednesday. 🌫🕸➍🅿🖳🐾♪

Thursley

Three Horseshoes Ⓛ
Dye House Road, GU8 6QD
☎ (01252) 703900 ⊕ threehorseshoesthursley.com
Surrey Hills Shere Drop; 1 changing beer (sourced locally) Ⓗ
This attractive, half-tiled country pub, between Thursley Common and the Devil's Punch Bowl, was saved from closure in 2004 when villagers grouped together to buy the freehold. It usually serves two or three local ales. The cosy front bar has two fireplaces and wooden beams and can get busy during meal times. There is also an extensive dining area at the rear. The garden overlooks fields stretching up to the Hindhead Hills. Closed Monday and Tuesday. 🌫🕸➍🅿🐾🛜♪

Upper Hale

Alfred Free House
9 Bishops Road, GU9 0JA
☎ (01252) 820385 ⊕ thealfredfreehouse.co.uk
4 changing beers (sourced nationally; often Disruption is Brewing, Wantsum) Ⓗ
This friendly, cosy, local free house, tucked away down a narrow residential road, serves four regularly changing ales sourced nationally, and always includes at least one dark beer. All beers currently on tap are displayed on a blackboard and are regularly updated on their website. Closed all day Monday and lunchtime Tuesday to Thursday. Q🕸♿♣🅿🖳(5)🐾

Walton on Thames

Walton Village 🍽 Ⓛ
29 High Street, KT12 1DG
☎ (01932) 254431 ⊕ thewaltonvillage.com
Hogs Back TEA; 2 changing beers (sourced locally) Ⓗ
Modern high-street pub in a converted shop premises, featuring exposed brickwork and wood panels. The large front bar has a raised seating area and there is a room to the rear for private events. A wide range of food is served all day, prepared in an open-plan kitchen in the centre of the pub. It attracts a diverse clientele. A popular quiz night is held on Thursday. Other attractions include a table tennis table and mini dog bar with water and treats. 🌫🕸➍🕩♿♣➍🖳🐾🛜

> There can't be a good living where there is not good drinking.
> **Benjamin Franklin**

Weir Ⓛ
Waterside Drive, KT12 2JB
☎ (01932) 784530 ⊕ weirhotel.co.uk
Brakspear Gravity; 2 changing beers (sourced locally) Ⓗ
The Weir's superb riverside location, with extensive outside seating and free moorings, attracts walkers, cyclists, boaters and families. It's a fair way from the town centre, but a nice walk. The Victorian-style bar area is mainly carpeted, with comfortable upholstered benches around the walls, and more intimate areas at the front and rear. The interior features copper pans, plates, ornaments and old pictures. Up to two changing beers are served, usually from local breweries. Accommodation is available in six rooms.
🌫🕸🛏🕩♣🅿🖳(564) 🐾🛜

West Horsley

Barley Mow Ⓛ
181 The Street, KT24 6HR
☎ (01483) 282693 ⊕ barleymowhorsley.com
Fuller's London Pride; Hogs Back TEA; Surrey Hills Ranmore, Shere Drop Ⓗ
A classic pub set in the heart of the Surrey Hills. The large building, which features some flagstone flooring, incorporates the Malting House to the rear, which is available for functions. Thai food is available at lunch and dinner, with traditional pub fare at lunchtimes (no food on Sun). The garden has a large open grassed area, which is great for dogs, and has seating dotted around. Will open on request at 11.30am for the bus from Guildford. Closed Monday lunchtime.
🌫🕸➍🅿🖳(478) 🐾🛜♪

West Molesey

Royal Oak ✅
317 Walton Road, KT8 2QG (On B369)
☎ (020) 8979 5452
Fuller's London Pride; St Austell Tribute; Timothy Taylor Landlord Ⓗ
Situated next to the church, this pub dates from about 1860 and is very much at the heart of the community. The comfortably furnished open-plan bar is divided into two areas, with a quiet lounge area to the left. Wood panelling gives it a traditional pub feel, along with oak beams, horse brasses and plates. Families are welcome until 8pm and there is a secure garden to the rear. Live music plays every other Saturday, and there are open mic nights on Monday and Wednesday.
🌫🕸♿♣🅿🖳(411,461) 🐾🛜♪

Weybourne

Running Stream ✅
66 Weybourne Road, GU9 9HE
☎ (01252) 323750
Greene King IPA, Abbot; Hardys & Hansons Bitter; Timothy Taylor Dark Mild Ⓗ
A good old-fashioned, friendly, traditional locals' pub. It is horseshoe-shaped, surrounding a central bar with tables dotted around the perimeter and bar-stools at the bar. The handpumps dispense up to six beers depending on demand, including a dark beer. The home-cooked food includes vegetarian, vegan and gluten-free options (phone ahead for bookings). There is a pleasant garden at the rear. Q🕸🕩♣🅿🖳🐾🛜

Whyteleafe

Radius Arms

205 Godstone Road, CR3 0EL (on A22)
☎ 07514 916172
4 changing beers (sourced nationally) Ⓗ/Ⓖ
This friendly and welcoming micropub brings choice to this part of Surrey with its ever-changing selection of beer and cider. There are at least four cask ales on offer, along with four KeyKegs and up to 12 ciders. A pumpclip-festooned ceiling and furniture recycled from the Olympic Park are just some of the quirky features. There is also a small library. Closed Monday. Q❀≈♦🛇🖵❀

Woking

Herbert Wells Ⓛ ✅

51-57 Chertsey Road, GU21 5AJ
☎ (01483) 722818
Greene King Abbot; Ruddles Best Bitter; Sharp's Doom Bar; 7 changing beers (sourced nationally) Ⓗ
A varied range of up to seven guest beers are served at this popular town-centre Wetherspoon, which is close to bus stops and the railway station. The large open-plan bar is decorated with HG Wells-inspired features, including an invisible man sitting in the window and its own time machine. A wealth of information about local history covers the walls of both the main bar and the smaller side room. Children are accommodated when eating. Q🛏🕽&≈🖵🛜

Woking Railway Athletic Club

Goldsworth Road, GU21 6JT (behind offices at E end of Goldsworth Rd) TQ003585
☎ (01483) 598499
3 changing beers (sourced nationally) Ⓗ
Lively club tucked away near Victoria Arch, serving three or four beers. The long, narrow, single-storied building is broken up into separate areas by the position of the bar and function room area. Walls are decorated with old railway pictures. Children are welcome at all times. Show a CAMRA membership card or copy of this Guide for entry. Local CAMRA Club of the Year five out of the last six years. 🛏≈♣🖵🛜

Wonersh

Grantley Arms Ⓛ

The Street, GU5 0PE
☎ (01483) 893351 ⊕ thegrantleyarms.co.uk
Surrey Hills Shere Drop; Young's London Original; 1 changing beer (often Hogs Back) Ⓗ
Half-timbered village pub dating from the late 16th century. A recent refurbishment exposed more of the frame of the building, creating a bright and cheerful interior. Food is the main focus and meals are served all day. Despite this, there are tables available in the bar for drinkers and there is no pressure to eat. Buses stop outside, including evening and Sunday services from Cranleigh and Guildford. 🛏❀🕽&🖵🖵(53,63)❀🛜

Woodmansterne

Woodman ✅

Woodmansterne Street, SM7 3NL (on B278)
☎ (01737) 371841
Harvey's Sussex Best Bitter; Sharp's Doom Bar; 2 changing beers (sourced locally; often Surrey Hills) Ⓗ
This recently and extensively refurbished busy village pub has one large horseshoe-shaped bar. It is bright and spacious, and mostly given over to dining, but drinkers are also welcome. There is a large beer garden that includes covered external seating. Tuesday is poker night, Thursday is quiz night, and there is live music on the last Friday of the month. 🛏❀🕽&♣🖵(166)❀🛜♫

Worplesdon

Fox Inn Ⓛ

Fox Corner, GU3 3PP
☎ 07841 204004 ⊕ thefoxinnfoxcorner.com
6 changing beers (sourced nationally; often Dorking, Surrey Hills, Triple fff) Ⓗ
A convivial and welcoming free house, set well back from the road. The four separate rooms have subdued lighting and low beams and contain an eclectic collection of effects that make the rooms interesting without being cluttered. Outside is a patio and beyond that a substantial garden. Food Is provided by a different pop-up stall each evening. 🛏❀🕽🖵(28,91)❀🛜♫

Wrecclesham

Sandrock Ⓛ

Sandrock Hill Road, GU10 4NS SU830444
☎ (01252) 447289 ⊕ sandrockwrecclesham.co.uk
Bowman Swift One; Butcombe Gold; Exmoor Gold; St Austell Proper Job; Timothy Taylor Landlord; Triple fff Moondance; 2 changing beers (sourced nationally; often Fuller's) Ⓗ
Traditional pub with a contemporary feel, offering seven regular cask ales, including Fuller's London Pride, plus a guest ale. Thai food is available in a separate restaurant (Wed-Sun eve and weekend lunchtimes). There is a patio garden terrace at the rear, and a small car park. Live music is performed once a month on a Saturday. Opens at 4pm on weekdays. Q🛏❀🕽&♣🖵(16,17)❀🛜♫

A short history of the Good Beer Guide

The Good Beer Guide was first published in 1972 and was just 18 pages long. Rather than a printed and bound edition, it was just a collection of sheets of paper stapled together and posted out to CAMRA members. The first printed edition was published in 1974 and contained a comment on Watney's brewery that was considered libellous, causing the first print run to be pulped and the description for the brewery to be revised. There are a few copies of the first print run out there, but they change hands for a fair amount of money.

There has been an edition of the Guide printed annually since 1974, meaning it is now in its 52nd year. The longest serving editor was Roger Protz, who edited the Guide from 1978-1983 and 2000-2018. It has grown from 96 pages in 1974 to 912 pages for this edition, with 4,500 pubs listed and more than 1,700 breweries.

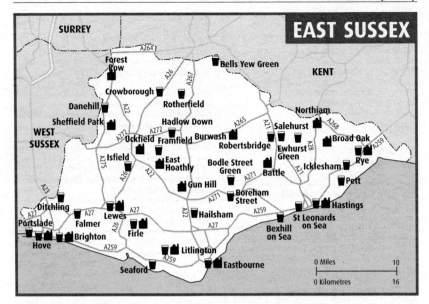

Bells Yew Green

Brecknock Arms ✓
Bayham Road, TN3 9BJ
☎ (01892) 750237 ⊕ thebrecknockarmspub.com
Harvey's Sisters, Sussex Best Bitter; 1 changing beer (sourced locally; often Harvey's) Ⓗ
A 10-minute walk from Frant railway station, the Brecknock is a traditional country pub on a crossroads in the village centre. It is family run and a warm welcome and good service are assured. Traditional pub meals and at least three Harvey's cask ales are usually available. In the garden there is a large outbuilding used for special events and the September beer festival, while a converted building in the car park serves as a TV and games room. Q☺❀◐&⟆(Frant)♣P🖳❀🛜♪

Bexhill on Sea

Albatross Club (RAFA) Ⓛ
15 Marina Arcade, TN40 1JS (on seafront 200yds E of De La Warr Pavilion)
☎ (01424) 212916 ⊕ bexhillrafa.co.uk
5 changing beers Ⓗ
The 1066 RAFA Club has a varied range of local and national real ales and ciders. In 2016 the club was the National CAMRA Club of the Year, and it is regularly voted local CAMRA Club of the Year. Two beer festivals are held each year, popular events for locals. CAMRA members are welcome to be signed in on making a minimum donation of £1 to RAF charities. Entertainment is on offer some evenings and occasionally at weekends.
Q☺◐&⟆(Bexhill) ●🖳❀🛜♪

Brickmaker's Alehouse ♥ Ⓛ
27 Sea Road, TN40 1EE
☎ (01424) 602778 ⊕ brickmakersalehouse.co.uk
5 changing beers Ⓖ
A friendly welcome awaits real ale and cider enthusiasts at Bexhill's only micropub located two minutes' walk from Bexhill station and local buses, and a short walk from the seafront. Owned by two CAMRA members whose passion is real ale and cider, drinkers can expect at least five ales dispensed from the cask in a temperature-controlled display, ciders, and also a good

selection of canned and bottled beers and ciders. Local CAMRA Pub of the Year 2022, 2023 and 2024.
Q☺⟆(Bexhill) ♣●🖳❀🛜♪

Picture Playhouse Ⓛ ✓
36-38 Western Road, TN40 1DY
☎ (01424) 819500
Greene King Abbot; Ruddles Best Bitter; Sharp's Doom Bar; 5 changing beers (often Franklins, Long Man, Old Dairy) Ⓗ
This large and spacious pub has been sympathetically converted from a derelict former cinema, retaining significant elements of the original and embracing the décor of its heyday. Information boards provide a mine of information about local achievements and personalities. Real ale is front and centre and the changing beers are varied and interesting, showcasing local as well as national breweries. There is a weekly quiz on Mondays. Beer festivals and Meet the Brewer events occur from time to time. ☺❀◐&⟆(Bexhill)🖳🛜

Bodle Street Green

White Horse Inn Ⓛ
White Horse Lane, BN27 4RE
☎ (01323) 833243
Harvey's Sussex Best Bitter; 2 changing beers (sourced locally; often Long Man) Ⓗ
This pleasant traditional rural free house dating from the 1850s makes a return to this Guide for the first time since 1977. Following closure it reopened with a local family as licensees. Refurbished and redecorated throughout, including an upgraded cellar, the main bar and drinking area are to your left as you enter. Situated in the heart of rural East Sussex it is popular with walkers and cyclists. Good pub food is available. Quiz nights are held and occasional live music. Q☺❀◐P❀🛜♪

Boreham Street

Bull's Head Ⓛ
The Strait, BN27 4SG
☎ (01323) 831981 ⊕ bullsheadborehamstreet.com
Harvey's Sussex Best Bitter; 2 changing beers (sourced locally; often Harvey's) Ⓗ

The original Harvey's tied pub has been in the Guide for many years because of its range of Harvey's beers. It also offers good wholesome food and is a local hub for many events. With a large garden, car park and campsite it is a popular holiday location. Ideal for walkers, the pub is close to the 1066 Country Walk and is dog friendly throughout. The internal décor is rustic with wooden flooring, furniture and timber-panelled walls.
Q✿⭢☃◑AP🖫(98) ✿☮♪

Brighton

Basketmakers Arms ★ ✪
12 Gloucester Road, BN1 4AD
☎ (01273) 689006 ⊕ basket-makers-brighton.co.uk
Fuller's London Pride, ESB; Gale's Seafarers Ale, HSB; 4 changing beers (sourced nationally; often Dark Star) Ⓗ
A much-loved Brighton institution, this busy two-room street-corner pub, popular with young and old alike, is located on the edge of Brighton's famous bohemian North Laine. Eight handpumps serve a selection of the Fuller's range plus guests. Locally sourced home-made food is available every day, with seafood Saturday and popular traditional Sunday roasts. The walls are adorned with old metal signs and tobacco tins. Live jazz music is on the first Sunday of every month. ✿✿◑⭢🖫✿☮♪

Brighton Bierhaus Ⓛ
161 Edward Street, BN2 0JB
☎ (01273) 686386 ⊕ brightonbierhaus.pub
5 changing beers (sourced nationally; often Brighton Bier, Downlands) Ⓗ
This single-bar pub is centrally situated near the Law Courts, Royal Pavilion and Brighton Pier. It serves up to five changing beers on handpump along with keg and bottled beers and a real cider. Food may be ordered from various local carry-out establishments and occasionally there is food available from pop-up vendors in the bar. There is a free cheeseboard on Sundays. The muted television shows sport during major tournaments. Card payments only. ✿✿●🖫✿☮♪

Evening Star Ⓛ
55-56 Surrey Street, BN1 3PB (200yds S of station)
☎ (01273) 328931 ⊕ eveningstarpub.co.uk
7 changing beers (sourced regionally; often Burning Sky, Downlands, Vibrant Forest) Ⓗ
A classic, friendly pub/alehouse, five minutes' walk from the station, majoring in good real ale and craft beers. It has a warm, cosy interior and tables outside. The original home of Dark Star brewery, formerly housed in the cellar, it is now an independent free house. Ten handpumps dispense seven real ales, often from local breweries, and three real ciders. ✿♿⭢♣●🖫✿☮

Great Eastern Ⓛ ✪
103 Trafalgar Street, BN1 4ER
☎ (01273) 677654
5 changing beers Ⓗ
A small, traditional and atmospheric single-bar pub located at the northern edge of Brighton's vibrant North Laine area. The pub is a short walk from Brighton station and close to the main St Peter's bus stops. Five, often local, guest beers are available, alongside craft beers and spirits. No food, and no machines. At weekends DJs play classic jazz, blues, soul and rock from a record deck at the end of the bar. ✿⭢🖫✿☮

Haus on the Hill Ⓛ
58 Southover Street, Hanover, BN2 9UF
☎ (01273) 601419 ⊕ hausonthehill.pub

4 changing beers (sourced locally; often Brighton Bier, Downlands) Ⓗ
This pub, previously the Southover, is now operated by Brighton Bier. Being at the top of a steep hill it is probably best approached by bus. There are two function rooms upstairs and a covered patio for smokers. Conversation is the norm here and there is no TV or jukebox. Beers are mainly from local breweries, always including a dark beer plus a real cider. A number of bottled and keg beers, both British and foreign, complete the range. Q✿⭢◑♣●🖫(18,23)✿☮

Hole in the Wall
Queensbury Mews, BN1 2FE
☎ (01273) 763961 ⊕ theholeinthewall.net
4 changing beers (sourced nationally; often Hand, Oakham, Thornbridge) Ⓗ
Formerly the Queensbury Arms, this cosy two-bar traditional pub is tucked away behind the Metropole hotel. The walls display posters from old Brighton seaside shows. Tap takeovers and Meet the Brewer events are organised. Toad can be played in the back bar. Keg beers and three ciders (two bag in a box and one real), sourced from small batch producers are served in addition to real ale, with the latter always including a dark beer. Q♣●🖫✿☮

Lord Nelson Inn Ⓛ ✪
36 Trafalgar Street, BN1 4ED
☎ (01273) 695872 ⊕ lordnelsonbrighton.co.uk
Harvey's Sussex Best Bitter; 4 changing beers (sourced locally; often Harvey's) Ⓗ
This comfortable, pleasantly decorated pub has three distinct drinking spaces, modelled on the historic multi-room layout. An extensive range of Harvey's cask beers is always on offer, including seasonal brews. The pub is located in the bustling North Laine district close the main railway station. There is an extensive food menu and cocktail list. Events include quiz night on Tuesday, singles night on Thursday and regular live music evenings. ✿◑⭢🖫✿☮♪

Prince Albert ★ Ⓛ
48 Trafalgar Street, BN1 4ED
☎ (01273) 730499 ⊕ princealbertbrighton.co.uk

REAL ALE BREWERIES

1648 🍺 East Hoathly
360° ✦ Sheffield Park
Battle ✦ Battle
Beak ✦ Lewes
Beer Me 🍺 Eastbourne
Brewing Brothers 🍺 ✦ Hastings
Brighton Bier Brighton
BRZN Lewes
Burning Sky Firle
FILO Hastings
Flying Trunk Forest Row
Gun ✦ Gun Hill
Hand 🍺 ✦ Brighton
Harvey's Lewes
Laine 🍺 Brighton
Lakedown ✦ Burwash
Long Man ✦ Litlington
Loud Shirt ✦ Brighton
Old Tree Brighton
Rother Valley Northiam
Three Acre Uckfield
Three Legs ✦ Broad Oak
UnBarred ✦ Brighton
Watchmaker's Arms 🍺 Hove
Waterworks ✦ Rye (NEW)

5 changing beers (sourced locally; often Burning Sky, Long Man) Ⓗ
Vibrant multi-room pub close to Brighton station. There is a public bar, small saloon bar, two other large rooms without bar counters and an upstairs music room. Decoration and paintwork are 1970s style and highly colourful. There is a small external courtyard at the rear, and several tables on the pavement outside the pub. Real cider and perry are prominently advertised and there are five handpumps. No meals are served, but food can be brought in from the many local suppliers in North Laine. Ᏸ❀≠♣●Ⓡ❀☞♪

Crowborough

Cooper's Arms Ⓛ
Coopers Lane, TN6 1SN
☎ (01892) 654796 ⊕ coopersarmscrow.com
Harvey's Sussex Best Bitter; 3 changing beers (sourced nationally) Ⓗ
A friendly drinkers' local celebrating its 21st consecutive year in the Guide. As well as the regular Harvey's Sussex Best Bitter, two or three changing cask ales are offered, often sourced locally. Food is not usually available other than packaged snacks. Beer festivals are held throughout the year, with up to 12 handpumps in operation. Two wood-burning stoves keep the pub warm in winter while the pleasant garden with extensive views is available for the warmer months. Q Ᏸ❀P❀

Crowborough Cross ✅
Beacon Road, TN6 1AF
☎ (01892) 662555
Greene King IPA, Abbot; Sharp's Doom Bar; 3 changing beers (sourced nationally) Ⓗ
A listed, late 18th-century, former coaching inn, this Wetherspoon pub is on three levels with a series of drinking booths behind the long bar. The guest ales are often from local breweries. Originally named the Red Cross, the use of this emblem was protected by the Geneva Conventions of 1949. The original name is thought to come from coach stopping points being marked by red crosses on maps for coachmen who were unable to read or write. Ᏸ❀◐&ᴀᴿ(29,228)☞

Wheatsheaf Ⓛ ✅
Mount Pleasant, TN6 2NF
☎ (01892) 663756 ⊕ wheatsheafcrowborough.co.uk
Harvey's Sussex Best Bitter; 2 changing beers (sourced locally; often Harvey's) Ⓗ
Downhill from the town centre and close to the station you can find the Wheatsheaf, a white weatherboarded Harvey's pub dating from the 1700s. Pictures of its history are to be found in each of the three seating areas surrounding a central bar. Real fires burn during winter months and there is an outside seating area with colourful hanging baskets during warmer times. Lunches are available from Tuesday to Saturday and evening meals from Tuesday to Friday.
Q Ᏸ❀◐≠♣P❀(228)❀☞♪

Danehill

Coach & Horses ★ Ⓛ
School Lane, RH17 7JF
☎ (01825) 740369 ⊕ coachandhorses.co
Harvey's Sussex Best Bitter; 1 changing beer (sourced locally; often 360 Degree, Long Man) Ⓗ
A traditional country pub dating from 1847 and retaining many original features. The public and saloon bars have real fires and simple farmhouse-style furniture. Locally produced Black Pig cider is always on the bar, and

occasionally its perry too. The separate restaurant area serves locally sourced, high-quality food. The large garden is a delight in summer and includes a children's play area. Convenient for nearby Ashdown Forest, Sheffield Park gardens and Bluebell Railway. Closed Monday and Tuesday. Q❀◐♣●P❀(270)❀☞

Ditchling

White Horse Ⓛ
16 West Street, BN6 8TS
☎ (01273) 842006 ⊕ whitehorseditchling.com
Harvey's Sussex Best Bitter; 3 changing beers (sourced locally; often Long Man, Three Acre) Ⓗ
This 12th-century inn lies below the parish church in the picturesque, historic village of Ditchling. Its cellar leads to a network of tunnels under the village, thought to have been used for smuggling in times past. The accommodation at the White Horse can cater for weddings, birthday parties or as a stopover while walking the South Downs Way. Log fires in winter, excellent food and ever-changing quality guest beers are certain to fortify the traveller.
Q Ᏸ❀≠◐P❀(167,168) ❀☞♪

Eastbourne

Beerarama
7B Bolton Road, BN21 3JU
☎ 07702 757916 ⊕ beerarama.co.uk
2 changing beers (often Abyss, Beak)
An inclusive welcoming craft beer bar which opened in the centre of town in 2022. Of the six beer lines at least two serve real ale from membrane kegs. Draft beers, bottles and cans are sourced from across the United Kingdom and include local offerings such as Abyss, Beak and Burning Sky. Real cider is served, usually locally made Ascension. There is occasional live music, vinyl DJs and a monthly quiz. Ᏸ❀◐≠♣●Ⓡ❀☞♪

Crown Ⓛ
22 Crown Street, Old Town, BN21 1PB
☎ (01323) 724654
Harvey's Sussex Best Bitter; Long Man Long Blonde Ⓗ**; Timothy Taylor Landlord** Ⓗ**/**Ⓖ**; 2 changing beers** Ⓖ
This popular and friendly pub is located in the Old Town area of Eastbourne and is a regular entry in the Guide. It has a range of well-kept beers from national and local brewers. Three or four beer festivals are held during the year. As well as the two main rooms in the pub, there is large garden, which is the site for occasional music concerts in summer months. Ᏸ❀Ⓡ❀☞♪

Hurst Arms Ⓛ
76 Willingdon Road, Ocklynge, BN21 1TW
☎ (01323) 419440 ⊕ thehurstarms.com
Harvey's Sussex Best Bitter; 4 changing beers (sourced locally; often Harvey's) Ⓗ
This classic two-bar public house serves the full range of Harvey's beer including some one-off seasonal beers. The pub has won many awards from CAMRA and appears in this Guide on a regular basis. The public bar hosts regular pool tournaments and darts matches. The quiet saloon bar is ideal for small groups meeting to discuss the latest topical issues of the day. The small, west-facing front garden catches the evening setting sun.
❀&♣P❀☞

Lamb Inn ★ Ⓛ ✅
36 High Street, Old Town, BN21 1HH
☎ (01323) 720545 ⊕ thelambeastbourne.co.uk

Harvey's Sussex Best Bitter, Armada Ale; 1 changing beer (sourced locally; often Harvey's) Ⓗ
A hospitable three-roomed historic pub with manager, Natalie, at the helm for 15 years. Taking pride in its beers, it serves well-regarded high-quality food. There is a first-floor function room with regular comedy, theatre and quizzes, along with live music downstairs. Four B&B rooms are named after Harvey's beers. Don't miss the illuminated well en-route to the toilets and, if it is not busy, ask to see the cellars and crypt dating back to 1180. ⏁❀✦❶⑀⬥⬥✦P🚆❀❀🎵

London & County Ⓛ ✅

46 Terminus Road, BN21 3LX
☎ (01323) 746310
Greene King Abbot; Ruddles Best Bitter; Sharp's Doom Bar; 3 changing beers (sourced nationally) Ⓗ
A Wetherspoon Lloyds No. 1 bar directly opposite Eastbourne railway station and close to bus stops. It has been listed in this Guide for over 10 years. The building is a former London and County Bank built in 1880. It has a two-storey layout, with the upper floor hireable for functions. There is some outside street seating. Good-value food is served all day. There is a DJ on Friday and Saturday evenings. ⏁❀❶⬥⬀🚆P❀

Ninkaci

Unit 9 The Enterprise Centre, BN21 1BD
☎ (01323) 573528
3 changing beers
A craft beer store and tap room recognised for local ale. It is located inside Eastbourne Enterprise Centre adjacent to the railway station, convenient for train and bus services. The centre, previously a goods depot for the former London, Brighton and South Coast Railway company now hosts independent shops and fooderies. Evening access when centre is closed is via a rear door. Real ale is dispensed from membrane kegs. There is a monthly jazz and soul club and a resident Saturday DJ.
❀⬀⬥❶🚆❀❀🎵

Ewhurst Green

White Dog Inn Ⓛ ✅

Village Street, TN32 5TD
☎ (01580) 830264 ⊕ thewhitedogewhurst.co.uk
Harvey's Sussex Best Bitter; house beer (by Rother Valley); 2 changing beers Ⓗ
Exposed beams, hops and horse brasses are part of the atmosphere of this traditional old English rural pub; split between bar, games room and restaurant, the latter having a large mural of Bodiam Castle on the wall. Here you'll find excellent food with ingredients sourced locally and scallops a speciality. Outside, overlooking Bodiam Castle, there is a wood-fired pizza oven with a bar. Weddings and functions are catered for with glamping available to hire. A beer festival is held in September. Q⏁❀⑀❶⚓⬥⬥P🚆(349)❀❀🎵

Falmer

Swan Inn ★ Ⓛ ✅

Middle Street, BN1 9PD (just off A27 in N of village)
☎ (01273) 681842
Palmers Tally Ho!; 5 changing beers (sourced regionally; often Downlands, Long Man, Palmers) Ⓗ
This is a traditional family-run free house in the village of Falmer near the universities. It has three bar areas and a barn with bar available for functions. Food is available, but check for times. The pub gets busy when Brighton and Hove Albion play at home. It opens at varying times on match days and will open in the event of Monday

evening games. There are small outside seating areas at both sides of the pub.
Q⏁❀❶⬥⬀⬥✦P🚆(28,29)❀❀🎵

Firle

Ram Inn ★ ✅

The Street, BN8 6NS
☎ (01273) 858222 ⊕ raminn.co.uk
Harvey's Sussex Best Bitter; 3 changing beers (sourced locally; often Burning Sky, Long Man) Ⓗ
Village pub convenient for walkers on the South Downs Way. Four handpumps often serve a beer from the nearby Burning Sky brewery, plus one other local ale and a cider or perry. The three main rooms all have an open fire. Families are most welcome, but children are not allowed in the bar area. There are large outside seating areas to the side and rear of the pub. A restaurant-style menu is offered. Glynde station 20 minutes' walk away. ⏁❀⑀❶⬥✦P🚆(125,125)❀❀

Framfield

Hare & Hounds Ⓛ

The Street, TN22 5NJ
☎ (01825) 890118 ⊕ hareandhounds.net
Harvey's Sussex Best Bitter; 1 changing beer (sourced locally) Ⓗ
Warm, family-friendly village pub dating from 1428, the bar features a snug sofa area with low beams, eclectic knick-knacks and a large inglenook fireplace. Food is served lunchtime and evenings Tuesday to Saturday, with a roast on Sundays. Parking is extensive, children can enjoy the garden play area and there are regular gigs and open mic nights. Local beer is from Three Acre, local cider from Big Nose & Beardy. Local CAMRA Pub of the Year 2020-2022. Q⏁❀❀❶⬥⚓⬥P🚆❀❀🎵

Hadlow Down

New Inn ★ Ⓛ

Main Road, TN22 4HJ (on the 272)
Harvey's Sisters, Sussex Best Bitter; 1 changing beer (often Harvey's) Ⓗ
A traditional village pub with important historic pub interior fittings such as ceramic spirit casks and a panelled counter dating from 1885 when the pub was rebuilt following a fire. This is a no-frills venue designed for good company and good conversation – there is no room here for machines or music! Renowned locally for excellently kept beer and a warm welcome. No food is available apart from bar snacks. This is a cash only pub – no card payments accepted. Q⏁⚓⬥P🚆(248)❀🎵

Hailsham

George Hotel Ⓛ ✅

3 George Street, BN27 1AD
☎ (01323) 445120
Greene King Abbot; Ruddles Best Bitter; Sharp's Doom Bar; 2 changing beers (sourced nationally) Ⓗ
A town-centre pub, convenient for local shops and businesses, popular with locals especially at the weekends when families often visit. As a Wetherspoon pub, it always serves the three regular ales, a real cider or perry and at least two guest beers, at least one being local. There is plenty of outdoor sitting, both in the garden and on a side terrace. It celebrated 10 years in this Guide in 2024, an achievement proudly displayed on the handpumps. Q⏁❀❶⬥⬥🚆P❀

Hastings

Albion ★ 🅛

33 George Street, Old Town, TN34 3EA

☎ (01424) 439156 ⊕ albionhastings.com

Harvey's Sussex Best Bitter; 3 changing beers (sourced nationally; often Lakedown) 🅗

This Old Town pub has established a reputation with its award-winning pies and pasties. It has been identified by CAMRA as having a nationally important pub interior, with attractive wooden panelling containing clan tartans, dating from when it was owned by Youngers of Edinburgh, and a rare zinc-covered bar. There are acoustic live folk and skiffle performances on Tuesday and Saturday. Food is also served from the Pasty Shack on the seafront side of the pub. 🅠🕿🕯🌢♣🍴🚍🐾🛜🎵

Dolphin 🅛 ⊘

11-12 Rock-A-Nore Road, Old Town, TN34 3DW

☎ (01424) 434326 ⊕ thedolphinpub.co.uk

360 Degree Bluebell Best; Dark Star Hophead; Harvey's Sussex Best Bitter; Young's London Special; 3 changing beers (sourced nationally) 🅗

This cosy 18th-century pub, often used as the start or end point of pub tours of Hastings, is located at the eastern end of town, adjacent to the iconic net drying huts and the home of the beach-launched fishing fleet. Filled with lovely memorabilia associated with the fishing community, the pub offers a range of weekly activities, with bingo on Tuesday, a quiz on Thursday and a meat raffle on Sunday, as well as regular live music. 🅠🕿🕯🍴🚍🐾🛜🎵

Jenny Lind ★ 🅛 ⊘

69 High Street, Old Town, TN34 3EW

☎ (01424) 421392 ⊕ jennylindhastings.co.uk

Greene King Abbot; Gun Project Babylon Pale Ale; Long Man Best Bitter; 5 changing beers (often 360 Degree) 🅗

In the centre of the Old Town the pub has a large front bar, used for popular live music events including the Fat Tuesday tour. Completely Scuppered Shanty Men perform every Tuesday. The cosy back bar, favoured by locals, has an open fire and bar billiards table. Stairs lead to the attractive terraced rear gardens. Up to 10 handpumps are available. The pub also has an annual dark beer festival and is a participant in the Hastings Tap Takeover held each October. 🅠🕿🕯🍴♣🐾🚍🐾🛜🎵

Jolly Fisherman 🅛

3 East Beach Street, Old Town, TN34 3AR

☎ (01424) 428811 ⊕ jollyfishermanhastings.com

2 changing beers (sourced nationally) 🅟

Hastings first micropub has an attractively decorated frontage and once stood right on the quayside. Historic black and white photographs show the pub's long-standing links to the fishing community. A quirky mix of furniture helps create a friendly environment with a wood-burning stove taking centre stage in winter. Seven craft keg and two cask ales are regularly available as well as seven ciders. The pub participates in the Hastings Tap Takeover and the Old Town Cider Festival. 🕿♣🐾🚍🐾🛜

Hove

Foghorn 🍺 🅛

55 Boundary Road, BN3 4EF

☎ (01273) 419362 ⊕ thefoghornmicro.com

5 changing beers (sourced regionally; often Burning Sky, Only With Love) 🅖

This popular micropub has become an established part of the local scene since it opened in 2018 The single bar is filled with wooden tables and seating, including tall stools. Beers and real ciders are dispensed from a chilled stillroom to the rear of the bar. The pub is often busy with a vibrant and welcoming atmosphere created by the friendly local crowd. Local CAMRA Pub of the Year 2024. Occasional pop-up food vans operate at the side of the pub. 🅠🕿🕯🕭(Portslade)🐾🚍🐾🛜

Neptune Inn 🅛 ⊘

10 Victoria Terrace, BN3 2WB (on the coast road E of King Alfred leisure complex)

☎ (01273) 736390 ⊕ theneptunelivemusicbar.co.uk

Harvey's Sussex Best Bitter; 4 changing beers (sourced locally; often Burning Sky, Long Man) 🅗

This is a traditional single-bar Victorian pub, close to the King Alfred centre and Hove seafront, committed to serving high-quality real ale. A reclining figure of Neptune rests above the old Courage signage at the front. Five beers are available including ever-changing guests, plus an occasional real cider during the summer months. Dogs are welcome. Live music features strongly with blues or rock every Friday and jazz Sundays; see the website for details. 🚍(700)🐾🎵

Poets Ale & Smoke House 🅛

33 Montgomery Street, BN3 5BF

☎ (01273) 272212 ⊕ thepoets.pub

Harvey's IPA, Sussex Best Bitter; 3 changing beers (sourced locally; often Harvey's) 🅗

This is a street-corner Harvey's tied house in the Poets Corner District of Hove, managed by a local pub company. The public bar shows sports events on a big screen TV whereas the saloon is quieter. There is outside seating at the front and a patio area to the rear. An extensive food menu, including vegetarian and vegan options, is served Monday to Saturday plus roasts on Sunday. A function room is available upstairs. 🕯🍴🕭(Aldrington)🚍🐾

Watchmaker's Arms 🅛

84 Goldstone Villas, BN3 3RU

☎ (01273) 776307 ⊕ thewatchmakersarms.co.uk

5 changing beers (sourced regionally; often Downlands, Fyne Ales, Watchmaker's Arms) 🅖

This micropub has a small outside seating area on the pavement outside the premises with two tables, which are well-used. The pub generally has four cask beers on sale, served from a cold room behind the bar, these rotate fortnightly. Details of beers currently on sale are given on the pub website. The cask beers are almost always from small breweries, with many from Sussex, Hampshire, and Kent. Real cider is also always available, mainly sourced from local producers. 🅠♣🚍(7,21)🐾🛜

Icklesham

Queen's Head 🅛

Parsonage Lane, TN36 4BL (opp village hall)

☎ (01424) 814552 ⊕ queenshead.com

Greene King Abbot; Harvey's Sussex Best Bitter; 2 changing beers (sourced locally) 🅗

Built in 1632 as two dwellings before becoming a pub in 1831, this delightful 17th-century inn has been in this Guide for over 40 years. Open fires, excellent good-value home-made food, two beer gardens, a pétanque piste and superb views over the Brede Valley all make it popular with locals, walkers on the nearby 1066 Country Walk and other visitors. There is live music most Sundays and a fortnightly pub quiz. 🅠🕿🕯🍴♣🐾🚍(100)🐾🛜🎵

Robin Hood 🅛

Main Road, TN36 4BD (on A259; W end of village)

☎ (01424) 814277

4 changing beers (sourced nationally; often Greene King) ⊞
This warm, friendly locals' pub dating from the 17th century has a striking ceiling display of hops, coppers and brasses built up over the past 20 years. There is an open fire and a large dining area to the rear offering home-cooked food. Usually four real ales, including at least one local real ale, and up to 12 real ciders are served. The pub has a pool table, and its large garden has a children's play area. Camper vans can be accommodated by prior arrangement. Local CAMRA Cider Pub of the Year 2024.
Q❄❀◐よ♣♠P🚲(100) ❀🐾🛜

Isfield

Laughing Fish 🅛 ✅
Station Road, TN22 5XB (off A26 between Lewes and Uckfield)
☎ (01825) 750349 ⊕ laughingfishisfield.com
Long Man Best Bitter; 2 changing beers (sourced locally; often Gun, Long Man) ⊞
Formerly the Half Moon, then the Station Hotel, this 1860s pub is next to the preserved Lavender Line. WWII brought the custom of Canadian troops, not without incident. In the 1950s it was the HQ of the District Angling Club, the probable origin of the present name. The beers are from the SIBA portfolio of Sussex breweries. Good pub food is served it has a range of games including bar billiards. There is quiz night and occasional live music events.
❄❀◐よ▲♣♠P🚲(29) ❀🛜

Lewes

Black Horse 🅛
55 Western Road, BN7 1RS
☎ (01273) 473653 ⊕ blackhorselewes.co.uk
Burning Sky Plateau; Harvey's Sussex Best Bitter; 3 changing beers (sourced regionally) ⊞
A Greene King Local Heroes pub that allows the licensee to source and stock Sussex ales and produce. This traditional community pub in the western end of the town has feature bay windows and a large main bar with a real fire together with a quieter back bar. Four TVs show most sporting events. Home-made food includes vegan options. The pub's teams play a wide variety of games including toad-in-the-hole, cribbage and cricket.
❄❀◐よ♣🚲(28,29) ❀🛜

Brewers Arms 🅛
91 High Street, BN7 1XN (near Lewes Castle)
☎ (01273) 475524 ⊕ thebrewersarmslewes.com
Harvey's Sussex Best Bitter; 4 changing beers (sourced regionally; often Burning Sky, Gun, Harvey's) ⊞
A two-bar pub with separate characteristics, the front bar being quiet and more food-oriented with the back bar offering darts and pool. There is an annual beer festival. Can you spot the bull? The pub has a stoolball team and is popular on match days with Lewes FC, Brighton and Hove Albion and away fans. Food, including traditional breakfasts, is served until evening. The exterior features the former owners Page & Overton's Croydon Ales signage. ❀◐≠♣♠🚲(28,29)❀🛜

Dorset 🅛 ✅
22 Malling Street, BN7 2RD
☎ (01273) 474823 ⊕ thedorsetlewes.co.uk
Harvey's Sussex Best Bitter; 3 changing beers (sourced locally; often Harvey's) ⊞
Refurbished in 2006, this Harvey's tied house has several drinking and dining areas, a large patio and six

reasonably priced en-suite bedrooms. It serves up to four ales on handpump. An extensive menu features traditional home-cooked dishes and an ever-changing fish menu using ingredients fresh from Newhaven. It is the home of the Cliffe Bonfire Society – the largest of the five Lewes bonfire societies. ❀🛏◐よ≠♣🚲(28,29)

Elephant & Castle 🅛
White Hill, BN7 2DJ (off Fisher St, near old police station)
☎ (01273) 473797
Harvey's Sussex Best Bitter; 4 changing beers (sourced nationally) ⊞
A spacious pub with three rooms able to show football, rugby, and other sports in different areas. On Thursday a large selection of craft bottled and canned beer is available to consume on the premises at take-away prices. There is a large function room upstairs available for hire. The pub is home to a number of clubs including the Commercial Square Bonfire Society. Folk Club is on a Saturday. The food is locally sourced.
❀◐≠♣🚲(127,132) 🛜

Gardener's Arms 🅛
46 Cliffe High Street, BN7 2AN
☎ (01273) 474808
Harvey's Sussex Best Bitter; 5 changing beers (sourced nationally; often Gun, Harvey's, Rother Valley) ⊞
A traditional, genuine free house near Harvey's brewery in Cliffe High Street. It is a one-roomed pub with a wooden floor and central bar. Five changing guest ales are dispensed, generally sourced from small breweries across the country, and a real cider is always available. A dark beer festival is held in March. The pub is popular with Lewes and Brighton FC fans on match days. No children allowed, but dogs are made welcome. Outside seating is at the front and side of premises.
≠♣♠🚲(28,29) ❀🛜

John Harvey Tavern 🅛 ✅
1 Bear Yard, Cliffe High Street, BN7 2AN (opp Harveys Brewery)
☎ (01273) 479880 ⊕ johnharveytavern.co.uk
Harvey's IPA ⊞, Sussex Best Bitter Ⓖ, Armada Ale ⊞; 3 changing beers (sourced locally; often Harvey's) ⊞/Ⓖ
Housed in a former stable block of the Bear Inn, opposite Harvey's brewery and next to the River Ouse. The bar boasts wooden beams, a slate floor, log burner and two large wine vats converted to cosy seating areas. Children are only allowed in the restaurant. There is a large function/dining room upstairs. The outside tables are a suntrap in summer and therefore popular. There is live music on the last Saturday of every month.
Q❄◐≠♣🚲(28,29) ❀🛜♪

Lansdown Arms 🅛
36 Lansdown Place, BN7 2JU
☎ (01273) 470711
Harvey's Sussex Best Bitter; Timothy Taylor Landlord; Thornbridge Jaipur; 1 changing beer (sourced locally; often Gun, Long Man) ⊞
Close to the railway station at the foot of a steep hill, this smallish pub is popular with fans and visitors to both Lewes FC and Brighton and Hove Albion on match days. Simply furnished, this dark and cosy pub was built in 1827, before the arrival of the railway in Lewes, and was, at one time, a Whitbread house. It hosts popular live music, regularly featuring local bands, and has a free jukebox. Local artists work is displayed on the walls.
❄◐≠🚲❀🛜♪

Lewes Arms ★ L ✔

1 Mount Place, BN7 1YH

☎ (01273) 473152 🌐 lewesarms.co.uk

Dark Star Hophead; Fuller's London Pride; Gale's Seafarers Ale, HSB; Harvey's Sussex Best Bitter; 2 changing beers (sourced regionally) H

This characterful corner pub comprises three small rooms plus a central lobby with serving hatch, upstairs function room containing a small theatre stage and an outside terrace. Toad-in-the-hole is played here. The food offering is limited to pizza. The pub is home to the world pea-throwing championship, dwyle flunking, spaniel racing and other unusual events. A three-day music festival is hosted in August and an annual pantomime in March. Occasionally a real cider is available.

Q🐴❀◑≠♣🚌(28,29)🐾📶♫

Royal Oak L

3 Station Street, BN7 2DA

☎ (01273) 474803 🌐 royaloaklewes.co.uk

Harvey's Sussex Best Bitter; 3 changing beers (sourced nationally; often Bedlam) H

This single-room pub at the top of the station hill is the birthplace of Lewes FC (1875) and home to the Waterloo Bonfire Society. The good food is complemented by a range of five beers, with usually at least one from Bedlam. The function room upstairs has its own bar which hosts regular live music sessions. There are DJs in the bar on Friday nights and sometimes karaoke sessions. At the back is a 'secret' garden.

❀◑≠♣🚌🐾📶♫

Litlington

Plough & Harrow ★ L ✔

The Street, BN26 5RE

☎ (01323) 870632 🌐 ploughandharrowlitlington.co.uk

Long Man Best Bitter, Rising Giant; 3 changing beers (sourced locally; often Long Man) H

Parts of this pub, situated in a valley cutting through the South Downs, date from the 17th century. It has with a large bar and a small cosy snug and is tied to the Long Man brewery from the same village. Of its six handpumps five follow the tie with the sixth having an occasional guest from another local source. It is popular with locals and tourists alike, including walkers on the Downs. Good quality food is served daily.

🐴❀◑♣P🚌🐾📶♫

Pett

Royal Oak L ✔

Pett Road, TN35 4HG

☎ (01424) 812515 🌐 royaloakpett.com

Harvey's Sussex Best Bitter; 3 changing beers (sourced locally) H

The Oak is a lovely 18th-century Grade II-listed building with a good selection of four local beers. Regular live music and quizzes feature. There is a separate dining area, and an extensive menu of quality food is on offer. There is a warming inglenook fireplace but mind your head on the low beams! The pub supports the Pett Level Rescue Boat Charity. It has a large, pleasant garden with a pétanque pisté. Q🐴❀◑♠P🚌(347)🐾📶♫

Portslade

Stags Head Inn L

35 High Street, Old Portslade, BN41 2LH

☎ (01273) 973799

Harvey's Sussex Best Bitter; 2 changing beers (sourced nationally; often Long Man) H

This friendly, traditional two-bar local in the heart of Portslade Old Village was formerly the brewery tap for the Dudney brewery (closed 1930), the buildings of which still stand nearby. There is a comfortably furnished saloon bar with a larger public bar extended to the rear. The regular beer is from Sussex with guests either sourced locally or from farther afield. Note the old Watney's and Tamplins signage behind each bar.

🐴❀♣🚌(1,1A)🐾📶

Stanley Arms L

47 Wolseley Road, BN41 1SS (on corner of Wolseley Rd and Stanley Rd)

☎ (01273) 701738

Harvey's Sussex Best Bitter; 4 changing beers (sourced regionally; often Downlands, Harvey's, Long Man) H

A good, old-fashioned, back-street pub, this two-bar gem is the hub of the community. Five beers are served, mainly but not exclusively from Sussex brewers and always including a dark beer. Quiz night is every Wednesday, live music on Friday and Saturday, with Open Mic nights every other Thursday plus live TV sports. A colourful heated patio smoking area is a feature. Children are welcome until 9pm. Takeaway food can be delivered to the pub.

🐴❀≠(Fishersgate)♣🚌(2,46)🐾📶♫

Robertsbridge

George Inn L

High Street, TN32 5AW

☎ (01580) 880315 🌐 thegeorgerobertsbridge.co.uk

Harvey's Sussex Best Bitter; 2 changing beers (sourced locally) H

The George is an imposing building with a red-tiled front that faces the centre of the village with views down the High Street and of the distinctive war memorial clock tower. There is a good-sized comfortable bar with a dining area to the left. This 18th-century coaching inn has a friendly relaxed atmosphere, enhanced by the warming inglenook fireplace. There are regular events held, with details available on the website. Breakfast is available to non-residents. 🐴❀🛏◑♿≠P🚌🐾📶♫

Rotherfield

King's Arms 🏆 L

High Street, TN6 3LJ

☎ (01892) 853441 🌐 katn6.com

Harvey's Sussex Best Bitter; 3 changing beers (sourced locally) H

This 17th-century coaching inn in the heart of an historic village features an extensive terrace and gardens offering unspoilt views over the surrounding countryside. Inglenook fireplaces warm diners in winter months, whilst the gardens offer ample space for alfresco dining. Beers and food served from their varied menu are usually sourced locally, with fresh eggs coming from the pub's own chickens. Q🐴❀◑♿♣P🚌(252)🐾📶♫

Rye

Waterworks L

Tower Street, TN31 7AT

☎ (01797) 224110 🌐 ryewaterworks.co.uk

Waterworks Golden Flush, UrRYEnal, I Pee A Lot, Pissoir; 3 changing beers (sourced locally) G

Over its 300-year history the building has been the town's pumphouse, soup kitchen and toilets. Reinvented as a micropub in 2018, the well, soup coppers and open fireplace remain as features. A friendly welcome and award-winning Scotch eggs and pork pies are always available. The Sunday lunchtime cheese club has strict rules: 'Bring cheese. Eat cheese. No cheese? Hard cheese, you're not in the club!' Local CAMRA Cider Pub of the Year 2023. Q ▧ 🛇 🟎 ♣ ♠ 🎗 🟎 ❖ 🛈

St Leonards on Sea

Nag's Head 🗓

8-9 Gensing Road, TN38 0ER
☎ (01424) 445973
Harvey's Sussex Best Bitter; 3 changing beers (sourced locally; often Gun, Long Man) ⊞
Well worth finding, this historic back-street local is where author of The Ragged-Trousered Philanthropists, Robert Tressell used to drink. The front entrance leads into the U-shaped bar with its relaxed atmosphere. There is a pleasant courtyard at the back of the pub. A fair pricing structure is in place and a local beer is always on tap on one of the five handpumps. There is live music every Saturday and Sunday and regular quizzes are held. Q ▧ 🛇 🟎 ≉ (Warrior Square) 🟎 ❖ 🛈

Tower

251 London Road, Bohemia, TN37 6NB
☎ (01424) 721773
Dark Star Hophead; Fuller's ESB; 5 changing beers (sourced nationally) ⊞
This lively community pub has a U-shaped bar, traditional décor, sofas and a wood-burning stove, all creating a convivial atmosphere. It regularly hosts live music, holds a popular beer festival in February, and organises occasional visits to breweries and sporting events. Sports fans can view all main football, rugby and cricket matches alongside other sports. Seven cask ales and at least six ciders are on offer. The pub celebrated 10 consecutive years in this Guide in 2023.
▧ ≉ (Warrior Square) ♣ ● 🛈 🟎 ❖ 🛈 🛈

Salehurst

Salehurst Halt 🗓

Church Lane, TN32 5PH (follow Church Ln from the A21 Robertsbridge roundabout)
☎ (01580) 880620 ⊕ salehursthalt.co.uk
Harvey's Sussex Best Bitter; 2 changing beers (sourced locally) ⊞
A family-run, friendly free house, keeping the atmosphere of a country pub with hops above the bar, exposed beams, farmhouse chairs, scrubbed tables and settees. The Halt is committed to serving local ales and ciders, and diners have a daily changing blackboard menu with an ethos of big flavours and rough edges, locally sourced where possible. Upstairs there is an events room for weddings and private parties. The cottage garden has delightful views across the Rother Valley countryside. Q ▧ 🛇 🟎 ♣ ● ❖ 🛈 🛈

Seaford

Old Boot Inn 🗓

16 South Street, BN25 1PE
☎ (01323) 895454
Harvey's Sussex Best Bitter; 4 changing beers (sourced regionally; often 360 Degree, Gun, Harvey's) ⊞
This deceptively large pub, under the same ownership as the Gardener's Arms in Lewes, has entrances in both South Street and High Street. Wheelchair access is possible. There are plenty of tables and food is served, with a wide range of roasts on Sundays. Harvey's Best Bitter is always to be found on one of the six handpumps

along with Old Ale in season. Four ever-changing guests and six bag in box ciders complete the range.
▧ 🛇 🟎 🛇 ≉ ● 🟎 ❖ 🛈 🛈

Steamworks 🗓

Cafe Unit, Seaford Station, Station Approach, BN25 2AR
☎ (01323) 895541
4 changing beers (sourced locally; often 360 Degree, Bedlam, Long Man) 🄶
Right on the station platform the Steamworks is a two-room buffet bar which is busy with coffee service to the early morning commuters and then becomes a micropub with four interesting, normally local, beers dispensed using an unusual gravity system. The décor and furniture is distressed industrial sanded-down woodwork as if the Ragged Trousered Philanthropists had only recently left! Entrance is both from the street and station platform. Cider is Silly Moo. Snack food, such as pasties, is available. Q ▧ 🛇 ≉ ● 🟎 ❖ 🛈

SUSSEX (WEST)

Arundel

King's Arms 🗓

36 Tarrant Street, BN18 9DN
☎ (01903) 885569
Fuller's London Pride; 4 changing beers (sourced regionally) ⊞
The King's Arms is the oldest pub in Arundel, dating from circa 1625. Situated in a small but vibrant street off the High Street this is a lively drinker's pub where conversation rules. Popular with locals and visitors alike it has two bars and a patio garden with a smoking area. No food is served but customers can bring their own. The pub is involved in many of the events that take place in the town. A wide selection of non-alcoholic drinks is served. Q ▧ 🛇 🟎 ♣ 🟎 (85) ❖ 🛈

Ashurst

Fountain Inn 🗓

Horsham Road, BN44 3AP (on the B2135)
☎ (01403) 710219 ⊕ fountainashurst.com
Harvey's Sussex Best Bitter; 3 changing beers (sourced locally; often Long Man) ⊞
The Fountain is a Grade II-listed building dating back to the 17th century. It has two bars plus a restaurant with flagstone flooring, exposed beams and an open fire. The large garden has a barn which doubles as a skittle alley and function room. The pub is popular as a classic car and bike rendezvous point. Q ▧ 🛇 🟎 ♣ 🛇 ♣ P 🟎 (17) ❖ 🛈

Barns Green

Queen's Head 🗓

Chapel Road, RH13 0PS
☎ (01403) 730436 ⊕ thequeensheadbarnsgreen.co.uk
Dark Star Hophead; Harvey's Sussex Best Bitter; 1 changing beer (sourced regionally) ⊞
A cosy 17th-century village pub, with old timber beams and a large inglenook fireplace used in winter. It is mainly open plan, with three seating areas and a small separate room. A garden with a covered seating area is at the back. There is a quiz night on the second Tuesday of the month, an open mic night on the first Thursday of the month, and a charity coffee morning on the last Friday of the month. Q ▧ 🛇 🟎 🛇 ♣ P 🟎 ❖ 🛈 🛈

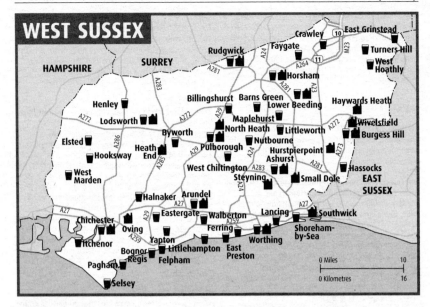

WEST SUSSEX

Billingshurst

Billi Tap 🅛
44 High Street, RH14 9NY
2 changing beers (often Brolly, Little Monster) 🅗
Opened in 2021, this welcoming High Street micropub is the brewery tap for Brolly and Little Monster breweries, with two cask ales and eight keg lines, mainly from those brewers. The beer range is ever-changing, usually with a local cider and a well-stocked fridge of cans as well. Food is provided some days, particularly Saturdays, by food trucks that park behind the pub, with a Sunday cheeseboard (check social media for more information). You are also welcome to eat local takeaways in the pub. Closed Mondays. Q🛏♣🚪(100)♣

Bognor Regis

Dog & Duck 🅛
3 The Steyne, PO21 1TX
☎ (01243) 865751
3 changing beers (sourced regionally; often Goldmark, Staggeringly Good, Triple fff) 🅗
This old pub, formerly the Star & Garter, then the Elizabeth II, is now the home of a micropub that moved in 2023. Three changing cask ales are served, one usually a stronger beer. There is a friendly atmosphere with tasters available from knowledgeable staff. Regular tap takeovers are held for local brewers. There is also a large range of interesting bottled and canned beers from local and regional breweries. Closed Mondays.
🛏🍴🚪(600)♣🛜♪

Hatter's Inn
2-10 Queensway, PO21 1QT (at W end of High St opp Iceland)
☎ (01243) 840206
Greene King Abbot; Ruddles Best Bitter; Sharp's Doom Bar; 3 changing beers (sourced nationally) 🅗
Large town-centre Wetherspoon that was formerly a Sainsbury's store, part of a concrete 60s retail development at one end of the main shopping street. The usual Wetherspoon beer range of regulars plus changing guests (sourced from a national list) can be found, plus good-value food all day. There is a large patio garden for outside drinking as well as offering a smokers' area. Public parking is available in Queensway car park or the adjacent multi-storey. 🛏❀🕭♿🚲🚪🛜

Burgess Hill

Six Gold Martlets ❷
49-51 Church Walk, RH15 9AE
☎ (01444) 231250
Greene King Abbot, IPA; Sharp's Doom Bar; 6 changing beers (sourced nationally) 🅗
Situated in the pedestrianised heart of the town's shopping area, this is a shop conversion that has had

REAL ALE BREWERIES
Adur Steyning
Aleworks Horsham (NEW)
Arundel ✦ Arundel
Bestens ✦ Burgess Hill
Blue Shed Horsham (NEW)
Brewery 288 Heath End
Brewhouse & Kitchen 🍺 Horsham
Brewhouse & Kitchen 🍺 Worthing
Brolly ✦ Horsham
Cloak & Dagger Worthing
Downlands Small Dole
Escapist Chichester
Fauna ✦ Arundel
Firebird ✦ Rudgwick
Goldmark Arundel
Gribble 🍺 Oving
Hairy Dog ✦ Wivelsfield
Heathen ✦ Haywards Heath
Hepworth ✦ North Heath
Horsham ✦ Horsham
Hurst Hurstpierpoint
Kissingate ✦ Lower Beeding
Langham Lodsworth
North Garden Burgess Hill (NEW)
Pin-Up Southwick
Ridgeway Pulborough
Sussex Small Batch Arundel
Top-Notch Haywards Heath
Wingtip Ashurst

many incarnations, including Curry's and Woolworths; it adjoins the Martlets and Marketplace shopping centres. The interior decoration commemorates the area's pottery and brickmaking industrial heritage. The name comes from the heraldic arms of Sussex. The town of Burgess Hill straddles the East/West Sussex border. ざ❶&≭⊟令

Byworth

Black Horse Inn 🄻

The Street, GU28 0HL (leave Petworth going E on the A283 for about 1 mile then right into The Street) SU987211

☎ (01798) 342424 ∰ blackhorsebyworth.co.uk

Hogs Back TEA; Young's London Original; 2 changing beers (sourced locally; often Arundel) Ⓗ

Friendly, unspoilt Grade II-listed village pub dating from 1791. Inside, this untouched 16th-century inn has the perfect olde-worlde country look and feel. The front bar has a traditional atmosphere with its large fireplace and real fire in winter. Old photographs and prints hang on the walls. The bar is separate from the restaurant and has an excellent selection of beer which changes regularly and is sourced from local breweries. A Guide regular, and previous local CAMRA Pub of the Year. Q ざ ⊛❶♣●P⊟(1) ❀令

Chichester

Bell Inn

3 Broyle Road, PO19 6AT (on A286 just N of Northgate, ½ mile from station)

☎ (01243) 783388 ∰ thebellinnchichester.com

3 changing beers (sourced locally; often Goldmark, Langham, Staggeringly Good) Ⓗ

Cosy and comfortable city local with a traditional ambience enhanced by exposed brickwork, wood panelling and beams. A rear patio garden with covered smoking area is heated in winter. The pub tends to be busiest when the Festival Theatre is open, pre- and post-show. The three beers are from mostly Sussex and Hampshire micros, complemented by a monthly changing food menu. There is a small parking area and a public car park opposite. Closed on Monday in winter. Q ざ ⊛❶P⊟(60) ❀令♫

Chichester Inn 🄻

38 West Street, PO19 1RP (at Westgate roundabout)

☎ (01243) 783185 ∰ chichesterinn.co.uk

Harvey's Sussex Best Bitter; 3 changing beers (sourced regionally; often Langham, Vibrant Forest) Ⓗ

Pleasant two-bar pub with a real fire in the front bar surrounded by comfortable chairs, and a mix of seating and table types elsewhere. The larger public bar to the rear features regular live music on Monday, Friday, and Saturday evenings. Outside is an attractive walled garden with a heated and covered smoking area. Four B&B rooms are available. Food includes Sunday lunches. The well-kept real ales include LocAles, and darker beers appear regularly. ⊛⊷❶≭♣●P⊟❀令♫

Eastgate

4 The Hornet, PO19 7JG (500yds E of Market Cross)

☎ (01243) 774877 ∰ eastgatechichester.co.uk

Dark Star Hophead; Fuller's London Pride; Gale's Seafarers Ale, HSB; 1 changing beer (sourced nationally; often Fuller's) Ⓗ

Welcoming town pub with an open-plan bar and tables for diners. Good quality traditional pub meals are served daily. There is a heated patio garden to the rear, which is

the venue for a beer festival in July. The pub attracts locals, holidaymakers, and shoppers from the nearby market, with a warm welcome and traditional pub games such as darts, cribbage, and pool. Music is turned up on Friday and Saturday late evenings, while live bands perform once a month. ざ⊛❶♣⊟❀令♫

Escapist

Crane Street, PO19 1LJ (turn W halfway up North St from Chichester Cross)

☎ (01243) 776599 ∰ theescapistchichester.co.uk

6 changing beers (often Escapist, Howling Hops, Liquid Light) Ⓚ

A micropub in a pedestrianised road off North Street. The draught offering consists of six taps pouring keg and KeyKeg beers, usually with at least one from their own microbrewery. There is also a wide choice of canned beer. No food is served except crisps and nuts, but you are spoilt for choice of cafés in the neighbourhood. There is currently seating for about 20 in the well-ventilated interior and a little more outside when weather permits. The atmosphere is enhanced by interesting music played unobtrusively. ざ❶&≭●P⊟(700)❀令♫

Hole in the Wall

1A St Martins Street, PO19 1NP (just off East St, almost opp the back door to Marks & Spencer)

☎ (01243) 788877 ∰ theholeinthewall-pub.co.uk

Big Smoke Solaris Session Pale Ale; Harvey's Sussex Best Bitter; 3 changing beers (sourced nationally; often Big Smoke) Ⓗ

The building is believed to have started as a 17th-century brewery and was later used as a debtors' prison. This traditional pub is now knocked-through, wrapping around the bar to form three areas featuring brick pillars and painted wood panelling, creating a cosy, friendly atmosphere. There are two open fires in winter. Operated by Big Smoke Brewing Company, there are 12 handpumps, including four for real cider, plus a keg wall with 20 craft beers. ざ⊛❶≭●P⊟❀令♫

Little Monster Tap

23 The Hornet, PO19 7JL (from the Market Cross head due E)

☎ (01243) 696387 ∰ littlemonsterbrew.com

3 changing beers (sourced nationally) Ⓖ

This busy split-level micropub whose brewery is situated about five miles north of the city, has plenty of standing room at the bar in addition to seating both downstairs and upstairs. Staff are friendly and knowledgeable. There are 10 taps for Little Monster keg beers as well as the cask offering, and a large range of interesting canned ales and foreign beers. The pub offers Meet the Brewer sessions, quizzes and music nights. Q ざ●⊟❀令

Crawley

Brewery Shades 🄻

85 High Street, RH10 1BA

☎ (01293) 514255 ∰ breweryshades.co.uk

Timothy Taylor Landlord; 7 changing beers (sourced regionally; often Vocation) Ⓗ

Possibly the oldest building in Crawley High Street, the pub dates back to the 1400s and comes complete with two active ghosts. The licensee has a true passion and skill for the trade, demonstrated by the inspired range of up to eight guest ales and up to six ciders, plus keg and cans. At least one dark ale is usually on. Good food is served during the day and evening – check the specials board. ざ⊛❶≭●⊟令

East Grinstead

Engine Room ▼ Ⓛ
The Old Mill, 45 London Road, RH19 1AW
☎ (01342) 327145 ⊕ theengineroomeg.com
5 changing beers (sourced locally) Ⓖ
Up a path between the shops close to Whitehall bus stop in London Road, the pub is a downstairs labyrinth of small seating areas, good for small groups to hold conversations. Between five and seven ever-changing cask ales are served on gravity, plus four via membrane keg and six or seven ciders. Beer festivals held in March and October. Live music is on Tuesday evenings. Due to the location downstairs, access is not disability friendly. Closed Mondays. Q ≠●⑪🗑🛜♪

Old Dunnings Mill Ⓛ ✅
Dunnings Road, RH19 4AT
☎ (01342) 821080 ⊕ olddunningsmill.co.uk
Harvey's Sussex Best Bitter; 3 changing beers (often Harvey's) Ⓗ
Originally a 15th-century mill before being converted into a pub in 1970, it has been adapted and extended over the years and is now a cosy and welcoming pub owned by Harvey's of Lewes. The upper level is a large bar with dining area attached, and there are more dining areas on the lower levels. There is a large garden in front and a patio with a modern waterwheel to the rear. Families and pets are welcome. 🐕❀◑ⓓ&P🗑(84)❀🛜♪

East Preston

SP Alehouse
23 Sea Road, BN16 1JN
☎ 07736 928347
House beer (by Langham); 1 changing beer (often Firebird) Ⓖ
This friendly micropub in East Preston opened in 2020. It is nicely decorated with much wood in view plus pumpclips on the walls and mixture of high- and low-level seating inside. It sells the house beer, plus cask ales from a cool room behind the bar, mainly sourced from local breweries. At least four good quality craft keg beers are available, plus cider, wines, gin, soft drinks and a traditional mead. Bar snacks are available with a free cheeseboard on a Sunday. ♣●🗑(700)❀

Eastergate

Wilkes Head Ⓛ ✅
Church Lane, PO20 3UT (off A29 in old village, 350yds S of B2233 roundabout, 1½ miles W of Barnham station) SU943053
☎ (01243) 543380 ⊕ thewilkeshead.co.uk
Flower Pots Pots Bitter; 5 changing beers (sourced nationally; often Palmers, Timothy Taylor) Ⓗ
Small Grade II-listed red-brick pub built in 1803 and named after 18th-century radical John Wilkes. There is a cosy lounge left of the central bar and to the right a larger room with inglenook fireplace. There is a separate restaurant, and a permanent marquee with seating outside in the large garden. Regular beer and cider festivals are held, and six real ales are always available. Buses from Bognor, Chichester and Littlehampton stop nearby. A frequent local CAMRA Pub of the Year, winning most recently in 2023. Q🐕❀◑&♣●P🗑🛜♪

Elsted

Three Horseshoes ★
GU29 0JY (at E end of village)
☎ (01730) 825746 ⊕ 3hs.co.uk

Bowman Swift One; Flower Pots Pots Bitter; Hop Back Crop Circle; 2 changing beers (sourced locally) Ⓖ
Old and cosy rural inn divided into small rooms, including one reserved for dining and one with a blazing wood-burning stove in winter. Outside, the large, pleasant garden enjoys superb views of the South Downs. In summer there are four beers (mainly from local micros), and three in winter, all served by gravity from a stillage alongside the bar. Meals are substantial and of high quality. This is a popular and homely pub, which you will be reluctant to leave. Q🐕❀◑♣P❀

Faygate

Frog & Nightgown Ⓛ
Wimlands Lane, RH12 4SS
☎ (01293) 852764 ⊕ thefrogandnightgown.co.uk
Harvey's Sussex Best Bitter; Surrey Hills Ranmore; 2 changing beers (sourced locally) Ⓗ
Vibrant, cosy pub that was comprehensively refurbished after changing hands in 2015. There are up to four real ales available. Regular events include quiz nights, classic car meets, live music and open mic nights. A pizzeria restaurant was added to the rear of the pub in 2021, in addition to the tearoom annex. Known as the fastest pub in West Sussex due to its motorsport connections. Q🐕❀◑P🗑❀🛜

Felpham

Fox Inn ★
Waterloo Road, PO22 7EH (turn right at the post office, then right again)
☎ (01243) 829363 ⊕ thefoxfelpham.com
Dark Star Hophead; Palmers Dorset Gold, 200; Timothy Taylor Landlord; 3 changing beers (sourced nationally; often Palmers, Timothy Taylor) Ⓗ
The Fox Inn was built after the war to replace a former pub destroyed by fire. Note the stone slab inset on the front of the building proclaiming Henty & Constable's ales. The original public bar is now the restaurant, although meals can also be eaten in the main bar. There is wood panelling throughout, numerous photographs adorning the walls and a large garden. A changing selection of real ales is served often sourced from Timothy Taylor and Palmers. Regular tap takeovers are held. Q🐕❀◑♣P🗑(600)❀🛜♪

George Inn
102 Felpham Road, PO22 7PL (In the village 120yds from Felpham Way traffic lights)
☎ (01243) 824177 ⊕ georgeinnfelpham.co.uk
Goldmark Dave, Liquid Gold, American Pale Ⓗ
A pleasant two-bar pub with a small locals' bar on the right with a TV. A larger bar to the left has a fire. This then leads into a small dining area on the right or to the back where there is a large conservatory leading to a pleasant, enclosed garden. A choice of three cask beers from Goldmark are offered. Q🐕❀◑&●P🗑(600,700)❀🛜♪

Ferring

Henty Arms Ⓛ ✅
2 Ferring Lane, BN12 6QY (just N of level crossing in Ferring)
☎ (01903) 241254 ⊕ hentyarms.co.uk
Adnams Ghost Ship; Harvey's Sussex Best Bitter; Sharp's Doom Bar Ⓗ
The Henty Arms was constructed on the present site in 1830, which predates the nearby railway line. It was then called the New Inn and was renamed the Henty

Arms in 1927 when the brewers were Henty & Constable. Reopened after refurbishment in April 2023, there are two bar areas although one area is largely used for food. A good food menu offers homemade dishes. There is a large beer garden which is used for the annual beer festival in July. ✧❀⊕ℙ♖❀✿

Halnaker

Anglesey Arms ✅
Stane Street, PO18 0NQ (on A285)
☎ (01243) 699644 ⊕ theangleseyarms.com
Timothy Taylor Landlord ℍ/🅰; 3 changing beers (sourced nationally; often Flower Pots, Hogs Back, Pennine) ℍ
Close to the Goodwood Estate, which owns the freehold, and to the Tinwood vineyard, this family-run, listed, Georgian pub and dining room features a wood and flagstone-floored public bar with a log fire, giving it the atmosphere of the traditional village pub, plus a comfortable restaurant renowned for good food made with local produce. The large garden features a boules pisté, and morris dancers perform on occasional summer evenings. Four handpumps serve a changing selection of nationally sourced beers.
Q✧❀⊕&🅰ℙ(55,99) ❀✿♪

Hassocks

BN6 Craft Beer & Tap 🅛
54 Keymer Road, BN6 8AR
☎ (01234) 567890 ⊕ thebn6tap.co.uk
3 changing beers (sourced locally; often Goldmark, Hurst, Long Man) 🅖
Micropub opened in a former shop, specialising in Sussex-made drink products. This includes cask beer, (served by gravity from a cool room), craft/keg beers, wines and gins. A cask beer from Hurst brewery is normally available. The long narrow bar leads to a small rear garden. The traditional Sussex pub game of toad-in-the-hole is a feature. A disabled access toilet is provided, and the bar has fully disabled access from the street.
Q❀&≠♣♖✿

Keymer & Hassocks Sports & Social Club
Adastra Hall, Keymer Road, BN6 8QH
☎ (01273) 842962 ⊕ khssc.co.uk
Harvey's Sussex Best Bitter; Long Man Best Bitter; 2 changing beers (sourced locally; often Harvey's, Long Man) ℍ
Founded in 1922, this members-only club based in Adastra Park features an award-winning bar, a busy events calendar, some of the best snooker and pool facilities in mid Sussex, free wireless internet, HD television sets showing all major sporting events and a dartboard. CAMRA members are welcome on production of current membership card. Local CAMRA Club of the Year 2023. The four handpumps serve beer at club prices.
❀≠♣ℙ♖✿

Henley

Duke of Cumberland ★ 🅛
GU27 3HQ (off A286, 2 miles N of Midhurst) SU894258
☎ (01428) 652280 ⊕ dukeofcumberland.com
Harvey's Sussex Best Bitter; Langham Hip Hop; Timothy Taylor Landlord; 1 changing beer (sourced locally; often Langham) 🅖
Stunning 15th-century inn nestling against the hillside in over three acres of terraced gardens with extensive views. The rustic front bar has scrubbed-top tables and

benches, plus log fires at both ends, while to the rear is a dining extension that blends in perfectly with the original pub and offers much-needed additional space. Outside is a smokers' shelter with its own wood-burner. A former local CAMRA Pub of the Year, this is a rural gem. May close Sunday evenings in winter. Q❀⊕♣ℙ♖(70)❀✿

Hooksway

Royal Oak
PO18 9JZ SU815163
☎ (01243) 535257 ⊕ royaloakhooksway.co.uk
Bowman Swift One, Hop Hearted; Langham Hip Hop; 1 changing beer (often Langham) ℍ
An idyllic, unspoilt country pub in walking country, on the South Downs Way; perfect for getting away from it all. Popular with hikers, horse riders, and young families, there is a large garden with play area for children. In winter two log fires greet you. On offer are three permanent real ales and a regular guest, mainly from local breweries. An extensive menu caters for all tastes, including a varied children's menu. Check opening days and times before visiting. Q❀⊕ℙ❀♪

Horsham

Anchor Tap 🅛
16 East Street, RH12 1HL
3 changing beers (sourced nationally) ℍ
Now free of tie, this popular pub continues to offer customers an eclectic choice of brews. The knowledgeable team behind the bar source interesting beers both local and from afar. There are three handpumps in use, plus a back bar dispensing 10 keg beers. Originally the pub was the 'tap' of the Anchor Hotel. In January 1975 a Horsham Branch of CAMRA was formed here. ✧&≠♦♖✿

Black Jug 🅛
31 North Street, RH12 1RJ
☎ (01403) 253526
Firebird Parody; Harvey's Sussex Best Bitter; 2 changing beers (sourced nationally) ℍ
A large, bustling town-centre pub, the Jug is something of a Horsham institution. It has a welcoming interior with bookshelves, pictures, a fire and friendly efficient staff. Two regular ales are available with rotating guests, a cider and an extensive range of whisky and gin. Excellent food is served all day, and the pub is equally popular as a venue to meet and chat with no intrusive music. It is close to the railway station and arts complex.
Q✧❀⊕&≠♣♖✿

Brolly Brewing 🅛
Unit 8 Redkiln Close, RH13 5QL
☎ (01403) 252459 ⊕ brollybrewing.co.uk
4 changing beers (often Brolly) ℍ
The new brewery tap for Brolly Brewing, on what was formerly the site of Chapeau brewery, opened in June 2023. They have transformed the space, and now offer four handpulls and a keg wall with 12 craft taps; roughly half Brolly beers and half guest ales, with a full bar drinks range. Food trucks visit most Fridays and Saturdays, and there is weekend live music; check the website for details. Closed Monday and Tuesday. ✧&♦♖❀✿♪

King's Arms 🅛
64 Bishopric, RH12 1QN
☎ (01403) 451468 ⊕ kingsarmshorsham.com
5 changing beers (sourced locally) ℍ
This 18th-century coaching inn in the town centre was the King & Barnes brewery tap and is situated in The

Bishopric, some 100 yards from the site of the former brewery. A comfortable two-bar pub, with five handpumps serving mostly local ales and two keg lines. Food is served, including quality Sunday roasts. Live music plays every Friday and some other nights, with Monday quiz nights and Thursday open mic on alternate weeks. ❄️◑▯🖥️📶♪

Malt Shovel ⛓️

15 Springfield Road, RH12 2PG
☎ (01403) 252302
6 changing beers (sourced regionally; often Surrey Hills) Ⓗ
Close to the town centre, the pub has six handpumps on year-round, plus two ciders and a mix of bottles and canned ales. It doesn't stock any regular ales but has a focus on local beers and usually offers at least one dark ale. There is live music every Saturday night, regular open mic and jam events. The landlord and his friendly staff take great pride in the real ale. There is good parking for a town-centre pub. ❄️◑▯&♣️🖥️P🖥️😃📶♪

Piries Bar ⛓️

15 Piries Place, RH12 1NY (narrow alley adjoining Horsham's Carfax)
☎ (01403) 267846 ⊕ piriesbar.com
Timothy Taylor Landlord; 1 changing beer (often 360 Degree, Long Man) Ⓗ
A 15th-century building with exposed original timber beams, the pub is tucked away down a narrow alley adjoining Horsham's Carfax. It comprises a small downstairs room, an upstairs lounge bar, and a small modern extension which is in character with the building. Evenings here can be lively, with karaoke on Sundays, quiz nights Mondays and Tuesdays and occasional live music. With two cask ales always on the go, this bar is well worth a visit. ➷◑⇌🖥️😃📶

Itchenor

Ship ★

The Street, PO20 7AH (turn off the B2179 following signs for village and pub)
☎ (01243) 512284 ⊕ theshipinnitchenor.co.uk
Arundel Castle; Langham Best; St Austell Proper Job; 1 changing beer (sourced regionally; often Long Man) Ⓗ
Nestling in the heart of the beautiful sailing village of Itchenor in an Area of Outstanding Natural Beauty, the pub is popular with locals and visitors alike, providing the perfect pit-stop for walkers and cyclists enjoying the nearby coastal footpaths and the Salterns Way. The cosy bar is complemented by a separate restaurant area, pleasant front patio and further outside seating and a bar at the back. Accommodation also available. May be closed on Monday and Tuesday in winter.
Q➷❄️🍴◑&P😃📶

Lancing

Stanley Ale House ⛓️

5 Queensway, BN15 9AY (N of Lancing railway station)
☎ (01903) 366820 ⊕ thestanleyalehouse.com
Downlands Best; Langham Arapaho; 3 changing beers (sourced regionally; often Gun, Iron Pier) Ⓖ
This former launderette opened as a family-run micropub/alehouse in 2014. Located 200 yards north of the railway station, near local shops, it offers several changing ales, plus ciders, wine and spirits. The owners have listened to customers so now have both keg and cask beers available. Bar snacks are available. There is ample seating, inside and outside. A regular quiz night is

on Thursdays, with live music on Sunday afternoons and other events. A variety of board games are available.
Q➷❄️🐕&⇌♣️●🖥️😃📶♪

Littlehampton

New Inn ✓

5 Norfolk Road, BN17 5PL (N from Sea Rd)
☎ (01903) 713112 ⊕ newinnla.co.uk
Harvey's Sussex Best Bitter; 2 changing beers (sourced nationally; often Long Man, Timothy Taylor) Ⓗ
The New Inn is a friendly community pub, just a short walk from the beach, offering regularly changing ales. This traditional inn has two bar areas – the front bar has ample seating, a real fire and hosts weekly pub quizzes and regular charity events, while the rear bar has a pool table and dartboard, as well as showing live sport. A free jukebox is a feature of Monday nights. There is a heated courtyard at the back. ➷❄️◑♣️🖥️😃📶

Littleworth

Windmill

Littleworth Lane, RH13 8EJ (from A24 or A272 follow signs to Partridge Green along the B2135 on which the pub is signposted)
☎ (01403) 710308 ⊕ windmilllittleworth.com
Harvey's Sussex Best Bitter; 2 changing beers (sourced regionally; often Long Man, Only With Love) Ⓗ
Popular independently-owned country pub with friendly staff and locals. This 17th-century inn retains many original features including stone floors and low beams. There is an inglenook fire in the lounge and a wood-burner in the bar. The pub serves one regular and two changing ales supporting local breweries. Freshly prepared food is offered, plus pizza in the garden in summertime. The inn has seven characterful bedrooms giving an opportunity for an overnight stay.
Q➷❄️🍴◑&P🖥️(17)😃📶

Lodsworth

Langham Brewery Tap

The Granary, Langham Lane, GU28 9BU (½ mile N of A272 at Halfway Bridge) SU92682260
☎ (01798) 860861 ⊕ langhambrewery.co.uk
Langham Session Bitter, Hip Hop, TRIPLE XXX, Arapaho; house beer (by Langham) Ⓗ**; 7 changing beers (sourced locally; often Langham)** Ⓖ
A new brewery tap opened in 2021, converted from outbuildings of the 18th-century granary barn that houses the brewery itself. Fronting onto a courtyard behind the brewery there is indoor and outdoor seating and a bar with five handpumps plus six keg taps dispensing a selection of Langham beers. Additional beers (as available) can be fetched from the brewery's cold store across the yard, and take-outs of Langham's cask-conditioned, keg, bottled and canned beers can also be purchased. ➷❄️&♣️P😃📶♪

Lower Beeding

Kissingate Brewery ⛓️

Pole Barn, Church Lane Farm Estate, Church Lane, RH13 6LU
☎ (01403) 891335 ⊕ kissingate.co.uk
Kissingate Sussex, Black Cherry Mild, Chennai; 4 changing beers (sourced locally; often Kissingate) Ⓖ
This is the taproom for the Kissingate brewery. You will find a selection of beers from their range served on

gravity, plus cider and perry from local producers such as Black Pig, Seacider, and JB as well as a well-stocked bar. Events include Saturday festivals in May and October, and curry nights, and there is a function area upstairs. Closed on Sunday and Monday. ও✿৬Å♠Pᵈ♠ি♪

Maplehurst

White Horse Ⓛ
Park Lane, RH13 6LL
☎ (01403) 891208 ⊕ whitehorsemaplehurst.co.uk
4 changing beers (often Downlands, Harvey's, Kissingate) Ⓗ
Under the same ownership for 43 years, this splendid, welcoming country pub celebrates 40 consecutive years in the Guide, and is popular with locals, cyclists, and walkers. The cosy interior, with its unusually wide wooden bar, boasts real fires and many interesting artefacts. Good honest fare is provided, with the emphasis on beer and conversation. Many local ales feature, with a good selection of dark brews. Local JB cider is also available, along with other ciders. Closed Monday and Tuesday. Q♣✿✪◗♣♠P♠ি

Nutbourne

Rising Sun Ⓛ
The Street, RH20 2HE (on A283 from Storrington, turn right after bridge over River Chilt) TQ075188
☎ (01798) 812191
Fuller's London Pride; Harvey's Sussex Best Bitter; St Austell Tribute; 1 changing beer (sourced locally; often Only With Love) Ⓗ
This 16th-century, unspoilt village free house is a fine old stone building, with ironstone in its construction. The front part is Victorian, and it has a listed outdoor privy. The bare floored drinking area contrasts with the separate well-appointed restaurant, but the pub has retained its character. A traditional drinker's pub with enthusiastic staff and live music from time to time. The landlord celebrated 40 years running this pub in 2023. Food is sourced locally when possible. Q✿◗♣♠ি♪

Pagham

Inglenook ♟ Ⓛ
255 Pagham Road, PO21 3QB SZ892986
☎ (01243) 262495 ⊕ the-inglenook.com
Fuller's London Pride; Langham Hip Hop; 4 changing beers (sourced nationally; often Arbor, Brighton Bier, Downlands) Ⓗ
A 16th-century Grade II-listed hotel, restaurant, and free house. There is always a selection of excellent well-hopped real ales available from highly regarded microbreweries alongside local ciders. The cosy bar areas, popular with locals and visitors alike, have real fires and there is a large garden to the rear and a patio area at the front. A frequent local CAMRA Pub of the Year, winning most recently in 2024. Q♣✿✪◗♠Pᵈ♣(600)♠ি

Pulborough

White Horse
Mare Hill, RH20 2DY (on A283 on E outskirts of the town)
☎ (01798) 872189 ⊕ whitehorsepulborough.com
Dark Star Hophead; Fuller's London Pride; Gale's HSB Ⓗ
Popular drinker's pub situated half a mile east of town centre. The pub was saved from closure in 1989 after a campaign by locals and CAMRA. Bar staff offer a warm welcome to visitors. The pub has views across Pulborough Brooks nature reserve and it is near to Goodwood and Parham House. There is a menu of specially selected wines, sparkling wines and Champagne – a great favourite is the locally produced Nyetimber. Food is served all sessions. There is a car park opposite but beware crossing the busy A283. ও✿◗♣(1)♠ি

Rudgwick

Firebird Brewery Ⓛ
Lynwick Street, RH12 3UW
☎ (01403) 823180 ⊕ firebirdbrewing.com
Firebird Two Horses, Parody, Paleface APA; 5 changing beers (sourced locally) Ⓟ
The brewery has a mezzanine level which has been converted to a smart bar area, serving up to eight Firebird beers on cask and keg, plus a full bar selection. Street food from changing vendors is available outside on Friday and Saturday nights when additional tables are set up on the ground floor of the brewery. Open daytime all week but evenings only Friday and Saturday. ও◗৬P♣(63)♠ি

Selsey

Hopp Inn
153 High Street, PO20 0QB
☎ 07743 275093 ⊕ TheHoppInn.co.uk
Harvey's Sussex Best Bitter; Langham Best; Vibrant Forest PUPA; 3 changing beers (sourced nationally; often Harvey's, Langham, Vibrant Forest) Ⓖ
Popular friendly family-run micropub in Selsey High Street. A community hub, all are welcome, including dogs. Three nationally sourced changing gravity dispense cask ales are always available, with craft keg beers and lagers, bottled drinks, wines and spirits and a large range of real ciders. There is small courtyard at the front with outside seating. There are regular fun general knowledge and music quizzes, food nights, open mic and karaoke nights and live music most Sundays. Crib is regularly played. Q♣Å♣♠◗♣(51)♠ি♪

Shoreham-by-Sea

Buckingham Arms
35 Brunswick Road, BN43 5WA (opp railway station)
☎ (01273) 453660 ⊕ thebuckinghamarms.co.uk
Harvey's Sussex Best Bitter; Sharp's Doom Bar; 4 changing beers (sourced nationally; often Harvey's) Ⓗ
The pub is a traditional family-run free house with a spacious bar area, adjacent to Shoreham-by-Sea railway station. Six handpumps serve two regular and up to four changing guest beers. A rear patio garden and front decking area are ideal for the sun-seekers. The pub features regular Sky Sports TV and occasional live music. Check the website and Facebook for details of events. ✿⇌♣♣(2,2A)♠ি♪

Duke of Wellington Ⓛ
368 Brighton Road, BN43 6RE (on A259)
☎ (01273) 441297 ⊕ dukeofwellingtonbrewhouse.co.uk
Gun Zamzama IPA; 6 changing beers (sourced regionally; often Dark Star, Downlands, Titanic) Ⓗ
Welcoming free house with seven cask beers on offer from Sussex and beyond which always includes a dark beer. The single bar has bench seating and a log fire in winter. There is a regular quiz on Monday, live music Friday, Saturday, and Sunday and open mic and folk nights every other Thursday. Regular beer festivals

including a wassail. The patio garden is a suntrap in the summer months and heated in the winter. Takeaway food can be eaten in the pub.
🛇❀❉⏳♣🍴🚆(2,700) ❀🛜♪

Piston Broke 🅛
88 High Street, BN43 5DB
☎ (01273) 440036
4 changing beers (sourced locally; often 360 Degree, Downlands, Long Man) Ⓖ
Facing the Ropetackle roundabout, this single-bar pub is a rare outlet for gravity-dispensed beers and ciders in the town. The basically brown and cream décor has a wine bar feel and, if there's a theme, it is motor racing with memorabilia on the walls and furniture converted from engine blocks. There is a decent wine list. The pub was previously called the Lazy Toad. Quiz night every Tuesday and various live music events advertised outside the pub.
❉♣🍴🚆(2,700) ❀🛜♪

Turners Hill

Crown 🅛
East Street, RH10 4PT
☎ (01342) 715218 ⏺ thecrownturnershill.co.uk
Harvey's Sussex Best Bitter; 2 changing beers (sourced regionally; often St Austell)
A tastefully decorated 16th-century farmhouse and 17th-century barn with Jacobean oak beams, go to make up this pub which was converted to an inn in 1706. Leather settees surround a large open fire in the bar area, with another open fire in the restaurant, which serves traditional English dishes. There are three handpumps, with Harvey's Best the house beer, alongside a St Austell ale and a seasonal guest.
Q🛇❀🅓❦🅐♣🚆(84,272) ❀🛜

Walberton

Holly Tree 🅛
The Street, BN18 0PH
☎ (01243) 553110 ⏺ hollytreewalberton.com
Harvey's Sussex Best Bitter; 3 changing beers (sourced locally; often 360 Degree, Goldmark, Langham)
Victorian village pub, reopened in 2013 after a lengthy closure. The owners have carried out a thorough refurbishment and extended the pub, transforming it into a popular venue for drinkers and diners alike. The decor is unusual, with several rooms having a mixture of furniture interacting with a range of wall decorations, mirrors, ornaments, and pictures. The original two front bars have been retained, and in the right-hand one four handpumps dispense mainly local beers. Food is served Tuesday to Saturday and is available in the main restaurant or private dining room (for up to 10 people). Biannual beer festivals are held.
Q🛇❀🅓❦♣🚆(66A,85A) ❀🛜♪

West Chiltington

Five Bells 🍸 🅛
Smock Alley, RH20 2QX (1 mile S of West Chiltington old village centre) TQ092171
☎ (01798) 812143
5 changing beers (sourced nationally; often Firebird, Harvey's, Long Man)
This friendly village free house is a Guide regular. Dating from 1935, this former King & Barnes pub has been run by the same couple since 1983. The handpumps are on what is probably Sussex's longest copper top counter. Local and regional ales are served, with one usually a

dark ale. There is a large copper hooded open fire. Locally sourced home-cooked food is served in the bar and large conservatory. Local CAMRA Pub of the Year 2024.
Q❀❦🅓P🚆(1,74) ❀🛜

West Hoathly

Cat 🅛
Queen's Square, North Lane, RH19 4PP
☎ (01342) 810369 ⏺ catinn.co.uk
Firebird Parody; Harvey's Sussex Best Bitter; 2 changing beers (often Hairy Dog, Harvey's, Long Man)
Set in a picturesque hilltop village, opposite the church, in the heart of the Sussex countryside, this 16th-century free house is within reach of several attractions. It retains oak beams and two inglenook fireplaces. There is an outside terrace, where food and drink can be consumed in the summer months. Four local ales are on the bar along with high-quality food, using mostly local suppliers. This cosy pub has four letting rooms. Closed Monday and Tuesday. Q🛇❀❉🅓❦🅐P🚆(84)❀🛜

West Marden

Victoria 🅛
PO18 9EN (just W of B2146 in village centre)
☎ (023) 9263 1330 ⏺ victoriainnwestmarden.com
Harvey's Sussex Best Bitter; Langham Hip Hop; 1 changing beer (sourced locally; often Hogs Back, Langham, Otter)
Traditional old rural inn at the heart of its tiny downland community, free of all ties having been purchased by an enthusiastic young couple in 2021. The pub supports country pursuits including walking, riding and shooting. With a log-burning stove for cold evenings, there are several intimate spaces in which to drink and enjoy the home-made pies. The front garden has splendid views of the surrounding hills. Changing beers feature mainly local breweries alongside others from further afield. A beer festival is held in December.
Q🛇❀🅓🅐♣P🚆(54) ❀🛜♪

Worthing

Egremont 🅛
32 Brighton Road, BN11 3ED (a short walk from seafront and town centre)
☎ (01903) 530180 ⏺ theegremont.co.uk
Harvey's Sussex Best Bitter; 3 changing beers (sourced locally; often Goldmark, Harvey's, Only With Love)
An attractive late-Georgian gem with quirky interior. The pub was refurbished in 2015 but kept the exterior signage and stained glass windows which show it was originally owned by Kemp Town brewery of Brighton. Handpumps deliver four rotating ales plus two ciders, with keg beers and over 50 gins also available. The Egremont has a reputation for its home-made food, having won two awards. Sunday roasts are substantial and very popular. Live music plays on Friday and Saturday evenings. 🛇🅓♣🍴❀🛜

George & Dragon 🅛
1 High Street, Tarring, BN14 7NN (at S end of Tarring High St, not to be confused with Worthing High St)
☎ (01903) 202497 ⏺ george-n-dragon.co.uk
Greene King Abbot; Harvey's Sussex Best Bitter; Timothy Taylor Landlord; 2 changing beers (often Long Man, Thornbridge)
A 17th-century coaching inn in the unspoilt part of Tarring village. The pub sign is unusual in that it sits

above the horizontal bar from the time when double decker buses used to drive up the high street. A traditional locals' pub, it has oak beams throughout and a choice of several split-level seating areas, including a cosy lounge and an enclosed rear garden, with a suntrap patio. The bar still has Watneys signage. Good pub food is served. ⏱☆◑⇌(West)♣P🖵(7,16)☻♪

Green Man Ale & Cider House 🅛

17 South Street, Tarring, BN14 7LG (40yds N of West Worthing railway crossing)
☎ 07984 793877
5 changing beers (sourced regionally; often Downlands, Tring, Wantsum) Ⓖ
Worthing's third micropub opened in 2016 near West Worthing railway crossing. The temperature-controlled cool room is visible from the pub which is furnished with high level tables, benches and stools arranged to encourage interaction and chat. The pub is known for a friendly atmosphere and consistently well-kept constantly changing ales from local and national brewers, gravity-dispensed and always including a dark ale. Six ciders, one perry, gins and wine are also served. Cash only. Local CAMRA Cider Pub of the Year 2024.
Q⇌(West) ♣●🖵(7,10) ☻

Hare & Hounds 🅛 ✪

79-81 Portland Road, BN11 1QG
☎ (01903) 230085 ⊕ hareandhoundsworthing.co.uk
Harvey's Sussex Best Bitter; St Austell Proper Job; Timothy Taylor Landlord; 1 changing beer (sourced regionally; often Flack Manor) Ⓗ
Located a short walk from the shopping precinct in the heart of Worthing, this 18th-century Grade II-listed flint building became a pub in 1814, extending into the adjoining property in the 1990s. The large, wood-panelled U-shaped bar leads to the rear conservatory and covered patio. The pub always has a selection of local and national ales, often with a dark ale in winter. A good-value food menu including specials. Live jazz is on Tuesday, with a quiz on Wednesday. Dogs are not permitted. Q⏱☆◑⇌🖵🛜♪

Parsonage Bar & Restaurant 🅛

6-10 High Street, Tarring, BN14 7NN (at S end of Tarring High St, not to be confused with Worthing High St)
☎ (01903) 820140 ⊕ theparsonage.co.uk
Burning Sky Plateau; Harvey's Sussex Best Bitter; 1 changing beer (sourced locally; often Harvey's) Ⓗ
Situated in the heart of Tarring village, this lovely Grade II-listed 15th-century building was originally three cottages, and has been in this Guide continuously for 12 years. It has been a quality restaurant since 1987 but from 2013 has offered several well-kept local ales, usually with a dark ale in winter. Customers are welcome to drink without having a meal, although the set menu is good value. The courtyard garden is great for the warmer weather. Q☆◑⇌(West)🖵(6,16)☻🛜

Selden Arms 🅛

41 Lyndhurst Road, BN11 2DB (5 mins from the centre of town and 2 mins from Worthing Hospital on Lyndhurst Rd)
☎ (01903) 532517 ⊕ seldenarms.co.uk
5 changing beers (sourced nationally; often Bristol Beer Factory, Five Points, Vocation) Ⓗ
This welcoming free house has been in the Guide for many years. Under new ownership since April 2023, pub has been redecorated but otherwise few changes have been made. The handpumps serve a regularly changing selection of local and national ales, and there is also a selection of craft keg beers, cans and bottles, including a range of bottled Belgian beers. A blackboard displays the beer and cider available. A log fire is lit in winter. An annual winter beer festival is held in February. Local CAMRA Pub of the Year 2022. ⇌♣●🖵☻

Three Fishes ✪

56 Chapel Road, BN11 1BE
☎ (01903) 288640
Greene King Abbot; Ruddles Best Bitter; Sharp's Doom Bar; 4 changing beers Ⓗ
Number 56 Chapel Road had previously been Worthing Corporation Electricity Board showrooms and on the front of the building is a blue emblem with three fishes, part of Worthing Corporation's coat of arms. It has been a Wetherspoon pub for some years (formerly a Lloyds No. 1) and it offers the usual Wetherspoon food and drink selection, with plenty of seating both upstairs and downstairs. In addition to the regular ales, a changing selection of guest ales are available. ⏱◑⛨⇌🖵(1)🛜

Toad in the Hole

1 Newlands Road, BN11 1JR (just S of railway bridge and Morrisons)
☎ (01903) 233488
Hand Bird, Chop; Three Acre IPA Ⓗ
Built in the 1870s, formerly the Castle Alehouse, this pub was taken over by HandBrewCo and reopened in early March 2022. The pub sells mainly beers from the brewery which is located in West Worthing. It is a short walk from Worthing town centre and station. The Sussex pub game Toad is available for customers to play. Three cask ales are stocked plus a good selection of keg beers and canned beers from HandBrewCo and other brewers. Live jazz plays on Sunday afternoons. ⏱♣🖵☻🛜♪

Yapton

Maypole 🅛

Maypole Lane, BN18 0DP (off B2132 ½ mile N of village; pedestrian access across railway from Lake Ln, 1 mile E of Barnham station) SU978042
☎ (01243) 551417
Downlands omb; Fauna Tree Planter IPA; house beer (by Lister's); 2 changing beers (sourced locally; often Downlands, Pitchfork) Ⓗ
Small 18th-century characterful flint-built free house hidden away from the village centre, down a narrow lane ending in a pedestrian crossing over the railway. The cosy, often lively, lounge boasts a large inglenook with a wood-burning stove and a row of six handpumps dispensing up to four beers usually from local breweries. There is also a traditional public bar with jukebox and darts. Dogs are welcome throughout the pub.
Q⏱☆▲♣P🖵☻🛜♪

By George!

It was my Uncle George who discovered that alcohol was a food well in advance of modern medical thought.
P G Wodehouse, The Inimitable Jeeves

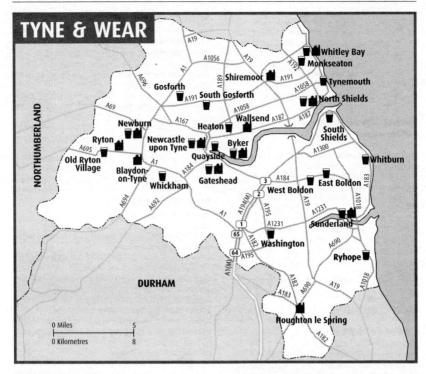

TYNE & WEAR

DURHAM

0 Miles 5
0 Kilometres 8

East Boldon

Boldon Cricket Club L
Sunderland Road, NE36 0BT
☎ (0191) 536 4180 ⊕ boldon.play-cricket.com
2 changing beers (sourced regionally) Ⓗ
The family-friendly cricket club has a single, roomy bar
with pool table, dartboard and TVs which show sport.
Both of the two handpulls have Maxim beers. There are
squash courts to the left of the bar and a function room
to the right. An outside drinking area overlooks the
cricket pitch in front of the club. There is a small car park
beside the club, with Metro and bus links a short walk
away. ⧉❀⅋♣P⧄(9)🛜

Grey Horse L ✓
Front Street, NE36 0SJ
☎ (0191) 519 1796
6 changing beers (sourced nationally) Ⓗ
Distinctively fronted building which has a single open-
plan room with a number of separate seating areas.
There are six handpulls with five changing beers and one
cider or perry. There is seating outside the front of the
pub and a beer garden and car park at the rear. A
largescreen TV in the bar shows regular sporting events.
Upstairs is a function room that can be hired. Food is
served daily from an extensive menu.
⧉❀🍺&⅋P🛜🛜

Mid Boldon Club L
60 Front Street, NE36 0SH
☎ 07799 311358
4 changing beers (sourced nationally) Ⓗ
This local gem of a club has four ever-changing,
competitively-priced cask ales from local and national
breweries covering a range of styles and strengths. The
club boasts a magnificent old snooker table, Sky TV,
subdued background music and frequent music nights.
Guests can expect a warm welcome – just ring the

doorbell to gain access. Close to local rail and bus
services. Current regional CAMRA Club of the Year.
Q⧄♣⅋🛜🛜🛜♫

Gateshead

Microbus 🍸
2 High Level Parade, NE8 2AJ
⊕ microbus.pub
6 changing beers (sourced nationally) Ⓗ
A campervan-themed micropub in a railway arch
opposite the entrance to High Level Bridge. This quirky
pub is adorned with paraphernalia reflecting the owners'
enthusiasm for these vehicles. Six handpulls and 10 taps
dispense a wide selection of beers, mainly from northern
breweries, with usually two dark beers. There is a bus
stop directly outside the pub with services provided by
Go North East with a real time departure display inside
the pub so you know when your next (southbound only)
bus is coming. ⧉❀➤(Newcastle)⧄●🐾🛜🛜

Old Fox L
10-14 Carlisle Street, Felling, NE10 0HQ
☎ (0191) 447 1980
5 changing beers (sourced nationally) Ⓗ
Only a short walk from Felling Metro station is this
traditional, single-room community pub with a roaring
fire in the winter months. Ales are sourced from national
and local breweries. Snacks and Sunday lunches are
available. There is live music over the weekend, and the
dartboard is in frequent use. A friendly and welcoming
pub with a beer garden at the rear.
⧉❀➤(Heworth) ⧄(Felling) ♣⅋🛜🛜♫

Station East L
Hills Street, NE8 2AS
☎ (0191) 477 2602
**3 changing beers (sourced nationally; often Hadrian
Border)** Ⓗ /Ⓐ

Hardian Border brewery's first pub occupies the site of the former Gateshead East Station and Railway Hotel. Formerly a small pub, the building has been stripped back and enlarged and is now open and spacious. There is a pleasant mezzanine floor above the main room and a further arched room to the rear below another railway bridge. A rear room is available for functions.
Q&₹(Newcastle) 유♠문

Wheat Sheaf ★ 🗓

26 Carlisle Street, Felling, NE10 0HQ
☎ (0191) 597 8404
Big Lamp Sunny Daze, Bitter, Prince Bishop Ale; 2 changing beers (sourced nationally) H

Welcoming street-corner pub owned by Big Lamp brewery and patronised by a loyal band of regulars who often travel quite a distance to drink here. The pub features some original details, mismatched furniture, and real coal fires when needed. The outdoor toilets have original Victorian urinals. There is a fortnightly Monday night quiz, traditional folk music featuring local musicians on Tuesday night, and dominoes on Wednesday night. An original CAMRA clock keeps time behind the bar. Snacks are available.
🕭&₹(Heworth) 유(Felling) ♣🖵(27,93) ♥ 🕯 ♫

Monkseaton

Crafty Cold Well

2 Cauldwelll Lane, NE25 8LN
4 changing beers (sourced nationally) H

The owner of this pub is dedicated to bringing something different to the local real ale scene. The four changing handpulls always include a dark beer, and there is always a changing real cider. The front room is accessed from street level, with steps to the back room and servery (ask at bar for ramp for disabled access to the back room). Opening times may vary so check before visiting. 🕭&묘묘(57,57A)🕯

Newburn

Keelman 🗓

Grange Road, NE15 8ND
☎ (0191) 267 1689 ⊕ biglampbrewers.co.uk
Big Lamp Sunny Daze, Bitter, Summerhill Stout, Prince Bishop Ale, Keelman Brown; 1 changing beer (sourced nationally) H

This tastefully converted, Grade II-listed former pumping station is now home to the Big Lamp brewery – the Keelman is the brewery tap. A conservatory restaurant serves excellent food, and quality accommodation is provided in the adjacent Keelman's Lodge and Salmon Cottage. Attractively situated by the Tyne Riverside Country Park, Sea to Sea cycleway and Hadrian's Wall National Trail. 🕭&🛏🕪🛆P묘(22,71)🕯

Tyne Amateur Rowing Club 🗓

Water Row, NE15 8NL
⊕ tynerowingclub.org
4 changing beers (sourced nationally; often Hadrian Border, Firebrick) H

Modern rowing club building with balcony overlooking the River Tyne and bridge at Newburn, about seven miles west of Newcastle city centre. Originally founded in 1852, it is one of the oldest sporting clubs in the country. There is a function space available for hire. Coffee, and snacks are available during the day. Walkers are particularly welcome, and National Cycle Route 72 passes the front of the building. It has a large car park.
🕭&🖵(22,62) ♥ 🕯

Newcastle upon Tyne: Byker

Cumberland Arms ★ 🗓

James Place Street, NE6 1LD (off Byker Bank)
☎ (0191) 265 6151 ⊕ thecumberlandarms.co.uk
House beer (by Northern Alchemy); 4 changing beers (sourced nationally) H

Standing in a prominent position overlooking the lower Ouseburn Valley, this three-storey pub was rebuilt over 100 years ago and has changed relatively little since then. It usually offers up to 12 ciders and perries. Winter and summer beer festivals are held each year. It is home to traditional dance and music groups. Closing time may vary. Accommodation is in four en-suite rooms. A multiple CAMRA regional Cider Pub of the Year.
Q🕭&🛏🖰(Byker) ♣P🕯🕯 ♫

Free Trade Inn 🗓

St Lawrence Road, NE6 1AP
☎ (0191) 265 5764
Fyne Jarl; house beer (by Almasty); 5 changing beers (sourced nationally) H

Unique former Scottish & Newcastle pub with wonderful views of the Tyne bridges and Newcastle and Gateshead quaysides. Up to nine beers and five ciders are available on the bar. Interesting ales come from far and wide, with regular tap takeovers and an extensive range of foreign bottled beers. Service is smiling, friendly and knowledgeable. The jukebox is a classic – and free – and the beer garden is excellent. The pub hosts regular pop-up food vendors. A former local CAMRA Pub of the Year and Cider Pub of the Year.
Q🕭&🛏(Byker) ♣♠🖵(Q3) ♥ 🕯

Full Circle Brew Co Taproom 🗓

167 Walker Road, Hoults Yard, NE6 2HL
☎ (0191) 481 4114 ⊕ fullcirclebrew.co.uk
4 changing beers (sourced locally; often Full Circle) A

Full Circle brewing started in 2020 and their brewery tap is located on a balcony overlooking the brewery itself. It serves a small range of cask ales and a larger range of keg beers from Full Circle, plus collaborations and

REAL ALE BREWERIES

Almasty ♦ Newcastle upon Tyne / Shiremoor
Anarchy ♦ Newcastle upon Tyne
Big Lamp Newburn
Brewlab ♦ Sunderland
Brinkburn Street ♦ Newcastle upon Tyne: Byker
Cullercoats Wallsend
Darwin North Shields
Dog & Rabbit ⬛ Whitley Bay
Firebrick Blaydon-on-Tyne
Flash House ♦ North Shields
Full Circle ♦ Newcastle upon Tyne
Great North Eastern ♦ Gateshead
Hadrian Border Newburn
Maxim ♦ Houghton le Spring
North Pier Sunderland
Northern Alchemy ♦ Newcastle upon Tyne: Byker
Out There Newcastle upon Tyne
Stu Brew Newcastle upon Tyne
Tavernale ⬛ Newcastle upon Tyne (brewing suspended)
Thirsty Moose Ryton
Three Kings North Shields
Two by Two Newcastle upon Tyne: Byker
Tyne Bank Newcastle upon Tyne
Vaux ♦ Sunderland
Wear Sunderland (NEW)
Whitley Bay Whitley Bay
Wylam ♦ Newcastle upon Tyne

seasonal beers from other small brewers. Pizzas are made to order. The new beer garden holds up to 60 people. ▶♿P

Two by Two Brewery Tap 🅛
Unit 8, Morley's Yard, NE6 1PQ
☎ 07723 959168 ⊕ twobytwobrewing.com
2 changing beers (sourced locally; often Two by Two) Ⓗ
Two by Two recently moved its brewing operation to Byker and opened a brewery tap. It serves two cask beers from Two by Two and eight keg lines. The bottle fridge is stocked with beer and cider including gluten-free and non-alcoholic options. It hosts occasional food vendors, live music, and DJs, and there are regular quiz nights. Dogs are welcome and the tap even holds monthly dog socials. ♨(Byker)❀♪

Newcastle upon Tyne: City Centre

Bacchus 🅛
42-48 High Bridge, NE1 6BX
☎ (0191) 261 1008
Anarchy Blonde Star; Fyne Jarl; 7 changing beers (sourced nationally) Ⓗ
This smart, city-centre pub boasts nine handpumps offering a wide range of rapidly changing guest beers, with one pump dedicated to cider. A large range of draught and bottled foreign beers is also available. Photographs and posters showing the region's proud, world-leading former industries cover the walls. The pub can get busy on match days. Winner of many local CAMRA awards. ⛴♿≠(Newcastle)♨(Monument)❀ 🛜

Bodega 🅛
125 Westgate Road, NE1 4AG
☎ (0191) 221 1552 ⊕ sjf.co.uk/the-bodega
Fyne Jarl; 7 changing beers (sourced nationally) Ⓗ
Two fine, stained-glass domes are the architectural highlights of this pub, which is popular with football and music fans. The interior offers a number of standing and seating areas, with separate booths for more intimate drinking. A number of old brewery mirrors adorn the walls, and TVs show sporting events. Eight handpumps dispense beers from Oakham and Fyne, and there is a good selection of foreign bottled beers. A range of ciders, including some real cider served from the cellar, is also available. ≠(Newcastle)♨(Central Station)♣❀🛜

Bridge Hotel 🅛
Castle Garth, NE1 1RQ
☎ (0191) 232 6400
Sharp's Doom Bar; 8 changing beers (sourced nationally) Ⓗ
Large Fitzgerald's pub next to Stephenson's spectacular High Level Bridge. The rear windows and patio have views of the city walls, River Tyne and Gateshead Quays. The main bar area, which features many stained-glass windows, is divided into a number of seating areas, with a raised section at the rear. Guest beers come from far and wide. What is claimed to be the oldest folk club in the country is among live music events held in the upstairs function room.
🎯◐≠(Newcastle) ♨(Central Station) ❀🛜♪

Fitzgeralds 🅛
60 Grey Street, NE1 6AF
☎ (0191) 230 1350
Anarchy Blonde Star; Ossett White Rat; 4 changing beers (sourced nationally) Ⓗ

A large, open-plan pub that is much bigger inside than it appears from the outside. The bar is at the back of the pub and has six handpulls serving local and national beers, usually including a dark beer. There is plenty of seating in various areas, and a large area in front of the bar which is kept clear for standing.
≠(Newcastle) ♨(Monument) 🚌(53,Q3) 🛜

Five Swans 🆗
14 St Mary's Place, NE1 7PG
☎ (0191) 211 1140
Sharp's Doom Bar; Ruddles Best Bitter; Greene King Abbot; 6 changing beers (sourced nationally) Ⓗ
Popular, multi-roomed Wetherspoon pub opposite Newcastle Civic Centre and close to the main shopping areas. The beer range includes guests from all the local brewers, plus some from further afield. Food is served all day. There is an outside drinking area to the front of the pub and a 'secret' courtyard through the maze of rooms. Children are welcome until 9pm. The pub area can be booked for private functions.
Q⛴❀◐♿≠(Manors) ♨(Haymarket) ♣🚌🛜

Lady Greys 🅛 🆗
20 Shakespeare Street, NE1 6AQ
☎ (0191) 232 5932 ⊕ ladygreys.co.uk
8 changing beers (sourced nationally) Ⓗ
Close to the historic Theatre Royal and busy shopping areas, it is good to see this pub, formerly the Adelphi, adding itself to the city-centre real ale scene. Beers are often from local brewers Hadrian Border, Allendale and others, with guests from all over the country. A recent refurbishment has added four more handpumps.
◐≠(Newcastle) ♨(Monument) ❀❀🛜

Mean-Eyed Cat 🅛
1 St Thomas Street, NE1 4LE
☎ (0191) 222 0952
Ossett White Rat; house beer (by Almasty); 4 changing beers (sourced nationally) Ⓗ
Situated in a former newsagent's in the street opposite Haymarket bus station, this one-room micropub opened in 2018 with six handpumps. It serves beers from local, national and international suppliers, alongside a range of eight craft keg beers. A good selection of up to six ciders is available – traditional still and served from the cellar. Mexican spirits are also on offer. There are street food pop-ups on occasion. ♨(Haymarket)❀🚌❀

Newcastle Tap
Ground Floor, Baron House, 4 Neville Street, NE1 5EN
☎ (0191) 261 6636 ⊕ tapnewcastle.com
6 changing beers (sourced nationally) Ⓗ
An open-plan single room on the ground floor of a former office block next to the Head of Steam and opposite Central Station and the Royal Station Hotel. The beer casks and kegs are displayed behind glass on a mezzanine above the bar. Cask beers are now dispensed by handpumps on the bar, with a tap wall behind for keg beers. Pizzas are served all day. Closing times may vary.
◐≠(Newcastle) ♨(Central Station) ❀🚌

Town Mouse Ale House 🅛
Basement, 11 St Mary's Place, NE1 7PG
⊕ townmousealehouse.co.uk
6 changing beers (sourced nationally) Ⓗ
This well-designed micropub is in the basement of a former coffee shop and has space for around 50 people. The bar area is to the front, with more seating to the rear. A large blackboard gives details of the six cask beers and larger range of keg and bottled beers. Local CAMRA Pub of the Year 2023. 🎯♨(Haymarket)♣❀❀

Trent House 🗒

1-2 Leazes Lane, NE1 4QT
☎ (0191) 261 2154
5 changing beers (sourced nationally) ⓗ
Friendly and laid-back, this pub is very popular with students and home to the best jukebox in town, featuring an eclectic mix of classic rock, jazz and electronica. There is an upstairs room with a pool table, and board games are available from the bar. The pub has a nightly happy hour from 8pm-9pm, with cask ales at reduced prices. ✍(Haymarket)♣🚐🎜

Wobbly Duck

4 Eldon Square, NE1 7JG
5 changing beers (sourced nationally; often Almasty) ⓗ
Micropub that opened in 2021 in a basement down a few stairs in a row of Georgian terraced houses in Eldon Square, near the shopping centre. A thorough refurbishment has given the interior a rustic feel. There are tables outside the front, as well as an enclosed paved outdoor driving area, the 'Wobbly Garden', at the rear, with outdoor heaters. A sister pub to the Old Fox in Felling and Beer Street in Newcastle.
🌸⇌(Newcastle) ✍(Monument) ●●

Newcastle upon Tyne: Gosforth

Gosforth Hotel 🗒 ✅

205 High Street, NE3 1HQ
☎ (0191) 285 6617
8 changing beers (sourced nationally; often Anarchy) ⓗ
Located on the corner of a busy junction at the top of the High Street, this is a stalwart of the lively Gosforth pub scene. Popular with a wide clientele, from nearby office workers to locals and students, the pub often gets busy. The rear bar opens at 5pm Monday to Thursday and midday Friday to Sunday. A good range of local ales is always available. ◖▷&✍(Regent Centre)🚐🎜

Newcastle upon Tyne: Heaton

Chillingham 🗒

89-91 Chillingham Road, NE6 5XL
☎ (0191) 265 3992
6 changing beers (sourced nationally) ⓗ
Close to Chillingham Road Metro station, this large, two-roomed pub comprises a comfortable lounge and a bar with sports shown on TVs. It offers an excellent choice of local microbrewery beers, plus bottled beers, whiskies and a wine of the month. The function room upstairs hosts regular quiz nights, and the food menu is popular with locals and visitors.
🌸◖✍(Chillingham Road) ♣🚐(62,63) 🎜

Elder Beer Café 🗒

290 Chillingham Road, NE6 5LQ
🌐 elderbeer.co.uk
Rigg & Furrow Run Hop Run; 1 changing beer (sourced nationally) ⓗ
This former shop unit on the main road opened in 2021 as a bottle shop. It expanded in 2022, and now offers real ales from smaller national breweries, plus 10 keg taps, and a wide range of local and continental bottled and canned beers. Limited snacks are available but customers can bring their own food. There is a garden to the rear. Card payments only. 🌸●🚐(62,63)🎜

Heaton Tap 🗒

41A Warton Terrace, NE6 5LS
☎ (0191) 276 2674

2 changing beers (sourced locally) ⓗ
Welcoming micropub and bottle shop just off Chillingham Road in Heaton. The shop is in the front room and has a good range of premium bottled beers. The newly refurbished lounge area is to the rear, and there is an outside drinking area at the front. Two real ales are served, often including some from the wood as well as local ales. Regular events include quiz nights and a book club. 🌸🚐(1,62)

Newcastle upon Tyne: Quayside

Bridge Tavern 🗒

7 Akenside Hill, NE1 3UF
☎ (0191) 261 9966 🌐 thebridgetavern.com
House beer (by Wylam); 8 changing beers (sourced nationally) ⓗ
The Bridge Tavern is situated between the stanchions of the North East's most iconic landmark —The Tyne Bridge. This modern, open-plan bar is also home to a microbrewery on the ground floor of the pub, in full view of the customers. There is an extensive real ale offering, with a house beer by Wylam, alongside a quality food menu. There is a ground floor beer garden, and upstairs is a second bar and roof terrace.
🌷🌸◖&⇌(Newcastle) ✍(Central Station) 🚐(53,Q3) ●🎜

Crown Posada ★ 🗒

31 Side, NE1 3JE
☎ (0191) 232 1269 🌐 crownposada.co.uk
6 changing beers (sourced nationally) ⓗ
Recognised by CAMRA as having a regionally important historic pub interior, this pub has been sympathetically refurbished over the years by the owners and is an oasis of calm and peace near the busy Quayside drinking, dining and clubbing circuit. The narrow street frontage shows two impressive stained-glass windows, behind which lies a small snug, the bar counter and a longer seating area. There's an interesting coffered ceiling, local photographs, and cartoons of long-gone customers and staff on the walls. Local small brewers are enthusiastically supported, with three regular local ales. ⇌(Newcastle) ✍(Central Station) 🚐(53,QA) 🎜

Newcastle upon Tyne: South Gosforth

Victory ✅

43 Killingworth Road, NE3 1SY
☎ (0191) 285 1254 🌐 victorysouthgosforth.co.uk
Great North Eastern Rivet Catcher; Timothy Taylor Landlord; Wainwright Gold; 3 changing beers (sourced nationally)
Established on this site since 1861, this lively pub takes its name from Nelson's flagship and once served the local mining community. Essentially a single room, there are two lounge areas each side of the entrance with some seating near the bar. A rear lounge overlooks the Ouseburn. Food is served all day, and there are regular quiz nights. 🌸◖▷&✍(South Gosforth)🅿🚐●🎜

North Shields

Enigma Tap

60 Bedford Street, NE29 0AL
☎ 07792 822063
4 changing beers (sourced nationally) ⓗ
Micropub in a former shop unit just off the main Northumberland Square. There is a seating area near the front entrance and a narrower raised area towards the rear incorporating the photograph-covered bar and craft

beer tap board. Outside is a small patio in the back yard for outdoor drinking. Beers are from local and regional breweries. ⑄⊛🅟♣●🚻☀

Seven Stars ⑃

7 Albion Road, NE30 2RJ
☎ (0191) 257 3982
House beer (by Three Kings); 4 changing beers (sourced nationally) Ⓗ
Recently refurbished single-roomed pub that serves up to five real ales; a house beer from Three Kings brewery and four others. Seven craft beers from local breweries and other brewers around the country are also available. A small courtyard to rear provides an outdoor drinking area. Bar snacks including Scotch eggs, pork pies and cheese boards are available. Q⊛♿🚻☀📶

Old Ryton Village

Olde Cross ⑃

Barmoor Lane, NE40 3QP
☎ (0191) 447 4250 ⊕ yeoldecrossryton.com
Fyne Jarl; 4 changing beers (sourced locally) Ⓗ
This community-owned inn in the Tyne Valley is an attractive Edwardian half-timbered local in a lovely setting by the village green and the cross it is named after. The original Cross Inn dates from the mid-19th century and was partly rebuilt in 1909. The pub is a centre for the local community, hosting entertainment and activities. Two community events – the hirings, which take place in spring and autumn, and the annual carols at Christmas – are held on the village green. Winner of a CAMRA Pub Saving Award in 2020.
⑄♿♣🚻(R3)☀📶

Ryhope

Guide Post ⑃ ✅

Ryhope Street South, SR2 0RN
☎ (0191) 523 5735
Maxim Double Maxim; 2 changing beers (sourced nationally) Ⓗ
Friendly, popular and comfortable street-corner local run by an enthusiastic landlord who is passionate about his ale. There are three handpulls with Maxim Double Maxim always on, plus two changing guest beers. There are sports TVs, a pool table, and regular weekend entertainment, with dominoes on Sunday. There is a pleasant enclosed garden at the rear of the pub.
⑄⊛♣🚻☀📶♪

South Shields

Cask Lounge ⑃

1 Charlotte Terrace, NE33 1QQ
☎ 07513 906703
6 changing beers (sourced nationally) Ⓗ
South Shields' first micropub, in a former housing office opposite the town hall, is run by an experienced couple who value the principle of the micropub, encouraging conversation with no TVs or gambling machines. There are six handpulls dispensing regular changing real ales. The pub's two rooms have comfortable seating throughout, soft carpeting and background music. An ever-growing collection of pumpclips adorns the bar area. ⊛♿🚻🚻📶

Marine 🍷 ⑃

230 Ocean Road, NE33 2JQ
☎ (0191) 455 0280 ⊕ the-marine.co.uk
Allendale Golden Plover; Draught Bass; 6 changing beers (sourced nationally) Ⓗ

Dating from 1868, this family-run free house is opposite Marine Park, near the seafront. Up to six changing and two regular cask ales are available. Left of the bar are raised areas for customers to sit in social groups. There is a games area to the right and a function room upstairs. Non-intrusive background music is played and pub food is served daily. Local CAMRA Pub of the Year 2024
⑄◗♿🚻♣●🚻☀📶

Steamboat ⑃ ✅

27 Mill Dam, NE33 1EQ (follow signs for Customs House)
☎ (0191) 454 0134
7 changing beers (sourced nationally) Ⓗ
The only pub in the North East to be awarded a Gold Award as part of CAMRA's 50 celebrations, the Steamboat is full of character. Located opposite the Custom House, the split-level bar and small lounge are decorated in a nautical theme. Note the certificates adorning the walls. There are nine handpulls serving real ale and two boxed ciders. Popular beer festivals are held, as well as regular music nights. It is a 10-minute walk from the public transport interchange. 🚻●🚻☀📶♪

Sunderland: City Centre

Chaplins ⑃

40 Stockton Road, SR1 3NR
☎ (0191) 565 3964
6 changing beers (sourced nationally) Ⓗ
This friendly city-centre pub has six real ale handpulls and one for real cider. The house beer, Happy Chappie, comes from Darwin brewery. There is plenty of seating either side of the main entrance, as well as outside. Some of the table tops depict scenes of Sunderland's industrial heritage. Good-value food is served every day, and a quiz is held on Thursday evening. It is handy for public transport, with Park Lane Interchange two minutes away. ⊛◗♿🚅(Sunderland)🚋(Park Lane)●🚻📶

Cooper Rose ⑃ ✅

2-4 Albion Place, SR1 3NG
☎ (0191) 514 8530
Ruddles Best Bitter; Greene King Abbot; Sharp's Doom Bar; 4 changing beers (sourced nationally) Ⓗ
Named after the Cooper Rose vaccinator used by Dr Henry Renney who lived in Albion Place in the 1890s, this pub was opened in 2011. It has a long ground-floor bar and a smaller bar upstairs. A roof terrace has been added and outside seating at the rear. Photographs are displayed around the pub depicting local figures from Sunderland's past. The beer selection varies, and reasonably-priced food is available all day.
Q⑄⊛◗♿🚅(Sunderland) 🚋(Park Lane) 🚻📶

Dun Cow ★ ⑃

9 High Street West, SR1 3HA
☎ (0191) 567 2262 ⊕ pubculture.com/duncow
Allendale Pennine Pale; 5 changing beers (sourced nationally) Ⓗ
A Grade II-listed architectural gem of a building, next door to the Sunderland Empire. It has been recognised by CAMRA as having a nationally important historic pub interior. It won two CAMRA/Historic England Awards for best restoration and conservation after a refurbishment in 2014, and underwent another makeover in 2021. A plaque outside shows the pub's history. Real ale features on up to eight handpulls, plus a real cider. A limited food menu is available until 6pm.
Q◗♿🚅🚋(Sunderland) ●🚻☀📶♪

Fitzgeralds ⑃

12-14 Green Terrace, SR1 3PZ
☎ (0191) 567 0852

Titanic Plum Porter; 8 changing beers (sourced nationally) ⓗ
A Grade II-listed pub that has been in the Guide since 1983. It serves two regular beers and up to seven guest beers. The pub comprises a large main bar with a number of seating areas. To the right is the smaller, quieter, nautically-themed Chart Room. Meals are served daily until 3pm. Note the small wooden barrels on top of the bar back. The pub is also known as Fitzys.
ⓗ☸◐≠Ⓡ(Park Lane) ☐♠ 🖤

Ivy House 🗈
7A Worcester Terrace, SR2 7AW
☎ (0191) 567 3399
6 changing beers (sourced nationally) ⓗ
Tucked away close to Park Lane public transport interchange, the Ivy House is well worth seeking out. Six changing guest ales feature, plus an extensive range of international bottled beers which are displayed on a blackboard facing the bar. Home-made pizzas and burgers are prepared in the open kitchen. There are themed meal nights and a Wednesday night quiz. Live music usually features on the second Saturday and last Sunday of the month. ☸◐◣≠Ⓡ(Park Lane)P☐♠ ♫

Museum Vaults 🗈
33 Silksworth Row, SR1 3QJ
☎ (0191) 565 9443
2 changing beers (sourced nationally) ⓗ
This small former beer house is on the edge of the city centre and has been run by the same family for over 40 years. The single room is divided in two and both feature open fires. There are up to two cask beers on offer, always from local breweries. The Vaults is a regular outlet for student brews from Brewlab nearby. The real ale is complemented by a small range of canned and bottled beers. ♿≠Ⓡ(Millfield)☐♠ 🖤 ♫

Ship Isis 🗈
26 Silksworth Row, SR1 3QJ
☎ (0191) 567 3720 ⊕ theshipisis.uk
5 changing beers (sourced nationally) ⓗ
Dating from 1885, the Ship Isis was restored to its original splendour in 2011. The bar has seven handpulls offering up to five cask beers and two ciders. A range of bottled and canned beers is also available. There is a quieter snug, and upstairs is a function room. The walls are adorned with old photographs. Food is available and Monday is quiz night. Home to the Wear Beer microbrewery ☸◐♿≠Ⓡ(Millfield)♦☐♠ 🖤 ♫

Sunderland: North

Avenue 🗈
26 Zetland Street, SR6 0EQ (just off Roker Ave)
☎ (0191) 567 7412
6 changing beers (sourced nationally) ⓗ
A 15-minute walk from the Stadium of Light, this local pub is just off Roker Avenue. There are up to six changing real ales, both local and national, and up to 18 real ciders. On Thursday nights there is a popular quiz, and a domino handicap on Sundays. A function room can be used as an overflow if the main bar is busy. Local CAMRA Cider Pub of the Year 2024. ☸♿♣♦P☐(E1)♠ 🖤

Harbour View
Harbour View, SR6 0NU
☎ (0191) 567 1402
6 changing beers (sourced nationally) ⓗ
A modern local pub opposite Roker Harbour and close to the beach. It has six handpulls dispensing regularly changing real ales. It is a true home for real ale lovers and a relaxing place, with additional seating outside. An

excellent selection of background music is played, while every Thursday evening the pub holds a popular live acoustic and blues speakeasy. There is a function room available upstairs. ☸P☐(E1,18)♠ ♫

Lighthouse 🗈
7 Sea Road, Fulwell, SR6 9BP
☎ 07817 884157
Maxim Double Maxim; 3 changing beers (sourced nationally) ⓗ
Sunderland's first micropub is in the centre of Fulwell. The former café was transformed into a small but comfortable bar in 2019. There is an outdoor drinking area at the rear and a small room upstairs. Four handpulls offer largely local beers, often from Maxim brewery, and real cider makes a rare appearance. A lack of TV and background music enhances the experience. Nearby are frequent buses to Sunderland and South Shields. Seaburn Metro is 10 minutes' walk. Q☸Ⓡ(Seaburn)☐♠

Tynemouth

Tynemouth Lodge Hotel 🗈
Tynemouth Road, NE30 4AA
☎ (0191) 257 7565 ⊕ tynemouthlodgehotel.net
Black Sheep Best Bitter; Hadrian Border Tyneside Blonde, Grainger Ale; Marston's Pedigree; 1 changing beer (sourced locally; often Hadrian Border) ⓗ
An externally tiled 1799 free house, next to a former house of correction, which has featured in every issue of the Guide since 1983. It recently celebrated 40 years under the same ownership. The comfortable pub has a U-shaped lounge, with the bar on one side and a serving hatch on the other. It is an ideal stopping-off point for those completing the Sea to Sea cycle route.
Q☸ⓇP☐(1) 🖤

Washington

Courtyard 🗈
Biddick Lane, NE38 8AB
☎ (0191) 417 0445 ⊕ thecourtyardbar.co.uk
8 changing beers (sourced nationally) ⓗ
A longtime regular in the Guide, this light and airy café bar is located in the Washington Arts Centre, and offers a warm welcome to drinkers and food lovers. Eight changing handpulls serve real ales from local, regional and national breweries. An extensive range of food is served in the afternoon and early evening. Outdoor seating is available in the spacious courtyard. Two popular beer festivals are held over the Easter and August bank holidays. ☸♿◐♣P☐♠ 🖤

Sir William De Wessyngton 🗈 ✅
2-3 Victoria Road, NE37 2SY
☎ (0191) 418 0100
Ruddles Best Bitter; Greene King Abbot; Sharp's Doom Bar; 4 changing beers (sourced nationally) ⓗ
A large, open-plan pub in a former ice-cream parlour and snooker hall, named after a Norman knight and lord of the manor whose descendants emigrated to the United States. As well as the three regular real ales, it offers at least four guest ales, some from local microbreweries. Good-value food is available all day. Twice yearly beer festivals are held in spring and autumn. It is opposite Concord bus station. Q☸☸◐♿P☐ 🖤

Steps 🗈
47 Spout Lane, NE38 7HP
☎ (0191) 415 0733
Greene King Abbot; 4 changing beers (sourced nationally) ⓗ

Known as the Spout Lane Inn when it opened in 1894, this popular community pub was renamed the Steps in 1976. The small, comfortable and friendly single-room lounge bar is divided into two drinking areas, with pictures of old Washington decorating the walls. The pub offers up to four reasonably-priced changing beers, which are often selected by the regulars, with some from local microbreweries. Quizzes are held Tuesday and Thursday nights. Opening hours vary. Q ❧ ❀ ♣ P ➡ (81,82) ☏ ♪

West Boldon

Black Horse L
Rectory Bank, NE36 0QQ (off A184)
☎ (0191) 536 1814
2 changing beers (sourced nationally) ⊞
Iconic coaching inn-style pub that can trace its history back to at least the early 1700s. The interior is split between a bar/lounge and restaurant, with the walls, furniture and ceiling decorated with bric-a-brac and photos taken by the owner. Two handpulls serve changing local ales, normally light session ales. Meals can be taken in the bar or in the partially covered area outside. ❀ ◑ ⅃ P ➡ ❀

Whickham

One Eyed Stag L
5 The Square, NE16 4JB
☎ (0191) 488 4713
4 changing beers (sourced locally) ⊞
A fairly recent addition to the pubs of Whickham, this micropub has a tile-topped bar with four handpumps serving beer from local microbreweries. Blackboards adorn the wall behind the bar giving details of the beers and other drinks available. There is an interesting light fitting covering most of the ceiling and an electric stove in an alcove to the right. ⅃ P ➡ (6,69) ❀ ☏

Whitburn

Blue's Micro Pub L
1A Percy Terrace, SR6 7EW
5 changing beers (sourced nationally) ⊞
In the centre of Whitburn village, this friendly micropub offers five cask ale handpulls, up to six real ciders and five keg taps. Craft bottles and cans are also available. There is an outdoor area and further seating upstairs with a games room. A cask and wine club is held on

Wednesday, Thursday is Pie and a Pint night, Friday is quiz night, and there is a free cheeseboard every Sunday. Card only payment. Buses to Sunderland and South Shields stop outside the door. Q ❀ ♣ ➡ ❀

Whitley Bay

Dog & Rabbit L
36 Park View, NE26 2TH
☎ 07944 552716
6 changing beers (sourced nationally) ⊞
This micropub, converted from a women's clothing shop, is a welcome addition to the number of pubs in the area. The corner bar has six handpumps serving mostly local beers. The owner's microbrewery has been installed in the pub, brewing Dog & Rabbit's beers. With no music, Wi-Fi or sports TV, conversation is encouraged among visitors. A former local CAMRA Pub of the Year. Q ❧ ⍨ (Monkseaton) ➡ ❀

Rockcliffe Arms
Algernon Place, NE26 2DT
☎ (0191) 253 1299
4 changing beers (sourced nationally; often Whitley Bay) ⊞
Outstanding back-street ex-Fitzgerald's pub, a few minutes walk from the Metro station, and now run by the Whitley Bay Brewing Co. This one-room establishment has distinct bar and lounge areas with a snug in between. It serves four constantly changing beers, details of which are explained on notices above the dividing arch. Regular darts and domino matches are held in the snug. It is popular with locals and real ale drinkers. ❀ ⍨ ♣ ➡ (1)

Split Chimp L
Unit 1, Ground Floor, Spanish City Dome, Marine Avenue, NE26 1BG
⊕ splitchimp.pub
House beer (by Three Kings); 3 changing beers (sourced nationally) ⊞
Micropub that opened in 2019 in one of the external units of the recently refurbished Spanish City, overlooking the promenade along the North Sea coast. Its single room has a long bar counter facing the entrance, with seating around the periphery. The house beer from Three Kings is supplemented by a changing range of four beers from near and far. Winter opening hours vary so check ahead. ❧ ❀ ● ➡ ❀

Spores for thought

Yeast is a fungus, a single cell plant that can convert a sugary liquid into equal proportions of alcohol and carbon dioxide. There are two basic types of yeast used in brewing, one for ale and one for lager. (The yeasts used to make the Belgian beers known as gueuze and lambic are wild spores in the atmosphere). It is often said that ale is produced by 'top fermentation' and lager by 'bottom fermentation'. While it is true that during ale fermentation a thick blanket of yeast head and protein is created on top of the liquid while only a thin slick appears on top of fermenting lager, the descriptions are seriously misleading. Yeast works at all levels of the sugar-rich liquid in order to turn malt sugars into alcohol. If yeast worked only at the top or bottom of the liquid, a substantial proportion of sugar would not be fermented. Ale is fermented at a high temperature, lager at a much lower one. The furious speed of ale fermentation creates the yeast head and with it the rich, fruity aromas and flavours that are typical of the style. It is more accurate to describe the ale method as 'warm fermentation' and the lager one as 'cold fermentation'.

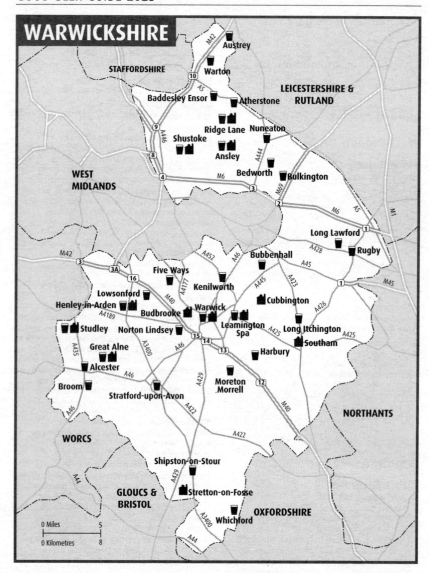

WARWICKSHIRE

Alcester

Holly Bush Inn ★

37 Henley Street, B49 5QX (opp town hall and church)
☎ (01789) 507370 ⊕ thehollybushinn.co.uk
Everards Sunchaser, Tiger; 2 changing beers ⊞
An Everards tied house offering Tiger and Sunchaser as
regular ales, plus one or two changing beers. There are
two bars and an additional room used for live sports, pub
games and live music on Friday and Saturday, with a pub
quiz on Sunday. This historic and traditional English public
house has an excellent beer garden, and welcomes
children and dogs. Closed Monday. Q⏰❀◑♿♣❄☂♪

Royal Oak

44 High Street, B49 5AB
☎ (01789) 565211 ⊕ theroyaloakalcester.co.uk
**3 changing beers (sourced nationally; often
Butcombe, Ossett, Theakston)** ⊞

Friendly 18th-century Grade II-listed building, with an
open-plan layout including snug areas, a log fire, and a
small rear garden with outside seating. The landlord and
her staff, including the specially appointed cellarman,
have a passion for their varied selection of real ales and
ciders. Regular live music sessions are held on Thursday,
and often themed food events on Friday evening, plus a
good Sunday lunch. A former local CAMRA award-winner.
⏰❀◑♿●🚌❄☂♪

Turks Head

4 High Street, B49 5AD
☎ (01789) 765948 ⊕ theturkshead.net
**Wye Valley Butty Bach; 2 changing beers (sourced
nationally; often St Austell, Salopian, Timothy
Taylor)** ⊞

A busy, centrally located pub, with exposed beams and
roaring log fires, that is well worth a visit. The landlords
have been here for 22 years and are dedicated to real
ale. Beers are sourced from regional breweries as well as

from Yorkshire and South Wales. Good food is served in a separate dining room, and there is a quiet garden. The pub provides street bars during the annual town food festivals. CAMRA Warwickshire Pub of the Year 2022. ☺⊛⏪&⬛(247,X19) ❀ 🛜

Ansley

Lord Nelson Inn ⏸

Birmingham Road, CV10 9PQ
☎ (024) 7639 2305 ⊕ thelordnelsoninnansley.co.uk
Sperrin Ansley Mild, Head Hunter, Band of Brothers, Third Party, Thick as Thieves; 3 changing beers ⊞
This nautically-themed pub has been run by the same family since 1974, incorporating a brewery at the rear of the building since 2012. Nine handpulls dispense their own Sperrin brews, plus guests from microbreweries. An extensive food menu is served, with meal nights and tribute nights hosted, plus a monthly quiz held in the Victory restaurant. The suntrap courtyard garden is a venue for a beer festival and barbecue in August. This is the pub's 31st consecutive entry in the Guide.
☺⊛⏪&P⬛❀🛜♪

Atherstone

Angel Ale House ⏸

24 Church Street, CV9 1HA
☎ 07525 183056
Leatherbritches Mad Ruby; Oakham Citra; 3 changing beers ⊞
Prominent pub on the market square, next to the church with its rare octagonal tower. The pub features an inglenook fireplace with log-burning stove. There are five real ales, often local, and always including a dark beer, plus up to 10 real ciders. Customers can select music from a large vinyl selection, which is a popular feature, plus there are occasional live bands. The pub is popular with dog owners (and their canine companions).
⊛≈♣P⬛(48,65) ❀♪

Austrey

Bird in Hand

Main Road, CV9 3EB
☎ (01827) 830260 ⊕ birdinhandaustrey.co.uk
Marston's Pedigree; house beer (by Marston's); 4 changing beers ⊞
This attractive thatched and timber-framed pub dates from the 15th century and is the focal point of this small rural village. Note the ancient octagonal wayside cross by the front entrance. There is a small bar room, a snug to the rear, and a large lounge featuring a number of intimate areas. The sizeable garden to the rear has a large pop-up marquee available for functions. Up to four guest ales offer interesting choices, and usually include a dark beer. Q☺⊛⏪&♣♣P⬛❀🛜

Baddesley Ensor

Red Lion

The Common, CV9 2BT (from the Grendon roundabout on A5 go S up Boot Hill) SP273983
☎ (01827) 718186
Greene King Abbot; Marston's Pedigree; 3 changing beers (often Grasshopper, Green Duck) ⊞
Welcoming and traditional village pub whose character hasn't changed for several decades. The interior is spacious but intimate; a music-free environment where community issues dominate the conversations amongst the local clientele. One of the two fires is a real log fire which adds further character. Opposite the pub is a

colliery wheel memorial recognising the pit head workings that operated in the area until 1989.
Q♣P⬛❀🛜

Bedworth

Bear & Ragged Staff ✓

50 King Street, CV12 8JA (in town centre)
☎ (024) 7649 4340
Greene King Abbot; Ruddles Best Bitter; Sharp's Doom Bar; 3 changing beers (often Byatt's, Purity) ⊞
A long, narrow Wetherspoon pub, converted from a former toyshop, with photos and articles featuring the history of Bedworth displayed throughout. The rear section of the pub is used as a family area. Outside there is a small patio area with hanging baskets and pot plants. As well as the regular beers, there are three guest beers, many from local microbreweries. ☺⊛⏪&≈🛜

Broom

Broom Tavern ⏸

32 High Street, B50 4HL
☎ (01789) 778199 ⊕ broomtavern.co.uk
North Cotswold Shagweaver; Wye Valley HPA; 1 changing beer (often Purity, St Austell) ⊞
A lovely brick and timber multi-room building retaining a great amount of character. It has been tastefully made over, while keeping the cosy snug and log fire in winter. It was reopened by two experienced chefs who now serve great food, made with local ingredients, at lunchtime and in the evenings. Local beers are frequently served here, plus at least one real cider. There is a choice of beer gardens, and dogs are welcome.
Q⊛⏪♣P❀

Bubbenhall

Malt Shovel ⏸

Lower End, CV8 3BW
☎ (024) 7630 1141
Church End Fallen Angel; Fuller's London Pride; Greene King Abbot; Sharp's Doom Bar ⊞
Traditional Grade II-listed village pub dating from the 17th century. The large comfortable lounge at the front caters mainly for diners, while the smaller bar to the rear is a more traditional drinking area which is popular with the locals. Dogs are only allowed in the bar. Good quality home-cooked food is served Tuesday to Saturday at lunchtime and in the evening, and at lunchtime on Sunday. There is a large garden to the rear for the summer months. Q☺⊛⏪P⬛(24)❀

REAL ALE BREWERIES

Church End Ridge Lane
Church Farm ⚲ Budbrooke
Fizzy Moon 🍺 Leamington Spa
Fosse Way Southam
Freestyle 🍺 Shustoke
Henley Mile Henley-in-Arden (NEW)
North Cotswold Stretton-on-Fosse
Purity Great Alne
Slaughterhouse Warwick
Sperrin 🍺 Ansley
Warwickshire Cubbington
Weatheroak Studley
Windmill Hill Leamington Spa

Bulkington

Weavers Arms

12 Long Street, CV12 9JZ

☎ (024) 7631 4415 🌐 weaversarms.co.uk

Draught Bass; 2 changing beers (sourced nationally) Ⓗ

Family-owned two-roomed traditional village pub converted from weavers' cottages. It has a wood-panelled games room, log-burning fireplace and slate floor. A large, well kept beer garden accommodates barbecues in summer. The pub is worth visiting for the quality of its Bass, and the friendly banter from the landlord. Children are welcome and private functions are catered for. The Weavers Walkers and Hillbilly Golf Society hold regular meetings here. ❀♣🚌(56)🐾📶

Five Ways

Case is Altered ★ 𝕃

Case Lane, CV35 7JD (off Five Ways Rd near A4141/A4177 jct) SP225701

☎ (01926) 484206 🌐 caseisaltered.com

North Cotswold Cotswold Best; Wye Valley Butty Bach; 4 changing beers (sourced locally; often North Cotswold) Ⓗ

A classic unspoilt country pub with a bar and separate snug, identified by CAMRA as having a historic pub interior of regional importance. The current landlady has been here for more than 30 years, after taking over from her grandmother. The traditional bar billiards table still takes old sixpences, which can be bought from the bar. Memorabilia includes a Victorian print of a former Leamington brewer, a clock from another old local brewer, and a propeller from a World War I fighter plane. Monday is cribbage night. Q❀♿♣P

Great Alne

Mother Huffcap 𝕃

Spernall Lane, B49 6HY

☎ (01789) 638005 🌐 motherhuffcap.co.uk

Wye Valley HPA; 2 changing beers (often Purity, Timothy Taylor) Ⓗ

An early 18th-century, Grade II-listed building houses this country pub, which reopened in 2021 under new owners to serve the local community, after being closed for nearly three years. The Purity beers, and Hogan's cider in summer, are produced less than three miles from this free house. Locally sourced food is prepared on-site to be eaten in or taken away. The menu includes gluten-free, vegetarian and vegan options. Bus X19 passes the door. There is a good sized car park and a garden.
❀◐♿●P🚌(X19)🐾📶♫

Harbury

Crown Inn Café & Public House

Crown Street, CV33 9HE

☎ (01926) 614995 🌐 crowninnharbury.co.uk

Adnams Ghost Ship; Butcombe Original; 1 changing beer (sourced nationally) Ⓗ

Located in the picturesque village of Harbury, this 1785 Grade II-listed building is constructed of local limestone. Inside is a cozy bar, a comfortable long lounge area at the rear, and a separate restaurant. There is a covered drinking area outside at the rear. The bar normally features two regular beers and one changing guest. Occasional music nights and quizzes are hosted.
Q❀◐♿▲♣P🚌(200)🐾📶♫

Henley-in-Arden

Three Tuns 🏆

103 High Street, B95 5AT

☎ (01564) 792723

Church End Goat's Milk; Fuller's London Pride; Sharp's Doom Bar; Wye Valley Butty Bach; 1 changing beer (sourced locally; often Church End) Ⓗ

A small, unpretentious 16th-century drinkers' pub with a single bar serving two rooms. Popular with locals, many of whom come here to play darts and cribbage, the pub is usually busy and the atmosphere is always friendly. Five real ales are served in consistently good condition. No hot food is served, though pub snacks, plus home-made sausage rolls and cobs are usually available. Parking is on the main street outside the pub.
Q♿⇌♣🚌(X20)🐾📶

Kenilworth

Ale Rooms & Gin Bar 𝕃

7 Smalley Place, CV8 1QG (opp clock tower)

☎ (01926) 513087

6 changing beers (sourced regionally; often Church End, Silhill) Ⓗ

A light, airy and welcoming contemporary bar in a pleasant location. Up to six changing real ales are on offer, and a large selection of gins. Live music is hosted every Friday, and an interesting collection of album covers adorns the walls. Upstairs is a chill-out lounge available for private hire and community use. In front of the pub there is a seating area from where customers can watch the world go by. ♿⇌🚌(11,X17)🐾📶♫

Engine

8 Mill End, CV8 2HP (on E edge of town)

☎ (01926) 853341

M&B Brew XI; Sharp's Doom Bar; 2 changing beers (sourced nationally) Ⓗ

A very comfortable single-roomed pub close to Kenilworth Common and the railway line. The pub name has nothing to do with trains – it was originally home to a pumping engine for a nearby forge. The pub is community and charity focused, and was presented with the Heart of Community Award in 2020, against stiff national competition. It is popular with those watching televised sport. A rear conservatory is a relatively recent addition. Guest beer pumps are at the back of the bar.
❀♣🚌(X68,X17)

Old Bakery 🏆 𝕃

12 High Street, CV8 1LZ (near A429/A452 jct)

☎ (01926) 864111 🌐 theoldbakerykenilworth.co.uk

Wye Valley HPA; 3 changing beers (sourced regionally) Ⓗ

Small pub in a former bakery in the old town, close to Abbey Fields and Kenilworth Castle. Beams, bare floorboards, rustic furniture, subtle lighting and pictures generate a cosy feel to the main bar and separate snug. This independent, family-run free house offers frequently changing guest ales and quality coffee. A mix of locals and visitors, plus guests occupying the 14 en-suite rooms, encourages conversation. There is limited disabled parking and access at the rear of the premises. Local CAMRA Pub of the Year 2024.
Q❀🛏♿P🚌(11)🐾📶

Leamington Spa

Benjamin Satchwell ✔

112-114 The Parade, CV32 4AQ (almost opp town hall)

☎ (01926) 883733

Greene King Abbot; Ruddles Best Bitter; Sharp's Doom Bar; 4 changing beers (often Hook Norton, Marston's, Silhill) Ⓗ
Named after a renowned local benefactor who discovered Leamington's second spring in 1784, this pub bears all the hallmarks of the Wetherspoon style. Converted from two shops, it is large, stretching back to Bedford Street. The building's split levels have been used well to create comfortable seating areas. The upper level hosts an impressively long bar. Wall panels depict local history and personalities. ⛄◐♿⇌🚌ᯤ

New Inn
197 Leam Terrace, CV31 1DW
☎ (01926) 422861 🌐 thenewinnleamington.co.uk
Eagle IPA; Sharp's Doom Bar, Atlantic, Sea Fury; 2 changing beers (often Byatt's) Ⓗ
A traditional pub in a wide Victorian terrace on the outskirts of town. The original pub has been extended into the property next door. A central door opens directly onto the bar, with a seating area to the left and a games area to the right leading to an extension at the rear. Outside is a good-sized walled garden. Quality home-cooked food is served. A quiz is hosted fortnightly on Wednesday. ⛄❀◐♿♣🚌(63,64)🐾ᯤ♫

Long Itchington

Harvester
The Square, CV47 9PE (off A423 at village pond, then first left)
☎ (01926) 812698 🌐 theharvesterinn.co.uk
3 changing beers (often Church End, Purity) Ⓗ
White-fronted pub near the village pond, on the corner of the square. Inside is a main bar, a small drinking area, and a restaurant specialising in good-value steaks. The ale range changes frequently, usually supporting smaller breweries. Real cider and a Belgian fruit beer are also on the bar. The pub hosts a beer festival each May bank holiday. A large walled courtyard garden to the rear has a wood-fired pizza oven. Gruntfuttocks Speciality Pickles can be purchased to take home.
Q⛄❀◐♿▲●🚌(64)🐾ᯤ♫

Long Lawford

Lawford Arms
Main Street, CV23 9AY
☎ (01788) 221295
Black Country Bradley's Finest Golden; M&B Brew XI; 3 changing beers (sourced nationally) Ⓗ
Purchased in 1992, the Lawford Arms was the first pub bought by Angus McMeeking, founder and chairman of Black Country Ales. This recently refurbished popular village local is warm and welcoming. One of the guest beers is always a dark ale, and two handpulled ciders are available. Traditional bar snacks include freshly made cobs and pork pies. Local CAMRA Country Pub of the Year 2023. ⛄❀♿♣P🚌(R86)🐾ᯤ♫

Lowsonford

Fleur de Lys
Lapworth Street, B95 5HJ (in centre of village, alongside canal)
☎ (01564) 782431 🌐 thefleur.co.uk
Greene King Abbot; St Austell Tribute; Timothy Taylor Landlord; 1 changing beer Ⓗ
Rambling country pub in a 17th-century, Grade II-listed building. There are several separate rooms and numerous tables, chairs and settles. Open fires give it a welcoming feel, as do the friendly staff. Good food is served, including an interesting selection of pies (the pub is where Fleur de Lys pies originated). The pub is popular with locals and people from further afield, especially in summer, thanks to its canalside location. Watch out for the low beams! Q⛄❀◐P🐾ᯤ

Moreton Morrell

Black Horse
CV35 9AR
☎ (01926) 954550 🌐 theblackhorsemm.co.uk
Purity Pure Gold; 2 changing beers (sourced regionally; often Hook Norton, North Cotswold, Salopian) Ⓗ
Situated in the heart of the village, this traditional pub has been sympathetically refurbished to be in keeping with its history. Two wood-burning stoves add comfort in the winter, and the terrace and garden enjoy the sunshine in summer months. Real ale is a crucial part of the pub's identity and beers are changed regularly, supporting both local and national breweries. Families and dogs are welcome. Four sound-proofed rooms are available to let. ⛄❀🛏♿🚌(77A)🐾ᯤ

Norton Lindsey

New Inn Ⓛ ✔
Main Street, CV35 8JA
☎ (01926) 258411 🌐 thenewinn.pub
Greene King IPA; 4 changing beers (sourced locally; often Blue Monkey, Church End, Slaughterhouse) Ⓗ
Warwickshire's first community-owned pub opened in 2017 after fundraising saved it from closure (it was purchased by a collective of more than 200 people). Located on a street corner in the heart of the village, the pub features a wooden floor and an open-plan interior that gives a light and airy feel. Food is locally sourced, with many specials on offer. Circular walks start and end at the pub. Local CAMRA Pub of the Year from 2021 to 2023. Q⛄❀◐P🐾ᯤ

Nuneaton

Felix Holt Ⓛ ✔
3 Stratford Street, CV11 5BS
☎ (024) 7634 7785
Greene King Abbot; Ruddles Best Bitter; Sharp's Doom Bar; 4 changing beers (often Byatt's, Oakham) Ⓗ
Large Wetherspoon outlet in the town centre. The pub takes its name from a novel by George Eliot, and the literary theme is reflected in the decor of books and pictures of local history. Look out for the comical metal sculptures on the walls. A good range of guest beers includes local ales. There are tables and chairs outside for alfresco drinking and eating. Q⛄◐♿⇌🚌ᯤ

Lord Hop Ⓛ
38 Queens Road, CV11 5JX
☎ (024) 7798 1869 🌐 lordhopnuneaton.co.uk
4 changing beers Ⓗ
Town-centre micropub on two floors; the large upper floor boasts settees, a small library, and a selection of board games. Four or more real ales are served from handpull, with up to eight ciders or perries from the chiller. Wine, gins, bottled lager and soft drinks are also sold. Snacks are available, or bring your own takeaway. CAMRA magazines are provided for reading. No under-18s are permitted, and assistance dogs only. Regular local CAMRA Pub of the Year contender. Q⇌P🚌ᯤ

Ridge Lane

Church End Brewery Tap ♚ Ⅼ

CV10 0RD (2 miles SW of Atherstone)
☎ (01827) 713080 ⊕ churchendbrewery.co.uk
Church End Goat's Milk, Gravediggers Ale, What the Fox's Hat, Fallen Angel; 4 changing beers ℍ
This brewery tap is hidden from the road, but can be accessed opposite Tom Piper Close. The brewery is visible from the bar area. Eight handpulls serve the bar and vestry, with a mild always on tap. Ciders are dispensed direct from the barrel. Under 18s are allowed inside the vestry until 6pm and are welcome in the garden meadow. A monthly quiz night is hosted. Brewery tours are available by prior arrangement. Open Thursday to Sunday, plus Wednesday evenings in summer.
Q ⊛ ♿ ♣ ⌂ P ♞ ❀ 🌐 ♪

Rugby

Merchants Inn Ⅼ

5-7 Little Church Street, CV21 3AN
☎ (01788) 571119
Nethergate Suffolk County Best Bitter; Oakham Bishops Farewell; Purity Mad Goose ℍ**; 6 changing beers (sourced nationally)** ℍ**/**ⓖ
Popular town-centre pub with flagstone floors and an open fire. The interior is a museum of brewery memorabilia, with a large room to the rear that doubles as a function room. Rugby and cricket are popular on the TV. Activities are held throughout the year and include Belgian and German nights, beer festivals, and gin and cider weekends. Locally produced snacks include pork pies and sausage rolls. A former local CAMRA Pub of the Year. ⊛ ♿ ♣ ♞ P ℍ ♞ ❀ 🌐 ♪

Raglan Arms

50 Dunchurch Road, CV22 6AD (on A426 near to gyratory and town centre)
☎ (01788) 221296
Black Country Bradley's Finest Golden, Pig on the Wall, Fireside; 6 changing beers (sourced nationally) ℍ
A friendly pub with a warm welcome. There is a bar with darts and skittles, a lounge, and a cosy snug which doubles as a meeting room. The regular ales are complemented by seasonal Black Country brews, plus six guest beers from regional and local breweries. Bar snacks include freshly made cobs, home-made Scotch eggs and locally made pork pies. Quiz nights are held weekly on Thursday and there is occasional live music. Well-behaved dogs are welcome. ⊛ ♣ ♞ P ♞ ❀ 🌐 ♪

Seven Stars ♚ Ⅼ

40 Albert Square, CV21 2SH
☎ (01788) 535478 ⊕ sevenstarsrugby.co.uk
Byatt's Platinum Blonde; Everards Tiger, Old Original; 7 changing beers (sourced nationally) ℍ
Traditional multi-roomed community pub with a focus on quality beer and cider. Its 14 handpumps dispense an ever-changing selection of light and dark ales, plus four ciders which are augmented by six craft beers. Food highlights include pie and pint on Wednesday evenings. Home-made Scotch eggs and pork pies plus filled rolls are available. Rugby is popular on the bar's TVs. Current local CAMRA Pub of the Year. No children after 7pm. Closed on Monday. Q ⊛ ⊘ ⇌ ♣ ♞ P ♞ ❀ 🌐 ♪

Squirrel Inn Ⅼ

33 Church Street, CV21 3PU
☎ (01788) 578527
4 changing beers (sourced nationally; often Dow Bridge, Nuttycombe, Phipps NBC) ℍ
A warm welcome is guaranteed at this historic free house, Rugby's 'jewel in the town'. A real fire and pictures of old Rugby contribute to the intimate ambience. Ales from Dow Bridge, Parkway Brewing and Phipps breweries are frequently served alongside Marston's beers and two ciders. Live music is a regular feature on Saturday evening, and there is an open mic night on Wednesday. National CAMRA Golden Award winner. ♣ ♞ ♞ ❀ 🌐 ♪

Victoria Inn ★

1 Lower Hillmorton Road, CV21 3ST
☎ (01788) 544374
Oakham Citra; 4 changing beers (sourced nationally; often Abbeydale, Hook Norton, Titanic) ℍ
A beautiful Victorian corner pub just outside the town centre. This true gem is the last of its kind in Rugby. Built in a wedge shape, the multi-roomed local features a traditional bar, larger refurbished lounge, and two relatively new snugs converted from the kitchen and store room. Filled rolls are available at the weekend. The pub shows sport on TV and hosts quiz nights on Thursday and Sunday. ⊛ ♣ ♞ ❀ 🌐

Shipston-on-Stour

Black Horse Inn Ⅼ

Station Road, CV36 4BT
☎ (01608) 238489 ⊕ blackhorseshipston.co.uk
Prescott Hill Climb; 2 changing beers (sourced regionally; often North Cotswold, Wye Valley) ℍ
This stone-built, thatched pub is the oldest in town – it has held a licence since 1540. There are two bars, each with an open fire for winter warmth. Three handpumps serve two regular and one changing ale. There is plenty of garden space, with a covered smoking area and a stage for live music in summer. Food is provided by Copper Grill, offering many types of gourmet burgers. A cider festival is usually held on August bank holiday.
Q ⊛ ⊘ ◗ ♣ P ♞ ❀ 🌐 ♪

Thirst Edition ♚

46 Church Street, CV36 4AS
☎ 07345 390114 ⊕ thirstedition.co.uk
North Cotswold Shagweaver ℍ**; 4 changing beers (sourced regionally; often Abbeydale, Castle Rock, Thornbridge)** ⓖ
A continuous beer festival goes on at this micropub, with over 1,400 different ales being served since it opened in 2018 (though there have been duplicates, often sourced from local breweries such as North Cotswold). A dozen still ciders and numerous gins are also available. Live music is hosted on two Fridays each month. Since opening, a popular Thursday quiz night has raised many thousands of pounds for local causes. Bus 50 from Stratford stops nearby. CAMRA Warwickshire County Pub of the Year 2023. Q ♣ ♞ (50) ♞ 🌐 ♪

Shustoke

Griffin Inn ♚ Ⅼ

Church Road, B46 2LB (on B4116 on sharp bend)
☎ (01675) 481205
Theakston Old Peculier; Wye Valley Butty Bach; 8 changing beers (sourced nationally; often Oakham) ℍ
Family-owned rural pub which has championed real ale for over four decades. The spacious but intimate interior features a stone bar, inglenook fireplaces and beams decorated with ancient beer mats. No music interrupts the hum of conversation. There is always one real cider, and up to four in summer. Children are welcome on the

beer terrace, in the conservatory, and on the extensive meadow-style garden. Home-cooked lunches are served (no food Sun). Q✿☺☆❀▲♣P❀❀🕏

Plough Inn

The Green, B46 2AN

☎ (01675) 481557 ⊕ theploughinnshustoke.co.uk

Draught Bass; 4 changing beers 🅗

Over 200 years old, this attractive pub sits on the village green. There are four low-ceilinged rooms around the bar, a modern conservatory to the rear, and a separate games room. The pleasant beer terrace to the front now includes cosy, enclosed pods which can be booked for dining. There is also a pets' corner to the rear. The pub is popular for food and features eating areas where dogs are welcome. ✿☺⬤☆❀♣P❀❀

Stratford-upon-Avon

Garrick ●

25 High Street, CV37 6AU (opp town hall)

☎ (01789) 292186

Greene King Abbot; house beer (by Greene King); 2 changing beers (sourced regionally; often Greene King, North Cotswold, Prescott) 🅗

The oldest pub in Stratford-upon-Avon. There has been an inn on this site since medieval times. This Grade II-listed pub has authentic olde-worlde charm, with a fine, timbered frontage, wooden beams, flagstone floors and irregular sized rooms. There is a rear bar with a restaurant and a cosy front bar. It has been under new management since 2023 and well-kept Greene King ales and regular guest ales feature. Popular with locals and also theatre-goers. Dogs are welcome.
✿☺⬤≠(Stratford Upon Avon)🚌❀❀❀♪

Stratford Alehouse 🄻

12B Greenhill Street, CV37 6LF

☎ 07746 807966 ⊕ thestratfordalehouse.com

4 changing beers (sourced nationally; often Byatt's, North Cotswold, XT) 🄶

This friendly, one-bar micropub has just celebrated its 10th birthday. A range of gravity cask ales are offered, with a dark beer always available, along with Hogan's cider, craft cans, wines and gins. It can get very busy and lively, especially when vinyl music is being played. Over 1,600 different beers from more than 400 breweries have been served in the last decade. Savoury snacks are sold and free doggy biscuits are provided.
≠(Stratford Upon Avon)⬤🚌❀❀♪

Studley

Weatheroak Tap House 🄻

21A High Street, B80 7HN

☎ (01527) 854433 ⊕ weatheroakbrewery.co.uk

Weatheroak Bees Knees, Victoria Works; 3 changing beers (sourced locally; often Beowulf, Church End) 🅗

Popular and welcoming micropub with two small, cosy rooms. It is the outlet for the nearby Weatheroak brewery, whose beers are available, including their own stout in winter, alongside guests from other small breweries. Basic snacks and packs of sweets are available, and takeaway food can be brought in from the chip shop next door. The pub prides itself on supporting local community events Q✿☆♣⬤P🚌(X19,247)❀❀

Warton

Office at Warton 🄻

Church Road, B79 0JN

☎ (01827) 894001 ⊕ theofficeatwarton.co.uk

Draught Bass; 2 changing beers (often Church End, Oakham) 🅗

Community-focused pub catering for a wide audience, particularly as this is now the last remaining pub in the village. The large bar area features largescreen TVs, usually showing sport and horse racing. There is a raised side area and a comfy upstairs room with a pool table. Open fires feature both upstairs and downstairs. A suntrap beer terrace on two levels is to the rear. Regular live music and quizzes are held. ✿☺♣P❀❀♪

Warwick

Ale Hub Warwick

Chase Meadow Square, Narrow Hall Meadow, CV34 6BT

Wye Valley Butty Bach; 3 changing beers (sourced nationally) 🅗

The Ale Hub in Warwick is the seventh pub opened by this small, family-owned chain of pubs. With four handpumps offering Butty Bach permanently and three revolving ales, they pride themselves on selling well-kept real ales, as well as a range of other beverages, including craft beers. The relaxed atmosphere and weekly quiz and bingo nights are helping this pub become a real community hub. Q♿P🚌

Cape of Good Hope 🄻

66 Lower Cape, CV34 5DP (off Cape Rd)

☎ (01926) 498138 ⊕ thecapeofgoodhopepub.com

Church Farm Session IPA; Hook Norton Hooky; Purity Mad Goose; Wye Valley Butty Bach; 2 changing beers (often Full Circle, Odyssey, Tiny Rebel) 🅗

Historic alehouse on the Grand Union Canal, dating from 1798, and welcoming to canal users and locals. The original building on the waterside is now the front bar, with a modern extension to the rear. Internal decorations feature canal memorabilia, including interesting maps. Four permanent real ales are offered, along with two locally sourced guest beers. The friendly staff are knowledgeable, and proud to serve local ales and food. There is outside seating by the canal, next to a busy double lock. ✿☺🖢⬤♣P🚌(G1)❀❀

Eagle

The Holloway, CV34 4SJ

☎ (01926) 493673

3 changing beers (sourced nationally; often Attic, North Cotswold, Siren) 🅗

Warwick's smallest pub is located in an old cellar tucked away on the famous Holloway just off the square. This quirky, friendly little pub, frequented by locals and visitors, has three changing cask beers and two craft taps. Seating is cosy, with some seats on the pavement outside. It has featured over 300 real ales and over 200 craft ales in its two years. There is often themed music playing. ✿☺▲❀❀

Four Penny Pub 🏆

27-29 Crompton Street, CV34 6HJ (near racecourse, between A429 and A4189)

☎ (01926) 491360 ⊕ 4pennyhotel.co.uk

6 changing beers (sourced nationally; often Church Farm, Hook Norton) 🅗

Housed in a Georgian building dating from around 1800, this pub lies a short distance from the town centre, close to the racecourse and castle. The single, split-level room has a contemporary feel and a relaxed atmosphere, and there is a large outside seating area. A selection of traditional pub classics and old favourites are served, as well as daily specials. Good, home-made roasts are served on Sunday. Local CAMRA Pub of the Year 2024.
Q✿☺❀🖢⬤▲⬤🚌❀❀♪

Old Post Office L

12 West Street, CV34 6AN

☎ 07764 244302

North Cotswold Shagweaver Ⓗ; 3 changing beers (often Attic, Byatt's, Church End) Ⓗ/Ⓖ

Warwick's first micropub was converted from an old post office and opened in 2014. It is a traditional, yet quirky pub, with an interesting interior. Popular with real ale enthusiasts and local residents, the pub has a diverse choice of constantly rotating real and craft ales, including five handpulled cask ales, four craft keg beer taps, lager, and up to three real ciders. A range of wines, spirits, quality whiskies and alcohol-free drinks are also sold. A winner of local CAMRA Pub of the Year on several occasions. Q ☼ Å ◑ ₴ ❀ ☏ ♪

Wild Boar L

27 Lakin Road, CV34 5BU

☎ (01926) 499968 ● wildboarwarwick.co.uk

Slaughterhouse Saddleback Best Bitter; 5 changing beers (often Everards, Slaughterhouse) Ⓗ

Award-winning Project William community pub, close to the railway station. Housed in an end-of-terrace Victorian building, it has a bar, snug and separate beer hall that was formerly a skittle alley. The pub is the taphouse for Slaughterhouse brewery. Regular beers include

Slaughterhouse, Everards and guest ales. Outside is an attractive patio hop garden – the hops are used for Slaughterhouse's annual brew, the Hop Head. Q ☼ ☀ ◑ ⇌ ♠ ₴ (X17) ❀ ☏ ♪

Whichford

Norman Knight L

CV36 5PE (2 miles E of A3400 at Long Compton, facing village green)

☎ (01608) 684621 ● thenormanknight.co.uk

Hook Norton Hooky; Prescott Hill Climb; house beer (by Goff's); 2 changing beers (sourced regionally; often Goff's, Purity, XT) Ⓗ

A friendly pub in the centre of this picturesque village, popular with locals and visitors. Its attractive decor and stone-flagged floor contribute to a cosy and comfortable ambience. High-quality food features locally sourced ingredients where possible. It holds monthly music nights, and in summer hosts classic car meetings on the third Thursday of the month. Muddy boots and muddy paws are always welcome. Accommodation is available in high-spec glamping pods behind the garden. Motorhomes are welcome and electric car charging is available. Q ☼ ☀ ⇌ ◑ Å ♣ ♠ P ₴ ❀ ☏ ♪

Eagle, Warwick (Photo: Emma Haines)

WEST MIDLANDS

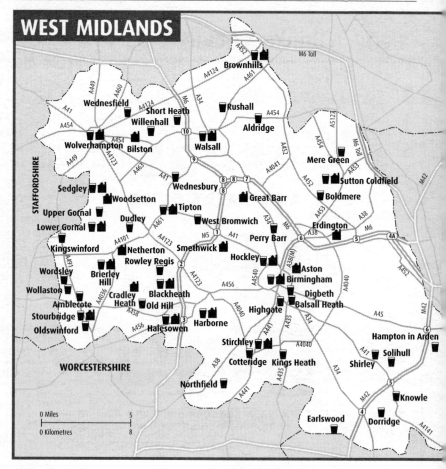

Aldridge

Turtle's Head 🅛

14 Croft Parade, WS9 8LY
☎ 07513 320525 ⊕ theturtleshead.co.uk
3 changing beers (sourced regionally) 🅗
Opened in 2015, this micropub in the centre of Aldridge, within a shopping parade, offers a warm welcome. It serves a range of three ever-changing ales, mainly from local and regional breweries. Bar snacks include freshly-made cobs, scratchings and complimentary cheese and pâté on Sunday. Customers may bring their own food if they are drinking. Closed on Monday except for bank holidays. Discounts are available on Tuesday.
🍷🏵🅰🖶🕸🛜

Amblecote

Red Lion

147 Brettell Lane, DY8 4BA
☎ (01384) 671743
Holden's Golden Glow; Salopian Oracle, Lemon Dream; 3 changing beers (sourced nationally; often Salopian) 🅗
This smart and inviting pub which exudes class is partly owned by the Furious Pub Company and was refurbished in 2021. It is popular with a wide customer mix and can get busy on Friday and Saturday nights. Full meals and a selection of freshly made cobs and pies are served all

day. A selection of real ales with two changing guests from small breweries, both local and national, are on the bar. A dress code operates on Thursday to Sunday after 7pm. Q🍴🅰🖶(6,16)🛜🎵

Robin Hood 🍷 🅛

196 Collis Street, DY8 4EQ (on A4102 one way street; off Brettell Ln A461)
☎ 07436 821120
Bathams Best Bitter; Enville Ginger Beer; St Austell Proper Job; Three Tuns XXX; Wye Valley HPA; 3 changing beers (sourced nationally) 🅗
A traditional Black Country local with fine ales and always a warm welcome; 2025 will see the pub celebrate 170 years as a licenced house. The front rooms house a wonderful beer bottle collection including international and historic brews. The pub serves freshly-made cobs and pork pies, and features some national guest ales but the LocAle scheme is emphasised on more local beers on permanent sale. The rear outside area now has a permanent marquee.
Q🍷🏵🅰🍴👶🖶(6,16) 🛜

Starving Rascal 🅛

1 Brettell Lane, DY8 4BN
☎ (01384) 481083
Black Country Bradley's Finest Golden, Pig on the Wall, Fireside; 7 changing beers (sourced nationally) 🅗

Bathams Best Bitter; Church End Goat's Milk; Enville Ale; Wye Valley HPA, Butty Bach ⊞

An oasis in an otherwise cask ale desert, this is a two-roomed traditional pub with a central bar. The left-hand room, as you enter, has an 80-inch screen for sport, with a smaller TV above the bar in the right-hand room, but no screens in the rear seating area, popular with diners. The pub also boasts a large, covered patio for warmer weather, and a function room is upstairs. A superb tandoori menu is served evenings and all day Sunday. Conveniently located for Edgbaston cricket ground. Q☆⛱❄️🅿️🚊(50)☻🛜

Birmingham: City Centre

Bacchus 🅛

Burlington Arcade, New Street, B2 4JH
☎ (0121) 632 5445
Purity Pure UBU; Sharp's Doom Bar; St Austell Nicholson's Pale Ale; 3 changing beers (sourced nationally; often Purity) ⊞
Hidden away below the Burlington Hotel (formerly the Midland), this pub has a number of distinct areas of discrete seating, many with a unique historic theme. A separate dining area is available, but meals can be eaten anywhere in the pub. It is part of the Nicholson's chain, and is handily situated opposite Grand Central tram stop and New Street station.
⊞🅖♿️➤(New Street) 🅡(Grand Central) 🚊🛜♪

Bull 🅛

1 Price Street, B4 6JU (off St Chads Queensway)
☎ (0121) 333 6757 ⊕ thebullbirmingham.co.uk
Church End Gravediggers Ale; Hook Norton Old Hooky; Oakham Citra; 1 changing beer (sourced nationally; often Backyard, Burning Soul, Green Duck) ⊞
A quirky country-style pub in the centre of Birmingham, near Aston University. This popular back-street local, with friendly staff, is one of the oldest pubs in Birmingham and has a comfortable and homely feel. Two distinct drinking areas surround a U-shaped bar with a smaller back room offering more privacy. A collection of 300 jugs adorns the ceiling, along with a number of old pictures and memorabilia. A small garden area is at the rear. Traditional, hearty pub food is served and guest beers change regularly. There are 11 en-suite bedrooms available. ☆⛱🛏️🍴🅖♿️➤(Snow Hill)🅡(St Chads)🅿️🚊☻🛜

Cherry Reds 🅛

88-92 John Bright Street, B1 1BN
☎ (0121) 643 5716 ⊕ cherryreds.com
Birmingham Pale Brummie; 3 changing beers (sourced regionally; often Attic) ⊞
Stylish independent café bar a stone's throw from New Street station. The downstairs bar is small but there is additional seating upstairs, accessed via a steep staircase. Several cask ales are available, supplemented by a range of craft keg, bottles and cans. The food menu is extensive and freshly made with plenty of options for vegetarians, and is well-known for home-made cakes. Two function rooms are available for hire.
☆🍴♿️➤(New Street) 🅡(Grand Central) ♠️🚊🛜♪

Colmore

116 Colmore Row, B3 3BD
☎ (0121) 238 1041 ⊕ colmoretap.co.uk
Thornbridge Astryd, Brother Rabbit, Lord Marples, Jaipur; 5 changing beers (sourced nationally; often Saltaire) ⊞
This Thornbridge pub is a worthy winner of a CAMRA design award in the conversion to pub category. It retains extensive wood panelling and high quality fixtures and fittings from its previous days when it was a bank. Four

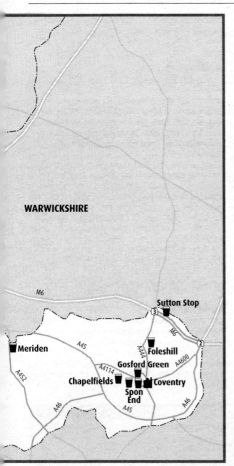

WARWICKSHIRE

M6

Sutton Stop
③

Meriden   A45   Foleshill   A4600   ②
A4114   Gosford Green
A452   Chapelfields   Coventry
Spon End
A46   A45

Purchased by Black Country Ales in 2020, and refurbished during the last Covid lockdown, the bar now has a central servery for all areas upstairs. Downstairs is a cosy little room for events and functions. The pub is nationally famous as being reputedly haunted. Two ciders are on handpull but may not be real. The car park has been removed to provide an enclosed garden.
♿️♣️🅿️🚊(6)☻🛜♪

Swan 🅛

10 Brettell Lane, DY8 4BN (on A461, ½ mile after A491)
☎ (01384) 591600
Enville Ale; Holden's Golden Glow; Salopian Oracle; Wye Valley HPA; 4 changing beers ⊞
This free house has been totally refurbished by the owners of the Red Lion down the road. There is now only one room served by a central bar. The difficult entry with the old serving hatch has gone, allowing customers to walk straight to the bar. The original metal bar separator in the lounge is now used as a garden feature. The derelict buildings to the rear have gone and a tidy smoking area has been created. Only cobs and snacks are available. ⛱🚊(6)☻🛜♪

Birmingham: Balsall Heath

Old Moseley Arms ★ 🅛

53 Tindal Street, B12 9QU (400yds off Moseley Rd)
☎ (0121) 440 1954 ⊕ oldmoseleyarms.co.uk

regular Thornbridge beers are served plus five guests and additional craft beers from Pivovar as well as 20 gins. A comprehensive pizza menu is also available, including gluten-free options. There is a pool table downstairs. It can get busy with office workers after work.
⛄🍺👫♿≹(New Street) ᚏ(Town Hall) ♣🚌🌸🎵🛜

Craven Arms 🄻
47 Upper Gough Street, B1 1JG (in sidestreet nr the Mailbox)
☎ (0121) 269 4113
Black Country Bradley's Finest Golden, Pig on the Wall, Fireside; 7 changing beers (sourced nationally; often Fixed Wheel, Mallinsons, Salopian) ⑭
This early 19th-century former Holder's outlet, restored and refurbished in 2022 by Black Country Ales, sports an attractive blue-tiled exterior and a cosy one room interior. Handpulls take prominence on the bar and, in addition to three permanent Black Country beers, seven changing guest casks come from breweries across Birmingham and the West Midlands. Three changing craft keg beers and cider are also served. Cobs, pork pies and sausage rolls are available at most times and a real fire may await when cold.
⛄♿≹(New Street) ᚏ(Town Hall) 🌸🛜🎵

Post Office Vaults 🄻
84 New Street, B2 4BA (entrances on both New St and Pinfold St)
☎ (0121) 643 7354 ⊕ postofficevaults.co.uk
Hobsons Mild; house beer (by Kinver); 4 changing beers (sourced nationally; often Abbeydale, Oakham) ⑭
A subterranean pub, situated close to New Street station, accessed by a single red door on New Street near Victoria Square or from the rear on Pinfold Street. Six real ales, a selection of ciders, a large selection of foreign bottled beers, and a range of cans and bottles are served. It is a destination pub for foreign beer enthusiasts. Food isn't served but customers are welcome to bring their own and cutlery can be provided. Bar billiards can be played free of charge.
Q≹(New Street) ᚏ(Town Hall) ♣🍔🚌🌸🛜

Prince of Wales
84 Cambridge Street, B1 2NP (behind ICC/NIA and Rep theatre)
☎ (0121) 269 4125
Black Country Bradley's Finest Golden, Chain Ale, Pig on the Wall; 7 changing beers (sourced nationally) ⑭
A well-loved pub that continues to thrive after a sympathetic refurbishment by Black Country Ales in 2022. This single-room pub is a welcome oasis for the community, close to Centenary Square, the ICC, NIA and the Rep theatre. Expect the usual Black Country beers plus up to seven guests. Freshly-made cobs and pasties are on offer. Quiz night is fortnightly on Tuesday. An interesting display of old views of Birmingham adorn the walls. ᚏ(Library)🍔🚌🌸🛜

Pure Craft Bar & Kitchen 🄻
30 Waterloo Street, B2 5TJ (5 mins from New Street and Snow Hill stations)
☎ (0121) 237 5666 ⊕ purecraftbars.com
Purity Bunny Hop, Pure Gold, Jimbo, Mad Goose, Pure UBU ⑭
Purity brewery's first outlet, set in a traditional building with an industrial interior in the centre of the business district. The open and welcoming bar features Purity beers on cask and 14 keg lines, including some guests from smaller breweries. Basic seating is available in the main bar area and the two smaller rooms downstairs; the latter two can be booked for functions. There is an

emphasis on gourmet food and tables are available to book online. It can get busy with office workers after work. ⛄🍺≹(New Street)ᚏ(Town Hall)🚌🌸🛜

Wellington 🄻
37 Bennetts Hill, B2 5SN (5 mins from New Street and Snow Hill stations)
☎ (0121) 269 4112 ⊕ thewellingtonrealale.co.uk
Black Country Bradley's Finest Golden, Pig on the Wall, Fireside; Froth Blowers Piffle Snonker; Oakham Citra; Wye Valley HPA; 11 changing beers (sourced nationally; often Fixed Wheel, Froth Blowers, Titanic) ⑭
A Guide regular, this Black Country Ales local has been run by the same landlord for 18 years. There are 27 handpulls over two floors, dispensing seven regular beers and nine guests. A broad range of whiskies, rums and gins are available from the impressive back fitting. The suntrap roof terrace is a hidden oasis in the urban landscape. Regular quizzes, folk nights and cheese nights are held. Food is not served – feel free to bring your own and plates will be provided.
Q🌸♿≹(Snow Hill) ᚏ(Grand Central) ♣P🚌🛜🎵

Birmingham: Cotteridge

RedBeer'd 🄻
1891 Pershore Road, B30 3DJ
2 changing beers (often Halton Turner) ⑭
Set over two floors this micropub in a converted shop is conveniently located for Kings Norton railway station. Serving from two cask handpulls and up to 10 keg taps, beers are often from local breweries such as Halton Turner and Leviathan. Up to four ciders or perries from

REAL ALE BREWERIES	
52 Degrees	Brownhills
AJä s	Walsall
Angel Ales	Halesowen
Attic 🌾	Birmingham
Banks's	Wolverhampton
Bathams	Brierley Hill
Birmingham	Birmingham
Black Country	Lower Gornal
Brewhouse & Kitchen 🍴	Sutton Coldfield
Burning Soul	Birmingham: Hockley
Byatt's 🌾	Coventry
Craddock's	Stourbridge (brewing suspended)
Cult Of Oak	Netherton
Davenports	Smethwick
Dhillon's 🌾	Coventry
Fixed Wheel 🌾	Blackheath
Fountain	Cradley Heath
Froth Blowers	Erdington
Glasshouse	Stirchley
Green Duck 🌾	Stourbridge
Holden's	Woodsetton
Indian	Great Barr
Leviathan 🌾	Sutton Coldfield
Mashionistas	Coventry
New Invention 🌾	Walsall
Newbridge	Bilston
Olde Swan 🍴	Netherton
Ostlers 🍴	Harborne
Rock & Roll 🌾	Birmingham
Sarah Hughes 🍴	Sedgley
Silhill 🌾	Birmingham: Aston
Toll End 🍴	Tipton
Twisted Barrel	Coventry
Two Towers	Birmingham
Underground Medicine	Coventry

Hogans and Oliver's are also served. Comfier seating is available on the ground floor, while upstairs features chairs and barrels. The toilet is located upstairs. Dogs are welcome and encouraged. Third and half pints are available. Card payment only. Drinkers can bring food from outside. ⛄≒(Kings Norton)●🍴🚻♿🕸

Birmingham: Digbeth

Spotted Dog ★ 🅛
104 Warwick Street, B12 0NH
☎ (0121) 772 3822
Castle Rock Harvest Pale; Holden's Black Country Mild; 2 changing beers (sourced nationally) 🅗
A multi-roomed traditional pub, family-owned, with the same landlord since the 1980s. Rugby and Irish sports are shown on largescreen TVs. Outside is an extensive covered garden and smoking area with heaters, a large real fireplace, a barbecue, a projection screen and eclectic adornments. Traditional Irish music night is on alternate Mondays, jazz night on Tuesday, and the pub is the home of Na Madrai golf society and the Digbeth O'lympics. There is a competitively priced cask mild on the bar. Busy when Birmingham City play at home.
⛄❀♿≒(Bordesley) ●🍴🚻♿🎵

Birmingham: Harborne

Hop Garden
19 Metchley Lane, B17 0HT (100yds from High St, at back of M&S)
☎ (0121) 427 7904 🌐 hopgarden.pub
5 changing beers (sourced nationally) 🅗
Small and cosy pub just off the main High Street. The pub is serious about craft beer, to the point of rarely stocking many mainstream products. It serves five real ales from small and local breweries, up to 10 craft beers and four traditional ciders. There is also an interesting selection of bottled beers. The decor is original and eclectic. Outside there is heated seating for 82 people, which can be hired. For events, bookings and a beer board please visit their website. Q⛄❀🍴♿♣●🚻♿🎵

White Horse 🅛
2 York Street, B17 0HG
☎ (0121) 608 7641 🌐 whitehorseharborne.com
Church End Gravediggers Ale; Greene King Abbot; 3 changing beers (sourced regionally; often Holden's, Thornbridge, Wye Valley) 🅗
Small, friendly, traditional community pub just off Harborne High Street. Beers from Ostlers brewery, based at the back of the pub, as well as guests on up to six handpulls are served. A two-room pub, the smaller room has four rotating craft beers on KeyKeg (occasionally keg) from Ostlers and other small breweries. Check availability in real time via the beer board on their website. There is also a gig guide showing upcoming artists for Saturday night live music. TVs throughout the pub show sport. Q❀♿●🚻♿🕸🎵

Birmingham: Highgate

Lamp Tavern 🅛
157 Barford Street, B5 6AH (550yds from A441 Pershore Rd near bottom of Hurst St)
Hobsons Town Crier; 2 changing beers (sourced nationally; often AJs, Froth Blowers, Fuller's) 🅗
A hidden gem of a pub with a small single bar, almost the last of its kind, on the edge of Digbeth. Run by the same landlord since 1993, it has a homely feel despite its industrial location. It can close early if there are no customers, so ring ahead if intending a later visit. A

function room at the back holds about 35 people. A folk club is held on Friday evenings. The bar is cash only, and nearest cash points are on Digbeth High Street or Hurst Street. Closed Monday, Tuesday and Thursday.
⛄♿🚻♿🎵

Birmingham: Hockley

1000 Trades
16 Frederick Street, B1 3HE
☎ (0121) 233 6293 🌐 1000trades.org.uk
4 changing beers (sourced nationally) 🅗
Sporting bare boards and brickwork, this bar has two distinct areas. The front bar area offers a small number of tables around an open fire, while the raised rear section has booth-style seating for eating and drinking. Up to four cask beers are served along with four keg lines for craft beers. The food is upmarket and from guest chefs and pop-ups. Sunday lunches are popular and booking is advised. A variety of events are hosted including open mic, theatre and themed music nights. The pin badge wall downstairs honours this 19th-century building's history.
❀🍴≒(Jewellery Quarter) 🚋(Jewellery Quarter) ❀🕸🎵

Burning Soul Brewery 🅛
Unit 1, 51 Mott Street, B19 3HE
🌐 burningsoulbrewshop.co.uk
13 changing beers (sourced locally; often Burning Soul)
A brewery and taproom just off Great Hampton Street in Hockley. One cask handpull and 11 KeyKeg lines all dispense live beer. Situated on an industrial estate, the decor is functional but comfortable, and there is outdoor decking for the warmer months. A good range of canned beer is available. Only open Friday and Saturday, opening hours can vary, check social media for details. Card payment is preferred.
❀≒(Jewellery Quarter) 🚋(St Paul's) ♣P🚻

Church
22 Great Hampton Street, B18 6AQ
☎ 07878 843703 🌐 thechurchjq.co.uk
Everards Sunchaser, Tiger; 2 changing beers (often Attic, Everards) 🅗
A street-corner pub with separate restaurant area and suntrap roof garden, it was extensively refurbished in 2022 and is now described as a pub and dining room. The main building has two rooms, one being the main bar and the other a snug for more relaxed drinking. It is a handy base from which to explore the Jewellery Quarter. A high-quality food menu is available throughout the day. Card payment only.
⛄❀🍴≒(Jewellery Quarter) 🚋(Jewellery Quarter) 🚋(16,74) ❀🕸

Rock & Roll Brewhouse 🅛
19 Hall Street, B18 6BS
☎ 07922 554181
Rock & Roll Voodoo Mild; 2 changing beers (sourced locally; often Rock & Roll) 🅗
A quirky brewery taproom on the first floor above the brewery, in the heart of the Jewellery Quarter, it is well worth checking out. Three real ales are available, all brewed on-site and vegan. There is a focus on a love of music, with memorabilia adorning the walls, books available to read and live music. When live music isn't being performed a set list of vinyls are played, often themed around music news that week. Check social media for details. It can get busy when bands are playing. Only open Friday and Saturday.
❀≒(Jewellery Quarter) 🚋(St Paul's) ●🚻❀🎵

Birmingham: Kings Heath

Hop & Scotch 🍷 ⓛ
9 Institute Road, B14 7EG
☎ (0121) 679 8807 ⊕ hopscotchbrum.com
5 changing beers (sourced regionally; often Attic, Green Duck, Infinity) Ⓗ
One-room micropub just off Kings Heath High Street. Five cask beers, usually local, are served, plus a mixture of local and national craft beers, a cider, and usually a German beer, on keg or KeyKeg across 10 taps. Bottled and canned ales are also sold. The bar attracts a wide age range and can get busy in the evening. Dogs are welcome with dog snacks offered. Its sister venue is two doors down, with an emphasis on European beer. Local CAMRA Pub of the Year 2023. ➤&●🗐❀🕿♪

Kings Heath Cricket & Sports Club
Charlton House, 247 Alcester Road South, B14 6DT
☎ (0121) 444 1913 ⊕ kingsheathsportsclub.com
Wye Valley HPA, Butty Bach; 1 changing beer (sourced regionally) Ⓗ
A welcoming two-roomed sports club, just south of Kings Heath. Upon entering, the right-hand room is a small, cosy lounge, while the left-hand room is a large sports bar complete with two large TV screens, a dartboard and several snooker tables. There is parking to the front of the building, as well as a large Pay & Display car park to the rear. Regular quiz nights are held plus live music in the function room. CAMRA members are asked to sign the visitors guest book. Q➤❀🕽&♣P🗐🕿

Red Lion
229 Vicarage Road, B14 7LY
☎ (0121) 444 2803
Birmingham Pale Brummie; Purity Pure UBU; 3 changing beers (sourced nationally) Ⓗ
A Grade II-listed imposing neo-gothic designed pub built in 1908. It has an open-plan design decorated in the Ember Inns style that incorporates original features. It was refurbished in 2023. There is a large garden at the front and plenty of parking spaces to the rear. The focus is on food, but three or four cask beers are available at all times. Regular quizzes are held Sunday and Thursday with poker on Monday night. Ale prices are reduced on Monday and Thursday. ➤❀🕽&P🗐🕿♪

Birmingham: Northfield

Black Horse ★ ⓛ ✅
Bristol Road South, B31 2QT (opp Sainsbury's)
☎ (0121) 477 1800
Greene King Abbot; Ruddles Best Bitter; Sharp's Doom Bar; 4 changing beers (sourced nationally; often Purity, Silhill) Ⓗ
A Grade II-listed Brewer's Tudor pub, it has been identified by CAMRA as having a nationally important historic pub interior after being refurbished and reopened by Wetherspoon in 2010. Built in 1929 to the Bateman & Bateman design, this midland roadhouse replaced an earlier, smaller pub that had been on the site. It is a multi-room pub with an extravagant half-timbered exterior, baronial hall with tie-beam roof, and barrel-vaulted lobby. There is a large car park to the side and a bowling green to the rear. A function room is available upstairs. Q➤❀🕽&➤(Northfield)P🗐🕿

Birmingham: Perry Barr

Arthur Robertson ✅
51-53 One Stop Retail Park, Walsall Road, B42 1AA
☎ (0121) 332 5910

Greene King Abbot; Ruddles Best Bitter; 2 changing beers Ⓗ
A popular, large open-plan Wetherspoon at the One Stop shopping centre in Perry Barr, it was named after Birchfield Harriers' very first Olympian and medal winner. The manager tries to keep three local guest ales available alongside the standard offerings when possible, and the standard Wetherspoon food menu is served. It can get busy when Aston Villa are playing at home. Q➤❀🕽&➤(Perry Barr)P🗐🕿

Birmingham: Stirchley

Birmingham Brewing Company Taproom
Unit 15 Stirchley Trading Estate, Hazelwell Road, B30 2PF
☎ (0121) 724 0399 ⊕ birminghambrewingcompany.co.uk
Birmingham Bitter Brummie; 2 changing beers (sourced locally; often Birmingham) Ⓗ
Craft beer brewery and tap on Stirchley Trading Estate. The tap is open Thursday to Sunday, serving up to four cask beers and four kegs, including one low/no alcohol option. Locally made ciders, as well as wines, spirits and soft drinks are also sold. Food is available at weekends from a changing lineup of street food vendors. A large outdoor seating area is available during summer months. ➤❀➤(Bournville) ●🗐❀♪

Wildcat Tap
1381-1383 Pershore Road, B30 2JR
☎ (0121) 213 2623 ⊕ stirchleywildcat.co.uk
4 changing beers (sourced nationally) Ⓗ
Located on the Pershore Road, this independent bar is spacious for a micropub, with adequate seating, although does get busy at weekends with a mixed age group clientele. The beer range of cask and keg is adventurous and interesting, with up to four cask beers on handpump and eight craft keg lines, complemented by a selection of bottled craft beers, gin, whisky and soft drinks. A vast array of tabletop games are available to play. Convenient for buses 27, 45, and 47 and close to Bournville railway station. ➤&➤(Bournville)●🗐❀🕿

Blackheath

Britannia ✅
124 Halesowen Street, B65 0ES
☎ (0121) 559 0010
Greene King Abbot; Ruddles Best Bitter Ⓗ**; Sharp's Doom Bar** Ⓗ/Ⓖ**; 6 changing beers (sourced nationally)** Ⓗ
An L-shaped Wetherspoon outlet in the heart of Blackheath. The garden at the rear provides a pleasant space away from the main A4099. The exposed brick façade is often decorated with hanging baskets in the warmer seasons. Six changing beers are accompanied by three permanent beers. Pictures placed throughout the pub depict local monuments and historic characters. Food is served all day, every day. A small car park for customers can be accessed via Cross Street. ➤❀🕽&➤(Rowley Regis)♣P🗐🕿

Cyder & Cobb
167 Halesowen Street, B65 0ES (exit Market Place island onto Halesowen St; pub is on the right)
☎ 07849 402244
Ludlow Blonde; Wye Valley HPA; 3 changing beers (sourced nationally; often Oakham, Salopian, Thornbridge) Ⓗ
An intimate and well-appointed micropub which opened in 2021. The interior contains six wooden tables and

benches. A standing bar serves up to four beers, with guests sourced nationally, and a selection of real ciders. A variety of small breweries are usually featured. Easy-listening music is played, and it is a easy way to spend a few hours. A selection of cobs and pies are available. ⏰&≠(Rowley Regis)♣●🅿❄🛜♪

Old Bush Revived

44 Powke Lane, B65 0AD
☎ (0121) 599 7963
Black Country Bradley's Finest Golden Ⓗ, Pig on the Wall Ⓗ/Ⓟ, Fireside; 8 changing beers (often Black Country) Ⓗ
Former Marston's pub that has been acquired and extensively refurbished by Black Country Ales; it was their 46th acquisition. The work has given a very open-plan feel to this accessible one-roomed pub with a real fire. Ten ales and two ciders are served on handpull (the ciders may sometimes be real). Outside is a partially covered patio area to the rear, bench seating to the side, and a car park. ⏰❄≠(Old Hill)♣●🅿🖂

Boldmere

Bishop Vesey Ⓛ

63 Boldmere Road, B73 5XA
☎ (0121) 355 5077
Greene King Abbot; Oakham Citra; Ruddles Best Bitter; Sharp's Doom Bar; 7 changing beers (sourced nationally; often Backyard, Oakham) Ⓗ
Named after a 16th-century Bishop and the town's greatest benefactor, who is recognised with a carved wooden pulpit by the entrance. A good mix of guest beers are offered, many from local microbreweries, along with good-value food. As well as extensive seating areas upstairs and down, there is a spacious rooftop garden, and a smaller beer garden downstairs to the rear. The building was constructed in 1931 and was formerly a builders' merchants and joinery works. ⏰❄Ⓓ&≠(Wylde Green)♣🖂🛜

Boldmere Tap

363 Boldmere Road, B73 5HE
☎ (0121) 386 2218
Joule's Pure Blonde, Pale Ale, Slumbering Monk; 1 changing beer Ⓗ
Formerly a bottle shop, this corner premises has been operated by Joule's for a decade. There is lots of reclaimed wood, including some intricate carved panels, plus a number of elegant stained glass panels. The main room, containing a log fire for colder days, splits into a number of intimate areas, with a large room to the side which in turn leads to a small function room. ⏰Ⓓ≠(Chester Road)♣🅿🖂❄🛜

Brierley Hill

Rose & Crown Ⓛ

161 Bank Street, DY5 3DD (on B4179)
☎ (01384) 936166
Holden's Black Country Bitter, Golden Glow, Special; 1 changing beer (often Holden's) Ⓗ
This traditional pub was originally two terraced properties. One end of the bar is dominated by a dartboard. A conservatory provides extra space and is used as a function room, opening onto a small garden with tables and benches. There is a bus stop outside, or a five-minute walk takes you to Brierley Hill High Street, which is served by several bus routes. Holden's seasonal beers are rotated. Q⏰❄♣🅿🖂❄🛜

Vine ★

10 Delph Road, DY5 2TN
☎ (01384) 78293
Bathams Mild Ale, Best Bitter Ⓗ
An unspoilt brewery tap with an ornately decorated façade proclaiming the Shakespearian quotation 'Blessing of your heart, you brew good ale'. An elongated pub with a labyrinthine feel, the front bar is staunchly traditional, while the larger rear room has its own servery, leather seating and a dartboard. The homely lounge was partly converted from former brewery offices. Local specialties such as faggots and home-made pies are served weekdays, with generously filled rolls and pork pies at all times. Q⏰❄Ⓓ♣🅿🖂(8)❄🛜

Brownhills

Jiggers Whistle Ⓛ

5-7 High Street, WS8 6ED
☎ 07854 356976
3 changing beers (sourced regionally) Ⓗ
Opened in 2017, this micropub has one room split into three interconnected drinking areas. It offers a wide range of cask and craft beers and some real ciders. As well as beers from regional breweries, its own beers are produced locally by both Backyard and Green Duck breweries. Bar snacks are available at weekends. The owners, who offer customers a warm and friendly welcome, are keen to support local events and groups, including a darts team. Closed on Tuesday. Q⏰♣●🅿🖂❄🛜

Swan Ⓛ

93 Pelsall Road, WS8 7DL (10 mins walk from Brownhills town centre)
☎ (01543) 548033
Black Country Bradley's Finest Golden, Fireside; 8 changing beers (sourced nationally; often Salopian, Black Country) Ⓗ
A cracking local pub, refurbished by Black Country Ales in 2023, comprising a large single room with a real fire, served by a single bar. There is an outside drinking area at the front of the pub, and a partially covered seating area to the rear. As well as the regular Black Country Ales, up to six guest beers and two ciders are on the bar. The Swan is a comfortable and welcoming venue for both locals and visitors and is a recent local CAMRA Pub of the Year. ⏰❄&♣🅿🖂(8)❄🛜♪

Coventry: Chapelfields

Hearsall Inn Ⓛ

45 Craven Street, CV5 8DS (1 mile W of city centre, off Allesley Old Rd)
☎ (024) 7671 5729 🌐 hearsallinn.com
Church End Goat's Milk; Draught Bass; 2 changing beers (sourced nationally; often Greene King) Ⓗ
Built in the 1850s to serve the historic watchmaking district, this free house has been in the same family's ownership for over 25 years. It has separate bar and lounge areas and a paved patio at the front with a wall-mounted defibrillator. The pub is home to a darts team and hosts traditional Irish music on Tuesday night as well as local community meetings. Four handpumps dispense local and regional beers. Freshly-made batches are available throughout the day. ⏰❄♣🖂❄🛜

Coventry: City Centre

Earl of Mercia ✔

18 High Street, CV1 5RE

☎ (024) 7643 3990
Greene King Abbot; Ruddles Best Bitter; Sharp's Doom Bar; 5 changing beers (sourced nationally; often Byatt's) ⊞

A popular Wetherspoon pub converted from a bank built in the Victorian era and named after Leofric, Earl of Mercia, who founded Coventry's first cathedral in 1043 with his wife Godiva. Offering a fine view of the Council House through large windows, it is split into ground floor and mezzanine levels and has a patio on the wide pavement at the front. It is handily situated for the historic cathedral quarter, university and city centre shops. Occasional tap takeovers are held. ⑃❀⊕�⇌☐☎

Gatehouse Tavern ⅃

44-46 Hill Street, CV1 4AN (close to Belgrade Theatre and Spon St, near J8 of ring road)
☎ (024) 7663 0140
Draught Bass; M&B Brew XI; 4 changing beers (sourced locally, often Byatt's, Church End) ⊞

A unique pub, rebuilt by the landlord from the shell of the former Leigh Mills gatehouse. A long-term entry in the Guide, it is dedicated to high-quality real ale, good-value food and televised sports of all kinds; the latter evidenced by the depiction of the rugby Six Nations emblems in a stained-glass window. There is a monthly pub quiz, plus live music every Sunday and open mic every other Tuesday. The raised beer garden is the largest in the city centre and is popular during the summer months. ⑃❀⊕◑☐❀☎♪

Golden Cross ⅃ ✔

8 Hay Lane, CV1 5RF (near the old cathedral ruins)
☎ (024) 7655 1855 ⊕ thegoldencrosscoventry.co.uk
Bath Ales Gem; Titanic Plum Porter; 2 changing beers (sourced locally) ⊞

One of two claimants to being the oldest pub in the city, this timber-framed pub was built in 1583 on the site of the Coventry mint, opposite the cathedrals. Although much damage was done by the owners in the 1970s, great effort has been made to restore it to something more in keeping with its heritage. Good quality food is served daily. One local ale is always on tap. Live music is held at the weekend and open mic on Tuesday. ❀◑☐❀♪

Hops d'Amour ⚲ ⅃

67 Corporation Street, CV1 1GX
☎ (024) 7767 2100 ⊕ hops-damour.business.site
6 changing beers (sourced nationally) ⊞

Multiple award-winning family-owned micropub, which offers six cask and seven keg beers, one of which is gluten-free, from both local brewers and others rarely seen in the area, plus boxed ciders. Bottled and canned drinks are also available to drink in or take away. Conversation takes the place of electronic entertainment or gaming machines. Runner-up in the National Cider Pub of the Year 2023 and local CAMRA Pub of the Year and Cider Pub of the Year 2024. Q♠☐❀

Old Windmill ★ ⅃ ✔

22-23 Spon Street, CV1 3BA
☎ (024) 7625 1717 ⊕ theoldwindmillcoventry.co.uk
Morland Old Speckled Hen; Theakston Old Peculier; Timothy Taylor Landlord; 4 changing beers (sourced regionally; often Byatt's, North Cotswold, Sperrin) ⊞

A fantastic 15th-century Grade II-listed building run by the Brown family from 1931 to 1975; locals called it Ma Browns. It is an atmospheric pub with several rooms, two of which have welcoming real fires, and inglenooks. The Victorian brewery can also be seen. Food is recommended and comprises pork pies and cold platters

of meats, bread and interesting cheeses. Beer festivals are held at least twice a year. Character and history abound in this old hostelry, which is even reputed to have a ghost. ❀♣☐❀☎♪

Town Wall Tavern ★ ✔

Bond Street, CV1 4AH (behind Belgrade Theatre)
☎ (024) 7622 0963
Brains Rev James Original; Draught Bass; Theakston Old Peculier; Wye Valley HPA; 2 changing beers (sourced nationally; often Purity, Theakston) ⊞

Nestled between modern buildings, this is an oasis in time behind the Belgrade Theatre, which can be overlooked from a small sheltered outside area. Patrons can choose from the lounge, the bar, or the Donkey Box snug, so named after a local character is reputed to have brought a donkey into it. An old Atkinson brewery window marks the original external wall. Up to six real ales are available. Good-value food is cooked to order. Closed on Monday. ◑☐❀

Coventry: Foleshill

Byatt's Brewhouse Bar ⅃

Unit 7-8 Lythalls Lane Industrial Estate, Lythalls Lane, CV6 6FL
☎ (024) 7663 7996 ⊕ byattsbrewery.co.uk
6 changing beers (sourced locally; often Byatt's) ⊞

Pleasant bar attached to the brewery on a small industrial estate. It showcases up to six rotating real ales and craft beers from Byatt's range. Drinkers can enjoy the ground floor taproom with pumpclips adorning the beams, or the mezzanine area containing a collection of commissioned artworks. The bar is only open on Thursday and Friday, plus days when Coventry City are playing at home. The venue is available for private functions and brewery tours. ⑃ᵭP☐❀☎♪

Coventry: Gosford Green

Twisted Barrel Brewery & Tap House ⅃

Unit 11 FarGo Village, Far Gosford Street, CV1 5ED
☎ (024) 7610 1701 ⊕ twistedbarrelale.co.uk
1 changing beer (sourced locally; often Twisted Barrel)

Large taphouse in FarGo Village which is home to over 40 independent artisanal businesses. It has 16 keg lines, with one cask beer from the brewery always available. A small, vegan food offering is offered at busy times. Beers can be enjoyed inside overlooking the brewery, or outside in the Village over a range of seating. Regular events include the popular Home Brew Club. Closed Monday and Tuesday. ⑃ᵭᵭ☐❀☎♪

Coventry: Spon End

Broomfield Tavern ⅃

14-16 Broomfield Place, CV5 6GY (adjacent to the rugby ground but hidden from the main road)
☎ (024) 7663 0969
Froth Blowers Piffle Snonker; 7 changing beers (sourced nationally) ⊞

A genuine free house and thriving community local. Despite lengthy renovations the pub remains cosy, with a fire in the winter and extending a warm welcome to all, including dogs. A wide variety of ales is offered with some being served from oak casks. It can get busy during early evenings and before and after rugby matches at the nearby Butts Park Arena, although outside seating is now available on the roadside. Filled batches are often for sale on rugby match days. Q❀♠☐❀♪

Coventry: Sutton Stop

Greyhound Inn

Sutton Stop, Hawkesbury Junction, CV6 6DF (off Grange Rd at the jct of Coventry and Oxford canals)
☎ (024) 7745 4992 ⊕ thegreyhoundsuttonstop.co.uk
Draught Bass; Everards Old Original; 2 changing beers (sourced nationally; often Everards, Timothy Taylor) ⊞
Popular canalside pub dating from the 1830s, at Hawkesbury Junction where the Coventry and Oxford canals meet. The front patio area is an idyllic setting to watch the activity on the canal and take in the industrial architecture. In winter drinkers can enjoy a real fire in the cosy bar area. At the rear there is a separate bar and garden for summer events. A wide range of food is served in the bar and restaurant, with booking recommended. Q७❀❶▶P♠(22)❀ ⟲ ♫

Dorridge

Knowle & Dorridge Cricket Club ✓

Station Road, B93 8ET (corner of Station Rd and Grove Rd)
☎ (01564) 774338 ⊕ knowleanddorridgecc.co.uk
3 changing beers (sourced nationally; often Abbeydale, Salopian) ⊞
This established cricket club is set in an upmarket residential area. Visitors are welcome to try the ever-changing range of up to three cask conditioned ales, always in excellent condition and often from interesting breweries. There are no entry restrictions, but club members are able to purchase drinks at a reduced price. There is outside seating to watch top-class cricket in the Birmingham league. Bar snacks and filled rolls are usually available. Local CAMRA Club of the Year three years in succession. ७❀&≠♠P♠(S2,S3)❀ ⟲

Knowle & Dorridge Racquets Club

Grove Road, B93 0PH
☎ (01564) 772342 ⊕ kdrc.info
2 changing beers (sourced nationally; often Abbeydale, Salopian) ⊞
Local racquet sports club with a growing membership, now augmented by an open-door policy for people who want to sample their well-kept, rotating guest ale selection. Salopian, Abbeydale and Thornbridge are among the breweries that are regularly represented at the bar. There is a good-sized outdoor area with clear views of the tennis courts and the cricket pitch of the Knowle & Dorridge Cricket Club. ❀&≠♠P♠(S2,S3)⟲

Dudley

Malt Shovel L

46 Tower Street, DY1 1NB (located off the Broadway A459; opp Dudley College Evolve Campus)
☎ (01384) 252735
Holden's Golden Glow; Wye Valley Butty Bach; 3 changing beers (sourced nationally; often Abbeydale, Oakham) ⊞
Originally known as the Lord Wellington in the 19th century, this exciting and trendy town-centre establishment is now part of the Red Pub Co portfolio. As such, there is a popular balance of both locally-produced cask beers and modern, national breweries on the bar. Yorkshire breweries are often showcased. The mixture of seating styles includes classic benches, which contrast nicely with the high stools. There is a small number of gaming and betting machines. ७❶P♠❀ ⟲ ♫

Earlswood

Bull's Head

7 Limekiln Lane, B94 6BU
☎ (01564) 700368 ⊕ bullsheadearlswood.co.uk
Thwaites Original, IPA, Gold; 1 changing beer (often Thwaites) ⊞
Originally built in 1740 for the navvies constructing the Stratford-upon-Avon canal, this Grade II-listed pub is a linked and extended collection of late 18th and early 19th-century two-storey whitewashed brick buildings. It is rumoured to be haunted by the ghost of a 17th-century lime kiln worker. A pub since 1832, it was refurbished in the 1990s and has a comfortable, welcoming interior with a large real fire.
Q७❀❶&P♠❀ ⟲

Halesowen

Crafty Pint H'ales'owen L

8 Wassell Road, B63 4JU
☎ 07823 880240
Wye Valley HPA, Butty Bach; 5 changing beers (sourced nationally) ⊞
A micropub run by a local resident that expanded the bar into the adjacent building in 2022. Traditional ales, cider, wines and beverages are sold and coffee is generally available during the week, along with crusty cobs, pork pies and sausage rolls. No children are allowed in the evening. May close early on Saturday, so it is worth checking opening hours in advance. Closed on Monday.
Q७❀♠P♠(142,192)❀ ⟲

King Edward VII L ✓

88 Stourbridge Road, B63 3UP
☎ (0121) 602 2537
Holden's Golden Glow; Wye Valley Butty Bach; 6 changing beers (sourced nationally) ⊞
Friendly, comfortable pub next to Halesowen Town football ground, on the main road just out of the town centre, towards Stourbridge. A large front lounge and smaller rear lounge with sports TV are both served by a central bar selling up to eight real ales plus one cider. Bar snacks are served Wednesday to Sunday. This is one of several pubs close by that sell good quality real ale.
७❀&♠P♠(9) ♠

Roberto's Bar

55 High Street, B63 3BG
☎ 07939 957338
2 changing beers (sourced nationally) ⊞
Roberto's Bar is owned by Roberto Ross who closed his Birmingham bar and opened this one in Halesowen late 2022. Two rotating cask ales are always available, as well as a choice of several UK KeyKeg beers, Belgian speciality beers, and several real ciders. Cask prices are usually lower than similar venues in the area. Opening hours may vary through winter. Keep an eye open for beers from Cult of Oak, Roberto's brewery in Netherton.
&♠♠

Swan L

282 Long Lane, B62 9JY
☎ (0121) 269 4111
Black Country Bradley's Finest Golden, Pig on the Wall, Fireside; 9 changing beers ⊞
Former local CAMRA Pub of the Year, this popular, comfortable pub was saved from the bulldozers in 2014 by local campaigners and Black Country Ales. The central bar serves two main drinking areas. Twelve ales and five real ciders are available, as well as a fine selection of gins. Regular beer festivals are held. A staircase leads to the toilets and gives access to the garden and smoking

area to the rear. Parking is limited at the pub but there is adequate street parking nearby.
Q❀♿♣●P🚌(14,X8) 📶 ♫

Hampton in Arden

White Lion ✔

10 High Street, B92 0AA
☎ (01675) 442833 🌐 thewhitelioninn.com
Otter Ale; St Austell Proper Job; Timothy Taylor Boltmaker; Wye Valley HPA; 1 changing beer (sourced nationally; often M
A charming 17th-century timber-framed Grade II-listed building, the White Lion has been licensed since 1838. It comrises an L-shaped lounge and dining area with a separate public bar, both with lovely real fires. The dining area is light, airy and open-plan. Quality British pub food with a French accent is served, and the quantity and quality of real ales is always of the highest level. The pub looks to rotate two of its regular beers every five to six months. This traditional country pub is well worth a visit.
♘❀🛏◐♿⇌(Hampton-in-Arden) P🚌(82) 🐾📶

Kingswinford

Ale Hub

15 Market Street, DY6 9JS
Wye Valley Butty Bach; 2 changing beers (sourced nationally; often North Cotswold, Thornbridge) Ⓗ
A warm welcome is guaranteed at this thriving town-centre micropub which opened in 2022, serving 3 beers including 2 ever-changing guest beers, nationally sourced, and at least one cider. A number of KeyKeg products and craft cans are also available plus one real cider. The pub is friendly, has a real customer mix and dogs are welcome as are children to 6pm. Weekly quiz and bingo nights are held. Q♘◐♿●P🚌🐾♫

Bridge Inn

118 Moss Grove, DY6 9HH (A491)
☎ (01384) 293880
Black Country Bradley's Finest Golden, Chain Ale, Pig on the Wall, Fireside; 5 changing beers (sourced nationally; often Black Country) Ⓗ
Open-plan Black Country Ales pub that is deservedly popular with a wide mix of customers. It offers a broad range of up to nine cask beers along with ciders, some of which may be real. Cobs, pork pies, sausage rolls and samosas (sourced locally) are available daily. The accent is very much on a homely feel with a lot of community atmosphere and it is well worth a visit.
Q♘❀♿♣●P🚌🐾📶

Cottage

534 High Street, DY6 8AW
☎ 07967 630495
Wye Valley HPA; 3 changing beers (sourced nationally; often Enville, Timothy Taylor, Wye Valley) Ⓗ
Comfortable pub set on two levels serving a good menu including lunchtime specials. A carvery on Sunday also supplies meat for delicious sandwiches and cobs. The layout is L-shaped with diners and drinkers intermingling throughout this spacious pub. Changing beers are always pale session ales. A range of country wines is also available. The frontage would not look out of place on a postcard and the interior is homely and inviting.
Q♘◐P🖥🚌🐾📶

Knowle

Ale Rooms

1592 High Street, B93 0LF
☎ (01564) 400040
7 changing beers (sourced nationally; often Church End, Silhill) Ⓗ
This micropub on the High Street, in a converted shop that was formerly a funeral director's, is a welcome addition to the Knowle pub scene. The pub stocks at least one real ale from the local Silhill brewery, along with one from Church End, guest ales, real cider, wines and spirits, including speciality gins. There is free Wi-Fi and the usual pub snacks are available. A former local CAMRA Pub of the Year and West Midlands Pub of the Year 2019.
●🚌(S3) 🐾📶♫

Lower Gornal

Fountain Inn

8 Temple Street, DY3 2PE (on B4157, 5 mins from Gornal Wood bus station)
☎ (01384) 596317
Greene King Abbot; Hobsons Town Crier; Wye Valley HPA, Butty Bach; 6 changing beers (sourced nationally; often Fountain Ales) Ⓗ
This venue is a destination for both quality real ales and pub food. To the rear, the courtyard with bench tables has been refurbished to a high standard. Up to 10 real ales are served, and those conditioning in the cellar are listed on a board opposite the main bar. There is an elevated, separate restaurant to the rear of the pub.
♘❀◐♣🚌(17/A,27/A) 🐾

Mere Green

Ale Hub

4 Hill Village Road, B75 5BA
Wye Valley Butty Bach; 3 changing beers (sourced nationally) Ⓗ
A former solicitor's office which gained a new life in 2021 when it reopened as a micropub, part of a small chain of bars of the same name. As well as the central area, a smaller room is to the rear. The three guest ales are generally from smaller brewers. Craft beers, wines, and a range of gins are available. There is a monthly bingo night and weekly quiz night on Monday.
♘⇌(Butlers Lane) 🚌🐾📶

Mare Pool ✔

294 Lichfield Road, B74 2UG (behind shops on E side of Lichfield Rd)
☎ (0121) 323 1070
Greene King IPA, Abbot; Oakham Citra; Sharp's Doom Bar; 4 changing beers Ⓗ
Part of a shopping precinct constructed in the 1970s, this is a large open-plan premises serving a well-priced food menu all day. Inside, artwork adorning the walls depicts the nearby waters, in testimony to the name of the area which historically suffered from poor drainage. The watery theme is reflected in the decor, with hundreds of hanging glass droplets. The comfortable interior is complemented by café-style seating outside at the front, plus an enclosed beer terrace to the side.
Q♘❀◐♿⇌(Four Oaks) P🚌📶

Meriden

Queen's Head

Old Road, CV7 7JP
☎ (01676) 522256 🌐 queensheadmeriden.com

Draught Bass; 3 changing beers (sourced nationally; often Leeds, Oakham, Sharp's) ⊞
Nestled on the old main road to Coventry, now a single-track lane, this is reputed to be Meriden's oldest hostelry. The licensees of over 20 years welcome you to this traditional single-roomed, split-level pub which is popular with the local community and diners seeking good-value lunches Monday to Saturday. Horse brasses, pictures and memorabilia add to the ambience in the two distinct drinking areas. Beer and drinks are supplied to the independent Meriden Spice restaurant upstairs which opens in the evening. ✪❶✚P🚍(X1,82)✿🛜

Old Hill

Wheelie Thirsty 🄻
215 Halesowen Road, B64 6HE
☎ 07876 808468
Fixed Wheel Wheelie Pale, Chain Reaction Pale Ale, Blackheath Stout, No Brakes IPA; 4 changing beers (often Fixed Wheel) ⊞
Located on the high street, this is the second outlet for Fixed Wheel brewery. With a wide cross-section of customers, it is popular with out-of-town visitors, but remains a real community pub. A range of up to four ciders, a guest cask ale and an enterprising variety of craft keg beers are also served. Monthly events such as quiz and pizza nights take place, with musical events in the afternoon every second Sunday.
👪✪❶✚🍴🚍(19,X10) ✿🛜♪

Oldswinford

Seven Stars ★ 🄻
Brook Road, DY8 1NQ (on B4186, opp the roadway to the front entrance of Stourbridge Junction station)
☎ (01384) 441566
Black Country Bradley's Finest Golden, Chain Ale, Pig on the Wall, Fireside; 9 changing beers ⊞
A magnificent Edwardian Grade II-listed building; look out for the ornate tiling and timber bar inside. There are two bars with three rooms – lounge, bar and snug – plus a function room, letting rooms, and a garden area to the side and rear. Twenty five handpulls are split between the two bars, featuring both BCA beers and guest ales, with three of the pulls used for cider. Limited snacks are available in the week.
👪✪🍴❶♿⇄(Stourbridge Junction) ✚🍴P🚍(142,7) ✿🛜♪

Rowley Regis

Britannia Pub & Brewery
Rowley Village, B65 9AT
☎ (0121) 559 3415
House beer (by Holden's); 3 changing beers (sourced regionally; often Church End, Holden's, Salopian) ⊞
Following a high-specification refurbishment, this multi-roomed pub reopened in 2017 offering a welcome combination of real ales, real ciders and hearty food. The bay windows in the shabby chic lounge provide natural lighting and there are multiple real fires throughout the building. The lounge, bar and conservatory are all spacious, and each room has a unique feel. Blues and rock bands regularly perform in the conservatory area.
Q👪✪🍴❶♿✚🍴P🚍(X8,14A) ✿🛜♪

Rushall

Manor Arms ★
Park Road, off Daw End Lane, WS4 1LG (off B4154 at canal bridge)

☎ (01922) 642333
Banks's Amber Ale, Sunbeam; Wainwright Gold; Wychwood Hobgoblin Gold ⊞
A canalside pub, founded around 1105 and rebuilt in the 17th century, it is thought to have held a licence for ale since 1248. The pub retains exposed beams and open fires in both bars. Handpulls are situated along the wall, resulting in it being known locally as the pub with no bar. Situated next to a country park and nature reserve, it is a little off the beaten track but well worth a visit. Closed on Tuesday. Q👪✿❀P🚍(997)✿

Sedgley

Beacon Hotel 🍷 ★ 🄻
129 Bilston Street, DY3 1JE (A463)
☎ (01902) 883380 ⊕ sarahhughesbrewery.co.uk
Sarah Hughes Pale Amber, Sedgley Surprise, Dark Ruby Mild; 2 changing beers (sourced nationally) ⊞
A unique destination pub, the brewery tap for Sarah Hughes also offers progressive guest beers. This Grade II-listed pub is brimming with character, and is deservedly popular – queues have been known to assemble ahead of opening time. The biggest selling beer by some margin is the award-winning Sarah Hughes Dark Ruby Mild. The large garden has children's play facilities at the rear and is used to host various annual events such as Black Country Day. Q👪✿❀P🚍(229,224)

White Lion Inn
104 Bilston Street, DY3 1JF
☎ (01902) 685232
Oakham Bishops Farewell; 3 changing beers (often Olde Swan, Salopian, Thornbridge) ⊞
Large wet-only pub serving a range of pale and often hoppy beers. It is popular with TV sports fans. What was previously the restaurant is now a quieter drinking lounge, also used for meetings and functions. There is a small garden with benches at the rear. The pub is served by a large car park next door, accessed via Claremont Road. ❀P🚍(229,224)🛜♪

Shirley

Ale Hub
277 Longmore Road, B90 3ER
⊕ alehub.co.uk
Wye Valley Butty Bach; 3 changing beers (sourced nationally) ⊞
Housed in a former newsagent shop, this is part of a growing family-run micropub enterprise. Four well-kept ales are available at all times from national breweries, including the regular Wye Valley Butty Bach. Ale Hub specialises in cask ales, craft beers and a variety of gins, and offers classic pub snacks. There is a regular quiz night on Monday, and a bingo evening on the first Tuesday of the month. 👪♿🚍(6,76)✿🛜♪

Shaking Hand
Unit 24 Parkgate, Stratford Road, B90 3GG
☎ (0121) 733 1176 ⊕ theshakinghand.co.uk
4 changing beers (sourced nationally) ⊞
A friendly, light and airy, though small, single-room pub in the Shirley Parkgate shopping centre near Asda. Four regularly changing guest ales, including a dark ale, are served, from local and national independent breweries, as well as five craft keg/KeyKeg beers. The pub has all of the feel of a micropub but has embraced some of the needs of the modern clientele such as sports television and background music. A changing range of canned craft beer is also available. There is always a warm welcome and excellent quality beer. 👪♿P🚍✿🛜

Short Heath

Duke of Cambridge 🄻
82 Coltham Road, WV12 5QD
☎ (01922) 712038
Black Country Bradley's Finest Golden, Pig on the Wall, Fireside; 9 changing beers (sourced nationally; often Blue Monkey, Green Duck, Salopian) 🄷
A homely, welcoming pub converted from 17th-century cottages. The public bar has a stove and original wooden beams, and an array of handpulls dispense beers from Black Country Ales, alongside many changing beers and a few ciders. The quieter lounge has been tastefully refurbished and has its own bar. A rear room caters for darts and pool, and is used for functions and beer festivals. Traditional bar snacks, cobs and pork pies are available. A beer garden is at the rear.
🌡️❀♣👜🚉(41,69) ☻♪

Solihull

Fieldhouse
10 Knightcote Drive, B91 3JU
☎ (0121) 703 9209
Purity Pure UBU; St Austell Tribute, Proper Job; Timothy Taylor Landlord; 2 changing beers (sourced nationally; often Black Sheep, Titanic) 🄷
Part of the Ember Inns chain, this large, modern pub is tastefully decorated and comfortably furnished. It features three large fires - one real, two coal-effect - and pleasant patio areas. Six ales are normally served, with two guest ales from across the country. Often busy, the pub attracts a wide range of ages. Regular quiz nights are held on Sunday and Tuesday, and on Monday and Thursday all cask ales are discounted. The pub also holds monthly tribute acts and occasional Meet the Brewer events, as well as sponsoring the local football team, the Fieldhouse. 🌡️❀◑👜🚉(A9,5)♀♪

Pup & Duckling ♟
1 Hatchford Brook Road, B92 9AG
☎ (0121) 247 8358 ⊕ pupandduckling.co.uk
8 changing beers (sourced nationally; often Shiny) 🄷
A family-run three-room micropub, serving up to eight real ales and two craft beers. The main front room has a bar and a bottle store, and the middle and extended back rooms provide extra seating, as does the garden area. Bar snacks are available and customers can bring their own food from takeaways close by. Local breweries are often featured, but the landlord also has a knack of obtaining interesting beers from national independents. Regular beer updates can be found online, and a regular Thursday quiz has raised thousands for local charities.
Q❀🚉(73,X2) ☻♀

Stourbridge

Hop Vault
9 Market Street, DY8 1AB
☎ 07858 312883 ⊕ thehopvault.com
3 changing beers (sourced nationally) 🄷
Recently opened specialist bottle shop selling cans and bottles from all over the country and Europe, some of which are bottle conditioned. A tasting room is now open offering 15 keg taps and three cask beers plus cans and bottles from the cold store. Extensions to the bar area are planned. The premises used to be a bank vault and more recently the hi-fi shop Music Matters. Closed on Monday.
⇌(Town) P🚉

Queen's Head 🄻
111 Enville Street, DY8 3TQ
☎ (01384) 881701

Black Country Bradley's Finest Golden, Pig on the Wall, Fireside; 7 changing beers (sourced nationally) 🄷
Purchased by Black Country Ales in 2018, this is a real ale-centric pub with 12 handpulls, situated just a short walk from Stourbridge town centre. At the rear is a comfortable heated smoking shelter, and a separate function room with a newly renovated skittle alley, ideal for events and private functions. Regular live music and comedy events now feature. Bar snacks are available. Former local CAMRA Pub of the Year. ❀♣👜🚉(25,8)☻♪

Royal Exchange 🄻
75 Enville Street, DY8 1XW (on A458 just off ring road)
☎ (01384) 396726
Bathams Mild Ale, Best Bitter 🄷
This pub has a busy traditional bar to the front and a newly extended small, cosy lounge to the rear, accessed through a side passage. The bar is decorated with a small collection of whisky bottles and boxes, pewter tankards and foreign bank notes. The beer is served in handled glasses on request. A large beer garden to the rear contains a heated smoking area. Bathams XXX is available in winter only. A public car park is directly opposite. Q❀👣♣P🚉(8,25)

Sutton Coldfield

Duke Inn
12 Duke Street, B72 1RJ
☎ 07946 655363
Brains Rev James Original; Greene King Abbot; Wye Valley HPA; 1 changing beer 🄷
An ornate back-street venue with striking overhead lanterns adorning the façade. Regulars play darts in the main bar that features a pale wood gantry complete with mirrors and clock. A simple small lounge to the rear is more cosy and used for various community and entertainment activities. The corridor abutting the bar features elaborate floor tiles, decorated mirrors, and even a short panel of snob screens. Outside is a sizeable grass garden where children are welcome.
❀⇌♣P🚉☻♀

Station ⬤
44 Station Street, B73 6AT (near Sutton station southbound platform)
☎ (0121) 362 4961
Sharp's Doom Bar; Timothy Taylor Landlord; 2 changing beers (sourced nationally) 🄷
Located adjacent to Sutton Coldfield station, this large venue is popular with a range of clientele including commuters, diners, and sport spectators. The mural on the external wall claims 'Sutton's most divine beer garden'. Two national core beers are accompanied by up to two guest beers. Quizzes, live music and comedy nights are among the entertainment. In summer, the multi-level beer terrace to the rear hosts DJs and live music. 🌡️❀◑👣♣🚉☻♀♪

Tipton

Fountain
51 Owen Street, DY4 8HE
☎ (0121) 522 3606
Greene King Abbot; Wye Valley HPA; 2 changing beers (sourced nationally; often Salopian) 🄷
A canalside pub in the heart of the Black Country, enjoyed by boaters and locals alike. In the mid-19th century it was a training base for Tipton-born British heavyweight prize fighter William Perry, better known as the Tipton Slasher. His statue stands in Coronation

Gardens opposite. Food is served Monday to Thursday lunchtime. Cobs and pork pies are available throughout the day. Greene King Abbot Ale and Wye Valley HPA are served, plus two changing guest ales which are usually pale beers. Q❁❂◐≠P🖵❀🛜

Rising Sun 🅛

116 Horseley Road, DY4 7NH (off B4517)

☎ (0121) 557 1940

Black Country Bradley's Finest Golden, Pig on the Wall, Fireside; 7 changing beers (sourced nationally) Ⓗ

A former CAMRA National Pub of the Year which reopened in 2013 following refurbishment by Black Country Ales. This imposing Victorian hostelry has two distinct rooms warmed by open fires, and a large yard at the rear with patio heaters and an outbuilding. There are seven changing guest beers plus the three Black Country Ales core beers, and up to five traditional ciders. Cobs are served. Great Bridge, a 10-minute walk away, has frequent bus services to Dudley, West Bromwich and Birmingham. ❁♣●🖵❀🛜♪

Upper Gornal

Britannia ★ 🅛

109 Kent Street, DY3 1UX (on A459)

☎ (01902) 883253

Bathams Mild Ale, Best Bitter Ⓗ

Dating from the early 19th century, this inn has been identified by CAMRA as having a nationally important historic pub interior because of the taproom at the rear with its wall-mounted handpulls. Service can be obtained from the front bar, itself a comfortable place to be. There is also a family/games room with a TV. Behind the building is the former brewhouse and the garden. Large cobs and pork pies are sold. The pub is on the main bus route between Wolverhampton and Dudley.
❂❁♣🖵(1)❀🛜

Jolly Crispin

25 Clarence Street, DY3 1UL (A459)

☎ (0121) 520 8899

Abbeydale Absolution; Oakham Citra, Bishops Farewell; 5 changing beers (sourced nationally; often Blue Bee, Neepsend, Saltaire) Ⓗ

A popular free house which was brought under the Red Pub Company umbrella in 2021. Changing beers are sourced from a wide array of breweries. The spacious lounge encourages conversation, and there is also a smaller bar and an outbuilding with largescreen TVs showing sport. A variety of crusty cobs are available every day, with fillings such as hot pork with stuffing and roast potatoes on Friday and Saturday. Regular tap takeovers and beer festivals are held.
❂❁♣●P🖵(1)❀🛜♪

Walsall

Black Country Arms 🅛

High Street, WS1 1QW (in market, opp Asda)

☎ (01922) 662720 ⊕ blackcountryarms.co.uk

Black Country Bradley's Finest Golden, Pig on the Wall, Fireside; 13 changing beers (sourced nationally; often Mallinsons, Salopian, Titanic) Ⓗ

A short walk from the train and bus station, this pub has an impressive selection of constantly changing real ales and sometimes a real cider. It is open-plan with comfortable seating and quieter areas. In winter, warming comfort is provided by an open fire with a tiled cast iron surround. The staff offer a warm welcome to all, even during busier periods. Pub meals are available

during the day from Tuesday to Saturday. Entertainment is held regularly on Saturday night and there are sports TVs spread around the pub. Dogs are welcome in all areas. ❁◐≠♣●P🖵❀🛜♪

Fountain Inn 🅛

49 Lower Forster Street, WS1 1XB (off A4148 ring road)

☎ (01922) 633307

9 changing beers (sourced regionally; often Green Duck, Silhill) Ⓗ

Two rooms are served by a central bar dispensing nine changing beers in this family-run pub which has a friendly atmosphere and welcoming staff. Bar snacks include pork pies and filled rolls. Vinyl nights take place once a month, live tribute acts are on most Saturdays, and a weekly pizza night on Thursday is popular. The heated outdoor terrace provides shelter for smokers and alfresco drinkers Q❂❁≠♣●🖵(977,997)❀♪

St Matthew's Hall ⊘

Lichfield Street, WS1 1SX (adj to Town Hall)

☎ (01922) 700820

Greene King Abbot; Ruddles Best Bitter; Sharp's Doom Bar; 4 changing beers (sourced nationally) Ⓗ

A stunning Grade II-listed Wetherspoon pub in the centre of Walsall, easily accessible by public transport and with plenty of parking nearby. The interior features library shelves, dining tables, comfy seating areas, and an airy conservatory, while outside is a large beer garden. Beer festivals feature throughout the year and entertainment is hosted every Friday and Saturday evening until late. A changing selection of ales supplements the three regular beers and food is served all day. Children are welcome until evening. ❂❁◐♿≠●🖵❀🛜♪

Victoria 🅛

23 Lower Rushall Street, WS1 2AA

☎ (01922) 635866

Banks's Sunbeam; Church End Gravediggers Ale; Wye Valley Butty Bach; 3 changing beers (sourced regionally; often AJ's, Fixed Wheel, Salopian) Ⓗ

Popular two-roomed pub, dating from 1845, close to the town centre. It has a pleasant garden and smoking facilities at the rear, where there is also a large Pay & Display car park. Steaks are available on Wednesday and traditional lunches on Sunday. Open mic and quiz nights are held regularly. Friday night blues, Sunday evening live entertainment and retro games nights are held on a monthly cycle. A pool table is located upstairs. Local beers are available and sometimes a real cider.
❂❁◐≠♣●🖵❀🛜♪

Walsall Arms

17 Bank Street, WS1 2EP (behind the Royal Hotel, off A34)

☎ 07837 302075

Wye Valley Bitter, HPA, Butty Bach; 3 changing beers (sourced regionally; often Salopian) Ⓗ

A refurbished back-street pub with a comfy carpeted bar area and another small bar accessed via the passageway. It is just a short walk from Walsall town centre, behind the Royal Hotel. The pub features an open fire, old Walsall photographs and has two TV screens. A patio painted in Italianate fashion is at the rear. Traditional Sunday lunches are available, with themed food every Thursday evening (pre-orders only). Live music is played most Saturdays and karaoke is hosted on Friday and Sunday evenings. ❁◐♿♣🖵(51,377)❀🛜♪

Walsall Cricket Club

Gorway Road, WS1 3BE (off A34, by university campus)

☎ (01922) 622094 ⊕ walsall.play-cricket.com

Wye Valley HPA; 1 changing beer (sourced regionally; often Backyard, Castle Rock) Ⓗ

On a fine summer's day the sound of leather on willow welcomes you at this green oasis on the outskirts of town. The club room has had a major renovation and now provides luxurious comfort and a panoramic view of the field. It contains local cricket memorabilia and two large TV screens. There is occasional entertainment and the venue is popular for function hire. CAMRA members may visit by showing a valid membership card. Closed Monday to Thursday and Sunday hours are reduced in winter. ⏰✿&♿P🚉(51)🐕🛜

Wheatsheaf 🅛

4 Birmingham Road, WS1 2NA

🌐 wheatsheafwalsall.business.site

Wye Valley HPA, Butty Bach; 2 changing beers (sourced locally; often Enville, Green Duck) Ⓗ

Friendly, open-plan community local with live music most weekends. Four real ales are served including two changing beers from local brewers. Games night is held every Tuesday evening. Live music is very much a feature of the pub with rehearsal evenings on Wednesday, open mic on Thursday, bands every Friday and Saturday, and jazz on Sunday afternoon. ⏰≠♿🚉(51)🐕🛜♪

Wednesbury

Bellwether ⊘

3-4 Walsall Street, WS10 9BZ

☎ (0121) 502 6404

Greene King Abbot; Oakham JHB; Ruddles Best Bitter; 7 changing beers (sourced nationally) Ⓗ

Just off the marketplace and main shopping area, this pub has a large L-shaped room on a split level. Open-plan seating is to the front of the bar with more intimate bench seating found at the rear. The pub is decorated with images of historic events and characters associated with the town. The large garden area at the rear offers a tranquil oasis for contemplation. Ten handpulls serve the usual Wetherspoon regulars plus seven changing beers. Food is served all day. Q⏰✿◑&♿♦🚉🛜

Olde Leathern Bottel ⊘

40 Vicarage Road, WS10 9DW (just off A461; bus 311 from Walsall is 5 mins' walk)

☎ (0121) 505 0230

4 changing beers (sourced nationally; often Adnams, Hook Norton, Wye Valley) Ⓗ

The front areas of the pub are cottages dating from 1510, while a later extension contains a comfy lounge. The small snug is often used as a function room. The four rooms have many old photos, with the bar displaying one of the pub from 1887 and a map of Wednesday from 1846. Live solo artists perform on Saturday night and there is a regular quiz on Sunday. The four changing beers are sourced from around the country. ⏰✿◑♦P🚉(11)🐕🛜♪

Wednesfield

Vine ★ 🅛

35 Lichfield Road, WV11 1TN

☎ (01902) 733529

Black Country Bradley's Finest Golden, Pig on the Wall, Fireside; 6 changing beers (sourced nationally) Ⓗ

Built in 1938, this Grade II-listed community local has been identified by CAMRA as having a nationally important historic pub interior. It is a rare intact example of a simple inter-war working-class pub, which has retained its original separate bar, lounge and snug. Darts

and dominoes are played and there are TVs showing sport. A covered smoking shelter and a beer garden provide outdoor areas. Cobs and pork pies are available at all times. ⏰✿♦P🚉(59,60)🐕🛜♪

West Bromwich

Royal Oak 🅛 ⊘

14 Newton Street, B71 3RQ (down side road off A4031 Hollyhedge Rd)

☎ (0121) 294 4140

St Austell Proper Job; Wye Valley HPA; 2 changing beers (sourced nationally) Ⓗ

Traditional back-street local comprising two small rooms with TVs showing sport in both; the bar on the left is adorned with West Bromwich Albion memorabilia and the quieter lounge is on the right. There is a terrace in the rear yard for smokers and two benches outside the front of the pub for basking in the summer. Parking is available in the street. Bar snacks are available. ⏰✿♦🚉(4,4A) 🐕🛜

Three Horseshoes 🅛

86 Witton Lane, B71 2AQ

☎ (0121) 269 4115

Black Country Bradley's Finest Golden, Pig on the Wall, Fireside; 4 changing beers (sourced nationally) Ⓗ

A refurbished one-roomed pub, taken on by Black Country Ales in 2016, with 10 handpulls installed. The spacious interior is furnished in a traditional style and there is a large beer garden for enjoying fine weather. The staff of this expansive hostelry offer a warm welcome and create a friendly atmosphere. Beers are from Black Country Ales, as well as regional and national breweries. TVs show live sport, and fresh cobs and pork pies are available all day. ⏰✿&♦P🚉(79,49)🐕🛜♪

Willenhall

Robin Hood 🏆 🅛

54 The Crescent, WV13 2QR (200yds from A462/B4464 jct)

☎ (01902) 271753

Black Country Bradley's Finest Golden, Pig on the Wall Ⓗ, Fireside Ⓗ/Ⓖ; 6 changing beers (sourced nationally) Ⓗ

A traditional-style public house with welcoming staff and a friendly clientele. The L-shaped interior has a warming real fire during the winter months. There are up to nine real ales on the bar and sometimes real ciders. A variety of cobs, hot pies and pork pies are available throughout the day. Quizzes are held on Thursday and a local archery club meets on adjacent land on Saturday. Local CAMRA Pub of the Year 2024. ✿♦🚉P🚉(529)🐕🛜

Three Crowns ⊘

72 Stafford Street, WV13 1RT

☎ (01902) 636579

3 changing beers (often Dartmoor, Nethergate, St Austell) Ⓗ

Town-centre pub dating from 1842, recently tastefully refurbished, comprising a comfortably furnished L-shaped bar, with a pool table and TV showing sports. A beer garden is to the rear. There are regular DJs, karaoke, or live music on Friday, Saturday and Sunday evenings, and pub games are played. Bar snacks are available. The local lock museum and Willenhall's famous local street market are nearby. Parking near the pub is limited. ✿♦🚉(529) 🐕🛜♪

Wollaston

Unicorn L

145 Bridgnorth Road, DY8 3NX (on A458 towards Bridgnorth)
☎ (01384) 394823
Bathams Mild Ale, Best Bitter Ⓗ

A former brewhouse purchased by Bathams, the Unicorn has barely altered in appearance since the Billingham family sold up in the early 1990s. It is a traditional two-bar drinking house, with a small back room where children are welcome. The pub is popular with all ages, and conversation is the order of the day. The brewhouse remains but is no longer in use. Fresh cobs – with hot pork and stuffing on Saturday lunchtime – are available on request. Bathams XXX is available in winter only.
Q ⏱ 🏵 ♿ P 🚲 (7,8) ✿ 🎵

Wolverhampton

Chindit

113 Merridale Road, WV3 9SE
☎ 07986 773487
7 changing beers (sourced nationally; often Oakham, Robinsons, St Austell) Ⓗ

Built in the 1950s as an off-licence, the first landlord here served in the Chindit Regiment in Burma in WWII and named it after his comrades. It is believed to be the only pub in the country honouring Major General Orde Wingate's WWII special forces; their history is displayed in the lounge. The two-roomed pub consists of a small lounge and a bar and offers up to seven, changing, nationally sourced ales. Live music features at weekends with Irish music every other Wednesday.
⏱ 🏵 ♣ P 🚲 (3,4) ✿ 🎵

Combermere Arms ★

90 Chapel Ash, WV3 0TY (on A41, Tettenhall Rd)
☎ (01902) 421880
Timothy Taylor Landlord; 5 changing beers (sourced nationally) Ⓗ

A Grade II-listed building with original sash windows. Situated a short walk or bus ride from the city centre, the pub comprises three charming rooms with cosy fireplaces replete with classic adverts. Pie, sausage and cheese-tasting festivals are held annually and there is occasional live entertainment. The rear has a courtyard and beer garden. The renowned tree in the Gents is still growing despite being trimmed. Hurst View cider is usually available. Q ⏱ 🏵 🏵 P 🚲 ✿ 🎵

Great Western L

9 Sun Street, WV10 0DG (pedestrian access from city centre via railway station car park and Corn Hill)
☎ (01902) 351090
Bathams Best Bitter; Holden's Black Country Mild, Black Country Bitter, Golden Glow, Special; 2 changing beers (sourced regionally; often Holden's) Ⓗ

A Grade II-listed, former CAMRA National Pub of the Year situated near the former low-level railway station, sympathetically refurbished in 2021. It attracts a varied clientele, including a rock climbing club and railway enthusiast groups. Four rooms consist of bar, snug, lounge and conservatory, all featuring railway or Wolves FC memorabilia, and four cosy real fires blaze in the winter. Meals are served at lunchtime and until 7pm, but not on Sunday. Cobs and pork pies are available every day. Q ⏱ 🏵 🏵 ◑ ⇌ ☰ (Station) ♣ P 🚲 ✿ 🎵

Hail to the Ale ♟ L

2 Pendeford Avenue, Claregate, WV6 9EF (at Claregate Island bus stop)
☎ 07846 562910 ⊕ mortonbrewery.co.uk/httahome.htm
6 changing beers (sourced locally; often Newbridge) Ⓗ

Having celebrated its 10th anniversary in 2023, this welcoming one-room beer and conversation-focused micropub was the first in the West Midlands. It also has an outside seating area. Six handpulls serve Newbridge beers plus guests, usually from local microbreweries, and three or more ciders or perries are also stocked. Locally-sourced pies, cheese, sausage rolls and Scotch eggs are available along with fine wines. Check the website for bank holiday hours, events and holiday closures.
Q ⏱ 🏵 ♿ ♣ 🏵 P 🚲 (5,6) ✿ 🎵

Keg & Comfort

474 Stafford Road, Oxley, WV10 6AN
☎ 07952 631032 ⊕ kegandcomfort.co.uk
4 changing beers (sourced locally) Ⓗ

The city's second micropub opened in 2018 in a former bank. The contemporary-styled main room has a striking custom-built bar made using coloured bottles, and seating for around 40 people. A small side room houses a large sofa and games cupboard. The pub's attention to detail gives it a welcoming atmosphere. Four changing ales – one dark – five ciders or perries and a selection of fruit wines are served. Local CAMRA Pub of the Year and Cider Pub of the Year 2023. Q ⏱ 🏵 ♿ ♣ 🏵 P 🚲 (3,4) ✿ 🎵

Lych Gate Tavern L

44 Queen Square, WV1 1TX (off Queen Square, opp Barclays bank, by St Peter's church)
☎ (01902) 399516
Black Country Bradley's Finest Golden, Pig on the Wall, Fireside; 6 changing beers (sourced nationally; often Black Country, Salopian) Ⓗ

A warm and friendly, traditional city-centre pub housed in one of the oldest buildings in Wolverhampton. The Georgian frontage dates from 1726 and the timber-framed rear is circa 1500. Featuring 10 handpumps, the bar area is located down a short flight of stairs with a function room upstairs. All floors have lift access. A rear courtyard provides outdoor seating. Cobs are served but customers may bring their own food, with plates and cutlery provided. Q ⏱ 🏵 ♿ ⇌ ☰ (St George's) ♣ ● 🚲 ✿ 🎵 🛜

Penn Bowling & Social Club

10 Manor Road, Penn, WV4 5PY
☎ (01902) 342516 ⊕ pennbowlingclub.com
4 changing beers (sourced nationally; often Enville, Green Duck, Newbridge) Ⓗ

The hub of this family-friendly community club is a large room which overlooks the floodlit crown bowling green. It also features a largescreen TV for sports. A smaller quiet room, the Red Room, is accessed from the main bar. A large function room is used for regular events and entertainment, and the patio area is ideal for watching bowls matches during the season. A children's adventure playground and seating area are outside. Cobs and bar snacks are available. Two annual beer festivals are held.
⏱ 🏵 ♿ ♣ P 🚲 (16) ✿ 🛜 🎵

Posada ★

48 Lichfield Street, WV1 1DG
Wye Valley HPA; 3 changing beers (sourced nationally; often Bath Ales, Ossett, Robinsons) Ⓗ

Dating from 1886, this Victorian Grade II-listed city-centre pub has a ceramic tiled exterior and interior tiled walls, original bar fittings – including rare snob screens – and is little altered since a remodelling in 1900 by local architect Fred T. Beck. It attracts a varied clientele, and is quiet during the day but busy in the evening and weekends, especially when Wolverhampton Wanderers are at home. There is a courtyard to the rear with a smoking area. Lunchtime meals are served by an arrangement with the next door café. Cobs are also served. ♿🐕⬅️🚆(St George's)🚃♪

Royal Oak 🅛 ✅
70 Compton Road, WV3 9PH
☎ (01902) 422845 ⊕ theoakchapelash.com
Banks's Mild, Amber Ale, Sunbeam; Marston's Old Empire; Wainwright Amber; 1 changing beer (sourced locally) Ⓗ

A friendly hostelry, just a short walk or bus ride from the city centre, serving a wide range of real ales from Marston's portfolio plus one SIBA guest. Open mic is hosted on Tuesday and live bands perform on Friday, as well as Sunday afternoons in summer. Part of the community, it raises money for charities and is the headquarters of the Old Wulfrunians Hockey Club. Pub and local history memorabilia are on display. Cobs and Scotch eggs are served. Covered, heated outdoor seating is available. ♿🐕♿♣P🚃(10,9)❀☂♪

Starting Gate
134 Birches Barn Road, Penn Fields, WV3 7BG
☎ 07834 673888
5 changing beers (sourced regionally; often Ludlow, Sarah Hughes, Wye Valley) Ⓗ

Opened in 2018, this small outlet occupies a former bank branch and retains the original counter and wings. The impressive rear door to the garden, which offers covered seating, also reflects its previous use. The small bar area leads to a cosy lounge, with another lounge upstairs reached by open spiral staircase. The paintings, silks and other memorabilia signal the owner's brother's interest in horse racing, hence the name of the pub. It is warm and welcoming with friendly local regulars.
Q❀♿♣🚃(2)☂☎

Summer House
290 Newhampton Road West, Whitmore Reans, WV6 0RS
☎ (01902) 745213
St Austell Proper Job; 3 changing beers (often Enville, Wye Valley) Ⓗ

A friendly community pub dating back to the 1860s. The bar features a roaring real fire in winter and is decorated with football memorabilia. The central servery links a comfortable lounge, with displays of local history on the walls, and a dining area where a Nepalese menu is available. There is a large garden for barbecues and outside drinking, and a covered, heated area for smokers. Q❀🐕◑♿🚃(6)❀☂♪

Swan 🅛
Bridgnorth Road, Compton, WV6 8AE (at Compton Island, A454)
☎ (01902) 754736 ⊕ swanwolverhampton.co.uk

Banks's Mild, Amber Ale, Sunbeam; Marston's Old Empire; Wainwright Gold; 1 changing beer (sourced nationally) Ⓗ

Built around 1780, this Grade II-listed former coaching inn is popular with locals, boaters, ramblers and cyclists alike, as it is close to the Staffordshire & Worcestershire Canal and Smestow Valley Nature Reserve. The bar is the place for lively banter, and there is also a games room and a quieter snug. Quizzes are held on Tuesday, a darts team plays on Wednesday and folk group on Thursday. The pub hosts an annual charity dog show and the weekly local pigeon flyers' club. Q🐕❀♣P🚃❀☂♪

Wordsley

Bird in Hand
57 John Street, DY8 5YS
☎ 07905 342711
Enville Ale; Hobsons Town Crier; Holden's Golden Glow; 3 changing beers (sourced nationally) Ⓗ

A Red Pub Company pub and the current local CAMRA Pub of the Year. This traditional back-street corner local has a wide customer mix and serves an enterprising range of up to three guest beers, including some rarely seen in the area. The pub exudes an air of friendliness and homeliness. Rooms include a bar with live TV sports, a quiet lounge and an outside covered seating area with heating. It is close to the Stourbridge Canal, with moorings a few minutes walk away.
Q🐕❀◑♣🚃(16,17/A)❀☂

New Inn 🅛
117 High Street, DY8 5QR (A491)
☎ (01384) 295614
Bathams Mild Ale, Best Bitter Ⓗ

Acquired by Daniel Batham Ltd in 2008, this L-shaped bar serves a single room with a small annexe at one end, plus a patio area and pleasant garden outside. A variety of cobs are available. Children are welcome in the garden but are not allowed in the pub. Bathams Mild Ale, only available in certain pubs across the Bathams estate, is sold. ♿❀♣P🚃❀☂

Queen's Head 🅛
129 High Street, DY8 5QS (A491)
☎ (01384) 881606
Black Country Bradley's Finest Golden, Pig on the Wall, Fireside; 6 changing beers (sourced nationally; often Fixed Wheel) Ⓗ

A comfortable roadside pub on the main A491 Stourbridge to Wolverhampton road. The layout echoes its multi-roomed past although most of the actual walls have gone, and the decor is cosy Victorian or Edwardian in style. Up to nine real ales, with three from the parent brewery, and a traditional cider are sold. To the right is an area that has a largescreen TV and dartboard. The pub now sells food Wednesday to Sunday (booking required Sun). ♿❀◑♣♣P🚃❀☂♪

The importance of the pub

Perhaps the workman spends, night after night, more than he should on beer. Let us remember, if he needs excuse, that his employers have found him no better place and no better amusement than to sit in a tavern, drink beer (generally in moderation), and talk and smoke tobacco. Why not? A respectable tavern is a very harmless place; the society which meets there is the society of the workman; it's his life; without it he might as well have been a factory hand of the good old time – such hands were 40 years ago; and then he should have but two journeys a day – one from bed to mill, and the other from mill to bed. **Walter Besant, As We Are and As We May Be, 1903**

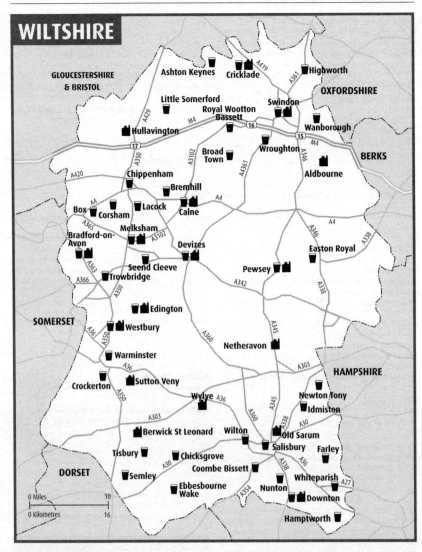

WILTSHIRE

Ashton Keynes

White Hart 🅛 ✅

High Road, SN6 6NX

☎ (01285) 861247 ⊕ thewhitehartashtonkeynes.com

Ramsbury Gold; St Austell Tribute; 2 changing beers (sourced nationally; often Broadtown, Dartmoor) ℍ

This popular community pub in the Cotswold Water Park has three distinct areas: a small bar with games and TV, the main bar area, and the restaurant area. There is also a large function room at the back. There are four real ales, two of them constantly changing guests. The good quality food uses locally sourced ingredients. Outside there is a secluded garden at the back and one of the four village crosses at the front. ♿🛏🍴♣️🅿️🚲(93A) 🐕🛜♪

Box

Quarryman's Arms 🅛 ✅

Box Hill, SN13 8HN

☎ (01225) 743569

Butcombe Original, Gold; 1 changing beer (sourced regionally; often Butcombe) ℍ

A Butcombe brewery pub in a hamlet off the A4 between Box and Corsham with fantastic views over the Bybrook valley towards Bath. This 250-year-old pub is popular with locals and visitors. A high quality varied menu is offered in the restaurant, bar and garden and includes breakfasts (served 8-10am). There is a car park, and although disabled access is limited, assistance is provided. The steep walk up from the bus stop is well worth it. ♿🛏🍴🚃🍴♣️🅿️🐕🛜♪

Bradford-on-Avon

Castle Inn

Mount Pleasant, BA15 1SJ

☎ (01225) 309317 ⊕ thecastleinnboa.co.uk

Palmers IPA; 3 changing beers (sourced locally; often Parkway, Twisted) ℍ

A very popular, comfortable pub, commanding splendid views across the town towards Salisbury Plain. The 2008 refurbishment earned a National CAMRA award. A wide range of handpulled real ales is complemented by excellent food. The guest beers are usually sourced from microbreweries in Wiltshire, Bristol, and East Somerset. There is a good sized garden at the front and children are welcome. ♿🍴🚫🕒◑🅿�👶≋🅿🚆(D1)👶⚭

Stumble Inn
Market Street, BA15 1LL
☎ (01225) 862115
4 changing beers (sourced locally; often Cheddar Ales, Hop Back, Kettlesmith) Ⓗ/Ⓖ
This characterful micropub opened in 2017 in the ground floor of what was a local club in the town centre. The main bar is in the back room, with a good-sized, comfortable room at the front overlooking the street, both decorated with much pub memorabilia and signage. There is a changing range of up to four beers, with two on handpump and one or two on gravity, usually from West Country breweries. May be closed Sunday to Wednesday. Q♿🕒≋♣●🚆(D1)👶⚭

Three Horseshoes
55 Frome Road, BA15 1LA
☎ (01225) 865876
3 changing beers (sourced locally; often Parkway, Stonehenge, Twisted) Ⓗ
The Horseshoes is a lively old coaching inn at the edge of the town centre, next to the rail station. It comes complete with the old wooden door where the horses went through to a yard. At the bar there are usually three constantly changing beers, often local. Live (and loud) bands play on Friday, Saturday, and Sunday nights. Out the back there is a small garden/terrace with seating. Limited parking at the rear. 🎵≋♣🚆(D1)👶⚭♪

Bremhill

Dumb Post Inn ✪
Dumb Post Hill, SN11 9JZ (1 mile N of A4, W of Calne)
☎ (01249) 813192 ● thedumb-post.com
Sharp's Doom Bar; 2 changing beers (sourced locally; often Butcombe, Ramsbury) Ⓗ
This free house stands in an elevated position between Chippenham and Calne, with a large terrace looking south over the Bowood Estate and beyond. There is plenty of seating for diners to enjoy award-winning food from either the traditional pub fare or gastropub menu. It is believed the inn got its name from the custom of postmen on carrier wagons pinning letters on a post outside the inn for the local people, in the days before the Royal Mail. Q♿🍴◑🅿👶⚭

Broad Town

Hop Chapel Ⓛ
29 Broad Town Road, SN4 7RB
☎ 07889 078648 ● broadtownbrewery.co.uk
Broadtown Best Bitter; 3 changing beers (often Broadtown) Ⓗ
Originally the site of the Broadtown microbrewery (the brewery has now scaled up and moved to Calne), the Hop Chapel is themed as a monastic style taproom, beautifully completed with ornate reclaimed wood, vintage glass panelling, stained-glass windows, and a pipe organ. Events and music festivals are held throughout the year, with regular food vendors visiting. There are alpacas in the field outside. ♿🎵●🅿👶⚭♪

Calne

Piggy Bank Micropub
The Old Bank House, The Strand, SN11 0EN
☎ (01249) 815362 ● piggybankpub.co.uk
1 changing beer (sourced locally; often Stealth) Ⓗ
Calne's first micropub opened in 2021, in a former bank in the centre of the town. The layout encourages conversation, and the emphasis is on community atmosphere, with no loud music or TV. You can even sit and drink in the former safe. The cask ales and keg beers are provided by Stealth Brew Co of Melksham, who normally have at least six of their own keg beers on tap, plus guests, and a cider. Card payment only.
Q♿🕒🚆(55)👶⚭♪

Chicksgrove

Compasses Inn Ⓛ
SP3 6NB
☎ (01722) 714318 ● thecompassesinn.com
Butcombe Original; 2 changing beers (sourced locally; often Hattie Brown's, Nuttycombe) Ⓗ
Set in the middle of the beautiful Wiltshire countryside, this 14th-century thatched cottage features flagstone floors, wooden beams and a large inglenook fireplace, with the the bar in the cellar. Local breweries are usually represented among the guest beers. Once a resting place for smugglers between Poole and Warminster, it now offers visitors a warm welcome, good ale, excellent food, accommodation, wonderful views and some peace and quiet. Q♿🍴🚫◑♣●🅿👶⚭♪

Chippenham

Flying Monk
6 Market Place, SN15 3HD
☎ (01249) 460662
North Cotswold Windrush Ale; 4 changing beers (sourced nationally; often North Cotswold, Tollgate) Ⓗ
Situated beside the historic Buttercross, the pub offers Belgian and craft beers and three draught ciders in addition to cask ales. The main bar is open plan with a small lounge up a short flight of stairs. There are periodic live music and other performances and a twice-monthly meat raffle. The annual Chippenham Folk Festival at the end of May has performances outside the pub. Not normally open on Sunday evenings. ♿≋●🚆👶⚭♪

REAL ALE BREWERIES

Arkell's Swindon
Broadtown ✦ Calne
Broadtown Calne
Dark Revolution ✦ Old Sarum
Downton ✦ Downton
Drink Valley 🍺 Swindon
Flying Monk ✦ Hullavington
Hop Back Downton
Hop Kettle 🍺 Cricklade
Hop Kettle Swindon
Kettlesmith ✦ Bradford-On-Avon
Moonraker Sutton Veny (NEW)
Ramsbury Aldbourne
Rude Giant Wylye
Rusty Garage ✦ Swindon
Stealth Melksham
Stone Daisy Berwick St Leonard
Stonehenge Netheravon
Three Daggers Edington
True Story ✦ Westbury
Twisted Westbury
Wadworth Devizes
World's End 🍺 Pewsey

Old Road Tavern ✓

Old Road, SN15 1JA

☎ (01249) 247080

Bath Ales Gem; Dark Star Hophead; Stonehenge Danish Dynamite; 3 changing beers (sourced nationally; often Harvey's, Hop Union, Timothy Taylor) Ⓗ

This popular local is a genuine community pub, with quality ales served by friendly and welcoming staff. The bar and lounge are separated by a central serving area. Bar snacks, including Panda's baps, are always available. There is a large enclosed garden, and a cabin with heated seats. The pub is a venue for the annual Chippenham Folk Festival in May. ⌖≈♣✿🐕♿ ♪

Three Crowns Ⓛ

18 The Causeway, SN15 3DB (S of town centre)

☎ (01249) 449029 ⊕ threecrownschippenham.co.uk

Broadtown Best Bitter; 6 changing beers (sourced nationally; often Broadtown) Ⓗ

An early 18th-century pub with a main bar, complete with log-burner, and a cider/snug bar. The excellent range of real ales usually includes at least two dark ales. At least three ciders and one perry are served from a separate bar. It is a peaceful pub, with few noisy distractions, and hosts popular quiz nights, as well as darts and cheese clubs. Food is limited to snacks, with filled rolls and pork pies at the weekend. Q⌖≈♣●P🚗♿🐕♿ ♪

Coombe Bissett

Fox & Goose Ⓛ

Blandford Road, SP5 4LE

☎ (01722) 718437 ⊕ foxandgoose-coombebissett.co.uk

Sharp's Doom Bar; 2 changing beers (sourced nationally) Ⓗ

An 18th-century coaching inn on the A354, three miles south of Salisbury. This popular and welcoming community pub has a local village atmosphere. Divided into a bar and dining area, it offers an extensive menu with ever-changing specials. Outside are pleasant gardens and a covered smoking area. Guest ales are from local and national breweries. Local CAMRA Rural Pub of the Year 2023. ⌖✿◑P🚗(20,29)♿♿

Corsham

Flemish Weaver ♈

63 High Street, SN13 0EZ

☎ (01249) 591959 ⊕ flemishweaver.co.uk

House beer (by Ramsbury); 3 changing beers (sourced nationally; often St Austell, Wadworth) Ⓗ

A 17th-century ale house which gets its name from the Flemish weavers who fled religious persecution and who in turn enhanced the town's woollen industry. This charming building, in the oldest part of Corsham, was refurbished in 2022 and is an intriguing and characterful pub with many nooks and crannies. They rightly pride themselves on the quality of their food and beer. The garden area is currently undergoing conservation work but should be reinstated in 2025. Local CAMRA Pub of the Year 2024. ⌖◑♣🚗♿

Three Brewers

51 Priory Street, SN13 0AS

☎ (01249) 701733 ⊕ threebrewerscorsham.co.uk

Draught Bass; 2 changing beers (sourced nationally; often Stonehenge, Timothy Taylor) Ⓗ

Welcoming traditional community pub, serving real ale, high-quality hot and cold snacks, coffee and cake. The two good-sized rooms – a bar and snug – have tables and

seating. Events such as quiz nights and bingo are hosted. The games room, with skittle alley, pool table, darts and board games, also serves as a meeting room. A pleasant beer garden is at the rear. Runner-up in the 2023 Wiltshire Life awards. ⌖✿◑♣P🚗(231)♿♿ ♪

Cricklade

Red Lion Ⓛ

74 High Street, SN6 6DD

☎ (01793) 750776 ⊕ theredlioncricklade.co.uk

Hop Kettle Ordinary Bitter, North Wall; St Austell Tribute, Proper Job; 5 changing beers (sourced nationally; often Hop Kettle, St Austell) Ⓗ

A friendly, popular and comfortable pub next door to the original Hop Kettle microbrewery. Part of the old Saxon town wall is incorporated within the building. There are nine real ales on offer, split between Hop Kettle, St Austell, and guests from elsewhere. The large garden has a covered seating area and hosts beer festivals. It is popular with walkers and is close to the source of the River Thames. Excellent food is served and there are five rooms for B&B. Q⌖✿≈◑●🚗♿♿

Crockerton

Bath Arms (Shearwater)

Clay Street, BA12 8AJ

☎ (01985) 221852 ⊕ atthebatharms.co.uk

4 changing beers (often Gritchie, Stone Daisy, Stonehenge) Ⓟ

Reopened in summer 2023 after being closed for some years, this charming 17th-century pub on the edge of the Longleat Estate has had a huge refurbishment, both inside and out, and is now a lovely, comfortable country inn. It has two bar areas, with seating for drinkers, and a smart dining room. Free of tie, it has up to six changing real ales (four in winter), all from local brewers. Q⌖✿≈◑●&P♿

Devizes

British Lion ✓

9 Estcourt Street, SN10 1LQ (on A361 opp Kwik Fit)

☎ (01380) 720665 ⊕ britishliondevizes.co.uk

4 changing beers (sourced nationally; often Palmers, Stonehenge) Ⓗ

The British has been ever-present in the Guide for over 30 years and is not to be missed. An unpretentious free house with wooden floors, cosy settles and an eclectic group of talkative regulars, it is an essential port of call in town. There are four handpumps and the beers change frequently throughout the week. Time it right and you can savour eight different real ales. The knowledgeable landlord is always pleased to offer his advice. ✿●P🚗(49)♿

Silk Mercer ✓

37-38 St John's Street, SN10 1BL

☎ (01380) 736760

Greene King Abbot; Ruddles Best Bitter; Sharp's Doom Bar; 3 changing beers (sourced nationally) Ⓗ

The Mercer occupies a Grade II-listed building just off the town's central market place. At least five ales are available at all times from all areas of the UK, including the standard Wetherspoon offerings. Regular beer festivals are held, during which up to 50 ales are available. Food is served all day. Q◑P🚗♿

Southgate Inn

Potterne Road, SN10 5BY

☎ (01380) 722872

Hop Back GFB, Fuggle Stone, Crop Circle, Taiphoon, Entire Stout, Summer Lightning; 1 changing beer (sourced nationally) G
A regular Guide entry, this cosy, friendly pub has three separate bar areas, with lots of nooks and crannies and a large courtyard area. There are usually several ales, still ciders and perry available at any time straight from the cask, including Hop Back offerings and a guest ale. There is live music throughout the weekend, an acoustic jam session every Wednesday, and a ukelele group on a Friday afternoon. Well-behaved dogs are welcome.
⛵❀♣♠P⟨(2,210) ❀❖✿♪

White Bear ❂
33 Monday Market Street, SN10 1DN
☎ (01380) 727588
Wadworth Henry's IPA; 5 changing beers (sourced nationally) H
Now in the Guide for a sixth consecutive year, this old coaching inn, with original beams and open fires, dates from the 1500s. The six handpumps serve up to two Wadworth ales, plus up to four guest ales. A dark beer is usually available and a still cider. Food is served all week and dogs are welcome. There is no car park but there is plenty of on-street parking and public car parks close by.
🏠◑❖✿

Downton

Goat at Downton
The Borough, SP5 3LY
☎ (01725) 535353 ⊕ thegoatatdownton.co.uk
Hop Back GFB; house beer (by Piddle); 2 changing beers (sourced locally; often Gritchie) H
Former coaching inn from the 13th century with four large rooms and inglenooks, it has been modernised but retains the village pub atmosphere. The cosy snug is perfect for private parties or just a cup of tea by the fire. There are informal and more formal dining areas serving an interesting modern menu with old favouties mixed in. It has a large enclosed garden with a fire pit and a children's play area. Q⛵❀◑P⟨(X3,44)❖

Easton Royal

Bruce Arms ★ 𝕃
Easton Road, SN9 5LR
☎ (01672) 810216 ⊕ brucearms.co.uk
Butcombe Original; St Austell Tribute; 2 changing beers (sourced regionally; often Ramsbury) H
This mid-19th-century local has been identified by CAMRA as having a nationally important historic pub interior. The small, cosy bar has furniture that probably goes back to the 1850s, and there is also a lounge with easy chairs and a piano. It has a campsite with full facilities, making it a good venue for meetings and rallies. Sunday lunch is served all year, otherwise food times vary seasonally. Q⛵❀◑▲P❖✿

Ebbesbourne Wake

Horseshoe ★
The Cross, SP5 5JF
☎ (01722) 780474 ⊕ thehorseshoe-inn.co.uk
Bowman Swift One; Gritchie English Lore; 1 changing beer (sourced locally; often Hattie Brown's, Otter, Palmers) G
Unspoilt 18th-century inn in a remote rural setting at the foot of an ox drove, run by the same family for 53 years and by the present landlord for 37. It has been identifiedby CAMRA as having a nationally important historic pub interior. There are two small bars displaying

an impressive collection of old farm implements, and a pleasant garden. The original serving hatch just inside the front door is still in use. Good local food is available Wednesday to Sunday. Real cider is usually available. Local CAMRA Rural Pub of the Year 2019-2022.
Q⛵❀◑▲♠P⟨(29) ❖

Edington

Three Daggers
Westbury Road, BA13 4PG
☎ (01380) 830940 ⊕ threedaggers.co.uk
Three Daggers Daggers Ale, Daggers Edge; 1 changing beer (sourced regionally; often Three Daggers) H
Upmarket pub and restaurant with its own on-site brewery. The main bar has three distinct drinking areas, with exposed beams, settles and reclaimed wooden furniture giving it a traditional feel. A separate dining room overlooks a lovely garden at the rear. The brewery and farm shop share a separate oak timbered, barn-style building. Normally serving three beers, this may reduce at quiet times of year. Excellent accommodation is available. Q⛵❀❀◑🛏▲P⟨(87,87A)❖✿

Farley

Hook & Glove
The Street, SP5 1AB
☎ (01722) 712247 ⊕ thehookandglove.co.uk
2 changing beers (sourced regionally) H
Five miles east of Salisbury, this pub lies in the Clarendon forest, which is excellent for walking. There is a snug bar and a larger bar/restaurant area, both of which boast wood fires in winter. The pub is well known for its food, with meals cooked using locally sourced produce. Outside is a large fenced area which is safe for children. Well-behaved dogs on leads are welcome. Two pétanque terrains are available during the summer months; booking is free. Q⛵❀◑🛏P⟨(37)❖✿

Hamptworth

Cuckoo Inn ♟
Hamptworth Road, SP5 2DU
☎ (01794) 338461
Hop Back Summer Lightning; Palmers Dorset Gold; house beer (by Hop Back); 3 changing beers (sourced regionally; often Downton, Exmoor) G
A traditional, friendly, country pub. The main bar area is a cosy square room, and there are three further rooms to sit in, one with a large fire. There is a large garden area to the front and more secluded areas to the rear. Ciders are a speciality, with a large and varying selection on offer. A good range of local and regional real ale is served straight from the cask. Beer festivals, with music, are held in May and September. Local CAMRA cider Pub of the Year 2023 and 2024, and Pub of the Year 2024.
Q⛵❀◑▲♣♠P❖✿♪

Highworth

Rose & Crown
19 The Green, SN6 7DB
☎ (01793) 764699
Sharp's Doom Bar, Sea Fury; 3 changing beers (sourced nationally; often Timothy Taylor, Young's) H
This free house is one of the oldest pubs in Highworth, and the friendly staff make it popular with locals. The inside features wooden beams decorated with hops and old adverting signs on the walls. There are five handpumps serving three changing ales and two Sharp's regulars. Breakfast is served Tuesday to Friday and there

is a good-value lunch menu. Occasional folk sessions are hosted. At the back is a large garden with a boules pitch. ⏚✿⟡♣P🍴(7)✿🐾♫

Idmiston

Earl of Normanton ✅
Tidworth Road, SP4 0AG
☎ (01980) 610251 ⊕ theearlofnormanton.co.uk
Hop Back Summer Lightning; St Austell Tribute; 2 changing beers (sourced locally; often Exmoor) ⊞
Popular and welcoming roadside pub that is warmed by two real fires in winter months. An extension has increased the dining area and added new indoor toilets, both with disabled facilities. Good-value home-cooked food is served, with a traditional roast on Sunday lunchtimes. There is a small, pleasant garden on the terraced hill behind the pub with a fabulous view across the River Bourne to the countryside beyond. The selection of ales is changed regularly. Q⏚✿⟡♣P🍴🐾🛜

Lacock

Bell Inn 🅛
The Wharf, SN15 2PJ
☎ (01249) 730308 ⊕ thebellatlacock.co.uk
House beer (by Hop Union); 3 changing beers (sourced regionally; often Hop Union, Palmers) ⊞
A popular free house outside Lacock village, to the south-east towards Bowden Hill. Friendly and welcoming staff serve the house and guest ales, plus a good and varied food menu. The pub has extensive seating indoors and outdoors, and there is also a pleasant barn, with wood-burner, providing additional drinking and dining space, where at least two beer festivals are held each year. It is an ideal finishing point for walks around Bewley Common and Bowden Hill. Q⏚✿⟡♣P🍴🐾🛜♫

Little Somerford

Somerford Arms ✅
The Hill, SN15 5JP
☎ (01666) 826535 ⊕ somerfordarms.com
Sharp's Doom Bar; 2 changing beers (sourced locally; often Flying Monk, Uley) ⊞
A warm and welcoming gastropub near Malmesbury, which has a large dining room with a small separate bar at the back, a conservatory, and an outdoor seating area. Three or four ales are generally available, but the emphasis is on high-quality food, with seasonal menus including vegan, gluten-free and dairy-free options. It is advisable to book a table online if eating. ⏚✿⟡♣P🍴(91)🛜

Melksham

Hiding Place Micropub
15 High Street, SN12 6JY
☎ (01225) 899022 ⊕ thehidingplace.co.uk
3 changing beers (sourced locally; often Stealth) ⊞
Two-storey micropub with tables downstairs in a bright and welcoming open-plan area, and comfortable sofas upstairs. It is run in conjunction with nearby the Stealth brewery, whose beers are found on the bar. Cider is served by gravity from a chilled cellar directly behind the bar, and there is also an extensive range of keg beers, wines, spirits and high-quality snacks including tapas. Opening hours are limited. Card payment only. Q⏚⟡♣🐾🛜

Market Tavern
18 Market Place, SN12 6EX
☎ (01225) 587396 ⊕ themelkshammarkettavern.co.uk
5 changing beers (sourced locally; often Frome, Three Daggers) ⊞
Reopened in 2021 following a change of ownership and a major refurbishment in a traditional tavern style. The quality food, an array of frequently changing ales, and friendly staff make it well worth a visit. The attractive building, with parts dating from the 18th century, has many booths, a quirky layout and decor, and three log-burners. Hops, hanging from the ceiling, are a major feature, along with comfortable chairs and seating. Outside is a lovely courtyard. ⏚✿⟡♣🍴🐾♫

Newton Tony

Malet Arms 🅛
SP4 0HF
☎ (01980) 629279 ⊕ maletarms.co.uk
4 changing beers (sourced locally) ⊞
Charming and historic pub in the conservation area of the village, with the River Bourne flowing past in winter. The window in the larger bar is reputed to come from a Spanish galleon. Run by the same family for 25 years, the landlord is as enthusiastic and proud of his high-quality food as he is of his ales. Four mainly local beers change weekly, often featuring Butts, Ramsbury, Stonehenge and Butcombe; Old Rosie cider is also served. Walkers and dogs are welcome. Q⏚✿⟡P🐾

Nunton

Radnor Arms 🅛
SP5 4HS
☎ (01722) 329722 ⊕ theradnor.com
St Austell Tribute; 3 changing beers (sourced locally; often Hop Back) ⊞
A popular, spacious pub dating from 1853 and named after the local landowner. The landlady and her staff offer a warm welcome to all, including families, children and dogs. Three dining areas adjoin the main bar, and an extensive and regularly changing menu is provided to suit all tastes. The large open garden extends to the river and has a secure children's playground. The pub hosts an annual summer festival. There is a milk vending machine in the car park. Q⏚✿⟡♣P🍴(44)🐾🛜♫

Pewsey

Crown Inn 🅛
60 Wilcot Road, SN9 5EL
☎ (01672) 562653 ⊕ thecrowninnpewsey.com
5 changing beers (sourced locally; often Butts, Stonehenge, World's End) ⊞
This traditional local is the brewery tap for the World's End microbrewery at the back of the site. It always features at least two of their own beers among the five on offer. The small bar has an attractive stone and brick fireplace in the centre. There is a regular poetry night and live music every Thursday, including a ukulele group on the last Thursday of the month. Food is only served on Friday evening, theme nights and Sunday lunch, unless by prior arrangement. Q⏚✿♣🛜♣🐾(X5)🐾🛜♫

Shed Alehouse 🅛
20 North Street, SN9 5EX
☎ 07769 812643 ⊕ theshedalehouse.com
5 changing beers (sourced regionally) ⊞
A former shop converted to a cosy micropub, the decor is wooden with tools to resemble its namesake. A free house with five handpumps serving a changing range of

beers from local and regional brewers, a tally of the number of different beers served is kept, with 1,250 from 2015 to early 2024. There are also real ciders and a craft pilsner. There is not much space inside, so you will soon get to know your fellow drinkers. No dogs allowed. Q❋⊱≉♣⬤➡(X5)

Royal Wootton Bassett

Five Bells ▼ ℂ ✅
Wood Street, SN4 7BD
☎ (01793) 849422
7 changing beers (sourced nationally; often Bristol Beer Factory, Hop Kettle (Swindon), St Austell) ⊞
Dating from before 1841, this busy and cosy traditional thatched local has a beamed ceiling and open fires. The landlord and landlady of this free house have run it for nearly 25 years. There are seven handpumps for changing real ales and one for Old Rosie cider. Food is served at lunchtimes and most evenings (not Sun or Mon). The pub has darts and crib teams. Multiple local CAMRA Pub of the Year and ever present in the Guide since 2002. ❋❀➡P➡(55,31)❀ ᗗ

Salisbury

Duke of York ℂ
34 York Road, SP2 7AS
☎ 07881 812218
Hop Back GFB, Summer Lightning; 5 changing beers (sourced locally; often Downton, Stonehenge) ⊞
A popular free house selling local beers and traditional cider. It is a community-focused pub, and home to the Fisherton History Society who meet on the second Wednesday of each month. Informal quiz nights are held on Sunday evenings, and there are other occasional events. The pub produces its own magazine with interesting articles and adverts from local businesses. Local CAMRA Pub of the Year 2023. ❋≉♣⬤➡❀ ᗗ

Haunch of Venison ★ ℂ
1 Minster Street, SP1 1TB
☎ (01722) 411313 ⊕ haunchpub.co.uk
Downton New Forest Ale; Hop Back GFB, Summer Lightning; 1 changing beer (sourced regionally) ⊞
A fine old inn which has been identified by CAMRA as having a nationally important historic pub interior. The main bar, The Commons, has a rare, pewter-topped, bar. A tiny second bar features old spirits taps and floor tiles recovered many years ago from a refurbishment of the cathedral. Upstairs, the House of Lords area contains the mummified hand of a card cheat. On the top floor are two separate dining rooms, one with a fireplace dating back to 1588. ⊱❶≉➡❀ ᗗ

Rai d'Or ★ ℂ
69 Brown Street, SP1 2AS
☎ (01722) 327137 ⊕ raidor.co.uk
2 changing beers (sourced locally; often Downton) ⊞
A 13th-century city-centre free house with a blue plaque commemorating a landlady from the 14th century. It has been identified by CAMRA as having a nationally important historic pub interior. The open fire, log-burner and low ceilings make for an appealing ambience. Reasonably-priced Thai food is complemented by two ever-changing beers, usually one of which is local. It can be busy at food times but bar drinkers are always welcome and you can call ahead if you prefer to be seated. Food is served from 5.30pm Tuesday to Saturday. A regular in the Guide since 2004. ⊱❶♣⬤➡❀ ᗗ

Village Freehouse ℂ
33 Wilton Road, SP2 7EF
☎ (01722) 329707
Downton Quadhop; 2 changing beers (sourced nationally) ⊞
A fully refurbished, lively pub near the train station. Microbrewery beers come from near and far, and there is always at least one dark brew, a stout, porter or mild, available with customer requests welcome. Teams are fielded in the local crib, cricket and football leagues. Two silent TVs show live sport most of the time. Filled rolls are available, or customers can bring their own food. Three-time local CAMRA Pub of the Year. ≉➡❀ ᗗ

Winchester Gate ℂ
113-117 Rampart Road, SP1 1JA
☎ (01722) 503362 ⊕ thewinchestergate.com
4 changing beers (sourced regionally; often Dark Revolution) ⊞
Characterful free house, an inn since the 17th century, which once provided for travellers at the city's east tollgate. Four handpumps offer changing ales, and real cider is often available. Beer and cider festivals are held, sometimes in association with live music events. A small, partially covered, garden offers a pleasant area to sit out in the summer. The pub is known as a live music venue, with events every Friday and Saturday night. ❋⬤P➡❀ ᗗ ♪

Wyndham Arms ℂ
27 Estcourt Road, SP1 3AS
☎ (01722) 331026
Hop Back GFB, Citra, Crop Circle, Summer Lightning; 1 changing beer (often Hop Back) ⊞
The birthplace of the Hop Back brewery, now celebrating 38 consecutive years in the Guide. This traditional ale house has a single bar serving a selection of Hop Back ales, normally with Taiphoon in summer and Entire Stout alternating with their monthly specials in winter, or a seasonal brew. Two small rooms off the main bar area provide quiet spaces and more seating. This is a pub for conversation, good-natured banter and fine ales. A former local CAMRA Pub of the Year. ⊱♣➡❀

Seend Cleeve

Brewery Inn
SN12 6PX
☎ (01380) 828463
Butcombe Original; Otter Ale; 1 changing beer (sourced locally; often Palmers, Ramsbury, Twisted) ⊞
A popular and welcoming pub near the Kennet and Avon Canal, with a strong community focus. This was acknowledged by residents, with a Community Help award during the pandemic. The outside area has dining pods, a decking area, and a large hidden beer garden. Inside the pub is a bar area and a pool/TV room that can also be used for dining. Regular quiz nights and local traditions such as the annual pumpkin competition and the inter-village cricket match are hosted. Q⊱❋❶♣P❀ ᗗ

Semley

Benett Arms
Village Green, SP7 9AS (1 mile E of A350) ST891270
☎ (01747) 830221 ⊕ thebenettarms-semley.co.uk
4 changing beers (often Salcombe, Twisted, Wriggle Valley)
A genuine free house sitting by the green and pond in a quiet village in an area popular with walkers. It has two

bars, plus a marquee and tables on the green opposite. There are four beers and a locally sourced cider to choose from. Excellent home-cooked food is served every day. A warm welcome is offered to all, including dogs. Three letting rooms and a shepherd's hut are available. Q☰❀✿☕♿P❀🐾🛜

Swindon

Ashford ✪
17-18 Ashford Road, SN1 3NT
☎ (01793) 534643 ∰ theashford.co.uk
Greene King IPA, Yardbird; Morland Old Speckled Hen; 1 changing beer (often Greene King) Ⓗ
Fully refurbished during lockdown, this is a contemporary club in the heart of Swindon Old Town. Established in 1896, it boasts great music and entertainment, Sky Sports, numerous dartboards, a pool table, and a function room suitable for parties, corporate events and meetings. There are two large projector screens with surround sound and four flatscreen TVs showing sport (normally muted). Non-members sign in at the bar, and new members are always welcome. Local CAMRA Club of the Year 2023 and 2024. ☰♿♣🚌(22,25)❀🛜♪

Beehive ✪
55 Prospect Hill, SN1 3JS
☎ (01793) 523187 ∰ bee-hive.co.uk
House beer (by Greene King); 5 changing beers (sourced regionally; often Greene King, Hardys & Hansons) Ⓗ
This four-room pub retains its quirky charm and layout. It dates from 1871 and was built on a corner on a hill, giving a nearly triangular layout on five different levels. It is a popular live music venue, hosting performances on most Thursday and Friday nights. Art is displayed for sale and there is a special seat next to Maxine the Mannequin. The long-standing landlord is proud of its community role, traditional feel and extensive support of local charities. ♣🚌❀🛜♪

Drink Valley Ⓛ
Unit C Fleet Square, SN1 1RQ
☎ (01793) 692980 ∰ thedrinkvalley.com
6 changing beers (sourced nationally; often Drink Valley) Ⓗ
This is Swindon's newest brewpub, with the brewing kit visible just behind the bar. It has a smart, modern appearance, with an airy, café-style layout. Four of the six handpumps serve Drink Valley beers, with two handpumps for guests, and there are also 12 keg taps for craft beers and ciders. A couple of beer festivals take place through the year. Good-value Indian street food is available most days. ☰❀✿♿➔🚌(22)❀🛜

Glue Pot
5 Emlyn Square, SN1 5BP
☎ (01793) 497420
Downton New Forest Ale; Hop Back Citra, Crop Circle, Entire Stout, Summer Lightning; 3 changing beers (sourced regionally; often Downton, Hawkshead, Hop Back) Ⓗ
An unspoilt corner pub, part of the historic GWR Railway Village built in the 1840s. It has a seven Hop Back or Downton real ales available including seasonal ones, plus one guest beer. It is a leading real cider pub and always stocks a wide range. it is normally quiet, but can get busy on weekend evenings. Monday is Book and Beer club night and there is a quiz on Wednesday evenings. Rolls and other snacks are available. Local CAMRA Cider Pub of the Year 2024. Q❀➔♣🚌🐾♪

Hop Inn Ⓛ
8 Devizes Road, SN1 4BH
☎ (01793) 613005 ∰ hopinnswindon.co.uk
House beer (by Ramsbury); 7 changing beers (sourced regionally; often Arbor) Ⓗ
This genuine free house has eight handpumps serving seven constantly changing guest ales, which are often from the South West region and include at least one dark beer. It also has six box ciders available. The interior is decorated in an eclectic style, including tables and chairs made from reclaimed wood and church pews. Local artworks are often featured. Interesting, good-value, food is available from the 'Hop Nosh' kitchen. Regular events are held such as quizzes, comedy nights and live music. Local CAMRA Cider Pub of the Year 2023. ☰❀◑●🚌❀🛜♪

Little Hop
7 Devizes Road, SN1 4BJ
∰ littlehop.co.uk
5 changing beers (sourced nationally; often Arbor) Ⓗ
The Little Hop was Swindon's first micropub and began the real ale revival in Devizes Road. The small, quirky pub has five handpumps dispensing a forever changing range of beers. In the corner of the pub is a well-stocked beer fridge. The colourful interior often features local art. Food can be ordered from the kitchen of the Hop Inn two doors away. Regular events include discos, life classes, and 'quiet times'. Q◑♿●🚌(9,11)❀🛜

Savoy Ⓛ ✪
38-40 Regent Street, SN1 1JL
☎ (01793) 533970
Greene King Abbot; Ruddles Best Bitter; Sharp's Doom Bar; 9 changing beers (sourced nationally; often Hop Union, Stonehenge, Windsor & Eton) Ⓗ
The ground floor of this former 1930s town centre cinema was converted to become the oldest Wetherspoon in Swindon. The spacious interior has many different levels and separated areas. The walls are adorned with photos and written information relating to the old cinema. Two small TVs are mainly silent. Toilet facilities are on same floor. The long bar has a very large selection of well-kept beers. The atmosphere is friendly and it is close to theatre, cinema, restaurants and shopping. ☰❀◑♿♣●🚌🛜

Tap & Brew Ⓛ
51 Devizes Road, SN1 4BG
∰ hop-kettle.com
6 changing beers (sourced locally; often Hop Kettle (Cricklade), Hop Kettle (Swindon)) Ⓗ
The Tap & Brew opened in 2019 and features a plain and functional interior with a variety of seating options. The six handpumps and 12 keg taps sell a full range of Hop Kettle beers. There is a small outside drinking area at the front and a larger open area at the back of the pub. Street food is provided by Scratch Kitchen. Customers can also purchase Hop Kettle merchandise and beers to takeaway. Q❀◑♿●🚌(9,22)❀

Tisbury

Boot Inn Ⓛ
High Street, SP3 6PS
☎ (01747) 870363
3 changing beers (sourced regionally) Ⓖ
Fine village free house built of Chilmark stone, licensed since 1768 and run by the same family since 1976. It has a relaxed, friendly atmosphere and offers a cordial welcome to all. Join in the conversation at the bar or find a quiet table at which to enjoy well-kept ales served

from casks behind the bar. Excellent food is served both in the pub and for takeaway. There is an attractive, spacious, garden. Q ☎ ❀ ◑ ⬤ ⇌ ♣ ♠ P 🚆 (25,26) ❀ 🛜

Trowbridge

Rose & Crown
36 Stallard Street, BA14 9AA
☎ (01225) 938936 ⊕ roseandcrown.uk.com
Butcombe Original; Stone Daisy Cow Down; 1 changing beer (sourced regionally; often Otter) Ⓗ
Pleasant bar with two areas located either side of the main entrance, with a single servery. Both have a light and airy yet cosy feel, with leather armchairs and banquette seating. It is close to Trowbridge station and a live train departure display means you needn't rush your drink. Premier League football and other sports are shown on screens in each bar. There is a monthly quiz night, usually on the second Thursday. Stone Daisy beer may be replaced by a guest. ❀ & ⇌ 🚆 ❀ 🛜

Wanborough

New Calley Arms Ⓛ
2 Ham Road, SN4 0DF
☎ (01793) 790615
Sharp's Doom Bar; 3 changing beers (sourced regionally; often Frome, Hop Kettle (Swindon), Ramsbury) Ⓗ
This traditional 19th-century pub is situated in the beautiful village of Wanborough and is equally popular with locals and visitors. The pub has a light and airy feel, with an open fire and log-burner to make it cosy in the winter. Four real ales are served, three of them changing guests sourced regionally. Good, honest food is made with the finest ingredients. The highlight of the year is the annual beer festival, which raises funds for the local church. ☎ ❀ ◑ ♣ P 🚆 ❀ 🛜 ♪

Warminster

Fox & Hounds
6 Deverill Road, BA12 9QP
☎ (01985) 216711
Greene King Abbot; St Austell Tribute; 1 changing beer (sourced regionally) Ⓗ
A friendly two-bar local: the main bar has a pool table and sport TV at the rear, while a quiet snug bar is on the right-hand side of the entrance. There is a large skittle alley and function room out at the back. Regular ciders are from Rich's, Inch's and Thatcher's, with three from Weymouth and perhaps a guest. The changing ale is often St Austell Tribute. A local CAMRA multiple award-winning pub. Q ❀ & ♣ ♠ P 🚆 ❀ 🛜

Westbury

Angel
3 Church Street, BA13 3BY
☎ (01373) 822648

4 changing beers (sourced regionally; often Twisted) Ⓗ
A lovely old pub tucked away in the centre of town. There is a warren of rooms, with a snug at the front, off the main bar, and a library with a huge collection of the owner's books. There are up to four beers, normally at least two from local brewer Twisted, with others from the South and the West Country. A couple of local ciders are also normally available. There is often live music and sporting events on TV. ❀ ⇌ ♣ ♠ 🚆 (D1) ❀ 🛜 ♪

Whiteparish

Parish Lantern Ⓛ
Romsey Road, SP5 2SA
☎ (01794) 884392 ⊕ theparishlanternwhiteparish.co.uk
Flower Pots Buster's Best; Hop Back Citra; St Austell Cornish Best Bitter, Proper Job; 1 changing beer (sourced locally) Ⓗ
A welcoming pub run by the same couple since 1991. The single bar has a central fireplace and areas for dining and darts. Guest beers are from Hop Back, Downton or other local breweries. There are family events on bank holidays and occasional beer festivals. Food is served at lunchtimes and in the evenings, and there are regular themed nights. A spacious garden with play equipment for children leads to a camping area with space for five caravans. Q ☎ ❀ ◑ Å ♣ P 🚆 (X7) ❀ 🛜

Wilton

Bear Inn
12 West Street, SP2 0DF
☎ (01722) 742468
Flack Manor Flack's Double Drop; Hop Back Summer Lightning; 1 changing beer (sourced locally) Ⓗ
A traditional, wooden-beamed, 16th-century pub in the heart of historic Wilton town. It has a friendly atmosphere in which to enjoy a selection of cask ales in front of the log fire or, at sunnier times, in the walled garden. Fielding crib and darts teams, this really is the hub of the community. An annual beer festival on the August bank holiday promotes cask ales, ciders and local bands. ☎ ❀ ◑ ♣ 🚆 ❀ 🛜

Wroughton

Carters Rest Ⓛ
57 High Street, SN4 9JU
☎ 07816 134966
Goff's Cheltenham Gold; 6 changing beers (sourced regionally) Ⓗ
First mentioned in 1671, the pub was extensively altered around 1912 to give its current Victorian appearance, with two rooms with a shared bar. It has long been renowned for its good beer. The current range of ales numbers seven, rising to eight at the weekend. They are mostly from small independent breweries within a 50 mile radius, although occasionally they may be from further afield. Monday is darts night, Wednesday crib and Thursday poker. Q ☎ ❀ & ♣ P 🚆 (9,49) ❀ 🛜

A quart a day keeps the doctor away

A judicious labourer would probably always have some ale in his house, and have small beer for the general drink. There is no reason why he should not keep Christmas as well as the farmer; and when he is mowing, reaping, or is at any other hard work, a quart, or three pints, of really good fat ale a-day is by no means too much.

William Cobbett, Cottage Economy, 1822

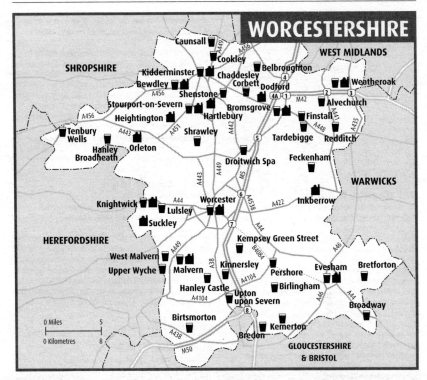

Alvechurch

Weighbridge 🍺 Ⅼ

Scarfield Wharf, Scarfield Hill, B48 7SQ (follow signs to marina from village) SP022721.

☎ (0121) 445 5111 ⏣ the-weighbridge.co.uk

Hobsons Mild; house beer (by Woodcote); 4 changing beers (sourced locally) Ⓗ

This cosy canalside pub is a thriving community asset that has won many CAMRA awards. It was built at the same time as the construction of the Birmingham to Worcester canal in the early 1800s. The regular beer, Bridge 60, is a unique pale ale from Woodcote brewery, while the changing beers are locally sourced, with real ciders and craft ales also available. Home-cooked food and a popular Sunday lunch are served. It holds two beer festivals a year, plus other events.

Q🌑🕏🕴🕭🕈🕪🕃P🕀♪

Belbroughton

Holly Bush Inn

Stourbridge Road, DY9 9UG (on A491 Stourbridge Rd)

☎ (01562) 730207

Hobsons Mild, Town Crier; Holden's Black Country Bitter; 1 changing beer (sourced regionally) Ⓗ

Set back from the A491, this traditional, characterful inn was originally built in the 1700s, and has been run by the same family for over 30 years. Hobsons beers are served along with guest ales and real cider. It comprises a lounge/dining area, a central bar area with an open fire, and a small raised restaurant. The traditional pub menu includes good-value specials, plus fish and vegetarian options. It is the winner of local CAMRA awards, including Pub of the Year. Dogs are welcome.

Q🌑🕏🕴🕪🕃P🕭(318) 🐾

Bewdley

Bewdley Brewery Tap 🍺

Lax Lane, DY12 2DZ (Lax Ln is off Severn Side S, the Tap is at back of brewery)

☎ (01299) 405148 ⏣ bewdleybrewery.co.uk

Bewdley Worcestershire Way, Baldwin IPA, Jubilee, Worcestershire Sway, William Mucklow's Dark Mild; 1 changing beer (sourced locally; often Bewdley) Ⓗ

Bewdley brewery produces a range of six regular cask ales, seasonal beers and bottled beers, some for the Severn Valley Railway. The taproom, at the rear of the brewery, is adorned with railway memorabilia and is a lively pub with a friendly welcome. Six of the brewery's cask and seasonal ales are served through half-pint pulls, giving each pint a perfectly clear dispense. The full range of bottled beers is available. Closed on Monday except bank holidays. Local CAMRA Gold Pub of the year 2024.

🌑🕃P🕭🕀

Black Boy Ⅼ

50 Wyre Hill, DY12 2UE (up Sandy Bank from Cleobury Rd at Welch Gate)

☎ (01299) 400088 ⏣ theblackboybewdley.co.uk

Bewdley Worcestershire Way; Wye Valley Butty Bach; 3 changing beers (sourced locally; often Enville, Hobsons, Three Tuns) Ⓗ

Perched above the town, this friendly inn is worth the climb. The attractive, half-timbered building dates from 1462, with a beamed interior and open fire in winter. Up to five beers are served, plus a real cider or two. Cobs and pork pies are available, and hot meals at the end of the week. Attractions include bar skittles, bagatelle, board games and shove-ha'penny. A folk session is hosted on the second Wednesday of each month and a quiz on Sunday. Closed on Monday.

Q🌑🕏🕴🕙🕪🕃(8,292) 🕀🕀♪

Great Western ⓛ

Kidderminster Road, DY12 1BY (near SVR station – walk past the signal box and under viaduct)

☎ (01299) 488828

Bewdley 2857, Worcestershire Way; 3 changing beers (sourced locally; often Ludlow, Wye Valley) ⓗ
Conveniently located a short walk from the Severn Valley Railway station, the pub's traditional interior has a railway theme. Overlooking the bar is an upper level from which to admire the fine, glazed, decorative tiling. Pub snacks such as cobs and tasty local pork pies are in keeping with the traditional pub ambience. On the bar are five real ales, including the house beer, 2857 from Bewdley, named after a GWR locomotive sometimes seen on the nearby railway viaduct. ⑧❀☒♣P🚃❀?

Old Waggon & Horses ⓛ

91 Kidderminster Road, DY12 1DG (on Bewdley to Kidderminster road at Catchem's End)

☎ (01299) 403170

Bathams Mild Ale, Best Bitter; Ludlow Gold; 1 changing beer (often Timothy Taylor, Three Tuns, Wye Valley) ⓗ
Popular and friendly pub with a central bar serving three distinct areas. The small wooden-floored snug has a dartboard; the larger room has a wood-burner and roll-down screen for sporting events, though at most times conversation prevails. Changing ales come from regional and national breweries. Lunchtime and evening meals are available from Wednesday to Saturday, with a lunchtime carvery on Sunday (two sittings). Fresh cobs and pork pies are always available. The attractive terraced flower garden is on many levels.
Q⑧❀☒①❀♣P🚃❀?♪

Real Ale Tavern ⓛ

67 Load Street, DY12 2AW (in centre of main street)

☎ (01299) 404972

Black Country Bradley's Finest Golden, Chain Ale, Pig on the Wall, Fireside; 6 changing beers (sourced nationally; often Front Row, Mallinsons, Saltaire) ⓗ
A traditionally styled pub, converted from a bank. The cosy front lounge has an open fire in winter and leads into another area, then another, all the way to the back of the pub. It specialises in real ales, with an impressive array of 12 handpulls dispensing beers from Black Country Ales, as well as local and national breweries, and sometimes including two real ciders. The current beers are displayed on screens making it easy to order at the bar. Cobs and pies are always available.
Q❀♣☒♣🚃❀?

Birlingham

Swan Inn

Church Street, WR10 3AQ

☎ (01386) 750485 ⊕ theswaninn.co.uk

Goff's Cheltenham Gold; 1 changing beer (often Purity, Three Tuns) ⓗ
A pretty, thatched free house tucked away at the edge of this quiet village. Although the emphasis is on dining, there is a small, separate, cosy black-and-white beamed bar. The conservatory overlooking the nice garden is for dining, with fresh fish featuring on the menu. The log cabin-style covered seating in the garden is ideal for outdoor drinking. Q⑧❀☒①P🚃(565A)❀?

Birtsmorton

Farmers Arms ★

Birts Street, WR13 6AP (off B4208) SO790363

☎ (01684) 833308 ⊕ farmersarmsbirtsmorton.co.uk

Hook Norton Hooky, Old Hooky; Wye Valley Butty Bach; 2 changing beers (sourced locally; often Hobsons) ⓗ
Grade II-listed black-and-white village pub dating from 1480, in a quiet spot down a country lane. The large bar area has a splendid inglenook fireplace while the cosy lounge has old settles and low beams. Good-value, home-made, traditional food is on offer daily. Beer from a small local independent brewery is often available. The safe, spacious garden, with swings, provides fine views of the Malvern Hills. A caravan site is nearby.
Q⑧❀☒①♣❀P❀?

Bredon

Fox & Hounds Inn ⓛ

Church Street, GL20 7LA

☎ (01684) 772377 ⊕ thefoxandhoundsbredon.co.uk

Donnington BB, Cotswold Gold, SBA ⓗ
A black-and-white, thatched village pub owned by Donnington brewery of Stow-on-the-Wold. The interior is decorated in rustic style with modern furnishings. It is mainly laid out for dining, with the space divided into separate areas. Paninis and sandwiches are served at lunchtime Wednesday to Saturday. Jazz nights are hosted, and events around major sporting occasions. The pub may close early if quiet. ❀①P♪

Bretforton

Fleece Inn ♈ ★ ⓛ

The Cross, WR11 7JE (near to the church)

☎ (01386) 831173 ⊕ thefleeceinn.co.uk

Purity Mad Goose; Uley Pigs Ear; Wye Valley Bitter; 3 changing beers (sourced nationally; often North Cotswold, Purity, Wye Valley) ⓗ
A 15th-century timber-framed village pub owned by the National Trust, on the edge of the Cotswolds. It is recognised by CAMRA as having a nationally important historic pub interior and has a world-famous 17th-century pewter collection. The pub has its own orchard garden which is very popular with families in summer, and the food comes highly recommended. Morris dancers and music feature all year round. Not to be missed if you are in the area. Local CAMRA Pub of the Year 2024. Q⑧❀☒①♣❀♣P🚃❀?♪

Broadway

Crown & Trumpet Inn ⓛ ✅

14 Church Street, WR12 7AE

☎ (01386) 853202 🌐 crownandtrumpet.co.uk
Goff's Cheltenham Gold; North Cotswold Shagweaver; Timothy Taylor Landlord; 1 changing beer (sourced locally; often North Cotswold) Ⓗ
Picturesque 17th-century Cotswold-stone inn just off the village green. It is a lovely pub with lots of character, oak beams, a log fire, and Flowers brewery memorabilia. Classic and local pub dishes are served alongside local and guest ales, plus several ciders and perries. Entertainment is hosted on Friday and Saturday. Accommodation is available. Worth a visit if you are on the Cotswold Way or touring Shakespeare's Country. Q✿🛏◖♣♥🤝🎵

Bromsgrove

Golden Cross Hotel Ⓛ ✔
20 High Street, B61 8HH (S end of High St)
☎ (01527) 870005
Greene King Abbot; Ruddles Best Bitter; Sharp's Doom Bar; 9 changing beers (sourced regionally) Ⓗ
A busy town-centre Wetherspoon pub in a former hotel and coachhouse. It is split-level and has 12 booths with stained-glass surrounds and an open fire. Daily themed food deals and manager's specials are always on offer. Three regular core beers are served, plus nine various guests, many from local breweries. The licensee asks for suggestions on beer choices and reacts to feedback. During seasonal festivals cask ales from across the UK are promoted. ♿✿◖🅿🚆♥

Hop Pole Inn ✔
78 Birmingham Road, B61 0DF
☎ 07522 847127 🌐 hop-pole.com
Wye Valley HPA, Butty Bach; house beer (by Woodcote); 2 changing beers (sourced regionally; often Woodcote) Ⓗ
An end-of-terrace pub close to the town centre, this community-style local has a great atmosphere. It features bands covering various music styles every Friday and Saturday. The bar area gives an excellent view of the stage, with comfortable chairs at the front. An upstairs games room has a pool table where league matches are played. There is a smoking area in the beer garden to the rear. Dogs are permitted in the pub but not in the beer garden grassed area. ♿✿🐕♣♥🚆♥🎵

Ladybird Inn Ⓛ
2 Finstall Road, B60 2DZ (on B4184 on corner of roundabout near station) SO969695
☎ (01527) 878014 🌐 ladybirdinn.co.uk
Bathams Best Bitter; Sharp's Solar Wave; Wye Valley HPA, Butty Bach; 1 changing beer (often Brew61) Ⓗ
This popular community local is situated near the town's railway station. Decor is light and airy, with a large busy bar to the front and a lounge with a polished wooden floor to the rear. A meeting room is available on the first floor and a function room suitable for parties is on the ground floor. Homemade filled rolls and other substantial snacks are available throughout the day. ♿✿&≠♣🅿♥🎵

Little Ale House
21 Worcester Road, B61 7DL (corner of Station St)
☎ 07791 698641
5 changing beers (often Hartlebury, Three Tuns, Woodcote) Ⓖ
A micropub with a cosy atmosphere, featuring raised seating and tables mounted on large wooden barrels. There is also seating available outside on the street. Up to five ales are dispensed by gravity, alternating between breweries such as Woodcote, Hartlebury and Three Tuns, and a good range of ciders and perries are

available. Dogs are welcome. A council car park is nearby and the bus station is a five-minute walk away. Q♿✿♣♥🚆♥♥

Caunsall

Anchor Inn Ⓛ
Caunsall, DY11 5YL (off A449 Kidderminster to Wolverhampton road)
☎ (01562) 850254 🌐 theanchorinncaunsall.co.uk
Hobsons Town Crier; Ludlow Gold; Wye Valley HPA, Butty Bach Ⓗ
Friendly village inn renowned for its excellent real ales, traditional cider, well-filled cobs and pork pies. The central doorway leads into the bar, with its 1920s furniture and horse racing memorabilia. Outside, the garden is a suntrap in summer. The pub is easily reached from the nearby canal, and is well worth stopping off for, but it is popular and can get busy, especially at lunchtimes and weekends. It has won many local CAMRA awards, including Bronze Pub of the Year in 2022 and Silver in 2023. Q♿✿♣♥🅿🚆(9A,9C)♥♥

Chaddesley Corbett

Swan Ⓛ
High Street, DY10 4SD SO892737
☎ (01562) 777302 🌐 theswanchaddesleycorbett.co.uk
Bathams Mild Ale, Best Bitter Ⓗ
Dating from 1606, this traditional pub features a public bar, side room with a real fire, and an impressive lounge with a raised area for entertainment. Cobs and pies are available at lunchtime. Quiz nights, jazz nights and open mic nights are held regularly. There is a large garden and children's play area overlooking beautiful countryside. Bathams Best Bitter was first brewed for this pub, and Bathams XXX is available in December. The pub is popular with walkers and cyclists. Q♿✿♪A♣🅿🚆(52)♥♥🎵

Cookley

Cookley Village Hall & Sports Club Ⓛ
Lea Lane, DY10 3RH (near St Peter's Church)
☎ (01562) 850055 🌐 cookleyvillagehall.co.uk
Sharp's Doom Bar; Wye Valley HPA, Butty Bach; 2 changing beers (sourced locally; often Hobsons, St Austell, Wye Valley) Ⓗ
Popular sports club and village hall which welcomes signed-in visitors and card-carrying CAMRA members (though club members benefit from discounted bar prices). The well-presented beers are from Wye Valley, with two changing guest ales from local and other breweries. An outside hatch serves barbecue-style food at weekends, and on other days during the spring and summer months. Various sports and leisure clubs are resident and the hall is available for event hire. ♿✿◖&🅿🚆(9A,9C)♥♥🎵

Droitwich Spa

Hop Pole Ⓛ
40 Friar Street, WR9 8ED (100yds from Norbury Theatre)
☎ (01905) 770155
Bathams Best Bitter; Wye Valley HPA, Butty Bach; 2 changing beers (sourced regionally; often Woodcote) Ⓗ
An 18th-century pub in the old part of Droitwich, close to the Norbury Theatre. Over 300 guest beers have been served since the current licensees took over in 2020. Cobs, Scotch eggs and pork pies are available. Outside is a heated patio area for smokers, plus an undercover

seated garden, and a large outdoor stage for use in summer. Safe moorings are available on the nearby Droitwich canal. ▷⚜❄✦♣●P🖵🐕🎵

Talbot
19 High Street, WR9 8EJ
☎ (01905) 773871
Craddock's Saxon Gold, Crazy Sheep, Monarch's Way; 4 changing beers (sourced regionally) Ⓗ
Friendly, traditional inn with a front bar, large rear room, beer garden and terrace. Eight handpumps serve the Craddock's beer range, plus other changing beers, offering a good range of styles. The Craddock's loyalty card scheme is operated here. The food menu is based on traditional pub dishes, with home-cooked Sunday lunches. The pub holds occasional themed nights, live music and a monthly quiz.
Q▷⚜❄✦●P🖵(144,354)🐕🎵

Evesham

Red Lion Ⓛ
6 Market Place, WR11 4RW
☎ (01386) 429123 ● redlionevesham.co.uk
Butcombe Original; North Cotswold Moreton Mild; 2 changing beers (sourced regionally) Ⓗ
Community local tucked away in the corner of Market Place, with a main bar, seating area at the front and side, and a smaller snug with its own bar and inglenook fireplace. Regular live music sessions are held throughout the week. There is no TV or food, although you are welcome to order from nearby food outlets. Four handpumps serve real ale, two changing, and one real cider. Winner of a local CAMRA special award in 2023.
Q▷⚜❄✦●🖵🐕🎵

Trumpet Inn Ⓛ ✅
13 Merstow Green, WR11 4BD (off Merstow Green car park)
☎ (01386) 442816
Hook Norton Hooky, Off The Hook, Old Hooky; 1 changing beer (often Hook Norton) Ⓗ
Friendly and welcoming traditional pub – probably the most westerly outlet of the Hook Norton tied estate – tucked away at the southern end of the High Street opposite the Merstow Green car park. It has a large grassed garden at the rear and further seating is available at the front. Home-made food is served daily, with many weekly specials and Sunday roasts. Regular darts matches are held and live sports are on TV. Local CAMRA Pub of the Year 2023. ▷⚜🕊▲❄✦🖵🐕🎵

Feckenham

Rose & Crown
High Street, B96 6HS
☎ (01527) 892188 ● roseandcrownfeckenham.co.uk
Brakspear Oxford Gold; 3 changing beers (sourced locally; often Brew61, Prescott, Purity) Ⓗ
A welcoming, family-run, Grade II-listed village pub standing in the pretty village of Feckenham. It has a cosy lounge with wooden settles and a traditional bar. Up to four changing real ales and at least one real cider are always available, as well as a wide menu of classic pub meals. At the rear is a large enclosed beer garden with a number of summer houses. Parking is limited, but there is a free car park 200 yards away.
Q▷⚜🕊♣🖵(354)🐕🎵

Finstall

Cross Inn Ⓛ
34 Alcester Road, B60 1EW (on B4184 Finstall corner)
☎ (01527) 577328
Black Country Bradley's Finest Golden, Pig on the Wall, Fireside; 4 changing beers (sourced regionally; often Burton Bridge, Silhill, Titanic) Ⓗ
A popular and welcoming community pub in the heart of the village, run by Black Country Ales. Seven handpumps dispense real ales, including at least one dark beer, alongside two ciders. Fresh cobs are always available with complimentary salad. It has a comfortable open-plan lounge, while outside is an extensive area that features a heated decking area and a small marquee for screening sporting events. The pub fundraises for the Primrose Hospice and hosts events for local community groups. ▷⚜🕊♣●P🖵(52,52A)🐕🎵

Hanley Broadheath

Fox Inn Ⓛ
WR15 8QS (on B4204 E of Tenbury Wells) SO671652
☎ (01886) 853189
Banks's Sunbeam; Bathams Best Bitter; 1 changing beer Ⓗ
A large, 16th-century, black-and-white timbered free house. The bar is decorated with hops and has a large fireplace with a wood-burning stove. The panelled dining area is separated from the bar by wooden beams. The games room has a pool table, TV and dartboard. Home-made food, including Sunday lunch, is available, with bar snacks at any time. Q▷⚜🕊▲♣P🖵(309)🐕🎵

Hanley Castle

Three Kings ★ Ⓛ
Church End, WR8 0BL (signed off B4211) SO838420
☎ (01684) 592686
Butcombe Original; 4 changing beers (often Beowulf, Hop Shed, Malvern Hills) Ⓗ
This unspoilt 15th-century country pub has been identified by CAMRA as having a nationally important historic pub interior. There is a small snug with a large inglenook, serving hatch and settle wall. Nell's Lounge has another inglenook and plenty of beams and is reached through the side entrance; there is also a small side room with no bar. Three guest ales are often from local breweries and include a stout or porter. Live music features on Sunday evening, with regular lunchtime singalong on Fridays. Cash only. Q▷⚜●P🖵(332)🐕🎵

Kemerton

Crown Ⓛ
High Street, GL20 7HP
☎ (01386) 725020 ● thecrownkemerton.co.uk
Wye Valley HPA, Butty Bach; 1 changing beer (often Goff's) Ⓗ
A delightful old pub in the centre of an idyllic Cotswold village at the foot of the famous Bredon Hill. It is run by two locals who are passionate about providing a great experience and is ideal for walkers. A traditional log fire greets customers in the cosy bar. There is a courtyard behind and a separate dining room serving meals prepared with local produce. B&B accommodation is available for those wishing to stay longer.
⚜🛏◑♣🖵(540)🐕🎵

Kempsey Green Street

Huntsman Inn 🅛

Green Street, WR5 3QB (from A38 at Kempsey via Post Office Ln) SO868490

☎ (01905) 820336

Bathams Best Bitter; Greene King IPA; Morland Original Bitter 🅗

A 300-year-old former farmhouse that is now a cosy and friendly multi-roomed local with exposed beams. A small main bar with a real fire is to the front, with a larger bar down steps to the rear. A separate restaurant serves reasonably-priced home-cooked food, but the pub is closed at lunchtimes during the week. There is also a skittle alley with its own bar, an attractive garden and a large car park. Dogs are welcome in the bar and lounge. ♿❀◑♣P♥

Kidderminster

Bear & Wolf 🅛

11-17 Worcester Street, DY10 1EA

☎ (01562) 227150

House beer (by Fixed Wheel); 5 changing beers (sourced nationally; often Mallinsons, Moor Beer, Vocation) 🅗

Modern, town-centre pub opened in 2019 and specialising in real ales, ciders and canned craft beers. It is deceptively spacious, with a mix of sofas, tables and high perches. Quiet background music encourages conversation and on weekends live music is featured. There are six real ales from local and regional breweries, always including a dark ale, some unusual beers, and a variety of cans in the fridge. Pork pies and Scotch eggs are available all day. Local CAMRA Gold Pub of the Year 2022 and 2023. ♿≒●P♥🎵

Chester Tavern 🅛

211 Chester Road, DY10 1TN

☎ (01562) 630010 ⊕ thechestertavern.co.uk

Bewdley Red Hill; Wye Valley HPA; 2 changing beers (sourced nationally; often Attic, Millstone, Woodcote) 🅗

Modern and spacious community pub and acoustic music venue, specialising in changing beers not commonly found in the area. The large lounge has an attractive wooden bar and there is a Mediterranean-style beer garden. There are four real ales, always one from Bewdley and Wye Valley, and two changing beers sourced from independent breweries. Pork pies and rolls are available. Open mic night is the last Tuesday of the month and acoustic artists play on Thursday evenings and Sunday afternoons. Q♿❀≒🖥(125,192)♥🎵

King & Castle 🅛

Comberton Hil, DY10 1QX (next to main line station and part of the Severn Valley Railway terminus)

☎ (01562) 747505

Bathams Best Bitter; Bewdley Worcestershire Way; Hobsons Town Crier; 3 changing beers (sourced regionally; often Bewdley, Three Tuns, Titanic) 🅗

Atmospheric recreation of a GWR terminus station bar and waiting room on the Severn Valley Railway. Handpumps dispense six beers from local and regional breweries. Pub meals, cobs and snacks are available from the bar on most days, and a full menu when trains are running. Bottled beers from Bewdley are served on the trains, and pubs along the line attract visitors using the railway. Local CAMRA Gold Pub of the Year 2019 and Bronze in 2020. Closed on Monday except bank holidays. Q♿❀◑&≒P🖥♥🎵

Weavers Real Ale House 🅛

98 Comberton Hill, DY10 1QH (30yds down hill from railway station)

Three Tuns XXX; 7 changing beers (sourced nationally; often Church End, Kinver, Ludlow) 🅗

One-room conversational bar serving eight interesting and changing real ales, always including at least one dark ale, and up to four ciders on handpump, sometimes including a perry, along with craft beers on tap. Cobs are always available. It is near the railway station and convenient for a pint and a chat on the way into town. CAMRA National Pub of the Year Finalist 2018, local Silver Cider Pub of the Year 2019, and local Silver Pub of the Year 2022. Q♿&≒●🖥♥🎵🎶

Kinnersley

Royal Oak

WR8 9JR

☎ (01905) 371482 ⊕ theroyaloakkinnersley.co.uk

Hobsons Mild; Wye Valley Butty Bach; 2 changing beers (often Butcombe, Wye Valley) 🅗

A rural pub at the centre of a quiet village, with a front bar and separate restaurant areas behind, and patio benches outside at the front. The changing beers are often from small local breweries. Live music features on the last weekend of each month. Children and dogs are welcome. It is close to the National Trust's Croome Park. B&B accommodation is offered in the converted stable block. Q♿❀🛏◑&Å♣P🖥♥🎵🎶

Knightwick

Talbot 🅛

WR6 5PH (on B4197, 400yds from A44 jct)

☎ (01886) 821235 ⊕ the-talbot.co.uk

Teme Valley T'Other, This, That 🅗; 1 changing beer (often Teme Valley) 🅖

A 14th-century coaching inn with a large lounge bar, divided into two by a huge fireplace, and a separate taproom. At the rear is a small wood-panelled restaurant that serves an imaginative menu using local ingredients, and there is also an attractive conservatory. A beer garden is to the side and another across the old road, which now doubles as a car park, leading down to the river. A food trailer operates in the summer for alfresco dining. The Teme Valley brewery is located behind the pub. Dogs and walkers are welcome. Q♿❀🛏◑&Å♣P🖥(420)♥🎵🎶

Lulsley

Fox & Hounds 🅛

WR6 5QT

☎ (01886) 821228 ⊕ foxandhoundslulsley.com

Ledbury Gold; Wye Valley HPA; 2 changing beers (often Goff's, Hobsons) 🅗

A large pub in a rural village, with two bars from the original Victorian building, warmed by an open fire, and with level access from the front door. The pub has been extended with a large dining room, and a conservatory on the side featuring a baby grand. An extensive garden and children's play area is to the rear, with the river Teme and the Worcestershire Way beyond. Local beers and local produce are on the menu. A beer festival is held on the spring bank holiday. Q♿❀◑●P♥🎵

Malvern

Morgan 🅛 ✅

52 Clarence Road, WR14 3EQ

☎ (01684) 578575
Wye Valley Bitter, HPA, Butty Bach; 1 changing beer (sourced locally; often Wye Valley) Ⓗ
Named after the town's Morgan car factory, this Wye Valley brewery-owned pub serves their full range, plus a guest craft keg. The interior is open plan, with comfy settees in a slightly raised seating area. Brewery and car pictures decorate the walls. The landscaped patio has ample seating. Activities include a monthly book club and weekly quizzes. The TV is only turned on for major sporting events. A ramp can be requested for wheelchair access to the main bar.
ⓣ❀⑪⟨⟩♿≒(Great Malvern) ♣🚆❀🛜♪

Nag's Head Ⓛ

19-21 Bank Street, WR14 2JG (near Graham Rd by Link Top common)
☎ (01684) 574373 ⊕ nagsheadmalvern.co.uk
Banks's Amber Ale; Hook Norton Old Hooky; Wainwright Gold; 8 changing beers (often Otter) Ⓗ
A free house serving three permanent beers and guests from around the country, plus two draught ciders. Nooks and crannies filled with mismatched furniture and foliage provide a homely environment and the pub is busy throughout the week. Several fires burn brightly in winter. Quality food is served in the bar and separate restaurant, which has level access (though the bar does not). There is a large, covered, heated outdoor area to the front and a quiet garden hidden away at the rear. The car park is small, but there is ample on-street parking. Dogs are welcome (and numerous).
Q❀⑪▶♣🚆🚌(44) ❀🛜♪

Weavers ♟

14 Church Street, WR14 2AY
5 changing beers Ⓗ
Modern craft and draught ale bar in a former shop, with level access to the bar and ground floor. A few tables are outside on the street in summer and a patio garden to the rear. The room upstairs has comfy sofas, a dartboard and board games. Five handpumps serve real ales and two dispense draught still cider, plus there are five craft keg lines. No food is served, but you can bring your own. Cheese nibbles are served on Sunday. There is no car park, but plenty of parking is available around town.
❀♿≒(Great Malvern) ♣🚌❀

Pershore

Millers Arms ✪

8 Bridge Street, WR10 1AT
☎ (01386) 553575 ⊕ millersarmspershore.co.uk
Wadworth Horizon, 6X; 1 changing beer (often Wadworth) Ⓗ
Spacious Wadsworth's pub on the main street. It is divided into several cosy areas, which retain a lovely, old-style pub atmosphere that is enhanced in the winter by a roaring log fire. Seating is at tables or on comfy settees. It is open daily, with food available every day, including Sunday roasts. A monthly quiz is held on Sunday, and live bands appear on Fridays. ⑪▶🚌❀♪

Redditch

Black Tap

Church Green East, B98 8BP (near top of Church Green East, opp fountain)
☎ (01527) 584165
4 changing beers (sourced regionally; often Hobsons, Oakham) Ⓗ
Redditch's only micropub is a former brewpub offering varied and interesting beers. The main bar has a roaring

fire, which adds to the friendly atmosphere. It is conveniently located near the town centre and serves a changing range of beers and ciders. A small side room can be booked on request. Live music usually features at the weekend once or twice a month. Parking is available at a Pay & Display car park in the nearby Quadrant.
ⓣ❀≒♣▶P🚌❀🛜♪

Shenstone

Plough Ⓛ

Shenstone Village, DY10 4DL (off A450/A448)
SO865735
☎ (01562) 777340
Bathams Mild Ale, Best Bitter Ⓗ
Traditional rural pub that has been at the heart of the village since 1840. The long single bar serves the public bar and two lounge areas, both of which have real fires. Bathams Mild and Bitter are served all year, while the stronger XXX is available during December. Cobs, pork pies and bar snacks are usually available. A large enclosed courtyard serves as an overflow, and there is a small patio to the front. Q ⓣ❀♿♣P❀🛜

Shrawley

New Inn Ⓛ

New Inn Lane, WR6 6TE (B4196 between Stourport and Worcester)
☎ (01299) 822701
Wye Valley HPA, Butty Bach; 1 changing beer (sourced nationally; often Bewdley, Hobsons, Otter) Ⓗ
An independent community pub in the Worcestershire countryside, with a lounge bar, log-burners and a separate restaurant area. Being close to Shrawley Woods, it is well placed for a pint after a walk; dogs are welcome. Light snacks are served at lunchtime and a full menu is available in the evening. Traditional lunches are served until 5pm on Sunday. The spacious garden has plenty of seating and is attractively illuminated. Wye Valley and other beers are available. Closed on Monday except bank holidays. Q ⓣ❀⑪▶♿♣P🚌(294,296)❀🛜

Stourport-on-Severn

Black Star Ⓛ ✪

Mitton Street, DY13 8YP (just off top end of High St, next to the canal)
☎ (01299) 488838 ⊕ theblackstar.co.uk
Ludlow Gold; Wye Valley The Hopfather, HPA, Butty Bach, Wholesome Stout; 5 changing beers (sourced regionally; often Hobsons, Three Tuns) Ⓗ
Situated next to the the canal, there are moorings just through the bridge towards the basins. An attractive beer garden with a shelter, tables and raised flowerbeds overlooks the canal. The changing range of beers is from Wye Valley and regional breweries. The menu includes steaks, fish, burgers, vegetarian and vegan options, sandwiches, baguettes and a variety of home-cooked meals. Food is served all week except Monday and Sunday evening. Local CAMRA Gold Pub of the Year 2020 and Bronze in 2023 and 2024. ⓣ❀⑪▶🚌❀🛜♪

Hollybush Ⓛ

Mitton Street, DY13 9AA (a short walk from main street down Gilgal)
☎ (01299) 660650
Black Country Bradley's Finest Golden, Pig on the Wall, Fireside; Sharp's Doom Bar; 4 changing beers (sourced nationally; often Mallinsons, Salopian) Ⓗ

A welcoming pub serving up to eight real ales from independent breweries in a relaxed and friendly atmosphere. A single bar serves a split-level lounge that has many ancient timbers, a snug and an upstairs function room containing a dartboard. The flower-filled beer garden at the rear, accessed from upstairs, is a tranquil suntrap in summer. Good-value cobs, pork pies and Scotch eggs are available. Regular evening events include live music, quizzes, cheese nights and live TV sports. Local CAMRA Silver Pub of the Year 2024. Q ⅏ ☕ ♣ ☐ ❀ 🛜 ♪

Tardebigge

Alestones

Unit 23 Tardebigge Court, B97 6QW
☎ (01527) 275254 ⊕ alestones.co.uk
4 changing beers (sourced locally) H
A well-maintained micropub sitting in a courtyard alongside several small independent shops and businesses. There is a constantly changing range of four beers available, usually including a golden ale, dark beer and a best bitter as well as real cider and perry. Though extended to the rear and side, the pub still retains its cosy, convivial atmosphere, but now with room to stretch your legs. Local musicians are hosted once a month on Sundays. Pub snacks are usually available. Q ⅏ ☕ ● P ☐ (52,52A) ♪

Tenbury Wells

Market Tavern

Market Square, WR15 8BL
☎ (01584) 810982
Black Country Bradley's Finest Golden, Pig on the Wall, Fireside; 7 changing beers (often Woodcote) H
Situated next to the historic Grade II-listed market hall, the Market Tavern has been extensively refurbished by Black Country Ales. The bar is smartly decorated and split into three smaller areas on different levels. There are prints of the old town on the walls, and a dartboard in the lower area. Specialising not only in real ales from their own microbrewery in Lower Gornal, the pub also offers a selection of six guest ales and two guest ciders. Bar snacks are available daily. Q ⅏ ☕ ♣ ● ☐ ❀ 🛜

Upper Wyche

Wyche Inn L

Wyche Road, WR14 4EQ (on B4218, follow signs from Malvern to Colwall)
☎ (01684) 575396 ⊕ thewycheinn.co.uk
Wye Valley HPA; 3 changing beers (sourced regionally; often Ledbury) H
Situated above Great Malvern, this free house is the highest pub in Worcestershire, with panoramic views towards the Cotswolds from the bar and patio. The top bar leads to the patio and has a dedicated dining area, and the lower bar features a dartboard. The regular real ales are paired with others from small and microbreweries. Green-hop beers are available throughout October. Home-made food is served. Closed on Monday, except bank holidays (when it closes on Tue). Q ☕ ⛺ ⅏ ♣ P ☐ (675) ❀ 🛜 ♪

Upton upon Severn

Olde Anchor Inn L ✓

5 High Street, WR8 0HQ
☎ (01684) 593735 ⊕ anchorupton.co.uk
Hobsons Best; St Austell Tribute; Sharp's Doom Bar; Wye Valley Butty Bach; 2 changing beers H

An old, oak-beamed pub dating from 1601 and mentioned in Cromwell's dispatches. There are low ceilings and many small rooms and alcoves, plus a patio garden and a few tables at the front. The bar, featuring a large fireplace and range, is separate from the restaurant area. An additional wood-panelled function room is available for meetings and parties. Sandwiches and a full food menu are available. Q ☕ ⅏ ⛺ ☐ ❀ 🛜 ♪

Weatheroak

Coach & Horses Inn L

Weatheroak Hill, B48 7EA (Alvechurch to Wythall road) SP057740
☎ (01564) 823386 ⊕ coachandhorsesinn.uk
Holden's Golden Glow; Hook Norton Old Hooky; Weatheroak Hill Slow Lane, IPA, Cofton Common; 5 changing beers (sourced nationally; often Hobsons, St Austell) H
Home to the Weatheroak Hill brewery (which is in the old coach house at the front), this award-winning country free house has been in the same family since 1968. It has a traditional bar, with a real fire and quarry tiled floor. There is also a modern lounge-bar and a separate restaurant. The large garden wraps around the pub and is popular in the summer. Fresh cobs are regularly available. The old Roman road, Icknield Street, runs alongside. ⛺ ☕ ⅏ ⅏ ♣ P ❀ 🛜

West Malvern

Brewers Arms L

Lower Dingle, WR14 4BQ (S end of village, down track by pub sign on B4232)
☎ (01684) 550609 ⊕ brewersarmswestmalvern.co.uk
6 changing beers (often Hobsons, Hop Shed, Wye Valley) H
Taken over by the community in 2022, this is an ideal refreshment stop for visitors to the Malvern Hills. Up to six real ales are available from local breweries. Most food is home-made. The main pub can get busy, but extra space is available in the function room across the yard. The garden offers splendid views across to the Black Mountains. A popular quiz is held on the first Tuesday of the month. It is open on bank holiday Mondays, with Sunday hours for food and drink. Q ☕ ⅏ ⅏ ♣ ● ☐ (675) ❀ 🛜 ♪

Worcester

Ale Hub Micropub L

Unit 1B Abbotsbury Court, WR5 3TY
⊕ alehub.co.uk
Wye Valley Butty Bach; 3 changing beers (sourced locally; often Bewdley, Dancing Duck, Salopian) H
Opened in 2021, this micropub is in a converted shop premises close to Tesco superstore, in the residential district of St Peter's to the south of the city, and accessible by bus. It offers Butty Bach and three changing, and often unusual, handpulled ales, alongside cocktails and craft keg. There is a warm, friendly atmosphere, and weekly bingo and quiz nights are held. There is level access to the bar. Dogs are welcome. Q ☕ ☐ (32) ❀ ♪

Dragon Inn

51 The Tything, WR1 1JT (on A449, 300yds N of Foregate St station)
☎ (01905) 25845 ⊕ thedragoninnworcester.co.uk
Church End Goat's Milk, Gravediggers Ale, What the Fox's Hat, Fallen Angel; 4 changing beers (often Bewdley, Church End, Slaughterhouse) H

A Georgian building on the edge of the city centre run by Church End Brewery. A selection of ales from the brewery are served, along with some from other UK microbreweries. The room at the front has a cosy fire, while the bar is towards the back. The old passageway to the side has seating and is decorated with odds and ends. The yard behind features another covered area, with a log-burner for colder months, and more seating beyond. There is easy level access through the gates at the rear. Bar snacks such as Scotch eggs are always available. Q✿❄☀(Foregate Street)♣🍴🚌❀🛜♪

Imperial Tavern ⓛ

35 St Nicholas Street, WR1 1UW

☎ (01905) 619472

Black Country Bradley's Finest Golden, Pig on the Wall, Fireside; 6 changing beers (often Black Country, M&B, Salopian) Ⓗ

This smart city pub is run by Black Country Ales. It serves three real ales from the brewery alongside up to six from small breweries around the country and up to six real ciders. Three drinking areas are joined by the bar running front to back, and there is level access to the bar. Pictures of old Worcester pubs and street scenes decorate all the walls. Cobs are available at lunchtime. Real time train information for Foregate Street station is shown. Q🐾👶♿❄(Foregate Street)♣🍴🚌❀🛜♪

Oil Basin Brewhouse

7 Copenhagen Street, WR1 2HB

☎ 07964 196194

Wintrip Butchers Beastly Best; 3 changing beers (often Salopian) Ⓗ

A small, dimly-lit bar, just off the High Street, with comfy chairs, beamed ceiling and bare boards. A variety of interesting real ales, mostly local, and craft keg are sold, as well as a good selection of craft beers and ciders from the fridge. Extra seating is available upstairs, where you can also find wood-fired oven pizzas. There is level access to the bar and toilets. ◗❄(Foregate Street)♣🚌❀🛜♪

Plough ⓛ

23 Fish Street, WR1 2HN (on Deansway)

☎ (01905) 21381

Hobsons Best; 4 changing beers (sourced regionally; often Salopian) Ⓗ

A Grade II-listed pub near the cathedral. A short flight of steps leads to a tiny bar, with rooms leading off to either side. The beers usually come from breweries in Worcestershire and the surrounding counties, but occasionally are from small breweries further afield. Draught cider and perry is from Barbourne in the city. There is also an ever-changing range of whiskies for the connoisseur. Outside there is a small patio area. Filled rolls are available Friday to Sunday. Q🐾✿❄(Foregate Street)♣🍴🚌❀♪

Fox & Hounds, Lulsley (Photo: Andy Checketts Consultancy)

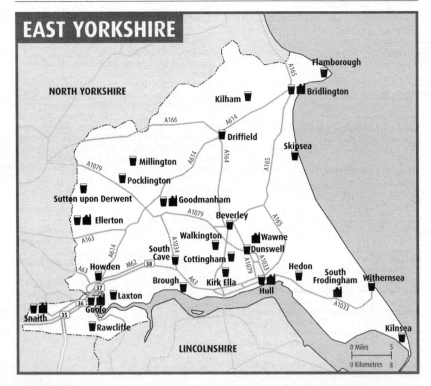

EAST YORKSHIRE

Beverley

Chequers Micropub 🅛

15 Swaby's Yard, Dyer Lane, HU17 9BZ (off Saturday Market)

☎ 07964 227906

5 changing beers (sourced regionally; often Great Newsome, North Riding, Rooster's) 🅗

Yorkshire's first micropub opened in 2013 in an old patisserie in a pleasant secluded yard between Tesco and Saturday Market, close to the bus station. The friendly bar encourages conversation in the absence of TV, sport, music and Wi-Fi. Board games and cards are available. There is a popular outside seating area and the pub is dog friendly. Q✿⚘♣️●🖪❀

Dog & Duck 🅛

33 Ladygate, HU17 8BH (off Saturday Market adjacent to Browns store)

☎ (01482) 862419 ⊕ bedandbreakfastbeverley.com

Black Sheep Best Bitter; Great Newsome Sleck Dust; Timothy Taylor Landlord; 2 changing beers (sourced regionally; often Rudgate, Yorkshire Heart) 🅗

The pub was built in the 1930s and has been run by the same family since 1972. It is comprised of three distinct areas: a bar with a period brick fireplace and bentwood seating, a front lounge with an open fire, and a rear snug. The good-value lunches are popular. Guest accommodation is provided in six purpose-built self-contained rooms to the rear with dedicated parking. Close to Beverley bus station. ⛺🛏️《●♣️●🖪❀🛜

Monks Walk 🅛

19 Highgate, HU17 0DN

☎ (01482) 880871 ⊕ monkswalkinn.com

5 changing beers (sourced regionally; often Great Newsome, Sharp's, Wold Top) 🅗/🅖

Dating back to the 13th century and built as a merchant's warehouse, conversation is encouraged at this genuine free house. Access is via a medieval passageway to the front bar, pool room and lounge with an open fire. The rear courtyard and secret beer garden have views of the nearby minster. Five handpumps offer pale, bitter, dark and strong ales. Wood-fired pizzas are served during the summer months. Wednesday is folk night, with live music upstairs most Friday and Saturday nights. Q⛺🏵️《≷♣️●🖪❀🛜♫

Bridlington

Brunswick Hotel 🅛

13 Manor Street, YO15 2SA

☎ (01262) 672186 ⊕ bridlingtonhotel.co.uk

Wold Top Headland Red, Wold Gold, Scarborough Fair IPA; 1 changing beer (sourced locally) 🅗

Situated in the centre of the town, close to the harbour, it is known by locals as the Brunnie. The public bar comprises two recently refurbished rooms, with a separate games room featuring two pool tables and four dartboards and equipped with TVs for live sport. Beers from Wold Top brewery have been featured for many years and are complemented by a rotating guest beer. ⛺🛏️≷♣️🖪🛜♫

Old Ship Inn ✅

90 St John Street, YO16 7JS

☎ (01262) 401906

Bridgehouse Porter; 6 changing beers (sourced nationally; often Acorn, Rudgate, Yorkshire Heart) 🅗

Offering a genuine warm welcome this multi-zoned pub located in Bridlington's historic Old Town features photographs of bygone Whitby by Frank Meadow Sutcliffe and others of Bridlington itself. Furnished comfortably throughout, it is backed by a superb enclosed beer garden with designated decked smoking

area. The handpull beers comprise a delightful mix of largely local as well national brewers. It is dog friendly but children are not permitted. A good stepping off point for exploring the old town's many pleasing features.
இ&&▲௫(124,5A) ⬤ ⬤ ♫

Pack Horse ⓛ
7 Market Place, YO16 4QJ
☎ (01262) 603502
Theakston Old Peculier; 3 changing beers (sourced regionally; often Bingley) ⓗ
With stocks outside and a restored brewery dray in the yard its easy to take a liking to this lovingly restored 17th-century establishment. Three separate areas flow around the central bar which are supplemented by the extensive rear courtyard. Bridlington Brewery Compay beers, now produced in the centre of Bridlington, are featured on the bar together with other ales usually sourced within Yorkshire. ⓢ⬤♣Pఱ⬤♠

Telegraph ⓛ
110 Quay Road, YO16 4JB (10 minutes from Rail station)
☎ 07411 281651
Wold Top Anglers Reward; 3 changing beers (sourced nationally; often Pennine, Wold Top) ⓗ
A popular local, family run, community focused pub situated a short walk from the railway station and en-route to Bridlington Old Town. The welcoming one room interior is divided into three distinct areas; one hosts the pool table and a television for sports coverage, while the main bar area also has plentiful seating; with the final area a comfortable lounge. There is also an extensive, well furnished, walled beer garden featuring a chimnea, to the right hand side and rear of the pub.
Qఱ⇌♣Pఱ⬤♠♫

Three B's Micropub ⓨ ⓛ
2 Marshall Avenue, YO15 2DS
☎ (01262) 604235 ⊕ threebspubbrid.co.uk
Acorn Barnsley Bitter; 3 changing beers (sourced locally; often Blue Bee, Half Moon, North Riding) ⓗ
Marketed as Bridlington's real ale destination the ever-present Barnsley Bitter is joined on the bar by three never repeated beers, sourced primarily from Yorkshire. To date approximately 800 different beers have been sold. A cider selection of up to 12, largely sourced regionally, has led to several CAMRA awards including the finals of national Cider Pub of the Year in 2023. Snacks in the form of excellent home-made sausage rolls as well as pie and peas are usually available.
Qⓢ⬤ⓘ&⇌♣⬤ఱ⬤♠♫

Brough

Centurion Arms ⓨ ⓛ
39 Skillings Lane, HU15 1BA
☎ 07936 569982
4 changing beers (sourced regionally; often Great Newsome, Half Moon, Wold Top) ⓗ
Located among a number of small businesses the Centurion is unlike any other pubs in the area. The interior is eclectically decorated with local artwork, an extensive collection of pumpclips and a variety of other paraphernalia. The pub serves an ever-changing variety of real ales and cider and also has a range of wines, keg beers and spirits. Social interaction and conversation is encouraged. Dogs are welcome, with treats provided. Local CAMRA Town Pub of the Year 2022 and 2023.
ⓢ⬤&⇌♣⬤Pఱ(55) ⬤

Cottingham

Hugh Fitz-Baldric ⓨ ⓛ
144 Hallgate, HU5 4BD
6 changing beers (sourced nationally; often Great Newsome, Oakham, Titanic) ⓗ
Converted from a shop on the main street of the largest village in England, this pub consists of one room with quiet corners. It is furnished with repurposed items and a log burner adds cosiness in winter. Altogether this makes for a peaceful place to enjoy the range of real ales, gins and other drinks reflecting changing trends. Children are welcome until evening, and dogs are allowed in the beer garden. Local CAMRA Village Pub of the Year 2023.
Qⓢ⬤ఱ⇌ఱ

Driffield

Butcher's Dog
57 Market Place, YO25 6AW (entrance is via the archway)
☎ (01377) 252229 ⊕ thebutchersdog.co.uk
6 changing beers (sourced locally; often Half Moon, Wold Top) ⓗ
This characterful micropub, now firmly established in the centre of the town, presents a long if slightly narrow room facing out onto the Main Road. An independently operated back room provides a food service. The beers are generally presented in colour order on the bar, dark to light. Dogs are welcome. Thursday afternoon features open mic sessions with live music sessions also staged. The pub provides an inclusive space for all.
Qⓢ⇌⬤Pఱ⬤♠♫

Spread Eagle
1-2 Exchange Street, YO25 6LJ
☎ (01377) 253073
Theakston Best Bitter; 3 changing beers (sourced locally; often Great Newsome, Ossett) ⓗ
Within easy walking distance of the town centre, this recently refurbished establishment offers a warm welcome and constantly changing range of beers. The main room offers comfortable furnishings and is well used by locals and attached sporting teams. A pool table is located to the right-hand side of the bar and televised live sport is popular at weekends. A quieter lounge area is to the left of the bar. An outdoor seating area is also available. ⓢ⬤&⇌♣Pఱ♫

Dunswell

Ship Inn ⓛ
Beverley Road, HU6 0AJ
☎ (01482) 854458 ⊕ shipsquarters.co.uk
3 changing beers (sourced regionally; often Black Sheep, Great Newsome) ⓗ

REAL ALE BREWERIES
Aitcheson's Wawne
All Hallows 🍺 Goodmanham (brewing suspended)
Atom Hull
Belschnickel Hull
Bridbrewer 🍺 Bridlington
Bridlington 🍺 Bridlington
Great Newsome South Frodingham
Half Moon 🍺 Ellerton
Old Mill 🍺 Snaith
Spotlight Goole (brewing suspended)
Woolybutt Hull
Yorkshire Brewhouse Hull

An attractive food-oriented free house fronting the Hull to Beverley road with maritime connections. There is nautical memorabilia relating to the trade on the nearby River Hull, and other interesting displays on the pub's walls. Log fires and a wood burner provide a cosy atmosphere. The outbuildings have been converted to create en-suite accommodation. The large garden has an outside bar and barbecue for summer events. 🛏️🍽️🕐🅟💳♿🅿🚌🅦🛜

Ellerton

Boot & Shoe
Main Street, YO42 4PB
☎ (01757) 288346
House beer (by Dark Horse) Ⓗ
A welcoming country village inn dating from the 17th century. Unusually, the building wraps around a very large tree. There is a cosy bar with exposed brick, a side bar served via a hatch, and two further rooms. All have real fireplaces, low ceilings and even lower doorways (watch your head). To the rear is a pleasant sunny patio and a large grassy beer garden. Q🕐♣🅿💳

Flamborough

Viking Hotel
North Marine Road, YO15 1BA
☎ (01262) 851455 🌐 the-viking.co.uk
3 changing beers (sourced regionally; often Rudgate, Wensleydale, Wold Top) Ⓗ
It is a pleasant walk from Flamborough's North Landing and the nearby Haven Caravan Park to this seemingly isolated pub divided into four separated areas. Delightful views across fields feature the two Flamborough lighthouses and offer glimpses of the local wildlife. Good food and well-kept beer are matched by a cheerful welcome to all comers. Real fires feature during the winter months. The pub does get very busy during holiday seasons. Q🛏️🍽️🅟🕐🅦♿🅿🚌💳🛜🎵

Goodmanham

Goodmanham Arms Ⓛ
Main Street, YO43 3JA
☎ (01430) 873849
All Hallows No Notion Porter, Ragged Robyn; Hambleton Stallion Amber; Ossett Yorkshire Blonde; Theakston Best Bitter; 3 changing beers (sourced locally; often All Hallows, Hambleton) Ⓗ
A family run atmospheric and cosy village local with attached All Hallows brewery in a beautiful setting close to the Wolds Way. Log fires and candlelight warm the two main bars in winter and a variety of outdoor seating spaces are available for warmer times. Freshly cooked meals are served every lunchtime as well as on Monday and Wednesday evenings. Dogs are welcome, except when food is being served. Frequent winner of the local CAMRA Village Pub of the Year. Q🛏️🕐🅟💳♿🛜🎵

Goole

Tom Pudding
20 Pasture Road, DN14 6EZ (2 mins' walk from Goole station)
☎ 07563 830828
4 changing beers (sourced regionally; often Great Newsome, Hambleton, Wold Top) Ⓗ
Opened in 2017 this micropub with interesting internal brickwork and an exposed wooden beamed ceiling was once a newsagents. It was started by two CAMRA members with an enthusiasm for real ale. The pub can

accommodate up to 50 people, and is often sought out by travelling football fans on their way to Hull and Doncaster. Four ales, frequently Hambleton or Wold Top, include a gluten free beer. Up to four real ciders from producers such as Henry Weston and Dudda's Tun are stocked. ⏚♣🅟🚌(155,X55)💳🎵

Hedon

Hed'On Inn
7 Watmaughs Arcade, St Augustine Gate, HU12 8EZ
☎ (01964) 601100
Black Sheep Best Bitter; 4 changing beers (sourced nationally; often Banks's, Castle Rock, Great Newsome) Ⓗ
This micropub was converted from the office of a carpet shop. Situated adjacent to a car park in the centre of this old market town, the premises are decorated with recycled items from the East Riding. It has one regular beer and four changing beers which include all styles. Real cider is also available. A quiz night is held every Wednesday. Music is played from a jukebox. Monthly live music is hosted; see Facebook for information. ♿♣🅟🅿🎵

Howden

Tailor's Chalk Ⓛ
3 Market Place, DN14 7BJ
☎ 07496 865180
3 changing beers (sourced regionally; often Great Newsome, Rudgate, Shadow Bridge) Ⓗ
Small family-run micropub situated in former tailor's shop consisting of a small single bar. It bills itself as Howden's smallest pub. Three cask beers are on offer, typically from regional breweries such as Wold Top or Great Newsome, and several craft keg beers. Check its Facebook page for updates to opening hours and community events. Q🛏️🅟(55)🛜🎵

Hull

Admiral of the Humber Ⓛ ✅
1 Anlaby Road, HU1 2NR
☎ (01482) 381850
Batemans XXXB; Greene King Abbot; Ruddles Best Bitter; Sharp's Doom Bar; 6 changing beers (sourced nationally; often Great Newsome, Rooster's, Titanic) Ⓗ
A Wetherspoon hotel in a former paint and wallpaper shop on the site of the Master Mariner almshouses built in 1834 by Trinity House and destroyed by enemy bombing in WWII. The Admiral of the Humber is the title held by the Lord Mayor of Hull. There is a large open-air roof terrace for non-smokers and smokers (closes 10pm). The Connexion Live Arena is nearby. The pub is away-supporter friendly for visiting sports teams. Q🛏️🍽️🕐♿🚮🅿🛜

Alexandra Hotel ★ Ⓛ
69 Hessle Road, HU3 2AB (by car use satnav to Ropery St; on foot from Interchange head S via Midland St and Porter St to green footbridge then past Vauxhall Tavern)
☎ (01482) 327455 🌐 alexandrahotelhull.co.uk
7 changing beers (sourced locally; often Mallinsons, Rudgate, Yorkshire Heart)
Known as The Alex, new ownership in 2019 transformed this Grade II-listed Victorian pub into a real ale gem with up to seven cask ales, including at least one dark beer and several real ciders. Good conversation features highly along with motorsport themed memorabilia. There is a fine bar back and (now electric) gas light

fittings inside with terracotta tiling outside. The pub supports local charities and picks up/drops off locally for donations. Home of the Parrot brewery.
🛇🕷🚻♿♠P🛅🖵👿♪

George Hotel
Land Of Green Ginger, HU1 2EA
☎ (01482) 226373
Timothy Taylor Landlord; 4 changing beers (sourced nationally; often Adnams, Wye Valley) 🅗
The George Hotel is located in the heart of Hull's Old Town and reputedly has the smallest pub window in England. A grey lady is also said to roam the hallway from its former coaching inn days. A welcoming ground floor bar has many of its original period fittings. The second bar upstairs has TVs for sporting events and is available for hire. The bars are well stocked with a good selection of real ales, ciders and other drinks. ♠🖵

Hop & Vine 🍸 ⓛ
24 Albion Street, HU1 3TG (250yds from Hull New Theatre and Central Library)
☎ 07507 719259
4 changing beers (sourced nationally; often Acorn, Salopian, Wishbone) 🅗
A cosy basement bar free house serving three to four changing guest beers, largely from independent Yorkshire breweries. Oversized lined glasses are used for real ales. Six still ciders and perries are stocked along with many bottled continental beers and a good selection of international whiskies, including ones from Yorkshire's own distillery. Pub games are available including Nine Men's Morris and Shove Ha'penny and there is a monthly Sunday games night. Local CAMRA City Pub of the Year 2022 and 2023. 🛇🕷♿▲🍴♠♦🛅🖵👿🛜

Minerva Hotel ⓛ
Nelson Street, HU1 1XE
☎ (01482) 210025 ⊕ minerva-hull.co.uk
Tetley Bitter; 5 changing beers (sourced regionally; often Ossett, Westgate) 🅗
Overlooking the Humber estuary and Victoria Pier, the Minerva has stood here since 1829. It is just around the corner from the marina and also connected to The Deep visitor attraction by a footbridge at the mouth of the River Hull. Inside, photos and memorabilia are a reminder of the area's maritime past. The central bar serves various rooms including the tiny three-seat snug – the smallest in the country. The former brewhouse was converted into a seating area and is available for functions. 🛇🕷🕪🖵(16)🛜

Pave ⓛ
16-20 Princes Avenue, HU5 3QA
☎ (01482) 333181 ⊕ pavebar.co.uk
Wainwright Amber; 4 changing beers (sourced regionally; often Brass Castle, North Riding, Rooster's) 🅗
The original pavement café in this popular area of the city, this continental-style bar attracts a diverse range of customers. There are four guest ales, usually regional or local, and a varied range of European draught and bottled beers. A changing cider is also sold. Close to the local sports stadium and away-supporter friendly. Free live music is provided on some Sunday afternoons; Facebook for details. 🛇🕷♿♠🖵(5)🛜♪

Scale & Feather
21 Scale Lane, HU1 1LF
☎ 07808 832295
4 changing beers (sourced nationally; often Carnival, Marble, Rudgate) 🅗

Large independent single-room pub with an upper floor function room situated in the heart of Hull's Old Town. This traditional pub with a modern interior is friendly, with a great atmosphere, serving a multitude of different drinks including four changing cask ales, craft beers and cocktails. Pizzas are available on Friday and Saturday nights. A small smoking area can be found at the rear of the property. 🛇♦🖵👿🛜

Ship Inn
43 Hodgson Street, HU8 7EY (from city centre go E over North Bridge, left onto Cleveland St then left onto Hodgson St)
☎ (01482) 228171 ⊕ shipinnhull.co.uk
Great Newsome Holderness Dark; Rudgate Battleaxe; 4 changing beers (sourced regionally; often Brass Castle, Brew York, Vocation) 🅗
Tucked away off New Cleveland Street, this 200-year-old pub is packed with history. A traditional pub with a warm welcome, there are photos illustrating the area on the walls, and seating area heated by a traditional log burner, as well as a dining area and function space. There is a large, sheltered, fully lit outdoor seating area complete with outdoor barbecue for summer events. Fish & chips are available on Friday and breakfast is served on Sunday, with booking available for both.
Q🕷♦♠♦P🖵(10)👿♪

St John's Hotel ★
10 Queens Road, HU5 2PY
☎ (01482) 341013 ⊕ stjohnshotelhull.co.uk
Courage Directors; Marston's Old Empire; Wainwright Gold; 3 changing beers (sourced nationally; often Banks's, Brains, Tetley) 🅗
Unspoilt Grade II-listed community local which was once a regular haunt of the late poet laureate, Philip Larkin. Built in 1865 and remodelled by Hull brewery in 1904-5, it has been identified by CAMRA as having a nationally important historic pub interior. Both the front, L-shaped, public bar and rear lounge, with original bench seating, encourage friendly conversation. Another larger room houses a pool table. There are two separate outside areas. Live music/open mic occurs every Tuesday, and cask ale is discounted on Monday. Occasional beer festivals are held. Q🛇🕷🕪♠P🖵👿🛜♪

Station Inn ⓛ
202 Beverley Road, HU5 1AA
4 changing beers (sourced regionally; often Abbeydale, Pennine, Rudgate) 🅗
Mid-Victorian pub built to serve the Stepney station on the Hull to Hornsea railway line. It has a mock-Tudor façade and has been extensively restored to a high standard. A great feature in the public bar is an open fire and the bar front. The back bar, also with open fire, is used for regular Station Singarounds and live music. Check the Facebook page for regular updates on beer and cider selections. 🛇🕷♠♦🖵👿♪

White Hart ★ ⓛ ✅
109 Alfred Gelder Street, HU1 1EP
☎ 07538 470546 ⊕ whiteharthullpub.co.uk
5 changing beers (sourced regionally; often Brew York, Great Newsome, Vocation) 🅗
Located 100 yards past the Guildhall on the edge of the Old Town, the pub is a Grade II-listed building with a half-timber frontage. It as been identified by CAMRA as having a nationally important historic pub interior with a rare example of a ceramic bar made by Burmantofts of Leeds, as were many other features such as the original bar back which dates from 1904. Both bars have large TV screens showing sport. A well stocked bar caters for all tastes. 🛇🕷🕪♠♦P🖵👿🛜♪

Kilham

Old Star Inn
Church Street, YO25 4RG
☎ (01262) 420619
Theakston Best Bitter; 2 changing beers (sourced regionally; often Great Newsome, Helmsley, Ossett) Ⓗ
Located in the centre of the village, opposite the imposing church, this delightful, beamed-ceiling pub contains three distinct areas off the bar. In winter two of these areas have real fires, giving it a homely and welcoming atmosphere. A corridor gives access to the sizeable garden at rear. Locally sourced, high-quality food is served all day. Locals, walkers, bikers and cyclists are all made equally welcome. The local Raven Hill brewery shares some familial links. Beers are usually source from the Yorkshire area. Q❄❀🕙&♿♣P🐾🐕🎵

Kilnsea

Crown & Anchor Ⓛ
Kilnsea Road, HU12 0UB
☎ (01964) 650276 ⊕ crownandchorkilnsea.co.uk
Tetley Bitter; Timothy Taylor Landlord; 1 changing beer (often Great Newsome) Ⓗ
Enjoy spectacular views over the River Humber of wading birds, ships and sunsets at Yorkshire's most easterly pub – an ideal stop-off for Spurn National Nature Reserve. It comprises a bar, dining room, saloon and large beer garden. Three real ales include a changing local ale. Food is locally sourced and freshly prepared, with a Sunday carvery, vegetarian options, vegan specials and lighter lunch time options available. Close to campsites and the beach. Q❄❀🕙♿♣P🐾🎵

Kirk Ella

Beech Tree
South Ella Way, HU10 7LS
☎ (01482) 654350
Dark Star Hophead; Sharp's Doom Bar; 6 changing beers (sourced nationally; often Black Sheep, Theakston, Timothy Taylor) Ⓗ
Open-plan pub on the western outskirts of Hull, owned by a pub company committed to cask ale. Up to eight real ales are available, including at least one dark beer; try-before-you-buy is encouraged. Food is served every day with brunch on weekends. Wednesday is quiz night. Families with children are welcome and a real fire makes for a hospitable winter feel. Buses stop close to the pub until early evening, with a later bus only 10 minutes away. ❄❀🕙♿P🚌(154)🐕

Laxton

Bricklayers Arms
Front Street, DN14 7TS
☎ (01430) 432029
3 changing beers (sourced regionally; often Great Newsome, Rudgate, Wold Top) Ⓗ
A 19th-century building in the centre of the village of Laxton with a bar, lounge, snug and games room. The pub serves three cask ales, all from regional breweries. Home-cooked meals are served Thursday, Friday and Sunday and use locally sourced ingredients. Thursday is pie night, Friday is fish night and Sunday is traditional lunch. May close early on Tuesday. Q❄🕙🚲(Saltmarshe) ♣P🐾🎵

Millington

Gait
Main Street, YO42 1TX
☎ (01759) 302045 ⊕ thegaitinn.co.uk
Black Sheep Best Bitter; Ossett Yorkshire Blonde; Theakston Best Bitter; 2 changing beers (sourced locally; often Bradfield, Half Moon, Wold Top) Ⓗ
Delightful Yorkshire Wolds pub, providing a warm welcome to locals and the many walkers enjoying the attractions of Millington Woods and Pastures. An idiosyncratic bar is filled with ornaments and local pictures with an old Yorkshire map on the ceiling. Wood-burning stoves provide warmth in winter. Hearty, home-made food is served from an extensive menu which includes Fish Fridays. A beer festival is held in July. Quiz night is every other Wednesday. A large pleasant beer garden includes a covered area. ❄❀🕙♣P🐾🐕

Pocklington

Market Tap
11-13 Market Place, YO42 2AS
☎ (01759) 307783
Brew York Fennec Blonde, Maris the Otter, Calmer Chameleon, Tonkoko; 4 changing beers (sourced locally; often Brew York) Ⓗ
Situated overlooking the market place, this 19th-century building provides a light, spacious and modern feel over two floors. An extensive range of eight cask beers and several craft keg beers are nearly all from Brew York, with occasional beers from other local breweries. Off sales of wines, beers and ciders are available too. It has an outdoor pavement area for drinking and that bistro feel! There is a popular weekly quiz night. ❄🕙♿🚌🐾🐕

Rawcliffe

Jemmy Hirst 🍷 ✅
26 Riverside, DN14 8RN (from village green turn N on Chapel Ln)
☎ (01405) 837902
Timothy Taylor Landlord; 5 changing beers (sourced locally; often Bradfield, Little Critters, Ossett) Ⓗ
A traditional award-winning free house in the heart of the village. The pub is famed for its warm welcome and is a community hub, hosting a wide variety of events, clubs and live music. Landlady Jill has invested in modernising the cellar and introducing more ales and drinks while still maintaining the much-loved traditional interior. Overlooking the River Aire, the pub has an open fire and is both dog and family-friendly. A must for fans of a proper local pub. Q❄❀🚲♣P🚌(401,88)🐾

Skipsea

Board Inn
Back Street, YO25 8SW (off B1242)
☎ (01262) 469845 ⊕ board-inn.co.uk
2 changing beers (sourced locally) Ⓗ
Situated one mile from the sea in the village conservation area this homely pub, dating from 1642, is popular with locals and is a mecca for holiday makers. A traditional two-roomed bar and lounge, three beers are reduced to two in winter. A 60 cover restaurant serves home-prepared food using locally sourced produce. Booking is recommended for Sunday lunches. Functions are catered for. Walkers, cyclists and dogs are welcome. Closed on Monday and Tuesday in winter. Q❄❀🕙&♣P🚌(130) 🐾🐕🎵

Snaith

Plough Inn ✪
Shearburn Terrace, DN14 9JJ
☎ (01405) 480106 ⊕ ploughinnsnaith.com
Don Valley Atomic Blonde, Gongoozler, Go Your Own Way; 2 changing beers (sourced nationally; often Nailmaker, Rudgate, Settle) ⊞
The Plough Inn is a Grade II-listed, traditional pub. It has two main rooms, both served by one central bar. The public bar has a large fireplace with log burner, while the lounge is cosier with chesterfield sofas and armchairs. The large, paved beer garden has a raised sun terrace and stables that contain a pool table and dartboard. Home-cooked food is available daily, including Sunday dinners. Various events and live music nights are hosted throughout the year. ☎❀🛏◑👪❤♣️P🚬(401)❤♪

South Cave

Bear Inn
61 Market Place, HU15 2AS
☎ (01430) 422482
4 changing beers (sourced nationally; often Lancaster, Timothy Taylor, Wold Top) ⊞
The Bear Inn is situated in the South Cave Conservation Area, less than a mile from the A63/M62. This 150-year-old pub serves food and has a regularly changing selection of cask beers. It has a recently remodelled main bar, a conservatory and a beer garden. The pub holds quizzes, has live music and shows live sports on TV. It is listed as an Asset of Community Value.
☎❀◑Å♣P🚬❤🛜♪

Sutton Upon Derwent

St Vincent Arms 🄻
Main Street, YO41 4BN
☎ (01904) 608349 ⊕ stvincentarms.co.uk
Fuller's London Pride; Kirkstall Three Swords; Timothy Taylor Golden Best, Landlord; Theakston Old Peculier; 1 changing beer (sourced nationally) ⊞
This pretty white-painted village free house has been owned by three generations of the same family. The pub offers an excellent range of beers, with five regular and one changing guest ale, usually from a local independent brewer. The cosy bar to the right, featuring a large Fuller, Smith & Turner mirror, is popular with locals. Another small bar to the left, with a serving hatch, leads to the dining rooms. This pub offers great service with excellent food beyond the usual pub fare. Q☎❀◑P

Walkington

Barrel Inn
35 East End, HU17 8RX
☎ 07550 078833
Thwaites IPA; Wainwright Gold ⊞
Friendly drinkers' local in a quiet three-pub village, one of only a handful of Thwaites pubs in East Yorkshire. The front bar, with a log fire and beamed ceiling, has a step leading to a connecting lounge, also with a log fire. To the rear is a secluded cottage-style garden. Families and dogs are welcome. Although essentially a quiet pub, major football matches and some other sporting events are shown. Thursday is quiz night. The pub is popular with Beverley racegoers. ☎❀♣P🚬❤♪

Withernsea

Captain Williams
6 The Promenade, HU19 2DP

☎ (01964) 270084
4 changing beers (sourced nationally; often Bradfield, Great Newsome, Timothy Taylor) ⊞
Formerly known as the Marine Bar, it was originally built in 1893 by builder and owner Captain William Newman. Refurbished with a nautical feature wall it has panoramic views of the beach and North Sea. Four changing beers are sourced nationally. Food is served, with a Wednesday pizza night, Sunday lunch, and other menus Thursday to Saturday. Accommodation includes en-suite rooms and three chalets. Families and dogs are welcome.
☎❀🛏◑P🚬❤♪

Old BoatShed 🄻
2 Seaside Road, HU19 2DL
☎ 07812 446689
4 changing beers (sourced regionally; often Great Newsome, Ossett, Wold Top) ⊞
Built as the town's lifeboat station in 1881 this became a micropub in 2016, retaining some original features. There are four cask pumps with at least three on all the time. There is no TV or gaming machines which makes for a comfortable and pleasant atmosphere. Beer and cider can be sampled as three thirds on a beer bat. There is a comfortable seating veranda outside. Live acoustic music is held monthly. Community-focused, children and dogs are welcome. Q☎❀♣🚬❤♪

YORKSHIRE (NORTH)

Ainderby Steeple

Wellington Heifer 🄻
DL7 9PU
☎ (01609) 775718 ⊕ thewellingtonheifer.co.uk
Timothy Taylor Landlord; 1 changing beer (often Black Sheep, Wensleydale) ⊞
Comfortable pub catering for locals and diners. The emphasis is on food, but pride is taken in consistently serving good beer. The pub is on a bend on the main A684 Northallerton to Bedale road, opposite the church referenced in the village's name. There are five B&B rooms and a new function room with panoramic views looking over fields to the River Swale. The pub has its own 50Kw charging point for electric cars, available to customers. Q☎❀🛏◑P🚬(54)❤🛜

Appleton Wiske

Lord Nelson
High Street, DL6 2AD
☎ (01609) 881351 ⊕ lordnelsoninn.uk
Theakston Best Bitter; 1 changing beer (sourced nationally) ⊞
A true local's pub located facing the beautiful village green in the centre of the picturesque award-winning village of Appleton Wiske, near Northallerton. The pub is divided into two rooms, one set out for meals and the other a welcoming bar for drinkers. Takeout food is available Friday and Saturday evening, with sit-in Sunday lunch. Two beers are always on – a traditional house bitter and a rotating local lighter beer. Thursday themed dining is available during the year, check the website for details. ❀◑P❤

Appletreewick

Craven Arms 🄻
BD23 6DA
☎ (01756) 720270 ⊕ craven-cruckbarn.co.uk

Dark Horse Craven Bitter, Hetton Pale Ale; Theakston Old Peculier; Wharfedale Wharfedale Blonde; 2 changing beers (sourced regionally) Ⓗ
Multi-roomed free house dating from 1548, with stone-flagged floors, oak beams and gas lighting. The bar features an original Yorkshire range while the cosy taproom has an open fire and ring the bull. A snug behind the bar leads to the cruck barn, built in 2006 using ancient techniques. This can be hired for functions and hosts occasional events including music and a beer festival in October. Two additional guest beers are added in summer. Accommodation is in three shepherd's huts.
Q✦🕮♿Å♣🚲🅿🚃(74A) ✿🛜🎵

Askrigg

Crown Inn Ⓛ ✅

Main Street, DL8 3HQ
☎ (01969) 650387 🌐 crowninnaskrigg.co.uk
Theakston Best Bitter; Wensleydale Semer Water; 2 changing beers (sourced locally; often Theakston, Wensleydale) Ⓗ
Family-run pub at the top of the main street, which attracts a good mix of locals and visitors, and is particularly popular for its bar meals sourced from local suppliers, with takeaway pies available. The interior has been partly opened out but retains much of its traditional character, with an impressive range in the cosy snug, and open fires to warm cold walkers seeking shelter from the fells. Check the website for winter opening hours.
✦🕮◑Å♣🅿🚃✿🛜

Beal

Jenny Wren

Main Street, DN14 0SS
☎ (01977) 328404
3 changing beers (sourced regionally; often Rudgate) Ⓗ
Quirky but traditional pub with an interesting front bar room preserved in original condition for over 50 years. There are three rooms of varying size, from a small snug to a large main bar, with both drinking and dining areas. Sky Sports available in the tap room, leaving the lounge area free for conversation. There is level access to the building. Three changing guest ales including seasonal specials. The pub was formerly the King's Head. Quiz night is Tuesday. ✦🕮◑🅿🚃(476)🛜🎵

Beck Hole

Birch Hall Inn ★ Ⓛ

YO22 5LE (approx 1 mile N of Goathland)
☎ (01947) 896245
Black Sheep Best Bitter; 2 changing beers (sourced regionally) Ⓗ
Unspoilt, family-run rural gem, resting among a hamlet of cottages, run by an accomplished fine artist celebrating 44 years of continuous service to the trade. It comprises a small Big Bar and an even smaller Small Bar, and which, uniquely, both sandwich an even smaller traditional sweet shop. Pleasant outdoor drinking facilities overlook the Murk Esk. Sandwiches, pies, beer, cake and sweets are always available. Opening hours change in winter. A must visit pub! Q✦🕮♿♣🛜✿

Bentham

Hoggs 'n' Heifers

Main Street, LA2 7HF (on Auction Mart Yard)
☎ (015242) 98950
Kirkby Lonsdale Monumental; 2 changing beers Ⓗ

Looking like what it is – the top floor of a barn – it was converted to a pub in 1986, complete with bare floorboards and stonework. A variety of furniture includes grotesque wooden shapes made by the landlord. Mostly open to the rafters, the loft space houses a Harley and a motor scooter. The clientele is quite mixed. Opening hours may vary during school holidays. ✿Å⇌🅿🚃(80)✿🛜🎵

Bishopthorpe

Bishopthorpe Sports & Social Club Ⓛ

12 Main Street, YO23 2RB
☎ (01904) 707185 🌐 bishopthorpeclub.co.uk
Black Sheep Best Bitter; Ossett White Rat; 3 changing beers (sourced regionally; often Bradfield, Daleside, Goose Eye) Ⓗ
A multiple winner of local CAMRA Club of the Year, most recently in 2023, it welcomes non-members and dispenses cask beers through five handpulls with three rotating guests and often a dark beer is available. The St Patrick's beer festival, held in the function room, encourages all to enjoy an extended range of real ales and ciders and raise money for the support of local community sports teams. With sports channels and pub games it's a popular and vibrant venue which provides the music for the annual village festival.
✦♿Å♣🅿🚃✿🛜🎵

Marcia Inn Ⓛ ✅

29 Main Street, YO23 2RA
☎ (01904) 706185 🌐 marciainnbishopthorpe.co.uk
Leeds Pale; Timothy Taylor Landlord; 2 changing beers (sourced locally; often Half Moon, Rooster's, Rudgate) Ⓗ
With a landlord passionate about real ale, this award-winning, popular community local serves four cask beers which are mainly LocAle. There's relaxed and friendly atmosphere, pub games, Wednesday quiz nights plus support for local teams and clubs. Outside is a large rear garden with covered and heated seating and a children's play area. A good range of food is on offer. On-site brewery Bishy BrewHouse is planned to open in the near future. Q✦🕮♿Å♣🅿🚃(11)✿🛜🎵

Blakey Ridge

Lion Inn

YO62 7LQ
☎ (01751) 417320 🌐 lionblakey.co.uk
Black Sheep Best Bitter; Copper Dragon Golden Pippin; Morland Old Speckled Hen; Theakston Best Bitter, Old Peculier; 3 changing beers (often Theakston) Ⓗ
In an isolated position above Rosedale and Farndale, this is the highest pub in the North Yorkshire Moors. The area is steeped in history, from ancient crosses to 19th-century iron workings. This historic inn has offered food, drink and shelter for well over 400 years. The heavily beamed and bare-stone-walled interior has several interconnected seating areas and a separate restaurant with several roaring fires in winter. ✦🕮◑♿Å🅿✿🎵

Boroughbridge

Black Bull Inn Ⓛ

6 St James Square, YO51 9AR
☎ (01423) 322413
Daleside Blonde; 2 changing beers (often Pennine, Rudgate, Timothy Taylor) Ⓗ
Nestling in a corner of the market square the inn has been serving ale since it was first built in 1278. A Grade

NORTH YORKSHIRE

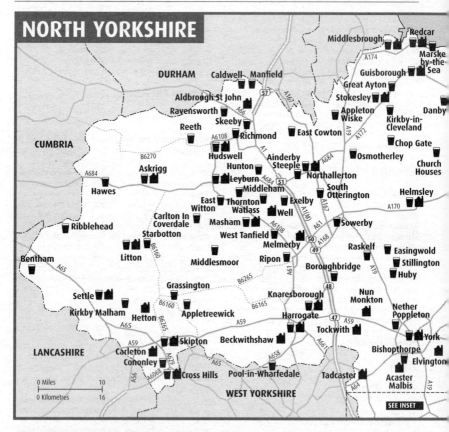

II-listed gem, it is well kept and comfortably furnished and is popular with locals and tourists alike; it also has a resident ghost. Three drinking and dining areas include a small cosy snug and a larger bar with open fires and good-value beers. Thai food is served Wednesday to Sunday and can also be ordered for takeaway. The ancient Roman site of Aldborough (Isurium) is nearby. Q ❄ 🏠 ⏰ 🍴 👜 ♣ P 🚲 (21,82) 🐾 🛜

Tap on the Tutt ★ 🅛 ✅

Bridge Street, YO51 9LF
☎ (01423) 322314 ⊕ taponthetutt.co.uk
Copper Dragon Golden Pippin; Daleside Bitter; Rudgate Jorvik Blonde; Timothy Taylor Golden Best; 2 changing beers (sourced locally; often Daleside, Rooster's, Rudgate) 🅗
A pub that was renovated in the 1930s and untouched until it closed in 2007. Thankfully subsequently reopened, it retains an outstanding 1930s interior but with some modernisation, however the wood and stained glass remains largely untouched. The pub also retains its original multi-room layout although in a concession to the modern world there are a number of TV screens. There are three handpumps in each bar. A beer list on a blackboard opposite the left-hand bar lists the ales including ABVs and prices.
🏠 ❄ ⏰ ♣ P 🚲 (21,82) 🐾 🛜

Burn

Wheatsheaf 🅛

Main Road, YO8 8LJ
☎ (01757) 270614 ⊕ wheatsheafburn.co.uk

5 changing beers (often Brown Cow, Ossett, Timothy Taylor) 🅗
Traditional country pub serving a varied range of guest beers mainly from Yorkshire breweries and popular for its excellent, reasonably-priced food. There is a collection of artefacts from bygone days and memorabilia of 578 and 431 Squadrons stationed at Burn in World War II. The Wheatsheaf stages regular beer festivals, quiz nights and many other activities. Q ❄ 🏠 ⏰ 👜 ♣ P 🚲 (476,405) 🐾 🛜 ♫

Burniston

Oak Wheel ✅

17-19 Coastal Road, YO13 0HR
☎ (01723) 870230 ⊕ theoakwheel.com
Timothy Taylor Boltmaker, Landlord; 1 changing beer (sourced regionally) 🅗
A friendly, large-roomed, village pub which prides itself on a warm welcome for locals and visitors alike. There are two regular handpulled ales together with a guest. The traditional meals are home-cooked using locally sourced ingredients, with daily specials available, and served evenings (not Sun) and weekend lunchtimes (Fri-Sun). Patio doors lead to the large garden with bench seating. An open log fire can be enjoyed during the winter months. En-suite accommodation is available.
🏠 ❄ ⏰ 👜 ♣ P 🚲 🛜

Caldwell

Brownlow Arms

DL11 7QH
☎ (01325) 718471 ⊕ brownlowarms.co.uk

☎ (01642) 778334 ⊕ the-buck-inn.co.uk
3 changing beers (sourced regionally) ℍ
Set amid a walkers' paradise, and close to the route of
Wainwright's Coast-to-Coast walk, this picturesque
family-run village pub offers a truly Yorkshire experience
with a Teutonic twist. Three handpulls and seven
especially imported draught lagers, brewed under the
508 year-old German Purity Laws, are served, together
with real home-made food, again half Yorkshire/half
German. There are six en-suite bedrooms, some
designated dog friendly, while free camping is offered to
those campers who also choose to dine here.
Q ☺ ☺ ♨ ◁ ◑ ⅄ ♣ P ⬚ (M4) ♥ ☕ ☎

Church Houses

Feversham Arms
YO62 7LF
☎ (01751) 433206 ⊕ fevershamarmsinn.co.uk
3 changing beers (sourced regionally) ℍ

Timothy Taylor Landlord; 2 changing beers (sourced
nationally) ℍ
The Brownlow Arms, set in the quiet village of Caldwell,
could be described as the perfect country inn. It boasts a
fine dining restaurant as well as two cosy bars with open
log fires where you are guaranteed to find some
welcoming locals. Serving three cask ales which always
includes Timothy Taylor Landlord, the others are ever-
changing but often from Yorkshire Dales although
requests are always welcome! Q ☺ ☺ ◑ ♣ P ♥ ☕

Carlton in Coverdale

Foresters Arms ⓛ
DL8 4BB
☎ (01969) 640272 ⊕ forestersarmscoverdale.com
**Wensleydale Gamekeeper; 4 changing beers (sourced
locally; often Black Sheep, Timothy Taylor, Yorkshire
Dales)** ℍ
Worth seeking out, this 250-year-old free house is
named after the Foresters Friendly Society, a mutual aid
body for local people in this picturesque area. It is on the
Dales cycle route and convenient for the Forbidden
Corner eccentric folly garden (advanced booking
essential). Owned by the community since 2011, the
pub's low-beamed ceilings and open fire contribute to its
character, with wooden settles fashioned from pews
from the former village church. Q ☺ ☺ ◑ ♣ P ♥ ☕ ♪

Chop Gate

Buck Inn
TS9 7JL (on the B1257, between Stokesley and Helmsley)

A stunning stone-built community country pub with a warm welcome situated in Farndale, in the middle of the North York Moors National Park. Farndale is famous for its wild daffodils that line the river Dove and the surrounding hills. The pub serves quality food and two to three changing beers, often LocAles. 🏵️🚲🍴◑P

Cloughton

Hayburn Wyke Hotel 🅛
Newlands Road, YO13 0AU (off the Ravenscar road, 1½ miles N of jct with the A171)
☎ (01723) 870202 🌐 hayburnwykeinn.co.uk
Black Sheep Special Ale; Theakston Old Peculier; 1 changing beer (sourced regionally; often Wold Top) Ⓗ
An 18th-century coaching inn in woodland next to the cinder track marking the old Scarborough to Whitby railway, and only minutes away from the Cleveland Way coastal path and adjacent rocky beach, making it popular with cyclists and walkers. Home-made food is served lunchtimes and evenings (not Mon eve), with the Sunday carvery a local favourite. En-suite accommodation is available. Outside is a well-provisioned children's play space and a sizeable heated smoking area. Operates reduced hours in winter.
Q🕱🛏️🏵️🚲◑Å♣P🖵(115)🏵️🎵

Cononley

New Inn 🅛 ✅
Main Street, BD20 8NR
☎ (01535) 636302
Timothy Taylor Golden Best, Boltmaker, Knowle Spring, Landlord, Landlord Dark; 1 changing beer (sourced locally) Ⓗ
This Timothy Taylor's tied house is a real local community pub with mullioned windows and low-beamed ceilings. The bar area is warmed by a wood-burning stove in a huge stone fireplace. Pot plants and china animals adorn the shelves and windowsills. Although just a short walk from Cononley railway station, if catching a train south allow time at the level crossing as the barriers often come down early. Quiz night is on Tuesday. A special beer from Timothy Taylor is occasionally offered.
🕱🏵️Å⇌♣🖵(78A)🏵️

Cross Hills

Craven Brew Co Tap Room 🅛
Midland Mills, Station Road, BD20 7DT (in industrial estate on right over railway bridge from Cross Hills)
☎ (01535) 637451 🌐 cravenbrew.co.uk
Craven Session Pale Ale, Black Angus Porter; 3 changing beers (sourced locally; often Craven, Kirkstall) Ⓗ
This is the tap room in the industrial unit that houses Craven Brew Co. The emphasis in the bar is on good company, friendly chatter and the appreciation of good beer. The main area features patio doors overlooking picnic tables. There is a more cosy snug behind the bar and an upstairs room with bar billiards. Five reasonably-priced ales are available, with at least four supplied by Craven Brew Co. Occasional music evenings and events are held. Q🕱🏵️◑&P🖵(66)🏵️📶

Gallagher's Ale House 🅛
1-3 East Keltus, BD20 8TD (in village centre)
☎ 07985 154469
5 changing beers (sourced nationally) Ⓗ
This popular micropub is located in what used to be Gallagher's bookmakers shop. The five changing ales usually include a dark beer, a pale bitter and a strong or

speciality beer. The cellar can be viewed through a window to the left of the bar. No electronic music or TV disturbs the conversation. Parking is available adjacent to the Co-op store round the corner.
Q🏵️♣🚗🖵(M4,66)🏵️📶🎵

Danby

Duke of Wellington 🅛
West Lane, YO21 2LY (300yds N of railway station)
☎ (01287) 660351 🌐 dukeofwellingtondanby.co.uk
Copper Dragon Scotts 1816; Daleside Bitter; 1 changing beer (sourced regionally) Ⓗ
This 18th-century inn is set in idyllic countryside, close to the Moors National Park Centre and the local traditional baker's shop. The inn was used as a recruiting post during the Napoleonic Wars. A cast-iron plaque of the first Duke of Wellington, unearthed during restorations, hangs above the fireplace. All beers are from Yorkshire. At lunchtime, sandwiches can be brought into the pub. During the evening, the kitchen offers traditional British home-cooked meals at their very best, using local produce. Q🕱🛏️◑⇌♣🚗🏵️

Easingwold

George Hotel 🅛
Market Place, YO61 3AD
☎ (01347) 821698 🌐 georgehoteleasingwold.com
Black Sheep Best Bitter; Ilkley Blonde; 6 changing beers (sourced regionally) Ⓗ
Old coaching inn which had a Georgian makeover and a much more recent spruce up. With eight beer lines and a focus on local ales this is not one to miss if in the Easingwold area. The 'coming soon' board only adds to the temptation. A recently opened up side room adds to the bay window seats from which it is a joy to watch the activity in the bustling market square. Accommodation is in 16 luxury rooms. Q🕱🛏️◑&P🖵📶

East Cowton

Beeswing ✅
Main Road, DL7 0BD
☎ (01325) 378349 🌐 thebeeswing.weebly.com
3 changing beers (sourced nationally) Ⓗ
Traditional country village pub with two bars, a pool room and a highly rated restaurant. Named after a locally-bred champion racehorse, there are numerous racing references. Real fires create a relaxing atmosphere. Up to three ever-changing beers come from breweries countrywide, with one craft beer. The staff are supportive and welcoming. Regular music nights, quizzes and a pool table are enjoyed by the local community.
Q🕱🏵️◑&♣P🏵️📶

East Witton

Cover Bridge Inn 🅛
DL8 4SQ (½ mile N of village on A6108 to Middleham)
☎ (01969) 623250 🌐 thecoverbridgeinn.co.uk
Black Sheep Best Bitter; Timothy Taylor Landlord; Theakston Old Peculier; 5 changing beers (sourced regionally; often Rudgate, Wensleydale) Ⓗ
A splendidly traditional Dales inn. The River Cover runs along the foot of the attractive garden and play area, near its confluence with the River Ure. Fathom out the door latch and you will be able to enjoy the warm welcome in the unspoiled public bar, or sit in the tiny lounge or pleasant beer garden. There is a choice of local beers and guests, and the ham and eggs on the food menu has a strong following. Middleham Castle and

Jervaulx Abbey are both within a couple of miles. An increasingly rare outlet for Old Peculier on handpull. Q⏚🕭🌢🖭🕪🌡♣🅿🖭(159) 🌢🛜🎵

Egton

Wheatsheaf Inn 🅛
YO21 1TZ
☎ (01947) 895271
Black Sheep Best Bitter; Timothy Taylor Landlord; 1 changing beer 🅗
Winner of many industry and CAMRA awards, this Grade II-listed 19th-century pub only serves Yorkshire beers. Church pews, country collectables and a roaring range add to the ambiance. The first class restaurant has been superbly refurbished, and local meat, game and fish feature. The grassy areas to the front and boules to the rear are ideal for lazy summer drinking. Three high-class letting bedrooms are available. Q⏚🕭🌢🖭🕪♣🅿🖭🌢🛜

Egton Bridge

Horseshoe Hotel
YO21 1XE
☎ (01947) 895245 ⊕ thehorseshoehotel.co.uk
Theakston Best Bitter; 3 changing beers (sourced regionally) 🅗
Secluded unspoilt 18th-century gem nestled in a horseshoe-shaped hollow. Located in beautiful countryside, it can accessed by road, from the railway station or by walking over the stepping stones across the River Esk. Old-fashioned settles and a large fire furnish the bar, while picnic tables make outdoor drinking a pleasure. Four handpumps feature some interesting beers. A farm shop has recently been added, while an outdoor bar, with two extra handpulls, opens during summer. Accommodation is in six en-suite bedrooms. Q⏚🕭🌢🖭🕪🚆(Egton) ♣🅿🖭(95) 🌢🛜

Exelby

Exelby Green Dragon 🅛
High Row, DL8 2HA
☎ (01677) 427715 ⊕ exelbygreendragon.co.uk
Black Sheep Best Bitter; 3 changing beers (sourced regionally; often Ossett, Rudgate, Wensleydale) 🅗
The knocked-through interior of this community-owned pub provides a number of separate areas, featuring two wood-burning stoves. A spacious separate restaurant opens onto the decked terraced beer garden. Numerous village activities include the folk club, book club, gardening club, a weekly coffee morning and the monthly women's group (aka the Dragons). A popular beer and cider festival is held on the August bank holiday weekend. Opening times vary according to season. Real cider is available. Cask ales are sold at reduced prices on Tuesday evenings. ⏚🕭🌢🖭🕪♿🍴🅿🌢🛜

Filey

Cobblers Arms
2 Union Street, YO14 9DZ
☎ (01723) 512511
Wainwright Gold; 4 changing beers (sourced regionally; often Great Newsome, Rudgate, Wold Top) 🅗
Formerly a cobblers shop, this micropub is located in the centre of Filey. The front bar encourages conversation and there is a smaller snug to the rear which is available for meetings. Alongside the permanent real ale the bar offers four changing guest ales (three in winter) with real cider always available. The pub is dog and family

friendly. There is a regular quiz on a Tuesday night with a pie and a pint deal offered on Friday and Saturday. Q⏚🕭🌢🚆🖭(12,13) 🌢🛜🎵

Station Hotel
15 Church Street, YO14 9ED
☎ (01723) 515117 ⊕ thestationhotelfiley.co.uk
Bradfield Farmers Blonde; Fuller's London Pride; Rudgate Ruby Mild; Timothy Taylor Landlord; Tetley Bitter 🅗
Known locally as the Top House, the Station Hotel is a thriving pub which boasts five eating and drinking areas; the main bar, quiet lounge, pool room, conservatory and beer garden/smoking area. Popular with locals and visitors alike, the pub offers five real ales throughout the year. Home-made food is served all day every day during tourist season. Accommodation is available in three chalets separate from the main pub. Regular entertainment includes live music, karaoke, a quiz night and Tuesday bingo. 🕭🌢🖭🕪🍴🚆🖭(12,13)🌢🛜🎵

Grassington

Black Horse Hotel 🅛 ✅
Garrs Lane, BD23 5AT
☎ (01756) 752770 ⊕ blackhorsehotelgrassington.co.uk
Black Sheep Respire; Dark Horse Blonde Beauty, Hetton Pale Ale; Tetley Bitter; 2 changing beers (sourced nationally) 🅗
A 17th-century inn in the centre of the village. The bar area has a bright feel to it and is warmed by a large wood-fired stove. An extensive food menu is available in both the main bar and separate dining room. Accommodation comprises of 15 en-suite bedrooms. The Black Horse hosts a quiz on Wednesdays, live music on Friday nights, and acoustic artists on Sunday teatimes. Q⏚🕭🌢🖭🕪🖭(72,74A) 🌢🛜

Foresters Arms 🅛 ✅
20 Main Street, BD23 5AA
☎ (01756) 752349 ⊕ forestersarmsgrassington.co.uk
Black Sheep Best Bitter, Riggwelter; Timothy Taylor Dark Mild, Landlord; Tetley Bitter; 1 changing beer (sourced locally; often Black Sheep) 🅗
Located just off the cobbled town square, the Foresters is a lively inn, run by the same family for decades, and popular with locals and visitors alike. The main bar and pool/TV area are to the left and further seating to the right leads to a separate dining room. Accommodation is available in seven en-suite rooms and fishing permits for the local River Wharfe can be bought at the pub. Monday is quiz night. Secure cycle storage is available for staying guests. 🕭🌢🖭🕪♣🖭(72,72B)🌢🛜🔄🎵

Great Ayton

Tannery
4 The Arcade, High Street, TS9 6BW (continue through the Arcade's entrance archway for 50yds)
☎ (01642) 909030 ⊕ thetanneryayton.co.uk
4 changing beers (sourced regionally) 🅗
Set back from the High Street within a courtyard, this former hairdresser's has been tastefully refurbished and is now the village's micropub. Opened in 2018 by experienced licensees, it has always attracted a discerning clientele. Four rotating guest beers generally include a stout or a porter, while craft ales and an extensive gin menu are also served by knowledgeable staff. Third-pint bats are available. Free cheese and biscuit evenings are hosted, with any donations going to charity. Q♿🖭(28,81)🌢

Grosmont

Crossing Club

Co-operative Building, Front Street, YO22 5QE (opp NYMR car park – ring front door bell for entry)
☎ 07766 197744
4 changing beers (sourced regionally) Ⓗ

Set amid beautiful scenery in the Esk Valley, this local CAMRA Club of the Year 2024 is located opposite the NYMR/Esk Valley railway stations in the village's original Co-op's delivery bay. Converted 26 years ago, a warm welcome always awaits CAMRA members. Over 1,800 different beers have been served during the club's history. Members are now also brewing their own beer, Preservation Ale, a 4% ABV blonde available exclusively in the club. Railway enthusiasts will enjoy the memorabilia adorning the walls. There is stepped access to both the bar and toilets. Q⇌♣♿🍽️

Guisborough

Guisborough Brewery Tap Ⓛ

14 South Buck Way, TS14 7FJ (off Rectory Ln behind M&S Foodhall)
☎ 07703 002858 ⊕ guisboroughbrewery.co.uk
Guisborough Dark Habit, Daze, Nut Kin, BOBA, Dangerous Brian, Vypa; 3 changing beers (sourced locally; often Guisborough) Ⓗ

Conversation inevitably flows freely on Fridays and Saturdays, when a varied selection of three of the brewery's portfolio of 13 beers, and which include a hazelnut porter and a chilli stout, are served. Most of the brewery's beers are also usually available in bottles for off-sales. All of the beers are suitable for vegetarians and vegans. Food stalls and live bands are becoming a regular feature during the warmer months, with details posted on GuisBrew social media pages. P🛏️♪

Monk Ⓛ

27 Church Street, TS14 6HG (at E end of Westgate)
☎ (01287) 205058
Timothy Taylor Landlord; 3 changing beers (sourced regionally) Ⓗ

This contemporary venue is an upmarket addition to the town's social life and attracts a discerning clientele. It sits opposite Gisborough Priory, which was razed to the ground by King Henry VIII in 1540. Legend has it that a 12th-century Black Monk made use of a tunnel, discovered during recent renovations, for his nefarious night-time activities. The tunnel's access steps are on view. Four beers, with a couple from the town's local brewery, are served. Better-value tasing paddles are available. ♿🛏️(5,X93)🍽️🎐♪

Harrogate

Devonshire Tap House Ⓛ

10 Devonshire Place, HG1 4AA
☎ (01423) 568702
Ossett Yorkshire Blonde; Timothy Taylor Boltmaker; 5 changing beers (often Ilkley, Kirkstall, Turning Point) Ⓗ

A short walk out of town to High Harrogate brings you to this old pub, formerly the Devonshire Arms, then 10 Devonshire Place, and in its current guise since 2019. It retains its original semicircular counter with stained glass canopy, wood flooring throughout and a mix of wooden benches, tables and chairs. Four handpumps each side of the bar dispense largely changing beers from mostly Yorkshire breweries, together with boxed ciders from Lilley's. There are 12 keg lines and a beer fridge. Food offering is pizzas, including gluten-free and vegan options. 🐕🏡🍷⇌🛏️🍽️🎐

Harrogate Tap 🍷 Ⓛ

Station Parade, HG1 1TE
☎ (01423) 501644 ⊕ harrogatetap.co.uk
12 changing beers (often Harrogate, Rooster's, Tapped) Ⓗ

Popular with both locals and the many visitors to Harrogate, this is an impressive transformation of a neglected railway building into a fine pub of similar style to the Tapped Brew Company's other bars at York and Sheffield stations. A diverse range of cask ales is available across 12 handpulls, always including a dark and a gluten-free beer, together with boxed ciders such as Lilley's or Pulp, craft kegs and bottled world beers. Bar snacks are also available. Local CAMRA Pub of the Year 2023 and 2024. 🐕♿⇌🛏️🍽️

Little Ale House

7 Cheltenham Crescent, HG1 1DH
⊕ alehouseharrogate.co.uk
5 changing beers Ⓗ

Award-winning micropub, comprising one main room with the counter at the back, a downstairs cellar room, and front and rear outside spaces. Seating is at tables with a mix of chairs in the front part of the pub; there are stools around a cask near the bar. Five handpumps dispense cask ales, always including a dark, there are boxed ciders from a changing list of producers, occasionally including a real cider such as Thornborough, KeyKeg beer, whiskies and small-batch gins. The rear yard has bench seating, with service from a window in summer. Card payments only. Q🐕🍷🛏️🍽️

Major Tom's Social Ⓛ

The Ginnel, HG1 2RB
☎ (01423) 566984 ⊕ majortomssocial.co.uk
3 changing beers (often Northern Monk, Rooster's, Turning Point) Ⓗ

Café bar in a former antiques emporium above a vintage shop in a busy nightlife area of Harrogate town centre, providing real ale, craft keg, pizza, music and art. Simply furnished, with wooden tables and chairs, décor is a mix of styles to suit its eclectic customers, and includes artwork for sale. Four handpumps dispense a variety of ales, usually from a range of smaller breweries, often including the local Rooster's and Turning Point. A real cider such as Dudda's Tun is usually available. Local CAMRA Cider Pub of the Year 2023. Card payments preferred. 🐕🍷⇌♿🛏️🍽️🎐♪

Oatlands Ⓛ

1 Coronation Grove, HG2 8BY
☎ (01423) 871534 ⊕ theoatlands.co.uk
Leeds Pale; Rooster's Yankee; Tetley Bitter Ⓗ

Popular social club in a relatively dry area south of Harrogate town centre serving three cask ales, two of which are sourced from local breweries, including nearby Rooster's. Established in 1899, and rebranded as the Oatlands in 2019, the club comprises two large rooms downstairs; to the right-hand side is the main bar with plenty of comfortable seating, a pool table and dartboard, and to the left a concert room where entertainment events are held. Upstairs are snooker and table tennis tables. Non-members are welcome but must sign in. Local CAMRA Club of the Year. 🐕🍷⇌(Hornbeam Park) ♣P🛏️🍽️🎐♪

Old Bell Ⓛ

6 Royal Parade, HG1 2SZ
☎ (01423) 507930
Hawkshead Windermere Pale; Kirkstall Three Swords; 4 changing beers (often First Chop, Rooster's, Theakston) Ⓗ

One of a dwindling number of Market Town Taverns establishments, the Old Bell was one of this pubco's earliest pubs, opened in 1999. It is located on the site of the Blue Bell Inn which closed in 1815 and was later demolished. President Bill Clinton visited the inn during a visit to Harrogate in 2001. Later the same year the pub expanded into the former Farrah's toffee shop, where there is a collection of Farrah's memorabilia. Six handpumps dispense real ales from local and northern breweries. Food is served every day. ✿🕭🕩🍴🍽♿🛜♪

Starling 🅛

47 Oxford Street, HG1 1PW
☎ (01423) 531310 ⊕ murmurationbars.co.uk
Daleside Blonde; Kirkstall Three Swords; Theakston Best Bitter; Timothy Taylor Landlord; 3 changing beers (sourced locally) Ⓗ
Popular bar in the centre of Harrogate serving a well-chosen mix of mostly Yorkshire ales, some from smaller breweries, and usually including a dark beer. There are also boxed ciders, usually Lilley's, and 10 keg lines. The beers are displayed on TV screens, with a live feed to the website. Decorated in modern style, the building is actually over 200 years old. As well as the downstairs bar area there are two large rooms upstairs, and a small courtyard garden at the rear. Stonebaked pizzas are a favourite here. Card payments preferred. ✿🌂🕩🍴🍽♿🛜

Tap on Tower Street 🅛 ✅

Tower Street, HG1 1HS
☎ (01423) 565600 ⊕ thetapontowerstreet.co.uk
Ilkley Mary Jane; 6 changing beers (often Rooster's, Timothy Taylor) Ⓗ
Street-corner pub close to West Park Stray, comprising three small rooms, a large outside space at the front with bench tables under retractable awnings, and a rear yard with seating. Food is available all day, mainly in the form of hot and cold snacks rather than formal cooked meals. Takeaway bottles and cans are available from fridges in the public bar, and the rear room has a selection of over 300 board games. Four handpumps in each of the front bars serve Yorkshire ales; one pump is devoted to cider, usually Old Rosie. ✿🌂🕩🍴🍽♿🛜🛜

Winter Gardens 🅛 ✅

4 Royal Baths, HG1 2WH
☎ (01423) 877010
Greene King Abbot; Ruddles Best Bitter; Sharp's Doom Bar; Theakston Old Peculier; house beer (by Daleside); 5 changing beers Ⓗ
Converted from part of the Royal Baths complex in 2002, this magnificent building has a spacious interior reached from the Parliament Street entrance by a sweeping Hollywood-style bifurcated stone staircase which carries you down to the high-ceilinged bar area below. The pub serves the usual Wetherspoon core range of beers, plus numerous locally sourced guests available across three sets of handpumps atop the long L-shaped bar; the local Daleside brewery provides a house beer. Boxed ciders are also available, such as Thistly Cross or Westons. Step-free access is from the lower entrance, in The Ginnel. ✿🌂🕩👵🍴🛜

Hawes

Fountain Hotel 🅛

Market Place, DL8 3RD
☎ (01969) 667206 ⊕ fountainhawes.co.uk
Black Sheep Best Bitter; 4 changing beers (sourced locally; often Theakston, Wensleydale, Yorkshire Dales) Ⓗ

A thriving Dales community pub that is located on the Pennine Way and is popular with walkers and other outdoor enthusiasts. In the same hands for over 30 years, this 17th-century inn has a spacious interior and offers good-value food, served until 9pm in summer. There is sports TV and up to four guest ales are usually available, often from local breweries such as Wensleydale, Yorkshire Dales and Theakston. ✿🛏🕩🏕♣🅿🖃♿🛜♪

White Hart Inn 🅛

Main Street, DL8 3QL (on one-way system, westbound)
☎ (01969) 667214 ⊕ whitehartharwes.co.uk
Black Sheep Best Bitter; 4 changing beers (sourced locally; often Pennine, Wensleydale, Yorkshire Dales) Ⓗ
Comfortable 16th-century coaching inn on the town's short one-way system. A large dining room is popular with visitors and a smaller bar features an attractive stone hearth and mock wood panelling, which works remarkably well. Guest beers are often from the local Yorkshire Dales, Wensleydale and Pennine breweries. Food is served daily, including beef and lamb from the family farm. ✿🛏🕩🏕♣🖃♿🛜♪

Helmsley

Helmsley Brewing Co

18 Bridge Street, YO62 5DX
☎ (01439) 771014 ⊕ helmsleybrewingco.co.uk
Helmsley Yorkshire Legend, Striding the Riding, Howardian Gold; 1 changing beer (sourced locally; often Helmsley) Ⓗ
This brewery tap for the Helmsley Brewing Company is close to the market square in picturesque Helmsley village, the only market town in the North York Moors National Park, and the perfect base for enjoying the wider area. Three regular beers plus one changing beer are all from their own range. Brewery tours and the onsite shop complete the full beer experience. There is a large, covered beer garden and a cosy cocktail bar upstairs is available for hire. 🖃♿🛜♪

Huby

Mended Drum 🅛

Tollerton Road, YO61 1HT
☎ (01347) 810264 ⊕ themendeddrum.com
Goose Eye Bitter; 4 changing beers (sourced locally; often Bone Machine, Brass Castle, Northern Monk) Ⓗ
The lively centre of this rural community, with a Terry Pratchett connection, is a former local CAMRA Pub of the Year. Welcoming families, dogs and cyclists, this large, open-plan pub is bigger than it looks. Its knowledgeable landlord serves an interesting range of changing local beers and real ciders. There are two beer festivals a year and a quiz night on the second Thursday of the month. A quality menu of modern street food is served, with vegetarian, vegan and gluten-free options. ✿🌂🕩👵🏕♣🅿🖃(40)♿🛜♪

Hudswell

George & Dragon 🅛

DL11 6BL
☎ (01748) 518373 ⊕ georgeanddragonhudswell.co.uk
Rudgate Ruby Mild; Wensleydale Falconer; 5 changing beers (sourced locally) Ⓗ
At the heart of the village, this homely multi-roomed country inn was CAMRA National Pub of the Year in 2016, a runner-up in 2020, and has been Champion Pub of Yorkshire several times. A pleasant walk from Richmond (if you do not mind the 300+ steps!) brings you to the

pub's large beer terrace with fantastic panoramic views over the Swale valley. Owned by the community, it boasts its own library, shop, allotments and other community facilities. Roasts are available on Sundays. Real cider is served. Q♿☆🕭🅔▲♣🛏P🚐(30)🏠🛜♪

Hunton

Countryman's Inn 🍷 Ⓛ
South View, DL8 1PY
☎ (01677) 450554 ⊕ countrymansinn.co.uk
5 changing beers (sourced locally; often Pennine, Theakston, Wensleydale) Ⓗ
Welcoming free house which survived near-closure after a lively campaign by villagers and is now thriving under community ownership. Separate drinking areas offer comfortable seating around a central bar. Coffee mornings on Mondays and Thursdays, and regular quiz nights contribute to local charities. Every September the village is host to the Hunton Steam Gathering, boasting a collection of antique steam vehicles.
Q♿☆🖾🕭🅔▲♣P🚐(155)🏠🛜♪

Kirk Smeaton

Shoulder of Mutton
Main Street, WF8 3JY (follow signs from A1)
☎ (01977) 620348
Black Sheep Best Bitter; 1 changing beer (sourced regionally; often Bradfield) Ⓗ
This welcoming traditional village pub is popular with walkers and the local community and is convenient for the Went Valley and Brockdale Nature Reserve. The quality of the well-kept real ales is superb. This award-winning free house comprises a large lounge with open fires and a separate cosy snug. Outside there is ample parking and a spacious beer garden with a covered and heated shelter for smokers. Quiz night is Tuesday.
Q♿☆♣P🌞🛜

Kirkby Malham

Victoria Inn Ⓛ ✅
BD23 4BS
☎ (01729) 830499 ⊕ victoriakirkbymalham.co.uk
Craven Best Yorkshire Bitter; Dark Horse Hetton Pale Ale; Timothy Taylor Knowle Spring; 2 changing beers (sourced regionally; often Craven, Timothy Taylor) Ⓗ
Adjacent to the church, this pub was built in 1840. There's a cosy, stone-flagged front bar with a real fire, a tiny snug off the corridor and a dining room with a wood-burning stove. Muddy boot, dog and family friendly. Well worth trying, especially in summer and at weekends when the pubs in Malham itself can get very busy. Benches outside soak up the summer sunshine and have a substantial awning to keep the rain off too. Two guest ales are available in high season. Closed on Mondays and some lunchtimes. ♿☆🖾🕭▲♣P🚐(75,210)🌞🛜

Kirkby-in-Cleveland

Black Swan
Busby Lane, TS9 7AW (800yds W of B1257) NZ539060
☎ (01642) 712512 ⊕ theblackswankirkby.co.uk
Bradfield Farmers Blonde; Sharp's Doom Bar; Timothy Taylor Landlord; Wainwright Gold; 1 changing beer (sourced regionally) Ⓗ
Nestling at the foot of the Cleveland Hills at the crossroads of this ancient village, this warm and cosy free house is under the stewardship of a licensee of over 25 years standing, and where a genuine welcome is always afforded from the friendly staff. It comprises a bar, an

adjacent pool room, a lounge/restaurant, a conservatory and a patio seating area. Four regular beers and a guest are available. Good-value meals are served, including daily specials. ♿☆🕭🅔♿♣P🚐(89)🌞🛜

Knaresborough

Blind Jack's Ⓛ
19 Market Place, HG5 8AL
⊕ blindjackspub.co.uk
Black Sheep Best Bitter; 5 changing beers (sourced nationally) Ⓗ
An entry in the Guide for over 30 years, this is a Georgian listed building with bare-brick walls and wooden floorboards, comprising two small rooms downstairs and two similar rooms up a steep staircase. A sociable pub, popular with both locals and visitors who appreciate the excellent selection of ales and friendly ambience. The diverse beer range includes at least one dark and one gluten-free choice, as well as a range of craft kegs. Of particular interest is the trompe l'oeil painting on the exterior which features the pub's namesake, Blind Jack Metcalf. Q🚲🚐🌞🛜

Cross Keys Ⓛ ✅
17 Cheapside, HG5 8AX
☎ (01423) 863562
Ossett Butterley, Yorkshire Blonde, White Rat, Silver King; 2 changing beers (sourced locally; often Ossett, Rudgate, Turning Point) Ⓗ
Traditional pub welcoming locals and visitors alike, a former Tetley's house refurbished by Ossett brewery in its trademark style of stone-flagged floors, bare-brick walls and stained glass. Six cask ales are served, mostly from the Ossett stable, with occasional beers from other breweries. Boxed ciders are available, mostly Lilley's, and sometimes a real cider such as Seacider. A popular quiz night is held on Thursdays, live bands play on Saturday nights monthly, and on the first Sunday of every month, a DJ plays motown, soul and funk records. ♿☆🚲🚐🛜🕭♪

Half Moon Ⓛ ✅
1 Abbey Road, HG5 8HY
☎ (01423) 313461 ⊕ thehalfmoonfreehouse.com
Rooster's YPA; 3 changing beers (sourced locally; often Kirkstall, Sunbeam, Turning Point) Ⓗ
Friendly staff give a warm welcome at this popular free house, where exposed brickwork, original sash windows, real fire and wood-burning stove all contribute to its cosy atmosphere. A small courtyard at the back of the pub has tables, chairs and some benches under heated awnings; dogs are welcome in the outside area. Four handpumps dispense a well-chosen mix of cask ales, mostly from smaller Yorkshire breweries. A grazing menu of meat and cheese boards complements the beers and is served every day, with pizzas on weekday evenings. Coffee and home-made cakes are also available.
♿☆🕭🚲🚐(8)🛜♪

Six Poor Folk Ⓛ ✅
25 Castlegate, HG5 8AR
☎ (01423) 869918 ⊕ sixpoorfolk.co.uk
4 changing beers (often Timothy Taylor) Ⓗ
Former almshouse near the market square dating back to the 15th century, now a quirky bar serving an ever-changing selection of real ales from national and Yorkshire breweries. Downstairs is a mix of café-type seating and armchairs around a wood-burning-style stove. There is a mezzanine level with a smaller room upstairs, and an enclosed courtyard at the back. A varied menu of small and large plates, lunch and tapas is served, with roasts on Sundays and home-made specials

that change regularly. The pub hosts a quiz on Wednesdays and a DJ plays soul and funk music on Friday evenings. ⬤✿❁❶≒🛏☀🛜♫

Lastingham

Blacksmith's Arms
Anserdale Lane, YO62 6TN
☎ (01751) 417247 ⊕ blacksmithsarmslastingham.co.uk
Theakston Best Bitter, Old Peculier; 2 changing beers (sourced regionally; often Daleside, Rudgate) H
Pretty stone pub in a conservation village opposite St Mary's church which is famous for its 11th-century crypt. The interior comprises a cosy bar with York range lit in winter, a snug, and two dining rooms. Excellent quality food including local game dishes is served alongside interesting guest beers and a changing guest cider, often Thistly Cross. A secluded beer garden to the rear now includes a pizza oven. This remote pub is popular with locals, walkers and shooting parties. Q⬤✿❁❶❷

Leavening

Jolly Farmers L
Main Street, YO17 9SA
☎ (01653) 658276
Ossett Yorkshire Blonde; Timothy Taylor Boltmaker; 1 changing beer (sourced regionally; often Great Newsome, Half Moon) H
A popular stopping off point for ramblers as well as locals, this 17th-century pub is on the edge of the Yorkshire Wolds between York and Malton. With its low ceilings and tiled floors, the pub is homely and welcoming, serving a range of local and regional ales, and locally sourced food, including fish & chip Fridays. The pub has a tradional bar with real fire, and an intriguing series of other rooms. The outside drinking area boasts table football and a cask of drinking water for dogs complete with handpump! Q⬤✿❁❶⅃P❷☀🛜

Leyburn

King's Head L
Grove Square, DL8 5AE
☎ (01969) 622694
Theakston Best Bitter; Timothy Taylor Landlord; Wensleydale Semer Water; 1 changing beer (sourced locally; often Wensleydale) H
Set off the main market place, at the junction of the moor road and the Richmond road, this friendly locals' pub is a rare example of a wet-led house in this tourist area, offering a selection of well-kept cask ales at attractive prices. An enthusiastic provider of sports TV, especially football, which is well-supported, and supplier of regular live music. The interior is knocked through, but the bar, lounge and games room have the feel of separate areas. It has a pool table, two dartboards, fruit machines, open fires and the only jukebox in town. ⬤≒❁🛏❷☀♫

Litton

Queens Arms L ✅
BD23 5QJ (in Littondale approx 5 miles from B6160)
☎ (01756) 770096 ⊕ queensarmslitton.co.uk
LAMB Bitter, Pale, Queens Ale; 1 changing beer (sourced locally; often LAMB) H
Transformed into a pub in 1843, with open fires, mullioned windows, oak-beamed ceilings and a stone-flagged bar area. Outside there is a garden with tables and chairs, which provide stunning views of the surrounding valley. The emphasis is on the locally

sourced food – booking is recommended. The dining room is available for private functions. The two or three changing beers will include LAMB beers (the brewery is behind the pub but not a connected business). ⬤✿🛏❶♣❷🛜

Malton

Blue Ball ★
14 Newbiggin, YO17 7JF
☎ (01653) 690692
Tetley Bitter; Timothy Taylor Landlord; 1 changing beer (sourced nationally) H
This Grade II-listed establishment, popular with locals, dates back to the 16th century and has been identified by CAMRA as having a nationally important historic pub interior, featuring in CAMRA Yorkshire's Real Heritage Pubs guide. Retaining much of its original character, it consists of a series of small rooms on different levels connected by a sloping passage and has a small central bar. A rear courtyard has seating. Home-cooked food is served Thursday to Sunday.
Q⬤✿❁⅃👤≒♣P🚃(840,843) ❷🛜♫

Brass Castle Brewery Tap House L
10 Yorkersgate, YO17 7AB
⊕ brasscastle.co.uk
Brass Castle Hoptical Illusion, Bad Kitty; 3 changing beers (sourced locally; often Brass Castle) H
Located in front of the brewery, just off Malton town centre, it is a short walk from the railway and bus stations. The single-roomed bar is a rustic design style with one wall covered with barrel staves. It has five regular changing cask ales with six KeyKeg ales and lager, predominantly from the brewery, alongside brewery cans, foreign bottled beers, canned cider, wines and spirits. Bar snacks are sold or you can bring in takeaways from elsewhere. Two upstairs rooms have seating and a bar billiards table, and there is a small smoking/drinking area to rear.
⬤✿≒♣🚃(843,840) ❷♫

Omni
22 Market Place, YO17 7LX
☎ (01653) 692302
4 changing beers (sourced regionally; often Great Newsome, Pennine) H
This family-run bar has rooms on the ground and first floor with a bright modern feel. A good range of ales, gins, wines and champagne are available with a food offering of Yorkshire tapas served daily until evening. External tables to the front of the building, overlooking the historic market place, are popular in warmer weather and cater for smokers. The venue is family friendly and accommodating to dog owners.
⬤✿❶👤≒🖥🚃(840,843) ❷

Manfield

Crown Inn L
Vicars Lane, DL2 2RF (500yds from B6275)
☎ (01325) 374243 ⊕ thecrowninnmanfield.co.uk
Timothy Taylor Landlord H**; Village White Boar** H**/**P**; 2 changing beers (sourced nationally)** H
This 18th-century inn in a quiet village has been voted local CAMRA Country Pub of the Year 17 times, and was previously Yorkshire Pub of the Year. It has two bars – with a real log fire in main bar – a games room and an extensive beer garden. A mix of locals and visitors create a friendly atmosphere. Beers from regional and national breweries are dispensed from four handpumps.
Q⬤✿❶♣P🖥🚃(29) ❷🛜

Marske-by-the-Sea

Clarendon ⓛ
88-90 High Street, TS11 7BA
☎ (01642) 490005
Black Sheep Best Bitter; Camerons Strongarm; Copper Dragon Golden Pippin; Theakston Best Bitter, Old Peculier; 1 changing beer (sourced regionally) Ⓗ
The Middle House, as it is also known, is a popular large one-room locals' pub, where little has changed since the 1960s. Six beers are served from the central mahogany island bar, a rarity on Teesside. The walls are adorned with interesting photographs of yesteryear. There is no TV, no pool table, no children nor teenagers, just regulars indulging in convivial conversation. There is no catering either, but tea and coffee are always available.
Q✿❀≉(Marske) P🚌(X3,X4) 🛜

Smugglers Den ⓛ
7 Redcar Road, TS11 6AA (next to St Marks church)
☎ 07802 469727
4 changing beers (sourced locally) Ⓗ
Located in the centre of town, this converted quaint, and recently refurbished two-story cottage is still a rather quirky, but equally stylish and friendly microbar. Now in its fifth year of operation, four rotating LocAle guest beers are served in the downstairs bar, where a log-burner keeps everybody warm. Two additional rooms upstairs are also available, one housing a pool table. Live music takes place on Friday and Saturday evenings. Open Thursday to Sunday. ≉(Marske)♣🚌(X3,X4)✿♪

Masham

White Bear ⓛ ✅
Wellgarth, HG4 4EN
☎ (01765) 689319 ⊕ whitebearmasham.co.uk
Theakston Best Bitter, Lightfoot, Old Peculier; 1 changing beer (often Theakston) Ⓗ
Theakston's only pub, an award-winning venue and a great favourite with the locals as well as directors and staff from the brewery. A large dining area to the left and a cosy taproom to the right offer exclusively Theakston's beers. Unusually for the Yorkshire Dales, this building was a victim of wartime bombing, following which it was derelict for many years before it was rescued and renovated to a high standard. A popular beer festival is hosted in June featuring over 30 real ales. Licensed from 11am. ➤✿🛏🍽◑&♣P✿🛜

Middleham

Black Bull Inn ⓛ
Market Place, DL8 4NX
☎ (01969) 624792 ⊕ theblackbullinn.co.uk
Theakston Best Bitter; Wensleydale Semer Water; 2 changing beers (sourced locally; often Yorkshire Dales) Ⓗ
Friendly family-owned pub with a good selection of real ales in a major racehorse-training centre. It has three rooms, the largest more for dining than drinking, with TVs in each bar. It serves good-quality food and has a log-burner in the main bar. A good centre for Dales walking, it also offers tailor-made cycling packages for all the Tour de Yorkshire enthusiasts. ➤🛏🚌(159)✿🛜♪

Middlesbrough

Chapel @ Whitehouse Street Ⓨ
Whitehouse Street, TS5 4BY (adjacent to St Cuthbert's Church, near Newport bridge)
☎ (01642) 214441 ⊕ whitehousestreet.co.uk

6 changing beers (sourced nationally) Ⓗ
This former Primitive Methodist Mission Hall, dating to 1890, and located at the west end of the town has been sympathetically renovated, retaining many original features from its former use. The refurbishment has provided a bright, airy, friendly atmosphere. Six beers, ranging from lighter ales to darker beers and stouts are dispensed on a rotating guest basis. Third-pint glasses are served on bespoke Chapel miniature pews. Live music and beer/cider festivals feature. Local CAMRA Pub of the Year 2024. ➤✿&▲♣●P🛏✿🛜♪

Infant Hercules ⓛ
84 Grange Road, TS1 2LS (jst S of Cleveland Centre and N of university campus)
☎ 07980 321626
4 changing beers Ⓗ
A warm welcome is always guaranteed at this successful micropub, located in the town's original solicitors' quarter and handy for the Law Courts and the Riverside Stadium. Now in its 10th year, the pub has developed a national reputation among discerning away football supporters, resulting in a tremendous atmosphere on matchdays. This local CAMRA award-winner is named after Gladstone's description of the town in 1862, after witnessing the town's ship building and steel furnaces. Third-pint tasting bats are available. ➤✿≉🚌✿🛜

Isaac Wilson ⓛ
61 Wilson Street, TS1 1SF (at N end of town, close to railway station)
☎ (01642) 247708
11 changing beers (sourced nationally) Ⓗ
Always busy, this popular pub is named after a 19th-century railway industry magnate and company director of the world's first railway, the Stockton and Darlington. The Isaac, a former Wetherspoon's conversion of the old Law Courts, gained new owners in 2017, improving on the chain's existing formula. An eclectic range of 11 guest beers, together with good-value food, are served. The single room interior has walls adorned with photographs of old Middlesbrough. Third-pint glasses are available. ➤◑&≉🚌🛜

Middlesmoor

Crown Hotel ⓛ
Main Street, HG3 5ST
☎ (01423) 755204
Black Sheep Best Bitter; Dark Horse Hetton Pale Ale; Theakston Best Bitter; 1 changing beer (sourced locally; often Black Sheep, Harrogate) Ⓗ
The last pub in Nidderdale in a small hilltop village where the tarmacked road ends and becomes the Nidderdale Way footpath. A very traditional old pub, this former shooting lodge has glorious views down the dale. It has a three-room set-up with the servery in the main room and comfortable seating and eating areas to the sides. Decorated in the traditional no-nonsense fashion for Dales pubs. There are a selection of walking sticks available for purchase in the bar. Opening times may vary in winter. ➤✿🛏◑▲♣P✿🛜↻

Nether Poppleton

Lord Nelson
9 Main Street, YO26 6HS
☎ (01904) 341066 ⊕ lordnelsonpoppleton.com
Timothy Taylor Landlord; 3 changing beers Ⓗ
Welcoming family-run free house close to a bend in the river Ouse in a 300-year-old farmhouse offering four, usually Yorkshire, cask ales and a range of craft kegs.

Excellent evening tapas and Sunday lunches are served. Games including darts, dominoes and cards are available and there is a Tuesday night quiz. At the back is a beer garden with a large shelter. ☺❀◑♣♠(10)❀📶

Northallerton

Mason's Arms ★
82 High Street, DL7 8EG
☎ (01609) 773465
Wainwright Gold ⊞
This small old-fashioned town-centre pub retains many original features, including a smoke room, a cosy drinking area around the bar opposite an unusual open snug, and a games room to the rear. It has been identified by CAMRA as having a regionally important historic pub interior, with a preserved entrance vestibule and the original bar woodwork. Karaoke is popular on Friday and Saturday nights. ◑♣❀📶♪

Oddfellows Arms ⅃
251 High Street, DL7 8DJ (off main part of High St, behind parish church)
☎ (01609) 259107
3 changing beers (sourced regionally; often Ossett, Wensleydale) ⊞
Hidden behind the parish church, by the cemetery gates, the Oddies does not appear to be on the High Street, despite its address. A thriving back-street community pub, it handles a mainly local trade and is popular with darts players, TV football fans and church bell-ringers. Refurbished in a simple but traditional style with an open-plan interior, there is a games room upstairs and a secluded beer garden to the rear. ☺❀♣🍽🚍❀📶♪

Origin ⅃
2 Friarage Street, DL6 1DP (just off High St near hospital)
☎ (01609) 775900 ● originsocial.co.uk
4 changing beers (sourced regionally; often Kirkstall, Ossett, Wensleydale) ⊞
Just off the busy High Street this smart bar opened in 2021 marketed as a 'small plates restaurant bar'. The focus is on tapas-style food, served both in the downstairs bar and the upstairs restaurant, however, drinkers are made very welcome, and can choose from up to four well-kept ales on handpump, as well as a range of interesting keg craft beers and wine from an extensive wine list. Guest beers often feature Brew York and Three Brothers. ☺◑♿🚍❀📶♪

Stumble Inn ⅃
4 Garthway Arcade, DL7 8NS (in pedestrian arcade off High St next to Grovers shop)
☎ 07817 568042
5 changing beers (sourced regionally) ⊞
This friendly and cosy micropub is just off the town's high street, down a small shopping arcade opposite the town hall. It serves a selection of local ales, craft beers and up to 20 ciders, and staff are keen to offer tasting advice and guidance. With no music, gaming machines, Wi-Fi, children or sports TV, there is just good old-fashioned chat plus a quiz on the last Sunday each month and seasonal beer and cider festivals. The beer selection always includes a dark beer. Q●🚍❀

Old Malton

Royal Oak Pub & Kitchen
47 Town Street, YO17 7HB (400yds off A64 Malton bypass)
☎ (01653) 696968 ● theroyaloakoldmalton.co.uk

House beer (by Yorkshire Heart); 3 changing beers (sourced regionally; often Lord's, Rudgate) ⊞
Historic Grade II-listed inn situated off the A64 near to Eden Camp military museum. The entrance corridor, with a cosy snug room off, opens onto a larger room with original beams (complete with brasses) and a log fire, which then leads to an extensive beer garden. A house beer, Royal Oak Pale Ale, and three changing ales are served on handpumps, complemented by a traditional home-cooked menu. An annual beer festival is held on Father's Day each June. Families and dogs are welcome. Q☺❀◑♿♣●P🚍(840) ❀📶♪

Osgodby

Wadkin Arms ⅃
Cliffe Road, YO8 5HU
☎ (01757) 702391
Ossett Yorkshire Blonde; Timothy Taylor Landlord; 3 changing beers (sourced nationally; often Marston's) ⊞
A true community pub at the heart of the village with five handpumps dispensing ales largely sourced from Yorkshire breweries. The Wadkin has a homely feel with open fires and friendly welcome and is home to locals and visitors alike. The nearby Trans Pennine Trail sees cyclists and walkers visiting in the summer months and a local bus service passes too. You will see much evidence of CAMRA sympathies on display. ☺❀▲♣P🚍(4)❀📶♪

Osmotherley

Golden Lion ⅃
6 West End, DL6 3AA
☎ (01609) 883526 ● goldenlionosmotherley.co.uk
Timothy Taylor Landlord; 2 changing beers (sourced locally; often Helmsley, Wold Top) ⊞
Set in the centre of a picturesque village on the edge of the North York Moors National Park and at the start of the long-distance Lyke Wake Walk, this old inn is popular with hikers, casual visitors and locals. Much of the focus is on high-quality food but drinkers are always made welcome, and the view from the outside drinking tables makes them popular on fine days. Two changing beers are from local or Yorkshire breweries. Dogs are welcome with well-behaved owners. Q🛏◑▲🚍(80,89)❀📶

Pickering

Sun Inn ♀ ⅃
136 Westgate, YO18 8BB (on A170, 400yds W of traffic lights in town centre)
☎ (01751) 473661 ● thesuninn-pickering.co.uk
Tetley Bitter; 5 changing beers (sourced regionally; often Helmsley) ⊞
Located close to the NYMR steam railway, this friendly local is the current local CAMRA Rural Pub of the Year. Six real ales are offered, often from Yorkshire micros, together with several traditional ciders. A cosy bar with a real fire leads to a separate room, ideal for families and special events. The large beer garden hosts an annual beer festival in September. Regular events include acoustic music, vinyl nights and weekly charity quizzes. Dogs (on leads), children and walkers are welcome. ☺❀♿🚶♣●🍽🚍(128,840) ❀♪

Pool-in-Wharfedale

Hunters Inn ⅃
Harrogate Road, LS21 2PS
Abbeydale Moonshine; Black Sheep Best Bitter; Morland Old Speckled Hen; Ossett Yorkshire Blonde,

White Rat; 3 changing beers (often Bradfield, Copper Dragon, Goose Eye) ⏢
Situated on the main Harrogate to Bradford road with views across lower Wharfedale, this is a single-storey building looking slightly out of place in Yorkshire. The large open-plan interior incorporates a raised area at one end with a warming real fire during the colder months. The long bar houses an array of handpumps dispensing a varied selection of ales sourced mainly from Yorkshire breweries. There is a pool table and video jukebox at one end of the main bar. Children are allowed during the day, accompanied by an adult. 🜚⊛♣P🚪(X52,A2)⊛🎵🕚🎵

Raskelf

Old Black Bull ⅃
North End, YO61 3LF
☎ (01347) 821431 ⏢ oldblackbull.com
Theakston Best Bitter; 2 changing beers ⏢
Free to choose, but still fond of its Theakstons, this authentic country pub goes from strength to strength. The central wood-burner is a special feature, keeping everyone warm in the colder months. Convenient bus links to York and Thirsk remove any excuse not to try this award-winning pub, which is well worth the effort of the journey. Closed Tuesdays and Monday lunchtimes.
🜚⊕♣P🚪(30)⊛

Ravensworth

Bay Horse ⅃
The Green, DL11 7ET
☎ (01325) 494437 ⏢ thebayhorseravensworth.co.uk
Theakston Best Bitter, Old Peculier; Wensleydale Semer Water; 1 changing beer (sourced regionally) ⏢
The Bay Horse is a traditional country pub serving high-quality food and drink in a warm and vibrant atmosphere. Refurbished and reopened in 2022, it offers a front bar for drinkers, a snug and restaurant for dining and an outdoor back garden for alfresco meals. The pub boasts an ever-changing selection of real ale from local and national brewers. Dogs on leads are welcome in bar and snug area. Children must be supervised and are only permitted in the evenings if dining. 🜚⊛⊕♣🎵🎵

Redcar

Rita's Pantry ⅃
1 Esplanade, TS10 3AA (opp Beacon)
☎ 07730 445483
3 changing beers (sourced nationally) ⏢
A former amusement arcade has been put to better use as the town's first micropub. Situated on the seafront, from where the 7,000-year-old petrified forest can be seen at low tide, a warm welcome is extended to CAMRA members, locals and visitors alike. Three interesting rotating beers are served and third-pint glasses are available. The amiable licensee hosts various social events, including a music quiz on Sunday. The pub gets rave reviews on social media.
⊛♿🚄(Central) 🚪(X3,X4) ⊛🎵🎵

Reeth

Black Bull ⅃
High Row, DL11 6SZ
☎ (01748) 884213 ⏢ theblackbullreeth.co.uk
Black Sheep Best Bitter; Theakston Best Bitter, Old Peculier; house beer (by Marston's); 1 changing beer ⏢
This characterful old inn is also known as 'the bottom house'. The cosy bar area has old settles round an open

fire; to the rear is a raised area with pool table. The Vic room provides a smartly revamped dining area. The pub sign was originally hung upside down following a widely publicised dispute between a previous licensee and the National Park Planning Authority. The pub may close early if quiet. 🜚🍴⊕♿♣🚪(30)⊛🎵🎵

Buck Hotel ⅃ ✅
DL11 6SW
☎ (01748) 884545 ⏢ thebuckreeth.co.uk
Black Sheep Best Bitter; 4 changing beers (often Allendale, Pennine, Theakston) ⏢
Originally an 18th-century coaching inn, the pub is sited prominently at the top of the green, and is therefore also known as 'the top house'. It retains many original features with beamed ceilings, an open fire and an ice house. Tables on the patio at the front offer stunning views over the dale, while the beer garden (closed in winter) is a suntrap. In high season meals may be served later than the usual times, and all meals are on a first-come first-served basis. 🜚⊛🍴⊕♿♣🚪(30)⊛🎵

Ribblehead

Station Inn
Low Sleights Road, LA6 3AS (on B6255 nr B6479 jct)
☎ (015242) 41274 ⏢ thestationinnribblehead.com
Black Sheep Best Bitter, Riggwelter; house beer (by Tirril); 2 changing beers (sourced locally; often Settle) ⏢
Built in 1874 at the same time as the nearby viaduct, this is a welcome refuge in a bleak spot in the midst of superb walking country and much used by hikers. Refurbished in 2017 to provide a rustic look throughout, there is a cheery range in the snug. The pub is frequented by a surprisingly large number of locals. There is a good train service, but buses are rare. A bunk barn is available next door – the wild camping behind the pub is no more. 🜚⊛🍴⊕🚄♣P🚪(830)⊛🎵🎵

Richmond

Buck Inn ⅃ ✅
29 Newbiggin, DL10 4DX
☎ (01748) 517300
Timothy Taylor Landlord; 2 changing beers (often Wensleydale) ⏢
Rambling old characterful free house situated on a cobbled street near the market place. There is a small snug at the front, comfortably furnished eating areas and a main bar to the rear which features dartboard, pool table and sports TV. Beyond this is the suntrap beer garden with its spectacular views over the River Swale and the Norman castle. Meal times vary according to the season, so it is worth checking beforehand. Guest beers usually include a local brew. Q🜚⊛🍴⊕♣🚪⊛🎵🎵

No 29 Alehouse & Gin Bar ⅃
29 Frenchgate, DL10 4HZ
☎ (01748) 850491
⏢ number-29-alehouse-gin-bar.business.site
3 changing beers (sourced locally; often Mithril, Rudgate, Wensleydale) ⏢
Real ale, craft beer, gin, wine and tapas bar located just off the foot of Richmond's market place on the road down to the former station complex. The single, small bar has simple decor with a wooden floor. Food such as cured meat and cheese sharing boards, ploughman's and various delicious tapas dishes are available. May close early if quiet. Beers are usually local or regional, often from Mithril, Rudgate and Wensleydale breweries.
⊕🚪⊛

Ripon

One Eyed Rat ⓛ
51 Allhallowgate, HG4 1LQ
☎ (01765) 607704
Ossett White Rat; Saltaire Blonde; 4 changing beers (sourced locally; often Ilkley, Pennine, Vocation) Ⓗ
A real ale destination in Ripon over many decades and a regular entry in the Guide, this Grade II-listed building is set within a terrace of 200-year-old houses, its narrow frontage leading to a warm and welcoming hostelry. The pub has a long, narrow interior with traditional seating and an open fire. There is a large garden at the rear, with a sizeable covered area. A varied selection of cask ales are served, often including a dark beer and, in summer, a real cider from Orchards of Husthwaite. Q ★ ❀ ● ₽ ❀ ♻

Portly Pig
5B Kirkgate, HG4 1PA
☎ 07944 394565
3 changing beers (sourced locally) Ⓗ
Bar and bottle shop opened in September 2023 serving three cask ales mainly from smaller local breweries together with five keg beers, cans and bottles. A small room downstairs accommodates the bar and bottle shop while upstairs there are two small rooms. Current beer selection, together with ABVs and prices, is displayed on the wall behind the bar. Food is not served but pizzas can be ordered from the Italian restaurant opposite for consumption in the pub. The premises served as the borough police station during the late 19th century. ★ ₽ ❀ ᯤ ♪

Royal Oak ✓
36 Kirkgate, HG4 1PB
☎ (01765) 602284 ⊕ royaloakripon.co.uk
Timothy Taylor Golden Best, Boltmaker, Landlord, Landlord Dark; 2 changing beers (often Ossett, Saltaire, Timothy Taylor) Ⓗ
Old coaching inn located between the cathedral and Market Square with a modern airy feel to its interior while retaining period features. Timothy Taylor's most northerly tied house, the Royal Oak serves a top-quality range of their beers alongside one other pale from another Yorkshire brewery, and there is an emphasis on locally sourced food. Accommodation is available in six en-suite bedrooms. At the Obelisk in the nearby Market Square at 9pm every night, the Ripon Hornblower sets the night watch as has happened each night for the last 1,000 years. ★ ❀ ⬤ ❀ ₽ ❀ ᯤ

Water Rat ⓛ ✓
24 Bondgate Green, HG4 1QW
☎ (01765) 602251 ⊕ thewaterrat.co.uk
Rudgate Jorvik Blonde; Theakston Best Bitter; 2 changing beers (often Acorn, Ilkley, Rudgate) Ⓗ
Located by the side of the River Skell with a grand view of Ripon Cathedral and the river from its large windows and riverside terrace, this is Ripon's only riverside pub, in fact so close to the river that it has been flooded in the past. An emphasis on affordable home-cooked traditional English pub food means it tends to get busy at times. Four Yorkshire ales are served. There is a small drinking area near the bar, and a snug at the front. Quiz night is Sunday and Northern Soul vinyl nights are held monthly. ★ ❀ ⬤ ₽ ❀ ᯤ

Robin Hood's Bay

Bay Hotel ⓛ
The Dock, YO22 4SJ (at the end of a very steep road, down towards the bay from top car park)
☎ (01947) 880278
Adnams Ghost Ship; Theakston Best Bitter, Lightfoot; Wainwright Gold Ⓗ
This magnificent Grade II-listed building dating from 1822 is the finish line for Wainwright's Coast-to-Coast 192-mile walk from St Bees. The bottom bar, named in his honour, provides access to the Dock patio, situated at the seawater's edge and which provides superb panoramic sea views. With a licensee of over 25 years' service, a friendly welcome awaits regulars, visitors, their children and their dogs. A good-value home-cooked menu is available. Access to this part of the village is not easy for the less mobile. ★ ❀ ⥤ ⬤ ₽ (X93) ❀

Saltburn-by-the-Sea

Saltburn Cricket, Bowls & Tennis Club ⓛ
Marske Mill Lane, TS12 1HJ (next to leisure centre)
☎ (01287) 622761 ⊕ saltburn.play-cricket.com
3 changing beers (sourced nationally) Ⓗ
Members of CAMRA are made most welcome at this thriving club and local CAMRA multi-award winner, including Club of the Year 2023. Located north of the town and within walking distance of transport links, the club is well supported by the local community. Now celebrating 28 years of continuous Guide recognition, three beers are served, often not even lasting the evening. An enthusiastic steward hosts a variety of events. The balcony, ideal for lazy summer afternoons, overlooks the cricket field. ♿ ⥤ (Saltburn) ♣ P ₽ (X3,X4) ❀

Scarborough

Craft Bar
7 Northway, YO11 1JH
☎ 07460 311059
4 changing beers (sourced nationally; often Brass Castle, North Riding Brewery) Ⓗ
A recent welcome addition to the Scarborough beer scene, the bar is located opposite Stephen Joseph Theatre and adjacent to Scarborough railway station. A single-room shop conversation with a mix of contemporary and vintage furnishings. Four cask ales, 13 craft keg taps and a selection of ciders together with a range of wines and spirits are available. An extensive choice of bottles and cans can be drunk onsite or taken away. There is regular live music at weekends and a quiz night on alternate Wednesdays. ★ ⥤ ⬤ ₽ ❀ ᯤ ♪

North Riding Brew Pub ⓛ
161-163 North Marine Road, YO12 7HU
☎ (01723) 370004 ⊕ northridingbrewpub.com
6 changing beers (sourced locally; often North Riding Brewery, North Riding Brewpub) Ⓗ
Scarborough's only brewpub, serving at least six continually-changing beers from local breweries and microbreweries around the UK. It always has one or more beer from North Riding brewery together with some brewed on the premises. These are complemented by up to six craft keg beers from around the world, and an extensive range of craft bottled beers. There is a public bar, complete with pool table, and a quiet comfortable lounge, both with real fires. Quiz night is on Thursday. Q ★ ⥤ ♣ ⬤ ₽ (843,X94) ❀ ᯤ

Scarborough Borough Council Employees Welfare Club ⓛ
Dean Road, YO12 7QS
☎ (01723) 364593
3 changing beers (sourced regionally; often Great Newsome, Mallinsons, North Riding Brewery) Ⓗ

GOOD BEER GUIDE 2025

Close to the town centre this club, dating from 1935, comprises a large bar area with an adjacent snooker room. The three cask ales often feature one from Mallinsons, reflecting the preference of the steward, and a dark beer. Club teams participate in local snooker, darts and domino leagues. The club welcomes guests and is popular with cricket goers especially during Scarborough CC hosted Yorkshire county games when the club opens early. An outdoor drinking/smoking area is available. Customers can bring in and consume their own food. ♿✿≉♣🚌🚃(11,333) 🐾

Scholars Bar ♟

6 Somerset Terrace, YO11 2PA

☎ (01723) 372826

Hambleton Nightmare Porter; Ossett Yorkshire Blonde, White Rat; Theakston Old Peculier; 5 changing beers (sourced regionally; often Brew York, Rat, Turning Point) Ⓗ

A warm, friendly atmosphere prevails at this busy town-centre pub at the main shopping centre. The large front bar is dominated by TV screens showing major sporting events and there is a smaller area to the left rear of the bar. Four regular beers plus a range of guest beers, usually from Yorkshire microbreweries are offered together with Theakston Old Peculier served from a wooden cask, plus real ciders from Mr Whitehead's. The Thursday night quiz is popular. Current local CAMRA Town Pub of the Year. ≉♣🍴🚃(10)🐾🛜

Stumble Inn

59 Westborough, YO11 1TS (approx 200yds SW of railway station)

☎ (01723) 372128 ⊕ stumbleinn.co.uk

6 changing beers (sourced nationally; often North Riding Brewery, Whitby) Ⓗ

Scarborough's first micropub and winner of many local and regional CAMRA awards. Located a short walk from the railway station and bus stops, the pub benefits from an external seating area to the front, open until 9pm. Six regularly changing guest ales, one sourced locally, with the old pumpclips decorating the walls, are supplemented by regular brewery takeovers. A number of real ciders are sold. A cheeseboard is available on Sundays. A true community beacon supporting charities and other fundraising causes and events. Q✿≉♣🚃🐾

Tap & Spile ✔

94 Falsgrave Road, YO12 5AZ

☎ (01723) 347534

Ossett White Rat; Sharp's Doom Bar; Timothy Taylor Landlord; Theakston Old Peculier Ⓗ

Located in the popular Falsgrave area, this sympathetically restored Grade II-listed public house offers four permanent cask ales. There are two main rooms, with dogs welcome in the public bar, plus a small quiet snug featuring local memorabilia. The pub is renowned for its live music and shows TV sports in the bar. Traditional lunch is served on Sunday only. A well-appointed beer garden, situated to the rear, is popular in warmer weather and caters for smokers. Q♿✿🐕🚲≉♣🅿🚃🐾🛜♪

Valley Bar Ⓛ

51 Valley Road, YO11 2LX

☎ (01723) 372593 ⊕ valleybar.co.uk

5 changing beers (sourced nationally; often Scarborough) Ⓗ

This spacious independently run bar with quirky decor is divided into several areas, with a separate pool room and a small function room. The pub is popular with locals but also attracts many visitors. Promoting a strong community emphasis the pub operates a book exchange

scheme and hosts an open mic night on Wednesday evenings. A nicely cultivated beer garden with several covered shelters caters for smokers and is well used during the summer months. Accommodation is available. ✿🛏♣🐕🛜♪

Selby

Doghouse Ⓛ

8 Park Street, YO8 4PW

☎ (01757) 703163

5 changing beers (often Great Newsome, Little Black Dog, Westgate) Ⓗ

Selby's first craft beer café featuring five cask beers, together with four ciders and a large range of craft keg beers. The upstairs room is a meeting place for many local groups and there is a weekly quiz night, regular live music and occasional guest food suppliers. You can be sure of a warm welcome at this family-run bar. ✿≉🐕♪

Settle

Golden Lion Ⓛ ✔

Duke Street, BD24 9DU

☎ (01729) 822203 ⊕ goldenlionsettle.co.uk

Thwaites Original, IPA, Gold; 2 changing beers (sourced nationally; often Dark Horse, Settle, Thwaites) Ⓗ

Built around 1670, this Thwaites managed former coaching inn has two comfortable high-ceilinged rooms for drinking. The main bar has wood panelling, a grand staircase and a huge fireplace. The Lion's Den is accessed from the bar or via a low door off the street. The separate dining area is bright and colourful. Outside seating is in the sheltered yard. Breakfast is served from opening. The external door is locked at 10pm except for residents. ♿✿🛏🍴🅰≉🐾🛜♪

Talbot Arms Ⓛ

High Street, BD24 9EX

☎ (01729) 823924 ⊕ talbotsettle.co.uk

Settle Ribblehead Bitter; house beer (by Settle); 2 changing beers (sourced regionally; often Craven, Wensleydale, Wishbone) Ⓗ

This family-run free house, claiming to be the oldest pub in town, offers a welcoming and friendly atmosphere. In winter a stove glows in the large stone feature fireplace to the left. A pleasant, terraced beer garden is at the rear. The guest beers are usually from Cumbria, Lancashire or Yorkshire. The Ribblehead Bitter is badged with an original Mainline pumpclip. A 'Bingo' quiz is held on the first and third Monday of month. Good-value food served daily; with booking advisable weekends and school holidays. Limited parking is available through the arch behind the pub. Opening hours vary in winter. ♿✿🍴🅰≉♣🅿🚃🐾🛜♪

Skeeby

Travellers Rest Ⓛ

22 Richmond Road, DL10 5DS

☎ (01325) 651011 ⊕ thetravellersrestskeeby.co.uk

House beer (by Mithril); 2 changing beers (sourced locally) Ⓗ

This pub is the area's first community-owned pub, reopened in May 2023 after 15 years being shut and derelict. The pub was awarded a CAMRA Pub Saving award after 250 locals raised £320,000 to rebuild it. This welcoming local has bar, lounge and garden room, with a lovely spacious garden at the rear. Darts and quoits teams play, with bingo on Mondays. Three local ales are offered, including a house beer, Community Gold, from

Mithril Ales. Food is served every day except for Monday and Tuesday, when only snacks are available.
Q⭢☕P🅿♿

Skipton

Beer Engine 🍷 Ⓛ
1 Albert Street, BD23 1JD
☎ 07930 810763
6 changing beers (sourced nationally) 🅷
A well-established micropub in a tiny street between the town centre and the canal. Six handpumps dispense varying beers, always including one blonde or pale ale and one dark beer, plus a character beer. The cask beers are stored in a large refrigerated cabinet behind the bar. There is also a craft keg font section, with keg products stored in a separate cupboard. The ambience is friendly and welcoming. Well-behaved dogs are welcome. Local CAMRA Pub of the Year 2024, and Yorkshire Pub of the Year 2024. Q⭢☕➔🚃♿🛜

Woolly Sheep Ⓛ ✓
38 Sheep Street, BD23 1HY
☎ (01756) 700966 🌐 woollysheepinn.co.uk
Timothy Taylor Dark Mild, Golden Best, Boltmaker, Knowle Spring, Landlord, Landlord Dark 🅷
This 18th-century pub at the bottom of the high street is handy for the bus station and town-centre shops. The cosy front lounge has a roaring fire in winter; the area around the main bar has stone flags and the traditional cobbled courtyard has decking with comfortable seating, a canopy and heaters. The split-level restaurant serves food throughout the day. Accommodation is in 12 en-suite rooms upstairs. All six regular Timothy Taylor beers are served, plus an occasional special. ⭢☕🛏🍴➔🚃🛜

Snainton

Peacock
66 High Street, YO13 9AJ
☎ (01723) 859257
Tetley Bitter; 3 changing beers (sourced regionally; often North Riding Brewery) 🅷
This single-roomed local is located on the A170 Scarborough to Pickering road in the heart of Snainton village. A regular beer plus up to three guests are offered. The pub has teams in local pool and darts leagues. Monthly quizzes raise funds for local charities. There is occasional live entertainment. Parking is available. It has a small smoking/drinking area outside the main entrance. ⭢♿P🅿(128)♿🛜♫

South Otterington

Otterington Shorthorn Ⓛ
DL7 9HP
☎ (01609) 773816 🌐 otteringtonshorthorn.co.uk
Daleside Bitter; 2 changing beers (sourced locally; often Ossett, Rudgate) 🅷
Old free house situated on the A167 crossroads, with a comfortable interior opened out into a carpeted lounge bar with an eating area in a separate room off the bar. Guest ales are usually sourced from small Yorkshire breweries and often include a dark beer. There is no accommodation, but the pub has its own holiday let to the rear. Takeaway meals are available.
Q⭢🍴♿🚃P♫

Sowerby

Crown & Anchor Ⓛ ✓
138 Front Street, YO7 1JN (in village ½ mile from Thirsk town centre)
☎ (01845) 522448
Black Sheep Best Bitter; Bradfield Farmers Blonde; Theakston Best Bitter; 2 changing beers (sourced regionally; often Ossett, Pennine, Saltaire) 🅷
A true community pub at the heart of this attractive village on the edge of Thirsk. Several beer or cider festivals each year use the outside bar at the rear. Inside there are several drinking areas with occasional live music and good, no-nonsense food all day ranging from bar snacks to Sunday lunches (booking advised). Guest beers are usually from Yorkshire breweries.
Q☕🍴♿♣P🅿♿🛜♫

Staithes

Cod & Lobster Inn
High Street, TS13 5BH (at the end of the High St, just before the sea)
☎ (01947) 840330 🌐 codandlobster.co.uk
Black Sheep Best Bitter; Helmsley Howardian Gold; Timothy Taylor Boltmaker; York Guzzler 🅷
Superbly positioned at the seawater's edge, in this picturesque sleepy fishing village, the pub comprises a large open-plan room where four beers are served. Good-value traditional meals are served, together with a children's menu. On sunny days a pleasant patio, overlooking the chilly sea, becomes popular. However, during high tides, combined with north-easterly winds, you are advised to use the roadside door or risk getting wet. Access to this part of the village is not ideal for the less mobile. ⭢☕🍴

Starbotton

Fox & Hounds Ⓛ
BD23 5HY
☎ (01756) 760269 🌐 foxandhoundsstarbotton.co.uk
4 changing beers (sourced locally; often Dark Horse, Wensleydale, Yorkshire Dales) 🅷
A family-run, whitewashed 17th-century inn, divided into two cosy rooms, with flagstone floors and a large stone fireplace enhancing the atmosphere. In fine weather the sheltered patio at the front provides extra seating and is good for basking in the Yorkshire sunshine. A locally brewed golden ale and dark beer are served alongside the regular beers. Open Wednesday to Sunday. The daytime community-run bus stops outside.
⭢☕🍴🍴♣P🅿♿

Stillington

White Bear Ⓛ
Main Street, YO61 1JU
☎ (01347) 810338 🌐 thewhitebearinn-york.co.uk
Leeds Pale; house beer (by Rudgate); 3 changing beers (sourced regionally) 🅷
Family-run village pub of exceptional quality. It is here that you can appreciate the benefits of well-managed autovac which provides fresh beer with Yorkshire liveliness. With dining to the left and traditional pub atmosphere to the right, you cannot go wrong. A local CAMRA award-winner, this is a pub definitely worth making the effort to visit if you are not already a lucky regular. Closed Monday, Tuesday and Wednesday and Thursday lunchtime. ⭢☕🍴🍴♣P🅿(40)♿🛜↺

Stokesley

White Swan ⓛ ✅

1 West End, TS9 5BL (at W end of town, 150yds beyond shops)
☎ (01642) 714985 ⊕ whiteswanstokesley.co.uk
Captain Cook Sunset, Slipway, Endeavour, Skippy, Black Porter, Schooner; 3 changing beers (sourced nationally) ℍ
Home of the Captain Cook brewery, this friendly 18th-century pub is at the west end of this pretty market town. Eight handpulls serve five beers from the Captain Cook portfolio of 11 beers, together with three interesting guests, while two real ciders are also always available. Beer festivals are held at Easter and in October. Open mic night is Tuesday, quiz night is Wednesday, and music night is Thursday. The sheltered outdoor drinking area overlooks the brewery. Over-18s only, please.
✿♣🏠🚐(89,28) 🐾🛜♪

Thornton Watlass

Buck Inn ▼ ⓛ ✅

Village Green, HG4 4AH
☎ (01677) 422461 ⊕ buckwatlass.co.uk
Black Sheep Best Bitter; Timothy Taylor Landlord; Theakston Best Bitter; Wensleydale Falconer; 1 changing beer (sourced locally; often Pennine, Rudgate, Three Brothers) ℍ
Overlooking the village green, this traditional country inn, with five letting rooms, features a cosy bar room with a real fire, a lounge/dining room and a large function room known as the Long Room. The building has been refurbished throughout by the owners, while retaining a village pub atmosphere. Excellent meals are available and four regular Yorkshire beers are served, with a changing ale added in summer. Live music is hosted on Sunday lunchtimes once a quarter. The Bedale to Masham bus stops nearby on Tuesdays, Wednesdays and Fridays. Local CAMRA Pub of the Year 2024.
✿🛏🕪P🚐(144) 🐾🛜♪

Ugthorpe

Black Bull Inn ⓛ

Postgate Way, YO21 2BQ
☎ (01947) 840286 ⊕ blackbullwhitby.co.uk
Theakston Old Peculier; 1 changing beer (sourced regionally) ℍ
Drinkers and diners travel from far and wide to visit this Grade II-listed traditional, pantiled country inn, where photographs of yesteryear adorn the walls. This comfortable, family-run establishment comprises a main bar, snug, restaurant and games room. The guest beers complement the Old Peculier, and change weekly. Portions of the home-cooked food are such that going home hungry is not an option. Impressive outdoor drinking facilities provide wonderful views over the North York Moors. Q🛏🕪&♣P

West Tanfield

Bull Inn ⓛ ✅

Church Street, HG4 5JQ
☎ (01677) 470678 ⊕ thebullwesttanfield.co.uk
Theakston Best Bitter; 3 changing beers (sourced locally; often Pennine, Rooster's, Rudgate) ℍ
This food-led pub with a open-plan layout of two rooms and a dining area is equally welcoming to drinkers. It has what is claimed to be the best riverside pub garden in Yorkshire. Nearby is the oft photographed Marmion Tower and the Lightwater Valley theme park. Meals are served lunchtime and evenings on weekdays (not Tue in winter) and all day at weekends. Cask ales from the nearby Masham breweries are always served, together with changing beers from other Yorkshire breweries.
🛏✿🛏🕪♣P🚐(159) 🐾🛜

Whitby

Arch & Abbey

2-4 Skinner Street, YO21 3AJ (at S end of Skinner Street, towards St Hilda's Terrace)
4 changing beers (sourced regionally) ℍ
This popular micropub and café, situated close to the noted Botham's bakery, is operated by enthusiastic licensees who strive to adhere to the original micropub norms. A successful crowd-funded start-up, it is located in what was a truly old-fashioned ladies' dress shop that would not look out of place in a heritage museum. Four interesting beers, six or more mixed ciders, and a huge range of spirits, all distilled in Yorkshire, are served, together with soups and light bites.
Q🛏🕪♿🏠🚐(X93,840) 🐾🛜

Beer O'Clock

11 Flowergate, YO21 3BA
Timothy Taylor Landlord; 3 changing beers (sourced regionally) ℍ
Until recently Mason's greengrocers, it is well worth the short climb to visit this relaxing and contemporary addition to the town's micropub circuit. The only 'Beer O'Clock' in the country is now well established, with friendly, enthusiastic and knowledgeable bar staff serving an interesting selection of guest beers. These normally include a dark beer, together with the regular Timothy Taylor's Landlord. Three ciders are also served together with Whitby's own gin.
Q&♿🏠🚐(X93,840) 🐾🛜

Black Horse ★ ⓛ ✅

91 Church Street, YO22 4BH (on E side of swing bridge on the way to Abbey steps, close to market place)
☎ (01947) 602906 ⊕ the-black-horse.com
5 changing beers (sourced nationally) ℍ
This busy little multi-roomed gem, dating from the 1600s, offers a warm welcome. The frontage, with its frosted glass, together with one of Europe's oldest public serving bars, was built in the 1880s and remains largely unchanged. Beers from the Punch list are served from five handpumps. Snuff and Yorkshire tapas are also served and hot drinks are always available. Local charitable causes are supported. Accommodation is in four bedrooms. Q🛏🛏&🕪♿🚐(X93,840)🐾🛜♪

Little Angel ⓛ ✅

18 Flowergate, YO21 3BA (200yds W of swing bridge, 200yds N of railway/bus stations)
☎ (01947) 820475 ⊕ littleangelwhitby.co.uk
9 changing beers (sourced regionally) ℍ
Now the home of Lady Luck brewery, locals and visitors alike are afforded a genuine friendly welcome at this extremely popular pub, where, it is rumoured, the remains of Whitby Castle form part of the structure. Largescreen sports TVs, live music, an outdoor beer terrace, and even a horse mount for those requiring this facility, complement the nine beers served to three separate rooms from a three-sided central bar. Local CAMRA Pub of the Year for three years running.
🛏🛏♿♣🚐(X93,840) 🐾🛜♪

Quirky Den

11 Grape Lane, YO22 4BA (E side of swing bridge)
☎ 07961 090646

Theakston Old Peculier; 4 changing beers (sourced regionally) Ⓗ
Opened in 2018, this is a rather special gem of a micropub, with so much packed into such a small space. A genuine welcome is assured from the enthusiastic and knowledgeable owners. There are four handpulls, and the pub is noted for serving Theakston Old Peculier directly from wooden sherry casks. An extensive range of gins are also available. Charitable causes are supported. It closes in the New Year, once the pub has been drunk dry, and reopens in March. ≈🚆(X93,840)🌸

Station Inn Ⓛ ✅

New Quay Road, YO21 1DH (opp bus and NYMR/EVR stations)
☎ (01947) 600498
Black Sheep Best Bitter; Ossett Yorkshire Blonde, Silver King; Timothy Taylor Boltmaker; Theakston Old Peculier; Whitby Jet Black; 2 changing beers (sourced regionally) Ⓗ
Next to the harbour and marina, this popular multi-room pub is under the proud stewardship of an enthusiastic licensee who ensures that the eight beers, including two guests, always encompass an eclectic range of varying beer styles. Being situated directly opposite the bus station and NYMR/Esk Valley railway station, this pub has become the discerning travellers' waiting room. Live music features three evenings a week. There are four letting bedrooms. 🛏≈🛜🚆(X93,840)🌸🎵

Waiting Room Ⓛ

2 Whitby Station, Langborne Road, YO21 1YN (by the main entrance to the NYMR/EVR station)
6 changing beers (sourced nationally) Ⓗ
Located on the platform that the NYMR steam trains use, the friendly staff at Whitby's first micropub strive to adhere to the original micropub values: no keg beers/lagers, no spirits, no jukebox, no TV. Six handpumps and several real ales and fruit ciders help to promote a pleasant atmosphere with lots of convivial conversation. The six-yard-square pub gets busy at times, so please do not be disappointed if there isn't any room. Local CAMRA Cider Pub of the Year. Q♿🛜🚆(X93,840)🌸🎵

Whitby Brewery Tap Ⓛ

East Cliff, YO22 4JR (at the top of the 199 steps)
☎ (01947) 228871 ⊕ whitby-brewery.com
Whitby Abbey Blonde, Whitby Whaler, Saltwick Nab, Smugglers Gold, Jet Black, IPA Ⓗ
Away from the hustle and bustle of the town, perched on the cliff edge in the shadow of the famous abbey, the brewery includes a small bar that serves up to four of the brewery's seven beers, together with a bottle shop. Drinkers imbibe close to the liquor tank, mash tun and copper, or sit in the courtyard when the weather isn't too inclement. Tours are available. During summer, the brewery can be accessed using the town's tour bus. Q🐕🧒🌳♿⛺≈P🚆(840,X93)🌸

York

Ackhorne Ⓛ

9 St Martins Lane, YO1 6LN
☎ (01904) 671421
Ainsty Cool Citra; Rudgate Jorvik Blonde, Ruby Mild; house beer (by Half Moon); 2 changing beers (sourced locally; often Brew York, Rooster's, Yorkshire Heart) Ⓗ
This traditional 18th-century pub, with six cask ales, is hidden off the beaten track down a narrow cobbled lane at the bottom of Micklegate. Partially open plan, with separate areas up a couple of steps or through an archway. There's a pleasant and heated beer garden on a

raised area to the back of the pub. It appeals to all age groups with a friendly family atmosphere. Bar snacks and pies are available as are bar billiards, dominos and darts. On Sunday, lunch is on offer along with an evening quiz. 🐕🧒🍽♿♣🚆🎵

Blue Bell ★ Ⓛ ✅

53 Fossgate, YO1 9TF
☎ (01904) 654904 ⊕ bluebellyork.com
Bradfield Farmers Blonde; Rudgate Ruby Mild; Timothy Taylor Landlord; Wold Top Bitter; house beer (by Brass Castle); 2 changing beers (sourced locally; often Bradfield, Half Moon, Rooster's) Ⓗ
Beautiful small Edwardian pub, with a Grade II*-listed historic interior from 1903, preserving a rich character and a unique feel. A central bar supplies the front bar, rear lounge area and side corridor with rare original fold-down seats. A small but very popular pub, a strict no-groups policy is applied and entry can be restricted if busy. Bar snacks and pork pies, with homemade chutney, are available, and a free cheeseboard on Sunday afternoons. Multiple winner of local CAMRA awards. Q♿♣🚆🌸🍽?

Brew York Beer Hall & Tap Room Ⓛ

Unit 6 Enterprise Complex, Walmgate, YO1 9TT
☎ (01904) 848448 ⊕ brewyork.co.uk
Brew York Fennec Blonde, Maris the Otter, Calmer Chameleon, Tonkoko; 6 changing beers (often Brew York) Ⓗ
Brew York opened outside the city centre in 2001. The Tap Room is inside the original brewery and the Beer Hall in the adjacent old maltings. There is plentiful seating in both venues by the brew tanks and outside in the beer garden by the River Foss. Ten cask ales and around 30 keg or KeyKeg choices give drinkers plenty to choose from. Innovative fresh food is available with a good vegan choice. Please note that the Tap Room is closed Monday, Tuesday, and weekday afternoons. Card payments only. 🐕🧒🍽♿🚆🌸?🎵

Fox ★

168 Holgate Road, YO24 4DQ
☎ (01904) 787722
Ossett Butterley, Yorkshire Blonde, White Rat, Silver King, Excelsius; 3 changing beers (sourced regionally; often Fernandes, Ossett, Rat) Ⓗ
Set in the Holgate district of York, the Fox is a pub whose history is linked to the golden age of rail. It was sympathetically restored by Ossett brewery in 2014. Beer festivals in the spring and summer always prove popular, with outdoor catering on a regular basis throughout the year. It has the largest beer garden in York with a serving hatch open on busy days. There is always a great atmosphere. Please check social media for up-to-date events. 🐕🌳P🚆(1,5)🌸?🔄🎵

Golden Ball ★ Ⓛ

2 Cromwell Road, YO1 6DU
☎ (01904) 849040 ⊕ goldenballyork.co.uk
Acorn Barnsley Bitter; Ainsty Assassin; 4 changing beers (sourced regionally; often Rooster's, Rudgate, Yorkshire Heart) Ⓗ
A fine Victorian street-corner community-run local with an impressive glazed brick exterior that was extensively refurbished by John Smiths in 1929. Grade II-listed, it has four very different rooms: a main bar, side room with bar billiards table, comfortable lounge and snug. Outside is a large south-facing beer garden. Six handpumps serve three permanent ales plus three changing guests. Local produce is on sale in the bar as well as Scotch eggs, pork pies, and nuts. Q🐕🧒🌳≈♣🌸🎵

Maltings 🄻

Tanners Moat, YO1 6HU

☎ (01904) 655387 ⊕ maltings.co.uk

Black Sheep Best Bitter; 7 changing beers (sourced nationally; often Rooster's) ⊞

The Maltings has been a must for beer-lovers for 30 years continuously improving to stay ahead of the competition. The beer range and quality is excellent covering all styles and strengths, both in cask and keg, along with a good selection of real cider. The food options are fairly typical for a pub, but the quality, quantity and value are outstanding. An extension added a few years ago provides more space and an outdoor area while maintaining the pub's unique character. Q🕮🕮🞱🖵🎵

Market Cat

6 Jubbergate, YO1 8RT

☎ (01904) 637023 ⊕ marketcatyork.co.uk

Thornbridge Lord Marples, Jaipur; 6 changing beers (often Hawkshead, Tapped, Thornbridge) ⊞

Operated by Thornbridge and Pivovar UK, this three storey building has seating on all three floors with excellent views across the Shambles Market and towards the minster from the upper two. Pizza is served. A changing range of real ales are dispensed from eight handpumps with a mixture of beers from Thornbridge, Tapped and other breweries. 🕮🕮🞱🖵🕮

Phoenix Inn ★

75 George Street, YO1 9PT

☎ (01904) 656401 ⊕ phoenixinnyork.co.uk

Saltaire South Island ⊞; **Timothy Taylor Landlord** ⊞/🄶; **3 changing beers (sourced regionally; often Saltaire, Wold Top)** ⊞

Local CAMRA Pub of the Year 2023, the Phoenix Inn is known across the city as a home of great real ale and jazz evenings. When there is no music, enjoy your beer by the log fire passing the time chatting to fellow drinkers. In warmer months, the enclosed garden offers the opportunity to relax with a pint while admiring the fine views of York's historic walls. A true gem and not to be missed. Q🕮🞱🖵🕮🎵

Rook & Gaskill 🄻

12 Lawrence Street, YO10 3WP

☎ (01904) 671548 ⊕ rookandgaskillyork.co.uk

4 changing beers (sourced nationally; often Brass Castle, Castle Rock, Turning Point) ⊞

This thriving community pub, across the road from Walmgate Bar, is home to locals, students and beer devotees. A wide and changing range and styles of reasonably-priced ales (including from onsite brewery) and LocAles are served. Six cask lines, 20 KeyKeg taps and three real ciders cater for all tastes. A good range of food cooked to order, a Thursday night quiz and a host of other events make this a pub worth visiting. 🕮🞱🖵🕮🞱

Slip Inn 🄻

Clementhorpe, YO23 1AN

☎ (01904) 621793

Leeds Pale; Rudgate Ruby Mild; Timothy Taylor Boltmaker; 5 changing beers (sourced nationally; often Brass Castle, Marble, Turning Point) ⊞

The Slip Inn is a thriving independent free house that's a community local, with two bars, a snug, and a sheltered courtyard beer garden. A major investment in 2019 created a dedicated outside festival bar and doubled the range on the bar, so you'll always find a good choice of cask ales. The pub hosts regular beer festivals and live music events and supports traditional pub games including darts, dominoes and cribbage. 🕮🞱🖵(11)🕮🎵

Swan 🍺 ★ 🄻

16 Bishopgate Street, YO23 1JH

☎ (01904) 634968 ⊕ theswanyork.co.uk

Half Moon Dark Masquerade; Timothy Taylor Landlord; Tetley Tetley Bitter; house beer (by Half Moon); 4 changing beers (sourced nationally; often Brass Castle, Half Moon, Settle) ⊞

Step inside this historic Grade II-listed Tetley Heritage pub to enjoy eight cask beers, including two darks and a house blonde, with four regulars and ever-changing guests from across the UK. The range of taste and styles of high-quality beer means there is a mini beer festival every day which is complemented by seasonal festivals in conjunction with the Slip round the corner. There is seating in the front or back room, the traditional West Riding-style drinking lobby or in the partially-covered beer garden. Local CAMRA Pub of the Year 2024. 🕮🞱🖵(11,26)🕮

Waggon & Horses 🄻

19 Lawrence Street, YO10 3BP

☎ (01904) 637478 ⊕ waggonandhorsesyork.com

Batemans XB; Oakham Citra; 5 changing beers (sourced nationally; often Ossett, Rat, Riverhead) ⊞

The Waggon & Horses is a classic multi-roomed real ale pub with impressive beer garden and bar billiards table. Tom and Paulina have recently celebrated their 10-year anniversary as landlords and over the last decade cultivated a well-deserved reputation for an ever-changing rotation of guest beers, including less common stouts and porters as well as occasional beers from the wood. 🕮🞱🖵🕮🞱

York Tap

Railway Station, Station Road, YO24 1AB

☎ (01904) 659009 ⊕ yorktap.com

Timothy Taylor Boltmaker, Knowle Spring, Landlord, Landlord Dark; 14 changing beers (sourced nationally; often Anarchy, Tapped, Thornbridge) ⊞

This conversion of the Victorian tea rooms on York station was opened as a pub in 2011. The ornate ceiling, Art Deco stained glass windows, terrazzo floors and stained glass ceiling domes create an award-winning backdrop to the central bar with 20 handpumps. On sale are 18 cask beers plus two ciders or perries, as well as a large range of keg and bottled beer. The beers are sourced by parent company Pivovar from many of Britain's finest breweries. All styles and strengths are represented. No meals are served, though pies are available at the bar. 🕮🞱🖵🕮

YORKSHIRE (SOUTH)

Armthorpe

Horse & Groom

Nutwell Lane, DN3 3JU (at edge of village on the road to Cantley)

☎ (01302) 831658

Pheasantry Best Bitter; 1 changing beer (sourced nationally; often Oakham, Otter) ⊞

The second oldest existing building in the village, this traditional pub used to be a coach house. Welcoming and traditional in style, with a cosy bar and spacious lounge with dining area. There is a large beer garden with seating. Events include a Tuesday music quiz, a general quiz on Sunday and a disco/music quiz on the first Saturday of the month. Traditional home-made pub food is served. The pub is the base for a darts team and the Golf Society. 🕮🞱🖵(81,82)🕮

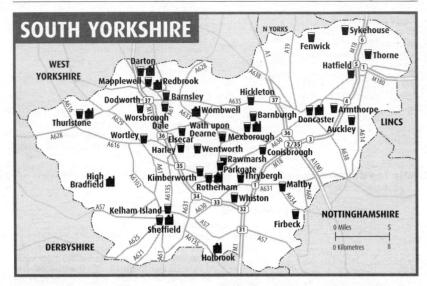

SOUTH YORKSHIRE

Auckley

Eagle & Child ✅
24 Main Street, DN9 3HS
☎ (01302) 770406 🌐 eagleandchildauckley.co.uk
Acorn Barnsley Bitter; Black Sheep Best Bitter; Timothy Taylor Landlord; 2 changing beers (sourced regionally; often Abbeydale, Milestone) Ⓗ
A much-loved pub, on the main road in the village, and winner of numerous CAMRA awards. Dating from early 19th century, it has real character. There are two bars, one with a TV, the other quieter, with tables for bar meals. The separate restaurant is decorated with photographs of local historic interest, and home-cooked meals have a deserved reputation. There is an outside seating area and beer garden.
Q🛏️🕱🌜◐▲♣P🚌(57f) 🐕🛜

Barnburgh

Coach & Horses ★
High Street, DN5 7EP
☎ (01709) 352045
Don Valley Atomic Blonde, Go Your Own Way; 3 changing beers (sourced regionally; often Black Sheep, Don Valley, Timothy Taylor) Ⓗ
This Grade II-isted pub with its unchanged multi-room layout and Art Deco grandeur has been identified by CAMRA as having a nationally important historic pub interior. In 2020 it was purchased by enlightened new owners, from the Don Valley brewery, and they have carried out an exemplary refurbishment. Look out for the Andy Capp mural in the tap room, the very rare sash screens and the Whitworth Ales logos. Real ales are from Don Valley brewery, supported by guest ales, with up to five ales available at any time.
🛏️🕱◐♣P🚌(219) 🐕🛜🎜

Barnsley

George & Dragon Ⓛ
41-43 Summer Lane, S70 2NW
☎ (01226) 219316
4 changing beers (sourced locally) Ⓗ
Reopened in 2020 following a thorough refurbishment which included reinstatement of real ale, four constantly-changing cask ales are all from local breweries and always include a dark beer. Quality keg and canned beers are also available. With a two-room layout, the main bar is dominated by the splendid counter and bar back and comfy bench seating. Both rooms have been tastefully decorated and adorned with attractive prints. There is a sizeable outdoor drinking area. Occasional live music is planned. Q🛏️🕱🌜≠P🚌(43,44)🎜

REAL ALE BREWERIES

1086 ✦ Doncaster
Abbeydale Sheffield
Acorn Wombwell
Blue Bee Sheffield
Both Barrels Mexborough
Bradfield Sheffield: High Bradfield
brewSocial Sheffield
Chantry Rotherham
Dead Parrot Sheffield
Doncaster 🍺 Doncaster
Emmanuales Sheffield
Exit 33 Sheffield (brewing suspended)
Fuggle Bunny Sheffield: Holbrook
Gorilla ✦ Mexborough
Grizzly Grains Sheffield
Heist ✦ Sheffield
Imperial 🍺 Mexborough
Jolly Boys ✦ Redbrook
Kibble 🍺 Thurlstone
Little Critters Sheffield
Little Mesters ✦ Sheffield
Lost Industry Sheffield
Loxley 🍺 Sheffield
Nailmaker ✦ Darton
Neepsend ✦ Sheffield
On the Edge Sheffield
St Mars of the Desert ✦ Sheffield
Stancill Sheffield
Tapped 🍺 Sheffield
Toolmakers ✦ Sheffield
Triple Point ✦ Sheffield
True North Sheffield
White Rose Mexborough
Woodland ✦ Sheffield

Heaven & Ale 🏆 L

66 Agnes Road, S70 1NH

☎ 07981 703786

4 changing beers (sourced nationally) H

This former old Co-op has had a wonderful conversion into a multi-roomed pub, with three rooms on the ground floor and a function room upstairs. The outside drinking area to the front is popular. The four real ales are from small micro and regional breweries across the whole of the UK, but a couple are often local to the area. A former local and regional CAMRA Pub of the Year. (43,44)

Jolly Tap on the Arcade L

31 The Arcade, S70 2QP (53.553344,-1.480003)

jollyboysbrewery.co.uk

Jolly Boys Blonde; 4 changing beers (sourced locally; often Hilltop, Jolly Boys) H

Barnsley's first micropub was opened in 2017 by Two Roses brewery. This tiny one-up one-down pub is now owned by the Jolly Boys brewery. It serves up to five real ales alongside a choice of craft beers, all sourced locally. The pub is situated in the lovely Victorian Arcade and was a cake shop before becoming the micropub. The staff are welcoming and knowledgeable on the cask and craft beers on offer. Q

Nailmaker Tap 2 L

Unit 2B, Gateway Plaza, Sackville Street, S70 2RD

Nailmaker Jester Pale Ale, Cardinal Sin, Clout Stout; 1 changing beer (sourced regionally) H

This micropub near the entrance to the Gateway Plaza complex opened in 2018. It is split over two levels with a mezzanine floor looking over part of the ground floor. A café bar outdoor drinking area was added in 2019 and is popular in the summer months. The pub offers four changing real ales, craft beers and cider, and is renowned for its gin selection. No children under-12. P

Old No 7 L

7 Market Hill, S70 2PX

☎ (01226) 244735

Acorn Barnsley Bitter, Blonde, Yorkshire Pride; 6 changing beers (sourced locally) H

This is popular town cenre ale house offers a range of up to eight real ales from Acorn and other micro breweries, also a wide range of craft and continental beers. This is the 12th consecutive year in the Guide. The downstairs bar is available for functions, meetings etc and opens match days and busy Friday and Saturday evenings. Regular Live Music.

Spiral City L

26-30 The Arcade, S70 2QN

☎ (01226) 283013

3 changing beers (sourced locally) H

Stylish bar opened in 2021 which is the latest adornment to the town's characterful Victorian Arcade. The split-level ground floor is decked out in Art Deco style. Upstairs are two drinking areas in similar vein, one featuring a marvellous original Rock-ola jukebox. On the walls are artworks by owners Dean and Fiona. The three handpumps offer a changing choice of local beers while the seven keg fonts also rotate. Also on the premises is the excellent Vinyl Underground record shop.

Conisbrough

Terminus

2 New Hill, DN12 3HA (10 mins walk downhill from town centre)

☎ 07397 853206

4 changing beers (sourced locally) H

This micropub adjacent to a former trolleybus terminus gives a warm and friendly welcome to all. It has four, usually local, rotating cask ales. The decor reflects local history with a large wall picturing eight local men who all joined up to serve in WWI on the same day. The bar surround has historic dates for Conisbrough on it. Dogs have their own treat jar on the bar. Quiz night is on Wednesdays. It is close to the castle and a 20-minute walk from the station. Q (X78,221)

Darton

Anvil Arms L

28 Church Street, S75 5HG

☎ (01226) 805225

Nailmaker Yorkshire Bitter, Cardinal Sin, Clout Stout; 1 changing beer (sourced locally; often Don Valley) H

Formally the Old Co-op Ale House, it has been taken into ownership of the Nailmaker brewery, with six real ales and three ciders on handpull, and a 12-tap beer wall. During lockdown sympathetic updates to the pub included adding new seating to outdoor drinking areas to the front and side of the building, while keeping the features people have come to love like the stone brick walls and log fire. This micropub, has definitely cemented itself on the Mapplewell and Darton real ale corridor. Q (X10)

Dodworth

Dodworth Tap

Station Road, S75 3JA

Ossett White Rat; house beer (by Nailmaker); 2 changing beers (sourced regionally; often Nailmaker, Timothy Taylor) H

Close to Dodworth railway station, this pub was brought back from the brink in 2020 by the people who run the Darton Tap, who have lovingly restored the pub to its former glory. Now serving up to four real ales including a house beer, an extensive spirit collection and a good selection of craft beers, a huge open fire place lost until the recent renovations, is now a feature. The refurbishment of the upper parts of the pub to create a function room were completed in 2021, and the huge beer garden has been revamped. P (21A,22)

Doncaster

Doncaster Brewery Tap 🏆 L

7 Young Street, DN1 3EL

☎ (01302) 376436 doncasterbrewery.co.uk

Doncaster Sand House; 4 changing beers (sourced locally; often Doncaster) H

Convenient for the city centre, DBT as it's becoming known as, has recently celebrated being open for 10 years and is the winner of several CAMRA awards. Up to six beers are available with a further six handpumps devoted to traditional cider and perries, all served in lined glasses. The new Dystopia bar upstairs offers a selection of craft beers. There's always something going on at DBT – quiz nights are held on Tuesdays, spoken word night on Thursdays and ukulele sessions are held once a month on Saturdays. Q (15,81)

Draughtsman Alehouse

Station Court, DN1 1PE (on Platform 3B of Doncaster Station)

☎ 07999 874660 ∰ thedraughtsmanalehouse.co.uk

3 changing beers (sourced regionally) Ⓗ

Located on platform 3B of Doncaster Railway Station, this former Victorian buffet bar had stood empty for 18 years. Reopened in 2017, it is the project of one man, Russell Thompson, who now runs it in partnership with his son Luke. Real ales are changed regularly and sourced from regional brewers. Locally made pies are usually available. Do be sure to inspect the fantastic Victorian wall tiles, and engineering drawings of steam locomotives. ❀≠⊟(29)❧

Hallcross

33-34 Hall Gate, DN1 3NL

∰ hallcrossdoncaster.co.uk

Stocks St Leger Gold, Select, Old Horizontal; 3 changing beers (sourced nationally; often Acorn, Little Critters, Rudgate) Ⓗ

Situated in a prominent location overlooking a busy road junction at the top of one of the city's main streets, this pub has done much to improve the real ale scene in Doncaster. The Hallcross is the home of the resurrected Stocks beers, once brewed on the premises, and now brewed by Welbeck Abbey. Up to three guest ales are sourced nationwide, although one is often from Rudgate. Sports fans are well catered for in the front bar, and the rear courtyard also contains an undercover snug. ❀⅋≠⊟(21,25)❧❦♪

Leopard ✔

2 West Street, DN1 3AA (less than 5 mins walk from the railway station)

☎ (01302) 739460 ∰ leopard-doncaster.co.uk

6 changing beers (sourced regionally; often Acorn, Stancill, Titanic) Ⓗ

This street-corner pub, located close to the city centre and transport interchange, offers a wide range of beer styles, including a stout or porter. It has a superb tiled frontage, recalling its days as a Warwick & Richardson's house. There are two rooms downstairs, and a large concert room upstairs, which often hosts live music at weekends. The pub is run by Doncaster Culture & Leisure Trust, and beers from their own 1086 brewery can often be found on the bar. ❀⓪≠♣✿⊟(71,72)❧❦♪

Little Plough ★ Ⓛ

8 West Laith Gate, DN1 1SF (close to Frenchgate shopping centre, 5 mins walk from railway station)

☎ (01302) 738310

Acorn Barnsley Bitter; Bradfield Farmers Blonde; 2 changing beers (sourced regionally) Ⓗ

A friendly haven for anyone wishing to escape the hustle and bustle of the city centre. Up to four cask ales are served on handpump in the front bar. The interior is little-changed since 1934, a fact proved by plans that can be seen in the corridor. It has been identified by CAMRA as having a nationally important historic pub interior. There is a comfortable lounge at the rear, usually quiet except on Sunday evenings when the pub is taken over by a fun quiz night. Q❀❦♣⊟❦❧

Queen (Crafthouse & Kitchen)

1 Sunny Bar, DN1 1LY (on the corner of Sunny Bar and Market Place)

5 changing beers (sourced nationally) Ⓗ

Old established marketplace pub, recently revived under new ownership. An interior created out of unusual boarding sets the scene and the pub has drawn many new customers, many to sample the atmosphere, real ales and music at weekends. Situated close to the historic Corn Exchange and bustling market, this is a welcome addition to the town's real ale scene. There are five changing real ales plus two ciders, typically from Gwynt y Ddraig or Celtic Marches. Q❀⅋≠●⊟(15)❦❧♪

Elsecar

Maison Du Biere Ⓛ

Wath Road, S74 8HJ (in Elsecar Heritage Centre, Unit 15)

☎ (01226) 805255 ∰ maisondubiere.com

Changing beers (sourced nationally)

This popular beer shop and tap is in the heart of the historic heritage centre, serving over 400 bottled, canned, draught beers and ciders, 20 lines of craft/draught beers and four real ciders. The knowledgeable staff can navigate you on a taste experience. The tap is popular with locals and visitors alike who also come for the many events held in the heritage centre. ♿❀⅋≠♣●P⊟(66,227)❦❧♪

Market Hotel Ⓛ

2-4 Wentworth Road, S74 8EP

☎ (01226) 742240

Acorn Barnsley Gold; 4 changing beers (often Acorn, Bradfield) Ⓗ

Multi-roomed pub with a popular drinking corridor. Look for the 'Horse and Gig For Hire' sign chiselled into the stonework. Constantly-changing beers from local microbreweries are charged at the same price regardless of strength. To the rear is a beer garden with a large brick-built barbecue. Next to Elsecar Heritage Centre, it is a popular meeting place for various groups and welcomes walkers enjoying the open scenic countryside. Q❀➤≠♣P⊟(66,227)❦

Fenwick

Baxter Arms

Fenwick Lane, DN6 0HA (between Askern and Moss)

☎ (01302) 702671

Theakston Best Bitter; 2 changing beers (often Black Sheep, Pennine, Stancill) Ⓗ

A family-owned country pub with traditionally furnished lounge decorated with country pursuits and pictures. A snug area has a full-sized snooker table. Reasonably priced food is available daily, and quiz night is Wednesday. Three well-kept real ales from independent breweries are served. Outside there is a small seating area at the front and a lawned area with benches at the side, all surrounded by high hedges. Ample parking is available. A welcoming rural gem. Q➤❀⓪▲♣P❦❧

Firbeck

Black Lion Ⓛ

9 New Road, S81 8JY (opp village hall)

☎ (01709) 812575 ∰ bit.ly/2VZpqE

Chantry New York Pale; Timothy Taylor Landlord; 2 changing beers (sourced locally; often Abbeydale, Bradfield, Stancill) Ⓗ

Traditional village free house, reopened in 2017 after a period of closure. It attracts drinkers, diners, walkers and the local community. Four real ales are offered and the two changing beers usually come from local microbreweries. The renowned food is freshly cooked to order. Pictures of old Firbeck adorn the walls of the snug area. The number 20 bus only serves the village Monday to Saturday daytime. Handy for the ruins of Roche Abbey and countryside walks. Open every day, but closes early on Sunday evenings. Q➤❀⓪♣P⊟(20)❦♪

Harley

Horseshoe L

9 Harley Road, S62 7UD (off A6135 on B6090, 1 mile from Wentworth)

☎ (01226) 742204 ● thehorseshoeharley.co.uk

Neepsend Blonde; 2 changing beers (often Acorn, Little Critters) H

Cosy village local and community hub, that has been in the same family for many years. Real ales change frequently and often come from local breweries. Opens at 4pm Monday to Saturday and all day on Sunday. Food available Monday, Friday and Saturday evenings with a carvery on Sunday afternoons. Home to sports teams, it is busy when the pool team are at home and when the village gala is held in July. There is some seating in front of the pub with a small outside area to the rear.
❀✲❶♣P☲(44) ❀♫

Hatfield

Jack Hawley at the Grange L

Manor Road, DN7 6SB

☎ 07769 927603

Timothy Taylor Boltmaker; 4 changing beers (sourced regionally; often Don Valley, Pheasantry, Welbeck Abbey) H

This micro is the project of a real ale enthusiast who was previously landlord of the Black Swan in Asselby. Access is via a staircase to the first floor. There is a long, narrow lounge with mixed seating. One wall has four guitars, which may be played by competent players, the other has the story of Jack Hawley, a local character from the 19th century, who was renowned for his hospitality.
Q❀♣♣P☲(84,87A) ♫

Hickleton

Hickleton Village Hall Club L

Castle Hill Lane, DN5 7BG

☎ (01709) 895867

2 changing beers (sourced regionally; often Black Sheep, Timothy Taylor) H

Cosy and comfortable village club in an attractive conservation village. Two real ales are available on handpull, usually, but not always from Yorkshire breweries. Membership is open to all, with card-carrying CAMRA members and other guests welcome. The real fire is perfect for sitting next to on cold evenings. Tuesday night is quiz night, and the third Thursday of each month Pie night. Puddings are also available. A warm welcome awaits. Q❀♣♣(X19)❀

Kimberworth

Steptoes Café Bar L

192 High Street, S61 2DT

☎ (01709) 431637

4 changing beers (sourced regionally; often Gorilla, Pheasantry, Welbeck Abbey) H

Café bar and micropub in a former hair salon. After a faltering start due to Covid lockdowns, it reopened in 2021. Real ales on the four handpumps come from microbreweries near and far and can often be rare. Luxury coffees and teas, wines, spirits and cakes are also on offer. Cosy and welcoming with interesting décor. Some snacks are available. Open all day every day. QP☲

Wilton L

255 Kimberworth Road, S61 1HF

☎ (01709) 551100

2 changing beers (sourced locally; often Chantry, Little Critters) H

Welcoming street-corner locals' pub with two handpumps, at the start of old Kimberworth village. It is close to Bradgate Park and to the main route between Rotherham and Meadowhall Retail Park. Bought from Enterprise Inns by a private individual in 2017 it is leased to Clare and Martin. The former two-roomed layout has been opened out, with a central bar serving all areas. Changing guest beers are sourced from local microbreweries, often Chantry or Little Critters. Closed Monday lunchtimes. ♣☲☂

Maltby

Queens Hotel ●

Tickhill Road, S66 7NQ (on A631)

☎ (01709) 812494

Greene King Abbot; Ruddles Best Bitter; Sharp's Doom Bar; 4 changing beers (sourced locally; often Bradfield, Stancill) H

Former residential hotel and pub on a busy crossroads, completely refurbished and reopened by Wetherspoon after a lengthy period of closure. Now firmly established, this spacious pub has an attractive family dining area offering typical Wetherspoon value-for-money food and drink. Maltby is not blessed with many real ale outlets and the Queens has raised its profile in the township. Regular Meet the Brewer nights are held. Next to Coronation Park and handy for Maltby Crags and Roche Abbey. Open all day every day from 8am.
☎❀✲❶☧P☲(X1,X2) ☂

Mapplewell

Talbot Inn L

Towngate, S75 6AS

☎ (01226) 385629 ● thetalbotmapplewell.co.uk

4 changing beers (sourced locally; often Millstone, Nailmaker) H

The first and original tap for Nailmaker brewery, this pub spearheaded the real ale revival in the area, with four rotating beers from the brewery and occasional guests and tap takeovers from the likes of Magic Rock and North brewing. This pub is extremely popular with locals, who come for a quick pint and a meal or for the ever-popular Speed Quiz. During 2021 the pub had a extensive sympathetic refurbishment from top to bottom, including the exterior. Food is served at all tables daily, or in the popular restaurant upstairs. Q☎❀✲❶♣P☲(1,X10)❀☂

Wentworth Arms L

Greenside, S75 6AU

☎ (01226) 390702 ● wentwortharms.co.uk

4 changing beers (sourced regionally; often Nailmaker) H

Sister pub to the Talbot, this popular relaxed place is well know for its excellent and ever-changing array of real ale and craft beers. The pub has a well cared for beer garden with lovely festoon lighting. During 2020 refurbishment work to the upstairs area created a new bar called the loft to host private events or just as a great place to chill and relax with a beer with friends. This pub has firmly positioned itself as a prominent participant in the real ale triangle of Mapplewell, Darton and Baurgh Green.
❀❶☧P☲(1,X10) ❀☂

Mexborough

Gorilla Beer Hall

Canalside Industrial Estate, Cliff Street, S64 9HU (on dual carriageway across road from bus interchange)
☎ 07933 078364 ⊕ gorillabrewing.co.uk
Gorilla Vanilla Gorilla; 3 changing beers (sourced nationally; often Bradfield, Don Valley, Gorilla) Ⓗ
The Gorilla Beer Hall is located on the canalside, adjacent to the main road through Mexborough and is ideally situated for local bus and rail services. There are five handpumps in each bar serving beers brewed in the adjacent brewery, usually including a dark beer and the award winning Ape-X IPA. Weekends are sometimes ticket-only live music, but at these times the upstairs taproom is opened for a quieter environment. Gift sets are also available to take away. Street food is available. ⽅⽊⽁⽓⽍P⽐⽎⽏♪

Imperial Brewery Tap Ⓛ

Cliff Street, S64 9HU (opp bus station)
☎ (01709) 584000 ⊕ mightyimperial.com
Imperial Classical Bitter, Platinum Blonde, Nah Then, Stout Wi' Nowt Tekkn' Owt; 4 changing beers (sourced locally; often Imperial) Ⓗ
A friendly brewery tap with lots to offer, especially for music lovers. It has a main entertainment bar, separate lounge area plus games/function room. The six handpumps serve two permanent Imperial beers, with four rotating from Imperial, local or national breweries. Entertainment ranges from a battle of the bands on Tuesday, karaoke on Wednesday, an award-winning acoustic night on Thursday to a wide range of live music on Friday Saturday and Sunday. Closed Mondays and Tuesdays. ⽅⽊⽁⽓⽄⽐(220,221)⽎⽏♪

Old Market Hall ⊘

Market Street, S64 9QA
☎ (01709) 599820
Greene King Abbot; Ruddles Best Bitter; Sharp's Doom Bar; 4 changing beers (often Exmoor, Hook Norton) Ⓗ
Town centre JD Wetherspoon art the end of Market Street, as the name suggests, converted from the Market Hall. It is a large-single room bar, with both high and low seating, catering for all age groups. Good-value food is served, with a selection of constantly changing real ales joining the three regulars. There is an outside seating area. Close to the bus and railway station. Q⽅⽊⽁⽄⽓P⽐(221)⽏

Parkgate

Little Haven Micro Bar Ⓛ

19 Broad Street, S62 6DX
☎ (01709) 710134
⊕ the-little-haven-micro-bar.business.site
3 changing beers (sourced locally; often Chantry, Little Critters) Ⓗ
Friendly, welcoming micropub, opened in 2018 in a former post office, but moved across the road to larger premises in early 2024. Three handpumps and four craft taps see local microbreweries often favoured. Nibbles, a jukebox, and board games are available, with acoustic music on Tuesday and Saturday evenings. Limited outside seating is accessed via pub. Food may be brought in from nearby takeaways. A welcome break from Parkgate Retail World and 15 minutes' walk from the tram/train stop there. Q⽊⽄⽐⽎⽏♪

Rawmarsh

Something BREW INN Ⓛ

2 Stocks Lane, S62 6NL (behind the Star pub)
☎ 07717 502307
3 changing beers (sourced locally; often Abbeydale, Bradfield, Chantry) Ⓗ
This micropub and coffee house in a former office building opened in 2018. The changing real ales are often from Chantry and other local microbreweries. Craft keg, bottled beers and boxed cider – some of it real – is also sold. The L-shaped room is tastefully decorated. Outside seating provided at the front and rear of the pub. Entertainment is provided by Sunday jam sessions and occasional guest singers plus Wednesday quiz nights. Closed on Monday and Tuesday. Q⽊⽁⽐⽎⽏⽏♪

Rotherham

Bluecoat Ⓛ

The Crofts, S60 2DJ (behind town hall, off Moorgate Rd A618)
☎ (01709) 539500
Greene King Abbot; Ruddles Best Bitter; Sharp's Doom Bar; Welbeck Abbey Cavendish; 6 changing beers (sourced regionally) Ⓗ
Former charity school, opened in 1776 by the Ffeofees of Rotherham. It became a pub named Ffeofees in 1981 then a Wetherspoon in 2001. Up to 10 handpulled beers include seven changing guest beers, with local and national microbreweries favoured. Most of the cider sold is not real. A Guide regular, and winner of numerous local CAMRA awards. Pictures of old Rotherham adorn the walls and a blue plaque on the façade commemorates its history. ⽅⽊⽁⽄⽓≢(Central)♣P⽐⽏

Cutlers Arms ★ Ⓛ

29 Westgate, S60 1BQ
☎ (01709) 382581
Chantry New York Pale, Iron and Steel Bitter, Diamond Black Stout; house beer (by Chantry); 2 changing beers (sourced locally; often Chantry) Ⓗ
Dating from 1825 and rebuilt for Stones brewery of Sheffield in 1907, it was saved from demolition in 2004, following a Grade II listing. Restored to Edwardian splendour by Chantry brewery, it reopened in 2014. The pub retains original art nouveau windows, tiling and curved bar counter with dividing screen and has been identified by CAMRA as having a nationally important historic pub interior. The full range of Chantry beers, two real ciders and quality craft beers available. It can be busy with live music at weekends. Snacks are available. ⽊⽁≢(Central)⽄⽐⽎⽏♪

Dragon's Tap ⽋ Ⓛ

477 Herringthorpe Valley Road, Broom, S65 3AD
☎ 07864 680301
Chantry New York Pale; 5 changing beers (sourced regionally) Ⓗ
Micropub opened in 2018 in a former DIY shop, it is simply but tastefully decorated with modern art prints. Six changing beers are sourced from local and national microbreweries, with four craft keg beers and bottled beers available. No food is served, save for snacks, but you can bring in food from nearby takeaways. There are tables at the front of the pub. There's a general knowledge quiz on Wednesday evening and live acoustic music on the third Sunday of the month in the upstairs room. Q⽊⽄⽀P⽐(X1,X2)⽎♪

Homestead ⊘

Wickersley Road, Broom, S60 3PJ (jct of Broom Ln)
☎ (01709) 838984

2 changing beers H

This imposing pub with an extensive garden area at the front of the building is a former farmhouse, hence the name. The interior has been opened out with several distinct areas served by a central bar. It specialises in sizzling steak dishes that are served from lunchtime until early evening. The arrival of the new manager has seen the real ale range rise to two, which can be from near and far. Cask Club on Tuesdays. Close to Herringthorpe Stadium and playing fields, it has a large car park and small outside seating area to the rear.

ᗘ⊛❶ᕉᏢᖯ(X1) ♪

New York Tavern L

84 Westgate, S60 1BD (jct of Coke Ln)

☎ (01709) 371155

Chantry New York Pale, Iron & Steel Bitter, Diamond Black Stout, Special Reserve; 3 changing beers (often Chantry) H

Wedge-shaped house that became a pub in 1856. It was refurbished and reopened by Chantry brewery in 2013 as a real ale-led pub. Previously the Prince of Wales Feathers, it was renamed after a pub demolished when the nearby ring road was built, but retains the same manager as when the Feathers. At least six Chantry beers and two real ciders or perries are available, at very competitive prices. Snuff and bar snacks available. Handy for New York Stadium, with Rotherham United memorabilia on display. ⇌(Central)♠ᖯ❀ 🛜 ♪

Sheffield: Central

Bath Hotel ★ ✅

66-68 Victoria Street, S3 7QL

☎ (0114) 249 5151

Abbeydale Deception; Acorn Barnsley Bitter; Thornbridge Jaipur IPA; 2 changing beers (sourced regionally; often Abbeydale, Bradfield, Thornbridge) H

A careful restoration of the 1930s historic pub interior, identified by CAMRA as nationally important, gained this two-roomed pub a conservation award. The bar lies between the tiled lounge, a small corridor drinking area and the cosy well-upholstered snug. There are usually three regular cask beers and three guest cask beers available. Food is light snacks only.

Qᖯ(University of Sheffield) ♣ᖯ❀

Dog & Partridge L ✅

56 Trippet Lane, S1 4EL

☎ 07354 471376 ⊕ thedogsheffield.com

4 changing beers (sourced regionally; often Abbeydale, Blue Bee, Chantry) H

Behind an impressive Gilmour's brewery frontage, lies a comfortable multi-roomed pub served by a central bar. To the right of the entrance is a spacious taproom with dartboard, and on the left a smaller seating area. Behind the servery is a cosy snug with a hatch for service and a lounge at the rear which often features live music. The four changing beers are usually sourced from local breweries. A popular quiz is held Tuesday evenings.

ᗘ⊛❶ᖯ(City Hall) ♣ᖯ❀🛜

Grapes ★ L

80 Trippet Lane, S1 4EL

☎ (0114) 249 0909 ⊕ thegrapessheffield.wordpress.com

Abbeydale Moonshine; Stancill Barnsley Bitter H

Centred around a tiled corridor drinking area, the three rooms comprise a snug, lounge and pool room. The pub has been identified by CAMRA as having a nationally important historic pub interior. The sign outside reads Flynn's as a reference to the Flynn family who have owned the pub for over 40 years. It offers two cask

beers, and bar food Monday to Saturday lunchtimes. Live traditional Irish music plays in the back room six days a week, mainly folk sessions. Cash only.

⊛ᖯ(City Hall) ♣ᖯ♪

Head of Steam L ✅

103-107 Norfolk Street, S1 2JE

☎ (0114) 272 2128

Camerons Strongarm; 8 changing beers (sourced regionally; often Abbeydale, Camerons) H

A pub for some 20 years, this former bank was acquired by Cameron's brewery in 2015 and, after extensive refurbishment, reopened as part of the Head of Steam chain. Behind the imposing frontage the large single room is served by a central island bar, with a separate seating area at the rear leading on to an outside drinking area in Tudor Square. In addition to the brewer's own beers, the handpumps usually dispense beers from independent breweries in Yorkshire and the North East.

⊛❶ᕉ⇌ᖯ(Cathedral) ᖯ❀🛜 ♪

Old Shoe

Unit 20 Orchard Square, S1 2FB

☎ 07470 312505 ⊕ theoldshoebar.com

2 changing beers (often Shiny, Track, White Dog) H

Specialist cider and craft beer bar, based in a unit that used to be a shoe shop. This joint venture between the Bear on Abbeydale Road and the Cider Hole/Exemption Cider opened in 2023, with the latter relocating here. Two constantly changing cask ales are available with a beer menu, and they produce their own cider on the premises. You can order food for collection from the Sheffield Plate food court and from Proove pizza.

ᕉ⇌ᖯ(Cathedral) ♠ᖯ❀

Perch L

44 Garden Street, S1 4BJ

10 changing beers (sourced locally; often Dead Parrot) H

The taproom of the Dead Parrot brewery, featuring their beers and guests. Décor is comfortable industrial chic, including large settees. Burgers, wings and pizzas are available. A covered courtyard now hosts regular events including bands and beer festivals. The brewery is behind the bar, at the side of the courtyard. Up to 10 cask beers are served, depending on availability, and there is an extensive range of bottled beers. Identified by CAMRA as an outstanding conversion of former industrial premises.

❶ᖯᖯ(City Hall)

Red Deer L ✅

18 Pitt Street, S1 4DD

☎ (0114) 263 4000 ⊕ thereddeersheffield.co.uk

7 changing beers (sourced regionally; often Abbeydale, Black Sheep, Titanic) H

A genuine, traditional local in the heart of the city. The small frontage of the original three-roomed pub hides an open-plan interior extended to the rear with a gallery seating area. As well as the impressive range of up to eight cask beers, there is also a selection of continental bottled beers. Meals are served lunchtimes and evenings daily. A popular quiz is held Tuesday night, and an upstairs function room is available for bookings.

⊛❶ᖯ(West Street) ᖯ❀🛜 ♪

Rutland Arms L

86 Brown Street, S1 2BS

☎ (0114) 272 9003 ⊕ rutlandarmssheffield.co.uk

Blue Bee Reet Pale; 6 changing beers (sourced regionally; often Abbeydale, Blue Bee, Cloudwater) H

Occupying a corner site in the Cultural Industries Quarter and near Sheffield's main railway station, the pub has

operated as a free house since 2009. The comfortable interior provides ample seating either side of the central entrance, and the walls are covered in the pumpclips and font badges of the huge number of guest beers that have featured over the years. The beers are mostly from local and regional microbreweries. Food is served daily.
👁️❄️◑⬤🚶♿🚌(Sheffield Station) ●🚌🛒🐾📶

Sheffield Tap ★ 🄻
Platform 1B, Sheffield Station, Sheaf Street, S1 2BP
☎ (0114) 273 7558 ⊕ sheffieldtap.com
Thornbridge Jaipur; 9 changing beers (sourced nationally; often Tapped) ⊞
Opened in 2009 this was originally the first class refreshment room for Sheffield Midland Station, built in 1904. After years of neglect the main bar area has been subject of an award-winning restoration retaining many original features. It has been identified by CAMRA as having a nationally important historic pub interior. Further seating has been provided in the entrance corridor and to the right of the bar. Usually three beers are from the on-site Tapped brewery, opened in 2013 in the impressive former dining room and which can be viewed behind a glass screen. Foreign beer includes over 200 bottled beers.
Q👁️❄️🛒♿🚶♿(Sheffield Station) ●🚌🛒📶

Triple Point Brewing 🄻
178 Shoreham Street, S1 4SQ
☎ (0114) 229 4769 ⊕ triplepointbrewing.co.uk
Triple Point Gold; 3 changing beers (often Triple Point) ⊞
Impressive conversion of an industrial warehouse-type building formerly used as a carpet showroom. Opened in 2019 in the premises originally operated by the former Sentinel brewery, the brewhouse is visible from the extensive seating area. The bar has four handpumps offering a selection of the core range and seasonal beers. The food offering is from Twisted Burger. There is an extensive beer garden to the front of the building.
🛒♿🚶♿(Granville Rd) P🚌📶

Vocation & Co.
113-117 Devonshire Street, S3 7SB
☎ (0114) 241 0810
5 changing beers (often Vocation) ⊞
Formally the Old House, this pub is run by Vocation brewery from Hebden Bridge. There are seating areas either side of the entrance corridor leading into the main bar area, with table service. Burgers, chicken wings and loaded fries are available throughout the day. With five cask beers, 22 keg lines, bottled world beers, cocktails and gins, there's something to tempt everyone. Outdoor seating is available. 👁️◑♿🚶♿(West Street)🚌

Sheffield: East

Chantry Inn ★ 🄻
400 Handsworth Road, Handsworth, S13 9BZ
☎ (0114) 288 9117
Chantry New York Pale, Iron and Steel Bitter, Diamond Black Stout; 2 changing beers (sourced regionally; often Chantry) ⊞
Housed in a former ecclesiastical building dating from the 13th century, in the churchyard of St Mary's Church, this is believed to be one of only four UK pubs set in consecrated ground. Becoming the Cross Keys pub in 1804, the name was changed to the Chantry Inn in 2019 when it was taken over by the Chantry brewery of Rotherham. The three rooms, taproom, lounge and snug at the rear are served from a central bar. 🛒●🚌🛒📶

Oxbow
103 Furnace Lane, Woodhouse Mill, S13 9XD
4 changing beers (often Moor Beer, Neepsend, Wild Weather) ⊞
A micropub in a suburban area of East Sheffield. Four cask beers are offered from different (often Sheffield) breweries, and also five craft keg beer lines, plus craft beer in cans. A new permanent outdoor covered heated seating area has increased capacity. There is a fortnightly quiz evening and regular visiting food vans. Note that this is a cashless bar, cards only.
🚶(Woodhouse) 🚌(52) 🛒

Sheffield: Kelham Island

Crow Inn 🄻
35 Scotland Street, S3 7BS
☎ (0114) 201 0096 ⊕ thecrowinn.co.uk
Abbeydale Heathen; 4 changing beers (sourced nationally; often Abbeydale, Arbor) ⊞
The former Old Crown Inn, after several years as just a hotel, reopened in 2019 as a freehouse under its new name, the Crow Inn. The old pub layout is still discernible, with two comfortably furnished seating areas either side of the entrance corridor which leads to the bar area. With five handpumps and 11 keg lines, a wide range of cask and craft beers is available, together with a large spirit range including 40 malt whiskies. There are also seven hotel rooms.
🛒🚤♿♿(Cathedral) ●🚌🛒📶

Fat Cat ★
23 Alma Street, S3 8SA
☎ (0114) 249 4801 ⊕ thefatcat.co.uk
Timothy Taylor Landlord; 8 changing beers (sourced nationally; often Neepsend, Thornbridge) ⊞
Opened in 1981 this is the pub that started the real ale revolution in the area. Beers from around the country are served, occasionally including Kelham Island Pale Rider brewed by Thornbridge. Vegetarian and gluten-free dishes feature on the menu. Food is available from lunchtime to evening Monday to Friday, and until late afternoon at weekends. The walls are covered with many awards. Q👁️❄️◑♿♿(Shalesmoor)●P🚌🛒

Kelham Island Tavern 🏆 🄻
62 Russell Street, S3 8RW
☎ (0114) 272 2482
Abbeydale Moonshine; Acorn Barnsley Bitter; Blue Bee American 5 Hop; 9 changing beers (sourced nationally; often Abbeydale, Blue Bee, North Riding) ⊞
Former CAMRA National Pub of the Year and regular regional and local winner, this small gem was rescued from dereliction in 2002. Twelve handpumps dispense an impressive range of beers, always including a mild, a porter and a stout. At the rear of the L-shaped front bar area, a conservatory has been added and in the warmer months you can relax in the pub's multi award-winning beer garden. Regular folk music features.
Q👁️🛒♿(Shalesmoor) ♣🚌🛒🐾🎵

Shakespeare's Ale & Cider House 🄻
146-148 Gibraltar Street, S3 8UB
☎ (0114) 275 5959
Abbeydale Deception; RedWillow Feckless; 5 changing beers (sourced nationally; often Bad Seed, Blue Bee, North Riding) ⊞
Originally built in 1821, it reopened as a freehouse in 2011 following a refurbishment including incorporation into the pub of the archway to the rear yard. The central bar serves three rooms including the extension and there

is a further room across the corridor. The eight handpumps have featured over 6,000 different beers over the last 10 years, and up to 100 whiskies are also available. There is regular live music and beer festivals are held twice a year. ✿Ω(Shalesmoor)♣🖴❀🛜♪

Wellington ★ ⅃

1 Henry Street, S3 7EQ
☎ (0114) 249 2295
Neepsend Blonde; 4 changing beers (sourced regionally; often Neepsend, Rooster's) Ⓗ
A traditional two-roomed local opened as a free house in 1993. This Sheaf Inns group pub has been sympathetically refurbished, and the rooms are comfortably furnished and welcoming. The handpumps feature at least three Neepsend beers and up to three changing guests mainly from micros. An extensive range of malt whiskies is also on offer.
Q✿Ω(Shalesmoor)♣🖴❀

Sheffield: North

Blake Hotel ⅃

53 Blake Street, Upperthorpe, S6 3JQ
☎ (0114) 233 9336
Neepsend Blonde; 5 changing beers (sourced regionally; often Blue Bee, Neepsend) Ⓗ
This extensively restored community pub is located at the top of a steep hill (pedestrian handrails provided). It retains many Victorian features, including etched windows and mirrors. To the rear is a large decked garden. The pub has one of the largest whisky selections in Sheffield and a growing range of other spirits. No electronic games, TV or jukebox. The Blake reopened in 2010 after being closed for seven years.
Q✿Ω(Langsett)♣❀🖴(31)❀

Blind Monkey ✅

279 Whitehouse Lane, Walkley, S6 2WA
☎ (0114) 233 0015
Don Valley Atomic Blonde, Gongoozler, Go Your Own Way; 2 changing beers Ⓗ
Reopened in 2018 by the owners of Don Valley brewery after a period lying empty, an extensive renovation has been done with great care. The formally open-plan pub is split into four separate areas. Decor was obtained from a large variety of sources. Much is 'of age', little is recent. The outside area is well planned and offers a comfortable experience on sunnier days. The pub has been identified by CAMRA as an outstanding restoration.
⛾✿◖Ω(Langsett)🖴(135)

Commercial ⅃

107 Station Road, Chapeltown, S35 2XF
☎ (0114) 246 9066
Abbeydale Moonshine; 7 changing beers (sourced nationally; often Durham, Neepsend, White Rose) Ⓗ
Built in 1890 by long-closed Strout's brewery of Neepsend in Sheffield, this friendly well-established free house provides six guest beers, including a porter or stout, together with at least one real cider. A central island bar serves the games room, lounge and tap room. There is a rear outdoor area, and an upstairs function room with regular folk sessions. Beer festivals are occasionally held. Monthly tutored whisky tastings take advantage of the extensive range. No meals Sunday evening. ⛾✿◖⇌(Chapeltown)♣●🖴❀🛜♪

Gardeners Rest ⅃ ✅

105 Neepsend Lane, Neepsend, S3 8AT
☎ (0114) 272 4978 🌐 thegardenersrest.co.uk
6 changing beers (sourced nationally; often Chin Chin, Helmsley, White Rose) Ⓗ

Taken over by the Gardeners Rest Community Society in 2017 after a share issue, this friendly pub provides guest beers from independent breweries sourced nationwide. There is live music at weekends and regular beer festivals. The cosy Dram Shop includes a bar billiards table and to the rear is a conservatory leading to an eclectically decorated beer garden overlooking the River Don. Q✿♿Ω(Infirmary Road)♣🖴🖴❀♪

Raven

35 Palm Street, Walkley, S6 2XF
☎ (0114) 234 5905
6 changing beers (often Loxley) Ⓗ
A traditional family-friendly community pub with a large beer garden. Operated by the owners of the Wisewood Inn and Loxley brewery, six cask beers are offered (including four from Loxley brewery) as well as nine craft keg taps. Food comprises bar snacks such as pork pies and sausage rolls. Events include live music, open mic nights, karaoke and a weekly quiz night on Thursday.
⛾✿Ω(Bamforth Street)🖴❀♪

Wisewood Inn ⅃

539 Loxley Road, Loxley, S6 6RR
☎ (0114) 233 4310
6 changing beers (often Bradfield, Loxley, Stancill) Ⓗ
Sister pub to the Raven in nearly Walkley, the main bar has three rooms, including a pool room. Below is the cellar bar, which is available for hire, and adjacent is Loxley brewery, which commenced production in 2018. A large garden to the rear overlooks the Loxley Valley. In addition to Loxley beers, the five handpumps invariably include local beers and there are also eight keg taps. The extensive food menu includes continental sausages, pizzas and tapas. ⛾✿◖●♣P🖴❀🛜♪

Sheffield: South

Beer Engine ⅃

17 Cemetery Road, S11 8FJ
☎ (0114) 272 1356 🌐 beerenginesheffield.com
Neepsend Blonde; 5 changing beers (sourced nationally; often Arbor, Manchester, Neepsend) Ⓗ
This traditional style multi-roomed pub, cosy with a great atmosphere, reopened in 2015 following a sympathetic refurbishment. A generous choice of high-quality drinks are provided for its wide-ranging clientele. The six changing cask beers come from an interesting mix of microbreweries in Sheffield and across the country. Excellent, mainly tapas-style food is served each evening. The large beer garden has a covered heated area. ✿●●🖴❀🛜

Broadfield ⅃

452 Abbeydale Road, Nether Edge, S7 1FR
☎ (0114) 255 0200 🌐 thebroadfield.co.uk
Abbeydale Moonshine; 5 changing beers (sourced nationally; often Abbeydale, Ilkley, True North) Ⓗ
Dating from 1896, the Broadfield has established a deserved reputation for quality food served daily, with an extensive menu including hearty meat pies and home-made sausages. There are nine cask ales including beers from owners True North, and large ranges of bottled beers and whiskies. The pub, located in the city's Antiques Quarter, has a great atmosphere, and is now a leading player in the local social scene. ⛾✿◖♿🖴❀🛜

Brothers Arms ⅃

106 Well Road, Heeley, S8 9TZ
☎ (0114) 258 3544
Abbeydale Deception; 7 changing beers (sourced nationally) Ⓗ

A classic, traditional local. Although the interior is open plan, it is designed so the various areas of seating and games area all feel individual and cosy. The pub's name reflects its association with locally well known parody ukulele band The Everly Pregnant Brothers and live music is hosted every Thursday evening. The bar features eight real ales with six changing guests, together with a real cider. A quiz is held on Tuesdays. ⏰🏠♣P🚪🐾🛜🎵

Sheaf View L

25 Gleadless Road, Heeley, S2 3AA

☎ (0114) 249 6455

Neepsend Blonde; 7 changing beers (sourced regionally; often Neepsend, Pictish, Saltaire) Ⓗ

A 19th-century pub near Heeley City Farm, the Sheaf experienced a chequered history before becoming a real ale oasis after reopening as a freehouse in 2000. The walls and shelves are adorned with assorted breweriana and provide an ideal background for good drinking and conversation. A wide range of international beers, together with malt whiskies and a real cider complement the eight reasonably-priced real ales. A busy pub, especially on Sheffield United match days.

Q🏠&♣♥P🚪🐾

Sheffield: West

Beer House L

623 Ecclesall Road, Sharrow, S11 8PT

🌐 the-beer-house-172.mytoggle.io

6 changing beers (sourced nationally; often Abbeydale, Blue Bee, Neepsend) Ⓗ

Sheffield's first micropub opened in a small former shop unit in 2014 with capacity for around 40 people. The front of two rooms has level access from the street and contains the bar with its bank of six handpumps displaying a regularly changing range of beers mainly from microbreweries, with local breweries well represented. The raised back room is focused around the fireplace. There is a quiz on Wednesday evenings. Outdoor seating is available to the front and in the rear beer garden. Q⏰🏠♣🚪🐾🛜

Rising Sun L ✅

471 Fulwood Road, Nether Green, S10 3QA

☎ (0114) 230 3855 🌐 risingsunsheffield.co.uk

Abbeydale Daily Bread, Moonshine, Absolution; 7 changing beers (sourced regionally; often Blue Bee, Revolutions, Welbeck Abbey) Ⓗ

This pub is a large suburban roadhouse operated by local brewer Abbeydale. There are two comfortably furnished rooms with a log-burning fire between the main bar and the glass-roofed extension, which also has glass panels in the end wall. A range of four Abbeydale real ales are always served, with three or four guest real ales mainly from micros. Quizzes are on Sunday evenings. Q⏰🏠🍽&♣♥P🚪(120,83A)🐾🛜

Sykehouse

Old George Inn

Broad Lane, DN14 9AU (on main road, in centre of village)

☎ (01405) 785635 🌐 oldgeorgeinnsykehouse.co.uk

3 changing beers (often Sharp's, Timothy Taylor) Ⓗ

A large, characterful 200-year-old building with a spacious, open-plan bar area featuring a log-burning stove and flagstone floors, with recently refurbished furniture and fittings. There is another seating area and function room off the main bar area. Rustic oak beams abound, hinting at the building's past. A separate games room has a pool table. Outside is a camping field, patio

area, garden and ample parking. Breakfast, lunch and evening meals are served daily, with booking advisable on Sundays. ⏰🏠🍺🍽&▲♣P🚪(84B)🐾🛜🎵

Thorne

Windmill

19 Queen Street, DN8 5AA

☎ (01405) 812866

Little Critters White Wolf; Stancill Barnsley Bitter; 2 changing beers (sourced regionally; often Abbeydale, Timothy Taylor) Ⓗ

Situated on a street parallel with the main road, this friendly community pub offers up to four well-kept real ales sourced from small independent breweries. The pub has a smart lounge with a conservatory area linked by an archway to another room with a pool table. Outside there are ample drinking facilities and a garden area with play equipment. Quiz night is on a Sunday. ⏰🏠🚂(North)♣P🚪(87,88A)🐾🛜

Thrybergh

Deer Park Tap L

Deer Park Farm Complex, Doncaster Road, S65 4BH (on A630)

☎ (01709) 854440

3 changing beers (sourced regionally; often Chantry, Little Critters, Welbeck Abbey) Ⓗ

Micropub in the Deer Park Farm complex off Doncaster Road, opened in early 2022. It was created in an empty building on a site that already contained a licensed tea room and delicatessen. The three handpumps serve real ales at a competitive price, favouring local and regional microbreweries. The cosy interior is warmed by a log-burner fire and an upstairs area is accessed via a wooden staircase. Food is available daily. Q🏠🍽▲P🚪(X3)🐾

Thurlstone

Huntsman L

136 Manchester Road, S36 9QW (on main A628 through village)

☎ (01226) 764892 🌐 huntsmanthurlstone.co.uk

Black Sheep Best Bitter; Timothy Taylor Landlord; 4 changing beers (sourced nationally) Ⓗ

Friendly drinking and talking pub makes up this pub's lifeblood. Throw in old-fashioned pub games, LocAle and a seriously dog-friendly attitude, and it just shouldn't be passed by. The choice of six real ales has contributed to the Huntsman being in the Guide for 13 consecutive years. The location of this village local on a main trans-Pennine route provides an interesting mixture of regulars and passing trade. Food is served Tuesday evening and Sunday lunchtime only. There is no jukebox or TVs but Wednesday evening is live music night. Q⏰🏠🍽♣🚪(21)🐾🛜🎵

Wath upon Dearne

Wath Tap L

49 High Street, S63 7QB

☎ (01709) 872150

6 changing beers (sourced regionally; often Chin Chin, North Riding) Ⓗ

A warm welcome is guaranteed at Rotherham's first micropub, opened in 2016 in a former butcher's shop. Six changing real ales, mostly from local breweries, and five real ciders are served. These are listed on chalkboards by the bar. Food may be brought in from the surrounding takeaways. Seats at the front of the pub shelter under the original shop canopy. The pub was extended to the rear to create a separate room. Jam sessions are sometimes held and board games are available. Q&♣🖶☺🛜♪

Wentworth

George & Dragon 🅛
85 Main Street, S62 7TN (stands back from road on B6090)
☎ (01226) 742440 🌐 georgeanddragonwentworth.com
Theakston Old Peculier; Timothy Taylor Landlord; 5 changing beers (sourced locally; often Bradfield, Chantry, Geeves) 🅷
Impressive village free house, licensed since 1804, standing back from the road in the centre of the village. It offers seven real ales from local and regional brewers. There is a front patio, with a large garden and children's adventure playground at the rear. It also houses a craft shop and the Hoober Room, available for hire. Home-cooked food is served from an extensive menu, with a pop-up Pie Shop every Saturday and Sunday afternoon. Handy for historic Wentworth Woodhouse, Needle's Eye and Hoober Stand. Access is also available from the parish church behind. Q❧🕭❀❶▶P🖶(44,7)☺🛜♪

Whiston

Sitwell Park Golf Club 🅛 ✅
Shrogswood Road, S60 4BY (off A631 East Bawtry road)
☎ (01709) 792064 🌐 sitwellgolf.co.uk
4 changing beers (sourced locally; often Acorn, Welbeck Abbey, Chantry) 🅷
Private members club, founded in 1913, open to the general public. The clubhouse usually stocks four real ales, often from local microbreweries such as Chantry, Acorn and Welbeck Abbey. A range of bar meals, sandwiches and hot and cold snacks is available. There is a bar area and lounge, and two snooker tables. The sun lounge and balcony give panoramic views across the golf course and the countryside beyond. Function rooms are available. Golf Club and other local memorabilia adorn the walls. Please note Shrogswood Road is not well lit at night. ❀❶&♣P🖶(3,19,19a)♪

Worsbrough Dale

Boatman's Rest
Edmunds Road, S70 4TD
☎ (01226) 286620
Greene King IPA 🅷
A multi-roomed pub full of coal mining knick-knacks. A spacious function room to the rear is often used for private events. A narrow lounge and bar seating area are very comfortable, the latter having a roaring fire during cold weather. The Trans Pennine Trail runs by the pub. The pub is set way back from the main roads and the bottom of Edmunds Road and is well-known for its good home-cooked food. ❀❶▶♣P🖶(67)

Wortley

Wortley Men's Club 🅛
Reading Room Lane, S35 7DB (situated in the centre of the village at the back of the Wortley Arms pub)
☎ (0114) 288 2066 🌐 wortleymensclub.co.uk
Timothy Taylor Landlord; 3 changing beers (sourced locally) 🅷
This is a multiple CAMRA award-winning club with titles including local, regional, and national Club of the Year. This is the 12th consecutive year the club has been in the Guide. Show your CAMRA membership card or a copy of this Guide on entry. The club is situated in the pretty rural

village of Wortley near to Wortley Hall and gardens. The lovely building has exposed timber frames, ornate ceilings, wooden panelling and a real fire. Guest ales are sourced from local and national breweries. The club runs an annual beer festival in July. Q❀&♣●P🖶(23,23A)♪

YORKSHIRE (WEST)

Ackworth

Boot & Shoe 🅛 ✅
Wakefield Road, WF7 7DF (on A638)
☎ (01977) 610218
2 changing beers (sourced regionally; often Ossett) 🅷
A busy village pub, dating back to the late 16th century, it has been extensively refurbished but retains its original features, including the open fire iron range. This is a well established pub in the Guide. Wood-fired pizzas and sweet food are served daily. There is a quiz nights are on Thursday, with live music every Saturday. All live sporting events are shown. The large Mediterranean style beer garden includes external bar with a covered heated area for live music. ❀❶▶●P🖶☺🛜♪

Armitage Bridge

Armitage Bridge Monkey Club 🅛
Dean Brook Road, HD4 7PB
☎ 07980 897105
Abbeydale Deception; house beer (by Empire); 2 changing beers (sourced locally; often Empire) 🅷
Refurbished and air-conditioned, this thriving and friendly little club in the hamlet of Armitage Bridge serves up to two permanent and two changing guest beers: one from Empire, generally a porter, and a pale guest beer from Yorkshire. A regular local CAMRA Club of the Year, it is well worth seeking out and a great place to relax with a pint on an evening. There is a pool room upstairs. No affiliation and no membership are required. ❧❀&♣🖶🛜♻♪

Batley

Cellar Bar
51 Station Road, WF17 5SU (opp Batley rail station)
☎ (01924) 444178 🌐 thecellarbar.weebly.com
Acorn Barnsley Bitter; Kirkstall Kirkstall Bitter; Ossett Yorkshire Blonde; 1 changing beer (sourced regionally; often Acorn) 🅷
In the basement of a Grade II-listed building with fine stonework, this atmospheric bar serves well-kept ales from four handpumps. An upstairs function room seats up to 40 and has a separate bar available. There is occasional live music. The bar has a mix of comfortable seating and the area is sometimes used as a film set, with its cobbled street and heritage industrial buildings. A screen inside shows live train times. ❧❀⇌♣🖶(112,212)☺🛜♻♪

Bingley

Brown Cow 🅛 ✅
Ireland Bridge, BD16 2QX
☎ (01274) 564345 🌐 browncowbingley.com
Timothy Taylor Golden Best, Boltmaker, Knowle Spring, Landlord, Landlord Dark; 2 changing beers (sourced locally; often Timothy Taylor) 🅷
On the riverside next to a 13th-century bridge, a warm welcome awaits all at this comfortable, traditional hostelry. Although popular for dining, for those just wanting a drink, armchairs and bar-stools are present closer to the bar. The beer garden to the rear was

refurbished and extended in 2023. An extensive range of Timothy Taylor real ales and international bottled beers are offered. An upstairs room is suitable for small functions and meetings. Live music often plays on Saturday evenings and there is a Tuesday quiz night. ⛥✿◑⟡⬥≉P⊞✿🛜♫

Chip N Ern ⓛ

73 Main Street, BD16 2JA
☎ 07930 317098
7 changing beers (sourced locally; often Barker Bridge, Bingley, Darkland) Ⓗ

A popular micropub in the local real ale scene. The wood-panelled ground floor bar has a distinctive and eclectic range of decorations. Seven cask ales include a varying range from local and regional breweries. Four craft keg taps behind the bar often feature local breweries. Additional seating is available in the more modern-styled upstairs room. A folk jam night takes place on Wednesday. Close to the railway station and handy for exploring the famous Five Rise Locks on the adjacent Leeds-Liverpool Canal. Closing times may vary depending upon demand. ⛥⬥≉⊞✿🛜♫

Myrtle Grove ⓛ ✓

141 Main Street, BD16 1AJ
☎ (01274) 568637
Goose Eye Chinook Blonde; Greene King Abbot; Ruddles Best Bitter; Sharp's Doom Bar; 6 changing beers (sourced nationally; often Bridgehouse, Elland, Titanic) Ⓗ

This town centre Wetherspoon outlet, originally a cinema, comprises a large single room and retains the high ceiling. Cosy alcoves with high backed settles occupy the back wall. The pub is popular with all age groups and walkers are welcome. There are ten real ale handpulls, usually including at least six guest beers and with local breweries often represented. A cider is also offered by handpull. Bus stops are immediately adjacent to the pub and the railway station is nearby. Q⛥◑⬥≉⊞🛜

Peacock Bar ⓛ

Wellington Street, BD16 2NB (opp railway station)
☎ 07480 711643 ● peacockbar.co.uk
5 changing beers (sourced regionally; often Bingley, Vocation, Wishbone) Ⓗ

A sister pub to the Peacock Bar in Bradford, this modern basement pub, opposite the railway station, comprises a small bar area and an adjacent larger room downstairs. Up to five varying real ales are usually from local and regional breweries and can include beers from the wood. One pump is dedicated to dark beers and another often has higher ABV beers. Two rotating craft keg beers, a wheat beer, lagers and cider on keg taps plus an extensive range of bottled and canned craft beers add to the offering. Indian-style street food is available and incredibly popular. ⛥◑≉⊞✿🛜

Birkenshaw

Halfway House ⓛ

1 Whitehall Road East, BD11 2EQ (A58/A651 jct)
☎ (01274) 680614 ● thehalfwayhousepub.co.uk
Ossett White Rat; 5 changing beers (sourced regionally; often Black Sheep, Bosun's, Theakston) Ⓗ

Traditional ex-Tetley local pub with homely lounge, situated on a busy crossroads. Events include Tuesday pool, a music quiz on Thursdays and live music on Saturday evenings. Three tied and three free of tie beers are mostly from Yorkshire breweries and usually include darker styles. Available food is homemade pizzas and burgers. Cask club on Monday to Wednesday features

ales at bargain prices. Buses 254 and 255 pass the pub, with 283 and 283A under 10 minutes' walk away. ⛥✿◑⟡⬥P⊞(254,255) ✿🛜♫

Birstall

Black Bull ⓛ ✓

5 Kirkgate, WF17 9HE (off A652 near jct of A643)
☎ (01274) 865609
Black Sheep Best Bitter; Ossett White Rat; 2 changing beers (sourced nationally; often Acorn, Bradfield, Timothy Taylor) Ⓗ

A stone-built 17th-century community pub that has been important through the centuries. The upper room was used as a local Magistrate's Court in times gone by, and is still preserved and used for functions. On the ground floor is a snug, a main bar area and a side room. There is an open fire in the winter amid comfortable, traditional surroundings while behind is a car park and a tidy beer garden. Traditional board games are available, with free pool on Wednesdays. An ale club is on Monday. ⛥✿⬥P⊞(200,283) ✿↺♫

Bradford

Boar & Fable

30 North Parade, BD1 3HZ
● boarandfable.com
3 changing beers (sourced regionally; often Vocation, Wilde Child, Wishbone) Ⓗ

Opened in 2020, this small, stylish and comfortable bar gets its name from the legend of a ferocious boar that lived in the woods where Bradford now stands. It comprises a ground-floor room, with additional seating in a basement area. Three handpulls serve a varying range of usually locally-sourced real ales. Nine keg taps offer an additional selection of beers, often including a dark beer and a sour. An extensive selection of bottled and canned beers is stocked. ⛥≉(Forster Square) ⊞✿🛜♫

Corn Dolly ⓨ ⓛ

110 Bolton Road, BD1 4DE
☎ (01274) 720219 ● corndolly.pub
Abbeydale Moonshine; Moorhouse's White Witch; Timothy Taylor Boltmaker; 5 changing beers (sourced regionally; often Bridgehouse, Durham, Pictish) Ⓗ

Award-winning traditional freehouse run by the same family since 1989. Close to the city centre and Forster Square railway station. Previously called the Wharfe, due to its location near to the former Bradford canal, it first opened its doors in 1834. An open-plan layout incorporates a games area to one end. Good-value food served Thursday and Friday lunchtimes. It has a friendly atmosphere and is popular before Bradford City matches. A large collection of pumpclips adorns the beams. ✿◑⬥≉(Forster Square) ⟡P⊞(640,641) ↺♫

Exchange Craft Beer House ⓛ

14 Market Street, BD1 1LH
☎ (01274) 306078 ● exchangecraftbeer.co.uk
6 changing beers (sourced regionally; often Craven, Nightjar, Verdant) Ⓗ

Under the Victorian splendour of the Wool Exchange building, this cellar bar has a light and airy feel. Open-plan with a large seating area and bar under a brick barrel ceiling with a smaller raised seating area near the entrance. Six handpulls usually feature at least one real ale from owner, Nightjar brewery, plus others from local and regional breweries, or further afield, in a variety of styles from light to dark. Real cider and pies are also available. ⛥◗≉(Forster Square) ⟡⊞✿🛜♫

WEST YORKSHIRE

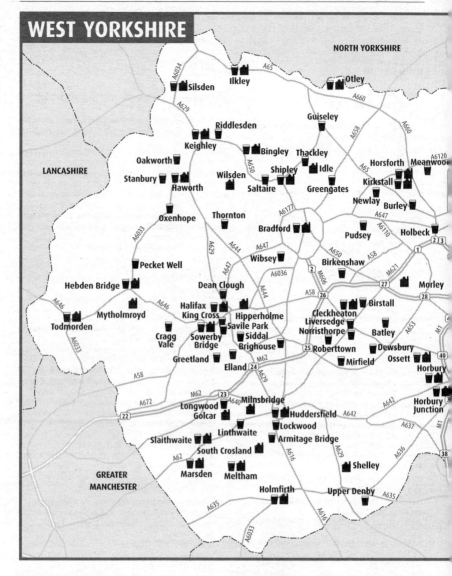

NORTH YORKSHIRE

LANCASHIRE

GREATER
MANCHESTER

Silsden · Ilkley · Otley · Guiseley · Riddlesden · Keighley · Bingley · Thackley · Horsforth · Meanwoo · Oakworth · Shipley · Idle · Kirkstall · Stanbury · Wilsden · Greengates · Newlay · Burley · Haworth · Saltaire · Pudsey · Holbeck · Oxenhope · Thornton · Bradford · Wibsey · Birkenshaw · Pecket Well · Morley · Hebden Bridge · Dean Clough · Birstall · Halifax · King Cross · Hipperholme · Cleckheaton · Batley · Mytholmroyd · Savile Park · Liversedge · Dewsbury · Todmorden · Cragg Vale · Sowerby Bridge · Siddal · Norristhorpe · Ossett · Greetland · Brighouse · Roberttown · Mirfield · Horbury · Elland · Horbury Junction · Longwood · Milnsbridge · Golcar · Huddersfield · Slaithwaite · Lockwood · Linthwaite · Armitage Bridge · Shelley · South Crosland · Marsden · Meltham · Holmfirth · Upper Denby

Fighting Cock L

21-23 Preston Street, BD7 1JE (close to Grattans, off Thornton Rd)
☎ (01274) 726907

Timothy Taylor Boltmaker, Landlord; Theakston Old Peculier; 5 changing beers (sourced nationally; often Blue Monkey, MBH Beer, Phoenix) ⊞

Drinkers' paradise in an industrial area, this multi-award winning traditionally-styled freehouse is 20 minutes' walk from the city centre and close to bus routes along Thornton Road and Legrams Lane. Its unpretentious feel appeals to a wide variety of people from loyal locals to well-travelled real ale enthusiasts. Up to eight real ales usually include at least one dark beer. Keg beers, ciders and foreign bottled beers are also offered. The jukebox has an extensive and eclectic choice of music. Good-value lunches are served Monday to Saturday. There is a large beer garden opposite the pub. ❀⑬🖪🏠🐾🛜ひ♪

Jacob's Well L

5 Kent Street, BD1 5RL (by Jacobs Well roundabout at end of Hall Ings)
☎ (01274) 395628 ⊕ jacobs-well.co.uk

Abbeydale Deception; Half Moon Dark Masquerade; Sunbeam Bright Day; 3 changing beers (sourced regionally; often Bingley, Craven, Torrside) ⊞

Traditionally-styled real ale and cider freehouse, dating from 1811, formerly known as Jacob's Beer House. The open-plan layout has a rustic feel, with a snug to the side of the bar. Nine handpulls offer a varying range of six real ales from local and regional independents and up to three real ciders from local producers. Numerous boxed ciders and perries are also available. Eight keg taps offer a range of European beers and a cider. The handmade pies include some interesting fillings. Sit outside and watch the city bustle while supping good ale.
❀⑬≉(Interchange) ●🖪🐾🛜ひ♪

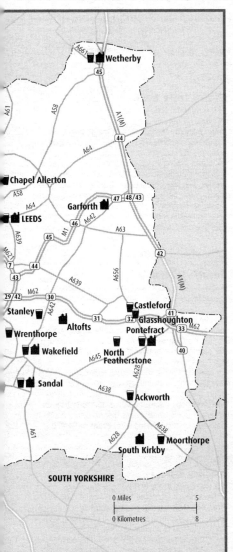

Multi-award winning modern café-style bar located in the city's independent quarter selling ale, vinyl and ham! Four handpulls serve constantly changing real ales sourced regionally in varying styles and including a dark beer. Real cider and perry are offered. Nine craft keg beers, many from independent brewers, are on tap. Food is offered in a charcuterie style specialising in hams and cheeses from Spain. In the upstairs mezzanine area, it is possible to purchase vinyl records. Payment by card only. 🍽️🏮🌳🕭(Forster Square) ●🚇♣️🐕🛜🔁

Brighouse

Crafty Fox L
44 Commercial Street, HD6 1AQ
☎ 07847 205425 ⊕ craftyfox.bar
6 changing beers (sourced nationally; often Church End, Salopian, Vocation) 🅗
A family-run bar on the main shopping street, with a back door opening into Brighouse bus station. The industrial-style interior has wood-panelled walls, pallet tables and stools. The upstairs room has similar decor and is available for private functions and meetings. Blind beer tastings are organised once a month, and live acts and a quiz are hosted weekly. Open Wednesday to Sunday. 🏮🕭🚇🐕🛜🔁♪

Market Tavern L
2 Ship Street, HD6 1JX
☎ (01484) 769852
6 changing beers (sourced nationally; often Abbeydale, Neepsend, Salopian) 🅗
Micropub in a single-storey former pork pie factory next to the canalside open-air market. It has comfortable seating in the bar, a small snug by the entrance and a sheltered outside drinking area. At least one dark beer and two changing real ciders are on sale at all times. Snacks are available for customers and their dogs. Open Wednesday to Sunday and bank holiday Mondays. Q🏮🐕🕭●🚇🐕🛜

Castleford

Glass Blower ✓
15 Bank Street, WF10 1JD (rear access from Aire St car parks, off road by Allinson flour mill)
☎ (01977) 520390
Greene King Abbot; Ruddles Best Bitter; Sharp's Doom Bar; 4 changing beers (often Acorn, Bradfield, Leeds) 🅗
Characterful former post office converted by Wetherspoon. Four guest beers are available, usually including one dark and one special from microbrewers. The name refers to the town's history of glass bottle making, with some examples on display. Locally born sculptor Henry Moore is represented via reproductions adorning the walls. It is a popular venue for families and rugby fans on match days. Regular Meet the Brewer events and brewery visits are arranged. Children are welcome in the family area. 🏮🏮🍽️🐕🕭🚇🛜

Junction L
Carlton Street, WF10 1EE (enter Castleford on A655, pub is on corner with Carlton St at top of town centre)
☎ (01977) 277750 ⊕ thejunctionpubcastleford.com
Daleside Bitter 🅗; Old Mill Traditional Bitter 🅗/🅖; Stancill Blonde; 6 changing beers (sourced locally; often Half Moon) 🅗
This rejuvenated pub specialises in beers from the landlord's own wooden casks. Up to six changing guest ales are available in the wood from enterprising local brewers. The large L-shaped bar is kept warm with open

Lord Clyde L
86 Thornton Road, BD1 2DG (On B6145)
☎ (01274) 371848
5 changing beers (often Kirkby Lonsdale, Ossett, Stancill) 🅗
On the edge of the city centre, this pub has a 'village local' atmosphere. Originally multi-roomed, it has been opened out, with comfortable leather seating throughout. There is a lounge to the left of the entrance and a games room to the right. Five handpulls offer a varying range of real ales, usually from local and regional breweries. The large beer garden to the rear is popular in good weather. Sports TV, on multiple screens, is a key feature. 🏮🕭(Forster Square)♣️🚇🛜🔁

Record Café
45-47 North Parade, BD1 3JH
☎ (01274) 723143 ⊕ therecordcafe.co.uk
4 changing beers (sourced regionally; often Big Trip, North Riding, Wishbone) 🅗

fires and a stove-heated snug can be used for functions. Folk afternoons are on the last Sunday of the month. Dog friendly. Handily situated for both the bus and railway stations. Q☆≠♣₽🌸🛜ੳ

Cleckheaton

Mill Valley Brewery Tap 🄻
Woodroyd Mills, South Parade, BD19 3AF
☎ 07565 229560 ⊕ millvalleybrewery.co.uk
Mill Valley Luddite Ale, Panther Ale, Yorkshire Bitter, Mill Blonde; 2 changing beers (sourced locally; often Mill Valley) 🄷
This brewery tap, tucked away in a courtyard, opens alternate Thursdays for comedy nights and other events, plus every Friday, Saturday and Sunday. Beers are of a range of styles from the nearby Mill Valley brewery, together with gins, spirits, wines and cider. Frequent live acts include popular comedy performers (first Thu) and music acts (mainly Sat), and there is a Sunday quiz. The adjoining café serves a useful range of meals and tempting snacks. ☆🕙♣₽➡(200,254)🌸🛜♪

Cragg Vale

Robin Hood 🄻
Cragg Road, HX7 5SQ (on B6138 1½ miles S of Mytholmroyd)
☎ (01422) 885899
Timothy Taylor Boltmaker, Landlord; 1 changing beer (sourced regionally; often Church End, Goose Eye, Small World) 🄷
Friendly, welcoming traditional split-level free house in a beautiful wooded valley and situated on the longest continuous hill climb in England, which is popular with competitive cyclists. There are also excellent walks nearby. On entering, the cosy bar – with a real fire in winter – is to the right and the larger dining room is to the left. Food is served Wednesday to Sunday. Two Timothy Taylor beers are complemented by a guest beer from regional breweries. Q☆🕙◑▲➡(900,901)🌸🛜ੳ

Dewsbury

Shepherd's Boy 🄻
157 Huddersfield Road, WF13 2RP (on A644 ½ mile W of town)
☎ (01924) 454116
Ossett Butterley, Yorkshire Blonde, White Rat, Silver King; 2 changing beers (sourced regionally; often Ossett, Vocation) 🄷
A trademark brick arch separates four comfortable drinking areas in this fine, friendly community pub, the reconstruction by Ossett brewery of a former Webster's pub. The hidden beer garden behind and below the pub is fine for summer days. Monday is poker night, Thursday is quiz night with food. Home-made snacks are sometimes sold. Ossett seasonal specials and independent guests are often available, in a range of styles. 🕸♣₽➡(202,203)🌸🛜ੳ♪

West Riding Refreshment Rooms 🄻
Dewsbury Railway Station, Wellington Road, WF13 1HF
☎ (01924) 459193
Timothy Taylor Landlord; Vocation Heart & Soul; 7 changing beers (sourced nationally; often Black Sheep, Vocation) 🄷
Located in the Grade II-listed former waiting rooms on Dewsbury station, this multi-award winning pub celebrated its 30th anniversary in 2024. The 10 handpumps dispense a range of well-kept real ales and

an occasional real cider. Lunches are served daily and pizzas are available until evening. Live music plays on some weekends throughout the year. Parking is in the railway station car parks. 🕸🕙🕭≠♣🚌₽🌸🛜ੳ♪

Elland

Elland Craft & Tap 🄻
102 Southgate, HX5 0EP
☎ (01422) 370630 ⊕ craftandtap.co.uk
House beer (by Millstone); 4 changing beers (sourced regionally; often Goose Eye, Blue Bee, Nightjar) 🄷
A community hub next to the market square, renowned for its friendly, convivial atmosphere. A converted bank with taproom and bar and a lower lounge area, is popular with locals, visitors and CAMRA members. There is always one bitter and one dark beer on handpull, plus the house ale from the local Millstone brewery. It has floral displays in summer and a private room upstairs for hire. Quiz night is Wednesday. Q☆🕙🕸🕭🚌₽(501,X1)🌸🛜

Glasshoughton

George V WMC 🄻
Holywell House, 124 Front Street, WF10 4RN (on A639 at roundabout with Holywell Ln B6136)
☎ (01977) 552775
Old Mill Traditional Bitter; 2 changing beers (sourced regionally; often Black Sheep, Old Mill, Ossett) 🄷
CAMRA members showing their cards can be signed-in at this popular and comfortable working men's club. The club has a large concert room and a bar lounge. Events are held most nights of the week include live entertainment Friday and Saturday. At the rear is a large, secure children's play area. The bar prices represent extremely good value. The club is an ambassador for Castleford Tigers which means that tickets for home matches can be purchased here. ☆🕸🕭♣₽🛜♪

Greengates

Cracker Barrel
832 Harrogate Road, BD10 0RA
Tetley Bitter; 4 changing beers (sourced regionally; often Daleside, Harrogate, Sunbeam) 🄷
Small, friendly, family-run micropub comprising a single room with the bar positioned to the right-hand side. It has a cosy, homely feel. In addition to the regular Tetley Bitter, a further four handpulls serve an ever-varying range of real ales, often including a dark beer, from regional breweries. The outside seating to the front is next to a busy main road. The small, secluded beer garden to the rear is much quieter. Family and dog friendly. ☆🕸₽🌸🛜ੳ

Greetland

Greetland Social Club 🄻
222 Rochdale Road, HX4 8JE
☎ (01422) 372966
2 changing beers (sourced regionally; often Goose Eye, Vocation) 🄷
A community-based social club open seven days a week with welcoming atmosphere, always offering two rotating real ales from local and regional breweries. The club is open to the public and members receive beer discounts. It consists of a lounge, games room with two snooker tables and function room that hosts regular music, open mic, comedy and charity events. There is an outside drinking shelter and buses stop outside the door. Local CAMRA Club of the Year 2023. 🕸♣🚌🌸🛜ੳ♪

Guiseley

Coopers L

4-6 Otley Road, LS20 8AH

☎ (01943) 878835

Hawkshead Windermere Pale; Theakston Best Bitter; 4 changing beers (sourced locally; often Kirkstall, MBH Beer, Theakston) Ⓗ

Modern-style bar converted from a former Co-op store. There is a main bar area, separate dining area and upstairs function room. Up to six cask beers are served, generally from Yorkshire or northern breweries. There is a dark beer in the winter months and large selection of other beers on tap and in bottles and cans. The large upstairs function room has occasional music events and a monthly comedy club and this area also serves as extra dining space. Asian street food is served. Card payment only. ➳❀◗◖ὠ⇌🖳❀🛜🎵

Guiseley Factory Workers Club L

6 Town Street, LS20 9DT

☎ (01943) 874793 ⊕ guiseleyfactoryworkersclub.co.uk

Black Sheep Best Bitter; 2 changing beers (sourced locally; often Acorn, Black Sheep, Craven) Ⓗ

Multi-award winning, three-roomed club founded over 100 years ago by the Yeadon and Guiseley Factory Workers Union. The bar serves both the lounge and the concert room and has changing guest ales sourced both locally and nationally. There is a snooker room with TV lounge and a large beer garden with lawn and stone-flagged patio. Occasional concerts are held at weekends. The club hosts many local clubs and organisations. CAMRA members are welcome with this Guide or a membership card. ❀⇌♣♿🅿🖳(27,34)❀🛜🎵

Halifax: Dean Clough

Stod Fold Dean Clough L

Dean Clough Mills, HX3 5AX

☎ (01422) 355600 ⊕ stodfolddeanclough.co.uk

Stod Fold Gold, West APA, Dark Porter, Dr Harris; 3 changing beers (sourced locally; often Stod Fold) Ⓗ

A sympathetically restored, industrial chic bar tucked just inside the architecturally significant Dean Clough Mills. Seven handpumps serve five core Stod Fold Brewing Company beers, plus seasonal beers from its brewery. Food is provided by the Stod Fold Yorkshire Kitchen, with a range of meals and snacks. There are monthly comedy nights, live music planned for Sundays and a monthly supper club. The outside seating area has heaters for cooler days. The bar recently expanded into the adjacent unit, offering private functions. ➳❀◗◖ὠ🖳❀🛜🎵

Halifax: King Cross

Wainhouse Tavern L ✓

Upper Washer Lane, Pye Nest, HX2 7DR (via Edwards Rd off Pye Nest Rd; buses to Pye Nest or King Cross)

☎ (01422) 339998

House beer (by Rudgate); 5 changing beers (sourced regionally; often Mallinsons, Rooster's, Rudgate) Ⓗ

Formerly home to the industrialist JE Wainhouse, famous for his elegant tower nearby, this pub became the Royal Hotel in the 1960s and acquired freehold status in 2014 as the Wainhouse Tavern. It boasts interesting architectural and decorative features and comprises a comfortable lower lounge bar at the front and a larger bar behind with pub games area and plenty of seating at tables. A good selection of beers is available, with home-cooked meals served most evenings and at weekends. ➳❀◗◖♣🅿🖳(579,586) ❀🛜🎵

REAL ALE BREWERIES

Anthology ✦ Leeds
Barker Bridge Bradford
Barker's South Crosland
BEEspoke ▤ Shipley
Bingley ✦ Wilsden
Bini ✦ Leeds
Bone Idle Idle
Bosun's ✦ Wetherby
Bridgehouse Keighley
Briggs Signature Huddersfield
Briscoe's Otley (brewing suspended)
Chevin Otley
Chin Chin South Kirkby
Cobbydale ▤ Silsden
Cooper Hill Leeds
Darkland Halifax
DMC ✦ Wakefield
Eagles Crag ✦ Todmorden
Empire Slaithwaite
Farmers Haworth
Fernandes ▤ Wakefield
Frisky Bear ✦ Leeds: Morley
Goose Eye ✦ Bingley
Halifax Steam ▤ Hipperholme
Henry Smith ▤ Pontefract
Hogs Head ▤ Sowerby Bridge
Horbury ▤ Horbury
Horsforth ✦ Leeds: Horsforth
Ilkley Ilkley
Kirkstall ✦ Leeds: Kirkstall
Legitimate Industries Leeds
Linfit Huddersfield
Lords Golcar

Luddite ▤ Horbury Junction
Magic Rock ✦ Huddersfield
Mallinsons Huddersfield
Meanwood ✦ Leeds
Mill Valley ✦ Cleckheaton
Milltown Milnsbridge
Morton Collins ▤ Sandal
Nightjar Mytholmroyd
Nook ▤ Holmfirth
North ✦ Leeds
Northern Monk ✦ Leeds
Ossett ✦ Ossett
Quirky ✦ Leeds: Garforth
Rat ▤ Huddersfield
Riverhead ▤ Marsden
Salt ▤ Shipley
Saltaire ✦ Shipley
Shadow ✦ Otley
Small World Shelley
Stod Fold Halifax
Stubbee ✦ Bradford
Sunbeam Leeds
Tarn 51 ▤ Altofts
Three Fiends Meltham
Tigertops Wakefield
Timothy Taylor Keighley
Truth Hurts ✦ Leeds: Morley
Vocation Hebden Bridge
Wetherby ✦ Wetherby
Wharfedale ▤ Ilkley
Wilde Child ✦ Leeds
Wishbone ✦ Keighley
Zapato ✦ Marsden

Halifax: Savile Park

Big Six ★ L

10 Horsfall Street, HX1 3HG (adjacent to Spring Edge Park at the top of Free School Ln)
☎ 07878 854447 ⊕ linktr.ee/bigsixinnhalifax
Old Mill Traditional Bitter; 4 changing beers (sourced regionally; often Brass Castle, Phoenix, Wensleydale) Ⓗ

A hidden gem in a row of terraces, with several cosy fireplaces and original features, this welcoming pub majors on good beer, real cider and conversation. Identified by CAMRA as having a regionally important historic pub interior, it has a through corridor separating the bar and games room from the two lounges. The pub's name derives from a mineral water company that operated here a century ago, whose memorabilia adorn the walls. A generously-sized garden is situated behind the pub. ♿❀♣♠🚌(577)♥↻

Halifax: Siddal

Cross Keys L

3 Whitegate, HX3 9AE
☎ (01422) 300348 ⊕ crosskeyshalifax.co.uk
8 changing beers (sourced regionally; often Wensleydale, Wilde Child, Goose Eye) Ⓗ

This 17th-century tavern has a real traditional feel. A snug beside the bar opens up to a much larger room with a central inglenook fireplace which is particularly cosy in winter. A smaller room behind the bar is ideal for small groups and for meetings. Live music is often featured on Sunday afternoons. Walkers and cyclists are always welcome. There is a large, heated, covered outdoor area often used for events including the annual beer and music festival on the second weekend of August. Local, CAMRA Pub of the Year 2023. ❀♣P🚌(541,542)♥🎵

Halifax: Town Centre

Dukes L

16-18 Market Arcade, HX1 1NX
☎ 07305 100054
4 changing beers (sourced nationally; often Anthology, Atom, Northern Monk) Ⓗ

Located within a Victorian arcade, this popular microbar serves four real ales and one real cider, all from handpumps. A wide range of keg and bottled beers is available. High and low-level seating is provided over two floors. Outdoor benches and tables are in the arcade. Hot sauces, modern art and various merchandise are available to buy. Various events are held throughout the year including beer festivals, poetry readings and makers markets. Card payments only. ♿❀♣♠●🚌♥🎵

København L

6 Westgate Arcade, HX1 1DJ
⊕ kobenhavn.beer
6 changing beers (sourced nationally; often Arbor, Marble, Vocation) Ⓗ

A spacious, minimalist, Scandinavian-style bar that opened in Westgate Arcade in central Halifax in 2019. It has three tiered seating areas plus a covered outdoor drinking space in the arcade itself. Six beers are served on handpump, always including a dark brew, and there are also 24 keg lines in a wide range of styles. A private function room is available upstairs. ♿❀♿🚆🚌♥↻

Meandering Bear L

21-23 Union Street, HX1 1PR
☎ 07807 136520 ⊕ meanderingbear.co.uk
5 changing beers (sourced nationally; often Wishbone, Neptune, Torrside) Ⓗ

This modern bar is located close to Halifax Piece Hall and Westgate Arcade in the town centre. Its name is derived from a large bear that escaped from Halifax Zoo in 1913. The classy interior incorporates comfortable seating and is split level, with the bar on a higher level. Five beers are provided on handpull, one usually dark, and there are seven keg lines. Locally sourced/made bar food is available. Occasional beer festivals and Meet the Brewer nights are held. ◖🚆🚌♥🎵

Three Pigeons ★ L ✅

1 Sun Fold, South Parade, HX1 2LX
☎ (01422) 347001
Ossett Butterley, Yorkshire Blonde, White Rat, Silver King; 4 changing beers (sourced regionally) Ⓗ

A striking octagonal drinking lobby forms the hub from which five distinctive rooms radiate in this Art Deco pub, built in 1932 by Websters brewery. Sensitively refurbished and maintained by Ossett brewery, this venue attracts a variety of local groups and societies along with football and rugby enthusiasts. Four Ossett beers are always available. Four guest beers also feature, which usually include a stout or a porter. Q❀🚆♣P🚌♥↻

Upper George L ✅

Crown Street, HX1 1TT (front entrance off Cheapside, down Upper George Yard; can also be accessed via passage between shops in Crown St)
☎ (01422) 353614
Greene King IPA; 7 changing beers (sourced nationally; often Acorn, Kirkstall) Ⓗ

A town-centre pub, in a historic building, with a friendly atmosphere and knowledgeable staff. The recently-refurbished interior retains traditional design and features, with several rooms around a central bar area and large outdoor courtyard. This northern outpost of Suffolk-based Greene King always offers one of the brewery's beers, plus seven changing beers usually sourced regionally, including a porter or stout. Half a dozen large TV screens show sport and there is a separate pool room. Live rock bands play on Saturday. ❀🚆♣●🚌♥🎵

Victorian Craft Beer Café 🍷 L

18-22 Powell Street, HX1 1LN
⊕ victorian.beer
9 changing beers (sourced nationally; often Arbor, Bristol Beer Factory, Vocation) Ⓗ

A multi-award winning bar, situated close to the Victoria Theatre, celebrating its 10th anniversary this year. With wooden floors throughout and varying rooms, it has recently been extended again. Offering 28 beers on draught, including nine on cask, and a selection of Belgian and world beers, it has become famous for its annual Back in Black Festival where it swaps all draught lines to dark beers. Local CAMRA Pub of the Year 2024. Q♿🚆🚌♥↻🎵

Vocation & Co Halifax L

13-17 Alexandra Street, HX1 1BS
☎ (01422) 252149
Vocation Bread & Butter, Heart & Soul; 5 changing beers (sourced locally; often Vocation) Ⓗ

Popular town-centre bar owned by Vocation brewery. It features a ground-floor taproom with seven cask and 18 keg lines. On the second floor is the Projectionist Bar with one cask and six keg lines. There is also an attractive roof terrace with four keg lines, seasonal spritz menu and a range of cocktails. Freshly prepared New York-style pizzas are served on the premises. A range of canned beers are available. ♿❀◖🚆🚌♥🎵

Haworth

Fleece Inn L ✓

67 Main Street, BD22 8DA
☎ (01535) 642172 ⊕ fleeceinnhaworth.co.uk
Timothy Taylor Golden Best, Boltmaker, Knowle Spring, Landlord, Landlord Dark; 1 changing beer (often Timothy Taylor) Ⓗ
A stone-built coaching inn on Haworth's famous cobbled Main Street, with spectacular views over the Worth Valley and close to the KWVR historic heritage railway. A cosy room to the right and a lower-level dining area offer quiet alternatives to the busy bar. Locally sourced food and accommodation are offered, and breakfast is available to all. The beer garden is three storeys up from the bar, on the roof. A Timothy Taylor tied house, popular with tourists and locals alike. ⏰✿🍺🅍♿🅰🎐🚗🐾📶

Hebden Bridge

Drink L

15 Market Street, HX7 6EU
☎ (01422) 844366
3 changing beers (sourced regionally; often Brew York, North, Vocation) Ⓗ
Specialist bottle shop and sampling room with small bar to the rear and an upstairs lounge. Three handpumps dispense a range of rotating pale and hoppy beers from independent northern breweries, with one handpump in the winter mainly dedicated to dark beers. Real cider is also available. The decor is minimalist with works from local artists exhibited. A wide range of bottled beers and real cider can be consumed on and off the premises. Customers are welcome to bring in their own food. ⏰🎐🚗🐾📶🕒♫

Fox & Goose L

7 Heptonstall Road, HX7 6AZ (at traffic lights on jct of A646 and Heptonstall Rd)
☎ (01422) 648052 ⊕ foxandgoose.org
Pictish Brewers Gold; 5 changing beers (sourced nationally; often Eagles Crag, Torrside, Wishbone) Ⓗ
West Yorkshire's first community co-operative pub extends a warm welcome to locals and visitors alike. A single bar serves three different rooms and an upstairs covered, heated beer garden. The main bar is warmed by a real fire in winter while the room to the left exhibits the work of local artists and often hosts live music. The snug to the right has a dartboard. At least one vegan beer and one dark beer are usually available. A former local CAMRA Pub of the Year. Q✿🅰♣🍺🚗🚌(590,592) 🐾📶♫

Nightjar L

New Road, HX7 8AD
☎ (01422) 713015 ⊕ nightjarhebden.co.uk
Nightjar Lost In Ikea; 2 changing beers (sourced nationally; often Blackedge, Bristol Beer Factory, Nailmaker) Ⓗ
Opened in 2017 in the listed Picture House building, this compact micropub is the tap for the Mytholmroyd-based Nightjar Brew Co. It serves three real ales, often two from its own brewery and a guest from another small independent. A range of craft keg beers is also available. Stripped-back brick walls and a flagstone floor offset the tiny brick-built bar and unusual split olivewood tables. There are additional tables and seating on the pavement outside. ⏰✿🎐♣🍺🚗🐾📶

Old Gate Bar & Restaurant L

1-5 Old Gate, HX7 8JP
☎ (01422) 843993 ⊕ oldgatehebden.co.uk

Timothy Taylor Landlord; Vocation Bread & Butter; 6 changing beers (sourced nationally; often Marble, Rooster's, Thornbridge) Ⓗ
This smart, modern and popular bar serves quality food all day in the bar and upstairs restaurant. A striking copper-topped bar serves two regular and six rotating real ales, one always a dark. Disabled access to each level of the split-level bar area is via separate doors off the patio fronting the pub. The large windows provide good views for people-watching from armchairs, benches and sofas. Regular and frequent bus services pass along the road outside. ⏰✿🅍♿🅰🎐🚌🚗🐾📶🕒

Holmfirth

Nook (Rose & Crown) L ✓

7 Victoria Square, HD9 2DN (down alley behind Kirkwood charity shop)
☎ (01484) 682373 ⊕ thenookbrewhouse.co.uk
Nook Baby Blond, SIPA, Best, Blond, Oat Stout; 4 changing beers (often Nook) Ⓗ
The Nook, properly the Rose & Crown, dates from 1754, and is a legendary real ale pub in the village. Owned and run by the Roberts family for two generations, it has been dispensing beers from its own adjacent brewhouse since 2009, alongside a real cider. Home-cooked food is served Friday to Sunday. There is a popular folk evening, usually held on the first Sunday of the month. Real ale festivals are held on the weekend before Easter and on the August bank holiday. The log fire is particularly warming on cold winter nights. ⏰✿🍺🅍♣🍴🚗🐾📶🕒♫

Horbury

Boons Horbury ✓

6 Queen Street, WF4 6LP (in town centre off B6128 Horbury to Ossett road, opp Co-op)
☎ (01924) 280442
Timothy Taylor Landlord; 6 changing beers (sourced nationally; often Abbeydale, Chantry) Ⓗ
This popular community pub located in the centre of town just off the High Street attracts people of all ages. The interior is based on a traditional layout around a central bar with Rugby League memorabilia on the walls. A sizeable outdoor drinking area is well used in summer. A guest cider is availabke and there is a beer festival on the first weekend in June. ✿🅰♣🍺🚗🐾📶

Cricketers Arms

22 Cluntergate, WF4 5AG (Cluntergate is a right fork off the High Street at its lower end)
☎ (01924) 261263
Timothy Taylor Landlord; 6 changing beers (sourced regionally; often Abbeydale, RedWillow, White Rabbit) Ⓗ
On the edge of the town centre this former Melbourne/ Tetley's house is now a genuine free house and winner of several local CAMRA awards. A poker night is held on Monday, a quiz night on Wednesday and meat raffle on Friday. Open mic night is on the second Sunday of each month and live music on the last Sunday. It also stocks a range of craft, keg and gluten-free beers. Q⏰✿🎐♣🍺P🚗🐾📶🕒♫

Horbury Junction

Calder Vale Hotel L

Millfield Rd, WF4 5EB (from main A642 road follow signage through housing estate to Horbury Junction industrial area; pedestrian access from canal side via tubular bridge)

☎ (01924) 277658
House beer (by Luddite); 6 changing beers (sourced locally; often Luddite) Ⓗ
Established in 1874 this lovingly restored Victorian Commercial Hotel is steeped in local industrial history. Reopened in 2019, it is home to the Luddite brewery, and has already been voted Yorkshire's dog-friendliest pub. It boasts Yorkshire stone floors and log-burning fires. There is a delightful garden and nearby canal walks. It hosts street food weekends and occasional entertainment in an upstairs room.
Q ⌂ ❧ ⊛ ① & ♣ ● P � ❀ ♫

Horsforth

Granville's Beer & Gin House Ⓛ
24 Long Row, LS18 5AA
☎ (0113) 258 2661 ● granvilleshouse.co.uk
5 changing beers (sourced locally; often Vocation, Wilde Child) Ⓗ
Former shop unit, now long and relatively narrow one-room pub, with the bar separating front and rear areas, the latter giving access to further covered seating outside. There are also a couple of tables out the front. The décor is eclectic; doors decorate one wall, panelling another, bare brick yet another, while the floor is part tiled, part parquet. The inner front door handle is a repurposed pump handle. Children are allowed until early evening. Closed on Mondays in winter.
⌂ ⊛ ⊟ ❀ ♥

Huddersfield

County Beerhouse ☝ ✅
4 Princess Street, HD1 2TT
☎ (01484) 959722
Timothy Taylor Landlord; 5 changing beers (sourced regionally; often Little Critters, Vocation) Ⓗ
The County is now run by Beerhouses. Freshly refurbished in a contemporary style with an Art Deco twist, it retains the original bar and coving partitions. Magnet windows and a John Smiths exterior lamp are retained as a cheeky nod to previous ownership. Six handpumps dispense beers sourced from Yorkshire, mainly from micros, and there are five craft keg lines. There is a rear function room, and the pub is handy for a drink after an event in Huddersfield Town Hall. Occasional food events also take place. Local CAMRA Pub of the Year 2024. ⌂ ⊛ ⊟ ❀ ♥ ♫

Grove Ⓛ
2 Spring Grove Street, HD1 4BP
☎ (01484) 318325 ● thegrove.pub
Kirkstall Pale Ale; Oakham Citra; Thornbridge Jaipur; Vocation Bread & Butter; 6 changing beers (sourced regionally; often Mallinsons, Marble) Ⓗ
The Grove has a style of its own, expressed through its eye-catching artwork. A veritable drinkers' paradise with 10 handpulled ales taking in the full range of styles and strengths. Featured breweries always include Kirkstall, Mallinsons, Marble, Oakham, Thornbridge and Vocation. Two craft ciders are always available and there is a superb menu of over 20 craft kegs, 100+ bottled and canned beers and a comprehensive spirits range. The Grove is also famed for its live bands and quirky snacks. It is a must for visitors to Huddersfield.
Q ⌂ ❧ & ≢ ♣ ● ⊟ ❀ ♥ ♫

Head of Steam Ⓛ
St George's Square, HD1 1JF (in station buildings, on right when exiting station)
☎ (01484) 454533

Camerons Strongarm, Road Crew; Timothy Taylor Dark Mild; Vocation Bread & Butter; house beer (by Camerons); 9 changing beers Ⓗ
One of the famous pair of real-ale 'bookends' at the railway station, and a favourite calling point on the Ale Trail. This is a large, 4-roomed pub, and each room has its own character and its own locals. One bar is dedicated to cask and one to keg. The pub's beer range is outstanding, with up to 14 real ales on sale and also 26 keg beers. This is complemented by four real ciders/perries and an extensive British and world bottle range. Pieminister pies, mash and peas are served. Local CAMRA Mild Pub of the Year 2024. ⌂ ① & ≢ ♣ ● ⊟ ❀ ♥ ♫

King's Head
St George's Square, HD1 1JF (in station buildings, on left when exiting station)
Bradfield Farmers Blonde; Magic Rock Ringmaster; Timothy Taylor Landlord; 7 changing beers (sourced regionally; often Abbeydale, Oakham, Pictish) Ⓗ
A friendly welcome always awaits you in this award-winning pub. Situated in the Grade I-listed railway station and winner of a railway heritage award, it has been carefully restored with features including a beautiful tiled floor, wood panelling and wood-burning stoves. It serves four permanent and six rotating beers from breweries near and far. A mild, a dark beer, and one real cider are always available. Live music plays on Sunday afternoon. Hot food is served on match days.
① ≢ ● ⊟ ❀ ♥ ♫

Rat & Ratchet Ⓛ
40 Chapel Hill, HD1 3EB (on A616, just off the ring road; car park at rear)
☎ (01484) 542400
Ossett Butterley, Yorkshire Blonde, White Rat, Silver King; Rat King Rat; 5 changing beers (sourced regionally; often Fernandes, Riverhead, Small World) Ⓗ
Multi award-winning pub owned by Ossett, with the on-site Rat microbrewery. The large open-plan main area still retains the feel of separate rooms. Nine handpumps offer beers from a range of breweries including the firm's own, with two permanent dark ales available. A generous range of ciders and perries are stocked. The pub has a dartboard, and it hosts live music on the second and fourth Thursday of the month. There is a quiz on Wednesday. Local CAMRA Pub of the Year 2022. ⌂ ⊛ ♣ ● P ⊟ ❀ ♥ ♥ ♫

Sportsman ★ Ⓛ ✅
1 St John's Road, HD1 5AY
☎ (01484) 421929
Timothy Taylor Boltmaker; 7 changing beers (sourced regionally; often Brass Castle, Thornbridge, Vocation) Ⓗ
This 1930s pub, with a 1950s refit by Hammonds (note the windows), is a previous winner of the CAMRA English Heritage Conservation Pub Design award. The main room has a superb curved central bar, a parquet floor and an interesting wooden entrance. Eight ales are arranged in strength order, with one or more dark beers always available. There is an excellent real cider offering. Regular Meet the Brewer/Cider producer nights are hosted, and two rooms off are regularly used for meetings, such as poker and music clubs. There is a large outside drinking area. Local CAMRA Cider Pub of the Year 2022-2024. ⌂ ⊛ ❀ ● ⊟ ❀ ♥ ♥ ♫

Ilkley

Flying Duck Ⓛ ✅
16 Church Street, LS29 9DS (on A65)

☎ (01943) 609587 ⊕ theflyingduck.co.uk
Dark Horse Hetton Pale Ale; Wharfedale Black, Blonde, Best; 4 changing beers (sourced regionally; often Helmsley, Rooster's, Wharfedale) Ⓗ
Beautifully refurbished Grade-II listed traditional-style pub close to the town centre. Originally constructed as a farmhouse in 1709, it is reputed to be Ilkley's oldest pub building. It retains many original features including Yorkstone and oak flooring, beamed ceilings, internal stonework and mullioned windows. Up to eight real ales are available, including four regulars from the in-house brewery. Real ciders are also sold. Wharfedale brewery is located to the rear. Closed on Mondays except bank holidays. ⌂✿◑≑♠🖪♞🌣🥄♫

Keighley

Brown Cow Ⓛ
5 Cross Leeds Street, BD21 2LQ
☎ (01535) 382423
Timothy Taylor Boltmaker; 4 changing beers Ⓗ
A short walk from the town centre, this family-run free house is about quality, choice and customer comfort. Up to five guest beers come mainly from local micros, featuring at least one session beer, a strong one and a dark one. A quiz takes place on the second and last Wednesday of the month. The Brown Cow is a regular meeting place for community groups and a regular CAMRA award winner. A no bad language policy is in place. ⌂✿♣♠🖪♞🌣

Taylor's on the Green Ⓛ ✔
Church Street, BD21 5HT
☎ (01535) 603053 ⊕ taylorsonthegreen.co.uk
Timothy Taylor Dark Mild, Golden Best, Boltmaker, Knowle Spring, Landlord, Landlord Dark Ⓗ
Timothy Taylor's managed house with a light and airy interior courtesy of a large atrium. The walls are decorated with photos of Taylor's long history and brewing process. A long bar boasts the full range of Taylor's cask ales, and a special cask may occasionally replace one of the six regular beers. Wood flooring leads you through a choice of booths, high stools, armchairs, sofas or wooden tables and chairs, and on to a part-heated outdoor area. There is an on-site brewery shop. ⌂✿◑♿≑♠🖪🌣♫

Leeds: Burley

Cardigan Arms ★ Ⓛ
364 Kirkstall Road, LS4 2HQ
☎ (0113) 226 3154 ⊕ cardiganarms.co.uk
Kirkstall Bitter, Pale Ale, Three Swords, Dissolution IPA, Black Band Porter; 1 changing beer (sourced locally; often Anthology, Kirkstall, Vocation) Ⓗ
The Cardigan Arms was always been a jewel in the Leeds pub heritage crown, but several years ago Kirkstall brewery brought it back to its former glory. There are four rooms, a drinking lobby and an upstairs function room. Whether you seek a traditional tap room, ornate woodwork, etched glass or bell pushes, the Cardigan has it all. Built in 1893 to an elaborate Italianate style it was named after the Earl of Cardigan who was a major landowner in the area.
⌂✿◑♿≑(Burley Park) ♣🖪🌣🥄♫

Dave's Pies & Ale Ⓛ
350 Kirkstall Road, LS4 2HQ
☎ (0113) 278 4555
Daleside Blonde; 2 changing beers (often Ilkley, Stancill, Wilde Child) Ⓗ

This small venue has a cosy and traditional feel despite only opening in 2021. Large windows face Kirkstall Road allowing you to watch the world go by. One wall is covered with old mirrors from brewers and distillers. The traditional looking bar hosts three handpulls with beers usually from Yorkshire breweries. A fridge offers a small but interesting range of beers from local breweries including alcohol-free ones. A variety of pork pies served with peas is also available. ⌂✿≑(Burley Park)♠🖪🌣

Kirkstall Brewery Tap & Kitchen Ⓛ
100 Kirkstall Road, LS3 1HJ
☎ (0113) 898 0280 ⊕ kirkstallbrewerytap.co.uk
Kirkstall Pale Ale, Three Swords, Black Band Porter; 4 changing beers (sourced locally; often Kirkstall, Leeds) Ⓗ
Traditional one-room pub set inside the thoroughly modern Kirkstall brewery – look out for the big K on the outside! On the bar there are seven cask ales and 12 keg taps. The single room is decorated with all manner of brewery and pub memorabilia collected over several years – from relatively common enamel advertisements and mirrors from long lost breweries to pub signs and partition screens. The food available is mostly pizza, salads and sides. ⌂✿◑♿🖪🌣

Leeds: Chapel Allerton

Regent Ⓛ ✔
15-17 Regent Street, LS7 4PE
☎ (0113) 293 9395
Greene King IPA; Leeds Pale, Best; 2 changing beers (sourced locally; often Goose Eye, Kirkstall, Saltaire) Ⓗ
Two-roomed stone-built Victorian pub in the heart of Chapel Allerton but with a traditional village pub atmosphere. Built in the early 19th century it has been a pub since at least the 1840s. The public bar is to the left and the lounge to the right. The central bar serves both rooms and five cask ales are available, mostly from local breweries. Quiz nights take place on Tuesdays and Thursdays and occasional theme nights are held. Dogs are welcome in the public bar. ⌂✿♿♣🖪🌣

Leeds: City Centre

Banker's Cat
29 Boar Lane, LS1 5DA
☎ (0113) 440 7998 ⊕ bankerscat.co.uk
Thornbridge Astryd, Lord Marples, Jaipur; 5 changing beers (often Buxton, Thornbridge) Ⓗ
Intimate yet lively pub a stone's throw from the train station, with rich mahogany and low lighting harking back to a simpler yet more decadent age. Thornbridge and Pivovar's love of cats is evident in this former bank, surpassed only by their love for providing quality real ale. The Thornbridge brewery classics are supported by a host of rotating beers (watch out for Jaipur X at 10%), with an impressive cask arsenal too. The old vault makes for an ideal function room. ♿≑🖪🌣

Duck & Drake Ⓛ ✔
43 Kirkgate, LS2 7DR
☎ (0113) 245 5432 ⊕ duckndrake.co.uk
Bridgehouse Blonde; Rooster's Yankee; Timothy Taylor Landlord; Theakston Old Peculier; Yorkshire Heart Ghost Porter; 9 changing beers (sourced locally; often Daleside, Saltaire) Ⓗ
Fine example of a two-roomed Victorian corner pub retaining many original features. Wood-floored throughout, some of the floorboards having survived 200 years of trade. The central bar with 15 handpumps serves

both rooms. The pork pies are not to be missed. Live music plays most nights. The Gents toilets feature traditional porcelain units from J Duckett and Son Ltd of Burnley. The beer garden is well maintained and a pleasant place to enjoy a pint on a sunny afternoon. ✿◑♿⇌🚋☺🛜♨🌙

Head of Steam 🅛

13 Mill Hill, LS1 5DQ
☎ (0113) 243 6618
Camerons Strongarm, Road Crew; Timothy Taylor Boltmaker; 4 changing beers (often Camerons, Ilkley, Wilde Child) Ⓗ
Attractive three-storey stone and brick pub with a curved frontage. The octagonal island bar hosts beers from all around the world, including a good range of cask ales and a very impressive array of draught Belgian beers for this side of the channel. Cavernous in both appearance and acoustically, there are several distinct areas: a few tables close to the bar, an alcove for live music – including jazz on Sundays – a raised area to the rear and an upstairs balcony area. ⇌🚋☺🛜🌙

Lamb & Flag 🅛

1 Church Row, LS2 7HD
☎ (0113) 243 1255 🌐 lambandflagleeds.co.uk
Leeds Pale, Yorkshire Gold, Best, Midnight Bell; 4 changing beers (sourced locally; often Brass Castle, Brew York, Kirkstall) Ⓗ
This 19thh-century brick-built pub is on a corner site overlooked by Leeds Minster (formally Leeds Parish Church). After a long period of closure, a few years ago it was tastefully restored and reopened under the current name. There are two floors with various different areas. The decor is exposed brickwork and timbers with large windows. Upstairs is a balcony with seating and views of the minster. Outside is a large covered courtyard. ☺✿◑♿⇌🚋☺🛜

North Bar 🅛

24 New Briggate, LS1 6NU
☎ (0113) 242 4540 🌐 northbar.com/northbar
North Vanishing Point; 1 changing beer (sourced locally; often North) Ⓗ
Small pioneering beer bar which opened way back in 1997 and has always had a relaxed, friendly atmosphere. A slick design is contrasted nicely with metal and neon signs of various Belgian breweries. The cask ales on the bar are joined by a range of keg offerings in a wide variety of styles and ABVs, many from North brewery. Packed fridges provide an interesting selection of UK and international beers, many of which are available to take away. ✿◑➧⇌🚋☺🌙

Scarbrough Hotel

Bishopgate Street, LS1 5DY
☎ (0113) 243 4590
St Austell Nicholson's Pale Ale; Tetley Bitter; 5 changing beers (sourced nationally; often Oakham, Theakston, Timothy Taylor) Ⓗ
Named after its first owner, Henry Scarbrough, rather than the seaside town and commonly misspelled. The building first became a pub in 1826. A beautifully tiled exterior leads to a long bar opposite the entrance with seating areas to either side. This is a busy ale house providing a convenient spot to wait for a train from across the road and with an array of cask delights sourced from around the country, so all travelers will feel right at home. ✿◑♿⇌🚋🛜🌙

Tapped Leeds 🅛

51 Boar Lane, LS1 5EL
☎ (0113) 244 1953 🌐 tappedleeds.co.uk

House beer (by Tapped (Leeds)); 6 changing beers (often Kirkstall, Tapped (Sheffield)) Ⓖ
Blending retro and modern designs, Tapped Leeds hosts a wide variety of draught beers and ciders, with a good list of bottled and canned beers and ciders too. This is an ideal venue for a newcomer to the world of beer, as most styles are represented here. Two of the beers available are brewed on site in the large copper tanks along the wall opposite the bar. Freshly baked pizzas are served until two hours before closing. ☺✿◑♿⇌🚋🛜

Templar ★ 🅛 ✅

2 Templar Street, LS2 7NU
☎ (0113) 243 0318
Bradfield Farmers Blonde; Kirkstall Three Swords; Tetley Bitter; 5 changing beers (sourced locally; often Acorn, Greene King, Pennine) Ⓗ
Grade II-listed with fine wood panelling from 1928 and splendid exterior with green and cream Burmantofts tiling, this is a traditional city-centre local pub. The bowing courtier logo can be seen in the leaded window panes from when it was a Melbourne brewery pub. The cask beers are mainly from Yorkshire with a couple from the Greene King stable. The landlord and many staff have served at the pub for over 30 years. Under-18s are not allowed. ✿⇌♣🛜♨

Town Hall Tavern 🅛 ✅

17 Westgate, LS1 2RA
☎ (0113) 244 0965
Timothy Taylor Dark Mild, Golden Best, Boltmaker, Knowle Spring, Landlord, Landlord Dark Ⓗ
Small traditional inter-war brick-built pub which dates from 1926 and is opposite the law courts on Westgate near the Town Hall and Leeds Central Library. The pub consists of a single room with open alcoves to the left and right of the door. Along the left-hand wall is the bar with its range of Timothy Taylor beers on six handpumps. The decor includes black and white photographs of Leeds from times past on the walls. ✿◑🚋☺🛜

Wapentake 🅛

92 Kirkgate, LS2 7DJ
☎ (0113) 243 6248
2 changing beers (sourced locally; often Kirkstall, Nailmaker) Ⓗ
Located on one of Leeds' oldest streets Wapentake, from an old word to describe an administrative area, is a little piece of Yorkshire. It opens in the morning for the coffee and brunch crowd before drinkers arrive later. The bare boards and shabby chic furniture create a cozy, homely atmosphere, with the downstairs for chat and upstairs for TV. A place for individuality and relaxation that feels a world away from the hustle and bustle of the city centre. ☺✿◑⇌🚋☺🛜🌙

Whitelock's Ale House ★ 🅛

Turk's Head Yard, LS1 6HB (off Briggate)
☎ (0113) 245 3950 🌐 whitelocksleeds.com
Five Points XPA, Railway Porter; Kirkstall Kirkstall Pale Ale; Timothy Taylor Landlord; Theakston Old Peculier; 4 changing beers (sourced locally; often Anthology, Kirkstall, Rooster's) Ⓗ
Described by John Betjeman as the very heart of Leeds, Whitelock's dates from 1715 and has an interior largely unchanged since 1895 with a feast of mirrors, polished metal and woodwork, stained glass and faience tiling. Time may have stood still here, but Whitelock's hosts a changing array of quality ales. The outside yard is shared with the Turk's Head bar and has many covered and heated tables. Locally sourced food is served every day with both lunch and dinner menus. ✿◑⇌🚋☺🛜

Leeds: Holbeck

Grove Inn ★ 🄻

Back Row, LS11 5PL

☎ (0113) 244 2085

Daleside Blonde; 7 changing beers (often Acorn, Ilkley, Wye Valley) 🄷

Dating from 1832, and remodelled in 1928-29, the front rooms have been recently restored after a fire. A fine example of a traditional four-room corridor pub there is a tiled entranceway that leads to two small rooms on the right and a traditional tap room with dartboard on the left. The rear Concert Room is an interwar addition and retains some original perimeter seating. Music is a strong feature and some form of performance can be heard most nights. ⊛🄳≋♣🄳🏵🛜🕙♫

Leeds: Kirkstall

Kirkstall Bridge Inn 🄻

12 Bridge Road, LS5 3BW

☎ (0113) 278 4044 🌐 kirkstallbridge.co.uk

Kirkstall Pale Ale, Three Swords, Dissolution IPA, Black Band Porter; 2 changing beers (sourced locally; often Brew York, Five Points, Vocation) 🄷

Stone-built roadside pub next to the river Aire. Inside the walls are decorated with pub memorabilia, chiefly mirrors. The main bar, at road level, has six handpumps predominantly serving Kirkstall brewery beers. Additionally there are 12 keg lines which also include Kirkstall beers. An easy-to-miss snug is behind the bar. Down some steep stone stairs will level with the beer garden entrance is a second bar. The disabled toilet is also at this lower level. ♿⊛🄳≋(Headingley)P🄳🏵🛜

West End House ✅

26 Abbey Road, LS5 3HS

☎ (0113) 246 4945

3 changing beers (sourced nationally; often Ilkley, Ossett) 🄷

Stone-built busy local community pub and a beer house since at least 1867. It is located on the A65 adjacent to Kirkstall Leisure Centre, close to Kirkstall Abbey and half a mile from Headingley railway station. Normally three cask ales are available often from Ossett or Ilkley breweries. Good-quality traditional British pub food is served. There is a small beer garden and smoking area outside. Partial level access from the rear entrance. Regular quiz nights are held. ♿⊛🄳≋(Headingley) 🄳(33,34) 🏵🛜🕙

Leeds: Meanwood

Terminus Tap Room & Bottle Shop

8A Stonegate Road, LS6 4HY

☎ (0113) 318 5821 🌐 terminustap.co.uk

4 changing beers (sourced locally; often Abbeydale, Meanwood, Ridgeside) 🄷

Meanwood brewery tap set back from the main road, the entrance to this two-storey pub is across a wooden decked patio. The bar is downstairs in a stone-walled room with wooden floor and bifold windows. Small tables with individual pot plants complete the modern homely look. At least two of the cask ales are from Meanwood brewery along with other beers. Upstairs is a similar large room. There are often pop-up street food vendors onsite at weekends. ♿⊛🄳🏵♫

Leeds: Newlay

Abbey Inn 🄻

99 Pollard Lane, LS13 1EQ (vehicle access from B6157 only)

☎ (0113) 258 1248

Kirkstall Three Swords, Black Band Porter; 2 changing beers (sourced locally; often Ilkley, Rooster's, Yorkshire Heart) 🄷

A stone-built former farmhouse, dating from 1714, which nestles between the River Aire and Leeds-Liverpool Canal. A celebrated community pub, the Abbey showcases a selection of predominantly local ales usually including a dark beer. The Abbey bustles with friendly locals throughout the week and events include a folk night and quizzes. Ample seating outside attracts dog walkers, cyclists and families. Accessible by road from Pollard Lane, on foot over Pollard Bridge or along the canal from the Kirkstall Forge Station. ♿⊛🄳≋(Kirkstall Forge) ♣P🏵🛜🕙♫

Linthwaite

Sair 🄻 ✅

139 Lane Top, HD7 5SG (top of Hoyle Ing, off A62)

☎ (01484) 842370

Linfit Bitter, Gold Medal, Old Eli; 2 changing beers (sourced regionally; often Empire, Vocation) 🄷

Overlooking the Colne Valley, the Sair is a multi-roomed stone-built pub of great character. Four rooms, each with a real fire, are served from a central bar. Up to five different beers are available. The three Linfit beers are now brewed at nearby South Crosland. At the heart of the local community, the pub gives a warm welcome to locals, visitors and their dogs. Pizza is served Thursday to Saturday in the evenings. Live music is regularly hosted. A former National CAMRA Pub of the Year. Q⊛🄳♣🄳🏵🛜🕙♫

Liversedge

Black Bull 🍺 🄻 ✅

37 Halifax Road, WF15 6JR (on A649, close to A62)

☎ (01924) 403779

Ossett Butterley, Yorkshire Blonde, White Rat, Silver King, Excelsius; 3 changing beers (sourced nationally; often Abbeydale, Ossett, Rat) 🄷

Ossett brewery's first pub and a Guide entry for over 20 years, the pub is a popular, sociable community local with a warm welcome. The five rooms each have unique styles, providing comfort and atmosphere. On offer are a stout or porter plus guest beers from the group and independents. Quiz night is Tuesday, darts and dominoes Mondays in local league, acoustic sessions on Sunday teatimes monthly. A fine, sheltered beer garden sits by a stream. The 229 bus route is 400 yards away. Q♿⊛🄳♣P🄳(200,229) 🏵🛜🕙♫

Lockwood

Shoulder of Mutton ★

11 Neale Road, HD1 3TN

🌐 shoulderofmuttonlockwood.com

Abbeydale Moonshine; Saltaire Blonde; 5 changing beers (sourced nationally; often Oakham, Small World, Titanic) 🄷

Well-run back-street local offering a decent selection of real ales from brewers including Abbeydale, Saltaire and Oakham. It has a medium-sized bar with two snug rooms either side and a pool room upstairs. A CAMRA award winner, the pub features in CAMRA's Yorkshire's Real Heritage Pubs book, with its dark wood interior and lead-

lined windows. Easily reached by a regular bus service and close to Lockwood train station.
Q☕🏧🅦◧⏰♿🅿️🚪❄️🐾🛜🕐♪

Longwood

Dusty Miller Inn 🅛 ✅
2 Gilead Road, HD3 4XH
☎ 07990 883932 🌐 dustymillerlongwood.com
Milltown Platinum Blonde, Tigers Tail, Black Jack Porter; Timothy Taylor Landlord; 2 changing beers Ⓗ
Local historic photographs and stone floors dominate at this pub. The interior is open plan but has three distinct areas. Six real ales are served, showcasing three Milltown brews. Alongside are two changing guests, always including a dark beer, plus a permanent cider. There are great views up the Colne Valley from the outside benches. Regular walking groups meet on Sundays. Q☕🏧♿🅿️🚪(356)❄️🛜🕐

Marsden

Riverhead Brewery Tap 🅛 ✅
2 Peel Street, HD7 6BR
☎ (01484) 844324 🌐 theriverheadmarsden.co.uk
Ossett Silver King, Excelsius; Riverhead March Haigh, Redbrook Premium; 5 changing beers (often Salt, Riverhead) Ⓗ
At the centre of village life, the Riverhead is a modern brewpub owned by Ossett brewery. The microbrewery is visible from the bar: beer doesn't get more LocAle than this. Nine beers are served: four Riverhead beers, three from Ossett plus guests. A dark beer is usually available. The Bank Room and the upstairs room have comfy seating and outside there is a riverside terrace for alfresco drinking. A popular venue for locals, visitors and their dogs. Local CAMRA Pub of the Year 2023.
🏧🅦♿🅦🚪(185)❄️🛜🕐

Meltham

Travellers Rest 🍸 ✅
Slaithwaite Road, HD9 5NH
☎ (01484) 851320 🌐 travellersrestmeltham.co.uk
Milltown Platinum Blonde; Timothy Taylor Landlord; 6 changing beers (sourced regionally; often Milltown) Ⓗ
Located at the edge of the South Pennine Moors, the pub offers stunning views which can be enjoyed from the spacious beer garden. It serves as the Milltown brewery tap. The pub is arranged on two levels and has modern decor following a refurbishment in 2017. Eight handpumps feature beers from Milltown and other breweries, as well as a real cider. Always providing a friendly welcome, this local CAMRA Rural Pub of the Year 2023-2024 is well worth the effort to visit.
🏧🅦🛏️♿🅦🚪(335,324)❄️🛜🕐♪

Mirfield

Flowerpot 🅛 ✅
65 Calder Road, WF14 8NN (over river, 400yds S of railway station)
☎ (01924) 496939
Ossett Butterley, Yorkshire Blonde, White Rat, Silver King, Voodoo, Excelsius; 1 changing beer (sourced locally; often 4Ts, Ossett, Rat) Ⓗ
An 1807 pub tastefully restored by Ossett brewery, decorated in a charming rustic style with an impressive tile flowerpot as the centrepiece. There are four separate drinking areas and real fires. There is a terrace and a fine riverside beer garden. Up to nine ales are offered from

Ossett's breweries and independents, usually including a mild or stout, plus sometimes a real cider. It is an easy walk from to Mirfield town centre, with access to the Brighouse to Mirfield canal walk.
🏧🅦♿🅦🚪(261)❄️🛜🕐♪

Knowl Club 🅛
17 Knowl Road, WF14 8DQ
☎ (01924) 493301 🌐 knowlclubmirfield.com
Saltaire Blonde; 2 changing beers (sourced regionally; often Black Sheep, Timothy Taylor, Titanic) Ⓗ
The former Mirfield Liberal Club is open to both members and the public, holding both Club and Public House licences. Ideal for a quiet pint, it has a single bar occupying a long well-furnished room offering up to four beers, plus a private function room and pool table downstairs and a well-furnished snooker room upstairs. A small car park at the rear is accessed down an adjacent narrow alley, as is the small beer garden. Closed Mondays and weekday lunchtimes. Local CAMRA Club of the Year 2024 🏧♿🅦◧🅿️🚪(203,205)❄️🛜🕐

Navigation Tavern
6 Station Road, WF14 8NL (next to Mirfield railway station)
☎ (01924) 492476 🌐 navigationtavern.co.uk
Small World Long Moor Pale; Theakston Lightfoot, Old Peculier; Vocation Bread & Butter; 2 changing beers (sourced regionally; often Acorn, Darkland, Durham) Ⓗ
A recently refurbished family-run free house, the pub attracts a wide range of age groups and drinkers. One side is traditionally furnished while the other is more popular with younger drinkers. Proud of its Donegal history, it often hosts live music and the large, sheltered canalside beer garden is used for charity and occasional concerts. Winter comfort is aided by a large wood-burning fire. Free moorings for patrons.
🏧🅦◧♿🅦🚪(205,203)❄️🛜♪

Moorthorpe

Mallard 🅛
Moorthorpe Railway Station, Barnsley Road, WF9 3AT (follow signage for Moorthorpe railway station)
☎ 07842 725903 🌐 jollyboysbrewery.co.uk
Jolly Boys Blonde, Jolly Collier Porter Ⓗ**; 4 changing beers (often Jolly Boys, Silver Brewhouse)** Ⓗ/Ⓖ
Jolly Boys brewery have recently reopened this sympathetically restored railway-themed bar on Moorthorpe station (on the Leeds to Sheffield line via Wakefield). Beers are mainly brewed by Jolly Boys but guest cask beers from Silver Brewhouse also feature. There are occasional quiz nights and live music events and the Pullman Lounge function room is free to hire. Cask beer is sold at at a reduced price on Tuesday.
🅦🅿️🚪❄️♪

Norristhorpe

Rising Sun 🅛
254 Norristhorpe Lane, WF15 7AN (0.4 miles off A62)
☎ (01924) 400190
Abbeydale Moonshine; Bradfield Farmers Blonde; Saltaire Blonde; Timothy Taylor Landlord; 2 changing beers (sourced locally; often Timothy Taylor) Ⓗ
This village local has a spacious bar and cosy lounge areas with exposed brickwork and real fires. Beers are mainly from Yorkshire. Every Tuesday there is a popular prize quiz, and occasional live music is advertised on Facebook. There is a large, well-maintained beer garden

with extensive views over the valley towards Mirfield and Emley Moor. Marquee hire is available. The 229 bus is a 10-minute walk. Q♿🅿️🚬(261,229)🍴🐕🛜🔌♪

North Featherstone

Bradley Arms 🅛

96 Willow Lane, WF7 6BJ (on B6128 Castleford to Featherstone road, opp St Wilfrid's High School)
☎ (01977) 704256 🌐 thebradleyarms.co.uk
Nailmaker Wapentake; house beer (by Acorn); 2 changing beers (sourced regionally) 🖐
Traditional multi-roomed pub with a large outdoor drinking area. The pub is rich in local history with links to the Featherstone Massacre of 1893. Cunninghame Graham gave his first speech on worker's rights here; note the inscription over the fireplace in the Tap Room. Weekly live music evenings are held, there is a quiz night on Wednesday and there are occasional pop-up food events. Q♿🍴🅿️🚬🛜♪

Oakworth

Oakworth Social Club 🅛

Chapel Lane, BD22 7HY
☎ (01535) 643931
Saltaire Blonde; Timothy Taylor Golden Best; 1 changing beer 🖐
Friendly and welcoming, this imposing Victorian building on the main thoroughfare was originally built as the Liberal Club in the late 19th century. Now a social club with a thriving membership, it has a comfortable front lounge and a back bar with traditional games and a TV. Upstairs, a third room caters for functions and meetings. Quiz night is Monday, and regular live music events are staged (see Facebook for details). Local CAMRA Club of the Year 2022. ♿🍴♣️🅿️(K7)🛜🔌♪

Ossett

Brewers Pride 🅛 ✓

Low Mill Road, Healey, WF5 8ND (in Healey Mills industrial area beside River Calder)
☎ (01924) 273865
Ossett Yorkshire Blonde, White Rat, Silver King; Rudgate Ruby Mild; 3 changing beers (often Ossett) 🖐
One of the best free houses in the area for many years was sold to Ossett brewery in 2018. The pub is on the outskirts of the town in a regenerated industrial area close to the Calder and Hebble canal. Under the guidance of Stephen (Chalky) Whyte the pub is finding its feet again after the transition from free to tied house. Good-value meals are served. Q♿🍴♣️🅿️(102)🐕🔌♪

Prop'ur Baa 🅛

3 New Street, WF5 8BH
☎ (01924) 265530
Abbeydale Moonshine; 4 changing beers (often North Riding (Brewery)) 🖐
Family-owned micropub near the Town Hall, established since 2019. A single bar with five handpumps serving real ales from mainly Yorkshire breweries, it also has an extensive selection of gins. Complimentary tapas is served on Fridays and a cheeseboard on Sundays. A quiz night is on Wednesday with the proceeds going to local charities of the winners choice, and there are occasional acoustic live music sessions. An atmospheric, dog-friendly pub. Q🅿️🛜♪

Otley

Black Horse 🅛

2 Westgate, LS21 3AS
☎ (01943) 465950 🌐 blackhorseotley.co.uk
Kirkstall Pale Ale, Three Swords, Dissolution IPA, Black Band Porter; 4 changing beers (sourced locally; often Anthology, Craven, Kirkstall) 🖐
The Black Horse is an impressive corner building dating from the start of the 20th century with a Victorian-style interior. The imposing entrance on the corner of the building takes you into the main bar area with its wooden floor and array of brewery mirrors on the walls. To the left of the bar is the tap room and to the right of bar an opening leads to additional seating areas. There is also a large covered outside seating area. Q♿🍴🛏️🍽️🚻🅿️🛜♪

Curious Hop Biere Café

9 Orchard Gate, LS21 3NX
☎ (01943) 467150 🌐 curioushop.com/bar
3 changing beers (sourced regionally; often Chevin, MBH Beer, Thornbridge) 🖐
Small independent bar which opened in November 2022 after a refurbishment of the premises. The main single room is wooden-floored, has a low partition down the middle and beer signs and mirrors on the walls. On the bar are three handpumps serving mainly northern beers and behind it on the white-tiled back wall are 10 keg fonts. A locally produced cider is normally available. There is an additional seating area upstairs which can also be booked for meetings. ♿🚻♣️🛜🛜

Horse & Farrier 🅛

7 Bridge Street, LS21 1BQ
☎ (01943) 468400
Hawkshead Windermere Pale; Theakston Best Bitter; 2 changing beers (sourced locally; often Kirkstall, Rooster's) 🖐
Previously called the Three Horse Shoes until a refurbishment in 2010, this is an open-plan pub dating from the second half of the 19th century with one large room divided into three wood-floored drinking areas and a carpeted area. The bar is to the left hand side of the room. Upstairs is a function room and there is an outdoor seating area in a narrow yard at the rear of the pub. An open mic night takes place on Thursday. ♿🍴🛏️🚻🅿️🛜♪

Junction Inn 🅛 ✓

44 Bondgate, LS21 1AD
Ossett Yorkshire Blonde; Timothy Taylor Boltmaker, Knowle Spring, Landlord; Theakston Old Peculier; 3 changing beers 🖐
A solid-looking stone-built pub on a prominent street-corner site on the approach from Leeds. To the front, roadside tables allow for outdoor drinking. Inside, the pub consists of a single room with a central fireplace and comfortable fixed seating which runs around the walls. Decoration in the half-panelled room includes a collection of pictures of old Otley. To the rear of the building is a covered and heating outside seating area. Children are allowed until evening. ♿🍴♣️🚻🔌♪

Old Cock 🅛

11-13 Crossgate, LS21 1AA
☎ (01943) 464424
Daleside Blonde; Timothy Taylor Landlord; Theakston Best Bitter; 6 changing beers (sourced locally; often Acorn, Brass Castle, Rooster's) 🖐
Award-winning genuine free house which has been cleverly converted from a former café in such a way that you would think it has been a pub for many years. There

are two low-ceilinged rooms downstairs with stone-flagged floors and a further room upstairs. The guest ales are mostly from local breweries. At least one dark beer is regularly available, usually a mild as well as a stout or porter. There is a small outdoor drinking area. No admittance to under-18s. Q✿&♿️☕🚫🛆🐕🚱🔊Ⓤ

Oxenhope

Bay Horse 🄻 ✅
20 Uppertown, BD22 9LN (on A6033)
☎ (01535) 642921
Rudgate Jorvik Blonde; Timothy Taylor Landlord; Vocation Heart & Soul; 4 changing beers (sourced regionally; often Goose Eye) Ⓗ
A friendly village local that welcomes families and dogs. It has a pleasant single-bar setup with a real fire, a cosy room to the rear, and a separate seating area up a flight of steps. The guest beers come from local breweries such as Bowland and Goose Eye. The pub is one of the main stopping points for the annual village charity Straw Race. Regular live music is a feature.
🚶✿🚲♣️🅿️🚌(B3,K14) 🐕🚱🔊

Pecket Well

Robin Hood 🄻
Keighley Road, HX7 8QR
☎ (01422) 842593 🌐 robinhoodinnhebden.co.uk
Timothy Taylor Landlord; 3 changing beers (sourced regionally; often Abbeydale, Moorhouse's, Stubbee) Ⓗ
This comfortable 17th-century inn commands superb views across Crimsworth Dean and towards Stoodley Pike which can be enjoyed from the extensive garden seating areas. The main room is pleasantly divided up to accommodate both drinkers and diners. A separate area within an impressive vaulted stone arch is also available for those who are eating, while a third room with a large stone fireplace provides a further snug area. A wide range of food and wines are available.
✿🍴🍽️🅿️🚌(B3,595) 🐕🚱

Pontefract

Old Grocers 🄻
25 Beastfair, WF8 1AL
5 changing beers (sourced locally) Ⓗ
Pontefract's first micropub with seating for around 60 people over two floors and a small outdoor area. There is a regularly changing selection of five cask beers, mainly from Yorkshire breweries, also real cider. A quiz night is held every Wednesday and there are regular acoustic music sessions at weekends. A folk club meets on the last Sunday of the month.
Q🚶✿🚆(Tanshelf) ♣️🚌🐕Ⓤ🔊

Robin Hood 🄻
4 Wakefield Road, WF8 4HN (at Town End jct of A645 Wakefield Rd)
☎ (01977) 702231
10 changing beers (sourced regionally; often Abbeydale, Henry Smith, Kirkstall) Ⓗ
Recently bought and totally refurbished by a local landlord, the Robin has been a pub since 1791 when it was owned by the Duchy of Lancaster. It is the home of the Henry Smith brewery which is named after the son of the present owner. There is a folk session on Sundays and live music on Thursdays. Home to Britain's longest-running vinyl club, the Cat Club. There are two outside drinking areas. Q🚶✿🅿️🚌🐕🔊

Pudsey

Fleece 🄻 ✅
100 Fartown, LS28 8LU
☎ (0113) 236 2748
Copper Dragon Golden Pippin; Tetley Bitter; Timothy Taylor Landlord; Wainwright Gold; 1 changing beer (sourced locally; often Timothy Taylor) Ⓗ
On the outskirts of Pudsey (about a 20-minute walk from centre) lies this welcoming and cosy local. It is a handsome pub with parking at the front and hidden-away garden around the back. Inside, the lounge on the right is long and blue with much comfy upholstery and movie-related bits and bobs. The snug on the left is only slightly more basic with a tiled floor, wood-burning fire and rustic charm. The central bar has a jar of treats for dogs who are welcome until evening.
✿🅿️🚌(4F,205) 🐕🚱🔊

Riddlesden

Applegarth Club 🄻
Banks Lane, BD20 5PD
☎ (01535) 603611
4 changing beers (sourced regionally) Ⓗ
A large old house with superb views over the Aire Valley, this private members club serves up to four beers sourced locally and further afield. Non-members are welcome to sign in for a drink, but regular ale visitors expected to join. Members have use of two full-size snooker tables, a pool table, and a dartboard. Quiz nights are the second and fourth Wednesday of the month, and various other events are held. Local CAMRA Club of the Year 2023 and 2024. 🚶✿♣️🅿️🚌(K4)🐕

Roberttown

New Inn 🄻 ✅
Roberttown Lane, WF15 7NP
☎ (01924) 500483 🌐 newinnroberttown.co.uk
Abbeydale Moonshine; Bradfield Farmers Blonde; Timothy Taylor Landlord; 3 changing beers (sourced regionally; often Wilde Child) Ⓗ
A free house at the heart of the local community, comprising a taproom, the main lounge area, a pool room and a side room suitable for functions. Outside is a sunny seating area and a smoking shelter. There is a popular quiz with supper on Wednesdays, occasional live music at weekends, a popular charitable 'knit & natter' night on Mondays and free grub Friday teatimes. The 229 bus is 10 minutes' walk. May close early if quiet.
🚶✿♣️🅿️🚌(260,261) 🐕🚱Ⓤ🔊

Saltaire

Cap & Collar 🄻
4 Queens Road, BD18 4SJ
🌐 tinyurl.com/capncollar
3 changing beers (sourced nationally; often Bristol Beer Factory, Marble, Wishbone) Ⓗ
Popular modern micropub accommodating up to 35 customers. It has a beer garden and smoking area to the rear with an additional outside seating to the front. Up to four real ales are often from local breweries but can also be from further afield. Additionally, up to four beers from independent breweries are dispensed using the KeyKeg system. There is a good selection of bottle-conditioned ales. Real cider served by bag in box and in bottles. The pub hosts homebrew and book club meetings.
Q🚶✿🚆🍴🐕🚱🔊

Fanny's Ale House L

63 Saltaire Road, BD18 3JN (on A657)
☎ (01274) 588051

Timothy Taylor Boltmaker, Landlord, Landlord Dark; 6 changing beers (sourced regionally; often Bingley, Craven, Moorhouse's) ⊞

Located near the UNESCO World Heritage Site of Saltaire village and the historic Salts Mill, this cosy pub is popular with residents and visitors alike. It was refurbished and reopened in 2021 under a change of ownership. The various extensions over its lifetime has created a maze of rooms with stairs and narrow passageways. Three regular ales and up to six guests are offered. The gas-lit lounge on the ground floor and real fires add nicely to the welcome. ⏱≠🚪🐾↻

SALT Beer Factory & Kitchen L ✓

199 Bingley Road, BD18 4DH
☎ (01274) 582111

Ossett Butterley, Yorkshire Blonde, White Rat, Silver King; 5 changing beers (sourced regionally; often Rat, SALT London, Wilde Child) ⊞

Large pub built within an old tramshed, originally constructed in 1904, now part of the Ossett brewery pub chain. It has a large open-plan main room with horseshoe bar, dining room offset to one side and upper mezzanine dining area. There is also access to the adjacent SALT Beer Factory. Real ales are mainly from Ossett brewery and associated brands with some guests. The large outdoor seating area is popular in good weather. Excellent meals include freshly made wood-fired pizzas. Busy at weekends. ⏱🐾◑≠♣🅿🚪🛜↻♫

Sandal

Star L ✓

Standbridge Lane, WF2 7DY (near Asda on the A6186 which links A61 and A636)
☎ (01924) 229674

5 changing beers (sourced regionally; often Morton Collins)

A cosy pub dating from 1821, witha stream-side beer garden. The Star is leased by the Morton Collins brewery and serves or or two of their beers plus four or five guests mainly from local breweries. The brewery has recently moved into the pub. It is a very welcoming pub with an open-plan layout and open fires in winter. A quiz night is held on Tuesday. There is a function room for hire. The pub hosts annual beer festivals.
Q⏱🐾◑&♣🅿(106)🐾🛜

Shipley

Crafty Kernel L

16 Kirkgate, BD18 3QN
☎ 07932 239195

4 changing beers (sourced regionally; often Abbeydale, Darkland, Wishbone) ⊞

Modern, smart pub located in a former shop unit near the Market Square and bus interchange. The open-plan ground floor room contains the bar. There is further seating in an upstairs room. Four handpulls serve a varying range and styles of real ale, usually from regional brewers. A variety of craft keg beers are offered, as is real cider and an extensive wine selection. The beers include gluten-free options including, usually, at least one real ale. Live music plays on Sunday evenings. ⏱🐾◑&≠🍴🚪🛜♫

Fox L

41 Briggate, BD17 7BP
☎ (01274) 594826 ⊕ thefoxshipley.co.uk

BEEspoke Plan Bee; 5 changing beers (sourced regionally; often Craven, Oaks, Small World) ⊞

Popular, independent, single-roomed café-style bar which is friendly and welcoming. Simply but smartly furnished featuring recycled church pews. Six handpulled ales include regulars from the in-house BEEspoke microbrewery and constantly varying guests beers. Real ciders, often including one from a local producer, are available as are a wide range of international bottled beers. Handy when waiting for trains as the station is close by. There is often live music on a Saturday night, when it can become very busy. ⏱🐾&≠🍴🐾🛜♫

Silsden

Counting House L

23 Kirkgate, BD20 0AJ
☎ 07756 634827

Dark Horse Hetton Pale Ale; 3 changing beers (sourced regionally; often Ilkley, Saltaire) ⊞

A brightly decorated bar with a welcoming atmosphere, it previously the branch of a bank, hence the name. The interior features exposed brickwork, interesting light fittings, and multiple clocks and mirrors. The L-shaped drinking/dining area has plenty of tables and small standing spaces at the bar and by the door. Three guest beers change weekly and are usually from local suppliers. Special events nights are a regular feature.
⏱🐾▲🚪(62,903)🍴🛜♫

Slaithwaite

Commercial L

1 Carr Lane, HD7 5AN (in village centre, off A62)
☎ (01484) 846258

Empire Moonrakers Mild; house beer (by Empire); 6 changing beers (often Goose Eye, Wensleydale) ⊞

This popular freehouse enjoys deserved success. Eight handpumps serve a variety of beer styles – the keenly-priced house beers are supplied by Empire brewery and include a permanent mild. A ninth pump serves a real cider. The open-plan interior retains the feel of separate drinking areas, one featuring a real fire. Walkers and their dogs are welcome and the pub is a popular stop on the Transpennine Rail Ale Trail. There is a pool room upstairs. Local CAMRA Mild Pub of the Year 2023.
🐾≠🚪🐾↻

Sowerby Bridge

Puzzle Hall L

21 Hollins Mill Lane, HX6 2RF (400yds from A58)
☎ (01422) 835237 ⊕ puzzlehall.org.uk

6 changing beers (sourced regionally; often Acorn, Big Trip, Mallinsons) ⊞

Located between the River Calder and the Rochdale Canal, this 18th-century gem has a proud history as a live music venue. The building once included a brewery; the tower is incorporated into the staff accommodation. Closed in 2016, it reopened as a community-owned pub in 2019, winning a CAMRA pub saving award. The single bar serves two rooms and a large partly-covered yard. Various clubs meet at the pub, and it hosts live music both inside and, in warmer weather, in the yard.
⏱🐾&≠🍴🚪🐾🛜♫

Stanbury

Friendly L

54 Main Street, BD22 0HB (in village centre)
☎ (01535) 645528

House beer (by Settle); 2 changing beers (sourced nationally; often Craven, Goose Eye, Small World) ⊞
Popular village local living up to its name, which also attracts those walking the Pennine Way or an afternoon stroll. This small pub retains a traditional layout with small lounges either side of a central bar plus a separate games room. There are south-facing benches outside the front door, and a small beer garden beyond the car park with impressive views across the valley. Only two miles from Haworth but a million miles from its tourist hustle and bustle. ⑤❀▲♣️Ρ🖵(B1,K14)❀⑆

Wuthering Heights Inn ⓛ

Main Street, BD22 0HB (in village centre)
☎ (01535) 643332 ⊕ thewutheringheights.co.uk
Craven Best Yorkshire Bitter; Moorhouse's White Witch; 2 changing beers (sourced regionally) ⊞
Set in a farming village, this popular, friendly inn dates from 1763. Warmed by log-burners, the traditional main bar displays photographs showing the history of the Stanbury. The cosy dining room has a Bronte theme, and there is a third room that can be booked for parties and meetings. The rear garden has spectacular views down the Worth Valley and a separate camping area (no caravans). There is a quiz every Thursday. Well-behaved dogs and children are welcome.
⑤❀😴◑▲♣️Ρ🖵(B1,K14)❀⑆

Stanley

Graziers Inn

116 Aberford Road, WF3 4NN (on A 642 at bottom of hill after hospitals, near jct with road to Stanley Ferry)
☎ (01924) 200283
Abbeydale Moonshine; Timothy Taylor Landlord; 3 changing beers (sourced regionally; often Theakston) ⊞
The pub dates from 1890 and is a deserved addition to the Guide. It has served consistently good quality beers for a number of years. Traditional and welcoming this pub boasts numerous rooms separated from a central bar. Copper-topped tables and a real fire in winter add to the atmosphere. There are many pictures of old Stanley adorning the walls. Q⑤❀👌◑♣️Ρ❀⑆ひ♪

Thackley

Ainsbury ⓛ

7 Thackley Road, BD10 0RS (on jct of Thackley Rd, Ainsbury Ave and Crag Hill Rd)
☎ 07743 222138
3 changing beers (sourced regionally; often Acorn, Nailmaker, Sunbeam) ⊞
A warm, friendly welcome is assured in this popular micropub. Formerly a corner shop it is located within a residential area. A small downstairs room houses the bar and limited seating. Stone-flagged floors and much woodwork are present, creating a clean, comfortable environment. A slightly larger room upstairs provides more seating with tables. Space can be at a premium at busy times. Three handpulls serving a varying range of real ales. Q⑤●🖵❀ひ

Black Rat ⓛ

530 Leeds Road, BD10 8JH
☎ 07525 006906
4 changing beers (sourced locally; often Kirkstall, Rudgate, White Rose) ⊞
Previously a florist shop, this micropub with capacity for approximately 15 people changed ownership in 2022 but has maintained the standards for which it was known. A friendly welcome is assured. As there is no music, TV or games machines, conversation and banter is key. A varying selection of four real ales, primarily from Yorkshire breweries, is offered with one line dedicated to dark beers. It can be very busy, especially first thing after a working day. Q👌●🖵❀

Thornton

Watchmaker ⓛ ✅

South Square, BD13 3LD (off Thornton Rd)
⊕ thewatchmaker.co.uk
Ossett Yorkshire Blonde; Timothy Taylor Landlord; 2 changing beers (sourced regionally; often Craven, Ossett, Titanic) ⊞
Small and friendly micropub with two small rooms on the ground floor with the bar to the front. It has a cosy, traditional appearance with plenty of timber on display and an old range in the rear room. Four handpulls serve two regular cask ales plus varying guests, usually including a dark beer. A courtyard provides additional outdoor seating and access to the toilets which are separate from the pub. There is also a communal beer garden to the rear down some steep steps.
Q⑤❀🖵(67,607)❀⑆

Todmorden

Alehouse ⓛ

52 Patmos, Burnley Road, OL14 5EY
☎ 07407 747956
Eagles Crag Pale Eagle; 4 changing beers (sourced regionally; often Helmsley, Whitworth) ⊞
A welcoming micropub located in a row of shops with a partially-covered patio at the front. The bar is located at the rear of the single room, whose walls feature work by local artists, often for sale. Four changing ales usually include a dark option and Eagles Crag K++ (a dry-hopped version of Golden Eagle) is offered on KeyKeg. There is occasional live music, mostly on Sunday afternoons. Opening hours may be reduced over autumn and winter.
❀🚲●🖵❀⑆♪

Upper Denby

George Inn ⓛ ✅

114 Denby Lane, HD8 8UE
☎ (01484) 861347 ⊕ thegeorgeinn-upperdenby.co.uk
Timothy Taylor Landlord; Tetley Bitter; 2 changing beers (sourced locally; often Acorn, Nailmaker, Small World) ⊞
This family-run village pub and free house is a regular winner of the local CAMRA Rural Pub of the Year and was Welcome To Yorkshire's Favourite Pub 2021. The pub is split into two separate areas – a comfortable lounge and a tap room. It is well known for its home-made pie and peas and walks. Cyclists, walkers and dogs are welcome, and families until evening. Q⑤❀◑▲♣️Ρ❀⑆

Wakefield

Harry's Bar ⓛ

107B Westgate, WF1 1EL (turn right from Westgate station, cross the road at the traffic lights and the pub is at the back of the car park on the right)
☎ (01924) 373773
Wensleydale Gamekeeper; house beer (by Chin Chin); 7 changing beers (often Mallinsons) ⊞
This small, one-roomed pub is set in an alleyway just off Westgate. A real fire and a bare brick and wood interior plus vintage sporting pictures enhance this small, cosy pub. There is also a fantastic view of Wakefield's famous 99-arch viaduct, if only steam trains were a regular

feature. It has a selection of bottled Belgian beers. An extensive decking area has been added to the side of the pub. Q☺⛲&♿(Westgate)♦P🅿🚲📶🕙♪

Luis Bar + Fernandes Wakefield 🄻

5 Avison Yard, Kirkgate, WF1 1UA (turn right 100yds S of the George St/Kirkgate jct near Scartop Pine)
☎ (01924) 386348 ⊕ luisbar.co.uk
House beer (by Fernandes) 🄷/🄶; 10 changing beers (sourced locally; often Chin Chin, Fernandes, Tigertops) 🄷
Independent pub and microbrewery housed in a 19th-century malthouse. The bar is named as a tribute to Jose Luis Fernandes, a Portuguese immigrant who built the original malthouse as part of Fernandes Old Bridge brewery. Old pub signs and coach lights adorn the walls of the pub which is situated over two floors. The brewery is located in the cellar, the bar is situated on the first floor with additional seating on the second floor.
Q☺♿(Kirkgate)♣♠P🅿🚲📶🕙♪

Old Printworks 🄻

107A Westgate, WF1 1EL (down an alley off main Westgate next door to Harry's Bar)
☎ 07771 861129
Oakham Citra; Ossett White Rat; 4 changing beers (sourced regionally) 🄷
One-room pub in an alleyway just off Westgate. A former printworks with pictures of print working adorning the walls. The bar was rescued from the Union pub, which was nearby on Horbury Road and closed a few years ago. The six handpulls usually have one dark beer and beers from Abbeydale, Acorn, Ossett and Oakham. Live music plays on Tuesdays and bank holiday Sundays.
⛲♿(Westgate)♣P🅿🚲📶🕙♪

Polka Hop 🄻

60 George Street, WF1 1DL (turn right out of Westgate station, left at Westgate then right at traffic lights, bear left at bottom of hill, pub is on the left after 200yds)
☎ (01924) 609760 ⊕ thepolkahop.co.uk
Bradfield Farmers Blonde; Sunbeam Parachuting Hedgehog; 2 changing beers (sourced regionally) 🄷
After major refurbishment the pub reopened as the Polka Hop in 2018. The Polka Hop is a dance performed by morris dancers – the new owner is a member of the local morris group. The bar has been relocated to a former recess, creating a comfortable seating area with secluded corners, and a real fire complements the warm welcome. Numerous board games are provided. Access from the street is difficult for wheelchairs.
Q☺♿(Westgate)♣🚌(443,444)🚲📶♪

Wakefield Labour Club 🄻

18 Vicarage Street, WF1 1QX (at the top of Kirkgate, round the corner from former Wakey Tavern)
☎ (01924) 215626 ⊕ theredshed.org.uk
5 changing beers (sourced regionally) 🄷
The Wakefield Labour Club (AKA Red Shed) is a repurposed army hut that has been extensively refurbished inside and out. It is home to many union, community and charity groups. A quiz night is every Wednesday, with regular music events and open mic nights on the last Saturday of the month. There are two rooms, one of which can be hired for functions. There is an extensive collection of union plates and badges adoring the walls. Dogs and well-behaved visitors welcome. Q☺&♿(Kirkgate)♣P🅿🚲♪

Wetherby

Bosun's Brewing Co Tap Room

15 Sandbeck Park, Sandbeck Lane, LS22 7TW
☎ (01937) 277337 ⊕ bosunsbrewery.com/pages/tap-room
5 changing beers (often Bosun's) 🄷
Brewery tap room in an industrial estate to the north of Wetherby. Up to five beers from Bosun's Brewing core range can be found on the bar. Outdoor seating is provided in warmer weather. Pork pies are available plus pizza on Fridays and Saturdays and sometimes pop-up food vendors will be onsite. The tap room may open additional hours for special events such as comedy nights and for sporting events, see social media for details.
☺⛲🅿🚲🍴

Wibsey

Dog & Gun 🄻

142-144 St Enoch's Road, BD6 3BU
☎ (01274) 677727 ⊕ thedogandgun.co.uk
Tetley Bitter; 3 changing beers (sourced regionally; often Empire, Ossett, Timothy Taylor) 🄷
Warm and welcoming traditional local on the outskirts of Bradford. Inside, it has three distinct areas with different feels. The bar serves the smart lounge, with another smaller room to the side. A further lounge is located to the rear. A regular real ale and three guest beers, usually from local and regional breweries, are available. The large beer garden to the rear includes an outside bar and pizza oven. On the bus route between Bradford and Wibsey. ☺⛲♣P🅿🚲📶🕙♪

Hooper Micropub 🄻

209 High Street, BD6 1JU
⊕ thehoopermicropub.co.uk
5 changing beers (sourced regionally; often Bridgehouse, Stancill, Wishbone) 🄷
Cosy, friendly, split-level micropub in the urban village of Wibsey and popular with locals and those from further afield. The bar is situated on the upper level and there is comfortable seating in the lower part. Five handpulls offer a varying selection of beers that are primarily sourced from the Yorkshire region but also occasionally from further afield. Photographs of old Wibsey provide a simple relief from the otherwise minimalist décor. Closing times may vary depending upon the demand.
Q☺♣🅿🚲📶♪

Wrenthorpe

New Wheel Inn 🄻

145 Wrenthorpe Road, WF2 0JN
☎ (01924) 960281
Black Sheep Best Bitter; Timothy Taylor Landlord; house beer (by Wainwright); 1 changing beer (sourced locally) 🄷
The New Wheel is a traditional village pub at the heart of the local community showing live sporting events and live music, alongside quiz nights, seasonal markets and family events. The pub consistently supports various local charities with fundraising throughout the year. The focus is strongly on the local community, with in-house football and pool teams. Q☺&♿♣P🅿🚲📶🕙♪

Not all chemicals are bad. Without chemicals such as hydrogen and oxygen, for example, there would be no way to make water, a vital ingredient in beer. **Dave Barry**

The Modern Homebrewer

Andy Parker and Jamil Zainasheff

A hands-on, practical guide to the most modern and up-to-date homebrewing ingredients, equipment, and processes. Written by two award-winning homebrewing experts-turned professional brewers, this new book will equip novices and more experienced brewers with the skills they need to produce professional quality beer at home.

- Features 40 world-class recipes from around the globe to try with your new-found skills.
- All recipes are also available on video and accessed via QR codes printed in the book.

RRP: £18.99   **ISBN**: 978-1-85249-389-9

For this and other books on beer and pubs, visit CAMRA's online bookshop at **shop1.camra.org.uk** or call 01727 867201.

Discounts are available for CAMRA members.

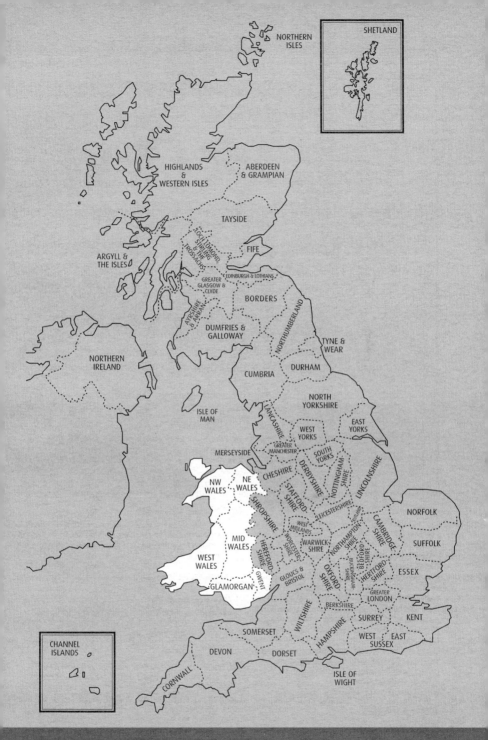

NORTHERN
ISLES

SHETLAND

HIGHLANDS
&
WESTERN ISLES

ABERDEEN
& GRAMPIAN

TAYSIDE

LOCH LOMOND,
STIRLING &
THE TROSSACHS

FIFE

ARGYLL &
THE ISLES

GREATER
GLASGOW &
CLYDE

EDINBURGH & LOTHIANS

BORDERS

AYRSHIRE & ARRAN

DUMFRIES &
GALLOWAY

NORTHUMBERLAND

TYNE &
WEAR

NORTHERN
IRELAND

CUMBRIA

DURHAM

ISLE OF
MAN

NORTH
YORKSHIRE

LANCASHIRE

MERSEYSIDE

WEST
YORKS

EAST
YORKS

GREATER
MANCHESTER

CHESHIRE

SOUTH
YORKS

NW
WALES

NE
WALES

DERBYSHIRE

NOTTINGHAM-
SHIRE

LINCOLNSHIRE

SHROPSHIRE

STAFFORD-
SHIRE

LEICESTERSHIRE

NORFOLK

MID
WALES

WEST
WALES

HEREFORD-
SHIRE

WEST
MIDLANDS

WORCESTER-
SHIRE

WARWICK-
SHIRE

NORTHAMPTON-
SHIRE

RUTLAND

CAMBRIDGE-
SHIRE

SUFFOLK

BUCKINGHAMSHIRE

BEDFORD-
SHIRE

HERTFORD-
SHIRE

ESSEX

GLAMORGAN

GWENT

GLOUCS &
BRISTOL

OXFORD-
SHIRE

GREATER
LONDON

BERKSHIRE

SURREY

KENT

WILTSHIRE

HAMPSHIRE

WEST
SUSSEX

EAST
SUSSEX

SOMERSET

DEVON

DORSET

ISLE OF
WIGHT

CORNWALL

CHANNEL
ISLANDS

Wales

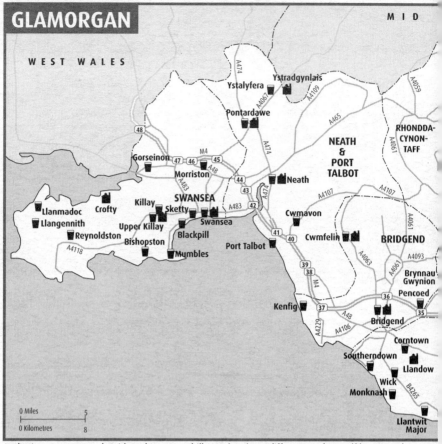

GLAMORGAN

MID

WEST WALES

Authority areas covered: Bridgend UA, Caerphilly UA (part), Cardiff UA, Merthyr Tydfil UA, Neath & Port Talbot UA, Rhondda, Cynon & Taff UA, Swansea UA, Vale of Glamorgan UA

Aberdare

Ieuan ap Iago ✓
6 High Street, CF44 7AA
☎ (01685) 880080
Greene King IPA, Abbot; 4 changing beers (sourced nationally) 🅷
Busy Wetherspoon pub in town centre, convenient for public transport. It is named after Ieuan ap Iago (Evan James), writer of the Welsh national anthem lyrics, and a proud son of Aberdare. Beers rotate quickly, but good choice is always present. The usual extensive food service is offered. Dare Valley Country Park is not far away, offering camping pitches. There is a public car park opposite. ✤🏠🍽🅳🅰♿➔🅿🛜

National Tap 🅛
Cross Street, CF44 7EG
☎ (01685) 267310 ⊕ greytreesbrewery.com
Grey Trees Diggers Gold, Drummer Boy, Mosaic Pale Ale, Afghan Pale; 3 changing beers (sourced regionally; often Grey Trees, Purple Moose, Salopian) 🅷
Small, comfortable micropub in the town's main street. It is the local outlet for award-winning Grey Trees brewery. Four of its beers are always available alongside guests sourced nationally, with craft beers also on offer. Seating is available at a mix of high and low tables. A subtle

military theme can be found among both the memorabilia and the Grey Trees beer names.
Q✤🏠🍽♿➔🛜🎵

Aberthin

Hare & Hounds
Aberthin Road, CF71 7LG
☎ (01446) 774892 ⊕ hareandhoundsaberthin.com
Wye Valley HPA; 2 changing beers (sourced regionally; often Glamorgan, Grey Trees, Vale of Glamorgan) 🅷
Characterful village pub whose cosy public bar with thick stone walls, wooden beams and log fire is the focal point where the locals gather. The rustic-style dining area serves award-winning high-quality food, with some of the ingredients grown by the chef. A full menu is also available in the bar. The guest ales are mainly sourced locally, and the cider is often from Llanblethian Orchards. The beer garden has its own bar shack and occasionally hosts live music. Dogs are welcome. Parking is limited.
Q✤🏠🍽🅳♣🌳🅿🚌(321) 🐾🛜🎵

Barry

Barry West End Club
54 St Nicholas Road, CF62 6QY
☎ (01446) 735739 ⊕ barrywestendclub.webs.com

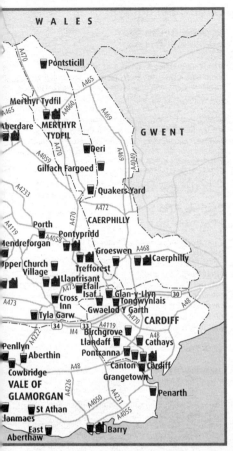

Greene King Abbot; Ruddles Best Bitter; Sharp's Doom Bar; 2 changing beers (sourced nationally) ⓗ
This spacious Wetherspoon pub is named after a landowner and legal reformer of the 1800s. It opened in 2009, in a building that was previously a market hall, theatre and bank, the vault of which remains and is used as a seating area. A large mural above the side entrance depicts life in old Barry, with many more pictures of the town inside. A larger range of beers is available during sporting events. Q ☎ ❀ ◑ ⓓ ⟲ ⇌ ▣ (96,304) ❦

Bishopston

Joiners Arms L

50 Bishopston Road, SA3 3EJ
☎ (01792) 232658
Gower Gold; Marston's Pedigree; Wadworth 6X; 2 changing beers (sourced nationally; often Exmoor, Grey Trees) ⓗ
Situated in the heart of the village, this 1860s stone-built free house remains popular with locals and visitors. The five cask handpumps are located in the rear lounge area of the two-room pub. Good-value food is served some lunchtimes and most evenings (except Mon and Sun eve) and there are occasional music events, usually around public holidays. Sporting events are shown on large screens. There is a small car park, and outdoor seating at the front. ☎ ❀ ◑ P ▣ (14) ❀ ❦ ♫

Blackpill

Woodman

120 Mumbles Road, SA3 5AS (near turn off for B4436, opp Blackpill Lido)
☎ (01792) 402700
3 changing beers (sourced nationally; often Greene King) ⓗ
Historic pub and restaurant dating back to 1819, situated on the main seafront road and the entrance to the

Sharp's Doom Bar; Wye Valley HPA; 2 changing beers (sourced nationally; often Wainwright) ⓗ
Overlooking the old harbour and housed in a large, multi-floored red-brick building, this busy venue is home to cricket, football, snooker and skittles teams as well as chess, scuba diving and fishing clubs, among others. Visiting CAMRA members are treated as honorary club members. Pub grub, live music on weekends, and a friendly atmosphere makes this club an essential visit, enhanced by two beer festivals a year. A multiple local CAMRA Club of the Year. Q ☎ ❀ ◑ ⓓ ⟲ ⇌ ▣ (96,304) ❦ ♫

Butterfly Collector L

50A Holton Road, CF63 4HE
☎ (07542) 673794
4 changing beers (sourced regionally; often Grey Trees, Vale of Glamorgan) ⓖ
Formerly a shop, this small, single-room venue has no bar but instead provides table service, with customers ordering from the current offering displayed on a blackboard. Up to four predominantly Welsh cask ales are served on gravity, accompanied by a craft keg beer. Most of the cider is fruit flavoured. The former licensee is a keen fan of The Jam and named the pub after one of their songs. The memorabilia extends into a series of tiles in the toilet. Q ☎ ⇌ (Dock) ▣ (304,96) ❀ ❦ ♫

Sir Samuel Romilly ✪

8 Romilly Buildings, Broad Street, CF62 7AU
☎ (01446) 724900

beautiful Clyne Gardens. The deceptively spacious interior is attractively furnished, with various nooks and alcoves. It is popular with families and diners, but also welcomes those only seeking liquid refreshment. An ever-changing range of ales is offered. There are three outside seating areas, including a beer garden.
☊❀◑♿P🐾📶

Bridgend

Coach [L]

37 Cowbridge Road, CF31 3DH

Coach 303; 3 changing beers (sourced nationally; often Coach, New Bristol, Thornbridge) [H]

An incredible commitment to real ale and independent producers has been the basis for the running of this pub since the current owners took over. Basically furnished but comfortable, it features a framed collage of brewery beermats adorning the walls. Events include open mic nights, outings and two beer festivals a year. The owners began brewing in 2018, and the brewery is visible from inside the pub. Two Coach cask beers are usually on sale alongside several craft beers.
Q☊❀≹♣🚌(303,X2)🐾📶♫

Wyndham Arms ✓

Dunraven Place, CF31 1JE

☎ (01656) 673571

Greene King IPA, Abbot [H]**; Sharp's Doom Bar** [H]/[G]**; 3 changing beers (sourced nationally)** [H]

Named after a centuries-old local family, this pub dates from 1792. It is split into three distinct sections, with a variety of seating options including areas more suited to dining. The pub opens at 7am to serve breakfast and non-alcoholic drinks, and the bar opens at 9am. Beers from Welsh breweries dominate. There are 25 en-suite bedrooms available, and a conference room can be hired. Q☊🛏◑♿≹📶

Brynnau Gwynion

Mountain Hare

Brynna Road, CF35 6PG

☎ (01656) 860453

3 changing beers (sourced nationally; often Glamorgan, Wye Valley) [H]

This typical Welsh village inn has featured in the Guide for many years, and has been owned by the same family for over 40 years. It has a traditional public bar, games room and a lovely, old, stone-walled lounge. The licensee began brewing on-site in 2014 and occasionally showcases his own beers. Sport is often on the TV in this rugby lovers' pub. Staff and locals are most welcoming to visitors. Closed Tuesday. Q☊❀◑♿♣P🚌(63,404)🐾📶

Caerphilly

Malcolm Uphill ✓

89-91 Cardiff Road, CF83 1FQ

☎ (029) 2076 0720

Greene King Abbot; Ruddles Best Bitter; Sharp's Doom Bar; 2 changing beers (sourced nationally; often Glamorgan, Rhymney) [H]

Comfortable and convenient Wetherspoon outlet near the main bus and rail transport hub. Usually two or three guest beers are on sale, particularly at weekends, and up to two ciders. Food service is available throughout the day. The pub can be busy later in the week and at weekends. It hosts a quiz on Sunday, when it tends to be a bit quieter. A separate accessible entrance can be used on request. ☊◑♿≹🚌📶

Cardiff: Birchgrove

Aneurin Bevan ✓

Caerphilly Road, CF14 4AD

☎ (029) 2054 4280

Greene King Abbot; Ruddles Best Bitter; Sharp's Doom Bar; 4 changing beers (sourced nationally) [H]

Popular Wetherspoon pub, smaller and more intimate than many, set in the middle of a busy road junction to the north of Gabalfa flyover. It is located near the main hospital, and its name honours the chief architect of the NHS. It offers the usual Wetherspoon food and range of changing cask ales. Live subtitled news (on silent) runs throughout the day. Extra outside dining space has been added. ☊❀◑♿●P🚌(27)📶

Cardiff: Canton

Chapter Arts Centre

Market Road, Canton, CF5 1QE

☎ (029) 2030 4400 🌐 chapter.org

Brains Rev James Original; 4 changing beers (sourced nationally) [H]

A lively and eclectic arts centre/cinema complex in a converted Victorian school, just off a busy main road. The guest beers are sourced from across the UK, and usually include small independents, supplemented by a local ale. A number of fridges contain a good range of bottled beers from continental producers, with the emphasis on those originating in Germany. They also provide good-value, freshly prepared food.
☊❀◑♿≹(Ninian Park) P🚌🐾📶♫

Lansdowne

71 Beda Road, CF5 1LX (off Cowbridge Road E)

☎ (029) 2022 1312

3 changing beers (sourced regionally; often Grey Trees, Wye Valley) [H]

A community-oriented street-corner pub created from an attractive conversion of a former hotel (whose name is still visible in the stonework). The open-plan layout has three distinct areas set around a large central bar. The guest beers constantly change and often includes a dark beer. Good-quality home-cooked food is available, with widely renowned Sunday lunches. It is family and dog friendly. ☊❀◑♿≹(Ninian Park)♣●🚌(96)🐾

Cardiff: Cathays

Cathays Beer House

109 Crwys Road, CF24 4NF

3 changing beers (sourced nationally; often 4Ts, Bristol Beer Factory) [G]

This single-room micropub, housed in a former post office, with a small terrace to the front, is a welcome real ale addition to this part of Cardiff. The basic decor and seating belies the welcoming and friendly atmosphere. It serves up to four ales on gravity dispense from across the UK, alongside a selection of boxed ciders. A former local CAMRA Cider Pub of the Year. Q☊❀♿●🚌(9)🐾📶

Cardiff: City Centre

Central Bar ✓

39 Windsor Place, CF10 3BW

☎ (029) 2078 0260

Greene King Abbot; Ruddles Best Bitter; Sharp's Doom Bar; 5 changing beers (sourced nationally) [H]

A popular Wetherspoon pub just off Queen Street near its eastern end. This former night club has an upper storey used as an additional bar, open most of the time. There is an outdoor drinking area at the rear. The pub is a regular outlet for the full range of available guest beers – up to five at any one time – as well as a number of real ciders and perries. ⮜✿❀🅙♿️≢(Queen Street)🛜

Flute & Tankard
4 Windsor Place, CF10 3BX
☎ (029) 2039 8315 ⊕ thefluteandtankard.com
5 changing beers (sourced nationally) Ⓗ
A one-bar pub just off Queen Street at eastern end. It has established itself as the city centre's leading real ale pub in terms of range and quality of its beers. An excellent choice of traditional ciders is also available. An upstairs function room hosts musical performances, often jazz, and events such as comedy nights. A former local CAMRA Pub of the Year and all-Wales Cider and Perry Pub of the Year. Open from 3pm daily, but closed when there are rugby internationals at the nearby Principality Stadium.
Q≢(Queen Street) ● ♫

Gatekeeper ✅
9-10 Westgate Street, CF10 1DD
☎ (029) 2064 6020
Greene King Abbot; 4 changing beers (sourced nationally) Ⓗ
A former theatre, then auction rooms, and now a JD Wetherspoon pub. As well as the usual listed beer, a choice of guest beers, often local, is available. The pub is spread across three levels: the downstairs bar services the two lower drinking areas while the balcony bar (not always open) services the upper floor, which is accessible by lift as well as stairs. Entry after 9pm is via the rear entrance in Womanby Street.
⮜✿❀🅙♿️≢(Central) 🛜

Old Arcade ★ 🅛
14 Church Street, CF10 1BG
☎ (029) 2021 7999 ⊕ oldarcadecardiff.co.uk
Brains Dark, Bitter, SA, SA Gold, Rev James Original Ⓗ
The Old Arcade is one of the most famous rugby pubs in the world. Though later refurbishments have given the pub a modern feel, it is well worth a visit to see the contrast of early-20th century fittings in the front bar with some of late-Victorian vintage in the back bar. It is always busy when there is an event at the nearby Principality Stadium, particularly rugby matches. Live sport is shown across several screens.
🅙♿️≢(Central) 🛜 ♫

Owain Glyndwr ✅
10 St John Street, CF10 1GL
☎ (029) 2022 1980
4 changing beers (sourced nationally; often Bristol Beer Factory, Gower, Mumbles) Ⓗ
A pub near the castle with a circular exterior, which has increased its cask offering since refurbishment. Five handpumps dispense beers from mainly Welsh micros. There is a large bar and plenty of seating inside, and outdoor seating at the front of the pub. Several TVs show live sport. It gets busy when the Welsh ruby team are playing at the nearby Principality Stadium.
❀🅙♿️≢(Central) ❀ 🛜

Pen & Wig ✅
1 Park Grove, CF10 3BJ
☎ (029) 2037 1217
8 changing beers (sourced nationally; often Vale of Glamorgan, Grey Trees, Mumbles) Ⓗ
A large, converted Victorian terraced house, just off the city centre and near the national museum and university. The clientele is mainly professional during the day, with students taking over in the evening. The beer range is from local, regional and national breweries. Prices are at the higher end for the area. The pub hosts monthly Meet

the Brewer nights and brewery takeovers. The large garden includes a covered section and a smokers' area. It features a special menu for dogs.
❀🅙♿️≢(Cathays) ● ❀ 🛜

Tiny Rebel 🅛
26 Westgate Street, CF10 1DD
☎ (07377) 414204 ⊕ tinyrebel.co.uk
Tiny Rebel Cwtch; 4 changing beers (sourced nationally; often Grey Trees, Kirkstall, Tiny Rebel) Ⓗ
Landmark pub only a short drop-kick from the Principality Stadium. A variety of rooms are spread over two floors, all decorated in the brewery's trademark quirky style. The selection of cask ales is from across the UK, and there are usually at least two boxed ciders on handpump. It serves an eclectic food menu. Monthly quizzes, open mic nights and special events are held on the last Monday in the month. Card payment only.
❀🅙♿️≢(Central) ● ❀ 🛜 ♫

Cardiff: Grangetown

Grange
134 Penarth Road, CF11 6NJ
☎ (029) 2025 0669
Wye Valley Butty Bach; 3 changing beers (sourced regionally) Ⓗ
This corner pub at a busy road junction was refurbished in 2017 after years of neglect by the previous owner. It is now run by an enthusiastic landlord and has a real community focus. There are two large rooms divided by a central bar, plus a function room. Outside is a big garden with a covered area and pizza oven. There is regular live music, a weekly quiz and great food. Up to three changing beers are offered, often from local small breweries. Q⮜❀🅙≢(Grangetown)🔥🖵♫

Cardiff: Gwaelod y Garth

Gwaelod y Garth Inn
Main Road, CF15 9HH ST116839
☎ (029) 208 0408 ⊕ gwaelodygarthinn.co.uk
6 changing beers (sourced nationally; often Thornbridge) Ⓗ
A characterful stone-built village local on the edge of Cardiff, on the lower slopes of Garth mountain. Frequented by locals, walkers and cyclists, it is the focus of the village. The pub sports eight handpumps offering a range of real ales along with two traditional ciders. There is a separate games room next to the bar area, and a high-quality restaurant upstairs. Dogs are catered for with their own menu. Q⮜❀🅙♿️🔥🖵P🖵(26B)❀ 🛜

Cardiff: Llandaff

Heathcock
58-60 Bridge Street, CF5 2EN
☎ (029) 2115 2290 ⊕ heathcockcardiff.com
Glamorgan Cwrw Gorslas/Bluestone Bitter; Wye Valley HPA; 3 changing beers (sourced regionally) Ⓗ
Situated at a junction on the main road, this pub has seen its fortunes revived under new management. A central bar serves an adjoining public bar and lounge, and the pleasant outdoor area at the rear of the premises has an additional dining area in a former skittles alley. The cosy and traditional bar has a small fireplace and a mix of furniture. The lounge is spacious and doubles as a dining room. ❀🅙♿️🖵❀ 🛜 ♫

WALES

Cardiff: Pontcanna

Halfway 🍺

247 Cathedral Road, CF11 9PP

☎ (029) 2066 7135

Brains Bitter, SA, SA Gold; 1 changing beer (sourced locally; often Brains) Ⓗ

Bustling Victorian pub with a varied clientele in the urban village of Pontcanna. The large open-plan interior offers a number of comfortable areas for drinking and dining, and food is served all day. Sporting events are shown on multiple TV screens, which are silent except for big games. Monday night is quiz night. The skittle alley is available to hire. ☼✿⏰♿♣♠🖶🌸🏳️‍🌈🎵

Cardiff: Tongwynlais

Lewis Arms 🍺

1 Mill Road, CF15 7JP ST133822

☎ (029) 2081 0330 ⊕ lewisarmspubcardiff.co.uk

Brains SA, SA Gold, Rev James Original Ⓗ

A centrally located village tavern with a solid Brains beer portfolio. It has a good reputation for food, which is served throughout the day. The airy interior sports modern decor and clean lines. For the more energetic, it offers a convenient stop on the way to or from Castell Coch, which is a short but steep walk up the hillside behind. There are regular bus services outside. Q☼✿⏰♿P🖶(132) 🌸🏳️‍🌈

Corntown

Golden Mile

Corntown Road, CF35 5BA

☎ (01656) 654884 ⊕ thegoldenmile.co.uk

3 changing beers (sourced nationally; often Draught Bass, Glamorgan, Sharp's) Ⓗ

Large pub with stunning views across the Glamorgan countryside. The double-sided bar serves both the restaurant and the bar areas, although food is available in all parts of the pub. Decor is modern but complements the exposed stonework, creating a homely atmosphere. The beer garden is a delight in the summer and also provides a play area for children. Three beers are usually available, and occasionally a fourth is added. Four en-suite rooms are available. Q☼✿⏰♿P🏳️‍🌈

Cowbridge

1 Town Hall Square 🍺

1 Town Hall Square, CF71 7DD

☎ (01446) 775217 ⊕ 1townhallsquare.com

Coach Bridgend Pale Ale; 3 changing beers (sourced nationally; often Coach, Thornbridge, Tiny Rebel) Ⓗ

A fairly recent addition to the local beer scene, aimed squarely at the beer enthusiast. There is a small bar with a seating area off it, and two rooms upstairs. The decor is traditional, with exposed stonework, tiled and wooden floors and low beams. The entrance courtyard is a pleasant suntrap on a sunny day. Food is not served but customers are welcome to bring their own. Under the same ownership as the Coach brewpub in Bridgend. ✿♣🖶(X2,321) 🌸🏳️‍🌈🎵

Bear Hotel

63 High Street, CF71 7AF

☎ (01446) 774814 ⊕ bearhotel.com

Sharp's Doom Bar; 2 changing beers (sourced nationally; often Glamorgan, Wye Valley) Ⓗ

Formerly an 18th century coaching inn, this smart hotel is located in the centre of Cowbridge. It was originally a townhouse and some of the 16th-century features

remain. Two bars either side of the entrance corridor serve real ale, with up to three guest beers also generally available. A rear courtyard offers outdoor drinking and a heated and covered smoking area. An extensive menu of main meals and snacks is always available. ✿🚪⏰P🖶(X2,321)🌸🏳️‍🌈

Cross Inn

Cross Inn Hotel

Main Road, CF72 8AZ

☎ (01443) 223431

Wye Valley HPA; 2 changing beers (sourced nationally; often Fuller's, Sharp's) Ⓗ

This traditional pub attracts a strong following from locals and visitors. The large single room is divided into a bar area and comfortable lounge, in which home-prepared meals are served. Curry night is Wednesday, and Sunday lunches are popular. A narrow entrance leads through to the rear car park and a pleasant outdoor drinking area with covered booths. A frequent local CAMRA award-winner. Q✿⏰♿♣P🖶(124)🌸🏳️‍🌈

Cwmavon

Brit

London Row, SA12 9AH (from Port Talbot, take B4286 to Cwmavon, turn right after about a mile, signed Maesteg, pub is 200yds on right)

☎ (01639) 680247

2 changing beers (sourced regionally) Ⓗ

Renovated in 2014 in an eclectic but cosy style, this pub has four handpumps serving two ciders and two rotating real ales, usually from a local brewery. The pub hosts a beer festival in June and is also noted for its good food. It has a lovely riverside garden, and is dog friendly. A former local CAMRA Pub of the Year. It may occasionally be closed on Monday and Tuesday in January and February. Q☼✿🚪⏰♿P🌸🏳️‍🌈

Cwmfelin

Cross Inn 🍺

Maesteg Road, CF34 9LB

☎ (01656) 732476 ⊕ cerddinbrewery.co.uk

Cerddin Solar, Cascade; 3 changing beers (sourced locally; often Cerddin) Ⓗ

Home to the Cerddin brewery and acting as its brewery tap, this is a must-visit pub and a long-standing fixture in this Guide. Alongside its five cask beers, a good range of bottle-conditioned beers is also available. This traditional two-roomed Valleys inn offers a warm welcome, with friendly locals and knowledgeable staff. There is a patio area directly outside the brewery. A multiple CAMRA award winner. Q✿≈(Garth)♣🖶🖶(71)🌸🏳️‍🌈🎵

Deri

Baileys Arms

Bailey Street, CF81 9HX

☎ (01443) 830214

Grey Trees Diggers Gold Ⓗ

Friendly traditional pub near the centre of Deri village, with the front entrance at right angles to the street. There is a spacious and comfortable front bar, plus a back room for pool and darts. Another Grey Trees beer occasionally substitutes for the regular beer, Diggers Gold. The Darran Valley cycle path passes close by, with access at the back of the car park. ✿♣P🖶(1)

East Aberthaw

Blue Anchor ★
CF62 3DD
☎ (01446) 750329 ⊕ blueanchoraberthaw.com
Theakston Old Peculier; Wadworth 6X; Wye Valley HPA; 2 changing beers (sourced regionally; often Glamorgan, Harbwr) Ⓗ
Dating from 1380, this attractive thatched pub has been in the same family for over 75 years. Its thick stone walls house a labyrinth of rooms, with stone floors, wooden beams and open fires adding to the character and making the pub a tourist attraction for ale and food lovers. Up to five ales and award-winning food are served in the bar and the restaurant. The guest beer and cider are often locally produced. Q🏠🕏🌣◑▶🚲(304)♣

Efail Isaf

Carpenters Arms 🄻
Heol Ffrwd Philip, CF38 1AR
☎ 07989 383479
2 changing beers (sourced locally; often Vale of Glamorgan, Well Drawn) Ⓗ
Friendly traditional locals' pub with two comfortably furnished bars which are usually opened into one. One real ale is always available, and two at weekends. South Wales brewery beers of varying styles are often on tap. Weekly events include a quiz on Tuesday, poker on Wednesday, and 'rock & roll bingo' on Thursday. A large room with dartboards for the pub's darts teams and for casual players can be hired. A south-facing patio is popular on sunny days. 🕏♣P🚲(90)♣♪

Gilfach Fargoed

Gilfach Workmens Club
87-89 Park Place, CF81 8LX
☎ (01443) 830210
2 changing beers (sourced nationally; often Glamorgan, Oakham) Ⓗ
The long-established members' club is a friendly destination, where visitors are always welcome. The front bar has comfortable lounge seating and a sports TV, which is usually silenced. There is also a large function room and a skittle alley. The only outlet for guest beers in the upper Rhymney Valley, the Workies has two constantly changing beers from a variety of local and national sources. ≈♣◐♪

Glan-y-llyn

Fagins Craft Beer House & Art Café
9 Cardiff Road, CF15 7QD
☎ (029) 2081 1800
2 changing beers (sourced regionally; often Grey Trees, Twt Lol) Ⓗ
A popular free house with a front bar and a larger room hidden beyond. The ales are generally hoppy pale or golden, and usually feature local breweries such as Glamorgan or Twt Lol. Thornbridge Jaipur is a frequent choice from further afield, while one real cider is also available. Good-value classic pub meals are served later in the week, including Sunday lunch, and there is occasional live music. Taffs Well railway station is a 15-minute walk away. Q🏠🕏◑◆🚲(132)♣🍴♪

Gorseinon

Mardy Inn ✅
117 High Street, SA4 4BR
☎ (01792) 890600

Greene King IPA, Abbot; Sharp's Doom Bar; 2 changing beers (sourced nationally) Ⓗ
This Wetherspoon pub was formerly a traditional high street pub. Following a major refurbishment, it is now modern in style. The large single bar has an adjoining airy extension looking over the furnished patio area. Many interesting pictures of old Gorseinon adorn the walls, depicting the town and its inhabitants in years gone by. TVs display news and sport. 🏠🕏◑◆P♣🍴

Groeswen

White Cross Inn
CF15 7UT (overlooking Groeswen Chapel)
☎ (029) 2085 1332
4 changing beers (sourced nationally) Ⓗ
This independent free house is a rural gem, overlooking the town of Caerphilly. It offers excellent choice and value from its four handpumps. The beer range constantly changes, each pump offering a different style, including a dark. Three bottled ciders from local maker Williams Brothers are also available. Home-made ham and cheese rolls are on offer at the bar. The pub has an eclectic social calendar. Access is unsuitable for large vehicles. Q🏠🕏♣◆P♣🍴♪

Hendreforgan

Griffin Inn 🍺 ★ 🄻
CF39 8YL (from Tonyrefail on A4093, turn down lane after Gilfach Goch village sign)
☎ (01443) 675144
Glamorgan Cwrw Gorslas/Bluestone Bitter, Jemima's Pitchfork Ⓗ
This warm, characterful pub has been in the same family for more than 60 years. Though out of the way, it is well worth the effort to find. The immaculate decor features oak furniture, gleaming brassware and memorabilia everywhere you look, and there are roaring fires in winter. The bar operates on a cash only basis, and an original Victorian till remains in use. Local CAMRA Pub of the Year 2024. Under-18s are not allowed inside. Q🕏AP🚲(150,172)♣

Kenfig

Prince of Wales ★
CF33 4PR
☎ (01656) 740356 ⊕ princeofwalesinn.co.uk
Draught Bass Ⓖ; 2 changing beers (sourced regionally; often Gower) Ⓗ/Ⓖ
An award-winning heritage inn dating from the 15th century and steeped in local history. Visitors can expect three quality ales on gravity, good, locally sourced food and a warm welcome. Family friendly and popular with dog walkers, the pub is comfortable and cosy. Outside there is a stunning view over Kenfig Nature Reserve. The Draught Bass is renowned throughout the local area. Guest beers and cider are occasionally available. Q🏠🕏◑≈(Pyle) P♣🍴

Killay

Village Bar Café ✅
5-6 Swan Court, The Precinct, SA2 7BA
☎ (01792) 203311
Sharp's Doom Bar; 2 changing beers (sourced regionally; often Glamorgan, Grey Trees, Tenby) Ⓗ
Situated at the rear of a small shopping precinct in Killay on the gateway to Gower, the Village has changed its focus from a traditional pub to a café bar. It retains a single split-level bar that offers three real ales. There is a

quiz on Monday afternoons and Tuesday evenings. Breakfasts and light meals (toasties, sandwiches) are on offer up to early afternoons. 🐴❀◐♣P🐾📶♫

Llangennith

King's Head

SA3 1HX

☎ (01792) 386212 🌐 kingsheadgower.co.uk

4 changing beers (sourced regionally; often Evan Evans) [H]

Previously a row of three 17th-century stone-built cottages, this large pub has two separate bars and a variety of seating rooms, plus outside seating at the front and rear. Ales from local breweries are available (up to four in summer, fewer in winter), and a variety of home-made food is served throughout the day. It is situated at the western end of the Gower Peninsular, a short distance from Llangennith beach.
🐴❀🛏◐⛺♣●P🚌(116) 🐾📶

Llanmadoc

Britannia Inn ✔

SA3 1DB

☎ (01792) 386624 🌐 britanniagower.com

Gower Gold; Sharp's Doom Bar; 1 changing beer (sourced nationally; often Wye Valley) [H]

This picturesque 17th-century pub is partly constructed from timbers of ships wrecked on the nearby coast. A cosy bar at the entrance serves good food and beer, while the rear area has been converted into a fine dining restaurant. There is a beer terrace at the front, while a large beer garden at the rear gives stunning views over the nearby estuary and North Gower Marshes, and has a play area for children. 🐴❀◐⛺♣P🚌(116)🐾📶

Llanmaes

Blacksmith's Arms

Tyle House Close, CF61 2XR

☎ (01446) 795996

Timothy Taylor Landlord; Wye Valley HPA; 1 changing beer (sourced nationally) [H]

A popular village pub consisting of a large, open-plan, split-level room separated into three distinct areas: a drinking space with a log fire, relaxed dining area and a dedicated restaurant (also available as a function room). The large patio at the front is a suntrap in summer. Live music features on the last Friday of each month.
Q🐴❀◐⛺♣P🐾📶♫

Llantrisant

Wheatsheaf Hotel

High Street, CF72 8BQ

☎ (01443) 229367

2 changing beers (sourced regionally; often Grey Trees, Ludlow, Wye Valley) [H]

A welcoming free house that is popular with all age groups. Three rooms off the bar each have an eclectic range of furniture and fittings, including cosy sofas, and one has a real fire. The ales are predominantly from South Wales and border counties. In addition to darts and cards, there is a quiz on Tuesday and occasional live music at weekends. Buses stop outside and parking is available a short walk away. Q♣🚌(100,404)

Llantwit Major

Old Swan Inn [L]

Church Street, CF61 1SB

☎ (01446) 792230

3 changing beers (sourced locally; often Bluestone, Tomos & Lilford, Vale of Glamorgan) [H]

The town's oldest pub is near the historic St Illtyd's Church and opposite the town hall. It has a popular front bar and a modern restaurant at the back, both of which serve excellent food and an ever-changing range of up to four ales, often locally sourced. Beer festivals are held in spring and summer and feature local live bands. A weekly quiz is held on Tuesday evening; steak night is Wednesday. The town car park is nearby.
Q🐴❀◐🚆P🚌(303,304) 🐾📶♫

White Hart Inn

Wine Street, CF61 1RZ

☎ (01446) 796956 🌐 oldwhitehart.uk

3 changing beers (sourced nationally; often Glamorgan, Tomos & Lilford, Wadworth) [H]

Dating back to the 15th century, this Grade II-listed pub is set in the picturesque town square. The cosy public bar has a large log-burner and two TVs. Three ales are served, and the separate restaurant offers a range of traditional food. A large beer garden at the back hosts popular music events and occasional small beer festivals. Seating outside at the front catches the afternoon sun.
🐴❀🛏◐⛺🚆♣🚌(303,304) 🐾📶♫

Merthyr Tydfil

Dic Penderyn ✔

102 High Street, CF47 8AP

☎ (01685) 385786

Greene King IPA, Abbot; Sharp's Doom Bar; 2 changing beers (sourced regionally; often Evan Evans, Glamorgan, Rhymney) [H]

Wetherspoon outlet in the town centre named after the martyr Richard Lewis, better known as as Dic Penderyn. Seating is on the ground floor in the main bar area, with upstairs outdoor seating overlooking Penderyn Square and the beautiful Redhouse Cymru Arts Centre building. Historic displays recall the town's heritage in iron production, and the pioneering run of the Penydarren steam locomotive in 1802. An extensive food menu is available throughout the day. 🐴❀◐♿🚆●▯🚌📶

Winchester [L]

1A Castle Street, CF47 8BG

☎ (01653) 79758

Rhymney Hobby Horse, Export; 2 changing beers (sourced locally; often Rhymney) [H]

The copper-topped tables and a coal fire in winter months make for a cosy atmosphere in this popular town-centre venue. The ales are attractively priced draught Rhymney beers, with mini-kegs, gift sets and other brewery merchandise available for sale. The pub is nice and quiet when the sports TV is not on. Children are not admitted. 🚆🚌🐾📶

Monknash

Plough & Harrow ★

CF71 7QQ

☎ (01656) 890209 🌐 ploughandharrowmonknash.co.uk

Draught Bass' [G]; Glamorgan Jemima's Pitchfork [H]; 2 changing beers (sourced nationally; often Wye Valley) [H]/[G]

Renowned 14th-century pub, originally a monastic farmhouse, retaining many original features and with an eclectic furnishing style that is always a surprise to newcomers. Up to four real ales are available on handpump or gravity, with local breweries well supported, plus ciders and perries from local producers.

Good pub meals are cooked from scratch using locally sourced ingredients. The large canopy-covered beer garden hosts festivals and live music in summer. Four holiday apartments are available. A former local CAMRA Pub of the Year. Q✿☎🅿🍴🅿🖰(303)🌸♪

Morriston

Red Lion Inn ✔
49 Sway Road, SA6 6JA (near Morriston Cross opp fire station)
☎ (01792) 761870
Greene King Abbot; Sharp's Doom Bar; 4 changing beers (sourced nationally) Ⓗ
This deceptively spacious Wetherspoon has a large, comfortable, open-plan room with a log fire in the front of the pub and high bar-stools at the back. Guest ales often include at least one from a local brewery. A number of pictures on the walls depict the long-gone industrial history of the area. A community board by the main door advertises various local events. ☎✿☎🅿🖰🅿🌳

Mumbles

Beaufort Arms 🏆 Ⓛ
1 Castle Road, Norton, SA3 5TF (on a busy jct of minor roads, near A4067 'Mumbles Road' and seafront footpath)
☎ (01792) 736127
Draught Bass; Glamorgan Jemima's Pitchfork; Sharp's Atlantic; 1 changing beer (sourced regionally; often Mantle, Mumbles) Ⓗ
A charming 18th-century village local with a welcoming atmosphere. Tastefully renovated since acquisition from a pub group, its popularity with locals has only gone up since the beer range was increased. A traditional main bar has a TV and dartboard, and there is also a small, comfortable lounge; both rooms have real fires. There is a small beer garden at the rear. A quiz is held on Tuesday. Cash only. Local CAMRA Pub of the Year. ☎✿♣🌳🌳

Pilot Inn Ⓛ
726 Mumbles Road, SA3 4EL
☎ 07897 895511
Draught Bass; 6 changing beers (sourced locally; often Pilot Brewery) Ⓗ
Friendly, welcoming local on the seafront at Mumbles, home to the Pilot Brewery. Seven ales are always available, usually including up to three rotating beers brewed on site. A wide range of bottled ciders is available and hot drinks are also served. This historic pub, built in 1849, is next to the coastal path and is popular with lifeboatmen, locals, real ale fans, walkers and cyclists among others. A multiple CAMRA award winner. Q☎♣🅿🌳🌳

Taproom Ⓛ
29 Newton Road, SA3 4AS (in main shopping street, next to Tesco store)
☎ (01792) 439899 🌐 gowerbrewery.com
Gower Gold, Power Ⓗ
Effectively a combination of traditional taproom and café, this small pie-and-pint pub opened in 2023 as a joint venture between Gower brewery and Pieminister. The long, narrow, attractively styled modern room has table seating, and an L-shaped bar to the rear has stools alongside. The food menu is based around pies or small-plate dishes. Opening times may vary. ☎🅿🌳🌳♪

Ty Cwrw
650 Mumbles Road, SA3 4EA (on main seafront road, next to Carlton Hotel)
☎ 07488 298344
4 changing beers (sourced regionally; often Grey Trees, Harbwr, Tomos Watkin) Ⓗ
Small and friendly, independently owned pub whose name is Welsh for beer house. Four real ales and six craft keg beers, all sourced from a variety of Welsh or independent breweries, are listed on a large blackboard. Although the frontage looks narrow from the outside, there is a second room behind the front room and the long wooden bar. Both rooms are decorated in a light, modern style and display a range of paintings from local artists. ☎✿♣🅿🌳🌳

Victoria Inn
21 Westbourne Place, SA3 4DB (in a small side street off Mumbles Rd; turn right at Davies Bakery, opp Boots, then turn left opp the coffee shop onto Gloucester Pl)
☎ 07388 160331
Bristol Beer Factory Independence; Draught Bass; Oakham Citra; 2 changing beers (sourced nationally; often Courage, Glamorgan) Ⓗ
Traditional and popular corner local in the heart of Mumbles, dating from the 1860s. It is decorated in a traditional dark, comfortable style, and retains some original features, including a well in the bar area, which was the source of water in the days when the pub brewed its own beer. Live music plays most Sunday evenings and there is a quiz on Wednesday evenings. ☎✿♣🌳🌳♪

Neath

Borough Arms
2 New Henry Street, SA11 1PH (off Briton Ferry road, near the Stockham's Corner roundabout)
☎ (01639) 644902
Draught Bass; 3 changing beers (sourced regionally; often Glamorgan, Grey Trees) Ⓗ
This emphasis in this welcoming, homely local is very much on ales and conversation. The landlord and brewer occasionally has his own ales on tap, but there is always a good choice from regional breweries. The pub holds an annual GlastonBorough festival in May, featuring live music, and has a beer festival over the August bank holiday. Live acoustic music plays every Wednesday. Cash only please. Well worth the 10-minute walk from the town centre. Q✿🚲🌳♪

David Protheroe ✔
7 Windsor Road, SA11 1LS (opp railway station)
☎ (01639) 622130
Greene King Abbot; Ruddles Best Bitter; Sharp's Doom Bar; 5 changing beers (sourced nationally; often Brains, Evan Evans) Ⓗ
Former police station and courthouse named after the first policeman in Neath. This Wetherspoon is ideally situated in the centre of town, directly opposite the railway station and a short walk from the bus terminus. It features three permanent beers and up to five guests on the roster, and often includes a locally brewed ale. Real ciders are also available. ☎✿🅿🖰🚲🌳

Penarth

Pilot 🏆
67 Queen's Road, CF64 1DJ
☎ (029) 2071 0615 🌐 thepilotpenarth.co.uk
2 changing beers (sourced regionally; often Bluestone, Glamorgan, Grey Trees) Ⓗ

This pub has a long-established reputation for high-quality beer, wine and food. Its ales focus on Welsh breweries, with more unusual offerings from around the country. There is pleasant seating outside at the front for sunny days, and the log-fired stove is comfortable in the winter. The restaurant serves home-cooked Mediterranean-style food; booking is recommended at peak times. The front bar is dog-friendly until 6pm. Closed Monday. Current local CAMRA Pub of the Year.
Q✿⦰❍&≉(Dingle Road)🚌(94,305)🐾🛜♪

Windsor
95 Windsor Road, CF64 1JE
☎ (029) 2070 8675
2 changing beers (sourced nationally; often Marston's, Young's) ℍ

Following a change in emphasis from dining to a more traditional pub, the Windsor offers a comfortable environment with a variety of seating to accommodate groups of different sizes. Classic pub food is available with a range of daily specials. It has a pool table and hosts entertainment through the week, including live bands, quizzes and comedy nights. When not hosting events, it is usually quiet, and a perfect place for a good conversation over ales chosen from the Marston's range.
Q✿&≉(Dingle Road)🚌(92,94)🐾🛜♪

Pencoed

Little Penybont Arms
13 Penybont Road, CF35 5PY
☎ 07734 767937
2 changing beers (sourced nationally; often Salopian) ⑥

Cosy micropub offering a couple of changing beers on gravity dispense, several ciders and a large selection of single malt whiskies and gins. The Steak & Stamp restaurant next door is under the same ownership and drinks from the pub are also available there. Since opening, the pub has built up a strong local following. Craft keg beer is also available. Closed Tuesday.
Q✿✿⦰≉♣🚌(404,63)🐾🛜

Penllyn

Fox
CF71 7RQ
☎ (01446) 772352 ⊕ thefoxatpenllyn.co.uk
3 changing beers (sourced nationally; often Cwrw, St Austell, Wye Valley) ℍ

A warm welcome is guaranteed at this community-owned village local. Within its thick stone walls, a stone-floored main bar area and cosy log fire greet you in the colder months. A separate restaurant serves meals using locally sourced produce. To the rear is a large enclosed garden where children can play safely, while at the front a neat patio area is popular on warmer days.
Q✿✿⦰AP🚌(X2)🐾🛜

Pontardawe

Pontardawe Inn
123 Herbert Street, SA8 4ED (off A4067 into town, pub is off A474 flyover)
☎ (01792) 447562 ⊕ pontardaweinnpub.co.uk
5 changing beers (sourced nationally; often Marston's) ℍ

Former Welsh longhouse later converted to a drover's pub, situated alongside the river Tawe and the local cycle path. A side room and stable were added in 1850 by the Royal Mail as a sorting depot. The central bar serves up to five changing ales, including one locally sourced,

alongside a range of real ciders. Food is served daily in this multi award-winning pub. Seasonal beer festivals plus music festivals are held, with live music also featuring at weekends. ✿✿⦰◐&♣♣P🐾🛜♪

Pontsticill

Red Cow ℒ
Main Road, CF48 2UN (in centre of village)
☎ (01585) 387775
Wye Valley Bitter; house beer (by Grey Trees); 3 changing beers (sourced locally; often Grey Trees, Wye Valley) ℍ

Warm and welcoming pub set in beautiful countryside, and within sight of the Brecon Mountain Railway, is a comfortable place to stop for a beer and a bite, with a menu offering wholesome pub food. The Wye Valley guest beer is often Butty Bach. The bar is a good size, neat and well furnished, and covered outdoor seating is also available. It is a popular destination for family groups and hikers, and is dog-friendly, with a garden and large car park. Q✿✿⦰♣P🐾🛜

Pontypridd

Bunch of Grapes ℒ ✅
Ynysangharad Road, CF37 4DA (off A4054)
☎ (01443) 402934 ⊕ bunchofgrapes.pub
Cwrw Otley O1; 8 changing beers (sourced nationally; often Cwrw Otley, Grey Trees, Salopian) ℍ

Located just outside the town centre, this busy and well-loved pub boasts many awards for beer and food. The rear elevation has been extensively refurbished, benefitting both bar and restaurant. Cwrw Otley microbrewery adds to the attractions, with its beers served alongside the numerous guests. A variety of styles are covered, plus craft beers and ciders. The restaurant is highly acclaimed, with a menu featuring locally sourced choices. Special food and drink events occur throughout the year. Q✿✿⦰≉♣P🚌🐾🛜♪

Clwb y Bont
85A Taff Street, CF37 4SL (off Taff St in town centre, behind Boots)
☎ (01443) 491424
1 changing beer (sourced locally; often Glamorgan, Grey Trees, Twt Lol) ℍ

Formerly a brewery and blacksmith's, this social club was founded in 1983. Although its main aim is to promote the Welsh language and culture, it hosts a diverse range of events, including regular music sessions, in addition to being a social meeting place. There is a bar and function room downstairs, and a smaller one upstairs. Beers from local independent craft brewers are favoured, with one cask beer and a range of bottled beers. Visitors are welcome. ≉🚌♪

Llanover Arms ★
Bridge Street, CF37 4PE (opp N entrance to Ynysangharad Park, off A470)
☎ (01443) 403215
3 changing beers (sourced regionally) ℍ

A short walk from Pontypridd bus station across the town's historic bridge, this popular free house was built to serve boatmen on the Glamorgan Canal in the late 18th century. Each of the three rooms has its own distinct atmosphere, and the walls are festooned with a variety of artefacts including old mirrors, paintings and clocks. The front bar serves two or three real ales, usually pale or golden, predominantly from breweries uncommon for the area. There is a pleasant outside seating area. Q✿≉♣🚌🐾♪

Patriot Bar 🄻

25B Taff Street, CF37 4UA

☎ (01443) 407915

Rhymney Hobby Horse, Bitter, Export; 2 changing beers (sourced locally; often Rhymney) 🄷

A Rhymney brewery tied house, near the bus station and a short walk from the railway station. Known locally as the Wonky Bar, it is a lively pub with no frills, and enjoys a loyal clientele. It offers well-kept, good-value beers that sell fast. ⇌🚌🐾📶

Tumble Inn ✔

4-9 Broadway, CF37 1BA

☎ (01443) 484390

Greene King Abbot; Ruddles Best Bitter; Sharp's Doom Bar; 2 changing beers (sourced nationally; often Glamorgan, Rhymney) 🄷

Spacious Wetherspoon bar near the impressive railway station and the main shopping area, and handy for several main bus routes. It once served as the town's main post office. The open-plan space is mainly on one level with two smaller raised tiers, served by a single bar. A pleasant outdoor patio is divided into smoking and non-smoking areas, and overlooks the River Taff. 👶❀◑♿⇌🚌📶

Port Talbot

Lord Caradoc ✔

69-73 Station Road, SA13 1NW (5 mins' walk from Port Talbot Parkway railway station)

☎ (01639) 896007

Greene King Abbot; Ruddles Best Bitter; Sharp's Doom Bar; 3 changing beers (sourced nationally) 🄷

Wetherspoon pub on the main shopping street, with a spacious, open-plan layout and a family-friendly area. The choice of beers is open to suggestion from customers, with a wide range always available. A locally brewed ale is frequently on offer, and up to three real ciders are also available. The walls are adorned with photographs of the town from times gone by and famous local people. The pub has been repeatedly recognised by Wetherspoon for its high standard of catering. 👶❀◑♿⇌(Parkway) P📶

Porth

Rheola 🄻

Rheola Road, CF39 0LF

☎ (01443) 682633

Rhymney Bitter, Export; 1 changing beer (sourced locally; often Rhymney) 🄷

Friendly local pub serving three well-kept, good-value cask ales from Rhymney brewery. The bar room has a pool table, dartboard and jukebox, and is often quite lively. The separate lounge is quieter, though less so at weekends. Various activities include a quiz, and usually live music at weekends. The pub is situated near the confluence of the two Rhondda rivers, and is well served by rail and bus. ❀⇌♣P🚌(120,132)📶♫

Quakers Yard

Glantaff Inn

Cardiff Road, CF46 5AH

☎ (01443) 411101 🌐 glantaffinn.com

2 changing beers (sourced nationally; often Grey Trees, Wadworth, Wye Valley) 🄷

Pleasant and friendly pub overlooking the River Taff. Good-value food is served daily in the main bar, and in a dining room upstairs; booking is advised, particularly at weekends when live entertainment often features. Sunday lunches are served 12-4pm, reverting to the bar menu for Sunday evening. Bunkhouse accommodation for up to six guests is available. May close early on quiet weekdays. 👶❀🛏◑♿⇌🚌(7,78)🐾📶♫

Reynoldston

King Arthur Hotel 🄻

Higher Green, SA3 1AD (on village green)

☎ (01792) 390775 🌐 kingarthurhotel.co.uk

Fuller's London Pride; Gower Gold; Sharp's Doom Bar; 1 changing beer (sourced regionally; often Glamorgan, Tenby, Tiny Rebel) 🄷

Popular, traditional, family-owned hotel and an acclaimed wedding venue, situated at the foot of Cefn Bryn hill in beautiful Gower, overlooking the village green. Covered outdoor seating is available by the pub entrance, as well as a large seating area on the green itself. The cosy, atmospheric main and rear bars are open all day to drinkers and diners – there is also a separate restaurant. Home-cooked main meals and bar snacks made with local produce are available all day, and breakfasts for non-residents from 9-11am. 👶❀🛏◑♿P📶♫

St Athan

Roost

Rock Road, CF62 4PG

☎ (01446) 753715 🌐 theroostonrockroad.com

Wye Valley HPA; 1 changing beer (sourced nationally; often Glamorgan, Wye Valley) 🄷

A major refurbishment of this pub – formerly the Four Bells – has created a more modern interior style but with some original features remaining such as the floorboards, which now form the bar front. Comfy sofas and chairs surround the log-burner alongside tall tables and stools in the drinking area. Outside there is a patio and grassy area where outdoor events such as barbecues can be held in the summer. Food is of a high standard and the menu is varied with locally sourced, seasonal offerings. Accommodation is in five en-suite rooms. Closed Monday. Q👶❀🛏◑P🚌(304)📶

Sketty

Vivian Arms

106 Gower Road, SA2 9BT (at Sketty Cross, jct of A4118 and A4216)

☎ (01792) 516194 🌐 vivianarmspubswansea.co.uk

Brains SA, Rev James Original; Marston's Pedigree; 2 changing beers (sourced nationally) 🄷

Situated on the main crossroads in Sketty, this spacious pub offers reasonably-priced meals daily, including a popular Sunday lunch. It has a mixture of seating areas and plenty of TV screens throughout the pub showing live sport. Live music features on Friday and open mic on the first Monday of the month. There is a general knowledge quiz on Sunday and a Wednesday music quiz. 👶❀◑♣🐾📶♫

Southerndown

Three Golden Cups

CF32 0RW

☎ (01656) 880432 🌐 thethreegoldencups.co.uk

Sharp's Doom Bar; 1 changing beer (sourced locally; often Glamorgan, Gower) 🄷

One of the few pubs on the Glamorgan Heritage Coast from which you can actually see the sea. The restaurant/lounge has a stone and wooden decor and is named after the Maria Jose, a ship wrecked nearby in 1914.

Music evenings are held regularly and summer barbecues are popular. The campsite is adjacent to the pub, bookable from March. ⏱🏴🕙🅿️▲♣🖿🖳(303)🌺

Swansea

Bank Statement ✅
57-58 Wind Street, SA1 1EP
☎ (01792) 455477
Greene King Abbot; Sharp's Doom Bar; 3 changing beers (sourced nationally) Ⓗ
A former bank, sympathetically transformed by Wetherspoon while retaining its original ornate interior. The pub is at the heart of the city's busy bar quarter and has a large ground floor with plenty of seating. Additional seating is available on the upstairs terrace. Is is popular with all ages throughout the week. It regularly shows sports events on its many screens. The bottled beer selection includes some real ales. ⏱🕙🔥⬥🥾🔊

Brunswick Arms
3 Duke Street, SA1 4HS (between St Helens Rd and Walter Rd)
☎ (01792) 465676 ⊕ brunswickswansea.com
Butcombe Original; Wye Valley Butty Bach Ⓗ**; 3 changing beers (sourced nationally)** Ⓗ/Ⓖ
Side-street pub with the air of a country inn in the city. Wooden beams and comfortable seating create a traditional, relaxing atmosphere. A popular general knowledge quiz is held on Monday, and a music quiz on Thursday. There are usually up to five beers available and one of the changing beers is gravity dispensed, often from a local brewery. 🕙⬥🔥🖳(200)🔊

No Sign Bar ★ Ⓛ
56 Wind Street, SA1 1EG
☎ (01792) 465300 ⊕ nosignwinebar.com
Gower Gold; 3 changing beers (sourced regionally; often Butcombe, Mumbles, Tiny Rebel) Ⓗ
Historic narrow bar established in 1690, formerly known as Mundays Wine Bar and reputedly a regular haunt of Dylan Thomas. Architectural signs from various periods of the pub's past remain, some dividing the interior into separate bar areas. Quality food and wine are available, with up to five real ciders on sale. Live music features in the bar on Friday, Saturday and often Sunday evenings. ⏱🏴🕙⬥🔥🌺🔊♪

Potter's Wheel
85-86 The Kingsway, SA1 5JE
☎ (01792) 465113
Ruddles Best Bitter; Sharp's Doom Bar; 5 changing beers (sourced nationally) Ⓗ
A city-centre Wetherspoon pub with a long, sprawling bar area that attracts a wide mix of customers. An interesting selection of guest beers is available, with a noticeable commitment to local breweries, plus real cider. Photographs on the walls feature many local dignitaries associated with the area's industrial past, particularly ceramics and pottery. Look for the CAMRA noticeboard and beer suggestion box. ⏱🕙🔥⬥🔊

Queen's Hotel
Gloucester Place, SA1 1TY (near Waterfront Museum)
☎ (01792) 521531
Theakston Best Bitter, Old Peculier; 2 changing beers (sourced nationally; often Bristol Beer Factory, Fuller's, Glamorgan) Ⓗ
This vibrant free house is near the Dylan Thomas Theatre, City Museum, National Waterfront Museum and marina. The walls display photographs depicting Swansea's rich maritime heritage. The pub enjoys strong local support, and home-cooked lunches are popular. Evening

entertainment includes a Sunday quiz and live music on Saturday. This is a rare local outlet for Theakston Old Peculier, in addition to a seasonal guest beer often from a local microbrewery. A former local CAMRA Pub of the Year. 🕙🔥♣🌺🔊♪

Uplands Tavern ✅
42 Uplands Crescent, Uplands, SA2 0PG
☎ (01792) 458242
Greene King IPA, Abbot; 2 changing beers (sourced nationally) Ⓗ
Situated in the heart of Swansea's student quarter, the Tav attracts regulars from all walks of life, and enjoys a reputation for the quality and variety of its live music at weekends, and most Wednesdays, and Monday open mic nights. The large, single-room pub is a former haunt of Dylan Thomas, who is commemorated in a separate snug area. It has a large heated outdoor drinking area. Quiz night is on Tuesday. 🏴⬥🔥🌺🔊♪

Trefforest

Otley Brewpub & Kitchen Ⓛ
7 Forest Road, CF37 1SY
☎ (01443) 402033 ⊕ otleybrewpubandkitchen.com
Mabby Blue; 1 changing beer (sourced regionally; often Mabby) Ⓗ
Friendly brewpub, close to the university, serving a selection of cask and craft beers and showcasing its own in-house microbrewery. The spacious, open-plan layout is well furnished. Staff are welcoming and informative. A modern menu features tasty street food and vegetarian options, plus traditional Sunday lunches. Close to the train station and buses to Pontypridd. Closed Monday and Tuesday. ⏱🏴🕙🔥♣🥾🖳(90,100)🌺🔊

Rickards Arms
61 Park Street, CF37 1SN
☎ (01443) 402305
⊕ therickardsarms-pontypridd.foodndrink.uk
2 changing beers (sourced locally; often Cwrw Otley, Grey Trees) Ⓗ
Traditional, family-owned pub, popular with students from the nearby university. Beers are always well kept and good quality, and classic pub meals are served at reasonable prices. The pub has several drinking areas, each of different character, including a vaulted cellar. The beer garden is popular but note that access is via the upper floor. It opens early until late seven days a week, with food served at most times. Handy for buses and trains. ⏱🏴🕙🔥♣🖳(90,100)🌺🔊

Tyla Garw

Boar's Head
Coedcae Lane, CF72 9EZ (600yds from A473 over level crossing)
☎ (01443) 225400
2 changing beers (sourced nationally; often Glamorgan) Ⓗ
Popular free house, with high wooden settles in the bar area and a more contemporary layout at the rear. At least one Glamorgan beer is usually on, but guests can be more unusual for the area. Two other rooms serve as dining areas, with a classic pub menu (booking advised for Sun lunch). There is a popular coffee shop at the rear and an enclosed patio is ideal for alfresco drinking or dining. There is a shortcut to Pontyclun railway station. Q⏱🏴🕙🚋(Pontyclun) 🅿️🌺

Upper Church Village

Farmers Arms

St Illtyds Road, CF38 1EB

☎ (01443) 205766

3 changing beers (sourced nationally; often Wye Valley) Ⓗ

Welcoming village local, popular with all ages, with one large bar and a smaller room. Wye Valley Butty Bach is often available, plus various other beers, some of which are unusual for the area. There is a popular quiz night on Tuesday, occasional live music, and events such as drinks tasting evenings and Q&A sessions with sporting personalities. Pizzas and burgers are served from the large split-level garden and patio on summer weekends. Q☺P및(90,100)☺♫

Upper Killay

Railway Inn ★ ᴸ

553 Gower Road, SA2 7DS

☎ (01792) 203946

Swansea Bishopswood Bitter, Original Wood, Three Cliffs Gold; 2 changing beers (sourced nationally) Ⓗ

Classic locals' pub set in woodlands. The adjacent former railway line forms part of route four of the National Cycle Network. There are two small rooms at the front, one of which is the main snug/bar, with a larger lounge at the rear. In winter the fire in the lounge provides welcome warmth and cheer. Swansea Brewing Company has moved alongside the pub and should be available regularly. An outside area hosts barbeques and music events. Thursday is quiz night. Q☺♣➡P및☺♫

Wick

Star Inn

Ewenny Road, CF71 7QA

☎ (01656) 890080 ⊕ thestarinnwick.co.uk

Wye Valley HPA; 2 changing beers (sourced regionally; often Glamorgan) Ⓗ

Originally three farm cottages, the interior comprises a traditional bar with pew seating and a lounge/diner with flagstone flooring – both warmed by log-burning fires – and an upstairs pool/function room. The friendly landlady, staff and locals make this a very pleasant place to visit. Good food is available, with the meat supplied by a nearby award-winning farm butcher. Dogs are welcome in the bar. A former local CAMRA Pub of the Year. Q⊃☺❶♣P및(303)☺�

Ystalyfera

Wern Fawr ★ ᴸ

47 Wern Road, SA9 2LX (on main road through Ystalyfera)

☎ (01639) 843625

9 Lives Amber, Dark, Gold; 1 changing beer (sourced nationally) Ⓗ

Entering this quirky pub is like stepping back in time. Run by the same family for three generations, this two-roomed pub is full of industrial heritage from the local area. It has a a cosy lounge and a friendly locals' bar with an old-fashioned stove that keeps the room warm in winter. The beers are brewed locally by 9Lives Brewing, with one changing guest beer being served. Q♣및(X6,121)☺

Owain Glyndwr, Cardiff: City Centre (Photo: Tom Bastin / Flickr CC BY 2.0)

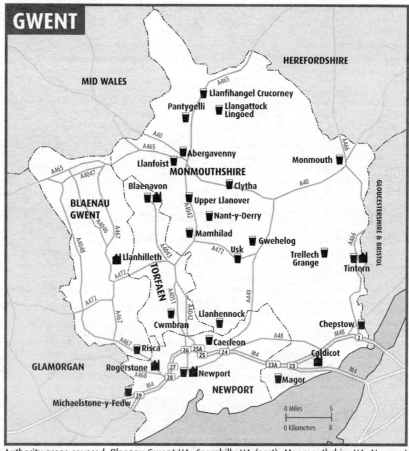

GWENT

Authority areas covered: Blaenau Gwent UA, Caerphilly UA (part), Monmouthshire UA, Newport UA, Torfaen UA

Abergavenny

Coliseum ✓
Lion Street, NP7 5PH
☎ (01873) 736960
Greene King Abbot; Ruddles Best Bitter; Sharp's Doom Bar; 3 changing beers (sourced nationally) ⊞
Wetherspoon pub in a former cinema. A spiral staircase leads up to a large open-plan bar with two raised areas, and skylights make it light and airy. Local scenes are dotted around the walls giving information on the history of the town and cinema. It can get busy – and noisy – at weekends. Major live sporting events are shown on the big screen. There is a smoking balcony at the rear. ॐ✿◑ሌ≠⊟ᔑ

Grofield ⅃
Baker Street, NP7 5BB
☎ (01873) 858939 ⊕ grofield.com
Sharp's Doom Bar; house beer (by Tomos & Lilford); 1 changing beer (sourced nationally; often Wye Valley) ⊞
Just off the main pedestrianised area and next to the cinema, this family-run free house has a hugely experienced licensee. To the rear is a large, well-maintained garden, which provides a green oasis in the centre of town on sunny days. Popular pub meals are served daily, except Mondays; booking is recommended.

A well-attended pub quiz is held every Sunday evening, while enthusiastic men's and women's darts teams participate in the local league. ॐ✿◑≠♣⊟

Station Hotel ★
37 Brecon Road, NP7 5UH
☎ (01873) 854759
Marstons Draught Bass; Wye Valley HPA, Butty Bach ⊞
The Station remains a traditional, unspoilt pub, although both the station and the Abergavenny to Brecon railway it refers to are long gone. This solid building of local stone has been identified by CAMRA as having a nationally important historic pub interior: much of the original Victorian interior remains, with its separate bar and lounge plus a small outside drinking area. The pub hosts a Wednesday night quiz and often features music on Fridays with a band or open mic evening. ≠P⊟✿♪

Blaenavon

Lion Hotel
41 Broad Street, NP4 9NH
☎ (01495) 792516 ⊕ thelionhotelblaenavon.co.uk
Glamorgan Jemima's Pitchfork; 2 changing beers (sourced regionally; often Glamorgan, Tomos & Lilford) ⊞

This comfortable hotel provides a handy base from which to explore the local industrial World Heritage sites, including Big Pit and the Pontypool & Blaenavon Railway. It has built a deserved reputation for excellent food, which is available in the traditional public bar or the separate restaurant area. Two handpumps usually dispense locally sourced ales which may vary according to customer preferences. Look out for the plaque outside which describes a tumultuous chapter in the town's past. ⏱☆🐾◐≢(High Level) P🏠(X24,30) 🛜

Caerleon

Bell Inn ✅
Bulmore Road, NP18 1QQ
☎ (01633) 420613 ⊕ thebellcaerleon.co.uk
Timothy Taylor Landlord; Wye Valley HPA, Butty Bach 🅷
Set in a quiet back street, this 17th-century pub has an impressive stone façade, behind which are a low-beamed fireside bar and adjoining snug decorated with prints of local interest. The popular restaurant offers high-quality dishes. The rear courtyard and garden provide a quiet refuge and also a stage for events and live music in fine weather. The real ale range is stable and reflects the preferences of the regulars.
⏱☆◐♣♠P🏠🐾🛜♪

Red Lion ✅
Backhall Street, NP18 1AR
☎ (01633) 423323
Wye Valley HPA, Butty Bach; 1 changing beer (sourced regionally; often Bath Ales) 🅷
Originally a 17th-century coaching inn, this back-street pub attracts a loyal following from customers both local and from further afield. The open-plan interior links what were once a separate public bar and lounge, with a screened and more secluded higher-level area. At the rear is a spacious garden that has an ancient Roman wall as part of its perimeter. Alongside the regular guest ales, food is a big attraction and it is advisable to book a table if eating. ⏱☆◐♣🏠🐾🛜♪

White Hart
28 High Street, NP18 1AE
☎ (01633) 430999
Greene King Abbot 🅷
A village favourite where the pleasant front and rear section are linked by a stand-up drinking area alongside an impressive central bar that is open on three sides. The decor features polished wood panelling. The bicentennial family tree of the former Courage brewery, whose beers it used to sell, is of interest. Abbot Ale is the beer of choice for the locals. There is often live music at weekends, sometimes in the garden in summer. Winter opening hours may be shorter. ⏱☆♣🏠(27,29)🐾🛜♪

Chepstow

Beaufort Hotel ✅
Beaufort Square, St Mary's Street, NP16 5EP
☎ (01291) 622497 ⊕ beauforthotelchepstow.com
Butcombe Adam Henson's Rare Breed; Sharp's Doom Bar; St Austell Proper Job; 1 changing beer (sourced regionally) 🅷
Popular with locals and the business community, this relaxed town-centre hotel sports a single L-shaped bar, recently refurbished, with a large side room for busy times. An air of reassuring continuity pervades; a clue to its longevity is offered by panels above the bar that announce the Beaufort Hotel as dating from around 1650. Wall panels frame local scenes, and a glass cabinet

displays racing colours either side of a picture of the great champion jockey Lester Piggot.
Q⏱☆🐾◐≢P🏠🐾🛜♪

Queen's Head 🍺
12 Moor Street, NP16 5DD
☎ 07793 889613 ⊕ queensheadchepstow.co.uk
6 changing beers (sourced regionally; often Glamorgan, Grey Trees, Twt Lol) 🅷
The success of the area's first micropub is evidenced by its multiple CAMRA awards. The bar counter makes for a welcoming sight, with an array of handpumps serving up a variety of styles and strengths and favouring Welsh brews. Beer flights of three third-pints are popular. Natural ciders and perries are also offered. Two linked seated areas are unspoiled by features such as TV, and it takes only a few people to generate a pleasant and relaxing atmosphere. Q≢♠P🏠🐾♪

Three Tuns Inn 🅛
32 Bridge Street, NP16 5EY
☎ (01291) 645797
Kingstone Llandogo Trow; Wye Valley Butty Bach; 3 changing beers (sourced regionally; often Butcombe, Kingstone) 🅷
Attractive old inn nestling at the historic heart of this town, close to the River Wye and even closer to Chepstow Castle. The two-level bar gives the pub a distinctly traditional feel, and the five real ales on offer reflect an enthusiasm for local breweries. A small room to the back gives access to an attractive garden. Live music sessions feature on Saturday evenings and Sunday afternoons. ⏱☆🐾◐≢P🏠🐾🛜♪

Clytha

Clytha Arms
Groesonen Road, NP7 9BW (on the B4598 old road between Abergavenny and Raglan)
☎ (01873) 840206 ⊕ clytha-arms.com
4 changing beers (sourced nationally; often Uley) 🅷
Featured in this Guide for over 30 consecutive years under the same skilled licensees, this popular country gastropub is well worth seeking out. A riot of wooden furniture is spread across the airy bar, lounge and dining areas, where good food always sits side-by-side with great beers, ciders and perries. Real ale drinkers are treated to an ever-changing variety of beers from around the UK, while new local breweries are also well supported. Q⏱☆🐾◐♣♠P🏠(83)🐾♪

Cwmbran

Bush Inn 🅛
Graig Road, Upper Cwmbran, NP44 5AN
☎ (01633) 483764 ⊕ thebushuppercwmbran.co.uk
3 changing beers (sourced regionally; often Glamorgan) 🅷
Cosy mountainside pub that was once four cottages before becoming the community hub it is today. It has two distinct sections, both with fireplaces, catering for

drinkers through the day and for diners in the evening, with live music on a Friday. Beers are usually local, but regional ales occasionally appear. Pictures of the locality during its industrialised days dot the walls. There are good views over Cwmbran in fine weather.
🛏️🕽🌔♣🌢P🗟(1) 🍴🛜♪

John Fielding ✅
1 Caradoc Road, Southville, NP44 1PP
☎ (01633) 833760
Greene King Abbot; Ruddles Best Bitter; Sharp's Doom Bar; 2 changing beers (sourced nationally) Ⓗ
Centrally located Wetherspoon pub close to transport links. The chain's formula of serving good-value food and drinks make this a busy place throughout the day and night. It is a welcome outlet for good real ale in the town; the two changing guest ales accompanying the regular beers are often supplied by local breweries. Seasonal real ale festivals inject further variety. Named after a local hero from Rorke's Drift in the Zulu Wars, the pub maintains links with today's service veterans.
Q🛏️🕽🌔🕽&🌢♣P🗟🛜

Queen Inn
Upper Cwmbran Road, Upper Cwmbran, NP44 5AX
☎ (01633) 484252 ∰ thequeeninn.uk
2 changing beers (sourced regionally) Ⓗ
Attractive pub with a rural backdrop and a bubbling mountain stream at the front. It was formerly three dwellings, and this is reflected in the interior layout of restaurant, public bar and lounge. There are extensive outdoor facilities including a children's play area. The popular menu is entirely plant-based, with ingredients sourced from local producers. Where possible the ales are also vegan and supplied from a local brewery.
🛏️🕽🌔♣🌢P🗟(1) 🍴♪

Gwehelog

Hall Inn Ⓛ
Old Raglan Road, NP15 1RB
☎ (01291) 672381 ∰ thehallinn.co.uk
Glamorgan Cwrw Gorslas/Bluestone Bitter; Wye Valley Butty Bach Ⓗ
This handsome, traditional rural inn has open fireplaces, thick walls and low-beamed ceilings. A couple of deer heads look down approvingly on a cosy and comfortable setting for drinkers and diners, the latter in a linked room that is handy for the bar. A reputation for well-kept ales and good home-cooked meals ensures a busy trade, particularly at weekends, and everyone gets a cheerful welcome. A garden and patio allow alfresco drinking alongside a paddock with chickens and livestock.
🛏️🕽🌔♣P🗟(60) 🛜

Llanfihangel Crucorney

Skirrid Mountain Inn
Hereford Road, NP7 8DH
☎ (01873) 890258 ∰ skirridmountaininn.co.uk
Wye Valley Butty Bach; 1 changing beer (sourced locally; often Wye Valley) Ⓗ
An ancient pub, where Owain Glyndwr is said to have rallied his troops, and where the infamous Judge Jeffries hanged people for alleged involvement in the 17th-century Monmouth Uprising. Named after the local mountain, the pub is in the centre of the village, bypassed by the A465. The village marks the start of the beautiful valley that makes its way through the Black Mountains to Llanthony and the whole area is popular with walkers and lovers of the outdoors.
Q🏢🕽🌔♣P🗟(X3) 🍴

Llanfoist

Bridge Inn
Merthyr Road, NP7 9LH
☎ (01873) 854831 ∰ bridgellanfoist.com
Evan Evans Cwrw; Glamorgan Jemima's Pitchfork; Wye Valley Butty Bach Ⓗ
Situated on the edge of the Brecon Beacons National Park is this attractive pub, named after the adjacent stone bridge across the River Usk. Inside, there is a split-level bar, the lower level sporting a wood-burning stove. TV screens are only switched on for major sporting events, and, like the occasional live music, are never allowed to overwhelm the sound of conversation. The popular garden has views across Abergavenny's Castle Meadows and the hills beyond. B&B accommodation is available. 🛏️🏢🕽🌔♣P🗟(A3,X4)🍴🛜♪

Llangattock Lingoed

Hunter's Moon Inn
NP7 8RR (2 miles off B4521 Abergavenny-Ross old road at Llanvetherine, at road bridge at end of village) SO361201
☎ (01873) 821499 ∰ hunters-moon-inn.co.uk
Wye Valley HPA Ⓗ/Ⓖ**, Butty Bach** Ⓗ**; 1 changing beer (sourced regionally; often Grey Trees)** Ⓗ/Ⓖ
Archetypal village pub in a glorious location next to the medieval church and Offa's Dyke path. Inside, bare stone walls, flagstone floors, low ceilings and exposed beams reflect the building's antiquity. You can sample the good food and beer in the small bar or the adjacent dining room, but on warm summer days you may prefer to drink outside in the gardens, either near the pond and its natural waterfall or looking out over the church and countryside. Q🛏️🏢🕽🌔♣🍴🛜

Llanhennock

Wheatsheaf ★
NP18 1LT (turn right 1 mile along Usk Road heading N from Caerleon, then bear left at the fork) ST353927
☎ (01633) 420468
Fuller's London Pride; 2 changing beers (sourced regionally; often Fuller's, Timothy Taylor, Wye Valley) Ⓗ
A long-standing fixture in the Guide, this excellent rural pub sits in delightful surroundings that offer extensive views. Its open fire and secluded garden make it an ideal year-round destination. Inside, the public bar usually offers a local beer to complement the national brands, and is crammed with historic photographs and memorabilia. The smaller snug is reputed to have a romantic presence. The game of boules is played in the car park. Q🛏️🏢Å♣P🍴🛜

Magor

Wheatsheaf ✅
The Square, NP26 3HN
☎ (01633) 880608
4 changing beers (sourced regionally) Ⓗ
Large, friendly pub in the centre of a bustling village, with exposed stonework and wooden beams offering character and reflecting its age. The traditional bar has pub games, and two other comfortable and well-furnished areas are divided by a two-sided fireplace, which is welcome on colder days. There is also a spacious restaurant. Four frequently-changing ales feature a range of styles from local, regional and national brewers.
🛏️🏢🕽&♣P🗟(X74) 🍴🛜

Mamhilad

Horseshoe Inn ✓
Old Abergavenny Road, NP4 8QZ
☎ (01873) 880542 ⊕ horseshoe.wales
House beer (by Tomos & Lilford); 2 changing beers (sourced regionally; often Tomos & Lilford) Ⓗ
Styled as a 'public house and bistro', this country pub is a few minutes' walk from the Monmouthshire and Brecon Canal. Deceptively large, it has a traditional slate-flagged bar with log-burner, extending into a small dining area. There is also a separate restaurant in which the high-quality food can be enjoyed. The surrounding countryside draws ramblers during the year, many seeking refreshment here. On the bar, a locally brewed house ale is supplemented by two guests plus a range of ciders.
Q ☺ ⊛ ◑ 🅐 ♣ P ✿ 🖙

Michaelstone-y-Fedw

Cefn Mably Arms
CF3 6XS (turn N off A48 at Castleton and follow the road for just over a mile)
☎ (01633) 680347 ⊕ cefnmablyarms.com
Wye Valley HPA, Butty Bach; 1 changing beer (sourced regionally) Ⓗ
Originally a farmhouse built in 1550 before becoming a pub in the mid 19th century, this remote but busy country inn has an emphasis on food with an excellent range of freshly prepared meals. The interior layout reflects the culinary focus, and is divided into three dining areas. Two regular well-kept ales and a guest (which may be dropped during the winter months) are served alongside ciders and wines. Outside are attractive areas to front and rear, with an ancient oak dominating the car park. There is no local bus service; the nearest stop is the A48, at least a mile away. Children under 10 are not permitted. Q ☺ ⊛ ◑ P ✿ 🖙

Monmouth

King's Head Hotel
8 Agincourt Square, NP25 3DY
☎ (01600) 713417
Greene King Abbot; Ruddles Best Bitter; Sharp's Doom Bar; 2 changing beers (sourced nationally) Ⓗ
This Wetherspoon adaptation of a 17th-century hotel has several separate spaces across two levels. Many original features have been incorporated into an excellent restoration that includes a family room with a royal Stuart theme. It retains the ambience of an old building, with historic pictures, artwork and many books in a number of areas in which to dine, or simply enjoy a choice of ales and other two local ciders.
Q ☺ ⊛ ⚞ ◑ ⅊ ♿ 🅐 🖥 🖙

Nant-y-Derry

Foxhunter Inn
NP7 9DN (over railway line after passing through Penperlleni, or just before railway bridge if travelling from E)
☎ (01873) 881101 ⊕ foxhunterinn.com
Glamorgan Thunderbird; Rhymney Bevans Bitter; Wye Valley Butty Bach; 2 changing beers (sourced regionally) Ⓗ
Grade II-listed building that first became a pub after serving for a century as the stationmaster's house and then a tea room for the long-gone Nant-y-Derry station. Its attractive rural location and excellent reputation for food and the selection of beers is reflected in its popularity. The garden has two heated wooden pods to

extend its use beyond the warmer weather. Occasional entertainment is offered. Well-behaved dogs are welcome. Closed Monday and Tuesday in winter.
Q ☺ ⊛ ◑ ⅊ ♿ P ✿

Newport

Alexandra 🅛
32 Commercial Street, NP20 1HP
☎ (01633) 376721
Rhymney Export; 1 changing beer (sourced locally; often Rhymney) Ⓗ
Named after Newport's Alexandra Dock, this popular pub is a recent conversion of a former bank and is the first Rhymney pub in the city. Modern styling and traditional pub character combine neatly to make this a vibrant part of Newport's pub scene, and competitively priced Rhymney ales are a draw. Alcoves and a raised rear level with high-table seating provide space for socialising at any time of the day. Several TV screens show music programmes and popular sporting events. ✿♿⚞🖥🖙♪

Cellar Door
5 Clytha Park Road, NP20 4NZ
☎ 07930 857897 ⊕ cellardoor.netlify.app
3 changing beers (sourced nationally) Ⓗ
Previously a small shop, Newport's pioneering micropub is a locals' favourite, with a comfortable bar, snug and covered outside area at the rear. Handpulls for two real ales and two real ciders are joined by three fonts for craft brews and a chilled cabinet which includes local but hard-to-find Anglo-Oregon beers. As a respite from TV and gaming machines, regularly changing modern artwork provides a background for conversation. There is live music on Sunday evenings. Q ✿ ⊛ ♣ ♠ 🖥 ✿ ♪

Godfrey Morgan 🅛 ✓
158 Chepstow Road, Maindee, NP19 8EG
☎ (01633) 221928
Brains SA; Greene King Abbot; Ruddles Best Bitter; Sharp's Doom Bar; 2 changing beers (sourced nationally; often Rhymney) Ⓗ
This open-plan Wetherspoon pub was once a cinema and photos of old film stars with local connections are displayed amidst the Art Deco-style surroundings. The usual range of national and regional ales are available, plus more interesting options. The pub takes its name from the 1st Viscount Tredegar, who survived the Charge of the Light Brigade. A small car park is at the rear, with some or all of the charge refundable with your custom.
Q ☺ ⊛ ◑ ♿ 🅐 P ⊟ (8,73) 🖙

John Wallace Linton 🅛 ✓
19-21 Cambrian Road, NP20 4AD (off Queensway)
☎ (01633) 251752
Greene King Abbot; Ruddles Best Bitter; Sharp's Doom Bar; 3 changing beers (sourced nationally; often Brains) Ⓗ
JD Wetherspoon's first Welsh outlet remains as popular as ever. Attracting both regular customers and passing

---

Burton beer makes me blithe,
French wine makes me sick.
I'm devoted to ale,
And to ale I will stick.
Henceforth let the grape
To the barleycorn bow;
Here's to success to the farmer,
And God speed the plough.
Traditional

trade, it is well placed for Newport's entertainment quarter and handy for public transport services. It is named after local World War II naval hero, John Wallace (Tubby) Linton and a corner of the pub is devoted to his exploits. The familiar food and drinks packages are available, and there are usually interesting guest ales on offer, as well as seasonal beer and cider festivals.
🏃😋🛒🕩&≠🅿🏡📶

Pen & Wig 🇱
22-24 Stow Hill, NP20 1JD
☎ (01633) 666818 ⊕ jwbpubs.com/penandwig
Draught Bass; Glamorgan Jemima's Pitchfork; 3 changing beers (sourced regionally; often Brecon, Quantock, Tudor) Ⓗ
Bustling city-centre pub attracting a varied clientele who are attracted by a good choice of ales that always includes a dark potion and the resident Bass. The open-plan layout offers several linked sections, each with TV screens, so you are unlikely to miss key sporting moments. The food offering is substantial and popular, including a Sunday carvery. A spacious function room caters for various groups, while the large decked patio at the rear gets busy in fine weather.
😋🕩≠♠🅿🏡(151) 🦮 🎵

Ruperra Arms 🇱
73 Caerphilly Road, Bassaleg, NP10 8LJ
☎ (01633) 376167 ⊕ theruperraarms.com
Glamorgan Welsh Pale Ale; Greene King Abbot; 2 changing beers (sourced nationally) Ⓗ
Popular roadside tavern offering a fine selection of well-kept ales. A selection of freshly prepared food is available all day, though booking is advised for the evening. The pub is divided into two rooms, and a large outside drinking/smoking area sits next to the smallish car park. In winter, a roaring gas fire warms up the thirsty traveller. Though generally peaceful, the pub can get busy when live sports are broadcast on TV screens. It takes its name from Ruperra Castle, which is not far away. Q🏃😋🕩&≠(Pye Corner)🅿🏡(50)🦮📶🎵

St Julian Inn
Caerleon Road, NP18 1QA
☎ (01633) 243548 ⊕ stjulian.co.uk
Bath Ales Gem; Fuller's London Pride; 2 changing beers (sourced nationally; often Bristol Beer Factory, Ludlow, Quantock) Ⓗ
This roadside pub overlooking the River Usk has enjoyed an unbroken decades-long run in this Guide, which bears testimony to the quality of its ales. An elliptic island bar is surrounded by a public bar, wood-panelled lounge and games area, with a riverside balcony popular in finer weather. There are now two guest pumps which typically serve beer of a light and hoppy style. There is also a downstairs skittles alley/function room. Live jazz features on a Friday afternoon.
🏃😋🕩♠🅿🏡(27,60) 🦮📶🎵

'What is your best – your very best – ale a glass?'
'Twopence-halfpenny,' says the landlord, 'is the price of the genuine Stunning Ale.'
'Then,' says I, producing the money, 'Just draw me a glass of the Genuine Stunning, if you please, with a good head to it.'
Charles Dickens,
David Copperfield

Weird Dad Brewery Tap 🇱
23 Caerleon Road, NP19 7BU
☎ (01633) 244238 ⊕ weirddad.co.uk
3 changing beers (often Weird Dad) Ⓗ/Ⓖ
An established fixture of the growing breed of micropubs, this pub is the outlet for the Weird Dad nanobrewery, which is housed at the back. A friendly vibe permeates the two small conjoined spaces and there is invariably someone willing to join you in conversation if you wish. A wide range of cask and keg beers is on offer, with a variety of packaged product also available to drink in or take out. A small smoking area/beer garden is next door. Closes at 8pm. Q😋≠🏡🦮📶

Pantygelli

Crown Inn 🇱
Old Hereford Road, NP7 7HR
☎ (01873) 853314 ⊕ thecrownatpantygelli.com
Wye Valley HPA, Butty Bach; 1 changing beer (sourced regionally; often Rhymney) Ⓗ
Just north of Abergavenny, with clear views from the patio across to the Skirrid mountain, this gastropub has an established reputation for beer and food; booking for meals is recommended. Hearty breakfasts are available till noon at weekends, ideal for those exploring the local countryside. A changing local Welsh independent guest beer and locally produced hand-pulled cider supports the core line-up. 🏃😋🕩♣🦮🅿

Risca

Prince of Wales
Dixon Place, NP11 6PY
☎ (01633) 612616
1 changing beer (often Wye Valley) Ⓗ
Two-roomed pub just off the towpath of what remains of the Risca branch of the Monmouthshire and Brecon Canal. An old Welsh brewer's light shines above the entrance to the sporting-themed main bar. Food is served in the adjoining contemporary-styled lounge. The pub is difficult to get to by car, but is popular with cyclists and walkers. A steep climb from the main road is rewarded with fine mountain views over the valley from an outside seating area.
🏃😋🛏🕩≠(Risca & Pontymister)♣🅿🏡(R1)🦮📶

Tintern

Wye Valley Hotel 🇱
Monmouth Road, NP16 6SQ
☎ (01291) 689441 ⊕ thewyevalleyhotel.co.uk
Wye Valley Bitter; 1 changing beer (sourced locally; often Kingstone) Ⓗ
This distinctive hotel has been family-run for many years and provides a warm welcome. Its comfortable bar, surrounded by a lengthy shelf displaying an impressive range of beer bottles from several decades, sports two well-kept ales, at least one of which is from the nearby Kingstone brewery. Home-cooked meals are served in the bar and in the silver-service restaurant. It makes a fine base from which to explore the Wye Valley.
🏃😋🛏🕩&Ⓐ🅿🏡(69) 🦮📶

Trellech Grange

Fountain Inn 🇱
NP16 6QW (turn left in Tintern by the Royal George and follow road towards Trelleck) SO503011
☎ (01291) 689303 ⊕ fountaininntrellech.co.uk

Rhymney Export; Wye Valley Butty Bach; 1 changing beer (sourced locally; often Rhymney) ⊞
A fine, 17th-century drovers' inn, in the countryside a few miles from Tintern Abbey. Rebuilt in the original style after being burned down in 1964. Although it is somewhat off the beaten track, it is worth seeking out. Three well-kept ales are always available alongside one local cider, complementing the home-cooked food. In winter, two real fires keep you cosy, and the welcoming garden has its own brook. Hours may vary so check ahead, especially in winter. Closed Mondays.
⏰❀◑♠♣P❀🛜♪

Upper Llanover

Goose & Cuckoo 🅛

NP7 9ER (turn off the A4042 Pontypool-Abergavenny road at the sign to Upper Llanover at the end of Llanover village, then follow signs to the Goose) SO292073
☎ (01873) 880277 ⊕ thegooseandcuckoo.com
3 changing beers (sourced regionally) ⊞
An isolated, stone-built, hilltop pub at the end of a long single-track lane, set in beautiful countryside with extensive views from the gardens. This time-capsule pub has remained virtually unchanged for many years, with flagstone floor and a wood-burning stove. It is popular with residents scattered across surrounding hillsides as well as with visiting walkers and cyclists. Originally a cider house called the New Inn, the 'Goose' and 'Cuckoo' were the nicknames of a couple who ran the pub in the 19th century. A multiple winner of local CAMRA Country Pub of the Year. Q⏰❀◑♣P❀♪

Usk

Castle Inn

7 Twyn Square, NP15 1BH
☎ (01291) 673037 ⊕ castleinnusk.co.uk
Butcombe Adam Henson's Rare Breed; Wye Valley Butty Bach; 1 changing beer (sourced nationally) ⊞
This pub has a reputation for good food and good accommodation. A deceptively long interior initially presents a small public bar to the left and a cosy snug to the right. A long corridor then leads you to two tastefully furnished restaurant rooms, one in a conservatory, before the back leads into the garden. There is limited car parking space immediately to the front, but a public car park is close by. Note the Whitbread PLC 1742 plaque on the outside wall. ⏰❀◑◑🖨(60,63)❀🛜♪

King's Head Hotel

18 Old Market Street, NP15 1AL
☎ (01291) 672963 ⊕ kingsheadusk.com
Fuller's London Pride; Glamorgan Jemima's Pitchfork; Wye Valley Butty Bach ⊞
The low-beamed lounge bar in this 16th-century hotel offers a cosy refuge, particularly on cold days with the large fireplace blazing away. Walls and ceilings are adorned with rural and music memorabilia, old books and other interesting artefacts. The ale range reflects the preferences of locals and rarely changes, but is mostly local. Diners are well catered for with several bespoke dishes. En-suite accommodation is available for those wishing to stay and explore the area.
Q⏰◑◑♿❀P🖨(60,63) ❀🛜

Come on in, the water's lovely

The importance of water to the brewing process is often overlooked. Most people know that barley malt and hops are the main ingredients used in beer making and that yeast turns malt sugars into alcohol. But 93% of even the strongest beer is made up of water – and the quality of the water is essential to the taste and character of the finished product.

Brewers call the water they use in the brewing process 'liquor' to distinguish it from cleaning water. Brewing liquor, whether it comes from natural wells or the public supply, will be filtered and cleaned to ensure its absolute purity. Care will be taken, however, to ensure that vital salts and irons are not removed during the filtering process, as they are essential to the production of cask beer.

The benchmark for brewing liquor is Burton upon Trent in the English Midlands. The natural spring waters of the Trent Valley have rich deposits of calcium and magnesium sulphates – also known as gypsum and Epsom salts. Salt is a flavour-enhancer and the sulphates in Burton liquor bring out the finest flavours from malts and hops. Since the 19th century, ale brewers throughout Britain and other countries have added salts to 'Burtonise' their liquor.

It's fascinating to compare the levels of salts in the water of three famous brewing locations: Burton, London and Pilsen. Pilsen is the home of the first golden lager beer, Pilsner. Brewers of genuine lager beers want comparatively soft brewing liquor to balance the toasted malt and gentle, spicy hop nature of their beers. Pilsen water has total salts of 30 parts per million, with minute amounts of calcium and magnesium.

London, once celebrated as a dark beer region, famous for mild, porter and stout, has 463 total salts per million, with high levels of sodium and carbonate. (Dublin, another dark beer city, has similar water to London's). Burton liquor has an astonishing level of total salts of 1,226 per million. If this figure is further broken down, Burton liquor is rich in magnesium, calcium, other sulphates and carbonate.

MID-WALES

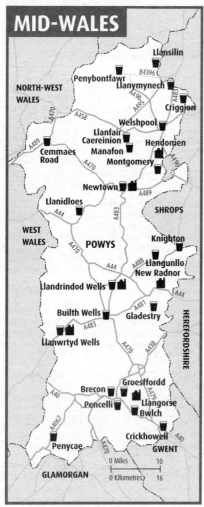

NORTH-WEST WALES

Llansilin

Penybontfawr

B4396

Llanymynech

A490

A495

A483

Criggion

A458

A470

Welshpool

Llanfair Caereinion

Cemmaes Road

Manafon

Hendomen

A490

Montgomery

A470

Newtown

A489

Llanidloes

A483

SHROPS

A44

WEST WALES

A470

POWYS

Knighton

A44

A488

Llangunllo

New Radnor

Llandrindod Wells

A44

Builth Wells

A481

A483

Gladestry

A470

A438

Llanwrtyd Wells

Groesffordd

A470

A479

Brecon

Pencelli

Llangorse

Bwlch

A40

A4067

Crickhowell

A40

Penycae

A470

GWENT

GLAMORGAN

0 Miles 10
0 Kilometres 16

HEREFORDSHIRE

Authority area covered: Powys UA

Brecon

Brecon Tap
6 Bulwark, LD3 7LB
☎ (01874) 622888
4 changing beers (sourced regionally) ⑂
In a prime town-centre location, this contemporary-style bar has a light and airy feel, with comfortable seating throughout and walls lined with bottle-filled shelves. Three or four varying guest ales are served, often from Welsh breweries, sometimes further afield. There is also an interesting range of international and UK craft ales. Simple food in the form of good-value pies, sandwiches and the like are available. Bottled beers, wines, craft spirits and local artisan produce are available for off-sales. Q ♿ ⑈ ◑ ♠ ⑂ ♣ ☂

Clarence
25 The Watton, LD3 7ED
☎ (01874) 622810 ● clarenceinn.co.uk
Wye Valley Bitter, Butty Bach; 1 changing beer (sourced regionally; often Wye Valley) ⑂
Formerly a coach house in bygone times, this two-room town-centre community pub has a contemporary and

relaxed atmosphere. The newly extended front bar with its log-burner tends to be frequented by locals, while the larger back bar is popular with diners. The large screen draws a crowd for big sporting events. The spacious garden has a performance space and is a major attraction, especially during the Brecon Jazz Festival. Guest beers are generally sourced from local breweries. ♿ ⊛ ⑈ ◑ ♣ ♠ ♣ ♪

George Hotel ⊘
1 George Street, LD3 7LD (just off The Struet)
☎ (01874) 620250
Greene King IPA; Sharp's Doom Bar; 2 changing beers (sourced nationally) ⑂
A former 16th-century coaching inn, now a Wetherspoon house, bringing additional choice to the town centre. The interior has been significantly expanded, with a large bar area at the back and numerous spaces leading off. Up to six ales are available, the usual national brands being supplemented by others from smaller breweries. Food is available throughout the day. The pub has accommodation in four rooms. ♿ ⊛ ⑈ ◑ ♿ ⑂ ♪

Hop In Beer & Gin House
37 The Watton, LD3 7EG
☎ (01874) 622092 ● hopinbeerandgin.co.uk
2 changing beers (sourced regionally; often Grey Trees) ⑂
Established in 2020 in difficult circumstances, the Hop In has quickly built an excellent reputation and following. The beer offering consists of two regularly changing real ales, five craft ales on tap, and a wide range of bottled and canned beers. An equally impressive range of around 40 gins is available, which the knowledgeable staff are happy to advise on. Though compact, the pub has ground-floor and first-floor drinking areas and a small courtyard outside at the rear. Excellent food is served, for which booking is essential. Q ♿ ⊛ ◑ ♠ ♣

Builth Wells

Fountain Inn ⊘
7-9 Broad Street, LD2 3DT
☎ (01982) 553888
Wye Valley Butty Bach; 3 changing beers (sourced nationally; often Salopian, Tiny Rebel) ⑂
Town-centre pub that is popular with locals. Decorated in a modern style, the Fountain retains a traditional feel with plenty of stonework, wood, floorboards and a welcoming wood-burner. The pub serves up to four real ales, which change regularly, plus a real cider. Sports TVs show major events, and pool and darts are available in the bar. Next door is a café section and upstairs terrace with a view of the River Wye. ◑ ♣ ♠ P

Bwlch

New Inn
Brecon Road, LD3 7RQ (on A40 between Brecon and Crickhowell)
☎ (01874) 730215 ● beaconsbackpackers.co.uk
Wye Valley Butty Bach; 2 changing beers (sourced nationally; often Grey Trees, Oakham) ⑂

REAL ALE BREWERIES

Heart of Wales 🍺 Llanwrtyd Wells
Hwgga 🌀 Llandrindod Wells
Left Bank Llangorse
Monty's 🍺 Hendomen
Radnorshire New Radnor
Wilderness Newtown

Lively and cosy village pub, popular both with locals and visitors. A comfortable dining area sits to the side of the bar, with armchairs around a huge fireplace. Two interesting guests supplement the regular ale, and excellent, good-value, home-cooked food is available evenings and at lunchtime at the weekend; the pies are deservedly popular. Bunkhouse accommodation is available, making it perfect for exploring the surrounding Brecon Beacons and Black Mountains. Former local and regional CAMRA award winner. Q 🕏 🛏 🌜 ♣ 👜 P 🐾 🎵

Cemmaes Road

Dovey Valley Hotel ★

SY20 8JZ

☎ (01650) 511335 ● doveyvalleyhotel.com

2 changing beers (sourced regionally; often Conwy, Monty's, Wye Valley) H

Saved from the threat of closure in 2013, this unspoiled gem is now run as a pub and guesthouse and serves a quality range of mainly Welsh ales. It has been identified by CAMRA has having a nationally important historic pub interior, and features original fittings, slate flooring, and an open fire. It also includes a photo of the now-defunct Cemmaes Road signal box. The pub has a large beer garden and covered seating area. Delicious locally-made pork pies are served with pickles. Dogs are welcome. Q 🕏 🏵 🛏 🌜 ♣ P 🖵 (T12) 🐾 🎵

Crickhowell

Bear Hotel ★

High Street, NP8 1BW (in town centre)

☎ (01873) 810408 ● bearhotel.co.uk

Brains Rev James Original; Timothy Taylor Landlord; 2 changing beers (sourced regionally; often Glamorgan, Gower, Grey Trees) H

Originally a 15th-century coaching inn, this is now an award-winning hotel and Guide regular. Its grand, multi-roomed bar features exposed beams, wood panelling, fine settles and an eclectic selection of furnishings and decorations. The two bar rooms have exposed fireplaces, as does one of the side rooms. There are usually four ales to choose from, with guests often from independent Welsh breweries. Food is excellent and the varied menu features local produce. An excellent base for exploring the surrounding Black Mountains and Brecon Beacons National Park. Q 🕏 🏵 🛏 🌜 ⅙ ♣ P 🐾

Treebeards Bar

54 High Street, NP8 1BH

☎ (01873) 268668

3 changing beers (sourced regionally; often Grey Trees) G

Micropub in the heart of town, occupying part of what was once the Corn Exchange pub before it was converted into award-winning smaller units. Established in recent years, it has built a good reputation and has brought variety to the local drinking scene. The comfortable bar has a friendly, cosy atmosphere and offers up to three real ales served straight from the cask, together with a selection of craft ales, mainly from Welsh independent breweries. 🕏 👜 🎵

Criggion

Admiral Rodney Inn

SY5 9AU

☎ (01938) 570313 ● theadmiralrodneycriggion.co.uk

Wye Valley Butty Bach; 1 changing beer (sourced locally; often Hafod) H

Though refurbished, this rural inn, dating back to the mid-18th century, remains unspoiled. It is named after Admiral Rodney who harvested local oak to build his ships, and who is honoured with a pillar on the adjacent Criggion Hill. Two fireplaces feature in the large open-plan front bar. A secluded drinking area lies off to the right of this, and a restaurant area to the left, with a smaller eating area to the rear. Q 🕏 🏵 🛏 🌜 ⅙ ♣ P 🐾 🎵

Gladestry

Royal Oak Inn

HR5 3NR

☎ (01544) 370586 ● theroyaloakgladestry.co.uk

Wye Valley Butty Bach; 2 changing beers (sourced regionally) H

A 17th-century country inn in the centre of the village, run by an experienced couple and also doubling up as the home of the village shop. Three real ales are available, with the two changing beers from Hobsons, Three Tuns or Ludlow breweries. It opens most lunchtimes and evenings. Walkers, and dogs on leads are welcome. Accommodation is available in two 5-star suites, making it a good base for walking the Offa's Dyke National Trail. Q 🕏 🏵 🛏 🌜 👜 ♣ P 🐾 🎵

Groesffordd

Three Horseshoes

LD3 7SN (just off B4558 in centre of village)

☎ (01874) 665672 ● threehorseshoesgroesffordd.co.uk

St Austell Tribute; 2 changing beers (sourced regionally) H

Busy village-centre pub in the heart of the Brecon Beacons, boasting superb views from the front and rear outdoor seating areas. The pub is only a 10-minute walk from the Brynich lock on the Monmouthshire and Brecon Canal and is a popular stop for boaters and other visitors. The emphasis is very much on food, which is excellent, but the ales are always varied and interesting. Brynich Caravan Site and the Brecon YHA are also nearby. 🕏 🏵 🌜 ⅙ ♣ 👜 🐾 🎵

Knighton

Watsons Ale House

24 High Street, LD7 1AT (near clock tower, up pedestrian street, on left next to chippy)

☎ (01547) 740017

3 changing beers (sourced nationally) H

Popular micropub that was previously a tea room and before that a butcher's shop (spot the hooks and cold-room door). They sell Skyborry cider and perry, locally produced in the town. Order your food at the chippy next door to have with your drinks. There are also occasional pizza nights for takeaway or delivery. Walkers and dogs are welcome. Q 🏵 🌜 ⇌ 👜 🖵 (46) 🐾 🎵

Y Banc

5 Broad Street, LD7 1BW (near clock tower)

☎ (01547) 520009 ● thebankknighton.com

Ludlow Gold; 1 changing beer (sourced regionally) H

Originally a Midland bank built in 1896, the building was converted to a bar and restaurant in 2018. The modern decor includes a bespoke decorative ceiling and radiators, and the old vault is now a quirky room with dining tables inside. There is piped music but no TV or other noise source. There is a small seated patio at the front. It hosts regular quiz nights to raise money for charity. 🌜 ⅙ ⇌ 👜 🖵 (41) 🐾 🎵

Llandrindod Wells

Arvon Ale House ♥
Temple Street, LD1 5DP
☎ (01597) 821647
5 changing beers (sourced regionally; often Wye Valley) Ⓗ
The first micropub in this part of Wales and a welcome addition to the Llandrindod pub scene. Formerly a shop premises, the pub is small and perfectly formed: a proper alehouse for the quiet enjoyment of beer with no extraneous attractions. Beer is sourced from Wales, the borders and the Midlands, and at least four real ciders are offered. It holds a folk music session on the second and fourth Sunday of every month. A former CAMRA National Pub of the Year and Cider Pub of the Year.
Q ⏰ ➰ ≷ (Llandrindod) ♣ ❀ ❀ ♪

Temple Bar
Fiveways, Temple Street, LD1 5HG
☎ (01597) 825405 ⊕ thetemplebar.co.uk
Wye Valley HPA, Butty Bach; 1 changing beer (sourced nationally) Ⓗ
This two-room bar reopened in 2023 under new management. It is located in the southern end of town, over the road from the Cycle Museum. Beers are mostly from Wye Vally, and food is also served, with separate lunch and evening menus. There is exterior seating to the front and side. It closes at 4pm daily for menu and kitchen change. ➰ ◑ ≷ (Llandrindod) ⊒ (T4) ❀ ❀ ⚡

Llanfair Caereinion

Goat Hotel
High Street, SY21 0QS (off A485)
☎ (01938) 810428 ⊕ thegoathotel.co.uk
3 changing beers (sourced locally; often Stonehouse) Ⓗ
Excellent 300-year-old beamed coaching inn whose welcoming atmosphere attracts both locals and tourists. The plush lounge, dominated by an impressive large inglenook and open fire, has comfortable large armchairs and sofas. A dining room serves home-cooked food, and a games room is situated at the rear. The choice of real ale usually contains a Shropshire beer. Watch out for the low-beam entrance to the Gents.
Q ➰ ❀ ⇔ ◑ ♣ P ⊒ (87) ❀ ⚡

Llangunllo

Greyhound ℒ
LD7 1SP (off A488 on B4356, in village centre)
☎ (01547) 550400
2 changing beers (sourced nationally) Ⓗ
A 16th-century village pub set in picturesque countryside. It is the first stop on the Wales Glyndwr Way long-distance footpath. As you would expect from a pub owned by CAMRA members, the beer is well kept. They also serve Weston's Family Reserve cider. There are regular open mic sessions. No food available.
Q ➰ ❀ Å ♣ ❀ P ❀ ♪

Llanidloes

Red Lion
Long Bridge Street, SY18 6EE
☎ (01686) 412270 ⊕ redlionllanidloes.com
Brains Rev James Original; Wye Valley Butty Bach; 2 changing beers (sourced locally; often Monty's) Ⓗ
A Grade II-listed hotel that started life as a coaching inn in the mid-17th century. There are two large contrasting rooms: the games bar has pool, darts and TV; the other is

a cosy lounge bar with leather Chesterfield sofas and a wood-panelled fireplace. There are up to four beers served, with guest beers normally sourced from local breweries. Food is served all day. Note the imposing red lion above the front door.
➰ ❀ ⇔ ◑ ♿ ♣ P ⊒ (X75,525) ❀ ⚡ ♪

Whistling Badger at the Royal Head
4 Short Bridge Street, SY18 6AD
☎ (01686) 412583 ⊕ thewhistlingbadger.co.uk
Wye Valley HPA, Butty Bach; 1 changing beer (sourced regionally) Ⓗ
This was formerly two adjacent pubs, the Royal Oak and the King's Head, which merged in the 1960s, and renamed again after a short closure in 2017. Now tastefully refurbished, it consists of two rooms: the larger retains its original beams and a large stone inglenook, while the smaller room is presented in a wine-bar style and set up for dining. Food is served in both bars during the evening. ➰ ❀ ⇔ ◑ P ⊒ (X75,525) ⚡ ♪

Llansilin

Wynnstay Inn
SY10 7QB
☎ (01691) 791355
2 changing beers (sourced regionally) Ⓗ
Built in 1784, the Grade II-listed Wynnstay is the last of five inns that the village once supported. The pub consists of a public bar, lounge and pool room. A separate dining room can also be used for small functions. The inn is close to attractions, including Pistyll Rhaeadr waterfall, Offa's Dyke walk, and the Tanat Valley. Two beers are available and a real fire makes for a cosy, warm visit. Q ➰ ❀ ⇔ ◑ ♿ Å ♣ P ❀ ⚡

Llanwrtyd Wells

Neuadd Arms Hotel ★ ℒ
The Square, LD5 4RB
☎ (01591) 610236 ⊕ neuaddarmshotel.co.uk
6 changing beers (sourced regionally; often Felinfoel, Monty's, Purple Moose) Ⓗ
This large Victorian hotel serves as the tap for the Heart of Wales brewery. The Bells Bar features a large fireplace and an eclectic mix of furniture. The bells, formerly used to summon servants, remain on one wall, along with the winners' boards from some of the town's famous and unusual competitions. The lounge bar is a little more formal. The hotel takes part in the town's annual events, including a major beer festival over two weekends in November. They serve a good range of real ciders.
Q ❀ ⇔ ◑ ≷ (Llanwrtyd) ♣ ❀ P ❀

Llanymynech

Dolphin Inn
North Street, SY22 6ER
☎ (01691) 839672 ⊕ thedolphininn.co.uk
2 changing beers (sourced locally) Ⓗ
This former coaching inn is one of the oldest buildings in Llanymynech, with some parts dating back to 1517. It was supposedly renamed after Sidney Godolphin, who inherited a local estate via marriage. The large bar at the front leads down a few steps to a well-appointed restaurant at the rear. Both ales are sourced from a local brewery such as Stonehouse. A large, walled beer garden provides a refuge and safe space for children.
➰ ❀ ⇔ ◑ ♿ P ❀ ⚡ ♪

Manafon

Beehive Inn

SY21 8BL

☎ (01686) 651007

Salopian Oracle, Shropshire Gold [H]

A black-and-white timbered Rhiw valley local in the heart of the village, next to the church. Established in the 1650s as a drover's inn, it has original beams and settles throughout. It was originally a lot smaller, but other rooms were added over the years. A large beer garden is at the rear. The pub closes during January. Q🛋❀♣P📶

Montgomery

Crown Inn

Castle Street, SY15 6PW

☎ (01686) 668533

Wye Valley HPA, Butty Bach [H]

Traditional local in a town that once supported a multitude of hostelries. The public bar is long and quite narrow, with a pool and games area at the rear. A small snug opposite the public bar contains a large array of trophies. There are also benches outside. Beware of the low beams in the bar area. The pub supports a large number of local sports teams. ❀♿♣🚌(71,81)📶

Newtown

Brew Hub

13 High Street, SY16 2NX (on the High St between Iceland and Lloyd's Bank)

☎ (01686) 610491

4 changing beers (sourced nationally) [H]/[G]

Newtown's first café bar has seen many uses over previous years, including as a hairdresser's, a health food shop and a patisserie. It serves one ale on handpull, three via gravity from bag in box, and two ciders. Eight beers on craft taps and a number of excellent whiskies, rums, brandies and gins are also available. There is table seating in the front half, and wall benches and stools to the rear. There is an outdoor covered area to the rear. Q❀🚆🍎📶

Railway Tavern

Old Kerry Road, SY16 1BH (off A483)

☎ (01686) 626156

Wye Valley HPA; 2 changing beers (sourced nationally; often Timothy Taylor) [H]

Thus unspoilt local close to the railway station consists of two areas: a lower bar has a piano and a handy electronic timetable showing train arrivals and departures; and a rear space offers benches, tables and a TV for sporting events. The three beers on offer are usually sourced from regional or small breweries. Outside toilets are located through the passageway, but mind the step. Q❀🚆♣🚌(T4,X75)

Pencelli

Royal Oak 🏆

LD3 7LX

☎ (01874) 665396 🌐 theroyaloakpencelli.com

Wye Valley Butty Bach; 3 changing beers (sourced regionally; often Grey Trees, Tudor) [H]

Comfortable and friendly family-run pub in a quiet village by the Monmouthshire and Brecon Canal. Its extended opening hours are welcome in this part of the Brecon Beacons. The regular ale is supplemented with up to three others, usually from independent Welsh breweries. The pretty garden next to the canal is a delight on a sunny day. It is popular with walkers, cyclists and boaters, with mooring available next to the garden. Local CAMRA Pub of the Year 2023 and 2024.
Q🛋❀◐♿⛺♣🍎P🍺🐾📶♫

Penybontfawr

Railway Inn

SY10 0NU

☎ (01691) 860447 🌐 the-railway-inn.co.uk

2 changing beers (sourced nationally; often Three Tuns) [H]

Dating from the 18th century, this Grade II-listed village pub was named after the now long-gone Cambrian railway. Many original features remain, including a slate floor, large fireplace, and settles in the bar. It consists of a lounge/dining room, public bar and a small snug (the Farmers' Room). Two ales are usually available. The menu features locally sourced food wherever possible. The pub does not have a car park, but there is a free one 100 yards away. Q🛋❀◐♿♣P🐾📶♫

Penycae

Ancient Briton

Brecon Road, SA9 1YY (on A4067 Swansea to Brecon road, N of Abercrave)

☎ (01639) 730273

5 changing beers (sourced nationally; often Glamorgan, Grey Trees, Pitchfork) [H]

Situated on the A4067 Swansea to Brecon road, in the Brecon Beacons National Park, this welcoming, family-friendly pub offers a wide range of ales and ciders, as well as high-quality food. Car parking is plentiful on site, and there is a campsite attached. It is ideal for campers and walkers and close to the famous Dan yr Ogof show caves and Craig y Nos castle. Multiple local CAMRA Pub of the Year winner. 🛋❀🛏◐♿⛺♣P🚌(T6)🐾📶♫

Welshpool

Old Bakehouse

14 Church Street, SY21 7DP

☎ (01938) 558860

4 changing beers (sourced locally; often Clun, Salopian, Stonehouse) [H]

A micropub that opened in 2021 on the site of an old bakehouse. Four changing local real ales are served alongside cider, wines and a small selection of local spirits. No TVs, fruit machines or jukebox means good, old-fashioned conversation rules. A relaxed environment in which you can unwind on your own or with friends. There is an upstairs area with tables, armchairs, board games and books, and an outside enclosed drinking area. Takeaway containers are available. Q🛋❀♿🚆♣🍎🐾

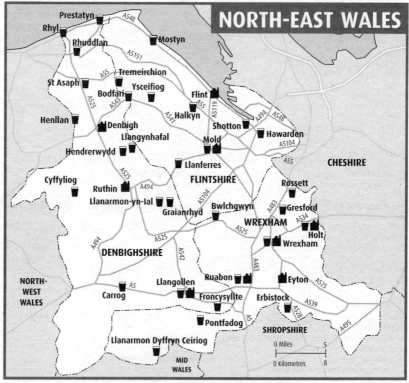

NORTH-EAST WALES

Authority areas covered: Denbighshire UA, Flintshire UA, Wrexham UA

Bodfari

Dinorben Arms 🛏

B5429, LL16 4DA (off A541, down B5429, 350yds on right) SJ092701

☎ (01745) 775090

Purple Moose Cwrw Eryri/Snowdonia Ale; Timothy Taylor Boltmaker; 4 changing beers (sourced locally) ⊞

Reputedly established in 1640, the building was derelict for eight years before being restored by the current owners. The spacious interior has several dining areas, serving food all day. The tower, with its elevated position by the 16th-century church, offers fine views across the Vale of Clwyd. Though primarily a popular destination pub for meals, it offers a good selection of real ales, including two regular and four guest beers mostly sourced from local micros. ⏱✿🍴&🅿🚌(14)🌸🏵

Bwlchgwyn

King's Head Inn 🛏

24 Ruthin Road, LL11 5UT

☎ (01978) 753089

2 changing beers (often Big Hand) ⊞

Small and friendly free house standing on the main road through Wales' highest village. The entrance is through a well furnished room, with a wood burner to the left and large TV to the right. To the side is another comfortable room with banquette seating. The pub offers hearty and good value bar meals, with two locally sourced beers on handpump. Bus services during opening hours are limited. ⏱✿🍴🅿🏵♪

Carrog

Grouse Inn

B5437, LL21 9AT (on B5437, off A5 at Llidiart Y Parc)

☎ (01490) 430272 🌐 thegrouseinncarrog.co.uk

JW Lees Bitter, Founder's; 1 changing beer (often JW Lees) ⊞

This friendly, family-run pub was originally a farm and brewhouse and has a single bar serving several rooms. A tasteful refurbishment was undertaken in 2020 without losing any of its character. Generous home-cooked food can be eaten in most areas of the pub. A large outside covered patio area offers splendid views of the Dee Valley, Berwyn Mountains and the 1660-vintage Carrog Bridge. Carrog station on the Llangollen-Corwen railway is a short walk away. Q⏱✿🌳🍴♿🅰🚲🅿🚌(T3,55)🌸🏵

Cyffyliog

Red Lion Hotel ★ 🛏

LL15 2DN (4 miles W of Ruthin, off B5105 at Llanfwrog)

☎ (01824) 710375 🌐 redlionhotel.wixsite.com

House beer (by Facer's); 1 changing beer (sourced locally) ⊞

Family-run village inn with parts dating back to the 17th century. The focal point is the welcoming lounge with its open fire and bar. A cosy adjacent dining area leads to a further dining/function room, and the public bar includes a pool table and TV. Don't miss the Gents toilet, which is bedecked in numerous different wall tiles from a bombed Liverpool factory. Wednesday quiz nights and Thursday curry nights are popular. The pub also doubles up as the village shop. Q⏱🍴🅰♣🅿🏵🛜♪

Erbistock

Boat

LL13 0DL (follow signs from the A528, just over 1 mile W of Overton)
☎ (01978) 280205 ● theboataterbistock.co.uk
Big Hand Seren; Stonehouse Station Bitter; Timothy Taylor Landlord; 2 changing beers (sourced regionally; often Salopian, Weetwood) Ⓗ
The Boat dates back to the 13th century and has a wonderful picturesque location. The building takes advantage of its southerly outlook with outdoor seating offering exceptional views of the idyllic banks of the River Dee. The split-level bar, with handpumps on both sides, serves up to four cask beers, often from local breweries. The pub is mainly laid out for dining but there is also plenty of space for drinkers. Q🏠⊕🕙&≟P🐾

Froncysyllte

Aqueduct Inn

Holyhead Road, LL20 7PY (on the A5)
☎ (01691) 777118
4 changing beers (sourced locally; often Izaak Walton, Weetwood) Ⓗ
A welcoming freehouse on the busy A5. The small central bar room leads to a games room, with a TV on the right and a comfortable lounge with a wood-burning stove to the left. Outside, the veranda offers panoramic views of the Pontcysyllte Aqueduct on the Llangollen Canal. Not to be missed is the mural that covers one gable end of the pub. Up to four changing ales are available. Food is served daily, with a traditional roast on Sunday.
🏠🏠🚅🕙♣P🖶(64) 🐾 🛜

Graianrhyd

Rose & Crown

Llanarmon Road, CH7 4QW (on B5430 off A5104)
☎ (01824) 780727 ● theroseandcrownpub.co.uk
Wye Valley HPA; 2 changing beers Ⓗ
An early-19th-century traditional pub with a strong local following. The long bar serves two rooms, the main one with an open fire, copper-topped tables and a vast array of pumpclips. Guest beers are usually from local breweries. It is popular with tourists, walkers, fell runners and cyclists. Finishers in the local Dash in the Dark can fuel up on the customary post-ride chip baps, as do those taking prt in in Three Taverns choir walking tour in May.
Q🏠🏠🕙♣P🖶(2) 🐾 ⸬

Gresford

Griffin Inn ★

Church Green, LL12 8RG
☎ (01978) 855280
2 changing beers (sourced nationally; often Timothy Taylor) Ⓗ
Friendly community pub run by the same landlady since 1973. Lively conversation at the bar does not impinge on the quieter corners. The irregular, open-plan layout is adorned with many interesting pictures. It is sited where pilgrims came to drink in the Middle Ages, opposite All Saints Church, whose bells are one of the Seven Wonders of Wales. There's a lawned area to the side with seating. The number 1 Chester to Wrexham bus stops in the village less than half a mile away. Q🏠🏠♣P🖶(1)🛜

Pant-yr-Ochain Ⓛ

Old Wrexham Road, LL12 8TY (off A5156, E from A483 follow signs to The Flash)
☎ (01978) 853525

Purple Moose Cwrw Eryri/Snowdonia Ale; Timothy Taylor Landlord; Titanic Plum Porter; Weetwood Eastgate; house beer (by Brightside); 4 changing beers (sourced regionally) Ⓗ
Impressive 16th-century dower house that retains many historical features and sits beside a small lake within extensive gardens. The central room, dominated by a large double-fronted bar, leads to a variety of seating areas including a garden room, a small snug behind the period inglenook fireplace, and the patio and lawn outside. Though hugely popular, the pub retains a quiet feel. Food is served all day and five regular beers are supplemented by four guests and often a draught cider.
Q🏠🏠🕙&♣P🐾 🛜

Halkyn

Blue Bell Inn Ⓛ

Rhosesmor Road, CH8 8DL (on B5123)
☎ (01352) 780309
JW Lees Bitter; 3 changing beers (sourced locally; often Facer's) Ⓗ
A traditional rural pub on Halkyn Mountain, the Blue Bell is a good base for exploring the local countryside and enjoying the free guided walks around the area. Built in 1700 and named after a local privateer's boat, the pub has a strong community focus and hosts regular events and societies. The beer range usually includes North Wales breweries – often Facer's – and is accompanied by a wide selection of real ciders. 🏠🏠⏶♣P🖶(126)🐾 🛜

Hawarden

Glynne Arms Ⓛ

3 Glynne Way, CH5 3NS
☎ (01244) 569988 ● theglynnearms.co.uk
Facer's This Splendid Ale; 2 changing beers (sourced locally; often Weetwood) Ⓗ
A 200-year-old coaching inn at the heart of the village, this is a comfortable place to try locally-sourced beers and good quality food. The semicircular bar serves both bar area and adjacent dining room, and there is also a separate restaurant with a real fire. Decor is sympathetic to the period of the building, with several references to the village's most famous resident, William Gladstone. Popular with walkers visiting the nearby castle and park.
🏠🏠🕙&⇌♣P🖶(4,11) 🐾 🛜 ♪

Hendrerwydd

White Horse Inn Ⓛ

LL16 4LL (signed from B5429, near Llandyrnog)
☎ (01824) 790218 ● whitehorserestaurant.co.uk
2 changing beers Ⓗ
Rambling but cosy oak-beamed 16th-century inn that has been tastefully refurbished. Entrance is into the lounge, with dining areas off both sides. A snug bar to the right has a roaring fire in winter and a pool room sits

REAL ALE BREWERIES

Beech Avenue Holt
Big Hand Wrexham
Black Cloak Denbigh
Denbigh (Dinbych) Denbigh
Facer's Flint
Hafod Mold
Llangollen 🍺 Llangollen
Magic Dragon Eyton
McGivern 🍺 Ruabon
Reaction Ruthin
Sandstone Wrexham

behind the bar. Two ever-changing guest beers are sourced from local breweries. The restaurant is popular and highly rated for its locally sourced food. Dogs are allowed in the snug. Q✆🏠🕽🏵🍴&▲P🚫(76)🌟

Henllan

Llindir Inn
Llindir Street, LL16 5BH
☎ 07896 649862
2 changing beers (sourced locally) 🅷
A 13th-century, Grade II-listed thatched freehouse opposite the local church and its detached tower. The spacious interior retains its character, with separate areas that include a games room. There are extensive views of the surrounding countryside to the rear. Wood-fired sourdough pizzas are available Thursday to Saturday, and the beer range usually includes ales from Chapter and Geipel. The unusual name relates to flax, which was once a local mainstay crop. Q✆🏵🕽♣P🚫(66)🌟🔊

Holt

White Lion 🅛
Castle Street, LL13 9YW
☎ (01829) 270345
2 changing beers (often Stonehouse) 🅷
An attractive, black-and-white fronted, village free house that is popular with locals. Recently refurbished to create a single pub, there is now a lounge/bar with a wood-burner, and a TV that is usually restricted to showing rugby. Dominoes and pool are played, and there is some outside seating in front of the pub. Opening times may vary so phone ahead to check. Beers are usually from local breweries. Q✆♣P🚫🌟🔊

Llanarmon Dyffryn Ceiriog

Hand at Llanarmon
LL20 7LD (end of B4500 from Chirk)
☎ (01691) 600666 ⊕ thehandhotel.co.uk
Stonehouse Station Bitter; Weetwood Cheshire Cat; 1 changing beer (sourced locally) 🅷
Cosy free house situated in a scenic location at the head of the delightful Ceiriog Valley and marked by a giant hand sculpture. There are always three real ales available, usually sourced locally. Food and accommodation are both of a very high standard; it is advisable to book a table at busy times. In addition there is a spa onsite. The real fire is very welcome in winter. This dog-friendly pub is popular with cyclists, walkers and tourists. Q✆🏠🏨🕽&♣P🚫(64)🌟🔊

Llanarmon-yn-Ial

Raven Inn
Ffordd-Rhew-Ial, CH7 4QE (signed 500yds W of B5430)
☎ (01824) 780833 ⊕ raveninn.co.uk
Purple Moose Cwrw Eryri/Snowdonia Ale; 2 changing beers (sourced locally) 🅷
Run with the help of volunteers for more than a decade, this delightful old pub goes from strength to strength, with all profits benefitting the community. It has a friendly and inviting ambience from the moment you enter. The bar serves three guest ales in two carpeted areas, with a tiled area to one side. There is also outside seating. Excellent, locally sourced, home-cooked food is available Thursday to Sunday. Accommodation is available in three self-catering rooms. Q✆🏠🏵🏨🕽&♣P🚫(2)🌟🔊🎵

Llanferres

Druid Inn ✅
Ruthin Road, CH7 5SN (on A494, 4½ miles from Mold, 5½ miles from Ruthin)
☎ (01352) 810225 ⊕ druid-inn.co.uk
Purple Moose Cwrw Eryri/Snowdonia Ale, Cwrw Glaslyn/Glaslyn Ale; 1 changing beer 🅷
The entrance to the Druid Inn leads to three distinct areas. The bar is to the right and has a friendly feel with a low, timber-beamed ceiling and open log fire. The restaurant is to the left. Meals can also be eaten in the bar. Accommodation is available in five bedrooms and a self-contained flat upstairs. Usually there are two beers from Purple Moose and one guest beer. Q✆🏠🏨🕽P🚫🌟🔊

Llangollen

Corn Mill
Dee Lane, LL20 8PN (on town side, W of River Dee bridge)
☎ (01978) 869555
Facer's Dave's Hoppy Beer; house beer (by Brightside); 3 changing beers (sourced nationally) 🅷
A splendid conversion of a flour mill that incorporates the water wheel. It has a series of open-plan rooms spread over three levels, with bars on the first two floors. It is primarily a restaurant, and the drinking area is confined to the ground floor bar and the large outside decking area, which has unparalleled views across the River Dee to the restored steam railway station. Five handpumps serve three regularly changing beers. High-quality food is served throughout the day. Q✆🏠🕽&▲⇌●🚫(5,T3)🌟🔊

Sun Inn 🅛
49 Regent Street, LL20 8HN (400yds E of town centre on A5)
☎ (01978) 860079
Ossett White Rat; 5 changing beers (sourced nationally) 🅷
A free house whose large front lounge has two open fires and a stage for live music. A smaller snug at the rear has mirrored panels and a large TV screen. This room is accessed via an enclosed, partly covered rear seating terrace. The pub has a late licence, with music from Wednesday to Saturday; last entry at 11pm. The pub can get busy later in the evening, especially at weekends, but it is quieter in the early evening. 🏵▲⇌♣●🚫(5,T3)🌟🔊🎵

Sun Trevor
Sun Bank, LL20 8EG
☎ (01978) 860651 ⊕ suntrevor.co.uk
2 changing beers (sourced locally; often Stonehouse, Weetwood) 🅷
An 18th-century pub overlooking the Llangollen Canal. The bar and lounge area features a large inglenook fireplace festooned with brasses and photos. There is a large separate dining area. Two changing beers are usually from local breweries. Food is served until late evening. Outside seating is available, including some under a small marquee. A quiz night is held on Wednesday. Popular with walkers, cyclists and narrow boaters. There is access from the canal and bus stop opposite. Q✆🏠🕽&P🚫(5,T3)🌟🔊

Llangynhafal

Golden Lion Inn
LL16 4LN (at village crossroads)
☎ (01824) 790451 ⊕ thegoldenlioninnllangynhafal.com

House beer (by Facer's); 1 changing beer (sourced locally) Ⓗ
Traditional and welcoming 18th-century village inn at the foothills of the Clwydian hills. The bar serves two distinct areas: the bar with its pool table, and the lounge leading down to a dining area. The enthusiastic landlord has been at the helm for well over a decade, and takes particular pride in his beers and whiskies. The guest beer is often from a local brewery. There is a campsite to the rear. A regular of the Route 76 bus beer festival.
Q✿🛏🕮●P🖵(76) ✿ 🛜

Mold

Glasfryn 🄻
Raikes Lane, CH7 6LR (off A5119 ½ mile N of Mold)
☎ (01352) 750500 ⊕ glasfryn-mold.co.uk
Brunning & Price Original; Purple Moose Cwrw Eryri/ Snowdonia Ale; 4 changing beers Ⓗ
Near to Theatre Clwyd and set in its own grounds opposite the civic centre, this large, upmarket pub and restaurant was once the residence for circuit judges attending the nearby court. It is operated by Brunning & Price, and the interior is decorated in their usual style. The emphasis is on food, served all day in three dining areas. There are extensive views over the surrounding countryside from the large beer garden.
Q✿🕮🌶◑&P🖵(28) ✿ 🛜

Gold Cape ✔
8-8A Wrexham Street, CH7 1ES (next to Market Square crossroads)
☎ (01352) 705920
Greene King Abbot; Ruddles Best Bitter; Sharp's Doom Bar; 3 changing beers Ⓗ
Situated in the historic market town of Mold, this Wetherspoon pub is named after a 4,000-year-old solid gold ceremonial cape found nearby in 1831. It was made from a single sheet of beaten gold, and embellished with intense decoration. The original, which has been restored and is in the British Museum, is possibly the best example of prehistoric craftsmanship in Europe. A copy is on display in Mold Library. The cape is of part of the town's history displayed on the pub walls, along with a panel about local writer Daniel Owen. Q✿◑▲🅡🛜

Mold Alehouse 🍷 🄻
Unit 2 Earl Chambers, Earl Road, CH7 1AL
☎ (01352) 218188
4 changing beers (sourced nationally; often Cwrw Ial, Facer's, Hafod) Ⓗ
Since opening in 2016, this micropub has won many CAMRA awards, including Welsh Pub of the Year. It has gained a strong following based on good beer and conversation. It is centrally located, in a Grade II-listed building opposite the town hall. The four cask ales include a dark beer, accompanied by five KeyKeg lines and four ciders. Although no food is served, a café in the same building is accessible via the same entrance.
Q●🖵✿🛜

Mostyn

Lletty Hotel 🄻
Coast Road, CH8 9HF
2 changing beers (sourced locally; often Conwy, Magic Dragon, Purple Moose) Ⓗ
This Grade II-listed, late 18th-century Georgian inn reopened as a hotel in 2023 after nine years of closure and a year of refurbishment. Real ales on offer include those from Conwy and Purple Moose, and are continually rotated. There is also a regular keg beer from a local

microbrewery. Beers on offer are updated weekly on Facebook to give advance notice of availability. Food is also available. Q✿🛏P🖵✿

Pontfadog

Swan Inn
Llanarmon Road, LL20 7AR (on B4500 next to post office)
☎ (01691) 718273 ⊕ theswaninnpontfadog.com
Stonehouse Cambrian Gold; 1 changing beer (sourced locally; often Stonehouse) Ⓗ
Welcoming village free house in the scenic Ceiriog valley. The cosy, red-tiled bar, where the locals tend to congregate, features a central fireplace which separates the TV and darts area from the servery. A dining room to the side often has themed food nights. An outside area is accessed through the dining room. More outside space is being developed to include decking and a bridge over the small brook. Call ahead if travelling, especially in winter, as opening hours may change.
Q✿🌶🛏◑&🌿P🖵(64) ✿ 🛜

Prestatyn

Bar 236 🄻
236 High Street, LL19 9BP
☎ (01745) 850084 ⊕ bar236.co.uk
2 changing beers (sourced locally) Ⓗ
This café bar at the top of the High Street opened its doors in 2010, and was fully refurbished 10 years later. One L-shaped room has a minimalist but pleasant feel, with its wood-boarded floor and blue-tiled bar front. It is glass-fronted on two sides, giving open views inside and outside. TV sport is shown, and there is live music at weekends. ✿➔🖵✿🛜♫

Halcyon Quest Hotel 🄻
17 Gronant Road, LL19 9DT (on A547 just E of town centre)
☎ (01745) 852442 ⊕ hqpencadlys.wales
Facer's Flintshire Bitter; 3 changing beers (sourced nationally) Ⓗ
A long-standing supporter of cask beer, the HQ – as it is known locally – is located in the southern end of town, a short distance from the High Street. The single room is packed with sporting and other memorabilia, including a rowing boat suspended from the ceiling dedicated to JR Hartley of fly-fishing fame. The extensive garden patio area at the rear has a covered area popular for outside drinking in the summer months.
✿🌶🛏🍴P🖵(35,36) ✿ 🛜

Rhuddlan

Castle Inn
Castle Street, LL18 5AE
Theakston Best Bitter; 1 changing beer (sourced nationally) Ⓗ
Friendly pub opposite the 13th-century ruins of Rhuddlan Castle. It has two large rooms separated by the central bar, and a sizeable covered outdoor area to the rear. Two cask ales are served, with Theakston's being a regular. The pub is popular with locals, and also attracts many tourists visiting the castle. A small car park located opposite is for patrons of the pub. 🌶🌿P🖵✿

Rhyl

Cob & Pen 🄻 ✔
143 High Street, LL18 1UF
☎ (01745) 350446

Facer's Mountain Mild, Flintshire Bitter; 2 changing beers ⊞

A town-centre pub, recently refurbished, close to railway and bus stations. It consists of three separate areas and includes a pool room, traditional snug and a dining area, all served from a central bar. A large, partially covered beer garden is to the rear. Local brewers and microbreweries feature in the beer range, which usually includes a cask mild, a rarity for the area. The pub hosts quiz nights and televised sports events, which adds to its popularity. ⏰⊛⊲⊅≈♣⊟⊛❄

Esplanade Club

86 Rhyl Coast Road, LL18 3PP (on A548, 1 mile E of centre, on left next to Spar local)
☎ (01745) 338344
2 changing beers ⊞

Friendly and welcoming club on the main coast road in the Tynewydd area of Rhyl. Two real ales are served, from local and national brewers. The club also caters for the many holiday parks on its doorstep and welcomes families and pets. The three-quarter-size snooker table is an attraction. A former local CAMRA Club of the Year. ⏰⊛♣⊟(11,35)❄❄

Sussex ✓

20-26 Sussex Street, LL18 1SG
☎ (01745) 362910
Greene King Abbot; Ruddles Best Bitter; 3 changing beers ⊞

This Wetherspoon pub, in the pedestrianised town centre, was formerly a Wesleyan Chapel and an Old Comrades Club. It has a spacious interior decorated with illustrated panels of local interest. Numerous gaming machines and TV screens provide entertainment for the locals and visitors. Guest beers are mainly from the Wetherspoon seasonal list but may also include beers from North Wales. Q⏰⊲⊅≈⊟❄

Tafarn Fach Micropub at Rhyl 🄻

2 St Margarets Buildings, St Margarets Drive, LL18 2HT (on A525, ½ mile from centre)
☎ 07908 957116
3 changing beers (sourced locally) ⊞

A welcome addition to the Rhyl pub landscape, on the outskirts of town. Originally called the Dove, the first in a small chain of the former Dovecote brewery, it is now run by locals, and the brewery links are entirely historic. Ales are now typically from Purple Moose and Conwy breweries. Local craft beer is available on KeyKeg and in cans from Wild Horse, Polly's and other Welsh breweries. Q⏰⊛♥⊟(51)❄♪

Rossett

Golden Lion ✓

Chester Road, LL12 0HN
☎ (01244) 555300 ⊕ thegoldenlionrossett.co.uk
Timothy Taylor Landlord; Theakston Best Bitter; 1 changing beer (often Hydes) ⊞

Situated midway between Chester and Wrexham, this large whitewashed building has plenty of nooks and crannies, attractive bric-a-brac for wall decoration, and smart, traditional furniture. It is popular with diners, but the bar area remains the domain of the humble drinker. A discount on cask ales is offered on Monday. A large garden sports a tepee. The pub claims to have a resident, harmless ghost known as Old Jeffrey. ⏰⊛⊲⊅⊟(1)❄

Ruabon

Bridge End Inn 🄻

5 Bridge Street, LL14 6DA
☎ (01978) 810881 ⊕ bridgeendruabon.co.uk
7 changing beers (sourced nationally; often Ossett, Rat, Salopian) ⊞

Welcoming, traditional, community-focused local, close to Ruabon station, with three low-ceilinged rooms and a covered outdoor drinking area. It has deservedly won numerous awards since its revitalisation by the owners, including CAMRA National Pub of the Year. The changing range of up to seven cask ales may occasionally include a brew from the on-site McGivern brewery, plus a porter or a stout. There is also usually a real cider. Families and well-behaved dogs are welcome in the lounge. Q⏰⊛♣≈♣⊛P⊟(5)❄❄♪

St Asaph

New Inn ✓

Lower Denbigh Road, LL17 0EF
☎ 07874 055314
JW Lees Manchester Pale Ale, Bitter, Dragon's Fire; 1 changing beer (often JW Lees) ⊞

The interior of the pub consists of a main lounge bar area, a pool room off with dartboard, and a separate back bar with a real open fire and dartboard. There is also a raised outdoor area to the rear with a large landscaped garden below. The pub backs onto the River Elwy, with easy access for dog walkers, and there is a large car park. It serves three core JW Lees beers, plus one from their experimental range. Closed on Tuesday from April to September. Q⏰⊛♣P⊟(51)❄

Shotton

Central Hotel ✓

2-4 Chester Road West, CH5 1BX
☎ (01244) 845510
Greene King Abbot; Sharp's Doom Bar; 2 changing beers (sourced nationally; often Purple Moose) ⊞

A local landmark, built in the early 1920s, beside the railway station. Following a major refurbishment in 2008, it reverted to its original name. The interior is in typical Wetherspoon mock-Edwardian, with a large single bar partially separated into three similarly furnished areas. Two changing guest beers are served alongside two regulars. At the front is an open seating area between the pub and the street. Monthly events include Meet the Brewer evenings. ⏰⊛⊲⊅♣≈P⊟(10, 11)❄

Tremeirchion

Salusbury

LL17 0UN (1 mile S of A55 from jct 30)
☎ (01745) 710532 ⊕ salusburyarms.co.uk
Timothy Taylor Landlord; 3 changing beers (sourced locally) ⊞

Welcoming, traditional village pub, parts of which are reputed to date back to the time of Magna Carta. Several discrete areas include dining rooms, a snug, and a meeting room. There is a large outdoor area with a children's play area. Beers are generally sourced from local micros, with two real ales available alongside keg beers. It became a Community Pub in 2023. ⏰⊛♣♣♣P❄❄♪

Wrexham

Elihu Yale ✓

44-46 Regent Street, LL11 1RR

☎ (01978) 366646
Greene King Abbot; Ruddles Best Bitter; Sharp's Doom Bar; 3 changing beers (sourced nationally) Ⓗ
Named after the founder of Yale University who is buried in the town, this is now the only Wetherspoon in Wrexham. Formerly a cinema, the single-room pub has several distinct areas, with the quieter part towards the front. One beer is usually from a North Wales brewery and there is also a cider. The pub is close to both rail and bus stations. Families welcome until 10pm.
Q ⏱ 🌙 ❶ ♿ ≋ (Central) 🚌 🛜

Magic Dragon Brewery Tap 🍷 Ⓛ ✅

13 Charles Street, LL13 8BT
☎ (01978) 365156
Magic Dragon Eyton Gold; 3 changing beers (sourced regionally; often Magic Dragon) Ⓗ
This single-room pub is the tap for the Wrexham-based Magic Dragon brewery. Situated on the edge of what was known as the Beast Market, the building started off as the Elephant & Castle before becoming other businesses, and finally returning to its roots as a pub. Four handpumps dispense at least three Magic Dragon beers, including one or more dark ales. Live music features every weekend, alternating between Friday and Saturday nights. Local CAMRA Pub of the Year 2024.
Q ≋ (Central) 🍴 🚌 🐾 🛜 🎵

Royal Oak

35 High Street, LL13 8HY
☎ (01978) 364111
Joule's Pure Blonde, Pale Ale, Slumbering Monk Ⓗ
Often known locally as the Polish Embassy, this Grade II-listed pub has a long, narrow interior, with a real fire, lots of wood panels and many brewery mirrors. Look out for the antelope head. The small roof garden is open between April and September. Food is not served but you can bring your own. Pub games are popular.
Q ⏱ ♿ ≋ (Central) ♣ 🍴 🚌 🐾 🛜

Ysceifiog

Fox ★

Ysceifiog Village Road, CH8 8NJ (signed from B5121)
☎ (01352) 720241 🌐 foxinnysceifiog.co.uk
Brains Bitter; Cwrw Llyn Porth Neigwl; 1 changing beer Ⓗ
Built around 1730, the Fox is a rare gem in a peaceful village location. Its unspoilt interior has four small rooms, two of them for dining. Of particular interest is the bar with its unique sliding door and settles. It has been identified by CAMRA as having a nationally important historic interior. The beer range usually includes a brew from Cwrw Llyn. Booking is recommended for the popular Sunday lunches. A children's playground sits outside. Q ⏱ 🌙 ❶ ♣ 🍴 P 🐾 🛜

Royal Oak, Wrexham (Photo: Tom Bastin / Flickr CC BY 2.0)

NORTH-WEST WALES

Authority areas covered: Anglesey UA, Conwy UA, Gwynedd UA

Aberdaron

Ty Newydd
LL53 8BE
☎ (01758) 760207 ⊕ gwesty-tynewydd.co.uk
4 changing beers (sourced locally; often Purple Moose) Ⓗ

The hotel is situated at the centre of a picturesque and historic village at the end of the Llyn Peninsula. Beers are generally from local breweries, and lunch, evening menus and afternoon teas are available. An outside terrace has stunning beach and sea views. Eleven en-suite bedrooms are available. The Wales coastal footpath passes through the village. Bus services run from Pwllheli. Q ➲ ➽ ◑ ▲ 🚌 🛜

Abergele

Hoptimist Ⓛ
32 Market Street, LL22 7AA
☎ 07538 336718
3 changing beers (sourced regionally) Ⓟ

An innovative use of a former building society provided Abergele with its first micropub in 2018. Originally a joint venture between Cwrw Ial and Dovecote breweries, it was taken over by local family in 2021. Full information regarding the beers on offer are clearly displayed on a large blackboard on the back wall with third-pint glasses

available. A bank of taps offers a selection of cask ales and keg beers with one-pint take-out containers also available. Q ➲ ➽ ❄ ➽ (Abergele & Pensarn) 🚌 ❀ 🎵

Amlwch Port

Adelphi Vaults
Quay Street, LL68 9HD
☎ (01407) 831754 ⊕ adelphivaults.com
4 changing beers (sourced locally; often Purple Moose) Ⓗ

Built in the 1800s, this nautically themed two-room pub is near the the old port. Several museums nearby depict the bygone copper industry. The pub has four changing beers that are mainly sourced from Welsh breweries. The small beer garden at the rear is a suntrap in summer. It is situated on the Anglesey Coastal Path, and popular with locals and tourists. Q ➲ ❄ ◑ ♣ ❀ 🛜 🎵

Bala

Goat/Yr Afr
41 High Street, LL23 7AF
☎ (01678) 521817
Wye Valley Butty Bach Ⓗ

Centrally located Admiral Taverns pub welcoming families and dogs. A central bar has a lounge and dining area on one side, with extensive comfy seating along its full length and plenty of tables and chairs. On the other side, the bar room has a pool table, dartboard and TVs showing sports channels. Outside, a live entertainment space includes a large covered seating area, gazebos and a yard. Friday and Saturday evenings are often karaoke/disco nights. ✿❀◐⚅♿▲♣️🅿️🚪(T3)❀🎵

STORI 🅛

101 High Street, LL23 7AE (on A494 in town centre, opp Old Bulls Head and Co-op)
☎ (01678) 520501 ⊕ storibeers.wales
1 changing beer (sourced locally) 🅖
A bottle shop with a taproom located in this popular town, close to the lake and other attractions. The taproom is accessed through the shop, which has a wide range of beers and beer-related merchandise, with the emphasis on local products. Cask and craft keg beers are available to either take away or enjoy in the cosy tasting room. The opening hours vary continually, so check on website. Q❀🚪(T3)❀

Bangor

Black Bull Inn (Tarw Du) ✅

107 High Street, LL57 1NS
☎ (01248) 387900
Greene King Abbot; 5 changing beers 🅗
A Wetherspoon pub in a converted church and presbytery at the top of the High Street. It has a long bar and spacious seating areas on two levels. A large outside patio overlooks upper Bangor and the university, and a lower-level beer garden provides excellent outside drinking spots. It is popular with students and busy during term time. ✿❀◐♿≠🎵

Globe

Albert Street, LL57 2EY
☎ (01248) 362095
4 changing beers (sourced nationally; often Ossett, St Austell) 🅗
Traditional back-street pub in upper Bangor, popular with locals and students. It is decorated with Welsh sporting photos and membrobilia, and is often busy when sporting events are shown on the multiple large screens. Four handpumps serve a rotating range of both national and local beers. A varied mix of ticketed gigs are hosted on an occasional basis, during which access can be restricted. ◐≠♣🚪🎵

Patrick's

59 Holyhead Road, LL57 2HE
☎ (01248) 353062
3 changing beers (sourced regionally; often Big Bog, Facer's) 🅗
Lively Irish-themed bar in upper Bangor, popular both with locals and students at Bangor University. The bar has numerous TVs displaying sporting events. Three handpumps dispense a regularly changing range of beers, including from North Wales breweries. The pub is on the bus route towards Menai Straits, and near the railway station. Opening hours are extended for sports events and late-night drinking. ≠🚪🎵

Barmouth

Myrddins Tap 🏆

Staffordshire House, Church Street, LL42 1EH
☎ (01341) 388060 ⊕ myrddinsbrewery.com
6 changing beers (often Myrddins) 🅟
Established in 2014, the taphouse for Myrddins brewery is on the main road through the town and close to the

beach and coastal path. The six real ales offered usually include two of their own and four locally brewed choices, alongside five real ciders. The single small room is cosy, with plenty of seating. There is also a good range of Welsh bottled beers, along with many gins they have distilled themselves. Closed Tuesday and Wednesday. ✿◐≠❀🚪❀

Royal Hotel

King Edward Street, LL42 1AB
☎ (01341) 213992 ⊕ theroyalbarmouth.co.uk
4 changing beers 🅗
The pub is located underneath the main hotel with access from the main road. It is a two storey bar with the main bar next to the pub entrance; a second lower level includes a pool table and a full-sized snooker table. There are three handpumps in each bar and at least three ales are usually served, possibly more. It is full of character and an eclectic mix of items are displayed around the walls and ceiling. A small beer garden is situated to the rear. Beers are usually sourced from Welsh breweries. ✿🛏◐▲♣❀☆🎵

Beaumaris

Castle Court Hotel ✅

Castle Square, LL58 8DA
☎ (01248) 810078 ⊕ castlecourtbeaumaris.co.uk
2 changing beers (sourced regionally) 🅗
Situated in the centre of this historic town, overlooking the castle, the former White Lion has been renovated by the current owners. It has a small beer garden at the rear, though in spring and summer the castle square provides an outdoor seating area. The two changing guest beers are from small independent breweries. Lunchtime meals are served, but only in the school holidays. ✿❀🛏▲🚪☆🎵

Brithdir

Cross Foxes

LL40 2SG (jct of A470 and A487)
☎ (01341) 421001 ⊕ crossfoxes.co.uk
3 changing beers (sourced locally) 🅗/🅖
This five-star hotel, in an extensively refurbished Grade II-listed building is situated near the foot of Cader Idris mountains, four miles from the historic town of Dolgellau. Beers are usually from local breweries. Breakfast is served and meals are available all day. It is popular with walkers, tourists and residents, and dogs are welcome in the bar area. Q✿🛏❀◐▲🅿️🚪(T2)❀☆

REAL ALE BREWERIES

Cader Dolgellau (brewing suspended)
Conwy ✦ Llysfaen
Cwrw Nant Pentrefoelas
Cybi ✦ Holyhead: Anglesey
Geipel Corwen
Lleu Penygroes
Llyn ✦ Nefyn
Mona Gaerwen: Anglesey
Myrddins Barmouth
Purple Moose Porthmadog
Snowdon Craft Mochdre (brewing suspended)
Snowdonia Parc 🍺 Waunfawr
Ty Mo Caernarfon
Wild Horse ✦ Llandudno

Caernarfon

Anglesey Arms Hotel
Slate Quay, LL55 1SG
☎ (01286) 672158
3 changing beers (sourced locally) ⊞
An historic pub in a superb location, with amazing views across the Menai Straits to Anglesey. Built up against the town walls and next to Caernarfon Castle, the pub attracts a mix of locals and tourists. The two rooms have a bar running between them which usually serves at least three ales. There is plenty of outdoor seating beside the seawall, where you can enjoy the birdlife and breathtaking sunsets. The Welsh Highland Railway station is a short walk away. ✿🏠➰❄🅿🚪😺🎵

Black Boy Inn ★ ✅
Northgate Street, LL55 1RW
☎ (01286) 673604 ⊕ black-boy-inn.com
5 changing beers (sourced regionally) ⊞
Characterful pub set within the town walls between the marina and castle. The historic town, a World Heritage Site, is well worth a visit, ending with a welcome pint at the Black Boy. The public bar and small lounge are warmed by roaring fires. A good range of food is served as well as a good selection of guest beers. There is a drinking area outside on the traffic-free street. A previous local CAMRA Pub of the Year award winner.
✿🏠🍽➰❤♣🅿🚪😺

Tafarn Y Porth ✅
7-9 Eastgate Street, LL55 1AG (just off Bangor Rd near post office)
☎ (01286) 662920
Greene King Abbot; 5 changing beers (sourced nationally) ⊞
This Wetherspoon pub is located in a converted supermarket, adjacent to the historic town walls and close to the castle. It takes its name from its location near to the east gate. It has a large open-plan interior and a spacious, partly covered courtyard outside with plenty of seating. The real ale range often includes local Welsh ales. The pub is in the centre of the historic town and convenient for the Welsh Highland Railway, which takes you to the heart of Snowdonia. Q✿🏠❄🍽🔔A➰❤♣🅿🚪😺

Colwyn Bay

Bay Hop ♥
17 Penrhyn Road, LL29 8LG
4 changing beers (sourced regionally) ⊞
Multi award-winning micropub and bottle shop with a friendly, welcoming atmosphere. The beers, ciders and perries on offer are displayed on the blackboard. Furnishings include wooden settles and chairs around large and small tables. An extensive range of bottles and cans are available for drinking in or taking out. Pizzas from Johnny Dough's can be delivered on Monday evenings. A former CAMRA North Wales Pub of the Year and local CAMRA Pub of the Year on several occasions.
✿❄➰●🚪(12,13) 😺🎵

Black Cloak Taproom 🅛
71 Abergele Road, LL29 7RU
☎ (01492) 330274
3 changing beers (sourced regionally) ⊞
Opened in 2018, this former brewpub has now expanded and the brewery moved to Denbigh. The pub continues as the tap room for Black Cloak beers while also featuring interesting and unusual brews from all over the UK including a large selection of canned and bottled beers available to drink in or take away. It has comfortable seating and a convivial atmosphere with a covered

outdoor area at the rear and tables at the front. Occasional music and quiz nights are held.
✿🌟❄●🚪😺🎵

Pen-y-Bryn
Pen-y-Bryn Road, LL29 6DD
☎ (01492) 533360
Brunning & Price Original; 4 changing beers (sourced regionally; often Timothy Taylor) ⊞
Large, open-plan pub furnished with bookcases and old furniture, featuring real fires during the winter. The walls are decorated with old photographs and memorabilia from the local area. The terrace and garden offer panoramic views over the Bay of Colwyn and the Great Orme. Food is served throughout the day, with the menu updated daily on the website. A boardroom-style function room, for celebrations and meetings, has been created in the cellar and opens out onto the garden.
✿🌟🍽🔔🅿🚪(23) 😺🎵

Conwy

Albion Ale House ★ 🅛
Upper Gate Street, LL32 8RF
☎ (01492) 582484
8 changing beers (sourced locally) ⊞
This multi-roomed pub has been identified by CAMRA as having a nationally important historic interior. Each room retains the original 1920s features, with several having interesting fireplaces. No music, TV or fruit machines intrude. The pub serves beers from all over Wales and the UK, but showcases local breweries such as Conwy, Purple Moose and Snowdon Craft. Paddles for three or six third-pints are offered. A selection of fine wines and malt whiskies is also served. Q✿🌟❄♣🚪(5,19)😺🎵

Bank of Conwy
1 Lancaster Square, LL32 8HT
☎ (01492) 573741 ⊕ thebankofconwy.wales
3 changing beers (sourced regionally) ⊞
Craft beer bar opened in a Grade II-listed former bank. Many of the original fittings remain, with the bank counter now being the bar and the downstairs seating area sporting the fortified door. An extensive selection of beers is available in cask, keg and bottled form, with a large wine and gin selection. Food is available daily until early evening, with breakfasts at weekends. Sausages are available for dogs. Wednesday night is music night.
✿❄❄🚪😺🎵

Mulberry
Conwy Marina, Morfa Drive, LL32 8GU
☎ (01492) 583350
Robinsons Dizzy Blonde, Unicorn; house beer (by Robinsons); 1 changing beer (sourced regionally) ⊞
Nautically themed new-build Robinsons pub that first opened in 1998 as part of an extensive marina development. The spacious ground floor has a full-length bar and features a rowing boat suspended from the ceiling. An open stairwell leads to the first-floor bar and restaurant with magnificent views over the Conwy estuary to Deganwy Castle. A front decking area overlooks the marina, with a barbecue and a pirate ship serving as the children's play area.
✿🌟🍽♣🅿🚪(27) 😺🎵

Dolgellau

Torrent Walk Hotel 🅛
Smithfield Street, LL40 1AA
☎ (01341) 422858
4 changing beers (sourced nationally) ⊞

An 18th-century hotel in the historic town centre. It retains most of its multi-roomed interior and old fireplaces, though the bar fittings date from circa 1970. Note the Coffee Room etched panel in the door from the lobby to the right-hand room. A regularly changing range of four ales is mostly from Welsh breweries. Dolgellau is an ideal base for walking in the Cadar Idris area. A former local CAMRA Pub of the Year. ✦✦✦✦✦✦

Llanbedr

Ty Mawr Hotel
LL45 2HH
☎ (01341) 241440 ⊕ tymawrhotel.com
4 changing beers Ⓗ
Small country hotel set in its own grounds. The modern lounge bar has a slate-flagged floor and cosy wood-burning stove. Unusual flying memorabilia reflect connections with the local airfield. French windows open out on a veranda and landscaped terrace with seating. A beer festival is held in a marquee on the lawn each summer. It is popular with locals and walkers, and dogs and children are welcome. Bar meals are served at lunchtime and evenings. Q✦✦✦✦✦✦✦

Llandderfel

Bryntirion Inn Ⓛ
B4401, LL23 7RA (on B4401, 4 miles E of Bala)
☎ (01678) 530205 ⊕ bryntirioninn.co.uk
Purple Moose Cwrw Eryri/Snowdonia Ale; 1 changing beer (sourced locally) Ⓗ
Dating back to 1695, this former hunting lodge and coaching inn overlooks the Dee Valley. The cosy and comfortable bar area, with a log fire, is open all day. There are a number of other rooms to accommodate diners and families, including a large function room for special events. There is also a small covered and heated courtyard at the rear. The guest beer varies and is from local or national brewers. Two en-suite guest rooms are available upstairs. Q✦✦✦✦✦P(T3)✦✦

Llandudno

Albert Ⓛ
56 Madoc Street, LL30 2TW
☎ (01492) 877188
Conwy Clogwyn Gold; Timothy Taylor Landlord; 2 changing beers (sourced regionally) Ⓗ
Just off the town centre and close to the railway station this popular pub/restaurant offers several handpulled beers from local and independent breweries as well as a range of meals, available throughout the day. The décor is modern, with a range of interesting photographs and pictures on display. The beers on offer are clearly displayed on blackboards above and beside the L shaped bar. There is a covered seating area at the front of the building. ✦✦✦✦✦(5,12)✦✦

Cask & Apple Ⓛ
29 Mostyn Avenue, Craig Y Don, LL30 1YS
☎ 07733 152242
4 changing beers (sourced regionally) Ⓗ
Micropub opened in 2023 as an attractive shop conversion, with imaginative repurposing of old scaffold timber used for the bar and its surrounds. Raised seating at the front windows overlooks the outdoor area, which consists of two picnic tables, with cover provided by the shop veranda. The owners have a good trade reputation, having previously run the nearby multi award-winning Penrhyn Arms. ✦✦✦(5,12)✦✦

Cottage Loaf Ⓛ
Market Street, LL30 2SR
☎ (01492) 870762 ⊕ the-cottageloaf.co.uk
Conwy Welsh Pride; Timothy Taylor Landlord; 2 changing beers (sourced regionally) Ⓗ
The building was converted to a pub in 1980 and its name refers to the previous occupant, a bakery. The interior features stone-flagged floors, an impressive fireplace and a raised, timber-floored area. Much of the wood came from the Flying Foam, a schooner shipwrecked at Llandudno's West Shore. The Loaf is a popular meeting place for all ages, with home-cooked food served all day, every day. To the rear is a conservatory-style restaurant area with an enclosed outdoor terrace. ✦✦✦✦✦(5,12)✦♪

Snowdon
11 Tudno Street, LL30 2HB
☎ (01492) 872166 ⊕ thesnowdon.co.uk
Draught Bass; Timothy Taylor Landlord; house beer (by Coach House); 3 changing beers (sourced regionally) Ⓗ
The Snowdon is one of the oldest pubs in Llandudno, featuring a large main drinking area with an attractive Snowdon mirror above the fireplace. The ale range includes house beer Coach House 1852. The raised pavement garden drinking area has a fine view of the Great Orme, and the goats if you are lucky. The pub has won the Llandudno in Bloom award for its floral display several times in recent years. ✦✦✦✦(5,12)✦✦

Tapps Ⓛ
35 Madoc Street, LL30 2TL
☎ (01492) 870956
Conwy Welsh Pride; 4 changing beers (sourced regionally) Ⓗ
Llandudno's first micropub opened in 2017 in a former cake shop. It features an open-plan bar at the front and a small snug to the rear. Welsh beer features prominently, and there is a large bottled beer selection to drink in or take away. Third-pint glasses are available. One of the tables is a chess board which transforms into a backgammon or card table. Other board games are provided, and there are books that can be borrowed. ✦✦✦✦(5,12) ✦✦

Llanelian-yn-Rhos

White Lion Inn ✔
LL29 8YA
☎ (01492) 515807 ⊕ whitelioninn.co.uk
Theakston Best Bitter; 2 changing beers (sourced regionally) Ⓗ
A regular in the Guide for over 30 years, this 16th-century inn, in the hills above Old Colwyn, next to St Elian's church, offers a warm welcome. Two stone white lions guard the entrance which leads into the bar area with its slate-flagged flooring, large comfortable chairs and log fires. Decorative stained glass is mounted above the bar in the tiny snug. The restaurant serves home-cooked food. Tuesday is jazz night and Thursday is quiz night. Q✦✦✦✦P✦✦♪

Llysfaen

MASH Ⓛ
Unit 2 Ty Mawr Enterprise Park, off Tan Y Graig Road, LL29 8UE
☎ (01492) 514305 ⊕ conwybrewery.co.uk
Conwy Clogwyn Gold; 3 changing beers (sourced locally) Ⓗ

Micropub and Conwy brewery tap that has become a community hub since opening in 2018. It serves a range of ales, wine and spirits, with tea, coffee and soft drinks also available. Recent refurbishment has provided further indoor drinking space, complete with a largescreen TV, which is available for functions. The fingerpost at the front corner of the brewery will lead you to views over the bay of Colwyn towards the Great Orme. Third-pint glasses are available. ⅋❀P🚃❀🛜♪

Maentwrog

Grapes Hotel 🄻

LL41 4HN (on A496 near A487 jct)
☎ (01766) 590365 ● grapeshotelsnowdonia.co.uk
3 changing beers (sourced locally) Ⓗ
This former coaching inn dates back to the 17th century and overlooks the Vale of Ffestiniog. The interior comprises a lounge, public bar, veranda and large dining room, and there is a sheltered beer garden at the rear. Most of the beers are locally sourced. The village is an ideal spot for a stop while visiting Snowdonia, with the railway station nearby on the heritage Ffestiniog line.
Q⅋❀🐕⌑❶👶♿♣♠P🚃

Marianglas

Parciau Arms

LL73 8NY
☎ (01248) 853766
4 changing beers (sourced nationally; often Conwy) Ⓗ
Set on a sizeable plot on the edge of the village, adjacent to a camping site, this free house has up to four ales, often from Conwy. Its stained-glass windows and wood-panelled interior, along with nautical themed pictures and memorabilia, give it character. In summer the lawned beer garden is popular, while an open fire provides warmth in winter when the opening hours are reduced. ⅋❀♠P❀

Nefyn

Bragdy Llyn

Ffordd Dewi Sant, LL53 6EG
☎ (01758) 721981 ● cwrwllyn.cymru
Cwrw Llyn Brenin Enlli, Cwrw Glyndwr, Seithenyn; 1 changing beer (sourced locally) Ⓗ
A friendly bar located within the modern Cwrw Llyn brewery on the edge of the village, near the coast and picturesque village of Porthdinllaen. A range of the brewery's ales are always available. Large glass windows provide a view of the brewery. Tours are available on request and include tasters of the core range of ales. ♿P

Old Colwyn

Crafty Fox

355 Abergele Road, LL29 9PL
☎ 07733 531766
Coach House Farriers Best Bitter, Post Horn Premium Pale Ale; 2 changing beers (sourced regionally) Ⓗ
Old Colwyn's first micropub opened in 2018 in two ex-retail units. The main entrance leads into the former

> A glass of bitter beer or pale ale, taken with the principal meal of the day, does more good and less harm than any medicine the physician can prescribe.
> **Dr Carpenter, 1750**

tattoo parlour, now the bar, and features tables upcycled from cast-iron Singer sewing machine bases with oak drop-leaf tabletops. The former butcher's is repurposed as a lounge, with comfortable leather sofas. The bar wall carries an interesting selection of photographs comparing the present street scene with that of a century ago. Q⅋♠🚃❀🛜

Penmachno

Eagles 🄻

LL24 0UG
☎ (01690) 760177 ● eaglespenmachno.co.uk
Greene King IPA; 2 changing beers (sourced locally) Ⓗ
Traditional pub set in a peaceful village in a secluded valley at the heart of Snowdonia, four miles from Betws-y-coed. A wood-burning stove ensures a warm welcome during winter months. There is always at least one local ale on offer. The pub prides itself on being the centre of community activities; local musicians perform on the first Wednesday of each month. The secluded rear garden has delightful views up the valley. Q⅋❀🍽️♠🚃(19)❀🛜

Penrhynside

Cross Keys Inn 🄻

Pendre Road, LL30 3DD (off B5115)
☎ (01492) 330850 ● crosskeysinn2015.wixsite.com
Facer's Flintshire Bitter; Greene King Abbot; 2 changing beers (sourced regionally) Ⓗ
This family-owned free house dates from the 19th century and serves local beers and guests from across the UK. Among the font offerings are three German beers. A cosy front room sports a central bar, and both the rear and side lounges boast unrivalled views of the surrounding area towards Penrhyn Bay and beyond. TVs are available for sporting events. Quiz night is the second and fourth Thursday of the month. Dogs are welcome, and children until 7pm. ⅋🚃(12,14)❀🛜

Penrhyn Arms

Pendre Road, LL30 3BY (off B5115)
☎ 07943 123146 ● penrhynarms.com
Banks's Amber Ale; 3 changing beers (sourced regionally) Ⓗ
This welcoming free house offers guest beers from around the country. The spacious single-room pub has an L-shaped central bar, seating around large tables and two real fires. Food highlights include Wednesday curry night, Thursday pie night and Sunday lunch, and wood-fired pizzas are available every night. The rear conservatory leads up to a raised landscaped garden terrace with extensive views of the coastline. Live jazz plays on Monday and occasional music on Saturday.
⅋❀❶🚃❀♪

Porthdinllaen

Ty Coch Inn

LL53 6DB (access on foot only)
☎ (01758) 720498 ● tycoch.co.uk
2 changing beers (sourced regionally) Ⓗ
Opened in 1842 to serve local fishermen, this pub enjoys a prominent position on the beach at beautiful Porthdinllaen, and is reachable only on foot, either along the beach (except at high tide) or by a pleasant walk across the golf course. It is rated as one of the top beach bars in the world, and views from the tables by the beach certainly justify the claim. Always check off-season opening times. ⅋❶❀

Porthmadog

Australia ✓
31-35 High Street, LL49 9LR
☎ (01766) 515957
Purple Moose Cwrw Eryri/Snowdonia Ale, Cwrw Ysgawen/Elderflower Ale, Ochr Dywyll y Mws/Dark Side of the Moose; 3 changing beers (sourced locally; often Purple Moose) Ⓗ
A pub since 1864, the Australia was taken over by Purple Moose Brewing in 2017 and serves as their taphouse. It is in the centre of town next to the bus stops. Two rooms are served by a long wooden bar with six handpumps, serving most of the brewery's core real ale range as well as seasonal and special occasion beers. There is a small outdoor seating area at the back. It is near the Ffestiniog and Welsh Highland Railway Station. 🏠◐🍴♿🚆🚌🐾❄🛜

Spooner's Bar
Harbour Station, LL49 9NF
☎ (01766) 516032 🌐 spoonerspub.co.uk
Purple Moose Cwrw Eryri/Snowdonia Ale; 4 changing beers (sourced nationally) Ⓗ
A bar situated in the terminus of the world-famous Ffestiniog Railway and Welsh Highland Railway, with steam trains outside the door most of the year. At least three ales are available, including a changing range from local and national breweries. The bar is adjacent to the café/restaurant, with outdoor seating overlooking the platforms and the scenic coast. Food is served every lunchtime, and evening meals from Tuesday to Saturday, but check hours out of season. A former local CAMRA Pub of the Year. Q🏠◐Å🚆(Harbour)🚌🛜

Red Wharf Bay

Ship Inn ✓
LL75 8RJ (off A5025 between Pentraeth and Benllech)
☎ (01248) 852568 🌐 shipinnredwharfbay.co.uk
House beer (by Facer's); 2 changing beers Ⓗ
Red Wharf Bay was once a busy port exporting coal and fertilisers in the 18th and 19th centuries. Previously known as the Quay, the Ship enjoys an excellent reputation for its bar and restaurant, with meals served lunchtimes and evenings. It gets busy with locals and visitors in the summer. The garden has panoramic views across the bay to south-east Anglesey. The resort town of Benllech is two miles away and the coastal path passes the front door. Q🏠☕◐♿P🐾

Rhos-on-Sea

Tapps at Rhos Ⓛ
1 Everard Road, LL28 4EY
☎ (01492) 870956
Conwy Welsh Pride; 4 changing beers (sourced regionally) Ⓗ
An open-plan micropub that opened in 2023 as a partner business to the Tapps pub in Llandudno. The rooms is furnished with random wooden tables and chairs, and examples of local photographs and paintings adorn the walls. Tiles on the ceiling and walls help to soften the acoustics and lend the bar a relaxed atmosphere. There is a piano in the small back room. Chess and other board games are played on Monday. Cheese is served on a Tuesday. 🏠☕🚌🐾🛜

Rhoscolyn

White Eagle
LL65 2NJ (off B4545, signed Traeth Beach)
☎ (01407) 860267 🌐 white-eagle.co.uk
6 changing beers (often Conwy, Weetwood) Ⓗ
Saved from closure by new owners some years ago, this pub was renovated and rebuilt and has an airy, brasserie-style ambience. Excellent food is available lunchtimes and evenings, and all day during the school holidays. Outside is a fine patio with superb views over Caernarfon Bay and the Llyn Peninsula to Bardsey Island. The nearby beach offers safe swimming, with a warden on duty in the summer months. The pub is also close to the coastal footpath. Q🏠◐♿Å♣P

Tremadog

Union Inn ✓
7 Market Square, LL49 9RB
☎ (01766) 512748 🌐 union-inn.com
1 changing beer Ⓗ
Friendly village local situated on the village square, with two separate cosy bars and a restaurant at the rear. The pub has a policy of using locally sourced produce, and the ale range features mainly local beers. Children are welcome, and there are board games available. Excellent food is served in the bar and restaurant. Tremadog was the birthplace of Lawrence of Arabia. Frequent bus services pass by. Q🏠☕◐♿Å🚆(Porthmadog)🐾🚌(1A,T2)

Tudweiliog

Lion Hotel
LL53 8ND (on B4417)
☎ (01758) 770244 🌐 lionhoteltudweiliog.co.uk
3 changing beers (often Purple Moose) Ⓗ
A 300-year-old village inn on the glorious north coast of the Llyn Peninsula, with cliffs and beaches a mile away by footpath, or a little further by road. Up to three ales are served depending on the season, with Purple Moose a firm favourite. This free house has a large beer garden and a restaurant serving good pub meals. It is accessible by number 8 bus from Pwllheli during the day only. Q🏠☕🛏◐♿Å🚌(8)🐾🛜

Waunfawr

Snowdonia Parc
Beddgelert Road, LL55 4AQ
☎ (01286) 650409 🌐 snowdonia-park.co.uk
House beer (by Snowdonia Parc); 5 changing beers (often Snowdonia Parc) Ⓗ
Home of the Snowdonia brewery, this is a popular pub for walkers, climbers and families (it has a children's play area). Meals are served all day. The pub adjoins Waunfawr station on the Welsh Highland Railway. You can stop off here before continuing on one of the most scenic sections of narrow gauge railway in Britain. There is a large campsite adjacent on the riverside. Multiple local CAMRA Pub of the Year. Q🏠☕◐♿Å🚆♣🐾P🚌🛜

For we could not now take time for further search (to land our ship) our victuals being much spent especially our beer.
Log of the Mayflower

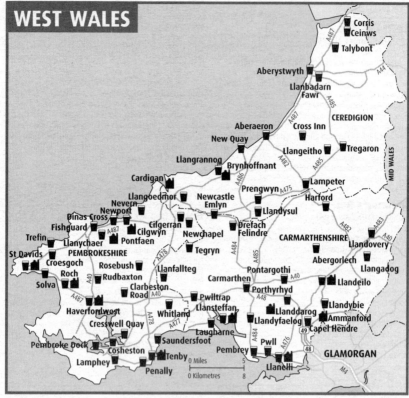

WEST WALES

Authority areas covered: Carmarthenshire UA, Ceredigion UA, Pembrokeshire UA

Aberaeron

Cadwgan Inn

10 Market Street, SA46 0AU (Off A487, overlooking harbour)
☎ (01545) 570149
Wye Valley Bitter; 2 changing beers (sourced nationally; often Mantle, Tinworks) Ⓗ
Named after the last ship built in the attractive regency town of Aberaeron, this old-style single-bar pub offers a friendly welcome and lively conversation. It is popular for its sports coverage, mainly rugby and racing. Guest beers are from a wide range of small and regional breweries. The sizeable paved terraced area at the front is a real suntrap. Opposite is a free, but busy harbourside public car park. Buses T1 and T5 stop nearby from Aberystwyth, Cardigan and Carmarthen. Q❀▲♿(T1,T5)❀🏵♪

Abergorlech

Black Lion

Abergorlech Road, SA32 7SN
☎ (01558) 685271 ⊕ blacklionabergorlech.co.uk
2 changing beers (sourced regionally; often Evan Evans, Harbwr) Ⓗ
Traditional village pub that is also a restaurant and coffee shop. It serves home-made food, including cakes, largely produced and sourced locally in Wales. Just a few steps from the pub you can take advantage of signposted walks in the Brechfa forest or the thrilling Brechfa Mountain Bike Trails. The car park provides bike-locking facilities and muddy bikers are always welcome, as the 300-year-old stone floor in the bar is easily cleaned. Open Thursday to Sunday. ❀🏵◑▶▲P❀🏵♪

Aberystwyth

Bottle & Barrel

14 Cambrian Place, SY23 1NT
☎ (01970) 625888 ⊕ bottleandbarrel.cymru
2 changing beers (sourced nationally; often Lucky 7, Polly's) Ⓗ
This modern, town-centre, mid-terrace bar provides a cosy atmosphere in which to enjoy a drink. At the front of the building is a relaxed area with comfy armchairs and wooden tables, and at the rear a number of high tables. At the very back the small garden with tables and chairs is a suntrap in the summer. The bar offers two cask ale pumps, 14 keg lines with a focus on Welsh breweries, and real cider. There is an on-site bottle shop. ❀🏵❀♣♿☐❀🏵

Glengower Hotel

3 Victoria Terrace, SY23 2DH (on seafront at N end of promenade)
☎ (01970) 626191 ⊕ glengower.co.uk
Mantle Rock Steady, MOHO; Wye Valley Butty Bach; 2 changing beers (sourced regionally; often Ludlow, Purple Moose, Timothy Taylor) Ⓗ
A warm and welcoming pub with rooms. Outside seating on its suntrap front terrace offers stunning views over Cardigan Bay. Inside is a light and airy bar, a quieter dining area, and a large back room. Cask beers are usually sourced from Welsh micros or independent breweries close to the border. Good-quality food is served all day Monday to Saturday and until early evening Sunday. Dogs are welcome, with water and biscuits at the bar. Q❀🏵❀◑▶▲♣♿❀🏵

Ship & Castle

1 High Street, SY23 1JG
☎ 07773 778785
Castle Rock Harvest Pale; Wye Valley Butty Bach; 3 changing beers (sourced nationally; often Oakham, Salopian, Tiny Rebel) Ⓗ

Aberystwyth's flagship pub offers microbrewery guest ales from the UK and Ireland, as well as beers from the likes of Polly's and Tiny Rebel in keg, bottles and cans. Cider and perry are available from Gwynt y Ddraig. A platter of five third-pint cask ales is available. The decor reflects the pub's name and history. It gets busy on rugby match days, but is welcoming at all times. ➪★▲≈♣🖶👹🕾🎜

Capel Hendre

King's Head Hotel

Waterloo Road, SA18 3SF
☎ (01269) 842377
2 changing beers (sourced regionally; often Glamorgan, Zoo) Ⓗ

A local village pub tucked away just three miles from M4 junction 49, and a couple of miles from the former mining town of Ammanford. There is a main bar and dining room, with a sliding door leading to a separate snug. Usually two, sometimes three, real ales are sourced from Wales; Glamorganshire, Bluestone and Neath breweries are often represented. It has a large car park and garden. ➪❀⇦◑&🖶P🖶(128,129)👹🕾🎜

Carmarthen

Coracle Tavern

1 Cambrian Place, SA31 1QG
☎ (01267) 469489
2 changing beers (sourced regionally; often Glamorgan, Robinsons) Ⓗ

Situated in the centre of town, close to the main shopping area, this friendly free house offers a warm welcome to locals and visitors alike. The large, open-plan bar area has comfy sofas, and there is a separate seating area upstairs that can be booked for private gatherings. Darts are a popular activity and a number of teams are hosted. Local CAMRA meetings are sometimes held here. ≈♣

Friends Arms

Old St Clears Road, SA31 3HH (W of town centre at bottom of Monument Hill B3412)
☎ (01267) 234073
Thornbridge Jaipur IPA; 1 changing beer (sourced regionally; often Gower, Wye Valley) Ⓗ

Excellent local hostelry half a mile from Carmarthen town centre. Two well-kept ales are always available, joined occasionally by a third in the summer. A cosy and friendly atmosphere and a warm welcome is enhanced by two open fires. The open-plan seated bar area has live sports channels and is popular with fans. There is also a smaller side room. A former local CAMRA Pub of the Year. It hosts beer festivals in early summer and in December. ➪❀♣🖶(222,322)👹🕾🎜

Hen Dderwen ⊘

47-48 King Street, SA31 1BH
☎ (01267) 242050
Glamorgan Jemima's Pitchfork; Gower Power; Greene King Abbot; Ruddles Best Bitter; Sharp's Doom Bar; 3 changing beers (sourced nationally) Ⓗ

A Wetherspoon pub named after the local legend of Merlin and an ancient oak tree, which is depicted throughout the premises. A recent extensive refurbishment includes a first-floor dining area and extensive roof terrace. Local Welsh ales are always available as well as a good selection of ales from around the UK. It also has a good selection of bottled and canned local and international craft beers. There are international beer festivals in the spring and autumn, and a summer cider festival. Food is served all day. ➪◑&≈🕾

Rose & Crown Hotel

114 Lammas Street, SA31 3AE
☎ (01267) 232050 ⊕ roseandcrowncarmarthen.co.uk
Evan Evans Cwrw; 1 changing beer (sourced nationally; often Fuller's, Glamorgan) Ⓗ

Large, popular town-centre pub with friendly staff and well-kept ale. A long bar serves numerous segregated drinking areas. Towards the rear of the premises is a separate restaurant area, offering a wide selection of pub food; Sunday lunches are particularly popular. A large outside area has a heated covered patio and widescreen TV. Local CAMRA Pub of the Year. ❀⇦◑≈P🕾🎜

Stag & Pheasant 🏆

34 Spilman Street, SA31 1LQ
☎ 07578 986586
4 changing beers (sourced nationally; often Bath Ales, Otter, Theakston) Ⓗ/Ⓖ

A busy locals' pub with a warm and friendly atmosphere, on the main street, making it a popular venue for tourists and regulars. The pub boasts an excellent beer garden with outdoor heaters at the rear. There are two large TV screens showing sporting events. The landlord is keen on his real ale offering, with four well-kept beers always available, including one on gravity straight from the cask. ❀&≈♣👹🕾

Ceinws

Tafarn Dwynant

SY20 9HA (off A487, 3 miles N of Machynlleth)
☎ (01654) 761660
2 changing beers (sourced regionally; often Mantle, Wye Valley) Ⓗ

Friendly two-room community pub. Down a few steps from a wood-floored bar serving Welsh or border ales is a small seated lounge. A small front terrace offers fantastic views along the wooded Dulas valley and alfresco drinking. The landlord is an artist and his paintings adorns the walls. Hourly buses ply the A487 across the river bridge 300 yards north of the village. Opening hours may vary, so ring ahead to check. Q➪❀▲♣🖶(T2)👹🕾🎜

REAL ALE BREWERIES

Bluestone ✦ Cilgwyn
Cardigan ✦ Brynhoffnant
Coles Family 🍺 Llanddarog
Core of the Poodle Haverfordwest
Electro Cardigan (brewing suspended)
Evan Evans Llandeilo
Felinfoel Llanelli
Gwaun Valley ✦ Pontfaen
Harbwr Tenby 🍺 Tenby
Mantle Cardigan
Pererin Llansteffan (NEW)
St David's Old Farmhouse St Davids
Tenby ✦ Tenby
Tinworks ✦ Llanelli
Victoria Inn 🍺 Roch
Zoo Ammanford

Cilgerran

Mason's Arms

Cwnce, SA43 2SR
☎ 07989 990461
Mantle Cwrw Teifi; 1 changing beer (sourced regionally) Ⓗ
Also known as the Rampin, this characterful and atmospheric pub is thought to have first opened in 1836. It is a small cosy and friendly village local, with an open fire (old kitchen range). Two real ales are served, one changing regularly, usually from a local brewery. Various charity events are held during the year, and there is the occasional musical evening. Check winter opening times before visiting. A former local CAMRA Pub of the Year.
Ꮞ❀Å♣P❀

Clarbeston Road

Cross Inn

SA63 4UL (N of railway station)
☎ (01437) 731506
Evan Evans Warrior; Glamorgan Jemima's Pitchfork; 1 changing beer (sourced regionally; often Bluestone) Ⓗ
This multi-roomed village inn has stone and wood floors and original oak beams, and is well worth seeking out. The large bar area houses pool, sports TV and a jukebox, and is complemented by two small snugs. A dining room serves reasonably priced home-cooked food Thursday to Saturday evenings and Sunday lunchtime. Outside there are more spacious drinking areas. The beer range is sourced regionally and nationally, and a beer festival is held in summer. Q❀Ꮞ❀◑&≈♣P🖵(313)❀🛜

Corris

Slater's Arms ★

Bridge Street, SY20 9SP
☎ (01654) 761324 ⊕ slatersarmscorris.co.uk
3 changing beers (sourced regionally; often Big Bog, Evan Evans, Purple Moose) Ⓗ
Named after what was formerly the main trade of the townsfolk in Corris, this Grade II-listed village pub is popular with locals and visitors. The main bar has some traditional features such as slate flooring and a decorative mantelshelf above a large inglenook fireplace. In winter a blazing log-burner is a welcome sight. A dining area at the rear is for Sunday lunches only. Walkers, families and well-behaved dogs are welcome. Accommodation in four en-suite double bedrooms.
ᏎⓀ◑Å🛏🖵(34) ❀🛜♫

Cosheston

Brewery Inn

SA72 4UD
☎ (01646) 686678 ⊕ thebreweryinn.com
2 changing beers (sourced regionally; often Brains, Glamorgan) Ⓗ
This Grade II-listed free house was once accommodation for monks, with its own brewhouse situated in the outbuildings behind. Brewing ceased in 1889. The light and airy stone-built inn boasts a traditional slate floor and beamed ceiling. To one side is a drinking area in front of a log fire. Ingredients for the extensive menu are sourced locally, including the fresh fish. It is worth checking opening hours in winter before travelling.
Q❀Ꮞ❀Ⓚ◑&Å P🖵❀🛜♫

Cresswell Quay

Cresselly Arms 🍷 ★

SA68 0TE
☎ (01646) 629904
Hancocks HB; Wye Valley Butty Bach; 2 changing beers (sourced regionally; often Bluestone, Mantle) Ⓗ
Situated on the Cresswell River, this 250-year-old, ivy-covered hostelry is like a throwback to the Victorian age. The homely farm kitchen interior, where a roaring fire burns in the hearth, is a haven for locals and visitors. Accessible by boat from the Milford Haven estuary at high tide, the pub also lies on a series of interesting walking routes. No food is served. Local and Wales CAMRA Pub of the Year 2024. Q❀❀&ÅP🖵(361)♫

Croesgoch

Artramont Arms

SA62 5JP (on A487)
☎ (01348) 831309
2 changing beers (sourced regionally; often Gwaun Valley, Tiny Rebel) Ⓗ
A friendly, family-run village local that has been a licensed premises since the 1700s, and which has, in the past, had a post office wing and sold petrol. The public bar has a tiled floor, and there is also a lounge and outdoor drinking area. Local ales are often available. There is also a small library for customers. Check winter opening times before visiting. Ꮞ❀♣●P🖵(T11)❀

Cross Inn

Rhos yr Hafod Inn 🍷

SY23 5NB (at B4337/B4577 crossroads)
☎ (01974) 272644
2 changing beers (sourced regionally; often Mantle, Purple Moose, Tudor) Ⓗ
Friendly, family-run pub offering two constantly changing ales from Welsh breweries and a warm welcome. The choice of drinking areas comprises a front bar, which is popular in the early evening with lively locals, and a comfortable rear bar. Sunny days can be enjoyed in the roadside drinking area or the large rear garden. There is ample parking. Events include an August beer festival. Hours vary in January so check in advance. A former local CAMRA Pub of the Year. Q❀❀♣P❀🛜

Dinas Cross

Freemasons Arms

Spencer Buildings, SA42 0UW (on A487 coast road, midway between Fishguard and Newport)
☎ (01348) 811674
Coles Family Llanddarog; Gower Gold Ⓗ
Traditional sea captains' meeting place in the Pembrokeshire National Park. The pub has been tastefully refurbished, retaining its original character, and is conveniently placed for attractive beaches and the coastal path. The main bar has a cosy open fire, with a dining area at the side. It is on a main bus route. Check winter opening times. Q❀❀Ⓚ&Å♣P🖵(T5)❀🛜♫

Drefach Felindre

John Y Gwas

SA44 5XG SN354383
☎ (01559) 370469
Robinsons Trooper; 3 changing beers (sourced regionally; often Brains, Glamorgan) Ⓗ

This early 19th-century village tavern, with its striking yellow and black livery, attracts locals and tourists alike. The landlord offers a friendly and enthusiastic welcome with one permanent and three well-kept and changing beers, plus a wide variety of bottled beers and ciders. The cosy interior features snugs and a wood-burning stove, and the walls and ceiling are adorned with Trooper ale branding. Food is available every night. A beer festival, hosting over 10 different ales, is held over the August bank holiday weekend.
🕭🏵🌶🅿🖵(460) 🏵🛜♫

Fishguard

Royal Oak Inn
Market Square, SA65 9HA
☎ (01348) 218632 🌐 royaloakfishguard.co.uk
Felinfoel Double Dragon; Glamorgan Jemima's Pitchfork; Sharp's Doom Bar; 1 changing beer (sourced regionally; often Cardigan, Evan Evans, Gwaun Valley) 🄷
This Grade II-listed pub is famous for its place in history. In 1797 the French unsuccessfully attempted an invasion on the west coast of Wales, only to be thwarted by the locals. This was the last invasion attempt to land in Britain. A peace treaty was signed between the British and French in the bar area. The pub is sparingly decorated, with exposed stone and wooden beams, and with little reference to its notable past. A former local CAMRA Pub of the Year. Q🕭🏵🌶🅰🌶♫

Harford

Tafarn Jem
SA48 8HF
☎ (01558) 650633
1 changing beer (sourced regionally; often Glamorgan) 🄷
Welcoming 19th-century pub named after the landlady, and previously known as Mountain Cottage, which hints at the stunning views. The main interior is open plan, with two distinct areas; a comfortable small bar and a larger room with a pool table and seating. Booking is essential for the occasional steak/curry nights. A touring caravan site is located about a mile and a half from the pub, and a glamping site is just a quarter of a mile away. 🌶🅰🌶🅿🏵🛜

Haverfordwest

William Owen 🄻 ✅
6 Quay Street, SA61 1BG
☎ (01437) 771900
Greene King IPA, Abbot; Sharp's Doom Bar; 3 changing beers (sourced regionally; often Bluestone, Glamorgan) 🄷
Pembrokeshire's first Wetherspoon outlet occupies a handsome 19th-century building that was reputedly built in 1856 for Joseph Thomas, a corn and manure merchant, by local architect William Owen. It also has been a saddler's and more recently the Wilton House Hotel. Beer from one of the county's breweries is regularly available. The pub offers the chain's usual menus and promotional deals, and opens at 8am for breakfast. Q🕭🏵🌶♿🛜

Lampeter

Nag's Head
14 Bridge Street, SA48 7HG
☎ (01570) 218517

Sharp's Doom Bar; 1 changing beer (sourced regionally; often Evan Evans, Glamorgan) 🄷
This town-centre pub was refurbished in 2018 and now features a modern and bright horseshoe-shaped bar area. It is a friendly and fun pub, with a good mix of customers – locals, students and tourists. It shows most live sports events on TV and has live music every Friday night. It also offers B&B, evening basket meals Monday to Saturday, Sunday lunch, and a function room. 🕭🏵🛏🌶🖵🏵🛜♫

Lamphey

Dial Inn
The Ridgeway, SA71 5NU
☎ (01646) 672927
House beer (by Felinfoel); 2 changing beers (sourced regionally; often Brains, Mantle, Purple Moose) 🄷
Former Georgian dower house, now a friendly and welcoming village local in the Pembrokeshire countryside, a short walk from the medieval summer palace of the Bishops of St David's. The pub prides itself on its Welsh produce for both food and ales, and the Lamphey IPA is brewed by Felinfoel. It has a spacious interior and a beer garden. It is convenient for the Lamphey railway station on the Pembroke Dock to Swansea line. 🕭🏵🌶🚆🌶🖵(349)🏵

Laugharne

New Three Mariners Inn
Victoria Street, SA33 4SE
☎ (01994) 427426
2 changing beers (sourced nationally; often Courage, Evan Evans, Gower) 🄷
Popular locals' pub in the centre of this historic town, only yards from its early 11th-century castle. The pub moved to its current site when the original ale house opposite was converted to a carpentry shop. Two ales are served; one in winter. Evening meals are available, and there is a weekly quiz night. Dylan Thomas lived in the town for a number of years and he and wife Caitlin are buried in the graveyard of St Martin's Church. 🕭🏵🛏🌶♿🅰🌶🏵🛜

Llanbadarn Fawr

Black Lion
SY23 3RA
☎ (01970) 636632
Wye Valley Butty Bach; 1 changing beer (sourced nationally; often Wye Valley) 🄷
A mile from Aberystwyth, this modernised pub is popular with locals and students. The spacious main bar has seating at one end, darts and pool at the other. A large function room and equally large beer garden can be found at the rear. This garden has a delightful air of rural seclusion and a large, bespoke barbecue. Quizzes are held every other Friday, and pub teams play darts, pool and poker. There is a carvery on a Sunday. Q🕭🏵🌶🅿🖵(526, X47) 🏵🛜♫

Llandeilo

Hen Vic
82 New Road, SA19 6DF
☎ (01558) 822596
3 changing beers (sourced nationally; often Glamorgan, Mumbles, Oakham) 🄷
A lively and welcoming locals' pub. It was originally a sports club, but has been a pub for the past 20 years. Three constantly-changing and well-kept beers are

always available. There are several large TVs showing sport in the bar, and there is a separate pool room. The dining area has just had a major refurbishment and is to the front of the pub. ☎◑✿♣P무(X13, 281)✿✦♪

Salutation Inn

33 New Road, SA19 6DF

☎ (01558) 824255

Wye Valley Butty Bach; 2 changing beers (sourced nationally; often Gower, Greene King) ⊞

A locals' pub near the town centre, where friendly staff dispense three well-kept beers. The pub is separated into two areas, with a pool table to one side and a wood fire in the other. It offers an open mic session on a Tuesday as well as live music on most weekends. There is a garden and function area at the rear. The pub holds a beer festival in the summer. ✿ᐠ≉♣무✿✦♪

Llandovery

Whitehall

1 High Street, SA20 0PU

☎ (01550) 721139

Mantle MOHO, Cwrw Teifi; 1 changing beer (sourced regionally) ⊞

Friendly 17th-century pub in the town centre, warmed by cosy log fires in the winter. Three well-kept ales are served; two in the winter. There is seating at the front of the pub and a beer garden to the rear. The availability of meals at weekends can be limited, so booking ahead is recommended. It is the home of the Llandovery Vintage Tractor club. The darts team competes on a Thursday evening. ☎✿ᐠ◑≉♣무(280,281)✿✦♪

Llandybie

Ivy Bush

18 Church Street, SA18 3HZ (100yds from church)

☎ (01269) 850272

Timothy Taylor Landlord; 1 changing beer (sourced nationally; often Exmoor) ⊞

This friendly local was modernised several years ago and has a single bar with two comfortable seating areas. Pub games and quizzes are run weekly, and a largescreen TV shows sport. Timothy Taylor Landlord plus at least one regularly-changing guest is usually available. The train station nearby is on the Heart of Wales line. The local bird-watching group hold their meetings here. ☎✿≉♣P🖩무(103,X13) ✦♪

Llandyfaelog

Red Lion

SA17 5PR (300yds off A484)

☎ (01267) 267530 ⊕ redlionllandyfaelog.co.uk

Wye Valley Butty Bach; 2 changing beers (sourced nationally; often Butcombe, Glamorgan) ⊞

This popular, family-run village pub is at the heart of the community. A warm welcome and friendly service are offered, alongside three well-kept ales. A large public bar is complemented by a restaurant and a separate family room, while a separate annexe hosts concerts and functions. Bar and restaurant meals are available; booking is recommended. Q☎ᐠ◑ᐠ♣A무(198,X12)✦

Llandysul

Porth Hotel

Church Street, SA44 4QS SN418407

☎ (01559) 362202 ⊕ porthhotel.co.uk

2 changing beers (sourced regionally; often Glamorgan) ⊞

Originally a 17th-century coaching inn, now a family-run village hotel on the banks of the River Teifi. It has a bar and restaurant and function room areas. The public rooms still feature the original oak beams and panels. Food and drink is sourced locally where possible. At the rear of the hotel is a customer car park and lawned rear garden on the bank of the Teifi. It is ideal for access to walks and fishing. ☎✿ᐠ◑♣🖩P✿✦

Llanelli

New Drovers

32-34 Thomas Street, SA15 3JA (just below Thomas Arms Hotel, on opp side; it can be hard to spot as there is little to indicate that it is a public house)

☎ 07707 894070

Felinfoel Double Dragon; Fuller's London Pride; 2 changing beers (sourced nationally; often Evan Evans) ⊞

Quirky town-centre pub with no pub sign other than a brass plaque near the door – which makes you feel as if you are entering a solicitor's office rather than a pub. The large, open-plan bar area serves four real ales, and there are a couple of side rooms for quiet drinking. No smoking is allowed in the beer garden or outside areas. It hosts monthly food events; booking essential. The pub has a strict over-25s admission policy. Closed Monday to Wednesday. Q✿ᐠ◑♪

Stradey Arms

1 Stradey Road, SA15 4ET

☎ (01554) 753332 ⊕ thestradeyarms.com

Brains Rev James Original; 1 changing beer (sourced nationally; often Marston's) ⊞

A popular pub on the outskirts of town, with a comfortable bar and separate restaurant. The friendly and welcoming staff add to the overall pleasant ambience. Real ale is served from two handpumps on the bar. A varied menu of freshly-prepared food is served during the week, replaced on Sundays with a lunchtime carvery. It is a popular venue for sporting events, especially rugby internationals. ☎✿◑ᐠ≉P✿✦♪

Tinhouse ⅃

14 Vaughan Street, SA15 3TY

Tinworks Cwrw Grav, Old Castle Pale; 1 changing beer (sourced nationally; often Vocation) ⊞

This pub opened in 2023 and is the taphouse for the Tinworks brewery. The large, open plan single room has tables and chairs arranged throughout. Three handpumps dispense Tinworks beers alongside a guest ale, and a wide selection of craft keg beers is also available. It is popular with locals, and a meeting place for sports fans taking advantage of mulitple TV screens. Pizza made on-site is available. ◑≉🖩무

York Palace ⊘

51 Stepney Street, SA15 3YA (opp Town Hall Square Gardens)

☎ (01554) 758609

Greene King Abbot; Ruddles Best Bitter; 7 changing beers (sourced regionally; often Glamorgan, Gower, Tomos Watkin) ⊞

A refurbished former picture palace retaining much of the original decor. It offers a good selection of ales from around the world, including a wide range of bottled and canned craft beers. It also boasts a varied selection of boxes and bottled ciders, occasionally on handpull. There are two international beer festivals in the spring and autumn of each year, and a cider festival each summer. The pub hosts a number of Meet the Brewer sessions throughout the year. Food is served all day. Q◑ᐠ≉✦

Llanfallteg

Plash

SA34 0UN (off A40 at Llanddewi Velfrey)

☎ (01437) 563472 ⊕ theplashinn.co.uk

Wye Valley Butty Bach; 2 changing beers (sourced nationally) 🄷

At the centre of village life, this welcoming, terrace-style cottage pub has been an inn for more than 180 years. The guest beers are usually from small, independent breweries. Home-cooked food, using locally sourced ingredients, is available, with specials on Wednesday, Thursday and Friday. There is a quiz night on a Tuesday and a folk night, plus a number of other special nights throughout each month. An accessible entrance is to the rear. A former local CAMRA Pub of the Year which has celebrated 10 continuous years in the Guide.

Q 🏠 🏵 🍺 🌙 👤 🅿 😺 🛜 🎵

Llangadog

Red Lion

Church Street, SA19 9AA

☎ (01550) 777228

Glamorgan Jemima's Pitchfork; Gower Power; 1 changing beer (sourced regionally) 🄷

A traditional, characterful and charming coaching inn with a history that dates back to the early 1600s. The Grade II-listed building has been refurbished, and consists of a small bar area adjacent to a larger seating space. You will find a genuine warm welcome in comfortable and relaxed surroundings.

Q 🏠 🏵 👤 🌂 👤 🅿 🛜

Llangeitho

Three Horseshoe Inn

SY25 6TW

☎ (01974) 821244

2 changing beers (sourced regionally; often Evan Evans, Gower, Wye Valley) 🄷

A traditional pub run by the same family for 25 years, offering a warm welcome to visitors. The friendly landlord is a keen supporter of real ale and Welsh breweries. The main bar features quirky seating areas, and there is a dining room and function room. Outside is a sunny rear garden with a large undercover seating area. Good-value evening meals and Sunday lunch is served, but no food at other times. Pool and darts are played, and there is a monthly open mic night and quiz.

🏠 🏵 🍺 👤 🚌 (585) 😺 🛜 🎵

Llangoedmor

Penllwyndu

B4570, SA43 2LY (on B4570, 4 ½ miles from Cardigan) SN240458

☎ (01239) 682533

Hancocks HB; Mantle MOHO; 1 changing beer (sourced regionally; often Glamorgan) 🄷

Old-fashioned alehouse standing at an isolated crossroads where Cardigan's evil-doers were once hanged – the pub sign is worthy of close inspection. The cheerful and welcoming public bar retains its quaintness, with a slate floor, inglenook fireplace and wood-burner. Good home-cooked food, including traditional favourites, is available all day in the bar and the separate restaurant. Free live music plays on the third Thursday evening of the month. 🏠 🏵 🍺 👤 🎵

Llangrannog

Pentre Arms Hotel

SA44 6SP (at seaward end of B4321/B4334)

☎ (01239) 654345 ⊕ pentrearms.co.uk

Bluestone Bedrock Blonde; Mantle MOHO; Purple Moose Cwrw Glaslyn/Glaslyn Ale 🄷

Set on the Wales Coast Path in a pretty village, this cosy pub has tremendous sea views from the huge window in the bar and its small decking area. Inside are a main bar, a games room (pool, darts) and dining room. Two Welsh real ales are served, three at busier times, and hearty pub food, including lunchtime sandwiches and fresh fish from Easter to October. Live music features on summer weekends. Dogs are welcome in the bar. B&B accommodation is available. There is a free car park half a mile away. Q 🏠 🏨 🍺 👤 🚌 (552) 😺 🛜 🎵

Llansteffan

Castle Inn

The Square, SA33 5JG

☎ (01267) 241225

Sharp's Doom Bar; house beer (by Evan Evans); 1 changing beer (sourced regionally; often Evan Evans) 🄷

A traditional pub committed to real ale, with a relaxing atmosphere and friendly staff. The interior has been completely redecorated and the toilets renovated. The open-plan layout also includes plenty of cosy corners in which to relax in relative peace and quiet. It hosts a number of local community groups, and provides bar snacks from a basic menu. There is an outside sitting area overlooking the village square.

Q 🏠 🏵 🍺 👤 🚌 (227) 😺 🛜

Llanychaer

Bridge End Inn 🄻

SA65 9TB (on B4313, 2 miles SW of Fishguard)

☎ (01348) 872545

Gwaun Valley Cwrw Melyn 🄷**; 1 changing beer (sourced locally; often Evan Evans, Gwaun Valley)** 🄷/🄶

Known locally as the Bont, this friendly country pub is over 150 years old and nestles in the beautiful Gwaun Valley at a bridging point across the river. The cosy bar, with log fires in winter, serves mainly local real ales and sometimes a guest ale from further afield. It features an external water wheel and a pretty garden at the rear. Free snacks are often on the bar on Friday evenings, but otherwise no food is served. A former local CAMRA Pub of the Year. Q 🏠 🏵 👤 🌂 😺 🚌 (345) 😺 🛜

Nevern

Trewern Arms 🄻

SA42 0NB (off A487, 2 mile N of Newport)

☎ (01239) 820395 ⊕ trewernarms.com

3 changing beers (sourced regionally; often Bluestone, Harbwr, Mantle) 🄷

A picturesque 16th-century pub nestled deep within a secluded valley astride the banks of the River Nevern. It is near St Brynach's Church, noted for its ancient Celtic High Cross, Ogham Stone and Bleeding Yew. The village is less than a mile from the beautiful fishing town of Newport. The pub makes a great base from which to experience some of the best walks in West Wales. Open Friday to Sunday in winter.

Q 🏠 🏵 🍺 👤 🌂 🅿 🚌 (T5) 😺 🛜 🎵

New Quay

Black Lion
Glanmor Terrace, SA45 9PT
☎ (01545) 560122 ● blacklionnewquay.co.uk
Purple Moose Cwrw Glaslyn/Glaslyn Ale; 1 changing beer (sourced nationally; often Sharp's) Ⓗ
Perched at the top of a steep street, this striking, contemporary-style Grade II-listed hotel has connections with Dylan Thomas. The bar serves Purple Moose, supplemented with a second beer for the summer, and gets busy during big games on the TV. The separate dining areas offer excellent quality food. Local art and photography is displayed throughout. A large garden with children's play area provides stunning sea views. Live music plays during the August festival. Accommodation is in nine rooms. Dogs are allowed only in the garden. Q✿⏰🏠◑🍴A♣🚃(T5)🛜

Newcastle Emlyn

Bunch of Grapes ●
Bridge Street, SA38 9DU
☎ (01239) 711185
Sharp's Sea Fury; 1 changing beer (sourced nationally; often Wye Valley) Ⓗ
Dating back to the 17th century, this Grade II*-listed building is reputed to have been built from the ruins of the nearby 13th-century castle. It offers a great place to eat, drink and relax, either in the warmth of the pub, or in the enclosed rear garden, which has a children's play area and a covered smoking shelter.
✿⏰◑🍴♣🚃P🚃(460)🛜🎵

Pelican Inn
Sycamore Street, SA38 9AP
☎ (01239) 710034
Draught Bass Ⓖ; 1 changing beer (sourced regionally; often Mantle) Ⓗ
This high street pub is easily spotted by its yellow frontage. It offers old-fashioned charm and features original fittings and a real fire. Bass is served by gravity behind the bar, alongside a changing guest served via handpump. The small bar at the front has cosy seating, and to the rear is a larger and more open seated space, with a pool table and dartboard. More enclosed seating is available outside to the rear. ✿♣🚃(460)

Newchapel

Ffynnone Arms
SA37 0EH
☎ (01239) 841800 ● ffynnonearms.co.uk
Wye Valley Butty Bach; 2 changing beers (sourced locally; often Cardigan, Mantle) Ⓗ
A charming traditional 18th-century pub on the border of Pembrokeshire, Carmarthenshire and Ceredigion. Local ales are often available and supplemented with those sourced more widely. Welsh cider Gwynt y Ddraig is also sold. The landlady prides herself on the food, and offers menus free of gluten, dairy and sugar, with most produce sourced locally. On Wednesday evening fish & chips is served, and there is a Sunday carvery.
Q✿⏰◑🍴P🎵

Newport

Royal Oak
West Street, SA42 0TA
☎ (01239) 820632 ● theroyaloaknewport.co.uk
Greene King IPA; Sharp's Atlantic; 1 changing beer (sourced nationally) Ⓗ

This 18th-century town-centre free house retains all the charm and atmosphere of its roots, with oak beams, a tiled bar area and other original features. Food is served throughout the day, and the wide-ranging menu displays a strong Indian theme alongside many pub favourites. A changing guest ale complements the two standard nationally sourced beers. A pensioners' lunch is served on Tuesday. Q✿⏰◑🍴P🛜

Pembrey

Ship Aground Inn
Ashburnham Road, SA16 0TL
☎ (01554) 835724
2 changing beers (sourced nationally; often Brains, Timothy Taylor) Ⓗ
A friendly, welcoming pub on the B4311 between Pembrey and Burry Port, popular with locals and visitors alike. The open plan bar area has tables where customers can order bar meals, while a separate room houses a larger restaurant area serving freshly cooked meals. It is adjacent to National Cycle Route 4. Outside at the front is a large garden seating area. ✿⏰◑P🚃(X11)🐾🛜

Pembroke Dock

First & Last
London Road, SA72 6TX (on A477)
☎ (01646) 682687
Brains Rev James Original; Sharp's Doom Bar; 1 changing beer (sourced nationally; often Fuller's) Ⓗ
Friendly single-bar local run by the same family for 50 years. The guest beer can be local to national. Food is good pub fare. There is a popular quirky Sunday evening quiz. Formerly the Commercial, the pub acquired its current more distinctive name in 1991 to reflect its edge-of-town location. It is handy for the Cleddau Bridge, giving easy access to Haverfordwest and the historic dockyard. It is also convenient for the ferry to Ireland. ✿⏰◑🚆P🛜

Penally

Cross Inn
SA70 7PU
☎ (01834) 844665 ● crossinnpenally.co.uk
Sharp's Doom Bar; 2 changing beers (sourced regionally) Ⓗ
Situated in a picturesque village with some well-preserved Georgian and Victorian houses, this pub features military and sporting themes, with shields of regiments stationed in a nearby barracks adorning the walls alongside local pictures. The sporting prowess of the locals is evident from the cups and shields on the trophy shelf. A signed photo and a set of darts used by Phil 'The Power' Taylor is framed in an alcove. The wood and brick bar leads to the restaurant where food is sometimes available – phone to check in advance. ✿⏰◑A🚆♣🚃(349,358)🐾

Pontargothi

Cresselly Arms
Llannon Road, A40, SA32 7NG
☎ 07437 605570
4 changing beers (sourced regionally; often Glamorgan, Rhymney, Wye Valley) Ⓗ
Refurbished and reopened in 2023, this family-friendly riverside pub offers open country views and a very warm welcome. The bar serves four changing ales with a strong Welsh focus. A large separate lounge area has comfortable seating and a wood fire, and there is

another seating area adjacent to the bar. Outside is a large riverside garden with extensive seating.
🐴❀♣P🚌(281) 🐾

Porthyrhyd

Mansel Arms

Banc y Mansel, SA32 8BS (on B4310 between Porthyrhyd and Drefach)
☎ (01267) 275305 🌐 themanselarms.co.uk
5 changing beers (sourced regionally; often Evan Evans, Grey Trees, Rhymney) [H]/[G]
Friendly and welcoming 18th-century former coaching inn with wood fires in both bars. The landlord is passionate about real ale and encourages customers to taste and experience the variety of flavours. An in-house cask ale members' club has been established, with regular brewery visits and brewers' speaker/taster events. Five ever-changing cask ales, from local and regional brewers, are available on handpump Friday to Sunday, with at least three available during week. A former CAMRA Regional and National Pub of the Year.
🐴❀◖◗♣🍎P🚌(129) 🐾📶♫

Prengwyn

Gwarcefel Arms

Prengwyn, SA44 4LU (on crossroads of A475 and B4476) SN424442
☎ (01559) 363126
Sharp's Doom Bar; 1 changing beer (sourced nationally) [H]
Traditional stone-built pub standing at the junction of five roads. It has a main bar with wood-burner and pool table, and seating around the walls. A rear snug with cosy seating is open at busier times. The large restaurant serves evening meals and Sunday lunches, and can cater for functions and private parties. Fish & chips are a speciality. A beer garden and car park are to the rear.
🐴❀◗♣P🐾📶

Pwll

Colliers Arms

77 Pwll Road, SA15 4BD
☎ (01554) 406421
Sharp's Doom Bar; 2 changing beers (sourced regionally; often Brains, Glamorgan, Tiny Rebel) [H]
A popular local pub on road between Llanelli and Burry Port. The bar splits the interior space into two distinct areas: to the left, a smaller seating area has sports TV, and to the right there is a larger restaurant space. Three real ales are served. Outside, there is seating at the front with good views over the Burry Inlet, and there is also a large seating area to the rear. Community events are hosted as well as regular quiz nights and live music.
🐴❀🛏◖◗♣P🐾♫

Pwlltrap

White Lion

SA33 4AT
☎ (01994) 230370 🌐 whitelion-pwlltrap.co.uk
Greene King Abbot; Sharp's Sea Fury; 1 changing beer (sourced nationally; often Courage, Fuller's) [H]
Featured in this Guide for over 10 years, this roadside pub, just outside St Clears on the road to Whitland, is warm and welcoming with a real fire in winter months. It has an olde-worlde charm, with oak beams and panelled walls. There is a large annexe restaurant serving good food, and takeaway meals are also available. Local teams for pool and darts are hosted, and a large TV screen shows regular sports. Of the three cask beers, two are on at any time in the winter and all three in the summer.
Q◖◗♿♣P🚌(224,322) 🐾📶

Roch

Victoria Inn

SA62 6AW (on A487)
☎ (01437) 710426 🌐 thevictoriainnroch.com
Victoria Inn NewgAle, Fine & Dandy, Malt 'n Rock, Resolution Porter; 1 changing beer (sourced locally; often Victoria Inn) [H]
This gem of a locals' pub, with views across St Brides Bay, offers a warm welcome. It dates from 1851, though parts of the pub are older. Much of its olde-worlde charm is retained in the form of beamed ceilings and low doorways. It recently become a brewpub, and the five beers on offer are all brewed on-site. There is also a beer carry-out service. Food is available except Monday, and Friday is curry-and-a-pint night. There is occasional live music. Q🐴❀🛏◖◗⛺🍎P🚌(T11)📶♫

Rosebush

Tafarn Sinc ✔

SA66 7QU
☎ (01437) 532214 🌐 tafarnsinc.cymru
3 changing beers (sourced nationally; often Gwaun Valley, Harbwr, Sharp's) [H]
A Victorian hotel built in 1876 to attract tourists to the Preseli Mountains when the Clunderwen to Rosebush railway line was opened. Originally called the Preselly Hotel, it closed in 1992, but was later bought by locals, refurbished and renamed Tafarn Sinc. The building features in the history and social life of the area, and its interior is full of olde-world character and charm. Its location in the heart of the Preseli Mountains ensures scenic views, whether driving or walking. The hotel is noted for local food. 🐴❀◖◗♿⛺P🐾

Rudbaxton

Corner Piece Inn

A40, SA62 5PG (on A40 to Fishguard, 2 miles from Haverfordwest on turning to Spittal)
☎ (01437) 742185 🌐 cornerpiece.wales
2 changing beers (sourced regionally; often Mantle) [H]
The first pub for two miles from Haverfordwest in one direction and Wolfs Castle in the other, on the side of the busy A40. The owners of this cosy, three-roomed pub are very enthusiastic about their real ales, and serve good ale and good food. There are two changing real ales, normally from Mantle. Wednesday is pie night and and fish is served on Friday. It has outside seating, with play equipment, though the busy road is noisy. Opens at noon on bank holiday Mondays and in school holidays.
Q🐴❀◖◗⛺P🚌(T5) 🐾

St Davids

Farmers Arms

14-16 Goat Street, SA62 6RF (down hill to left of square)
☎ (01437) 721666 🌐 farmersstdavids.co.uk
Felinfoel Double Dragon; Sharp's Atlantic; 1 changing beer (sourced nationally) [H]
This traditional three-room city pub is the westernmost in Wales. The top bar is mainly for dining, with a smaller room off (the Coxswains) which serves the patio and is the social meeting place for the St David's lifeboat crew. The Glue Pot bar is where the locals tend to gather

WALES

around the fire. An outside patio offers views of the cathedral and has a seasonal bar. Winter opening times vary and food may not be available – check beforehand. In addition to the two regular ales, there are one or two guest ales. ⚲🏠🅭🛍🚲🅰♣🚇🖵(T11)🌂🛜🎵

Saundersfoot

Royal Oak Inn
Wogan Terrace, SA69 9HA
☎ (01834) 812546 🌐 theroyaloaksaundersfoot.co.uk
Glamorgan Cwrw Gorslas; Bluestone Bitter; house beer (by Glamorgan); 3 changing beers (sourced regionally; often Brains, Mantle) ⊞
An old pub and restaurant in the centre of town which boasts a wide selection of real ales with a Welsh flavour. To the right on entering, a cosy drinkers' bar welcomes locals and visitors. To the left is another bar and a dedicated restaurant where meals are served from the extensive menu. Food is available throughout the day during the summer months. At the front is a heated terrace with sea and harbour views. ⚲🏠🅭🛍🅰🖵(381)🌂

Solva

Ship
15 Main Street, SA62 6UU (on A487)
☎ (01437) 721528 🌐 theshipsolva.co.uk
Banks's Amber Ale; Wye Valley Butty Bach; 1 changing beer (sourced nationally; often Wye Valley) ⊞
Families are made particularly welcome at this traditional pub which features black and white timbers inside and out. The Sunday roast is popular, and authentic Indian curries are served in the evening, with free delivery available. An outdoor smoking area is covered and heated, and ample parking is available nearby overlooking the picturesque harbour. Winter opening times may vary; check before visiting. A former local CAMRA Pub of the Year. ⚲🏠🍴🅭🛍🅰P🖵(T11)🌂🛜

Talybont

White Lion/Llew Gwyn
SY24 5ER
☎ (01970) 832245
Wainwright Gold; Wychwood Hobgoblin Gold; 1 changing beer (sourced nationally; often Wye Valley) ⊞
A proper community local at the heart of village life. The main slate-floored room is heated by a solid fuel stove, with separate games and dining rooms serviced from the central bar. Interesting local memorabilia adorns most of the walls. The large beer garden features a children's playground. A popular Sunday lunch is served. There is an antique shop on the premises. Camper vans are welcome. Bus services in the evening and on Sundays are limited. Q⚲🏠🅭🛍🅰♣P🖵(T28)🌂🛜🎵

Tegryn

Butcher's Arms
SA35 0BL
☎ 07494 801623
Gower Gold; 1 changing beer (sourced regionally; often Bluestone) ⊞
The Butcher's Arms is a friendly rural pub off the beaten track, a few miles from the A478 and on National Cycle Route 47. It has been attractively refurbished, with local slate on the walls and floor. It has a games room with a mobile skittle alley along with traditional pub games. A beer festival is held every July. Q⚲🍴🛍♣P🌂🛜

Tenby

Harbwr Tap & Kitchen 🅛
St Julian Street, SA70 7AS
☎ (01834) 842273 🌐 harbwr.wales
Harbwr M V Enterprise, Caldey Lollipop, RFA Sir Galahad; 1 changing beer (sourced locally; often Harbwr) ⊞
Situated in quaint St Julian Street, which links the town square to the harbour and beaches, the pub is the brewery tap for the adjacent Tenby Harbour brewery and sells their full range of beers. Although the bar area is large, it has a cosy feel, with beams, a stove, and Tenby memorabilia adorning the walls. A sunny walled beer garden is to the rear. Food is served all day, with locally-sourced fresh fish and other produce on the menu. ⚲🏠🅭🅰🍴🖵🌂🛜🎵

Trefin

Ship Inn
Ffordd y Felin, SA62 5AX
☎ (01348) 831798 🌐 theshipinntrefin.com
Sharp's Sea Fury; 1 changing beer (sourced regionally; often Bluestone) ⊞
A characterful 200-year-old stone-built country pub with origins as a fishing cottage. It is full of of traditional rustic features such as exposed beams and an open fire. Outside seating offers terrific coastal views to complement your drink or meal. It is generally quiet in the winter, but busy in the summer. Meals are served in the evening and also at lunch during the warmer months. Opening times are extended for summer. Located just 200 yards from the Pembrokeshire Coast Path and ideal for walkers. ⚲🏠🅭🛍♣P🖵(T11)🌂🛜🎵

Tregaron

Talbot ★ ✅
The Square, SY25 6JL
☎ (01974) 298208 🌐 ytalbot.com
2 changing beers (sourced regionally; often Evan Evans, Mantle, Wye Valley) ⊞
A heritage pub of immense character. It has a front bar with an open fire, settles and huge beams, a snug with an inglenook fireplace, a rear main bar and a restaurant. An ever-changing range of real ales from Wales and the Borders is available. Excellent-quality food is served in the bars and restaurant, from a menu including local meat, fish and cheese. There is a rear patio and beautifully landscaped beer garden with memorial to the circus elephant reputedly buried here. January hours vary so check in advance. Q⚲🏠🍴🅭🛍🅰♣P🖵(585,588)🌂🛜

Whitland

Station House Hotel
St John Street, SA34 0AP
☎ (01994) 240556 🌐 stationhousewhitland.co.uk
Felinfoel Double Dragon ℗; 4 changing beers (sourced nationally; often Felinfoel, Sharp's, Wye Valley) ⊞
A warm welcome is always on tap at this friendly family-run pub. Very much a locals' pub for all ages, it has something for everyone, with pool and darts teams, and bingo on Sunday evenings. A small room is available for those looking for a quiet corner. Five well-kept and ever-changing beers are always available. There is a large covered outside area at the rear, with individual booths. The pub is only 50 yards from the train station. 🏠🅭🍴♣P🌂🛜

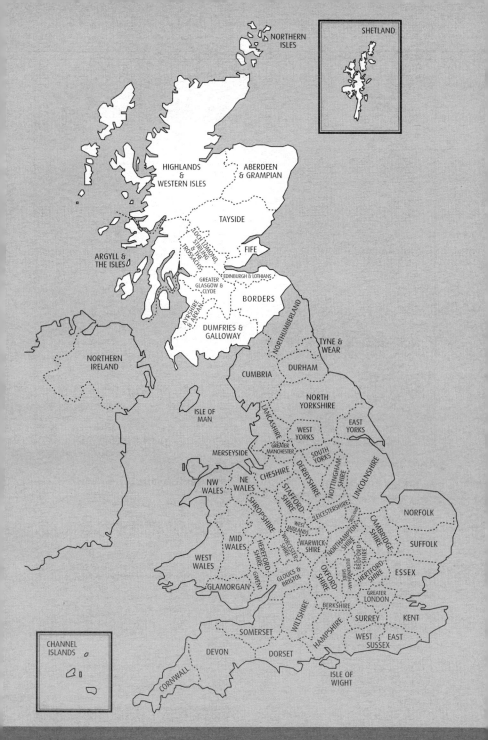

NORTHERN ISLES

SHETLAND

HIGHLANDS & WESTERN ISLES

ABERDEEN & GRAMPIAN

TAYSIDE

FIFE

LOCH LOMOND STIRLING & THE TROSSACHS

ARGYLL & THE ISLES

GREATER GLASGOW & CLYDE

EDINBURGH & LOTHIANS

BORDERS

AYRSHIRE & ARRAN

DUMFRIES & GALLOWAY

NORTHERN IRELAND

NORTHUMBERLAND

TYNE & WEAR

CUMBRIA

DURHAM

ISLE OF MAN

LANCASHIRE

NORTH YORKSHIRE

EAST YORKS

WEST YORKS

MERSEYSIDE

GREATER MANCHESTER

SOUTH YORKS

CHESHIRE

DERBYSHIRE

NOTTINGHAM-SHIRE

LINCOLNSHIRE

NW WALES

NE WALES

STAFFORD-SHIRE

SHROPSHIRE

LEICESTERSHIRE

NORFOLK

WEST MIDLANDS

CAMBRIDGE-SHIRE

MID WALES

HEREFORD-SHIRE

WORCESTER-SHIRE

WARWICK-SHIRE

NORTHAMPTON-SHIRE

BEDFORD-SHIRE

SUFFOLK

WEST WALES

GWENT

GLOUCS & BRISTOL

OXFORD-SHIRE

BUCKINGHAMSHIRE

HERTFORD-SHIRE

ESSEX

GLAMORGAN

BERKSHIRE

GREATER LONDON

WILTSHIRE

SURREY

KENT

SOMERSET

HAMPSHIRE

WEST SUSSEX

EAST SUSSEX

CHANNEL ISLANDS

DEVON

DORSET

ISLE OF WIGHT

CORNWALL

Scotland

ABERDEEN & GRAMPIAN

Aberdeen

Archibald Simpson ✓

5 Castle Street, AB11 5BQ (E end of Union St)
☎ (01224) 621365
Belhaven 80/-; Greene King Abbot; Sharp's Doom Bar; 9 changing beers (sourced nationally; often Orkney, Stewart) ⊞
The former headquarters of Clydesdale Bank, this Wetherspoon is in one of the many monumental granite buildings in central Aberdeen designed by local architect Archibald Simpson. It has a pillared entrance and retains many original architectural features; the main room is a central hall with a high ceiling and additional seating areas to the side. Twelve handpumps offer beers, mostly from Scottish breweries. There is a narrow outside drinking space on the pavement. Beer festivals are held several times a year. ☕◑ㅊ≐♣☂🖵🛜

Ferryhill House Hotel

169 Bon Accord Street, AB11 6UA (10 mins' walk from Union St)
☎ (01224) 590867 ● ferryhillhousehotel.co.uk
Orkney Corncrake; Timothy Taylor Landlord; 1 changing beer (sourced regionally) ⊞
A small city-centre hotel in a quiet residential area. Two regular beers are offered, with the occasional cask from another brewery, in the large, modern, lounge bar, which also has a large selection of malt whiskies. There is also a large restaurant and a conservatory. A wheelchair access ramp leads to the front door. There are tables and chairs in the extensive garden, which features a children's play area. Duthie Park, with its famous Winter Gardens, is close by. ☕🛏🍴◑ㅊ≐🅿🖵(17,17A)🛜

Globe Inn ♟

13-15 North Silver Street, AB10 1RJ (off Golden Square)
☎ (01224) 641171 ● the-globe-inn.com
3 changing beers (sourced regionally; often Cromarty, Stewart, Swannay) ⊞
This convivial open-plan pub reverted to private ownership in 2018 after being run by Belhaven. It now serves up to three beers from a variety of Scottish breweries. Excellent food is served all day, including in the beer garden, which may be partially covered in poor weather. HM Theatre and the Music Hall are nearby. Reasonably priced en-suite accommodation is available. Opens from 9am and alcohol served from 11am. Local CAMRA Pub of the Year 2024. ☕🛏🍴◑ㅊ≐🐾🖵🛜

Grill ★

213 Union Street, AB11 6BA
☎ (01224) 583563 ● thegrillaberdeen.co.uk
4 changing beers (sourced regionally; often Cromarty, Orkney, Stewart) ⊞

REAL ALE BREWERIES

Braemar Braemar
Burnside Laurencekirk
Fierce ✎ Aberdeen
Keith Mulben
Matheson Banff (NEW)
Quiet 🍴 Banchory
Six° North Laurencekirk
Spey Valley Mulben
Speyside Forres
Twisted Ankle Aboyne

ABERDEEN & GRAMPIAN

With an exquisite interior redesigned in 1926, this is the only pub in the area identified by CAMRA as having a nationally important historic pub interior. It has been part of the McGinty's Group since 2019. The ale pumps are now all in a central position, offering guest beers, mainly from various Scottish breweries. The large selection of whiskies has won many awards. Bar snacks, including stovies, are available. Musicians appearing at the Music Hall opposite often visit during concert breaks. ⇌🚌🛜

Justice Mill ✅
423 Union Street, AB11 6DA
☎ (01224) 252410
Belhaven 80/-; Greene King Abbot; Sharp's Doom Bar; 3 changing beers (sourced nationally; often Broughton, Spey Valley, Stewart) Ⓗ
Long, narrow Wetherspoon outlet, refurbished in May 2024, with raised seating near the bar and booths at both the main entrance and at the rear entrance on Justice Mill Lane. The quiet, family-friendly atmosphere during the day changes to a louder one favoured by a younger clientele in the evenings. There is often a DJ playing from 8pm at weekends. The pub has two statement art pieces: a statue of an upside-down man, and a fire behind glass. 🛏️🕽&⇌🚌🛜

Krakatoa
2 Trinity Quay, AB11 5AA (facing quayside at bottom of Market St)
☎ (01224) 587602 ⊕ krakatoa.bar
10 changing beers (sourced regionally; often Cromarty, Harviestoun, Swannay) Ⓟ
This historic harbourside bar, owned by the Black Cat Worker Collective, changes character from a friendly, laid-back one to a raucous rock bar on weekend evenings, when there may be a cover charge. The eclectic jukebox is popular with the varied clientele who may participte on Wednesday evenings in rock karaoke. A wide selection of Scottish ales is served on up to 12 American-style fonts, and a varied selection of Belgian beers and ciders is also available, as well as a good cocktail list. &⇌♣🕽🖥🛜🎜

Number 10 Bar & Restaurant
10 Queens Terrace, AB10 1XL (short walk W from top of Union St)
☎ (01224) 631928 ⊕ no10aberdeen.co.uk
Harviestoun Bitter & Twisted; Timothy Taylor Landlord; 1 changing beer (sourced regionally; often Cromarty, Fyne, Stewart) Ⓗ
This popular basement bar has a contemporary interior featuring exposed granite walls, traditional herringbone floors and dark wood furnishings. It has two seating areas to the right and left as you come in, with several TV screens showing sports. The bar along the back wall has three handpumps selling some varied ales. A wide choice of meals is available in the restaurant in the former Number 9, with an additional separate menu in the bar. 🕽🚇(11,13)🛜

Prince of Wales ★ ✅
7 St Nicholas Lane, AB10 1HF (lane opp Marks & Spencer, parallel to Union St)
☎ (01224) 640597
Greene King IPA, Yardbird, Abbot; 5 changing beers (sourced regionally; often Cromarty, Fyne, Stewart) Ⓗ
One of the oldest bars in Aberdeen, the Prince has possibly the longest bar counter in the city, a large following of regulars and a friendly atmosphere buzzing with conversation. The bar offers a varied selection of ales from up to eight pumps, mostly from Scottish breweries, with tasters for the undecided. Good-value

food is served daily. A prize quiz is held on a Thursday and open mic nights on Friday. It may close an hour early if not busy. Q🛏️🕽⇌🚇🛜🎜

Queen Vic
126 Rosemount Place, AB25 2YU (10 mins' walk from W end of Union St)
☎ (01224) 638500 ⊕ queenvicaberdeen.co.uk
Timothy Taylor Landlord; 3 changing beers (sourced nationally; often Cromarty, Orkney, Swannay) Ⓗ
A cosy, one-room locals' bar, slightly off the beaten track in two converted shops in the Rosemount residential area. Sports events are frequently shown on TV, when the pub can get extremely busy. Guest cask ales are mainly from a variety of Scottish breweries. A popular quiz featuring a Play Your Cards Right jackpot is held on Monday evening, and live bands play occasionally at weekends. No food, but customers can order in. A former local and city CAMRA Pub of the Year. 🚇(3,3A)🌸🛜🎜

St Machar Bar
97 High Street, AB24 3EN (near Kings College)
☎ (01224) 483079
3 changing beers (sourced regionally; often Cromarty, Orkney, Stewart) Ⓗ
Located in the Old Aberdeen conservation area amid the university buildings, this historic pub is frequented by academia and locals alike. The bar features a splendid Thomson Marshall Aulton Brewery mirror and an original Devanha one. Three beers are available from a variety of Scottish breweries and a large TV screen displays current and coming beer details. The pub has a reputation as a whisky destination and hosts monthly tastings. Food is burgers and buckets. The bar is home to a darts team and university football and rugby teams. Local and City CAMRA Pub of the Year 2023. 🌞🕽🚃🚇(20)🌸🛜

Aboyne

Boat Inn
Charlestown Road, AB34 5EL (N bank of River Dee next to Aboyne Bridge)
☎ (01339) 886137 ⊕ theboatinnaboyne.co.uk
3 changing beers (sourced nationally; often Belhaven) Ⓗ
Popular riverside inn with a food-oriented lounge. Junior diners (and adults) may request to see the model train, complete with sound effects, traverse the entire pub at picture-rail height upon completion of their meal. The Shed public bar has a recess at the back used for live music nights. Three ales are served in summer, two in winter, usually at least one from Belhaven and another from a local brewery. Breakfast is served. Fifteen twin rooms and a family room are available for overnight stays. Q🛏️🛌🕽&♣P🌸🛜🎜

Ballater

Alexandra Hotel
12 Bridge Square, AB35 5QJ
☎ (01339) 755376 ⊕ alexandrahotelballater.co.uk
Cairngorm Trade Winds; 2 changing beers (sourced regionally; often Cairngorm) Ⓗ
Originally built as a private home in 1800, this friendly, family-owned lounge bar became the Alexandra Hotel in 1915. It is popular both with locals and those visiting for bar suppers. Three Cairngorm ales are available in summer; generally just two in winter. Benches outside at the front are ideal for alfresco drinking and there is a beer garden to rear. A handy stop-off on your way to Braemar for the Highland Games or on a visit with the royals at Balmoral. 🛏️🌞🛌🕽&🚃🚇(201)🌸🛜

565

Balmoral Bar

1 Netherley Place, AB35 5QE
☎ (01339) 755462
Braemar Pale; 1 changing beer (often Cairngorm) ⓗ
Smart, modern public bar, situated on a corner opposite the village square in this picturesque Deeside vllage. Six large screens show sports and news while the adjacent pool room also has two large screens. An old poster on the wall shows the coach timetable from Aberdeen of days gone by. It is one of the few pubs where you can find local beer from Braemar. Food is served every day. ⓑⓄⓁＡ♣ꮲ(201) ✿♥ 🎵

Glenaden Hotel

6 Church Square, AB35 5NE
☎ (01339) 755488
2 changing beers (sourced regionally; often Caledonian) ⓗ
Situated on the far side of the picturesque town square, this small hotel displays a prominent external sign for its Barrel Lounge. It normally serves three beers during busy periods, usually Scottish, and darker ales are apparently favoured by the locals. A large function suite and beer garden may be found at the rear of the hotel. A free car park is next door. Qⓑ⊛Ⓚ⑪♣ꮲꮲ(201)✿♥🎵

Banchory

Ravenswood Club (Royal British Legion)

25 Ramsay Road, AB31 5TS (up Mount St from A93, then 2nd right)
☎ (01330) 822347 ⊕ banchorylegion.co.uk
2 changing beers (sourced nationally) ⓗ
Large British Legion club with a comfortable lounge adjoining the pool and TV room and a spacious function room frequently used by local clubs and societies as well as members. Darts and snooker are popular and played most evenings. The two handpumps offer excellent value and the beer choice is constantly changing, with the quality consistently second to none. An elevated terrace has fine views of the Deeside hills. Show this Guide or your CAMRA membership card for entry. CAMRA Regional Club of the Year 2024. ⓑ⊛Ⓚ⑪ⓁＡ♣ꮲ🎵

Banff

Market Arms

5 High Shore, AB45 1DB
☎ (01261) 818616
1 changing beer (sourced nationally; often Morland, Ruddles, Timothy Taylor) ⓗ
This fine building is one of the oldest in historic Banff, dating back to 1585. The courtyard at the back retains many original features and is used as an alfresco drinking area. The long public bar has several fine examples of historic brewery and distillery mirrors. One of the two handpumps always serves a changing beer, with two beers on at weekends and holidays. The impressive upstairs lounge is used mainly for meals. ⓑ⑪ꮲ✿♥

Braemar

Fife Arms Hotel

Mar Road, AB35 5YN
☎ (01339) 720200 ⊕ thefifearms.com
Cairngorm Gold; 1 changing beer (sourced locally; often Cairngorm) ⓗ
The Fife Arms reopened in 2018 as an upmarket hotel after major refurbishment. The Flying Stag bar serves two Cairngorm ales on handpull. A feature of the bar is the

hundreds of antlers intertwined with a stuffed stag seemingly flying out from behind the bar. The hotel itself has a strong Scottish theme throughout. Each bedroom is dedicated to a local place, person or event. The hotel also features prominent works by leading artists. ⓑ⊛Ⓚ⑪ⓁＡ♣ꮲ(201,202) ✿♥

Invercauld Mews

Glenshee Road, AB35 5YR
☎ 07710 596629
Cairngorm Stag, Trade Winds; 2 changing beers (often Braemar, Cairngorm) ⓗ
The Mews Bar lies in a separate building behind the Invercauld Hotel and reopened in 2020 after a full refurbishment that restored the bar to the way it looked when it closed in 2002. Four new handpulls were installed, with ales supplied by Cairngorm brewery and the local Braemar brewery. Four beers are available all year round. There is substantial outdoor seating on the grass outside. it is not open till 3pm midweek, and 2pm weekends, though hours may be subject to seasonal change. QⓑⓁＡ♣ꮲ(201)✿♥

Charlestown of Aberlour

Mash Tun

8 Broomfield Square, AB38 9QP
☎ (01340) 881771 ⊕ mashtun-aberlour.com
2 changing beers (sourced locally; often Cairngorm, Spey Valley) ⓗ
A busy traditional bar with a full collection of Glenfarclas bottles in a cabinet plus a large number of other malts. Built in 1896 as the Station Bar, a pledge in the title deeds allowed a name change if the railway closed – but it must revert to the Station Bar if a train ever pulls up again outside! There is an outside decking area and a heated cigar pavilion. The Speyside Way is just outside the door, and the River Spey itself, making it popular with fishermen. Closed in the afternoon Monday to Thursday. ⓑ⊛Ⓚ⑪Ａꮲ(36)✿♥

Craigellachie

Highlander Inn

10 Victoria Street, AB38 9SR (A95, opp post office)
☎ (01340) 881446 ⊕ whiskyinn.com
3 changing beers (sourced regionally; often Cairngorm, Orkney, Spey Valley) ⓗ
Picturesque whisky and cask ale bar on Speyside's Whisky Trail, twinned with the Highlander Whisky Bar in Tokyo. It offers a fine selection of malt whiskies, including many Japanese ones, plus up to three ales. CRAC (Craigellachie Real Ale Club) meet here on the first Wednesday of the month, and its members help to choose the pub's guest ales. An outside decked area with tables and chairs is a delight for alfresco dining and drinking on a sunny afternoon. ⓑ⊛Ⓚ⑪Ａꮲ(36)♥🎵

Spey Inn (Craigellachie Hotel)

Victoria Street, AB38 9SR
☎ (01340) 881204 ⊕ craigellachiehotel.com
2 changing beers (sourced locally; often Cairngorm, Spey Valley) ⓗ
Situated in the beautiful village of Craigellachie, next to the Fiddich and Spey rivers, this impressive Victorian building boasts picturesque views. The bar, formerly the Copper Dog, is below the hotel, and though mostly dedicated to dining, has a cosy, dimly lit area dedicated to drinking. There are over 800 whiskies in the Quaich Bar, with tasting sessions available. It can get busy, especially during whisky festivals. Booking recommended if eating. ⓑ⊛Ⓚ⑪Ⓛꮲ(36)✿♥🎵

Elgin

Muckle Cross ✅

34 High Street, IV30 1BU
☎ (01343) 559030
Belhaven 80/-; Greene King Abbot; Sharp's Doom Bar; 6 changing beers (sourced regionally; often Orkney) ⑈

A typical small Wetherspoon pub converted from what was once a bicycle repair shop. Refurbished in 2018, the pleasant long room has ample seating and a family area. It is popular and can get busy at weekends. Twelve handpumps (some duplicated) offer a wide range of beers from UK and Scottish microbreweries, and ciders are available during the annual cider fest. Now the only real ale outlet in the Elgin area. Two beer festivals are held annually. Q🏠🐾⚫🕩🛢�‖↔♣🖵🛜

Ellon

Tolbooth

21-23 Station Road, AB41 9AE (opp public library)
☎ (01358) 721308
3 changing beers (sourced nationally; often Cairngorm, Cromarty, Orkney) ⑈

A large pub, popular with all ages, close to the centre of the town and just a short walk from the bus stops on Market Street. There are separate seating areas on split levels, as well as an airy conservatory with barrel tables, and a patio garden area for alfresco drinking. Two Scottish and one English guest ale, often Directors or London Pride, are usually available. No food is served. It is a few minutes' walk from buses to Aberdeen or Peterhead/Fraserburgh. 🏠🐾⚫♣🖵🛢🛜🎵

Forres

Mosset Tavern

Gordon Street, IV36 1DY
☎ (01309) 672981 ⊕ mossettavern.com
5 changing beers (sourced locally; often Cairngorm, Cromarty, Swannay) ⑈

Described as 'the country pub in the heart of Forres', this smart, popular Scottish lounge bar/restaurant is next to the Mosset burn and pond. Friendly, efficient staff serve ale from a single handpump in the lounge and up to five in the spacious and comfortable public bar, where there are pool tables and large screens showing sport. A large function room is also available. Live music plays on Friday evening, and there is a pub quiz every Tuesday. 🏠🐾🚄⚫🕩🛢↔♣🖵(10)🛜🎵

Fraserburgh

Elizabethan Bar & Lounge

36 Union Grove, AB43 9PH (10 mins' walk from A90)
☎ (01346) 510464
3 changing beers (sourced regionally; often Kelburn) ⑈

Set in the middle of a housing estate, with a mock-Tudor exterior, the pub has a public bar, games room with four dartboards and two pool tables, and a lounge bar with a largescreen sports TV. It has an excellent reputation for offering a wide range of quality Scottish ales, and also features an extensive range of malts – the largest collection in the area. The beach, harbour and lighthouse museum are a mile away. Not normally open till 5pm Monday to Thursday, although hours may vary dependant on live football on TV. 🏠🛢🖲♣🖵🛜🎵

Garlogie

Garlogie Inn

AB32 6RX (on B9125 just before jct with B9119)
☎ (01224) 743212 ⊕ garlogieinn.com
1 changing beer (sourced regionally; often Cairngorm) ⑈

This roadside inn dates from the early 19th century and has been owned and run by the same family since 1986. Numerous extensions have been added to the original building, forming a large restaurant area. It has an excellent reputation for its food; booking is advised. Drinkers are welcome in the small bar area, which has a collection of coffee mugs hanging up, each one relating to a football club. The one beer is sourced from a variety of local and regional breweries. Drum Castle and Cullerlie stone circle are close by. Q🏠🐾⚫🕩🖵(X18)🛜🎵

Gourdon

Harbour Bar

William Street, DD10 0LW
☎ (01561) 361337
2 changing beers (often Burnside, Loch Lomond)

Traditional seafaring decor abounds in this harbourside howff. It has a public bar, a smaller tap room with heavy-topped swivelling bar stools, and a separate pool room with more seating. Handy for the Maggie Law lifeboat museum and next door to the locally renowned Quayside Fish & Chip restaurant. Last orders for pub food is 15 minutes before closing time. The local post office operates here on Friday mornings. 🏠🐾⚫🕩🛢🖲♣🖵(X7)🛜🎵

Inverurie

Gordon Highlander ✅

West High Street, AB51 3QQ
☎ (01467) 626780
Belhaven 80/-; Greene King Abbot; Sharp's Doom Bar; 4 changing beers (sourced nationally; often Orkney) ⑈

A fine Wetherspoon conversion of a splendid Art Deco building that used to be the Victoria Cinema. The name refers to a locomotive built at the now defunct Inverurie Locomotive Works and there are many references to this throughout the pub. The famous Gordon Highlander Regiment also features prominently, with displays and a large mural. The books on the shelves are free to read and take home, with donations welcome. There are at least three guest ales, the occasional real cider, and the usual Wetherspoon beer festivals. 🏠⚫♣↔🖵(10,37)🛜

Methlick

Ythanview Hotel

Main Street, AB41 7DT
☎ (01651) 806235
2 changing beers (sourced regionally; often Fyne, Swannay) ⑈

Traditional inn in the village centre, home to the MCC (Methlick Cricket Club) at nearby Lairds. Log fires warm both the lounge bar at the front and the friendly sports-themed public bar at the rear. Beers are exclusively from Scottish micros. The restaurant is renowned for the owner's special chicken curry, and steak night on Thursday is popular. Meals are served all day at weekends. Live music and quiz nights take place on most Saturdays. Close to several attractions. Closed Monday to Friday afternoons and closes at 7pm Monday and Tuesday. 🏠🐾🚄⚫🕩♣🖵(290,291)🛜🎵

Newtonhill

Newton Arms
10 Old Mill Road, AB39 3TZ
☎ (01569) 730227
1 changing beer (sourced regionally; often Cromarty, Orkney) Ⓗ
Traditional village local with a classic, dark-wood panelled public bar, featuring 1950s bar counters, intriguing under-counter shelves for drinks, and an original Devanha brewery mirror. The lounge at the side has light-wood panelling and tables. Customers are welcome to bring in a curry from the takeaway next door; cutlery and plates will be provided. Up to two beers may be available in the public bar only, but usually just one. There is an east-facing patio to the rear for alfresco drinking. ☎⊛♣⊋(7)⊛❖♪

Oldmeldrum

Redgarth
Kirk Brae, AB51 0DJ (signposted off A947)
☎ (01651) 872353 ⊕ redgarth.com
4 changing beers (sourced regionally; often Cromarty, Fyne, Swannay) Ⓖ
Offering a warm welcome and excellent views of the eastern Grampian mountains, the Redgarth is a winner of many CAMRA awards, it retains a strong reputation for its imaginative choice of Scottish beers. The emphasis is on excellent beers served on gravity, with three handpumps on the bar to show which ales are available. Extra choice is offered during occasional Brewer in Residence evenings. Meals are served in the bar and in a separate restaurant area. Closed Monday to Saturday afternoons. ☎⊛⊨⊲♪▲♣P☐(35,X35)❖♪

Peterhead

Cross Keys ✅
23-27 Chapel Street, AB42 1TH
☎ (01779) 483500
Belhaven 80/-; Greene King Abbot; Sharp's Doom Bar; 3 changing beers (sourced nationally; often Exmoor, Oakham, Orkney) Ⓗ
A typical Wetherspoon pub in the centre of a bustling port, close to the local museum. The pub is named after the chapel dedicated to St Peter that previously stood on the site. The long single room has the bar towards the front and a large seating area at the rear. A sheltered and heated area outside caters for hardy souls and smokers. Children are welcome until 9pm if dining. Alcohol served from 9am. Q☎⊛⊲♦⊞(69,63)❖

Pitmedden

Craft Bar
Tarves Road, AB41 7NX
☎ (01651) 842049 ⊕ thecraftpitmedden.wordpress.com
2 changing beers (sourced regionally; often Orkney, Spey Valley) Ⓗ
One-room corner pub run by an enthusiastic local CAMRA member. Old church pews provide seating for some of the tables around the walls; other tables have bench seating. Two handpumps serve ales from Scottish breweries, supplemented by a wide variety of KeyKeg beers from UK breweries. There is also a comprehensive range of bottled and canned beer for takeaway in the fridge, with much of the pub taken up as an off-licence (these may be consumed on the premises for a small fee). Occasional Brewer in Residence evenings are held. Snacks are available. Closed Monday and Tuesday. ☎▲♣P☐❖♪

Portsoy

Shore Inn
Church Street, AB45 2QR (overlooking harbour)
☎ (01261) 842831
2 changing beers (sourced regionally; often Kelburn, Spey Valley) Ⓗ
Cosy, comfortable, coastal howff with a warm welcome in winter and scenic views in summer of the oldest harbour on the Moray Coast (it was a location for the 2016 remake of Whisky Galore). The L-shaped room with low ceilings is a fine example of a nautical bar. Expect the pub to be busy during the Boat Festival in June. Only one beer is normally available in winter months. No food served. Not open till 2pm Monday to Friday. ☎⊛▲♣❖❖♪

Stonehaven

Marine Hotel ★
9-10 Shorehead, AB39 2JY (overlooking harbour)
☎ (01569) 762155 ⊕ marinehotelstonehaven.co.uk
6 changing beers (sourced regionally; often Cromarty, Fyne, Six Degrees North) Ⓗ
Once the only outlet for Six Degrees North cask ales, it is now often available in some independent pubs. The small harbourside hotel features simple wood panelling in the bar and a rustic lounge with an open fireplace. Seating outside offers a splendid view of the harbour. Usually at least one ale from Six Degrees North is served, plus several varieties from other breweries, numerous Belgian beers, and up to 18 craft keg beers. Dunnottar Castle is one mile south and an open-air bathing pool one mile north. ☎⊛⊨⊲♦▲☐☐(747,X7)❖❖

Ship Inn
5 Shorehead, AB39 2JY (on harbour front)
☎ (01569) 762617 ⊕ shipinnstonehaven.com
3 changing beers (sourced regionally; often Cromarty, Inveralmond, Orkney) Ⓗ
Built in 1771, this harbour-front hotel has a maritime-themed, wood-panelled bar and a small seating area outside overlooking the water. The long, narrow bar features a mirror from the defunct Devanha brewery. Two beers are available, both usually from the same Scottish brewery, plus an extensive range of malt whiskies. A modern restaurant with panoramic harbour views is adjacent to the bar; fish is the speciality and food is served all day at the weekend. Accommodation is available in 11 guest rooms. ☎⊛⊨⊲♦⊾▲☐(747,X7)❖❖

Westhill

Shepherds Rest
10 Straik Road, AB32 6HF (on A944, ½ mile from village)
☎ (01224) 740208
Greene King Abbot; 3 changing beers (sourced regionally; often Stewart, Williams Bros) Ⓗ
Built in 2000, this pub has a large, rustic-style interior with plenty of nooks and crannies providing some privacy if preferred. Much of the pub is set up for meals, but a large area between the main entrance and the bar is reserved for drinking. The three guest ales are generally from Scottish micros. It is popular with families and an extensive food menu is available all day. It opens for breakfast. The Premier Inn next door provides accommodation for travellers. ☎⊛⊨⊲♦⊾P☐❖❖

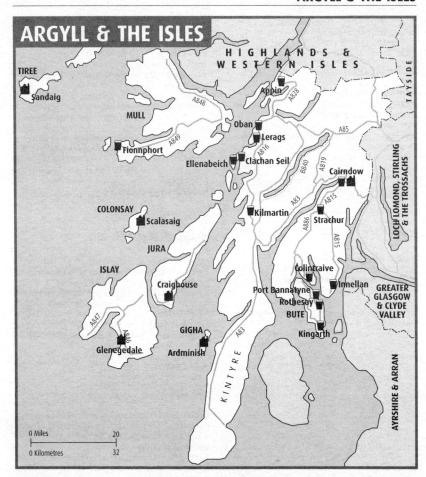

ARGYLL & THE ISLES

Appin

Creagan Inn

Creagan, PA38 4BQ (on A828 ½ mile N of Loch Creran bridge)

☎ (01631) 730250 ⊕ creaganinn.co.uk

Fyne Jarl Ⓗ

Originally a ferryman's house, the inn is set in a beautiful scenic location on the shores of Loch Creran. One handpump is available, selling Fyne Ales Jarl. Local produce is prominent on the menu, and it has a good selection of vegetarian/vegan options. There is a limited bus service from Oban and Fort William. Closed Monday to Wednesday outside the summer season and often closes for months in winter – phone ahead.

Q🕸️😊◐⟨⟩&P🚌(405,918) 🐾🍴🛜

Cairndow

Fyne Ales Brewery Tap Ⓛ

Achadunan, PA26 8BJ (up side road at head of Loch Fyne)

☎ (01499) 600120 ⊕ fyneales.com

Fyne Jarl; 4 changing beers (sourced locally; often Fyne) Ⓗ

Brewery tap and shop in what was originally a farm building. The bar, with its fine polished granite front, sells a range of beers from the brewery along with a full and varied selection of bottled beers. An impressive array of brewing award certificates can be seen above the shelves displaying the beers for sale. Light snacks are available at weekends but visitors are welcome to bring their own food and enjoy it al fresco in the brewery courtyard beer garden. The shop is normally open till 6pm daily, but closed on some public holidays.

Q🕸️😊🐾&P🍴🛜

Clachan Seil

Tigh-an-Truish Inn

PA34 4QZ

☎ (01852) 300242 ⊕ tigh-an-truish.co.uk

2 changing beers (sourced nationally; often Fyne) Ⓗ

This charming inn, located just over the 'Bridge over the Atlantic', is worth a diversion off the A816. The rustic wooden interior has an L-shaped counter with an unusual high bench seat (the Perch). Two handpumps (one in winter) serve Scottish ales. In summer the garden and patio are a delight. A door by the bar leads to

REAL ALE BREWERIES

Bun Dubh 🏴 Sandaig: Isle of Tiree
Colonsay Scalasaig: Isle of Colonsay
Fyne ✦ Cairndow
Gigha Ardminish: Isle of Gigha
Islay ✦ Glenegedale: Isle of Islay
Jura Isle of Jura: Craighouse

a modern dining area. Closed on Monday and Tuesday; other opening times can vary – phone ahead.
Q❀✍❶₱☐(418) ☘❄♫

Colintraive

Colintraive Hotel ℓ

PA22 3AS
☎ (01700) 841207 ⊕ colintraivehotel.com
Fyne Jarl ⊞
Hotel tucked away in a quiet village by the ferry crossing to the northern part of Bute. The welcoming and cosy public bar has a wooden floor, and a separate restaurant serves highly regarded, locally sourced food, including fish and game. The bar is popular with locals on Friday nights, and music is sometimes performed. The hotel is easily reached from Rothesay by bus and then ferry; check timetables before setting off as you may have to spend a few hours at Colintraive. Closed on Monday.
Q↻❀✍❶₱☐(478) ☘♫

Ellenabeich

Oyster Bar & Restaurant

PA34 4RQ
☎ (01852) 300121 ⊕ oysterbarealsdale.com
2 changing beers (sourced regionally; often Fyne, Loch Lomond) ⊞
A family-run pub by the harbour at the end of a row of whitewashed cottages once occupied by workers at the abandoned slate quarries, which are now flooded. The ale is generally from Scottish breweries. The small lounge bar opens out to the rear decking area offering stunning views of Scarba and Jura. Closed Mondays in winter. Opening times can vary according to the season, and how busy it is, so phone ahead.
Q❀❶も☐(418) ☘❄

Fionnphort

Keel Row

Isle of Mull, PA66 6BL
☎ (01681) 700458 ⊕ thekeelrowmull.co.uk
2 changing beers (sourced nationally; often Fyne, Timothy Taylor) ⊞
Traditional, granite stone pub, close to the Iona ferry and departure point for boat trips to Staffa. It was originally a private house, then a tea room, then a craft shop, before becoming a pub in 1993. After expansions and changes of ownership it is now in the hands of local investors hoping to continue to serve the local community and the tourist trade. Food is locally sourced where possible. Closed Monday to Wednesday and opens later on Thursdays in winter – phone ahead. ❀❶☐(496)☘❄♫

Innellan

Osborne

44 Shore Road, PA23 7TJ
☎ (01369) 830820 ⊕ theosborneinnellan.co.uk
3 changing beers (sourced nationally; often Fuller's, St Austell, Theakston) ⊞
A whitewashed seafront hotel a few miles south of Dunoon, built in 1869. The comfortable bar has a pool table to one side and a cosy lounge with a log fire. At the front is the conservatory dining room with excellent views across the Firth of Clyde. Any good weather can be enjoyed in a small outdoor area to one side. Unlike most Argyll pubs, beers are mainly from English breweries. No food on Mondays, and no evening meals on Sundays.
↻❀✍❶☐(489) ❄

Kilmartin

Kilmartin Hotel

PA31 8RQ (on A816 10 miles N of Lochgilphead)
☎ (01546) 510250 ⊕ kilmartin-hotel.com
3 changing beers (sourced regionally; often Fyne, Loch Lomond, Orkney) ⊞
A pleasant hotel set above Kilmartin Glen, one of Scotland's most important prehistoric sites. The small public bar to one side provides a cosy fireside nook and offers a good selection of whiskies to complement the real ale. Good home-cooked food is available in the evenings and when the bar is open at lunchtime. Children are welcome at meal times and pub games are available. Beers are mainly from Scottish breweries. Opens at 5pm Monday to Wednesday in winter.
↻❀✍❶もも₱☐(421,423) ☘❄

Kingarth

Kingarth Hotel

PA20 9LU (on A844 at jct for turn-off to Kilchattan)
☎ (01700) 831662 ⊕ kingarth-bute.co.uk
Fyne Jarl; 1 changing beer (sourced nationally; often Fyne) ⊞
A friendly welcome awaits you at this rare gem of a pub set in a secluded yet reachable location on the south of the Isle of Bute. Two handpumps (one in winter) serve Jarl and another beer usually from Fyne Ales. It is popular for relaxed dining. You can enjoy a stroll to Kilchattan Bay and return for a few beers and an alfresco meal under cover on the rear veranda, or tables on the front patio.
↻❀✍❶₱☐(490) ☘❄

Lerags

Barn

PA34 4SE (2 miles S of Oban on A816, turn right to Cologin Chalets and then first right after about 1 mile)
☎ (01631) 564501 ⊕ cologin.co.uk
1 changing beer (sourced locally; often Fyne) ⊞
Cologin farmhouse forms the centre of a range of holiday chalets and lodges in a secluded glen a couple of miles south of Oban. The Barn was originally the cattle byre and some of the slate stalls have been retained to provide the backrest for seating, helping to contribute to the cosy ambience. An enclosed veranda at the front provides extra seating and looks over the play area and duck pond. Closed Tuesday and Wednesday, hours can vary, especially in winter – phone ahead.
Q↻❀✍❶₱☘❄♫

Oban

Corryvreckan ✓

The Waterfront Centre, Railway Pier, PA34 4LW
☎ (01631) 568910
Belhaven 80/-; Greene King Abbot; Sharp's Doom Bar; 4 changing beers (sourced nationally) ⊞
Conveniently located Wetherspoon named after the famous whirlpool between Jura and Scarba. It is close to the railway and bus stations and the ferry terminal, with views across Oban Bay and the island of Kerrera. The interior has an exposed wood-panelled roof and the layout is open and spacious. A wide range of beers can be found, often from English breweries. The pub is enlivened by much nautical ephemera including a casting of a sea eagle. ↻❀❶もも☐❄

Markie Dans

1 Victoria Crescent, Corran Esplanade, PA34 5PN
☎ (01631) 564448 ⊕ markiedans.co.uk

1 changing beer (sourced regionally; often Fyne) ⊞
A cosy and welcoming locals' pub in the lower floor of a grand house overlooking Oban Bay. A pool table is available most days, however it is moved away when there is entertainment. An intimate snug off the main bar provides welcome seclusion for a quiet chat. One ale, usually one of Fyne Ales' less common beers, is served and can be enjoyed in the small terrace overlooking the bay. ⏰♿◑♣☕♿❀♪

Oban Inn ♀
1 Stafford Street, PA34 5NJ
☎ (01631) 567441 ⊕ obaninn.co.uk
3 changing beers (sourced regionally; often Fyne) ⊞
A traditional corner local, which originally opened in 1790, by the old harbour pier. The public bar retains its dark wood panelling and stone floors of Easdale slate. Maritime artefacts are displayed on the walls and currency notes from many nations cover the wooden beams. The comfortable lounge upstairs only occasionally has real ale, but it is worth taking a look to admire the stained-glass panels acquired from an Irish monastery. Local CAMRA Pub of the Year 2024.
♿◑♣☕❀♪

Port Bannatyne

Anchor Tavern
33 Marine Road, PA20 0LL
☎ (01700) 505617
Fyne Jarl ⊞
Community-owned free house pub and hub that opened in 2022. It is two miles along the coast to the north of Rothesay and offers views of Cowal and the opening of Loch Striven. The single room is comfortably decorated with nautical ephemera, including local sea charts. As well as a cask ale the pub serves keg beers brewed by Fyne Ales, and there is a fine selection of malt whiskies and gins distilled on the island. Often closed weekday evenings in winter. ☕(90,490)❀♿♪

Rothesay

Black Bull Inn
3 West Princes Street, PA20 9AF

☎ (01700) 505838 ⊕ blackbullrothesay.co.uk
2 changing beers (sourced regionally; often Fyne, Greene King) ⊞
A popular pub in the centre of the town, close to the ferry terminal, opposite the marina and within walking distance of all amenities, including the famous Victorian toilets. The pub has two bars and a separate dining area. The front entrance is closed in cold weather so it is worth checking round the back if it appears to be closed. Food serving times vary so phone ahead if you want to eat. Closed on winter Mondays. ◑♣☕(90,490)♿

Macs Bar ★
14-18 Castlehill Street, PA20 0DA
☎ (01700) 502417
1 changing beer (sourced nationally; often Orkney, Timothy Taylor) ⊞
Occupying the ground floor of a three-storey stone building opposite the entrance to Rothesay Castle, Macs has been in the same family since 1951. The pub is popular with locals but visitors are given a warm welcome. The cramped bar, decorated with Scottish women's football memorabilia, leads to a surprisingly spacious lounge area with leather seating and a pool table at the end. There are three dartboards and domino competitions are taken very seriously. ♣☕❀♪

Strachur

Creggans Inn ⌂
PA27 8BX (on A815 at N end of village)
☎ (01369) 860279 ⊕ creggans-inn.co.uk
2 changing beers (sourced locally; often Fyne) ⊞
A convenient stopping place along Loch Fyne. Named after a half-hanged sheep rustler of yore, the pub is comfortable, with a real fire and plenty of space for dining. Two handpumps offer a changing selection of beers, which can be enjoyed in the other lounges, the pool room or restaurant, or in the garden overlooking the loch. The games room and toilets are decorated with sea charts. The inn is usually closed throughout December and January. Q⏰♿⌂◑P☕(484,486)❀♿

The language of beer

Nose: the aroma. Gently swirl the beer to release the aroma. You will detect malt: grainy and biscuity, often likened to crackers or Ovaltine. When darker malts are used, the nose will have powerful hints of chocolate, coffee, nuts, vanilla, liquorice, molasses and such dried fruits as raisins and sultanas. Hops add superb aromas of resins, herbs, spices, fresh-mown grass and tart citrus fruit – lemon and orange are typical, with intense grapefruit notes from some American varieties. Sulphur may also be present when waters are 'Burtonised': i.e. gypsum and magnesium salts have been added to replicate the famous spring waters of Burton-on-Trent.

Palate: the appeal in the mouth. The tongue can detect sweetness, bitterness and saltiness as the beer passes over it. The rich flavours of malt will come to the fore but hop bitterness will also make a substantial impact. The tongue will also pick out the natural saltiness from the brewing water and fruit from darker malts, yeast and hops. Citrus notes often have a major impact on the palate.

Finish: the aftertaste, as the beer goes over the tongue and down the throat. The finish is often different to the nose. The aroma may be dominated by malt whereas hop flavours and bitterness can govern the finish. Darker malts will make their presence felt with roast, chocolate or coffee notes; fruit character may linger. Strong beers may end on a sweet or biscuity note but in bitters, bitterness and dryness come to the fore.

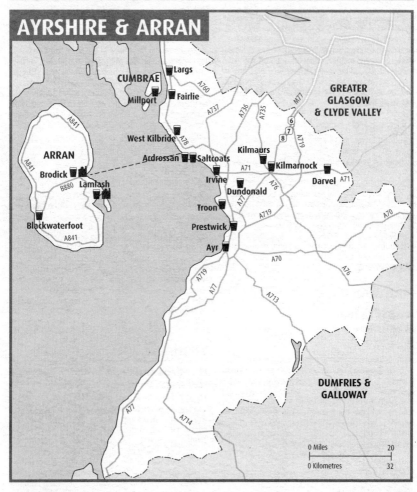

AYRSHIRE & ARRAN

Ardrossan

Ardrossan Academicals Rugby Club
Memorial Field Pavilion, Sorbie Road, KA22 8AP
(400yds NE of Ardrossan South Beach train station)
☎ (01294) 461651 ⊕ ardrossanrugby.com
1 changing beer (often Alechemy, Fyne, Orkney) ⊞/℗

An active sports club with a members' lounge selling one cask ale. Non-members can be signed in – one per night up to 12 times a year – and CAMRA members are very welcome to join. The club holds an annual beer festival. It opens at 1pm on Saturdays if there is a home rugby match. Local CAMRA Club of the Year 2024.
Q&⇌(South Beach) P❒♨(11,585) ❀❖ 🗢

Ayr

Chestnuts Hotel
52 Racecourse Road, KA7 2UZ (on A719)
☎ (01292) 264393 ⊕ chestnutshotel.com
2 changing beers (often Fyne, Morland, Timothy Taylor) ⊞

A sandstone villa that used to be a synagogue, with a stone bay window, real open fire and airy, timber-beamed vaulted ceiling with an array of whisky water jugs. It offers various seating/dining options, including barstools. The quiet, family-run bar has helpful staff and good food (booking advisable at weekends). There is a secure, south-facing garden to the side with varied seating, and a car park at the front. It is within walking distance to beach at Seafield. Q❁&♨◑◑&P❒(9)🗢

Wellingtons Bar
17 Wellington Square, KA7 1EZ
☎ (01292) 262794
3 changing beers (often Five Kingdoms, Kelburn, Loch Lomond) ⊞

A large Wellington boot advertises the location of this welcoming, long-established real ale basement bar that serves three constantly changing ales. It is close to the seafront, bus station and local government offices, and attracts tourists as well as local office workers. It hosts a popular Wednesday evening quiz. ♨◑⇌♨❖🗢♫

West Kirk ✅
58A Sandgate, KA7 1BX (close to bus station)
☎ (01292) 880416

REAL ALE BREWERIES

Arran ✎ Brodick: Isle of Arran
Arran Botanical Drinks Brodick: Isle of Arran
Seagate Lamlash: Isle of Arran

Belhaven 80/-; Greene King Abbot; Sharp's Doom Bar; 6 changing beers ⊞
This spacious Wetherspoon church conversion retains many original features. The vaulted ceiling is bathed in light, featuring a huge chandellier, and there is a balcony. Toilets are via the pulpit, and there is an accessible toilet downstairs. Various seating options include stools, tables and chairs and booths. A paved outside seating area on a busy road gets some sun. The news, with subtitles, is usually shown on small TV screens. It gets busy at weekends and during Ayr races. Food is served all day. Q❀❄❍❦♿⇌🚐🛜

Blackwaterfoot: Isle of Arran

Kinloch Hotel
KA27 8ET
☎ (01770) 860444 ⊕ kinloch-arran.com
House beer (by Kelburn); 1 changing beer (often Greene King, Kelburn) ⊞
A family-run hotel offering comfort and spectacular scenery. It has 37 bedrooms, a restaurant and three refurbished bars, and facilities include a heated indoor swimming pool, squash court and a sauna. Kelburn has taken on the role of brewing the house beer, Uisge Dubh. Well thought-out menus using local produce offer plenty of choice at lunch and dinner. A popular beer festival is held in August with a wide selection of ales on offer. ❄❀❦❍♿▲♣🚐(322,323)❀🛜

Brodick: Isle of Arran

Ormidale Hotel
Knowe Road, KA27 8BY (off A841 at W end of village)
☎ (01770) 302293 ⊕ ormidale-hotel.co.uk
Arran Blonde; 2 changing beers (often Inveralmond, Kelburn, Stewart) ⊞
A cosy, friendly and popular bar at the heart of a large sandstone hotel which has been owned by the Gilmore family since 1935. Three handpulls dispense well-kept ales throughout the year. Board games feature on Monday, a music quiz on Tuesday, rock & pop bingo on Wednesday, and a general knowledge quiz on Thursday provide additional entertainment. Occasional live music and plenty of chat also make this an ideal destination on the island. ❄❀❦❍♣🚐(322,324)❀🛜♪

Darvel

Black Bull Inn
24 West Main Street, KA17 0AQ
☎ 07860 355736
2 changing beers (often Five Kingdoms, Fyne, Orkney) ⊞
Dating from 1840, this former coaching inn retains much of its original character. The bar features a dark wooded gantry offering a wide selection of spirits. Many photographs adorn the interior, reflect the rich history of the former lace town. An open mic session is held on Wednesdays, and live bands play on Saturday evenings. There is no permanent kitchen, but a variety of food trucks visit regularly. Local CAMRA Pub of the Year 2023. ❀♣🚐(1,X71)❀🛜♪

Dundonald

Auchans
29-31 Main Street, KA2 9HH (on B730)
☎ (01563) 851472 ⊕ theauchans.co.uk
2 changing beers (often Fyne, Kelburn) ⊞
Friendly family-run restaurant-bar in the village of Dundonald. It features a varied food menu that will

appeal to all tastes. The comfortable lounge bar has views of the historic 14th-century castle and serves one or two regularly changing beers on handpump, mainly from local and regional breweries. Quiz night is Thursday. Q❄❀❍♿♣🚐(10,110)❀🛜♪

Fairlie

Village Inn
46 Bay Street, KA29 0AL
☎ (01475) 560059
2 changing beers ⊞
Known locally as the Mudhook, this is a community local serving good-value pub food in the lounge, conservatory, Fife Room and traditional public bar. One of the real ales is likely to be a pale beer of around 4% ABV. The walls are decorated with photos of Fife yachts which were built opposite. The pub hosts regular quizzes and board games nights, plus occasional live music and beer festivals. Pub games are also available. Dogs are welcome in the public bar, and children in other areas if eating. ❄❀❍♿♣🚐(585)❀🛜♪

Irvine

Auld Brig ✅
15 Fullarton Square, KA12 8EJ (opp Irvine station)
☎ (01294) 277818
Belhaven 80/-; Greene King Abbot; Sharp's Doom Bar; 3 changing beers ⊞
A large, modern Wetherspoon pub next to the west entrance to Rivergate shopping centre. Six of the 12 handpumps dispense a variety of real ales. Its sloping glass roof provides natural light to the front seating and mezzanine area, which features an art installation made from cotton rope. Also note the wooden doors on the wall and the various old photos. The rear downstairs area has a long, wooden bar, a tiled floor and subdued lighting. A quiz is held on the first Wednesday of the month. Q❄❀❍♿⇌🚐🛜

Kilmarnock

First Edition ✅
50-54 Bank Street, KA1 1ER
☎ (01563) 528833
2 changing beers (often Fyne, Loch Leven, Stewart) ⊞
Large, recently renovated town-centre pub in a former furniture shop in the town's historic core. Two ales are usually available from Scottish regional brewers. The pub serves food all day in bright surroundings, and the beer garden has some tables under cover. Numerous TV screens inside and five outside show sports, and a DJ features Friday to Sunday evenings. A quiz is held every Sunday. ❄❀❍♿⇌🚐❀🛜

Wheatsheaf Inn ✅
70 Portland Street, KA1 1JG
☎ (01563) 572483
Greene King Abbot; Ruddles Best Bitter; Sharp's Doom Bar; 3 changing beers ⊞
A large, modern pub incorporating the frontage of the original Wheatsheaf Hotel, an important coaching inn dating from the early 1700s. Robert Burns was first published in Kilmarnock and may have socialised here with his cronies, including Tam Samson who lived close by. The bar is divided into various seating areas and a quiet corner can be found even when busy. Six handpumps dispense a range of ales. The food is standard Wetherspoon fare. Licensed from 11am. ❄❀❍♿⇌🚐🛜

Kilmaurs

Weston Tavern
27 Main Street, KA3 2RQ
☎ (01563) 538805 ⊕ westontavern.co.uk
2 changing beers (often Broughton, Sulwath, Theakston) Ⓗ
Housed in the former manse of reformist minister David Smeaton, a contemporary of Robert Burns, this fully refurbished country pub and restaurant has a tiled floor, stone walls and a wood-burning fire. It sits beside the Jougs, a former jailhouse and tollbooth. Two handpumps serve ales from a rotating list of local breweries. The pub holds regular live music and quiz nights.
❄🕸🕪&≈♣P🖵(9,337) 🐾🛜♪

Lamlash: Isle of Arran

Pierhead Tavern
Shore Road, KA27 8JN
☎ (01770) 600418 ⊕ thepht.co.uk
2 changing beers (often Arran, Loch Lomond) Ⓗ
A traditional, welcoming village pub in the centre of Lamlash. Two handpumps in summer and one in winter dispense ales from a variety of Scottish brewers, including Arran. Live music plays on Saturday evenings, and occasionally Sunday afternoons, and a popular quiz is held on on Wednesday evenings. Pub grub is available until late evening. The views from the roof terrace across to Holy Isle are spectacular. ❄🕸🕪&▲♣🖵(323)🐾🛜♪

Largs

Paddle Steamer ✅
Gallowgate Street, KA30 8LX (on promenade)
☎ (01475) 686441
Belhaven 80/-; Greene King Abbot; Sharp's Doom Bar; 3 changing beers Ⓗ
Seafront Wetherspoon pub with a nautical theme, a feature fire in the middle, and a viewing window into the cellar. An outside balcony borders the promenade overlooked by wide windows with views to the Isles of Bute and Cumbrae. Models of the world-famous paddle steamer Waverley decorate the outside, while the real ship visits Largs in the summer. Licensed from 11am. The Cumbrae ferry terminal is only one minute away.
❄🕸🕪&≈🖵🛜

Millport: Isle of Cumbrae

Fraser's Bar Ⓛ
9 Cardiff Street, KA28 0AS (opp bus terminus)
☎ (01475) 530518
2 changing beers (often Broughton, Spey Valley) Ⓗ
Well maintained and tidy, this pub caters for visitors to the island as well as locals. Buses meet every ferry from Largs and terminate just across the road. Two handpumps serve mostly light-coloured ales, usually including one from a local brewery. Good-value pub food is available at lunchtime and early evening. The main bar has an open fire and a fine display of old Clyde steamer photographs. Children are welcome in the rear lounge until 10pm. Local CAMRA Pub of the Year 2023.
Q❄🕸🕪&♣🖵(320) 🛜

Prestwick

Prestwick Pioneer ✅
87 Main Street, KA9 1JS
☎ (01292) 473210
Greene King Abbot; Ruddles Best Bitter; 6 changing beers Ⓗ
Modern Wetherspoon pub in a former Woolworths store, named after the first Scottish Aviation Pioneer light aircraft, built in 1947 at the nearby airport. It has an airy feel, with a light-wood decor, and features photographs of early Open Championship golf at Prestwick, and of Elvis at the airport – the only place in the UK he set foot. Ten handpumps serve local and national ales and food is available. Licensed from 10am. ❄🕪&≈(Town)🖵🛜

Saltcoats

Salt Cot ✅
7 Hamilton Street, KA21 5DT
☎ (01294) 465924
Greene King Abbot; Ruddles Best Bitter; Sharp's Doom Bar; 3 changing beers Ⓗ
Wetherspoon conversion of a former cinema, named after the original cottages and salt pans of the old fishing community. The interior features memorabilia relating to the cinema, its entertainers and the community. There are TVs with sound occasionally turned up for special sporting events. At least one of the guest beers is usually sourced locally. Food is available all day. Licensed from 10am. Q❄🕪&≈🖵(11,585)🛜

Troon

Harbour Bar
169 Templehill, KA10 6BH (opp ferry terminal)
☎ (01292) 312668 ⊕ harbourbartroon.co.uk
1 changing beer (often Broughton) Ⓗ
Popular bar overlooking the North Bay. One real ale is available in the bar that serves both public and lounge areas, usually from Scottish breweries. There is also a good range of malt whiskies, gins and rums. Meals are served throughout the day, with a popular roast on Sundays. The bar has a jukebox and a hosts a monthly quiz on Thursday nights, live music on most Saturday nights, and jam nights on Wednesdays.
❄🕸🕪&♣P🖵🛜♪

Number Forty Seven
47 Templehill, KA10 6BQ
☎ (01292) 312814
Cairngorm Wildcat; Morland Old Speckled Hen; 3 changing beers (often Five Kingdoms, Greene King) Ⓗ
A long, single-room bar with seating booths plus tables and chairs. Six handpulls dispense real ales from Scottish and English breweries. Over-60s get a discount on full-priced drinks. Quiz night is Thursday. There is a pool table, a jukebox and a lot of TVs showing a variety of live sport. The gantry is stocked with a wide selection of different spirits. A DJ plays on Friday and Saturday nights when the bar moves into nightclub mode. Local CAMRA Pub of the Year 2023. &≈♣🖵(14,10)🐾🛜

West Kilbride

Twa Dugs
71 Main Street, KA23 9AW
☎ (01294) 822524
2 changing beers (often Five Kingdoms, Kelburn) Ⓗ
A popular, well-kept, comfortable pub in Scotland's Craft Town. A variety of real ales from local and national brewers are served from two handpulls. Live music on Saturdays, a pool table, and a regular quiz night entertain the regulars. The pub holds occasional beer festivals. Convenient for public transport. A renovation of the upper floors is currently underway and it is expected that food service will restart once completed.
&≈♣🖵(585,585A) 🐾🛜♪

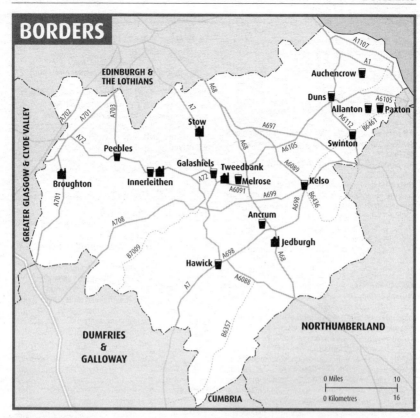

Allanton

Allanton Inn

Main Street, TD11 3JZ (on B6437)
☎ (01890) 818260 ⊕ allantoninn.co.uk
2 changing beers (sourced nationally; often Born, Fyne, Timothy Taylor) ⊞
Old 18th-century coaching inn with a bright and airy feel. It serves quality food in the dining rooms, and in the small bar area that overlooks the lovely beer garden, with views of the countryside beyond. The bar is attractively decorated, with artwork on the wall and comfortable cushioned benches. Families are welcome, and a children's menu and games are provided. Booking is strongly recommended. It is likely to be closed on Tuesday and Wednesday lunchtimes, and Sunday evenings in winter. Q☼❄🕮🍴◑♣P🛜

Ancrum

Ancrum Cross Keys ★

The Green, TD8 6XH (on B6400, off A68)
☎ (01835) 830242 ⊕ ancrumcrosskeys.com
Born Blonde, Amber ⊞
A 200-year-old inn, owned by Born brewery, perched above the Ale Water. Parts have been upgraded, but the front bar, with a real fire, has remained virtually untouched since 1906 and has pine panelling throughout. Beware the sliding door! There is also a comfy drinking/dining area and additional snug. Food features strongly (not Mon and Tue) and uses local produce that is sometimes foraged, with its 'Plough to Platter' ethos matching the brewery's 'Plough to Pint' philosophy. Families are welcome, with children's menu, play area and games provided. It is usually closed weekday afternoons all year, and Monday and Tuesday during winter. ☼❄🕮🍴🚃Å♣P🖭(68,51)❀🛜♪

Auchencrow

Craw Inn

TD14 5LS (signed from A1)
☎ (01890) 761253 ⊕ thecrawinn.co.uk
2 changing beers (sourced nationally; often Fyne, Loch Lomond, Timothy Taylor) ⊞
A friendly and revitalised, listed 18th-century country inn. The real ales are usually from smaller breweries, as can be seen from the numerous pumpclips on show. The cosy front bar has a wood-burning stove and tables for dining and drinking. Excellent home-cooked food is served in both the bar and well-appointed restaurant. There is also an additional back room with comfy settees and a TV. Likely to be closed on Monday, not open until 5pm Tuesday to Friday and may close early if no custom. Q☼❄🕮🍴◑♣P❀🛜

Duns

White Swan Hotel

31-32 Market Square, TD11 3AL
☎ (01361) 883338 ⊕ whiteswan-hotel.co.uk
2 changing beers (sourced locally; often Born, Hadrian Border, Loch Lomond) ⊞
Town-centre hotel with a deceptively spacious interior. The bar is a welcoming and comfortable room, with a friendly and lively clientele. There is a separate dining room, and a function room upstairs for special events. There is a good menu serving great-value meals.

Breakfasts and pensioner's lunches on Thursday are especially popular. Children are welcome until 9pm if eating. Likely to open at 9am with alcoholic drinks served from 11am. ⬛🏚◀🍴🚃(60,32)🌀 �🎵

Galashiels

Hunters Hall ✓
56 High Street, TD1 1SE (N end of centre)
☎ (01896) 759795
Belhaven 80/-; Greene King Abbot; 3 changing beers (sourced nationally; often Broughton, Sharp's, Stewart) ⓗ
This former Presbyterian church and school has been sympathetically restored to expose much of the original stonework, the high ceiling and the skylight roof panels. Historical photographs of Galashiels decorate the walls. The pub offers typical Wetherspoon's fare and caters for families, locals, visitors and students. Meals are served all day, with breakfast 8-12am and children's options. Real cider is generally only available during festivals. Likely to open at 8am with alcoholic drinks served from 11am. Q⬛🌀◀🍴&🅰🍴⬛🌀⑂

Salmon Inn
54 Bank Street, TD1 1EP (town centre, opp gardens)
☎ (01896) 752577 ⬛ salmoninn.co.uk
Caledonian Deuchars IPA; Timothy Taylor Landlord; 1 changing beer (sourced locally; often Born, Stow) ⓗ
A comfortable, friendly town-centre inn. The single L-shaped bar and adjacent bistro are split into three areas that are decorated with contemporary photographs of Galashiels and around. The changing real ales are often from smaller breweries. Good home-cooked meals are served all day (except Sun and Mon) and families are welcome at lunchtimes. The pub gets quite animated when sporting events are screened on TV. Runner-up in local CAMRA Real Ale Quality Award 2023. B&B accommodation available. ⬛🏚◀🍴&🅰🍴⬛⬛🌀⑂🎵

Hawick

Bourtree ✓
22 Bourtree Place, TD9 9HL (NE edge of town centre)
☎ (01450) 360450
Belhaven 80/-; Greene King Abbot; 3 changing beers (sourced nationally; often Oakham, Sharp's, Stewart) ⓗ
Built as the Hawick Conservative Club in 1897, this listed building has been stunningly transformed into a Wetherspoon pub. The original badminton and snooker halls form the main area and there are three other quieter sections. Photographs depict a history of Hawick life. Food is served all day with breakfast and children's options. Either bingo or a quiz is held on Wednesday evenings. Real cider is generally only available during festivals. Likely to open at 8am, with alcoholic drinks served from 11am. Q⬛🌀◀&🍴🍴⬛🌀⑂

Exchange Bar (Dalton's) ★
1 Silver Street, TD9 0AD (off SW end of High St)
☎ (01450) 376067
2 changing beers (sourced regionally; often Born, First & Last, Orkney) ⓗ
Tucked away near St Mary's Kirk, the pub used to overlook the Corn Exchange and took its name from that. However, a previous owner was called Dalton and that name has stuck ever since. Popular with locals, this Victorian gem has a bar featuring original dark-wood panelling and ornate cornice work. A comfy back lounge is used for parties, occasional karaoke and Sunday folk sessions. Children are not admitted. 🌀🅰🍴⬛🌀⑂🎵

Innerleithen

St Ronan's Hotel
High Street, EH44 6HF
☎ (01896) 831487 ⬛ stronanshotel.co.uk
1 changing beer (sourced regionally; often Born, Broughton, Stewart) ⓗ
This village hotel with a prominent blue-and-white exterior takes its name from a local saint. The public bar is long and narrow, with a wood-burning stove. A pool room leads off it, and two alcoves provide extra seating and a darts area. No food is served, but a pick-up service and packed lunches are available for Southern Upland Way walkers staying overnight. There is a garden play area and indoor games for children. Likely to open at 2pm Monday to Thursday and at 1pm Friday to Sunday. ⬛🌀🏚🅰🍴⬛(X62)🌀⑂🎵

Traquair Arms Hotel
Traquair Road, EH44 6PD (W edge of centre)
☎ (01896) 830229 ⬛ traquairarmshotel.co.uk
3 changing beers (sourced regionally; often Stewart, Tempest) ⓗ
Elegant 18th-century hotel in the scenic Tweed Valley offering accommodation in 14 en-suite rooms and six self-catering cottages. The comfortable lounge bar features a welcoming real fire, and a flagstoned sports bar with log-burner provides a thawing-out space for mountain bikers, walkers and anglers. A bistro area and separate restaurant offer plenty of room for diners. Meals are served all day at weekends and there is a children's menu. The bar may close earlier if quiet. ⬛🌀🏚◀&🅰🍴⬛(X62)🌀⑂

Kelso

1905
Crawford Street, TD5 7DP (off N corner of town square)
☎ (01573) 225556
3 changing beers (sourced regionally; often Born, Firebrick, Stewart) ⓗ
Formerly the Red Lion, this pub has a lively atmosphere when events are held, while at other times it has a pleasant, peaceful ambience. The main room has a fine wood and plastered vaulted ceiling, wood panelling and mosaic flooring. Brewery mirrors adorn the walls and are also inlaid into the bar gantry. Other areas with different styling lead off from the bar. Children are not admitted, except for some functions. Likely to be closed Monday. Q🌀🏚⬛🌀🌀⑂🎵

Cobbles Freehouse & Dining ♥
7 Bowmont Street, TD5 7JH (off N corner of town square)
☎ (01573) 223548 ⬛ cobbleskelso.co.uk
Tempest Armadillo; 1 changing beer (sourced locally; often Tempest) ⓗ
This gastropub is often busy with diners but drinkers are also welcome. The decor is bright and welcoming, with a bar warmed by a real fire. Food is served in the dining area throughout the day (but no evening meals are on Sun or lunches Wed to Fri) and should suit all tastes, including children. The beers are dedicated to Tempest

REAL ALE BREWERIES

Born Jedburgh
Broughton Broughton
Durty 🍺 Innerleithen
Stow Stow
Tempest 🍴 Tweedbank
Traquair House Innerleithen

ales. Local CAMRA Real Ale Quality Award winner in 2023, and 2024 Pub of the Year. Likely to be closed all day Monday and early afternoon Tuesdays and Sunday evenings. ⬥🏡🍴◖🦽🛏️🚃🐾🎵

Rutherfords

38 The Square, TD5 7HL
☎ 07933 887344
4 changing beers (sourced regionally; often Fyne, Hadrian Border, Loch Lomond) 🅗
This tiny shop conversion was the first micropub in Scotland. With no TV or music to distract, it is ideal for a friendly chat or playing board games. The area extends onto the pavement under canopies. The real ales are generally from smaller breweries, with third-pint tasting paddles available. Some simple bar snacks are provided. Children are only welcome until 3pm, with games provided. Likely to open all day in summer, but hours are reduced in winter. Q⬥🏡🍴🚃🐾🎵

Melrose

Burt's Hotel

Market Square, TD6 9PN
☎ (01896) 822285 🌐 burtshotel.co.uk
Timothy Taylor Landlord; 1 changing beer (sourced regionally; often Born, Tempest)
An elegant, family-run hotel with colourful window boxes providing a striking appearance in summer. The comfortable lounge bar reflects the country sporting interests of many of the clientele. The focus is unashamedly on food, which is excellent in both the bar and restaurant. Those visiting solely for a drink may find space limited at busy times. Children are permitted, with a menu provided. The Townhouse opposite has the same owners. Q⬥🏡🍴◖🦽🅰♣P🚃🐾🛜

George & Abbotsford Hotel

High Street, TD6 9PD (centre, NW of Market Square)
☎ (01896) 822308 🌐 georgeandabbotsfordmelrose.co.uk
Greene King Abbot; Tempest Armadillo; 2 changing beers (sourced regionally; often Orkney) 🅗
A spacious family-run hotel with a comfortable bar and lounges, offering a warm welcome to locals and visitors alike. The real ales offered are from both sides of the border. Food features prominently and is served all day, the menu being supplemented with various specials and children's options. The partially covered enclosed suntrap beer garden has plenty of seating. It is popular with walkers, cyclists, and Melrose rugby supporters, and is a pleasant walk from the rail terminus at Tweedbank. May close earlier if quiet. Q⬥🏡🍴◖🅰♣P🚃🐾🛜🎵

Paxton

Cross Inn

TD15 1TE (off B6461)
☎ (01289) 384877 🌐 thecrossinn.co.uk
Timothy Taylor Landlord; 2 changing beers (sourced nationally; often Fyne, Hadrian Border) 🅗
A friendly, rejuvenated 19th-century village local, with a small and welcoming stone-floored bar, and an attractive larger dining and function area. The seasonal plant arrangements throughout are a visual delight. At the front is a raised decking area for outside drinking and eating. The menu, along with daily specials, children's options and Sunday roasts, should appeal to most tastes. Likely to be closed Monday and Tuesday.
⬥🏡◖🦽🅰P🚃(32)🐾🛜🎵

Peebles

Bridge Inn (Trust) ★

Portbrae, EH45 8AW (W end of town centre)
☎ (01721) 720589 🌐 thebridgeinnpeebles.co.uk
3 changing beers (sourced nationally; often Cromarty, Orkney, Stewart) 🅗
Cheerful, welcoming pub also known as the Trust and once called the Tweedside Inn. The bright, comfortable bar is decorated with jugs, bottles, pictures of old Peebles and displays relating to outdoor pursuits. There is a cosy corner with a log-burner and a small room to the rear with a dartboard. The Gents has superb old fittings. The suntrap patio overlooks the river and hills beyond. Children are not admitted. Unlikely to open before 2.30pm on Mondays. Runner-up local CAMRA Pub of the Year 2024. 🏡🅰♣🚃🛜🎵

Swinton

Wheatsheaf Hotel

Main Street, TD11 3JJ (on A6112 in centre of village)
☎ (01890) 860257 🌐 eatdrinkstaywheatsheaf.com
1 changing beer (sourced regionally; often Firebrick, Hadrian Border) 🅗
Overlooking the village green, this relaxing and stylish country inn attracts locals, tourists and anglers. While the focus is on food and accommodation, the variety of comfortably furnished public rooms, including a cosy bar area, give a warm and welcoming feel, ensuring that drinkers are equally well catered for. The split level rear garden and front patio seats are popular in summer. There is a pie and a pint deal on the first Monday evening of each month. May close after Sunday lunch service in winter. Q⬥🏡🍴◖P🚃(32,34)🐾🛜🎵

Pepys on the road

Thence (from Salisbury) about 6 o'clock, and with a guide went over the smooth plain indeed till night; and then by a happy mistake, and that looked like an adventure, we were carried out of our way to a town where we would lie, since we could not go as far as we would. And there with great difficulty came about 10 at night to a little inn, where we were fain to go into a room where a pedlar was in bed, and made him rise; and there wife and I lay, and in a truckle-bed, Betty Turner and Willet. But good beds, and the master of the house a sober, understanding man, and I had a pleasant discourse with him about country matters. Up, finding our beds good, but we lousy; which made us merry. We set out, the reckoning and servants coming to 9s. 6d.

Samuel Pepys (1633-1703), diary for Thursday and Friday, 11 and 12 June 1668

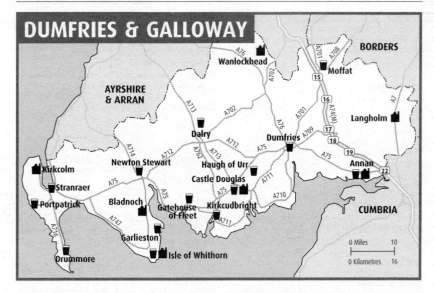

DUMFRIES & GALLOWAY

Annan

Blue Bell Inn 🍺 ★

10 High Street, DG12 6AG
☎ (01461) 202385
3 changing beers (sourced locally; often Five Kingdoms, Mote & Bailey) Ⓗ
Former coaching inn with some traditional features, notably the inter-war panelling on the walls and the bar counter, which are retained from its time as a State Management Scheme pub from up to 1972. The courtyard to the rear features the original stables and provides a pleasant seated area. The pub has an onsite brewery called Motte & Bailey, and their beers are only available here. Local CAMRA Pub of the Year 2024.
🕭❀🅰🍴♣🐶🅿🚏(79,383) 🐾🛜🎵

Castle Douglas

Sulwath Brewery Tap Room 🅛

209 King Street, DG7 1DT
☎ (01556) 504525 ⊕ sulwathbrewers.co.uk
Sulwath Black Galloway; 5 changing beers (sourced locally; often Sulwath) Ⓗ
The visitor centre for Sulwath brewery is a showcase for the brewery's beers, with four in cask-conditioned form, alongside other guest beers on occasion. One keg cider, usually from Westons, is also available. Dried hop bines decorate the walls and old wooden casks of various sizes provide some of the furniture. Brewery tours are available Monday and Friday. Occasionally open on Sunday for special events (see Facebook for details).
🕭🅰🅿🚏🐶🛜

Dalry

Clachan Inn 🍺

8-10 Main Street, DG7 3UW
☎ (01644) 430241 ⊕ theclachaninn.co.uk
3 changing beers (sourced regionally; often Five Kingdoms, Fyne) Ⓗ
Pub with a reputation for excellent food, cosy, well-equipped bedrooms and a welcoming atmosphere. The menu is varied, with excellent daily specials, and uses local produce. The pub has an attractive traditional main bar, a relaxing lounge bar, and a separate restaurant.

Both bars have wonderfully warming open log fires in winter. It is a handy stop for walkers on the Southern Upland Way. Winter opening hours may vary. Local CAMRA Pub of the Year 2024.
🕭🛏❀🍴◑👪♿🅰♣🅿🚏(520,521) 🐾🛜

Drummore

Ship Inn

5 Shore Street, DG9 9PU (turn left at end of A714, then left again)
☎ (01776) 840471
2 changing beers (often Fyne, Greene King, Timothy Taylor) Ⓗ
A family-run pub in Scotland's most southerly village on the shores of Luce Bay. Now serving real ale again after a gap of many years. It is close to the Mull of Galloway, with its lighthouse and foghorn, and Logan Botanic Garden, and is a great area for spotting seabirds. A welcome addition to this remote part of Galloway.
🕭🛏◑♣🚏(407) 🐾🎵

Dumfries

Cavens Arms 🍺

20 Buccleuch Street, DG1 2AH
☎ (01387) 252896 ⊕ cavensarms.com
Fyne Jarl; Morland Old Speckled Hen; Swannay Orkney IPA; Timothy Taylor Landlord; 4 changing beers (sourced nationally; often Thornbridge) Ⓗ
Busy, food-oriented pub that is popular with diners for its range of good-value meals. Drinkers are welcomed in the bar area, but seating can be limited during food service times. Outside, accessed by stairs or from the Whitesands, is an additional area including a covered barn. It serves five regular beers and three guests, which

REAL ALE BREWERIES

Borderlands 🔨 Langholm
Five Kingdoms Isle of Whithorn
Lola Rose 🍺 Wanlockhead
Mote & Bailey 🍺 Annan
Portpatrick Kirkcolm
Sulwath 🔨 Castle Douglas
Wigtown Bladnoch

are from a wide range of breweries, including some rarely seen in this area. Local CAMRA Town Pub of the Year 2024. ✿◑🖢&P🚲📶

Douglas Arms 🅛

75 Friars Vennel, DG1 2RQ

☎ (01387) 248236

2 changing beers (often Five Kingdoms) 🅗

Popular, recently refurbished, traditional town-centre bar with a warming fire in winter and a cosy snug. The beers on offer are often from smaller, less well-known breweries, and reflect the care taken by the licensee to give real ale drinkers something different. They are always featured on the pub's Facebook page. ☕≠🖢📶♪

Fleshers Arms

48 Loreburn Street, DG1 1HJ

☎ (01387) 256461

3 changing beers (often Five Kingdoms) 🅗

This popular pub, between the station and town centre, has been reopened by the previous licensee of the Tam O'Shanter. The large single room has modern seating to one side, and a pool table in a separate area to the rear. The building is reputed to be the oldest in Loreburn Street and was so named because of the proximity to a slaughterhouse that is long gone. ☕&≠♣🖢📶♪

Riverside Bar

Dock Park, DG1 2RY

☎ (01387) 254477

Morland Old Speckled Hen; 3 changing beers (sourced nationally) 🅗

An established feature on the Dumfries real ale scene. Comfortable and friendly, it has seating on two levels and a large conservatory. Three outside seating areas include a terrace with open views over Dock Park and access to walks both sides of the River Nith. The pub is accessible from the St Michaels area near Robert Burns Mausoleum or from Dock Park. Guest beers are sourced throughout the UK. ☕✿♣🖢📶♪

Robert the Bruce ✅

81 Buccleuch Street, DG1 2AB

☎ (01387) 270320

Belhaven 80/-; Greene King Abbot; Sharp's Doom Bar; 3 changing beers (sourced nationally) 🅗

This former Methodist church, sensitively converted by Wetherspoon in 2001, has a relaxed atmosphere and is a popular meeting place in the town centre. There is a pleasant outside seating area to the rear. The pub stands near the site where Robert the Bruce killed John Comyn in 1306, in an incident linked to Scotland's fight for independence. The food menu offers a range of good-value meals served all day, every day. Alcohol is served from 10am. A former local CAMRA Cider Pub of the Year. ☕✿◑&≠♣P🚲📶

Tam o' Shanter

113-117 Queensberry Street, DG1 1BH

☎ (01387) 256696

3 changing beers (sourced locally; often Five Kingdoms, Sulwath) 🅗

Established in 1630, this 17th-century coaching inn with a connection to Robert Burns has been a mainstay of the Dumfries beer scene for many years. Situated just off the High Street, the pub has been refurbished to an aesthetically pleasing standard without ruining the traditional bar. The twin booth snug is lovely, with the old stove made into a glass-fronted feature. Brand new toilets are on the ground floor, and there is an updated outdoor smoking/vaping area. ☕≠♣🖢📶

Garlieston

Harbour Inn 🍷

18 South Crescent, DG8 8BQ

☎ (01988) 600685 ● the-harbour-inn.co.uk

House beer (by Greene King); 2 changing beers (often Belhaven, Fyne, Greene King) 🅗

A well-established and well-known pub, dating back to 1700, in the village centre with scenic sea views over the bay. It is busy all year round with locals and holidaymakers. The friendly and cosy bar area now features a second handpump. Pub meals are served at lunchtime and evenings, and there is a separate restaurant area adjacent to the bar. This is a great place for coastal walking and fishing. The pub is dog friendly. Local CAMRA Pub of the Year 2024. Q☕≿✿🖾◑&🔥♣P🚲(415,416) 🖢📶♪

Gatehouse of Fleet

Masonic Arms

10 Ann Street, DG7 2HU

☎ (01557) 814335 ● masonicarms.co.uk

Caledonian Deuchars IPA; 1 changing beer (sourced locally; often Sulwath) 🅗

Built by local Masons in 1785, the pub is situated just off the east end of the main street in Gatehouse of Fleet, a lovely traditional village in the heart of the Stewartry. Exposed beams are a feature in the comfortable bar area, along with a real fire. Good, locally sourced food is served in the bar, the conservatory and the restaurant. There are daily specials, a weekly curry night, and a popular Sunday carvery. Winter opening times may vary. ☕✿◑AP🚲(431,500) 🖢📶♪

Haugh of Urr

Laurie Arms Hotel

11-13 Main Street, DG7 3YA

☎ (01556) 660246 ● haugh-of-urr.co.uk

4 changing beers (sourced nationally; often Caledonian, Five Kingdoms, Fyne) 🅗

Welcoming family-run pub and restaurant in a charming, quiet village, popular for its range of beers and freshly cooked food featuring local produce. It has a good village-pub atmosphere, enhanced on winter nights by the warming log fire in the bar. Up to four beers are available, depending on the season, mainly from independent breweries. National Cycle Route Seven passes nearby. Winter opening times may vary, so check before visiting. The pub is on the bus route between Dumfries, Dalbeattie and Castle Douglas. ☕✿◑♣P🚲(501) 🖢📶

Isle of Whithorn

Steam Packet Inn 🅛

Harbour Row, DG8 8LL (on B7004 from Whithorn)

☎ (01988) 500334 ● thesteampacketinn.co.uk

8 changing beers (often Five Kingdoms, Loch Lomond, Timothy Taylor) 🅗

Traditional and historic family-run hotel overlooking the harbour, welcoming to all, including pets. The public bar has stone walls and a multi-fuel stove, and there are pictures of the village and maritime events throughout. One guest ale is available, from a variety of breweries, along with up to seven beers from in-house brewery Five Kingdoms. Bottle-conditioned ales are also stocked. The extensive food menu features local produce. Q☕≿✿🖾◑AP🚲(415,416) 🖢📶

Kirkcudbright

Masonic Arms
19 Castle Street, DG6 4JA
☎ (01557) 330517 ⊕ masonic-arms.co.uk
2 changing beers (sourced nationally) Ⓗ

This friendly pub has been a firm favourite with real ale enthusiasts for many years. It serves one real ale year round, with two in summer months. It also features more than 50 malt whiskies and over 250 gins, as well as a good selection of world beers. There is a smaller back bar and a garden with a smoking area. Q❀&▲♣P☕❀♠♪

Selkirk Arms Hotel ✓
High Street, DG6 4JG
☎ (01557) 330402 ⊕ selkirkarmshotel.co.uk
2 changing beers (sourced nationally; often Five Kingdoms, Sulwath) Ⓗ

Refurbished 18th-century hotel with a restaurant, bistro and lounge bar, renowned for locally sourced food. Two real ales are available, sometimes three in summer, and there is also a good selection of malt whiskies and gins. The large garden area, with tables, is popular in summer. Robert Burns wrote his famous Selkirk Grace at the hotel in 1794. Kirkcudbright is notable for its artistic heritage and houses a number of interesting galleries and museums. Q♣❀❀◐&▲P☕❀♠

Moffat

Famous Star Hotel Ⓛ
44 High Street, DG10 9EF
☎ (01683) 220156 ⊕ famousstarhotel.co.uk
1 changing beer (sourced regionally; often Sulwath) Ⓗ

The Famous Star Hotel is recognised by the Guinness Book of Records as the narrowest detached hotel in the world. The building is only 20 feet wide and 162 feet long, but feels much bigger due to the clever use of internal space. Service is excellent, and there is at least one beer available all year round. There is a large public bar downstairs with entry at the rear, and a smaller lounge accessed from the front. Moffat is a good base for exploring the Southern Uplands and there are excellent walks nearby. ♠❀◐&▲♣☕♠♪

Newton Stewart

Creebridge House Hotel
Minnigaff, DG8 6NP (on B7079, E of river)
☎ (01671) 402121 ⊕ creebridge.co.uk
2 changing beers (often Five Kingdoms) Ⓗ

This traditional country house hotel is set in three acres of gardens and woodland next to the River Cree and close to the town centre. Two ales are available throughout the summer, with one at other times. Food choices are excellent and locally sourced meat, game and fish are served. The bar and lounge areas have real fires. Some charity events are held. There is also an outdoor bar when weather permits. Q♣❀❀◐&▲P☕(415,500) ❀♠

Portpatrick

Crown Hotel
9 North Crescent, DG9 8SX (opp harbour)
☎ (01776) 810261 ⊕ crownhotelportpatrick.com
2 changing beers (often Belhaven, Five Kingdoms, Sulwath) Ⓗ

Hotel overlooking the picturesque and historic harbour, with views on a clear day across to Ireland. The large, comfortable bar area at the front is adorned with fine pictures and ornaments, and warmed by an open fire. Two regularly changing ales are sourced from breweries across the UK, including the local Five Kingdoms brewery. Live music plays on Friday and Saturday nights. ♠❀❀◐&▲♣☕(367) ❀♠♪

Stranraer

Grapes ★
4-6 Bridge Street, DG9 7HY
☎ (01776) 703386
2 changing beers (often Bowness Bay, Coniston, Timothy Taylor) Ⓗ

Historic public bar, little altered in over 50 years. It has a comfortable snug bar downstairs, an upstairs Art Deco lounge/function room, and a sunny seated courtyard. Local musicians play in the public bar most Friday evenings, and touring American-style bands often perform in the public bar or upstairs. There is a strong commitment to real ales, often from Cumbria but also from all over the UK. Mini beer festivals are usually held annually. ♠❀&≈♣☕(500,358) ❀♠♪

Definitions

bivvy – beer
bumclink – inferior beer
bunker – beer
cooper – half stout, half porter
gatters – beer
shant of gatter – glass of beer
half and half – mixture of ale and porter, much favoured by medical students
humming – strong (as applied to drink)
ponge or pongelow – beer, half and half
purl – mixture of hot ale and sugar, with wormwood infused
rot-gut – bad
small beer shandy – gaffs ale and gingerbeer
shant – pot or quart (shant of bivvy – quart of beer)
swipes – soup or small beer
wobble-shop – shop where beer sold without a licence
J C Hotten, The Slang Dictionary, 1887

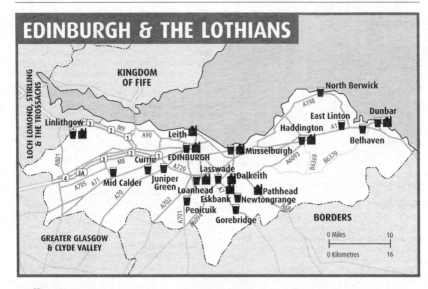

EDINBURGH & THE LOTHIANS

Belhaven

Brig & Barrel

8 High Street, EH42 1NP (1 mile W of Dunbar)
☎ (01368) 866847 ⊕ thebrigandbarrel.com
Harviestoun Schiehallion; 1 changing beer (sourced regionally; often Harviestoun) Ⓗ
A bright, comfortable bar overlooking the beer garden, with views to the Lammermuir Hills. It features a small horseshoe counter finished with reclaimed wood and barrels, a wooden floor, and a real fire. Meals are served all day in summer, and Friday to Sunday in winter. A children's menu and games are provided. The beer garden has heated booths as well as open tables. Local CAMRA Real Ale Quality Award runner-up in 2023. Likely to be closed Tuesday all year; not open until 4pm Monday to Wednesday in winter. Q❄️👪🍴◐🅰️▲�🚗♿🐾🎵

Currie

Riccarton Inn

198 Lanark Road West, EH14 5NX
☎ (0131) 449 2230 ⊕ riccartoninn.co.uk
4 changing beers (sourced regionally; often Broughton, Loch Leven, Stewart) Ⓗ
Originally a coaching inn, this pub has a long central bar with half-timbered walls and contemporary exposed stonework. There are attractive seating areas including booths next to the bar, and a separate restaurant area. Meals are served all day and include children's options. The decking at the front has southerly views to the Pentland Hills and there's a large beer garden at rear. Very handy for the Water of Leith walkway. ❄️👪🍴◐P🚗(44,45)🐾🛜

Dunbar

Volunteer Arms

17 Victoria Street, EH42 1HP (near swimming pool)
☎ (01368) 862278 ⊕ volunteerarmsdunbar.co.uk
2 changing beers (sourced regionally; often Cairngorm, Harviestoun, Stewart) Ⓗ
Close to Dunbar's harbour is this friendly traditional locals' pub. The cosy wood-panelled bar is decorated with lots of fishing- and lifeboat-oriented memorabilia, interesting photos, and a good selection of old pumpclip

badges on the ceiling. The upstairs restaurant offers an excellent, good-value menu, with an emphasis on seafood (all day except Wed and Thu). Food is also served downstairs. Families are welcome and a children's menu and games are provided.
Q❄️👪🍴◐▲🚲♣🚗🚗🐾🛜Ü🎵

East Linton

Crown & Kitchen

25-27 Bridge Street, EH40 3AG
☎ (01620) 860098 ⊕ crownandkitchen.com
1 changing beer (sourced regionally; often Fyne, Harviestoun, Stewart) Ⓗ
A long-established pub in the centre of a conservation village, with plain flooring and exposed stonework. The unusual features in the bar include 1940s engraved window screens depicting pub scenes, old Belhaven window adverts, and an impressive cabinet display of malt whiskies. The focus here is on good-quality food, which is served all day on Saturday and Sunday in the bar and restaurant. A menu, games and play area are all provided for children. It is unlikely to open before 3pm, with no food served on Monday and Tuesday.
❄️👪🍴◐🚲♿🚗🐾🛜

Edinburgh: Central

Abbotsford Bar & Restaurant ★

3-5 Rose Street, EH2 2PR
☎ (0131) 225 5276 ⊕ theabbotsford.com
Fyne Jarl Ⓗ/🅰️; **Timothy Taylor Landlord** 🅰️; **5 changing beers (sourced regionally; often Cromarty, Loch Lomond, Swannay)** Ⓗ/🅰️
This traditional Scottish bar features a magnificent island bar and gantry in dark mahogany that have been fixtures since 1902. The ornate plasterwork and corniced ceiling are outstanding. The room is predominantly furnished with large tables and wooden bench seating. There's an interesting selection of real ales served by handpump and tall fount. An extensive food menu is available all day in the bar and in the upstairs restaurant where ales can also be ordered, and where children over five are permitted.
Q❄️👪◐🚲≉(Waverley) ⏻(St Andrew Square) 🚗🐾🛜Ü

Black Cat

168 Rose Street, EH2 4BA
☎ (0131) 225 3349
2 changing beers (sourced regionally; often Bellfield, Harviestoun, Williams Bros) Ⓗ

A small, single-roomed bar, with pleasant modern styling including a wall-to-wall mirror. It is furnished with an eclectic range of tables, chairs and stools, including half-barrels and an upholstered banquette. It is a friendly, lively pub, especially when folk musicians arrive. Food is served all day. The two real ales, usually from smaller Scottish breweries, and an extensive range of malt whiskies may be sampled in taster 'flights'. Children are permitted until 8pm for hot meals. May be open till 3am during the Festival in August.
ॐ❀◑Ɽ(West End/Princes Street)🚌❀ 🛜 ♪

Bow Bar

80 West Bow, EH1 2HH (off Grassmarket)
☎ (0131) 226 7667 ⊕ thebowbar.co.uk
Cromarty Whiteout; Loch Lomond Silkie Stout; Stewart 80/-; 5 changing beers (sourced regionally; often Cromarty, Fyne, Swannay) Ⓐ

A classic one-roomed Scottish alehouse with seven traditional Scottish air pressure founts. The walls are festooned with original brewery mirrors and enamels from cigarette companies. The superb gantry features an award-winning selection of 400+ single malt whiskies and international bottled beers. The real ales tend to come from independent Scottish breweries. Beer festivals are held in January and July, along with frequent tap takeovers. Food is limited to gourmet pies, available 12-5pm. Children are not admitted.
Q≉(Waverley) Ɽ(Princes Street)🚌❀🛜Ʊ

Caley Picture House ✅

31 Lothian Road, EH1 2DJ (W edge of centre)
☎ (0131) 656 0752
Belhaven 80/-; Greene King Abbot; Sharp's Doom Bar; 9 changing beers (sourced nationally) Ⓗ

A stunning Wetherspoon renovation of a Grade B-listed former cinema, originally opened in 1923. The main bar has a superb screen-style backdrop, and is complemented by a smaller bar up in the 'gods', complete with plush, cinema-style seating. Meals are served all day and there is a children's menu. Be aware of the single-line queueing at the bar. Highly commended in the 2017 CAMRA Pub Design Awards. May open at 8am and serve alcoholic drinks from 9am (11am on Sun). ॐ◑⅋Ɽ(West End/Princes Street)🚌🛜

Guildford Arms ★

1 West Register Street, EH2 2AA (off E end of Princes St)
☎ (0131) 556 4312 ⊕ guildfordarms.com
Fyne Jarl; Loch Lomond Silkie Stout; Stewart Pentland IPA; Swannay Orkney IPA; Timothy Taylor Landlord; 5 changing beers (sourced nationally; often Campervan, Cromarty, Newbarns) Ⓗ

A large establishment built in the golden age of Victorian pub design. The high ceiling, cornices, friezes, window arches and screens are spectacular. There is a large standing area around the canopied bar, as well as extensive seating areas. The diverse range of real ales includes many from Scottish breweries. Meals and simple bar snacks are available all day, both downstairs and in the noteworthy upstairs gallery restaurant where children over five are permitted.
ॐ◑≉(Waverley) Ɽ(St Andrew Square)🚌❀🛜Ʊ

Halfway House

24 Fleshmarket Close, EH1 1BX (up steps opp Market St entrance to Waverley Station)
☎ (0131) 225 7101

4 changing beers (sourced regionally; often Alechemy, Broughton, Stewart) Ⓗ

A cosy, characterful bar hidden halfway down an Old Town close, decorated with railway memorabilia. The front of the small, often busy bar area has window seats, stools and tables. The rear area has more comfortable semi-circular booth seating where children over five may be permitted until 8pm if the pub is quiet. Heated pies, pasties and sausage rolls are available all day. The bar may stay open until 1am during busy times of year.
ॐ❀≉(Waverley) Ɽ(St Andrew Square)🚌❀🛜

Jolly Judge ♥

7 James Court, 493 Lawnmarket, EH1 2PB (in Old Town)
☎ (0131) 225 2831 ⊕ jollyjudge.co.uk
4 changing beers (sourced nationally; often Cromarty, Fyne, Tempest) Ⓗ

Comfortable small bar with an attractive painted ceiling hidden down a close just off the Royal Mile. Outdoor tables in the close provide extra seating. The real ales are usually from smaller UK-wide breweries, and sparklers are used occasionally. A varying selection of six ciders is also available. It is a welcome spot for refreshment after visiting the Old Town sights. Dogs are allowed inside, but no children. Local CAMRA Pub of the Year and Regional Cider Pub of the Year 2024.
Q❀❀(Waverley) Ɽ(Princes Street)🌶🚌❀🛜

Oxford Bar ★

8 Young Street, EH2 4JB (in New Town)
☎ (0131) 539 7119 ⊕ oxfordbar.co.uk
Fyne Jarl; 3 changing beers (sourced regionally; often Fyne Ales, Stewart) Ⓗ

A basic, busy drinking shop that is little changed since the late 19th century. The bar counter nearly fills the small front room but the side room is more spacious and is enhanced by a real fire and artworks for sale. The pub is renowned as a favourite of DI Rebus and his creator, Ian Rankin, and a haunt of many other famous and infamous characters over the years. Children are not admitted. A return tray is only used for Fyne Jarl.
QƗ(Princes Street)🚌❀🛜Ʊ

Ryrie's ★

1 Haymarket Terrace, EH12 5EY (1 mile W of centre)
☎ (0131) 337 0550 ⊕ ryries.bar
7 changing beers (sourced regionally; often Campervan, Loch Lomond, Tempest) Ⓗ

A classic Scottish bar in a listed building, tastefully refurbished in 2022, with a dark wooden interior, a fine gantry, and stained/leaded glass windows. It is popular with a varied clientele from the local community and

REAL ALE BREWERIES

Barney's Edinburgh
Belhaven Dunbar
Bellfield 🍂 Edinburgh
Campervan 🍂 Leith
Cross Borders 🍂 Eskbank
Hanging Bat 🍺 Edinburgh
Keller 🍺 Edinburgh
Kerr's Pathhead (NEW)
Moonwake 🍂 Leith
Newbarns 🍂 Leith
Newt Musselburgh
Otherworld Dalkeith
Pilot Edinburgh
Stewart 🍂 Loanhead
Strangers Linlithgow
Tartan Shark Edinburgh
Winton 🍂 Haddington

those using the adjacent station and gets busy when Heart of Midlothian FC are at home. An upstairs lounge is now a cocktail bar and there is a bar annexe down two steps. Traditional Scottish pub meals are served all day. Children are not admitted. ❀◑◗≠(Haymarket) ☷(Haymarket) ⬚❀≈↻

Standing Order ✪
62-66 George Street, EH2 2LR
☎ (0131) 225 4460
Belhaven 80/-; Greene King Abbot; Sharp's Doom Bar; 5 changing beers (sourced nationally; often Alechemy, Hadrian Border, Stewart) Ⓗ
Once the head Edinburgh office of the Union Bank, this Wetherspoon pub features a vast main bar with a superb high ceiling and polished granite pillars. There are three smaller rooms with tables for dining, one containing the old Chubb vault. Meals are served all day, and children are welcome in the family area until 8pm. It can be busy at peak times. May open at 8am; alcoholic drinks are served from 9am (11 on Sun).
Q✿❀◑◗&≈(Waverley) ☷(Princes Street) ●⬚≈

Edinburgh: East

Artisan
35 London Road, EH7 5BQ (1 mile E of centre)
☎ (0131) 661.1603 ⊕ theartisanbar.co.uk
3 changing beers (sourced regionally; often Bellfield, Fyne, Orkney) Ⓗ
Perched at the gable end of a terraced block of colony flats, this traditional bar has an ornate exterior, which features an eye-catching clock for a hanging sign. Two entrances lead into a spacious, wood-panelled room dominated by a large island bar and some fine mirrors. It is a friendly locals' pub, but though it can be busy when Hibernian FC are at home, it is normally relaxed. Several large screens show football, and the jukebox gets regular use. A separate function room is available for bookings. Children are not admitted. ❀❀❀≈↻

Bellfield Brewery Tap Room
46 Stanley Place, EH7 5TB (1 mile E of centre)
☎ (0131) 656 9390 ⊕ bellfieldbrewery.com
2 changing beers (often Bellfield)
The taproom is on the brewery site and tours and tastings are available. It has an excellent beer garden with covered booths. The cask ales are usually from Bellfield's standard range, but also occasional new pilot brews. All Bellfield ales are certified gluten-free. Food is available on a pop-up basis, with the choice changing every week. Children are welcome until 9pm. May be closed on Monday and Tuesday, and not open until 5pm Wednesday and Thursday and 2.30pm Friday.
✿❀◑&●⬚❀≈♪

Edinburgh: North

Dreadnought
72 North Fort Street, Leith, EH6 4HL (2 miles N of centre)
☎ 07876 351535 ⊕ dreadnoughtpub.com
4 changing beers (sourced nationally; often Brass Castle, Cromarty, Dark Revolution) Ⓗ
A welcoming one-roomed pub with big picture windows, a high ceiling with plaster cornicing, and an attractive old-fashioned bar gantry. A large photograph of HMS Dreadnought hangs on the wall along with other nautical items. The Brass Castle beers are all vegan and the cider is from Ascension. No food is prepared on-site, but pizza and burgers can be ordered from local outlets. Children are not admitted. May open at 4pm Monday to Thursday

afternoons and 2pm Friday to Sunday. Local CAMRA Pub of the Year runner-up in 2024.
❀◑☷(Newhaven) ♣●⬚❀≈♪

Henry Hall's Carriers Quarters ★
42 Bernard Street, Leith, EH6 6PR (2 miles N of centre)
☎ (0131) 554 4122 ⊕ carriersquarters.co.uk
2 changing beers (sourced regionally; often Fyne, Stewart) Ⓗ
This small, popular, cosy bar is said to be the oldest in the area. The front room contains the bar counter and has a small alcove with historical prints depicting life in Leith. The rear room has exposed stone walls and a large fireplace with a welcoming electric stove. The real ales are from Scottish breweries and there is a good selection of malt whiskies. Home-made pizzas are served all day. Children are not admitted. ◑☷(The Shore)♣●❀❀≈♪

Kay's Bar ✪
39 Jamaica Street West, EH3 6HF (off India St in New Town, ½ mile N of centre)
☎ (0131) 225 1858 ⊕ kaysbar.uk
Fyne Jarl; Theakston Best Bitter; Timothy Taylor Landlord; 3 changing beers (sourced regionally; often Loch Lomond, Stewart, Swannay) Ⓗ
A cosy and convivial pub that retains many features from its days as a Victorian wine merchant. Considering its relative compactness, it offers an impressive range of real ales and malt whiskies. If the front bar is busy, try the small room at the back. Meals are served lunchtimes Wednesday to Friday. Children are not admitted but dogs are allowed. Edinburgh winner of the CAMRA Real Ale Quality Award 2022. Q◑♣⬚❀≈↻

Old Eastway Tap
218 Easter Road, Leith, EH7 5QH (1 mile NE of centre)
☎ (0131) 259 3495 ⊕ crossborders.beer
Cross Borders Heavy; 3 changing beers (sourced nationally; often Cross Borders) Ⓗ
Cross Borders brewery's second pub was opened in 2021, with four cask and 16 craft keg lines, and was an instant hit with locals. The L-shaped bar is on a split level, and the decor is muted, with relatively low levels of lighting, to aid relaxation. Tap takeovers and meet the brewer events are held frequently. Meals consist of various types of hot dogs, mac 'n' cheese, and nachos. Children are not admitted. ❀◑☷(McDonald Road)♣●❀❀≈♪

Stockbridge Tap
2-4 Raeburn Place, Stockbridge, EH4 1HN (¾ mile N of centre)
☎ (0131) 343 3000
7 changing beers (sourced nationally; often Cromarty, Swannay) Ⓗ
A specialist real ale house offering unusual and interesting real ales from all over the UK and holding occasional beer festivals. The staff are keen and knowledgeable about the selection. The bright front area offers plenty of seating, and space for standing, while the rear has low tables and sofas. Both feature mirrors from lost breweries, including Murray's and Campbell's. A handy stop for those walking the Water of Leith path. Children are not admitted. &♣⬚❀≈

Teuchters Landing
1C Dock Place, Leith, EH6 6LU (2 miles N of centre)
☎ (0131) 554 7427 ⊕ teuchtersbar.co.uk
Caledonian Deuchars IPA; Fyne Jarl; Timothy Taylor Landlord; 1 changing beer (sourced regionally; often Black Isle, Orkney, Stewart) Ⓗ
Once the waiting room for the Leith to Aberdeen ferry, the pub features an attractive front bar with a wood-panelled ceiling edged with tiles featuring Scottish place

names from Teuchterland. There are two smaller rooms and a large conservatory that opens out on to a pontoon floating on the Water of Leith. The varied food menu is available all day. An excellent selection of malt whiskies is available. Children are permitted in the back rooms. May open at 10am; alcoholic drinks served from 11am. ⏰☆◑⅃⚠(Port of Leith) ♣♠🚐🍴🐾🤶

Edinburgh: South

Argyle Bar
15 Argyle Place, EH1 1JJ (1 mile S of centre)
☎ (0131) 221 9759
3 changing beers (sourced regionally; often Fyne, Harviestoun, Stewart) Ⓗ
Located on the ground floor of a corner tenement, this small pub has a loyal clientele drawn from locals and the transient student population. It comprises a single room on the ground floor and a basement room where various musical and other events are held. The bar has large windows overlooking the street and is furnished with comfortable banquette seating along two walls, central tables and chairs, and bar stools. The cask beer change regularly and are often from Scottish microbreweries. Food can be provided by arrangement. Children are not admitted. May not open until mid-afternoon. Card payments only. 🏮🚐🐾🤶♪

Bennets Bar ★
8 Leven Street, EH3 9LG (¾ mile SW of centre)
☎ (0131) 229 5143
Fyne Jarl Ⓐ; 3 changing beers (sourced regionally; often Orkney, Stewart) Ⓗ
A Grade B-listed building with a late-Victorian pub interior. Features include a magnificent gantry, Jeffrey's Brewery etched door panels, and a wonderful Bernard's mirror. A particularly unusual feature is the 'jug' bar, a small enclosed snug with a separate entrance and its own serving hatch. One of the four Aitken founts is still in use. The back-room bar (no real ale) offers a more modern environment with larger tables and can be hired. Food is available daily in both rooms. Live music weekly. ⏰🏮◑🍴🚐🐾🤶♪

Bennets of Morningside ✅
1 Maxwell Street, Morningside, EH10 5HT (1½ miles S of centre)
☎ (0131) 447 1903
Stewart Pentland IPA; Timothy Taylor Landlord; house beer (by Hadrian Border); 3 changing beers (sourced regionally; often Cromarty, Fyne, Loch Lomond) Ⓗ
A welcoming, traditional single-room tenement bar, popular with Morningside locals, with comfortable seating along three walls and a fine display of bottles behind the bar. Photographs of old Edinburgh and brewery mirrors adorn the walls and there is a stained-glass window at the back. Guest ales are mostly from Scotland while the permanent Bennets Ale is from Hadrian Border brewery in Gateshead. An outdoor drinking area is at the front. Children not admitted; dogs are welcome. 🏮♣♠🐾🤶

Cloisters Bar
26 Brougham Street, EH3 9JH (¾ miles SW of centre)
☎ (0131) 221 9997 ⊕ cloistersbar.com
Black Isle Yellowhammer; Cross Borders Heavy; Stewart Pentland IPA; 7 changing beers (sourced nationally; often Cromarty, Newbarns, Swannay) Ⓗ
Established in 1995 in the former All Saints Parsonage, this warm and friendly bar has retained many traditional features. The real ales are generally from interesting UK-wide breweries. Frequent tap takeovers and Meet the Brewer events are held. The wide range of single malt

whiskies, gins and rums does justice to the outstanding gantry. Meals are provided by Heavenly Scran, with a varied menu including vegan options and a roast on Sunday. Children under 16 are not admitted. Q◑⅃♣🚐🤶🎵♪

John Leslie ★
45-47 Ratcliffe Terrace, EH9 1SU (1½ miles S of centre)
☎ (0131) 667 7205
Timothy Taylor Landlord; house beer (by Hadrian Border); 2 changing beers (sourced nationally; often Stewart) Ⓗ
This superb tenement pub is divided in two by a fine mahogany counter, a gantry with a clock, and a mirrored snob screen with small 'ticket window' hatches. The bar has an alcove with banquettes, while the lounge has three areas: a small snug by the door, an area around the fire, and a quieter back area with banquette seating. The elaborate late 19th-century decorative plaster work includes a Lincrusta frieze. Children over two are permitted until 9pm. ⏰🏮🐾🤶🎵♪

Edinburgh: West

Athletic Arms (Diggers) ★ ✅
1-3 Angle Park Terrace, EH11 2JX (1½ miles SW of centre)
☎ (0131) 259 9948
Caledonian Deuchars IPA; house beer (by Stewart) Ⓗ; **4 changing beers (sourced nationally; often Fyne, Stewart, Timothy Taylor)** Ⓐ
Dating from 1897, this legendary Edinburgh pub gained the name Diggers due to its location between two graveyards. Banquette seating lines the walls and the wooden floor features a compass drawing. Two smaller back rooms, where children are permitted until 9pm if eating, have further seating and the larger has a dartboard. The gantry is graced by over 700 malt whiskies. The pub is busy when Hearts are playing at nearby Tynecastle. Return trays (Autovacs) are only used with the tall founts. The pies are outstanding. ⏰◑♣🚐🤶🎵🤶

Roseburn Bar ★ ✅
1 Roseburn Terrace, EH12 5NG (1½ miles W of centre)
☎ (0131) 337 1067 ⊕ roseburnbar.co.uk
Fyne Jarl; Stewart Pentland IPA; 1 changing beer (sourced regionally; often Cromarty) Ⓗ
A traditional pub, popular with local, and close to Murrayfield (for rugby) and Tynecastle (for football). It boasts high ceilings and a largely wooden interior, with interesting mirrors and period photos on the walls. There are numerous comfortable booths along the walls and two separate lounge areas. Multiple TVs show sporting events, though the volume is typically kept low. Pies and toasties are available. Live music plays on Friday and Saturday evenings. Children are not admitted. ♿⚠(Murrayfield Stadium) 🚐🤶🎵♪

Gorebridge

Stobsmill Inn (Bruntons)
25 Powdermill Brae, EH23 4HX (⅓ mile S of centre)
☎ (01875) 820202 ⊕ stobsmill.co.uk
1 changing beer (often Born, Loch Lomond, Stewart) Ⓗ
This small pub is now the only one in Gorebridge. The single-room bar has a long, L-shaped counter with bar stools, and an area with tables and chairs, benches and a large clock. The decor and skylight help to create a bright and welcoming interior. There is another attractive seating area, and downstairs is the Brunton Restaurant.

Food is served all day Thursday to Sunday. Entry is restricted to over-21s, unless dining. May be closed on Tuesday and Wednesday; opens at 5pm Monday. ⛄🐕🚬🐈☀🅿🏵(29,48) ✿🎵

Haddington

Golf Tavern

5 Bridge St., EH41 4AU
☎ (01620) 822327 ⊕ golftavernhaddington.co.uk
Hop Back Summer Lightning ⊞
A traditional locals' pub nestling behind the Waterside Bistro on the eastern side of the River Tyne, where a footbridge gives direct access to the town. The bar, with jugs, bottles and mirrors adorning the walls, has a horseshoe counter, pool table and a dartboard. The spacious lounge acts mainly as a popular restaurant and function room. Food is served all day on Saturdays and until 7pm on Sundays, with children's options available. The pub is renowned for its generous portions.
⛄🏵🍴🐕☀🅿🏵

Juniper Green

Kinleith Mill

604 Lanark Road, EH14 5EN
☎ (0131) 453 3214 ⊕ kinleithmill.com
Timothy Taylor Landlord; 2 changing beers (sourced regionally; often Fyne, Loch Leven, Stewart) ⊞
This well-maintained pub has a friendly atmosphere and welcomes locals and visitors alike. The large room is decorated with old village pictures and has an island bar counter separating the public bar and the lounge/dining areas. Meals are served all day and the menu offers children's options and monthly specials. A full range of sports is shown on TVs. Dogs are welcome but only allowed in the non-carpeted areas. The rear beer garden has fake grass and a part-covered decked area.
⛄🏵🍴🅿🏵(44,45) ✿🏵

Lasswade

Laird & Dog Inn ✓

5 High Street, EH18 1NA (A768, near river)
☎ (0131) 663 9219 ⊕ lairdanddoginn.co.uk
2 changing beers (sourced regionally; often Fyne, Harviestoun, Stewart) ⊞
Comfortable village local, just five miles from central Edinburgh. It has different areas for either a drink or a meal, furnished with a mixture of banquette seating and chairs. The walls are decorated with old photographs. There is also a conservatory restaurant with an unusual bottle-shaped well by the entrance and a mural explaining the origin of the village name. Meals are served all day and include children's options. May open at 7am; alcoholic drinks are served from 11am
⛄🏵🍴🐕☀🅿🏵✿🕐🎵

Linlithgow

Four Marys ▼ ✓

65-67 High Street, EH49 7ED
☎ (01506) 842171
Caledonian Deuchars IPA; house beer (by Greene King); 6 changing beers (sourced nationally; often Cromarty, Fyne, Orkney) ⊞
Close to Linlithgow Palace, birthplace of Mary Queen of Scots, the building dates back to around 1500 and is named after Mary's four ladies-in-waiting. Initially a dwelling house, the building has had several changes of use over the centuries – it was once a chemists run by the Waldie family whose most famous member, David,

helped establish the anaesthetic properties of chloroform in 1847. The pub serves good-quality food and an ever-changing range of real ales from Scottish and English breweries. Q⛄🏵🍴🐕🚬🅿🏵✿🎵

Platform 3 ✓

1A High Street, EH49 7AB
☎ (01506) 847405 ⊕ platform3.co.uk
Stewart Pentland IPA; 2 changing beers (sourced regionally; often Fyne, Stewart) ⊞
This friendly hostelry on the railway station approach has appeared in the Guide for over 20 consecutive years. It was originally the public bar of the hotel next door, before being renovated in 1998 as a pub in its own right. Look out for the miniature goods train that travels from the station above the bar, with ducks waiting for a train that never arrives. Two Scottish beers are served in addition to the regular ale. Dogs are welcomed with biscuits and water. A live train departures board keeps travellers informed. 🚬🐕🅿🏵✿🎵

Loanhead

Stewart Brewing Tap Room & Shop

26A Dryden Road, Bilston Glen Industrial Estate, EH20 9LZ (SE edge of industrial estate)
☎ (0131) 440 2442 ⊕ stewartbrewing.co.uk
2 changing beers (often Stewart)
This family-friendly taproom is open Wednesday and Thursday evenings and all day Friday to Sunday. It has two handpumps for real ales, lots of keg taps, and provides food in the form of freshly cooked pizzas. Beers are served in ⅓ or ⅔ sized measures. The shop is open during daytime hours and sells bottle- and can-conditioned beers and mini-casks. There is also an 18-tap growler station selling keg/tank beers which can be drunk in the shop or outdoor area. ⛄🏵🍴🐕🅿🏵🏵✿🏵

Mid Calder

Black Bull ★ ✓

Market Street, EH53 0AA
☎ (01506) 882170 ⊕ blackbullmidcalder.co.uk
3 changing beers (sourced regionally; often Stewart) ⊞
Established in 1747, this pub is at the heart of the community. It has a fine, old L-shaped public bar with wooden decor and a coal fire. There is also a comfortable open-plan lounge where food is served all day and families are welcome. Both rooms are decorated with country photos and prints. The changing real ales are chosen by customers. The public bar is only open from 3pm Friday and all day Saturday and Sunday.
⛄🏵🍴🐕🏵✿🏵

Musselburgh

David MacBeth Moir ✓

Bridge Street, EH21 6AG (opp The Brunton)
☎ (0131) 653 1060
Belhaven 80/-; Greene King Abbot; Sharp's Doom Bar; 2 changing beers (sourced nationally; often Broughton, Marston's, Williams Bros) ⊞
Wetherspoon pub converted from a 1930s cinema and named after a local physician and writer. Many original features have been beautifully restored, and the vast, single-roomed bar has Art Deco styling and artefacts from its cinematic past. There is a long bar counter with a good mix of real ales. Food is served all day. May open at 8am; alcoholic drinks served from 11am (12.30 Sun). Q⛄🏵🍴🏵✿

Levenhall Arms ★

10 Ravensheugh Road, EH21 7PP (B1348, 1 mile E of centre)

☎ (0131) 665 3220

Winton Peelywally; 1 changing beer (sourced regionally; often Born, Loch Leven) Ⓗ/Ⓐ

A friendly three-roomed hostelry dating from 1830 and close to the racecourse. The lively public bar is half-timber panelled with a wood effect floor. Dominoes is regularly played and the TV often shows sporting events. A smaller area leads off, with a dartboard and pictures of old local industries. The pleasant lounge, where families are welcome until 8pm, has comfortable seating and a second dartboard that is used for matches. No food is served. ⠿❀♿A♣P🚫❀🛜♪

Volunteer Arms (Staggs) ▽ ★

81 North High Street, EH21 6JE (behind the Brunton)

☎ (0131) 665 9654

Fyne Jarl; Oakham JHB, Citra, Bishops Farewell; 3 changing beers (sourced nationally; often Fyne Ales, Two by Two, Vocation) Ⓗ

Superb pub run by the same family since 1858. Its bar and snug are traditional, with wooden floors, wood panelling, mirrors from defunct local breweries, and an attractive gantry topped with old casks. The more modern lounge opens at the weekend. Real ales are mostly pale and hoppy but there is often a dark one, especially in winter. Children are permitted until 7.30pm in the lounge and snug. Local CAMRA Pub of the Year 2024, and winner of many previous awards.
⠿❀♣🚫❀🛜U

Newtongrange

Dean Tavern ★

80 Main Street, EH22 4NA

☎ (0131) 663 2419 ⊕ deantavern.co.uk

2 changing beers (sourced regionally; often Born, Loch Lomond, Stewart) Ⓗ

Excellent pub owned by the community and run on Gothenburg principles, with profits returned to local organisations. The spacious bar was designed to help miners recover from their day in darkness, with roof lights in a high ceiling supported by arched iron beams. There is also the Lamp Room restaurant and a function room with a large mural depicting the town's mining past. Meals are available all day (not Tue). Children are welcome until 8pm if dining. Local CAMRA Pub of the Year 2024 runner-up. ⠿❀◑♿A≒♣🚫❀🛜♪

North Berwick

Auld Hoose

19 Forth Street, EH39 4HX (N edge of centre)

☎ (01620) 892692 ⊕ auldhoosenorthberwick.co.uk

Greene King Abbot; Timothy Taylor Landlord; 1 changing beer (sourced regionally; often Broughton, Spey Valley, Williams Bros) Ⓗ

Built in 1896 and said to be the oldest pub in town, this friendly, traditional, high-ceilinged Scottish drinking shop has been tastefully updated. The bar has bare floorboards around a mahogany bar, carpeted areas, and a welcoming atmosphere enhanced by a real fire in winter. The gantry has four carved pillars and supports six old numbered whisky casks. The lounge, where children are permitted until 8pm, has varied seating, a pool table and pictures of sporting heroes. ⠿≒♣🚫❀🛜♪

Nether Abbey Hotel

20 Dirleton Avenue, EH39 4BQ (A198, ¾ mile W of centre)

☎ (01620) 892802 ⊕ netherabbey.co.uk

4 changing beers (sourced regionally; often Alechemy, Stewart, Williams Bros) Ⓗ

Family-run hotel in a stone-built villa with a bright, contemporary, open-plan interior. The Fly Half Bar is in a split-level glass extension, with large folding doors opening out onto an attractive patio. Real ales can be served without sparklers on request. The award-winning restaurant is famed for its freshly cooked food, available all day throughout the week (not Mon lunch). Well-behaved children are welcome until 8pm (7pm in the bar). ⠿❀📻◑♿A≒P🚫(124,X5)❀🛜♪

Ship Inn

7-9 Quality Street, EH39 4HJ (E edge of centre)

☎ (01620) 890699 ⊕ theshipinnnorthberwick.com

Fyne Jarl; 2 changing beers (sourced nationally; often Bellfield, Greene King, Stewart) Ⓗ

Friendly, spacious, often lively venue with an open-plan bar and a wide variety of seating and tables. The bar area has pine floorboards and a tastefully modernised bar and gantry. To the side and rear is a quiet, carpeted area (dogs not allowed) featuring maritime-themed artwork. It is popular for food, which is served all day until 8pm. There is a suntrap rear patio garden. ⠿❀📻◑🚫❀🛜♪

Penicuik

Navaar House Hotel

23 Bog Road, EH26 9BY (¼ mile W of centre)

☎ (01968) 672683 ⊕ navaarhouse.co.uk

Fyne Jarl; 1 changing beer (often Stewart) Ⓗ

A lively pub with a strong community spirit. The large bar is open plan, with a log/coal stove, TV screens and a pool table. A bistro serves locally sourced food at lunchtimes and evenings, and all day on Saturday and Sunday. Children are permitted in the restaurant only, which serves a dedicated menu for them. There is a small lounge by the bistro and pleasant beer garden. The bar opens at 3pm Monday to Friday but real ale can be enjoyed in the bistro and lounge before then. ⠿❀📻◑♣P🚫❀🛜

Return trays

Also known as an Autovac or beer economiser, a return tray is a device that collects beer spilled in the pouring process, recycles it by mixing it with fresh beer, and returns it to the glass. It can be identified by a stainless steel drip tray below the nozzle on a handpump, with a pipe connected from the bottom of the tray to the draw line of the cask. They are commonly found in use in Yorkshire and parts of south-east Scotland and have been seen in north-east Scotland and north-west England. A symbol will appear next to entries in the Guide where a return tray is in use on some or all of the beers (see inside cover key).

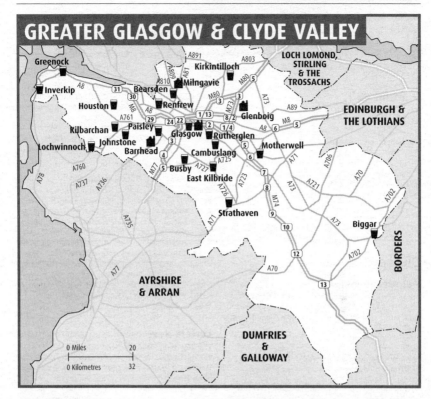

GREATER GLASGOW & CLYDE VALLEY

SCOTLAND

Bearsden

Burnbrae ✓

281 Milngavie Road, G61 3DQ

☎ (0141) 942 5951

6 changing beers (sourced nationally; often Greene King) Ⓗ

The Burnbrae is a popular eating place with room for drinkers at the bar and in the front room. There are four handpumps serving a Greene King regular supplemented by a range of beers, at least one from a Scottish brewery such as Fyne Ales or Kelburn. A visit to the pub can be combined with a stroll along the Allander Water or a visit to the Roman bath house in Bearsden, which is 15-minute walk away. ⚫✿❶&🄿🚯(60A,B10)🐾🛜

Biggar

Crown Inn

109-111 High Street, ML12 6DL

☎ (01899) 220116 🌐 thecrownbiggar.co.uk

6 changing beers (sourced nationally; often Belhaven, Morland) Ⓗ

This pleasant and friendly inn, in the centre of Biggar, has hundreds of years of tradition behind it, officially dating from the mid-17th century. The bar area is directly accessed from the street and there is a small, quiet room, conservatory and beer garden to the rear. Real ales are mainly from the Greene King stable and can be served in flights of three third-pints. ⚫✿❶🚯(91,101)🐾🛜🎵

Busby

White Cart Pub & Grill ✓

61 East Kilbride Road, G76 8HX

☎ (0141) 644 2711

Greene King IPA, Abbot; 2 changing beers (sourced nationally) Ⓗ

Located in the Busby Conservation Village, this lively Greene King pub has bright and spacious bar and large restaurant area. The extensive outdoor patio area at the front is used as a beer garden and restaurant and is popular in summer. There is also an area for families inside. An added bonus are the roaring fires in winter. ⚫✿❶&⇌🄿🚯🐾🛜

Cambuslang

John Fairweather ✓

52-58 Main Street, G72 7EP

☎ (0141) 646 2411

Belhaven 80/-; Greene King Abbot; Sharp's Doom Bar; 3 changing beers (sourced nationally) Ⓗ

An impressive Wetherspoon conversion of the former Savoy cinema and named after the man who designed it. Many original features have been restored, including seats that fold up when you stand, and the former stalls are watched over by models of movie-goers sitting in the balcony. At the back, past the dartboard, is an upstairs lounge leading to the beer garden. ✿❶&⇌♣🚯🛜

East Kilbride

Hay Stook ✓

26-36 Princes Avenue, G74 1JU (at the Brouster Gate entrance to shopping centre)

☎ (01355) 244323

Belhaven 80/-; Greene King Abbot; Sharp's Doom Bar; 3 changing beers (sourced nationally) Ⓗ

A Wetherspoon pub housed within Scotland's largest covered shopping mall. The pub is popular with shoppers and handy for the cinema complex, and is a short walk

587

from the bus station. Bare walls and a wooden ceiling give it a rustic air. The staircase up to the toilets neatly divides the pub between the family area to the left and the bar to the right. There is a beer garden beside the mall entrance which is popular with smokers.
🛏🟤🍴👥&≠�🔔

Hudsons ✓
14-16 Cornwall Way, G74 1JR
☎ (01355) 581040
3 changing beers (sourced regionally; often Alechemy, Loch Lomond) Ⓗ
Busy town-centre pub just outside the bus station and next to the town's main shopping centre. There is a narrow, elliptical-shaped bar, with couch-like seating down both sides. At the front there are chairs and a ledge by the windows, enabling customers to look out for the arrival of their buses. Bingo sessions are held every week, live music on Thursdays, and a DJ at the weekend. Despite being in the town centre it has the feel of a local community pub. &≠🚺👕🔔 ♪

Glasgow

Babbity Bowster
16-18 Blackfriars Street, Merchant City, G1 1PE
☎ (0141) 552 5055 ⊕ babbitybowster.com
Fyne Jarl; 2 changing beers (sourced nationally; often Kelburn, Spey Valley) Ⓗ
This unique pub-restaurant-hotel has a well-earned reputation for good beer, wine and food. Three cask beers are sold, usually from Scottish breweries. The downstairs bar generally has a low-key ambience, except on Wednesday and Saturday afternoons when lively traditional music plays. There is also jazz on the second Sunday of the month. The pub has a fair-sized beer garden for the odd sunny day.
🟤🍴🍴(High Street) 🚇(St Enoch) P🚌(CB4) 🔔 ♪

Ben Nevis
1147 Argyle Street, Finnieston, G3 8TB
☎ (0141) 576 5204 ⊕ thebennevisbar.com
2 changing beers (sourced nationally; often Fyne) Ⓗ
A corner tenement pub established around 1880. It was closed for a while, but reopened in 1999 as a rustic, Highland-themed bar with a large selection of malt whiskies, some of which appear to be precariously perched on sloping shelves. There is also a range of unusual canned and bottled beers. Ales are chosen from a wide range of breweries, normally at least one of which is Scottish. There is live folk music on Wednesday, Thursday and Sunday evenings.
🛏🟤≠(Exhibition Centre) 🚌👕🔔 ♪

Bon Accord
153 North Street, Charing Cross, G3 7DA
☎ (0141) 248 4427 ⊕ bonaccordpub.com
8 changing beers (sourced nationally; often Fyne Ales, Kelburn, Loch Lomond) Ⓗ
The Bon Accord has been at the forefront of the Glasgow real ale scene for over half a century and the tradition continues. Eight handpumps serve beer from all over the UK, often featuring local ales from lesser-known Scottish breweries. The pub has an impressive collection of malt whiskies and regularly hosts a whisky club on Tuesday evenings. A quiz night is on Wednesdays. Cider is often available, and good-value meals are served every day.
🛏🟤🍴&≠(Charing Cross) 🚇(St George's Cross) 🚌🔔 ♪

Counting House ✓
2 St Vincent Place, City Centre, G1 2DH
☎ (0141) 225 0160

Belhaven 80/-; Greene King Abbot; Sharp's Doom Bar; 5 changing beers (sourced nationally; often Stewart) Ⓗ
A busy Wetherspoon pub with an outside drinking area on George Square. It has up to eight cask ales, mainly featuring Scottish breweries. Designed as the Bank of Scotland's head Glasgow office by J T Rochead, it features sculptures by William Mossman, and an impressive collection of paintings, drawings and photographs are displayed throughout. A bottle store in an old strong room has a good range of bottles and canned beers.
🛏🟤&≠(Queen St) 🚇(Buchanan Street) 🚌🔔

Crystal Palace ✓
36 Jamaica Street, City Centre, G1 4QD
☎ (0141) 221 2624
Belhaven 80/-; Greene King Abbot; Sharp's Doom Bar; 6 changing beers (sourced nationally) Ⓗ
Inspired by London's Crystal Palace, this Wetherspoon pub is in a Victorian iron-framed former furniture house, close to Central Station. The large high windows give the pub a fresh, light feel during the daytime. There are two large bars, one on each floor, offering different guest beers. The original lift remains operational and serves all floors. Behind the lift on the ground floor is a more secluded area, making conversation easier.
🛏🟤🍴&≠(Central) 🚇(St Enoch) 🚌🔔

Curlers Rest
256-260 Byres Road, Hillhead, G12 8SH
☎ (0141) 341 0737
Stewart 80/-; house beer (by St Austell); 3 changing beers (sourced nationally; often Orkney) Ⓗ
Taking its name from a local curling pond, this quirky, West-End Nicholson's pub was originally a conversion from two 18th-century cottages. The large open-plan space is spread over two floors. The house beer is complemented by a range of Scottish and English real ales and a selection of world beers. There is a more limited range served in the upstairs bar, which has an open fire. There are three function rooms available for private parties. 🛏🟤🍴&🚇(Hillhead)🚌(8,90)👕🔔 ♪

Doublet
74 Park Road, Woodlands, G4 9JF
☎ (0141) 334 1982
3 changing beers (sourced regionally; often Alechemy, Orkney) Ⓗ
Corner tenement pub in a mock-Tudor style that opened its doors in 1961. The small, friendly locals' bar offers real ales from Scottish breweries and the opportunity for a good conversation. In addition, there is a range of bottled beers and a distinctive lager. The small lounge up the stairs to the rear is usually closed at quiet times, but it is available for large functions, and is often used as a music venue. 🟤🚇(Kelvinbridge)🚌👕🔔 ♪

REAL ALE BREWERIES
Dookit Glasgow
Drygate 🍺 Glasgow
Epochal Glasgow
Glasgow Beer Works Glasgow
Jaw 🍺 Milngavie (brewing suspended)
Kelburn Barrhead
Outlandish Glenboig
Overtone Glasgow
Shilling Glasgow
Simple Things Fermentations Glasgow
Up Front Glasgow
WEST 🍺 Glasgow

Drum & Monkey

91 St Vincent Street, City Centre, G2 5TF
☎ (0141) 221 6636
**St Austell Nicholson's Pale Ale; 6 changing beers
(sourced nationally; often Stewart)** Ⓗ

A corner pub, housed in a former American-style bank, with an opulent marble and wood-panelled interior and ornate ceilings. Convenient for both main railway stations and numerous bus routes, it is usually busy with a varied clientele. Families are allowed for dining and are welcome until 8pm. The large P-shaped central bar features seven handpumps offering a wide variety of different styles from well-known local and national favourites as well as new breweries.
🚲🕓🛇≉(Central) ᗡ(Buchanan Street) 🚌👹🛜🎵

Hengler's Circus

351-363 Sauchiehall Street, Charing Cross, G2 3HU
☎ (0141) 331 9810
**Caledonian Deuchars IPA; Greene King Abbot; Sharp's
Doom Bar; 7 changing beers (sourced nationally;
often Broughton)** Ⓗ

A Wetherspoon pub named after the indoor circus that used to be on the other side of Sauchiehall Street, closer to Charing Cross. It is an L-shaped pub, with the bar down both sides, and a family area to the right of the entrance. It is popular during the week with students and office workers, and busy at weekends. The pub is handy for the King's Theatre and other attractions.
Q🚲🕓🛇≉(Charing Cross) ᗡ(Cowcaddens) 🚌🛜

Horse Shoe ★

17-19 Drury Street, City Centre, G2 5AE
☎ (0141) 248 6368 ⊕ thehorseshoebarglasgow.co.uk
**4 changing beers (sourced nationally; often Stewart,
Timothy Taylor)** Ⓗ

Dating from 1870, this Victorian pub has been identified by CAMRA as having a nationally important historic pub interior. It also boasts Scotland's longest bar. The real ales are sourced from a wide selection of breweries. The pub is close to Central Station and the main bus routes, and can be busy in the evenings and at weekends. Above the bar there is a lounge/diner where children are welcome until the evenings, when karaoke often takes over. Sports TV is screened.
🚲🕓≉(Central) ᗡ(Buchanan Street) 🚌🛜

Koelschip Yard

686-688 Pollokshaws Road, Strathbungo, G41 2QB
☎ (0141) 423 2945 ⊕ koelschipyard.beer
**2 changing beers (sourced nationally; often
Newbarns, Thornbridge)** Ⓗ

Cosy beer lovers' bar in the south side of the city. Up to two real ales are available, from breweries throughout the UK. Scottish micros also feature regularly, making this a rare outlet for cask Dookit, Newbarns and Simple Things Fermentations. There are also 14 keg taps, ranging from Czech lagers to imperial stouts and IPAs. The impressive can and bottle list includes saisons and lambics. Occasional Meet the Brewer evenings are held. Card payment only. ≉(Queens Park)🚌👹🛜

Laurieston Bar ★

58 Bridge Street, Tradeston, G5 9HU
☎ (0141) 429 4528
**Fyne Jarl; 2 changing beers (sourced locally; often
Fyne)** Ⓗ

Friendly, unpretentious bar that is unchanged since the 1960s. The ales are found in the public bar, but can also be ordered at the counter in the lounge. It is popular with ale drinkers, gig-goers to the nearby Academy, and sub crawlers endeavouring to visit the closest pub to each subway station. The atmosphere is always convivial,

thanks to the excellent service. You may recognise the interior, which has appeared in films and TV shows. Cash only. ≉(Central)ᗡ(Bridge Street)🚌👹🛜

Lismore

206 Dumbarton Road, Partick, G11 6UN
☎ (0141) 576 0102
**1 changing beer (sourced regionally; often Brass
Castle, Broughton)** Ⓗ

There is a strong Highland connection in this split-level pub whose decor gives it an old-fashioned feel. The pub name is spelt in Gaelic by the side entrance, while stained-glass windows by local artists portray scenes from the infamous clearances, with the urinals dedicated to the Duke of Sutherland and other perpetrators. The cask ales can be found in the front bar along with a large selection of malt whiskies. Regular folk sessions are featured. ≉(Partick)ᗡ(Kelvinhall)🚌🛜🎵

Pot Still

154 Hope Street, City Centre, G2 2TH
☎ (0141) 333 0980 ⊕ thepotstill.co.uk
**4 changing beers (sourced regionally; often Kelburn,
Loch Leven, Orkney)** Ⓐ

This busy city-centre pub offers four Scottish beers served from tall founts. It has an impressive gantry accommodating a vast collection of malt whiskies. Visitors from all over the world are usually in attendance to sample the whisky, and tastings are held regularly. Food in the form of pies is available during the day. Due to its location and popularity, the bar is often packed, but it has a real, traditional pub atmosphere that is becoming all too rare. 🚲🕓≉(Central)ᗡ(Buchanan Street)🚌👹🛜

Scotia Bar ★

112-114 Stockwell Street, City Centre, G1 4LW
☎ (0141) 552 8681
**4 changing beers (sourced regionally; often
Broughton, Cromarty, Orkney)** Ⓗ

One of the oldest pubs in Glasgow, the Scotia Bar certainly looks the part with its half-timbered frontage, wood panelling, dark wooden benches and low ceilings. It has been a firm fixture on the folk music scene – the likes of Hamish Imlach and Billy Connolly performed here – and there are still regular sessions. Most of the seating is close to the L- shaped bar, and there is also a cosy snug. Beers are predominantly from Scottish breweries. Food consists of soup and pizza.
🕓≉(Argyle St) ᗡ(St Enoch) 🍴🚌👹🛜🎵

Sir John Moore ⊘

260-292 Argyle Street, City Centre, G2 8QW
☎ (0141) 222 1780
**Belhaven 80/-; Greene King Abbot; Sharp's Doom
Bar; 5 changing beers (sourced nationally)** Ⓗ

A Wetherspoon pub across the road from Glasgow Central Station's (lower level) Hope Street exit. It opens early and is handy for breakfast after a night on the sleeper. Converted from several shops into one very large room, it has several distinct areas marked with screens and a licensed pavement area. The pub takes its name from a Glasgow-born general whose likeness was cast from brass cannons to become the first statue to be unveiled in George Square in 1819.
🚲👹🕓🛇≉(Central) ᗡ(St Enoch) 🚌🛜

Society Room ⊘

151 West George Street, City Centre, G2 2JJ
☎ (0141) 229 7560
**Belhaven 80/-; Greene King Abbot; Sharp's Doom
Bar; 3 changing beers (sourced nationally; often
Stewart)** Ⓗ

The city's only Lloyd's No. 1 bar. The room's low ceiling and lack of windows at the back give it a cavernous feel. During the day, it is much like any other Wetherspoon, serving office workers and the retired community. In the evening it attracts a younger clientele and music plays from 8pm. There is a DJ from 9pm at weekends. Handpumps for the regular ales are situated near the entrance and the guests are towards the rear. ⛲❀◑Ġ⇌(Central) 🚇(Buchanan Street) 🚲🛜

State Bar

148 Holland Street, Charing Cross, G2 4NG
☎ (0141) 332 2159
Oakham Citra; house beer (by Stewart); 5 changing beers (sourced nationally; often Almasty, Oakham, Two by Two) Ⓗ
A regular local CAMRA award winner, this city-centre pub just off Sauchiehall Street is handy for restaurants and entertainment venues and gets busy at weekends. It has a traditional island bar, serving an ale choice that often includes unfined beers and strongly hopped beers rarely seen in Glasgow. Old pictures and showbills displayed around the walls reflect the pub's proximity to the King's Theatre. There are blues sessions on alternate Tuesdays. Ġ⇌(Charing Cross) 🚇(Cowcaddens) 🚲❀🛜ᶸ♪

Tennent's

191 Byres Road, Hillhead, G12 8TN
☎ (0141) 339 7203 ⊕ thetennentsbarglasgow.co.uk
7 changing beers (sourced nationally; often Draught Bass, Stewart, Titanic) Ⓗ
One of Glasgow's oldest pubs, dating from 1884, which still retains some of its Victorian finery, with tall columns supporting the high ceilings. The pub is on the West End's main street, close to Glasgow University, and is often busy. With its wide selection of real ales, this pub has been listed in the Guide for over 25 years. Food is served all day and sports are shown on several large TVs. There is a separate bar downstairs for live music and functions. ❀◑Ġ🚇(Hillhead) 🚲❀🛜♪

Three Craws

501 Crow Road, Jordanhill, G11 7DN
☎ (0141) 950 4518
Dark Star Hophead; 3 changing beers (sourced nationally; often Black Sheep, Titanic) Ⓗ
Modern open-plan bar and restaurant in a mainly residential part of Glasgow. Though there is a strong emphasis on food, an area near the bar and open fire is available for those just wanting a drink. The three or four beers come from various large and small breweries around the UK, and are available at a good price on Monday to Wednesday evenings at the Cask Beer Club. There is a quiz on Tuesday evenings. ⛲❀◑Ġ⇌(Jordanhill) P🚲🛜

Three Judges ✔

141 Dumbarton Road, Partick, G11 6PR
☎ (0141) 337 3055
9 changing beers (sourced nationally; often Fyne, Kelburn, Loch Leven) Ⓗ
For over 30 years this traditional corner pub has brought the best new real ales to Glasgow from all over the UK. A wide choice of real ales is supplemented with an ever-changing selection of three ciders (one on handpump, two bag in box) although these might not be real. Numerous local CAMRA awards adorn the walls. There is a quiz on Mondays and there are monthly jazz sessions on Sunday afternoons. No food is served but you can bring your own. ⇌(Partick) 🚇(Kelvinhall)❀🚲❀🛜♪

Greenock

James Watt ✔

80-92 Cathcart Street, PA15 1DD
☎ (01475) 722640
Greene King Abbot; Sharp's Doom Bar; 4 changing beers Ⓗ
Opposite Greenock Central Station and 200 yards from the bus station, this large open-plan Wetherspoon, in a former post office, is named after Greenock's most famous son. The chain's standard value-for-money food is available all day and beer festivals are hosted at various times throughout the year. This pub is a real ale oasis in a beer desert. ◑Ġ⇌(Central)🛜

Houston

Fox & Hounds Ⓛ

South Street, PA6 7EN
☎ (01505) 808604 ⊕ foxandhoundshouston.co.uk
Timothy Taylor Landlord; 4 changing beers (sourced nationally; often Fuller's, Fyne, Kelburn) Ⓗ
Excellent traditional village pub established in 1779, consisting of a bar, lounge and restaurant downstairs and a cocktail bar upstairs. The downstairs bar has five handpumps and an excellent selection of spirits, including around 130 whiskies, plus a selection of canned and bottled craft beers. Gastropub food made wholly on the premises is served throughout. An annual beer and music festival is held on the late May bank holiday weekend. There is a pool table upstairs and board games night is every Wednesday. Q⛲❀◑Ġ♣P🚲❀🛜

Inverkip

Inverkip Hotel

Main Street, PA16 0AS
☎ (01475) 521478 ⊕ inverkip.co.uk
Fyne Jarl Ⓗ
Small, family-run hotel located in the heart of a conservation village and just a short walk from the large Inverkip Marina. It is an ideal staging post for those just messing about on the river or passing through on the way to Largs and the Ayrshire coast. Food options range from snacks up to fine dining. The all-ticket 'Battle of The Brewer' nights are popular. ❀🛏◑⇌P🚲(578,580)🛜

Johnstone

Callum's Ⓛ

26 High Street, PA5 8AH
☎ (01505) 322925
3 changing beers Ⓗ
Popular town-centre pub in a real-ale desert, offering a friendly welcome, a comfortable atmosphere and three changing ales. Two large but unobtrusive TV screens feature major sporting events. A side lounge allows for some relaxation away from the main bar area. There are occasional events throughout the year, including live music and quiz nights. ⛲Ġ⇌🚲(36,38)🛜♪

Kilbarchan

Habbies Bar & Grill

25 New Street, PA10 2LN
☎ (01505) 706606
2 changing beers (sourced locally) Ⓗ
Busy, family-friendly local pub within a conservation village, close to the famous NTS Weaver's Cottage. It offeres a wide range of food, including family favourites, steak and curry nights, and weekend 'specials'. Afternoon teas are also offered. The beer garden is

popular in summer. Live sports are shown on large screens in a separate area. Live music features most Saturday nights, with a range of styles and an emphasis on supporting local musicians. ⬗❀◑⬗🅿🚆(38)♫

Kirkintilloch

Kirky Puffer ✔

1-11 Townhead, G66 1NG
☎ (0141) 775 4140
Belhaven 80/-; Greene King Abbot; Sharp's Doom Bar; 3 changing beers (sourced nationally; often Oakham, Thornbridge) Ⓗ

Large community-friendly Wetherspoon pub alongside the Forth and Clyde Canal. It features a modern interior with Rennie Mackintosh-like wood panelling. Off the main room is a sizeable family-friendly corner and more secluded alcoves. A wide selection of beers is available, including strong ales. There is an extensive beer garden at the rear. The pub is popular with locals, canal users and visitors to the Roman Antonine Wall. There are frequent buses to Glasgow. ⬗❀◑⬗🚆🛜

Lochwinnoch

Brown Bull

32 Main Street, PA12 4AH
☎ (01505) 843250
3 changing beers (sourced nationally; often Cromarty, Fyne, Kelburn) Ⓗ

More than 200 years old, this family-run pub attracts locals and visitors all year. An ever-changing range of ales is offered, with an emphasis on regional breweries. At the rear is a quirky outdoor seating area and garden with cooperage tools. It hosts live music monthly. It is close to Lochwinnoch RSPB reserve and Castle Semple loch and visitor centre. Q⬗❀🐾🚆(4, 307)♣♫

Motherwell

Brandon Works ✔

45-61 Merry Street, ML1 1JJ
☎ (01698) 210280
Caledonian Deuchars IPA; Greene King Abbot; Sharp's Doom Bar; 2 changing beers (often Kelburn, Loch Lomond) Ⓗ

This town-centre Wetherspoon pub takes its name from the ironworks that occupied the site until the 1960s. A wide range of cask ales is available, and these are shown on blackboards at each end of the bar. Seating is split into two parts, with wooden fencing separating an area more suited to dining from the lively bar area. Prints on the wall depict Motherwell's industrial past and its labour and trades union heritage. ⬗❀◑⬗🚆🛜

Paisley

Bull Inn 🍺 ★ ✔

7 New Street, PA1 1XU
☎ (0141) 849 0472
4 changing beers (sourced regionally; often Broughton, Loch Lomond) Ⓗ

Established in 1901 and identified by CAMRA as having a nationally important historic pub interior, this is the oldest inn in Paisley. The pub retains many original features, including stained-glass windows, three small snugs, and a spirit cask gantry, and boasts the only original set of spirit cocks left in Scotland. Live sport is regularly shown on large screens. Four changing guest ales feature, often from Broughton, Loch Lomond, Orkney and Spey Valley breweries. Local CAMRA Pub of the Year 2024. ⬗➤(Gilmour Street)🚆♣🛜

Last Post 🅻 ✔

2 County Square, PA1 1BN
☎ (0141) 849 6911
Belhaven 80/-; Greene King Abbot; Sharp's Doom Bar; 3 changing beers (often Kelburn, Stewart) Ⓗ

Large Wetherspoon converted from the town's main post office. It is open-plan and on two levels, with plenty of seating and wheelchair access. Wetherspoon's standard food menu is available. Next to Gilmour Street railway station and close to the bus station, so it is handy for a pint between trains or buses. Three guest ales are usually available. Q⬗❀◑⬗➤(Gilmour Street)🚆(9,36)♣🛜

Wee Howff

53 High Street, PA1 2AN
☎ (0141) 887 8299
2 changing beers (sourced nationally) Ⓗ

The Wee Howff is one of Paisley's oldest real ale pubs and has appeared in over 30 editions of this Guide. This small, traditional pub with a loyal regular clientele offers two guest ales from all over the UK. The jukebox caters for even the most eclectic of tastes. A little piece of ale heaven in an otherwise crowded area of cheap drinking establishments. ⬗➤(Gilmour Street)🚆(9,36)♣🛜♫

Renfrew

Lord of the Isles ✔

Unit 21 Xscape, Kings Inch Road, PA4 8XQ
☎ (0141) 886 8930
Belhaven 80/-; Greene King Abbot; Sharp's Doom Bar; 3 changing beers (sourced nationally) Ⓗ

Large and lively, purpose-built Wetherspoon establishment located at the XSite Leisure Complex. Photographs depicting the history of industry on the River Clyde are displayed on the walls, and a short stroll allows you to view ships in dock at the shipyard opposite. The outside seating area is a suntrap during warm summer days. Food is available all day and three changing guest ales are available. ⬗❀◑⬗🅿🚆🛜

Rutherglen

Ruadh-Ghleann ✔

40-44 Main Street, G73 2HY
☎ (0141) 613 2370
Belhaven 80/-; Greene King Abbot; Sharp's Doom Bar; 3 changing beers (sourced nationally) Ⓗ

Busy Wetherspoon located at the western end of the High Street. The small shop frontage leads to a long, narrow room brightened by large windows down the right-hand side, with the bar halfway down. There is a family area to the rear where you can see through a window into the cellar. There is a beer garden on two levels at the back. Q⬗❀◑⬗🚆🛜

Strathaven

Weavers ✔

1-3 Green Street, ML10 6LT
☎ 07749 332914
4 changing beers (sourced nationally; often Black Iris, Outlandish, Stewart) Ⓗ

Standing in the centre of the town, the pub has links to the 19th-century weaving industry and has been listed in the Guide for over 25 years. Sympathetically refurbished inside and out in 2022, the single room has modern and comfortable furnishings and is decorated with black and white pictures of film stars. There is an ever-changing range of ales featuring beers from breweries in the region, and some that are rarely seen in Scotland. A range of imported bottled beers is also available. ⬗🚆🛜

HIGHLANDS & WESTERN ISLES

PLEASE NOTE: Pubs may not serve real ale outside tourist season, or even be open at all. Opening hours may vary all year round. Please contact pubs before intended visit to check.

Applecross

Applecross Inn
Shore Street, IV54 8LR NG70974444
☎ (01520) 744262 ⊕ applecrossinn.co.uk
3 changing beers (sourced locally; often Applecross) Ⓗ
This remote, multi-award winning inn is reached via a hair-raising road over the steepest road pass in Britain, or by the longer scenic coastal route. Beers come from the local Applecross microbrewery. Renowned for its local seafood and venison, and with a massive chalkboard menu, this is a must for foodies. There are additional tables outside, with the 'Inn-Side-Out' Airstream caravan offering light refreshments and takeaways. The inn is a popular stop-off on the North Coast 500.
Ꮭ❀✿⊀❶♿ＡＰ🚪🐕🏮🛜

Ardgour

Ardgour Ales
The Manse, PH33 7AH (on A861, ½ mile from Corran Ferry terminal) NN008650
☎ (01855) 632321 ⊕ ardgourales.scot
5 changing beers (sourced locally; often Ardgour) Ⓗ
Situated in a stunning location on Loch Linnhe, and just a five-minute walk from the Corran Ferry, Ardgour Ales started brewing in 2020, with a broad range of award-winning beers named in Gaelic around the theme of the local Ardgour goats. A cleverly designed canopy provides an outside drinking area at the brewery, with added wood-fuelled fires to provide extra heat when required. An onsite bakery also provides bread loaves, and the Friday pizza night is always popular. Closed Monday.
Q Ꮭ❀✿⊀❶♿Ａ🚶≈(Fort William) ♣Ｐ🚪🐕🏮🛜

Aviemore

Balavoulin
125 Grampian Road, PH22 1RL (at N end of village)
☎ (01479) 812255 ⊕ thebalavoulin.co.uk
3 changing beers Ⓗ
The Bally reopened its doors in 2019 after a short closure for major refurbishment. It offers three real ales from Greene King, plus guest beers, and a font for cider. Located in the heart of Aviemore, the pub also has seven rooms for B&B, making it a great base to explore the Cairngorm National Park. A wide range of home-cooked food is available, using local suppliers.
Ꮭ❀✿⊀❶♿Ａ🚶≈Ｐ🚪(1,31) 🐕🛜

Cairngorm Hotel Ⓛ
77 Grampian Road, PH22 1PE
☎ (01479) 810233 ⊕ cairngorm.com
Cairngorm Gold, Stag Ⓗ
Opposite the train station and bus stop, this is the first watering hole for many after a long journey. The privately owned Cairngorm Hotel has a warm and familiar feel about it, with comfy seats in the lobby to the bar and seating under cover outside. Although not tied, Cairngorm beers feature on the two handpumps. Largescreen TVs show popular sporting events, and there

is Scottish entertainment for the many visitors most evenings. Food with a Scottish twist is available much of the day. ⏷❀⛬❶❻⚓⚰️🅿️🚲(31,32)🛜♪

Old Bridge Inn ⓛ
23 Dalfaber Road, PH22 1PU
☎ (01479) 811137 ⊕ oldbridgeinn.co.uk
4 changing beers (sourced regionally; often Cairngorm, Caledonian) Ⓗ
Close to the River Spey, this gem of a pub off the main drag is worth seeking out. The cosy, intimate inn, converted from a cottage in 1982, is an ideal place to relax after a busy day on the hills, or even just touring the area. Four handpumps offer a mix of local and regional beers. Booking is recommended for the low food-miles restaurant. Entertainment is laid on most nights. Self-catering accommodation is available in the adjacent bunkhouse. Handy for Strathspey Steam Railway. ⏷❀⛬❶❻⚓⚰️🅿️🚲(1,31)❀🛜♪

Badachro

Badachro Inn
IV21 2AA (B8056 to Red Point and Badachro) NG781736
☎ (01445) 741255 ⊕ badachroinn.com
2 changing beers (often Cairngorm, Ewebrew) Ⓗ
On the south side of Loch Gairloch, this single-bar inn remains essentially unchanged. The decking outside offers an idyllic location to watch the tide ebb and flow in the safe and secure anchorage that the inlet provides. Inside, a conservatory overlooks the inlet. It is a three-mile drive from the main road itself, but worth it for the ales and the superb seafood that is a speciality. You may miss the small sign to the pub on the road out of Gairloch, but you won't miss the big one.
Q⏷❀⛬❶❻🚲🛜

Carbost: Isle of Skye

Old Inn
IV47 8SR NG379318
☎ (01478) 640205 ⊕ theoldinnskye.co.uk
3 changing beers (often Cuillin, Isle of Skye) Ⓗ
On the shores of Loch Harport, the Old Inn nestles on the tideline. Outside, trestle tables take advantage of the island's spectacular views – there can be no better place to enjoy a pint. Seafood is top of the menu, with most of it coming from the loch. The pub is busy year-round with an eclectic mix of outdoor folk, and those touring Skye or visiting the Talisker Distillery close by.
Q⏷❀⛬❶❻❀🅿️🚲❀♪

Carrbridge

Cairn Hotel ⓛ
Main Road, PH23 3AS (just off the A9, on B9153)
☎ (01479) 841212 ⊕ cairnhotel.co.uk
3 changing beers (sourced regionally; often Cairngorm, Cromarty, Orkney) Ⓗ
The Cairn Hotel is the hub of this small village, with the lure of a warming open fire and excellent gastropub-style menus. The licensee selects the best cask ales from the Highlands and Islands for his three handpumps, so the pub is deservedly popular with devoted locals and the many visitors to the area. There are 14 rooms for overnight stays. The 1717 Packhorse Bridge and Landmark Forest Adventure Park are close by.
⏷❀⛬❶❻❀🅿️🚲(32,33)❀🛜

Cawdor

Cawdor Tavern
The Lane, IV12 5XP NH845500
☎ (01667) 404777 ⊕ cawdortavern.co.uk
Orkney Northern Light, Red MacGregor, Dark Island; 1 changing beer (sourced regionally; often Orkney) Ⓗ
Run by the same owners since 1994, who are also the proud owners of the Orkney (and Atlas) brewery at Quoyloo. Accordingly, up to five handpumps feature their beers. Oak panelling covers the walls of the public areas, including the spacious cosy bar with its water taps for whisky on the bar. The lounge is mainly for meals and includes a separate 'baronial' dining hall. The tempting menu caters for all tastes and ages – leave room for pudding! Q⏷❀⛬❶❻⚓🅿️🚲(2,20)🛜

Claddach Kirkibost: North Uist

Westford Inn
HS6 5EP (2½ miles NW of Clachan on A865)
NF7751066195
☎ (01876) 580653 ⊕ westfordinn.com
3 changing beers (sourced regionally; often Fyne, Isle of Skye) Ⓗ
The owners took on the Westford Inn in 2015 and have turned around its fortunes. The pub is very much the community hub, with live music and an annual beer festival. A second Skye ale is on rotation in winter, with three in summer, as well as a range of bottles and cans. Good-quality food is available to eat in or take away. This is one of the most remote pubs in the Guide, but well worth the effort. Accommodation is available in The Bothy, a former byre. May not open till 4pm Monday and Tuesday. Q⏷❀⛬❶❻⚓❀🅿️🚲❀🛜♪

Cromarty

Fishertown Inn ⓛ
Church Street, IV11 8XA
☎ (01381) 600988 ⊕ fishertowninn.com
Cromarty Happy Chappy Ⓗ
A family-run pub providing B&B accommodation and delicious home-made bar meals, served daily. A beer garden can be found to the rear, with some additional outdoor seating at the front on the street. A traditional music session is held on the second Friday of every month. Up to three handpumps serve beers from the nearby Cromarty brewery. The pub is opposite the NTS Hugh Miller's Cottage and Cromarty Courthouse, and

---

REAL ALE BREWERIES

Applecross Kishorn
Ardgour Ardgour
Black Isle Munlochy
Cairngorm Aviemore
Cromarty Davidston
Cuillin 🍺 Sligachan: Isle of Skye
Dun 🔌 Glenelg
Ewebrew Poolewe
Glen Spean Spean Bridge
Hanging Tree 🍺 Drumnadrochit
Isle of Eigg Galmisdale: Isle of Eigg
Isle of Harris Borrisdale: Isle of Harris
Isle of Skye Uig: Isle of Skye
John O'Groats 🔌 John O'Groats
Knoydart Inverie
Plockton Plockton
River Leven Kinlochleven
Strathcarron Strathcarron
Two Thirsty Men Grantown on Spey

SCOTLAND

close to the harbour from where dolphin-spotting tours leave. A two-car ferry operates during the summer to Nigg. Q☆♿🅿🏆⏸🔷👟♣🅿🚭(26,26A)🌞🛜♫

Dores

Dores Inn 🅛
IV2 6TR NH59753476
☎ (01463) 751203 🌐 thedoresinn.co.uk
4 changing beers (sourced regionally; often Cairngorm, Cromarty, Inveralmond) 🄷
On the shores of Loch Ness, the inn offers excellent Nessie-spotting opportunities. It is popular all year round, and a must-stop for the views alone. A cosy, wood-finished bar has up to four handpumps offering local and independent ales, plus an occasional English guest. During summer a second bar serves the beer garden. Great food is available all day. Open from 10am, full bar service from 11am (midday on Sun). There is a free local minibus service to/from Inverness. May be closed Monday in winter. Q☆♿⏸🔷🅿🚭(301,302)🌞🛜

Dornoch

Dornoch Castle Hotel 🅛
Castle Street, IV25 3SD
☎ (01862) 810216 🌐 dornochcastlehotel.com
Cromarty Happy Chappy 🄷
It is worth diverting off the A9 just to marvel at the interior of this hotel, parts of which date back to 1577. Up to three ales from Cairngorm, Cromarty and Orkney breweries are usually available, and there is a massive collection of 300 single malt whiskies. Food is available in the restaurant. Local attractions include the 13th-century cathedral opposite, plus the renowned golf course, and beaches. Q☆♿🏆⏸🔷👟♣🅿(X98,X99)🛜

Fort William

Ben Nevis Bar
103 High Street, PH33 6DG
☎ (01397) 702295 🌐 bennevisbarfortwilliam.com
House beer (by Hanging Tree); 1 changing beer (often Hanging Tree) 🄷
Built in 1806 and under new ownership since 2019, this pleasant, two-room, traditional locals' pub on the pedestrianised High Street is said to have a resident ghost in the loft. A decked area at the rear gives splendid views of Loch Linnhe. As well as the two ales, over 50 malt whiskies are stocked. The house beer is Ben Nevis from Hanging Tree. A food menu of classic pub favourites is available all day until 9pm. Live music plays at weekends. ☆♿⏸🔷👟♣🅿🌞🛜♫

Ben Nevis Inn 🅛
Achintee Road, Claggan, PH33 6TE NN12477293
☎ (01397) 701227 🌐 ben-nevis-inn.co.uk
2 changing beers (sourced locally; often Cairngorm, River Leven) 🄷
Traditional 200-year-old stone-built barn at the start of the Ben Nevis mountain path, popular with outdoor enthusiasts. The small bar counter has two handpumps offering local beers. The interior is warm, informal and friendly, with long, beer hall-style tables and a beckoning stove, and is festooned with mountaineering and skiing paraphernalia. A menu of hearty dishes is available until 9pm and changes daily. There is regular live music. The adjacent bunkhouse sleeps 24. Closed in November, and Monday to Wednesday from December to February. Q🏆🅿⏸🔷👟🅿

Grog & Gruel 🅛
66 High Street, PH33 6AE (on pedestrianised High St)
☎ (01397) 705078 🌐 grogandgruel.co.uk
6 changing beers (sourced regionally) 🄷
The Grog alehouse is busy all day every day with a mix of locals and tourists. A regular feature in the Guide, up to six handpumps dispense predominantly local, sometimes regional beers, making it a draw for the real ale connoisseur. The bar menu offers imaginative and interesting food at affordable prices all day. After 5pm the restaurant upstairs opens, offering a wider selection of fare for hungry hill walkers. Open mic features on most Friday evenings. ☆🔷👟🏆🚭♣🌞🛜♫

Fortrose

Anderson
Union Street, IV10 8TD (corner of High St)
☎ (01381) 620236 🌐 theanderson.co.uk
2 changing beers (sourced nationally; often Cromarty, Inveralmond) 🄷
A regular entry since 2005, the Anderson offers well-chosen ales, mostly local or regional, drawn from a 200-year-old cellar. The whisky lounge has a single cider handpump and more than 250 single malts. The restaurant has a reputation for excellence and is a popular destination for foodies. Regular music, quiz and special food nights throughout the year. Nine bedrooms are available. May not open till 4pm and closed Sunday to Wednesday in winter. Closed for about a month before Christmas – phone ahead to check.
Q☆♿🏆⏸🔷👟♣🅿🚭(26,26A)🌞🛜♫

Glencoe

Clachaig Inn 🅛
Glencoe, PH49 4HX (3 miles SE of village, off A82)
NN12705668
☎ (01855) 811252 🌐 clachaig.com
10 changing beers (sourced regionally; often Cairngorm, Loch Lomond, Orkney) 🄷
Set in a remote location among the spectacular hills and scenery of Glencoe, the Clachaig is a must for outdoor enthusiasts and beer aficionados alike. Having worked up a hunger on the hills, a huge choice of beers and hearty grub will replenish your energy. There are also more than 400 whiskies and 130 gins on offer. On cooler days, wood-burning stoves keep the three bars and snugs warm. Beer festivals are held during the year and music hosted most weekend evenings. It opens four days a week in winter – phone ahead. ☆🏆⏸🔷👟♣🅿🌞🛜♫

Glenmore

Pine Marten Bar & Scran
PH22 1QU (on ski road by Loch Morlich) NH974098
☎ (01479) 861253 🌐 aviemoreski.co.uk
Cairngorm Trade Winds, Black Gold, Wildcat 🄷
Though unassuming from the outside, this 'wee snug of a bar' has a welcoming wood-burning stove and a bar topped with three handpumps. The minimalist building is designed to emulate mountain refuges in Austria, Switzerland and Bavaria, and ice axes and skis festoon the walls, along with quirky artefacts from across Europe. The kitchen serves some great grub, and there is also a shop and ski hire. Accommodation includes glamping pods and a tree house. Live music plays most Friday and Saturday nights. ☆🏆⏸🔷👟♣🅿🚭🌞🛜♫

Inverness

Black Isle Bar L
68 Church Street, IV1 1EN
☎ (01463) 229920 ⊕ blackislebar.com
Black Isle Goldfinch, Red Kite, Hibernator; 1 changing beer (sourced locally; often Black Isle) Ⓟ
This popular bar opened in 2016, offering up to three real ales and 23 craft font beers. Two big screens show the eclectic beer menu, mostly from Black Isle, but with some guests, plus prices for pints, halves and thirds. The open-plan bar area offers a mix of seating. Upstairs, the secret garden utilises upcycled pallet tables and stools under a cover of reclaimed corrugated iron. Organic ingredients from the brewery farm are used in an interesting food menu, with pizzas the speciality.
Q✇⊞◑₠≠Pᵬ☻ 🖝

Castle Tavern L
1 View Place, IV2 4SA (top of Castle St)
☎ (01463) 718178 ⊕ castletavern.pub
5 changing beers (sourced regionally; often Cromarty, Isle of Skye, Loch Lomond) Ⓗ
Just a short walk from the town centre, the Castle Tavern is popular with tourists visiting the castle opposite, as well as locals who know their beer. Six handpumps offer an interesting rolling selection of beers, mostly from Scottish independents, and a changing cider. There is plenty of seating inside, but the covered area outside is always busy, even in winter, with panoramic views along the River Ness. Bar meals are available all day and the restaurant upstairs opens in the evening.
☎✿◑₠Å≠●Pᵬ☻🖝

Corriegarth L ✓
5-7 Heathmount Road, IV2 3JU
☎ (01463) 224411 ⊕ corriegarth.com
Cromarty Happy Chappy; 3 changing beers (sourced nationally) Ⓗ
A busy local in the quiet Crown area of Inverness, just 10 minutes from the town centre. The imposing red sandstone building was once a hotel, and also did a stint as a club for navy and RAF officers. Cromarty Happy Chappy features regularly, along with up to three other beers from further afield. There is a large area to sit outside in summer. Accommodation in nine boutique en-suite rooms. Q☎✿✇◑₠≠Pᵬ☻🖝

King's Highway
72-74 Church Street, IV1 1EN
☎ (01463) 251830
Caledonian Deuchars IPA; Fuller's London Pride; Greene King Abbot; Sharp's Doom Bar; changing beers Ⓗ
This city-centre Wetherspoon pub has offered good-value fare since 2001. Up to 10 handpumps feature mainly Scottish beers, many local to the area. It is a popular meeting point, and handy for the local buses and the train station, but even when busy you can always find a quiet place to sit and enjoy a pint. There is also a decked area outside. Accommodation is available. Breakfast is served from 7am and alcoholic drinks from 11am.
☎✿✇◑₠≠Pᵬ🖝

Number 27 L
27 Castle Street, IV2 3DU
☎ (01463) 241999 ⊕ number27inverness.com
4 changing beers (sourced regionally; often Cairngorm) Ⓗ
The entrance to this pub, opposite the castle, leads into a bar area with mixed seating and then on to a raised area towards the rear for dining. Four handpumps normally offer ales from Cairngorm, with other local breweries

making an occasional appearance. An extensive selection of keg and bottled beers is also offered. Food menus cater for both a quick pub lunch and a more substantial offering in the evening, and include an all-day children's menu. ☎◑₠≠Pᵬ🖝

Phoenix Ale House ★ L
106-110 Academy Street, IV1 1LX
☎ (01463) 240300 ⊕ phoenixalehouse.co.uk
10 changing beers (sourced nationally; often Cairngorm, Cromarty) Ⓗ
The Phoenix offers a selection of Scottish real ales from up to 10 handpumps. Identified by CAMRA as having a nationally important historic pub interior, the island bar is surrounded by a spittoon. Though most of the space is for standing only, it is popular with tourists as well as those who know their ales. It is now jointly owned with the Indian restaurant next door, where hearty meals are served all day. Q◑₠≠Pᵬ♫

John O'Groats

John O'Groats Brewery & Tap Room
The Last House, KW1 4YR
☎ 07842 401571 ⊕ johnogroatsbrewery.co.uk
4 changing beers (sourced locally; often John O'Groats) Ⓗ
The Last House is the taproom for the adjoining John O' Groats brewery. Situated just yards from the Pentland Firth, it is the most northerly pub and brewery in mainland Britain. Drinkers can sit in the small bar, or in the shop window overlooking the sea and Orkney Isles, or outside on nicer days. Four handpumps serve ales brewed next door, and the offering is seldom missing a Highland real cider. May close at 5pm January to May and October to December. Q✿Å●Pᵬ(77,80)

Kincraig

Suie Bar L
PH21 1NA (on B9152, just off A9) NH829057
☎ (01540) 651788 ⊕ thesuiebar.com
Cairngorm Trade Winds; 2 changing beers (sourced regionally; often Orkney) Ⓗ
It is worth pulling off the busy A9 and following the old road to seek out this wee gem of a country pub. From the outside it does not look much, but inside a warm Highland welcome is accompanied by four handpumps offering Cairngorm and some local Highland beers. A much-loved old stove has been replaced with a more modern, efficient model. The Suie holds a beer festival in late February and hosts music most weekends. Handy for the Kincraig Wildlife Park. ✿✇♣Pᵬ(32,32A)☻🖝♫

Lewiston

Loch Ness Inn
nr Drumnadrochit, IV63 6UW (W of the A82)
☎ (01456) 450991 ⊕ staylochness.co.uk
3 changing beers (sourced locally; often Cairngorm, Cromarty) Ⓗ
Dating from 1838, this traditional inn has rooms and a new bunkhouse. The restaurant is fiercely proud of the local provenance of its ingredients. The comfy bar features a welcoming stove and has up to three handpumps offering beers from mainly local breweries, occasionally Applecross. The inn is ideal for visiting Loch Ness and Urquhart Castle, or even walking the Great Glen Way. A free eight-seater courtesy bus is available for local pick-ups within five miles; call the pub.
☎✿✇◑₠Å♣Pᵬ🖝♫

Nairn

Bandstand 🏆 [L] ✔

Crescent Road, IV12 4NB (E end of town towards beach)
☎ (01667) 452341 🌐 thebandstandnairn.co.uk
5 changing beers (sourced nationally; often Cairngorm, Cromarty, Orkney) [H]
Overlooking the green, with its bandstand and the Moray Firth beyond, this bar has five handpumps offering a great selection of local and regional Scottish beers, including the occasional English ale. Popular spring and autumn beer festivals, said to be the biggest independent events in the UK, are accompanied by themed food and music acts over three days. The restaurant offers good-value quality food and live music plays at the weekend. Local CAMRA Pub of the Year 2024. Q👶❀🛏◐◑♿⛺🚆♣🍎P🚌(10,11)🐾📶♫

Havelock

Crescent Road, IV12 4NB (E end of town)
☎ (01667) 455500 🌐 havelocknairn.co.uk
Cromarty Happy Chappy; 3 changing beers (sourced regionally; often Cromarty, Loch Lomond, Orkney) [H]
The Havelock is a pub and hotel by the seaside in this popular tourist town. It has a welcoming, informal atmosphere and a lively bar. The two original handpumps on the bar were joined by a third, which appeared in 2022. Regular live music features, and there is karaoke on Sunday. 👶🛏◐◑♿🚆♣P🚌📶♫

Plockton

Plockton Hotel ✔

41 Harbour Street, IV52 8TN NG80293343
☎ (01599) 544274 🌐 plocktonhotel.co.uk
4 changing beers (often Cromarty, Fyne, Swannay) [H]
Plockton was the setting for TV's Hamish Macbeth, which is an attraction for visitors to the pretty village, many of whom arrive by train on the picturesque Kyle Line. The bar in this award-winning, family-run hotel proudly offers four handpumps dispensing an ever-changing range of beers from both local and regional breweries, which can be enjoyed on the terrace with breathtaking views across the bay. The food menu features locally sourced seafood, beef and venison. A real ale and gin festival is held in May. Q👶❀🛏◐◑♿P🐾📶♫

Portree

Isles Inn

Somerled Square, IV51 9EH (E side of main square)
☎ (01478) 612129
Isle of Skye Skye Gold, Skye Red [H]
The Isles Inn is situated in the central square of Portree and is an excellent base for exploring the island. The restaurant and bar are decorated in a Jacobean style. The menu features locally sourced ingredients, including langoustines, hand-dived scallops and local haggis, neeps and tatties. Vegetarian options also available. Two beers are usually on tap, together with a range of bottled beers and ciders. 🛏◐◑♿P🚌♫

Roy Bridge

Stronlossit Inn [L]

Main Street, PH31 4AG (on A86) NN27228117
☎ (01397) 712253 🌐 stronlossit.co.uk
3 changing beers (sourced locally; often Cairngorm, Isle of Skye, Orkney) [H]
The inn's location makes it attractive to those keen on the outdoors. The railway station is just over the road, so you can leave the car at home and arrive by train from Fort William. The train can also take you for a day trip to Corrour, to walk around Loch Ossian. Up to four handpumps dispense beers from various Scottish breweries. Great food is available all day, and there is accommodation to suit all budgets. Closed from November to February.
Q👶❀🛏◐◑♿⛺🚆🍎P🚌(19C,41)📶

Stornoway: Isle of Lewis

Crown Inn & Harbour Bar

Castle Street, HS1 2BD (close to ferry terminal)
☎ (01851) 703734 🌐 crownhotelstornoway.com
2 changing beers (sourced nationally; often Timothy Taylor) [H]
Located in the centre of Stornoway, minutes' walk from the ferry terminal and bus station, the lounge bar and Harbour View restaurant are accessed via the hotel while the large public Harbour Bar which features sports TV, pool and weekly live music sessions, has a separate entrance. Both bars sport two handpumps. In 1963 the Crown famously witnessed the 'Cherry Brandy Scandal', when the former Prince of Wales indulged in a nip while underage. An impressive range of over 120 gins is on offer. Opening hours vary seasonally.
👶🛏◐◑♣P🚌🐾📶♫

Whitebridge

Whitebridge Hotel [L]

IV2 6UN (B862 towards the SE side of Loch Ness) NH487152
☎ (01456) 486226 🌐 whitebridgehotel.co.uk
Cromarty Happy Chappy; 3 changing beers (often Black Isle) [H]
Built in 1899 on the quieter east side of Loch Ness, this hotel has fishing rights on three local lochs. Inside, the attractive pitch-pine panelled bar features a welcoming wood-burning stove. Three ales are usually available – with Cromarty's Happy Chappy being the principal choice – reducing to one or two in winter. The menu offers an excellent range of home-cooked meals and is well worth sampling. The hotel has a green tourism policy. Closed in February. Q❀🛏◐◑♿P🚌(14)🐾📶

The soul of beer

Brewers call barley malt the 'soul of beer'. While a great deal of attention has been rightly paid to hops in recent years, the role of malt in brewing must not be ignored. Malt contains starch that is converted to a special form of sugar known as maltose during the brewing process. It is maltose that is attacked by yeast during fermentation and turned into alcohol and carbon dioxide. Other grains can be used in brewing, notably wheat. But barley malt is the preferred grain as it gives a delightful biscuity / cracker / Ovaltine note to beer. Unlike wheat, barley has a husk that works as a natural filter during the first stage of brewing, known as the mash.

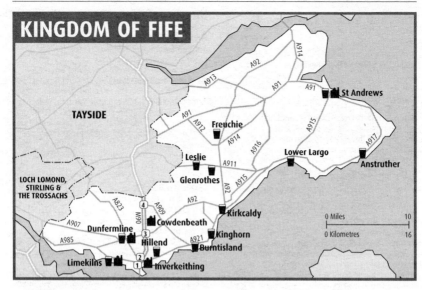

KINGDOM OF FIFE

Anstruther

Bank ✓

23-25 High Street East, KY10 3DQ
☎ (01333) 310189 ⊕ thebank-anstruther.co.uk
3 changing beers (sourced nationally; often Greene King, Spey Valley) Ⓗ

This charming, family-run bar and hotel boasts views of the Dreel Burn meeting the Firth of Forth, creating a picturesque backdrop for your evening dining experience. The Bank offers freshly prepared lunches and bar suppers sourced from local providers, alongside a delightful selection of real ales, draught beers, wines and spirits. Its expansive, well-tended gardens are a sanctuary in sunny weather, inviting guests to bask in the warmth and tranquillity of this idyllic setting. Only nine miles from all the famous golf courses in St Andrews. ❀😋🛏️🍴🚌(X60,95)❀ 🕏 ❅

Dreel Tavern

16 High Street, KY10 3DL
☎ (01333) 279238 ⊕ dreeltavern.co.uk
3 changing beers (sourced nationally; often Fyne, Stewart) Ⓗ

Inhabiting one of Anstruther's oldest buildings, this former coaching inn dates back 300 to 400 years and is steeped in history. The family-run establishment offers a blend of tradition and modernity, with locally sourced fine dining complementing its pub atmosphere. Locals and tourists can bask in sunshine in the beer garden overlooking the Dreel Burn, or enjoy cosy winter evenings by the open fire. Closed Monday and Tuesday. Q😋❀🍴♣🚌(95,X60) ❀ ❅ ♪

Burntisland

Sands Hotel ✓

Lochies Road, KY3 9JX
☎ (01592) 872230 ⊕ burntislandsands.co.uk
1 changing beer (sourced regionally; often Loch Leven, Stewart) Ⓗ

A warm welcome awaits at this family-run hotel by the seafront in this picturesque coastal resort. Burntisland is home to the second oldest Highland Games in the world (1652), held in mid-July alongside the town's annual fair. The hotel has a choice of restaurants and is renowned for

its high teas. There is also a popular outside area in which to relax and watch the trains go by. ❀🛏️🍴🅿️🚌(7) ❀ ❅

Dunfermline

Commercial Inn

13 Douglas Street, KY12 7EB
☎ (01383) 696994
6 changing beers (sourced nationally; often Harviestoun, Orkney, Stewart) Ⓗ

Located in the town centre, close to the main retail area, the pub attracts an eclectic clientele and gets busy on match days. Formerly a hotel, this 19th-century listed building is full of character and retains the high ceilings and decorative cornices of that period. A spiral staircase leads down to the lower levels. Local and regional CAMRA Pub of the Year 2022. 🍴❧(City)❀🚌❀❅♪

East Port ✓

7 East Port, KY12 7JG
☎ (01383) 736678
4 changing beers (sourced regionally; often Loch Leven, Loch Lomond, Stewart) Ⓗ

Standing on the high street, just a short distance from the main shopping area, this busy (especially on match days) town-centre pub is well worth a visit when out and about in Dunfermline. It is not simply a sports bar, but a great place to relax with a few drinks in one the many cosy booths. The interior features wood panelling and a wooden bar and gantry. Large TVs show various sports, and soft background music usually plays. Tables can be booked during large sporting events. There is live music on Friday and Saturday evenings. ❀♿❧(City)♣🚌❀❅

Guildhall & Linen Exchange ✅

79-83 High Street, KY12 7DR
☎ (01383) 625960
8 changing beers (sourced nationally; often
Belhaven, Greene King, Stewart) ⊞
This Wetherspoon outlet was a Guildhall and Linen
Exchange when Dunfermline was synonymous with fine
quality table linen. The Category A-listed building is now
a split-level pub and hotel. The interior is decorated with
a mix of modern and Art Deco features and displays
numerous pictures highlighting the town's past. It is in
the middle of the busy retail area, and a great place to
stop for a pint and a bite to eat
Q ☎ 🏠 ⌂ ◑ & ⇌ (City) 🚍 🛜

Freuchie

Albert Tavern

2 High Street, KY15 7EX
☎ 07876 178863 ⊕ alberttavern.wixsite.com
5 changing beers (sourced nationally; often
Phoenix) ⊞
Small, two-roomed pub in the village of Freuchie. Up to
five ales and at least two ciders are available in the bar,
which is decorated with pumpclips from ales that have
been sold previously. The staff are always friendly and
willing to share their ale knowledge. The lounge, on the
right when entering, has bench seating and a TV showing
sport, and children are welcome there until 8.30pm. A
multi-award winning CAMRA local, Scottish and Cider Pub
of the Year. May not open till 5pm Monday to Thursday.
Q ☎ 🏠 ♣ 🚍 (42,36) 🐾 🛜

Glenrothes

Golden Acorn ✅

1 North Street, KY7 5NA
☎ (01592) 755252
Belhaven 80/-; Greene King Abbot; Sharp's Doom
Bar; 5 changing beers (sourced nationally; often
Orkney, Purple Moose, Stewart) ⊞
A busy Wetherspoon pub catering to all tastes, with
themed menus and promotions available most days. The
large, open-plan interior has a family area to the rear,
and there are a number of TVs throughout, showing a
mixture of sports and news. Parking is available directly
in front of the pub – remember to register your car details
via the monitored parking system by the bar. There are
26 hotel rooms available. ☎ 🏠 ⌂ ◑ & P 🚍 🛜

Hillend

Hillend Tavern 🍸

37 Main Street, KY11 9ND
☎ (01383) 415391 ⊕ hillendtavern.co.uk
4 changing beers (sourced nationally; often
Cromarty, Harviestoun, Timothy Taylor) ⊞
A community-focused village pub near Dalgety Bay, with
cosy log fires creating a friendly and welcoming
atmosphere, a beer garden, and a selection of real ales.
The Tav, as it is known, has a traditional bar and spacious
area at the rear which is ideal for groups or functions. A
Dog Bar offers complimentary water and treats to well-
trained canines. Live music nights and the two quiz
nights a month are popular. CAMRA Regional Pub of the
Year 2023 and Local Pub of the Year 2024. May not open
till 4pm Monday to Thursday, 3pm Friday.
☎ 🏠 ⇌ (Dalgety Bay) ♣ 🚍 (7,87) 🐾 🛜 ♪

Kinghorn

Auld Hoose

6-8 Nethergate, KY3 9SY
☎ (01592) 891074
2 changing beers (sourced nationally; often
Marston's, Timothy Taylor) ⊞
A traditional two-room pub just off the main street of this
former Royal Burgh. It has a large bar area, with a
comfortable lounge at the side. It is popular with both
locals and visitors and makes an ideal refreshment stop
for Fife Coastal Path walkers. Lunches are served daily.
The pub hosts regular evening events such as live music,
karaoke and dominoes, with open mic sessions on
occasional Sundays. ◑ ⇌ ♣ 🚍 (7) 🐾 🛜

Crown Tavern Ⓛ

55-57 High Street, KY3 9UW
☎ (01592) 891363
2 changing beers (sourced nationally; often Loch
Leven, Loch Lomond) Ⓐ
Formerly known as the Middle Bar, this two-roomed pub
sits at the heart of Kinghorn, just a stroll from the train
station. It is a real community hub, and doubles as a
sports bar, boasting a large TV screen and multiple
smaller ones. Two ales are served from classic Scottish
tall founts, a rarity nowadays. Evening events include live
music. ⇌ 🚍 (7) 🐾 🛜 ♪

Kirkcaldy

Betty Nicols

297 High Street, KY1 1JL
☎ (01592) 590467
Fyne Jarl; 2 changing beers (sourced nationally; often
Fyne, Harviestoun, Oakham) ⊞
Located in the town's merchant quarter, this traditional
pub on the High Street boasts a cosy interior, with
vintage patterned tiles and comfortable seating. It serves
three real ales, often sourced from Fyne Ales, and offers
a bistro menu and a selection of bottled beers, wines,
and spirits. Regular quiz nights and other events add to
the lively atmosphere. ☎ ◑ & ⇌ 🚍 🐾 🛜 ♪

Harbour Bar ★

473 High Street, KY1 2SN
☎ (01592) 264270
4 changing beers (sourced nationally; often Brew
York, Harviestoun, Loch Lomond) ⊞
Established in 1924, this lively, historic pub serves a
diverse selection of real ales and Belgian beers. Housed
in a former ship chandler's dating from around 1870, the
building has been identified by CAMRA as having a
regionally important historic pub interior, and notably
retains its rare Jug Bar. Entertainment includes live music
and quizzes. Tucked behind the pub, in the old
sailmaker's workshop, is the dormant Fyfe brewery,
which is due for revival under new ownership. Closed in
January, and from Monday to Wednesday in other
months. Hours are subject to change, so please call
ahead. ☎ ♣ 🚍 (X60,X27) 🐾 🛜 ♪

Robert Nairn ✅

2-6 Kirk Wynd, KY1 1EH
☎ (01592) 205049
Belhaven 80/-; Greene King Abbot; 4 changing beers
(sourced nationally; often Broughton, Oakham,
Stewart) ⊞
Wetherspoon conversion of a former bank, just off the
town's main pedestrianised shopping area. It is named
after a member of the Nairn family, who helped put
Kirkcaldy on the map. The split-level lounge features
pictures of old Kirkcaldy. The pub attracts a mixed

clientele. Six quickly changing ales are served on handpull, and a roaring fire burns through the winter.
Q🐴✿◑♿🚆🚌📶

Leslie

Burns Tavern

184 High Street, KY6 3DB

☎ (01592) 741345

Timothy Taylor Landlord; 1 changing beer (sourced nationally) [H]

The Burns Tavern is very much the hub of the community. Located in the former paper-making town of Leslie, the pub consists of a lounge and public bar. The main bar is a split into two sections: the lower contains the main bar area, and the higher level contains a pool table. Sit back, relax and enjoy your pint of Timothy Taylor's Landlord while watching sporting events on the numerous TVs. The Burns also has a jukebox, mainly featuring music from the 60s to the 80s.
🐴🛏⛺♣P🚌(39A) 🐾

Limekilns

Bruce Arms [L]

2 Main Street, KY11 3HL

☎ (01383) 872259 🌐 brucearmslimekilns.co.uk

2 changing beers (sourced nationally; often Greene King, Timothy Taylor) [H]

A cosy and inviting pub nestled in the heart of this ancient village on the Fife Coastal Path. The pub affords breathtaking views across the Firth of Forth, all the way to towards the iconic bridges, as you enjoy a refreshing pint and some tasty food. Opens at 3.30pm on Monday and midday Tuesday to Friday. 🐴✿◑♣P🚌(6)🐾📶♫

Lower Largo

Railway Inn

1 Station Wynd, KY8 6BU

☎ (01333) 320239 🌐 railwayinnlargo.co.uk

5 changing beers (sourced regionally; often Fyne, Loch Lomond, Stewart) [H]

A friendly and traditional pub, dating back to 1749. Standing in the shadow of the old East Fife Railway viaduct in the picturesque village of Lower Largo, it is bedecked with railway memorabilia. In fair weather you can relax in the beer garden or sit at benches out the front, overlooking the harbour. Pies, toasties and bar snacks are available. It sits beside the Fife Coastal Path and is a handy respite for walkers.
Q🐴✿◑🚌(95,395) 🐾📶

St Andrews

Aikmans Bar & Bistro

32 Bell Street, KY16 9UX

☎ (01334) 477425 🌐 cellarbar.co.uk

3 changing beers (often MòR, Spey Valley, Swannay) [H]

Located just off South Street, Aikmans is a two-level venue, with the bistro at street level and the cellar bar below. This retro-style café-bar offers a relaxed atmosphere for tourists and students, be it for quick bite to eat or to sample one of the many beers on offer. In addition to the cask beers, a large range of draught and bottled European beers are available. 🐴◑🚌🐾♫

Central Bar ✔

77 Market Street, KY16 9NU

☎ (01334) 478296

3 changing beers (sourced nationally; often Belhaven, Greene King) [H]

The Central has a Victorian-style interior with an island bar, ornate ceiling and a fine collection of historic brewery mirrors. As the name suggests, this pub is situated in the busy cobbled market square of this historic university town. It attracts a wide range of customers – locals, tourists, students and golfers – all off whom can enjoy their drink on the small seated area out front. 🐴✿◑🚌🐾📶

Criterion [L]

99 South Street, KY16 9QW

☎ (01334) 474543 🌐 criterionstandrews.co.uk

House beer (by Stewart); 4 changing beers (sourced nationally; often Loch Lomond, MòR, St Andrews) [H]

One of the few family-run pubs in St Andrews, the Criterion was established back in 1874. It is situated on one of the main shopping streets and is popular with locals, tourists, students and golfers. The famous 'Cri-Pie' is served until 11.45pm. In addition to the four cask ales, a large selection of whiskies and gins are stocked. Children over five are allowed outside. Card payment only. 🐴✿◑🚌🐾📶♫

Whey Pat Tavern ✔

1 Bridge Street, KY16 9EX

☎ (01334) 477740

Greene King IPA; 3 changing beers (often Inveralmond, Timothy Taylor) [H]

The original birthplace of the Kingdom of Fife branch of CAMRA, the Whey Pat is a busy corner pub opposite the historic West Port, and convenient for the bus station. The pub is popular with the usual mix of locals, tourists, students and golfers. The two-levelled building has a busy public bar at the front, with a spacious lounge to the rear. ✿◑♿♣🚌🐾📶

SCOTLAND

Learned drinker

He was a learned man, of immense reading, but is much blamed for his unfaithfull quotations. His manner of studie was thus, he wore a long quilt cap, which came two or rather three inches at least over his eies, which served him as an umbrella to defend his eies from the light. About every three houres his man was to bring him a roll and a pot of ale to refocillate (refresh) his wasted spirits so he studied, and dranke, and munched some bread and this maintained him till night, and then he made a good supper.

An Oxford man, William Prynne (1600-69), as described by John Aubrey in Brief Lives, ed. John Buchanan-Brown, 2000

LOCH LOMOND, STIRLING & THE TROSSACHS

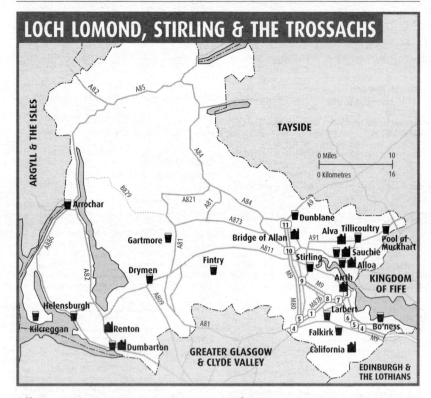

Alloa

Bobbing John ✅

46 Drysdale Street, FK10 1JL

☎ (01259) 222590

Belhaven 80/-; Greene King Abbot; Sharp's Doom Bar; 2 changing beers (sourced regionally; often Broughton, Kelburn, Williams Bros) ⓗ

Wetherspoon pub in a traditional three-storey sandstone building, purpose built in 1895 for the Alloa Co-operative Society. It is named after Alloa-born John Erskine who created industrial Alloa by developing the town as a coal mining centre. He was twice Secretary of State for Scotland under Queen Anne, but his frequent changes of political allegiance earned him the nickname 'Bobbing John'. Much of the building's original stonework has been retained and a Victorian shop front reintroduced. There is a warming firepit in the centre.

ᗧ🛏🏠🛜🛒♿👜🚃🚭🛜

Arrochar

Village Inn ✅

Shore Road, G83 7AX (down A814 from A83 jct)

☎ (01301) 702279

5 changing beers (sourced nationally; often Fyne, Loch Lomond) ⓗ

A picturesque inn, built in 1827 as the local manse, offering views over Loch Long to the Arrochar Alps. The bar and restaurant are decorated in a traditional Scottish country style. Five handpumps offer ales from a variety of Scottish breweries, though the choice is more limited in winter. The large front lawn is a pleasant spot to enjoy a beer looking over the loch. The pub is popular with locals, daytrippers, hillwalkers and weekending tourists staying at the inn. ᗧ🛏🏠🛜♿⛰🅿🚌(926,976)🐾🛜

Bo'ness

Corbie Inn

84 Corbiehall, EH51 0AS

☎ (01506) 825307 🌐 corbieinn.co.uk

3 changing beers (sourced nationally; often Kelburn, Loch Lomond, Strangers) ⓗ

Since 2011 the pub has been run by a family, passionate about real ale. Up to three ales are available, mainly from Scottish breweries, plus a few English. It has a large lounge area serving fine food. It is a real community pub involved in local charities, and is a supporter of Bo'ness Real Ale Society's festival. The large covered beer garden has a pizza oven and children's play area. Close to the Bo'ness and Kinneil Railway, Bo'ness Motor Museum and the Hippodrome (Scotland's oldest purpose-built picture house). Q🛏🏠🍴🛜♿🅿🚃🐾🛜

Drymen

Clachan Inn

2 The Square, G63 0BL

☎ (01360) 660824 🌐 clachaninndrymen.co.uk

2 changing beers (sourced regionally; often Belhaven, Loch Lomond) ⓗ

This popular free house, established in 1734, is the oldest licensed premises in Scotland. It has been recently refreshed, preserving many original features. Two handpumps dispense an ever-changing selection of excellent local and other Scottish beers. It offers a warm welcome to visitors, including walkers of the West Highland Way, tourists for Loch Lomond National Park, and dog owners. Quality meals and pizzas are served all day in the bar and separate restaurant.
と☎◑Å➡(309) ♣ ❀

Dumbarton

Captain James Lang ✔
97-99 High Street, G82 1LF
☎ (01389) 742112
Belhaven 80/-; Greene King Abbot; Sharp's Doom Bar; 2 changing beers (sourced nationally) Ⓗ
Converted from a former Woolworths store that opened in 2014, this Wetherspoon has a light, open layout, with a variety of seating options. The pub is named after the captain of the paddle steamer Leven, which was built in the town. Pictures on the wall pay tribute to Woolworths, the Cutty Sark and racing driver Jackie Stewart, who was born nearby. At the back there is a large beer garden overlooking the River Leven. Frequent trains and buses serve the area. Q ど❀◑♦≉(Central)➡≋❀

Dunblane

Tappit Hen ✔
Kirk Street, FK15 0AL
☎ (01786) 825226
5 changing beers (sourced regionally; often Fyne, Greene King, Spey Valley) Ⓗ
Taking its name from a type of Scottish pewter drinking vessel, this traditional, one-room pub stands opposite one of Scotland's oldest cathedrals. Refurbished in 2019 to an excellent standard, it has a friendly atmosphere, and the helpful and knowledgeable staff serve regularly changing beers from four guest pumps. The train station and car parking are close by. As well as charity and community events, the pub holds a successful real ale festival once a year. ≉➡❀❀

Falkirk

Wheatsheaf Inn ✔
16 Baxters Wynd, FK1 1PF
☎ (01324) 638282 ⊕ wheatsheaffalkirk.co.uk
3 changing beers (sourced nationally; often Cromarty, Kelburn, Orkney) Ⓗ
Falkirk's oldest public house, dating from the late 18th century, can be found off the High Street via one of the three vennels. Retaining much of its original character, the wood-panelled bar is furnished in traditional style, with interesting historical pub decor. A secluded suntrap beer garden is at the rear. Two guest beers come from breweries in Scotland and England. A must-visit venue near Falkirk's famous Steeple, with a friendly welcome for all from knowledgeable staff and fellow drinkers. Q❀≉(Grahamston) ➡❀❀♪

Fintry

Fintry Inn Ⓛ
23 Main Street, G63 0XA
☎ (01360) 860224 ⊕ fintryinn.co.uk
2 changing beers (sourced regionally; often Belhaven) Ⓗ
This traditional village public house dates from 1750, and though recently renovated, has kept its historic appearance. For many this will represent their idea of what a village pub should be – comfortable, cosy and welcoming. Beers from the on-site microbrewery, Fintry Brew Crew, are always available, along with one guest beer. It also has an extensive whisky selection and hosts popular comedy and music sessions. Food is served in the restaurant and an off-licence service is available. Closed Monday and Tuesday. Q ど❀☎◑♦P❀❀♪

Gartmore

Black Bull Hub & Pub
Main Street, FK8 3RW
☎ (01877) 382054 ⊕ blackbullgartmore.com
Harviestoun Schiehallion; 1 changing beer (sourced regionally; often Fyne, Orkney) Ⓗ
A community-owned pub and hotel that is the village hub. The fine old building is largely unspoiled and comprises a warren of small rooms, including two for dining, a historic society meeting room, and a cosy bar with a real fire. It is mainly staffed by enthusiastic and keen volunteers, supported by 14 paid employees. This family- and dog-friendly pub featured on the BBC TV series Saving Britain's Pubs with Tom Kerridge. Hours change throughout year so check the website. Q ど❀☎◑♦ÅP➡(X10A) ♣ ❀

Helensburgh

Ashton
74 West Princes Street, G84 8UG
☎ (01436) 675900
Fyne Jarl; Stewart Pentland IPA; Timothy Taylor Landlord Ⓗ
A warm welcome awaits at this genuine local where the bar has been tastefully modernised and decorated with a nautical theme while retaining its original charm. During the work a set of tiles depicting scenes from the Waverley novels was revealed. There is a snug up a few steps to the left opposite the bar and a small room for playing darts. Food can be ordered from local takeaways to eat in. Live music is a regular Saturday night feature. ❀≉(Central) ♣➡(1B,316) ♣ ❀ ♪

Commodore ✔
112-117 West Clyde Street, G84 8ES
☎ (01436) 676924
Sharp's Doom Bar; Stewart Jack Back Ⓗ
Just a short walk from the station, this bar offers scenic views of the Firth of Clyde and the Gareloch. In addition to the quality real ales, there is a wide selection of food in the informal restaurant. In good weather you can enjoy sitting in the popular garden to the front where you might spot seabirds, ships, the wrecked sugar boat, and the occasional submarine. The hotel upstairs is now a separate business. ❀◑♦P➡(1B)♣

Kilcreggan

Creggans
Princes Terrace, Shore Road, G84 0JJ
☎ (01436) 842700
2 changing beers (sourced nationally; often Timothy Taylor) Ⓗ
A single-room bar with a wooden floor and a mix of freestanding tables and chairs with shelves along the wall. It stands opposite the ferry pier to Gourock. Beers are from Timothy Taylor complemented with a regular guest ale. Live music can be heard from time to time. The front patio (where children are welcome) offers views of the ships making their way along the Firth of Clyde. Pub food is served daily. ❀◑♦➡(316)♣ ❀ ♪

Larbert

Station Hotel ✓
2 Foundry Loan, FK5 4AW
☎ (01324) 557186 ⊕ stationhotellarbert.com
3 changing beers (sourced nationally; often Brampton, Loch Lomond, Orkney) ⊞
A popular local next to Larbert railway station and on regular bus routes. Three cask ales are normally on offer, plus a variety of local, regional and national ales, and food is served daily. There are largescreen TVs showing sporting events. It prides itself on the support given to numerous local community groups. There is a large enclosed beer garden, and a cosy lounge area. It is the closest pub to CAMRA's Larbert Real Ale Festival, held in the nearby Dobbie Hall each spring.
🕭🏵🖾🕪🕭≠P🖵🏵🕭

Pool of Muckhart

Inn at Muckhart 🗓 ✓
FK14 7JN
☎ (01259) 781324 ⊕ theinnatmuckhart.com
Devon Original 70/-, 24K IPA, Pride ⊞
Single-storey old coaching inn in a picturesque rural village close to the Japanese Gardens, overlooked by the Ochil Hills. It has low ceilings, exposed timber construction and a welcoming open fire, with a beer garden to the side. It was recently extended to the rear, creating a large, bright room with seating and TV. The restaurant produces good-quality food, making it a popular with locals and tourists. It serves their own Devon Ales, which are brewed at its sister pub, the Mansfield Arms in Sauchie. Holiday cottages are attached. Q🕭🏵🖾🕪🕭AP🖵🏵🕭

Sauchie

Mansfield Arms 🗓 ✓
7 Main Street, FK10 3JR (in centre of village, 100yds from main road)
☎ (01259) 722020 ⊕ devonales.com/mansfield-arms
Devon Original 70/- ⊞, 24K IPA ⊞/Ⓖ, Pride ⊞
A traditional two-bar pub and the oldest operating microbrewery in the Wee County. Four Devon Ales are dispensed from three changing handpumps. The bar is family owned and run, and is popular with the locals who enjoy lively banter, and families come to enjoy the food served in the comfortable lounge. Both beer and meals are excellent value for money. The pub is on the Stirling-Alloa circular bus route. 🕭🕪🕭P🖵(52,H2)🏵🕭

Stirling

Allan Park
20 Allan Park, FK8 2QG
☎ (01786) 475336 ⊕ theallanparkstirling.co.uk
Cairngorm Cairngorm Gold; house beer (by Cairngorm); 1 changing beer (sourced regionally; often Loch Ness) ⊞
Dating back to 1880, this historic, listed Georgian building features a Roman Doric columned fanlight door. It has been refurbished in recent years, bringing a bright and airy feel to the various open-plan rooms and conservatory. It operates as a pub, hotel, restaurant and coffee shop, attracting visitors and locals. Although mainly set for dining, drinkers are welcome in the lower mezzanine and bar area, which often features beers from Cairngorm and Loch Ness breweries.
Q🕭🏵🖾🕪🕭≠P🖵🏵🕭

Birds & Bees 🗓
Easter Cornton Road, FK9 5PB (off Causewayhead Rd)
☎ (01786) 473663 ⊕ thebirdsandthebees-stirling.com
3 changing beers (sourced regionally; often Caledonian, Harviestoun) ⊞
A welcoming converted rustic farmstead, located between the historic National Wallace Monument and Stirling Castle, in a residential area on the outskirts of north Stirling. This award-winning gastropub serves locally sourced food, and three handpumps dispense a variety of Scottish ales. Two large beer gardens feature a permanent barbecue area in the courtyard and a pétanque pitch. This is a popular pub, with a good mix of locals and tourists. Q🕭🏵🕭🕪🕭🕭P🖵(C30)🏵🕭

Portcullis Hotel
Castle Wynd, FK8 1EG (next to Stirling Castle)
☎ (01786) 472290 ⊕ theportcullishotel.com
2 changing beers (sourced nationally; often Fyne, Orkney, Timothy Taylor) ⊞
Dating from 1787, this historic Category B-listed building, originally a grammar school, is now a hotel and bar next to the castle esplanade. Exposed stone walls, wood panelling and an open fireplace with an ornate surround create a warm and cosy atmosphere, attracting both tourists and locals. It has an excellent reputation for food (booking is advisable) and two ever-changing ales from north and south of the border, plus a good range of malt whiskies. 🕭🏵🖾🕪🕭≠P🖵🕭

Settle Inn
91 St Marys Wynd, FK8 1BU
3 changing beers (sourced regionally; often Alechemy, Orkney, Spey Valley) ⊞
Built in 1733, the Settle Inn stands on a hill leading to Stirling Castle and is the oldest pub in this ancient city. The atmospheric inn (with a few regular ghosts) is frequented by tourists, students and locals. The front bar is cosy and friendly, aided by a roaring fire with old curling stones in the hearth. The cavern-style room at the rear provides extra seating and hosts music events, plus a Sunday night quiz. Q≠🕭P🖵🏵🕭♪

Tillicoultry

Royal Arms
2 High Street, FK13 6AE
☎ (01259) 753037
3 changing beers (sourced nationally; often Fuller's, Theakston, Timothy Taylor) ⊞
This popular drinks-only pub, run by an enthusiastic owner, caters mainly for local trade, though visitors are made welcome. It has a dartboard, large sports TVs and a fruit machine, and is furnished with comfortable seating and bar stools, and features a Victorian fireplace with log-burner. A quieter side room with a small counter is ideal for families. There are three handpumps serving changing beers. 🏵🕭P(52)🏵🕭

Volunteer Arms
132 High Street, FK13 6DU
☎ (01259) 750368
2 changing beers (sourced nationally; often Fyne, Greene King, Harviestoun) ⊞
This unpretentious corner pub, near the village's main bus stop, offers a warm welcome to all, thanks mainly to the collective efforts of the enthusiastic landlord and his family. It has a small bar area with ample seating in three distinct bays on two levels. Large TVs cater for sports fans. This pub is a recent and key addition to the growing and thriving local real ale community and has received a local CAMRA Newcomer award. 🕭P🏵🕭♪

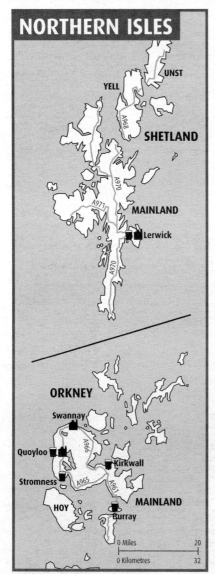

NORTHERN ISLES

(Map showing UNST, YELL, SHETLAND, MAINLAND, Lerwick, ORKNEY, Swannay, Quoyloo, Stromness, Kirkwall, HOY, MAINLAND, Burray)

0 Miles 20
0 Kilometres 32

Burray: Orkney

Sands Hotel

KW17 2SS (follow signs for pier at village)
☎ (01856) 731298 ⊕ thesandshotel.co.uk
Swannay Scapa Special ⊞
Situated in a small fishing village on the Island of Burray, just off mainland Orkney and overlooking the harbour and South Ronaldsay beyond, the Sands was originally a 19th-century fish store. It is popular with locals and visitors alike. Meals are served in the comfortable, friendly bar, or in the separate restaurant, both of which specialise in local seafood. Dive boats and yachts can tie up at the pier outside. Accommodation is in six en-suite bedrooms and two luxury suites, all with sea views. Kirkwall is eight miles to the north, and other attractions such as the Italian Chapel and Churchill Barriers are within easy reach. Closed weekday afternoons.
Q✿⌂◖&ẢP❀🌐

Kirkwall: Orkney

Auld Motor Hoose

26 Junction Road, KW15 1AB
☎ (01856) 871422 ⊕ auldmotorhoose.co.uk
Swannay Scapa Special ⊞
A friendly, motor-themed pub with a single bar room, featuring lots of motoring memorabilia and car parts scattered throughout. The jukebox tends to blast out rock classics. There is a regular quiz night, and live music, mainly at weekends, and the pub is one of the venues for the Orkney Rock Festival. An outside patio has a smoking area. It is the sister bar to the Torvhaug in Bridge Street and convenient for the bus station. Twice voted local CAMRA Pub of the Year. ✿&♣🖳(X1)❀🌐♪

Helgi's Bar 🍷

14 Harbour Street, KW15 1LE (by harbour)
☎ (01856) 879293 ⊕ helgis.co.uk
Swannay Scapa Special; 2 changing beers (sourced locally; often Swannay) ⊞
Converted from a former shipping office, this small, smart bar has the look of a modern café, with wood panelling and a floor of local stone. Special food nights where food is matched with ales are a highlight. Regular music sessions and a weekly Thursday quiz night are also hosted. It sits on the harbour front, where seafood is landed daily, and is a handy place to fill in time before island hopping on the many ferries to outlying parts. Local CAMRA Pub of the Year 2022-24. Closed Monday and opens at 3pm Tuesday and Wednesday. ◖&🖳🌐♪

Skippers Bar

Bridge Street, KW15 1LE (corner of Harbour St and Bridge St)
☎ (01856) 872232 ⊕ kirkwallhotel.com
2 changing beers (sourced locally; often Orkney) ⊞
Skippers Bar is a vibrant, busy bar, especially in the evenings, with a mainly youngish clientele and multiple TV screens. It is part of the Kirkwall Hotel, which overlooks the harbour. There is a large, separate lounge area with a whisky bar, often hosting functions and wedding parties. The bar may sell two ales in season and the lounge probably only one, and you can move between the two bars via a connecting corridor.
🏠◖♣❀🌐♪

St Ola Hotel

Harbour Street, KW15 1LE
☎ (01856) 875090 ⊕ stolahotel.co.uk
Swannay Scapa Special; 1 changing beer (sourced locally; often Swannay) ⊞
Built overlooking the harbour on the site of the Inns of Sinclair dating back to the 14th century, the Ola is a short walk from all of Kirkwall's major attractions. It has a traditional public bar, and a larger lounge to the rear where food is served. Ales are available in both bars, along with an extensive range of whiskies. A music session is held from 4pm Sundays on the last Sunday of the month, which can be lively during the summer. A former local CAMRA Pub of the Year.
✿⌂◖&♣🖳❀🌐♪

REAL ALE BREWERIES

Lerwick ✦ Lerwick: Shetland
Orkney ✦ Orkney: Quoyloo
Swannay Orkney: Swannay

SCOTLAND

Lerwick: Shetland

Lerwick Brewery Ⓛ

Ladies Drive, Staney Hill, ZE1 0NA (near A970)
☎ (01595) 694552 ⊕ lerwickbrewery.co.uk
2 changing beers (sourced locally; often Lerwick) Ⓗ
The brewery tap and shop has two handpumps serving Lerwick real ales along with bottled and canned beers, a wide range of spirits, wine and soft drinks. Brewery tours are held on Thursday and Friday at 2pm; advanced booking essential. There are brewery open days occasionally on some Saturdays and Sundays. The brewery is also available to hire for parties, events and meetings. Closed Monday. **P**

Quoyloo: Orkney

Orkney Brewery Visitor Centre

KW16 3LT
☎ (01856) 841777 ⊕ orkneybrewery.co.uk
4 changing beers (sourced locally; often Orkney) Ⓗ
The visitor centre is part of this award-winning brewery, established in 1988 and converted from the old schoolhouse. A selection of beers are available on cask,

and a wide variety of food includes Dark Island hotpot, a brewhouse burger, Westray rollmop herring, and Grimbister cheese with Dark Island chutney. The gift shop stocks beers and other brewery related products. May not be open all year round and hours are restricted; best to check in advance. ⟿◖P

Stromness: Orkney

Ferry Inn

10 John Street, KW16 3AD (opp ferry terminal)
☎ (01856) 850280 ⊕ ferryinn.com
Swannay Scapa Special; 2 changing beers (sourced locally; often Orkney, Swannay) Ⓗ
Reopened in 2022 following major refurbishment, the Ferry is an easy walk from the harbour front. It is popular with locals and visitors, including divers who come to Orkney to explore the sunken German fleet at Scapa Flow. Annual folk and blues festivals are held, with a marquee erected outside complete with an ale pump. The pub is handy for buses to Kirkwall and the mainland ferry from Scrabster. Nearby attractions include the Ring of Brodgar and Skara Brae village. A previous local CAMRA Pub of the Year. ❀☎◖❶ ▲♣P🚌(X1)❀ 🛜 ♫

Sands Hotel, Burray: Orkney (Photo: Stuart McMahon)

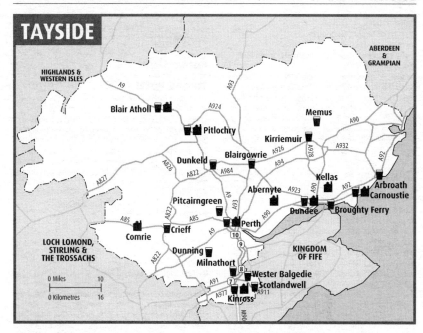

Arbroath

Corn Exchange ✔

14 Olympic Centre, Market Place, DD11 1HR

☎ (01241) 432430

Belhaven 80/-; Greene King Abbot; Sharp's Doom Bar; 3 changing beers (sourced nationally; often Stewart) Ⓗ

Located just off the High Street, this Wetherspoon is a conversion of a former 19th-century corn exchange. Although largely open-plan, there are a number of booths providing some privacy. A varied selection of real ales is always available. Boat trips offering fishing or a visit to the 200-year-old Bell Rock lighthouse can be taken from the nearby harbour. ⛬✿⬤♿≈🅿🛜

Blair Atholl

Atholl Arms Hotel Ⓛ

PH18 5SG

☎ (01796) 481205 ⊕ athollarmshotel.co.uk

Moulin Light, Braveheart, Ale of Atholl, Old Remedial Ⓗ

The Atholl Arms has a grand and imposing façade in the Victorian Highland style. The characterful Bothy Bar serves four ales produced by the local Moulin brewery, as well as freshly cooked food throughout the day. Blair Atholl and the surrounding area is a popular destination for walking, climbing, biking and sightseeing. Off-season Bothy Bar opening hours may be shorter, but ales can be brought through to the lounge bar. Open daily throughout the year.

Q⛬✿🛏⬤♿⚲≈🅿🚃(M91,87) ✿🛜

Blairgowrie

Ericht Alehouse

13 Wellmeadow, PH10 6ND

☎ (01250) 872469

6 changing beers (sourced regionally; often Loch Lomond, MòR, Windswept) Ⓗ

Classic town-centre pub with a friendly atmosphere. There are two seated areas separated by a well-stocked bar, and a wide range of ever-changing ales from Scottish breweries, lagers and ciders is served. There is no food, but customers are welcome to bring their own as long as they tidy up afterwards. A regular winner of local CAMRA Pub of the Year since 1999. It has been community-run since 2023, with enthusiastic volunteers behind the bar. Cash payment only. Closed Mondays and open 2-7pm Sundays; opens at 5pm other days.

Q♣⬤🛏✿🛜

Fair o' Blair

25-29 Allan Street, PH10 6AB

☎ (01250) 871890

Belhaven 80/-; Greene King Abbot; 4 changing beers (sourced regionally; often Stewart) Ⓗ

This Wetherspoon pub, managed by a real ale enthusiast, has a small beer garden to the rear on two levels, with disabled access to the lower of the two. Nearby is the Wellmeadow, centrepiece of the town, a grassy triangular plot hosting regular markets and outdoor entertainments. The practice of holding fairs and markets here began in 1824, including the famous Fair o' Blair itself, which was staged every July for many years. ⛬✿⬤♿♣🅿(57) 🛜

REAL ALE BREWERIES

71 Brewing ✦ Dundee
Abernyte Abernyte
Cullach ✦ Perth
Inveralmond Perth
Law Dundee
Loch Leven ✦ Kinross
MòR Kellas
Moulin 🍺 Pitlochry
Nat 20 Comrie
Shed 35 Carnoustie
Wasted Degrees ✦ Blair Atholl

Stormont Arms ★

101 Perth Street, PH10 6DT

☎ (01250) 873142

1 changing beer (sourced regionally; often MòR, Orkney) Ⓗ

Real ale is served from two handpumps in this traditional Scottish pub, with a public bar, lounge and small adjacent room. The friendly bar has a classic interior, with wooden bench seating and a dartboard (it hosts a darts team during the week). It is not open on Tuesdays, and may also close early if quiet, so check before travelling. It is a 10-minute walk from the town centre, but many buses stop nearby. Q♣🖰🐾🏵

Broughty Ferry

Fisherman's Tavern

12-16 Fort Street, DD5 2AD

☎ (01382) 775941 ⊕ fishermanstavern-broughtyferry.co.uk

5 changing beers (sourced nationally; often Greene King, MòR) Ⓗ

Licensed since 1857, this famous pub consists of three fishermen's cottages converted into a small hotel. The bar is to the right of the entrance, with a snug on the left, leading to the dining room/lounge, which has a real fire. The lounge to the rear has disabled access from Bell's Lane. A famed annual beer festival is held in July, run by the local lifeboat crew. Guest ales are from local Mòr brewing, and also around Britain. This Belhaven/Greene King managed house was refurbished in 2018.
🛏🏵🖰🕪🚃🐾🏵♪

Jolly's Hotel ✪

43A Gray Street, DD5 2BJ

☎ (01382) 734910

Belhaven 80/-; Greene King Abbot; Sharp's Doom Bar; 3 changing beers (sourced nationally) Ⓗ

Named after John Jolly, its proprietor for two decades in the late 19th century, this Wetherspoon hotel run by a real ale enthusiast has expanded considerably over the years. It features two large areas, one for drinking and dining, the other principally for dining. The numerous handpumps offer a wide selection of ales to a mixed clientele. An outdoor patio area has a good number of tables. Accommodation is in 25 en-suite rooms.
🛏🏵🖰🕪🛆🚃🖰(73) 🏵

Royal Arch ✪

285 Brook Street, DD5 2DS

☎ (01382) 779741 ⊕ the-royal-arch.co.uk

2 changing beers (sourced nationally; often 71 Brewing, Brakspear, MòR) Ⓗ

A popular, locally-owned pub in the centre of the Ferry. There are three TVs in the public bar for the many sports fans, and good-quality meals are served in the Art Deco lounge. Local ales, often from MòR Beers, and others from all over Britain are served through three handpumps. The gantry in the public bar was rescued in the past from the demolished Craigour Bar in Dens Road. The station is close by and train times are displayed on a screen in the bar. 🏵🕪🚃🖰(73)🐾🏵

Ship Inn

121 Fisher Street, DD5 2BR

☎ (01382) 779176 ⊕ theshipinn-broughtyferry.co.uk

Timothy Taylor Landlord; 2 changing beers (sourced regionally; often Orkney) Ⓗ

The Ship Inn is a traditional free house on the waterfront at Broughty Ferry, with views over the Tay towards Fife. Dating back to 1847, this cosy retreat is atmospheric and interesting, with several nautical features. Usually three well-kept real ales are available. A range of tasty bar

meals is on offer and there is a restaurant upstairs. There is pavement seating outside for the good weather.
🏵🛏🕪🐾🏵🏵

Carnoustie

Station Hotel

23 Station Road, DD7 6AR

☎ (01241) 852447 ⊕ stationhotelcarnoustie.com

Caledonian Deuchars IPA; Timothy Taylor Landlord; 1 changing beer (sourced nationally; often Orkney) Ⓗ

Beside Carnoustie railway station, the Station Hotel offers comfortable accommodation, a warm welcome and excellent pub food, including the famed steak pie and classic chicken curry. Both public and lounge bars provide the two regular real ales plus one changing guest beer. The hotel is just a short walk to the town's famous golf links, a venue for the Open Championship.
🛏🕪🚃♣🖰(73) 🐾🏵

Crieff

Tower

81 East High Street, PH7 3JA

☎ (01764) 650050 ⊕ thetowercrieff.com

1 changing beer (sourced regionally; often Hybrid, Loch Leven) Ⓗ

Small family-run gastropub close to the town centre. One real ale is served, usually from local breweries. The beams in the bar display some interesting and amusing proverbs and quotations. Quiz nights take place every second Wednesday. The large beer garden to the rear has great views south to the Ochil hills. It is open daily for food and drink. Accommodation is provided in five self-catering apartments. Q🛏🏵🖰🕪🖰(15)🐾🏵

Dundee

Bank Bar

7-9 Union Street, DD1 4BN

☎ (01382) 205037 ⊕ thebankbardundee.com

4 changing beers (sourced nationally; often 71 Brewing, Loch Lomond, MòR) Ⓗ

A former bank, with bare-boards floor, wooden furniture and a series of alcoves with tables in the tradition of older Scottish city pubs. Four ales are usually pouring, with at least one local contribution from MòR or 71 Brewing. Other popular guest beers feature regularly from Fyne, Orkney, Robinson (Trooper), Theakston (Old Peculier), Titanic (Cherry and Plum Porters) and Williams Bros. Food is served 12-6pm daily, and live music is performed Friday and Saturday nights. Local CAMRA Pub of the Year 2022. 🛏🕪🛆🚃🖰🐾🏵♪

Market

7-9 Seagate, DD1 2EG

☎ (01382) 224591 ⊕ marketdundee.co.uk

2 changing beers (sourced regionally; often Alechemy, Stewart) Ⓗ

Formerly the Capitol cinema, built in 1945, before being converted into a large Lloyds pub. A staircase rises to the large upper seating area which is mainly for families. Four handpumps serve two changing beers, with local ale from Law Brewing often featuring. It is popular with shoppers and those watching sport on 10 TVs or the large screen. It is lively on Friday and Saturday evenings with occasional live music. Open for breakfasts, with alcohol sales from 11am. 🛏🕪🛆🚃🖰(73)🏵♪

Phoenix

103 Nethergate, DD1 4DH

☎ (01382) 200014

Caledonian Deuchars IPA; Timothy Taylor Landlord; 3 changing beers (sourced regionally; often 71 Brewing, Loch Lomond, Orkney) ⊞
One of Dundee's oldest pubs, with sturdy wooden seats and tables, green leather benches, and a rare Ballingall Brewery mirror, all giving it a warm and cosy traditional character and great atmosphere. The location is handy for the Rep Theatre, Dundee Contemporary Arts and Bonar Hall. Five ales are on offer, with Scottish breweries well supported, along with excellent pub food provided at reasonable prices. Note that since the food is fresh, serving may finish early at busy times.
◑⇻🚆(73,16) ❀ 🤶

Speedwell Bar ⛾ ★ ✅
165-167 Perth Road, DD2 1AS
☎ (01382) 667783 🌐 speedwellbar.co.uk
3 changing beers (sourced nationally; often Inveralmond, Loch Leven) ⊞
Built in 1903 for James Speed, this pub is also known as Mennie's after the family who ran it for more than 50 years. The L-shaped bar is divided by a part-glazed screen and has a magnificent mahogany gantry and counter, dado-panelled walls and an anaglypta Jacobean ceiling. Two seated rooms are separate from the bar. There are usually three ales on offer, sourced from a wide variety of breweries, some local, many from elsewhere in Scotland, or from all over England.
◑🚆❀🤶♪

Dunkeld

Perth Arms 🅛
High Street, PH8 0AJ
☎ (01350) 727270
2 changing beers (sourced locally; often Cromarty, Orkney, Wasted Degrees) ⊞
Close to Dunkeld Cathedral, this establishment – first opened in 1795 – has been in the same family for almost 50 years, and is the oldest trading pub in the area. The cosy, one-room bar serves a mix of locals and tourists. Two handpumps usually dispense Scottish beers, one of them local, and food is served daily, with a carvery on Sunday. The secluded beer garden to rear also has a smoking area. 🏠🅿️◑🚆❀🤶♪

Dunning

Kirkstyle Inn ✅
Kirkstyle Square, PH2 0RR
☎ (01764) 684248 🌐 thekirkstyleinn.co.uk
House beer (by Marston's); 2 changing beers (sourced nationally; often Timothy Taylor) ⊞
A traditional village inn dating from 1760, overshadowed by the impressive Norman steeple of St Serf's Church, which is home to the ancient Dupplin Cross and other Pictish relics. One or two ales in the cosy public bar come from a variety of Scottish independents, as well as English and Welsh regional breweries. The pub usually serves its own real house ale, Risky Kelt. Open daily for food and drink, but from 5pm on Mondays.
🏠🅿️◑🚆(17) ❀🤶♪

Kinross

Loch Leven Brewery Taproom 🅛
Muirs, KY13 8AS
☎ (01577) 864881 🌐 lochleven.beer
Loch Leven Warrior Queen, Shining Knight, Outlaw King, King Slayer ⊞
Loch Leven's taproom is attached to the brewery and offers a choice of three beers on handpump from the full

cask range, while two keg taps dispense craft beers from Cold Town. Loch Leven Gins are also featured. Drinks may be consumed indoors or at tables outside. A growler dispenser enables cask beers to be purchased to take home. Bottled beers, brewery gifts and souvenirs may be purchased from the shop. Closed Monday, but check brewery website or social media for opening times.
❀🅿️🚆❀🤶♪

Kirriemuir

Airlie Arms
St Malcolm's Wynd, DD8 4HB
☎ (01575) 218080 🌐 airliearms.net
2 changing beers (sourced locally; often Burnside, MòR) ⊞
After lying closed for many years, this large, B-listed, 18th-century establishment was substantially renovated and reopened in 2015 by a local family, with real ale making a very welcome appearance. Since then the Airlie has gone from strength to strength. There are two handpumps on the bar serving changing real ales, usually locally sourced. Drinks are served from 11am. Food is served daily in the bar, with the restaurant open at weekends. 🏠❀🅿️◑♣🅿️🚆(21)❀🤶

Memus

Drovers Inn
DD8 3TY
☎ (01307) 860322 🌐 the-drovers.com
Timothy Taylor Landlord; 1 changing beer (often Harviestoun, MòR) ⊞
Located in the rural setting of Memus, just north of Forfar, and handily placed for the Angus Glens, the Drovers is a traditional Scottish inn with a contemporary look. An old range fire in the bar adds to the atmosphere, especially on a chilly day. Two ales are usually served, and excellent food using locally sourced seasonal produce is available daily. Food and drink are served every day; check for times. There is a large outdoor dining area with an adjoining play area for children.
Q🏠❀◑🅿️❀🤶

Milnathort

Village Inn
36 Wester Loan, KY13 9YH
☎ (01577) 863293
2 changing beers (sourced regionally) ⊞
Dating back to 1728, this friendly local has a semi open-plan interior featuring classic brewery mirrors and local historical photographs. The comfortable lounge area has low ceilings, exposed joists and stone walls, while the bar area is warmed by an open fire. The pub has been family-owned since 1985 and usually serves two or sometimes three beers, sourced from breweries across Scotland and beyond. Milnathort links some great cycling routes through the Ochils, via Burleigh Castle, to the more leisurely Loch Leven Heritage Trail. 🚆♣🚆❀🤶

Perth

Bunker
222 South Street, PH2 8NY
☎ (01738) 632000 🌐 thebunkergolflounge.co.uk
Timothy Taylor Landlord ⊞
Former bank converted to a lounge bar, with areas featuring golf simulators and a separate games room. A single handpump pours Timothy Taylor Landlord (or its dark version), and Cullach's Tayside IPA is available from membrane keg. Good pub grub includes the famous

Tabla curries from just across the road, available all day and well into evening. There is a water bowl at the door for thirsty four-legged customers. Closed on Monday. ⚄🕮❀🕪❧⬚❀🕯♪

Capital Asset ✔

26 Tay Street, PH1 5LQ
☎ (01738) 580457
Greene King Abbot; Sharp's Doom Bar; 4 changing beers (sourced nationally; often Stewart) 🅗
A Wetherspoon pub that was formerly a savings bank. The high ceilings and ornate cornices have been retained, and pictures of old Perth adorn the walls of the open-plan lounge which overlooks the River Tay. The large safe from its banking days can be found in the family area. A variety of six ales are dispensed, and food is available all day. Beer festivals twice a year are popular with local ale drinkers. The manager is a real ale enthusiast. Q⚄🕮❀🕪⬚❀🕯(7)🕯

Cherrybank Inn

210 Glasgow Road, PH2 0NA
☎ (01738) 624349 ⊕ cherrybankinn.co.uk
3 changing beers (sourced regionally; often Kelburn, Orkney, Stewart) 🅗
This 250-year-old, family-owned, former drovers' inn is a popular watering hole for locals and travellers alike. Three ales, generally from Scottish independent breweries, are dispensed by handpump in the public bar, or from the larger L-shaped lounge. As well as breakfasts, excellent bar lunches and evening meals are served daily. There is a large, sunny, elevated covered wooden decking area to the rear. The inn has seven en-suite rooms. ⚄🕮❀🕪P⬚❀🕯♪

Old Ship Inn ✔

31 High Street, PH1 5TJ (on Skinnergate)
☎ 07956 924767 ⊕ oldshipinnperth.co.uk
3 changing beers (sourced nationally; often Fyne, Greene King, Oakham) 🅗
Said to be the oldest pub in Perth, the Old Ship has traded under the same name since 1665. It was the city's oasis for real ale in the 1980s, and now offers one regular ale and two changing guest beers. A large oil painting of a sailing ship adds interest in the timber-lined bar, which is lightened by a frieze and white-painted ceiling. The upstairs lounge reopened as 'Above Board' in 2018 after a 20-year closure. 🕮❧P⬚(7)❀🕯

Silvery Tay

189 South Street, PH2 8NY
☎ (01738) 321119
1 changing beer (often Stewart) 🅗
Situated on the walking route from the railway station to the city centre, this pub is conveniently located at the historic South Street Port. The high-ceilinged single room has dark wood panelling and a fine staircase up to the closed first floor. There are a number of alcoved seating areas, making for privacy if desired. Real ale was reintroduced in 2019, and is usually from Stewart brewing. ❧⬚❀🕯♪

Pitcairngreen

Pitcairngreen Inn

Bridgeton Brae, PH1 3LP

☎ (01738) 583022 ⊕ pitcairngreeninn.co.uk
2 changing beers (sourced regionally; often Cromarty, Loch Lomond) 🅗
Adjacent to the village green, this is quite a large establishment with several different sections. Well-kept ales are served through three handpumps. This is one of the best places in Tayside for real ciders and perries, which are presented professionally. The pub has won several cider and food awards, including CAMRA Scotland and Northern Ireland Cider Pub of the Year. Normally closed Monday and Tuesday. Q⚄🕮❀🕪❧P⬚❀🕯♪

Pitlochry

Old Mill Inn

Mill Lane, PH16 5BH
☎ (01796) 474020 ⊕ theoldmillpitlochry.co.uk
4 changing beers (sourced regionally; often Cromarty, Orkney, Wasted Degrees) 🅗
Located in the centre of Pitlochry, this former 19th-century mill features a water wheel, still driven by the local stream, in the pub garden. This well-run, family-owned inn serves food from an extensive menu most of the day until 9pm, including breakfast. The large bar offers a varied selection of real ales, usually three or four from Scottish breweries, and cider too. Live music is a regular feature at weekends. Accommodation is available. ⚄🕮❧🕮❧⬚❀🕪❧P⬚❀🕯♪

Scotlandwell

Well Country Inn

Main Street, KY13 9JA
☎ (01592) 840444
1 changing beer (often Stewart) 🅗
A pleasant country inn under the imposing Bishop Hill, on the A911 between Kinross and Glenrothes. The village and pub take their name from the impressive canopied village well. The bar features real ale, normally from Stewart brewing, from two handpumps, with one pouring and another ale always tapped to follow. There is an impressive log-burning fire in the winter. The pub is popular with cyclists and walkers. Open every day from 4pm. B&B accommodation is provided in chalets adjacent to the inn. ⚄🕮❧🕮⬚P⬚(201)❀🕯

Wester Balgedie

Balgedie Toll Tavern 🅛

KY13 9HE (at jct of A911 and B919)
☎ (01592) 840212 ⊕ balgedietolltavern.com
Harviestoun Bitter & Twisted; Loch Leven Warrior Queen 🅗
Welcoming country tavern dating from 1534. There are seating areas on two levels, where a fine selection of meals and bar snacks is available. The old toll house is now the Harness Bar and features low ceilings, oak beams, horse brasses and wooden settles. Cask-conditioned beers from local breweries are served from two handpumps in the lower bar area. Food is served six days a week. Closed on Wednesdays, apart from quiz nights. ⚄🕮❀🕪❧P⬚(201)❀🕯♪

We would like to hear from you. If you think a pub not listed in the Guide is worthy of consideration, please let us know. Send us the name, full address and phone number (if known). If a pub in the Guide has given poor service, we would also like to know.
Email: **gbgeditor@camra.org.uk**

NORTHERN ISLES

SHETLAND

HIGHLANDS & WESTERN ISLES

ABERDEEN & GRAMPIAN

TAYSIDE

FIFE

ARGYLL & THE ISLES

LOCH LOMOND, STIRLING & THE TROSSACHS

EDINBURGH & LOTHIANS

GREATER GLASGOW & CLYDE

BORDERS

AYRSHIRE & ARRAN

DUMFRIES & GALLOWAY

NORTHUMBERLAND

TYNE & WEAR

NORTHERN IRELAND

CUMBRIA

DURHAM

ISLE OF MAN

NORTH YORKSHIRE

LANCASHIRE

WEST YORKS

EAST YORKS

MERSEYSIDE

GREATER MANCHESTER

SOUTH YORKS

LINCOLNSHIRE

CHESHIRE

DERBYSHIRE

NOTTINGHAM-SHIRE

NW WALES

NE WALES

NORFOLK

SHROPSHIRE

STAFFORD-SHIRE

LEICESTERSHIRE

CAMBRIDGE-SHIRE

SUFFOLK

MID WALES

WEST MIDLANDS

WORCESTER-SHIRE

WARWICK-SHIRE

NORTHAMPTON-SHIRE

BEDFORD-SHIRE

HERTFORD-SHIRE

ESSEX

HEREFORD-SHIRE

GWENT

WEST WALES

BUCKINGHAM

GLAMORGAN

GLOUCS & BRISTOL

OXFORD-SHIRE

GREATER LONDON

BERKSHIRE

WILTSHIRE

SURREY

KENT

SOMERSET

HAMPSHIRE

WEST SUSSEX

EAST SUSSEX

DEVON

DORSET

CORNWALL

ISLE OF WIGHT

CHANNEL ISLANDS

Northern Ireland
Channel Islands
Isle of Man

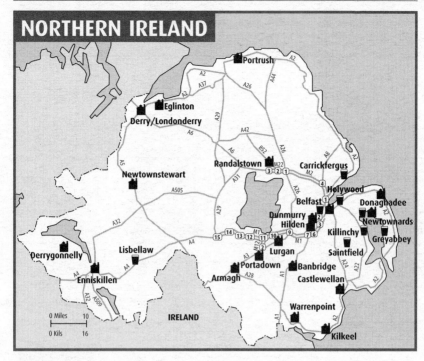

NORTHERN IRELAND

Belfast

Boundary Taproom

310 Newtownards Road, BT4 1HE
🌐 boundarybrewing.coop/pages/taproom
21 changing beers (sourced locally; often Boundary) Ⓟ
The taproom for Boundary brewery is a roomy, contemporary bar with long tables. Twenty taps dispense mainly Boundary's own beers plus guests. There are also fridges with bottles and cans from a variety of other breweries. Food can be brought in from a nearby pizzeria. **Q**&♿≉(Titanic Quarter)🚌

Bridge House ✔

37-43 Bedford Street, BT2 7EJ
☎ (028) 9072 7890
Greene King Abbot; Ruddles Best Bitter; Sharp's Doom Bar; changing beers (sourced nationally) Ⓗ
Large Wetherspoon pub close to the city centre. It has eight handpumps in the main bar, serving mainly national ales with some local ones from Whitewater. It is a popular watering hole and although it can get busy staff keep up with a fast and friendly service. It is open for food from 8am, with alcohol available from 11.30am (12.30 Sun). **Q**🛏🎧🐕♿≉(Great Victoria Street)🚌🛜

Bullhouse East

442-446 Newtownards Road, BT4 1HJ
☎ (028) 9013 8554 🌐 bullhousebrewco.com
Changing beers (sourced locally; often Bullhouse) Ⓟ
Bullhouse East is a craft beer bar a short walk up the Newtownards Road from Boundary's taproom. It is a bright, spacious bar with a beer garden at the back. Twenty taps serve a selection of Bullhouse's own beers, plus guests. A fridge also contains beers and ciders from several craft outlets. Wood-fired pizza is available, and the bar hosts the popular Bullapalooza street party.
Q🎧♿🍴🚌🐾🛜

Crown ★

46 Great Victoria Street, BT2 7BA (opp Europa Hotel and Great Victoria St station)

☎ (028) 9024 3187

St Austell Nicholson's Pale Ale; 5 changing beers (sourced regionally) Ⓗ
Fresh from a period of heritage conservation, the Crown looks as good as ever. The exterior has been enhanced while the interior retains all of its magnificent historic features. Five handpumps dispense a mixture of local and national ales. An additional pump has cider, sometimes real cider from the likes of Sandford Orchards.

REAL ALE BREWERIES

Ards Newtownards
Armagh Armagh
Baronscourt Newtownstewart
Beer Hut Kilkeel
Boundary ♦ Belfast
Bullhouse Belfast
Dopey Dick Derry
Fermanagh Derrygonnelly
Hercules Belfast
Hilden Hilden
Knockout Belfast
Lacada Portrush
Mashdown Banbridge
McCracken's Portadown
Modest Beer Randalstown
Mourne Mountains Warrenpoint
Norn Iron Dunmurry
Northbound Eglinton
Our Randalstown
Rough Brothers Derry / Londonderry
Sheelin Enniskillen
SpadeTown Lurgan
Twisted Kettle Donaghadee
Whitewater Castlewellan

Good food is available in the bar and in the dining rooms upstairs. A former local CAMRA Pub of the Year.
Q◐◐♿❄(Great Victoria Street) ●🚃

Deer's Head
1-3 Lower Garfield Street, BT1 1FP
☎ (028) 9023 4655 ⊕ thedeersheadbelfast.com
Changing beers (sourced locally; often Bell's) ℗
This old drinking emporium has been given a more modern makeover in recent years. It retains the long bar with globe lights, and the snugs along the windows, though the interior is much brighter than before. The Deer's Head is Belfast's only brewpub, and Bell's brewery can be seen through a glass screen, with signs showing what is being brewed. Good food is available, along with sport on TV, and there is music in the bar and upstairs. ◐♿🚃❄♫

Errigle Inn ★
312-320 Ormeau Road, BT7 2GE
☎ (028) 9064 1410 ⊕ errigle.com
4 changing beers (sourced locally; often Whitewater) Ⓗ
The Oak Lounge is the peaceful back bar of the Errigle Inn. The handpumps serve up to four ales from local breweries and occasional national brands. A handpulled cider is a regular feature, occasionally including real ciders such as Hunts. The Lounge is open from 5pm on weekdays and from 2pm at weekends. When it is not open staff will bring handpulled drinks into the main bar.
Q◐◐♿🚃❄♫

John Hewitt
51 Donegal Street, BT1 2FH (100yds from St Anne's Cathedral)
☎ (028) 9023 3768 ⊕ thejohnhewitt.com
Changing beers (sourced locally; often Boundary) ℗
Now part of Boundary brewery's portfolio, the John Hewitt is a popular bar in Belfast's Cathedral area. It features a large snug and a stage, and is a venue for live music. It is different from most bars in that it is run by the Belfast Unemployed Resource Centre, and profits go to fund their charitable work. Boundary beers and guests are served as well as a fridge with a selection of other craft beers. Closed on Mondays. Q👥♿🚃♫

McHughs
29-31 Queens Square, BT1 3FG (near Albert Clock)
☎ (028) 9050 9999 ⊕ mchughsbar.com
Whitewater Maggie's Leap IPA Ⓗ
McHughs is a bar in a Grade A-listed building, reputedly Belfast's oldest. It features the restored old bar which adjoins a more modern public bar. There is one handpump exclusively dispensing ales from Whitewater brewery. The restaurant upstairs serves good food, which can be eaten downstairs. Below the bar is a basement where music acts appear. Sporting events are also an attraction. Close to Albert Clock and Customs House Square. Q◐◐♿❄(Central)🚌🚃❄♫

Northern Lights
451 Ormeau Road, BT7 3GQ
☎ (028) 9029 0291 ⊕ galwaybaybrewery.com
Changing beers (sourced regionally) Ⓗ/℗
A corner bar on the Ormeau Road opposite the Errigle. It is a craft beer bar downstairs with a function area upstairs. There are 20 taps, with 10 from Galway brewery and the rest from others. A range of craft beers and ciders are also available in bottles and cans. There is a handpump but you need to phone in advance to see what is on. Good food is available. A former local CAMRA Pub of the Year. Q👥◐◐♿🚃❄

Sunflower
65 Union Street, BT1 2JG
☎ (028) 9023 2474 ⊕ sunflowerbelfast.com
1 changing beer (sourced locally) Ⓗ
Now under new management, the Sunflower continues to be a much-treasured outpost for real ale in Belfast. It is a one-room bar with a function room upstairs and a large beer garden. The bar features one handpump with ales mainly from local breweries, along with a selection of craft beers. Unusually, it does not sell Ireland's most famous beverage. Music is a big draw, with acts in the main bar and the lounge upstairs. 🏵🍴🚃❄❄♫

Woodworkers
20-22 Bradbury Place, BT7 1RS
☎ (028) 9087 1106 ⊕ woodworkersbelfast.com
Changing beers (sourced locally) ℗
This craft beer bar is part of Lavery's complex. It has up to 14 taps serving a variety of local, national and international beers. It was a former woodworkers shop and wood forms much of the decor. There is a restaurant area to one side of the bar and tables on the other. Good food is available, and drinks can be taken through to the main bar if you want to see sport on the many screens. Q👥◐♿❄(Botanic)🚃❄

Carrickfergus

Central Bar ✔
13-15 High Street, BT38 7AN (opp castle)
☎ (028) 9335 7840
Greene King Abbot; Ruddles Best Bitter; Sharp's Doom Bar; 2 changing beers (sourced regionally) Ⓗ
Community local with a dedicated clientele. The ground-floor public bar of this Wetherspoon pub can be a bit lively, and there is a family-friendly first-floor loggia-style sitting room with exposed timber trusses, affording inspirational views from its many windows over Belfast Lough and the adjacent 12th-century castle. Handpumps on both levels serve three house ales and guest ales, with a local ale from Whitewater brewery, is served from 11.30am (12.30pm Sun).
Q👥🏵◐♿❄🚃(563)

Greyabbey

Wildfowler Inn
1 Main Street, BT22 2NE (7 miles S of Newtownards on the A20)
☎ (028) 4278 8234 ⊕ wildfowlerinn.co.uk
2 changing beers (sourced locally; often Ards) Ⓚ
The Wildfowler is restaurant in a village seven miles south of Newtownards in County Down, and is an outlet for the nearby Ards brewery. The tap on the restaurant's bar dispenses a variety of their KeyKeg ales. Phone beforehand to check what is on. The restaurant serves good, locally sourced food. The bar is only open occasionally, though drinks can be taken ordered in the restaurant when buying food. A beer garden and off-road parking also feature. Q👥🏵◐♿P🚃

Holywood

Dirty Duck Ale House
3 Kinnegar Road, BT18 9JN
☎ (028) 9059 6666 ⊕ thedirtyduckalehouse.co.uk
3 changing beers (sourced nationally) Ⓗ
Perched near Belfast Lough, the Dirty Duck Ale House is a cosy haven, with its crackling fire, wooden beams and friendly staff. Good food, particularly seafood, is available in the bar and in the upstairs restaurant. Notably, it boasts three real ales, largely drawn from national and

local brands. It also has a beer garden, a collection of pumpclips, and a nook celebrating local golfing hero Rory McIlroy. A two-time former local CAMRA Pub of the Year. Q❄️✲◑🕹️🚲≢🛜

Killinchy

Daft Eddy's 🄻

Sketrick Island, BT23 6QH (2 miles N of Killinchey at Whiterock Bay)
☎ (028) 9754 1615 ⊕ dafteddys.co.uk
1 changing beer (sourced locally; often Whitewater)
This family-owned establishment has been in the same hands for many years, and is a rare example in Northern Ireland of a pub on an island accessed by a road over a causeway. It comprises a public bar, a highly recommended restaurant, and a coffee shop. The bar has been selling real ale for many years and now features handpulled ales from nearby Whitewater brewery.
Q❄️✲◑🕹️🅿️✿🛜

Lisbellaw

Dog & Duck Inn 🏆

30 Main Street, BT94 5ER
☎ (028) 6638 5371 ⊕ thedoganduckinn.com
14 changing beers (sourced locally; often Hercules, Lacada) Ⓗ/Ⓟ
The Dog & Duck specialises in independently made drinks. In addition to numerous taps, there are four handpumps, usually dispensing one real ale and up to three ciders. Real cider is often available from outlets like Sandford Orchards. Locally brewed ales such as Hercules and Lacada have appeared. Good food is served in the large dining area as well as a cosy room with a fire. The pub is also features the Glenwinny brewstillery, which produces small-batch Irish whiskey, poitin and rum. An annual beer festival is held the weekend before the late August Bank Holiday. Q❄️✲⛺◑🕹️🚲✿🐾🎵

Newtownards

Spirit Merchant ✓

54-56 Regent Street, BT23 4LP (opp bus station)
☎ (028) 9182 4270
Greene King Abbot; 5 changing beers (sourced nationally) Ⓗ
A one-bar Wetherspoon pub near Newtownards bus station. The building was formerly two Victorian houses which were combined, and the name recalls a previous pub. There are five handpumps pouring a variety of well-kept real ales. Inside are a number of areas to sit in, while outside there is a large beer garden. As with the other pubs in the chain, it is open from 8am, with alcohol available from 11.30am (12.30pm on Sun).
Q❄️✲◑🚲🚌(7) 🛜

Saintfield

White Horse

49-53 Main Street, BT24 7AB
☎ (028) 9751 1143 ⊕ whitehorsesaintfield.com
Whitewater Maggie's Leap IPA; 2 changing beers (sourced locally) Ⓗ
Formerly a coaching inn, and dating back over 200 years, the White Horse Inn is now a busy bar, restaurant and pizzeria. There are a number of different drinking areas: a reading room with a log stove, comfy booths, a first floor balcony, and a public bar area. The bar itself usually features two real ales from Whitewater brewery. A former local CAMRA Pub of the Year.
Q❄️✲◑🚲🚌(15,215) 🎵

Errigle Inn, Belfast (Photo: Stuart McMahon)

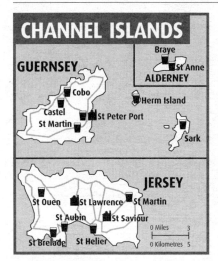

ALDERNEY
Braye

Divers Inn
Braye Street, GY9 3XT
☎ (01481) 822632 ⊕ brayebeach.com
2 changing beers (sourced nationally; often Fuller's, Sharp's) Ⓗ
Traditional pub with a great atmosphere, attached to the Braye Beach Hotel. It serves two real ales and has a good bar menu. The interior features wooden tables, chairs and counter, and is warmed by real fires. Walking through the bar area reveals sea views and a superb outdoor seating space overlooking the beach. Themed and musical events attract locals and visitors alike, and make this a must-visit location when on Alderney.
🛋️🌂◑♣

St Anne

Georgian House Hotel
54 Victoria Street, GY9 3UF
☎ (01481) 822471 ⊕ georgianalderney.com
Butcombe Original, Gold; 1 changing beer (sourced nationally; often Greene King, Morland) Ⓗ
Just up from the town church, the hotel extends a warm welcome to all. There is a pleasant garden which, in the summer months, has an outside bar (where casks can be found on the counter) and sometimes hosts live music. Meals are served all day (lunchtime only on Sun). Real cider also features during the summer. In winter there are two multi-fuel fires to make it warm and cosy.
🌂⊛🛋️◑🚿♥P🛜

GUERNSEY
Castel

Fleur du Jardin ✔
Kings Mills, GY5 7JT
☎ (01481) 257996 ⊕ fleurdujardin.com
Little Big Alan; 2 changing beers (sourced nationally; often Butcombe, Sharp's, Timothy Taylor) Ⓗ
A building of unique charm with two bars – one traditional, small and cosy, attached to the restaurant, the other renovated in a more contemporary style to create a comfortable, relaxing area to enjoy a beer. A door leads to a large covered patio and out to the garden. Menus in both the bar and restaurant feature fresh local produce. The car park can be busy in summer.
Q🌂🌂⊛🛋️◑🚿♥P🛜(61) ❀

Cobo

Rockmount Restaurant & Bar
Cobo Coast Road, GY5 7HB
☎ (01481) 252778 ⊕ therocky.gg
4 changing beers (often Randalls) Ⓗ
The pub comprises a large lounge bar and a taproom that shows sport on TV. There is also a public bar with a pool table and largescreen TV for sport. The lounge has an emphasis on food, served lunchtimes and evenings, but there are comfy chairs near the fire for drinkers. Five handpumps offer a changing range of beers, with one local regular ale from Randalls Brewery. You can also try a tasting paddle of different ales.
🌂⊛◑🚿♥P🛜(41,42) ❀❀🛜♪

Herm Island

Mermaid Tavern ✔
GY1 3HR (Trident ferry from St Peter Port)
☎ (01481) 750050 ⊕ herm.com/mermaid
House beer (by Liberation); 2 changing beers Ⓗ
A welcoming inn on the beautiful island of Herm, a short trip by ferry from Guernsey. The large courtyard is a popular spot in summer, while an open fire adds to the charm in winter. The house beer is Liberation's Herm Island Gold, brewed specially for the island. The pub holds regular themed music and food events, and hosts real ale and cider festivals in June and September. Check the Herm website for seasonal opening hours.
🌂⊛◑🍴♣❀❀🛜♪

St Martin

Les Douvres Hotel
La Fosse, GY4 6ER
☎ (01481) 238731 ⊕ lesdouvres.com
Little Big Alan; 2 changing beers (often Butcombe, Sharp's, Timothy Taylor) Ⓗ
Former 18th-century manor house, set in private gardens in St Martin near the south coast, two-and-a-half miles from St Peter Port, with cliff walks and Saints Bay fishing harbour close by. A well-maintained, changing range of beers is offered on three handpumps, and real cider during the season. Excellent meals, including pizzas, are served in the bar and separate restaurant. Live music features on Friday night and occasional Wednesdays.
⊛🛋️◑♥P🛜(81) ♪

St Peter Port

Red Lion
Les Banques, GY1 2RX
☎ (01481) 724042
4 changing beers (often Randalls) Ⓗ
Friendly pub on the northern outskirts of St Peter Port, with two bar areas – a lounge overlooking Belle Greve Bay to the front and a public area at the rear. Gluten-free beer is available in bottles, and real cider is served in summer. Numerous TVs show sport. Meat draws are held

NI &
ISLANDS

on Friday and Saturday evening. The pub is on several bus routes, and the cycle route between St Peter Port and St Sampson. ✿✿❶◆🍴♥️⚡

Ship & Crown ✦
North Esplanade, GY1 2NB
☎ (01481) 721368
Butcombe Original; Liberation Ale, Herm Island Gold, IPA Ⓗ
Traditional local on the town seafront, with fantastic views of the harbour, neighbouring islands, and Castle Cornet. It is popular with locals, yachtsman and tourists, and is an ideal pub to enjoy a pint and a good meal. It is decorated with photos of local shipwrecks, Guernsey, and the pub while under German occupation. Up to four Liberation and Butcombe ales are sometimes accompanied by real cider. Major sports events are shown in a friendly and lively atmosphere. ❶◆🍴♥️⚡

Slaughterhouse
Castle Pier, GY1 1AN
☎ (01481) 712123 ⊕ slaughterhouse.gg
3 changing beers (often Randalls) Ⓗ
Popular harbourside restaurant and pub that offers fine views over Havelet Bay and the harbour from its mezzanine restaurant and upper section of the large outdoor terrace. The Randalls-managed pub serves a changing range of up to six real ales, some from small breweries. Winner of a CAMRA design award in 2019 for its conversion from an abbatoir, hence the name.
✿❶♿🍴

Thomas de la Rue 🏆 ✦
9 The Pollet, GY1 1WQ
☎ (01481) 714990
Butcombe Original; 1 changing beer (often Liberation) Ⓗ
A traditional town pub in the heart of St Peter Port, overlooking the harbour and Castle Cornet. Popular with both locals and tourists, the de la Rue comprises a main bar with two handpumps serving a rotating selection of Liberation and Butcombe ales. Food ranges from sandwiches to pub classics such as burgers and fish & chips. Downstairs is the Front Room bar and terrace, which can be booked for private parties, but does not serve real ale. Local CAMRA Pub of the Year 2024.
✿✿❶P🍴⚡♫

JERSEY
St Aubin

Trafalgar Inn
Charing Cross, JE3 8AA
☎ (01534) 741184 ⊕ trafalgarinn.je
Liberation Ale, IPA; 2 changing beers (often Butcombe) Ⓗ
Traditional pub with two bars: the saloon bar is decked out like a ship but has no real ale; the public bar to the rear has four handpumps generally serving Liberation beers and the occasional guest ale. The pub can get busy during sporting events, and live music is generally played in the saloon bar on Friday and Saturday evening.
♿♣🍴(15) ♥️♫

St Brelade

Old Smugglers Inn ✦
Le Mont du Ouaisne, JE3 8AW
☎ (01534) 741510 ⊕ oldsmugglersinn.com
Draught Bass; house beer (by Liberation); 2 changing beers (often Marston's, Ringwood) Ⓗ

Perched on the edge of Ouaisne Bay, the Smugglers has been the crown jewel of the Jersey real ale scene for many years. Dating back to when pirates came to enjoy an ale or two here, it is set within granite-built fishermen's cottages, with foundations reputedly from the 13th century. Up to four ales are available, including the house beer brewed by Liberation. The pub is well known for its good food, with fresh daily specials.
Q✿❶P♥️⚡♫

St Helier

Lamplighter Ⓛ ✦
9 Mulcaster Street, JE2 3NJ
☎ (01534) 723119
5 changing beers (sourced nationally; often Fuller's, Marston's, Titanic) Ⓖ
A traditional pub with a modern feel. There are a predominance of television screens and the bar can get busy during sporting events. The gas lamps that gave the pub its name remain, though are no longer in use, and it retains the original antique pewter bar top. An ever-changing range of up to five real ales is available, all served direct from the cellar. 🍴♥️⚡

Prince of Wales Tavern ★
8 Hilgrove Street, JE2 4SL
☎ (01534) 737378
Fuller's London Pride; Timothy Taylor Landlord; 3 changing beers (sourced nationally; often Courage, Shepherd Neame) Ⓗ
This traditional pub is a pleasant oasis in the centre of town. The main bar is comfortable, and there are five handpumps serving a range of beers. Out back is a walled beer garden where quiet drinks can be enjoyed in the summer. No children are allowed, and the bar is cash only. ✿◆🍴♥️

St Ouen

Farmers Inn ✦
La Grande Route de St Ouen, JE3 2HY
☎ (01534) 485311
Butcombe Original; Liberation Herm Island Gold; 1 changing beer (often Liberation) Ⓗ
Situated in the hub of St Ouen, near the war memorial and parish hall, the rustic Farmers Inn is a typical country pub. It offers up to three ales, as well as a locally made cider, when available (usually April to July). Traditional pub food is served in generous portions. Best described as a friendly community local, there is a good chance of hearing Jersey French (Jerriais) spoken at the bar. There is an outside seating area to the front of the pub.
✿❶♣◆🍴

Moulin de Lecq ✦
Le Mont De La Greve De Lecq, JE3 2DT
☎ (01534) 482818 ⊕ moulindelecq.co.uk
Shepherd Neame Spitfire; house beer (by Liberation); 2 changing beers (often Marston's) Ⓗ
A converted 12th-century watermill, in the valley above the beach at Greve de Lecq. The waterwheel is still in place and the turning mechanism can be seen behind the bar. This free house offers a range of real ales. There is an adjoining restaurant that can be hired for functions. The children's play space and a barbecue area are used extensively in the summer. Pool can be played in the second-floor games room. Q✿✿❶♿♣◆P🍴♥️⚡♫

SARK
Sark

Bel Air

Harbour Hill, GY10 1SB

☎ (01481) 832052 🌐 belairinnsark.gg

2 changing beers (often Randalls) Ⓗ

Located at the top of Harbour Hill, this family-friendly pub is popular with tourists and local residents. Two handpumps serve a changing selection of local and national real ales, and a real cider. Pizza is available from noon until late, to eat in or take away. There is a cosy fire in winter, and a large garden and courtyard where barbecues and live music feature on summer weekends. Off-sales are available. 🏠🏡🕙&♣🐾🏵

Mermaid Tavern

Main Street, GY10 1SG

☎ (01481) 832022

Butcombe Original Ⓗ

Established before WWII, this pub is a little like Sark – an island that harks back to an earlier time. The decor has remained unchanged since the 1960s. Though a locals' pub, the Mermaid extends a warm welcome to visitors. It is child friendly and serves snacks such as pizza and sandwiches on request. There is an outdoor seating area. Darts and pool can be played, in addition to the jukebox and piano, which is available for spontaneous sing-songs, or a dance! Local events are held and there is a weekly meat draw. 🏠♣

Trafalgar Inn, St Aubin: Jersey (Photo: Hugh Llewelyn / Flickr CC BY-SA 2.0)

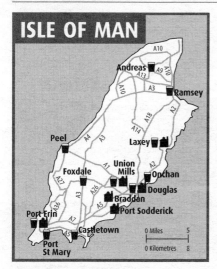

ISLE OF MAN

Andreas

Grosvenor Country Inn 🅛

Andreas Road, IM7 4HE
☎ (01624) 888007
Odin Manx Mild; Okell's Bitter; 2 changing beers (sourced nationally) 🅗
The Grosvenor is the most northerly pub on the island, with a real community feel and rural charm about it. There is a central bar serving diners on one side (booking at peak periods advised), with a separate, relaxed bar for drinkers and those playing darts. The beers are kept across the two bars. Live music and events such as horseracing nights feature on occasion. There is a large function room. 🌇🏠🍴🕕👤♿➡️🅿️🚪🐾🛜🎵

Castletown

Castle Arms 🅛 ✅

The Quay, IM9 1LD
☎ (01624) 824673
Okell's Manx Pale Ale, Bitter; 1 changing beer (sourced locally) 🅗
The Castle Arms, or Gluepot as it is often known, is thought to date from around 1750, and features on the Manx £5 note. It is situated in a stunning setting by the harbour and close to the castle, which dominates the centre of town. There are two rooms, one decorated with a nautical theme. There is an open mic night once a month, an occasional quiz, and there are plans to extend the outdoor seating areas. Q🌇🧒👤⛺🚶➡️🚪(1,2)🐾🛜🎵

George Hotel 🅛 ✅

The Parade, IM9 1LG
☎ (01624) 822533
Okell's Manx Pale Ale, Bitter; 1 changing beer (often Okell's) 🅗
Built in 1883, this imposing building overlooks Castletown square and the superbly preserved castle. It has been refurbished to a high standard and now offers B&B accommodation in 11 rooms. There is a large function area to the rear, which can accommodate at least 80 guests. On the walls are pictures of scenes from across the island. It is a family-friendly pub and offers a Sunday carvery. A Manx folk group meet here every Friday. Opens at noon in winter.
👤🛏️🕕♿➡️🚪(1) 🐾🛜

Sidings 🅛

Victoria Road, IM9 1EF (next to railway station)
☎ (01624) 823282
Bushy's Castletown Bitter, Bitter; Castle Rock Harvest Pale; Odin Manx Mild; Okell's Bitter; 8 changing beers (sourced nationally; often Castle Rock) 🅗
This former ticket office for the nearby steam railway has been a local CAMRA Pub of the Year on several occasions. It boasts an impressive array of a dozen real ales, frequently featuring several beers from Castle Rock brewery. It also has a reputation for good-value food. There is live music on the first Saturday of every month. There is a large garden area to the rear.
Q🌇🏠🕕♿➡️🚶➡️🚪(1,1A) 🐾🛜🎵

Douglas

Albert Hotel ★ ✅

3 Chapel Row, IM1 2BJ (near bus stands and indoor market)
☎ (01624) 673632
Bushy's Castletown Bitter; Odin Manx Mild, Laksaa Pale; Okell's Bitter; 1 changing beer (sourced locally) 🅗
Traditional, immaculately maintained pub close to the main sea terminal. It has two rooms: to the right is a games room with darts, pool and sports TV; to the left a smaller area with seating surrounding the walls to the rear. A central bar serves beers from several local breweries, there is also house brew, Jough (via Okell's), and, frequently, Kaneen's beers. Q➡️🚶🚌🐾🛜🎵

British Hotel 🅛 ✅

North Quay, IM1 4LB
☎ (01624) 616663
Okell's Manx Pale Ale, Bitter; 2 changing beers (sourced nationally) 🅗
Situated on Douglas North Quay, this imposing building has an open-plan interior with a central bar. The decor throughout has a London/British theme, with many photographs of past stars, and a section of London Tube map adorning the walls. Live music features frequently on Saturday evening. The outdoor areas overlooking the quayside are south facing and busy in the summer months. There is an upstairs area, The Embassy, which is available for functions, catering for up to 50. 🕕➡️🛜🎵

Cat With No Tail 🅛 ✅

Hailwood Court, Hailwood Avenue, IM2 7EA
☎ (01624) 616364
Okell's Bitter; 2 changing beers (sourced nationally; often Okell's, Timothy Taylor) 🅗
A modern pub serving the Grosveners Hill housing estate, two miles from central Douglas. It features a large games room, with two pool tables, a dartboard and largescreen TVs showing sport. Note the impressive brewery mirrors facing the bar on the back wall. There is also a quieter area where food is served. This leads to an extensive conservatory and outdoor area. Church services are held in the pub on Sundays. Q🌇🏠🕕♿➡️🚪🐾🛜🎵

REAL ALE BREWERIES

Burnside Laxey (NEW)
Bushy's Braddan
Kaneen's Union Mills
Kerroo ✦ Port Erin (NEW)
Odin Union Mills
Okell's Douglas
Radical Port Sodderick

Old Market Inn L

Chapel Row, IM1 2BJ

☎ 07624 381076

2 changing beers (sourced locally; often Bushy's) Ⓗ

This gem of a pub has remained unchanged for many years and is held in great affection by regulars and visitors. It features a tiny bar serving two small rooms. The cellars are thought to be some of the oldest man-made structures in Douglas. The pub is a greater supporter of the Isle of Man TT festival, and raises money for charitable causes. During race weeks a bespoke beer, Old Market Grog (OMG), is produced by Bushy's for the pub. ≉🖳🛜

Prospect Hotel L ✔

Prospect Hill, IM1 1ET

☎ (01624) 616773

Okell's Manx Pale Ale, Bitter; 5 changing beers (sourced nationally; often Okell's) Ⓗ

This pub in the heart of the Douglas finance sector, opened in 1857. It consists of a large open-plan area, with a mixture of seating and a raised area to the rear which is often in use for meetings. There are two banks of four handpumps, typically dispensing five to six cask ales. The walls are adorned with portraits of significant legal figures, some local. The pub hosts a popular quiz on Wednesday evening. ≉🖤🖳(3,11)🛜🛜

Queen's Hotel L

Queens Promenade, IM2 4NL (towards N end of promenade)

☎ (01624) 674438

Okell's Bitter; 2 changing beers (sourced nationally) Ⓗ

A large Heron & Brearley pub on Douglas promenade, dating from 1853. It comprises two rooms, as well as a games area to the right with pool and darts. In the summer months the pub stocks a real cider, available on the handpumps, which also frequently have Timothy Taylor Landlord. Outside are extensive outdoor heated areas, which are popular on summer evenings. Q🍴🌟🐟🕭≉(Derby Castle)🍀🖤🖳🛜🛜♪

Rover's Return L

11 Church Street, IM1 2AG (in pedestrianised area behind town hall)

☎ (01624) 676459

Bushy's Bitter; 5 changing beers (sourced nationally; often Bushy's) Ⓗ

Tucked away behind the town hall on a narrow street, the Rover's is an unusual pub that is full of surprises. The walls of the many small rooms are adorned with an eclectic mix of memorabilia, including a Blackburn Rovers room, historic photographs of many local pubs, and some handpumps made from firemen's hoses. Look out for the Bushy's foxes in The Last Suppage painting. There is a welcoming traditional open fire in colder months. This is the largest outlet for Bushy's beers in the capital. 🍺≉🍀🖤🖳🛜♪

Thirsty Pigeon L

38-40 Victoria Street, IM1 2LW

☎ (01624) 675584 🌐 thirstypigeon.com

Okell's Bitter; 3 changing beers (sourced nationally; often Kaneen's, Odin) Ⓗ

An open-plan, one-roomed pub in a former bank, the Thirsty Pigeon has only been in existence in the last decade or so but is already a Douglas institution. It stands in a prime location and is popular with all age groups, day and night. The casks, often containing local beers, are taken down to the former bank cellar vaults on an internal lift system. There is always live music on Friday and Saturday evenings. 🕭≉🖳🛜🛜♪

Woodbourne Hotel L ✔

Alexander Drive, IM2 3QF (in the Woodbourne area of Douglas)

☎ (01624) 676754

Okell's Manx Pale Ale, Bitter; 5 changing beers (sourced nationally; often Okell's) Ⓗ

This imposing Victorian pub serves the Woodbourne residential area. It comprises four rooms, split across two levels and served by three separate interconnected bar areas, a challenge for the bar staff, darting between bars. In addition there is a games area, where functions and live music occasionally take place. The cask ales are found in the central (formerly gents-only) bar. The pub raises money for charity, notably guide dogs. Q🌟🕭🍀🖳(3)🛜🛜♪

Foxdale

Baltic Inn L

1 Glentramman Terrace, IM4 3EE

☎ (01624) 801305 🌐 balticinn.pub

Okell's Manx Pale Ale, Bitter; 1 changing beer (sourced nationally) Ⓗ

The Baltic is very much the beating heart of Foxdale, a former mining village with a proud heritage. The pub supports several darts and pool teams, and has an unobtrusive TV for sport, with live music featuring frequently. There are two local Mheilleas held here annually. Note the rare photographs adorning the walls in the pool area, featuring the Foxdale mines in their heyday. The hotel has accommodation available. Q🛏🌟🕭🕭🍀🖳(4)🛜🛜♪

Laxey

Queen's Hotel L

New Road, IM4 7BP (600yds S of village centre)

☎ (01624) 861195

Bushy's Castletown Bitter, Bitter; Odin Laksaa Pale; 2 changing beers (sourced locally; often Odin) Ⓗ

A large open plan pub just south of the village centre. It has a comfortable and relaxed feel to it, and enjoys a dedicated local following. Live music features occasionally. The pub holds a popular weekly meat raffle draw on Sunday, and competes in local darts and pool leagues. To the rear is a garden area for summer months, directly overlooking the historic Manx Electric Railway line. 🛏🌟🕭≉🍀🖤P🖳(3,3A)🛜🛜♪

Onchan

Manx Arms L ✔

Main Road, IM3 1BE

☎ (01624) 675484

Okell's Manx Pale Ale, Bitter; 1 changing beer Ⓗ

A Heron & Brearley (Okell's) pub in the centre of Onchan village, next to the bus stop. It consists of two large rooms and bars, one focusing on TV for sport, with a games area to the rear. There is a quieter room to the right, which is used for live music events, with pictures celebrating the history of the vast holiday camps of yesteryear. 🕭🍀🖤P🖳🛜🛜♪

Peel

Miller's T'Ale

33 Michael Street, IM5 1HD

☎ 07624 307356

5 changing beers (sourced nationally) Ⓗ

This remains the island's only true micropub. It serves an ever-varying range of five real ales, many never previously seen here. In addition, there are up to six real ciders, plus two changing keg beers and one lager. There is a monthly quiz and a regular and highly popular Sunday cheeseboard. The pub underwent a substantial makeover in recent years. Check opening times in quieter months. Q⬤♿☐(5,6)❀🕸🛜

Port Erin

Falcon's Nest Hotel ⓛ
Station Road, IM9 6AF
☎ (01624) 834077 ⊕ thenest.im
Bushy's Bitter; 2 changing beers (sourced nationally) Ⓗ
The Falcon's Nest Hotel is undergoing a major refurbishment. While this is ongoing, the Port bar and restaurant, where three real ales are served, is at the rear of the building. This stylish, modern, open plan bar is being used for diners and drinkers while the front bars are refurbished, and has a relaxed and informal ambience. A second bar, the Ridler Under the Nest, is next door and also serves real ale.
Q🕸🍴◑≠♣P☐(1,2)❀🛜♫

Haven ⓛ ✅
Station Road, IM9 6AB
☎ (01624) 834030
Okell's Bitter Ⓗ
A spacious pub close to the bus and steam railway stations. The two rooms each have their own bar. To the rear is a predominantly locals' bar, with a pool table, two dartboards, and largescreen TVs for sport. To the front is a much larger bar, with huge windows, where live music features at the weekend. A guest ale can occasionally be available at peak periods. ≠♣P☐❀🛜♫

Station Hotel ⓛ ✅
Station Road, IM9 6AE
☎ (01624) 838991
Okell's Manx Pale Ale, Bitter; 1 changing beer (sourced nationally) Ⓗ
The Station is perfectly situated on arrival in Port Erin by steam train or by bus. It is a large open plan pub with ample tables for dining and drinking in a comfortable environment, with an overspill area to the right. A guest ale usually features in the summer months. As well as dining, there are a plethora of clubs and societies that use the pub, including the local Bradda WI, the MS Society, and a canasta card group. 🕸◑♿≠P☐❀🛜

Port St Mary

Albert Hotel ⓛ
Athol Street, IM9 5DS (opp harbour)
☎ (01624) 832118
Bushy's Bitter; Okell's Bitter; 2 changing beers (sourced nationally; often Kaneen's, Marston's) Ⓗ
The Albert enjoys picturesque views over the harbour. Run by the same landlady for 20 years, the pub is very much at the heart of the village. It comprises three rooms, with the beers spread across the two bars, and typically featuring a stronger ale such as Abbot or Old Empire, or one from local brewery Kaneen's. The games room has sports TV and can be lively at times. A former local CAMRA Pub of the Year on numerous occasions.
Q🕸♿♣☐(1)🛜

Railway Station Hotel ⓛ
Station Road, IM9 5LF
☎ (01624) 832494
Bushy's Bitter; Okell's Bitter; 2 changing beers (sourced locally) Ⓗ

An imposing building next to Port St Mary steam railway station, in a rural setting close to both Port Erin and Port St Mary. It has two rooms: a cosy, smaller bar with a roaring real fire in the winter, and a second sports bar, overlooking the station, with pool, darts and sports TV. Live bands often play, and many local clubs meet here, including a stamp club and chess club. There is accommodation in summer months.
Q🕸🍴♿≠♣P☐(1,2)🛜♫

Ramsey

Mitre ⓛ
16 Parliament Street, IM8 1AP
☎ (01624) 813045
Okell's Bitter; house beer (by Okell's); 2 changing beers (sourced locally) Ⓗ
A deceptively large pub, with entrances on the main street and on the quay. The main bar is upstairs, with excellent views over the working harbour. There is a second bar on the ground floor, which is used at busier times. The Cooil Bar is opened occasionally for special events. The pub is a huge supporter of local breweries, and the house beer is Jough Ale by Okell's. Live bands feature on a Saturday evening.
◑≠(Plaza)♣☐(3,3A)❀🛜♫

Plough ⓛ
46 Parliament Street, IM8 1AN
☎ (01624) 813323
Okell's Bitter; Timothy Taylor Landlord Ⓗ
On the main shopping street in Ramsey, the recently refurbished Plough is very much a locals' pub. It has two small rooms: the room to the right is sometimes closed off at quieter periods; the one to the left is where you will find the real ales. This room has a fire, and several largescreen TVs showing sport. The pub's two darts teams play in local leagues. ≠(Plaza)♣☐❀🛜

Trafalgar Hotel ⓛ ✅
West Quay, IM8 1DW
☎ (01624) 609247
Odin Manx Mild, Rhumsaa Bitter, Laksaa Pale; Timothy Taylor Landlord; 2 changing beers (sourced nationally; often Odin) Ⓗ
A friendly, welcoming and often busy pub opposite Ramsay's scenic harbour. Now linked with the local Odin brewery, it stocks many of its beers. The single room has tables and seating, and a further area to the rear. Local CAMRA Pub of the Year 2022 and 2023, and a finalist in the 2023 National Pub of the Year competition.
🕸≠(Plaza)♣☐❀🛜

Union Mills

Railway Inn ⓛ
Main Road, IM4 4NE
☎ (01624) 853006
Okell's Bitter; 5 changing beers (sourced nationally; often Bushy's, Kaneen's, Odin) Ⓗ
This three-roomed free house is one of the few pubs that serves cask beers from all the island's breweries. It is situated on the TT motorbike course, and its extensive garden areas offer an ideal viewing point to watch the races. The Jeff Castle Room at the front features memorabilia relating to West Bromwich Albion football club. A former local CAMRA Pub of the Year on several occasions. Q🕸▲♣P☐(5,5A)❀🛜

The Breweries

BREWERIES OVERVIEW

Is real ale reviving or is it in decline? The answer to that question depends on who you talk to in the brewing industry.

SIBA – the Society of Independent Brewers and Associates – that speaks for many smaller brewers, says it recorded a 10 per cent increase in sales of cask beer in 2024. Its members are returning to pre-Covid levels of production.

As a result of the dominance of the giant global brewers, many SIBA members are now buying pubs in order to have shop windows for their beers. They find it difficult or impossible to sell to pubs where the globals offer their products with deep discounts that would ruin small producers.

Andy Slee, the chief executive of SIBA, says that for nearly half his members survival is their top priority. The beer market is so skewed in favour of the globals that the independents struggle to find sufficient outlets for their beers. They have received little or no support from government when they have asked for cuts in energy bills and other inflationary costs.

Despite welcome reductions in excise duty for draught beer and rates for small brewers, British beer is still heavily taxed compared to most European countries, with around 30 per cent of the price of a pint going in duty and other taxes. The burden of taxes and production costs led to 69 breweries closing in 2023 and the toll continued the following year.

The major closures have come from the global brewers. Andy Slee accuses them of 'walking away from the cask sector.'

CLOSURES

Despite SIBA reporting a return to pre-Covid sales of cask ale, the globals say they have closed real ale breweries due to falling demand. Demand does tend to fall if no effort is made to promote cask while lager is given substantial support. The biggest British brewer as a result of buying Scottish and Newcastle's breweries and pubs in 2009, has closed the historic Caledonian Brewery in Edinburgh at the same time as it invested £1 million on a new lager brand. Reasons cited included Caledonian, dating from 1869, needed substantial investment but insiders say this would have been a fraction of the money spent on launching the new brand. It has also been criticised for grubbing up 300 acres of land on the Welsh border where apples for Bulmer's cider were grown. The orchards are

the size of 140 football pitches and environmentalists are concerned at the loss of the land for wildlife if, as expected, it will be used for house building. A slow down in cider sales was cited as the reason.

The cider orchards at Penrhos before they were chopped down

UNKIND CUTS

The Carlsberg Marston's Brewing Company (CMBC), formed in 2022, with the Danish giant controlling 60 per cent of the business, has closed Jennings in Cumbria, Ringwood in Hampshire and Wychwood in Oxfordshire. At the same time, it has dug deep to invest £10 million at its lager factory in Northampton.

In July CMBC announced the unkindest cut of all. After 190 years of brewing, Marston's is quitting and selling its breweries to Carlsberg for £206 million. Carlsberg also bought soft drinks company Britvic that month and said it would carry out a 'strategic review' of its entire business. It said it would supply Hobgoblin, Brakspear, Pedigree and Wainwright's ales to Marston's pubs but wouldn't be drawn on whether it would continue to brew Jenning's or Ringwood beers. The future of the two Marston's breweries in Burton and Wolverhampton would be part of the strategic review.

DECLINING INTEREST

The power of the global brewers is considerable. The big four – Heineken, CMBC, Molson Coors and AB InBev – produce 88 per cent of all the beer made in Britain. Add in Asahi of Japan, which owns Fuller's, and Diageo, owners of Guinness, and the top six brewers account for 90 per cent of production. With the exception of Asahi, which continues to brew Fuller's London Pride, ESB and Dark Start Hop Head, the national brewers have a declining interest in the cask sector.

GREENE SHOOTS

The one encouraging development on the national stage comes from Greene King. The Suffolk brewer plans to build a £40 million new brewery on a green field site outside Bury St Edmunds where it will produce cask ales as well as craft keg. Along with such cask staples as IPA, Abbot Ale and Old Speckled Hen, the brewer will produce seasonal and one-off beers.

Greene King's chief executive, Nick Mackenzie, says: 'We sell a significant amount of traditional cask ale. We are the No 1 cask ale group in the UK, with just shy of a 14 per cent share of the cask sector.'

With 2,600 pubs, Greene King will supply cask beers to all parts of the country. It will also brew Deuchar's IPA – a former CAMRA Champion Beer of Britain – at its Belhaven plant in Scotland following the closure of Caledonian.

HELP IS REQUIRED

Pub closures make grim reading. CAMRA estimates that 750 would close in the first half of 2024, following the loss of 500 the previous year. The closures are caused by charges for energy, rising business rates, and a mountain of taxes, including income tax and VAT.

Despite lower duty for draught beer, pubs continue to face unfair competition from supermarkets. Sir Tim Martin, the founder and chairman of the Wetherspoon pub group, has railed against the fact that supermarkets can claim back VAT on alcohol sales, allowing them to sell beer as cheaply as bottled water.

Brewing and pub retailing make a massive contribution to the British economy. They give employment to more than one million people and together account for a mighty £23.1 billion in all forms of taxation.

The new government cannot turn its back on such a vibrant part of the economy. It must come to the aid of breweries and pubs with a package that will provide them with lower energy bills, reduce duty still further and abolish the out-dated system of business rates.

And it must end the absurd anomaly of supermarkets undercutting pubs by not paying VAT.

Beer and pubs play a vital role in society. Cask ale is a style unique to this country while pubs are hubs of local communities. They need to be cherished and supported.

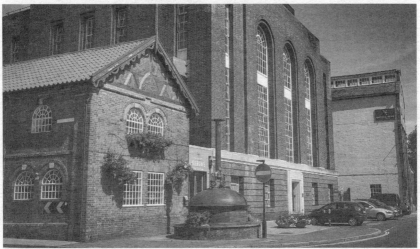

Greene King plan to build a new brewery just outside Bury St Edmunds

Former editor of The *Good Beer Guide*, Roger Protz is considered one of the leading beer writers in the world, with a long career in journalism and publishing, and having won multiple awards. Roger has authored many books on beer and pubs including *The Family Brewers of Britain*. Follow him on Twitter **@RogerProtzBeer** and **protzonbeer.co.uk**

HOW TO USE THE BREWERIES SECTION

Breweries listed include independent companies (regional, family, microbrewers and brewpubs), national brewers and global groups. If a brewery owns more than one site, these are mentioned. Within each brewery entry, regular beers are listed in increasing order of strength. Seasonal, occasional or one-off beers are not listed. Please consult brewery websites or social media for more information.

KEY TO BREWERY ENTRIES

BREWERY SYMBOLS

Brewpub: a pub that brews beer on the premises

Serve with tight sparkler: the brewery's beers can be acceptably served through a 'tight sparkler' attached to the nozzle of the beer pump, designed to give a thick collar of foam on the beer

Do not serve with tight sparkler: the brewery's beers should NOT be served through a tight sparkler. CAMRA is opposed to the growing tendency to serve southern-brewed beers with the aid of sparklers, which aerate the beer and tend to drive hop aroma and flavour into the head, altering the balance of the beer achieved in the brewery. When neither symbol is used it means the brewery in question has not stated a preference

Brewery tours available: check with individual breweries for details

Brewery shop: beer available to take away. Check opening hours in advance

LIVE Live beer: the brewery produces live beer in bottles, cans or other small formats

Seasonal beers: the brewery produces seasonal beers in addition to its regular range

V Vegan: the brewery produces vegan beers (check with brewery for further details. Not all beers produced may be vegan)

GF Gluten free: the brewery produces gluten-free beers (check with brewery for further details. Not all beers may be gluten free)

Taproom: the brewery features an onsite taproom (always check ahead with brewery for up-to-date information about opening times and events)

BEER STYLES

The following styles are listed after each beer name in the brewery section. Please refer to pages 11–13 for more information.

BARLEY	Barley wine	**RED**	Red ale
BROWN	Brown ale	**MILD**	Mild; session or strong
IPA	IPA; British or New World	**PORTER**	Porter; session or strong
OLD	Old ale	**STOUT**	Stout; session or strong
BITTER	Bitter; session or premium	**SPECIALITY**	Speciality beer; differently produced
BLOND	Blond ale; session or premium		or flavoured
GOLD	Golden ale; session or premium	**STRONG**	Strong ale
PALE	Pale ale; session or premium		

ABBREVIATIONS

ABV Stands for Alcohol by Volume, which is a measure of the percentage of alcohol in finished beer

SIBA Indicates a member of the Society of Independent Brewers

IFBB Indicates a member of the Independent Family Brewers of Britain

NOTE: The breweries information was correct at the time of going to press and every effort has been made to ensure that all regularly available cask-conditioned beers are included.

625

The Breweries

The breweries listed in this section include micro, small, family, regional, national and global companies. Please use the Beers index (p859) to help locate beers.

1086

Old Brewhouse, Cusworth Hall, Cusworth Lane, Doncaster, South Yorkshire, DN5 7TU
☎ (01302) 639880

Office: Doncaster Culture & Leisure Trust, The Dome, Doncaster Lakeside, Bawtry Road, Doncaster, DN4 7PD ⊕ 1086brewery.co.uk

⊙1086 was established in 2018, in the original brewhouse of Cusworth Hall, an 18th century, Grade I, country house in Cusworth, near Doncaster. The brewery shares space with its popular brewery tap, the Old Brewhouse. Beers are available in the taproom, and occasionally at the Leopard in Doncaster. ◆

14 Lock

🍺 **Canal Inn, 30 Bullbridge Hill, Bullbridge, Derbyshire, DE56 2EW**
☎ (01629) 534888 ⊕ thecanalatbullbridge.co.uk/14-lock-brewery

Commenced brewing in 2022, the brewery is located in the cellar of the Canal Inn at Bullbridge and supplies the four outlets of the Moorwood Hotel Group.

1648

🍺 **Old Stables Brewery, Mill Lane, East Hoathly, East Sussex, BN8 6QB**
☎ (01825) 840830 ⊕ 1648brewing.co.uk

⊠ The 1648 brewery, set up in the old stable block at the King's Head pub in 2003, derives its name from the year of the deposition of King Charles I. One pub is owned and more than 40 outlets are supplied. ‼🍺◆LIVE

Hop Pocket (ABV 3.7%) GOLD
Triple Champion (ABV 4%) BITTER
Signature (ABV 4.4%) GOLD
Laughing Frog (ABV 5.2%) BITTER

3 Brewers of St Albans SIBA

The Potato Shed, Symonds Hyde Farm, Symonds Hyde Lane, Hatfield, Hertfordshire, AL10 9BB
☎ (01707) 271636 ☎ 07941 854615
⊕ 3brewers.co.uk

⊠ Launched in 2013, the 3 Brewers of St Albans uses water from its own borehole. Cask and keg beers are supplied to local pubs, clubs and other outlets. Bottled beer and mini kegs are sold direct from the brewery. Its taproom is open Fridays and Saturdays plus summer Sundays and also offers coffee, teas and cakes. A mezzanine level with extra seating is regularly used by local artists for displays. Both mezzanine and brewery are available for private hire. Brewery tours and membership available. An annual music festival is held every September. ‼🍺◆V◆

Golden English Ale (ABV 3.8%) GOLD
Copper (ABV 3.9%) BITTER
Classic English Ale (ABV 4%) BITTER
Three Brewers Blonde (ABV 4.2%) BLOND
IPA (ABV 4.6%) PALE

Special English Ale (ABV 4.8%) BITTER
Contract brewed for B&T Brewery:
Shefford Bitter (ABV 3.8%) BITTER
Dragon Slayer (ABV 4.5%) GOLD

3 Locks SIBA

Arches N4 & N5, River Place, Hawley Wharf, Camden Town, London, NW1 8QG ⊕ 3locksbeer.com

Overlooking one of the eponymous Camden Locks, the brewery opened in 2022 in railway arches underneath the London Overground including adjacent taproom spaces and a future shop. Founded by the owner of a brewery on the Greek island of Pathos, a wide range of styles are now brewed (available at the taproom). No cask ale. ◆

3 Words (NEW)

Cornmill Road, Evesham, Worcestershire, WR11 2LL
⊕ 3wordsbrewing.uk

A nanobrewery that began brewing in Worcester in 2022 and in 2024 moved to Evesham, taking over the space at Cornmill Yard previously used by Little Beer Company. It specialises in bringing lesser-known beer styles to bars and bottle shops in the county. Beers are also available at the Cornmill Yard café-bar.

360°

Unit 24b, Bluebell Business Estate, Sheffield Park, East Sussex, TN22 3HQ
☎ (01825) 722375 ⊕ 360degreebrewing.com

⊠ Under different management since 2020 but still brewing at Sheffield Park, adjacent to the famous Bluebell Railway. The brewery is committed to producing high quality cask conditioned ales and has increased its output of craft keg and cans. ‼🍺◆◆

Double Act Pale (ABV 4.1%) GOLD
Bluebell Best (ABV 4.2%) BITTER
Session IPA (ABV 4.3%) PALE
Fastback Pale Ale (ABV 5%) PALE

3P's

Burton Road, Swadlincote, Woodville, Derbyshire, DE11 7JE ☎ 07590 285975 ⊕ 3psbrewery.co.uk

Innovative nanobrewery with a 600-litre Elite stainless steel two vessel system, founded in 2020 by an enthusiastic homebrewer. Using only the freshest natural ingredients, all beers are vegetarian and vegan-friendly (apart from the milk stout). 3P's brew beers with innovative twists throughout the year, alongside its core range. The name comes from Pits, Pots and Pipes for which Woodville was once renowned. Micropubs in Burton, Swadlincote and Derby are supplied. V

Bob "Ole" (ABV 4.5%) BITTER
Knocker Upper (ABV 4.8%) BLOND
Big Butty (ABV 5%) BITTER
Tubthumper (ABV 5.3%) PALE

627

4 Mice

🍴 Coach & Horses, Main Street, Bolton-by-Bowland, Clitheroe, BB7 4NW
☎ (01200) 447331
🌐 coachandhorsesribblevalley.co.uk

☺A four-barrel brewery in a gastro-pub, situated in the Trough of Bowland.

4Ts SIBA

Unit 20, Manor Industrial Estate, Lower Wash Lane, Latchford, Warrington, Cheshire, WA4 1PL
☎ (01925) 417820 ☎ 07917 730184
🌐 4tsbrewery.co.uk

Brewing continues several days a week on the 12-barrel kit. A large core range of beers is regularly produced with many one-off specials. The beers can be found in the Tavern, Church Street. The taproom is open once a month (Fri & Sat), please see social media for dates and opening times. ‼◆☕

SPA (ABV 3.8%) PALE
Light session beer, sweet fruity start and a long dry hop finale.
APA (ABV 4%) GOLD
WSB (ABV 4.2%) BITTER
IPA (ABV 4.6%) PALE
English Stout (ABV 5%) STOUT
Roast malt aromas with some sweet caramel developing into a stout with a dry roast bitter finish.

40FT SIBA

Bootyard, Abbot Street, Dalston, London, E8 3DP
☎ (020) 8126 6892

Office: The Printhouse, 18-20 Ashwin Street, Dalston, London, E8 3DL 🌐 40ftbrewery.com

This six-barrel microbrewery was established in 2015 in two 20ft shipping containers. It has since expanded to a total of 150ft. Beers are produced for its taproom as well as pubs, bars, restaurants and off-licences. Output is in kegs and cans with cask specials for local beer festivals and the taproom. ☕

52 Degrees SIBA

Unit 8a, Gatehouse Trading Estate, Lichfield Road, Brownhills, West Midlands, WS8 6JZ
🌐 52degreesbrewing.com

☺52 Degrees Brewing produces a range of beer styles in cask, keg, bottle and can. It is the home of Backyard Brewhouse, Grasshopper Brewery and the Warwickshire Beer Co. Beers can be found nationwide. ‼🍴◆

71 Brewing SIBA

36-40 Bellfield Street, Dundee, DD1 5HZ
☎ (01382) 203133 🌐 71brewing.com

Brewing began in 2016, producing craft keg and bottled beers. Although production is focused on canning, cask-conditioned ale made a welcome return to the Dundee area in 2023. Collaboration projects are popular with local start-up craft brewers. ‼🍴V☕

Cloud Fall (ABV 4.5%) PALE

8 Sail SIBA

Heckington Windmill, Hale Road, Heckington, Lincolnshire, NG34 9JW
☎ (01529) 469308 ☎ 07866 183479
🌐 8sailbrewery.co.uk

Established in 2010, 8 Sail Brewery operates on a six-barrel brew plant. It nestles in the shadow of Heckington Windmill, Britain's only eight-sailed windmill, from where it takes its name. The Mill helps to mill malted grain for the brewery. The shop stocks bottle-conditioned beers alongside local ciders. The front of the brewery has been converted into a Victorian-style bar, which has beer on handpump daily. The large outside area is weather dependent (hours may vary). 🍴◆LIVE☕

Windmill Bitter (ABV 3.8%) BITTER
Fenman (ABV 4.1%) BITTER
Froglet (ABV 4.2%) PALE
King John's Jewels (ABV 4.5%) GOLD
Victorian Porter (ABV 5%) PORTER

Brewed for Leila Cottage:
Leila's Lazy Days (ABV 3.6%) PALE
Ace Ale (ABV 3.8%) BITTER
Leila's One Off (ABV 5.1%) OLD

9 Lives

Unit 303, Ystradgynlais Workshops, Trawsffordd Road, Ystradgynlais, SA9 1BS ☎ 07743 559736
🌐 rob@9livesbrewing.co.uk

☺9 Lives Brewing was established in 2017 by Robert Scott, formerly brewer at the now defunct Bryncelyn Brewery, using the same six barrel capacity equipment. ‼◆LIVE V

Amber (ABV 4%) PALE
Pale amber with a hoppy aroma. A refreshing hoppy, fruity flavour with balancing bitterness; a similar lasting finish. A beer full of flavour for its gravity.
Dark (ABV 4%) MILD
Dark brown with an inviting aroma of malt, roast and fruit. A gentle bitterness mixes roast with malt, hops and fruit, giving a complex, satisfying and lasting finish.
Gold (ABV 4.5%) BITTER
An inviting aroma of hops, fruit and malt, and a golden colour. The tasty mix of hops, fruit, bitterness and background malt ends with a long, hoppy, bitter aftertaste. Full-bodied and drinkable.

A Bloke Down the Pub

See Potbelly

Abbey SIBA

Abbey Brewery, Camden Row, Bath, BA1 5LB
☎ (01225) 444437 🌐 abbeyales.co.uk

Founded in 1997 Abbey Ales was the first brewery in Bath for more than 50 years. It supplies more than 80 regular outlets within a 20-mile radius and its beers are more widely available in the South West via wholesalers. Three pubs are operated in Bath. ◆

Bath Best (ABV 4%) BITTER
Slight malt aroma, subtle caramel sweetness balanced with some hop bitterness and dark fruit on the palate, short dry aftertaste
Bath Pale Ale (ABV 4.2%) PALE
Bellringer (ABV 4.2%) BITTER
Refreshing and clean tasting with balanced flavours of pale fruit, English hops and biscuity malt before a bittersweet dry aftertaste.

Abbeydale SIBA

Unit 8, Aizlewood Road, Sheffield, South Yorkshire, S8 0YX
☎ (0114) 281 2712 🌐 abbeydalebrewery.co.uk

⊕Established in 1996, Abbeydale (one of the largest and longest standing Sheffield breweries), produced 200+ barrels a week in 2023 (75%+ was cask). At least one new beer produced weekly, often including the Dr Morton's range. Small batch, mixed fermentation and barrel-aged brews are created under its Funk Dungeon project. Substantial innovation, investment and expansion have enabled growth, including a substantial online and an export offering. One pub is owned, the Rising Sun, Nether Green. ♦GFV

Daily Bread (ABV 3.8%) BITTER
Well-balanced bitter, light brown in colour with a gentle caramel background finishing dry:
Deception (ABV 4.1%) PALE
Heathen (ABV 4.1%) PALE
Moonshine (ABV 4.3%) PALE
Absolution (ABV 5.3%) PALE
Black Mass (ABV 6.66%) STRONG

ABC

See Vale

Abernyte

South Latch Farm, Abernyte, Perthshire, PH14 9SU
☎ 07827 715915 ⊕ abernytebrewery.com

Established in 2016, the brewery overlooks the Carse of Gowrie. Brewing features a step mashing process in small batch, producing a range of unfiltered and naturally carbonated craft beers, packaged mainly in bottles. Cask beer is occasionally available. LIVE

Abyss SIBA

Unit 3, The Malthouse, Davey's Lane, Lewes, East Sussex, BN7 2BF ⊕ abyssbrewing.co.uk

⊗ Founded in Lewes in 2017, the brewery moved to its current premises at the old Southdown Brewery Malthouse in 2021. Cask beers are not normally produced but the onsite taproom (Thu-Sat) offers a changing range of modern style vegan-friendly keg beers from the eight-barrel brew plant. These can also be purchased to take away while home delivery is available (details online). Brewery tours (4-15 people, normally Sat) arranged by email. !!V♦

Accidental

Old Market Court, Morecambe, Lancashire, LA4 5HS
☎ 07930 592749 ⊕ accidentalbrewery.com

Initially a brewpub located on the edge of Lancaster city centre in an 18th century converted stable block, which opened in 2018. In 2021 it opened a new brewery in Morecambe where all production was moved to with the original site remaining as a brewery tap. Occasional cask ale is sometimes produced.

Acorn SIBA

Unit 3, Aldham Industrial Estate, Mitchell Road, Wombwell, Barnsley, South Yorkshire, S73 8HA
☎ (01226) 270734 ⊕ acorn-brewery.co.uk

⊕Acorn was set up in 2003 with a 10-barrel plant, expanding to 25 barrels when the brewery moved to larger premises. It currently has a 160-barrel a week capacity. All beers are produced using the Barnsley Bitter yeast strain, dating back to the 1850s. The brewery has recently changed ownership and is now owned by Sonas Capital. The staff remain and former owner Dave Hughes remains in a consultancy role. !!🍴♦LIVE

Yorkshire Pride (ABV 3.7%) BITTER
Golden session beer with pleasing fruit notes. A mouthwatering blend of malt and hops create a fruity taste which leads to a clean bitter finish.
Barnsley Bitter (ABV 3.8%) BITTER
Brown bitter, smooth malty bitterness throughout with notes of chocolate and caramel. Fruity bitter finish.
Blonde (ABV 4%) PALE
A clean-tasting, golden-coloured hoppy beer with a refreshing bitter and fruity aftertaste.
Barnsley Gold (ABV 4.3%) GOLD
Golden ale with fruit in the aroma with a hoppy and fruitiness flavour throughout. A well-hopped, clean, dry finish.
Malthouse (ABV 4.4%) BITTER
Old Moor Porter (ABV 4.4%) PORTER
A rich-tasting porter, smooth throughout with a hint of chocolate and a hint of liquorice. This is a moreish porter.
Gorlovka Imperial Stout (ABV 6%) STOUT
Black stout, rich and smooth and full of chocolate and liquorice flavours, with a fruity, creamy finish.

Adnams SIBA

Sole Bay Brewery, East Green, Southwold, Suffolk, IP18 6JW
☎ (01502) 727200 ⊕ adnams.co.uk

⊗ Adnams was founded in Southwold on the Suffolk coast in 1872, where it still brews today. It owns and manages eleven hotels, pubs and inns and has a number of partner pubs, as well as several retail stores. It remains an independent, values-based family business committed to a sustainable future. !!🍴♦V

Southwold Bitter (ABV 3.7%) BITTER
Impressive creamy copper-coloured session bitter with lingering earthy herbal hop, sweet nutty malt flavours and hints of caramel and fruit.
Mosaic (ABV 4.1%) PALE
Impressive pale ale with citrus, tropical fruit and peach hop, quenching bitterness, subdued sweet malt and a balanced dry aftertaste.
Ghost Ship (ABV 4.5%) PALE
Vibrant pale ale with lingering orange, lemon, crisp hoppiness and biscuity sweetness. Great balance and easy-drinking.
Broadside (ABV 4.7%) RED
Rich, malty and fruity ruby brown beer, balanced with hops in the mouth and ending fruity with sweet malt.

Adur

Brick Barn, Charlton Court, Mouse Lane, Steyning, West Sussex, BN44 3DG
☎ (01903) 867614

Office: 2 Sullington Way, Shoreham-by-Sea, BN43 6PJ
⊕ adurvalleycoop.com

⊗ Adur Brewery, nestled in the heart of the South Downs, was launched in 2008 on a 5.5-barrel plant, marking the return of brewing to the Adur Valley after an interval of nearly 100 years. The brewery was sold to the Adur Valley Co-operative in 2012, including the Adur Brewery name and recipes. A large part of the output is sold as bottle-conditioned beer, with certain brews in five-litre mini kegs. !!♦LIVE

Ropetackle Golden Ale (ABV 3.4%) GOLD
Hop Token: Amarillo (ABV 4%) BITTER
Hop Token: Summit (ABV 4%) BITTER
Velocity (ABV 4.4%) BITTER
Black William (ABV 5%) STOUT
Robbie's Red (ABV 5.2%) RED

Affinity

Grosvenor Arms, 17 Sidney Road, Stockwell, London, SW9 0TP ☎ 07904 391807 ⊕ affinitybrewco.com

Established in 2016 in a container in Tottenham Hale and expanded in 2017 to the Bermondsey Beer Mile, 2020 saw the brewery start afresh in the basement of the Grosvenor Arms. Run as a separate business; cask, keg and canned beers are available in the pub and now quite widely. Brewing is currently suspended. ✦

Ainsty

Manor Farm, Intake Lane, Acaster Malbis, York, North Yorkshire, YO23 3UJ
☎ (01904) 703233 ☎ 07983 604989
⊕ ainstyales.co.uk

⊛Based in the ancient York & Ainsty Wapentake in York, this award-winning brewery opened in 2016 with a 10-barrel kit, supplying venues mainly in Yorkshire, but also throughout the UK via wholesalers, and online shop. The taproom is open year round on Fridays, plus Saturdays May-October, with street food and live music. ‼☕✦✦

Northern Lights (ABV 3.6%) GOLD
Flummoxed Farmer (ABV 4%) BLOND
Bantam Best (ABV 4.2%) BITTER
Cool Citra (ABV 4.4%) PALE
This premium pale is packed with citrus flavor and has a strong fruity aroma and creamy hop laden aftertaste.
Assassin (ABV 4.9%) STOUT

Aitcheson's

Windham Farm, Ferry Road, Wawne, East Yorkshire, HU7 5XY ☎ 07456 063670

Office: 2 Wheelhouse Court, Hull, East Yorkshire, HU6 5BF ⊕ eastyorkshirebeer.co.uk

⊛Formerly the East Yorkshire Beer Company, Aitcheson's is a small batch brewery, established by Steve and Avril Aitcheson in a 17th century refurbished, former boatshed on the banks of the River Hull, in 2020. Beers are available in multiple formats. Brewing experience days are popular and are bookable in advance. ✦V

Endike Black (ABV 3.5%) MILD
Hazy Grapefruit IPA (ABV 4%) IPA
Vanilla Stout (ABV 4%) STOUT
King Billy Best Bitter (ABV 4.2%) BITTER
Earl de Grey EPA (ABV 4.5%) PALE
Oddfellows Red (ABV 4.8%) RED
Kiwi IPA (ABV 5%) PALE

Aither

12 Mill Way, Old Mill Lane Industrial Estate, Mansfield Woodhouse, Nottinghamshire, NG19 9BG ☎ 07703 828594 ✉ slawrence@aitherbrewery.co.uk

Taking its name from Greek mythology, and meaning 'from the heavens', Aither Brewery, was established in 2022 by Scott Lawrence and Ashleigh Hunt. It brews traditional English ales. Scott spent ten years at Batemans before setting up on his own. Beers are available in Mansfield and the wider Nottinghamshire area.

Equinox (ABV 3.8%) PALE
Artemis (ABV 4%) PALE
Sirius (ABV 4.2%) BLOND
Void (ABV 4.5%) BITTER
Aurora (ABV 5%) PORTER

AJ's

Unit 11, Ashmore Industrial Estate, Longacre Street, Walsall, West Midlands, WS2 8QG ☎ 07860 585911 ✉ ajs-ales@hotmail.com

⊠ Set up by experienced brewer Andy Dukes and his wife Charlotte, AJ's Ales was established in 2015 and uses a four-barrel plant with three fermenting vessels and a cool room. It brews three times a week, mainly supplying local pubs and further afield through local wholesalers. ✦

Blackjack Mild (ABV 3.6%) MILD
Stuck on Blondes (ABV 3.9%) BLOND
Best Bitter (ABV 4%) BITTER
Dukey's Delight (ABV 4.1%) GOLD
SPA (ABV 4.2%) PALE
Gold (ABV 4.3%) GOLD
Stuck in the Mud (ABV 4.3%) STOUT
Ruby (ABV 4.4%) BITTER
IPA (ABV 4.6%) PALE
Stuck in the Doghouse (ABV 4.7%) GOLD

Aldwark Artisan

Lydgate Farm, Aldwark, Matlock, Derbyshire, DE4 4HW
☎ (01629) 540720 ☎ 07834 353807
⊕ aabrewery.co.uk

⊠ This 10-barrel plant, housed in an old milking shed on a rural working farm, produced its first brew in 2017. Water comes from the farm's own bore hole, filtered through the strong limestone hills of the Peak District. It has created the 'AAA' range of craft ales.

Nostrum Gold (ABV 3.8%) GOLD
Elixir Gold (ABV 3.9%) GOLD
Baabarian Gold (ABV 4%) PALE
Roan (ABV 4%) BITTER
Nostrum Amber (ABV 4.2%) BITTER
Eight Million (ABV 4.5%) GOLD
Hare of the Hill (ABV 4.6%) BLOND
Aldwark Pale IPA (ABV 4.8%) PALE
Frankenstein (ABV 5.4%) PORTER

Aldworth

🍺 **Bell Inn, Aldworth, Berkshire, RG8 9SE**

Set up in 2022 in an old barn behind the Bell, which was CAMRA National Pub of the Year 2019. This nanobrewery is run by James Macaulay, son of the family who run the pub. James trained as a brewer at West Berkshire Brewery (now rebranded as Renegade). The brewery has a capacity of 163 litres (approx 1 barrel or 4x9 gallon firkins) and is understood to be supplying the pub only.

Aleworks (NEW)

Brookhouse Farm, Horsham, Sussex, RH13 8PY
☎ 07875 395432 ⊕ aleworksbrewingco.co.uk

Based on the beautiful Knepp Castle estate in West Sussex, Liam (originally a home brewer) and Harriet spent 18 months converting an old milking parlour into a fully operational brewery, launching in 2022. Their focus is traditional cask ale with modern flavours.

All Day Succa (ABV 4%) PALE
Into the Wild (ABV 4.2%) PALE
Stay Gold (ABV 4.2%) PALE
Sonder (ABV 4.3%) PALE
Southern Ranger (ABV 4.3%) BITTER
Maple Days (ABV 4.5%) SPECIALITY

Alfred's SIBA

Unit 6, Winnall Farm Industrial Estate, Easton Lane, Winchester, Hampshire, SO23 0HA
☎ (01962) 859999 ⊕ alfredsbrewery.co.uk

Alfred's is a 10-barrel, state-of-the-art brewery located close to the centre of Winchester. Production of Saxon Bronze is complemented by returning favourites and experimental beers. ▰♦

Saxon Bronze (ABV 3.8%) BITTER
Well-balanced, copper-coloured bitter, with minimal aroma. Malt dominates the taste with some hops in the finish.

All Day

Salle Moor Farm, Wood Dalling Road, Salle, Norfolk, NR10 4SB
☎ (01603) 327656 ☎ 07825 604887
⊕ alldaybrewing.co.uk

⊗ Housed in a centuries old barn, the brewery has its own hop yard and an adjoining organic orchard. Many of the beers are barrel-aged, or sours, or involve fruit grown at the brewery. They are available in the taproom and kitchen, along with vegan food, pizza, real cider, and raw kombucha. Home of the the Norfolk Hop Festival. ‼▰♦LIVE✦

All Hallows

⬛ Main Street, Goodmanham, East Yorkshire, YO43 3JA
☎ (01430) 873849 ✉ abbielogo@aol.co.uk

⊕Abbie Logozzi, landlady of the Goodmanham Arms, started brewing in 2012 in outbuildings behind the pub. The ex-Goodmanham Brewery buildings were purchased and a five-barrel plant installed. The brewery name comes from the adjacent 12th century All Hallows Church. Local legendary characters are used in the naming of some of the beers. Brews are supplied to the pub and some free trade. Brewing is currently suspended. ♦

All Nations

⬛ 20 Coalport Road, Madeley, Telford, Shropshire, TF7 5SU
☎ (01952) 585747 ✉ allnationsinn@btinternet.com

⊕One of the famous last four brewhouses left. Established in 1832, and run by just two families for the first 151 years. Then the Birtwhistles for 21 years. Now Andrew Brough continues the legacy of brewing traditional beers (as he has for more than a decade), on the ten-barrel plant, extending the brewing portfolio from one to four different beers.

Allanwater

⬛ Queens Lane, Bridge of Allan, FK9 4NY
☎ (01786) 834555 ☎ 07831 224242
⊕ allanwaterbrewhouse.co.uk

⊕Originally named Tinpot and then Wash House, the brewery was established in 2009 using a one-barrel plant designed to brew speciality beer. From 2018 all beers and branding are under the Allanwater Brewhouse name. The beer range varies depending on season and demand, which is increasing every year. ‼▰♦LIVE

Allendale SIBA

Allen Mill, Allendale, Northumberland, NE47 9EA
☎ (01434) 618686 ⊕ allendalebrewery.com

⊕Established in 2006, the brewery is a 20-barrel plant in a historic lead smelting mill in the heart of the North Pennines Area of Outstanding Natural Beauty. Many of the beers reflect the heritage and identity of the local area. Taproom events with music are held on the last Friday of the month during the warmer months. Contact the brewery or check on social media for details. ‼▰♦GF✦

Wagtail Best Bitter (ABV 3.8%) BITTER
Amber bitter with spicy aromas and a long, bitter finish.
Golden Plover (ABV 4%) BLOND
Light, refreshing, easy-drinking blonde beer with a clean finish.
Pennine Pale (ABV 4%) PALE
Fruity citrus aromas and a sweet full mouth are enveloped by a lasting hop bitterness, some malt and a satisfying dryness.
Hop On (ABV 4.7%) GOLD
Adder Lager (ABV 5%) SPECIALITY
Anvil (ABV 5.5%) IPA
Wolf (ABV 5.5%) RED
Full-bodied red ale with sweet fruitiness in the taste giving way to a roast bitter finish.
Wanderlust (ABV 6.5%) IPA
Dirty Deeds (ABV 6.6%) IPA

Allgates

See Wigan Brewhouse

Allkin (NEW)

Rendlye Farm, Tunbridge Wells, Kent, TN3 9LP
⊕ allkinbrewing.com

New brewery established after Good Things Brewery was struck by lightning in 2023 and burned to the ground.

Almasty

Unit A2A, Benfield Business Park, Benfield Road, Newcastle upon Tyne, NE6 4NQ
☎ (0191) 253 1639

Second Site: Unit 11, Algernon Industrial Estate, New York Road, Shiremoor, NE27 0NB
⊕ almastyshop.co.uk

⊗ Opened in 2014, Almasty brews across two sites. The original site in Shiremoor runs the mixed/natural fermentation and barrel-ageing programme. The newer site now produces the majority of output, which is a continuously changing range of unfined, unfiltered beers. These include heavily-hopped pale ales, IPAs and rich stouts. A taproom and shop located at Benfield Business Park is open during summer weekends. House beer pumpclips are made from screen-printed, hand-sawn logs. Beers are supplied nationwide. ‼▰♦V✦

Alnwick SIBA

Unit E-F, Hawkhill Business Park, Lesbury, Northumberland, NE66 3PG
☎ (01665) 830617 ☎ 07788 433499
⊕ alnwickbrewery.co.uk

Brewing started in the 1860s in the centre of Alnwick, the capital of Northumberland. The brewery was acquired in 1978 by Scottish brewer Dryboroughs, who closed it in 1986, but relaunched in 2003 with the assistance of the Duchess of Northumberland. Having expanded onto a 10-barrel plant in 2020, five core beers are now produced. Lockdown in 2020 also allowed some development onsite and a taproom and shop were opened. More than 50 outlets are supplied in the north of

England. The brewery acts as a distribution hub for beer festivals in the north of England as well as Scotland. ☞◆✦

Amber (ABV 3.8%) BITTER
Holy Island Bitter (ABV 3.8%) BITTER
Gold (ABV 4.2%) BLOND
American IPA (ABV 4.4%) PALE
IPA (ABV 4.5%) PALE

Alter Ego SIBA

Unit B2, Salcombe Road, Meadow Lane Industrial Estate, Alfreton, Derbyshire, DE55 7RG
☎ (01773) 475126 ☎ 07989 655828
✉ matt@alteregobrewing.co

Alter Ego upgraded in 2022 to a six-barrel brewery located in Alfreton producing full-flavoured, small-batch beers in cask and keg. The brewery's tap is the Tip Inn micropub, Loscoe. ◆

Echo Chamber (ABV 3.8%) PALE
Mr Brown (ABV 4.2%) BITTER
Blonde Protagonist (ABV 4.3%) BLOND
S'more Fire (ABV 5.2%) STOUT
Incognito (ABV 5.8%) IPA

Ambridge

Unit 2A, Priory Piece Business Park, Priory Farm Lane, Inkberrow, Worcestershire, WR7 4HT ☎ 07498 628238 ⊕ ambridgebrewery.co.uk

⊛Ambridge commenced brewing in 2013, initially for the family run pub, and expansion was achieved by acquiring the Wyre Piddle brewery. As well as the main beer range a number of seasonal and specials are brewed throughout the year. Occasional, small run bottling is also carried out. Brewing is currently suspended. ‼◆LIVE

Amity SIBA

🍴 15-16 Festoon Rooms, Sunny Bank Mills, Farsley, Leeds, West Yorkshire, LS28 5UJ ⊕ amitybrew.co

Launching in 2020 with its online shop, Amity Brew Co was founded by Russ Clarke (ex-BrewDog, Buxton, North Brewing Co, and Beer Hawk team member). Originally cuckoo brewing, its brewpub opened later the same year sporting a 10-hectolitre brew kit, producing modern interpretations of classic beer styles, as well as more experimental brews. No real ale. ‼☞✦

Ampersand SIBA

27-31 Sawmills Road, Diss, Norfolk, IP22 4GG
☎ (01379) 643944 ⊕ ampersandbrew.co

A small batch brewery established in 2017. Originally based on a family farm in South Norfolk, it relocated to Diss in 2021. ☞V✦

Bidon (ABV 3.9%) PALE
Bitter (ABV 3.9%) BITTER
Pale (ABV 3.9%) BITTER
The Cap Bitter (ABV 3.9%) BITTER
On the Wing (ABV 4.5%) PALE
Pulpit Pale (ABV 5%) PALE
Fruity, hoppy, and well-balanced in aroma and taste. Malt and a light hoppiness join bittersweet notes in the background.

Amwell Springs SIBA

Westfield Farm House, Westfield Road, Cholsey, Wallingford, Oxfordshire, OX10 9LS ☎ 07812 396619 ⊕ asbco.co.uk

Brewing began in 2017 on a 70-litre plant using water from a spring in the farmhouse grounds. Capacity expanded in 2019 to six barrels. Beers are available in local pubs. ☞LIVE✦

Chairman Dave (ABV 3.5%) BITTER
Stay Jammy (ABV 3.8%) BITTER
Rude Not To (ABV 4%) GOLD
Eazy Geez (ABV 4.5%) GOLD
Mad Gaz (ABV 5.2%) PALE

Anarchy SIBA

Unit A1, Benfield Business Park, Newcastle upon Tyne, NE6 4NQ
☎ (0191) 389 7580 ⊕ anarchybrewco.com

A 20-barrel brewery, started in 2012 in Morpeth, and moved to Newcastle upon Tyne in 2018. Its focus is on session beers, plus an eclectic mix of one-offs and collaborations with a host of breweries from the UK and across the globe. ‼LIVE V✦

Blonde Star (ABV 4.1%) BLOND
A sweet, gently-bittered, fruity beer.
Citra Star (ABV 4.1%) GOLD
Skin Deep (ABV 4.2%) PALE
Cult Leader (ABV 5.5%) PALE

Andwell SIBA

Andwell Lane, Andwell, Hampshire, RG27 9PA
☎ (01256) 761044 ⊕ andwells.com

⊠ Brewing commenced in 2008 on a 10-barrel plant. The brewery relocated and expanded in 2011 to an idyllic riverside location with a new bespoke 20-barrel plant. Beer is distributed to Hampshire, Surrey, Wiltshire, Berkshire, Greater London and the Isle of Wight. More than 200 outlets are supplied. In 2020 Andwells new brewhouse shop, bar and café opened behind the brewery. ‼☞◆

Resolute Bitter (ABV 3.8%) BITTER
An easy-drinking bitter. The malty aroma, leads into a similarly malty flavour with some bitterness and a sweetish finish.
Gold Muddler (ABV 3.9%) BLOND
Light golden blond ale. Aroma of hops and malt, characteristics carried into flavour with solid bitterness and dry, biscuity finish.
King John (ABV 4.2%) BITTER
Malty bitter, low in hops with loads of caramel and toffee. Underlying sweetness, leading to some dryness in the finish.

Angel

🍴 Angel, 7 Stoney Street, Nottingham, NG1 1LG
☎ 07908 942417
✉ barbookings@theangelmicrobrewery.co.uk

Situated inside one of Nottingham's oldest, haunted, and cave-filled pubs. The Angel Microbrewery uses a 2.5-barrel plant, nestled in the taproom of the 400-year-old pub. Beers are available at the Angel and the Golden Fleece in Nottingham. V

Angel Ales SIBA

62A Furlong Lane, Halesowen, West Midlands, B63 2TA ☎ 07986 382919 ⊕ angelales.co.uk

Angel Ales began commercial brewing in 2011. The brewery building has been a chapel of rest, a coffin makers workshop and a pattern makers before becoming a brewhouse. Beers are produced using organic ingredients where possible. !! ♦ LIVE V

Ale (ABV 4.1%) PALE
Krakow (ABV 4.5%) SPECIALITY
Zanzibar (ABV 5%) SPECIALITY

Angels & Demons

See McCanns

Anglo Oregon

Newport, NP19 4RR ☎ 07854 194966 ⊕ aobc.co.uk

Founded in the Forest of Dean in 2015, the brewery relocated to the owner's garage, in Nash, Newport, in 2017. It produces 330ml bottle-conditioned ales, brewing 240 litres once a month. The ales are centred around the Newport Levels Trilogy, The Chartists Trilogy and the Newport Heritage Trilogy. It no longer produces casks or kegs. It regularly produces special, commemorative ales. It has a license for off-sales from the brewery. LIVE

Animal

See XT

Anomaly

Glebe Gardens, Old Malden, KT3 5RU ☎ 07903 623993 ⊕ anomalybrewing.co.uk

Founded in 2017, beers started to appear at the end of 2018 brewed on a 100-litre home kit. Most production is available in bottles and cans but cask is sometimes available for pubs and at beer festivals.

Another Beer

Unit 3, Handley Park, Elvington Industrial Estate, York Road, Elvington, YO41 4AR ☎ 07403 264242 ⊕ anotherbeer.co.uk

Launched in 2019 by James Fawcett, Another Beer moved from York City Centre into the former Hop Studio site in Elvington in 2022. Additional space and increased brewing capacity has seen an expansion into cask production. Beers are available in York as well as having distribution across Yorkshire, Manchester and the Midlands. ♦

Anspach & Hobday SIBA

Unit 11, Valley Point Industrial Estate, Beddington Farm Road, Beddington, CR0 4WP
☎ (020) 3302 9669 ⊕ anspachandhobday.com

⊠ Anspach & Hobday began brewing in 2014. In 2020 the brewery moved to a new site near Croydon. In 2022 following the success of its nitro-porter, London Black, the brewery expanded to a 24-barrel kit. The original site, the Arch House (on the Bermondsey Beer Mile), is now the home of its taproom and barrel-aged and sour beers. ☲LIVE V

The Ordinary Bitter (ABV 3.4%) BITTER
Malty aroma with nutty sweetness. Malt builds and combines with hops, roasty chocolate and orange. Smooth, bitter and peppery finish.
The IPA (ABV 6%) IPA

Easy-drinking, hoppy New World IPA. Citrus and spicy peppercorns overlaid by biscuity malt and a bitter, dry, lemony finish.
The Porter (ABV 6.7%) PORTER
Roasted coffee notes throughout with caramel, dark fruit and hops in the flavour and lingering finish which is slightly dry.

Anthology

Unit 6, Armley Link, Armley Road, Leeds, West Yorkshire, LS12 2QN ⊕ anthologybrewing.co.uk

Established in 2018, Anthology is a small-batch, 2.5-barrel, Leeds-based brewery. Liam Kane brews an ever-evolving range of beers focussed on bold flavours. Beers are available in outlets around the city, and some further afield. Occasional taproom events throughout the warmer months (check social media). It also likes to work with artistic/charitable organisations. V♦

New England Session Pale (ABV 3.8%) PALE
Pale Ale (ABV 4%) BLOND

Antur

Brecon House, Elvicta Estate, Crickhowell, NP8 1DF
☎ (01873) 561278 ⊕ anturbrew.com

Showcasing the local landmarks within the Brecon Beacons National Park, Antur Brew Co opened in 2022 and relocated to its present site in 2024. 'Antur' being the Welsh word for 'Adventure' embodies the brewery ethos. Heavily influenced by German and American styles, its small-batch 500-litre output is canned onsite. Craft keg beers are available. !! ☲ ♦

Apex

Patson Hill Farm, Patson Hill Lane, Sherborne, Dorset, DT9 4SY ☎ 07817 806730 ⊕ apexbrewing.co

Apex Brewing Co was originally based in Corton Denham and moved to its current location in 2024 to allow expansion. Its mission is to brew beer to the highest standards using the latest technology. All beers are unfined and therefore slightly cloudy. V

Cut 'n' Shut (ABV 1.2%) PALE
Piston Popper (ABV 3.9%) PALE
Epic Prang (ABV 5%) SPECIALITY
Full Beams (ABV 5%) BITTER
Gear Grinder (ABV 5%) PALE
Grease Monkey (ABV 5%) PALE
Oil Leak (ABV 5%) STOUT
Old Rusty (ABV 5%) BITTER
Rear End (ABV 5%) GOLD
Road Kill (ABV 5%) PALE
Sticky Clutch (ABV 5%) SPECIALITY
Hot Lap (ABV 6.4%) IPA

Applecross

Russel Yard, Kishorn, Strathcarron, IV54 8XF
⊕ applecrossbrewingcompany.co.uk

Applecross Brewing Co was established in 2016 in the remote wilderness of the Applecross Estate in the Highlands of Scotland. All the beers are available in bottle and cask. The main cask outlet is the famous Applecross Inn.

Applecross (ABV 3.7%) PALE
Sanctuary (ABV 4%) RED
Inner Sound (ABV 4.7%) PORTER

Arbor SIBA

181 Easton Road, Easton, Bristol, BS5 0HQ
☎ (0117) 329 2711 ⊕ arborales.co.uk

⊗ Founded in 2007, Arbor has a 20-barrel brew length with 16 fermenting vessels. Willing to experiment, more than 300 beers have been produced. The current range reflects modern tastes and leans towards hoppy pale ales and IPAs plus some interesting red and dark ales. ♦ GF V

Mosaic Gluten Free (ABV 4%) PALE
Hoppy aroma, flavours of soft tropical fruit with floral notes on a light malt background leaving a gentle bittersweet aftertaste.

Motueka (ABV 4%) PALE

Shangri La (ABV 4.2%) PALE
Hoppy aroma, light malt background flavour supporting citrus and tropical fruits with pine needle hints before a clean, refreshing finish.

Blue Sky Drinking (ABV 4.4%) BITTER
Background malt overlaid with gentle hop bitterness, hints of dark fruit and subtle caramel before a clean, bittersweet finish.

C Bomb (ABV 4.7%) PALE
Distinctive New World hop aroma, citrus fruit and pine flavours bring bitterness to the palate continuing into the lingering aftertaste.

My Little Sabrony (ABV 5%) PALE

Why Kick a Moo Cow? (ABV 5.5%) PALE
A strong amber ale with malt and hops on the nose, flavours of tropical fruit and a dry bittersweet aftertaste.

Yakima Valley (ABV 7%) IPA
A strong, full-bodied IPA. Hoppy and very fruity. Sweetness is well-balanced with bitterness, lasting into a soft bitter aftertaste.

Archers

See Evan Evans

Ardgour SIBA

The Manse, Ardgour, PH33 7AH
☎ (01855) 632321 ⊕ ardgourales.scot

Opening in 2020, eight years after Fergus and Lizzy Stokes bought the crumbling Manse with a view to bringing great beer to Scotland's west coast, this new-build, five-barrel brewery is situated in the village of Ardgour on the edge of the remote Morvern and Ardnamurchan peninsulas. An onsite bakery is also in operation. ‼ 🍴 V

Eas Geal (ABV 3.4%) PALE
Boc Beag (ABV 3.6%) GOLD
Gobhar Shamhna (ABV 4.1%) RED
Gobhar Odhar (ABV 4.3%) BITTER
Bainne nan Gobhar (ABV 4.5%) STOUT
Boc Ban (ABV 5.1%) BITTER
Boc na Braiche (ABV 6.4%) PALE
Gobhar Reamhar (ABV 6.5%) STOUT

Ards

34B Carrowdore Road, Greyabbey, Newtownards, Co Down, BT22 2LX ☎ 07515 558406
✉ ardsbrewing@blackwood34.plus.com

Ards began brewing in 2011 using a 100-litre plant. A five-barrel plant is now in operation, allowing cask production in addition to the increasing range of bottle-conditioned and KeyKeg beers. Very much a local brewery with beers generally only supplied within a 15-mile radius. ♦ LIVE

Citra (ABV 4.8%) GOLD

Scrabo Gold (ABV 4.8%) GOLD
Hip Hop (ABV 5%) BITTER
Pig Island (ABV 5.2%) BITTER

Aristotle

c/o Unit 4, Silver House, Adelphi Way, Staveley, Derbyshire, S43 3LJ
☎ (01246) 470074 ☎ 07496 757619
✉ richard@silverbrewhouse.com

⊗ A splinter brewery company set up from within Silver Brewhouse to produce alternative beers on the same kit for cask, keg, bottles and can. ♦

Arkell's SIBA IFBB

Kingsdown, Swindon, Wiltshire, SN2 7RU
☎ (01793) 823026 ⊕ arkells.com

⊗ 2023 marked the 180th anniversary of Arkell's Brewery which was established in 1843 by John Arkell. The Arkell family still brew in the original Victorian brewhouse, one of the few remaining 'tower' breweries in Britain. The brewery owns nearly 100 pubs across Wiltshire, Gloucestershire, Oxfordshire, Berkshire and Hampshire. In 2018 a brewery shop and visitor centre opened onsite. Seasonal beers are brewed frequently, often linked to sporting and other national events. ‼ 🍴 ♦

Wiltshire Gold (ABV 3.7%) GOLD
Refreshing, hoppy pale ale, light in colour with a balance of sweet, malty and bitter tastes.

3B (ABV 4%) BITTER
A medium brown beer with a strong, sweetish malt/caramel flavour.

Hoperation IPA (ABV 4.2%) PALE
A light, hoppy pale ale with a refreshing palate and a slightly bitter aftertaste.

Arkwright Pal

See Silver

Armagh

Drumgraw Road, Armagh, Northern Ireland, BT60 2AD ☎ 07828 473199
✉ armaghbrewingco@gmail.com

A microbrewery based on the outskirts of Armagh, established in 2016.

Arran SIBA

Cladach, Brodick, Isle of Arran, KA27 8DE
☎ (01770) 302353

Office: Isle of Arran Brewery Guesthouse, Shore Road, Whiting Bay, Isle of Arran, KA27 8PZ
⊕ arranbrewery.co.uk

☺ The brewery opened in Brodick in 2000 using a 20-barrel plant with water sourced from the nearby mountains. It has its own in-house bottling plant, shop and taproom – brewery tours are also available. Local outlets are supplied direct, with the beers available around the UK via distributors. The brewery owns the rights to the former Devil's Dyke Brewery beers. ‼ 🍴 ♦ V ⊘

Guid Ale (ABV 3.8%) GOLD
A golden, refreshing session ale with a delicate balance of malt and fruit.

Dark (ABV 4.3%) BROWN
A well-balanced, malty beer, roast and hop in the taste and a dry, bitter finish. A traditional 'Scottish Heavy'.

Sunset (ABV 4.4%) GOLD

A mid-amber summer ale, light perfumed aroma, good balance of malt, fruit and hops with a pleasant dry finish.

Blonde (ABV 5%) SPECIALITY
A hoppy beer with substantial fruit balance. An aromatic strong golden ale that drinks below its weight.

Brewery Dug (ABV 5.5%) IPA
An American-style IPA with a refreshing citrus body and a dry, lemon zest, bitter finish.

Arran Botanical Drinks

Cladach Beach House, Brodick, KA27 8DE
☎ (01770) 302513 ⊕ arranbotanicaldrinks.com

Formerly known as Arran Gin, Arran Botanical Drinks is located at Cladach, overlooking Brodick Bay. Drinks can be enjoyed outdoors at the idyllic beachside location, often beside a large and warming bonfire. It has a small brewkit producing a couple of in-house bottle-conditioned and kegged beers using locally-foraged ingredients. There is a shop and tastings are available for all its products. ☛LIVE

Artefact SIBA

Bridge Farm, Bury Road, Ixworth, Suffolk, IP31 2HX
⊕ artefactbrewing.co.uk

Artefact Brewing is a nanobrewery established in 2020. The brainchild of husband-and-wife team James and Kat Lawson-Phillips, it operates from a cleverly converted shipping container in Ixworth, Suffolk. Committed to a classic core range and a variety of seasonal and special releases, Artefact has released more than 30 different beers so far, and won two national SIBA awards.

Dark Mild (ABV 3.2%) MILD
Session Pale Ale (ABV 3.8%) PALE
Ixworth Blonde (ABV 4.8%) GOLD
Finally an ESB (ABV 5.6%)
Amber Haze IPA (ABV 6.2%) IPA

Arundel

The Brewhouse Project, Lyminster Road, Arundel, West Sussex, BN17 7QL
☎ (01903) 733111 ⊕ arundelbrewery.co.uk

⊠ Founded in 1992, Arundel brewery is the historic town's first brewery in 70 years. It also brews for the Bison Crafthouse, Brighton. The Brewery has recently moved onsite to the Brewhouse Project, which serves as a taproom. ‼☛◆⬟

Black Stallion (ABV 3.7%) MILD
A dark mild with well-defined chocolate and roast character. The aftertaste is not powerful but the initial flavours remain in the clean finish.

Castle (ABV 3.8%) BITTER
A pale tawny beer with fruit and malt noticeable in the aroma. The flavour has a good balance of malt, fruit and hops, with a dry, hoppy finish.

Sussex Gold (ABV 4.2%) GOLD
A golden-coloured best bitter with a strong floral hop aroma. Clean-tasting and bitter for its strength, with a tangy citrus flavour. The initial hop and fruit die to a dry and bitter finish.

Sussex IPA (ABV 4.5%) PALE
Stronghold (ABV 4.7%) BITTER
A smooth, full-flavoured premium bitter. A good balance of malt, fruit and hops comes through in this rich, chestnut-coloured beer.

Wild Heaven (ABV 5.2%) PALE

Ascot

See Disruption is Brewing

Ashley Down

St Andrews, Bristol, BS6 5BY
☎ (0117) 983 6567 ☎ 07563 751200
✉ ashleydownbrewery@gmail.com

⊠ Ashley Down began brewing in 2011, in the owner's garage. It suffered a major fire in 2017. Production resumed 2022, in the owners reinstated garage, using a 3.5-barrel plant. A small range of beers are regularly brewed, that are interspersed with one-offs. ◆V

Ashover

Unit 1, Derby Road, Clay Cross, Derbyshire, S45 9AG
☎ (01246) 251859 ⊕ ashoverbrewery.com

⊠ Brewing began in 2007 on a 3.5-barrel plant in the garage of the cottage next to the Old Poets' Corner, Ashover. Moved to a 10-barrel brewery in the neighbouring village of Clay Cross in 2015. The brewery serves local freehouses across Derbyshire and further afield, including many festivals. It has won many CAMRA awards. ‼LIVE

Light Rale (ABV 3.7%) BITTER
Light in colour and taste, with initial sweet and malt flavours, leading to a bitter finish and aftertaste.

Font (ABV 3.8%) GOLD
Poets Tipple (ABV 4%) BITTER
Complex, tawny-coloured beer that drinks above its strength. Predominantly malty in flavour, with increasing bitterness towards the end.

Littlemoor Citra (ABV 4.1%) PALE
The Fabrick (ABV 4.4%) GOLD
Rainbows End (ABV 4.5%) GOLD
Slightly smooth, bitter golden beer with an initial sweetness. Grapefruit and lemon hop flavours come through strongly as the beer gets increasingly dry towards the finish, ending with a bitter, dry aftertaste.

Red Lion (ABV 4.6%) RED
Coffin Lane Stout (ABV 5%) STOUT
Stout with chocolate and coffee flavours, which are balanced by a little sweetness. The finish is long and quite dry.

Butts Pale Ale (ABV 5.5%) PALE
Pale and strong with a combination of bitter and sweet flavours leading to a warming yet bitter finish.

Milk Stout (ABV 6%) STOUT

Ashton

Cheltenham, Gloucestershire, GL53 9LW ☎ 07796 445822 ⊕ ashtonbrewery.co.uk

⊠ Nanobrewery established in Ashton Keynes, Wiltshire, in 2018. The brewery moved in 2020 to Cheltenham. A range of live beers are produced which are unfined cask and bottle-conditioned. LIVE V

Mosaic (ABV 4.4%) GOLD
Gold (ABV 4.5%) PALE
Shot In The Dark (ABV 4.6%) SPECIALITY
Hazy Blonde (ABV 4.8%) PALE

Atlantic

Unit 5, Indian Queens Trading Estate, Warren Road, Indian Queens, Cornwall, TR9 6TL
☎ (01726) 457506 ⊕ atlanticbrewery.com

⊠ Specialist microbrewery producing organic and vegan ales. All ales are unfiltered and finings-free. There are eleven core brews including four food-matched dining ales developed with Michelin recognised chef Nathan Outlaw. Casks are supplied locally and to London, with bottle-conditioned beers available nationally. ♦LIVE V✦

Soul Citra (ABV 4%) PALE
A gold beer with citrus hop aroma. Smooth and creamy mouthfeel with dominant citrus hop flavours. Moderate bitterness and sweetness.

Azores (ABV 4.2%) GOLD
Unfined gold beer. Citrus and resinous hops dominate the aroma and taste with tropical fruits. Refreshing bitter and dry finish.

Blue (ABV 4.5%) PORTER
Smooth, rich porter with heavy roast malt aroma and taste. Smoky liquorice, bitter coffee and chocolate flavours with sweet fruit.

Earl Grey PA (ABV 4.5%) SPECIALITY
Cloudy, amber, organic speciality ale. Hop aroma leads to powerful citrus fruit flavours becoming intense. Fairly bitter and dry.

Elderflower Blonde (ABV 4.5%) SPECIALITY
Pale yellow, light, crisp floral beer with elderflower nose. Elderflower and gooseberry fruits with soft citrus and pine hops flavours.

Mandarina Cornovia (ABV 4.5%) SPECIALITY
Pale gold speciality beer with full mandarin citrus fruit flavour matched by firm biscuit malt and resin/earthy hop notes.

Masala Chai PA (ABV 4.5%) SPECIALITY

Sea Salt Stout (ABV 4.5%) SPECIALITY
Coffee stout. Roast malt, chocolate and toffee aroma. Complex smoky malt with underlying resinous hops and peanuts, saltiness and sweetness.

Simcotica (ABV 4.5%) GOLD

Honey Ale (ABV 4.8%) SPECIALITY

Fistral Pilsner (ABV 5.2%) SPECIALITY
Full-flavoured, copper, wheat beer. Sweet, stone-fruit flavours blend with biscuit malt and citrus hops. Malt finish with hops and dryness.

Atom SIBA

Unit 4-5, Food & Tech Park, Malmo Road, Sutton Fields Industrial Estate, Hull, East Yorkshire, HU7 0YF
☎ (01482) 820572 ⊕ atombeers.com

⊠ Atom Brewing Co was founded in 2014 by Allan Rice and Sarah Thackray. Most of its production goes into can and keg, but cask ales are produced in rotation or on demand, around a core range. Atom's ethos is science and education-based, so working with local colleges, it runs regular brewing schools and classes. All beers are unfined and unfiltered (so naturally hazy). ‼♦GF V

Quantum State (ABV 4.2%) PALE

Catalyst (ABV 5.4%) PALE

Attic SIBA

29B Mary Vale Road, Stirchley, Birmingham, West Midlands, B30 2DA ☎ 07470 643758
⊕ atticbrew.com

⊠ Since its launch in 2018, this brewery (set in an industrial estate close to Bournville Railway Station) has increased the kit size, the range of beers and its fanbase. Main production is keg/KeyKeg but it also serves cask on the premises as well as in a number of Birmingham pubs and micropubs. The beer range encompasses a number of styles and strengths and includes collaborations. ✦

Austendyke

The Beeches, Austendyke Road, Weston Hills, Spalding, Lincolnshire, PE12 6BZ ☎ 07866 045778

Austendyke Ales began brewing in 2012 using a seven-barrel plant. The brewery is operated on a part-time basis by brewer Charlie Rawlings and business partner Nathan Marshall, who handles sales. The brewery owns and runs micropub the Prior's Oven, Spalding.

Long Lane (ABV 4%) BITTER

Sheep Market (ABV 4%) GOLD

Bakestraw Bitter (ABV 4.1%) PALE

Bake House (ABV 4.5%) BITTER

Holbeach High Street (ABV 4.5%) BITTER

Hogsgate (ABV 5%) BITTER

Avalanche

5 Goodwood Close, Burton Latimer, Northamptonshire, NN15 5WP
⊕ avalanchebrew.co.uk

Avalanche Brewery is a nanobrewery formed by two former homebrewers, aiming to put a modern twist on classic styles. Most cask beers produced are one-off beers to allow creativity to thrive. Beers are unfined and unfiltered. Output is primarily cask and keg alongside short canning runs. V

Pulsar (ABV 3.6%) PALE

Notts Pale (ABV 3.8%) PALE

Avid SIBA

Red Moss Farm, Quernmore, Lancaster, LA2 0QW
☎ 07976 275762 ⊕ avidbrewing.co.uk

Avid was established in 2015 by two experienced homebrewers. The 7.5-barrel microbrewery is based in picturesque Quernmore, near Lancaster. Water is sourced from a local borehole.

Axeljack (NEW)

Unit 5, Maesteg, CF34 0BQ

The brewery was set up by three members of the same family in 2023. Beers are packaged in cans, mini-kegs and plastic recyclable Uni-kegs. V

Axholme

See Docks

Azvex

Unit 16, King Edward Rise, Gibraltar Row, Liverpool, L3 7HJ ⊕ azvexbrewing.com

Azvex Brewing Co is a Liverpool-based brewery producing modern progressive beer. No real ale. ✦

B&T

See 3 Brewers

Babel

▤ **1 Lewis Cubitt Walk, Kings Cross, London, N1C 4DL**
☎ (020) 8161 4446 ⊕ babelbeerhouse.com

Opened in 2019 as Little Creatures, it is the UK outpost of Australia's Little Creatures, and is ultimately owned by Kirin's Lion Group. Lion sold its UK brewing interests to Odyssey Inns in 2022, later renamed In Good Company. The brewpub has been renamed to Babel Beerhouse. No cask ale. Brewing is currently suspended. ✦

Bacchus

🍺 Bacchus Hotel, 17 High Street, Sutton-on-Sea, Lincolnshire, LN12 2EY
☎ (01507) 441204 ⊕ bacchushotel.co.uk

Bacchus began brewing in 2010 and now has a two-barrel plant supplying the Bacchus Hotel. ‼LIVE

Backlash

7A Earls Court, Prudhoe, Northumberland, NE42 6QG
☎ (01661) 830934 ⊕ backlashbrewery.co.uk

Brewing commenced in 2018, initially on a small scale for marketing purposes at exhibitions worldwide. Beers are only produced in bespoke batches via pre-order for events and special occasions, and available in bottle, cask or keg.

Backyard

See 52 Degrees

Bad Bunny

Ambergate, Derbyshire, DE56 2EW ☎ 07519 605362
⊕ badbunnybrewery.co.uk

Founded by husband-and-wife team Mike and Clare Chettle, brewing commenced in 2019. They now run a 1000-litre plant at their home in Bullbridge, Derbyshire, supplying local pubs with fresh unfiltered casks as well as occasional can and bottle releases. 🛒♦LIVE V

Johnny Utah (ABV 5.5%) IPA

Badger

See Hall & Woodhouse

Badgworth (NEW) SIBA

Home Farm, Axbridge, Somerset, BS26 2QN

Badgworth Brewhouse is a family-owned microbrewery nestled in the heart of the English countryside in Somerset. Since its founding, it has been dedicated to crafting exceptional beers using only the finest ingredients and traditional brewing methods. A range of eight beers (classic and new styles) are available in cask, can and keg. ♦

Bakehouse

See Warwickshire

Bakers Dozen SIBA

Unit 5, Ketton Business Estate, Pit Lane, Ketton, PE9 3SZ
☎ (01780) 238180 ⊕ bakersdozenbrewing.co.uk

☺Baker's Dozen is a two-person microbrewery with brewing taking place on a five-barrel plant installed in 2015. The beers favour hoppy styles with some occasional brews unfined. ♦

Acoustic Landlady (ABV 3.4%) PALE
Jentacular (ABV 3.5%) GOLD
Magic Potion (ABV 3.8%) GOLD
Sinc Stream (ABV 4%) BITTER
Stamford Pale (ABV 4%) PALE
Cuthberts Fee (ABV 4.1%) BLOND
Straight Outta Ketton (ABV 4.5%) PALE
Electric Landlady (ABV 5%) GOLD
12 Second Panda (ABV 6%) IPA

Bang The Elephant

Unit 14, Bailey Brook Industrial Estate, Amber Drive, Langley Mill, Derbyshire, NG16 4BE ☎ 07539 652055
✉ bangtheelephantbrewing@hotmail.com

⊠ Bang The Elephant is a neo-Victorian, steam punk-inspired, six-barrel brewery, creating small batch beers for the cask, keg and bottle market. ♦V

Half Rats (ABV 4.4%) PALE
Sons of Liberty APA (ABV 5%) PALE
What Makes Larry Happy (ABV 5.2%) IPA
Odissi (ABV 6%) IPA

Bang-On

Unit 3, George Street, Bridgend Industrial Estate, Bridgend, CF31 3TS
☎ (01656) 760790 ⊕ bangonbrewery.beer

Established in 2016, this five-barrel plant produces a variety of unique beers concentrating on bottled beers. An onsite taproom is available for hire and private parties. An onsite shop sells all its bottled beer range. Limited edition beers are also available. A bespoke bottled beer service is offered with professionally designed personalised labels (minimum of six bottles). It also stocks a range of peanuts and chilli sauces including a Carolina Reaper option. ‼🛒V♦

Bank Top SIBA

The Pavilion, Ashworth Lane, Bolton, BL1 8RA
☎ (01204) 595800 ⊕ banktopbrewery.com

☺Bank Top was established in 1995. Since 2002, the brewery has occupied a Grade II-listed tennis pavilion housing an 11-barrel plant. Bank Top Brewery Estates was formed in 2010 and now owns three pubs, Bank Top Brewery Tap, Bank Top Ale House and Olde England Forever. ‼♦

Draymans Draught (ABV 3.6%) PALE
Bad to the Bone (ABV 4%) BITTER
Smooth, sweet malty drink with a light caramel background and hops with gentle bitterness that lasts.
Dark Mild (ABV 4%) MILD
Coffee roast aroma. Smooth mouthfeel, with roasted malt prominent throughout and some fruit. Gentle bitterness in aftertaste.
Flat Cap (ABV 4%) BITTER
Amber coloured beer with a malty aroma with lasting flavours of malt, fruit and bitter hops.
Pavilion Pale Ale (ABV 4.5%) PALE
A yellow beer with a citrus and hop aroma. With a peppery hoppiness and a dry bitter finish.
Nineteen Ninety Five (ABV 4.8%) PALE
Palomino Rising (ABV 5%) PALE
Port O Call (ABV 5%) SPECIALITY
A malty, fruity aroma, malt, roast and dark fruits in the bittersweet taste and finish. A complex, well-balanced beer.

Banks's

Park Brewery, Brewery Road, Wolverhampton, West Midlands, WV1 4JT
☎ (01902) 219833 ⊕ bankssbeer.co.uk

Banks's was founded as maltsters in 1840, commencing brewing in 1874 and moving to the current Park Brewery in 1875. It became the principal brewery of Wolverhampton and Dudley Breweries (W&DB), founded in 1890. In 2007 the Marston's name was adopted following the takeover by W&DB in 1999. A joint venture with Carlsberg in 2020 led to the renamed Carlsberg

Marston's Brewing Company. Alongside the traditional Banks's beers it also produces Wainwrights and Bombardier, as well as contract brewing. Part of Carlsberg Marston's Brewing Co. ‼▼

Amber Ale (ABV 3.4%) BITTER
A pale brown bitter with a pleasant balance of hops and malt. Hops continue from the taste through to a bittersweet aftertaste.
Mild (ABV 3.5%) MILD
An amber-coloured, well-balanced, refreshing session beer.
Sunbeam (ABV 4.2%) BLOND

Brewed for Carlsberg Marston's Brewing Co:
Tetley Bitter (ABV 3.7%) BITTER

Brewed for Marston's:
61 Deep (ABV 3.8%) GOLD
Light, golden to amber ale with intense tropical fruit and citrus aromas. Sweet tropical start with hints of spice. Hoppy bitterness overcomes the fruit and leaves a pleasant mouthwatering feel.
Wainwright Amber (ABV 4%) BITTER
Wainwright Gold (ABV 4.1%) GOLD

Brewed under the Bombardier brand name:
Bombardier (ABV 4.1%) BITTER
A heavy aroma of malt and raspberry jam. Traces of hops and bitterness are quickly submerged under a smooth, malty sweetness. A solid, rich finish.
Gold (ABV 4.1%) GOLD

Brewed under the Brakspear brand name:
Gravity (ABV 3.4%) BITTER
Oxford Gold (ABV 4%) GOLD
Special (ABV 4.3%) BITTER

Brewed under the Eagle Brewery name:
IPA (ABV 3.6%) PALE

Brewed under the Mansfield brand name:
Cask Ale (ABV 3.9%) BITTER

Brewed under the Ringwood brand name:
Razorback (ABV 3.8%) BITTER
Copper-coloured session bitter dominated by malt with some toffee and berry fruit character, leading to a short, bittersweet finish.
Boondoggle (ABV 4.2%) BITTER
Golden-coloured, light, easy-drinking session bitter. Quite malty with some peach and apricot nose and sweet tropical fruit palate.
Fortyniner (ABV 4.9%) BITTER
Caramel, biscuity aroma, with hints of damson, lead to a sweet taste, balanced with some malt, fruit and hop flavours.
Old Thumper (ABV 5.1%) BITTER
Powerful, sweet, copper-coloured bitter. A fruity aroma preludes a sweet, malty taste with fruit and caramel and a bittersweet aftertaste.

Brewed under the Wychwood brand name:
Hobgoblin Gold (ABV 4.2%) GOLD
Hobgoblin IPA (ABV 4.5%) PALE

Brewed under the Young's brand name:
London Original (ABV 3.7%) BITTER
London Special (ABV 4.5%) BITTER

Barker Bridge

Manor Farm, Station Road, Cullingworth, Bradford, BD13 5HN ☎ 07378 398982 ⊕ deepcliff.co.uk

Barker Bridge Brewery was founded in 2022 by Matthew Barker at the site of the former Old Spot Brewery.

Arch Blonde (ABV 4%) BLOND
3B's (ABV 4.2%) GOLD

Barker's

14 Midway, South Crosland, Huddersfield, West Yorkshire, HD4 7DA ☎ 07876 540211
✉ barkersbrewing@gmail.com

James Barker started as a homebrewer eight years ago, producing beers for friends. With invaluable help and guidance from Summer Wine Brewery and Neil at Milltown, he made the leap from homebrewer to commercial production in 2019. He continues to use his handbuilt, 60-litre brewplant, bottling a core range of seven beers. V

Barn Owl

Buildings Farm, Faringdon Road, Gozzards Ford, Oxfordshire, OX13 6QH ☎ 07724 551086

⊠ Located in an historic barn on a farm just outside Abingdon, brewing began in 2016 using a four-barrel plant. Beers can be found in local free trade outlets.

Old Scruttock's Bitter (ABV 3.9%) BITTER
Golden Gozzard (ABV 4%) GOLD
Gozzards Guzzler (ABV 4.4%) BITTER
Gozzards Glory (ABV 4.5%) BITTER
Old Scruttock's Dirigible (ABV 5%) PORTER

Barnaby's

The Old Stable, Hole Farm, Staverton, Devon, TQ11 0LA
☎ (01803) 762730 ⊕ barnabysbrewhouse.com

Organic brewery established in 2016 (Soil Association certified). Barnaby's Brewhouse is one of the most sustainable breweries in Britain, aiming in the near future to be completely off-grid. Occasional cask ale production. A planned doubling of the size of the premises will enable a four-fold increase in production. New beers have been added to the range. ♦V

Dark Dunkel (ABV 4.8%) SPECIALITY
Pilsner (ABV 4.8%) SPECIALITY
Red Helles (ABV 4.8%) SPECIALITY
English IPA (ABV 5.4%) PALE
Green Tomato Saison (ABV 6%) SPECIALITY

Barney's SIBA

Summerhall Brewery, 1 Summerhall, Edinburgh, EH9 1PL ☎ 07512 253660 ⊕ barneysbeer.com

☺The only microbrewery in Edinburgh's city centre, Barney's Beer was founded in 2010 and now brews on the site of the original 1800s Summerhall Brewery. Summerhall is Edinburgh's centre for the arts and science. ♦V

Loop Pale Ale (ABV 3.9%) PALE
Red Rye (ABV 4.5%) RED
Warming spicy notes from the rye malt create an interesting twist.
Volcano IPA (ABV 5%) PALE
Nice floral aroma to this moderately bitter IPA.

Barngates

▤ **Barngates, Ambleside, Cumbria, LA22 0NG**
☎ (01539) 436347 ⊕ drunkenduckinn.co.uk

☺Barngates was established in 1997 to supply only the Drunken Duck Inn. It became a limited company in 1999. Expansion over the years, plus a new purpose-built, 10-barrel plant in 2008, means it now supplies more than 150 outlets throughout Cumbria, Lancashire and Yorkshire. ‼

Pale (ABV 3.3%) PALE
A well-balanced, fruity, hoppy pale ale with plenty of flavour for its strength.

Cat Nap (ABV 3.6%) PALE
Pale beer, unapologetically bitter, with a dry, astringent finish.

Cracker (ABV 3.9%) BITTER
A full-bodied hoppy beer with some balancing sweetness and fruit. A cleverly constructed copper-coloured beer.

Brathay Gold (ABV 4%) PALE
Aroma of fruit, malt and hops is followed by plenty of fruit and bittering hops with a long, bitter finish.

Goodhew's Dry Stout (ABV 4.3%) STOUT
The inviting roast aroma leads to an easy-drinking, full-bodied and well-balanced roasty stout.

Tag Lag (ABV 4.4%) BITTER
This traditional bitter with fruit, noble hops, malt balance and a good body has a crisp, clean finish of hop bitterness.

Red Bull Terrier (ABV 4.8%) RED
An assertive roasty red beer with full mouthfeel. Initial sweetness and luscious fruit, give way to a lingering bitter finish.

Baron

Great Hormead, Hertfordshire, SG9 0PB
☎ (01763) 289924 ☎ 07936 357617
⊕ baronbrewing.co.uk

Launched 2021, Baron Brewing is run by Jack Baron. The focus is on modern styles. The 1,000 litre brewhouse allows for experimentation and a changing range of beers, including collaborations with other craft breweries. Beer is can and keg only, but there are plans for cask. A taproom opened 2022. There are plans for brewery experience days, and a range of new beer styles. A new smaller tank is being used for the small-batch experimental brews. ◆

Baronscourt

38 Baronscourt Road, Newtownstewart, Omagh, BT78 4EY ☎ 07788 839907
⊕ baronscourtbrewery.com

A family-run, farm-based brewery founded in 2018 nestled at the foot of the picturesque Bessie Bell mountain, close to Harry Avery's Castle, producing high end, hand-crafted, artisan beer. Brewery waste is directly fed back to livestock or sent to the local anaerobic digester thereby neutralising the carbon footprint.

Barsham SIBA

Estate Office, West Barsham, Fakenham, Norfolk, NR21 9NR
☎ (01328) 864459 ☎ 07920 181537
⊕ barshambrewery.co.uk

⊠ Barsham Brewery was purchased by the present brewers in 2017. Maris Otter barley is grown onsite and a private bore hole supplies water for the brewery.
⏚LIVE GF V

Oaks (ABV 3.6%) BITTER
Soft vanilla notes complement a creamy bittersweet maltiness. Hop and raisin add to the sweetish, well-rounded, easy-drinking character.

Norfolk Topper (ABV 3.8%) BITTER
Yellow, hop-dominated bitter. Citrus notes vie with bitterness to add depth. Quick, slightly astringent finish.

Pilgrims Ale (ABV 4%) BLOND
BOB (ABV 4.3%) BITTER
Stout Robin (ABV 4.5%) STOUT

Golden Close IPA (ABV 5%) PALE

Barum SIBA

▤ **c/o Reform Inn, Pilton High Street, Pilton, Barnstaple, Devon, EX31 1PD**
☎ (01271) 329994 ⊕ reforminn.co.uk/barum-brewery

⊠ Barum Brewery was established in 1996 by Tim Webster and is housed in a conversion attached to the Reform Inn, which is now run by Tim. The Reform continues to act as the brewery tap as well as serving other locally-sourced ales. Distribution is exclusively within Devon. ‼◆LIVE

Basement Beer

32 Upper York Street, Stokes Croft, Bristol, BS2 8QN
☎ 07702 430808 ⊕ basementbeer.co.uk

⊠ Basement expanded its brewing capacity in early 2023 and continues to brew a variety of innovative and progressive beers, supplying both the onsite taproom and a number of Bristol pubs and bars. Several of the beers feature collaborations with local tea blenders and coffee roasters. ◆V◆

Little Citra Single Hop Pale (ABV 3.4%) PALE
Hazy, straw-coloured beer with New World hop aroma, refreshing lemon and grapefruit flavours and a bittersweet fruity aftertaste.

Lost Horizon (ABV 5.9%) STOUT
Galaxy Hopping (ABV 6.2%) IPA
Juicy, hop-forward IPA with grapefruit to the fore and pineapple and tropical fruit undertones before a balanced, bittersweet finish.

Bason Bridge SIBA

Unit 2, 129 Church Road, Highbridge, Bason Bridge, Somerset, TA9 4RG
☎ (01278) 787210 ⊕ basonbridgebrewery.co.uk

⊠ Brewery founded in Somerset in 2018. Initially, two beers were brewed, but after the successful launch, many more are now available. All beer is brewed on the 20-barrel plant. ◆

Copper Ale (ABV 3.8%) BITTER
Double Hopped Pale Ale (ABV 4.2%) PALE
Amarillo Citra Pale Ale (ABV 4.3%) PALE
Bridge Best Bitter (ABV 4.4%) BITTER
Bridge Stout (ABV 5%) STOUT

Bat Country

Unit D, Whinwhistle Road, East Wellow, Romsey, SO51 6BH
☎ (01794) 331400 ⊕ batcountrybrewco.com

Bat Country Brew Co is a small-batch brewery founded in 2021 by two brothers. Located in Hampshire it produces a variety of different beers in various formats.

The Dirt (ABV 4.2%) BITTER
Echo Base (ABV 5.2%) PALE
Mosquito Pimpstick (ABV 5.6%) BITTER

Batemans SIBA IFBB

Salem Bridge Brewery, Mill Lane, Wainfleet, Lincolnshire, PE24 4JE
☎ (01754) 880317 ⊕ bateman.co.uk

☺Bateman's Brewery is one of Britain's few remaining independent, family-owned and managed brewers. Established in 1874, it has been brewing award-winning beers for four generations. Justifiably proud of its heritage it is, nevertheless, forward-looking and progressive. All of its tied and managed houses serve cask-conditioned beer. See website for seasonal and speciality beers. ‼ ᑲ ♦ ⬧

Dark M (ABV 3.4%) MILD
XB (ABV 3.7%) BITTER
A well-rounded, smooth malty beer with a blackcurrant fruity background. Hops flourish initially before giving way to a bittersweet dryness that enhances the mellow malty ending.
Gold (also known as Yella Belly Gold) (ABV 3.9%) GOLD
5G (ABV 4.2%) PALE
Salem Porter (ABV 4.8%) PORTER
A black and complex mix of chocolate, liquorice and cough elixir.
XXXB (ABV 4.8%) BITTER
A brilliant blend of malt, hops and fruit on the nose with a bitter bite over the top of a faintly banana maltiness that stays the course. A russet-tan brown classic.

Bath Ales

Hare Brewery, Southway Drive, Warmley, Bristol, BS30 5LW
☎ (0117) 947 4797 ⊕ bathales.com

⊠ Established in 1995, Bath Ales was taken over by St Austell in 2016. Since 2018 Bath Ales' beers have been brewed in a new high-tech brewery, including cask, bottling and kegging lines. During 2020-2021, the Hare Brewery layout was fine tuned and more automation added. In 2022, a new canning line was installed. In 2024, Gem was certified gluten-free by Coeliac UK. Brewing is also carried out for a range of St Austell beers, typically Tribute and Korev. 🍺 GF

Gem (ABV 4.1%) BITTER
Malt is to the fore with some caramel, spicy hop bitterness and hints of plummy fruit. Soft, balanced, bittersweet finish.

Bath Brew House SIBA

🍴 14 James Street West, Bath, BA1 2BX
☎ (01225) 805609

Office: City Pub Group, 2nd Floor, Essel House, London, W1W 7TH ⊕ thebathbrewhouse.com

⊠ Previously known as the James Street Brewery, Bath Brew House opened in 2013. It is owned by the City Pub Group, which has pubs and brewpubs in Wales and across the south of England. The compact brewery is on the ground floor, with the fermenting vessels and conditioning tanks on the first floor. The onsite brewer produces a wide range of beers – regular favourites alongside seasonal and one-off specials. ‼ 🍺 ♦ V

Bathams IFBB

Delph Brewery, Delph Road, Brierley Hill, West Midlands, DY5 2TN
☎ (01384) 77229 ⊕ bathams.com

☺A classic, Black Country, small brewery established in 1877. Tim and Matthew Batham represent the fifth generation to run the company. The Vine, one of the Black Country's most famous pubs, is also the brewery tap. The company has 12 tied houses and supplies around 30 other outlets. Batham's Best Bitter is sometimes delivered in 54-gallon hogsheads to meet demand. ♦

Mild Ale (ABV 3.5%) MILD

A fruity, dark brown mild with malty sweetness and a roast malt finish.
Best Bitter (ABV 4.3%) BITTER
A pale yellow, fruity, sweetish bitter, with a dry, hoppy finish. A good, light, refreshing beer.

Battersea

12-14 Arches Lane, Battersea Power Station, Nine Elms, London, SW11 8AB
☎ (020) 8161 2366

Second Site: Substation, Arch 8, Almond Road, South Bermondsey, London, SE16 3LR
⊕ batterseabrew.co.uk

Opened in 2018, the brewery consists of two railway arches, one for the brewery and one for the taproom. A second brewery with a taproom was opened in 2023 along the Bermondsey Beer Mile in the former home of Spartan Brewery. A changing range of beers is produced in cask and keg, available at the taprooms and in pubs run by the brewery owners, the Mosaic Pub Company. ♦

Admiral's Best Bitter (ABV 4.2%) BITTER
Malty amber bitter. Roast nuttiness on nose and taste remain with Seville orange, cocoa and dates. Dry bittersweet aftertaste.

Battle

Woodmans Yard, Battle, East Sussex, TN33 9QT
☎ (01424) 772838 ✉ hello@battlebrewery.co.uk

Battle Brewery is an eight-barrel brewery located in the heart of 1066 country in the historic town of Battle. Established in 2017, local pubs cafés and shops are supplied. A brewtap/micropub was opened in 2021 at the top of Battle High Street selling beers direct from the cask, plus its bottled range. 🍺 V ♦

Fyrds Gold (ABV 3.8%) GOLD
Conquest (ABV 4.1%) BITTER
One Hop Wonder (ABV 4.3%) PALE
Alan the Red (ABV 4.4%) RED
Black Arrow (ABV 4.5%) PORTER
Abbey Pale IPA (ABV 5%) PALE
Harolds EyePA (ABV 5.6%) PALE
Senlac Imperial Stout (ABV 10.5%) STOUT

Bayonet SIBA

Office: Cotswold Street, Brompton, DL6 2BX
⊕ bayonetbrewing.co.uk

Launched in 2021 by Serviceman Alex Postles the brewery is a part-time operation with long-term aims to expand into a functioning unit/taproom in Northallerton, North Yorkshire. Focusing on innovative, modern and exciting craft beers the brewery has firmly established itself in the local area and is rapidly spreading further afield. The three-beer core range is supported by a rotating array of specialist IPAs, pales and stouts that aim to showcase the breweries versatility and appeal. ♦ V

Bays SIBA

Aspen Way, Paignton, Devon, TQ4 7QR
☎ (01803) 555004 ⊕ baysbrewery.co.uk

Bays Brewery is a multiple award-winning, family-run business. Its passion is to brew premium ales using the finest local ingredients, while also supporting the community. It is committed to reducing its carbon footprint: It has 30kw of solar panels on the roof; spent grains are used by local farmers to feed their cattle; spent hops are used on local allotments as fertilisers; and the yeast extracts are sent to an anaerobic digester in Plymouth to help power the dairy farm. ‼🍴♦V

Topsail (ABV 4%) BITTER
A tawny session bitter with complex aroma. Malty, bitter taste leading to a long, dry and refreshing aftertaste.
Gold (ABV 4.3%) GOLD
Smooth, golden ale. Light aroma and taste of hops, malt and caramel. Lingering hoppy aftertaste.
Devon Dumpling (ABV 5.1%) BITTER
Strong ale, easily drinkable. Light aromas of hops and fruit continue through taste and lingering aftertaste.

BB18

🍺 **BB18 Brewing Tap, 31-33 Victoria Road, Earby, BB18 6UN ☎ 07908 591343**
✉ bb18brewing@gmail.com

☻Brewpub opened in 2020. A five-barrel plant is used.

Beach

See Milton

Beak

Unit 14, Cliffe Industrial Estate, Lewes, East Sussex, BN8 6JL
☎ (01273) 473094 ☎ 07985 708122
⊕ beakbrewery.com

Beak is an independent brewery and taproom in the historic brewing town of Lewes. It brews a wide range of beers, from hop-forward IPAs and best bitters, to saisons and imperial stouts. ♦

Bear Claw

Unit 3, Meantime Workshops, North Greenwich Road, Spittal, Northumberland, TD15 1RG ☎ 07919 276715
⊕ bearclawbrewery.weebly.com

Bear Claw began brewing in 2012 using a two-barrel plant, producing a variety of cask-conditioned ales and many bottle-conditioned beers, including some continental styles. All the beers are now fermented in oak, ex-wine barrels and conditioned for a minimum of one month with some being barrel-aged. LIVE ♦

Beartown SIBA

Bromley House, Spindle Street, Congleton, Cheshire, CW12 1QN
☎ (01260) 299964 ⊕ beartownbrewery.co.uk

☻ Beartown began brewing in 1994 and uses a 25-barrel plant. The brewery underwent a significant refurbishment in 2022. It supplies more than 250 outlets. ‼🍴♦

Glacier (ABV 3.6%) BLOND
Sweet fruity beer with gentle bitterness.
Best Bitter (ABV 3.7%) BITTER
Bear Ass (ABV 4%) BITTER
Kodiak (ABV 4%) PALE
Hops and fruit dominate the taste and follow through to the dryish aftertaste. Biscuity malt in the aroma and taste.
Skinful (ABV 4.2%) BITTER
Traditional bitter, malt and hops build together with some fruit. The bitterness lasts well in the finish.
Kahuna (ABV 4.5%) SPECIALITY
Passion fruit aromas dominate this very fruity beer. Some pleasant hops complement the sweetness and last well in the finish.
Lit (ABV 4.5%) BLOND

Fruity citrus aromas graduate into a sweet, fruity, hoppy body. The perception of bitterness increases in the finish.
Creme Bearlee (ABV 4.8%) SPECIALITY
Chocolate and vanilla aromas with malty, caramel and roasty flavours combine with a sweet body followed by a dry finish.

Beath SIBA

54 Foulford Road, Cowdenbeath, KY4 9AS ☎ 07792 369678 ⊕ beathbrewing.com

☻Beath began brewing in 2016, originally with a 20-litre capacity upgraded to 100-litre within a few months. There are plans for a further expansion. The beer range varies from week to week. LIVE

Mad World (ABV 4%) PORTER
Are You With Me (ABV 4.5%) BITTER
Ella Ella Ella (ABV 4.5%) SPECIALITY
Funky Town (ABV 5%) BITTER

Beavertown

Units 17 & 18, Lockwood Industrial Park, Mill Mead Road, Tottenham Hale, London, N17 9QP
☎ (020) 8525 9884

Second Site: Unit 7, Ponders End Industrial Estate, 102 East Duck Lees Lane, Ponders End, EN3 7SR
⊕ beavertownbrewery.co.uk

🗙 Beavertown opened its Tottenham Hale site in 2014 after small beginnings in De Beauvoir Town and Old Ford. A minority stake was sold to Heineken in 2018 and further investment saw the opening of 'Beaverworld' in Ponders End in 2020. Heineken completed 100% ownership in 2022. The brewery at the Tottenham Hotspur stadium closed in 2023. No cask ale. ♦

Beccles

The Studios, London Road, Brampton, Suffolk, NR34 8DQ ☎ 07815 519576
✉ info@becclesbrewco.co.uk

🗙 The brewery has been in production since 2019 and is now run by one of the original owners with the assistance of family and friends. It has a production run three times a week, with a 700-litre capacity. A core range of beers are regularly produced and can be found in local pubs. The beers are also available in bottle and mini-keg from the brewery, with bottles also available at some local shops. 🍴LIVE

Uncle Albert's (ABV 3%) MILD
Hodgkins Hop (ABV 3.6%) GOLD
Best (ABV 3.8%) BITTER
Beautiful Sky (ABV 4.2%) PALE
Neil, Neil Orange Peel (ABV 4.2%) GOLD
Paint the Town Red (ABV 4.5%) RED
Boney's Island (ABV 4.6%) STOUT
Nelson's Tree (ABV 4.8%) BITTER

Beech Avenue

Lodge Farm, Borras Road, Holt, LL13 9TE ☎ 07917 841304 ✉ info@beechavenuebrewery.co.uk

Brewing commenced using a 30-litre kitchen plant. In 2020 the brewery upscaled and relocated to eco-friendly converted farm builldings. Speciality fruit or dry-hopped beers are available at various times in addition to a range of cask-conditioned ales.

Gold (ABV 4%) GOLD
Pale (ABV 4.5%) PALE

GOOD BEER GUIDE 2025

Beer Engine SIBA

Newton St Cyres, Devon, EX5 5AX
☎ (01392) 851282 ⊕ thebeerengine.co.uk

⊠ The Beer Engine was established in 1983 and is the oldest working microbrewery in Devon. The brewery is visible in the downstairs bar in the pub through multiple viewing windows. Several outlets are supplied, as well as local beer festivals. ‼◆

Rail Ale (ABV 3.8%) BITTER
Piston Bitter (ABV 4.3%) BITTER
Sleeper Heavy (ABV 5.4%) BITTER

Beer Hut

14 Binnian Enterprise Park, Kilkeel, BT34 3NA
☎ 07885 566599 ✉ andrew@beerhutbrewing.co.uk

Microbrewery situated near Kilkeel harbour. Established in a flat pack hut using a 100 litre kit, it has since upscaled twice and now operates using a 1,000 litre plant. Further expansion is planned. V

Citra Ella (ABV 4.5%) GOLD
Fluffy Bunny (ABV 5%) SPECIALITY
Wahey IPA (ABV 5.6%) IPA
There's Something in the Water (ABV 6%) IPA
Simcoe Simon (ABV 6.5%) IPA
Ahoy Captain (ABV 7.4%) IPA

Beer Me

🯄 The Belgian Café, 11/23 Grand Parade, Eastbourne, East Sussex, BN21 3YN
☎ (01323) 729967 ⊕ beermebrewery.co.uk

⊠ Beer Me was launched in 2014 by the owners of the Belgian Café in Eastbourne, building on 10 years in the catering industry. It uses a 2.5-barrel plant and produces continental-style beers which are served direct from the brewery. ‼◆

Beer Riff

🯄 Pilot House Wharf, Swansea, SA1 1UN ☎ 07897 895511 ⊕ beerriffbrewing.com

⊠ An offshoot of Pilot Brewery Mumbles. The four-barrel brewery produces keg and canned beers that are unfiltered and unfined. It offers a variety of styles including one-offs. The integral tap house bar offers great views over Swansea Marina.

Beer Shack SIBA

🯄 Beer Shack, 22-24 King Street, Clitheroe, Lancashire, BB7 2EP
☎ (01200) 426368 ⊕ thebeershack.uk

This brewery first brewing in 2022, and is based above the Beer Shack.

Beer Station

🯄 3 Victoria Buildings, Victoria Road, Formby, Merseyside, L37 7DB
☎ (01704) 807450

☺A small half-barrel plant set up in 2019 at the rear of the Beer Station micropub, opposite Freshfield station. The beers are railway-themed and generally only available in the Beer Station, but are occasionally seen elsewhere.

Beerblefish SIBA

Unit 2A-4, Uplands Business Park, Blackhorse Lane, Walthamstow, London, E17 5QJ ☎ 07594 383195
⊕ beerblefish.co.uk

Starting at UBrew in Bermondsey in 2015, the Edmonton site began production in 2016. A move to Walthamstow occurred in 2021, to a site three times larger with a homely taproom. Capacity increased by subsequently buying the former Brew By Numbers kit. A series of hoppy pale ales and a range of Victorian heritage ales are available in cask, keg and bottles. LIVE V◆

Hoppy Little Fish (ABV 3.5%) PALE
Easy-drinking amber beer with a fruity biscuity taste. Fruity, slightly spicy, sweet aftertaste with a little dry bitterness.
Hackney TNT (ABV 4%) RED
Edmonton Best Bitter (ABV 4.3%) BITTER
Dark amber beer with sweet caramel balancing a growing bitterness. Slightly floral hops on nose and slightly dry, sweetish finish.
Pan Galactic Pale (ABV 4.6%) PALE
Amber, full-bodied beer with fruity tangerine notes with sweet biscuit. Aftertaste starts soft becoming bitter and dry. Floral, biscuity nose.
Blackbeerble Stout (ABV 5.2%) STOUT
1853 ESB (ABV 5.3%) BITTER
Sweet caramel flavour aroma and flavour with marmalade and a gentle developing spicy hoppiness becoming slightly bitter in the aftertaste.
1820 Porter (ABV 6.6%) PORTER
Aromas of brettanomyces, roast and black treacle, which are also in the sweet caramelised fruity flavour. Spicy, dry, bitter finish.
1892 IPA (ABV 6.9%) IPA
Brettanomyces and marmalade aroma. Full-bodied with apricot, honey, caramelised orange and brettanomyces. Strong, spicy, hoppy, bitter orange builds in the finish.

Beermats SIBA

New Yard, Winkburn, Nottinghamshire, NG22 8PQ
☎ (01636) 639004 ⊕ beermatsbeer.co.uk

☺Beermats was founded in 2017 by three friends while drinking in a pub. The brewery is located on the Winkburn Estate in old dairy buildings. Beers are named around the theme of the humble beermat. ‼🯄◆LIVE V◆

Charismatic (ABV 3.8%) BITTER
Dambusters Ale (ABV 3.8%) BITTER
Pragmatic (ABV 3.8%) BITTER
Format (ABV 3.9%) PALE
Team Mates (ABV 3.9%) PALE
Soul Mate (ABV 4.2%) GOLD
Diplomat (ABV 4.6%) STOUT
Ultimate (ABV 4.9%) RED

BEEspoke

🯄 Fox, 41 Briggate, Shipley, West Yorkshire, BD17 7BP
☎ (01274) 594826 ⊕ thefoxshipley.co.uk

☺Brewing began in 2015 in the cellar of the Fox pub using a one-barrel plant. Beers are available in cask and keg from the pub and at local beer festivals. Shiny Cowbird Spirit Company is a sister business. ◆

Beeston SIBA

Fransham Road Farm, Beeston, PE32 2LZ
☎ (01328) 700844 ☎ 07768 742763
⊕ beestonbrewery.co.uk

⊠ The brewery was established in 2006 in an old farm building using a five-barrel plant. Brewing water comes from a dedicated borehole and raw ingredients are sourced locally whenever possible. ‼♦LIVE

Light Wait (ABV 3.3%) BITTER
The Squirrel's Nuts (ABV 3.5%) MILD
Cherry, chocolate and vanilla aroma. A malt and cherry sweetness comes to the fore but quickly fades. Short finish.
Afternoon Delight (ABV 3.7%) PALE
A biscuity malt aroma. A smooth, well-balanced mix of malt and hop. Hints of marmalade in a long finish.
Worth the Wait (ABV 4.2%) BITTER
Hoppy throughout with a growing dryness. Complex and grainy with fruit notes, malt and understated bitterness.
Stirling (ABV 4.5%) BITTER
The Dry Road (ABV 4.8%) BITTER
Village Life (ABV 4.8%) BITTER
Copper-coloured with a nutty character. Malty throughout, a bittersweet background gives depth. Strong toffee apple finish.
On the Huh (ABV 5%) BITTER
A fruity raisin aroma. A bittersweet maltiness jousts with caramel and roast. A dry hoppiness adds to a strong finale.

Contract brewed for Brancaster Brewery:
Best (ABV 3.8%) BITTER
Malthouse Bitter (ABV 4.2%) BITTER

Beeston Hop

Enfield Street, Beeston, NG9 1DN
✉ john@beestonhop.co.uk

⊠ A nanobrewery launched in 2015, it moved back to Beeston in 2023, from a site in the City Centre. Produces cask and bottle-conditioned beer in a variety of styles. The beers are all unfined (vegan), unfiltered and unpasteurised. LIVE V

Beestonia (NEW)

Unit 5, Goodhill Court, Hallamsfield Road, Ilkeston, Derbyshire, DE7 4RT ✆ 07894 563731
✉ dave@beestonia.co.uk

A new family-run five-barrel brewery producing small batch recipes in cask and keg. ♦

Blonde (ABV 3.9%) BLOND

Belgian Brewer, The

Unit 11, The Links Business Centre, Raynham Road, Bishop's Stortford, Hertfordshire, CM23 5NZ
✆ (01279) 507515 ⊕ thebelgianbrewer.co.uk

Situated just outside Bishop's Stortford town centre, The Belgian Brewer is a small brewery and taproom. Established in 2018, it produces Belgian-style beers brewed to traditional Belgian methods using family recipes. Currently producing under 10,000 litres per month, demand is increasing week by week, especially for its speciality fruit beers. The brewery expanded to take on the premises next door to increase capacity and allow the creation of a function hall. ‼🍺♦LIVE V♦

Belhaven

Brewery Lane, Dunbar, EH42 1PE
✆ (01284) 763222

Office: Abbot House, Westgate Street, Bury St Edmunds, IP33 1QT ⊕ belhaven.co.uk

☺Belhaven is Scotland's oldest working brewery, established 1719. Nestling between the rolling hills of East Lothian and a beautiful bay (the meaning of Belhaven), it brews beers using 100% Scottish malted barley, fresh water from a local source and its own Belhaven yeast. Part of Greene King PLC. ‼🍺

80/- (ABV 4.2%) BITTER
St Andrew's Amber Ale (ABV 4.9%) BITTER
A bittersweet beer with lots of body. The malt, fruit and roast mingle throughout with hints of hop and caramel.

Contract brewed for Heineken
Deuchars IPA (ABV 3.8%) PALE
Gold with soft malt body and lightly fruity, citrus aroma and a touch of sulphur. Moderate bitterness with balancing sweetness.

Belleville

Units 36 & 38, Jaggard Way, Wandsworth Common, London, SW12 8SG
✆ (020) 8675 4768 ⊕ bellevillebrewing.co.uk

Belleville began brewing in 2012. It was set up by a group of parents from a local primary school, after the success of the head brewer's efforts at homebrewing for a beer festival at the school. It specialises in American-style beers, with a core range and quarterly seasonals, available in keg and can. The brewery tap is a few units along from the brewery and offers the core range and current seasonals plus occasional guest beers. Cask ale returned in 2024. ♦

Bellfield SIBA

46 Stanley Place, Edinburgh, EH7 5TB
✆ (0131) 656 9390 ⊕ bellfieldbrewery.com

☺Bellfield was established in 2014 and was the UK's first certified gluten-free brewery. It is accredited by Coeliac UK and registered with the Vegan Society. The new site with taproom and all-weather beer garden opened in 2019. Brewery tours with tasting are available Friday to Sunday. ‼🍺♦GF V♦

Lucky Spence Pale (ABV 3.5%) BITTER
Session Ale (ABV 3.8%) PALE
Light citrus tones flavour this balanced bitter.
Lawless Village IPA (ABV 4.5%) PALE
Deep amber with subtle citrus aroma and flavour, and medium malt body. Moderately bitter and hoppy which builds and lingers.
Jex-Blake IPA (ABV 5.6%) IPA

Bell's

🏠 **Deer's Head, 1-3 Lower Garfield Street, Belfast, BT1 1FP**
✆ (028) 9043 4655

Brewery within the Deer's Head pub, Belfast.

Belschnickel SIBA

146 Ella Street, Hull, HU5 3AU
✆ (01482) 348747 ⊕ belschnickel.co.uk

Launched in 2022, Belschnickel Brewery work on a small scale with a 50-litre brewhouse to produce a small core range of canned beers and bottle-conditioned speciality beers brewed for ageing. All the brewing, canning and packaging is completed in-house. All beers are unfiltered and unpasteurised. Its branding and labels are produced in collaboration with a local artist. LIVE

Ben's

Unit 17, Yarrow Business Centre, Yarrow Road,
Chorley, Lancashire, PR6 0LP
☎ (01257) 367480 ⊕ bensbrewery.co.uk

☺Established in 2021, the brewery is situated in part of
an office furniture suppliers showroom. The onsite
taproom is only open for special events. ✦

Arawak (ABV 3.8%) PALE
Wellington (ABV 3.8%) BLOND
Fruity and citrus resiny hop aromas and taste. Some
sweet body to balance, with a dry finish.
Beyond the Pale (ABV 4%) PALE
Mosaic (ABV 4%) GOLD
Citrus fruit aromas to begin, then hop bitterness which
lasts lengthily and is supported by the slightly sweet
body.
She is my Country Still (ABV 4%) PALE
The Light Brigade (ABV 4%) BLOND
Easy-drinking and balanced blond beer with some fruity
sweetness and a lasting bitter finale.
Alright Treacle (ABV 4.5%) SPECIALITY
Blighty (ABV 4.5%) PALE
The Duke (ABV 4.5%) BITTER
Sweet, malty aromas, some fruit and bitterness in the
taste with a drier hoppy bitter finish.
Mean Old Bastard (ABV 5.7%) STOUT
Proper Grafter (ABV 5.7%) STOUT

Contract brewed for Shed Beer:
Amarillo (ABV 3.6%) PALE
Mild (ABV 3.6%) MILD
Citra (ABV 4%) GOLD

Benjamin Franklin

See under F

Bentley Brook

Hilltop Farm, The Cliff, Matlock, Derbyshire, DE4 5FY
☎ 07483 831640 ⊕ bentleybrook.co.uk

⊠ Formed in 2018, this 6.5-barrel brewery was
previously located in the heart of Lumsdale Valley and
named after the local brook. It has since expanded and
moved to a nearby farm. It offers unfined, small batch
beers available to purchase in the local area and at the
brewery tap. LIVE

Beowulf

Forest of Merica, Chasewater Country Park, Pool Lane,
Brownhills, Staffordshire, WS8 7NL
☎ (01543) 454067 ☎ 07789 491801
⊕ beowulfbrewco.co.uk

Beowulf Brewery is noted for its long history of award-
winning ale. Both dark and light ales are brewed. The
ever expanding range of beers appear thoughout the
Midlands area. The brewery produces bottle-conditioned
beers, which can be purchased on site. Merchandise is
also available. ‼✦LIVE GF V

Beorma (ABV 3.9%) BITTER
A perfectly balanced session ale with a malty hint of fruit
giving way to a lingering bitterness. Background spice
excites the palate.
Zwodder (ABV 4%) PALE
Mango Sypian (ABV 4.3%) SPECIALITY
Chasewater Bitter (ABV 4.4%) BITTER
Golden bitter, hoppy throughout with citrus and hints of
malt. Long mouth-watering, bitter finish.
Black and Blueberry (ABV 4.5%) SPECIALITY
Boomer (ABV 4.5%) BITTER

Pale brown with lots of caramel aroma. Bitter start with a
sweet malty background which develops to a mouth-
watering finish with dry lips.
Chase Buster (ABV 4.5%) BLOND
Dark Raven (ABV 4.5%) MILD
So dark with apple and bonfire in the aroma, so sweet
and smooth like liquid toffee apples with a sudden bitter
finish.
Swordsman (ABV 4.5%) BITTER
Pale gold, light fruity aroma, tangy hoppy flavour. Faintly
hoppy finish.
Folded Cross (ABV 4.6%) BITTER
Malt and caramel aromas and tastes with hints of fruity
biscuits are nudged aside by the robust hops which give
lingering bitter edges.
Hurricane (ABV 4.6%) BITTER
Wuffa (ABV 4.6%) GOLD
Chocolate Porter (ABV 4.7%) PORTER
Dragon Smoke Stout (ABV 4.7%) STOUT
Black with a light brown creamy head. Tobacco,
chocolate, liquorice and mixed fruity hints on the aroma.
Bitterness fights through the sweet and roast flavours
and eventually dominates. Hints of a good port emerge.
Finn's Hall Porter (ABV 4.7%) PORTER
Dark chocolate aroma, after dinner mints, coffee and
fresh tobacco. Good bitterness with woodland hints of
Autumn. Long late bitterness with lip drying
moreishness.
Heroes Bitter (ABV 4.7%) BITTER
Gold colour, malt aroma, hoppy taste but sweetish finish.
Mercian Shine (ABV 5%) BITTER
Amber to pale gold with a good bitter and hoppy start
and a hint of nutmeg. Plenty of caramel and hops with
background malt leading to a good bitter finish with
caramel and hops lingering in the aftertaste.
Clout (ABV 6%) BITTER
Nordic Noir (ABV 6%) MILD
Dark brown with full liquorice aroma. Rich liquorice
tastes with subtle tastes of chocolate and cinnamon.
Gently moreish.
Beowulf IPA (ABV 7.2%) STRONG
Killer Stout (ABV 7.3%) STOUT

Bespoke SIBA

Church Farm, Church Street, Littledean,
Gloucestershire, GL14 3NL
☎ (01452) 929281 ⊕ bespokebrewery.co.uk

⊠ Brewing moved to premises at Littledean, with a farm
tap. Both cask-conditioned and keg beers are produced
using a 12-barrel plant. Beers are available from the farm
tap and brewery shop. Specially labelled bottles are
offered for celebratory occasions. ‼⬛✦✦

Saved by the Bell (ABV 3.8%) BITTER
Forest Gold (ABV 4%) GOLD
Beware the Bear (ABV 4.2%) BITTER
Going Off Half-Cocked (ABV 4.6%) PALE
Money for Old Rope (ABV 4.8%) STOUT
Over a Barrel (ABV 5%) OLD

Bestens

The Brickworks, Unit 5, Victoria Road, Burgess Hill,
West Sussex, RH15 9LH ⊕ bestensbrewery.co.uk

The brewery opened in 2018 in Lower Beeding as a one-
barrel plant, increasing to four-barrel capacity in 2020
and moving to Scaynes Hill in 2022 and then Burgess Hill
in 2024. The brewery operates a taproom in Haywards
Heath, the Tap, as well as a mobile outlet in the town.
Real ale is occasionally available. ✦

Bewdley SIBA

Unit 7, Bewdley Craft Centre, Lax Lane, Bewdley, Worcestershire, DY12 2DZ
☎ (01299) 405148 ⊕ bewdleybrewery.co.uk

⊠ Bewdley began brewing in 2008 on a six-barrel plant in an old school. This was upgraded to a 10-barrel plant in 2014. Beers are brewed with a railway theme for the nearby Severn Valley Railway. The brewery has an onsite tap and shop. Element gin is also produced. 🚩♦LIVE♦

Worcestershire Way (ABV 3.6%) GOLD
Refreshing golden ale with a citrus, faintly orange peel aroma, leads to a balanced hop, malt and grapefruit taste and a lingering hoppy finish.
Baldwin IPA (ABV 4.2%) GOLD
Jubilee (ABV 4.3%) BITTER
Pale colour, fruit and citrus aroma, sweet malt with underlying citrus taste.
Red Hill (ABV 4.4%) BITTER
Worcestershire Sway/ 2857 (ABV 5%) BITTER
Complex, amber-coloured bitter, sometimes badged as 2857. Fragrant malty aroma, well-balanced, slightly sweet malt and hops taste with hints of toffee and marmalade, malt with citrus and meadow grass finish.
William Mucklow's Dark Mild (ABV 6%) MILD
Dark in colour, malty, sweetish fruity flavour with slight liquorice finish.

Bexley SIBA

Unit 18, Manford Industrial Estate, Manor Road, Erith, DA8 2AJ
☎ (01322) 337368 ⊕ bexleybrewery.co.uk

Bexley Brewery was founded in 2014. Brewers Cliff and Jane Murphy produce regular, seasonal and experimental brews, all of which are gluten-free. The Bird & Barrel in Barnehurst, opened in 2018, replaced the taproom and the range of beers, including the Howbury specials, is available more widely in the local area. ♦GF V

Bursted Session Bitter (ABV 3.8%) BITTER
Quaffable, tawny bitter. Sweet biscuit with toffee, caramel and stone fruit notes, balanced with a gentle lingering bitter hoppy dryness.
Hills & Holes Kent Pale (ABV 3.8%) PALE
Golden Acre (ABV 4%) GOLD
Smooth golden ale with citrus aroma. Flavour is of grapefruit, hops and a strong bitterness, continuing in the dry, fruity finish.
Bexley's Own Beer (ABV 4.2%) BITTER
Pale brown beer with a balance of fudge, floral, piny hop with stone fruit. Bitterness grows in the dry finish.
Redhouse Premium (ABV 4.2%) BITTER
Strong malty aroma with fruit and hops. Malty caramel sweet flavour with bitter, earthy and spicy hops. Long, bittersweet finish.
Black Prince Porter (ABV 4.6%) PORTER
Creamy dark-brown porter with treacle aroma and hints of dark roast and fruit. Flavour has mocha, damsons, citrus and toffee.
Anchor Bay IPA (ABV 4.8%) PALE
A deep golden beer with a fruity, spicy aroma, citrus taste and an astringent finish.
Spike Island Stout (ABV 5.3%) STOUT
Well-balanced, light and easy-drinking. Chocolate and coffee are present along with dark berries on a sweet smooth mouthfeel.

Bianca Road

83-84 Enid Street, Bermondsey, London, SE16 3RA
⊕ biancaroad.com

After starting in 2016 in Peckham, the brewery moved to a bigger site in Bermondsey in 2017, and again in 2019 to two arches on the Bermondsey Beer Mile which incorporate the taproom. Output is in keg and cans. No cask ale. ♦

Bicester

≣ Angel, 102 Sheep Street, Bicester, Oxfordshire, OX26 6LP
☎ (01869) 360410 ⊕ theangelbicester.co.uk

Brewing commenced in 2017 in an outhouse behind the Angel, Bicester. Beers are brewed occasionally and supplied solely to the pub. Brewing is currently suspended.

Big Clock

≣ Grants, 1 Manchester Road, Accrington, Lancashire, BB5 2BQ
☎ (01254) 393938 ☎ 07766 163497
⊕ thebigclockbrewery.co.uk

☺Brewing commenced at the iconic Grants Pub and Brewhouse, just off Accrington town centre, in 2014. The specially-commissioned brewery can be viewed from the bar area. A new, smaller brewery has been installed. This is to run along side the existing larger six-barrel plant, for production of smaller, speciality beers for a new canning line. Beer is supplied to around a dozen outlets across East Lancashire.

Big Dig (NEW)

The Old Stables, North West Farm Buildings, Winterborne Kingston, Dorset, DT11 9AT
⊕ bigdigbrewhouse.uk

Founded by a group of seven enthusiasts and named after an extensive archeology dig on the farm where the brewery is situated, Big Dig first brewed in 2023. The initial portfolio of beers has been expanded, with more planned. ♦

Big Fish

c/o 45 Glenury Crescent, Stonehaven, AB39 3LF
✉ info@brewscotland.com

A nomad brewery established in 2017. Collaboration brews form part of the brewery strategy.

Big Hand SIBA

Unit A1, Abbey Close, Redwither Business Park, Wrexham, LL13 9XG
☎ (01978) 660709 ⊕ bighandbrewing.co.uk

☺Big Hand began brewing in 2013 and continues to operate from its 10-barrel plant on the outskirts of Wrexham, despite the sad loss of brewery founder Dave Shaw in 2022. It offers a broad-ranging selection of beers, including several experimental ales, that are widely available throughout North Wales and West Cheshire ♦

Seren (ABV 3.7%) PALE
Pili Pala (ABV 3.8%) PALE
Gold (ABV 3.9%) GOLD
Ostara (ABV 3.9%) BITTER
Pendragon (ABV 3.9%) BITTER
Little Monkey (ABV 4%) MILD
Sirrus (ABV 4%) PALE
Super Tidy (ABV 4%) PALE
Bastion (ABV 4.2%) BITTER
Freehand (ABV 4.2%) BITTER
Little Black S (ABV 4.2%)

Palewulf (ABV 4.2%) BITTER
Domino (ABV 4.4%) STOUT
Appaloosa (ABV 4.5%) PALE
Spectre (ABV 4.5%) STOUT
Havok (ABV 5%) PALE
Bad Gorilla (ABV 6%) MILD

Big Lamp

Grange Road, Newburn, Newcastle upon Tyne,
NE15 8NL
☎ (0191) 267 1689 ⊕ biglampbrewers.co.uk

☺The North East of England's oldest microbrewery celebrated 40 years in 2022. After relocating to a former water pumping station in 1997, it expanded to a 55-barrel plant. The brewery tap, Keelman, is next door with accommodation available. !! ♦LIVE

Sunny Daze (ABV 3.6%) GOLD
Golden, hoppy session bitter with a clean taste and finish.
Bitter (ABV 3.9%) BITTER
A clean-tasting bitter, full of hops and malt. A hint of fruit with a good, hoppy finish.
Lamplight Bitter (ABV 4.2%) BITTER
Summerhill Stout (ABV 4.4%) STOUT
A rich, tasty stout, dark in colour with a lasting rich roast character. Malty mouthfeel with a lingering finish.
Prince Bishop Ale (ABV 4.8%) GOLD
A refreshing, easy-drinking bitter. Golden in colour, full of fruit and hops. Strong bitterness with a spicy, dry finish.
Keelman Brown (ABV 5.7%) OLD

Big Penny

1 Priestley Way, Blackhorse Lane, Walthamstow,
London, E17 6AL
☎ (020) 3700 1040 ⊕ bigpenny.co.uk

The Truman's Brewery name was revived in 2010 with a brewery established on Fish Island in 2013. After a move to the former Crate brewery, Hackney Wick in 2020, they withdrew from brewing in 2022. A name change to Big Penny coincided with a start to contract brewing at Redchurch. Its Big Penny Social beer hall remains a major presence on the Blackhorse Beer Mile. No cask ale. ♦LIVE

Big Smoke SIBA

Unit D3, Sandown Industrial Estate, Esher, Surrey,
KT10 8BL
☎ (01372) 469606 ☎ 07859 884190
⊕ bigsmokebrew.co.uk

⊠ Brewing began at the Antelope, Surbiton, in 2014. In 2019 Big Smoke moved to a new purpose-built 30-hectolitre brewery in Esher with an onsite taproom. ♦V⛴

Solaris Session Pale Ale (ABV 3.8%) PALE
Unfined golden ale with bitter grapefruit flavour, some malt and a long dry bitter finish. Hoppy fruity nose.
Dark Wave Porter (ABV 5%) PORTER
Creamy, black porter with a dry roasty bitter character balanced by a caramelised sweetness.
Electric Eye Pale Ale (ABV 5%) PALE
Smooth golden ale with a fruity nose. Citrus and stone fruit flavours are overlaid with sweet biscuit and peppery, bitter hops.
Underworld (ABV 5%) SPECIALITY
Sweet smooth stout with hints of chocolate and coffee in the aroma and taste coupled with toasted nuts and vanilla.

Big Stone SIBA

Ashen Clough, Maynestone Road, Chinley,
Derbyshire, SK23 6AH ☎ 07867 652062
⊕ bigstonebeer.co.uk

This small operation started brewing on a 2.5-barrel kit in 2019. It is based in large out-buildings connected to a private house, on the outskirts of Chinley, in the heart of the Peak District. Beers are available in bottles from local outlets. Casks are supplied to a limited number of local pubs. An onsite spring provides all the water used in production. ♦LIVE V

Dimpus (ABV 3.5%) BITTER
Kinder Stout (ABV 4.2%) STOUT
Downfall (ABV 4.3%) PALE
Rough Rock (ABV 4.3%) BITTER
The Naze (ABV 4.5%) SPECIALITY
Edale Rocks (ABV 5%) SPECIALITY
Mount Famine (ABV 5.5%) IPA

Big Trip SIBA

Unit 5, City Court, Poland Street, Manchester, M4 6AL
☎ 07931 557943 ✉ jonny@bigtripbrewery.com

Big Trip commenced brewing in Ancoats in 2022, producing a variety of cask and keg beers, mainly hop-forward, hazy, unfiltered and unpasteurised. The keg range features low carbonation (1.2 volumes) with new limited run specials most months. Currently brewing three times per week. A brewery tap is planned. ♦V

Microdose (ABV 3.5%) PALE
Beautiful Things (ABV 4.2%) PALE
Desperately Seeking Dopamine (ABV 5.7%) IPA

Billericay SIBA

⚏ Essex Beer Shop, 54c Chapel Street, Billericay,
Essex, CM12 9LS
☎ (01277) 500121 ☎ 07788 373129
⊕ billericaybrewing.co.uk

With numerous regular beers and local distribution outlets, Billericay Brewing opened at its present site in 2014, using a 4.5-barrel plant. It has an adjacent, very popular, micropub and well-stocked beer shop. The brewery hosts plenty of food and drink events, and is dog friendly. !! 🍴♦LIVE

Zeppelin (ABV 3.8%) BITTER
Blonde (ABV 4%) GOLD
Dickie (ABV 4.2%) BITTER
Vanilla Bark (ABV 4.3%) SPECIALITY
Woody's Bark (ABV 4.3%) STOUT
Rhythm Stick (ABV 4.8%) BITTER
Sex & Drugs & Rock & Roll (ABV 5%) PALE
Barista (ABV 5.9%) SPECIALITY
Chapel Street Porter (ABV 5.9%) PORTER
Chilli Porter (ABV 5.9%) SPECIALITY
Mayflower Gold (ABV 6.5%) IPA

Bingley SIBA

Unit 2, Old Mill Yard, Shay Lane, Wilsden, West
Yorkshire, BD15 0DR
☎ (01535) 274285 ⊕ bingleybrewery.co.uk

Bingley is a small, family-run brewery that opened in 2014 using a six-barrel plant. It is located in a rural setting in the village of Wilsden, part of Bingley Rural Ward. Beers are distributed coast to coast and as far south as Derby. !! ♦

Endeavour (ABV 3.7%) BLOND
Goldy Locks Blonde (ABV 4%) BLOND

Azacca (ABV 4.1%) GOLD
Aire Gold (ABV 4.2%) GOLD
Session IPA (ABV 4.2%) GOLD
Steady State (ABV 4.2%) BITTER
Centennial (ABV 4.4%) GOLD
Tri State (ABV 4.5%) PALE
1848 Stout (ABV 4.8%) STOUT
Jamestown APA (ABV 5.4%) PALE

Bini

Unit 11, Sheepscar House, Leeds, West Yorkshire, LS7 1AD ⊕ binibrew.co

Microbrewery that launched in 2020. In 2023 it relocated from the edge of Ilkley Moor to the former Nomadic premises in central Leeds. Mainly producing craft keg beers. The Bini Tap House maintains a presence in Ilkley. Its onsite brewery taproom is open on Fridays and Saturdays. ◆

Biochemist

Boundary Road, Red Lodge, IP28 8JQ ☎ 07821 540237 ⊕ biochemistbrewery.com

Established in 2020, Biochemist Brewery is a part-time, 100-litre nanobrewery producing small-batch core beers and an experimental series. Brews can be bought online or at local markets. Small batches of seasonal, dry ciders also produced.

Birch Cottage

Birch Cottage, Wilne Road, Sawley, Derbyshire, NG10 3AP ☎ 07966 757407
✉ birchcottagebrewery@outlook.com

Birch Cottage is a nanobrewery established in 2018 brewing small batch beers. Its brewery tap, Sawley Junction, opened in 2018. ◆V

Footsteps (ABV 3.9%) GOLD
Bit 'O' 52 (ABV 4.3%) BITTER
Sawley Stout (ABV 4.3%) STOUT
BCB (Birch Cottage Bitter) (ABV 4.4%) BITTER
Windmill Stout (ABV 4.5%) STOUT
No Code (ABV 5.3%) GOLD
Big Hard Sun (ABV 5.8%) IPA

Birchover

🍴 Red Lion, Main Street, Birchover, Derbyshire, DE4 2BN
☎ (01629) 650363 ⊕ red-lion-birchover.co.uk

⊗ Brewing started at the Red Lion pub in the picturesque Peak District village of Birchover in 2016, and upgraded to a five-barrel plant by enthusiastic pub and brewery owner in 2017. Core range of beers are named after local Stanton Moor landmarks and are to be found alongside seasonal specials on the pub bar. ◆LIVE

Bird House (NEW)

Arch 1127, Bath Factory Estate, 41 Norwood Road, Herne Hill, London, SE24 9AJ
⊕ birdhousebrewing.com

Bird House started brewing in early 2024 in the arch formerly occupied by Canopy, which closed a year previously. The intention is to brew beers for the small Bird House pub chain, mostly in south and west London, and the taproom. No cask ale. ◆

Birdhouse

Revell Road, Downham Market, Norfolk, PE38 9SE
☎ 07858 628183 ⊕ birdhousebrewery.co.uk

⊗ Birdhouse Brewery, a picobrewery, was established in 2019 by Paul Bird. It produces 150 bottle-conditioned beers per batch, making it one of the smallest breweries in the country. It produces a range of nine beers. Available in shops, local markets and online. ◆V

Birmingham SIBA

Unit 17, Stirchley Trading Estate, Hazelwell Road, Birmingham, B30 2PF
☎ (0121) 724 0399 ☎ 07717 704929
⊕ birminghambrewingcompany.co.uk

Birmingham Brewing Co was established in 2016 and is based in a small unit on a trading estate in Stirchley. Its growing range of vegan and gluten-free beers are available in the trade in cask or keg, and also in cans direct from the brewery or many local bottle shops.
‼◆GFV

Pale Brummie (ABV 4%) PALE
Bitter Brummie (ABV 4.1%) BITTER

Contract brewed for Craddock's Brewery:
Saxon Gold (ABV 4%) BITTER
Crazy Sheep (ABV 4.5%) BITTER
Monarch's Way (ABV 4.5%) BITTER
Troll (ABV 5.4%) GOLD

Bishop Nick SIBA

33 East Street, Braintree, Essex, CM7 3JJ
☎ (01376) 349605 ⊕ bishopnick.com

⊗ Bishop Nick was launched in 2011 by Nelion Ridley, a member of the family that started Ridley's brewery near Chelmsford in 1842. In 2013 a new brewery was established in Braintree using a 20-barrel plant. �]◆

Ridley's Rite (ABV 3.6%) BITTER
Heresy (ABV 4%) GOLD
1555 (ABV 4.3%) BITTER
Devout (ABV 4.5%) STOUT
Martyr (ABV 5%) PALE
Divine (ABV 5.1%) BITTER

Bitter End

See Tirril

Black Bear

🍴 c/o Bear Inn, 8-10 North Street, Wiveliscombe, Somerset, TA4 2JY
☎ (01984) 623537 ⊕ blackbearbrewery.co.uk

⊗ Established in 2013, Black Bear is situated at the Bear Inn, Wiveliscombe, where Head Brewer Jon Coward and Assistant Brewer Peter Saxby create Black Bear Bitter and Goldihops, and a selection of seasonal offerings for the small estate of four pubs. Brewing is suspended. ◆

Black Box SIBA

18 Aviation Way, Southend Airport, Essex, SS2 6UN
☎ 07471 733719 ⊕ blackboxbrewery.co.uk

⊗ A brewery and taproom on the airport industrial estate, with an aircraft theme. Music and other events are held regularly. See social media for opening hours
V◆

Ground Speed (ABV 3.8%) PALE
Landing Gear (ABV 3.8%) BITTER
Golden Wings (ABV 4%) GOLD
Mild High Club (ABV 4.2%) MILD
First Class (ABV 4.4%) PALE
Kamikaze (ABV 4.4%) SPECIALITY

Spruce Goose (ABV 4.4%) PALE
Vulcan XL426 (ABV 4.5%) GOLD
Bird Strike (ABV 4.8%) PORTER
Coffee & Vanilla Porter (ABV 4.8%) PORTER
Auto Pilot (ABV 5%) BITTER
Lost Luggage (ABV 5%) BITTER

Black Cloak SIBA

**Units 1 & 2, Denbigh Enterprise Centre, Denbigh,
LL16 5TA ☎ 07701 031121**

Office: Glog Ddu Llangernyw, Abergele, LL22 8PS

☺Originally opened as a brewpub in Colwyn Bay in 2018, the brewery has now moved to a larger plant in Denbigh with increased capacity. It produces cask and keg beers with a core range and regular specials available at the Black Cloak Taproom, Colwyn Bay. 🍺♦

Pale (ABV 3.9%) GOLD
American Red (ABV 4.5%) RED
Porter (ABV 4.5%) PORTER
IPA (ABV 5%) PALE

Black Country IFBB

**Rear of Old Bulls Head, 1 Redhall Road, Lower Gornal,
West Midlands, DY3 2NU
☎ (01384) 401820**

**Office: 69 Third Avenue, Pensnett Trading Estate,
Kingswinford, DY6 7FD ⊕ blackcountryales.co.uk**

☺A compact brewery located at the back of the Bull's Head in Lower Gornal, which recommenced brewing in 2004. In 2012 much of the old equipment was replaced with a new kit, which can brew up to 15 barrels at a time and is currently doing so three times a week. The beers can be found in its own tied estate, as well as certain free houses nationwide. ‼♦

Bradley's Finest Golden (ABV 4.2%) GOLD
Chain Ale (ABV 4.2%) GOLD
Pig on the Wall (ABV 4.3%) MILD
Fireside (ABV 5%) BITTER

Black Dog

See Hambleton

Black Flag

**Unit 1D, New Road, Perranporth, Cornwall, TR6 0DL
☎ (01872) 858004 ⊕ blackflagbrewery.com**

⊗ Black Flag began brewing in 2013 and relocated to Perranporth in 2019. A new eight-barrel plant was installed in 2020 and the brewery began producing a wider range of beer styles using organic malts. All beers are unfined and unpasteurised, available in cans, bottles and kegs. Growlers of draught keg are sold or refilled in the taproom where wood-fired pizzas are a popular eat in or takeaway. ♦LIVE V🍽♦

Black Hole SIBA

**Unit 3A, Old Hall Mill Business Park, Alfreton Road,
Little Eaton, Derbyshire, DE21 5EJ
☎ (01283) 619943 ☎ 07812 812953
⊕ blackholebrewery.co.uk**

⊗ Black Hole was established 2007 with a 10-barrel plant in the former Ind Coope bottling stores, Burton-on-Trent (now demolished), but moved to its current location in 2017. Its fermenting capacity of 36 barrels enables production of up to four brews per week (some under the Little Eaton Brewery, and Mr Grundy's Brewery

names). Around 400 outlets are supplied direct, and many more via wholesalers. Since 2014, the brewery has been owned by GHH Llp, which also owned Mr Grundy's Brewery (closed). ‼♦

Bitter (ABV 3.8%) BITTER
Amber glow and malt and spicy hop aroma. Fresh, lively session beer hopped to give a clean crisp finish of hoppy dryness and touch of astringency.
Cosmic (ABV 4.2%) BITTER
Almost golden with an initial malt aroma. The complex balance of malt and English hops give lingering tastes of nuts, fruit and dry hoppy bitterness.
Supernova (ABV 4.8%) GOLD
Pure gold. Like marmalade made from Seville oranges and grapefruit the aroma mimics the sweet start but gives into the hops which deliver a dry, lingering bitter finish.
IPA (ABV 5.2%) PALE
Milky Way (ABV 6%) SPECIALITY
Honey and banana nose advises the sweet taste but not the sweet, dry spicy finish from this wheat beer.

Brewed for Small Beer, Lincoln:
Lincoln Imperial Ale (ABV 3.8%) BITTER

Brewed under the Little Eaton brand name:
Bates' Pale Ale (ABV 3.8%) PALE
Bagnall Bros. Bitter (ABV 4.2%) BITTER
Delver's Drop IPA (ABV 4.8%) SPECIALITY
Old Mill Stout (ABV 5%) SPECIALITY

Brewed under the Mr Grundy's brand name:
Passchendaele (ABV 3.9%) PALE
Big Willie (ABV 4.3%) GOLD
Sniper (ABV 4.6%) BITTER
Lord Kitchener (ABV 5.5%) IPA

Black Iris SIBA

**Unit 1, Shipstone Street, New Basford, Nottingham,
NG7 6GJ
☎ (0115) 979 1936 ⊕ blackirisbottleshop.co.uk**

☺Black Iris began brewing in 2011 using a six-barrel plant behind the Flowerpot pub in Derby. It expanded to a brand new 10-barrel plant in 2014 and relocated to premises in Nottingham. Beers are distributed nationally through wholesalers and by direct order to the local free trade. Innovation and collaboration ensure that new beers are consistently being added to the range. 🍺♦🔧

Snake Eyes (ABV 3.8%) GOLD
Golden-coloured ale with an intense hoppy aroma and taste with a lingering bitter finish.
Bleeding Heart (ABV 4.5%) BITTER
Red rye malty ale balanced with roast and hops and a bitter finish.
Endless Summer (ABV 4.5%) GOLD
Golden in colour with a tropical citrus fruit presence from aroma to aftertaste, with a gentle bitter finish.
Stab in the Dark (ABV 5%) STOUT
Black Stout with New Zealand hops, roast malt and coffee flavours and a moderate bitter finish.

Black Isle SIBA

**Old Allengrange, Munlochy, IV8 8NZ
☎ (01463) 811871 ⊕ blackislebrewery.com**

☺Black Isle Brewery was set up in 1998 in the heart of the Scottish Highlands. It expanded substantially in 2011 with a new brewhouse and bottling line. All beers are organic with Soil Association certification. ‼🍺♦V

Yellowhammer (ABV 3.9%) GOLD
A refreshing, hoppy golden ale with light grapefruit hop and peach flavour throughout. A short bitter finish.

Red Kite (ABV 4.2%) BITTER
Tawny ale with light malt on the nose and some red fruit on the palate and a hoppy background. Slight sweetness in the taste.
Heather Honey (ABV 4.6%) SPECIALITY
Sweet amber beer brewed with a background mix of organic malt, hops and Highland heather honey.
Porter (ABV 4.6%) PORTER
A hint of liquorice and burnt chocolate on the nose and a creamy mix of malt and fruit in the taste.
Blonde (ABV 5%) BLOND

Black Lodge

Kings Dock Street, Baltic Triangle, Liverpool, L1 8JU
☎ 07565 299879 ⊕ blacklodgebrewing.co.uk

Brewery producing experimental and speciality beers that can be sampled in its own taproom. Moved to current brewery in 2019 with ex-Mad Hatter brewery kit. Frequently brews specials and collaboration beers. Its cask beers are increasingly available in local pubs. ♦V♦

Crash on the Hill (ABV 3.9%) BLOND

Black Market

🍺 The Workman's, 43 High Street, Warsop, NG20 0AE
☎ 07824 363373

Beers first appeared at the Black Market in 2016. The 2.5-barrel plant is situated in the basement. There are four core beers regularly brewed. Most of the brews are consumed onsite, however it does provide to other pubs and outdoor festivals. V

Illicit (ABV 4.3%) PALE
Purple Haze (ABV 4.3%) PALE
Overdrive (ABV 4.5%) BITTER
Back in Black (ABV 5%) STOUT

Black Metal

Unit 20, M90 Commerce Park, Lathalmond, Dunfermline, KY12 0SJ
☎ (0131) 623 3411 ☎ 07711 295385
Office: Flat 10 / 7, Edinburgh, EH11 2PQ
⊕ blackmetalbrewery.com

Black Metal Brewery was established in Edinburgh in 2012 by two old friends; metalheads and inspired brewers. In 2021 operations moved to its own brewing site in Dunfermline. ♦LIVE

Will-o'-the-Wisp (ABV 6%) SPECIALITY
Blood Revenge (ABV 6.6%) SPECIALITY
Yggdrasil (ABV 6.6%) GOLD

Black Sheep

Wellgarth, Masham, Ripon, North Yorkshire, HG4 4EN
☎ (01765) 689227 ⊕ blacksheepbrewery.co.uk

☺Established in 1992 by Paul Theakston, a member of Masham's famous brewing family, the brewery operation is now run by his two sons. It is situated in the former Wellgarth Maltings and uses the traditional Yorkshire Square fermenting system. The company supplies the free trade across Yorkshire and the North, with national supply through pubcos and wholesale channels. Bought by Breal Capital in 2023 and now part of the rebranded Keystone Brewing Group of breweries. ‼🍺♦♦

Best Bitter (ABV 3.8%) BITTER
A malty amber beer with some hoppy and fruity notes, leading to a sweet finish balanced by bitterness throughout.

Respire (ABV 4%) PALE
Special Ale (ABV 4.4%) BITTER
Riggwelter (ABV 5.9%) BITTER
A dark brown fruity bitter which carries on to the dry, bitter finish.

Black Wolf

Unit 7c, Bandeath Industrial Estate, Throsk, Stirling, FK7 7NP
☎ (01786) 437187 ⊕ blackwolfbrewery.com

☺Established in 2005, the brewery is located in a former torpedo factory on the shores of the River Forth. In 2014 the brewery changed its name from Traditional Scottish Ales to Black Wolf Brewery and rebranded its range of beers. All Black Wolf beers are brewed on demand all year round at Throsk. The brewery also bottles beers for other breweries. Currently no cask ales are being produced but this may change in the future. ♦

Blackedge SIBA

🍺 Moreton Mill, Hampson Street, Horwich, BL6 7JH
☎ (01204) 692976 ☎ 07795 654895
⊕ blackedgebrewery.co.uk

☺Blackedge Brewery brews at a 10-barrel plant visible through a viewing window on the ground floor beneath the Brewery Bar – one of its two outlets. Its award-winning beers are available throughout north west England and beyond. A strong core range is supplemented by seasonal brews in both cask and unfiltered keg formats. Most are also canned onsite. ‼🍺♦LIVE

Session (ABV 3.4%) GOLD
Refreshing citrus hops, with a full-bodied citrus hop aroma. Clean dry finish with lingering bitter hops.
Zinc (ABV 3.4%) GOLD
Hop (ABV 3.8%) PALE
Assertively hoppy bitter beer. Citrus flavours with a lasting dry finish
Brewers Gold (ABV 3.9%) BLOND
Dark Mild (ABV 3.9%) MILD
Pleasant chocolate and malt aroma leads to a full-bodied beer with dark fruits, sustained malt presence and roasty finish.
Black (ABV 4%) STOUT
Well-rounded and creamy dark beer with roast malt and balanced sweetness. Dry, bitter roast finish.
Cascade (ABV 4%) BLOND
Pike (ABV 4%) PALE
Smooth, copper coloured beer with bitter hops and balanced sweetness, leading to a dry bitter finish.
West Coast (ABV 4.1%) GOLD
Citrus hop aroma and flavour. Sweet fruitiness balances lasting bitter hops.
Platinum (ABV 4.4%) BLOND
Blonde (ABV 4.5%) BLOND
Black Port (ABV 4.6%) SPECIALITY
Black beer with malty, fruity aroma. Rich, with chocolate and dark fruits to taste with a slightly drier finish.
Dark Rum (ABV 4.6%) SPECIALITY
Rich roast aroma and strong dry roast flavour. Accompanying taste of dried fruit and drawn-out, sweet finish.
IPA (ABV 4.7%) GOLD
Intense bitter hops with a long, drying finish.
Kiwi (ABV 5%) GOLD
Citrus hops and fruit in the aroma and taste. Sweetness supports the flavours as the bitterness builds in the finish.

Blackened Sun

3 Heathfield, Stacey Bushes, Milton Keynes,
Buckinghamshire, MK12 6HP ☎ 07963 529859
⊕ blackenedsunbrewing.co.uk

⊠ Blackened Sun began brewing in 2017 and is mainly
focused on brewing beers using Belgian yeast. The
brewery continues to diversify and innovate with its core
range. It is involved in other brewing projects including a
mixed fermentation programme and a project brewing
with local home brewers. ♦LIVE V✦

Blackfriars Tavern (NEW)

▤ Blackfriars Tavern, 94 Blackfriars Road, Great
Yarmouth, Norfolk, NR30 3BZ
⊕ blackfriarstavernbrewery.co.uk

Established in 2023 by the owner of the Blackfriars
Tavern, it uses local ingredients where possible, produces
regular ales, and a steady output of small batch, high
gravity beers across a variety of styles. Most beers are
named based on the Dominican Order (The Black Friars)
or local interest. ♦LIVE V

Blackjack SIBA

34-36 Irk Street, Manchester, M4 4JT
☎ (0161) 819 2767

Office: Smithfield Market Tavern, 37 Swan Street,
Manchester, M4 5JZ ⊕ blackjack-beers.com

☺Blackjack began in a railway arch in Manchester's
Green Quarter in 2012, and is now well established as
one of Manchester's foremost brewers of both modern
style and traditional ales. Beers are widely available
across the North of England and nationally as well as in
its own Smithfield Tavern, three Jack in the Box food
market bars, and the brewery taproom (open last
weekend of the month Mar-Oct – check socials for more
information). ‼♦V✦

Irk Street Pale Ale (ABV 3.8%) GOLD
Fruity citrus hoppy aromas progress into a sweet, fruity,
hoppy beer. Bitterness develops lessening the impact of
the fruity sweetness.
Jack in the Box (ABV 4%) BLOND
Fruition (ABV 4.2%) PALE
Pub Ale: Best Bitter (ABV 4.2%) BITTER
A complex malty sweetness characterises this beer,
which finishes with a malty hop bitterness.
Salvation! (ABV 4.5%) GOLD
Citrus hops to the fore starting with the aromas.
Bitterness develops on drinking with some fruity
sweetness to balance.
Early Days (ABV 4.6%) BITTER
Malty and fruity aromas lead to a sweet fruity beer
balanced by some gentle hops.
Manchester Stout (ABV 4.8%) STOUT

Blindmans SIBA

Talbot Farm, Leighton, Frome, Somerset, BA11 4PN
☎ (01749) 880038 ⊕ blindmansbrewery.co.uk

Established in 2002 in a converted milking parlour and
purchased by its current owners in 2004, this five-barrel
brewery has its own water spring. In addition to its core
range of ales, which are available locally and nationally,
the brewery produces bespoke branded beers for pubs
and other customers. ♦

Buff Amber (ABV 3.6%) BITTER
Funny Farm (ABV 4%) PALE
Golden Spring (ABV 4%) GOLD
Mine Beer (ABV 4.2%) BITTER

Icarus (ABV 4.5%) BITTER

Blondies (NEW)

Patchworks, 258 Church Road, Leyton, London,
E10 7JQ ⊕ blondiesbar.co.uk

After a long search for a venue (including a failed
attempt in Hackney Downs), the taproom opened in
2023 and the brewery was installed at the end of 2023
with the help of Mammoth Brewery. Initial beers came
from Mammoth and those from the onsite brewery
appeared in early 2024. The beers are available in keg at
the taproom and the original bar in Clapton. No cask ale.
✦

Blue Anchor

▤ 50 Coinagehall Street, Helston, Cornwall, TR13 8EL
☎ (01326) 562821 ⊕ spingoales.com

☺A 15th century, family-run thatched brewpub – the
oldest continuously brewing in the country. Home to the
world famous Spingo ales, from the brewery at the rear
of the Blue Anchor, using its own well water. It was built
sometime in the 18th century. Beforehand, Spingo was
brewed within the confines of the pub. The Spingo name
derives from the word "Stingo", used in the old English
dictionary of 1625, to describe British strong beer. ‼♦LIVE

Flora Daze (ABV 4%) BITTER
Pale brown bitter with flowery aroma, caramel and malt,
citrus hops and stone fruit in the mouth. Lingering bitter
finish.
Jubilee IPA (ABV 4.5%) PALE
Amber premium bitter with malty, fruity hop nose and
taste, balanced by fresh hop bitterness. Gentle bitter
finish with sweet malt.
Ben's Stout (ABV 4.8%) STOUT
Creamy dark stout with coffee roast aroma. Roast malt
with liquorice and cherry flavours. Bittersweet finish with
apples and cloves.
Spingo Middle (ABV 5%) BITTER
Heavy tawny ale with dominant malt and balancing
peppery hop bitterness. Nuts, spices and dates flavours.
Long, malty, earthy finish.
Spingo Special (ABV 6.6%) STRONG
Smooth, red, strong ale. Red wine aroma. Kaleidoscope
of powerful sweet stone fruits, smoky malt and hop
flavours. Vinous and earthy.

Blue Bee

Unit 29-30, Hoyland Road Industrial Estate, Sheffield,
South Yorkshire, S3 8AB ☎ 07375 659349
⊕ bluebeebrewery.co.uk

Established in 2010, this independently-owned, 10-
barrel brewery supplies throughout the East Midlands
and Yorkshire. The beers are often found further afield. A
session pale, an IPA and a stout are always available. In
addition, Blue Bee regularly produce innovative specials.
Most beers emphasise New World hops. ♦

Bessemer Blonde (ABV 4%) BLOND
Hillfoot Best Bitter (ABV 4%) BITTER
Reet Pale (ABV 4%) PALE
American 5 Hop (ABV 4.3%) PALE
Triple Hop (ABV 4.3%) PALE

Blue Bell

▤ Cranesgate South, Whaplode St Catherine,
Lincolnshire, PE12 6SN
☎ (01406) 540300 ☎ 07788 136663
⊕ thebluebell.net

⊕Founded in 1998 behind the Blue Bell pub. The brewery is owned by the pub after previously operating as a separate business. Beers are only available at the pub and to private customers. !! ♦ LIVE

Blue Monkey SIBA

10 Pentrich Road, Giltbrook Industrial Park, Giltbrook, Nottingham, Nottinghamshire, NG16 2UZ
☎ (0115) 938 5899 ⊕ bluemonkeybrewery.com

⊕Blue Monkey was established in 2008 as a 10-barrel plant, but moved in 2010 to a bigger site to meet increasing demand. It now brews around 15,000 pints a week to supply more than 1,000 local outlets, and selected national distributors. The brewery has four pubs all called the Organ Grinder (Nottingham, Arnold, Loughborough and Newark). !! 🏺

Marmoset (ABV 3.6%) BITTER
BG Sips (ABV 4%) PALE
Pale golden hoppy beer, brewed mainly with Brewers Gold hops. Very fruity and bitter.
Primate Best Bitter (ABV 4%) BITTER
Infinity IPA (ABV 4.6%) PALE
Chocolate Amaretto (ABV 4.9%) SPECIALITY
This Guerrilla is flavoured with chocolate and amaretto. Sweetness is the dominant characteristic and overtakes the usual malt and roast.
Chocolate Guerilla (ABV 4.9%) STOUT
Chocolate Orange (ABV 4.9%) SPECIALITY
Guerilla stout flavoured with chocolate and orange. The orange is mostly on the nose. A strong, bitter finish
Guerrilla (ABV 4.9%) STOUT
A creamy stout, full of roast malt flavour and a slightly sweet finish.
Ape Ale (ABV 5.4%) PALE
Intensely hopped strong golden ale with dry bitter finish
Infinity Plus 1 (ABV 5.6%) BITTER

Blue Shed (NEW)

17 Rook Way, Horsham, West Sussex, RH12 5FR

Established in 2023, Blue Shed is based in Horsham. ♦

Blue Square

See Truth Hurts

Bluestone SIBA

Tyriet, Cilgwyn, Pembrokeshire, SA42 0QW
☎ (01239) 820833 ⊕ bluestonebrewing.co.uk

⊗ Family-run business established in 2013 on a working farm in the Preseli Hills, within the Pembrokeshire Coast National Park. The 10-barrel brewery is housed in the 300-year-old dairy, and has a visitor facility and office (see website for opening times). Outdoor music and other events are held in the summer. Spring water, filtering down through the Preseli Bluestones to the brewery's well, gives the beers a unique taste. Local outlets plus wholesalers around the UK are supplied. Green Key accredited for environmental sustainability. 🏺 ♦ LIVE GF V✿

Bedrock Blonde (ABV 4%) BLOND
Stone Cold (ABV 4.2%) PALE
Hammerstone IPA (ABV 4.5%) PALE
Rocketeer (ABV 4.6%) BITTER

Bluntrock

Trewiston Lane, St Minver, Cornwall, PL27 6PY

Second Site: Pityme Industrial Estate, St Minver, Cornwall, PL27 6NS ⊕ bluntrockbrewery.co.uk

This nanobrewery commenced brewing as Lowlands Brewing in 2021 in four converted shipping containers using a one-barrel plant. It rebranded to Bluntrock in 2022. In 2024 a new 15-hectolitre brewery was opened 1km away with brewing also continuing on the original site. All beers are vegan and some are gluten-free. The Pityme taproom hosts regular music and food events. ♦ GF V✿

Right On (ABV 4.2%) BITTER
Gold (ABV 4.8%) GOLD

Blythe SIBA

Blythe House Farm, Lichfield Road, Hamstall Ridware, Staffordshire, WS15 3QQ
☎ (01889) 504461 ☎ 07483 248723
⊕ blythebrewery.co.uk

⊗ Blythe began brewing in 2003 using a 2.5-barrel plant in a converted barn. Only organic ingredients are used wherever possible. Following a buyout by two brothers in 2017, the brewery increased its range of beers. 15 outlets are supplied direct with others supplied by wholesalers throughout the region. !! ♦ LIVE

Bagot's Bitter (ABV 3.8%) BITTER
Amber in colour with a fruit start and sweetness which develops to a smooth, bitter finish. A lightly-hopped, easy-drinking beer.
Ridware Pale (ABV 4.3%) BITTER
Bright and golden with a bitter floral hop aroma and citrus taste. Good and hop-sharp, bitter and refreshing. Long, lingering bite with ripples of citrus across the tongue.
Summer Breeze (ABV 4.3%) BITTER
Staffie (ABV 4.4%) BITTER
Hoppy and grassy aroma with hints of sweetness from this amber beer. A touch of malt at the start is soon overwhelmed by hops. A full hoppy, mouth-watering finish.
Palmers Poison (ABV 4.5%) BITTER
Refreshing darkish beer. Tawny but light-headed. Coffee truffle aroma, pleasingly sweet to start but with a good hop mouthfeel.
Gold Rush (ABV 4.6%) BITTER
Dark Horse (ABV 4.7%) STOUT
Knobbled Horse (ABV 4.7%) SPECIALITY
Dark Ruby (ABV 5%) MILD
Johnsons (ABV 5.2%) PORTER
Black with a thick head. Refreshingly hoppy and full-bodied with lingering bitterness of chocolate, dates, coal smoke and liquorice.

BMAN

Unit 50, Monument Business Park, Warpsgrove Lane, Chalgrove, Oxfordshire, OX44 7RW
⊕ bmanbrewery.co.uk

Microbrewery focusing on craft and modern styles. Established by food scientist Alex Berryman in a freight container in 2021 and expanded to five hectolitre capacity (three barrels) in 2023. Production goes into cans and kegs, which can be purchased online and found in local outlets.

BOA (Brothers of Ale)

Unit 3, Anglo Buildings, Baldwin Road, Stourport-on-Severn, Worcestershire, DY13 9AX
☎ (01299) 489200 ☎ 07305 084490
✉ info@boabrewingcompany.co.uk

What started as a hobby soon became a passion and BOA Brewery was established in 2018, before opening its doors in 2019. It is situated in the heart of Stourport-on-Severn and produces New World-style hoppy beers. ✦

Peace Out (ABV 3.6%) BITTER
Lock N Load (ABV 4.2%) GOLD
The 7 (ABV 4.2%) BITTER
2 Step (ABV 4.4%) PALE
Re-wind (ABV 4.7%) GOLD
VVD Oatmeal Stout (ABV 4.7%) STOUT
Bone Idle (ABV 4.8%) GOLD
Loud Mouth (ABV 5.2%) GOLD

Boat Lane

Unit 3, Streamside Business Park, Boat Lane, Offenham, Evesham, Worcestershire, WR11 8RS
☎ (01386) 719558 ⊕ boatlanebrewery.co.uk

A microbrewery established in 2017 by Ian Hazeldene in a small village near Evesham. An ever-changing range of beers are brewed, with up to eight available in the brewery bar at weekends. ✦

Boden

4 Craigends Road, Glengarnock, KA14 3AE ☎ 07511 022231 ⊕ bodenbrewing.co.uk

Launched in the east end of Glasgow in 2019, Boden Brewing is a one-man operation now based in Ayrshire. Six core beers are available in bottle and keg.

Bohem

Unit 5, Littleline House, 41-43 West Road, Tottenham, London, N17 ORE
☎ (020) 8617 8350 ☎ 07455 502976
⊕ bohembrewery.com

Traditional Bohemian lagers, light and dark, brewed by Czech expats in North London. Beers are supplied widely, including the brewery tap, Bohem Tap Room, near Bowes Park Station. A second outlet was added in 2020, the Bohemia House in West Hampstead, replacing the former Czech club and specialising in Czech food to complement the beers. No cask ale.

Boilerhouse

See JW Lees (under L)

Bollington SIBA

Brook Mill, Parker Street, Macclesfield, Cheshire, SK11 7BQ
☎ (01625) 575380 ⊕ bollingtonbrewing.co.uk

⊗ Bollington began brewing in 2008 with the Vale Inn, Bollington, as the brewery tap. The Park Tavern, and the Fountain, both in Macclesfield, and the Cask Tavern, Poynton, are also owned, and in 2023 the Foundry in Congleton opened. The brewery moved to new premises in 2024, with a taproom due to open during the currency of this guide. Around 40 outlets are supplied direct. ‼◆

Chinook & Grapefruit (ABV 3.6%) GOLD
Ginger Brew (ABV 3.6%) SPECIALITY
White Nancy (ABV 3.6%) BLOND
Fruity hoppy aroma and a sweet body with hops providing balance. The bitterness continues with the fruit into a lasting finish.
Long Hop (ABV 3.9%) BLOND
A hoppy yellow beer with fruit and some sweetness for balance.
Best (ABV 4.2%) BITTER

A bitter beer with plenty of hop bitterness which dominates the fruity sweet malt flavours. The bitterness lasts and develops.
Oat Mill Stout (ABV 5%) STOUT
Smooth stout with a fruity sweet taste developing into a roast bitter finish with some hop, which intensifies on drinking.
Eastern Nights (ABV 5.6%) IPA
Peachy fruity aromas lead on to a sweet, fruity middle which gives way to hoppy bitterness. A complex beer.

Bond Brews

Units 3 & 4, South Barns, Gardeners Green Farm, Heathlands Road, Wokingham, Berkshire, RG40 3AS
☎ (01344) 775450 ⊕ bondbrews.co.uk

⊗ Bond Brews was established in 2015 using a six-barrel plant and produces a range of cask-conditioned and bottle-conditioned beers. Deliveries are made to pubs within a 30-mile radius and retail purchases are available from the brewery shop and online. Brewery tours and experience days are available by arrangement with the brewer. ‼🏪◆LIVE V

Goldi-hops (ABV 3.9%) PALE
A golden-coloured session pale ale with a fruit and hop aroma. Bramble and apple flavours lead to a lingering fruity, dry bitter aftertaste.
Best of British (ABV 4%) BITTER
Tawny-coloured session bitter, predominantly malty, hops and fruit aroma. Dried fruit, earthy caramel flavours lead to sweet nutty aftertaste.
Bengal Tiger (ABV 4.3%) PALE
A golden-coloured session pale ale with a hoppy, fruity aroma. Initial fruity flavour leads to an earthy bitterness and a long, dry, bitter finish.
Railway Porter (ABV 4.5%) PORTER
A brown-coloured session porter with roast malt and fruit aroma. Bitter and hoppy flavour with an earthy, peppery, bitter chocolate aftertaste.

Bone Idle

28 The Green, Idle, Bradford, West Yorkshire, BD10 9PX ☎ 07525 751574

Established in 2018 in a converted barn situated in the heart of Idle village. The brewery offers the public the opportunity to try brewing. All beers produced are sold exclusively in the Idle Draper pub next door. A mezzanine floor has a mini cinema/function room.

Boobytrap

Unit 7a/b, Upper Barn Farm, Bicester Road, Westcott, Buckinghamshire, HP18 0JX ☎ 07811 437185
⊕ boobytrapbrewery.com

A five-barrel brewhouse and taproom established by chef Philip Baker in 2021 and producing beer in cans. The taproom sells draught and canned beers to drink in or take out. ✦

Boot

See Little Brewing

Boot Town

c/o Bosworths Garden Centre, 110 Finedon Road, Burton Latimer, Northamptonshire, NN15 5QA
☎ 07958 331340 ⊕ boottownbrewery.co.uk

One-barrel microbrewery, established in 2017, based at the old Copper Kettle Homebrew Shop, producing an ever-changing range of beers with a modern craft theme, with output into KeyKegs, Sankey kegs and cans.

Bootleg

See Joseph Holt

Borderlands SIBA

116A High Street, Langholm, DG13 0DH ☎ 07843 896644 ⊕ borderlandsbrewery.co.uk

Brewing in the heart of Langholm, also known as 'The Muckle Toon'. Borderlands was founded by Stuart Campbell restoring brewing to the town, yards away from the historic brewery, after a break of over a century. Proudly nestled in the Esk Valley, the brewery is a 2.5-barrel plant brewing in small batches. Three core beers are supplemented by limited editions (all cask, bottle and can). Expanded into a new premises incorporating a taproom in 2022. ◆

Born SIBA

Lanton Mill, Jedburgh, TD8 6ST
☎ (01835) 830495 ☎ 07802 416494
✉ john@scottishbordersbrewery.com

Scotland's original plough-to-pint brewery, it started brewing as Scottish Borders Brewery in 2011, using its own barley, before changing name to Born in the Borders Brewery, and then Born Brewery in 2020. Beyond its core range of ales, projects have included the 'Wild Harvest' initiative, which sources locally-foraged ingredients. ‼ 🍴◆

Blonde (ABV 3.8%) GOLD
Well-balanced hop and malt flavour, with bitterness coming through.
Amber (ABV 4%) BITTER
An amber ale with a balance of malty sweetness and hop bitterness, fruity and easy to drink.
IPA (ABV 4.8%) PALE

Borough Arms

🍴 2 New Henry Street, Neath, SA11 2PH
☎ (01639) 644902 ⊕ boroughbreweryneath.com

☺The Borough Arms and Borough Brewery were purchased in early 2019 by the new landlord who is a former brewer with the now defunct Kite Brewery which has been absorbed by the Glamorgan Brewery. Beers are brewed occasionally at the rear of the pub for consumption in-house only.

Boscombe

Bournemouth, Dorset ☎ 07549 844099 ⊕ bbco.beer

⊠ A nanobrewery launched commercially in 2022 using a three-barrel plant in a converted outhouse of a residential property. Brewer Jarrod Thompson began homebrewing in his native Nashua in New Hampshire more than twenty years ago. No real ale. V

Boss

176 Neath Road, Landore, Swansea, SA1 2JT
☎ (01792) 381695 ⊕ bossbrewing.co.uk

⊠ Brewing currently suspended. ‼◆LIVE

Bosun's SIBA

Unit 15, Sandbeck Park, Sandbeck Lane, Wetherby, LS25 7TW
☎ (01937) 227337 ⊕ bosunsbrewery.com

☺The first brew was produced in 2013 by a father and son who had both served in the armed forces. The brewery relocated from Horbury to Huddersfield in 2018 and subsequently to Wetherby in 2021 under new ownership. The regular beers are produced on a 10-barrel plant with some nautical-themed names. Canned beers are available from the online shop. ‼🍴◆⚓

Tell No Tales (ABV 3.8%) BITTER
Bosun's Blonde (ABV 3.9%) BLOND
Maiden Voyage (ABV 3.9%) BITTER
Down the Hatch (ABV 4%) BITTER
King Neptune (ABV 4.3%) BITTER
IPA (ABV 5.6%) IPA
Tempest (ABV 5.6%) IPA

Both Barrels

56A Main Street, Mexborough, S64 9DU ☎ 07753 746618 ✉ anthony@bothbarrelsbrewing.com

Small-batch craft brewery specializing in a wide variety of beers and lagers, founded in 2021. Beers are available in all formats. No filtering or pasteurization of any products.

Botley

Botley Mills, Mill Hill, Botley, Hampshire, SO30 2GB
☎ (01489) 784867 ☎ 07909 337212
⊕ botleybreweryltd.com

⊠ Botley Brewery was established in 2010 and uses a five-barrel plant. A small bar next door, appropriately named the Hidden Tap, serves at least three of its ales. 🍴◆LIVE

HPA (ABV 3.8%) PALE
Citra Ass Down (ABV 4.6%) PALE
English IPA (ABV 5.1%) PALE
An earthy, rich and piney English IPA. Decent hoppiness with lasting, pronounced dryness, but a well-rounded malt character throughout.
Wildern (ABV 5.7%) RED

Bottle Brook

Church Street, Kilburn, Belper, Derbyshire, DE56 0LU
☎ (01332) 880051 ☎ 07971 189915

⊠ A sister brewery to Leadmill (qv), Bottle Brook was established in 2005 using a 2.5-barrel plant on a tower gravity system. New World hops are predominantly used. The core range of beers is supplemented by one-off brews.

Columbus (ABV 4%) GOLD
Heanor Pale Ale (ABV 4.2%) PALE
Roadrunner (ABV 4.8%) GOLD
Mellow Yellow (ABV 5.7%) GOLD
Rapture (ABV 5.9%) GOLD
Sand in the Wind (ABV 6.1%) GOLD

Boudicca

Office: Bakers Road, Norwich, NR3 3AZ ☎ 07864 321733 ⊕ boudiccabrewing.co.uk

⊠ Established in 2015, Boudicca Brewery was based on a North Norfolk estate until 2020. Its beers are currently contract brewed. It is an award-winning brewery exclusively producing vegan beers and one gluten-free, supplied to free trade outlets across East Anglia, including cafés, delicatessens and off-licences. ‼◆LIVE GF V

Queen of Hops (ABV 3.7%) PALE

Refreshing with a lasting finish. Fruity aroma, with hints of marmalade introducing a tangy burst of hops on the palate.

Three Tails Bitter (ABV 3.9%) BITTER
A bitter backbone dominates throughout. Malt, grapefruit and pepper in the first taste fades as a dry bitterness slowly grows.

One for the Woad (ABV 4%) MILD
A complex, malty, rich mild with a light, bitter finish from four hops.

Golden Torc (ABV 4.3%) GOLD
Malty bouquet with a hint of grassy hop. Biscuity beginning with a growing zesty citrus background appears. Clean grapefruit finish.

The Red Queen (ABV 4.5%) RED
Malt, dark fruits and caramel in nose and taste. Sweetness counters a growing hoppiness. Rye adds contrast and depth.

Spiral Stout (ABV 4.6%) STOUT
An aroma of dark autumnal berries. Full-bodied with undertones of dark chocolate and roasted malts with a gentle, lingering finish.

Prasto's Porter (ABV 5.2%) PORTER
Smooth and dark with molasses, malt and sweetness in aroma and taste. A roast toffee edge with a drying finish.

Boundary SIBA

Unit A5, 310 Portview Trade Centre, Newtownards Road, Belfast, BT4 1HE ⊕ boundarybrewing.coop

Boundary is a cooperative brewery based in Belfast, established in 2014. ♦◆

APA (ABV 3.5%) PALE
Export Stout (ABV 7%) STOUT
IPA (ABV 7%) IPA

Bowland SIBA

Holmes Mill, Greenacre Street, Clitheroe, Lancashire, BB7 1EB
☎ (01200) 443592 ⊕ bowlandbrewery.com

☺Founded in 2003, this family-run business uses a 30-barrel plant, together with a nanobrewery for experimental brews, and serves 250+ outlets. The site features a beer shop and beer hall with 42 handpumps featuring beers from Lancashire and beyond. ‼☴◆LIVE

Pheasant Plucker (ABV 3.7%) BITTER
Amber session bitter. Good hop/malt balance in aroma and flavour, raisin vine fruit ending in a growing bitter finish.

Gold (ABV 3.8%) PALE
Well-balanced, pale, hoppy ale with delicate citrus hop notes and a long dry bitter finish.

Boxer Blonde (ABV 4%) BLOND

Bumble (ABV 4%) SPECIALITY
Fruit and malty aroma some caramel and sweetness in the body and a rising dry bitter balance in the finish.

Hen Harrier (ABV 4%) PALE
Gentle aromas of malt, hops and fruit start this satisfying fruity bitter which has a lasting rich finish.

Buster IPA (ABV 4.5%) BITTER
Amber beer with sweet fruity flavours and rising hop bitterness.

Deer Stalker (ABV 4.5%) STOUT

Bowler's SIBA

84 Lincoln Road, Deeping Gate, Peterborough, Cambridgeshire, PE6 9BB ☎ 07480 064147
⊕ bowlers.beer

⊠ Established in 2019, Bowler's Brewery acquired the Hopshackle brand in 2023, and now brews a number of SIBA award-winning real ales under both brands. It supplies cask ales to pubs within the Peterborough and South Lincolnshire area. It also sells bottled beers via its online shop and a number of local outlets. ◆LIVE V

Simmarillo (ABV 3.8%) GOLD
The Duke (ABV 3.9%) BITTER
PE6 (ABV 4%) GOLD
King Street (ABV 4.2%) PALE
Special Bitter (ABV 4.3%) BITTER
Sundance (ABV 4.5%) GOLD
Brown Derby (ABV 4.8%) BROWN
Historic Porter (ABV 4.8%) PORTER
Hopnosis (ABV 5.2%) GOLD
Trusty Steed (ABV 5.5%) IPA

Bowman SIBA

Wallops Wood, Sheardley Lane, Droxford, Hampshire, SO32 3QY
☎ (01489) 878110 ⊕ bowman-ales.com

⊠ Brewing started in 2006. A new 40-barrel plant came on line in 2013, this is now working alongside the original 20-barrel plant. In addition to the standard beers, a range of seasonal brews and monthly specials are produced. ‼◆LIVE

Swift One (ABV 3.8%) BLOND
Easy-drinking blond, well-balanced, sweet biscuit maltiness and clean fresh hoppiness, leading to a bittersweet finish and gentle, dry hoppiness.

Meon Valley Bitter (ABV 3.9%) BITTER
Complex, well-balanced, traditional, copper-coloured bitter; sweet with initial maltiness in taste and aroma leading to a lingering bitterness.

Wallops Wood (ABV 4%) BITTER
Malt dominates this light brown session bitter. Some dried fruit flavours balanced by toffee notes and sweetness in the finish.

Quiver (ABV 4.5%) BITTER
Fruity best bitter, golden in colour with hoppy aroma leading through to a balanced, bittersweet taste and refreshing hoppy finish.

Hop Hearted (ABV 4.8%) GOLD

Bowness Bay SIBA

Unit 10, Castle Mills, Aynam Road, Kendal, Cumbria, LA9 7DE
☎ (01539) 726800 ☎ 07823 347763
⊕ bownessbaybrewing.co.uk

☺Bowness Bay Brewing moved to Kendal in 2015 and increased capacity from five to 16 barrels. Now expanded to a 2,500-litre, automated, four-vessel brewing system, capable of brewing up to six times a day. The original five-barrel plant is used for small experimental brews. In 2020 grant funding allowed expansion into keg beers. Onsite tap, the Barrel House, showcases the core range and seasonal specials. Live music space (since 2021), The Venue, hosts beer festivals, weddings and private parties. ‼◆◆

Fell Explorer (ABV 3.4%) BITTER
Lakeland Blonde (ABV 3.7%) BLOND
Swift Best (ABV 3.8%) BITTER
Hoppy bitter balanced by some malty sweetness and a little fruit.

Swan Blonde (ABV 4%) BLOND
Sweet, fruity mild beer with gentle bittering hops.

Fell Walker (ABV 4.1%) BLOND
A sweet fruity beer with gentle hop bittering and a drying finish.

Raven Red (ABV 4.2%) BITTER
Sweet, malty bitter with fruit and roast aromas, gentle hop bitterness and a dry finish.
Swan Gold (ABV 4.2%) BLOND
Fell Runner (ABV 4.6%) GOLD
Swan Black (ABV 4.6%) STOUT
Stout-like beer with a fruity raisiny middle, grainy mouthfeel and roast bitter finish.
Tern IPA (ABV 5%) PALE
Well-balanced with some sweet malt and fruit to balance the lingering hoppy finish.
Steamer IPA (ABV 5.7%) BLOND

Bowtie

78 Church Road, Watford, Hertfordshire, WD17 4PU
⊕ bowtiebrewers.co.uk

A one-barrel nanobrewery founded in 2018 in a specially designed brewshed. Commercial brewing began in 2019, offering three ranges of small batch beers; traditional, craft and speciality. Beers are mostly available in bottles but cask-conditioned beer is occasionally produced. ♦LIVE

Br3wery

2a Birkbeck Road, Beckenham, BR3 4SN
☎ (020) 3793 2765 ⊕ br3wery.com

Established at home in 2019, bigger batches of beer were later brewed at Birmingham Brewery. The brewery opened in a shop, doubling as a taproom, in 2021, and moved around the corner in 2023. The original taproom, part of the Local Brewery Loop, now has more space and the brewery doubles up as an occasional taproom space. A range of simply named styles is available at both sites. No cask ale. ✦

Bradfield SIBA

Watt House Farm, High Bradfield, Sheffield, South Yorkshire, S6 6LG
☎ (0114) 285 1118 ⊕ bradfieldbrewery.com

⊕One of the larger Sheffield breweries, Bradfield is based on a working farm in the Peak District National Park, and uses pure Millstone Grit spring water. This family-run business was established in 2005. Direct delivery in the Midlands and the North although beer is often supplied further afield and there is a local home delivery service. Monthly specials and occasional barrel-matured stout available. Four pubs are owned; King & Miller, Deepcar, Nag's Head, Loxley, Wharncliffe Arms, Wharncliffe Side, and White Hart, Bradwell. 🛒♦

Farmers Bitter (ABV 3.9%) BITTER
Farmers Blonde (ABV 4%) BLOND
Farmers Brown Cow (ABV 4.2%) BITTER
Farmers Steel Cow (ABV 4.5%) BITTER
Farmers Stout (ABV 4.5%) STOUT
Farmers 5K (ABV 5%) PALE
Farmers Pale Ale (ABV 5%) PALE
Farmers Sixer (ABV 6%) GOLD

Braemar SIBA

Airlie House, Chapel Brae, Braemar, AB35 5YT
☎ 07709 199914 ⊕ brewbraemar.uk

Small brewery founded in 2021 and located next to Hazelnut Patisserie. It produces cask and bottle-conditioned ales using Scottish malt and British hops. Bottled beers are available direct from the brewery.

Oat Stout (ABV 4%) STOUT
Braemar Pale (ABV 4.2%) PALE
Summer Sun (ABV 4.5%) GOLD

80/- (ABV 5%) BITTER

Brains SIBA IFBB

Dragon Brewery, Pacific Road, Cardiff, CF24 5HJ
☎ (029) 2040 2060 ⊕ sabrain.com

⊕In 2021, SA Brain put its freehold and leasehold pubs on the market. Most went to Carlsberg Marston's Brewing Co (25 year lease). Freeholds of the pub estate were sold to third party companies. Brains no longer own any pubs. Proceeds from the sale provided a foundation for the modern state-of-the-art facility, Dragon Brewery, to continue in Cardiff. Its beers are served in its former pubs, widely in the free trade and across the UK. Contract brewing and bottling is also undertaken. ♦

Dark (ABV 3.5%) MILD
A tasty, classic dark brown mild, a mix of malt, roast, caramel with a background of hops. Bittersweet, mellow and with a lasting finish of malt and roast.
Bitter (ABV 3.7%) BITTER
Amber-coloured with a gentle aroma of malt and hops. Malt, hops and bitterness combine in an easy-drinking beer with a bitter finish.
SA (ABV 4.2%) BITTER
A mellow, full-bodied beer. Gentle malt and hop aroma leads to a malty, hop and fruit mix with a balancing bitterness.
SA Gold (ABV 4.2%) GOLD
A golden beer with a hoppy aroma. Well-balanced with a zesty hop, malt, fruit and balancing bitterness; a similar satisfying finish.
Rev James Original (ABV 4.5%) BITTER
A faint malt and fruit aroma with malt and fruit flavours in the taste, initially bittersweet. Bitterness balances the flavour and makes this an easy-drinking beer.

Brakspear

See Banks's

Brampton SIBA

Units 4-5, Chatsworth Business Park, Chatsworth Road, Chesterfield, Derbyshire, S40 2AR
☎ (01246) 221680 ⊕ bramptonbrewery.co.uk

⊕The original Brampton Brewery closed in 1955. In 2007 a new brewery was established, and brewing commenced on an eight-barrel plant. Three tied houses are situated close to the brewery. ‼🛒♦LIVE

Golden Bud (ABV 3.8%) GOLD
Crisp and refreshing golden bitter with a pleasant balance of citrus, sweetness and bitter flavours. Light and easy to drink.
1302 (ABV 4%) PALE
Griffin (ABV 4.1%) PALE
Best (ABV 4.2%) BITTER
Classic, drinkable bitter with a predominantly malty taste, balanced by caramel sweetness and a developing bitterness in the aftertaste.
Impy Dark (ABV 4.3%) OLD
Strong roasted coffee aroma and a rich flavour of vine fruit and chocolate combine to make this a tasty mild ale.
Jerusalem (ABV 4.6%) BITTER
Tudor Rose (ABV 4.6%) PALE
Wasp Nest (ABV 5%) BITTER
Strong and complex with malt and hop flavours and a caramel sweetness.
Speciale (ABV 5.8%) IPA

Brancaster

See Beeston

Branscombe SIBA

Branscombe, Devon, EX12 3DP
☎ (01297) 630511 ⊕ branscombebrewery.co.uk

⊗ The brewery was set up in 1992 in cowsheds at the back of a National Trust-owned farm, overlooking the sea at Branscombe. The brewery owners converted the sheds and dug their own well for the water supply. In 2008 a new 25-barrel plant was shoehorned in through the roof to increase capacity. The brewery also makes its own Branscombe Cider and two varieties of gin. ♦LIVE

Branoc (ABV 3.8%) BITTER
Amber session bitter. Hops and malt throughout with good bitterness in taste and aftertaste.
Golden Fiddle (ABV 4%) GOLD
Summa This (ABV 4.2%) BITTER
Strong bitterness throughout, touch of grapefruit and tangerine notes with malty biscuitiness.
Summa That (ABV 5%) GOLD
A clear golden ale, hoppy fruity lemon aroma. Fruity taste with a bitter finish.

Brass Castle SIBA

10A Yorkersgate, Malton, North Yorkshire, YO17 7AB
☎ (01653) 698683 ⊕ brasscastle.co.uk

⊛Having begun life modestly in 2011 on a one-barrel kit in the owner's garage, the brewery, now based in the centre of Malton, expanded its capacity in 2023 from a 12 to 25-barrel state-of-the-art plant. All beers are vegan-friendly and certified gluten free. Alongside brewing a wide array of both traditional and modern interpretations of beer styles, the team have an occasional flair for the outlandish and use of unconventional ingredients. The adjacent brewery tap (open Tue-Sun), showcases up to ten draft beers, with more available for off-sales. !! ₹ ♦ GF V

Session Mini IPA (ABV 3.6%) PALE
Northern Blonde (ABV 3.9%) BLOND
Hoptical Illusion (ABV 4.3%) PALE
Misfit (ABV 4.3%) GOLD
Bluebell IPA (ABV 4.5%) IPA
Fruit Lupe (ABV 4.8%) PALE
Bad Kitty (ABV 5.5%) SPECIALITY
Sunshine (ABV 5.7%) IPA

Braybrooke (NEW) SIBA

Braybrooke Farm, Harborough Road, Braybrooke, Northamptonshire, LE16 8LJ ☎ 07711 637590

In 2017 three friends set up this specialist lager brewery on Braybrooke Farm, outside Market Harborough. Made using Bavarian lager yeast, German malt (milled onsite) and German hops, the beer is fermented more slowly at a lower temperature and then matured for 30 days. The bottles are unfiltered, unpasteurised and vegan. **V**

Brazenor's (NEW)

Maidenhead, Berkshire, SL6 5JW

Established in 2023, Brazenor's Brews is a nanobrewery producing a variety of beers in cans. All beers are unfiltered and unpasteurised.

Breakbeat (NEW)

Priory Road, Southampton, SO17 2JQ

Commercial home-based brewery of strong bottled beers that started brewing in 2023.

Breakwater

St Martin's Yard, Lorne Road, Dover, Kent, CT16 2AA
☎ (01304) 410144 ☎ 07979 867045
✉ andrea@breakwater.brewery.co.uk

⊗ Brewery and taproom behind Buckland Corn Mill in former industrial premises and on the site of the former Wellington Brewery. ♦♦

Dover Pale Ale (ABV 3.5%) BITTER
East Kent Gold (ABV 4.2%) GOLD
Red Ensign (ABV 4.2%) BITTER
Blue Ensign (ABV 4.3%) BITTER
Cowjuice Milk Stout (ABV 4.4%) STOUT
American Pale Ale (ABV 5%) PALE

Brecon

See Cold Black Label

Bredy (NEW)

Bredy Farm, Burton Bradstock, Dorset, DT6 4ND
☎ 07496 884837 ⊕ bredyfarm.com

Established in 2024, Bredy is a microbrewery based on a 300-acre farm in Dorset. The farm has a restaurant, camping (Apr-Sep), live music most weekends and hosts three music festivals across the summer.

Brentwood SIBA

Calcott Hall Farm, Ongar Road, Pilgrims Hatch, Brentwood, Essex, CM15 9HS
☎ (01277) 200483 ⊕ brentwoodbrewing.co.uk

⊗ Since its launch in 2006 Brentwood has steadily increased its capacity and distribution, relocating to a new purpose-built brewery unit in 2013 with a visitor centre. Seasonal and special beers are available including more unusual beer styles under the Elephant School brand name. All beers are gluten-free. !! ₹ ♦LIVE GF ♦

IPA (ABV 3.7%) PALE
Marvellous Maple Mild (ABV 3.7%) SPECIALITY
Legacy (ABV 4%) PALE
Best (ABV 4.2%) BITTER
Gold (ABV 4.3%) GOLD
Hope & Glory (ABV 4.5%) BITTER
Lumberjack (ABV 5.2%) BITTER
Chockwork Orange (ABV 6.5%) SPECIALITY

Brewed under the Elephant School brand name:
Aussie Blond (ABV 4%) BLOND

Brew Forest

Unit B1-B2, Setters Farm Workshops, Mount Pleasant Lane, Lymington, SO41 8LS ⊕ thebrewforest.com

Opened in 2022 by brother and sister team, David and Helen, the Brew Forest is a nanobrewery and taproom located in the New Forest. ♦

Brew Foundation

Office: 18 Jarrow Road, Sheffield, South Yorkshire, S11 8YB
☎ (0114) 282 3098 ☎ 07545 618894
⊕ thebrewfoundation.co.uk

Family-founded brewery. Following the passing of founder James, beers are currently being contract brewed at Wincle Brewery. The beer is available in Beer

Foundation outlets in Sheffield and occasionally distributed both east and west of the Pennines.

Pop (ABV 3.6%) PALE
Little Bitter That (ABV 3.8%) BITTER
Hops & Dreams (ABV 4%) PALE
Laughing Water (ABV 4.3%) BLOND
First Light (ABV 4.6%) PALE
Janet's Treat Porter (ABV 4.8%) SPECIALITY
Hop & Glory (ABV 4.9%) PALE
Bitter That (ABV 5%) BITTER

Brew Shed

Wellheads House, Sandilands, Limekilns, KY11 3JD
☎ 07484 727672 ⊕ brewshedbeers.wordpress.com

Brewing began in 2016 in a tiny brewery behind the owner's house; the first brewery in Limekilns since 1849. Brew Shed Beers revives a tradition of local breweries serving the neighbourhood.

Brew Toon SIBA

72a St Peter Street, Peterhead, AB42 1QB
☎ (01779) 560948 ⊕ brewtoon.co.uk

Established in 2017, beers are brewed in small batches. The brewery has an onsite café/bar. V

Brew Yonder

See Yonder

Brew York SIBA

Unit 6, Enterprise Complex, Walmgate, York, North Yorkshire, YO1 9TT
☎ (01904) 848448

Secondary Site: Handley Park, Outgang Lane, Osbaldwick, YO19 5UP ⊕ brewyork.co.uk

⊛Established in 2016, Brew York was born out of two friends' passion for beer and brewing. The original brewery is located within York's historic city walls, a 15-minute walk from the Station. A unique taproom and beer hall (including kitchen) with riverside beer garden sits alongside the original 10-barrel brewery which now specialises in barrel-aged and mixed fermentation beers. A new state-of-the-art, twin 30-barrel brewery has been built to the east of the city for larger scale production. ‼️🍺♦GFV♢

Minstermen Pride (ABV 3.7%) PALE
Maris the Otter (ABV 3.9%) BITTER
Calmer Chameleon (ABV 4.1%) PALE
Haze of Thunder (ABV 4.2%) PALE
Tonkoko (ABV 4.3%) SPECIALITY

Brew61 SIBA

Greenfields Farm, Upton Warren, Bromsgrove, B61 7EZ
☎ (01527) 879472 ⊕ brew61.co.uk

Tim Dunkley started brewing as a hobby, opening a small 'pub' for friends and family on the farm. As his brewing prowess grew the equipment he used grew, and he needed more space. A purpose-built brewery with newer, larger equipment, enabled him to supply a growing demand locally. Bottles and kegged ales are sold direct from the farm. 🍺

Greenfields Gold (ABV 3.8%) PALE
Grazing Girls (ABV 4.5%) GOLD
Hop On (ABV 4.5%) GOLD

BrewBoard SIBA

Unit B3, Button End Industrial Estate, Harston, Cambridgeshire, CB22 7GX
☎ (01223) 872131 ⊕ brewboard.co.uk

Founded in 2017 on a former brewery site just outside of Cambridge. The brewery has grown to include a 30-hectolitre brew kit and 12 conical fermenters. This growth allowed it to increase production of specials and introduce the Hammahed Hop series. A barrel-ageing programme is planned at an additional site in Newton. ‼️🍺GF♢

Ripchord (ABV 4.3%) PALE

Brewdog

Balmacassie Industrial Estate, Ellon, AB41 8BX
☎ (01358) 724924

Tower Hill: Unit 3, Minster Building, 21 Great Tower Street, Tower Hill, London, EC3N 5AR

Waterloo: Unit G, 01 The Sidings, Waterloo Station, Waterloo Road, London, SE1 7BH

Manchester: 144 Oxford Road, Manchester, M13 9GP
⊕ brewdog.com

Established in 2007 by James Watt and Martin Dickie. Most of the production goes into cans and keg. More than 50 bars now exist in the UK. The Tower Hill site opened 2018. The brewery occupies one end of a large, sunken bar. Regular onsite specials are available here. The Manchester outpost opened in 2019 followed by the Waterloo site in 2022, underneath the former Eurostar platforms at Waterloo Station. Claimed to be the largest bar in London, the brewery takes up but a small part. ‼️🍺

Brewers Folly

Ashton Farm House, Stanbridge, Wimborne, Dorset, BH21 4JD ☎ 07463 554434 ⊕ brewersfolly.co.uk

⊠ Founded in 2017, it is now brewing on a five-barrel plant in Stanbridge, with plans to move to Honeybrook Farm where it recently opened a good sized taproom (with meeting and function space). Direct deliveries throughout Dorset and much of Hampshire plus shipments further afield on request. ‼️🍺♦V♢

Session Pale Ale (ABV 4.2%) PALE
Summer Haze (ABV 4.6%) PALE
10w-40 (ABV 5%) STOUT
Chocolate Milk Porter (ABV 5%) PORTER
Azacca IPA (ABV 5.5%) IPA
Citra IPA (ABV 5.5%) IPA
Ekuanot IPA (ABV 5.5%) IPA
Kohatu IPA (ABV 5.5%) IPA
Mosaic IPA (ABV 5.5%) IPA
Sabro IPA (ABV 5.5%) IPA
Simco IPA (ABV 5.5%) IPA

Brewery 288

Burton Park Road, Heath End, Duncton, Petworth, West Sussex, GU28 0JU ☎ 07487 600288
⊕ brewery288.co.uk

Brewery 288 is a microbrewery specialising in traditional real ales. All beers are bottle-conditioned. LIVE

Brewhouse & Kitchen SIBA

🍴 Bournemouth: 154 Commercial Street, Bournemouth, Dorset, BH2 5LU
☎ (01202) 055221

Bristol: 31-35 Cotham Hill, Clifton, Bristol, BS6 6JY
☎ (0117) 973 3793

Cardiff: Sophia Close, Pontcanna, Cardiff, CF11 9HW

Chelmsford: Anne Knight Building, Chelmsford, Essex, CM1 1LW

Cheltenham: The Brewery Quarter, Henrietta Street, Cheltenham, Gloucestershire, GL50 4FA ☎ (01242) 509946

Chester: Forest House, Love Street, Chester, CH1 1QY ☎ (01244) 404990

Dorchester: 17 Weymouth Avenue, Dorchester, Dorset, DT1 1QY ☎ (01305) 265551

Gloucester Quay: Unit R1, St Anne Walk, Gloucester Quay, Gloucester, GL1 5SH ☎ (01452) 222965

Highbury: 2a Corsica Street, Highbury, London, N5 1JJ ☎ (020) 7226 1026

Horsham: 38 East Street, Horsham, RH12 1HL ☎ (01403) 788140

Hoxton: 397-400 Geffrye Street, Hoxton, London, E2 8HZ ☎ (020) 3861 8920

Lichfield: 1 Bird Street, Lichfield, Staffordshire, WS13 6PW ☎ (01543) 224740

Nottingham: Trent Bridge, Nottingham, Nottinghamshire, NG2 2GS ☎ (0115) 986 7960

Poole: 3 Dear Hay Lane, Poole, Dorset, BH15 1NZ ☎ (01202) 771246

Portsmouth: 26 Guildhall Walk, Portsmouth, Hampshire, PO1 2DD ☎ (023) 9289 1340

Southampton: 47 Highfield Lane, Southampton, Hampshire, SO17 1QD ☎ (023) 8055 5566

Southbourne: 147 Parkwood Road, Southbourne, Bournemouth, BH5 2BW ☎ (01202) 055209

Southsea: 51 Southsea Terrace, Southsea, Hampshire, PO5 3AU ☎ (023) 9281 8979

Sutton Coldfield: 8 Birmingham Road, Sutton Coldfield, West Midlands, B72 1QD ☎ (0121) 796 6838

Worthing: Wykeham Road, Worthing, West Sussex, BN11 4JD ⊕ brewhouseandkitchen.com

Brewing began in Portsmouth in 2013 – the first in a growing chain of Brewhouse and Kitchen brewpubs. There are now 21 in the chain (Milton Keynes and Islington have recently closed), each offering its own range of beers. Each brewery is on display to customers in the bar area. Carry outs and brewing experience days are available (check with each branch). ♦

Brewhouse

Tap & Vent Brewhouse, 26 Poulton Street, Kirkham, Lancashire, PR4 2AB ☎ 07738 275438 ⊕ lythambrewery.co.uk

☺Well-established, family-run brewery that began 2007 as Lytham Brewery. In 2021 it moved to Kirkham. Rebranding took place in 2022. The brewery relocated in 2024 to the rear of the Tap & Vent, Kirkham. ♦

Blonde (ABV 3.8%) BLOND
Triple C (ABV 4.1%) GOLD
Gold (ABV 4.2%) GOLD
Old Timer (ABV 4.6%) BLOND
Empire IPA (ABV 5.6%) IPA

Brewing Brothers

🏳 Imperial, 119 Queens Road, Hastings, East Sussex, TN34 1RL ☎ 07985 505810

Second site: 6-8 Burgess Road, Hastings, TN35 4NR ⊕ brewingbrothers.org

⊠ Brewing began in 2016 in the Imperial, Hastings. The brewery has a 2.5-barrel capacity with four fermenting vessels. A wide range of brother-themed beers have been brewed to date, including a collaboration with Half Man Half Burger. Up to eight beers on cask and keg can feature at any one time. A taproom and a 10-barrel brewery in Burgess Road opened in 2022. ♦V♪

Brewis

Unit 4, Coquet Enterprise Park, Amble, Northumberland, NE65 0PE ☎ (01665) 714818 ⊕ brewisbeer.co.uk

Brewis Beer Co is a family-run nanobrewery featuring a bottle shop and taproom. 🛒♪

Building Bridges (ABV 4.5%) PALE
Helm (ABV 4.7%) PORTER
Just Like Heaven (ABV 5.7%) IPA
Turning Tides (ABV 5.8%) IPA
Ebb & Flow (ABV 6.5%) IPA

Brewlab

1 West Quay Court, Sunderland Enterprise Park, Sunderland, SR5 2TE ☎ (0191) 549 9450 ⊕ brewlab.co.uk

☺Brewlab was founded in London in 1986, moved to Sunderland in 1991, and in 2011 moved to its present purpose-built facility. It provides training courses for UK and worldwide brewers, and also offers technical and analytical services at the Sunderland site. It brews throughout the year to build on the interesting things that students create and use its own skills to create high quality, innovative beers. These are sold at the regular taproom evenings onsite, and are also available in selected locals. ♦♪

Brewpoint SIBA

Cut Throat Lane, Bedford, MK41 7FY ☎ (01234) 244444 ⊕ brewpoint.co.uk

☺Brewpoint was launched in 2020 by Wells & Co, which has brewed in Bedford since 1876. The Brewpoint complex also houses the company head office and features conference and meeting rooms, a brewery shop and a taproom/restaurant, plus beer garden. Beers are also brewed for the John Bull brands in France, but few are cask-conditioned. ♬🛒♦♪

Anchorman (ABV 4.1%) PALE
Easy-drinking pale ale with a sweetish malty presence throughout and an unfolding gentle hop bitterness.

Brewshed

Place Farm, Ingham, Suffolk, IP31 1NQ ☎ (01284) 848066 ⊕ brewshedbrewery.co.uk

⊠ Brewshed began brewing in 2011 using a five-barrel plant in buildings located behind the Beerhouse (one of its outlets). It is now located in the nearby village of Ingham, using a 12-barrel plant, resulting in greater capacity and a more modern beer range with up to two seasonal beers usually available, plus a number of unusual KeyKeg beers. It supplies its own five pubs, one restaurant plus a limited free trade. ♦

Pale (ABV 3.9%) PALE
Kveik IPA (ABV 4.2%) PALE
Best Bitter (ABV 4.3%) BITTER
American Blonde (ABV 5.5%) BLOND

Brewsmith SIBA

Unit 11, Cuba Industrial Estate, Stubbins, Ramsbottom, Bury, BL0 0NE
☎ (01706) 829390 ⊕ brewsmithbeer.com

⊛Brewsmith is a 10-barrel microbrewery established in 2014 by the Smith family – James, Jennifer and Ted. It produces a range of cask and bottle-conditioned ales in traditional British beer styles. ‼♦LIVE

Mosaic (ABV 3.5%) PALE
Bitter (ABV 3.9%) PALE
Gold (ABV 4.2%) PALE
New Zealand Pale (ABV 4.2%) PALE
A deep golden beer with hoppy floral and citrus aromas. Pithy bitterness, with citrus and fruity notes in support.
Pale (ABV 4.2%) PALE
APA (ABV 5%) PALE
Oatmeal Stout (ABV 5.2%) STOUT

brewSocial SIBA

Princess Street, Sheffield, South Yorkshire, S4 7UU

Launched in 2022 brewSocial is a social enterprise dedicated to supporting and training people who are disadvantaged in the labour market. Located in a railway arch in Attercliffe and utilising the brewkit that was formerly in use at Little Ale Cart and then Neepsend. Brewery tap, theSocial, on Snig Hill is a regular outlet.

Brewster's SIBA

Unit 5, Burnside, Turnpike Close, Grantham, Lincolnshire, NG31 7XU
☎ (01476) 566000 ⊕ brewstersbrewery.com

⊠ Brewster is the old English term for a female brewer, and Sara Barton (who was named Brewer of the Year by the All Party Parliamentary Beer Group in 2018) is a modern example. Originally established in the Vale of Belvoir in 1998, it moved to Grantham in 2006. Brewster's produces a range of traditional and innovative beers with two regularly-changing ranges. ‼🛒♦V

Hophead (ABV 3.6%) BLOND
Marquis (ABV 3.8%) BITTER
A well-balanced and refreshing session bitter with maltiness and a dry, hoppy finish.
Aromantica (ABV 4.2%) BITTER
Hop A Doodle Doo (ABV 4.3%) BITTER
Decadence (ABV 4.4%) GOLD
Aromatic Porter (ABV 4.5%) PORTER
Dragon Street Porter (ABV 4.9%) PORTER
American Pale Ale (ABV 5%) PALE
Rundle Beck Bitter (ABV 5.5%) BITTER
Virago IPA (ABV 5.8%) IPA
IPA (ABV 6%) IPA

Briarbank SIBA

🍴 70 Fore Street, Ipswich, Suffolk, IP4 1LB
☎ (01473) 284000 ⊕ briarbank.org

The Briarbank Brewing Company was established in 2013, and is situated on the site of the old Lloyds Bank on Fore Street, Ipswich. The brewery is a two-barrel plant, and the bar above offers a core range of beers – including some speciality ales. ‼♦V

Brid's Cross (NEW) SIBA

c/o Serious Brewing Co Ltd, Unit C5, Fieldhouse Industrial Estate, Rochdale, OL12 0AA

Office: 1 The Warehouse, Anchor Quay, Penryn, Cornwall, TR10 8GZ

Established in 2024, Brid's Cross Brewing Ltd uses spare capacity at Serious Brewery, Rochdale.

Bridbrewer

🍴 2A Chapel Street / 5 King Street, Bridlington, East Yorkshire, YO15 2DN
☎ (01262) 674300 ☎ 07727 107435
⊕ bridbrewerandtaproom.co.uk

⊛After two years developing his recipes as a homebrewer Stuart Fisher launched his unfined beers commercially in 2020 from his brewpub located in central Bridlington. A 50-litre Braumeister kit is used and most beers are vegan-friendly and include golden IPAs, bitters and various stouts and porters, all available to drink in or takeaway from the bar. ‼🛒♦LIVE V

Bridge

Unit 15G, Newton Moor Industrial Estate, Lodge Street, Hyde, SK14 4LD ☎ 07948 617145
⊕ bridgebeers.co.uk/brewery

Bridge Beers commenced production in 2021 using a 2.5-barrel plant. Cask-conditioned and bottled ales are supplied to the brewery tap, located in the nearby town centre, as well as to other local outlets. 🛒

Citra (ABV 4%) PALE
El Dorado (ABV 4%) PALE
Galaxy (ABV 4%) PALE
4Bs (ABV 4.2%) BITTER
Mumbai (ABV 4.2%) GOLD
Dark Ruby Mild (ABV 4.5%) MILD
Dark Matter (ABV 4.7%) MILD

Bridgehouse SIBA

Airedale Heifer, Bradford Road, Sandbeds, Keighley, West Yorkshire, BD20 5LY
☎ (01535) 601222

Office: Unit 1, Aireworth Mills, Aireworth Road, Keighley, West Yorkshire, BD21 4DH
⊕ bridgehousebrewery.co.uk

⊛Bridgehouse began brewing in 2010. The brewery purchased the recipes and branding of Old Bear Brewery in 2014 and moved into its premises in Keighley. In 2015 the brewery relocated to its present address behind the Airedale Heifer pub in Sandbeds. Bridgehouse operate a bespoke 15-barrel brewery. Twelve pubs are operated. ‼♦

Tequila Blonde (ABV 3.8%) SPECIALITY
Initially sweet with hints of lime, finishing with a slight tingling aftertaste.
Blonde (ABV 4%) GOLD
Strong fruity aroma with a sharp burst of grapefruit on the tongue, touch of sweetness in the background. Bitter finish.
Aired Ale (ABV 4.1%) BITTER
Brown beer with malty aroma. Malt, hops and fruit in equal balance with lingering fruitiness in a long bitter finish.
Porter (ABV 4.5%) PORTER
Black beer with red hints. Aromas of malt and liquorice lead to coffee, chocolate and wine fruit flavours. Bitter finish.
Holy Cow (ABV 5.6%) BITTER
Strong ale with juicy malt and full hop flavour, citrus overtones. Light hop aroma and a bitter finish.

Bridgetown SIBA

32 Bridgetown, Totnes, Devon, TQ9 5AD

☎ (01803) 863214 (Pub) ☎ 07517 926040
⊕ albertinntotnes.com/bridgetown-brewery

⊗ Bridgetown started brewing in 2008 in the outbuildings of the Albert Inn, Totnes, though it is independent of the pub itself. A two-barrel plant is used. Steady growth now means a range of seven regular beers is brewed along with a growing range of seasonals. The beers are available in an increasing number of outlets. ‼🍺♦LIVE

Albert Ale (ABV 3.8%) BITTER
A pale brown bitter style ale. Malty biscuit dominates from start to finish with caramel and roast on the nose and in the aftertaste. There is a slight bitterness on the tongue.
Accolade (ABV 4.2%) BITTER
Bitter (ABV 4.2%) BITTER
Cheeky Blonde (ABV 4.5%) GOLD
Hoppy citrus nose, definite hoppy citrus taste with a bitter citrus finish.
Shark Island Stout (ABV 4.5%) STOUT
A smooth, black stout dominated by malt and roast throughout with a slight smokiness. There are subtle hints of liquorice and chocolate with some fruit and bitterness to be detected on the tongue and in the aftertaste.
Westcountry IPA (ABV 4.7%) PALE

Brewed for Providence, Plymouth:
Provvi Beys (ABV 4.5%) PALE
IPA-style beer. Earthy basic taste with citrus notes throughout and at finish.

Bridgnorth

See Severn Valley

Bridlington

🍴 10 Prospect Street, Bridlington, YO15 2AL
☎ (01262) 674418

Founded in 2014 in the grounds of the Telegraph Inn, Bridlington, it later moved to the rear of the Pack Horse, supplying the pub. It relocated again in 2019 to the rear of the Moon Tap pub. The beers and beer styles regularly change. Beers are available in the Moon Tap and Pack Horse.

Briggs Signature

c/o Unit 1, Waterhouse Mill, 65-71 Lockwood Road, Huddersfield, West Yorkshire, HD1 3QU ☎ 07427 668004 ⊕ briggssignatureales.weebly.com

⊗ Briggs Signature Ales started brewing in 2014 using spare capacity at Mallinsons (qv). Nick Briggs, also a member of the Mallinsons brewing team, produces a number of modern, hop-forward beers. 🍺LIVE

Northern Soul (ABV 3.8%) BITTER
Rock & Roll (ABV 4%) BITTER
Hip Hop (ABV 4.2%) GOLD
Techno (ABV 4.2%) BITTER
Blues (ABV 4.6%) GOLD
Metal (ABV 5%) PORTER

Brighton Bier

Unit 10, Bell Tower Industrial Estate, Roedean Road, Brighton, East Sussex, BN2 5RU ☎ 07967 681203
⊕ brightonbier.com

Brighton Bier was established in 2012. It operates a 15-barrel brewery close to the centre of the city and also owns the Brighton Bierhaus pub, in Brighton. Beers are available throughout the UK and exported to Europe and Asia.

Thirty Three (ABV 3.3%) GOLD
Brighton Bier (ABV 4%) GOLD
West Pier (ABV 4%) GOLD
Underdog (ABV 4.2%) BITTER
IPA (ABV 5%) PALE
No Name Stout (ABV 5%) STOUT
Grand Porter (ABV 5.2%) PORTER

Brightside SIBA

Unit 10, Dale Industrial Estate, Radcliffe, M26 1AD
☎ (0161) 725 9644 ⊕ brightsidebrewing.co.uk

⊗ Brightside is a 20-barrel, family-run brewery producing cask ales, craft keg beers and lagers. A broad range of styles is produced, and new seasonal casks are produced every 6-8 weeks to keep the line up interesting. It has a brewery shop onsite for collections, and a web shop for local and national deliveries. Brightside prides itself on working as sustainably as possible, by limiting energy expenditure, recycling and reusing waste. All Brightside beers are gluten-free, and suitable for vegans. 🍺♦GF V

Odin Blonde (ABV 3.8%) PALE
Fruity hop aromas. Moderate bitterness follows and persists into the finish. Some malt sweetness is evident.
B-Side Gold (ABV 4.2%) GOLD
Academy Ale IPA (ABV 4.5%) PALE
The Mancunian (ABV 4.5%) PALE
Full-bodied, sweet fruity beer with moderate bitter hops.
Maverick IPA (ABV 4.8%) PALE

Brewed for Brunning & Price Pub Co:
Original (ABV 3.8%) BITTER

Brightwater

9 Beaconsfield Road, Claygate, Surrey, KT10 0PN
☎ (01372) 462334 ☎ 07802 316389
⊕ brightbrew.co.uk

⊗ Established in 2013 at Claygate in Surrey, Brightwater is a five-barrel brewery producing traditional beers. The range is available at its brewery tap, Platform 3, outside Claygate Station, and other Surrey and South London pubs. LIVE GF

Little Nipper (ABV 3.3%) BITTER
A rather thin hoppy bitter with a hint of a citrus taste and a bitter, slightly dry finish.
Top Notch (ABV 3.6%) BITTER
Citrus notes dominant the aroma of this mid brown bitter. It has a reasonably well-balanced taste with some bitterness in the finish.
Ernest (ABV 3.7%) PALE
TPL (ABV 3.7%) BITTER
Village Green (ABV 3.8%) GOLD
Daisy Gold (ABV 4%) GOLD
Golden coloured ale with a moderate tropical fruit hoppy character and some balancing malt leading to a bittersweet finish.
Wild Orchid (ABV 4%) SPECIALITY
All Citra (ABV 4.3%) GOLD
Lip Smacker (ABV 4.8%) BITTER
Coal Porter (ABV 4.9%) PORTER

Brimstage SIBA

Home Farm, Brimstage, Merseyside, CH63 6HY
☎ (0151) 342 1181 ⊕ brimstagebrewery.com

Neil Young began brewing in 2006 using a 10-barrel plant in the heart of the Wirral countryside. Wirral's first brewery since the closure of the Birkenhead Brewery in the late 1960s. Since Neil passed away in 2018, his two sons now own the brewery. Outlets are supplied across the Wirral, Merseyside, Cheshire and North Wales. ‼♦

Sandpiper Light Ale (ABV 3.6%) GOLD
Trapper's Hat Bitter (ABV 3.8%) BITTER
A nicely balanced beer, strong malt aromas, sweet hoppy malt flavours and a smooth bitter finish.
Rhode Island Red (ABV 4%) RED
Red, smooth and well-balanced malty beer with a good dry aftertaste. Some fruitiness in the taste.
Elder Pale (ABV 4.1%) SPECIALITY
Scarecrow Bitter (ABV 4.2%) BITTER
This bitter has some bitterness and sweetness along with a little fruit. The hop flavours develop in the finish.
Oyster Catcher Stout (ABV 4.4%) STOUT
Shed Day Session IPA (ABV 4.4%) PALE
IPA (ABV 6%) PALE

Brinkburn Street SIBA

3 Hume Street, Byker, Newcastle Upon Tyne, NE6 1LN
☎ **(0191) 338 9039** ⊕ **brinkburnbrewery.co.uk**

Brewing began in 2015, much influenced by West Coast US beer styles. Citrus flavours and highly-hopped bitterness is a feature of many of its beers. The brewery relocated to a new site in 2018, which also incorporates a taproom. ♦

Fools Gold (ABV 3.8%) GOLD
The Pursuit of Hoppiness (ABV 3.9%) PALE
Byker Brown Ale (ABV 4.8%) BROWN

Briscoe's

Ash Grove, Otley, West Yorkshire, LS21 3EL
☎ **(01943) 466515** ✉ **briscoe.brewery@talktalk.net**

⊛The brewery was launched in 1998 by microbiologist and chemist Dr Paul Briscoe, in the cellar of his house, with a one-barrel brew length. The beers are available in local Otley pubs. Brewing is currently suspended.

Bristol Beer Factory

The Old Brewery, Durnford Street, Ashton, Bristol, BS3 2AW
☎ **(0117) 902 6317**

Office: 291 North Street, Ashton, Bristol, BS3 1JP
⊕ **bristolbeerfactory.co.uk**

⊗ A fiercely independent brewery at the heart of the Bristol beer scene since 2004. Currently based on North Street, the cultural hub of south Bristol, in a 200-year-old red brick building with 180 years of brewing heritage (including Ashton Gate Brewing Co, which closed in 1933). More than 40 beers are produced annually. Plans have been announced to move the taproom a few doors down the road to the Old Brewery and to relocate the brewery to Ashton Vale Trading Estate. ‼🏭♦🖤

Notorious (ABV 3.8%) BITTER
Fruity hop aroma, light malt on the palate overlaid with citrus and tropical fruits before a lingering dry bitter aftertaste.
Fortitude (ABV 4%) BITTER
Amber ale with a light malty base overlaid with traditional English hop flavours before a clean and slightly dry finish.
Milk Stout (ABV 4.5%) STOUT
Roasted malt aroma, creamy flavours of chocolate dusted cappuccino with dark stone and dried vine fruit, increasingly bitter aftertaste.
Independence (ABV 4.6%) PALE

Pine and fruity hop aroma, light malt background with tropical and citrus fruits on the palate. Clean refreshing bittersweet finish.

Brixton

Arches 547 & 548, Brixton Station Road, Brixton, London, SW9 8PF
☎ **(020) 3609 8880**

Second Site: Units 1 & 2, Dylan Road Estate, Dylan Road, Loughborough Junction, London, SE24 0HL
⊕ **brixtonbrewery.com**

The brewery opened in 2013 in central Brixton with beer names and branding reflecting the local area. An investment by Heineken in 2017 enabled expansion into a nearby industrial unit. As of 2021 Brixton is now owned outright by Heineken. The original arch is used for seasonal and experimental brews and the adjacent arch houses the taproom. The bulk of production is in KeyKeg, cans and bottles. ♦LIVE GF V⬦

Reliance Pale Ale (ABV 4.2%) PALE
Pale hazy gold beer with lemon zest and a growing bitterness. A little biscuit and apricot on the palate. Spicy hops finish.

Broadtown SIBA

The Old Coach House, 29 Broad Town Road, Calne, Wiltshire, SN4 7RB ☎ **07889 078648**

Second site: Porte Marsh Industrial Estate, 3 Maundrel Road, Calne, Wiltshire, SN11 9PU
⊕ **broadtownbrewery.co.uk**

Opened in 2019, Broadtown began brewing in the old coach house of the 19th century Hart brewery. 118 years on, the village has a brewery again. Broadtown has a range of core beers and produces an ever-changing list of seasonal and one-off ales. In 2021 the Hop Chapel, a Trappist-themed taproom and beer garden, opened onsite. The brewery is home to three alpacas and a lime green double-decker bus. A second larger site in Calne came on stream in 2022. 🏭♦LIVE GF V🖤

Spring Back (ABV 3.8%) GOLD
Fettler's Finest (ABV 4.7%) BITTER
Black Llama (ABV 4.8%) PORTER
Gricer's Choice (ABV 4.8%) PALE
Wide to Gauge (ABV 5.2%) PALE
Line of Sight (ABV 5.6%) IPA

Brockenhurst

Balmer Lawn Hotel, Lyndhurst Road, Brockenhurst, SO42 7ZB ✉ **feedback@smokindeer.co.uk**

A microbrewery located in the grounds of the Balmer Lawn Hotel & Spa.

Smokin Deer (ABV 3.8%) BITTER

Brockley SIBA

31 Harcourt Road, Brockley, London, SE4 2AJ
☎ **(020) 8691 4380**

Second Site: Unit 28, Chiltonian Industrial Estate, Manor Lane, Hither Green, London, SE12 0TX
⊕ **brockleybrewery.co.uk**

The original SE4 brewery has been trading since 2013 and now focuses on core cask ales and single-batch specials. In 2019, a new 20-barrel brewery was opened on the former site of the Chiltonian Biscuit factory in Hither Green. The brewery concentrates on brewing cask beers and supplying outlets across SE London. The whole range is vegan and available in the taprooms at both sites. ♦V✦

Pale Ale (ABV 4.1%) BITTER
Fragrant sweet nose leading to a hoppy citrus flavour. The aftertaste is sweet leading to a slightly bitter finish.
Red Ale (ABV 4.8%) RED
Malty with bitterness from the roast barley balanced by notes of red berries. Dry, roasty long aftertaste, which remains fruity.

Broken Drum

Heron Hill, Upper Belvedere, DA17 5ER ☎ 07803 131678 ⊕ thebrokendrum.co.uk

Homebrewer that started trial brewing for the Broken Drum micropub in Blackfen, before going commercial in 2018. Brewed in small batches for the micropub and local beer festivals. All output is in cask.

Brolly SIBA

Unit 8, Redkiln Close, Horsham, West Sussex, RH13 5QL ☎ 07720 847017 ⊕ brollybrewing.co.uk

⊛Brolly was established in 2017 and is located in Horsham. It is essentially a brewery with a bar specialising in modern and traditional cask, alongside globally-inspired keg beer. ‼♦V✦

Little Pearl (ABV 3.5%) STOUT
Aroha (ABV 3.8%) PALE
Lifeline (ABV 3.8%) MILD
Madre (ABV 4%) PALE
Choco-lots (ABV 4.1%) STOUT
Chub IPA (ABV 4.3%) PALE
Spanky McDanky (ABV 4.5%) PALE
C.O.W (ABV 4.8%) PALE
How Now (ABV 5%) BROWN
Natural Spring Water (ABV 5%) PALE
Jolly Brolly Brown Ale (ABV 5.2%) BROWN
Old Ale (ABV 5.4%) OLD
Together (ABV 10%) STOUT

Brooks

17 Birkenhead Road, Hoylake, Merseyside, CH47 5AE ⊕ brooks-brewhouse.co.uk

Brewing starting in 2017 at this nanobrewery, which predominately produces bottle-conditioned beers. LIVE

Broughton

Main Street, Broughton, ML12 6HQ ☎ (01899) 830345 ⊕ broughtonales.co.uk

⊛Founded in 1979, Broughton Ales was one of the first microbreweries. Broughton has developed since then, and though more than 60% of production goes into bottle for sale in Britain and abroad, it retains a sizeable range of cask ales. It merged with Consolidated Craft Breweries Group in 2022. All beers are suitable for vegetarians and Hopo Lager is certified gluten-free. ‼🍺♦

60 Shilling (ABV 3.8%) BITTER
Hopo Session IPA (ABV 3.8%) PALE
Dry-hopped pale ale with slightly tart, fruit taste and distinctive tang.
Merlin's Ale (ABV 4.2%) GOLD
A well-hopped, fruity flavour is balanced by malt in the taste. The finish is bittersweet, light but dry.
Hopo 2 Rivers IPA (ABV 4.6%) PALE
Beautifully hopped, robust bitter with a dry finish.
Wee Jock (ABV 4.6%) BROWN
Pleasant 80/- style. Light fruit and a malty sweetness.

Stout Jock (ABV 4.8%) STOUT
Glasgow Cross IPA (ABV 5%) PALE
A fruity, refreshing IPA with a good body and a pleasant hoppy flavour. A long lasting bitterness in the finish.
Hopo Proper IPA (ABV 5%) PALE
Old Jock (ABV 6.7%) STRONG
A bold Scotch ale, full bodied, sweetish and fruity in the finish.

BRUBL SIBA

Unit 3, Railway Arch, Victoria Business Centre, Neilston Street, Leamington Spa, Warwickshire, CV31 2AZ ⊕ brubl.beer

During the 2020 pandemic Nathan Barnes began brewing his own beer on a 150-litre kit in his garden shed. Proving adept at brewing, Nathan's new obsession led to him leaving his 30-year career in IT and setting up as a brewer. Securing premises in a railway arch in Leamington Spa in 2022, he now has a 1,000-litre brew kit. The taproom is open daily (except Mon). ✦

Bruha

Unit 4, Progress Way, Eye, Suffolk, IP23 7HU ☎ (01379) 882230 ⊕ bruhabrewing.co.uk

Established in 2014 as Station 119, Bruha was acquired in 2023 by the family who founded Aspall Cyder. New fermentation vessels and bright beer tanks are to be added to the 12-barrel brewhouse. All the beers have a contemporary yet subtle twist on traditional styles. LIVE ✦

Cupshot Bitter (ABV 3.4%)
Niksun Pale (ABV 4%) PALE
Lagom Gold (ABV 4.5%) GOLD

Bruhaha (NEW)

🍴 156 Wells Road, Bristol, BS4 2AG

⊛Moved to its current location in Totterdown in 2023, having originally started at the nearby Windmill Hill City Farm in 2021, Bruhaha are creating an ultra sustainable brewing model. Using low energy techniques such as Kveik yeasts, pressure fermentation and natural carbonation plus the farm animals receive the left-over grain from the brewing process. Always experimenting with styles and recipes to create beer from around the world without the food miles. ♦✦

Brunning & Price

See Brightside and St Austell

Brunswick SIBA

🍴 1 Railway Terrace, Derby, DE1 2RU ☎ (01332) 410055 ☎ 07534 401352 ⊕ brunswickbrewingcompany.co.uk

☒ Derby's oldest brewery. It is a 10-barrel tower plant built as an extension to the Brunswick Inn in 1991. Bought by Everards in 2002, the brewery is now run separately, yet in conjunction with the pub. It supplies the Brunswick Inn, Dead Poets Inn, Everards, wholesalers, and the free trade within 100 miles. Brunswick also swaps with other breweries. Beers are also produced under the Engine Shed Project brand name. ‼♦LIVE

White Feather (ABV 3.6%) PALE
Triple Hop (ABV 4%) BLOND
The Usual (ABV 4.2%) BITTER
Railway Porter (ABV 4.3%) PORTER
Rocket (ABV 4.7%) PALE

Black Sabbath (ABV 6%) OLD

Brewed under the Engine Shed Project brand name

Ubiquitous (ABV 6%) IPA

Brythonic

See Forest, The

BRZN

Highfield Farm, Lewes, BN8 5AR
✉ buybrzn@gmail.com

BRZN started in 2019, initally cuckoo brewing around Sussex, before moving into a central Brighton shipping container in 2020. In 2023 it moved to a large space outside Lewes, with plans to expand. A brewery tap, The BRZN Arms, opened in 2021. It has a single, rotating cask line with five rotating keg lines, gluten-free beer, cider, wines and spirits. Expect food popups every Friday-Saturday throughout warmer months.

Bucks Star

23 Twizel Close, Stonebridge, Milton Keynes, Buckinghamshire, MK13 0DX
☎ (01908) 590054 ⊕ bucksstar.beer

A solar-powered brewery which opened in 2015 using a 10-barrel, purpose-built plant. Only organic malt is used and no sugars or syrups are added. The beers are unfiltered, vegan, and primarily available through Bucks Star's own zero-waste innovation (Growler Swap). This range of beers are conditioned inside reusable glass growlers, and are available at farmers' markets locally, and at various London locations. The brewery tap opened in the opposite unit in 2020. ♦ ▬ LIVE V

Budweiser

Bureau, London, EC4A 1EN
☎ (0800) 655 6075

Budweiser (Magor): Magor Brewery, Magor, Monmouthshire, NP26 3DA

Budweiser (Samlesbury): Cuerdale Lane, Samlesbury, Preston, PR5 0XD ⊕ budweiserbrewinggroup.co.uk

No real ale.

Bull of the Woods

Brook Farm, Kirby Cane, Bungay, Norfolk, NR35 2PJ
☎ (01508) 518080 ☎ 07833 702658
⊕ bullofthewoods.co.uk

⊠ The brewery began production 2017. The brewery and shop are situated in the old milling barn on the family-owned farm. The head brewer gave up his tree surgery business to pursue his love of brewing. The brewery goes from strength to strength and continues to expand its range of eclectic styles and seasonal favourites. Various merchandise, along with a range of its bottled beers are available in the shop. ▬ ♦ LIVE V

Rock Steady (ABV 3.8%) BITTER
Traditional malt and hop signature with the added complexity of walnut and quinine flowing through. Long, increasingly bitter finish.
Satan Session (ABV 3.8%) PALE
Hacienda (ABV 4%) PALE
Woodstock (ABV 4.2%) IPA
Vapour Trail (ABV 4.3%) PALE
Well-balanced with grapefruit and mandarin complementing a hoppy bittersweet base. Floral notes quickly fade in a long drying finish.

Inca Gold (ABV 4.4%) GOLD
Pulsating lemon presence in aroma and taste looms over a balanced malt and hop foundation. A crisp dry finish develops.
Twisted Wheel (ABV 4.5%) BITTER
Strong marmalade notes with sweet malty support slowly fade behind a crisp, well-defined bitterness. Short peppery ending.
Loaded (ABV 4.9%) PALE
Banjo Hill (ABV 5%) IPA
Shine A Light IPA (ABV 6.4%) IPA
Hop, apricot and toffee underpin a full-bodied complex character. Bittersweet notes highlight a growing peppery dryness.

Bulletproof

91 Mutley Plain, Plymouth, Devon, PL4 6JJ ☎ 07703 733570

Office: Highlands, 1 Queen's Road, Lipson, Plymouth, PL4 7PJ ⊕ bulletproofbrewing.co

⊠ Small-scale brewery established in an outbuilding in 2016. It uses a 50-litre pilot plant to refine recipes before upscaling, using spare capacity at larger breweries. All beers are unfiltered and unfined. V♦

Bullfinch

Arches 886 & 887, Rosendale Road, Herne Hill, London, SE24 9EH ☎ 07795 546630
⊕ thebullfinchbrewery.co.uk

Bullfinch began brewing in 2014 sharing with Anspach & Hobday in Bermondsey, but opened in Herne Hill in 2016, using a 2.5-barrel plant. The beers are available in the taproom, at its Bull & Finch bar in Gipsy Hill (which now has its own kit – the So What brewery) and increasingly in local pubs. ♦ LIVE V♦

Bullhouse SIBA

22 Balmoral Road, Belfast, BT12 6QA ☎ 07749 877841 ⊕ bullhousebrewco.com

Bullhouse was set up in 2016 by beer enthusiast and homebrewer William Mayne at his family farm. The brewery has since relocated to Belfast and a brewery tap opened at 442-446 Newtownards Road, Belfast.

Road Trip (ABV 4%) GOLD
Small Axe (ABV 4.3%)
Frank the Tank (ABV 5%) SPECIALITY
The Dankness (ABV 5.5%)
Merc Bro (ABV 6.5%) SPECIALITY

Bun Dubh SIBA

▤ Ceabhar, Sandaig, Isle of Tiree, PA77 6XG
☎ (01879) 220684 ☎ 07792 789733
✉ bundubh@gmail.com

Duncan Castling began brewing on his picobrewery in 2016, then catering solely for his restaurant, Ceabhar. The brewery expanded into the adjoining former guesthouse during 2020 and 2021. With Tiree known as 'the Sunshine Isle', the installation of a solar thermal hot water tank allows for more energy conscious brewing. In 2024 the brewery began catering for outside events across the island. With an enviropunk ethos, all production goes into reusable containers, no bottles or cans, and availability, though wider, remains exclusive to the island. ♦

Bundobust SIBA

🍴 61-69 Oxford Street, Manchester, M1 6EJ
🌐 bundobust.com

Bundobust Brewery was established in 2020 but brews were not commercially available until 2021. Beer is exclusively for the Bundobust restaurant chain. No real ale but does real ale collaborations, primarily with Thornbridge.

Buntingford

Greys Brewhouse, Therfield Road, Royston, Hertfordshire, SG8 9NW
☎ (01763) 250749 ☎ 07851 743799
🌐 buntingfordbrewery.com

⊗ Brewing commenced on the current site in 2005, and has expanded to a capacity of approx 15 barrels per brew. Regular beers are brewed alongside seasonal, occasional brews and themed specials. An onsite well supplies water, and malt is sourced from East Anglia. All liquid waste is treated in a reed bed. The brewery is located on a conservation farm and a wide variety of birdlife is visible from the brewhouse. It is open to the public one day a month. ♦V

Twitchell (ABV 3.8%) BITTER
Hurricane (ABV 4%) BITTER
Single Hop Varieties (ABV 4%) GOLD
Polar Star (ABV 4.4%) GOLD
Riwaka Station (ABV 4.8%) PALE

Burning Sky SIBA

Place Barn, The Street, Firle, East Sussex, BN8 6LP
☎ (01273) 858080 🌐 burningskybeer.com

⊗ Burning Sky started brewing in 2013 using a 15-barrel plant, based on the Firle Estate in the South Downs. It is owned and run by Mark Tranter (ex-Dark Star head brewer). The brewery has its own yeast strains suited to the beer styles. It specialises in pale ales and Belgian-inspired farmhouse beers and has an extensive barrel-ageing programme. ♦LIVE

Plateau (ABV 3.5%) GOLD
Aurora (ABV 5.6%) PALE

Burning Soul

Unit 1, 51 Mott Street, Hockley, Birmingham, B19 3HE
☎ (0121) 439 1490 ☎ 07793 026624
🌐 burningsoulbrewing.com

Established in 2016, the name Burning Soul reflects a passion for beer and brewing. It is a five-barrel, full-mash brewery with an onsite tap. The brewery's varied range of live beer in KeyKeg, can or cask, is sold onsite or in a growing number of free trade outlets in the Midlands. This range includes sours, saisons, and very hoppy pales, alongside dark beers of all styles. 🍴 ☕♦V

Burnside Brew Shed (NEW)

Burnside, Minorca Hill, Laxey, Isle of Man, IM4 7ED

Small scale brewery that began brewing in early 2024.

Burnside SIBA

Unit 3, Laurencekirk Business Park, Laurencekirk, AB30 1EY
☎ (01561) 377316 🌐 burnsidebrewery.co.uk

⊗ Burnside began brewing in 2010 using a 2.5-barrel plant, and by 2012 had expanded to a 10-barrel plant. It changed ownership in 2018, and since then the focus has

been on developing a range of cask and bottle-conditioned beers, including new seasonal bottled beers, plus collaborations with local businesses. Beers are unfined and vegan-friendly. Barrel-aged beers are produced using Fettercairn Distillery casks. Alcohol free IPA and lager is available in bottles. Free delivery between Montrose, Banchory, Aberdeen, Dundee and everywhere in-between. It offers brewer experiences on scheduled Saturdays. 🍴☕LIVE V

New Tricks (ABV 3.8%) IPA
Lift & Shift (ABV 4%) PALE
Flint's Gold (ABV 4.1%) BITTER
Chain & Anchor (ABV 4.2%) PALE
Lost Shadow (ABV 4.4%) STOUT
Wild Rhino (ABV 4.5%) GOLD
Stone River (ABV 5%) IPA
Sunset Song (ABV 5.3%) BITTER

Burnt Mill

Badley, Ipswich, Suffolk, IP6 8RS ☎ 07791 961974
🌐 burntmillbrewery.com

This farm brewery was created by Charles O'Reilly in 2016 and is set in a former grain shed. In 2017 Sophie de Ronde joined the brewing team as Head Brewer. All beers brewed to date have been unfiltered and are available in both KeyKeg and 440ml cans.

Burton Bridge SIBA

24 Bridge Street, Burton upon Trent, Staffordshire, DE14 1SY
☎ (01283) 510573 🌐 burtonbridgebrewery.co.uk

⊕The brewery was established in 1982 by Bruce Wilkinson and Geoff Mumford. Following their retirement in 2024 it was merged with Planning Solutions, the owners of the Heritage Brewery brand. New head brewer, Al Wall, is formerly of Cloudwater in Manchester. The Burton Bridge Inn remains the brewery tap. 🍴☕♦LIVE

Golden Delicious (ABV 3.8%) BITTER
Burton classic with sulphurous aroma and well-balanced hops and fruit. An apple fruitiness, sharp and refreshing start leads to a lingering mouth-watering bitter finish with a hint of astringency. Light, crisp and refreshing.
Sovereign Gold (ABV 4%) BITTER
Sweet caramel aroma with a grassy hop start with malt overtones. Fresh and fruity with a bitterness that emerges and continues to develop.
XL Bitter (ABV 4%) BITTER
Burton classic with sulphurous aroma. Golden with fruit and hops and a characteristic lingering aftertaste hinting of toffee apple sweetness.
XL Mild (ABV 4%) MILD
Black treacle initial taste after liquorice aroma. Sweet finish with a touch of bitterness
Bridge Bitter (ABV 4.2%) BITTER
Gentle aroma of malt and fruit. Good, balanced start finishing with a robust hop mouthfeel.
Burton Porter (ABV 4.5%) PORTER
Chocolate aromas and sweet smooth taste of smoky roasted grain and coffee.
Damson Porter (ABV 4.5%) SPECIALITY
Faint roast, caramel and dark fruit nose. Cough mixture and Black Jack beginning. Uncomplicated profile with a fractious mix of bitter fruitiness and yeasty maltiness.
Draught Burton Ale (ABV 4.8%) BITTER
Fruity orange aroma leads to hoppy start, hop and fruit body then fruity aftertaste. Dry finish with fruity hints
Bramble Stout / Top Dog (ABV 5%) SPECIALITY
Smoky aroma with a fruit hint from black liquid. Roast start with briar dry fruit emerging then a sharp blackfruit

taste emerges to balance the burnt effect with a sweetish dry blackberry finish.

Stairway to Heaven (ABV 5%) BITTER
Golden bitter. A perfectly-balanced beer. The fruity and hoppy start leads to a hoppy body with a mouthwatering finish.

Festival Ale (ABV 5.5%) BITTER
Caramel aroma with plenty of hop taste balanced by a full-bodied, malty sweetness.

Thomas Sykes (ABV 10%) BARLEY
Kid in a sweetshop aroma. Rich, fruity, spirited tastes – warming and dangerously drinkable.

Brewed under the Heritage brand name:
Charrington IPA (ABV 4.5%) PALE
Masterpiece IPA (ABV 5.6%) IPA
Old-fashioned amber ale, strong with lots of bitterness.

Burton Road

Office: 65 Kingsfield Drive, Manchester, M12 6JL
✉ contact@burtonroadbrewing.co.uk

Established in 2015, a South Manchester brewery producing cask, keg, cans and bottles focusing on IPA and pale ales. Beer is contract brewed at MBH Beer (qv).

Burwell SIBA

Burwell, Cambridgeshire, CB25 0HQ ☎ 07788 311908
⊕ burwellbrewery.com

⊠ Richard Dolphin and Paul Belton established Burwell Brewery in 2019 in a purpose-built timber brewery at the bottom of Richard's garden. The plant, recently upgraded to 2.5-barrels, together with four conditioning tanks and produces beer in cask, bottle and bag-in-box. !!♦V

Beer Fuggled Best Bitter (ABV 4%) BITTER
Priory Wood Rauch (ABV 4%) BROWN
Judy's Hole Chocolate Porter (ABV 4.5%) PORTER
Margaret's Field Amber (ABV 5%) PALE
Moulin D'Etienne Wit Bier (ABV 5%) SPECIALITY
Stefans' Mü¥hle Weiss Bier (ABV 5%) SPECIALITY
Sunshine Pale Ale (ABV 5%) PALE
Double Beer Fuggled Special Bitter (ABV 5.5%) BITTER
Absolutely Beer Fuggled Extra Special Bitter (ABV 6.5%) STRONG

Bushy's SIBA

Mount Murray Brewery, Mount Murray, Braddan, Isle of Man, IM4 1JE
☎ (01624) 661244 ⊕ bushys.com

☺Launched in 1986 as a brewpub, Bushys relocated in 1990 when demand outgrew capacity. Bushys goes one step further than the Manx Pure Beer Law preferring the German Reinheitsgebot (Pure Beer Law). The brewery hosts a successful festival during the TT period. It distributes to many pubs and clubs throughout the Isle of Man. There are plans to move in 2024/2025 to a new site and visitor centre in Castletown. !!♦

Castletown Bitter (ABV 3.5%) BITTER
Bitter (ABV 3.8%) BITTER
A traditional malty and hoppy beer with good balnace. The fruit lasts through to the bitter finish.
Darkside (ABV 4%) MILD
Mannannan's Cloak (ABV 4%) BITTER
Triskellion (ABV 4%) GOLD
Classic (ABV 4.3%) BITTER
Bramble (ABV 4.4%) SPECIALITY
Buggane (ABV 4.4%) BITTER
Old Bushy Tail (ABV 4.5%) BITTER
Red (ABV 4.7%) RED

Star of India (ABV 5%) PALE

Buswells

⊟ Lime Kilns Pub, Watling Street, Burbage, Leicestershire, LE10 3ED
☎ (01455) 631158 ⊕ limekilnsinn.co.uk

Brewing started at the Lime Kilns pub, Burbage, in 2016 as a small-batch brewery. It expanded to a two-barrel plant in 2017, providing up to 14 ales for the pub and other outlets, on demand. Bespoke brews are provided for events including several local beer festivals. V

Butcombe

Cox's Green, Wrington, BS40 5PA
☎ (01934) 863963 ⊕ butcombe.com

⊗ Originally established in 1978, Butcombe moved to a purpose-built brewery with a 150-barrel plant in 2005. The brewery was bought by the Jersey-based Liberation Group in 2015. Around 500 outlets are supplied direct and similar numbers via wholesalers and pub companies. Butcombe opened a new distribution centre with a bottling line in Bridgewater in 2018. The brewery has an estate of around 60 managed pubs and 20 tenanted pubs. !!⟂♦GFV

Adam Henson's Rare Breed (ABV 3.8%) BITTER
Light-bodied, easy-drinking refreshing beer, sweet malt overlaid with soft bitterness and subtle hints of citrus and tropical fruit.
Original (ABV 4%) BITTER
Sweet-tasting bitter with malt dominating over a trace of dark fruit, both soon fade in the rapid ending.
Gold (ABV 4.4%) GOLD
Very light background malt supports floral hop aromas with sweet tropical fruit notes and gentle bitterness on the palate.

Contract brewed for Wickwar Brewery:
BOB (ABV 3.9%) BITTER
Malty aroma, caramel with some spice and floral hop notes on the palate with a gentle bitterness continuing into the dry aftertaste.

Buxton

Units 4A & B, Staden Business Park, Staden Lane, Buxton, Derbyshire, SK17 9RZ
☎ (01298) 24420 ⊕ buxtonbrewery.co.uk

☺Set up in 2009 as a five-barrel plant, Buxton now uses a 20-barrel plant. Its brewery tap is in Buxton and there is a tasting room at the brewery with views of the Derbyshire countryside. A wide range of small-batch beers is brewed throughout the year. Cask beers are distributed throughout the Peak District and are available nationally. Live beer is available in KeyKeg and cans using its own canning machine. Stronger beers are available in bottles. ⟂♦LIVE GF V♦

Hatchet (ABV 3.4%) PALE
Right to Roam (ABV 3.8%) BITTER
Deepdale (ABV 4%) PALE
Gatekeeper (ABV 4.1%) PORTER
SPA (ABV 4.1%) PALE
Best Bitter (ABV 4.2%) BITTER
Blonde (ABV 4.6%) BLOND
Double Back (ABV 4.6%) PALE
Featherbed (ABV 4.7%) PALE
Stacked (ABV 5.2%) PALE
Wild Boar (ABV 5.7%) BITTER
Axe Edge (ABV 6.8%) IPA

By the Horns SIBA

Unit 11-12, The IO Centre, Salbrook Road Industrial Estate, Salbrook Road, Redhill, Surrey, RH1 5GJ
☎ (020) 3417 7338 ⊕ bythehorns.co.uk

⊗ By the Horns began brewing in 2011 with a 5.5-barrel plant but outgrew the site by 2020. A new site in Salfords, Surrey opened in 2021. Cask is a big part of the production, with the rest in keg and cans. Its brewery tap is inside the AFC Wimbledon Stadium. Starting in 2024, the brewery will be opening a taproom on Saturdays, with live music events booked for Summer. Initially most products will be keg or can, but cask availability will increase. ⌷

Panowow (ABV 3.8%) BITTER
Stiff Upper Lip (ABV 3.8%) BITTER
Classic, amber-coloured bitter, well-balanced with hops throughout with hints of citrus and honey. Dry bitter finish.
Hopadelic (ABV 4.3%) GOLD
Smooth golden ale with grapefruit, gooseberry, citrus and lemon rind notes overlaid with hops. Building bitterness in the lingering finish.
Lambeth Walk (ABV 5.1%) PORTER
Black-ruby, full-bodied porter with black cherry, sultanas, coffee and a sweet treacle character. Developing, lingering, dark bitter roast cocoa.

Byatt's SIBA

Unit 7-8, Lythalls Lane Industrial Estate, Lythalls Lane, Coventry, CV6 6FL
☎ (02476) 637996 ⊕ byattsbrewery.co.uk

⊕ Since being established in 2011 Byatt's has been expanding and gained many fans with its extensive rotating beer list. This has made the increased range of beers very popular within the free trade as it can repeat popular brews throughout the year. A brewhouse bar with six handpumps also serves ciders on gravity. Tours and tasting sessions can be booked and private hire is available. Coventry Building Society Arena is nearby. ⌷⌷⌷LIVE⌷

Coventry Bitter (ABV 3.8%) BITTER
Easy-drinking session bitter. Has an earthy taste from the bitter hops used. The aftertaste retains the strong bitterness.
Platinum Blonde (ABV 3.9%) BLOND
A blond beer having hints of citrus and sulphur, with a mild lemony after taste tempered by fruit sweetness.
Phoenix Gold (ABV 4.2%) GOLD
A refreshing golden ale with an earthy taste. Leading to a crisp citrus hop notes in the aftertaste.
All Day Foreign Extra Stout (ABV 4.9%) STOUT
Session stout, roasted malt, dark chocolate and coffee. With a hint of liquorice.
Regal Blond (ABV 5.2%) GOLD
Strong golden ale. Citrus, vanilla and lemongrass notes. Powerful and hoppy. Smooth and refreshing.

C'84

See Cropton

Cabin

44 Brooksfield, Bildeston, Suffolk, IP7 7EJ ☎ 07990 845855 ⊕ cabinbrewery.co.uk

Owner and brewer Chris Smith has been brewing since 2013, with Cabin Ales available commercially since 2015. Demand soon outgrew the original plant and a new two-barrel kit was designed and installed in 2018.

Autumn Leaf (ABV 3.8%) BITTER
Chesn't (ABV 3.9%) BROWN
Gold Rush (ABV 4%) PALE
Mark's Gold (ABV 4%) PALE
Red Nek (ABV 4.3%) RED
Mary Celeste (ABV 4.5%) PALE
INNspiration (ABV 5%) PALE

Cader

Unit 4, Parc Menter, Marian Mawr Enterprise Park, Dolgellau, LL40 1UU
☎ (01341) 388080 ☎ 07546 272372
⊕ caderales.com

The five-barrel, purpose-built brewery is situated close to the centre of the picturesque market town of Dolgellau. Deliveries are made to the licensed trade in North and Mid-West Wales and beers in cask or bottle are available to the general public direct from the brewery. Brewing is suspended. ⌷⌷

Cairngorm SIBA

Unit 12, Dalfaber Industrial Estate, Aviemore, PH22 1ST
☎ (01479) 812222 ⊕ cairngormbrewery.com

⊕ Cairngorm brews using a 20-barrel plant. Now with its own bottling line, it supplies the free trade as far south as the central belt, and nationally via wholesalers. In 2016, in partnership with the Cobbs Group, it bought the brands of the Loch Ness Brewing Co and now brews selected beers under the Loch Ness brand name. ⌷⌷⌷⌷

Lochan (ABV 3.4%) BLOND
Nessies Monster Mash (ABV 4.1%) BITTER
A good, traditional, English-type bitter with plenty of bitterness, strong malt flavour and a red fruity background. Lingering bitterness in the aftertaste with diminishing sweetness.
Stag (ABV 4.1%) BITTER
A good mix of roasted malt, red fruits and hops throughout. This tawny brew also has plenty of malt in the lingering bittersweet aftertaste.
Trade Winds (ABV 4.3%) SPECIALITY
Award-winning brew with a strong elderflower and citrus fruity hop nose following on through to the bittersweet finish.
Black Gold (ABV 4.4%) STOUT
Roast malt dominates throughout, slight smokiness in aroma leading to a liquorice and blackcurrant background taste giving it a background sweetness. Very long, dry bitter finish. A worthy Championship winner.
Cairngorm Gold (ABV 4.5%) GOLD
Fruit and hops to the fore with a hint of caramel in this sweetish brew.
Highland IPA (ABV 5%) PALE
Refreshing, golden, well-balanced citrus American and South Pacific-hopped IPA. Some background biscuit and caramel.
Wildcat (ABV 5.1%) BITTER
A full-bodied, warming, strong bitter. Malt predominates but there is an underlying hop character through to the well-balanced aftertaste. Drinks dangerously less than its ABV.

Calverley's SIBA

23a Hooper Street, Cambridge, CB1 2NZ
☎ (01223) 312370 ☎ 07769 537342
⊕ calverleys.com

⊕ Brewery started in 2013 by brothers Sam and Tom Calverley. It is located in a converted stable yard close to the city centre. There is an adjacent taproom open for on and off-sales (Tue-Sat). The beer range varies continuously, and normally includes pale ales, lagers and dark beers, as well as more unusual styles, including sours. The beers are all unpasteurised and some are unfiltered. The beers are all served from keg and are also available in cans. ‼☛◆

Cambridge

▤ 1 King Street, Cambridge, CB1 1LH
☎ (01223) 858155 ⊕ thecambridgebrewhouse.com

⊗ Brewing began in 2013 at the onsite microbrewery in the Cambridge Brew House. ◆

Camden Town

Unit 1, Navigation Park, Morson Road, Ponders End, EN3 4TJ

Second Site: Arches 55-65, Wilin Street Mews, Kentish Town, London, NW5 3NN
⊕ camdentownbrewery.com

⊗ Bought by A-B InBev in 2016. A modern, automated brewhouse situated in railway arches underneath Kentish Town West Railway Station with an onsite brewery tap. A second brewery in Ponders End opened in 2017, and is the main production site, with a large taproom open for special events. No cask ale. ‼◆

Camerons

Lion Brewery, Stranton, Hartlepool, County Durham, TS24 7QS

☎ (01429) 852000 ⊕ cameronsbrewery.com

☺Camerons was founded in 1865, and is a family-owned business. Brewing is done by various team members, from office staff to brewery staff. A range of cask ales in association with the RNLI is produced throughout the year. A number of limited-run ales are produced through its Tooth & Claw pilot brewery. It also has a pub estate of more than 70 pubs, including the Head of Steam pubs. ‼☛◆

Sanctuary Pale Ale (ABV 3.8%) BITTER
Hoppy bitter with a sweet body and a drying finish.
Strongarm (ABV 4%) BITTER
Traditional sweet malty bitter with fruity aromas and caramel sweetness lasting into the finish.
Old Sea Dog (ABV 4.3%) BROWN
Boathouse Premium Blonde Beer (ABV 4.4%) BLOND
Road Crew (ABV 4.5%) PALE

Campervan SIBA

Bonnington Business Centre, 112 Jane Street, Leith, Edinburgh, EH6 5HG
☎ (0131) 553 3373 ☎ 07786 566000
⊕ campervanbrewery.com

Campervan began brewing in 2016 in a garage and an old campervan (hence the name). The van is still used for some events. A new 10-barrel facility in Leith was opened in 2017. Further expansion followed in 2024. Campervan's Lost in Leith Bar and Fermentaria houses an onsite barrel-ageing project. Campervan returned to cask ale production in 2022. LIVE ◆

Hoppy Camper (ABV 4.5%) PALE

Canterbury Ales SIBA

Unit 7, Stour Valley Business Park, Ashford Road, Chartham, Kent, CT4 7HF

☎ (01227) 732541 ☎ 07944 657978
⊕ canterburyales.co.uk

⊗ Brewing commenced in 2010. An eight-barrel plant is used. ‼◆

The Wife of Bath's Ale (ABV 3.9%) GOLD
A golden beer with strong bitterness and grapefruit hop character, leading to a long, dry finish.
The Reeve's Ale (ABV 4.1%) BITTER
The Miller's Ale (ABV 4.5%) RED

Canterbury Brewers SIBA

▤ Foundry Brew Pub, 77 Stour Street, Canterbury, Kent, CT1 2NR
☎ (01227) 455899
⊕ canterburybrewers-distillers.co.uk

⊗ Canterbury Brewers started in the Foundry Brewpub in the heart of Canterbury in 2011. The eight-barrel plant is purpose-built. Popular events are held there including the Kent Green Hop Festival (late September/early October). A wide range of spirits are now distilled in the brewpub, and up to three ciders are produced. ‼◆

Capitalist Hippy

See Gyle 59

Caps Off

Unit 4, Henson Close, South Church Industrial Estate, Bishop Auckland, County Durham, DL14 6QA ☎ 07900 551754 ⊕ capsoff.co.uk

Established in 2020, the brewery moved to larger premises in 2022 with new equipment and an onsite taproom. A wide range of styles is brewed. ◆

Have It! Best Bitter (ABV 4.1%) BITTER
A well-balanced, traditional bitter with crystal malt sweetness and a rising bitter finish.
Hot Wired Tuk Tuk (ABV 4.3%) PALE
Pale (ABV 4.3%) PALE
IPA (ABV 5%) PALE
Brown Ale (ABV 7.4%) STRONG

Captain Cook

Rear of White Swan, 1 West End, Stokesley, North Yorkshire, TS9 5BL
☎ (01642) 714985 ⊕ whiteswanstokesley.co.uk

☺The Captain Cook Brewery located behind the 18th Century White Swan pub celebrated its 25th anniversary in 2024. The brewery, which supplies the pub, uses a four-barrel plant. ‼◆

Cygnet (ABV 3.7%) IPA
Sunset (ABV 4%) GOLD
Slipway (ABV 4.2%) BLOND
Endeavour (ABV 4.3%) BROWN
Skippy (ABV 4.3%) GOLD
Black Porter (ABV 4.4%) PORTER
First Voyage (ABV 4.5%) PALE
Schooner (ABV 4.7%) STOUT

Cardigan (Teifi) SIBA

Y Bryn a'r Bragdy, Brynhoffnant, Llandysul, SA44 6EA
☎ (01239) 614974

Office: First Floor Offices – Ty Canol, Cardigan, SA43 1JL ⊕ cardiganbrewery.com

Cardigan Brewery Ltd – 'Bragdy Aberteifi' – is a craft microbrewery established in 2021, and is part of the Innkeeper (UK) Ltd Group. It produces a range of craft real ales, influenced by its surrounding area of the Welsh Coast. All are available through the medium of cask, keg and bottle-conditioned retail packs (V & VE) for the take home market. The brewery also installs cellar and dispense equipment and supplies the wholesale and on-trade market. !!LIVE V◆

Carleton (NEW)

The Butchers Shop, Park Lane, Carleton, North Yorkshire, BD23 3DJ

Launched in 2024, Carleton Brewing Company is a microbrewery producing a small core range of beers with occasional seasonal ales. Beers can usually be found in the Swan Inn, Carleton. ◆

Carlisle SIBA

Unit 2, 12a Kingstown Broadway, Kingstown Industrial Estate, Carlisle, Cumbria, CA3 0HA
☎ (01228) 594959 ☎ 07979 728780
⊕ carlislerealale.com

⊕Carlisle Brewing Company is a family-run brewery established in 2013. Initially using a 2.5-barrel plant in a shed behind the owner's freehouse, by 2015 it had expanded to a 10-barrel plant in an industrial unit. Beer is available in the Spinners Arms and other local outlets. !!◆GF

Cumbrian Bitter (ABV 3.7%) BITTER
Carlisle Bell (ABV 3.8%) PALE
Citadel (ABV 3.8%) PALE
Spun Gold (ABV 4.2%) BITTER
Sweet malty, fruity bitter with a lasting dry finish.
Flaxen (ABV 4.5%) BITTER
Magic Number (ABV 4.5%) BITTER

Carlsberg

Jacobson House, 140 Bridge Street, Northampton, NN1 1PZ
☎ (03457) 585685
Office: Carlsberg Marston's Brewing Co Ltd, Wolverhampton, WV1 4JT ⊕ carlsbergmarstons.co.uk

International lager brewery, which while brewing no real ales is a major distributor of cask beer. A joint venture with Marston's in 2020 led to the company being renamed Carlsberg Marston's Brewing Company.

Carnival

Unit 3, King Edward Industrial Estate, Gibraltar Row, Liverpool, L3 7HJ ⊕ carnivalbrewing.me

Brewery and taproom incorporated in 2017 and opened in 2019 by keen homebrewers Dominic Hope-Smith and Adrian Burke. Specialist styles are brewed and range from light through golden to dark beers. The brewery has a core range but also releases ad-hoc specials or collaborates with other local, national and international breweries to release further specials. It supplies online, retail, a few outlets in Liverpool, and beer festivals. Brewery tasting tours (Friday and Saturday) can be booked on the website. !!≡◆GFV◆

Carmen (ABV 4%) GOLD
Fruity peach/mango hop flavours balanced by sweetness and a dry, fruity bitter hop finish.
A Lovely Pint of Best Beside the Fire (ABV 4.4%) BITTER

Castle SIBA

Unit 9A, 7 Restormel Industrial Estate, Liddicoat Road, Lostwithiel, Cornwall, PL22 0HG ☎ 07880 349032
⊕ castlebrewery.co.uk

⊗ The brewery was established in 2007 using a one-barrel plant. A new 200-litre plant was added in 2016. All brews are unfined and are suitable for vegetarians and vegans. The brewery carries out its own bottling, and some for other breweries. ≡◆LIVE V

Restormel Gold (ABV 4.1%) PALE
Cornish Best Bitter (ABV 4.2%) BITTER
Daymark (ABV 5.1%) RED

Castle Eden

8 East Cliff Road, Spectrum Business Park, Seaham, SR7 7PS
☎ (0191) 581 5711 ☎ 07768 044484 ⊕ cebl.co.uk

Using the name of the former Castle Eden Brewery (having acquired the intellectual rights and recipes), a new 20-barrel commercial plant was installed in 2015 along with a bottling/kegging plant. Besides its own brand production, the brewery also contract bottles for several local and national companies. ≡◆

Blond (ABV 3.9%) BLOND
Ale (ABV 4.2%) BITTER
Faint malty and fruity aromas are precursors to a sweet, malty, gently-bittered beer with some hop presence, finishing dry.
Red (ABV 4.4%) RED
Black (ABV 4.6%) STOUT

Castle Rock SIBA

Queensbridge Road, Nottingham, NG2 1NB
☎ (0115) 985 1615 ⊕ castlerockbrewery.co.uk

⊕Castle Rock, established in 1998, quickly developed a reputation for producing high quality, consistent cask beers, which continues to this day, with five from the core range winning awards at national level. Throughout the year, Castle Rock brew an eclectic range of special and one-off beers in cask, keg and can, from the traditional to the more experimental and modern styles. !!≡◆LIVE GF V◆

Our House (ABV 3.4%) BLOND
A light, citrussy session pale with orange notes on the nose and a bitter hop taste and finish
Black Gold (ABV 3.8%) MILD
A dark ruby mild. Full-bodied and fairly bitter.
Harvest Pale (ABV 3.8%) PALE
Pale yellow beer, full of hop aroma and flavour. Refreshing with a mellowing aftertaste.
Preservation (ABV 4.4%) BITTER
A traditional copper-coloured English best bitter with malt predominant. Fairly bitter with a residual sweetness.
Oatmeal Stout (ABV 4.6%) STOUT
A sweet, malty session stout with hints of caramel, liquorice and dried fruits.
Elsie Mo (ABV 4.7%) GOLD
A strong golden ale with floral hops evident in the aroma. Citrus hops are mellowed by a slight sweetness.
Screech Owl (ABV 5.5%) IPA
A classic golden IPA with an intensely hoppy aroma and bitter taste with a little balancing sweetness.

Cat Asylum

12 Besthorpe Road, Collingham, Nottinghamshire, NG23 7NP

☎ (01636) 892229 ☎ 07773 502653
⊕ cat-asylum.com

☺Established in 2017, Cat Asylum is a microbrewery specialising in historic recipes from Britain and around the world. ‼️ ▣ ◆LIVE ⚲

Wee Moggie (ABV 3.8%) BLOND
Columbus Pale (ABV 4.9%) BLOND
Simcoe Pale Ale (ABV 5.1%) BLOND
The Big Smoke Stout (ABV 5.8%) PORTER
Newark IPA (ABV 6.1%) IPA

Celt Experience

See Evan Evans

Cerddin

▤ Cross Inn, Maesteg Road, Maesteg, Cwmfelin, CF34 9LB
☎ (01656) 732476 ☎ 07949 652237
⊕ cerddinbrewery.co.uk

Brewpub established in 2010 using a 2.5-barrel plant in a converted garage adjacent to the pub, now enlarged to a four-barrel plant. Beer is usually only available in the pub. Seasonal beers brewed ‼️◆LIVE V

Cerne Abbas

Chescombe Barn, Barton Meadows Farm, Cerne Abbas, Dorset, DT2 7JS
☎ (01300) 341999 ☎ 07506 303407

Office: Chescombe Barn, Barton Meadows Farm, Cerne Abbas, DT2 7JS ⊕ cerneabbasbrewery.com

⊠ Established in 2014 by Vic Irvine and Jodie Moore. Beers are made as naturally as possible using chalk-filtered water from its own spring. Many seasonal beers are produced, some with non-conventional ingredients. All beers are brewed with organic Maris Otter barley grown in the Cerne Valley. On the second Saturday in September each year, a community brew is produced using hops grown at the brewery and by people living in the village and surrounding areas. ‼️▣◆⚲

Ale (ABV 3.8%) BITTER
Gold/amber ale with gentle hop aroma. Refreshing balanced bittersweet taste. Long dry finish.
The Big Lubelski (ABV 3.9%) BLOND
Blonde (ABV 4.2%) BLOND
Hops to the fore in a new world style, fairly light on palate with spicy bitterness balanced with sweetness fading to astringency.
Danny's Brew (ABV 4.4%) BITTER
Tiger Tom Ruby Mild (ABV 4.4%) MILD
Mellow, malty ruby brown ale with hints of chocolate in aroma, taste and aftertaste. Malt balanced by bitterness leading to a dry slightly bitter aftertaste.
Leggless Jester (ABV 4.7%) GOLD
Mrs Vale's Ale (ABV 5.6%) OLD
Caramel and dried fruit have strong presence with warming enduring finish in this complex old ale. Presents as much stronger than the advised ABV.
Gurt Stout (ABV 6.2%) STOUT
Gurt Coconuts Rum Stout (ABV 7.2%) SPECIALITY
A strong, sweet stout with very prominent coconut elements in aroma, taste and aftertaste.

Chadlington SIBA

Blaythorne Farm, Cross's Lane, Chadlington, Oxfordshire, OX7 3NE
☎ (01608) 676823 ☎ 07931 482807
⊕ chadlingtonbrewery.com

Based in the Cotswolds, brewing began with small-batch brews, but the brewhouse, which opened in 2019 is capable of supplying a growing range of customers. The brewery utilises renewables and pure spring water. Family-owned, it makes visitors very welcome, hosting events, and holding Brew-your-Own days. The beers can frequently be found at the Tite Inn, Chadlington, which acts as the brewery tap.

Oxford Pale Ale (ABV 3.8%) PALE
Golden Ale (ABV 4%) GOLD
Oxford Blonde (ABV 4%) BLOND
Oxford Blue (ABV 4.2%) GOLD

Chain House

139-142 Market Street West, Preston, Lancashire, PR1 2HB ☎ 07707 511578

Office: 20 Brookdale, New Longton, Lancashire, PR4 4XL ⊕ chainhousebrewing.com

Brewing began in 2017. Popularity grew and beers occasionally appear in a handful of pubs in the Preston area. Producing predominantly keg and canned beers, there have been successful collaborations with breweries such as Rivington, Track and Drop Project. The brewery relocated into the heart of Preston in 2022, and includes a brewery tap with cask and keg lines. Chain House cask ale has been trialled at the tap. ⚲

Chalk Hill

▤ Rosary Road, Norwich, NR1 4DA
☎ (01603) 477077 ⊕ thecoachthorperoad.co.uk

⊠ Chalk Hill began production in 1993 on a 15-barrel plant. It supplies local pubs and festivals. A small plant is used to brew experimental beers, which if popular become part of the regular range. ‼️◆

Chantry SIBA

Unit 1-2, Callum Court, Gateway Industrial Estate, Parkgate, Rotherham, South Yorkshire, S62 6NR
☎ (01709) 711866 ⊕ chantrybrewery.co.uk

☺Brewing returned to Rotherham with the opening of Chantry in 2012. It uses the latest brewing technology in a 20-barrel plant built by Sheffield-based Moeschle UK. As well as the tap at the brewery (open Fri-Sat, with events most weekends), three other pubs are owned: Cutlers Arms and New York Tavern, Rotherham, and Chantry Inn, Handsworth, Sheffield. Delivery is nationwide, with free local delivery. ‼️▣◆

New York Pale (ABV 3.9%) PALE
Iron & Steel Bitter (ABV 4%) BITTER
Steelos (ABV 4.1%) PALE
Full Moon (ABV 4.2%) PALE
Diamond Black Stout (ABV 4.5%) STOUT
Kaldo (ABV 5.5%) BLOND
Mighty Millers (ABV 5.5%) BLOND
Special Reserve (ABV 6.3%) OLD

Chapel-en-le-Frith SIBA

5 Market Place, Chapel-en-le-Frith, Derbyshire, SK23 0EW ☎ 07951 524003
⊕ chapelcraftbrewing.co.uk

☺Opened in 2016, this small brewery is located at the rear of Chapel-en-le-Frith post office. The brewing kit consists of a single 200-litre capacity integrated system supplemented by a 20-litre trial kit. Bottles are available from the post office. Cask ales are available from a limited number of local outlets. ▣V

Siena (ABV 4.1%) GOLD
Isambard (ABV 4.4%) PALE
Busted Monkey (ABV 4.6%) BROWN
Craken Edge (ABV 4.6%) BITTER
Leningrad (ABV 5%) RED
Elysium Amber Ale (ABV 5.4%) BITTER
Acadian (ABV 5.6%) IPA
Hoppy as Funk (ABV 5.8%) IPA
Sinamarian Black IPA (ABV 6%) IPA

Charles Wells

See Eagle

Charnwood SIBA

22 Jubilee Drive, Loughborough, Leicestershire,
LE11 5XS
☎ (01509) 218666 ⊕ charnwoodbrewery.co.uk

☺Family-run, 10-barrel brewery established in 2014,
producing three core beers and up to three monthly
specials, with a wide range of styles. All beers are widely
available locally, including at its three micropubs, the
Sorrel Fox, Mountsorrel, the Hall Croft Tap, Shepshed, and
the Fox Cub, Barrow upon Soar. The front of the brewery
features a shop with large glass windows, giving a good
view into the brewery. It sells brewery merchandise,
bottled beers, mini-kegs, bag-in-box and local gins.
Online ordering is available for local deliveries. ⌷ ☰ ♦

Salvation (ABV 3.8%) GOLD
Vixen (ABV 4%) BITTER
Blue Fox (ABV 4.2%) GOLD

Chasing Everest

15 Ponteland Square, Blyth, NE24 4SH
⊕ chasingeverestbrew.com

Founded in 2018 by Zak Everest, focusing on small batch
brews. Many of the beers are dry-hopped, giving bold,
hoppy flavours. Brewing is currently suspended.

Checkstone

▤ First & Last Inn, 10 Church Street, Exmouth, Devon,
EX8 1PE
☎ (01395) 263275

Checkstone Brewery is a one-barrel plant inside the First
& Last pub, Exmouth, established in 2016. It is named
after the Checkstone reef outside the Exe Estuary. Like
the brewery, the beers are named after various sea
features around Exmouth. ♦

Cheddar SIBA

Winchester Farm, Draycott Road, Cheddar, BS27 3RP
☎ (01934) 744193 ⊕ cheddarales.co.uk

⊠ Established in 2006 in the heart of the Mendips,
Cheddar Ales has expanded capacity to enable it to brew
up to 100 barrels a week. Production is split
approximately 75% cask-conditioned ale, 25% bottle-
conditioned. Its bottling plant produces around 120,000
bottles annually and all bottled ales are gluten-free.
Around 450 outlets are supplied including pubs, clubs
and the off trade. A visitor centre and brewery tap
opened in 2020. ⌷ ☰ ♦ LIVE GF ♦

Bitter Bully (ABV 3.8%) BLOND
Light session bitter with flowery hops on the nose and a
dry, bitter finish.
Gorge Best (ABV 4%) BITTER

Nicely-balanced, English-style bitter with malty
backbone, gentle hop bitterness, hints of dark fruit and a
smooth, bittersweet finish.
Piney Sleight (ABV 4%) GOLD
Hoppy golden ale with bitter flavours of resinous pine,
light citrus fruit and delicate spice, before a long bitter
finish.
Potholer (ABV 4.3%) GOLD
Refreshing flavours combine soft fruit sweetness with
hop bitterness on a light malt background before a clean,
balanced finish.
Hardrock (ABV 4.4%) GOLD
Fruity hop aroma, balanced flavours of tropical fruit and
bitterness on a pale malt background before a clean,
bitter ending.
Totty Pot (ABV 4.4%) PORTER
Roasted malts dominate this smooth, well-flavoured
porter. Hints of coffee and rich fruits follow with a well-
balanced bitterness.
Crown & Glory (ABV 4.6%) BITTER
Lightly-hopped aroma, background malt balanced with
fruity hops in the crisp bittersweet flavour before a dry
and bitter finish.
Goat's Leap (ABV 5.5%) IPA
Light malt aroma with enticing toffee and red liquorice
hints. Traditional hop flavours and fruity sweetness, clean
bitter finish.

Chelmsford

2 Brewery Fields, Church Street, Great Baddow,
Chelmsford, Essex, CM2 7LE
☎ (01245) 476267 ⊕ chelmsfordbrewco.co.uk

⊠ Chelmsford Brew Co, established in 2017, is a family-
owned brewery located in Great Baddow, near the
former Baddow Brewery. A brewery shop and taproom is
open Thursday to Saturday, and online orders are
delivered free of charge to locations within 10 miles.
☰ V ♦

Blueshack Bitter (ABV 3.8%) BITTER
Cool Bay (ABV 3.9%) PALE
Port Jackson (ABV 4%) PORTER
Davy Dark (ABV 4.2%) MILD
Radio Wave (ABV 4.2%) PALE
Wild Coast (ABV 4.5%) IPA
Luxury Porter (ABV 4.6%) PORTER
Death of a Cowboy (ABV 4.7%) PALE
Mr Beard (ABV 5.2%) STOUT
Hand Grenade (ABV 5.3%) IPA

Cheshire Brew Brothers

See Oaks

Chevin

Office: 1 Mount Pisgah, Otley, West Yorkshire,
LS21 3DX ✉ chevinotley@gmail.com

Brewed in the shadow of the Chevin, in the famous pub
town of Otley, Chevin Brew Co specialises in small-batch
brews (cask, keg, and bottle). It is proud to use local
ingredients, and works with local artists for the labels. It
shares a small one-barrel brewery with sister brewery,
Marlowe Beer Project.

Danefield Pale (ABV 4.5%) PALE

Cheviot

Slainsfield, Cornhill on Tweed, Northumberland,
TD12 4TP ☎ 07778 478943 ⊕ cheviotbrewery.co.uk

Brewing commenced in 2018 in converted hunt kennels on the historic Ford & Etal estate. It is a 7.5-barrel plant producing ales named after local landmarks and historical figures. Bottles are supplied to local businesses while the full range is distributed from Edinburgh to Newcastle and beyond to over 200 outlets. ‼🍺◆

Sea Stack (ABV 3.7%) PALE
Upland Ale (ABV 3.8%) BITTER
ETale (ABV 4%) BITTER
Harbour Wall (ABV 4.2%) PALE
Black Hag (ABV 4.4%) STOUT
Trig Point (ABV 4.5%) PALE
Windy Gyle (ABV 4.7%) PALE
Menhir (ABV 5.1%) STOUT

Chiltern SIBA

Nash Lee Road, Terrick, Aylesbury, Buckinghamshire, HP17 0TQ
☎ (01296) 613647 🌐 chilternbrewery.co.uk

⊠ Founded in 1980 and located on a working farm, Chiltern was one of the first microbreweries in the country, and was expanded in 2023. Family-run, its emphasis has always been on producing natural, wholesome beers using the best British malt and hops (some grown in Buckinghamshire). Now run by the second generation, George and Tom, it supplies around 100 outlets including its tap, the King's Head, Aylesbury. Some bottled beers are suitable for vegans, and some are gluten-free. 🍺◆LIVE GF V

Chiltern Pale Ale (ABV 3.7%) PALE
An amber, refreshing beer with a slight fruit aroma, leading to a good malt/bitter balance in the mouth. The aftertaste is bitter and dry.
Chiltern Black (ABV 3.9%) PORTER
Beechwood Bitter (ABV 4.3%) BITTER
This pale brown beer has a balanced butterscotch/toffee aroma, with a slight hop note. The taste balances bitterness and sweetness, leading to a long bitter finish.

Chin Chin

Unit 53F, Lidgate Crescent, Langthwaite Grange Industrial Estate, South Kirkby, Pontefract, West Yorkshire, WF9 3NR ☎ 07896 253650
✉ david@chinchinbrewing.co.uk

☺David Currie founded the brewery in 2016 with his brother Andrew, before taking sole control. Initially utilising a one-barrel plant in domestic premises, in 2018 there was expansion to a five-barrel plant, and relocation to its current location. An expanding range of small batch beers is supplied across Yorkshire, and to festivals nationwide. ‼

Chislet (NEW) SIBA

Unit 32, Chislet Business Park, Chislet, Canterbury, CT3 4BY 🌐 chisletbrewery.co.uk

⊠ Chislet Brewery was setup in 2023 by John and Lewis who, after a number of years of home brewing, decided to take the plunge and setup a commercial microbrewery at Chislet Business Park. The focus is on traditional-style beers with a mix of local and worldwide hops. V

Church End SIBA

Ridge Lane, Nuneaton, Warwickshire, CV10 0RD
☎ (01827) 713080 🌐 churchendbrewery.co.uk

⊠ The brewery started in 1994 in an old coffin shop in Shustoke. It moved to its present site in 2001 and has expanded over the years. It currently operates a 24-barrel, purpose-built plant. Many one-off specials and old recipe beers are produced. Its award-winning beers are available throughout the Midlands. ‼🍺◆LIVE

Brewers Truth (ABV 3.6%) PALE
Goat's Milk (ABV 3.8%) PALE
Gravediggers Ale (ABV 3.8%) MILD
What the Fox's Hat (ABV 4.2%) BITTER
A beer with a malty aroma, and a hoppy and malty taste with some caramel flavour.
Vicar's Ruin (ABV 4.4%) PALE
A straw-coloured best bitter with an initially hoppy, bitter flavour, softening to a delicate malt finish.
Stout Coffin (ABV 4.6%) STOUT
Fallen Angel (ABV 5%) PALE

Church Farm SIBA

Church Farm, Church Lane, Budbrooke, Warwickshire, CV35 8QL ☎ 07980 012712
🌐 churchfarmbrewery.co.uk

Once a traditional farm with a large dairy herd, now a traditional brewery using a purpose-built, 20-barrel plant. Family-run with a keen environmental focus; malt and hops are sourced from local suppliers, whilst water is drawn from the farm's own well. Regular outlets are spread across central England, with some further afield. A mobile bar regularly attends Warwickshire food festivals, outdoor music and motorsport events. Brewery tap yard open Friday evenings and Saturdays (winter excepted). ‼LIVE◆

Pale Ale (ABV 3.8%) PALE
Session IPA (ABV 3.8%) PALE
Brown's Porter (ABV 4.2%) PORTER
Harry's Heifer (ABV 4.2%) BITTER
IPA (ABV 5%) PALE

Church Hanbrewery

Unit F2, New Yatt Business Centre, New Yatt, North Leigh, Oxfordshire, OX29 6TJ
☎ (01993) 774986 ☎ 07907 272617

Office: Tithe Barn South, Church Hanborough, OX29 8AB 🌐 churchhanbrewery.com

⊠ Brewing commenced in 2016 on a small scale in the owner's kitchen. A year later, a 250-litre plant was installed in a small industrial unit in New Yatt near Witney. It was upgraded to 500-litres in 2021. Now producing mainly bottles and keg, plus some cask for the taproom next door, and the Teardrop bar in Oxford's indoor market (one-off brews regularly seen in both). 🍺LIVE◆

Ale X IPA (ABV 4.5%) PALE
Rauk (ABV 5%) SPECIALITY
Red Beetter (ABV 5%) SPECIALITY
Bluenette (ABV 5.5%) PORTER
Mat Black (ABV 5.5%) PALE

City of Cambridge

See Wolf

Clark's

Office: 136 Westgate, Wakefield, West Yorkshire, WF2 9SW
☎ (01924) 373328 ☎ 07801 922473 🌐 hbclark.co.uk

☺Beers are contract brewed elsewhere. ◆

Brewed under the Westgate Brewery brand name:
WB Bitter (ABV 3.7%) BITTER

WB Blonde (ABV 3.9%) BLOND
Pale (ABV 4%) PALE

Clarkshaws

Arch 497, Ridgway Road, Loughborough Junction, London, SW9 7EX ☎ 07989 402687
⊕ clarkshaws.co.uk

Established 2013, Clarkshaws is a small brewery focusing on using UK ingredients for its core beers, and reducing beer miles. The beers are suitable for vegans and vegetarians (accredited by the Vegetarian Society). All beers are unfined and may be hazy. A small taproom operates onsite mainly at weekends for most of the year (check before travelling). V◆

Gorgon's Alive (ABV 4%) BITTER
Unfined golden coloured beer with spicy hops throughout. The flavour has hints of orange and peach with a dry bitterness.
Phoenix Rising (ABV 4%) BITTER
Tawny beer with a creamy toffee nose. Bananas, pineapple, hops and caramel flavours. Dryish, short, fruity biscuit finish.
Vegan Milk Stout (ABV 4.9%) STOUT
Coldharbour Hell Yeah Lager (ABV 5.3%)
SPECIALITY
Hellhound IPA (ABV 5.5%) IPA
British IPA with malt and growing orange marmalade notes with some subtle spiciness. The finish is dry and slightly bitter.

Clavell & Hind SIBA

Unit 2, Elmstone Business Park, Cheltenham, Gloucestershire, GL51 9SY
☎ (01242) 677118 ⊕ clavellandhind.co.uk

⊠ Clavell & Hind Brewery launched in 2018 in Birdlip before relocating in 2023 to the outskirts of Cheltenham. Taking its name from two infamous 17th century highwaymen its beer names take inspiration from that source. A 20-barrel brewkit is used and it has an onsite taproom. ‼◆❀

Coachman (ABV 3.8%) SPECIALITY
Blunderbuss (ABV 4.2%) GOLD

Clay Brow

256 Carfield, Skelmersdale, WN8 9DW ☎ 07769 581500 ⊠ claybrownano@gmail.com

Nanobrewery that started production in 2017. Together with its core beers and seasonal range, bespoke beers are produced for pubs, bars and other outlets. Beers are available in both cask and can.

Eclipse (ABV 5.4%) STOUT
Mr P's (ABV 5.7%) SPECIALITY
Mrs P's (ABV 6%) IPA

Clearwater

Unit 1, Little Court, Manteo Way, Gammaton Road, Bideford, EX39 4FG
☎ (01237) 420492 ☎ 07891 562005
⊕ clearwaterbrewery.co.uk

⊠ Established in 1998, Clearwater is a 10-barrel brewery regularly supplying more than 250 outlets across the South West and nationally with its Devon's Own-labelled beers. Beers are also available at the brewery tap, the Champ, Appledore. ‼🍺◆LIVE

Expedition Ale (ABV 3.7%) BROWN
Honey Beer (ABV 3.7%) SPECIALITY

Real Smiler (ABV 3.7%) GOLD
Eric's ESB (ABV 4.1%) BITTER
Mariners (ABV 4.2%) GOLD
Proper Ansome (ABV 4.2%) BITTER
A dark brown bitter in the style of a winter warmer.
Riff IPA (ABV 4.3%) PALE

Clevedon SIBA

Unit 1, Tweed Road Trading Estate, Clevedon, Somerset, BS21 6RR ☎ 07907 583415
⊠ les@clevedonbrewery.co.uk

⊠ A small brewery founded in 2016. Ownership changed in 2019. It is regarded as a local brewery by owners and patrons alike. Retail outlets are the taproom for cask and bottles, plus local markets for bottled beers. It focuses on using British malts and hops for its core beers. ‼🍺LIVE◆

Gold (ABV 3.8%) GOLD
BS21 (ABV 4.1%) BITTER
Best (ABV 4.4%) BITTER
Percy's Porter (ABV 4.4%) PORTER
Roasted malt with coffee and chocolate balanced with blackberry and liquorice notes on the palate before a short dry finish.
IPA (ABV 5%) PALE
Blonde (ABV 5.2%) BLOND

Clinkstone

The Steading, Seggiecrook, Insch, AB52 6NR ☎ 07583 027179 ⊠ info@clinkstonebrewing.com

Farm-based brewery commissioned in mid-2021. Clinkstone Brewing Company uses sustainable natural resources to produce hop-forward beers predominantly available in small pack formats. No real ale.

Cloak & Dagger SIBA

Unit 6a, Garcia Trading Estate, Canterbury Road, Worthing, West Sussex, BN13 1AL ☎ 07378 300570
⊕ cloakanddaggerbrewing.com

Cloak & Dagger was established by three friends from Brighton in 2017. Beers are available in can and keg, with the occasional cask beer (usually a stout). 🍺

Closet (NEW)

Office: 44 Hawkhill, Edinburgh, EH7 6LB
⊕ closetbrewing.com

Lucy Stevens began brewing soon after turning 18 with the most basic of equipment. Having now upgraded, and with more than 10 years of experience, she produces beers of unusual style and flavour in cans.

Cloudwater SIBA

Units 7-8, Piccadilly Trading Estate, Manchester, M1 2NP
☎ (0161) 661 5943 ⊕ cloudwaterbrew.co

Cloudwater specialises in producing modern takes on classic styles, with a leaning towards hazy, hop-forward beers. It also releases a series of wild, spontaneous and aged beers from its barrel project, with a strong focus on seasonality of both styles and ingredients. The brewery tap is adjacent. ‼◆

Clun SIBA

🍺 White Horse Inn, The Square, Clun, Shropshire, SY7 8JA
☎ (01588) 640523 ⊠ clunbrewery@gmail.com

⊚Established in 2007 behind the White Horse, Clun, as a microbrewery. A 2.5-barrel plant was installed in 2010, and brewing has increased steadily since then, with beers supplied to the trade across the West Midlands and the Welsh Marches. Cask, bottle-conditioned and bright beer is available for sale to the public. Ad-hoc brewery tours are available (enquire at bar). ♦

Loophole (ABV 3.5%) BITTER
Clun Pale Ale (ABV 4.1%) BITTER
Solar (ABV 4.3%) SPECIALITY
Green Man (ABV 4.4%) BITTER
Citadel (ABV 5.9%) BITTER

Coach

🍺 37 Cowbridge Road, Bridgend, CF31 3DH

Office: 2 Oldfield Road, Bocam Park, Bridgend, CF35 5LJ

The Coach Brewing Co is a four-barrel brewpub based at the award-winning freehouse of the same name. Launched in 2018, the brewery is visible in the pub. In addition to the regularly produced beers occasional seasonal additions are brewed. The beers are also available in keg. The brewery now own two other pub outlets, the Cross Inn, Cowbridge, and No. 1 Town Hall Square, Cowbridge.

Coach House SIBA

Wharf Street, Howley, Warrington, Cheshire, WA1 2DQ
☎ (01925) 232800 ⊕ coachhousebrewery.co.uk

Established in 1991 following the closure of the Greenall Whitley Brewery earlier that year, Coach House Brewing Company is the oldest cask ale producer in Cheshire. With a weekly fermentation capacity of 240 barrels, the company produces a core range of permanent beers, seasonal and special occasion brews as well as an extensive range of fruit and spice beers. ♦

Gunpowder Premium Mild (ABV 3.8%) MILD
Aromas of roast malts and caramel attract you to a pleasant sweet and toasty tasting mild with a gentle finish.
Cromwell Best Bitter (ABV 4%) BITTER
Blonde (ABV 4.1%) BLOND
Cheshire Gold (ABV 4.1%) PALE
Cheshire Oak (ABV 4.1%) BITTER
Dick Turpin Best Bitter (ABV 4.2%) BITTER
Malty, hoppy beer with some initial sweet flavours, leading to a short, bitter aftertaste.
Blueberry Classic Bitter (ABV 5%) SPECIALITY
A sweet beer with fruity esters and tasting predominately of blueberries, finishing dry.
Post Horn Premium Pale Ale (ABV 5%) BLOND

Coalition

Office: Hill View Close, Purley, CR8 1AU ☎ 07500 148699 ⊕ coalitionbrewing.co.uk

Founded in 2015. Brewed in the London surrounds, supplying pubs, restaurants, hotels and bars. Brewing lager, Pilsner, IPA and pale ales in kegs and bottles. No cask ale.

Coalshed

69 Pen-Y-Bryn, Caerphilly, CF83 2JZ

Based in Penyrheol, Caerphilly, this nanobrewery situated in a former coalshed in the garden of the brewer, produces a modern take on ales. V

Honey It's Going Down (ABV 4.3%) GOLD
Mosaic Monster (ABV 4.5%) PALE
Black as Coal (ABV 5%) SPECIALITY
Fallout (ABV 6.5%) IPA
Mango Madness (ABV 6.7%) SPECIALITY

Coastline

Far South End Cottage, Walney Island, Cumbria, LA14 3YQ

An old barn converted to a 2.5-barrel microbrewery, family-owned and run, located on the south end of Walney Island, Cumbria. Brewing began in 2023, supplying a number of local outlets. Presently Coastline brews five beers.

Cobbydale

🍺 Red Lion, 47 Kirkgate, Silsden, West Yorkshire, BD20 0AQ
☎ (01535) 930884 ☎ 07965 569885
⊕ cobbydalebrewery.co.uk

⊚Brewing began in 2017 at the Red Lion, Silsden. Originally only brewing one beer, others are now brewed on an occasional basis.

CoelBrew (NEW)

Avalon Business Park, St Andrews, KY16 0UB
⊕ coelbrew.com

Gluten-free brewery launched in 2022 and situated just outside of St Andrews. GF

Colbier (NEW)

Unit 7, 36 Canal Street, Bootle, Merseyside, L20 8AH
New brewery founded in Bootle in 2024 by two friends. Beers are named on a sound theme.

Legato (ABV 4.8%) STOUT

Colchester SIBA

Viaduct Brewhouse, Unit 16, Wakes Hall Business Centre, Wakes Colne, Essex, CO6 2DY
☎ (01787) 829422 ⊕ colchesterbrewery.com

⊠ Set up in 2012 by three friends, Tom Knox, Roger Clark and Andy Bone, the brewery utilises the double drop brewing method. Popular during the early 20th century this process requires additional brewing vessels in a two-tier system resulting in clean beer with pronounced flavours. ‼🍺♦LIVE

AKA Pale (ABV 3.7%) PALE
Metropolis (ABV 3.9%) GOLD
Jack Spitty's Smuggler's Ale (ABV 4%) BITTER
No. 1 (ABV 4.1%) BITTER
Sweeney Todd (ABV 4.2%) BITTER
Brazilian Coffee & Vanilla Porter (ABV 4.6%) SPECIALITY
Cat's Whiskers (ABV 4.8%) STOUT
Old King Coel London Porter (ABV 5%) PORTER

Cold Bath

🍺 46 Kings Road, Harrogate, North Yorkshire, HG1 5JW
☎ (03308) 807009 ⊕ coldbathbrewing.com

Launched in 2018, Cold Bath's onsite brewery can be viewed on the mezzanine level above the bar. All beers are available in the pub and the wider free trade. 10% of production is cask.

Cold Black Label SIBA

5 Squire Drive, Brynmenyn Industrial Estate, Bridgend, CF32 9TX
☎ (01656) 728081 ⊕ coldblacklabel.co.uk

Cold Black Label was initially founded in 2004, concentrating on its eponymous lager brand, and expanded into cask-conditioned beers 10 years later. In 2018, Cold Black Label and Brecon Brewing merged, with Buster Grant taking over all brewing, and 14 new beers were created. In 2019, Lithic Brewing joined the group, with these gluten-free beers mainly available in keg and can, with the occasional release of casks. Brewing is currently suspended. ☞V

Cold Town SIBA

8-10 Dunedin Street, Edinburgh, EH7 4JB
☎ (0131) 221 9978

Second Site: 4 Grassmarket, Edinburgh, EH1 2JU
⊕ coldtownbeer.com

Launched as a microbrewery in an old, disused church on Grassmarket in 2018, Cold Town evolved quickly and expanded to a larger site in 2019. The original brewery metamorphised into a bar and restaurant, Cold Town House, was upgraded and continues to produce some beers onsite. Beer is available in keg and can. ‼

Coles Family

🍺 White Hart Thatched Inn & Brewery, Llanddarog, SA32 8NT
☎ (01267) 275395 ⊕ coles.wales

Brewpub based in the White Hart Inn. It uses a one-barrel plant and also produces a cider. There is a separate distillery producing Welsh whisky and rum. Production invariably is for the pub only but an online ordering service is available for the take home trade. ♦

College Green

See Hilden

Collyfobble

🍺 Peacock at Barlow, Hackney Lane, Barlow, Derbyshire, S18 7TD
☎ (0114) 289 0340 ⊕ collyfobblebrewery.com

☺This impressive looking, gleaming 4.5-barrel plant is housed in the grounds of the Peacock at Barlow and can be viewed through the large glass panels built into the design. There is also a tasting room available to hire. The ales are brewed mainly for the Peacock although they are available wholesale and may be found at the neighouring Tickled Trout Inn and other local hostelries. ‼

Colonsay

The Brewery, Scalasaig, Isle of Colonsay, PA61 7YT
☎ (01951) 200190 ⊕ colonsaybrewery.co.uk

Colonsay began in 2007 on a five-barrel plant. Beer is mainly bottled or brewery-conditioned for the local trade. LIVE

Combe

Unit 4, Lundy View, Mullacott Cross Industrial Estate, Ilfracombe, Devon, EX34 8PY
☎ (01271) 267030 ☎ 07973 488409
⊕ combebrewingcompany.co.uk

⊗ Combe Brewing Co was established in early 2020, in a recently closed brewery. It produces bottle-conditioned ales to meet its small but growing client base. The owners, Richard and Michelle, have previous experience in the trade. A five-barrel plant is used. Bottle label artwork is designed by a local artist, Karen French. ‼☞LIVE◈

Harbour (ABV 3.7%) BITTER
Beach Blonde (ABV 4.1%) BLOND
Ruby Sunset (ABV 4.7%) RED
Dark and Stormy (ABV 5%) PORTER

Concrete Island

Pavilion Terrace, Wood Lane, Shepherd's Bush, London, W12 0HT ⊕ concreteislandbrewery.co.uk

Established as Small Beer Brewing in 2016, it was rebranded as Concrete Island Brewery in 2020. Run from a private flat near the Westway with a brew length of just 25 litres, it is one of the smallest commercial breweries. Unpasteurised and unfiltered beers are available in bottles. No cask ale.

Coniston

Coppermines Road, Coniston, Cumbria, LA21 8HL
☎ (01539) 441133 ⊕ conistonbrewery.com

☺The 10-barrel plant commenced brewing in 1995. The brewery is situated behind the Black Bull Inn, Coniston, and currently brews 40 barrels a week. Bluebird, XB and Old Man are bottle-conditioned and are brewed using Ridgeway Brewery. It supplies over 100 outlets with cask beers across the North West, and bottled beers are available in Asda, Sainsburys and Booths, as well as online. Bottled versions of Gold and Freebird (0.5% ABV) are gluten-free. ‼☞LIVE GF

Bluebird Bitter (ABV 3.4%) PALE
A yellow-gold, predominantly hoppy and fruity beer, well-balanced with some sweetness and a rising bitter finish.

Oliver's Light Ale (ABV 3.4%) BLOND
A fruity, hoppy, gently bittered straw-coloured beer with plenty of flavour for its strength.

Bluebird Premium XB (ABV 4.2%) PALE
Well-balanced, hoppy and fruity bitter. Bittersweet in the mouth with dryness building.

Old Man Ale (ABV 4.2%) RED

Special Oatmeal Stout (ABV 4.5%) STOUT
Well-balanced stout, fruity with a balanced ratio of malt to hop bitterness. A good starting point for novice stout drinkers.

K7 (ABV 4.7%) PALE
Balanced fruity hoppy bitter, plenty of body and a long hoppy bitter finish.

Thurstein Pilsner (ABV 4.8%) SPECIALITY
True to style; mild but unusually sweet, with a hoppy fruitiness.

Infinity IPA (ABV 6%) IPA
Impactful IPA. Fruity aromas persist in the powerful but well-balanced hoppiness and sweetness with nothing being lost in the finish.

No. 9 Barley Wine (ABV 8.5%) BARLEY
Hops and alcohol dominate with appropriate sweetness and fruit on the tongue. A full-bodied and beautifully balanced beer.

Consall Forge

3 Railway Cottages, Consall Forge, Staffordshire, ST9 0AJ

A one-barrel brewery set in the heart of the Staffordshire Moorlands adjacent to the Churnet Valley Railway. The Black Lion at Consall Forge is a regular outlet.

Dark Ruby Mild (ABV 5.2%) MILD
Equilibrium (ABV 6%) STOUT

Consett

🍺 Grey Horse Inn, 115 Sherburn Terrace, Consett, County Durham, DH8 6NE
☎ (01207) 591540 ⊕ consettaleworks.co.uk

☺Established in 2005, this four-barrel plant is located at the rear of the Grey Horse (Consett's oldest pub). The name, beers and branding commemorates the former steelworks in the town which closed in 1980. Beers are also available throughout the North East. New beers are launched at the twice yearly Grey Horse beer festivals. Vegan cask beers are available on request. ‼♦V

Pale Ale (ABV 3.8%) PALE
Steeltown (ABV 3.8%) BITTER
Balanced bitter with caramel and maltiness. Some fruit is evident in the sweet body and hops linger in the finish.
Steel River (ABV 4%) GOLD
Steelworkers Blonde (ABV 4%) BLOND
White Hot (ABV 4%) GOLD
A sweet fruity beer with citrus hops lasting well into the finish.
Men of Steel (ABV 4.2%) BITTER
Stout (ABV 4.3%) STOUT
Roasty and sweet with some interesting fruitiness. The hop combines with the roast malts for a satisfying and lasting finish.
Ironsand (ABV 4.4%) PALE
The Company (ABV 4.4%) GOLD
Porter (ABV 4.5%) PORTER
Sweet malts and caramel dominate throughout, with some fruit and a lasting finish.
Red Dust (ABV 4.5%) RED
Sweet, fruit and malt lead to a creamy, full bodied balanced red ale with caramel flavours and a lasting finish.
Stahlweizen (ABV 4.6%) SPECIALITY
Foreman's IPA (ABV 4.8%) PALE

Consortium

13D Cornmarket, Louth, LN11 9PY
☎ (01507) 600754

Second Site: Unit 10, Fairfield Industrial Estate, Louth, LN11 0YG ⊕ theconsortiumlouth.co.uk

☺The Consortium Brewing Company was setup in 2016 to serve the Consortium micropub and tasting lounge. It is situated in the Cornmarket of Louth, down a small passageway close to the Masons Arms. A large, diverse range of ale and gin styles is now brewed on the Fairfield Industrial Estate. It has produced more than 100 different ales since production started and bottle them for sale on the market (Wednesday, Friday, Saturday), within 20 metres of the pub. ‼♦✦

Lincolnshire Traditional Bitter (ABV 3.8%) BITTER
Wheres My Fiorucci (ABV 3.8%) BITTER
Aisey Dubitz (ABV 3.9%) BLOND
Farming County (ABV 4%) BITTER
Saturdays Blonde (ABV 4%) BITTER
Wet Pocket (ABV 4.1%) RED
Best Bitter (ABV 4.2%) BITTER
Pleasant Blonde (ABV 4.2%) BLOND
Executioners Assistant (ABV 4.3%) BLOND
Obliging Blonde (ABV 4.3%) BLOND
Black Frog (ABV 4.4%) BITTER
Queens (ABV 4.4%) GOLD

Willy Wickams Posthumous Ale (ABV 4.4%) BITTER
Englands Finest hour (ABV 4.5%) GOLD
Fat Cat Fuller (ABV 5%) SPECIALITY
Nicholas De Luda (ABV 5.4%) STOUT
Seek Medical Help (ABV 5.5%) IPA
Thanks Pa (ABV 6%) IPA

Conwy

Unit 2, Ty Mawr Enterprise Park, Tan y Graig Road, Llysfaen, LL29 8UE
☎ (01492) 514305 ⊕ conwybrewery.co.uk

☺Conwy started brewing in 2003, and was the first brewery in Conwy for at least 100 years. In 2013 it increased capacity and moved to bigger premises in Llysfaen with its own brewery tap, known as Mash. Around 100 outlets are supplied. Monthly seasonals are available as well as the West Coast range showcasing American-style beers. The Brewery is now owned by the Cadman Capital Group which also operates 360 Degrees brewery. ‼🍺♦LIVE✦

Clogwyn Gold (ABV 3.6%) PALE
Welsh Pride (ABV 4%) BITTER
Beachcomber Blonde (ABV 4.2%) BLOND
Honey Fayre (ABV 4.5%) SPECIALITY
Rampart (ABV 4.5%) BROWN
Golden Gate (ABV 5.5%) IPA

Cooper Hill

Highcliffe Industrial Estate, Bruntcliffe Lane, Morley, Leeds, LS27 9LR
☎ (0800) 783 2989 ⊕ cooperhillbrewery.co.uk

Commenced brewing in 2018 on equipment from the former Trinity Brewery, now relocated to Morley.

Best Bitter (ABV 3.8%) BITTER
Blonde (ABV 3.8%) BLOND
Golden Ale (ABV 4.2%) GOLD

Copper Dragon

Snaygill Industrial Estate, Keighley Road, Skipton, North Yorkshire, BD23 2QR
☎ (01756) 243243 ⊕ copperdragon.co.uk

☺Copper Dragon brew in Skipton using a 15-barrel plant. As well as the core range of Copper Dragon beers, Recoil Craft beers are also brewed, with both brands also featuring special editions.

Best Bitter (ABV 3.8%) BITTER
Refreshing amber coloured best bitter with a well-balanced malty and hoppy flavour.
Golden Pippin (ABV 3.9%) BLOND
Golden session beer, fruity and hoppy in aroma and taste. Citrus comes comes through in the aftertaste, which is increasingly bitter.
Black Gold (ABV 4%) MILD
Silver Myst (ABV 4%) SPECIALITY
Scotts 1816 (ABV 4.1%) BITTER

Brewed under the Recoil brand name:
Antidote (ABV 3.8%) BLOND

Copper Kettle

See Hydes

Copper Street

8 Copper Street, Brewery Square, Dorchester, DT1 1GH ☎ 07395 664390
⊕ copperstreetbrewery.co.uk

⊠ Established in 2018, the brewery is situated in the Brewery Square development, the former site of Eldridge Pope, next to Dorchester South Station. Its new owners are putting in larger equipment to increase production. There is a brewery tap and bottle shop open six days a week. Around 15 beers are brewed throughout the year and beer festivals are held regularly. ☒♦♠

Scramasax (ABV 4.1%) PALE
871 (ABV 4.3%) BITTER
Egbert's Stone (ABV 4.3%) BITTER
Shield Wall (ABV 4.3%) BITTER
Aethel Sword (ABV 4.5%) BITTER
Saxon Gold (ABV 4.7%) GOLD
Dark Ages (ABV 5.5%) PORTER

Copperhead (NEW)

Unit 6, Burke Road, Totnes, Devon, TQ9 6WL ☎ 07399 357445 ⊕ copperheadales.co.uk

New brewery established late 2022 in Newton Abbot, brewing a small but growing range of bottle-conditioned, vegan-friendly, live beers, brewed using only British ingredients. Cask-conditioned ales are available occasionally. It moved to new premises in Totnes in 2024. LIVE V

Core of the Poodle SIBA

26 Market Street, Haverfordwest, SA61 1NH

Core of the Poodle is a small brewery located at the back of the record and hifi shop at the 'top of town' in Haverfordwest. The aim is to brew beers for the year-round market and make them available from a few select locations in addition to the shop itself. ♦LIVE

Corinium

Unit 1a, The Old Kennels, Cirencester Park, Cirencester, Gloucestershire, GL7 1UR ☎ 07716 826467 ⊕ coriniumales.co.uk

⊠ Established in 2012, Corinium Ales brew classic and contemporary award-winning ales. It uses a five-barrel plant located in small, historic old kennels adjacent to the new Cirencester Park Visitor Centre, just outside the town centre. An onsite taproom showcases the range, which is also available at a growing number of local outlets, events and pubs. ☒☒♦LIVE V♠

Firebird VI (ABV 4%) BITTER
Corinium Gold I (ABV 4.2%) GOLD
Mosaic (ABV 4.5%) PALE
Plautus V (ABV 4.5%) PALE
Bodicacia IV (ABV 4.7%) PALE
Centurion II (ABV 4.7%) STOUT
Ale Caesar III (ABV 5%) PALE

Corn

🖥 **Corn Exchange/Kings Head Hotel, Ross-on-Wye, Herefordshire, HR9 5HL**

Small brewery in the Corn Exchange, part of the Kings Head Hotel in Ross-on Wye. Brewing mainly for the pub, the ales will find a way into the local free trade.

Cornish Crown

End Unit, Badger's Cross Farm, Badger's Cross, Penzance, Cornwall, TR20 8XE
☎ (01736) 449029 ☎ 07870 998986
⊕ cornishcrown.co.uk

⊠ This six-barrel brewery was launched in 2012 on a farm high above Mounts Bay by the brewer, and landlord, of the Crown Inn, Penzance, which acts as the brewery tap. Beer is available locally and as far as the Southampton Arms in London. ☒☒

Citra Boom (ABV 4%) GOLD
Causeway (ABV 4.1%) BITTER
Tawny bitter with a malty caramel nose. Initially malty with resinous, citrus hop bitterness emerging. Stone fruits. Long bitter finish.
Madagascan Vanilla Porter (ABV 5.2%) SPECIALITY
Dark vanilla porter. Roasted malt aromas. Molasses, treacle, liquorice flavours with raisin, fig/plum fruits and earthy hops. Roast, dry finish.

Cotleigh

See Nuttycombe

Cotswold

See Hawkstone

Cotswold Lion

Hartley Farm, Hartley Lane, Leckhampton Hill, Cheltenham, Gloucestershire, GL53 9QN
☎ (01242) 870164 ⊕ cotswoldlionbrewery.co.uk

Previously located in a grain store on a farm in the Cotswolds, Cotswold Lion brewery relocated in 2021. It produces a core range of five beers using a 10-barrel plant. Following founder Andy Forbes' decision to retire, the brewery was sold to new owners in 2024. ☒LIVE

Shepherd's Delight (ABV 3.6%) PALE
Hogget (ABV 3.8%) BITTER
Best in Show (ABV 4.2%) BITTER
Golden Fleece (ABV 4.4%) IPA
Drover's Return (ABV 5%) BITTER

Cottage Beer Project

Brewer's Cottage, Morebath, Tiverton, EX16 9BZ
☎ 07422 731152 ✉ dan@cottagebeerproject.co.uk

⊠ Opened in 2021 to brew bottle-conditioned beers in classic styles in 200-litre brew runs. Sold online, and at local retailers, cafés and events, primarily within Devon and Somerset. The core range is supported by seasonal and one-off beers, with occasional casks for special events. ♦LIVE V

Country Life SIBA

The Big Sheep, Abbotsham, Devon, EX39 5AP
☎ (01237) 420808 ☎ 07971 267790
⊕ countrylifebrewery.co.uk

⊠ Country Life is based at the Big Sheep tourist attraction. The brewery offers a beer demonstration and free samples in the shop during the peak season (April-October). A 15.5-barrel plant was installed in 2005, making Country Life the biggest brewery in North Devon. Regular, seasonal and bottle-conditioned beers are available at approximately 100 outlets, the brewery shop, and online. ☒☒♦LIVE

Old Appledore (ABV 3.7%) BITTER

Reef Break (ABV 4%) BITTER
Shore Break (ABV 4.4%) GOLD
Black Boar/Board Break (ABV 4.5%) PORTER
Golden Pig (ABV 4.7%) BITTER
Country Bumpkin (ABV 6%) OLD

Courier (NEW)

78b Temperance Street, Ardwick, Manchester, M12 6HU ✉ courierbrewingcompany@gmail.com

Nanobrewery located in a railway arch on Temperance Street. Founded in 2022, it specialises in the production of vegan-friendly craft beer while being focused on making as little impact on the environment as possible. It shares the brewery with Steelfish (qv). V

Courtyard SIBA

Gosfield Cottage, The Street, Gosfield, CO9 1TP
☎ (01787) 475993 ☎ 07710 230662
⊕ courtyardbrewery.co.uk

⊠ Courtyard Brewery uses a six-barrel plant designed to perfectly fit into a 19th century coach house in the north Essex village of Gosfield. It is run by two brewers passionate about producing ales traditionally, but with a 21st century twist. ◆LIVE ◢

IPA (ABV 3.8%) PALE
Gold (ABV 4.1%) GOLD
Dark (ABV 5%) PORTER

Cove

See Driftwood Spars

CrackleRock

The Old Cooperage, High Street, Botley, Hampshire, SO30 2EA ☎ 07733 232806 ⊕ cracklerock.co.uk

⊠ CrackleRock began brewing in 2014 at the Old Cooperage in the centre of Botley. Its taproom moved to larger premises near the brewery in 2018. ♨ ☛ ◆

Crackerjack (ABV 3.8%) PALE
Yellow beer with Saison-like characteristics of smoke throughout. Hops and bitterness noticeable in the taste, leading to a dry, hoppy finish.
Verified (ABV 4%) PALE
Fire Cracker (ABV 4.2%) BITTER
Malt and caramel characterise this traditional light brown bitter, with a background smokiness throughout, growing sweetness and a bittersweet aftertaste.
Gold Rush (ABV 4.5%) PALE
Well-rounded with noticeable tropical fruit and peach flavours. Sweet malt, hops and a moderate bittersweet finish, with a hint of smoke.
Dark Destroyer (ABV 4.9%) PORTER
Complex porter with red berries, chocolate, and some smokiness, combining malt with a lingering bitter finish, more fruit and smoke.
Crackatoa IPA (ABV 6.2%) PALE
Malty, amber-coloured pale ale with a warming aroma. Full-bodied, predominantly sweet in both the taste and finish.

Craddock's

Duke William, 25 Coventry Street, Stourbridge, West Midlands, DY8 1EP
☎ (01384) 440202 ⊕ craddocksbrewery.com

⊠ Craddock's beers are brewed exclusively for its pubs; the Duke William and the Plough & Harrow in Stourbridge, the King Charles, Worcester, the Talbot,

Droitwich and the Good Intent, Birmingham City Centre. The brewing is suspended, and currently contracted to Birmingham Brewing Company, with Green Duck brewing occasional seasonal beers. ◆LIVE

Craftsman

Abingdon, Oxfordshire, OX14 3TA

A 100-litre microbrewery in the owner's garage which started commercial production in 2021. Still trying new recipes, mostly flavoured stouts, which are bottled and sold in local markets, country fairs and similar places, plus the occasional cask. LIVE

Crafty SIBA

Thatched House Farm, Dunsfold Road, Dunsfold, Loxhill, Surrey, GU8 4BW
☎ (01483) 276300 ⊕ craftybrewing.co.uk

⊠ Established in 2014 behind the famous Dunsfold aerodrome, Crafty Brewing opened a new plant in 2019. It brews contemporary and traditional beer styles. The 'Crafty Cares' beers support various charities, including Surrey Search & Rescue. It supplies nearly 200 regional pubs, local shops and markets. All beers are available nationally to order online in mini-kegs, bottles and cans. The brewery hosts regular open days (see website for details). ☛ ◆ GF V

Loxhill Biscuit (ABV 3.6%) BITTER
Golden bitter which belies its strength. Initial biscuity aroma and taste with a dry bitter finish, from the Challenger hops.
Crafty One (ABV 3.9%) PALE
Golden-yellow beer with Chinook and Sorachi Ace hops. Tropical fruits aroma, leads to full dry fruity finish. Hints of coconut.
Blind Side (ABV 4%) BITTER
A traditional, light brown bitter. Predominantly malty throughout. Toffee and some roast character lead to a bittersweet finish.
Hop Tipple (ABV 4.2%) GOLD
Beautifully balanced pale ale. Light and easy-drinking with resinous modern hops and a crisp finish coming from dry-hopping.

Crafty Devil

Unit 3, The Stone Yard, Ninian Park Road, Cardiff, CF11 6HE ☎ 07555 779169
⊕ craftydevilbrewing.co.uk

⊠ Brewery has been in its location since 2017. It does not currently brew cask ale regularly, but produces bottled, canned and keg beer, which is supplied to markets and a number of other outlets in the local area. It currently operates two microbars, one in Cardiff and one in Penarth. ♨ ☛

Crafty Monkey SIBA

Benknowle Farm, Elwick, Hartlepool, TS27 3HF
⊕ shop.craftymonkey.beer

Brewing commenced in 2018 using a five-barrel plant in converted farm buildings. Beers are available throughout County Durham, Teesside and North Yorkshire. The brewery has a pop-up bar for events.

Telegraph Session IPA (ABV 3.8%) PALE
Moneypenny EPA (ABV 4%) PALE
New Era (ABV 4.3%) BITTER
Ruby Ruby Ruby Ruby (ABV 4.5%) RED
Malty and hoppy red beer, sweet centre and smooth texture with a somewhat drier finish.

Reward IPA (ABV 4.7%) PALE
Cemetery Gates (ABV 4.8%) PORTER
Black Celebration (ABV 5%) STOUT

Crafty Pint

🍺 Half Moon, 130 Northgate, Darlington, DL1 1QS
☎ (01325) 469965 ☎ 07804 305175

Established in 2013 in the cellar of the Half Moon in Darlington. Originally a 10-gallon brew length, it was upgraded to a one-barrel plant in 2015. One-off beers are produced occasionally and only available in the pub. ♦

Crate

See Purity

Craven SIBA

Units 9-0, Midland Mills, Station Road, Cross Hills, BD20 7DT
☎ (01535) 637451 ⊕ cravenbrew.co.uk

☺A cask-led and focused brewery established in Cross Hills in 2022. The 16-barrel plant brews twice weekly producing five core beers together with specials. The adjacent taproom is open daily. !! ◆

Session Pale Ale (ABV 3.7%) PALE
Balanced yellow premium bitter. Citrus hops on the nose with underlying orange sweetness that leads to a short, sweet finish.
Best Yorkshire Bitter (ABV 3.8%) BITTER
Light brown session bitter. Malt-led in taste, balanced with a roasty nuttiness and citrus overtones. Finish is increasingly bitter.
Extra Fine Ale (ABV 4.2%) GOLD
Hop-led yellow session bitter, with initial malt sweetness overtaken by a tropical fruitiness leading to a long bitter finish.
Black Angus Porter (ABV 4.5%) PORTER
Sweet malts and roast aroma. Tastes of bitter chocolate, liquorice and cherries. Finish is long and bitter with balancing fruity sweetness.
Pale Ale (ABV 4.8%) BITTER
Golden bitter, malty base overlaid with grassy hoppiness. Citrus fruit comes through and leads into a long, increasing bitter finish.

Creative Juices

Woodoaks Farm, Denham Way, Maple Cross, Rickmansworth, Hertfordshire, WD3 9XQ
☎ (01923) 771779
⊕ creativejuicesbrewingcompany.com

A craft brewery, taproom and beer garden that opened in 2019 in a renovated dairy building on a farm in Hertfordshire. Beers are unpasteurised and filtered and are either kegged or canned. No cask-conditioned ale is produced. ◆

Crich (NEW)

Unit 1D, Campbell Street, Belper, Derbyshire, DE56 1AP ☎ 07885 491329 ⊕ crichbrew.co.uk

Brewing since 2022, Crich Brewing Company produces modern, hop-forward craft beer in keg, cask and can from its microbrewery and taproom in the mill town of Belper, Derbyshire. ◆ ◆

Electric Avenue (ABV 4.2%) PALE
Stand (ABV 5%) PALE
58 Steps (ABV 5.8%) PALE
Rising Sun (ABV 6%) PALE

Modern Prometheus (ABV 6.66%) IPA

Cromarty SIBA

Davidston, Cromarty, IV11 8XD
☎ (01381) 600440 ⊕ cromartybrewing.co.uk

Family-owned, Cromarty began brewing in 2011 in a purpose-built brewhouse. Many awards have been garnered. Fermenting capacity was increased during 2014 and again in 2015. The varied portfolio of regular and occasional brews now surpasses 20. A bottling line was commissioned in 2017, a warehouse in 2018, and a canning line in 2019. The brewer is constantly trialling new recipes and collaboration brews. !! 🍴 ◆ V

Whiteout (ABV 3.8%) SPECIALITY
Happy Chappy (ABV 4.1%) GOLD
An excellent golden ale with plenty of hop character. Floral citric hop aroma with a good bitter taste which increases in aftertaste and balanced with malt.
Red Rocker (ABV 5%) SPECIALITY
Red-coloured rye hop monster with a malty background leading to a bitter finish.
Raptor IPA (ABV 5.5%) IPA
Rogue Wave (ABV 5.7%) IPA
Easy-drinking, strong peachy, citrus hoppy bitter.
Ghost Town (ABV 5.8%) PORTER
Classic, dark-roasted, malty porter with blackcurrant and liquorice background.
AKA IPA (ABV 6.7%) IPA
Strong IPA with a smooth, citrus hoppy taste.

Cronx SIBA

Unit 6, Vulcan Business Centre, Vulcan Way, New Addington, CR0 9UG
☎ (020) 3475 8848 ⊕ thecronx.com

Croydon-based microbrewery, opened in 2012, brewing a range of award-winning beers in cask, keg, bottles, cans and mini-kegs. Cronx has a dedicated bar within the Selhurst Park Stadium (open on Crystal Palace FC match days), and a bar on Croydon High Street serving both cask and keg beers. ◆LIVE

Old Town Bitter (ABV 3.8%) BITTER
Standard (ABV 3.8%) BITTER
Easy-drinking brown bitter with sweetish fudge and spicy hoppiness notes throughout. Malty bitter finish with a dryness that remains.
Kotchin (ABV 3.9%) SPECIALITY
Lemon and faint notes of pineapple on nose and palate. The growing dry spicy bitterness is balanced by honey flavours.
Nektar (ABV 4.5%) PALE
Full-bodied dark gold pale ale. Peach with citrus, sweet biscuit and floral hops, gently fade in the lingering bitter finish.
Pop Up! (ABV 5%) PALE
Amber pale ale. Malt, hops and passion fruit aromas. Hoppiness and fruitiness builds, balanced with some bitterness. Dry, bitter aftertaste.
Entire (ABV 5.2%) PORTER
Dark brown smooth porter with malt, chocolate and coffee aroma and flavours alongside damsons, sultanas and some hop bitterness.

Crooked

Units 12-15, The Garages, Leeds East Airport, Church Fenton, LS24 9SE ☎ 07890 526505
⊕ crookedbrewing.co.uk

☺After teaching homebrewing, Steve, Andy, Hudson and Mark started brewing in 2017 on the old RAF airfield at Church Fenton. Beers are increasingly available in a number of city centre pubs and bars in York and Leeds and many brews are canned for wider distribution. The brewery tap, Crooked Tap, opened in 2019 at Acomb Green, York. A second Crooked Tap opened in Driffield in 2022. ♦✦

Spokes (ABV 4%) BITTER
Standard Bitter (ABV 4.2%) BITTER
The Lash (ABV 4.4%) PALE
XX (ABV 4.6%) PALE
Rufus (ABV 4.8%) PORTER

Crooked River SIBA

c/o 2 Blooming Heather, Dearham, Cumbria, CA15 7EF ☎ **07888 141697** ⊕ **crooked-river.co.uk**

Initially starting brewing on a small scale in the autumn of 2022, most of the production is now cuckoo-brewed at Tractor Shed. Most of the beer is live beer in keg or can, but occasionally a cask beer may be produced.

Cropton

🍴 **Rear of New Inn, Main Street, Cropton, North Yorkshire, YO18 8HH**
☎ **(01751) 469800** ⊕ **croptonbrewery.co.uk**

⊚Established in 1984, the brewery was built behind the New Inn in 1994. After various incarnations the brewery returned to Lee family ownership in 2023. Beers are available throughout Yorkshire and nationally through wholesalers in various formats. ‼♦LIVE

Yorkshire Classic (ABV 4%) BITTER
Yorkshire Golden (ABV 4.2%) GOLD
Yorkshire Blackout (ABV 5%) PORTER

Cross Borders SIBA

28-1, Hardengreen Industrial Estate, Eskbank, EH22 3NX
☎ **(0131) 629 3990** ⊕ **crossborders.beer**

⊠ Established in 2016 by childhood friends Jonathan Wilson and Gary Munckton. Cross Borders brews traditional Scottish ales without pretension. The brewery has an onsite taproom open Friday-Saturday. ‼🍴✦

Hop Series Pale (ABV 3.8%) PALE
Notes of citrus on the nose with a balanced bitter finish.
Wee BRAW (ABV 4%) PALE
A fresh, fruity beer with lots of hops creating a great aroma and a lightly bitter aftertaste.
Heavy (ABV 4.1%) BITTER
A malt forward 'heavy', fruity with a slight bitterness not found in a traditional 80/-.
Bill's Beer (ABV 4.2%) PALE
Session IPA, a pale, full flavoured ale with zesty fruits and a clean finish
Porter (ABV 4.2%) PORTER
Flavours of coffee and chocolate come through in the finish of this easily drinkable porter.
Stout (ABV 5%) STOUT
BRAW (ABV 5.2%) PALE
Enticing citrus and tropical notes in the aroma of this juicy, refreshing golden ale.
IPA (ABV 6%) IPA

Crossed Anchors

🍴 **c/o Grapevine, 2 Victoria Road, Exmouth, Devon, EX8 1DL**
☎ **(01395) 222208** ☎ **07843 577608**

Second Site: 1 Fore Street, Topsham, Exeter, EX3 0HF
⊕ **crossedanchors.co.uk**

⊠ Crossed Anchors was established in 2015. In 2016 a six-barrel plant became operational in the old stables of the Grapevine in Exmouth town centre. In 2022 an additional two 2,100-litre conical fermenters were added. Beers are increasingly available across Devon and the south-west, as well as in the Grapevine. ‼🍴♦LIVE

Bitter Exe (ABV 4%) BITTER
American Pale Ale (ABV 4.2%) PALE
Very light brown coloured ale. Has a lot of sweet malt and fruit on aroma. Sweet tropical fruits dominate the taste with a slight bitter finish.
Tropical IPA (ABV 5.8%) IPA

Crossover Blendery

Lannock Manor Farm, Hitchin Road, Weston, Hertfordshire, SG4 7EE ⊕ **crossoverblendery.co.uk**

⊠ Founded in 2018, a small blendery operation producing 100% spontaneously-fermented beers aged in traditional vessels such as oak barrels. The aim is to source ingredients as close to the blendery as possible, working with farmers and growers directly, and promoting the produce through the beers. The taproom and shop opened in 2022 (see website for open hours). ‼🍴♦LIVE✦

Crouch Vale SIBA

23 Haltwhistle Road, South Woodham Ferrers, Essex, CM3 5ZA
☎ **(01245) 322744** ⊕ **crouchvale.co.uk**

⊠ Founded in 1981 by two CAMRA enthusiasts, Crouch Vale is well established as a major player in Essex brewing, having moved to larger premises in 2006. It supplies to various outlets as well as beer festivals throughout the region. A taproom (Tap Room 19) is onsite. One tied house, the Queen's Head in Chelmsford is owned. ‼🍴♦LIVE✦

Blackwater Mild (ABV 3.7%) MILD
Malty, fruity and full with a deep-ruby colour and a dry roast character.
Essex Boys Best Bitter (ABV 3.8%) BITTER
Brewers Gold (ABV 4%) PALE
Golden pale ale with striking citrus hop alongside biscuity malt supported by a sweet fruitiness.
Yakima Gold (ABV 4.2%) GOLD
Creamy session golden ale with aromatic citrus hop and a touch of biscuity malt.
Amarillo (ABV 5%) GOLD

Crown

🍴 **Crown, Green End, Little Staughton, Bedfordshire, MK44 2BU**
☎ **(01234) 376260** ⊕ **thecrownstaughton.com**

Brewing began in 2017 in a building behind the Crown public house. The brewery is owned and run by the landlord of the Crown, with the beers only being produced for the pub and local events. He occasionally brews a dark beer and hopes to create bottled options. ♦

Crown Brewhouse

🍴 **The Square, Elford, Staffordshire, B79 9DB**
☎ **(01827) 383602** ✉ **bluecatsup@hotmail.com**

A one-barrel plant, established in 2017, housed in a former store room attached to the Crown pub. Beers are brewed almost exclusively for the pub, but can be found at local beer festivals and events. Brewing is currently suspended.

Cuillin SIBA

Sligachan Hotel, Sligachan, Carbost, Isle of Skye, IV47 8SW ☎ 07795 250808 ⊕ cuillinbrewery.com

☺The five-barrel brewery opened in 2004 and is situated in central Skye at the foot of the Cuillin mountains. The water from the Cuillins provides a distinctive colour and taste to the ales. Beers are available onsite at the Sligachan Hotel and at several other pubs and hotels on the Isle of Skye. The brewery is open by appointment only in winter (November-March). ‼♦

Cullach

50 Princes Street, Perth, PH2 8LJ ☎ 07929 325890 ⊕ cullachbrewing.co.uk

⊠ The brewery opened in 2019 in an industrial unit on the outskirts of Perth. It moved into a retail unit closer to the town centre allowing a welcoming taproom to be set up for direct onsite sales. Some draught beers are real ale in KeyKeg and some cans are also produced. ➤LIVE V♦

Cullercoats

Westfield Court, Unit 19, Maurice Road Industrial Estate, Wallsend, Tyne & Wear, NE28 6BY ☎ 07837 637615 ⊕ cullercoatsbrewery.co.uk

☺Established in 2011, brewing takes place twice a week. The brewery champions English hops. ♦

Shuggy Boat Blonde (ABV 3.8%) BLOND
Lovely Nelly (ABV 3.9%) BITTER
Polly Donkin Oatmeal Stout (ABV 4.2%) STOUT
Fruity sweet and roast aromas precede a full bodied stout with a roast sweet caramel centre and a lingering finish.
Jack the Devil (ABV 4.5%) BITTER
Light brown bitter with a sweet fruit start. Bittering hops last well in the finish.
Grace Darling Gold (ABV 5%) GOLD

Cult Of Oak

Unit 15, Central Park Industrial Estate, Netherton, West Midlands, DY2 9NW ☎ 07530 193543

Cult of Oak was set up by beer sommelier Roberto Ross in 2019. Specialising in barrel-aged strong ales of varying styles, most of the beers are brewed collaboratively and are canned or bottled with some going into the trade or festivals in cask. Beers are available at Roberto's Bar, Birmingham.

Cumbrian SIBA

Old Hall Brewery, Hawkshead, Cumbria, LA22 0QF ☎ (01539) 436436 ⊕ cumbrianales.com

☺First established in 2003, the brewery is located in an idyllic position in a renovated barn on the shores of Esthwaite Water. The success of Loweswater Gold has meant the brewery is thriving. ‼♦

Esthwaite Bitter (ABV 3.8%) PALE
Robust refreshing bitter beer with plenty of hops, lasting well into the finish.
Langdale (ABV 4%) GOLD
Fresh grapefruit aromas with hoppy fruity flavours and crisp long hop finish, make for a well-balanced beer.
Grasmoor Dark Ale (ABV 4.3%) MILD
Dark fruity beer with complex character and roast nutty tones leading to a short refreshing finish.
Loweswater Gold (ABV 4.3%) BLOND
A dominant fruity body develops into a light bitter finish. A beer that belies its strength.

Curious

Unit 1, Victoria Road, Ashford, TN23 7HQ ☎ (01233) 552525 ⊕ curiousbrewery.com

⊠ Situated next to Ashford International Railway Station, this multi-million pound investment by parent company Chapel Down opened in 2019 and was sold to Risk Capital Partners in 2022. It is a modern, state-of-the-art brewery with a shop, tasting room (ground floor), bar and 120-seater restaurant (upstairs), featuring the core range plus special and seasonal brews. Products are widely available in keg, bottle and can. In 2023, the company acquired the brands of the now defunct Wild Beer Co. Tours and tastings are offered. ‼➤♦V⚓

Brewed under the Wild Beer Co brand name:
Bibble (ABV 4.2%) PALE

Cybi SIBA

Unit 4a, Penrhos Business Park, Holyhead, Anglesey, LL65 2FD
☎ (01407) 769651

Office: O'r Garw, Porthdafarch Road, Holyhead, LL65 2RU ⊕ bragdycybi.cymru

Family-run microbrewery on Holy Island established in 2020. It uses a 200-litre brewing system producing bottle-conditioned beers for local distribution on Anglesey. In 2021 the plant was relocated and upgraded to produce 1,600 litres in bottle and keg forms. Local ingredients are used in the production of some of the beers; including wild hops, Welsh coast kelp, and honey. There is an onsite taproom that has occasional tasting evenings. All beers are unfiltered and unpasteurised. ➤LIVE⚓

Daleside SIBA

Unit H5, Fifth Avenue, Hornbeam Park, Harrogate, North Yorkshire, HG2 8QT
☎ (01423) 880022 ⊕ dalesidebrewery.com

☺Daleside Brewery was established in the mid-1980s as Big End Brewery, changing its name in 1992 to Daleside. It moved to its current site in 1992. It was purchased by Rooster's Brewing Co in 2024 and production moved to Hornbeam Park with both companies operating individually. Beers are sold to local, regional and national customers and export markets include Denmark, Sweden and Australia. ➤♦

Bitter (ABV 3.7%) BITTER
Blonde (ABV 3.9%) BLOND
Old Leg Over (ABV 4.1%) BITTER
A fairly sweet and malty amber ale with hints of caramel and gentle hoppiness.
Monkey Wrench (ABV 5.3%) BITTER

Dancing Duck SIBA

1 John Cooper Buildings, Payne Street, Derby, DE22 3AZ
☎ (01332) 205582 ☎ 07581 122122
⊕ dancingduckbrewery.com

⊠ Dancing Duck was established in 2010 by Rachel Mathews using a 10-barrel brew plant. Its name comes from the local greeting 'ay up me duck'. The Exeter Arms in Derby is the brewery tap. ‼➤♦V

Quack Addict (ABV 3.8%) BITTER
Ay Up (ABV 3.9%) PALE
Brown Clough (ABV 4%) BITTER
Waitangi (ABV 4%) PALE
Ginger Ninja (ABV 4.1%) SPECIALITY

Nice Weather (ABV 4.1%) BITTER
Back Sack & Quack (ABV 4.2%) MILD
Donald *UCK! (ABV 4.2%) GOLD
Release the Quacken (ABV 4.2%) GOLD
Sapphire (ABV 4.2%) GOLD
22 (ABV 4.3%) BITTER
DCUK (ABV 4.3%) GOLD
Beaky Blinders (ABV 4.5%) GOLD
Dark Drake (ABV 4.5%) STOUT
Waddle It Be? (ABV 4.5%) PALE
Gold (ABV 4.7%) GOLD
Indian Porter (ABV 5%) PORTER
Abduction (ABV 5.5%) IPA
Imperial Drake (ABV 6.5%) STOUT

Dancing Man

Wool House, Town Quay, Southampton, Hampshire, SO14 2AR
☎ (023) 8083 6666 ⊕ dancingmanbrewery.co.uk

The Dancing Man opened in 2011 before moving to the historic Wool House in 2015. It recently underwent a large increase in brewing capacity. The outside seating, ideal for better weather, has been increased to almost 100. ‖ ☛ ♦ LIVE V

Dancing Men

Hill House Inn, The Hill, Happisburgh, Norfolk, NR12 0PW
☎ (01692) 650004 ☎ 07818 038768
⊕ hillhouseinn.co.uk

Brewing began in 2014 at the 16th century Hill House Inn on Happisburgh's fast-eroding clifftop. The microbrewery is named in honour of one of Sir Arthur Conan Doyle's Sherlock Holmes stories after he visited the pub in 1903. The five-barrel plant was acquired from Bees Brewery after its partial destruction in 2013. New recipes have been crafted using exclusive hops and barley including locally-grown Norfolk varieties. ‖ ♦

Dares

See Davenports

Dark Element (NEW) SIBA

c/o Unit 1, Lon Y Twyn, Caerphilly, CF83 1NW
✉ darkelementbrewco@gmail.com

A new brewery with an effective marketing campaign meaning canned beers can be found in a number of retail outlets locally and more recently, further afield.

Dark Horse SIBA

Coonlands Laithe, Hetton, Nr. Skipton, North Yorkshire, BD23 6LY
☎ (01756) 730555 ⊕ darkhorsebrewery.co.uk

Dark Horse began brewing in 2008. The brewery is based in an old hay barn within the Yorkshire Dales National Park. Around 50 outlets are supplied direct.

Craven Bitter (ABV 3.8%) BITTER
Well-balanced bitter with biscuity malt and fruit on the nose continuing into the taste. Bitterness increases in the finish.
Blonde Beauty (ABV 3.9%) GOLD
Well-balanced golden ale with citrus and hop aroma. Malty background.
Hetton Pale Ale (ABV 4.2%) PALE
Earthy bitterness on the palate overlaying a malty base and a spicy citrus character.
Night Jar (ABV 4.2%) BITTER

A malty, fruity bitter in aroma and taste. Caramel and dark fruits lace the finish

Dark Revolution

Unit 3-5, Lancaster Road, Old Sarum, Wiltshire, SP4 6FB
☎ (01722) 346255 ⊕ darkrevolution.co.uk

In the beautiful Wiltshire countryside, just north of Salisbury, Dark Revolution Brewery & Taproom is uniquely located in a tranquil setting, overlooking the historic airfield at Old Sarum. The 15-barrel brew plant has been producing beer since 2017. Homebrewers at heart, it is driven by innovation and curiosity. Its 50-litre test kit allows new techniques and flavour combination trials. ☛ ♦ LIVE V ♦

Orbital (ABV 3.4%) BLOND
So.LA (ABV 4.5%) PALE
A cloudy light naturally carbonated West Coast style pale ale that surprises the nose and the palate with citrus hoppy freshness that fades to dry citrus floral finish.
Velveteen (ABV 4.8%) STOUT

Dark Sky

Barclays Bank House, Market Place, Middleton-in-Teesdale, DL12 0QG ⊕ dskyb.co.uk

Brewing commenced in premises formerly occupied by Barclays Bank in Middleton-in-Teesdale, in an Area of Outstanding Natural Beauty in the North Pennines. Beers are brewed in small batches and the names are inspired by the local surroundings. Beers are available at the Teesdale Hotel in Middleton-in-Teesdale and other local outlets.

Dark Star

See Fuller's

Dark Tribe

Dog and Gun, High Street, East Butterwick, Lincolnshire, DN17 3AJ
☎ (01724) 782324 ⊕ darktribe.co.uk

Situated on the banks of the River Trent in the Dog & Gun pub, this 2.5-barrel brewing plant produces beers for the pub and local outlets. The award-winning brewery has been established since 1996. A range of one-off beers is produced throughout the year. ‖ ♦

Darkland

Unit 4c, Ladyship Business Park, Mill Lane, Halifax, West Yorkshire, HX3 6TA ☎ 07714 344723
⊕ darklandindiebrewco.com

Founded in 2018, Darkland is an award-winning microbrewery located on the outskirts of Halifax. Specialising in cask ales, it supplies the independent on trade both locally and nationally. Its brewery tap is open for special events at least once a month. ♦

Tower Blonde (ABV 3.8%) BLOND
Wildfire (ABV 3.8%) BITTER
Unmasked (ABV 5%) PORTER

Dartmoor SIBA

The Brewery, Station Road, Princetown, Devon, PL20 6QX
☎ (01822) 890789 ⊕ dartmoorbrewery.co.uk

Formerly named Princetown, Dartmoor Brewery was established in 1994. It is the highest brewery in England at 1,465 feet above sea level. In 2005 the brewery moved locally to a new, purpose-built building. In both

2012 and 2013 capacity was increased. In 2017 a further extension was built which now gives a brewing capacity of 540 barrels. The brewery is a traditional ale producer and all beer is brewed using English Malt. ‼🛒♦

Dartmoor IPA (ABV 4%) PALE
There is a flowery hop aroma and taste with a bitter aftertaste to this full-bodied, golden/amber-coloured beer.

Dragon's Breath (ABV 4.4%) SPECIALITY
Sweet, winter warmer best bitter. Full-bodied, sweet, fruity with treacle hints. Malt, roast and caramel from start to finish.

Legend (ABV 4.4%) BITTER
Complex beer full of aromas and flavours. Malt and caramel dominate balanced in an aftertaste of bitter hops. Well-rounded.

Jail Ale (ABV 4.8%) BITTER
Above average strength session ale. Complex and well-balanced, sweet and malty with fruit and hops. Well-rounded caramel and fruit with a bitter but pleasant aftertaste.

Darwin

14 Prospect Terrace, North Shields, NE30 1DX
☎ 07900 921276 ⊕ darwinbrewery.com

☺Darwin Brewery, established in Sunderland in 1994, is focused on making high quality cask ales, with great flavour and aroma. The brewery has a core range of five beers and monthly one-off or seasonal products. Since 2022, Darwin has shared premises and a 10-barrel brewhouse with Three Kings Brewery. The beer is mainly sold to outlets in the North East, but appears more regularly around the UK with increased work with distributors. ‼♦LIVE

Expedition (ABV 3.8%) PALE
Evolution (ABV 4%) BITTER
Beagle Blonde (ABV 4.1%) BLOND
Rare Stout (ABV 5%) STOUT
Rolling Hitch (ABV 5.2%) PALE

Datum Attitude

Tollesbury Road, Tolleshunt D'Arcy, Essex, CM9 8UA
☎ 07498 218283 ⊕ datumattitude.co.uk

A family-run, small-batch craft brewery established in 2021, producing unfiltered and unfined vegan-friendly beers. LIVE V

Davenports SIBA

Unit 5, Empire House, 11 New Street, Smethwick, West Midlands, B66 2AJ
☎ (0121) 565 5622
✉ info@davenportsbrewery.co.uk

☺Davenports brewery occupies part of a distribution warehouse in an industrial unit in Smethwick on the outskirts of Birmingham. The 7.5-barrel plant produces a selection of beers under the Davenports name with some occasional beers branded as being from the former Highgate brewery of Walsall, and Dares brewery of Birmingham. Beers can be found in its growing estate of tied houses, as well as the free trade. ♦

Mild (ABV 3.5%) MILD
Gold (ABV 3.9%) PALE
Original Bitter (ABV 4.2%) BITTER
IPA (ABV 4.4%) PALE

Dead Duck (NEW)

Hale, Hampshire, SP6 2NJ ☎ 07876 125386
⊕ deadduckbrewery.co.uk

Brewing began in 2023 using a bespoke two-barrel system producing four real ales in cask and canned live beer format. Operating from private property on the edge of the New Forest, Dead Duck supplies local pubs, shops and beer festivals with beers that reflect local places and forest folklore. LIVE

The Commoner (ABV 4%) BITTER
Colt Pixie (ABV 4.5%) BLOND
Sunny Haze (ABV 4.5%) PALE
Knightwood Oak (ABV 5%) SPECIALITY

Dead End Brew Machine

Office: Flat 1-2, 10 Lawrence Street, Glasgow, G11 5HQ ✉ chris@deadendbrewmachine.com

Dead End Brew Machine produce small batch, artisinal beers specialising in brettanomyces and saccharomycetes blends, augmented with fruit and spices. Beers are available in bottle and can. ♦LIVE

Dead Parrot

44 Garden Street, Sheffield, South Yorkshire, S1 4BJ

Established in Sheffield City Centre in 2018 by the Simmonite brothers. Expansion in recent years has seen increased production using a 15-barrel plant followed by the opening of a brewery tap, Perch, in 2022. In 2021 Jamie Allsopp approached Dead Parrot with the aim of recreating some original 19th century recipes from Allsopps of Burton.

Deeply Vale

Unit 25, Peel Industrial Estate, Chamberhall Street, Bury, BL9 0LU ☎ 07749 856043
⊕ deeplyvalebrewery.com

☺Deeply Vale is a family-run business established in 2012. The brewery's name immortalises the Deeply Vale area near Bury, famed for legendary 1970s music festivals. The range of traditional beers with a modern twist produced from the ten-barrel plant are distributed largely across North West England and West Yorkshire. ♦

DV US (ABV 3.8%) GOLD
Equilibrium (ABV 3.8%) GOLD
Crisp and refreshing bitter with a pale malt flavour and clean bitter hops. Dry finish with lingering hops.
Hop (ABV 3.8%) BITTER
Maverick (ABV 3.8%) PALE
Long-lasting hoppy pale beer with some sweetness, balancing malt and a hoppy, more bitter and dry conclusion.
White Wolf (ABV 3.8%) PALE
Citra Storm (ABV 4%) PALE
Optimum (ABV 4.2%) PALE
Initial malt, fruit and caramel flavours are soon replaced with a lasting hop bitterness.
DV8 (ABV 4.8%) STOUT
Subtle fruity sweetness accompanying luscious coffee roast. Clean, gentle malt finish with lingering sweetness. Coffee and raisin aroma.
Freebird (ABV 5.2%) PALE

Delphic

Mayors Lane, Newbury, Berkshire, RG14 5DR
☎ 07595 386568 ⊕ delphicbrewing.com

Thatcham's first craft brewery was established in 2019 by head brewer Tom Broadbank. It is a 2.5-barrel plant providing regular, seasonal and collaboration beers to local pubs, clubs and festivals. Bottles and cans are also available through well-established off-sales outlets in Berkshire, the online shop and at the new brewery site in Newbury. ‼️ 🍺 ♦ ⊘

Level Crossing (ABV 4.2%) BITTER
World's End (ABV 4.6%) PALE

Denbigh (Dinbych)

Crown Workshop, Crown Lane, Denbigh, LL16 3SY
☎ 07850 687701 ⊕ bragdybinbych.co.uk

⊗ Brewing commenced in 2012 at the rear of the Hope & Anchor pub relocating to the current premises in 2015. It now brews occasionally mainly to produce one-offs for special events and seasonal fairs. ♦ LIVE

Derailed

See Ludlow

Derby SIBA

Masons Place Business Park, Nottingham Road, Derby, DE21 6AQ
☎ (01332) 365366 ☎ 07887 556788
⊕ derbybrewing.co.uk

A family-run microbrewery, established in 2004 in the old Masons paintworks varnish shed by Trevor Harris, founder and former brewer at the Brunswick Inn, Derby (qv). The business has grown over the years; two venues are owned in Derbyshire, both of which are micropubs. Many outlets and retailers are supplied and there are up to four new beers available each month. ‼️ 🍺 ♦

Hop Till You Drop (ABV 3.9%) BLOND
Business as Usual (ABV 4.4%) BITTER
Penny's Porter (ABV 4.6%) PORTER
Dashingly Dark (ABV 4.8%) STOUT
Mercia IPA (ABV 5%) PALE
Quintessential (ABV 5.8%) GOLD

Devil's Dyke

See Arran

Devil's Pleasure

Higher Sigford Farm, Sigford, TQ12 6LD ☎ 07847 228249 ⊕ thedevilspleasure.com

Brewery founded in 2020 on the edge of Dartmoor National Park, near Newton Abbot. It specialises in brewing punchy, bold craft beers which are unfiltered and naturally hazy. V

Devon

🍴 **Mansfield Arms, 7 Main Street, Sauchie, FK10 3JR**
☎ (01259) 722020 ⊕ devonales.com

⊛ Named after the nearby River Devon and the former Devon colliery, the brewery was established in 1992 and run by the Gibson family to supply their two pubs, the Mansfield Arms, and the Inn at Muckhart. Beer is also available to the free trade. ‼️

Devon's Own

See Clearwater

DEYA SIBA

Unit 27, Lansdown Industrial Estate, Gloucester Road, Cheltenham, Gloucestershire, GL51 8PL
☎ (01242) 269189 ⊕ deyabrewing.com

DEYA Brewing Company was established in 2016. It brews innovative, hop-forward beers, all of which are unfiltered, unfined and unpasteurised, and available in keg and cans, with occasional casks. It has recently expanded into a new 25,000sq ft premises with a bespoke 40-hectolitre four-vessel brewhouse to significantly increase capacity. 🍺 V ⊘

Steady Rolling Man (ABV 5.2%) PALE

Dhillon's SIBA

14a Hales Industrial Estate, Rowleys Green Lane, Longford, Coventry, West Midlands, CV6 6AL
☎ (02476) 667413 ⊕ dhillonsbrewery.com

Established in 2014 as Lion Heart and relaunched as Dhillon's in 2015 with a new range of beers. The main focus is on craft bottled and canned beers but cask ales are also brewed. The brewery taproom is open Friday evenings and before football matches at the nearby Coventry Building Society Arena. ‼️ ♦ V ⊘

Bright Eyes GPA (ABV 3.8%) PALE
Fair Lady (ABV 4.5%) PALE
The Ambler Gambler (ABV 4.5%) GOLD
Red Rebel IPA (ABV 6.2%) IPA

Dhu Brew

See Stow

Digfield SIBA

Lilford Lodge Farm, Barnwell, Northamptonshire, PE8 5SA
☎ (01832) 273954 ⊕ digfield-ales.co.uk

⊗ Digfield Ales started brewing in 2005 and has continually expanded brewing capacity to keep up with demand. In 2012 it moved to a larger premises near Barnwell, where a reed bed was installed and the brewhouse was equiped with a new 15-barrel plant. More than 40 free houses are supplied. ♦

Fools Nook (ABV 3.8%) GOLD
The floral aroma, dominated by lavender and honey, belies the hoppy bitterness that comes through in the taste of this golden ale. A fruity balance lasts.
Chiffchaff (ABV 3.9%) GOLD
An amber-gold pale ale with a distinct hoppy aroma.
Barnwell Bitter (ABV 4%) BITTER
A fruity aroma introduces a beer in which sharp bitterness is balanced by dry, biscuity malt.
Old Crow Porter (ABV 4.3%) PORTER
A rich, full-bodied porter with a balanced roasted malt finish.
March Hare (ABV 4.4%) BLOND
A straw coloured premium ale with a subtle fruit flavour
Shacklebush (ABV 4.5%) BITTER
This amber brew begins with a balance of malt and hop on the nose which develops on the palate, complemented by a mounting bitterness. Good dry finish with lingering malt notes.
Mad Monk (ABV 4.8%) BITTER
Fruity beer with bitter, earthy hops in evidence.

Dionysiac

19 Oaklands Terrace, Darlington, DL3 6AX ☎ 07557 502083 ⊕ dionysiacbrewing.co.uk

Starting in 2021, this nanobrewery takes its name from Dionysus, the Greek god of drunken madness. Producing small batches of high quality, artisanal bottled beers, the beer names reflect local history. Production capacity doubled in 2024 following a complete upgrade of the brewery.

Disruption is Brewing SIBA

Unit 4, Camberley, GU15 3DL
☎ (01276) 686696 ⊕ disruptionisbrewing.co.uk

Founded in 2020 as the craft brewing arm of Ascot Brewing Company, the Disruption Is Brewing brand is now the single focus. It has won several awards for its beers, most notably its flagship pale ale, Chaos More Chaos. A heated 100-seat taproom is set on a mezzanine overlooking the brewery and features 20 taps (own, plus guest beers), and hosts comedy, trivia, music nights, and beer festivals (including Easter). ◆❖

Demockracy (ABV 4%) GOLD
Memoirs of a Geezer (ABV 4%) BITTER
Chaos More Chaos (ABV 5%) PALE
Shadow of Darkness (ABV 5%) STOUT

Distortion

647 Portslade Road, Battersea, London, SW8 3DH
☎ 07557 307452 ⊕ distortionbrewing.co.uk

⊠ Starting in the founder's garage in south London, the brewery was installed in a railway arch in 2020. The keg range is sold directly from serving tanks in the taproom (open Thursday-Sunday). No cask ale. ◆

DMC

78-79 Railway Street, Off Marsh Lane, Leeds, West Yorkshire, LS9 8HB ⊕ dmcbrewery.com

DMC Brewery, founded by husband and wife team Gez and Ele, produce the finest alcoholic ginger beer, made using fresh, natural ingredients, avoiding the use of synthetics, so the beers are gluten-free and mostly vegan. Four signature flavours, available for nationwide delivery, plus small batch, seasonal brews are produced. Its taproom is open Thursday to Saturday. GF V◆

Docker

Unit 14, Riverside Craft Centre, West Hythe, Folkestone, CT21 4NB
☎ (01303) 883220 ⊕ dockerbrewery.com

⊠ Brewing and baking commenced in 2016 inside a container on Folkestone Harbour Arm. Now brewing with a 10-barrel commercial plant, a stones throw from Hop Fuzz (qv), and Unit 1 pub, selling beers from both. Its brewery taps are at Sandgate and the Goods Shed, Canterbury. Its ethos is enviro-forward and local hops are used, some community grown. All beers are unfiltered and vegan. Cans are sold at retail outlets and online, kegs at pubs nationally. ‼🍴◆V

Old Dairy Red Top (ABV 3.8%) BITTER

Docks SIBA

The Church, King Edward Street, Grimsby, DN31 3JD
☎ (01472) 289795 ⊕ docksbeers.com

Brewing began in 2018 using a 15-barrel plant in a converted Edwardian Church in Grimsby. The brewery was originally named Axholme Brewing Co, with beers brewed under that name. ‼◆

Brewed under the Axholme Brewing Co name:
Magnitude (ABV 3.9%) PALE

Hard Graft (ABV 4%) PALE
Cleethorpes Pale Ale (ABV 4.2%) SPECIALITY
Lightning Pale Ale (ABV 4.3%) PALE
Graveyard Shift (ABV 4.5%) STOUT
Never Say Die (ABV 6%) IPA
Special Reserve (ABV 7.2%) STRONG
Powerful old ale. Amber-coloured beer with flavours of brandy and dried fruits.

Dr Morton's

See Abbeydale

Dog & Rabbit

🏠 36 Park View, Whitley Bay, Tyne & Wear, NE26 2TH
☎ 07944 552716 ⊕ dogandrabbitbrewery.co.uk

The Dog & Rabbit brewery was established in 2015 and relocated to its current premises as a small, one-barrel, micro-brewpub in 2016. LIVE

Dog Falls SIBA

Scaniport, Inverness, IV2 6DL ⊕ dogfallsbrewing.com

Microbrewery founded by Bob Masson in 2019, Dog Falls brew modern interpretations of international beer styles. Beers are unfined and unfiltered, available in can and keg. V

Dog's Window SIBA

8 Nant-Yr-Adar, Llangewydd Court, Bridgend, CF31 4TY ☎ 07929 292930
⊕ dogswindowbrewery.com

Dog's Window is a small-batch brewery which started production in 2018, producing a range of craft beers to its own recipes. It has a core range of four beers with an ever-changing list of limited editions (the Experimental Series). The mainstay of production is live canned beers, with the occasional keg and KeyKeg. The brewery sells cans direct to the public via its off license. 🍴◆LIVE V

Dolomite (NEW) SIBA

Unit 1, 6 Park View, Langwith, Nottinghamshire, NG20 9DE

Three friends, Huw, Nathan and Tom, are the brains behind Langwith-based Dolomite Brewery. Housed in an industrial unit, which is owned by Nathan's family, the brewery has the facilities to produce 20 casks of beer a week, which amounts to a total of 1,500 pints.

Dolphin SIBA

Woodley, Berkshire, RG5 4TL ☎ 07979 753391
⊕ dolphinbrewery.co.uk

A 130-litre brewery operating on a small scale from the garage of one of the brewers' parents. It produces bottled beers and occasional KeyKeg and specialises in niche styles; sours, gose, saisons, Brett and mixed fermentation beer, all of which are vegan. LIVE V

Don Valley

The Old Airfield, Belton Road, Sandtoft, Lincolnshire, DN8 5SX
☎ (01709) 580254 ☎ 07951 212722
⊕ donvalleybrewery.co.uk

☺The brewery, established in 2016, changed ownership in 2018. It moved in 2019 to a new site in Sandtoft in Lincolnshire with new brewing equipment, doubling the capacity. A canning line was installed in 2020. ◆❖

Bit o' That (ABV 4%) BITTER
Atomic Blonde (ABV 4.3%) BLOND
Gongoozler (ABV 4.5%) STOUT
Go Your Own Way (ABV 5%) GOLD

Doncaster

📧 7 Young Street, Doncaster, South Yorkshire,
DN1 3EL ☎ 07921 970941 ⊕ doncasterbrewery.co.uk

☺Established in 2012 and initially based at an industrial
unit in Kirk Sandall, Doncaster. In 2014 the brewery
moved to new premises in the city centre, using a 15-
barrel plant. The brewer frequently trials new recipes for
beers. ♦LIVE

Sand House (ABV 3.8%) BLOND
Handsome Pat (ABV 4%) SPECIALITY
Cheswold (ABV 4.2%) BITTER
Rebellious Monk (ABV 4.5%) STOUT
First Aviation (ABV 5%) PALE

Donnington IFBB

Upper Swell, Stow-on-the-Wold, Gloucestershire,
GL54 1EP
☎ (01451) 830603 ⊕ donnington-brewery.com

Thomas Arkell bought a 13th century watermill in 1827
and began brewing onsite in 1865. The waterwheel is
still in use. Thomas's descendant Claude owned and ran
the brewery until his death in 2007, supplying 20 outlets
direct. It has now passed to Claude's cousin, James Arkell,
also of Arkells Brewery, Swindon (qv). ⬛LIVE

BB (ABV 3.6%) BITTER
A pleasant amber bitter with a slight hop aroma, a good
balance of malt and hops in the mouth and a bitter
aftertaste.
Cotswold Gold (ABV 4%) GOLD
Citrus malty/sweet caramel aroma. Bright with
developing hops, fruit notes and malt. A dry hop bitter
finish with some citrus.
SBA (ABV 4.4%) BITTER
Malt dominates over bitterness in the subtle flavour of
this premium bitter, which has a hint of fruit and a dry
malty finish.

Donzoko

Office: Brougham Terrace, Hartlepool, County
Durham, TS24 8EY ☎ 07463 863647 ⊕ donzoko.org

Donzoko Brewing Company was founded by Reece Hugill
in 2017. It takes its inspiration and influences from
Germany and translates this beer tradition, combined
with techniques from modern UK and US craft brewing,
into its beers. It is a cuckoo brewery that has teamed up
with Gipsy Hill (qv) to produce its flagship lager in
London. Other beers are brewed at various breweries in
the North East. No real ale.

Dookit

Block 3, Unit 1, Tollcross Industrial Estate,
Causewayside Crescent, Glasgow, G32 8LJ ☎ 07792
889210 ⊕ dookitbrewing.co.uk

Established in 2020, Dookit originally brewed at Ride
Brewing before moving to its own premises in 2022. LIVE
Beers are available in bottle and keg.

Dopey Dick

Office: 4 Custom House Street, Derry, BT48 6AA
☎ (028) 7141 8920 ✉ dopeydickderry@gmail.com

A microbrewery founded in Derry. Beers can be found at
its sister pub, the Guildhall Taproom. Beers are contract
brewed.

Dorking SIBA

Aldhurst Farm, Temple Lane, Capel, Surrey, RH5 5HJ
☎ (01306) 877988 ⊕ dorkingbrewery.com

⊗ Dorking started brewing in 2008 at premises in west
Dorking. In 2017 production moved to a new, larger site
in Capel capable of producing 35,000 pints per week.
Beers can be found in Surrey, Sussex, Hampshire and
London. One tied house, the Old House in Dorking. All
beers are unfined. ‼⬛♦✦

Surrey XPA (ABV 3.8%) BITTER
Pilcrow Pale (ABV 4%) GOLD
Smokestack Lightnin' (ABV 4%) SPECIALITY
DB One (ABV 4.2%) BITTER
Hoppy best bitter with underlying orange fruit notes.
Some balancing malt sweetness in the taste leads to a
dry bitter finish.
Black Noise (ABV 4.5%) PORTER
Rich full flavoured porter with blackberries dominating
the aroma. Rounded bitterness with underlying hop
character throughout with a biscuity finish.
Red India (ABV 5%) RED
Five Claw (ABV 5.1%) PALE

Dorset (DBC) SIBA

Unit 7, Hybris Business Park, Warmwell Road,
Crossways, Dorset, DT2 8BF
☎ (01305) 777515 ⊕ dbcales.com

⊗ Founded in 1996, Dorset Brewing Company started in
Hope Square, Weymouth, which was once the home of
the Devenish and Groves breweries. In 2010 it moved to
purpose-built premises near Dorchester. Here spring
water is used in its state-of-the-art brewing equipment.
Beers are available in local pubs and selected outlets
throughout the South West. ‼⬛♦✦

Dorset Knob (ABV 3.9%) BITTER
Complex bitter ale with strong malt and fruit flavours
despite its light gravity.
Jurassic (ABV 4.2%) BITTER
Clean-tasting, easy-drinking bitter. Well-balanced with
lingering bitterness after moderate sweetness.
Origin (ABV 4.3%) GOLD
Durdle Door (ABV 5%) BITTER
A tawny hue and fruity aroma with a hint of pear drops
and good malty undertone, joined by hops and a little
roast malt in the taste. Lingering bittersweet finish.

Double-Barrelled SIBA

Unit 20, Stadium Way, Tilehurst, Reading, Berkshire,
RG30 6BX
☎ (0118) 942 8390 ⊕ doublebarrelled.co.uk

Brewing began in 2018 on a 15-barrel plant. The beer
range is extensive, concentrating on pale ales, IPAs and a
lager, but also including seasonal fruited sours and
stouts. The production of barrel-aged beers began in
2021. The occasional cask-conditioned beer is available
locally. Most beers are only brewed once, with regular
collaborations. The taproom is large and welcoming
(children and dogs), offering a variety of street food at
weekends. The majority of the beers are suitable for
vegans. ‼⬛V✦

Dove Street SIBA

82 St Helens Street, Ipswich, Suffolk, IP4 2LB

☎ (01473) 211270 ☎ 07880 707077
⊕ dovestreetbrewery.co.uk

⊠ Dove Street began brewing in 2011 using a 2.5-barrel plant in a garage opposite the Dove Street Inn. The pub, its sister pub and beer festivals are supplied. ‼

Underwood Mild (ABV 3.2%) MILD
Gladstone Guzzler (ABV 3.6%) BLOND
Dove Gold (ABV 4%) PALE
Incredible Taste Fantastic Clarity (ABV 4%) GOLD
Dove Elder (ABV 4.1%) SPECIALITY
Apples & Pears (ABV 4.2%) PALE
Ed Porter (ABV 4.5%) PORTER
Thirsty Walker (ABV 4.6%) BITTER

Dow Bridge

2-3 Rugby Road, Catthorpe, Leicestershire, LE17 6DA
☎ (01788) 869121 ☎ 07790 633525
⊕ dowbridgebrewery.co.uk

Dow Bridge commenced brewing in 2001 and takes its name from a local bridge where Watling Street spans the River Avon. The brewery uses English whole hops and malt with no adjuncts or additives. Seasonal and bottle-conditioned beers are also available. ☛ ♦ LIVE

Bonum Mild (ABV 3.5%) MILD
Complex dark brown, full-flavoured mild, with strong malt and roast flavours to the fore and continuing into the aftertaste, leading to a long, satisfying finish.
Acris (ABV 3.8%) BITTER
Centurion (ABV 4%) BITTER
Legion (ABV 4.1%) GOLD
Ratae'd (ABV 4.3%) BITTER
DB Dark (ABV 4.4%) MILD
Gladiator (ABV 4.5%) BITTER
Fosse Ale (ABV 4.8%) BITTER
Praetorian Porter (ABV 5%) PORTER
Onslaught (ABV 5.2%) BITTER

Downham Isle

19 Main Street, Littleport, Cambridgeshire, CB6 1PH
☎ (01353) 864795 ☎ 07732 927479
⊕ downhamislebrewery.co.uk

Downham Isle Brewery opened in 2016 in Little Downham, in the north eastern Cambridgeshire fens. Brewing real and craft ales, the customer base spans the Isle of Ely, Cambridge and Dusseldorf. Artisan small-batch brewing methods are used. The brewery moved to premises in Littleport in 2021. Normally four core ales are brewed, both cask and bottle conditioned. New beers, including specialist niche beers and seasonal beers, are planned during the currency of this Guide. ‼ ☛ ♦ LIVE V◆

Main Street Citra (ABV 3.5%) IPA
Goose Ely (ABV 3.7%) PALE
Moturiki Blowhole (ABV 5%) PALE
Duneham Ale (ABV 6%) BITTER

Downlands SIBA

Unit Z (2a), Mackley Industrial Estate, Small Dole, West Sussex, BN5 9XE
☎ (01273) 495596 ⊕ downlandsbrewery.com

⊠ A 10-barrel brewery set up in 2012 distributing beers across South East England. ‼ ♦

Root Thirteen (ABV 3.6%) GOLD
Best (ABV 4.1%) BITTER
Bramber (ABV 4.5%) BITTER
Devils Dyke Porter (ABV 5%) PORTER
Devils Dyke Salted Caramel (ABV 5%) SPECIALITY

Downton

Unit 11, Batten Road, Downton Industrial Estate, Downton, Wiltshire, SP5 3HU
☎ (01725) 513313 ⊕ downtonbrewery.com

⊠ Downton was set up in 2003. The brewery has a 20-barrel brew length and produces around 1,500 barrels a year. Around 100 outlets are supplied direct. A range of regular beers is produced together with speciality and experimental beers. The brewery offers an off-site mobile bar service and has an online shop. A taproom is open Friday. Sales of beer and merchandise are also available during normal brewery operating hours.
☛ ♦ LIVE ◆

New Forest Ale (ABV 3.8%) BITTER
An amber-coloured bitter with subtle aromas leading to good hopping on the palate. Some fruit and predominant hoppiness in the aftertaste.
Quadhop (ABV 3.9%) GOLD
Pale golden session beer, initially hoppy on the palate with some fruit and a strong hoppiness in the aftertaste. It's all about the hops.
Elderquad (ABV 4%) SPECIALITY
Golden yellow bitter with a floral fruity aroma leading to a good well-hopped taste with hints of elderflower. Dryish finish with good fruit and hop balance.
Honey Blonde (ABV 4.3%) SPECIALITY
Straw-coloured golden ale, easy-drinking with initial bitterness giving way to slight sweetness and a lingering balanced aftertaste.
Nelson's Delight (ABV 4.5%) SPECIALITY
Dream (ABV 4.8%) PALE
A premium pale ale with obvious Eastern European influences. Hoppy on aroma and taste with a particularly dry finish and a hint of lemon citrus notes.
Moonstruck (ABV 5.5%) BITTER
A dark ruby-coloured, premium bitter with malt and caramel in the aroma and taste which also carries notes of dried fruit and plum. A dry finish with some bitterness and a lingering taste.
Chimera IPA (ABV 6.8%) IPA
Golden yellow-coloured, strong IPA with a good balance of hops and fruit, slight sweetness and some malt notes, all through to the aftertaste.

Draycott

Low Farm, 30 Mill Road, Buckden, Cambridgeshire, PE19 5SS
☎ (01480) 812404 ☎ 07740 374710
⊕ draycottbrewery.co.uk

⊠ The brewery was set up by Jon and Jane Draycott in 2009, and is located in an old farm complex where they live. Focus is on bottle-conditioned beers which are available in a one-pint, traditionally-shaped bottle. Four regular beers are available, along with a cask beer brewed for the Grafham Trout pub, or to order. A seasonal ale made with local wild hops is also produced.
LIVE

Drenchfoot

Unit 9, Hill Fort Close, Thetford, Norfolk, IP241HS

Office: 65 Vicarage Road, Thetford, Norfolk, IP24 2LW
⊕ drenchfoot.co.uk

Drenchfoot is a 400-litre microbrewery supplying pubs and bars in Norfolk and Suffolk, selling bottles and polypins to the trade and direct to the public. V

Dragon Slayer (ABV 3.6%) BITTER
Don't Panic (ABV 5%) IPA
To Pee or not to Pee (ABV 5.8%) IPA

Driftwood Spars SIBA

Driftwood Brewery, Trevaunance Cove, St Agnes, TR5 0RY
☎ (01872) 552591 ⊕ driftwoodsparsbrewery.com

⊠ Established in 2000, production on the custom-built, five-barrel plant expanded with the installation of additional fermentation and conditioning capacity. Annual production now stands at 1,500 barrels. A small-batch beer range named Cove is produced, from which a portion of sales income is donated to local charities. ‼ ☗ ♦ LIVE GF V

Spars (ABV 3.8%) BITTER
Refreshing bitter with a balance of sweet malt and grassy, earthy hops, hedgerow and stone fruit flavours. Rising bitter finish.
Blue Hills Bitter (ABV 4%) BITTER
Amber with caramel malt aroma. Refreshing balance of non-citrus hops, malt and apple fruit. Long bitter, dry finish.
Bolster's Blood (ABV 5%) PORTER
Dark brown porter. Coal-smoke and peaty malt flavour with dark chocolate and dried fruits. Bitterness and burnt malt persist.
Lou's Brew (ABV 5%) GOLD
Golden beer laden with orange and grapefruit flavours, spice notes and some malt. Tropical fruit aromas and long-lasting tangy bitterness.
Stippy Stappy (ABV 5.5%) IPA
Alfie's Revenge (ABV 6.5%) STRONG
Rich strong red ale with dominant malt aroma and flavour. Kaleidoscope of dried and stone fruit, sweetness and light bitterness.

Drink Valley

▤ Unit C, Fleet Square, Swindon, Wiltshire, SN1 1RQ
☎ (01793) 692980 ⊕ thedrinkvalley.com

Drink Valley microbrewery opened in 2021. It has an open, airy, café-style layout to the bar area, where the brewing equipment can be seen. There is a core range of three ales but seasonal beers are also regularly available onsite. ♦

Drinkstone

Rattlesden Road, Drinkstone, Bury St Edmunds, Suffolk, IP30 9TL ☎ 07592 072140
⊕ drinkstoneales.co.uk

Drinkstone Ales is a 100-litre, part-time nanobrewery owned by Colin Field, and based in his converted garage. It commenced brewing in 2021, supplying local outlets and festivals. It concentrates on traditional cask ale using only English malt and hops, now available in bottles at local markets and fayres.

Bitter (ABV 3.8%) BITTER
Golden Ale (ABV 4%) GOLD
Uncle Percy's Solar Powered Pale Ale (ABV 4%) PALE
Farmers Ale (ABV 4.4%) RED
Road Apple Strong (ABV 5.2%) BITTER

Drone Valley SIBA

Unstone Industrial Complex, Main Road, Unstone, Dronfield, Derbyshire, S18 4AB ☎ 07794 277091
⊕ dronevalleybrewery.com

☺Community-owned, five-barrel brewery began brewing commercially in 2016. All the brewing processes are carried out by volunteers some of whom are fully qualified, experienced brewers. Being a community trust society all the profits go to local good causes. New owner members are always welcome. The onsite tap is open every Friday and Saturday afternoon and evening, with occasional events held on Sundays. Seasonal opening hours may apply, check website and social media for details. ‼ ☗ ♦ LIVE GF

Dronny Bottom Bitter (ABV 3.7%) BITTER
Derbyshire Blonde (ABV 4%) BLOND
Gosforth Gold (ABV 4%) GOLD
Coal Aston Porter (ABV 4.5%) PORTER
Fanshaw Blonde (ABV 4.5%) PALE
Amarillo (ABV 4.8%) PALE
Stubley Stout (ABV 5%) STOUT
IPA (ABV 5.2%) GOLD
Candelriggs (ABV 5.8%) MILD

Drop Kick (NEW)

The Millshed, Dorking, Surrey, RH5 4DX ☎ 07880 722835 ⊕ dropkickbrewing.co.uk

Drop Kick Brewing opened in 2023, taking over the site and kit of Trailhead. The owner, Fin, is a keen rugby fan and is a former brewer at Pilgrim. Beers are mainly keg but the occasional cask is produced. ♦

Drop Project SIBA

Unit 8, Willow Business Centre, 17 Willow Lane, Mitcham, CR4 4NX ⊕ drop-project.co.uk

Drop Project began brewing at Missing Link in Sussex until brewing commenced at Mitcham in 2021. Beers are mostly available in keg and can, including regular collaboration brews with other breweries and groups, and a growing range in cask. ♦

Drop The Anchor

9 East Close Farm, Lyndhurst Road, Hinton, Christchurch, BH23 7EF ☎ 07806 789946
⊕ droptheanchorbrewery.co.uk

⊠ Neil Hodgkinson began brewing in 2017 using a 2.5-barrel plant situated in the loft area of the Christchurch Emporium. The brewery has now relocated to Victorian farm buildings in Hinton in the New Forest. Beer is available in a number of local pubs and a small bar and shop is situated in the brewery (open Fri and Sat). All beers are unfined. ☗ ♦ LIVE ♠

Misty Mountain Hop (ABV 3.8%) GOLD
Silent Stones (ABV 4.7%) PALE
Tucktonia (ABV 4.7%) PALE
Black Dog Porter (ABV 4.9%) PORTER
The Admiral (ABV 5.2%) BROWN
Otakaro NZ Pale (ABV 5.5%) BLOND
40 Past Midnight (ABV 6%) SPECIALITY
Breaking Glass Hazelnut Latte Porter-Stout (ABV 6%) SPECIALITY
It's My Shadow (ABV 6%) SPECIALITY
The Phoenix IPA (ABV 6%) IPA

Drygate

▤ 85 Drygate, Glasgow, G4 0UT
☎ (0141) 212 8810 ⊕ drygate.com

⊠ Restaurant, bar and microbrewery, Drygate is a joint venture of Tennent's and Williams Bros, though operationally independent. The onsite brewery began production in 2014. A core range of keg and bottled beers is available. ‼ ♦

Dukeries

⬛ 18 Newcastle Avenue, Worksop, Nottinghamshire, S80 1ET

☎ (01909) 731171 ☎ 07500 119299

☺Founded in 2012 the brewery is located in the Dukeries Tap premises in the heart of Worksop. Beer brewed is available at the tap only, which is open every Saturday evening. ♦❧

Dummer Down (NEW) SIBA

Duxford Lane, Dummer, Basingstoke, RG25 2AR

☎ 07887 565502 ⊕ dummerdownbrewery.co.uk

Located on a family farm, this microbrewery and taproom first brewed towards the end of 2022. The taproom, open Friday and Saturday (closed Jan & Feb), is available for private hire. ❧

Dun

Corrary Farm, Glen Beag, Glenelg, IV40 8JX

☎ (01599) 522333 ⊕ dunbrewing.co.uk

☺Established in 2018, this small brewery is named after the two neighbouring Iron Age brochs (forts) – Dun Telve and Dun Troddan. Using its own spring water, organic ingredients and 100% renewable energy, Dun Brewing produces a range of craft beers, all unfiltered and vegan. Cask is available at the brewery's Dun Inn and the nearby Glenelg Inn. ☎♦V❧

Dungeon (NEW)

47 Sherbourne Drive, Hilton, Derbyshire, DE65 5NJ

☎ 07790 424377

A 200-litre nanobrewery offering cask and cans, with keg beers planned. Both craft and traditional style brews are produced, made to its own unique recipes. ♦

Mildly Evil Tom (ABV 4.1%) MILD
Is This a Joke (ABV 4.9%) STOUT
President Evil (ABV 5%) PALE

Dunham Massey

100 Oldfield Lane, Dunham Massey, WA14 4PE

☎ (0161) 929 0663 ⊕ dunhammasseybrewing.co.uk

☺Opened in 2007, Dunham Massey brews traditional North-Western ales using only English ingredients. Around 30 outlets are supplied directly, along with the three Costello's Bars, located in: Altrincham (opened 2010), Stockton Heath (opened 2013) and Warrington (opened 2022). A sister brewery, Lymm (qv), along with Lymm Brewery Tap both opened in 2013. ☎♦LIVE V

Castle Hill (ABV 3.5%) PALE
Little Bollington Bitter (ABV 3.7%) BITTER
Chocolate Cherry Mild (ABV 3.8%) SPECIALITY
Dunham Dark (ABV 3.8%) MILD
Big Tree Bitter (ABV 3.9%) BITTER
Obelisk (ABV 3.9%) BLOND
Alty Ale (ABV 4%) BLOND
Dunham Milk Stout (ABV 4%) STOUT
Landlady (ABV 4%) PALE
Dunham Stout (ABV 4.2%) STOUT
Dunham XPA (ABV 4.2%) PALE
Stamford Bitter (ABV 4.2%) BITTER
Deer Beer (ABV 4.5%) BITTER
Cheshire IPA (ABV 4.7%) PALE
Dunham Porter (ABV 5.2%) PORTER
East India Pale Ale (ABV 6%) IPA
Dunham Gold (ABV 7.2%) STRONG

Brewed for Lymm Brewery:

Bridgewater Blonde (ABV 4%) BLOND

Duration

Abbey Farm, River Road, West Acre, Norfolk, PE32 1UA

☎ (01760) 755436 ⊕ durationbeer.com

Duration Brewing make traditional and modern beers that reflect the rich agricultural landscape around them. Located at an idyllic and historic spot at West Acre Priory it produces wild and blended farm-style ales. Available in keg and cask, can and bottle (for live beer), the taproom opens every Saturday and Sunday from Easter to Oktoberfest, with tours every first Saturday of the month. ♨☎♦LIVE❧

Durham SIBA

Unit 6a, Bowburn North Industrial Estate, Bowburn, County Durham, DH6 5PF

☎ (0191) 377 1991 ⊕ durhambrewery.com

☺County Durham's oldest brewery, established in 1994. A core range of bottle, cask, mini-cask and keg beers is available all year round with two to three special brews appearing monthly. ♨☎LIVE V❧

Magus (ABV 3.8%) BLOND
Pale malt and hops define the character with a fruity aroma, a clean bitter mouthfeel, and lingering dry, citrus finish.
White Gold (ABV 4%) PALE
Hop and fruit aromas build in the mouth with added bitterness and sweet malts. Hop bitterness develops and lasts.
Dark Angel (ABV 4.3%) STOUT
A stout with malty roast aromas and flavours. Balanced with gentle hops, sweetness and a touch of fruit.
Alabaster (ABV 7.2%) STRONG

Durty

⬛ 4 Traquair Road, Innerleithen, EH44 6PD ☎ 07970 232192 ⊕ durtybrewing.com

With beers named after the mountain bike trails and landscape of the Tweed Valley, Durty Brewing brings a fresh perspective to its beers. Beers are available in cask, keg, bottle and can. ♦LIVE

Thunderstruck (ABV 4.5%) STOUT

Dynamite Valley

Units 5 & 6, Viaduct Works, Frog Hill, Ponsanooth, Cornwall, TR3 7JW

☎ (01872) 864532 ☎ 07990 887613
⊕ dynamitevalley.com

⊠ Dynamite Valley was set up in 2015 following a successful crowdfunding campaign and is located close to an historic gunpowder site near Falmouth. Beers are influenced by European and US beer styles. The brewery has expanded into bottling and canning. It has acquired the Rebel Brewery brand name and beers. ☎LIVE V

Gold Rush (ABV 4%) BITTER
Smooth gold bitter with light malt nose. Malt dominates throughout with bitterness, honey, apricot and pear drops. Long malty, bitter finish.
Ambrys Cornish Amber Ale (ABV 4.3%) BITTER
Amber bitter. Biscuit malt with stronger earthy hop and bitter character. Mixture of tropical fruits with citrus hints. Short finish.
Kennall Vale Pale (ABV 4.3%) PALE
Viaduct Pale Ale (ABV 4.4%) PALE

.

Gold, premium pale ale with honey and grapefruit aroma. Bitter citrus and pineapple hops and biscuit malt flavours with barley sugar.

TNT IPA (ABV 4.8%) PALE
Golden premium pale ale with malt and hop aroma. Heavy citrus hop bitterness with toffee apples, pear drops and malt balance.

Black Charge (ABV 5%) STOUT
Black, oatmeal-style, sweet stout. Powerful flavours of roast coffee, dark chocolate, malt and molasses throughout. Bitter, dry, short finish.

Frog Hill Cornish IPA (ABV 6%) IPA

Eagle

Havelock Street, Bedford, MK40 4LU
☎ (01234) 272766 ⊕ eaglebrewery.co.uk

Founded in 1876 and remained with the Wells Family until 2017, when the brewery and its brands were acquired by Marston's, and renamed Eagle Brewery. It brewed Young's beers after the closure of the Ram Brewery in 2007 and the popular Bedfordshire ale, Eagle IPA. In 2022 the brewery was sold to SA Damm and all production of cask beers transferred to other breweries in the Carlsberg Marston's Brewing Co. See Banks's for beer list. ‼️�♦

Eagles Crag

Unit 21, Robinwood Mill, Todmorden, West Yorkshire, OL14 8JA
☎ (01706) 810394 ⊕ eaglescragbrewery.com

Eagles Crag is named after, and overlooked by, a prominent landmark, famous in local folklore. Its eight-barrel plant is situated in a former textile mill. Commercial brewing began in 2017 and the two founders both have over 35 years of brewing experience. Expansion has led to a range of styles – including an occasional Imperial Stout aged in whisky casks. Beers can be fined as vegan on request. Eagles Crag supply more than 200 outlets in Lancashire, Yorkshire and Manchester. The brewery taproom opens during the last weekend of every month. 🚚♦V♻

Eagle of Light (ABV 3.4%) BITTER
The Eagle's Feather (ABV 3.8%) BITTER
Traditional Yorkshire bitter. Malty and fruity with a dry bitter finish.

Pale Eagle (ABV 4%) GOLD
Easy-drinking, well-balanced golden ale. Light citrus notes offset by a touch of sweetness giving a smooth bitter finish.

The Eagle's Strike (ABV 4%) GOLD
Golden in colour with citrus fruit prominent in the aroma and flavour. It has a crisp and bitter aftertaste.

The Eagle's Jester (ABV 4.3%) PALE
Fruity hop flavours combine with balanced malts leading to a refreshing, modern-style tasty pint.

Eagle of Kindness (ABV 4.4%) PALE
Pale ale with a golden blonde hue. Its hoppy character is balanced with notes of malt, packing a lot of flavour into a rounded body.

Black Eagle (ABV 4.6%) STOUT
Luscious black creamy stout. Dry roast flavours develop in the mouth. The aftertaste is bitter and crisp.

The Eagle has Landed (ABV 4.6%) BITTER
An amber best bitter with a good balance of fruit and malt. Moderate bitterness with a lingering malty finish.

Golden Eagle (ABV 4.7%) PALE
Classic, robust, well-balanced pale ale, pleasantly malty and fruity. It has a crisp and bitter farewell.

Eagle of Darkness (ABV 5%) PORTER

Refreshing dark brown porter. A subtle blend of chocolate malt and raisin-like fruit develops into a mellow sweet aftertaste.

Bald Eagle (ABV 6.9%) IPA
A big IPA with plenty of bittering; beautiful hoppy citrus aromas with plenty of fruit balanced by the malt flavours.

Earl Soham SIBA

Meadow Works, Cross Green, Debenham, Suffolk, IP14 6RP
☎ (01728) 861213 ⊕ earlsohambrewery.co.uk

Earl Soham was set up behind the Victoria pub in 1984 and continued there until 2001 when the brewery relocated, moving again in 2013 to Debenham. Around 30 outlets are supplied and two pubs are owned.
‼️�♦LIVE

Gannet Mild (ABV 3.3%) MILD
A beautifully balanced mild, sweet and fruity flavour with a lingering, coffee aftertaste.

Victoria Bitter (ABV 3.6%) BITTER
A light, fruity, amber session beer with a clean taste and a long, lingering hoppy aftertaste.

Elizabeth Ale (ABV 4%) BITTER
Sir Roger's Porter (ABV 4.2%) PORTER
Roast/coffee aroma and berry fruit introduce a full-bodied porter with roast/coffee flavours. Dry roast finish.

Albert Ale (ABV 4.4%) BITTER
Brandeston Gold (ABV 4.5%) GOLD
Popular beer brewed with local ingredients. Lovely sharp clean flavour, malty/hoppy and heavily laden with citrus fruit. Malty finish.

Earth Ale

Bothy Vineyard, Oakley Park, Faringdon Road, Frilford Heath, Oxfordshire, OX13 6QW ☎ 07508 553546 ⊕ earthale.com

After brewing at various London breweries, Earth Ale settled down at the Chocolate Factory complex in 2019, then moved to the Vale of the White Horse in 2021, using a six-barrel plant. A wide range of beers is available in kegs and cans. ♦

East London SIBA

Unit 45, Fairways Business Centre, Lammas Road, Leyton, London, E10 7QB
☎ (020) 8539 0805 ⊕ eastlondonbrewing.com

East London Brewing Company is an award-winning, 25-barrel brewery established in 2011 by Stu and Claire. The brewery brews a core range of regular beers available in cask, keg, bottle and can. Regular specials are made, including an annual green-hopped beer each September, in collaboration with Walthamstow Beer (a collective of small-batch hop growers). ♦LIVE

Pale Ale (ABV 4%) PALE
Amber beer with spicy hops, bitter lemon, tropical fruits and biscuit that are there in the dry aftertaste. Hoppy aroma.

Foundation Bitter (ABV 4.2%) BITTER
Orange marmalade, apricot and sultanas flavours overlaid with honey caramel, and roasty chocolate. Sweet, fruity, spicy, dry, bitter, roasty finish.

Nightwatchman (ABV 4.5%) BROWN
Malty caramel sweetness with a roast nuttiness and bitterness providing a good balance with dark fruits. Malty, sweet, dry aftertaste.

Cowcatcher American Pale Ale (ABV 4.8%) PALE

Smooth pale ale with sweet fruity aroma. Honey, grapefruit, tropical fruits and malt flavours and a dryish bitter aftertaste.

Jamboree (ABV 4.8%) BLOND
Slightly hoppy, bitter flavour with a gentle fruity character of orange and some malt. Long and bitter dry, spicy finish.

Quadrant Oatmeal Stout (ABV 5.5%) STOUT
Easy-drinking smooth stout with raisins and marmalade on a chocolaty roasty base with a touch of sweet black treacle.

Eden River SIBA

Unit 3, Hartness Road, Penrith, Cumbria, CA11 9BD
☎ (01768) 210565 ⊕ edenriverbrewco.uk

Originally named Eden Brewery, the name changed to Eden River in 2018. Set up in 2011, the brewery is now a 10-barrel plant and has been run by Andrew Hunter since 2019. The brewery has expanded its distribution to regional pubs and retail outlets, rebranding its labels and canning and bottling lines have been installed. ‼♦LIVE GF V

Fuggles (ABV 3.8%) PALE
Initially sweet, a gently hopped pale beer with a bitter finish.

Beacon (ABV 4%) BITTER

Penrith Porter (ABV 4%) PORTER

Emperor (ABV 4.6%) PALE
Fascinatingly fruity beer with balanced malt and hops and a hint of butterscotch combining to a rich bitter finish.

Edinburgh Beer Factory

The Works, Implement Road, West Barns, Dunbar, EH11 4EQ
☎ (0131) 442 4562 ⊕ edinburghbeerfactory.co.uk

Family-run brewery that was established in 2015. Packaging inspired by Leith-born artist Eduardo Paolozzi. The beers are available in bottle, keg and can. Brewing ceased in Edinburgh in 2022, before moving to West Barns, East Lothian. ‼◆

Eight Arch SIBA

Unit 1, Stone Lane Industrial Estate, Wimborne, Dorset, BH21 1HB
☎ (01202) 889254 ☎ 07554 445647
⊕ 8archbrewing.co.uk

⊠ Multi award-winning brewery established in 2014, originally using a five-barrel plant on an industrial estate on the outskirts of Wimborne. It expanded to 10 barrels in 2021, and moved to new premises across the road in 2024. A separate bar area, with a window overlooking the brew plant, has been installed. The taproom is open Fridays and Saturdays. ‼☰♦LIVE V◆

Session (ABV 3.8%) PALE
Square Logic (ABV 4.2%) PALE
Little Dragon (ABV 4.5%) SPECIALITY
Dainty (ABV 4.8%) PALE
Easy Life (ABV 5%) PALE
Corbel (ABV 5.5%) IPA
Strong golden ale with hops dominating yet balanced with bitterness.

Eko (NEW)

Unit 2A-2, Copeland Park, 133 Copeland Road, Peckham, London, SE15 3SN ⊕ ekobrewery.com

Brewing has taken place since 2018 at various breweries around the country and this continues to be the case following the opening of its brewery tap in Peckham. A brewery is planned to be installed in due course. No cask ale.

Electric Bear SIBA

Unit 12, Maltings Trading Estate, Locksbrook Road, Bath, BA1 3JL
☎ (01225) 424088 ⊕ electricbearbrewing.com

Electric Bear began brewing in 2015 using a purpose-built, 18-barrel plant, expanding capacity in 2016, 2018, and 2020. Its brewery tap showcases a selection of the range, including exclusive one-offs. A wide range of beer is available in cans and kegs and all are unfiltered, unfined and unpasteurised. It also offers a single, ever-changing cask-conditioned beer. ‼☰♦LIVE GF V◆

Gizmo (ABV 4%) PALE

Electro

Unit 19, Parc Teifi, Cardigan, SA43 1EW

Office: Glenydd Cwmin St Dogmaels, Cardigan, SA43 3HF ⊠ contact@electrobrewing.com

Artisan brewery with beers first appearing 2021. Some of the output is one-off cask beers. Brewing is currently suspended.

Elements

Unit 2, Upton Downs Farm, Upton, Burford, Oxfordshire, OX18 4LY ☎ 07984 308670
⊕ elementsbrewery.co.uk

Began brewing in 2018 on a six-barrel plant, producing small-batch, hop-forward beers. No real ale. ☰◆

Elephant School

See Brentwood

Elgood's SIBA

North Brink Brewery, Wisbech, Cambridgeshire, PE13 1LW
☎ (01945) 583160 ⊕ elgoods-brewery.co.uk

⊠ The North Brink brewery was established in 1795. Owned by the Elgood family since 1878, the fifth generation are now involved in running the business. Elgood's has approximately 30 tied pubs within a 50-mile radius of the brewery and a substantial free trade. Lambic-style beers are produced using the brewery's old open cooling trays as fermenting vessels. Off-sales are available year round from the shop in the brewery office (when the visitor centre is closed). ‼☰♦V

Black Dog (ABV 3.6%) MILD
Black-red mild with liquorice and chocolate. Dry roasty finish.

Cambridge Bitter (ABV 3.8%) BITTER
Fruit and malt on the nose with increasing hops and balancing malt on the palate. Dry finish.

Cambridge Gold (ABV 3.9%) GOLD
Session golden ale with big-hearted citrus hop and defined underlying malt. Pleasantly bittersweet with a sustained hop bitter finish.

Blackberry Porter (ABV 4.5%) SPECIALITY
A rich, full-bodied dark porter. With roast malt flavours complemented by sweet, juicy blackberry fruit.

Plum Porter (ABV 4.5%) SPECIALITY

Elmesthorpe

Church Farm Offices, Church Farm, Station Road, Elmesthorpe, Leicestershire, LE9 7SG ☎ 07754 321283 ⊕ elmesthorpebrewery.com

Elmesthorpe was established in 2017 by a beer enthusiast and pub landlord. The company has gone from strength to strength and now operates fives sites as well as supplying many pubs and taps in Leicestershire, Nottinghamshire, Warwickshire, Derbyshire and Staffordshire.

Tight Bar Steward (ABV 3.7%) MILD
CAPA (ABV 3.8%) BITTER
Aylmers Ale (ABV 4.1%) BITTER
Barons Best Bitter (ABV 4.3%) BITTER
Hansom Ale (ABV 4.4%) GOLD
Lord Cullens Ruby (ABV 4.5%) BITTER
Debbie Does (ABV 4.9%) GOLD
Ale O'Clock (ABV 5.2%) BITTER
Taking the Biscuit (ABV 5.3%) BITTER

Elmtree SIBA

Unit 10, Oakwood Industrial Estate, Harling Road, Snetterton, NR16 2JU
☎ (01953) 887065 ⊕ elmtreebeers.co.uk

⊠ Established in 2007, Elmtree brews on a six-barrel plant. More than 120 free trade outlets are supplied directly. The brewery specialises in high quality ales made with the best ingredients. Some of the strongest beers are only available in bottled-conditioned form. Bespoke beers for individual pubs are also brewed. !! ⬛♦LIVE V

Burston's Cuckoo (ABV 3.8%) GOLD
Assertive lemon hoppiness dominates a soft malty backdrop. A crisp bitterness gives definition to a slowly drying finale.
Bitter (ABV 4.2%) BITTER
Traditional malt and hop nose. Solid and well-balanced with a bittersweet hoppy maltiness throughout. Flowing, crisp, hoppy ending.
Norfolk's 80 Shilling Ale (ABV 4.5%) BITTER
Mixed fruit nose introduces a sweet fruity bitter with a bitter counterbalance. Short, drying finish.
Dark Horse Stout (ABV 5%) STOUT
Solid coffee and malt aroma. A cornucopia of vanilla, dark chocolate, and roast with a sweet foundation. Long, strong finale.
Golden Pale Ale (ABV 5%) PALE
Sweet fruity aroma with hints of honey. Even handed mix of lemon and crisp hoppiness with a defined bittering finale.
Nightlight Mild (ABV 5.7%) MILD
A heavy mix of liquorice, roast and malt infuses aroma and first taste. A sweet spiciness slowly develops.

Elusive SIBA

Units 3-5, Marino Way, Hogwood Lane Industrial Estate, Finchampstead, Berkshire, RG40 4RF
☎ (0118) 973 2153 ⊕ elusivebrewing.com

Established in 2016, award-winning Elusive Brewing has now expanded its capacity with a 60% increase in tank space, totalling 110HL. It produces a diverse range of cask, KeyKeg and canned beers (all unfiltered and unpasteurised). It continues to be involved in many brewery collaborations and tap takeovers. There is also a new shop for merchandise, and taproom (own beer and guests) with three flat screens which can play retro computer games, and a covered outdoor area in the summer. ⬛♦V◆

Microball (ABV 3.7%) MILD
Level Up (ABV 5%) RED
Overdrive (ABV 5.5%) IPA
Oregon Trail (ABV 5.8%) IPA
Spellbinder (ABV 6%) SPECIALITY

Elvington

Station Yard, York Road, Elvington, YO41 4EL
☎ (01904) 607167 ⊕ pivovarorders.co.uk/elvington-brewery

Part of the Pivovar Group, that includes the Tapped breweries in Sheffield and Leeds, that was established in 2021 to brew Mittel Pils lager for its pubs. The lager is brewed on a £1 million, German-built plant. No real ale. ◆

Emmanuales

70 Cromwell Street, Sheffield, S6 3RN ☎ 07881 995604 ⊕ emmanuales.co.uk

Emmanuales has been brewing beers of biblical proportions since 2014 AD, spreading the 'good news' one beer at a time. Drawing upon the heritage of the Christian faith, it is not out to force religion down people's throats – just beer! Following a sabbatical in 2018 resumption of brewing was further delayed by the pandemic but full production resumed in 2021. Production now mostly available in can but some bottle, keg and cask is packaged. LIVE

Emperor's

Unit 13, Bailey Brook Industrial Estate, Amber Drive, Langley Mill, Derbyshire, NG16 4BE
⊕ emperorsbrewery.co.uk

Former homebrewer now brewing imperial stouts and porters commercially.

Empire SIBA

The Old Boiler House, Unit 33, Upper Mills, Slaithwaite, Huddersfield, West Yorkshire, HD7 5HA
☎ (01484) 847343 ☎ 07966 592276
⊕ empirebrewing.com

☺Empire Brewing was set up in 2006 in a mill on the bank of the scenic Huddersfield Narrow Canal, close to the centre of Slaithwaite. In 2011 the brewery upgraded from a five-barrel to a 12-barrel plant. Beers are supplied to local free houses and through independent specialist beer agencies and wholesalers. !! ♦LIVE

Chocolate & Cherry Mild (ABV 3.8%) MILD
Golden Warrior (ABV 3.8%) GOLD
Moonrakers Mild (ABV 3.8%) MILD
Strikes Back (ABV 4%) GOLD
Charlie Don't Surf (ABV 4.2%) BLOND
West Coast Pale (ABV 4.3%) PALE
White Lion (ABV 4.3%) BLOND

Engine Shed Project

See Brunswick

Ennerdale SIBA

Chapel Row, Rowrah, Cumbria, CA26 3XS
☎ (01946) 862977 ⊕ ennerdalebrewery.co.uk

☺This family-owned brewery was established in 2010 using a 10-barrel plant in a converted barn. In 2016 the brewery moved to larger premises and expanded considerably with a brewery tap and restaurant. It distributes throughout Cumbria and the North of England. The tap is open Wednesday to Sunday. !! 🍴 ◆ GF ✦

Blonde (ABV 3.8%) BLOND
A sweet, fruity, light-coloured beer with gentle bitterness.
Darkest (ABV 4.2%) BROWN
Roast malty aromas and flavours combine with sweet fruitiness. The finish is of lasting dry roast malts.
Wild (ABV 4.2%) MILD
Fruity and hoppy beer with some balancing malt remaining in the long bitter finish.

Enville SIBA

Coxgreen, Hollies Lane, Enville, DY7 5LG
☎ (01384) 873728 ⊕ envilleales.com

⊠ Enville Brewery is sited on a picturesque Victorian, Grade II-listed farm complex, using natural well water, traditional steam brewing and a reed and willow-effluent plant. Enville Ale is infused with honey and is from a 19th century recipe for beekeeper's ale passed down from the former proprietor's great-great aunt. All beer is distributed in cask to a large, locally-based free trade. 🍴◆

Simpkiss (ABV 4%) BITTER
Caramel smooth start, caramel body with sweet malt and hop bite. Fruity hop finish, easing finish and satisfying.
White (ABV 4.2%) SPECIALITY
Yellow with a malt, hops and fruit aroma. Hoppy but sweet finish.
Ale (ABV 4.5%) SPECIALITY
Sweet malty aroma and taste, honey becomes apparent before bitterness finally dominates.
Old Porter (ABV 4.5%) PORTER
Black with a creamy head and sulphurous aroma. Sweet and fruity start with touches of spice. Good balance between sweet and bitter, but hops dominate the finish.
Ginger Beer (ABV 4.6%) SPECIALITY
Golden bright with gently gingered tangs. A drinkable beer with no acute flavours but a satisfying aftertaste of sweet hoppiness.

Epochal

Payne Street, Glasgow, G4 0LE ⊕ epochal.co.uk

Gareth Young founded Epochal in 2021. He specialises in what he describes as Scottish stock beer; brewed with whole cone hops and aged in wooden casks with dry hops and Brettanomyces yeast. All beers are naturally conditioned in bottle and keg. LIVE

Escape

Unit P, Dodd Lane Industrial Estate, Chorley Road, Westhoughton, BL5 3NA
☎ (01204) 228969 ⊕ escapebrewery.co.uk

Small brewery launched in Bolton in 2019 by three friends. Brews a range of regular and occasional beers on a 2.5-barrel kit previously owned by Porter Brewing Co. Has a microbar in Adlington, the Old Post Office, and an 18th century pub, the Collier's Arms in Aspull, both selling Escape and guest beers. V

Day Trip to Bangor (ABV 3.8%) PALE
If the Caravan's A Rockin' (ABV 3.8%) BLOND
Avoid Detection (ABV 4.2%) PALE
The Shackles Are Off (ABV 4.2%) PALE
Hoppy beer with a sweet citrus fruity centre and a long lasting bitter finish.
Erik Weiss (ABV 4.4%) PALE
Tom, Dick & Harry (ABV 4.5%) BITTER

Escapist

Unit 4a, Hambrook Business Centre, Cheesemans Lane, Chichester, PO18 8XP
☎ (01243) 776599 ☎ 07545 905610
⊕ theescapistchichester.co.uk

The Escapist Craft Beer Bar in Crane Street, Chichester, opened a brewery at Hambrook in the Sussex countryside in 2022. As well as producing its own beers, it participates in collaborations with like-minded brewers.

Essex Street

See Temple Brew House

Evan Evans SIBA

1 Rhosmaen Street, Llandeilo, Carmarthenshire, SA19 6LU
☎ (01558) 824455 ⊕ evanevansbrewery.com

⊠ Evan Evans brews six core beers and an array of seasonal beers. The company owns the Celt craft beer range, and produces the Fire Island brand of gluten-free bottle beers. The Evan-Evans beers form the traditional cask beer range. The Archers brand name is used for occasional beers. The brewery markets its own Redhog Wild Cider (gluten-free and vegan-friendly). The brewery also bottles its own beer brands as well as bottling for other independent breweries. !! 🍴◆LIVE

Best Welsh Beer (ABV 4%) BITTER
WPA (Welsh Pale Ale) (ABV 4.1%) PALE
Cwrw (ABV 4.2%) BITTER
Wrecker (ABV 4.5%) BITTER
Sea Scape (ABV 4.6%) GOLD
Warrior (ABV 4.6%) BITTER

Everards SIBA

Cooper Way, Everards Meadows, Leicester, LE19 2AN
☎ (0116) 201 4100 ⊕ everards.co.uk

☺Everards was established in 1849 by William Everard and remains an independent, sixth generation family company. Its state-of-the-art brewery, nestled within Everards Meadows, is home to an impressive beer hall, small-batch brewery and shop. It hosts weekly award-winning brewery tours. Everards has an estate of more than 150 pubs throughout the East Midlands and beyond, all run by independent business owners. !! 🍴◆✦

Sunchaser (ABV 4%) GOLD
Tiger (ABV 4.2%) BITTER
A mid-brown, well-balanced best bitter crafted for broad appeal, benefiting from a long, bittersweet finish.
Old Original (ABV 5.2%) BITTER
Full-bodied, mid-brown strong bitter with a pleasant rich, grainy mouthfeel. Well-balanced flavours, with malt slightly to the fore, merging into a long, satisfying finish.

Ewe Brew (Hampshire) (NEW)

🍺 **Andover Tap at the Lamb, Andover, Hampshire, SP10 2EA**

Microbrewery that opened in 2023 housed in the Andover Tap at the Lamb. Production is predominantly for consumption on site.

Ewebrew SIBA

2 Naast, Achnasheen, Poolewe, IV22 2LL ☎ 07494 310317 ⊕ ewebrew.beer

⊛Commissioned in early 2022, Ewebrew is the creation of James and Jo Struthers. Initially two core beers are brewed with an ever-evolving range coming on stream. A self catering holiday cottage is operated adjacent to the brewery. LIVE

Arctic Convoy (ABV 4.5%) BLOND
Firemore (ABV 5%) BITTER

Exale SIBA

Unit 2C, Uplands Business Park, Blackhorse Lane, Walthamstow, London, E17 5QJ ⊕ exalebrewing.com

Starting as Hale Brewery in Tottenham in 2017, expansion in 2019 saw a new brewery in Walthamstow and a new name. Most famous for Krankie, the Iron Brew Sour. The beers are produced in keg and cans with an increasing amount of occasional cask ale available, often in collaboration with other breweries. As well as the Three Colts in Bethnal Green, another bar will be added during the currency of this Guide. ◆

Exeter SIBA

Unit 1, Cowley Bridge Road, Exeter, Devon, EX4 4NX ☎ (01392) 259059 ⊕ exeterbrewery.co.uk

⊠ Exeter began brewing in 2003 and is the largest brewery in the city, distributing its products from Cornwall to Gloucester, and to London. It produces Avocet, Devon's original organic ale. It moved to its present site in 2012, having outgrown its previous location. !!☞◆⬥

Lighterman (ABV 3.4%) BITTER
Tomahawk (ABV 3.4%) BITTER
Avocet (ABV 3.9%) BITTER
A refreshing light ale, slight citrus/fruit on nose which comes out more on taste. An easy-drinking summer-style beer.
'fraid Not (ABV 4%) GOLD
Easy to drink and refreshing with a gentle lingering aftertaste.
Ferryman (ABV 4.2%) BITTER
A malty slightly spiced biscuit with a sweetness to the ale. An easy-drinking traditional session bitter.
County Best (ABV 4.6%) BITTER
An amber-coloured bitter, malty and fruity flavoured beer with a bittersweet finish.
Darkness (ABV 5.1%) STOUT
Full bodied stout. Roasted malt dominates the aroma. Complex taste with roast chocolate. Hints of liquorice in a bitter finish.
MC6 (Mash Concentration 6) (ABV 6%) OLD
An old ale with a sweet taste. Lots of malts and roasts blending together to give a lovely lasting aftertaste.

Exile

See Exmoor

Exit 33

Unit 1, Petre Drive, Sheffield, South Yorkshire, S4 7PZ ☎ (0114) 270 9991 ⊠ office@exit33.beer

⊛This eight-barrel brewery was founded in Sheffield in 2008 as Brew Company but rebranded as Exit 33 in 2014. In 2022 it began producing beers under the HQ Beers name. Social enterprise schemes are supported from the sales through the Harlequin, Sheffield. The plant and equipment is available for use by cuckoo breweries. Brewing is currently suspended. ◆V

Exmoor SIBA

Golden Hill Brewery, Old Brewery Road, Wiveliscombe, TA4 2PW ☎ (01984) 623798 ⊕ exmoorales.co.uk

Somerset's largest independent brewery was founded in 1980 in the old Hancock's brewery, which closed in 1959. In 2015 it moved to new, larger premises within 100 yards of the original site, doubling capacity. More than 400 outlets in the South West are supplied, plus others nationwide via wholesalers and pub chains. More recently it launched Pathfinder and Exile as modern craft sub-brands. ☞◆V

Ale (ABV 3.8%) BITTER
Mid-brown, medium-bodied session bitter. Mixture of malt and hops in the aroma and taste lead to a hoppy, bitter aftertaste.
Fox (ABV 4.2%) BITTER
Gold (ABV 4.5%) BITTER
Golden best bitter with balance of malt and fruity hop on the nose and palate with sweetness following. Bitter finish.
Islander (ABV 4.5%) PALE
Stag (ABV 4.8%) BITTER
A pale brown beer, with a malty taste and aroma, and a bitter finish.
Beast (ABV 6.6%) STRONG

Experimental

See Dog's Window

Eyam

Unit 4, Eyam Hall Craft Centre, Main Road, Eyam, Hope Valley, Derbyshire, S32 5QW ☎ (01433) 639795 ☎ 07976 432682 ⊕ eyamrealalecompany.com

Brewing began in 2017 using a 1.5-barrel plant producing keg and bottle-conditioned beers. Most output goes to its shop and events but 10 local outlets are also supplied. LIVE

Facer's

A8-9, Ashmount Enterprise Park, Aber Road, Flint, CH6 5YL ☎ 07713 566370 ⊕ facersbrewery.com

Set up in 2003 by the now retired Dave Facer, it is now operated by long time employee Toby Dunn. It is the oldest brewery in Flintshire. Sales average some 30 barrels per week to around 100 outlets in North Wales and North West England. !!◆

Mountain Mild (ABV 3.3%) MILD
Clwyd Gold (ABV 3.5%) BITTER
Clean tasting session bitter, mid-brown in colour with a full mouthfeel. The malty flavours are accompanied by increasing hoppiness in the bitter finish.
Flintshire Bitter (ABV 3.7%) BITTER
Well-balanced session bitter with a full mouthfeel. Some fruitiness in aroma and taste with increasing hoppy bitterness in the dry finish.
Abbey Blonde (ABV 4%) BITTER
Abbey Original (ABV 4%) BITTER
Abbey Red (ABV 4%) BITTER
North Star Porter (ABV 4%) PORTER
Dark, smooth, porter-style beer with good roast notes and hints of coffee and chocolate. Some initial sweetness and caramel flavours followed by a hoppy bitter aftertaste.
Game Changer (ABV 4.1%) BITTER
Sunny Bitter (ABV 4.2%) BITTER

An amber beer with a dry taste. The hop aroma continues into the taste where some faint fruit notes are also present. Lasting dry finish.

DHB (Dave's Hoppy Beer) (ABV 4.3%) BITTER
A dry-hopped version of Splendid Ale with some sweet flavours also coming through in the mainly hoppy, bitter taste.

This Splendid Ale (ABV 4.3%) BITTER
Refreshing tangy best bitter, yellow in colour with a sharp hoppy, bitter taste. Good citrus fruit undertones with hints of grapefruit throughout.

Landslide (ABV 4.9%) BITTER
Full-flavoured, complex premium bitter with tangy orange marmalade fruitiness in aroma and taste. Long-lasting hoppy flavours throughout.

Fairy Glen

5 The Corn Store, Heol Ty Gwyn, Maesteg, CF34 0BG
☎ 07968 847878

Office: 60 Oaklands Avenue, Bridgend, CF31 4ST

Keg-only brewery that produces for special events and not for pubs etc. Beers are pre-carbonated.

Falstaff

▤ **24 Society Place, Normanton, Derby, DE23 6UH**
☎ 07947 242710 ⊕ falstaffbrewery.co.uk

⊗ Attached to the Falstaff freehouse, the brewery dates from 1999 but was refurbished and reopened in 2003 under new management as a 3.5-barrel plant. Updated again in 2017, it now operates as a six-barrel plant producing a core range of six beers plus specials. More than 90 outlets are supplied. ♦

3 Faze (ABV 3.8%) GOLD
Fist Full of Hops (ABV 4.5%) GOLD
Phoenix (ABV 4.7%) BITTER
A smooth, tawny ale with fruit and hop, joined by plenty of malt in the mouth. A subtle sweetness produces a drinkable ale.
Smiling Assassin (ABV 5.2%) BITTER
Darkside (ABV 6%) MILD
Good, Bad & Drunk (ABV 6.2%) BITTER

Faringdon

▤ **1 Park Road, Faringdon, Oxfordshire, SN7 7BP**

Faringdon Brewery opened in 2010. After a period of closure, brewing restarted in 2019, stopped again when the brewer left in 2021, and restarted in 2023 with a new brewer. All beers are supplied to the brewery tap, the Swan, when available.

Farm to Fermenter

See Vault City

Farm Yard SIBA

Gulf Lane, Cockerham, Lancashire, LA2 0ER
☎ (01253) 799988 ⊕ farmyardbrew.co.uk

⊕The brewery, set up in 2017 on a remote farm, has continued to expand and diversify with an ever-changing array of beers to complement the core range. The brewery underwent rebranding in 2022. Onsite is a vibrant taproom (open Thu-Sun), with regular live bands and street food. ⅋🍴♦V♦

Holmes Stead (ABV 3.4%) BITTER
TVO 54 (ABV 3.7%) BLOND
Haybob (ABV 3.9%) GOLD
Sheaf (ABV 4.1%) BLOND

Hoof (ABV 4.3%) SPECIALITY
Coffee and chocolate aromas, sweet with roast malt flavours and a little bitterness, a bit of fruit to balance.
Chaff (ABV 4.7%) BLOND
Gulf (ABV 5.8%) IPA

Farmageddon

See Fermanagh

Farmers

Office: 98 Main Street, Haworth, West Yorkshire, BD22 8DP
☎ (01748) 886297 ⊠ farmersmuker@gmail.com

⊕Formerly known as Haworth Steam, the five-barrel brewery has been in the Gascoigne family for more than 30 years. Beers are supplied exclusively to the two family-owned establishments. Beers are also sold under the Whitechapel brand name. 🍴V

Farnham SIBA

2 Pierrepont Home Farm, Farnham, GU10 3BS
☎ (01252) 447240 ⊕ farnhambrewing.co.uk

⊗ Farnham Brewing Co (FBC) is a microbrewery nestling in the beautiful rural setting of the Surrey Hills Area of Outstanding Natural Beauty. Established by three local families, it brews a variety of ales from the traditional to modern IPAs and American pale ales. Visitors are welcome. ♦

Farr Brew SIBA

Great Revel End Farm, Gaddesden Lane, Redbourn, Hertfordshire, AL3 7AR ☎ 07967 998820
⊕ farrbrew.com

⊗ Farr Brew began brewing in 2014, expanding in 2016 with a new 10-barrel facility. Ecological and environmental concerns are at the forefront of everything Farr Brew does. Community engagement includes hop-growing, and a homebrewers competition. The brewery now runs several pubs around Hertfordshire: Reading Rooms, Wheathampstead; Rising Sun, Slip End; Red Cow, Harpenden; Eight Bells, Old Hatfield, and Elephant & Castle, Amwell. ⅋🍴♦♦

Chief Jester (ABV 3.6%) PALE
Our Greatest Golden (ABV 4.1%) GOLD
Our Best Bitter (ABV 4.2%) BITTER
Our Most Perfect Ale (ABV 4.2%) PALE
Pride Pale (ABV 4.2%) PALE
Farr Afield (ABV 4.3%) BITTER
Black Listed IBA (ABV 4.5%) PALE
Farr & Away (ABV 4.5%) PALE
Farr Apart (ABV 4.8%) PALE
Rusty Stag (ABV 4.8%) BITTER
Fresh Start (ABV 4.9%) PALE
1492 (ABV 5%) GOLD
Porter (ABV 5%) PORTER

Farriers Arms

▤ **The Forstal, Mersham, Kent, TN25 6NU**
☎ (01233) 720444 ⊕ thefarriersarms.com

⊗ Brewing commenced in 2010 in this brewpub owned by a consortium of villagers. ⅋♦

Fat Cat

98-100 Lawson Road, Norwich, NR3 4LF ☎ 07807 579517/ 07795 633368 ⊕ fatcatbrewery.co.uk

☒ Established in 2005 by the owner of the Fat Cat and Fat Cat & Canary pubs, it is located in the same building as the brewery tap (separately owned). Beers are available in other outlets, mainly within Norwich and Norfolk and also it is distributed by Small Beer of Lincoln. ♦ LIVE GF V

Norwich Bitter (ABV 3.8%) BITTER
Grapefruit on the nose. A strong hoppy bitterness with underlying maltiness adds depth and complexity. Softly drying finale.

Tom Cat (ABV 4.1%) GOLD
A crisp citrus character with lemon, lime and orange in aroma and taste. Bitterness grows as cut grass hoppiness fades.

Milk Stout (ABV 4.6%) STOUT

Incredible Pale Ale (ABV 5.2%) PALE
Big hit of hoppiness with lemon and peach fruitiness. Background maltiness soon disappears under a level sustained bitterness. Full bodied.

Marmalade (ABV 5.5%) BITTER
Orange and malt pervades both aroma and taste. A full bodied mix of balanced flavours. A bittersweet finish with hoppiness.

Wild Cat IPA (ABV 6%) IPA

Fat Head (NEW)

⬛ 127 High Street, Weston-super-Mare, Somerset, BS23 1NH ☎ 07873 536969
✉ management@fatheadbrewery.com

☒ A microbrewery set up by Sam Cureton and Tom Adams in the centre of Weston-super-Mare in 2023 with a commitment to quality, innovation and the environment. Its current capacity of five fermenters ensures at least six ales rotating seven days a week. Used grain is donated to Osprey Outdoors, a local environmental organisation that composts the grain for use by local allotments. The brewery also works with a local charity tree nursery meaning a tree is planted for every brewer's barrel sold. ♦

Fauna

Norfolk Estate Office, London Road, Arundel, West Sussex, BN18 9AS
☎ (01903) 863580 ☎ 07742 144340
⊕ faunabrewing.com

Combining three core values of conservation, environmentalism and good beer, Fauna Brewing was launched in 2021. The brewery work with three charity partners in aid of endangered species that benefit from each beer sale. ♠

Feisty

The Stables at Gable Manor, Wooburn Common Road, Wooburn Green, HP10 0JS ⊕ feistybeerco.com

A nanobrewery in converted stables, which began brewing commercially in 2022 with a capacity of 53 litres (0.65 barrels), but with plans to expand significantly. It currently produces EcoKegs, cans and occasional bottle-conditioned beers. It aims to specialise in higher ABV craft beers, stouts, and fruit-infused beers. Longer term it also aims to have one flagship cask-conditioned ale. It currently distributes to one or two local beer shops, taprooms and local markets. LIVE

Felday

⬛ Royal Oak, Village Green, Felday Glade, Holmbury St. Mary, Surrey, RH5 6PF
☎ (01306) 730654 ⊕ feldaybrewery.co.uk

Brewing began in 2017 on a custom-made plant in a small, purpose-built, building next to the Royal Oak pub car park. Almost all of the beer is supplied to the pub although it may very occasionally be seen elsewhere. ♦

Felinfoel SIBA

Farmers Row, Felinfoel, Llanelli, SA14 8LB
☎ (01554) 773357 ⊕ felinfoel-brewery.com

Founded in the 1830s, the company is still family-owned and is now the oldest brewery in Wales. The present buildings are Grade II*-listed and were built in the 1870s. It supplies cask ale to half its 84 houses, though some use top pressure dispense, and to approximately 350 free trade outlets. ‼ ⴹ ♦

Dragon Welsh IPA (ABV 3.6%) BITTER

Dragon Stout (ABV 4.1%) STOUT

Double Dragon (ABV 4.2%) BITTER
This pale brown beer has a malty, fruity aroma. The taste is also malt and fruit with a background hop presence throughout. A malty and fruity finish.

Nut Brown Ale (ABV 4.3%) BITTER

Celtic Pride (ABV 4.5%) BITTER

Dragons Heart (ABV 4.5%) BITTER

Welsh ESB (ABV 4.6%) BITTER

Double Dragon Export (ABV 4.7%) BITTER

Fell

Unit 27, Moor Lane Business Park, Flookburgh, Cumbria, LA11 7NG
☎ (01539) 558980 ⊕ fellbrewery.co.uk

☺ Fell Brewery was founded in 2013 by homebrewer Tim Bloomer and friend Andrew Carter, brewing beers inspired by their travels in the US and Belgium. Production capacity is 15 barrels. It has five retail outlets situated in Cartmel, Chorlton (near Manchester), and Penrith, with two (one an events space) in Kendal. The brewery is powered by solar panels. ♦

Ghyll (ABV 3.4%) PALE
Inviting citrus aromas follow through nicely in this hoppy bitter beer with fruit and sweetness present for balance.

Crag (ABV 3.8%) BITTER
A bitter beer with sweet malts, soon to be replaced by an increasing hop presence, giving a lasting bitter finish.

Tinderbox IPA (ABV 6.3%) IPA
A complex beer with bitterness. Moderate sweetness balances the resiny and citrus hop flavours until overtaken in a drying finish.

Fengate

Unit 3, Cobble Acre Park, Brick Kiln Road, Hevingham, Norfolk, NR10 5NL
☎ (01263) 479953 ☎ 07884 960697
✉ fengatebrewery@gmail.com

☒ Fengate Brewery was established in 2019. Head brewer and owner Alistair brews a selection of traditional ales with a mix of new beer styles. Beers can be found in pubs and bottle shops in the surrounding area. ⴹ ♦

Hudson's Bitter (ABV 3.6%) BITTER

3 Threads Smoked Porter (ABV 4%) PORTER

Cobble Acre Pale Ale (ABV 4.5%) PALE

West Coast IPA (ABV 4.8%) PALE

Extra Double Stout (ABV 9%) STOUT

Fermanagh

75 Main Street, Derrygonnelly, BT93 6HW
☎ (028) 6864 1254

Fermanagh Beer Company is a small-scale brewery producing a range of bottle-conditioned beers within their Inishmacsaint and Farmageddon brands. Draught is also available at the brewery's pub, Old Pal's Bar, Derrygonnelly, as well as at other outlets throughout the county, including the 5-star Lough Erne resort. **LIVE V**

Brewed under the Farmageddon brand name:
Gold (ABV 4.2%) PALE
Mosaic IPA (ABV 6.3%) IPA

Fernandes

🍺 **Luis Bar, 5 Avison Yard, Kirkgate, Wakefield, West Yorkshire, WF1 1UA** ☎ **07949 833138** ⊕ **luisbar.co.uk**

😊 Opened in 1997 and housed in a 19th century malthouse, Fernandes Brewery was sold to the Ossett Group in 2007. In 2021 it was extensively refurbished and reopened independent of Ossett as Luis Bar @ Fernandes Brewery. **!! ♦**

Ferry Ales SIBA

Ferry Hill Farm, Ferry Road, Fiskerton, Lincolnshire, LN3 4HU
☎ **(0800) 999 3226** ☎ **07790 241999**
⊕ **ferryalesbrewery.co.uk**

Ferry Ales Brewery (FAB) began brewing in 2016 using a five-barrel plant. It is situated just outside Fiskerton, Lincolnshire. Beers can be found in the Lincoln area and beyond. A range of between 12-15 beers are available in cask, keg, bottle and can. 🍽

Just Jane (ABV 3.8%) BITTER
49 SQN (ABV 4.9%) BITTER
Smokey Joe (ABV 4.9%) PORTER

Fierce SIBA

Unit 60, Howe Moss Terrace, Dyce, Aberdeen, AB21 0GR
☎ **(01224) 035035** ⊕ **fiercebeer.com**

The multi-award-winning Fierce Beer was established by Dave Grant and David McHardy, brewing its first beer in 2016. It produces a range of hoppy, fruity, dark and speciality beers. Production is in cask, KeyKeg and cans. Three bars are owned, in Aberdeen, Edinburgh and Manchester. **V♦**

Scottish Export (ABV 5%) PALE

Fierce & Noble

25 Mina Road, St Werburgh's, Bristol, BS2 9TA
☎ **(0117) 955 6666** ⊕ **fierceandnoble.com**

Founded in 2017 to supply beer to the Grounded community café chain in Bristol, beers can now be found across Bristol and the South West. A range of IPAs and occasional specials are brewed on an eight-barrel plant. The onsite taproom and brewery shop regularly hold events, and are open year round Wednesday-Sunday. **!! 🍽 ♦ ♪**

Session IPA (ABV 4.2%) PALE
American Pale Ale (ABV 5%) PALE
Abundant powerful hop flavours add pine and tropical fruit to the slightly sweet malt background, before a lingering bitter aftertaste

FILO

The Old Town Brewery, Torfield Cottage, 8 Old London Road, Hastings, East Sussex, TN34 3HA
☎ **(01424) 420212** ⊕ **filobrewing.co.uk**

⊠ Owners of the First In Last Out (FILO) set up their own brewery in the back of the pub in 1985, to become Hastings first brewpub. The current owners took over in 1988, and in 2011 relocated the brewery to the nearby Grade II-listed stable at Torfield Cottage. The brewery continues to supply ales to the FILO pub, together with many other pubs within Hastings, and throughout Sussex and Kent. ♦

Crofters (ABV 3.8%) BITTER
Churches Pale Ale (ABV 4.2%) PALE
Old Town Tom (ABV 4.5%) SPECIALITY
Gold (ABV 4.8%) GOLD

Fine Tuned SIBA

Unit 16, Wessex Park, Bancombe Trading Estate, Bancombe Road, Somerton, TA11 6SB
☎ **(01458) 897273** ☎ **07872 139945**
⊕ **finetunedbrewery.com**

Established in Langport, Somerset in 2016, but relocated to its current site in 2017. **♦LIVE**

Pitch Perfect (ABV 3.8%) BITTER
Langport Bitter (ABV 4%) BITTER
Sunshine Reggae (ABV 4.2%) PALE
Free Style (ABV 4.5%) GOLD
Twist and Stout (ABV 4.5%) STOUT
Hop Culture (ABV 5%) GOLD

Finney's

51 Wrockwardine Road, Wellington, Telford, Shropshire, TF1 3DA
☎ **(01952) 412224** ✉ **finney@blueyonder.co.uk**

A half-barrel capacity microbrewery supplying local pubs in Wellington and Oakengates as well as Shropshire beer festivals on an occasional basis since 2010. The brewery produces a small but steadily expanding range of hand-crafted ales in a range of styles, upon request from the pubs they appear in. Most made with traditional hop varieties. Beers produced commercially include an award-winning strong dark bitter and a pale bitter often produced for Christmas. Brewing is currently suspended.

Fire Island

See Evan Evans

Firebird SIBA

Old Rudgwick Brickworks, Lynwick Street, Rudgwick, West Sussex, RH12 3UW
☎ **(01403) 823180** ⊕ **firebirdbrewing.co.uk**

⊠ Firebird began brewing in 2013 and has grown rapidly with new beers, new vessels, an extended warehouse and an expanded team. There is an upstairs bar onsite. **!! 🍽 ♦ LIVE GF V♪**

Two Horses (ABV 3.8%) PALE
Parody (ABV 4.5%) PALE

Firebrand SIBA

Unit 2, Southgate Technology Park, Pennygillam Industrial Estate, Launceston, Cornwall, PL15 7ED
☎ **(01566) 86069** ⊕ **firebrandbrewing.co.uk**

⊠ Formerly known as Penpont and also as Altarnun, Firebrand began brewing in 2008 and has steadily increased its range and production since then. The award-winning brewery currently uses a 12-barrel plant. Beers are available in pubs across Cornwall. The tap has regular music events (details on website). **!! 🍽 ♦ LIVE ♪**

Shipwreck Coast (ABV 4%) PALE
Patchwork Rocket Pale (ABV 4.2%) PALE
Golden pale ale where bitter hop tastes dominate,
balanced by sweet malt, gentle dryness. Grapefruit,
tropical and vine fruits. Long finish.
West Coast Session IPA (ABV 4.2%) PALE
An Howl (ABV 4.8%) PALE
Amber/gold, hoppy pale ale with citrus and tropical fruit
flavours. Balanced by sweet, grainy and nutty malt and
robust bitterness.
Black Stuff Stout (ABV 5%) STOUT

Firebrick SIBA

**Units 10 & 11, Blaydon Business Centre, Cowen Road,
Blaydon-on-Tyne, Tyne & Wear, NE21 5TW
☎ (0191) 447 6543 ⊕ firebrickbrewery.com**

Firebrick began brewing on a 2.5-barrel plant in 2013,
expanding to a 15-barrel plant in 2014. Beers are mostly
available in pubs within the Tyne & Wear area and a few
outlets further afield. ♦ GF

Blaydon Brick (ABV 3.8%) BITTER
Traditional bitter with an attractive malty aroma and
taste. Some fruit and sweet body balanced by hop bitter
finish.
Coalface (ABV 3.9%) MILD
Elder Statesman (ABV 3.9%) BITTER
Tyne 9 (ABV 3.9%) SPECIALITY
Pagan Queen (ABV 4%) BLOND
Little Belgium (ABV 4.2%) SPECIALITY
Trade Star (ABV 4.2%) BITTER
Copper-coloured fruity bitter. Well-balanced with sweet
malts some fruitiness and a long hoppy bitter finish.
Stella Spark (ABV 4.4%) PALE
Well-balanced, sweet fruity and hoppy beer with a
lasting finish.
Toon Broon (ABV 4.6%) BITTER
Tasty, sweet, malty and fruity beer with some roast
crystal caramels and hop bitterness emerging nicely in
the finish.
Cushie Butterfield (ABV 5%) STOUT
Creamy with hints of blackcurrant and chocolate.
Complex balance of sweet malts, roast and hop
bitterness with a clean finish.
Wey-Aye PA (ABV 5.8%) IPA
Well-balanced IPA with citrus hops, fruit and sweetness.
The hops prevail in the finish.

Firehouse

**⊟ Gas Lamp Lounge, 13 Thames Street, Louth,
Lincolnshire, LN11 7AD
☎ (01507) 608202 ☎ 07961 772905
⊕ firehouse-brewery.co.uk**

⊛Owned by Jason Allen and Louise Darbon, Firehouse
Brewery was founded in 2014. It started production in
the village of Manby on part of the site of the former RAF
station. In 2016 a 2.5-barrel plant was purchased from
Fulstow Brewery and relocated to the Thames Street
Brewery in Louth. Beers are available in the free trade
and from the bar located at the brewery, the Gas Lamp
Lounge. ♦

Mainwarings Mild (ABV 3.6%) MILD
Marsh Mild (ABV 3.8%) MILD
FGB (ABV 3.9%) BITTER
Northway IPA (ABV 4.2%) PALE
Woodman Pale Ale (ABV 4.4%) BLOND
Pride of Fulstow (ABV 4.5%) PALE
Wobbly Weasel (ABV 4.9%) BITTER
Lincolnshire Country Bitter (ABV 5.1%) BITTER

FireRock

**20-24 Outram Street, Sutton-in-Ashfield,
Nottinghamshire, NG17 4FS ☎ 07875 331898
⊕ firerockbrewing.com**

⊛Now in its 6th year, FireRock Brewing Co is an
independent craft beer nanobrewery, bar and bottle
shop. It creates small-batch, modern beers with
everything from hazy pales and classic bitters, to pastry
sours and imperial stouts. The one-barrel brew kit is
housed inside the taproom, with beers produced
regularly in cask, keg and can. ♦

Firkin (NEW)

**⊟ Sainsbury's Depot, Unit 15, Whitburn Road,
Lewisham, London, SE13 7UQ
☎ (020) 8690 0969 ⊕ foxfirkin.com**

The brewery was installed at the Fox & Firkin in 2023,
reviving one of the earliest and longest lived brewpubs
in the original Bruce's Firkin chain, which brewed 1980-
1999. The beers are available at the bar but the brewery
is at the rear of the pub and they may be marketed
further afield in the future. No cask ale.

Firs

**⊟ Station Road, Codsall, Staffordshire, WV8 1BX
☎ (01902) 844674 ⊕ thefirscodsall.com**

Beers are brewed onsite in the CAMRA award-winning
Firs for the club and some local beer festivals.

First & Last SIBA

**Old Ambulance Station, Foundry Yard, Bellingham,
NE48 2DA ☎ 07757 286357
⊕ firstandlastbrewery.co.uk**

First & Last was established in 2016 by Red Kellie, a
founder member of Stu Brew (qv), in Newcastle upon
Tyne. Upgraded to a five-barrel plant in 2018, it relocated
eight miles up the road to Bellingham in 2022, with
further expansion to a 10-barrel plant plus the addition of
a shop and taproom. Outlets in Northumberland, Tyne
and Wear and the Scottish Borders are supplied. ▤♦♦

Mad Jack Ha' (ABV 3.8%) PALE
Call Out (ABV 4%) PALE
Red Rowan (ABV 4%) RED
Equinox (ABV 4.1%) PALE
Reiver (ABV 4.2%) BITTER
Stell (ABV 4.3%) STOUT
Amarillo (ABV 4.5%) PALE
Eclipse (ABV 5.6%) STOUT

First Chop

**B2 Barton Hall Business Park, Hardy Street, Eccles,
M30 7NB ☎ 07970 241398 ⊕ firstchop.co.uk**

Brewing began at Outstanding Brewery (qv) in Bury in
2012 before transferring to Salford in 2013. The brewery
relocated again to Eccles in 2017 with increased capacity.
It specialises in producing gluten-free beers. GF

AVA (ABV 3.5%) BLOND
POD (ABV 4.2%) SPECIALITY
IPA (ABV 5%) PALE
SYL (ABV 6.2%) IPA

Five Kingdoms SIBA

**22 Main Street, Isle of Whithorn, DG8 8LF
☎ (01988) 500334 ⊕ fivekingdomsbrewery.com**

Five Kingdoms was established in 2015 by Alastair Scoular, owner of the Steam Packet Inn, and Brendon Dennett, using a 2.5-barrel plant. It is situated in the harbourside village of Isle of Whithorn, the most southerly point of the Wigtownshire peninsula in Galloway, and a tourist and sailing hotspot. It supplies numerous local and Scottish outlets, selected national beer festivals, and the Steam Packet Inn. Brewery tours and expansion are planned. ‼◆LIVE

Bright Idea (ABV 3.8%) PALE
McGregors Mild (ABV 3.8%) MILD
Bitter X Blonde (ABV 4%) GOLD
Hillbillie (ABV 4%) PALE
Rebus (ABV 4%) PALE
Summerisle (ABV 4%) GOLD
An Invisible Hand (ABV 4.2%) BROWN
Private Idaho (ABV 4.5%) PALE
Renton (ABV 4.5%)
Wee McAsh Bitter (ABV 4.5%) BROWN
Prentice (ABV 4.6%) PALE
Calm Before The Storm (ABV 5%) STOUT
Bay of Plenty (ABV 6%) IPA
Captain Morrison's IPA (ABV 6.5%) STRONG
Dark Storm Stout (ABV 6.9%) STOUT

Five Points SIBA

61 Mare Street, Hackney, London, E8 4RG
☎ (020) 8533 7746 ⊕ fivepointsbrewing.co.uk

Five Points commenced brewing in 2013 in Hackney Downs. Crowdfunding in 2018 helped buy the Pembury Tavern. In 2020, the brewery moved into the existing warehouse facility in Mare Street. Crowdfunding in 2021 helped fund the addition of a taproom. Commitment to quality cask ale extends to a care scheme for stockists. ‼◆LIVE GF V◆

XPA (ABV 4%) GOLD
Smooth golden ale with strong grapefruit, mango and apricot over a rich tea biscuit flavour and a gentle, growing bitterness.
Best (ABV 4.1%) BITTER
Smooth, easy-drinking bitter with marmalade, pineapple, apricot, some sweet honey biscuit and a hint of hazelnut in the flavour.
Pale (ABV 4.4%) PALE
Well-balanced, slightly sweet beer with a hoppy bitterness, lemon and passion fruit leading to a dry, subtle bitter finish.
Railway Porter (ABV 4.8%) PORTER
Chocolate and currants on nose and smooth palate. Black treacle notes and a hint of orange. Roasty dry, peppery finish.

Fixed Wheel

Unit 9, Long Lane Trading Estate, Long Lane, Blackheath, West Midlands, B62 9LD ☎ 07766 162794 ⊕ fixedwheelbrewery.co.uk

⊠ Set up in 2014 by cycling and brewing enthusiasts Scott Povey and Sharon Bryant, this full mash brewery is situated on a trading estate on the Blackheath/Halesowen border. It brews several times a week using an eight-barrel plant. Alongside the core range, there are regular single hop and other specials. The award-winning ales are available throughout the Midlands and further afield. A canning plant was purchased in 2021 to service the expanding market for small package beers. ‼🍺◆LIVE◆

Through and Off (ABV 3.8%) PALE
Wheelie Pale (ABV 4.1%) PALE
Chain Reaction Pale Ale (ABV 4.2%) PALE

Blackheath Stout (ABV 5%) STOUT
No Brakes IPA (ABV 5.9%) IPA
Deceptive citrus and hop IPA. So light in taste it belies its gravity, with lots of lingering fruit and American hop flavours

Fizzy Moon

🍺 Fizzy Moon, 35 Regent Street, Leamington Spa, Warwickshire, CV32 5EE
☎ (01926) 888715 ⊕ fizzymoonbrewhouse.com

Fizzy Moon is a bar and microbrewery in the heart of Leamington Spa, brewing a range of small-batch beers, exclusively for consumption in the bar. All beers are unfined and so naturally hazy.

Flack Manor SIBA

8 Romsey Industrial Estate, Greatbridge Road, Romsey, Hampshire, SO51 0HR
☎ (01794) 518520 ⊕ flackmanor.co.uk

⊠ Flack Manor commenced brewing in 2010. It continues as the sole upholder of Romsey's long brewing tradition, and one of the few remaining breweries in the British Islands using the double-drop method. Its 20-barrel capacity was recently increased by the addition of a one-barrel pilot plant. All barley used is Maris Otter, and most beers contain only British hops. Flack's beers are supplied to many outlets within 50 miles of Romsey, and may also be found in JD Wetherspoon outlets. 🍺◆LIVE◆

Flack's Double Drop (ABV 3.7%) BITTER
A classic amber session bitter. Hops, malt and some bitterness in the taste, with more hop and some malt in the finish.
Romsey Gold (ABV 4%) GOLD
Lemony citrus on the nose with some smoke, biscuity sweetness, malty backbone and hints of pepper. Dry and citrus aftertaste.
Catcher (ABV 4.4%) BITTER
A well-balanced, amber best bitter with some fruit aroma and throughout with good hop bitterness in the balanced taste and finish.

Flash

Moss Top Farm, Moss Top Lane, Flash, Quarnford, Staffordshire, SK17 0TA ☎ 07967 592345
⊕ flashbrewery.uk

The brewery is located high in the Peak District and was founded by two friends who brew on a part-time basis. All natural ingredients are used including spring water and seaweed finings which make the beer suitable for vegans. Three bottle-conditioned beers are produced and are sold at Leek Market (only sales outlet). LIVE V

Flash House

Unit 1A, Northumberland Street, North Shields, NE30 1DS ☎ 07481 901875
⊕ flashhousebrewing.co.uk

Flash House was set up by Jack O'Keefe in 2016, after a life-long appreciation of ale. It aims to bring the best beer styles the world has to offer to the North East, and continues to produce new guest/seasonal ales rather than maintaining a core range in cask. The brewery and taproom are situated a short walk from North Shields town centre and the revamped North Shields Fish Quay. ◆

Flat Iron Square

🏠 45 Southwark Street, Southwark, London, SE1 9HP
🌐 flatironsquare.co.uk/drink/our-beers

This brewpub opened in 2021 as St Felix, changing its name in 2022. Owned by Lagunitas (Heineken UK), exclusive beers are brewed for the site and possibly some of the Lagunitas range as well. No cask ale.

Flipside

See Magpie

Floc

Unit 7a, Wincheap Industrial Estate, Cotton Road, Canterbury, Kent, CT1 3RB 🌐 flocbrewing.com

Floc is a community-driven brewery producing unfiltered, vegan-friendly beer in keg and can. It began on a one-barrel brew plant in Margate before moving to its new home in Canterbury. Its taproom is open at weekends. V◆

Flower Pots SIBA

Brandy Mount, Cheriton, Hampshire, SO24 0QQ
☎ (01962) 771735 🌐 theflowerpots.co.uk

⊗ Flower Pots began production in 2006, now making it Hampshire's oldest independent brewery. The 10-barrel brewery, and neighbouring pub of the same name, are in a pretty Hampshire village. In 2023, it obtained the ex Red Cat brewery in Winchester, allowing it to double its capacity by splitting brewing between the two sites. It brews six core beers, plus a monthly special. ◆

Perridge Pale (ABV 3.6%) GOLD
Very pale, easy-drinking golden ale. Honey-scented with high hops, grapefruit and bitterness throughout. Crisp with some citrus notes.
Pots Bitter (ABV 3.8%) BITTER
Refreshing, easy-going bitter. Dry, earthy hop flavours balanced by robust maltiness. Bitter throughout with hoppy aroma and dry, bitter finish.
Buster's Best (ABV 4.2%) BITTER
Beautiful, smooth dark brown beer. Nutty, biscuit and caramel throughout with a delicate bitter hop backbone that strengthens in the aftertaste.
Cheriton Porter (ABV 4.2%) PORTER
Dry porter packed with blackcurrant flavours. Distinctive chocolate roastiness and malty throughout, combining with pleasing bitterness leading to bittersweet finish.
Goodens Gold (ABV 4.8%) GOLD
Complex, full-bodied, golden-coloured ale, bursting with hops and citrus fruit and a snatch of sweetness, leading to a long, dry finish.
IPA (ABV 6%) IPA
Rich, full-bodied IPA with uncompromising hoppiness and strong grapefruit character, a robust maltiness and rich, fruity finish.

Flowerhorn

The Bridge Studios, 454 Western Avenue, Cardiff, CF5 3BL 🌐 flowerhorn.co.uk

Established in 2019 by two friends, Andrew and Arran. Brewing was initially on a nomad basis, and beers were available in bottle and keg only. In 2020 the brewery moved to its own premises in Cardiff with a bespoke five-barrel plant. A taproom is open Fridays-Saturdays. A canning line is planned. The brewery is also developing the Flowerhorn Dog Bakery project, using spent grains to make dog biscuits, with a portion of the profits donated to the Rescue Hotel, Cardiff. ◆

Flying Gang

Unit 3, Meadowfield Industrial Estate, Ponteland, Northumberland, NE20 9SD ☎ 07789 958782
🌐 flyinggangbrewing.com

Brewing commenced in 2021 in an industrial unit in Ponteland, also incorporating a taproom (open at weekends). The brewery is also involved in the running of the Left Luggage micropub in Monkseaton. ◆

Flying Monk SIBA

Unit 1, Bradfield Farm, Hullavington, Wiltshire, SN14 6EU
☎ (01666) 838415 🌐 flyingmonkbrewery.com

⊗ Named after Elmer, an 11th century monk at nearby Malmesbury Abbey who attempted flight from the abbey tower using self-made wings. Owned by the farm where it's located, allowing reduced waste by using brewery by-product as cattle feed. A stone-built barn next to the brewery has been attractively converted to a café tap, offering some of the brewery's cask and keg beers, and incorporating the shop which sells cans of the keg beers. 🍽◆V◆

Balance (ABV 4%) PALE
New Age (ABV 4%) PALE

Flying Trunk

The Cement Stores, Highgate Works, Tomtits Lane, Forest Row, East Sussex, RH18 5AT ☎ 07710 642848
✉ hello@flyingtrunkbrewery.co.uk

⊗ Brewing began in 2022 in premises formerly used by High Weald Brewery. Flying Trunk is a nanobrewery producing small batches of cask, live KeyKeg and bottle-conditioned beers, often as one-offs. Beers are available in selected free houses and other outlets, at local CAMRA and pub festivals, and in bottled form at local markets. ◆LIVE

Good Natured (ABV 4.3%) PALE

Fonthill SIBA

🏠 c/o The George, 29 Mount Ephraim, Tunbridge Wells, Kent, TN4 8AA
☎ (01892) 539492 🌐 fonthillbrewing.co.uk

⊗ Fonthill is a small-batch brewery located in the George pub. Beers are available in the pub as well as its two sister pubs in Tunbridge Wells.

Forest, The

The Old Workshop, Lydney Park Estate, Lydney, Gloucestershire, GL15 6BU ☎ 07766 652837
🌐 theforestbrewery.co.uk

Originally named Brythonic Beer (a trading name it still retains), The Forest nanobrewery began in a Bristol suburb in 2015. The brewery relocated several times within Gloucestershire, finally settling in Lydney. As well as the taproom, beers can be found at the Dog House micropub, and Forest Deli, both Coleford (mainly available bottle-conditioned, but the occasional cask beer also makes an appearance). ‼🍽LIVE◆

Forest Road SIBA

Unit 1a, Elizabeth Industrial Estate, Juno Way, South Bermondsey, London, SE14 5RW
☎ (020) 8691 8534 🌐 forestroad.com

Homebrewing at Forest Road, E8, at Van Eecke, Belgium, and Cropton, Yorkshire, are all part of Forest Road's history, before importing a brewery from San Francisco and setting up in South Bermondsey in 2021, including the onsite Emerald City Taproom. Cask is more widely available now including at its pub, the Quiet Night Inn, Westbourne Park, W11. ✦

Forge

Wilderland, Woolley Cross, Cornwall, EX23 9PW
☎ **(01288) 331669** ☎ **07837 487800**
✉ **forgebrewerybeer@gmail.com**

⊠ This multi-award-winning brewery was set up near Bideford in Devon by Dave Lang, who commenced brewing in 2008 using a five-barrel plant. The brewery relocated to Cornwall in 2017. ✦LIVE

Discovery (ABV 3.8%) BITTER
Gold-coloured bitter bursting with hops from start to finish. Some subtle hints of fruit to the discerning palate too.
Blonde (ABV 4%) BLOND
Pale ale with light citrus aroma. Zesty citrus hop in the mouth balanced by a little malt. Bitter and dry.
Litehouse (ABV 4.3%) PALE
Pale ale with faint tropical fruit hop aroma. Light balance of sweet malt and hop bitterness fading into a short finish.
IPA (ABV 4.5%) PALE
Rev Hawker (ABV 4.6%) BITTER
Tamar Source (ABV 4.6%) BITTER
Premium bitter with malt and earthy hop aroma. Dominant crystal malt with bitterness and sweet stone fruit flavours. Bitterness rises.

Fosse Way SIBA

Elms Farm, Plough Lane, Bishops Itchington, Southam, Warwickshire, CV47 2QG ☎ **07956 179999**
⊕ **fossebrew.co.uk**

⊠ In 2022 the brewery relocated and expanded, and a full time partner taken on (a former owner of the Red Moon brewery). The beer range includes a lager influenced by the owner's extensive experience in South Africa. Most production is bottled and sold in Warwickshire markets. Some Red Moon brands, plus ciders, have been added to the range. ✦LIVE

Aurora (ABV 3.6%) PALE
Sentinel (ABV 4.5%) BITTER
Dark Side (ABV 4.8%) PORTER

Fountain

Oak Street Industrial Estate, Cradley Heath, West Midlands, B64 5JY

Established in 2023 to produce beers for the Fountain Inn, Temple Street, Dudley. The new brewery bought the former Morton Brewery, Essington, near Wolverhampton, and switched production to Cradley Heath in summer 2023. The beers are also now being supplied to other pubs in the Black Country area.

Four Candles

⊟ 1 Sowell Street, St Peters, CT10 2AT ☎ **07947 062063** ⊕ **thefourcandles.co.uk**

⊠ Based in the cellar of the micropub of the same name, Four Candles uses a 2.5-barrel plant and produces up to 10 nine-gallon casks with each brew. Never brewing the same ale twice, the brewery supplies the micropub, which is named after the well-known Two Ronnies sketch. ‼

Four Priests

2 Finney's Lane, Middlewich, Cheshire, CW10 9DR
⊕ **fourpriests.co.uk**

☺Start-up brewery established in 2022 by homebrewer-turned-professional Andy Thomason. The name originates from the carvings on the Saxon crosses in nearby Sandbach. Founded with the 2.5-barrel kit from the now closed Goodall's brewery, capacity was increased to five barrels with the acquisition of further equipment from Crankshaft in Leyland. Three regular beers are supplied to local outlets, with occasional seasonal brews. Cans are available for UK-wide delivery from the website. ♦V

Moston Dragon (ABV 4%) BITTER
Cross Stout (ABV 4.2%) STOUT
Murgy Straight (ABV 4.2%) GOLD

Fourpure

Units 22 & 23, Bermondsey Trading Estate, Rotherhithe New Road, South Bermondsey, London, SE16 3LL
☎ **(02037) 442141** ⊕ **fourpure.com**

Fourpure began brewing in 2013. In 2018 the brewery was bought by Lion of Australia (ultimately owned by Kirin of Japan), and again sold in 2022 to Odyssey Inns, later renamed to In Good Company. A substantial taproom opened along from the brewery in 2019, becoming a popular start (or end!) to the Bermondsey Beer Mile. No cask ale. LIVE

Fownd (NEW)

Unit 3, Hill Street, Kidderminster, Worcestershire, DY11 6TD

The brewery was formed towards the end of 2023 from the ashes of Fownes brewery.

Fox

⊟ 22 Station Road, Heacham, Norfolk, PE31 7EX
☎ **(01485) 570345** ⊕ **foxbrewery.co.uk**

⊠ Based in an old cottage adjacent to the Fox & Hounds pub, Fox Brewery was established in 2002 and now supplies around 30 outlets as well as the pub. All the beers are brewed using malt from Crisps in Great Ryburgh. A hop garden next to the brewery, trialled during 2009, has been enlarged. ‼ ⏚ ♦LIVE

Best (ABV 3.9%) BITTER
Heacham Gold (ABV 3.9%) GOLD
Red Knocker (ABV 3.9%) BITTER
Hop Across the Pond (ABV 4.2%) PALE
Cerberus Stout (ABV 4.5%) STOUT
Nelson's Blood (ABV 4.7%) SPECIALITY
Fox Grizzly Bear (ABV 4.8%) SPECIALITY
IPA (ABV 5.2%) PALE

Frank & Otis

Unit 7, River Bridge Business Centre, Cardiff, CF15 7QR ☎ **07968 094270**
⊕ **frankandotisbrewing.co**

Business started in 2019 with all beers contract brewed. In 2021, it opened a one-barrel brewery for smaller bottle runs at Taffs Well near Cardiff. In 2022, production moved to Cardiff with bottling replaced by canning and an expansion into kegs. An additional vessel has recently been added and production is being expanded. ⏚

Benjamin Franklin

🍺 Three Horseshoes, 23 High Street, Ecton,
Northamptonshire, NN6 0QA
☎ (01604) 407446

The Benjamin Franklin is a microbrewery at the Three
Horseshoes in Ecton village. Its name is directly
associated with the family of one of the founding fathers
of the USA.

Freedom SIBA

1 Park Lodge House, Bagots Park, Abbots Bromley,
Staffordshire, WS15 3ES
☎ (01283) 840721 ● freedombrewery.com

Freedom specialises in producing hand-crafted English
lagers, all brewed in accordance with the German
Reinheitsgebot purity law. No real ale. ♯▤

Freestyle

🍺 Church Road, Shustoke, Warwickshire, B46 2LB
☎ (01675) 481205 ● griffininnshustoke.co.uk

Griffin Inn started brewing in 2008 in the old coffin shop
adjacent to the pub. In 2017 the brewery was updated to
a modern, more efficient 2.5-barrel plant. At this time
the name was changed to Freestyle though the business
is still owned by the Pugh family who run the Griffin.
Beers are available for the free trade as well as selling
through the pub. ♯♦

Freetime

19 St Lukes Court, Clarke Way, Winch Wen, Swansea,
SA1 7ER
☎ (01792) 713731 ☎ 07291 253227
● hello@freetimebeer.co

Small-batch brewery producing unfined beers. V

Fresh Standard SIBA

Unit 25, Merrets Mill Industrial Centre, Bath Road,
Woodchester, Stroud, Gloucestershire, GL5 5EX
☎ (01453) 802400

Office: 3 West Tynings, Nailsworth, GL6 0EH
● thefreshstandard.co.uk

⊗ Founded in 2020 by experienced brewer Richard
Taylor, in space rented from Artisan Ales. Initially
brewing two core beers, alongside one-off brews. It
relocated to its own premises, complete with taproom,
in 2022, when wife Charlotte joined the team. Beers may
be purchased from the website. ♦V♦

Horse Brass (ABV 4%) BITTER
Solution (ABV 4.8%) PALE
Red Mild (ABV 6%) MILD

Friday Beer

Unit 4, Link Business Centre, Link Way, Malvern,
Worcestershire, WR14 1UQ
☎ (01684) 572648 ● thefridaybeer.com

Founded in 2011, the Friday Beer Co primarily produces
bottle-conditioned ales. The range of bottles now sells
across the region and to a growing number of outlets,
from Birmingham to London, and south of the M4
corridor (including local restaurants and venues). Beer is
rarely available in cask form. Brewing is currently
suspended. ♯▤LIVE

Friendship Adventure

See Supercute

Frisky Bear

Unit 1, Vantage Point, Howley Park Road East,
Morley, Leeds, West Yorkshire, LS27 0SU ☎ 07590
540210 ● friskybear.com

☺Established in 2016, Frisky Bear was originally based
in Oscar's Bar in Morley Bottoms. An upgrade from one
barrel to six barrel in 2019 saw a relocation to an
industrial unit across town. The beers are available,
unfined, in cask, keg and can, on a regularly rotating
brewing schedule. ♦LIVE V♦

Grizzly Bear (ABV 4.5%) PALE

Frome SIBA

Unit L13, Marshall Way, Commerce Park, Frome,
BA11 2FB
☎ (01373) 467766 ● fromebrewingcompany.com

⊗ Formerly Milk Street Brewery, the business changed
its name in 2018. The brewery was established in 1999
behind the Griffin pub, Frome, before moving to an
industrial unit on the edge of town in 2016, and
increasing its capabilities to 60 barrels. Beer is supplied
direct to local outlets and wholesalers are used to
distribute further afield. ♦V

Funky Monkey (ABV 4%) BITTER
Ra (ABV 4.1%) GOLD
The Usual (ABV 4.4%) BITTER
Rounded ale with malty biscuit, caramel and hedgerow
fruit evident in aroma and taste, all lingering into the
balanced ending.
Zig-Zag Stout (ABV 4.5%) STOUT
Gulp IPA (ABV 4.8%) BITTER
Beer (ABV 5%) BLOND
Galaxy Australian Pale Ale (ABV 5.2%) PALE

Front Row SIBA

Unit A3, The Old School, Outclough Road, Stoke-on-
Trent, Staffordshire, ST8 7QD ☎ 07861 718673
● frontrowbrewing.co.uk

After starting operations in Congleton in 2012, Front Row
expanded from a 2.5-barrel to an eight-barrel plant in
2014. It moved to its current location at the end of 2018
to allow for a further increase in capacity. The brewery
tap, the Crafty Flanker, is in nearby Biddulph. A range of
occasional brews is also produced. ♯♦

Number 8 (ABV 3.7%) MILD
Crouch (ABV 3.8%) BITTER
LOHAG (Land of Hops & Glory) (ABV 3.8%) GOLD
Touch (ABV 4%) BITTER
Sin Bin (ABV 4.2%) GOLD
Try (ABV 4.2%) BITTER
Half-Time (ABV 4.5%) SPECIALITY
Pause (ABV 4.5%) STOUT
Red Roses (ABV 4.5%) STOUT
Wot No Cheyz (ABV 4.5%) STOUT
Pride (ABV 4.6%) BITTER
Blindside (ABV 4.7%) GOLD
Crafty Flanker (ABV 4.7%) GOLD
Rucked (ABV 5.2%) OLD
Converted (ABV 5.4%) PORTER
Oblensky (ABV 7.3%) PORTER

Froth Blowers

Unit P35, Hastingwood Industrial Park, Wood Lane, Erdington, West Midlands, B24 9QR ☎ 07966 935906
⊕ frothblowersbrewing.com

⊠ Froth Blowers began brewing in 2013. The name derived from the Ancient Order of Froth Blowers, an organisation dedicated to 'Lubrication in Moderation'! The brewery has the capacity to brew 20 barrels at a site only metres away from its original one, with most of the beers consumed within 30 miles of the brewery. In addition to the core range, half a dozen seasonal beers are brewed. Certain beers are sometimes available in five-litre minikegs. ◆

Piffle Snonker (ABV 3.8%) BLOND
Straw-coloured pale ale. Aroma is sweet and almost jammy with honey and a little malt and hop. Taste is well-balanced with a slightly hoppier aftertaste.
Bar-King Mad (ABV 4.2%) BITTER
Wellingtonian (ABV 4.3%) PALE
John Bull's Best (ABV 4.4%) BITTER
Gollop With Zest (ABV 4.5%) GOLD
A blonde beer with a floral start and a citric finish.
Hornswoggle (ABV 5%) BLOND

Fuddy Duck

Unit 12, Kirton Business Park, Willington Road, Kirton, Lincolnshire, PE20 1NN ☎ 07881 818875
⊕ thefuddyduckbrewery.co.uk

Small brewery based in Kirton near Boston, where brewing commenced in 2016.

Pale Ale (ABV 4%) PALE
American Red Ale (ABV 4.5%) RED
Blonde Ale (ABV 4.5%) SPECIALITY
Dark Porter (ABV 4.5%) PORTER
German Ale Altbier (ABV 4.5%) SPECIALITY
Biere De Garde (ABV 6.5%) SPECIALITY

Fuggle Bunny SIBA

Unit 1, Meadowbrook Park Industrial Estate, Station Road, Holbrook, Sheffield, South Yorkshire, S20 3PJ ☎ (0114) 248 4541 ☎ 07813 763347
⊕ fugglebunny.co.uk

⊠ Fuggle Bunny was established in 2014 and is an independent, family-run brewery. The plant, originally obtained from Flipside Brewery, has since been expanded. The core range is supplemented by occasional seasonal and special brews. Beers are delivered direct within a 40-mile radius of the brewery and are available nationally through wholesalers. Its first pub opened in Worksop in 2017. !! ☛

Chapter 5 Oh Crumbs (ABV 3.8%) BITTER
Chapter 9 La La Land (ABV 3.9%) PALE
Chapter 2 Cotton Tail (ABV 4%) GOLD
Chapter 6 Hazy Summer Daze (ABV 4.2%) GOLD
Chapter 8 Jammy Dodger (ABV 4.5%) BITTER
Chapter 1 New Beginnings (ABV 4.9%) BITTER
Chapter 3 Orchard Gold (ABV 5%) GOLD
Chapter 7 Russian Rare-Bit (ABV 5%) STOUT
Chapter 4 24 Carrot (ABV 6%) BITTER

Full Circle SIBA

Hoults Yard, Walker Road, Newcastle upon Tyne, NE6 2HL
☎ (0191) 481 4114 ⊕ fullcirclebrew.co.uk

Brewing began in 2019 in Hoult's Yard in Byker, another addition to the real ale scene in this area. ◆

Repeater (ABV 4.2%) PALE
Hoop (ABV 5.5%) IPA
Looper (ABV 6.4%) IPA

Full Mash

17 Lower Park Street, Stapleford, Nottinghamshire, NG9 8EW
☎ (0115) 949 9262 ⊕ fullmash.co.uk

☺Brewing commenced in 2003 and has grown steadily since, with a gradual expansion in outlets and capacity. ◆

Horse & Jockey (ABV 3.8%) GOLD
Easy-drinking golden ale with moderate hoppy aroma and finish.
Whistlin' Dixie (ABV 3.9%) BITTER
Séance (ABV 4%) GOLD
Predominantly hoppy golden beer, with a refreshing bitter finish.
Illuminati (ABV 4.2%) BITTER
Gently-hopped golden ale with initial hops and bitterness giving way to a short, bitter finish.
Wheat Ear (ABV 4.2%) SPECIALITY
Warlord (ABV 4.4%) BITTER
Amber-coloured beer with an initial malt taste leading to a dry, bitter finish.
Apparition (ABV 4.5%) BITTER
A pale hoppy bitter brewed with Brewers Gold hops.
Northern Lights (ABV 4.7%) STOUT
Manhattan (ABV 5.2%) PALE
Bhisti (ABV 6.2%) IPA

Fuller's

Griffin Brewery, Chiswick Lane South, Chiswick, London, W4 2QB
☎ (020) 8996 2400 ⊕ asahibeer.co.uk

⊠ The Griffin Brewery has stood for more than 360 years with the Fuller's name coming from the partnership formed in 1845. Gale's of Horndean was bought in 2005 and closed a year later. Dark Star of Sussex was bought in 2018 and closed in 2022. Gale's and Dark Star are now brewed at Chiswick with Dark Star returning after a year out at Meantime Brewery, until its closure in spring 2024. Fuller's sold its brewing interests to Asahi in 2019 but kept its pubs and hotels. !! ☛ ◆ LIVE ✦

Oliver's Island (ABV 3.8%) GOLD
Well-balanced golden ale with fruity aroma and flavour. Gentle bitter hoppiness balances a sweet malty character and short finish.
London Pride (ABV 4.1%) BITTER
The malty sweetness is balanced by spicy dry bitter hops, which linger. Orange, apricot, sultanas and toffee flavours provides complexity.
Bengal Lancer (ABV 5%) PALE
Smooth, full-flavoured beer. The sweet malty biscuit provides balance alongside caramelised orange, apricot and spicy hops. Growing dry bitterness.
ESB (ABV 5.5%) BITTER
Caramelised malt and fruit aroma. Orange marmalade with hops, caramel and raisins in this strong brown bitter. Long, bitter, malty dry finish.

Brewed under the Dark Star brand name:
Hophead (ABV 3.8%) GOLD
Smooth, refreshing, straw-coloured beer with a sweet malt flavour overlaying the hops and citrus fruit. Lingering hoppy bitter aftertaste.
American Pale Ale (ABV 4.7%) PALE
Light biscuit malt base complements the hoppy aroma, leading to flavours of grapefruit, orange and tropical fruits. Smooth sweetish finish.

Brewed under the Gale's brand name:

Seafarers Ale (ABV 3.6%) BITTER
A pale brown bitter, predominantly malty, with a refreshing balance of fruit and hops that lingers into the aftertaste where a dry bitterness unfolds.
HSB (ABV 4.8%) BITTER
Smooth complex beer with Demerara sugar, orange and sultanas flavours with hints of cocoa and a developing dry peppery hoppiness.

Funk Dungeon

See Abbeydale

Funky Hop Donkey

See Silver

Furnace

9 Duke Street, Derby, DE1 3BX
☎ (01332) 385981

Six-barrel brewhouse in the beer garden of the Furnace Inn on Duke Street. Supply is mainly for the pub, but beers can be seen at beer festivals and specialist pubs across the UK. V

Reprazent! (ABV 4.2%) SPECIALITY
Fun Sponge (ABV 4.3%) PALE
My Milk Stout (ABV 4.9%) STOUT

Futtle

Unit 2, The Bowhouse, St Monans, KY10 2FB
⊕ futtle.com

Organic farmhouse brewery producing European-style beers. A 1,000-litre 'coolship' (a shallow, open fermentation vessel), has been installed in the rafters of the brewery.

FutureState

Earley, Reading, RG6 5XF ⊕ futurestatebrew.com

A nanobrewery being run from the owner's domestic garage, producing a wide variety of beers and participating in many collaborative brews. It registered for commercial activity in 2020 and beer is only available through its web-based subscription club.

Fuzzchat

Jolly Coopers, 84 Wheelers Lane, Epsom, Surrey, KT18 7SD
☎ (01372) 723222 ⊕ fuzzchatbrewery.co.uk

Fuzzchat is Epsom's first brewery in more than 90 years. Housed behind the Jolly Coopers, it used to be an old blacksmith's cottage, recently restored after being derelict for several years. A Fuzzchat is anyone born on Epsom Common. ‼◆

Fuzzy Duck SIBA

18 Wood Street, Poulton Industrial Estate, Poulton le Fylde, Lancashire, FY6 8JY ☎ 07904 343729
⊕ fuzzyduckbrewery.co.uk

Fuzzy Duck was established in 2006. It relocated to Poulton-le-Fylde later that year, expanding capacity to an eight-barrel plant. The brewery delivers over a wide area of North-West England. A range of single-hopped beers is also available. Most beers are available bottle-conditioned. ‼◆LIVE V

Golden Cascade (ABV 3.8%) PALE
Mucky Duck (ABV 4%) STOUT

Pheasant Plucker (ABV 4.2%) BITTER
Cunning Stunt (ABV 4.3%) BITTER
Ruby Duck (ABV 5.3%) OLD

Fyne SIBA

Achadunan, Cairndow, PA26 8BJ
☎ (01499) 600120 ⊕ fyneales.com

Fyne Ales has been brewing since 2001 and is situated at the head of Loch Fyne. In 2012 an onsite tap was added. Expansion has allowed for the production of experimental brews. FyneFest runs annually, celebrating beer from the UK and beyond. ‼☵◆LIVE◆

Jarl (ABV 3.8%) GOLD
Strong citrus notes, through use of the Citra hop. A light, golden ale that can be drunk in any season.
Hurricane Jack (ABV 4.4%) GOLD
Vital Spark (ABV 4.4%) OLD
Avalanche (ABV 4.5%) GOLD
This true golden ale starts with stunning citrus hops on the nose. Well-balanced with good body and fruit balancing a refreshing hoppy taste, it finishes with a long bittersweet aftertaste.
Highlander (ABV 4.8%) BITTER
Full-bodied, bittersweet ale with a good dry hop finish. In the style of a Heavy although the malt is less pronounced and the sweetness ebbs away to leave a bitter, hoppy finish.

Gadds'

See Ramsgate

Gale's

See Fuller's

Gan Yam

Unit 3, Shap Road Industrial Estate, Kendal, Cumbria, LA9 6NZ ⊕ ganyambrewco.uk

Initially a commercial home-based brewery based in north London when founded in 2018, it relocated to Kendal in early 2021. An onsite taproom is open most months. ◆◆

PAL (ABV 3.9%) PALE
ALF (ABV 4.1%) BITTER
SIP (ABV 4.3%) PALE
KEN (ABV 5%) SPECIALITY
AYE (ABV 6%) IPA
TAR (ABV 7%) PORTER

Garden City

22 The Wynd, Letchworth Garden City, Hertfordshire, SG6 3EN ☎ 07932 739558
⊕ gardencitybrewery.co.uk

A brewbar established in 2016 using a 2.5-barrel plant, serving a selection of its own ales plus guests on gravity. ◆V◆

Gasworks

5 Jack Rosenthal Street, Manchester, M3 4LY
⊕ gasworksbrewbar.co.uk

Gasworks is a six-barrel brewpub from the team behind Dockyard, opened in 2016. It also supplies Salford Quays and Dockyard, Spinningfields.

Gates Burton

Reservoir Road, Burton upon Trent, Staffordshire, DE14 2BP
☎ (01283) 532567 ☎ 07957 930772
⊕ gatesburtonbrewery.co.uk

☺The Gates Burton Brewery was established in 2011 using a one-barrel plant. Now expanded to a three-barrel plant, representing cottage brewing at its finest. All beer is available in cask in the free trade. ‼◆

Reservoir (ABV 4.6%) BITTER
Light brown beer with a white head with a malt and hop aroma. Caramel starts before a spicy hop and malt middle leads to a mouth-watering bitter finish.
GBA (Gates Burton Ale) (ABV 4.8%) BITTER
Damn (ABV 5%) BITTER
Reservoir Gold (ABV 7.5%) BARLEY

Geipel SIBA

Pant Glas, Llangwm, Corwen, LL21 0RN
☎ (01490) 420838 ⊕ geipel.co.uk

Geipel commenced brewing in 2013 producing unpasteurised and unfiltered beers. The brewery specialises in lagers, drawing inspiration from the classic styles of Germany and beyond. Available in keg, KeyKeg and bottle. LIVE V

Gentlewood

Fir Tree Cottage, Tithe Barn, Gentleshaw, Staffordshire, WS15 4LR ☎ 07544 146900
✉ gentlewoodbrewery@hotmail.com

Gentlewood began in 2018 and is co-owned and run by Darren Williams and Ben Colthorpe. It is a Staffordshire-based brewery specialising in traditional cask ales using British hops and grain. Frequent seasonal brews complement the core range.

Heritage (ABV 4.2%) BITTER

George Samuel

Unit 3, Norland House Business Centre, Shildon, DL4 1HE ☎ 07840 892751

Named after the brewer's two sons, the brewery originally set up as a two-barrel plant in 2014 at the Duke of Wellington pub in Welbury near Northallerton, before moving to Spennymoor and closing in late 2018. The brewery reopened as an eight-barrel plant in 2020 in Shildon, the 'Cradle of the Railways', in a unit which formerly housed the offices of Shildon Wagon Works. ◆LIVE ◈

Locomotion No 1 (ABV 4%) BLOND
Citrus hops and fruity aromas are complemented by a moderate sweetness with rising and lasting dry bitterness at the end.
Leaves on the Line (ABV 4.2%) BITTER
Travelling Light (ABV 4.5%) BLOND
Well-hopped blond beer with a sweet body, some fruit and citrus hops remain in the crisp dry finish.
Harvey (ABV 5.2%) PORTER
A smooth malty beer with some fruity sweetness and a dry roast finish.
Terminus (ABV 5.5%) IPA
Fruity, hoppy beer with sweetness in the body lasting into the finish. A well-balanced English IPA.

George Shaw (NEW)

Office: Sefton Lodge, Earles Lane, Wincham, Cheshire, CW9 6EA

The original brewery was founded at the beginning of the 19th century and registered as Bedford Brewing & Malting Co Ltd in 1866. William Shaw was brewer, manager, and later owner. His son George inherited it in 1899. The name changed to George Shaw & Co Ltd 1902. Brewing ended by 1933. The name was revived in 2019. The new brewery owns the name rights, original trademark and has original recipes. Original/new recipes are being brewed by Dunham Massey Brewery to raise funds to build a new tap and brewery.

George's SIBA

Common Road, Great Wakering, Essex, SS3 0AG
☎ (01702) 826755 ☎ 07771 871255
⊕ georgesbrewery.com

⊗ George's Brewery and Hop Monster Brewing Company (qv) are owned by the same brewer, using the same plant. George's concentrates on traditional styles and Hop Monster on the more unusual. ‼➡◆LIVE

Wallasea Wench (ABV 3.6%) BITTER
Wakering Gold (ABV 3.8%) GOLD
Cockleboats (ABV 4%) BITTER
Olde Leigh Oyster & Cockle Stout (ABV 4.1%) STOUT
Pier City (ABV 4.1%) PALE
Banshee Porter (ABV 4.4%) SPECIALITY
Broadsword (ABV 4.7%) BITTER

Brewed under the Hop Monster Brewery name:
Absolutely Fuggled (ABV 4.2%) GOLD
Child of the Jago (ABV 4.4%) PALE

German Kraft

Mercato Metropolitano, 42 Newington Causeway, Borough, London, SE1 6DR

Second Site: Mercato Mayfair, 13a North Audley Street, Mayfair, London, W1K 6ZA

Third Site: Kraft Dalston, 130a Kingsland High Street, Dalston, London, E8 2LQ ⊕ germankraftbeer.com

Opening in 2017 with beer imported from a German brewery in Bavaria, Steinbach Brau. In 2018, the brewery officially opened near Elephant & Castle and beers were replicated onsite. The core range and seasonals reflect traditional German styles including lagering for four weeks. There are two further breweries with taprooms in Mayfair and Dalston and a bar (without a brewery) in Brixton. A further brewery, with a taproom, was opened in Vienna in 2023. No cask ale. ‼◆

Gert Lush

Hurn Farm Buildings, Ashmore Drove, Wells, Somerset, BA5 1NS ☎ 07476 662948
⊕ gertlushbeer.co.uk

Gert Lush is a craft brewery situated near Wells on the Somerset Levels. All beers are brewed using organic malt, hops, carefully-cultured yeasts and spring water and are suitable for vegans. Most are also gluten-free. No real ale. Brewing is currently suspended. GF V

Gigha

Ardminish, Isle of Gigha ⊕ isleofgighabrewing.co.uk

A microbrewery based on the Isle of Gigha, just off the Kintyre peninsula, on the west coast of Scotland. Its mobile brewery bar opens at weekends in the grounds of the Gigha Hotel.

Gilbert White's

Gilbert White's House, The Wakes, High Street, Selborne, Hampshire, GU34 3JH

☎ (01420) 511275 ⊕ gilbertwhiteshouse.org.uk/the-brewhouse

⊠ One-barrel nanobrewery staffed by volunteers, attached to the Gilbert White Museum. It produces bottled, cask-conditioned and keg beer using modern kit in Gilbert White's original brewhouse, dating from 1765. One brew uses an original recipe. Bottled beer is sold in the shop (Tue-Sun). Cask and keg beer is sold at its tied pub, the Jubilee Tap Room, Selborne village. It is also produced on demand for the free trade, festivals and other events. ☛◆LIVE

Six Quarters (ABV 3.9%) BLOND
Pale blond ale with a balance of hops and malt in the aroma, an initial zesty character and smooth, rounded finish.

Bostal (ABV 4.3%) BITTER
A traditional English bitter. Predominantly malty throughout, with some fruitiness. Smooth on the palate, with a short finish.

Hop Monster (ABV 4.5%) PALE
Balanced, well-rounded pale ale. Bready hop, floral and honey flavours. Malty richness and short finish with hints of apricot.

Capt. Lawrence Oates (ABV 4.7%) GOLD
Well-balanced premium golden ale with a pronounced fruitiness of apricot and peach. Some malt and hop, with a dry finish.

Gilbert's (ABV 4.7%) SPECIALITY
Smoked malt gives a smoky character throughout, with delicate fruity aromas, leading to a slightly sour and sweet aftertaste.

Zig Zag Ale (ABV 6.2%) OLD
A robust light brown ale with a creamy mouthfeel. Predominantly malty with dark fruits and a caramel sweetness throughout.

Gilt & Flint

Haye Farm, Haye Lane, Musbury, EX13 8ST ☎ 07904 035640 ⊕ giltandflint.com

This brewery is based on the beautiful Haye Farm in an Area of Outstanding Natural Beauty in East Devon. Using age old traditional brewing techniques, it has created organic, modern, New World, bottle-conditioned beers, ciders and soft drinks. All of the agricultural by-product goes to feed the free-range livestock on the farm. LIVE

Gipsy Hill SIBA

Unit 8, Hamilton Road Industrial Estate, 160 Hamilton Road, West Norwood, London, SE27 9SF
☎ (020) 8761 9061 ⊕ gipsyhillbrew.com

Gipsy Hill opened in 2014 at the same time and on the same site as London Beer Factory. It has since expanded into adjacent units and the taproom moved across the yard. A core range of four is supplemented by regular specials including alcohol free options, available in keg and cans. Cask is occasionally produced. It has also brewed some barrel-aged beers. ◆LIVE ♠

Glamorgan SIBA

Unit B, Llantrisant Business Park, Llantrisant, CF72 8LF
☎ (01443) 406080

Office: Unit J, Llantrisant Business Park, Llantrisant, CF72 8LF ⊕ glamorganbrewingco.com

☺ This family-owned and run brewery moved to its present site in 2013. Production capability has increased year-on-year. A range of core and seasonal beers are produced with special brews to mark notable events. Shop is open daily. Direct deliveries are made throughout Wales, and further afield by selected wholesalers and breweries. Major supermarkets are also supplied. In 2023 Glamorgan was awarded sole beer supplier to the Welsh Rugby Union and

Principality Stadium, Cardiff. In 2024 exports began to France and Norway. ☛◆

Cwrw Gorslas/ Bluestone Bitter (ABV 4%) BITTER
Welsh Pale Ale (ABV 4.1%) PALE
Jemimas Pitchfork (ABV 4.4%) GOLD
Thunderbird (ABV 4.5%) BITTER

Glasgow Beer Works SIBA

Block 23, Unit 2, Queenslie Industrial Estate, Glasgow, G33 4JJ
☎ (0141) 258 1661

Office: Pavillion 1, Finnieston Business Park, Minerva Way, Glasgow, G3 8AU ⊕ merchantcitybrewing.com

Established in 2017 as Merchant City Brewing using a 12-barrel plant, Glasgow Beer Works moved and rebranded in 2020. In addition to the core range, small pilot batches and barrel-aged beers are produced. 25 outlets are supplied direct, plus specialist off-licences across central Scotland. A pop-up bar in Osborne Street, beneath the John Byrne mural of Billy Connolly, opened in 2020. **GF**

Session Ale (ABV 3.9%) GOLD
Unit 1 Red Ale (ABV 4%) RED
American Pale Ale (ABV 4.7%) PALE
Vienna Lager (ABV 5%) SPECIALITY
IPA (ABV 5.8%) IPA

Glasshouse

Unit 6b, Waterside Business Park, Stirchley, B30 3DR ⊕ glasshousebeer.co.uk

Located at the far end of the business park, the brewery is easily accessed via the canal towpath. Beers are available in a variety of styles, tastes and strengths, mostly keg and KeyKeg, but occasionally in cask, either at the tap or in a number of Birmingham outlets. Brewery tap open Friday-Saturday (check before travelling). 70-80 beers were produced in 2023 with most seen in local micropubs.

Glastonbury

See Parkway

Glen Affric

Unit 2 & 3, Lightbox, Knox Street, Birkenhead, CH41 5JW ☎ 07742 020275

Office: 2-5 Knox Street, Birkenhead, CH41 5JW ⊕ glenaffricbrewery.com

⊠ Established in 2016, a small-batch brewery which in 2023 starting producing cask beers alongside the extensive keg range. Its tank farm allows for a flexible brew length. The brewery contract brews for other breweries. ‼☛

Glen Spean SIBA

Tirindrish, Spean Bridge, PH34 4EU ☎ 07511 869958 ⊕ glenspeanbrewing.com

Based in a converted steading, brewing began in 2018. ☛

Pale Blonde (ABV 3.4%) BLOND
Highbridge IPA (ABV 4%) BITTER
Red Revival (ABV 4.5%) BITTER

Globe

🏠 144 High Street West, Glossop, Derbyshire, SK13 8HJ

☎ **(01457) 852417** ⊕ **globepub.co.uk**

Globe was established in 2006 by Ron Brookes on a 2.5-barrel plant, in an old stable behind the Globe pub. His grandson Toby now is now the main brewer. The beers are mainly for the pub but special one-off brews are produced for beer festivals. ♦

Gloucester SIBA

Fox's Kiln, West Quay, The Docks, Gloucester, GL1 2LG
☎ **(01452) 668043** ☎ **07503 152749**
⊕ **gloucesterbrewery.co.uk**

⊠ Situated in the historic Gloucester Docks, brewing began in 2011 and has expanded into larger dockside premises to meet demand. Further expansion is planned. The original site is now its bar, named Tank. The full range of beers is regularly available in Gloucestershire and beyond. Beers are brewed in cask, keg and cans, most are unfined. A range of gins and vodkas is also distilled onsite. The brewery is committed to being carbon neutral. ‼ ⇌ ♦ LIVE V ⬦

Session Pale (ABV 3.7%) PALE
Gloucester Gold (ABV 3.9%) GOLD
Priory Pale (ABV 3.9%) GOLD
Cascade (ABV 4.2%) BITTER
Session IPA (ABV 4.5%) PALE
Dockside Dark (ABV 5.2%) PORTER
New England IPA (ABV 5.2%) PALE

Goacher's

Unit 8, Tovil Green Business Park, Burial Ground Lane, Tovil, Maidstone, Kent, ME15 6TA
☎ **(01622) 682112** ⊕ **goachers.com**

A traditional brewery that uses only malt and Kentish hops for all its beers. Phil and Debbie Goacher have concentrated on brewing good, wholesome beers without gimmicks. Two tied houses and around 30 free trade outlets in the mid-Kent area are supplied. Special is brewed for sale under house names. ‼ ♦

Real Mild Ale (ABV 3.4%) MILD
A rich, flavourful mild with moderate roast barley, and a generous helping of chocolate malt.
Fine Light Ale (ABV 3.7%) BITTER
A pale, golden brown bitter with a strong, floral, hoppy aroma and aftertaste. A hoppy and moderately malty session beer.
Special/House Ale (ABV 3.8%) BITTER
Best Dark Ale (ABV 4.1%) BITTER
Light brown bitter. Malt-forward aroma with roast and sweetness. The malty bittersweet holds to the aftertaste with gentle roasty dryness.
Crown Imperial Stout (ABV 4.5%) STOUT
A good, well-balanced roasty stout, dark and bitter with just a hint of caramel and a lingering creamy head.
Gold Star Strong Ale (ABV 5.1%) BLOND
A strong pale ale brewed from 100% Maris Otter malt and East Kent Goldings hops.

Godalming Beerworks

▤ **Star Inn, 17 Church Street, Godalming, Surrey, GU7 1EL**
☎ **(01483) 417717** ⊕ **godalming.beer**

⊠ A unique nanobrewery attached to a CAMRA award-winning cider pub, where the landlord takes part in the brewing process. ‼ ⬦

Goddards SIBA

Branstone Farm, Hale Common, Branstone, Sandown, Isle of Wight, PO36 0LT
☎ **(01983) 611011** ⊕ **goddardsbrewery.com**

⊠ Anthony Goddard established, what is now the oldest, active brewery on the Isle of Wight, in 1993. Originally occupying an 18th-century barn, a new brewery was built in 2008, quadrupling its capacity. It has since been increased again following a move to Branstone Farm in 2023. Goddards' remain a locally-focused business distributing ales on the island, and easily accessible to southern English counties. ♦ ⬦

Ale of Wight (ABV 3.8%) BITTER
Starboard! (ABV 4%) GOLD
Wight Squirrel (ABV 4.3%) BITTER
Fuggle Dee-Dum (ABV 4.8%) BITTER
Brown-coloured strong ale with plenty of malt and hops.

Godstone SIBA

Flower Farm, Oxted Road, Godstone, Surrey, RH9 8DE
☎ **07791 570731**

Office: Flower Farm Shop, Unit B8A, Godstone, RH9 8DE ⊕ **thegodstonebrewers.com**

⊠ The Godstone Brewers was established in 2015 using a one-barrel plant, but moved to larger premises on a farm in Godstone, where a taproom has recently been built. It now uses a 12-barrel plant to produce core beers, and a five-barrel plant for a variety of special and one-off brews. Beers are named with local themes. Local outlets are supplied. All beers are suitable for vegans. ‼ ⇌ ♦ LIVE V ⬦

Up, Up & Away (ABV 2.7%) GOLD
Trenchman's Hop (ABV 3.8%) BITTER
Redgate (ABV 4%) BITTER
Pondtail (ABV 4.1%) PALE
Junction 6 (ABV 4.2%) BLOND
Forever (ABV 4.3%) GOLD
Rusty's Ale (ABV 4.4%) BITTER
Tunnel Vision (ABV 4.6%) SPECIALITY
Buzz (ABV 4.7%) SPECIALITY
Bitter Entropy (ABV 5.3%) BITTER
Dubbel (ABV 5.5%) SPECIALITY
Polly's Potion (ABV 6.5%) PORTER

Goff's SIBA

9 Isbourne Way, Winchcombe, Cheltenham, Gloucestershire, GL54 5NS
☎ **(01242) 603383** ⊕ **goffsbrewery.com**

⊠ Goff's is a family concern that has been brewing cask-conditioned ales since 1994. The ales are available regionally in more than 200 outlets and nationally through wholesalers. Three regular ales are supplemented by the seasonal 'Jester' range (12 beers). ⇌ ♦ V

Lancer (ABV 3.8%) GOLD
Bright gold. Verbena, lemony-grass and light pear aroma. Light-bodied, easy-drinking, some citrus bitterness and long, drying finish.
Jouster (ABV 4%) BITTER
Earthy, pepper hop aroma. Relatively sweet, mild hop bitterness, some hedgerow fruits. Drying aftertaste but bitterness and fruit fade quickly.
Tournament (ABV 4%) BITTER
Earthy, spicy hops, sweet malt, hedgerow fruits aroma. Caramel/toffee, bitter English hops taste. Long finish with drying hops and fruit.
Cheltenham Gold (ABV 4.5%) GOLD

Bright gold, strong USA hop/citrus aroma. Balanced citrus hop, malt sweetness, with no dominating flavour. Citrus aftertaste, and long, drying finish.
White Knight (ABV 4.7%) BLOND
Bright, light malt aroma with fruit, hop and earthy sweetness. Citrus hops and fruit lead to a bitter, drying finish.

Golden Duck

Unit 2, Redhill Farm, Top Street, Appleby Magna, Leicestershire, DE12 7AH ☎ 07846 295179
⊕ goldenduckbrewery.com

Launched in 2012 using a five-barrel plant, Golden Duck is a family run microbrewery in Appleby Magna. Supplying beer to pubs and festivals around the surrounding area. Beers have a cricket-related theme. It also runs a tap bar at Sir John Moore School next door, where beer is served straight from the barrel. ♦LIVE

Hayles' Ale (ABV 3.8%) BITTER
Tinners Tipple (ABV 4.1%) GOLD
Golden Duck Extra Pale (ABV 4.2%) PALE
LFB (Lunns First Brew) (ABV 4.3%) GOLD
Lunnys No. 8 (ABV 4.8%) BITTER
Nosey Parker (ABV 5%) GOLD
For England (ABV 5.1%) GOLD
Reverend Green (ABV 5.5%) IPA

Golden River

160 Coronation Avenue, Bath, BA2 2JR

A 25-litre brew length nanobrewery operating from late 2022 and launched at Bath Beer Festival early 2023. Supplies beer in 20-litre bag in box.

Golden Triangle SIBA

Unit 9, Industrial Estate, Watton Road, Barford, Norfolk, NR9 4BG
☎ (01603) 757763 ☎ 07976 281132
⊕ goldentriangle.co.uk

⊠ Golden Triangle, named after an area of Norwich, has been brewing modern, hop-forward ales on a 10-barrel plant since 2011. Brewing is on an occasional basis, with the beers mainly found in the brewery tap, the Artichoke, Norwich, which was purchased in 2018. ♦

Goldmark SIBA

Unit 23, The Vinery, Arundel Road, Poling, Arundel, West Sussex, BN18 9PY
☎ (01903) 297838 ☎ 07900 555415
⊕ goldmarkbeers.co.uk

⊠ Brewery run by Mark Lehmann, an ex-biochemist, in Arundel, West Sussex. Commercially brewing since 2013 on a 12-barrel plant. The brewery specialises in pales and porters in cask. Seasonal brewery tours and takeaway from shop are available on Fridays and Saturdays. ‖ ☞ ♦LIVE

Session Pale (ABV 3.7%) PALE
Dave (ABV 3.8%) BITTER
Liquid Gold (ABV 4%) GOLD
Hop Idol (ABV 4.4%) PALE
Mosaic Pale (ABV 4.4%) PALE
American Pale (ABV 4.8%) PALE
Black Cherry (ABV 4.8%) PORTER
Sussex Warrior (ABV 4.8%) BITTER
Vertigo Craft Lager (ABV 4.8%) SPECIALITY
Pitch Shifter IPA (ABV 5%) PALE

Good Chemistry SIBA

Unit 2, William Street, St Philips, Bristol, BS2 0RG
☎ (0117) 903 9930

Office: 6 Beaconsfield Road, Bristol, BS8 2TS
⊕ goodchemistrybrewing.co.uk

⊠ Good Chemistry was established in 2015 in a warehouse in St Philips, Bristol, by Bob Cary and Kelly Sidgwick, using a 10-barrel plant. As the name suggests, all brewery and beer logos have a scientific theme. The brewery has a taproom and canned beer shop, and it also operates two pubs in Bristol: the historic King's Head, BS1, and The Good Measure, Redland. ☞ GF V♦

Time Lapse (ABV 3.8%) BITTER
Aroma and flavours are balanced with a malty foundation supporting soft fruit and light citrus with a hoppy bitterness which grows into the finish.
Natural Selection (ABV 4%) PALE
Hops and pale malt aromas, initially sweet body is followed by hoppy bitterness which continues into the short, dry finish.
Kokomo Weekday (ABV 4.3%) PALE
Hazy golden-coloured ale with hop and sweet fruit aroma which continues onto the palate before a short, bitter finish.

Good Stuff

⬛ Abdication, 89 Mansfield Road, Daybrook, Nottinghamshire, NG5 6BH ⊕ theabdication.co.uk

Good Stuff Brewing at The Abdication is a nanobrewery located inside the Abdication micropub. Capacity is 0.5-barrels so occasional beers can only be found at the pub and local beer festivals.

Goodh SIBA

Unit 3, Moorland Road Business Park, Indian Queens, Cornwall, TR9 6GX
☎ (01726) 839970 ☎ 07834 407964
⊕ goodhbrew.com

Goodh Brewing is now well established as a producer of kegged and canned beers, featuring numerous variations and names across a wide range of styles. Canned beers are retailed widely including at local farmers markets. The revived Skinners Brewery is also part of the Goodh family and its kegs feature at Skinners Tapyard at Newham Industrial Estate, Truro, alongside Skinners cask beers. ☞ V♦

Goodness SIBA

Unit 5a, Clarendon Yards, Coburg Road, Wood Green, London, N22 6TZ ⊕ thegoodnessbrew.co

⊠ A community-focused microbrewery with taproom, pizza oven and event space. It brews seven core beers, with many specials and one-offs, plus a range of single-hop beers. All are unfiltered, gluten-free and vegan, and variously available as cask, keg or can. Wood Green Hopping City is brewed annually with hops grown by the local community. GF V♦

Goodwood

The New Brewery, Stane Street, North Heath, West Sussex, RH20 1DJ ⊕ goodwood.com/estate/home-farm/goodwood-brewery

Beers are available in bottle and keg in restaurants and bars across the Goodwood estate and now available to order online. The beer is brewed by Hepworth (qv) using ingredients grown on the estate.

Goody SIBA

Bleangate Brewery, Braggs Lane, Herne, Kent, CT6 7NP
☎ (01227) 361555 ⊕ goodyales.co.uk

Goody Ales began brewing in 2012 using a 10-barrel plant. A wood-burning boiler is used to heat the water for the brews using wood from its copse, thereby minimising the use of non-renewable fuel. An onsite bar and shop, the Cathedral, is open (limited hours). ⊨♦LIVE♦

Good Evening (ABV 3.4%) MILD
Genesis (ABV 3.5%) RED
A dark ruby-coloured, single hop ale with a full flavour and lasting bitter finish.
Good Health (ABV 3.6%) BITTER
A honey-coloured, golden ale with a fresh, hoppy finish and undertone of zesty orange.
Good Life (ABV 3.9%) BLOND
Good Heavens (ABV 4.1%) BITTER
Good Sheppard (ABV 4.5%) BITTER
Deep amber ale with a warm vanilla twist on the palate and a soft feel on the tongue.
Goodness Gracious Me (ABV 4.8%) BITTER
Good Lord (ABV 5%) PORTER

Goose Eye SIBA

Unit S, Castlefield Industrial Estate, Crossflatts, Bingley, West Yorkshire, BD16 2AF
☎ (01274) 512743 ⊕ goose-eye-brewery.co.uk

☺Goose Eye is a family-run brewery established in 1991, supplying numerous regular and mainly local outlets, chiefly in Yorkshire and Lancashire. Goose Eye moved in 2017 to a custom-built brewery with a 20-barrel brew-length producing regular beers and monthly specials. The well-appointed brewery bar is open every Friday and Saturday, with food from independent vendors available every first Saturday of the month. ♦♦

Spring Wells (ABV 3.6%) PALE
Aromas of light malts, hops. Pink grapefruit, strong hoppiness, with a background of maltiness. Finish is long and increasingly bitter.
Bitter (ABV 3.9%) BITTER
Traditional Yorkshire brown session bitter. Well-balanced malt and hops with a pleasingly bitter finish.
Black Moor (ABV 3.9%) MILD
Black mild with rich maltiness which runs from aroma to finish. Vine fruits and dark chocolate create a balance finish.
Chinook Blonde (ABV 4.2%) BLOND
Assertive grapefruit hoppiness in the aroma and tropical fruit flavours, followed by a bitter finish.
Golden Goose (ABV 4.5%) BLOND
Over & Stout (ABV 5.2%) STOUT
A full-bodied stout with roasty malt flavours mingling with hops, dark fruit and liquorice on the palate. Growing bitter finish.
Pommies Revenge (ABV 5.2%) PALE
Golden strong bitter combining grassy hops, a cocktail of fruit flavours, a peppery hint and a hoppy, bitter finish.

Gorgeous

Church Farm, Warwick, CV35 8QL ☎ 07714 649988
⊕ gorgeousbrewery.com

⊠ Gorgeous inherited the brewing kit from London Brewing on the purchase of the Bull in Highgate, in 2017. In 2018, a newly-built brewhouse at the rear of the pub came on stream, but this was removed in 2022 at the insistence of the new pub owning company. The brewery is currently in storage until a new location is found, with beers brewed elsewhere in the meantime. LIVE V

Greedyguts (ABV 3.5%) GOLD
Glowfly (ABV 4%) BITTER
Pale brown, easy-drinking bitter with apples and orange aroma. Hops, orange and caramel flavours with a lingering, peppery bitter finish.
Geekhunter (ABV 4.2%) GOLD
Floral, sweet fruity aroma. Biscuity sweet with grapefruit, pineapple and ginger-like spiciness, gently fading in the dry, bitter, lingering finish.
Gunpowder (ABV 4.8%) BITTER
Amber, smooth beer with hoppy tangy nose. Flavour is of orange and biscuit with notes of bitter earthy hops.
Gravedigger (ABV 5%) SPECIALITY
Smooth vanilla milk stout with some fruit, black treacle and subtle vanilla notes. Slightly sweet finish with some vanilla.

Gorilla SIBA

Unit 3, Glasshouse Lane, Cliff Street, Mexborough, S64 9HU ☎ 07747 484368 ⊕ gorillabrewing.co.uk

Co-founders Jason White and Phil Paling launched Gorilla Brewing in 2020, utilising a six-barrel kit, next to the Sheffield and South Yorkshire Navigation canal. Two pubs are operated, Rockingham Tap, Swinton and Track & Sleeper on Knaresborough Station. ♦

Silverback Blonde (ABV 3.8%) PALE
Monkey Magic (ABV 4.5%) SPECIALITY
Orang-A-Tang (ABV 4.5%) SPECIALITY
Kong (ABV 6%) IPA
Vanilla Gorilla (ABV 6%) SPECIALITY

Gower SIBA

Unit 25, Crofty Industrial Estate, Penclawdd, Crofty, Swansea, SA4 3RS
☎ (01792) 850681 ⊕ gowerbrewery.com

⊠ Established in 2011 on a five-barrel brew plant at the Greyhound Inn, Llanrhidian. The brewery moved to a new 20-barrel brewery in Crofty, Gower, in 2015. Seasonal and speciality ales are brewed alongside established beers. Its onsite taproom was added in 2021. See online for event details. ‼⊨♦♦

Brew 1 (ABV 3.8%) BITTER
Best Bitter (ABV 4.5%) BITTER
Gold (ABV 4.5%) GOLD
Rumour (ABV 5%) RED
Shipwreck (ABV 5.1%) PALE
Power (ABV 5.5%) BITTER

Grain SIBA

South Farm, Tunbeck Road, Harleston, Norfolk, IP20 0BS
☎ (01986) 788884 ⊕ grainbrewery.co.uk

⊠ Grain Brewery was launched in 2006 by Geoff Wright and Phil Halls in a converted dairy in the Waveney Valley. It upgraded to an 18-barrel plant in 2012. Two pubs are owned: the Plough, Norwich, and the Spread Eagle, Ipswich. The taproom is open every Friday and Saturday. ‼⊨♦LIVE♦

Oak (ABV 3.8%) BITTER
Good balance of malt, toffee and bittersweet fruitiness. Caramel in initial taste fades as biscuit and bitterness dominate the aftertaste.
ThreeOneSix (ABV 3.9%) PALE

Hop and grapefruit dominate throughout as an underlying bitterness slowly stifles a delicate malty echo. Crisp and well-defined.
Best Bitter (ABV 4.2%) BITTER
Brazil nut and malt introduce this well-balanced, complex bitter. Bittersweet caramel notes flourish before a gently tapering malty finish.
Blackwood Stout (ABV 4.5%) STOUT
Red Nelson (ABV 4.7%) RED
Slate (ABV 6%) PORTER
Roast and dark fruits dominate throughout. Caramel and sweet malt add complexity and balance. Full-bodied with a short finish.
Lignum Vitae (ABV 6.5%) IPA
Orange, toffee and banana on the nose and first taste. A smooth digestive sweetness adds depth as bitterness slowly grows.

Grainstore SIBA

🍺 Station Approach, Oakham, Rutland, LE15 6RE
☎ (01572) 770065 ⊕ grainstorebrewery.com

☺Grainstore, the smallest county's largest brewery, has been in production since 1995, founded by Tony Davis and Mike Davies. After 45 years in the industry Tony decided to retire, handing the reins to his son, William, and Peter Atkinson. More than 200 outlets are supplied. Beers are also brewed under the Stoney Ford brand name. ‼◆⬥

Rutland Panther (ABV 3.4%) MILD
This superb reddish-black mild punches above its weight with malt and roast flavours combining to deliver a brew that can match the average stout for intensity of flavour.
Cooking (ABV 3.6%) BITTER
Tawny-coloured beer with malt and hops on the nose and a pleasant grainy mouthfeel. Hops and fruit flavours combine to give a bitterness that continues into a long finish.
Red Kite (ABV 3.8%) BITTER
Rutland Osprey (ABV 4%) GOLD
Triple B (ABV 4.2%) BITTER
Initially hops dominate over malt in both the aroma and taste, but fruit is there, too. All three linger in varying degrees in the sweetish aftertaste of this brown brew.
Zahara (ABV 4.2%) GOLD
Ten Fifty (ABV 5%) BITTER
Pungent banana and malt notes on the nose. On the palate, rich malt and fruit is joined by subtle hop on a bittersweet base. Dry malt aftertaste with some fruit.
Rutland Beast (ABV 5.3%) OLD
Nip (ABV 7.3%) BARLEY

Grampus

🍺 Grampus Inn, Lee Bay, Devon, EX34 8LR
☎ (01271) 862906 ⊕ thegrampus-inn.co.uk

⊠ Grampus was established in 2014 at the back of the Grampus Inn by Bill Harvey, the pub owner and brewer. It is a small plant using traditional brewing methods, but combining unique and unusual ingredients. All beers are available in the local area. A small batch gin distillery was added in 2019. ◆LIVE

Grasmere

Lake View Country House, Lake View Drive, Grasmere, Cumbria, LA22 9TD
☎ (01539) 435572 ☎ 07840 059561
⊕ grasmerepub.com

Brewing began in 2017 in old farm buildings at Lake View Country House. Beers are available at its nearby brewery tap and restaurant, the Good Sport. Cider is also produced.

Helles Lager (ABV 3.8%) SPECIALITY
Pale Ale (ABV 4%) BLOND
Sweet beer with a hint of bitterness and a drying finish.
Bitter (ABV 4.1%) BITTER
IPA (ABV 5.5%) IPA

Grasshopper

Unit F2, Langley Bridge Industrial Estate, Linkmel Road, Langley Mill, Derbyshire, NG16 3RZ
⊕ 52degreesbrewing.com

Grasshopper commenced brewing in 2017 using a purpose-built, 10-barrel plant. It came under the 52 Degrees Brewing umbrella in 2023.

Gravity Well

Unit 1, Compass West Industrial Estate, 33 West Road, Tottenham, London, N17 0XL ☎ 07833 226373
⊕ gravitywellbrewing.co.uk

Brewing started in 2018 in a railway arch in Leyton with a bigger taproom opening along the line in 2020. 2023 saw a move with new kit to Tottenham, into the same industrial estate as Redemption and the former OME brewery. The range of pale ales, sours and stouts (including double and imperial versions) is available in keg and cans. Cask is available for local beer festivals. ◆

Great Beyond SIBA

416-418 Union Walk, Hoxton, London, E2 8HP
☎ (020) 3398 6471 ⊕ greatbeyond.beer

Comprising three arches under the London Overground close to Hoxton Station; two arches contain the brewery, and one arch the comfy taproom (Wed-Sun and for special events). The seasoned brewers create a wide range of styles in keg and cans, available at the taproom and an increasing number of local bars. No cask ale. ◆

Great Corby SIBA

The Green, Great Corby, Cumbria, CA4 8LR
☎ (01228) 560899 ⊕ greatcorbybrewhouse.com

☺The brewery started in 2009 and has been locally-owned since 2020. The large sandstone former honey factory now houses the brewing area and offices. The former brewing site at the Forge, across the village green, is now used for cask washing. All beers are now gluten free. An additional two-barrel plant was installed in 2024 for one-off brews and specials. ‼◆GF

Corby Ale (ABV 3.4%) BITTER
A fruity session beer with sweetness leading to gentle bitterness in the aftertaste.
Fox Brown Ale (ABV 3.4%) BROWN
Malty aromas follow into the taste to dominate with some hop bitterness and fruit. Gentle bitterness balances the malty sweetness.
Tizzie Whizie (ABV 3.4%) PALE
Blonde (ABV 4%) BLOND
Some fruit in the aroma and then a sweet, fruity and lightly bittered taste which continues for a short time.
Lakeland Summit (ABV 4%) BLOND
Aroma and taste are dominated by fruity hops. Sweetness in the finish is joined with hop bitterness to create balance.
Stout (ABV 4.5%) STOUT
A roasty start with some caramel and gentle hops, a sweet body to balance, finishing drier with all flavours lasting.

Great Newsome SIBA

Great Newsome Farm, South Frodingham, East Yorkshire, HU12 0NR
☎ (01964) 612201 ⊕ greatnewsomebrewery.co.uk

☺Nestled in the Holderness countryside, Great Newsome began brewing in 2007 in renovated farm buildings. A range of beers is now brewed using barley from the farm and brewing can be seen from a viewing area. Expansion into other farm buildings in 2018, and again in 2019, increased brewing capacity to 20-barrels. A diversification in beer range to include organic and vegan beers was established in 2024 upon obtaining organic certification and the susequent purchase of the Little Valley brand. Contract brewing is carried out on behalf of other local breweries. Beer is distributed throughout the UK and overseas. ‼🍴♦GF V

Sleck Dust (ABV 3.8%) BLOND
Pricky Back Otchan (ABV 4.2%) BITTER
Frothingham Best (ABV 4.3%) BITTER
Holderness Dark (ABV 4.3%) MILD
Jem's Stout (ABV 4.3%) STOUT
Liquorice Lads Stout (ABV 4.3%) SPECIALITY

Brewed under the Little Valley brand name:
Withens Pale (ABV 3.9%) PALE
Creamy, light gold-coloured, refreshing ale. Fruity hop aroma, flavoured with hints of lemon and grapefruit. Clean, bitter aftertaste.
Cragg Bitter (ABV 4.2%) BITTER
Tawny best bitter with a creamy mouthfeel.
Tod's Blonde (ABV 5%) BLOND
Bright yellow, smooth golden beer with a citrus hop start and a dry finish. Fruity, with a hint of spice. Similar in style to a Belgian blonde beer.

Great North Eastern

Contract House (Unit E), Wellington Road, Dunston, Gateshead, NE11 9HS
☎ (0191) 447 4462 ⊕ gnebco.com

Brewing began in 2016 on a 10-barrel plant. In 2017 the brewery expanded into the adjacent premises and a tap and shop was opened, with an events space for live entertainment. Beers are supplied direct throughout the North East, and nationally via wholesalers. 🍴♦◆

Claspers Citra Blonde (ABV 3.8%) BLOND
Styrian Blonde (ABV 3.8%) BLOND
Gold (ABV 4%) GOLD
Rivet Catcher (ABV 4%) BITTER
Session bitter with sweet malts and hops continuing through to a lasting, dry, bitter finish.
Taiheke Sun (ABV 4.2%) PALE
Delta APA (ABV 4.5%) PALE
Foxtrot Premium Ale (ABV 4.5%) BITTER
GNE Stout (ABV 4.6%) STOUT
Graphite (ABV 4.6%) BROWN
Hopnicity (ABV 5%) PALE

Great Oakley SIBA

Ark Farm, High Street South, Tiffield, Northamptonshire, NN12 8AB
☎ (01327) 351759 ⊕ greatoakleybrewery.co.uk

⊠ Award-winning brewery established in 2005 in Great Oakley, relocating to Tiffield in 2012. It is run by Guy Jenkins who took over in 2017. More than 60 local outlets are supplied. ♦LIVE V

Daggerbill (ABV 3.4%) PALE
Welland Valley Mild (ABV 3.6%) MILD
Egret (ABV 3.8%) GOLD

Wagtail (ABV 3.9%) GOLD
Wot's Occurring (ABV 3.9%) BITTER
Sweetish aroma with caramel notes followed by a typical bitter biscuity flavour, with a slightly astringent aftertaste.
Walter Tull (ABV 4%) BITTER
Tiffield Thunderbolt (ABV 4.2%) BLOND
Light cirus aroma which builds on the flavour with citrus notes, grapefruit predominates and continues into the light bitter aftertaste.
Gobble (ABV 4.5%) BLOND
Delapre Dark (ABV 4.6%) OLD
Abbey Stout (ABV 5%) STOUT
Tailshaker (ABV 5%) GOLD

Great Western

See Hop Union

Green Arches

🍺 Arch 11, 15 Red Bank, Manchester, M4 4HF

Situated in the Green Quarter, Green Arches is a bar and brewery founded in 2023 by Sam and Lee, who both formerly brewed at Beatnik Republic. A range of beer styles is brewed and available in keg.

Green Dragon

🍺 29 Broad Street, Bungay, Suffolk, NR35 1EF
☎ (01986) 892681 ⊕ greendragonbungay.co.uk

⊠ The locally-famed Green Dragon is Bungay's liveliest pub and brewery. Established in 1991 by brothers Robert and William Pickard, Green Dragon beer is brewed onsite in an eight-barrel plant situated in a converted barn. ‼♦

Green Duck SIBA

Unit 13, Gainsborough Trading Estate, Rufford Road, Stourbridge, West Midlands, DY9 7ND
☎ (01384) 377666 ⊕ greenduckbrewery.co.uk

☺Green Duck began brewing in 2012 and relocated to its present site in Stourbridge in 2013. Experimental beers are brewed alongside a core range. The brewery has a taproom, the Badelynge Bar, where the brewing equipment is visible through a glass partition. Demand for small package beers saw the brewery invest in a canning plant together with Twisted Barrel Brewery in 2020. ‼♦◆

ZPA Zesty Pale Ale (ABV 3.8%) PALE
Session IPA (ABV 4%) PALE
Pale gold with a tropical aroma derived from mosaic hops. Very refreshing with a dry pine and resin aftertaste.
Blonde (ABV 4.2%) SPECIALITY
American Pale (ABV 4.5%) PALE

Green Jack SIBA

Argyle Place, Love Road, Lowestoft, Suffolk, NR32 2NZ
☎ (01502) 562863 ☎ 07902 219459
⊕ green-jack.com

⊠ After 10 years at Oulton Broad, Green Jack moved to the Triangle Tavern, Lowestoft in 2003 and then to a nearby 35-barrel plant in 2009. One pub is owned and more than 150 outlets supplied. ‼♦LIVE

Golden Best (ABV 3.8%) GOLD
Smooth, satisfying session golden ale with tangy citrus hops, well mixed with a malty sweetness, and a quenching bitter finish.
Nightingale (ABV 4%) BITTER

Malty and fruity amber bitter well-balanced by hop. A sweetish palate subsides as a satisfying bitterness develops.

LGM1 (ABV 4.2%) PALE
Refreshing pale ale with bold citrus hop flavours and a well-defined malty base. Background sweetness fades slowly as bitterness expands.

Orange Wheat Beer (ABV 4.2%) SPECIALITY
Marmalade aroma with a hint of hops, leading to a well-balanced blend of sweetness, hops and citrus with a malt background. Mixed fruit flavours in the aftertaste.

Trawlerboys Best Bitter (ABV 4.6%) BITTER
Tawny premium bitter with sweet malt gently balanced by caramel and fruit, and a gentle lingering hop bitterness providing contrast.

Lurcher Stout (ABV 4.8%) STOUT
Impressive creamy stout with spirited roast malt supported by a satisfying mix of hops and caramel. Lingering roast bitter finish.

Red Herring (ABV 5%) SPECIALITY
Gone Fishing ESB (ABV 5.5%) BITTER
Full-bodied, malty, fruity premium bitter with an amber glow and a background of hop flavours and caramel hints.

Mahseer IPA (ABV 5.8%) IPA
Pale amber brew with well-defined citrus hop, a background balance of malty sweetness and a lingering bittersweet finale.

Ripper (ABV 8.5%) BARLEY
Baltic Trader Export Stout (ABV 10.5%) STOUT
Imperious and complex with full roast malt throughout underscored by caramel and touches of liquorice, then a powerful sweetish finish.

Worthog (ABV 11%) STRONG

Green Mill

Harewood Arms, 2 Market Street, Broadbottom, SK14 6AX ☎ 07967 656887 ⊕ greenmillbrewery.com

Green Mill started brewing in 2007 on a 2.5-barrel plant and moved in 2010 to the Cask & Feather, Rochdale. The brewery relocated again in 2013 to the Harewood Arms, Broadbottom. A number of occasional beers are brewed. The brewery supplies beer to the Harewood Arms and a number of other pubs. ♦GF V

Gold (ABV 3.6%) GOLD
Northern Lights (ABV 4.5%) BLOND

Greene King

Westgate Brewery, Westgate Street, Bury St Edmunds, Suffolk, IP33 1QT ☎ (01284) 763222

Office: Abbot House, Westgate Street, Bury St Edmunds, Suffolk, IP33 1QT ⊕ greeneking.co.uk

Greene King has been brewing in the market town of Bury St Edmunds since 1799. It brews its beers using water drawn from artesian chalk wells below its brewhouse, as well as local East Anglian malt. Beers are also brewed under various brand names. The brewery has recently started brewing more frequent seasonal and collaboration beers again. ‼☕♦LIVE

IPA (ABV 3.4%) BITTER
Creamy, copper-coloured bitter with a meld of soft biscuity malt, hops, fruit and hints of caramel. Light, bitter, malty finish.

London Glory (ABV 4%) BITTER
Malt with hints of caramel, a backdrop of hop and a gentle bittersweet palate in this refreshing session bitter.

Yardbird (ABV 4%) PALE

Session pale ale with a fruity hop hit and a supporting malty sweetness. Fruity hop persists in a strong finale.

St Edmunds (ABV 4.2%) GOLD
Abbot (ABV 5%) BITTER
Mouth-filling premium bitter with sweet malt, caramel and redcurrant. Underpinning hop bitterness holds up well in a malty, fruity finish.

Brewed for Taylor Walker:
1730 (ABV 4%) BITTER

Brewed under the Hardys & Hanson brand name:
Bitter (ABV 3.9%) BITTER
Olde Trip (ABV 4.3%) BITTER

Brewed under the Morland brand name:
Original Bitter (ABV 4%) BITTER
Old Golden Hen (ABV 4.1%) GOLD
Smooth, easy-drinking golden ale with fruity hop underpinned by a malty sweetness.

Old Speckled Hen (ABV 4.5%) BITTER
Light-bodied, ruby-brown, premium bitter with caramel, fruit and malt, touches of background hops, and a developing gentle dryness.

Brewed under the Ruddles brand name:
Best Bitter (ABV 3.7%) BITTER
Easy-drinking amber/brown beer with gentle bitterness and some initial sweetness, fruit and muted hops. Dryness lingers in the aftertaste.

Grey Trees

Unit 17-20, Robertstown Business Park, Aberdare, CF44 8EZ
☎ (01685) 267077 ⊕ greytreesbrewing.com

National award-winning, family-owned brewery in the Welsh heartlands. From humble beginnings, the brewery moved to a new home at Robertstown, Aberdare in recent years, which now includes a brewery shop. It operates its own microbar, the National Tap, Aberdare. Beers are supplied to the free trade in south Wales and beyond. ‼☕♦LIVE

Caradog (ABV 3.9%) BITTER
Black Road Stout (ABV 4%) STOUT
Diggers Gold (ABV 4%) GOLD
Drummer Boy (ABV 4.2%) BITTER
Mosaic Pale Ale (ABV 4.2%) PALE
Valley Porter (ABV 4.6%) PORTER
JPR Pale (ABV 4.7%) PALE
Afghan Pale (ABV 5.4%) PALE

Gribble

Gribble Inn, Oving, West Sussex, PO20 2BP
☎ (01243) 786893 ⊕ gribbleinn.co.uk

Established in 1980 using a five-barrel plant, the Gribble Brewery is the longest-serving brewpub in the Sussex area, independently-owned and run by the licensees since 2005. A number of local outlets are supplied. ♦

Grid

Unit 21, Cuckoo Hill Farm, Hanslope, Milton Keynes, MK19 7HQ

A nanobrewery with a capacity of 350 litres (about two barrels) which started in 2023 and is believed to be producing beer in KeyKegs.

Griffin

See Freestyle

Grizzly Grains

Unit 6, Sheaf Gardens, Duchess Road, Sheffield, South Yorkshire, S2 4BB ☎ 07807 242545
✉ sambrewsbeers@gmail.com

Having purchased the equipment from Crosspool Alemakers in 2019, Sam Bennett commenced brewing in the Walkley area of Sheffield in 2020 before moving to an industrial unit in 2021. Sam produces a range of mostly one-off beers, including bottle-conditioned ales.
♦ LIVE

Grounding Angels

6 Rear Battle Hill, Hexham, Northumberland, NE46 1BB ☎ 07508 175512 ⊕ grounding-angels.com

Brewing started in 2018 by Jamie Robson, using his family's experience of owning global drinks brand Fentimans. Golden Promise malt is used as a base for all of the beers, which are distributed nationwide. Brewing is currently suspended.

Gruff (NEW)

7 Drum Field, Stratford St Mary, Suffolk, CO7 6NU ☎ 07970 667960 ✉ gruff-brewery.co.uk

Created by keen homebrewer Gareth in 2023, Gruff Brewery is named after his baseball nickname and reflects long friendships and a strong sense of local community. The obvious addition of 'Billy Goat' to Gareth's nickname by his teammates provided the basis of the logo. Starting on a 65-litre plant, plans were quickly drawn up to acquire a 200-litre kit to increase production. Local pubs, clubs and beer festivals are supplied with an initial range of four core beers.

Gold (ABV 4%) GOLD
Amber (ABV 4.1%) BITTER
Lawless APA (ABV 4.6%) PALE
P2 Porter (ABV 5.4%) PORTER

Grumpy Fish (NEW)

33 Harwood Close, Arnold, Nottinghamshire, NG5 8AB

Microbrewery that upgraded recently and now regularly appear on bars and at festivals around the Midlands.

GT

Unit 5, The Old Aerodrome, Chivenor Business Park, Braunton, Barnstaple, Devon, EX31 4AY ☎ (01271) 267420 ☎ 07909 515170 ⊕ gtales.co.uk

⊗ Established in 2013, GT Ales is housed in a World War II aircraft hangar at Chivenor. An onsite shop has been added to the five-barrel brewery. All award-winning core ales are available in cask, bottle (limited availability) and can. Limited edition, small-batch brews are regularly produced, and own brand beers are also brewed for local customers. ♦♦♦ LIVE

Thirst of Many (ABV 4.2%) BITTER
North Coast IPA (ABV 4.3%) PALE
Blonde Ambition (ABV 4.5%) BLOND

Guisborough

14 South Buck Way, Guisborough, North Yorkshire, TS14 7FJ ☎ 07703 002858
✉ info@guisboroughbrewery.co.uk

⊗ Established in 2020 using a five-barrel plant. The core range consists of an extensive range of thirteen beers, brewed on a rotational basis. The brewery bar is open most Fridays/ Saturdays, and Sundays for off-sales.

Events are held regularly, with food stalls and live bands becoming a regular feature. Visitors are made most welcome. ♦♦♦

Dark Habit (ABV 3.7%) MILD
Delight (ABV 3.7%) BITTER
Alchemy (ABV 3.8%) BITTER
Realm (ABV 3.9%) GOLD
Phoenix (ABV 4%) RED
Daze (ABV 4.3%) IPA
Elevator (ABV 4.5%) IPA
Nut Kin (ABV 4.5%) PORTER
BOBA (ABV 5%) BROWN
Dangerous Brian (ABV 5%) SPECIALITY
Vypa (ABV 5.5%) IPA

Gun SIBA

Hawthbush Farm, Gun Hill, Heathfield, East Sussex, TN21 0JX ☎ (01323) 700200 ☎ 07900 683355 ⊕ gunbrewery.co.uk

⊗ Gun Brewery is located on a beautiful 140-acre, organic, mixed farm in the Sussex Weald. After selling its first pint in 2015 and outgrowing the converted barn it started in, a brand new brewery and taproom were built on the farm, opening in 2022. Using its own spring water, a core range of beers is brewed with monthly specials as well as a barrel-ageing programme.
♦♦ LIVE GF V♦

Scaramanga Extra Pale (ABV 3.9%) PALE
Parabellum Milk Stout (ABV 4.1%) STOUT
Chummy Bluster Best Bitter (ABV 4.4%) BITTER
Project Babylon Pale Ale (ABV 4.6%) PALE
Zamzama IPA (ABV 6.5%) IPA

Gwaun Valley SIBA

Kilkiffeth Farm, Pontfaen, SA65 9TP ☎ 07854 767383 ⊕ gwaunvalleybrewery.com

Founded in 2009, this microbrewery produces traditional and experimental ales using water from its own well. It has won many awards since being taken on by homebrewer Nigel Smith in 2019. Ales are available in cask, keg and bottle. Tourists can hire a holiday cottage, tent, or caravan pitches, and enjoy folk music sessions once a month. ♦♦♦

Cwrw Melyn (ABV 4%) BLOND
Nutty Mild (ABV 4%) MILD
Cascade (ABV 4.3%) BLOND
Traditional Porter (ABV 4.3%) PORTER
Pembrokeshire Best Bitter (ABV 4.5%) BITTER
Cwrw Gwyn (ABV 5.3%) SPECIALITY

Gyle 59 SIBA

Sadborow Estate Yard, Thorncombe, Dorset, TA20 4PW ☎ (01297) 678990 ☎ 07508 691178 ⊕ gyle59.co.uk

⊗ Gyle 59 is a 10-barrel brewery that began commercial production in 2014. Bottling takes place onsite with bottles being available by mail order. ♦♦♦ LIVE V

Take It Easy (ABV 2.5%) BITTER
Freedom Hiker (ABV 3.7%) BITTER
Lyme Regis Ammonite (ABV 3.7%) BITTER
Toujours (ABV 4%) SPECIALITY
Vienna Session Lager (ABV 4.2%) SPECIALITY
Halcyon Daze (ABV 5%) SPECIALITY
IPA (ABV 5.3%) PALE
Nettle IPA (ABV 5.3%) SPECIALITY
Dorset GIPA (ABV 5.4%) SPECIALITY

Starstruck (ABV 6.6%) SPECIALITY
The Favourite (ABV 6.6%) PORTER
Double IPA (ABV 7.3%) IPA

Brewed under the Capitalist Hippy brand name:
Flower Power (ABV 4.3%) BITTER
Far Out (ABV 5%) PALE
Summer of Love (ABV 6.6%) STRONG

Hackney

Unit 10, Lockwood Way, Blackhorse Lane,
Walthamstow, London, E17 5RB
☎ (020) 3489 9595 ⊕ hackneybrewery.co.uk

⊗ Founded in 2011 in Haggerston and relocated in 2021 to Walthamstow, the brewery and taproom are at the northern tip of the growing Blackhorse Beer Mile. The core range is available on keg and in cans supplemented by regular specials including collaborations. Cask by request only or for special events. ♦🍴

Hackney Church SIBA

Arches 16 & 17, Bohemia Place, Hackney, London,
E8 1DU
☎ (020) 3795 8295 ⊕ hackneychurchbrew.co

Formerly known as St John at Hackney Brewery. Comprising two railway arches, the brewery is in one, the other, the atmospheric taproom. Mostly only available from the taproom for quality control, small quantities are now available from trusted outlets. Beers come from kegs or the tanks above the bar, or in bottles or cans for take away. All profits are used for worthy projects at the nearby parish church. No cask ale. 🍴

Hadrian Border SIBA

Unit 5, The Preserving Works, Newburn Industrial
Estate, Shelley Road, Newburn, Tyne & Wear,
NE15 9RT
☎ (0191) 264 9000 ⊕ hadrian-border-brewery.co.uk

☺ Celebrating 30 years of brewing, based in Newburn near Newcastle-upon-Tyne, using a 40-barrel plant, the brewery can produce up to 200 barrels per week. Beer is delivered directly to the area between Edinburgh, North Yorkshire, Carlisle and the East Coast, and is also available nationally through wholesalers. A three-barrel plant is used for experimental craft brews. One pub is run; the Station East, Gateshead. 🍴♦LIVE

Tyneside Blonde (ABV 3.9%) BLOND
Refreshing blonde ale with zesty notes and a clean, fruity finish.
Farne Island Pale Ale (ABV 4%) BITTER
A copper-coloured bitter with a refreshing malt/hop balance.
Northern Pale (ABV 4.1%) PALE
Secret Kingdom (ABV 4.3%) BITTER
Sweet bitter beer with a light malty taste and some roast to add to the pleasant finish.
Grainger Ale (ABV 4.6%) PALE
Northern IPA (ABV 5.2%) IPA
Ouseburn Porter (ABV 5.2%) PORTER
Traditional robust porter, made with chocolate and black malt. Distinct bitter coffee finish.

Hafod

Old Gas Works, Gas Lane, Mold, CH7 1UR ☎ 07901
386638

Office: Gorwel Hafod Road, Pantglas Gwernaffield,
Mold, CH7 5ES ⊕ welshbeer.com

☺ Hafod began brewing in 2011 on a small scale and upgraded to a new plant in the current premises in 2014, concentrating on beers in bottle and cask. The standard range is accompanied by regular seasonal and special brews throughout the year. The brewery shop operates on a click-and-collect basis and the brewery hosts occasional open days. 🍴♦

Little Marvel (ABV 3.4%) PALE
Solo (ABV 3.4%) PALE
Sunrise (ABV 3.8%) GOLD
Short Circuit (ABV 4%) PALE
London Pale (ABV 4.1%) GOLD
Moel Famau Ale (ABV 4.1%) PORTER
Fruitcake (ABV 4.5%) BITTER
Vanilla Porter (ABV 4.5%) PORTER
Landmark (ABV 4.6%) BITTER
Jigsaw (ABV 4.7%) PALE
Blanchard's ESB (ABV 5.1%) GOLD
Landmark Reserve (ABV 5.2%)
Freestyle (ABV 5.4%) IPA
Fruitcake, Brewers Reserve (ABV 5.5%) BITTER

Hairy Dog

Unit 38, More House Farm, Wivelsfield, West Sussex,
RH17 7RE
☎ (01444) 635003 ⊕ hairydogbrewery.beer

⊗ Overlooking the South Downs National Park, the brewery's ethos is to use Sussex ingredients wherever possible and to pursue a policy of sustainability. An onsite taproom is open Fridays. ♦

Gun Dog (ABV 0.4%) PALE
Hounded Best Bitter (ABV 4.1%) BITTER
Far-Fetched Pale Ale (ABV 4.2%) PALE
Bloodhound Red IPA (ABV 5.5%) RED

Hal's

22A Woodmancote, Dursley, Gloucestershire,
GL11 4AF ☎ 07765 890946

Hal's is a one-barrel microbrewery established in Dursley in 2016, occasionally producing a number of small-batch beers for the New Inn, Dursley, and beer festivals. Brewing is currently suspended. ♦

Half Bap Pour

See Mashdown

Half Moon

Forge House, Main Street, Ellerton, York, East
Yorkshire, YO42 4PB
☎ (01757) 288977 ☎ 07741 400508
⊕ halfmoonbrewery.co.uk

Established in 2013 by Tony and Jackie Rogers, the brewery is situated in a former blacksmith's forge with a capacity of 5.5-barrels. Brewing takes place two-three times a week. ♦LIVE GF🍴

Dark Masquerade (ABV 3.6%) MILD
Old Forge Bitter (ABV 3.8%) BITTER
F'Hops Sake (ABV 3.9%) BITTER

Halifax Steam

🏠 Conclave, Southedge Works, Brighouse Road,
Hipperholme, West Yorkshire, HX3 8EF ☎ 07506
022504 ⊕ halifax-steam.co.uk

☺ Brewing since 1999, the five-barrel plant supplies only the Cock o' the North. It is now reputedly the oldest brewery in Calderdale. A range of permanent beers and different rotating beers are brewed throughout the year. ◆

Hall & Woodhouse (Badger) IFBB

Bournemouth Road, Blandford St Mary, Blandford Forum, Dorset, DT11 9LS
☎ (01258) 452141 ⊕ hall-woodhouse.co.uk

⊠ Hall & Woodhouse has been brewing in the heart of the Dorset countryside since 1777. Owned and run by the seventh generation of the Woodhouse family, it brews with local spring water filtered through the Cretaceous chalk downs and drawn up 120ft from its wells.
A leading, independent UK brewer, its well-known range of Badger ales is award-winning, and it has an estate (around 200 pubs) across southern England. Its ales are available exclusively in Hall & Woodhouse public houses. ♦♣◆⦿

Badger Best Bitter (ABV 3.7%) BITTER
Well-balanced bitter with malt caramel sweetness and hop fruitiness.
Fursty Ferret (ABV 4.1%) BITTER
Easy-drinking best bitter with sweet bitterness that lingers into a dry aftertaste, with a hint of orange.
Tanglefoot (ABV 4.7%) GOLD
Relatively sweet-tasting and deceptive, given its strength. Pale malt provides caramel overtones and bittersweet finish.

Hall's (NEW)

Lubrication Ltd, Unit 3, Lubricant Distribution Centre, Snibston Drive, Coalville, Leicestershire, LE67 3NQ
☎ 07905 308888 ⊕ halls.beer

In 2023, Bill Hall founded Hall's Brewery. It only makes traditional cask ales. ◆

Hambleton SIBA

Melmerby Green Road, Melmerby, North Yorkshire, HG4 5NB
☎ (01765) 640108 ⊕ hambletonbrewery.co.uk

⦿ Established in 1991 by Nick Stafford in a barn at the bottom of his in-laws' garden. Now it is run by Nick's daughter Rachel and son-in-law Ben. Since 2007 it has operated from purpose-built premises near Ripon (100 barrels a week capacity). Along with a core range of eight beers, cask ale is contract brewed for Village Brewer, Black Dog and Wharfe Beer. A bottling line handles brands for others and a canning line was added in 2022, with unfiltered beers on sale locally and via the website. ♦♣◆GF

Session Pale (ABV 3.6%) PALE
Bootleggers Pale Ale (ABV 3.8%) PALE
Thoroughbred IPA (ABV 4%) PALE
Pink Grapefruit (ABV 4.1%) SPECIALITY
Stallion Amber (ABV 4.2%) BITTER
Stud Blonde (ABV 4.3%) GOLD
Black Forest (ABV 5%) SPECIALITY
Nightmare Porter (ABV 5%) STOUT

Contract brewed for Black Dog Brewery:
Whitby Abbey Ale (ABV 3.8%) BITTER
Schooner (ABV 4.2%) PALE
Rhatas (ABV 4.6%) BITTER

Contract brewed for Village Brewer:
White Boar (ABV 3.8%) BITTER
Bull (ABV 4%) GOLD

Contract brewed for Wharfe:
Verbeia (ABV 3.6%) BITTER

Tether Blond (ABV 3.8%) GOLD

Hammersmith

Lower Ground Floor, 106 Fulham Palace Road, Hammersmith, London, W6 9PL
⊕ hammersmithbrewery.co.uk

Brewing started in 2019 in premises formerly used by the unconnected Hoppy Collie brewery. The basement taproom (open Thursday-Saturday evenings) opened 2022. The beer range is dominated by hoppy pale ales, almost always with a stout and a lager, and sometimes a more niche beer such as a sour. No cask ale. ◆

Hammerton SIBA

Units 8 & 9, Roman Way Industrial Estate, 149 Roman Way, Barnsbury, London, N7 8XH
☎ (020) 3302 5880 ⊕ hammertonbrewery.co.uk

⊠ Hammerton began brewing in London in 1868, but ceased in the 1950s, and was later demolished. In 2014, a member of the Hammerton family resurrected the name and opened a new brewery in Barnsbury. Expanded in 2019 after crowdfunding, the taproom is open Thursday-Sunday, complemented by its nearby bar, the House of Hammerton. GF ◆

N1 (ABV 4.1%) PALE
Smooth pale ale with sweet caramel biscuit, grapefruit and Peach Melba. Finish is peppery, bittersweet with a dryness that lingers.
N7 (ABV 5.2%) PALE
Easy-drinking smooth pale ale. Sweet honey with grapefruit, apricot, earthy hops, hint of apricot. Spicy, sweet finish overlaid dry bitterness.

Hand SIBA

▤ 33 Upper St James's Street, Kemptown, Brighton, East Sussex, BN2 1JN
☎ (01273) 286693

Second site: Unit 6a, Garcia Trading Estate, Canterbury Road, Worthing, BN13 1AL ☎ (01273) 286693
⊕ handbrewco.com

⦿ Founded in 1989, Brighton's tiny Hand in Hand Brewpub hides the smallest commercially operating tower brewery in the world, and is the smaller sibling of its main production site in Worthing. The Worthing site houses a steam-heated 2,000-litre brew kit with a combined 28,000-litre fermenting capacity, plus two bright beer tanks and a canning line. This facility also offers a taproom, shop and brewery tours. ♦♣◆

Handsome

Bowstone Bridge Garage, Bowston, Kendal, Cumbria, LA8 9HD
☎ (0344) 848 0888 ⊕ handsomebrewery.co.uk

⦿ Founded in 2016 in the Lakes District following its previous existence as Houston Brewery in Scotland, Handsome is situated on the River Kent in an old MOT garage, formerly the blacksmiths for James Cropper's paper mills. In 2021, it opened a bar next to the River Kent in Kendal and another in Leeds.

Blonde (ABV 3.6%) BLOND
Top Knot (ABV 3.7%) PALE
Hound (ABV 4%) PALE
Stranger (ABV 4.2%) BITTER
Blacksmith (ABV 4.6%) STOUT
Bar Steward (ABV 4.8%) BITTER

Handyman

461 Smithdown Road, Liverpool, L15 3JL
☎ (0151) 722 7422 ⊕ handymansupermarket.co.uk

Brewing began in 2017 on a mezzanine above the bar of the Handyman pub. Both cask and craft beers are produced, using a 400-litre brew kit. Other outlets are also supplied. ♦

Pale (ABV 4.3%) GOLD
Golden Ale (ABV 4.5%) GOLD
Porter (ABV 5.2%) PORTER
American Red Ale (ABV 5.3%) RED
IPA (ABV 5.3%) PALE
Black IPA (ABV 6.7%) IPA

Hanging Bat

c/o Hanging Bat Beer Café, 133 Lothian Road, Edinburgh, EH3 9AD
☎ (0131) 229 0759
⊕ hangingbatbrewco.tumblr.com

☒ Brewing began in 2012 from within the Hanging Bat bar using a 50-litre brew kit from the United States.

Hanging Tree

Benleva Hotel, Kilmore Road, Drumnadrochit, IV63 6UH
☎ (01456) 450080

☺Hanging Tree began brewing in 2017 using a two-barrel brew plant in an old bothy in the grounds of the Benleva Hotel. Named after the 400-year-old chestnut tree growing in the garden, which was used as the hanging tree for the local area. Beers are available at a few local outlets.

Hanlons SIBA

Hill Farm, Half Moon Village, Newton St Cyres, Devon, EX5 5AE
☎ (01392) 851160 ⊕ hanlonsbrewery.com

☺Hanlons, one of Devon's largest brewers since 2013, supply a range of award-winning ales nationwide. The purpose-built brewery also has a shop, bar and restaurant. In 2019, it bought Prescott Ales of Cheltenham. ‼ 🍴 ♦LIVE ⚲

Firefly (ABV 3.7%) BITTER
Malty and fruity light bitter. Hints of orange in the taste.
Citra IPA (ABV 4%) PALE
An easy-drinking citrus and floral IPA.
Yellow Hammer (ABV 4.2%) PALE
Zesty fruit aroma, pineapples on taste with a nice sweetness counteracted by bitterness. Even though available all year, it has got a summer ale style to it.
Brewers Blend (ABV 4.5%) BITTER
Malty biscuit aroma, with a malty biscuit taste with lemons in the background. An easy-drinking bitter.
Port Stout (ABV 4.8%) SPECIALITY
Hints of caramel and port on aroma. Ruby port flavour with dried raisin taste with a slight hint of caramel and chocolate. All flavours carry through in aftertaste.
Stormstay (ABV 5%) BITTER
Tawny and full-bodied. Caramel with hints of malt on the nose. Triumvirate of malt, caramel, hops develop into lingering bitterness.

Brewed under the Prescott Ales name:
Hill Climb (ABV 3.8%) PALE
A late-hopped, straw-coloured session beer with a refreshing fruity finish.
Pit Stop (ABV 4%) PALE

Dark golden colour, biscuity malts with a citrus hop taste throughout.
Chequered Flag (ABV 4.2%) BITTER
A generously-hopped, amber-coloured ale with a malty finish.
Podium Finish (ABV 4.8%) SPECIALITY
Grand Prix (ABV 5%) BITTER
A dark amber-coloured strong ale with a rich, smooth finish.

Contract brewed for Wickwar Brewery:
Falling Star (ABV 4.2%) PALE
Gentle citrus aroma and a light malt background overlaid with bittersweet flavours of grapefruit and pineapple before a well-rounded, moreish finish.

Happy Valley

73 Oxford Road, Macclesfield, Cheshire, SK11 8JG
☎ (01625) 480988 ☎ 07768 107660
⊕ happyvalleybrewery.co.uk

☒ Happy Valley was established in 2010 using a 2.5-barrel plant located in Bollington. In 2018 the brewery was sold and relocated to Macclesfield, and is based at the Happy Valley Tap and Pizza aka 73 & Pizza pub. Brewing is currently suspended. ♦

Harbour

Trekillick Farm, Kirland, Bodmin, Cornwall, PL30 5BB
☎ (01208) 832131 ☎ 07870 305063
⊕ harbourbrewing.com

☒ Harbour is an innovative brewery founded on the outskirts of Bodmin in 2011. Brewed using local spring water, the regular beers are established in an increasing number of outlets. A new 30-barrel plant was installed in 2016, and more conditioning tanks in 2017. The brewery no longer produces cask beers, and is part owned by St Austell Brewery, who handle all distribution. ♦

Harbwr Tenby SIBA

Sargeants Lane, St Julian Street, Tenby, SA70 7BU
☎ (01834) 845797 ☎ 07815 046140
⊕ harbwr.wales

This is a five-barrel brewing plant in an outbuilding of the Harbwr Tap and Kitchen, its associated pub. The beers are available in the pub as well as in the brewery itself, which has a mezzanine bar area overlooking the brewery. Information boards explain the building's history and the brewing process. The brewery offers a tour package named "Hops and Hwyl". Beers are found at more than 20 outlets in South Wales. ‼♦

MV Enterprise (ABV 4%) PALE
North Star (ABV 4.2%) BITTER
Caldey Lollipop (ABV 4.5%) PALE
RFA Sir Galahad (ABV 4.6%) BITTER
La Nossa Signora (ABV 5%) SPECIALITY

Harby

Bottle & Glass, 5 High Street, Harby, Nottinghamshire, NG23 7EB
☎ (01522) 703438
⊕ wigandmitre-lincoln.blogspot.co.uk

Harby Brewstore is a four-barrel malt extract brewery established in 2015 and located at the Bottle & Glass in Harby. Most output goes to the three pubs in the small Wig & Mitre pub group; the Wig & Mitre, Lincoln, Caunton Beck, Caunton and the Bottle & Glass itself.

Hardline (NEW) SIBA

78 Sotheron Road, Watford, Hertfordshire, WD17 2QA
⊕ hardlinebrewery.com

Established in 2023 by Andrew Caird, Hardline currently operates in a disused ice cream factory. It produces seven styles of ales that benefit from being low carb, low calorie, gluten reduced, chemical-free and vegan-friendly. Available in cask and bottle. **V**

Hardys & Hansons

See Greene King

Harrison's

Unit 1, 108 Carolgate, Retford, Nottinghamshire, DN22 6AS ☎ 07850 228383 ⊕ harrisonsbrewery.com

⊛A three-barrel brewery built completely from scratch by brewer Christopher Harrison-Hawkes. The first brew was in 2018. Shortly afterwards four beers were available at its own pub, the Brew Shed (which stands metres from the brewery). In 2019, the pub moved next door to larger premises with an outside area next to the canal. 2019 saw the production of bottle-conditioned beers and in 2020, real ale in a can, produced and packaged onsite. ‼◆LIVE V

Vacant Gesture (ABV 3.8%) BLOND
Idaho 7 (ABV 3.9%) PALE
Best Bitter (ABV 4%) BITTER
Pale Ale (ABV 4%) PALE
Ruby Mild (ABV 4%) MILD
5 Pints All English Bitter (ABV 4.1%) BITTER
Sabro (ABV 4.1%) PALE
Proof of Concept (ABV 4.3%) PALE
Stout (ABV 4.3%) STOUT
American Brown Ale (ABV 4.9%) BROWN
Plum Porter (ABV 5.6%) PORTER
Porter (ABV 5.6%) PORTER
Planet Amarillo (ABV 6.9%) IPA

Harrogate SIBA

Unit 7, Hookstone Centre, Hookstone Chase, Harrogate, North Yorkshire, HG2 7HW ☎ 07593 259425 ⊕ harrogatebrewery.co.uk

⊛Established in 2013, the brewery also uses the names Spa Town Ales, and It's Quicker By Ale on its logo and pumpclips. The brewery has a capacity of 10 barrels, and brews 2-3 times each week. ▰◆

Nidd Mild (ABV 3.7%) MILD
Wavey Marms (ABV 3.8%) PALE
Harlow Blonde (ABV 3.9%) BLOND
Harrogate Pale (ABV 4.2%) GOLD
Cold Bath Gold (ABV 4.4%) BLOND
Pinewoods Pale Ale (ABV 4.4%) GOLD
Best (ABV 4.5%) BITTER
Stray All Day (ABV 4.6%) PALE
Plum Porter (ABV 4.8%) SPECIALITY
Salted Caramel Porter (ABV 4.8%) PORTER
Vanilla Porter (ABV 4.8%) SPECIALITY
Beeching Axe (ABV 5.2%) BITTER
Jumping The Shark (ABV 5.9%) IPA
Louis Louis (ABV 6%) STOUT
Kursaal Stout (ABV 6.7%) STOUT

Hartlebury

Station Park, Station Road, Hartlebury, Worcestershire, DY11 7YJ

☎ **(01299) 253617 ☎ 07831 570117**
✉ hartleburybrewingco@icloud.com

Formerly the site of Attwoods Brewery, the Hartlebury Brewing Co was established in 2019 by David Higgs, the owner of the Tap House pub adjacent to Hartlebury Railway Station. It supplies the Tap House and local free trade.

Bitter Strikes Back (ABV 3.8%) BITTER
Hooker (ABV 4%) PALE
Pale ale, malt and hops predominate on the nose, background berry fruits, then notes of grapefruit, hops, pear and melon in the taste. Finish is grapefruit fading into bitterness and finally malt.
Off the Rails (ABV 4.2%) GOLD
Golden ale, fruity aroma with a hint of honey sweetness, flavours of grapefruit, hint of nectarine and some toffee leading to a spicy aftertaste of grapefruit and a long bitter finish.
Rambo Mango (ABV 4.3%) SPECIALITY
Yellow speciality beer with mango, aromas of yeast, biscuit and a hint of mango, fruity bitter taste of hops, grapefruit, mango in the background followed by a long hoppy then bitter finish.
APA (ABV 4.5%) PALE
Smooth yellow ale, malt and hops predominate on the nose with some background berry fruits, grapefruit, hops and pear followed by grapefruit fading into bitterness and malt in the aftertaste.

Harvey's IFBB

Bridge Wharf Brewery, 6 Cliffe High Street, Lewes, East Sussex, BN7 2AH
☎ **(01273) 480209 ⊕ harveys.org.uk**

⊠ Established in 1790, this independent, family brewery operates from the banks of the River Ouse in Lewes. A major development in 1985 doubled the brewhouse capacity to more than 38,000 barrels a year. There are plans to re-establish small brew lengths of special beers, including replicating old recipes. Harvey's supplies real ale to all its 45 pubs and about 550 free trade outlets in the South East. ‼▰◆LIVE

Dark Mild (ABV 3%) MILD
A dark copper-brown colour. Roast malt dominates the aroma and palate leading to a sweet, caramel finish.
Sisters Table Beer (ABV 3.4%) PALE
Sussex Best Bitter (ABV 4%) BITTER
Full-bodied brown bitter. A hoppy aroma leads to a good malt and hop balance, and a dry aftertaste.
Old Ale (ABV 4.3%) OLD
Armada Ale (ABV 4.5%) BITTER
Hoppy amber best bitter. Well-balanced fruit and hops dominate throughout with a fruity palate.

Harviestoun SIBA

Alva Industrial Estate, Alva, FK12 5DQ
☎ **(01259) 769100 ⊕ harviestoun.com**

Harviestoun has grown from one-man brewing in a bucket in the back of a shed, in 1983, to a 60-barrel, multi award-winning brewery today. Now based in Alva, Scotland. Two cask ales produced all year round and monthly rotational ales. ‼▰◆LIVE

Bitter & Twisted (ABV 3.8%) GOLD
Refreshingly hoppy beer with fruit throughout. A bittersweet taste with a long bitter finish. A golden session beer.
Schiehallion (ABV 4.8%) SPECIALITY
A Scottish cask lager, brewed using a lager yeast and Hersbrucker hops. A hoppy aroma, with fruit and malt,

leads to a malty, bitter taste with floral hoppiness and a bitter finish.

Harwich Town

See WHARF

Hatherland

Hatherland Mill Farm, Lower Washfield, Tiverton, EX16 9PG
☎ (01398) 351165 ⊕ hatherland.co.uk

Owner and founder, Lawrence Bunning, decided to combine his love for beer with reutilising unused space on his family farm, setting up the brewery in the old dairy shed. Water is drawn from a bore hole. Passionate about the environment, solar energy is utilised from panels on the brewery roof and heat from the wood chip boiler. Brewing waste is used to feed the farm's prize-winning, rare-breed cattle. LIVE

Sand Martin (ABV 4.7%) PALE

Hattie Brown's

Whitecliff Farm, Whitecliff Road, Swanage, BH19 1RJ
☎ (01929) 439229

⊗ Hattie Brown's began brewing in 2014, moving to its present location in 2015. Owned by Jean Young and Kevin Hunt, who formerly ran the Square & Compass public house in Worth Matravers. The brewery increased capacity in 2023 to cope with demand.

HBA (ABV 3.8%) BITTER
Well-balanced session bitter with initial malt flavours followed by a balanced hop and sweet finish.
Moonlite (ABV 3.8%) PALE
Easy-drinking session pale ale, richly-hopped with refreshing strong citrus flavours and long lingering finish.
Mustang Sally (ABV 4.3%) BITTER
Agglestone (ABV 4.5%) BITTER
Kirrin Island (ABV 4.5%) PALE
Premium, blonde-coloured pale ale with hop flavours dominating the malt biscuit base.
Spangle (ABV 4.6%) BITTER
Sirius (ABV 4.8%) PALE
Swanage Nut (ABV 4.8%) BROWN
Full Moon (ABV 5%) GOLD
Herkules (ABV 5%) PALE
Crow Black (ABV 5.1%) PORTER
Excellent strong mild with roast aromas, and rich malt and dried fruit pudding flavours. Lovely lingering aftertaste. Deceptively easy-drinking.
Dog on the Roof (ABV 6%) GOLD

Hawkshead SIBA

Mill Yard, Staveley, Cumbria, LA8 9LR
☎ (01539) 822644 ⊕ hawksheadbrewery.co.uk

⊕ Established in 2002, it outgrew its original barn and moved to Staveley in 2006 to a purpose-built, 20-barrel brewery. Shortly afterwards a brewery tap was added, which has gained huge popularity. While a range of unpasteurised keg and small format beers are offered the majority of production is in cask. ‼ ➤ ♦ LIVE GF ♦

Bitter (ABV 3.4%) BITTER
Iti (ABV 3.4%) GOLD
Windermere Pale (ABV 3.4%) BLOND
Floral aromas with some malt presence evolves into citrus hop bitterness and a long bitter finish.
Mosaic Pale (ABV 4%) PALE

Strong citrus hops and fruity aromas continue with hop bitterness and a sweet body, finishing long and a little drier.
Red (ABV 4.2%) RED
Lakeland Gold (ABV 4.4%) BLOND
A beer with plenty of hop bitterness throughout, just enough sweetness and an impactful, dry, lasting bitter finish.
Dry Stone Stout (ABV 4.5%) STOUT
This black stout progresses from a slightly sweet, fruity start to a mouth filling balance of lasting dry roast and hop bitterness.
Prime Porter (ABV 4.9%) PORTER
Complex, dark brown beer with plenty of malt, fruit and roast taste. Satisfying full body with a clean finish.
Brune (ABV 5.6%) BROWN

Hawkstone

College Farm, Stow Road, Lower Slaughter, Bourton on the Water, Gloucestershire, GL54 2HN
☎ (01451) 824488 ⊕ hawkstone.co

An independent producer of craft lager and speciality keg beers. The brewery was established in 2005 and expanded in 2010. More than 150 outlets are supplied, mainly in the Cotswolds and London. The brewery changed ownership and name in 2022 (was Cotswold). ‼ ➤ ♦

Haworth Steam

See Farmers

Healey's

⧯ **Wellington Inn, Main Street, Loppergarth, Cumbria, LA12 0JL**
☎ (01229) 582388

Healey's began brewing in the Wellington Inn in 2012 using a custom-made, 2.5-barrel, stainless steel plant. The brewery can be viewed through full-length windows in the pub. A range of different cask beer styles are brewed and are available at a variety of local pubs in the area including in the Wellington itself. Electrical power is provided by solar panels.

Heaney Farmhouse SIBA

The Wood, 96a Ballymacombs Road, Bellaghy, BT45 8JP ⊕ heaney.ie

Founded in 2014. Initially beers were brewed at Boundary (qv) in Belfast while Mal and Suzy McCay's brewhouse project was being constructed on the farm in Bellaghy, Co Londonderry. In 2019 production began on its 100% renewable-powered brewery which utilises its own water supply. Favourites, seasonal and special beers are available in bottle and can. No real ale. ♦

Heart of Wales

⧯ **Stables Yard, Zion Street, Llanwrtyd Wells, LD5 4RD**
☎ (01591) 610236 ⊕ heartofwalesbrewery.co.uk

⊕ The brewery was set up with a six-barrel plant in 2006 in old stables at the rear of the Neuadd Arms Hotel. It uses water from the its own borehole. Seasonal brews celebrate local events such as the World Bogsnorkelling Championships. Cambrian Heart Ale was commissioned by, and is brewed for, the Cambrian Mountains Initiative, inspired by the Prince of Wales, which aims to promote and support rural producers and communities in the region. ‼ ➤ ♦ LIVE V

Heathen SIBA

Hop Sun, Triangle Road, Haywards Heath, West Sussex, RH16 4HW
☎ (01444) 456217 ☎ 07825 429428
⊕ heathenbrewers.co.uk

Heathen opened its new brewery in 2021, moving from the more restricted premises at the Grape & Grain off-licence into a barn. The new premises has an adjoining taproom (Thursday-Saturday). Beers are unfiltered, unpasteurised and mostly vegan-friendly, served via air pressure from tanks or in casks. !! ♦ LIVE V ⬧

Atemporal Rites (ABV 3.9%) PALE
Session IPA (ABV 4.7%) PALE
NEIPA (ABV 5.2%) GOLD

Heineken Royal Trafford

Royal Brewery, 201 Denmark Road, Manchester, M15 6LD

Office: 3-4 Broadway Park, Edinburgh, EH12 9JZ
☎ (0131) 528 1000 ⊕ heineken.com

No real ale.

Heist

107 Neepsend Lane, Sheffield, South Yorkshire, S3 8AT ⊕ heistbrewco.com

Established by Dan Hunt and Adam France in 2017 as a craft bar and bottle shop, Heist began brewing operations in Clowne, Derbyshire in 2018. The development of the new brewery and taproom site in Neepsend, Sheffield launched in mid 2021. It showcases 30 fresh beers on tap, alongside a strong community-focussed environment, welcoming to all the family. !! ⬧

Helmsley SIBA

18 Bridge Street, Helmsley, YO62 5DX
☎ (01439) 771014 ☎ 07525 434268
⊕ helmsleybrewingco.co.uk

☺Located within the North York Moors National Park, brewing began in 2014. The brewery has a viewing gallery, tasting room and taproom. Local pubs are supplied. !! ☰ LIVE ⬧

Yorkshire Legend (ABV 3.8%) BITTER
Striding the Riding (ABV 4%) BITTER
Howardian Gold (ABV 4.2%) GOLD
Honey (ABV 4.5%) SPECIALITY
H!PA (ABV 5.5%) IPA

Hemlock

37 Main Street, Hemington, Derbyshire, DE74 2RB
☎ 07791 057994 ✉ hembrew@yahoo.com

Established in 2015 in Leicestershire on the borders of Derbyshire and Notts, this two-barrel plant is located in the outbuildings of a lovely 17th Century thatched cottage in the village of Hemington. The brewery originally supplied beers in the immediate area. It has now branched out and supplies to Derbyshire, Nottinghamshire, Leicestershire & Staffordshire. It produces a number of pale ales and several seasonal beers. !! ♦ LIVE

Lemonhead (ABV 3.8%) GOLD
Harvest Moon (ABV 4.1%) GOLD
Twisterella (ABV 4.1%) PALE
Bossanova (ABV 4.3%) BLOND
Hoptimystic (ABV 4.3%) BITTER
Village Idiot (ABV 4.3%) BITTER

California Dreaming (ABV 4.5%) PALE

Henley Mile (NEW)

Station Road, Henley-in-Arden, Warwickshire, B95 5JD ⊕ thehenleymile.co.uk

A small brewery set up to serve the recently revived refreshment room at Henley-in-Arden station on the Birmingham to Stratford upon Avon railway line.

Henry Smith

🍺 **Robin Hood, 4 Wakefield Road, Pontefract, West Yorkshire, WF8 4HN** ☎ 07547 573378

☺Set up behind the Robin Hood pub in Pontefract by Dean Smith in 2019 with the help of Revolutions Brewery (where Head Brewer, Paul Windmill, learned to brew). The plant is the former James & Kirkman kit with a few tweaks.

Hepworth SIBA

Stane Street, North Heath, West Sussex, RH20 1DJ
☎ (01403) 269696 ⊕ hepworthbrewery.co.uk

⊠ Hepworth's began brewing in Horsham in 2001 moving to its present purpose-built site in 2016. Its organic status is ratified by the Soil Association. The brewery is also home to Ridgeway and Goodwood Breweries. There is a shop selling the full range of beer and a taproom, both open all day Monday to Saturday. !! ☰ ♦ LIVE V ⬧

Traditional Sussex Bitter (ABV 3.5%) BITTER
A fine, clean-tasting amber session beer. A bitter beer with a pleasant fruity and hoppy aroma that leads to a crisp, tangy taste. A long, dry finish.
Dark Horse (ABV 3.8%) BITTER
Summer Ale (ABV 3.8%) BITTER
Pullman First Class Ale (ABV 4.2%) BITTER
A sweet, nutty maltiness and fruitiness are balanced by hops and bitterness in this easy-drinking, pale brown best bitter. A subtle bitter aftertaste.
Prospect Organic (ABV 4.5%) GOLD
Classic Old Ale (ABV 4.8%) OLD
Iron Horse (ABV 4.8%) BITTER
There's a fruity, toffee aroma to this light brown, full-bodied bitter. A citrus flavour balanced by caramel and malt leads to a clean, dry finish.

Hercules

Unit 5b, Harbour Court, Heron Road, Sydenham, Holywood, Belfast, BT3 9HB
☎ (028) 9036 4516 ✉ niall@herculesbrewery.com

The original Hercules Brewing Company, founded in the 19th century, was one of 13 breweries in Belfast at the time. The company has been re-established to produce small batch brews using old brewing traditions. Its output is all under the Yardsman brand name.

Brewed under the Yardsman brand name:
IPA (ABV 4.3%) PALE
Lager (ABV 4.8%) SPECIALITY
Belfast Pale Ale (ABV 5.6%) GOLD

Hereford

🍺 **88 St Owen Street, Hereford, HR1 2QD**
☎ (01432) 342125 ✉ jfkenyon@aol.com

☺Although there has been a small brewery on this site since 1992, Hereford began life as the Spinning Dog Brewery in 2000, changing its name in 2010. After a period as primarily a brewpub, in 2017 it began to expand its distribution to pubs in Herefordshire and Pembrokeshire. ‼♦LIVE

Herefordshire Owd Bull (ABV 3.9%) BITTER
Dark (ABV 4%) MILD
HLA (Herefordshire Light Ale) (ABV 4%) PALE
Celtic Gold (ABV 4.5%) GOLD
Mutley's Revenge (ABV 4.8%) BITTER
Mutts Nuts (ABV 5%) BITTER

Hermitage

Heathwaite, Slanting Hill, Hermitage, Berkshire, RG18 9QG
☎ (01635) 200907 ☎ 07980 019484
⊕ hermitagebrewery.co.uk

⊠ Established in 2013 by semi-retired food science lecturer, Richard Marshall. After many years as a home brewer, the opportunity arose to go commercial. The 0.5-barrel brewery produces bottle-conditioned and some cask ales. Volumes vary, but is about 200 bottles per week. A range of six core beers and six seasonal and special brews are sold to local shops. Cask is sent to festivals and a few pubs along with polypins for events. Bespoke beers are produced occasionally by special request. LIVE

Tom Herrick's

The Stable House, Main Street, Carlton on Trent, NG23 6NW ☎ 07877 542331
✉ tomherricksbrewery@hotmail.com

Tom Herrick installed his bespoke, 2.5-barrel, stainless steel brewery at the front of his premises during 2014, and began small scale commercial brewing the following year. The brewery is only operated on a part-time basis with output going to festivals and local pubs.

Bomber Command (ABV 4.2%) BITTER

Hesket Newmarket SIBA

Old Crown Barn, Back Green, Hesket Newmarket, Cumbria, CA7 8JG
☎ (01697) 478066 ⊕ hesketbrewery.co.uk

☺Founded in 1988, and bought by a co-operative in 1999 to preserve a community amenity. Cask and keg beers are generally named after Cumbrian fells. Newer look beer styles have been introduced in recent years with traditional beers undergoing a rejuvenation. More than 10 cask ales are supplied across Cumbria with supply also available in bottles and cans. ‼♦

Skiddaw (ABV 3.6%) BITTER
Haystacks (ABV 3.7%) BLOND
Light, easy-drinking, thirst-quenching blond beer; pleasant for its strength.
Black Sail (ABV 4%) STOUT
A sweet stout with roast flavours
Helvellyn Gold (ABV 4%) BLOND
Doris' 90th Birthday Ale (ABV 4.3%) BITTER
Scafell Blonde (ABV 4.3%) PALE
A hoppy, sweet, fruity, pale-coloured bitter.
Brim Fell IPA (ABV 4.5%) PALE
Catbells (ABV 5%) PALE
An ale with a nice balance of fruity sweetness and bitterness, almost syrupy but with an unexpectedly dry finish.
Old Carrock Strong Ale (ABV 6%) OLD
Reddy brown strong ale, vine-fruity in flavour with slightly astringent finish.

Hetton Law

Hetton Law Farm, Lowick, Berwick upon Tweed, Northumberland, TD15 2UL
☎ (01289) 388558 ☎ 07889 457140
⊕ hettonlawbrewery.co.uk

Brewing began in 2015 using a 2.5-barrel plant. Run by retired dentists Judith and Nicholas Grasse, it uses local spring water and locally-grown malt, which gives the beers a distinctive character. Due to the size of the brewery, availability on draught and in bottles is effectively limited to the local area on both sides of the border. Brewing is currently suspended. ♦

Hex

66a Eastbourne Road, Birkdale, Southport, PR8 4DU
⊕ hexbrewing.co.uk

Brewery opened 2022. It brews classic style, vegan beers for cask and bottle. V

Hexhamshire SIBA

Dipton Mill Road, Hexham, Northumberland, NE46 1YA
☎ (01434) 606577 ⊕ hexhamshire.co.uk

Hexhamshire is Northumberland's oldest brewery and is run by the same family since it was founded in 1993. The Brooker family also run the brewery tap, the Dipton Mill. Outlets are supplied direct and via the SIBA Beerflex scheme.

Devil's Elbow (ABV 3.6%) BITTER
Amber brew full of hops and fruit, leading to a bitter finish.
Shire Bitter (ABV 3.8%) BITTER
A good balance of hops with fruity overtones, this amber beer makes an easy-drinking session bitter.
Blackhall English Stout (ABV 4%) STOUT
Devil's Water (ABV 4.1%) BITTER
Copper-coloured best bitter, well-balanced with a slightly fruity, hoppy finish.
Whapweasel (ABV 4.8%) BITTER
Malt and caramel flavours, hints of fruit, a sweet body and a quick dry finish.

Hidden SIBA

🪑 Seven Stars, 73 The Terrace, Penryn, Cornwall, TR10 8EL
☎ (01326) 531398

Office: Kernow House, Gas Hill, Newham, Truro, Cornwall, TR1 2XP ⊕ sevenstarspenryn.co.uk/micro-brewery

Brewing began in 2020 in an outbuilding of the Seven Stars pub in Penryn, using a 2.5-barrel plant. The two regular beers are accompanied by regular trialling of new one-off brews. The brewery can be seen from the pub terrace. V

Hideaway

2 Kansas Avenue, Salford, M50 2GL ☎ 07887 732725
⊕ hideawaybrewing.co.uk

Established as a nanobrewery in a garage in 2020, Hideaway Brewing Co has grown into a much larger enterprise. From brewing 25-litre batches, Dan Wright now has capacity for more than 1,200-litres per batch at the brewery's new home near Media City. The new brewery opened in 2023, followed six months later by the taproom and kitchen in 2024. ‼⚲

Highgate

See Davenports

Higsons

See Love Lane

Hilden

Hilden House, Grand Street, Hilden, Lisburn, Co Antrim, BT27 4TY
☎ (028) 9266 0800 ⊕ hildenbrewery.co.uk

☺Established in 1981, Hilden is Ireland's oldest independent brewery. Now in the second generation of family ownership, the beers are widely distributed across the UK. The beers are regularly available in JD Wetherspoon outlets in Northern Ireland. ‼️🍴◆

Nut Brown (ÄBV 3.8%) BITTER
Hilden Ale (ABV 4%) BITTER
An amber-coloured beer with an aroma of malt, hops and fruit. The balanced taste is slightly slanted towards hops, and hops are also prominent in the full, malty finish.
Barney's Brew (ABV 4.2%) SPECIALITY
Irish Stout (ABV 4.3%) STOUT
Scullion's Irish Ale (ABV 4.6%) BITTER
Twisted Hop (ABV 4.7%) BITTER
Halt (ABV 6.1%) RED

Brewed for College Green Brewery:
Headless Dog (ABV 4.3%) GOLD

Hill Island

Unit 7, Fowlers Yard, Back Silver Street, Durham, DH1 3RA ☎ 07740 932584
✉ hillisland73@gmail.com

☺Established in 2002, Hill Island is a literal translation of Dunholme, from which Durham is derived. It is part of Fowler's Yard Craft Workshops on the banks of the River Wear and can be reached by steps down from Silver Street. Nearly all production is sold through the pop-up bar which operates at the brewery most Saturdays (Facebook for updates) including weekends coinciding with Durham events such as the Durham Fire & Ice Festival, and the Durham Miner's Gala. ‼️🍴◆V◆

Hinks

1 Dimon Villas, Hamstreet Road, Ruckinge, Kent, TN26 2NT ☎ 07518 569041
✉ hinkscraftbrewery@gmail.com

⊗ Nanobrewery established in 2018 that occasionally retails bottle-conditioned ales. Brewing is currently suspended. ◆LIVE V

Hive Mind

Unit 5F, Severn Bridge Industrial Estate, Caldicot, Chepstow, NP26 5PR ☎ 07402 993998

Office: 19 River View, School Hill, Chepstow, NP16 5AX ⊕ wyevalleymeadery.co.uk

Hive Mind (part of Wye Valley Meadery) started brewing in 2021, offering beers infused with honey from its own hives. Bottles and casks are available. ‼️🍴◆

The Pollinator (ABV 3.8%) PALE
Golden Hour (ABV 4.5%) GOLD
Honey Citra IPA (ABV 5.7%) IPA
Big Smoke (ABV 7%) PORTER

Hiver

56 Stanworth Street, Bermondsey, London, SE1 3NY
☎ (020) 3198 9972 ⊕ hiverbeers.com

Beers are brewed at Hepworth in Sussex using London urban honey. The taproom is on the often overlooked Maltby Street Market side of the Bermondsey Beer Mile. Beers are available in keg, bottles and cans. No cask ale.

Hobsons SIBA

Newhouse Farm, Tenbury Road, Cleobury Mortimer, Shropshire, DY14 8RD
☎ (01299) 270837 ⊕ hobsons-brewery.co.uk

Established in 1993 in a former sawmill, Hobsons relocated to a farm site with more space in 1995. A second brewery, bottling plant and a warehouse have been added along with significant expansion to the first brewery. Beers are supplied within a 50-mile radius. The brewery utilises environmental sustainable technologies where possible. A visitor centre was added in 2014, which also now operates as a taproom. ‼️🍴LIVE◆

Mild (ABV 3.2%) MILD
A classic mild. Complex layers of taste come from roasted malts that predominate and give lots of flavour.
Twisted Spire (ABV 3.6%) GOLD
Best (ABV 3.8%) BITTER
A pale brown to amber, medium-bodied beer with strong hop character throughout. It is consequently bitter, but with malt discernible in the taste.
Old Prickly (ABV 4.2%) PALE
Town Crier (ABV 4.5%) GOLD

Hogs Back SIBA

Manor Farm, The Street, Tongham, Surrey, GU10 1DE
☎ (01252) 783000 ⊕ hogsback.co.uk

⊗ Established in 1992, this traditional, family-owned brewery boasts an extensive range of award-winning ales. In 2014 it planted its own hop garden (now 6,500 plants). The brewery is open for guided tours and the shop sells all its beers, plus 300+ of the best UK and World bottled beers, craft cans and cider. Its taproom is housed in a former hop kiln, offering a varied programme of live music, comedy, quizzes, live sports, and an annual September Hop Harvest festival. ‼️🍴◆LIVE◆

Surrey Nirvana (ABV 4%) PALE
Refreshing session pale ale. Sweet, moderately full-bodied leading to an initially sweet finish with hop bitterness becoming more evident.
TEA (ABV 4.2%) BITTER
A tawny-coloured best bitter with toffee and malt present in the nose. A well-rounded flavour with malt and a fruity sweetness.

Hogs Head

🍺 1 Stanley Street, Sowerby Bridge, West Yorkshire, HX6 2AH
☎ (01422) 836585 ⊕ thehogsheadbrewhouse.com

☺The Hogs Head Brewery opened in a huge 18th century former malthouse at the end of 2015. The sixteen-barrel brewhouse has increased from eight-barrels since 2018. The handsome copper and stainless steel brewing vats of the original brewery are on display at the back of the bar area with the newer brewing vessels located in a building adjacent to the pub. Almost all the production is sold on the premises with occasional casks being provided to beer festivals. ◆GF V

Holden's SIBA IFBB

George Street, Woodsetton, Dudley, West Midlands, DY1 4LW
☎ (01902) 880051 ⊕ holdensbrewery.co.uk

⊛A family brewery spanning four generations, Holden's began life as a brewpub in 1915. Continued expansion means it now has 18 tied pubs in its estate. !! ᴇ ♦

Black Country Mild (ABV 3.7%) MILD
A good, red/brown mild; a refreshing, light blend of roast malt, hops and fruit, dominated by malt throughout.

Black Country Bitter (ABV 3.9%) BITTER
A medium-bodied, golden ale; a light, well-balanced bitter with a subtle, dry, hoppy finish.

Golden Glow (ABV 4.4%) BITTER
Special (ABV 5.1%) BITTER
A sweet, malty, full-bodied amber ale with hops to balance in the taste and in the good, bittersweet finish.

Hollow Stone

See Shipstone's

Hollow Tree

3 Glen Road, Whatstandwell, Matlock, Derbyshire, DE4 5EH ☎ 07920 843754
⊕ hollowtreebrewing.co.uk

⊛Nanobrewery with five core beers. Brewing began in 2019. There are also limited and seasonal releases which use ingredients sourced and foraged from the local area. ♦LIVE

Holsworthy

Unit 5, Circuit Business Park, Clawton, Holsworthy, EX22 6RR
☎ (01566) 783678 ☎ 07879 401073
⊕ holsworthyales.co.uk

⊗ Holsworthy Ales is a 5.5-barrel microbrewery situated in the heart of Devon's Ruby Country. Brewing began commercially in 2011. Its intention is to make its beers taste as clean and natural as possible, so no chemicals or finings are added to the soft Devon water used in many of its ales. !! ᴇ ♦LIVE V

Paler Shade Of Ale (ABV 3.6%) PALE
Sunshine (ABV 4%) GOLD
St George (ABV 4.1%) GOLD
Bang On (ABV 4.2%) PALE
Muck 'n' Straw (ABV 4.4%) BITTER
Hops dominate with hints of malt in aroma and taste. Well-balanced with slight dryness in aftertaste.

Tamar Black (ABV 4.8%) STOUT
Hop on the Run (ABV 5%) PALE
An American-style IPA, packed full of vibrant hops, this beer has good body and lasting flavour. Unfined and expect that fruitiness taste.

Proper Lager (ABV 5%) SPECIALITY
Old Market Monk (ABV 6.1%) SPECIALITY

Joseph Holt SIBA IFBB

The Brewery, Empire Street, Cheetham, Manchester, M3 1JD
☎ (0161) 834 3285 ⊕ joseph-holt.com

⊛Founded in 1849, Joseph Holt is one of the UK's, leading, independent, family breweries. Now in its sixth generation, the business operates 123 pubs across Manchester and the North West and supplies ales to many pubs and clubs nationally. 2024 saw the 175th anniversary of the operation at its Manchester site and continued family ownership. ᴇ

Mild (ABV 3.2%) MILD
Fruity, malty nose. Roast, malt and hops in the taste, with strong bitterness and a dry malt and hop finish.
IPA (ABV 3.8%) BLOND
Bitter (ABV 4%) BITTER
Brown beer, malt and hops in the aroma. Bitter taste with a malty back ground, increasing hop bitterness to finish.

Two Hoots (ABV 4.2%) BITTER
Easy-drinking beer, smooth texture, well-balanced malty sweetness and gentle hops lead to a lasting bitter finish.

Brewed under the Bootleg brand name:
Chorlton Pale Ale (ABV 4%) PALE

Holy Goat SIBA

Unit 5, Mid Wynd, Dundee, DD1 4JG ⊕ holygoat.beer

Holy Goat is a Dundee based brewery specialising in the production of mixed fermentation and wood-aged beers. All beers are bottled with some available in can.

Hook Norton SIBA IFBB

Brewery Lane, Scotland End, Hook Norton, Oxfordshire, OX15 5NY
☎ (01608) 737210 ⊕ hooky.co.uk

⊗ One of the finest examples of a Victorian tower brewery, and the oldest independent brewery in Oxfordshire, Hook Norton has been brewing since 1849. The current premises were built in 1900 and still house much of the original machinery, including a 25hp steam engine. Shire horses make deliveries to local pubs. Family-owned, it combines its heritage with a modern approach. Various parts of the brewery are available for hire and customers can spend a day brewing their own beer. !! ᴇ ♦LIVE ✦

Hooky Mild (ABV 2.8%) MILD
A chestnut brown, easy-drinking mild. A complex malt and hop aroma give way to a well-balanced taste, leading to a long, hoppy finish that is unusual for a mild.

Hooky (ABV 3.5%) BITTER
A classic, golden session bitter. Hoppy and fruity aroma followed by a malt and hops taste and a continuing hoppy finish.

Off The Hook (ABV 4.3%) GOLD
Old Hooky (ABV 4.6%) BITTER
A strong bitter, tawny in colour. A well-rounded fruity taste with a balanced bitter finish.

Hop Back SIBA

Units 22-24, Batten Road Industrial Estate, Downton, Wiltshire, SP5 3HU
☎ (01725) 510986 ⊕ hopback.co.uk

⊗ Founded in 1987, Hop Back owns ten pubs and distributes nationally. The flagship beer, Summer Lightning, has won numerous CAMRA awards. Brewing regular and seasonal beers with a unique house yeast, and sourcing its primary English Hops from grower-owned cooperatives. !! ᴇ ♦LIVE GF V

GFB (ABV 3.4%) BITTER
A light gold, refreshing session bitter. The hoppy aroma leads to bitterness initially, lasting through to the finish with some fruit.

Citra (ABV 4%) BLOND
Pale yellow almost straw-coloured with lemon and grapefruit on the aroma and taste, rapidly developing a balanced hoppy aftertaste.

Fuggle Stone (ABV 4%) BITTER
Fresh-tasting, slightly sweet, malty session bitter with the sweetness and hops leading to a gentle dry aftertaste.

Crop Circle (ABV 4.2%) GOLD
A pale yellow best bitter with a fragrant hop aroma, complex hop, fruit and citrus flavours with a balanced hoppy, bitter/sweet aftertaste.

Taiphoon (ABV 4.2%) SPECIALITY
A clean-tasting, light fruity beer with hops and fruit on the aroma, complex hop character and lemongrass notes in the taste, slight sweetness balanced with some astringency in the aftertaste.

Entire Stout (ABV 4.5%) STOUT
A smooth, rich, ruby-black stout with strong roast and malt aromas and flavours, with a long bittersweet and malty aftertaste.

Summer Lightning (ABV 5%) BLOND
Strong golden ale with a hoppy aroma and slightly astringent bitterness in the taste, balanced with some fruit sweetness, in the dry aftertaste.

Hop Fuzz SIBA

Unit 8, Riverside Industrial Estate, West Hythe, Kent, CT21 4NB ☎ 07858 562878/ 07730 768881
⊕ hopfuzz.co.uk

⊠ Brewing since 2011 at a rural estate alongside the Royal Military Canal. Now sandwiched between Docker and its former taproom, Unit 1, where beers from both brewers are always available. The commercial plant is plumbed with a thermostatic cooling system for year-round consistency. Cask, kegs, and bottles are sold nationally. ◆

English (ABV 4%) BITTER
American (ABV 4.2%) GOLD
Martello (ABV 4.5%) RED

Hop Kettle SIBA

Swindon: Unit 4, Hawksworth Industrial Estate, Newcombe Drive, Swindon, SN6 6DD
☎ (01793) 490556

Second Site: Red Lion, High Street, Cricklade, SN6 6DD
⊕ hop-kettle.com

Brewing began in a barn behind the Red Lion Inn, Cricklade, in 2012, using a four-barrel plant. Brewing has since expanded to a 10-barrel brewery in Swindon whilst retaining the original Cricklade brewery. Both breweries produce a range of innovative and award-winning ales. Beer is supplied to its taprooms in Swindon, Cirencester and Gloucester, in addition to the free trade. The latest innovation is a beer van which can be hired to bring three cask ales and other beer to outdoor events. The brewery may relocate from the current Swindon address during the currency of this guide. ◆GF

COB (Cricklade Ordinary Bitter) (ABV 3.8%) BITTER
Dog Star (ABV 4%) PALE
North Wall (ABV 4.3%) BITTER
Lode Star (ABV 4.5%) PALE
Space Cowboy (ABV 4.7%) STOUT
Rising Star (ABV 4.8%) GOLD
East Star (ABV 5%) BITTER
Red Star (ABV 5.2%) RED
Evening Star (ABV 5.5%) PORTER
Flapjack Marmalade (ABV 7.8%) SPECIALITY

Hop Monster

See George's

Hop Shed SIBA

Old Chicken Shed, Stocks Farm, Suckley, Worcestershire, WR6 5EQ
☎ (01886) 884110 ☎ 07484 688026
⊕ hopshed.co.uk

Originally named Unity Brew House, brewing began in 2016, using a 10-barrel plant. Based in an old chicken shed on a commercial hop farm, the beers are named after breeds of chicken. An onsite bar is open on Fridays and Saturdays. ◆

Wybar (ABV 3.6%) BITTER
Sebright Golden Ale (ABV 3.8%) GOLD
Pekin (ABV 4%) PALE
Sultan (ABV 4.2%) GOLD
Frizzle British IPA (ABV 4.5%) GOLD

Hop Stuff

See Salt

Hop Union SIBA

20 Bonville Road, Brislington, Bristol, BS4 5QH
☎ (0117) 957 2842 ⊕ hopunionbrewery.co.uk

⊠ Originally established as Great Western in 2008, the brewery relocated and rebranded to Hop Union in 2021. The move has allowed for much-needed expansion and will enable canning and kegging onsite. One pub, the Rising Sun, Frampton Cotterell, is owned, as well as a shop at the new site. A taproom opened in 2022. ♯☰◆◈

Bonville Pale (ABV 4%) PALE
Hambrook Pale Ale/ HPA (ABV 4%) PALE
Hoppy, yellow pale ale with zesty citrus flavours and hints of tropical fruit, leading to a morish, bittersweet finish.

Maiden Voyage (ABV 4%) BITTER
Malty backbone with hints of caramel supporting a soft bitterness and subtle fruit flavours that continue into the balanced finish.

Scallywag (ABV 4.8%) BITTER
Moose River (ABV 5%) PALE
Light citrus aroma, delicate hop taste with long lasting bitter finish.

Hop Vine

◙ Hop Vine, Liverpool Road North, Burscough, Lancashire, L40 4BY
☎ (01704) 893799 ☎ 07920 002783
✉ mikejulie6465@gmail.com

☺Hop Vine began brewing in 2017 using the four-barrel plant of the defunct Burscough Brewery. It is situated in old stable buildings in the courtyard to the rear of the Hop Vine. Beer is usually only supplied to the pub and the Legh Arms, Mere Brow. ☰◆

Hop Yard

Elm Cottage, The Yard, Lewes Road, Forest Row, East Sussex, RH18 5AA
☎ (01342) 824272 ⊕ hopyardbrewing.co.uk

Hop Yard began brewing in 2014 using a 100-litre brew plant. However, its cask-conditioned beers are now brewed using spare capacity at Westerham Brewery (qv). Beers are only available at its onsite brewery bar. ☰

Hopewell (NEW)

◉ Lockdown Room, Corson House, Hopewell Square, London City Island, Leamouth, London, E14 0SY
☎ (020) 3633 4777 ⊕ thelockdownroom.com

The Lockdown Room opened as a result of the pandemic to serve the newly built community on London City Island. A brewery was installed on the mezzanine floor at the start of 2024 and at least one keg beer is usually available at the bar. Although it appears isolated, surrounded by the rivers Lea and Thames, access is by the short footbridge near the rear exit of Canning Town Station. No cask ale.

Hophurst

c/o Moreton Mill, Horwich, BL6 7JH
☎ (01942) 522333 ☎ 07938 949944
⊕ hophurstbrewery.co.uk

⊕Hophurst Brewery was started in 2014 by Stuart Hurst. Stuart's passion for producing craft ales, combined with 20 years of supporting businesses and re-skilling unemployed people, created a unique social enterprise brewery. It employs people over the age of 50 and guides them through its training programme. Twisted Vine Ale House is its award-winning microbar in Ashton-in Makerfield town centre. Stuart is currently brewing his beers at Blackedge Brewery (qv). !!♦

Flaxen (ABV 3.7%) PALE
Campfire (ABV 3.9%) MILD
Light-bodied beer with bitter roasted malt.
Twisted Vine (ABV 4.1%) PALE
Cosmati (ABV 4.2%) BLOND
Citrus hop fruity aromas lead to a sweet fruity body with gentle bitterness and plenty of hops.
Debonair (ABV 4.9%) STOUT
Porteresque (ABV 5.5%) STOUT
Complex dark beer, with roast and fruit in aroma. Strong roast flavour with a developing sweet fruitiness. Lasting roast finish.

Hopper House Brew Farm

Racecourse Road, Sedgefield, TS21 2HL ☎ 07947 874278 ⊕ hopperhousebrewfarm.co.uk

Brewing commenced in 2019 on a one-barrel plant situated in a working dairy farm on the outskirts of Sedgefield. There is a taproom in an old milking parlour, currently it only has a licence for the last weekend in the month and is open Friday (3-11pm) and Saturday (12-11pm). V♦

Hopshackle

See Bowler's

Hopstar SIBA

Unit 9, Rinus Business Park, Grimshaw Street, Darwen, BB3 2QX ☎ 07933 590159
⊕ hopstarbrewery.co.uk

⊕Hopstar first brewed in 2004 on a 2.5-barrel plant and expanded in 2010 to a new unit with a six-barrel plant. More than 100 outlets are supplied around Lancashire and the Greater Manchester area. The brewery tap is Number 39 in Darwen. !!♦LIVE

Chilli Beer (ABV 3.8%) SPECIALITY
Dark Knight (ABV 3.9%) MILD
Off t'Mill (ABV 3.9%) PALE
Smokey Joe's Black Beer (ABV 3.9%) STOUT
Lancashire Gold (ABV 4%) BLOND

Lush (ABV 4%) BITTER
JC (ABV 4.1%) BITTER

Hopworks

Unit 335, Ranglet Road, Walton Summit Centre, Bamber Bridge, Lancashire, PR5 8AR
⊕ hopworksbrewing.com

⊕Operating with a 10-barrel plant and nine fermenting vessels, this brewery started production in 2023. An ever-changing range of beers is produced, with all beers being live and served from membrane kegs. Occasional cask versions are also made available. ♦LIVE ♦

Horbury

◉ The Brewhouse, Cherry Tree Inn, 19 Church Street, Horbury, West Yorkshire, WF4 6LT ☎ 07970 299292

⊕Following the closure of Bob's Brewing Co, Horbury Ales took over the plant in 2016 and transferred production to the rear of the brewery tap, Cherry Tree Inn. Beers are available locally, regionally and nationally.

Now Then (ABV 3.8%) PALE
5 Hops (ABV 4.1%) PALE
First Light (ABV 4.1%) PALE
Tiramisu (ABV 4.3%) PORTER
Green Eyed Monster (ABV 4.5%) PALE

Horncastle

◉ Old Nicks Tavern, 8 North Street, Horncastle, Lincolnshire, LN9 5DX
☎ (01507) 526862 ⊕ horncastleales.co.uk

Brewing began in 2014 using a 3.75-barrel plant. The brewery is situated at the rear of Old Nicks Tavern with beer available in the pub plus other Lincolnshire outlets. It has its own bottling plant and a beer in box scheme is also available for pre-ordering. !!🍺

Hornes SIBA

19b Station Road, Bow Brickhill, Buckinghamshire, MK17 9JU
☎ (01908) 647724 ⊕ mkbeer.co.uk

A purpose-built, six-barrel brewery established in 2015 and producing a range of beers, several called Triple Goat after the three goats kept in a paddock at the brewery. Shop open by appointment only. Occasional events in the large garden. All beers are gluten-free. 🍺♦GF

Featherstone Amber Ale (ABV 3.6%) BITTER
Dark Fox (ABV 3.8%) BITTER
Triple Goat Pale Ale (ABV 3.9%) PALE
Ryestone (ABV 4%) RED
Unlocked Hornes (ABV 4.3%) GOLD
Triple Goat Porter (ABV 4.6%) PORTER
Triple Goat IPA (ABV 5%) PALE

Horsetown

See Malton

Horsforth SIBA

143 New Road Side, Horsforth, Leeds, West Yorkshire, LS18 5NX ☎ 07854 078330
⊕ horsforthbrewery.co.uk

⊕Brewing began on a part-time basis in 2017 in the owner's garage, and then moved on to a small unit. 2020 saw relocation to larger premises, which incorporate a shop and taproom. In addition to the flagship beer, an ever-changing range of specials is produced. The taproom is accessed through an opening on the main street. ◆V⚭

My Horse Came Fourth (ABV 3.5%) SPECIALITY
Horsforth Pale (ABV 4.5%) PALE
A modern, easy-drinking, hazy pale ale. Well-balanced with hops and gentle fruit such as peach and apricot.
Schwarz Rose (ABV 5%) SPECIALITY
Mosaic (ABV 5.1%) PALE
Weise Rose (ABV 5.4%) SPECIALITY
Aubretia (ABV 5.5%) IPA
Night Ryder (ABV 5.5%) RED
Rubis (ABV 6.2%) SPECIALITY

Horsham

Unit 3, Blatchford Close, Horsham, West Sussex, RH13 5RG ⊕ horshambrewerycompany.com

⊗ Horsham Brewery Company Ltd began brewing in early 2021 to sell to local pubs. Set up by Rohan and Tim, it brews a wide variety of beers and opened a taproom in 2022. The brewery brews cask and KeyKeg beer, with some also available in cans. All the beers are named after places local to Horsham. The brewery has a beer festival every September at the Drill Hall, Horsham. ◆⚭

Causeway (ABV 3.8%) PALE
Victory (ABV 3.8%) PALE
Trafalgar (ABV 4%) PALE
HBC (ABV 4.2%) BITTER
Sun Oak (ABV 4.2%) RED
Normandy (ABV 4.7%) SPECIALITY
Bishopric (ABV 5.2%) STOUT
Carfax (ABV 6.2%) IPA

Howfen

Westhoughton, BL5 2BN ⊕ howfenbrew.co

Howfen began brewing in 2018 and is situated in the owner's garage. It is named after the dialect word for Westhoughton.

Howl

Polmear Hill, Par, PL24 2AR
☎ (01726) 467254 ⊕ howlbrewery.co.uk

Howl Brewery is located just 300m from Par Sands. Craft ales are dreamed up, tested and perfected in small batches and the menu changes every couple of weeks. Hops-flavoured water is also available. No live beer.

Howling Hops SIBA

Unit 9a, Queen's Yard, White Post Lane, Hackney Wick, London, E9 5EN
☎ (020) 3583 8262 ⊕ howlinghops.co.uk

⊗ Brewing began in 2012 at the Cock Tavern in Hackney, later opening a new brewery and tank bar in 2015 in Hackney Wick. Beers are widely available and cover many styles from pale ales with varying hops, sours and dark beers. Available in keg and cans with a growing range of cask. ⚭

Howzat

🍴 **Cricketers Arms, Peter Street, St Helens, Merseyside, WA10 2EB**
☎ (01744) 758021

A brewery in the grounds of the Cricketer's Arms – a former CAMRA National Pub of the Year.

HQ Beers

See Exit 33

Sarah Hughes

🍴 **Beacon Hotel, 129 Bilston Street, Sedgley, West Midlands, DY3 1JE**
☎ (01902) 883381 ⊕ sarahhughesbrewery.co.uk

⊗ Nationally-renowned, Victorian tower brewery behind The Beacon Hotel which has been brewing since 1987. It attracts visitors from near and far. The brewery is famous for its Dark Ruby Mild which has a cult following. The beers are served in the Beacon Hotel as well as a growing number of free trade outlets. !!◆

Pale Amber (ABV 4%) BITTER
Sedgley Surprise (ABV 5%) BITTER
A bittersweet, medium-bodied, hoppy ale with some malt.
Dark Ruby Mild (ABV 6%) MILD
A dark ruby strong ale with a good balance of fruit and hops, leading to a pleasant, lingering hops and malt finish.

Humber Doucy SIBA

St Edmunds Garage, Broad Road, Bacton, Stowmarket, Suffolk, IP14 4HP
☎ (01449) 780151 ⊕ humberdoucybrew.co

Producing fresh, vegan-friendly beers from the heart of Suffolk, Humber Doucy started brewing in 2019 in an old MOT garage in Bacton, with a brewery shop located down the road, within the Jeffries of Bacton Subaru Dealership. Beers are available nationwide and in pubs, shops and restaurants across East Anglia in bottles, cask and keg. LIVE V

King Slayer (ABV 3.6%) BITTER
Friday Street (ABV 4%) PALE
Pale Ale (ABV 4.4%) PALE
Hedgerow (ABV 4.5%) SPECIALITY
Porter (ABV 5%) PORTER

Humpty Dumpty SIBA

Church Road, Reedham, Norfolk, NR13 3TZ
☎ (01493) 701818 ☎ 07843 248865
⊕ humptydumptybrewery.co.uk

⊗ Established in 1998, this 11-barrel, award-winning brewery continues to grow and expand its range of beers, including a new Norfolk Broads Brewing series of occasional one-off brews. !!🍺◆LIVE

Little Sharpie (ABV 3.8%) PALE
Complex and smooth with a crisp bitterness underpinning a buttery biscuit follow through. Lemon hoppiness in a long drying finish.
Branch Line Bitter (ABV 3.9%) BITTER
Lemon & Ginger (ABV 4%) SPECIALITY
Swallowtail (ABV 4%) PALE
Full-bodied marmalade and biscuit aroma with matching beginning. Grainy texture is enhanced by solid bitter notes flowing onward.
Broadland Sunrise (ABV 4.2%) BITTER
Red Mill (ABV 4.3%) BITTER
Full-bodied, robust and fruity. Coffee, dark fruits and caramel vie for dominance against a malty bitter base. Powerful, rich ending.
Reedcutter (ABV 4.4%) GOLD
A sweet, malty beer; golden-hued with a gentle malt background. Smooth and full-bodied with a quick, gentle finish.
Cheltenham Flyer (ABV 4.6%) BITTER

A full-flavoured golden, earthy bitter with a long, grainy finish. A strong hop bitterness dominates throughout. Little evidence of malt.

EAPA (East Anglian Pale Ale) (ABV 4.6%) PALE
Amber gold with an orange marmalade nose. A bittersweet caramel beginning slowly dries out as malty nuances fade away.

Railway Sleeper (ABV 5%) OLD
A rich Christmas pudding aroma introduces this delightfully fruity brew. Malt, sultanas and raisins dominate a bittersweet backdrop. Full-bodied, smooth finish.

Hurst

Highfileds Farm, Hurstpierpoint, West Sussex, BN6 9JT
☎ 07866 438953 ⊕ hurstbrewery.co.uk

Hurst was founded in 2012, but reviving a name dating back to 1862.

Founders Best Bitter (ABV 4.2%) BITTER
Keepers Gold (ABV 4.4%) SPECIALITY
Watchtower (ABV 5.5%) PORTER

Hush

Unit 4, Navigation Road, Northwich, Cheshire, CW8 1BE ☎ 07973 797500 ⊕ hushbrewing.co

⊛Established 2021 Hush has now relocated to its new premises in Northwich Town Centre. The five-barrel plant produces traditional and craft beers. Core beers, themed around the local area, are distributed locally to selected free trade outfits and festivals. The brewery tap (now completed) hosts events at the end of every month. Ever-changing seasonal and special beers, from across the range of beer styles, are brewed under the 'What the Hush' label. It also hosts Northwich Home Brew Crew meetings. ✦

My Grain is Earl (ABV 3.7%) PALE
Salt Town Stout (ABV 3.8%) STOUT
Northwich Pale Ale (ABV 4%) PALE
We Built This Citra On Rock Salts Home (ABV 4%) PALE
Weaver Las Vegas (ABV 4.3%) PALE
Beds Beneath Bitter (ABV 4.8%) BITTER
Sweet malty start, some caramel and roast flavours, gentle hops giving moderate bitterness and a dry finish.

Husk

5, Unit F, The Factory Project, 33 Factory Road, Silvertown, London, E16 2HB
☎ (020) 7474 3827 ⊕ huskbrewing.com

Originally starting in West Silvertown in 2015, 2023 saw a move to be part of the Factory Project, a creative work and event space in Silvertown itself. At the same time, a new taproom opened close to Canning Town Station, an important stop on the Jubilee Line and Docklands Light Railway. Brewing is currently suspended. LIVE

Hwgga SIBA

6 Park Crescent, Llandrindod Wells, LD1 6AB ☎ 07767 358932 ⊕ hwggabrew.com

Brewery name is a pseudo Welsh version of the Danish language term for 'cosy and welcoming' (hygge). Output can be casked, kegged or bottled, and a selection can always be sampled at the onsite taproom. Seasonal beers may also be available. The brewery delivers within a 30 mile radius of Llandrindod Wells. ‼ ☗ ✦

Elan Valley Pale (ABV 4.1%) PALE
Lover's Leap (ABV 4.5%) BITTER

Shaky Bridge (ABV 5%) BITTER

Hydes SIBA IFBB

The Beer Studio, 30 Kansas Avenue, Salford, M50 2GL
☎ (0161) 226 1317 ⊕ hydesbrewery.com

⊛Hydes Brewery has now been in the Manchester area for over 160 years. In 2012 it left the historic Queen's Brewery in Hulme and began brewing on a smaller, brand new site in Salford's MediaCity. The five core beers are brewed all year round and supplemented by 18 seasonal cask beers under the Ralf + Alf brand. The Beer Studio brand has been dropped. The new kegging line now produces Hydes' own lager, 'Dock 4', a nod to the old Ship Canal docks, alongside the Copper Kettle brands. ✦

1863 (ABV 3.5%) MILD
Lightly-hopped, pale brown session beer with some hops, malt and fruit in the taste and a short, dry finish.

Dark Ruby (ABV 3.5%) MILD
Reddy brown in colour, with a fruit and malt nose. Taste includes biscuity malt and fruit, with a satisfying aftertaste.

Hopster (ABV 3.8%) BLOND
Light-bodied blond beer with citrus aromas a fruity hop centre, and a lasting hop bitter finale.

Original (ABV 3.8%) BITTER
A malty nose, malt and an earthy hoppiness in the taste. A good bitterness through to the finish.

Lowry (ABV 4.7%) GOLD
Citrusy and strong bitterness along with bready malt follow the moderate hoppy aroma, ending with a lingering finish.

Ice Cream Factory

21 Fetter Lane, York, YO1 9TA ☎ 07880 547393
⊕ theicecreamfactory.com

Nano-brewery located in the old Capaldi's ice cream factory, established in 2017.

Iceni

The Walled Garden, Elveden Courtyard, London Road, Elveden, Suffolk, IP24 3TQ
☎ (01842) 878922 ☎ 07949 488113

Office: 70 Risbygate Street, Bury St Edmunds, IP33 3AZ ✉ icenibrewe@aol.com

The Iceni Brewery is owned by Brendan Moore, who set it up in 1995. In 2020 a micropub, the Magic Hammer, opened. ✦LIVE

Fine Soft Day (ABV 4%) BITTER
Golden-hued with toffee notes throughout. A creamy, lightly-hopped backdrop softly sinks into a pleasant sweetness.

Ideal Day

Crocadon Farm, St Mellion, Saltash, PL12 6RL

Ideal Day, established in 2023 near Saltash, makes beers focused on where the ingredients, especially grain, comes from and how it was farmed. Brewing inspiration comes from Belgian farmhouse traditions, classic British beers and modern innovation. It strives to create tasty beers while supporting farmers who are saving our soils and ecosystems with regenerative agriculture. One real ale is currently brewed.

Idle

🍺 White Hart Inn, Main Street, West Stockwith, Nottinghamshire, DN10 4EY
☎ (01427) 892672 ☎ 07831 618436
🌐 idlewhitehart.co.uk

☺Following the retirement of previous owners, Kevin Thacker purchased the pub and brewery. Kevin runs the brewery, with daughters Olivia and Katie taking ownership of the pub. Numerous refinements and improvements have been made to both. A varied, traditional menu has been maintained, some brewing recipes have been retained, and seasonal specials are likely to be introduced in the near future. The core beer range has reduced to four. Currently all in-house brews retain the Idle identity, with subtle descriptive changes. ‼◆

Ignition SIBA

Ground Floor, Sydenham Centre, 44a Sydenham Road, Sydenham, London, SE26 5QF 🌐 ignition.beer

Ignition is a not-for-profit, small South London brewery run by Brighter Horizons. It employs and trains people with learning disabilities to brew beer. An onsite taproom was opened in 2018 providing the staff with customer-facing experience and putting on a variety of regular events (see website). Beers, which are unfiltered, unpasteurised and suitable for vegans and vegetarians, are bottled for distribution or served from tanks in the taproom. LIVE V◢

Ilkley SIBA

40 Ashlands Road, Ilkley, West Yorkshire, LS29 8JT
☎ (01943) 604604 🌐 ilkleybrewery.co.uk

☺Ilkley Brewery was founded in 2009 and has expanded rapidly since. Ilkley beers can be found throughout the UK and are now exported into Europe. The brewery is a frequent sponsor of local beer festivals and also holds regular onsite social events and brewery tours. ‼◆LIVE GF

Mary Jane (ABV 3.4%) PALE
Joshua Jane (ABV 3.7%) BITTER
Mild Mary (ABV 3.8%) MILD
Promise (ABV 3.8%) GOLD
Blonde (ABV 3.9%) GOLD
Pale (ABV 4.2%) PALE
Alpha Beta (ABV 4.5%) IPA

Imperial

🍺 Arcadia Hall, Cliff Street, Mexborough, S64 9HU
☎ (01709) 584000 ☎ 07428 422703
✉ impbrewery@gmail.com

☺Brewing began in 2010 using a six-barrel tower brewery system located in the basement of the Imperial Club, Mexborough. Beer is available in the club as well as local outlets. ‼◆LIVE

Classical Bitter (ABV 3.9%) BITTER
Platinum Blonde (ABV 4%) BLOND
Bees Knees (ABV 4.2%) GOLD
Nah Then (ABV 4.5%) GOLD
Stout Wi' Nowt Tekkin' Owt (ABV 6%) STOUT

Inadequate

🍺 Holy Inadequate, 67 Etruria Old Road, Stoke-On-Trent, ST1 5PE
☎ (01782) 915170 ☎ 07771 358238
✉ paulcope.cope@gmail.com

☺This one-barrel plant commenced brewing behind the Holy Inadequate in 2018 and mainly supplies the pub with an ever-changing range of beers (up to four at any one time). Other local pubs are sometimes supplied, along with local beer festivals.

Incredible SIBA

214/224 Unit 1, Broomhill Road, Brislington, Bristol, BS4 5RG ☎ 07780 977073
🌐 incrediblebrewingcompany.com

⊠ This microbrewery specialises in producing small batches of beer using a 2.5-barrel plant. It was established in 2014 by head brewer Stephen Hall with the aim of promoting experimental beers and traditional recipes. Cask ales are available occasionally. ‼◆LIVE V

Independent Lakeland

See Strands

Indian SIBA

119b Baltimore Trading Estate, Baltimore Road, Great Barr, B42 1DD
☎ (0121) 296 9000 🌐 indianbrewery.com

Six-barrel brewery, established in 2005 as the Tunnel Brewery at the Lord Nelson Inn. It relocated to the picturesque stable block at Red House Farm in 2011. In 2015 Tunnel's owners went their separate ways, with Mike Walsh retaining the brewery and renaming it the Indian Brewery. Later that year it was sold to new owners and relocated to the outskirts of Birmingham. Beers are normally only found in its own two pubs. ‼

Summer (ABV 4%) GOLD
IPA (ABV 4.9%) PALE
Bombay Honey (ABV 5%) SPECIALITY
Peacock (ABV 5%) BITTER

Indie Rabble SIBA

27-28 The Arches, Alma Road, Windsor, Berkshire, SL4 1QZ ☎ 07983 736132 🌐 indierabble.co.uk

A 20-hectolitre brewery and taproom in a railway arch beneath the track for Windsor & Eton Central Station. Opened in 2023, it produces, by itself and also in collaboration with others, a range of cask and keg beers. ‼◆◢

Indigenous

Peacock Cottage, Main Street, Chaddleworth, Berkshire, RG20 7EH
☎ (01488) 505060 🌐 indigenousbrewery.co.uk

⊠ An occasional and informal microbrewer for many years, Kevin Brady established Indigenous in 2014, increasing production using a 2.5-barrel plant. Availability is restricted to local pubs, shops and an increasing number of regional beer festivals. ‼🍴◆LIVE

Baldrick (ABV 3.4%) MILD
Chinwag (ABV 4%) BITTER
Forager's Gold (ABV 4%) GOLD
Summer Solstice (ABV 4.1%) PALE
Billy No Mates (ABV 4.2%) PALE
Frisky Mare (ABV 4.2%) GOLD
Silly Moo (ABV 4.2%) STOUT
Tickety-Boo (ABV 4.2%) GOLD
Nutcracker (ABV 4.5%) OLD
Old Cadger (ABV 4.5%) BITTER
Monocle (ABV 4.6%) STOUT
Moonstruck (ABV 4.8%) PORTER

Nosey Parker (ABV 5.5%) MILD
AMMO Belle (ABV 5.6%) IPA
Double Warp (ABV 5.8%) STOUT

Industrial

See Silver

Inferno

17 Station Street, Tewkesbury, GL20 5NJ
☎ (01684) 294873 ☎ 07854 949731
✉ infernobrewery@yahoo.com

⊗ Inferno began in 2018, after many years of home brewing, using a 2.5-barrel kit which was installed in 2019. As well as its core range, a number of seasonal ales are brewed. The beers are available in local Gloucestershire pubs, clubs and at beer festivals. ♦⬦

Mild Burn (ABV 3.8%) MILD
Spark (ABV 3.8%) PALE
Bright gold, spicy hop, tropical fruit aroma. Balanced malt, new world hops, stone fruit, peach, papaya fades to bitter citrus.
Helles Fire (ABV 4%) SPECIALITY
Golden Embers (ABV 4.2%) PALE
Citrus hop aroma, mandarin, white pepper, earthy notes, minimal malt. Initial sweetness leads to a long, dry, bitter, citrus aftertaste.
Tinder Box (ABV 4.5%) PALE
Dark colour, hedgerow fruits, spice and a malty nose. Earthy, bittersweet autumn fruits with some caramel. Long, bitter dry finish.
Cinder Stout (ABV 4.8%) STOUT
Soft roast, vanilla nose. Light roast and body. Chocolate, coffee, Crunchy Bar, raisins/dates. Finish is dry, soft coffee, dark fruit.
Wheat Storm (ABV 5%) SPECIALITY
Fresh, zingy Belgian Wit beer. Yeasty banana, clove, coriander and pear esters. Wheat, biscuit, and spicy banana with floral and wood.
Mental Martha (ABV 5.5%) SPECIALITY
Vulcan (ABV 5.5%) PORTER
Prometheus (ABV 5.8%) IPA
Triple-hopped, bright, spicy, earthy aroma with oyster mushroom notes and honey. Spicy hops, strong malt backbone. Long bitter finish.

Infinity

Sladepool Farm Road, Birmingham, B14 5EB
☎ (0121) 405 8058 ☎ 07915 948058
⊕ infinitybrewing.uk

Infinity Brewing Company was established in 2020 and is a one-barrel nanobrewery producing small-batch craft beer in Birmingham. It makes small-batch brew runs, which allows trials of different recipes and flavours.

Inishmacsaint

See Fermanagh

Inkspot

Rookery Barn, The Rookery, 40 Streatham Common South, Streatham Common, London, SW16 3BX
☎ (020) 8679 7322 ☎ 07747 607803
⊕ theinkspotbrewery.com

Started in 2012 as Perfect Blend after a bar in Streatham, the brewery subsequently changed its name to Inkspot. Brewing began at its own premises in the middle of Streatham Common in 2018. Its Art & Craft bottle shops

are the best places to find the beers along with when the taproom is open for 'shutters up' events. No cask ale. ⬦

Inner Bay SIBA

Seacliffe Villa, Hill Street, Inverkeithing, KY11 1AB
⊕ innerbay.co.uk

Brewing began in 2016. Inner Bay is a family-run brewery using traditional ingredients and methods producing bottle-conditioned beers in small batches.

INNformal

14 Charnham Street, Hungerford, Berkshire, RG17 0ES
⊕ john-o-gaunt-hungerford.co.uk

⊗ The INNformal brewery was established in 2015 and moved to Hungerford in 2019 when it expanded to a four-barrel plant. A selection of the beers can always be found at its affiliated pub, the John O'Gaunt Inn, Hungerford. ‼♦

INN Session (ABV 3.5%) PALE
INN House Bitter (ABV 4.1%) BITTER
INN Deep (ABV 5%) STOUT
INN Alcatraz (ABV 5.9%) IPA
INN Darkness (ABV 6%) PORTER
Alice INN Wonderland (ABV 7.1%) STRONG

Innis & Gunn SIBA

See Inveralmond

Intrepid SIBA

Unit 12, Vincent Works, Stretfield Road, Bradwell, Derbyshire, S33 9HG ☎ 07936 174364
⊕ intrepidbrewing.co

Based in the Hope Valley in the Peak District, Intrepid commenced brewing in 2014 using an eight-barrel plant located in an old smelting mill. It is a small-batch brewery, producing beers in cask, keg and bottle.

Inveralmond

22 Inveralmond Place, Inveralmond Industrial Estate, Perth, PH1 3TS
☎ (01738) 449448 ⊕ inveralmond-brewery.co.uk

☺Established in 1997, Inveralmond was the first brewery in Perth for more than 30 years. In 2016, it became part of the Innis & Gunn family, an independent Scottish brewer based in Edinburgh. I&G makes no real ale but the Inveralmond range continues. ‼🖩♦

Ossian (ABV 4.1%) GOLD
Well-balanced best bitter with a dry finish. This full-bodied amber ale is dominated by fruit and hop with a bittersweet character although excessive caramel can distract from this.
Lia Fail (ABV 4.7%) BITTER
A dark, robust, full-bodied beer with a deep malty taste. Smooth texture and balanced finish.

Iron Pier SIBA

Units 6 & 7, May Industrial Estate, May Avenue, Northfleet, Gravesend, Kent, DA11 8RU
☎ (01474) 569460 ⊕ ironpier.beer

⊗ Iron Pier Brewery was established in 2017 using a 15-barrel plant. It takes its name from the oldest iron pier in existence, located on the River Thames at Gravesend. An onsite taproom offers the brewery's beers plus other local brews. ‼♦V⬦

Perry St Pale (ABV 3.7%) GOLD

Joined at the Hop Pale Ale (ABV 3.8%) GOLD
Bitter (ABV 4%) BITTER
Wealdway (ABV 4.5%) GOLD
Cast Iron Stout (ABV 4.7%) STOUT
Rosherville Red (ABV 4.8%) RED
A lovely red, crisp with a hint of spice, with a nice butterscotch finish.
From the Wave (ABV 6.4%) PALE

Isaac Poad SIBA

Office: Hay House, Baxby Manor, Husthwaite, North Yorkshire, YO61 4PW
☎ (01423) 358114 ⊕ isaacpoadbrewing.co.uk

☺Established in 2016 by a local grain merchant, which formerly supplied malting barley to local maltsters, the brewery continues despite the subsequent demise of the parent company. Pending construction of its own brew plant, production is actually carried out at another local brewery. ◆

No.86 Golden Ale (ABV 3.6%) GOLD
1863 Best Bitter (ABV 3.8%) BITTER
No.91 Craft Ale (ABV 3.9%) GOLD
All Four Yorkshire Red Ale (ABV 4.2%) RED
No.84 India Pale Ale (ABV 4.5%) PALE
Piccadilly Porter (ABV 4.8%) PORTER

Isca SIBA

Court Farm, Holcombe, Devon, EX7 0JT ☎ 07773 444501 ✉ iscaales@yahoo.co.uk

⊠ Established in a disused milking parlour in 2009, Isca has developed a large range of ales. Seasonal and special brews are often available at beer festivals, including outside of the region. ◆LIVE V

Citra (ABV 3.8%) GOLD
Dawlish Summer (ABV 3.8%) GOLD
Golden Ale (ABV 3.8%) GOLD
Dawlish Bitter (ABV 4.2%) BITTER
Glorious Devon (ABV 4.4%) GOLD
Gold (ABV 4.5%) GOLD
Holcombe White (ABV 4.5%) SPECIALITY
Dawlish Pale (ABV 5%) PALE
Black IPA (ABV 6%) IPA
Devon Pale (ABV 6.8%) IPA

Isla Vale

Margate, Kent, CT9 5DJ
☎ (01843) 292451 ☎ 07980 174616
⊕ islavalealesmiths.co.uk

⊠ Isla Vale was established in 2014 from a residential address in Westbrook (Margate) and supplies local micropubs. A one-barrel plant is used to brew its core range as well as a specially commissioned beer for the Wheel Alehouse, Birchington. Outlets are supplied locally. Brewing is currently suspended. ◆

Island SIBA

Dinglers Farm, Yarmouth Road, Newport, Isle of Wight, PO30 4LZ
☎ (01983) 821711 ⊕ islandbrewery.co.uk

⊠ Island Brewery is the realisation of Tom Minshull's ambition to brew real ales to complement the existing family-owned drinks distribution business. Brewing commenced in 2010 using a 12-barrel brewery. More than 100 outlets are supplied direct. ‼◆

Nipper Bitter (ABV 3.8%) GOLD
Wight Gold (ABV 4%) BITTER
Yachtsmans Ale (ABV 4.2%) BITTER

Wight Knight (ABV 4.5%) BITTER
Vectis Venom (ABV 4.8%) BITTER
Earls RDA (ABV 5%) STOUT

Islay SIBA

Glenegedale, Isle of Islay, PA42 7AS
☎ (01496) 810014 ✉ info@islayales.com

☺The only brewery on an island famous for its malt whiskies, Islay Ales started brewing in 2004 and continues to use a four-barrel plant. Originally situated in converted farm buildings in Bridgend, it moved in 2024 to new premises in Glenegedale. The brewery tap is the only outlet for the brewery's cask-conditioned beers. ‼🛒◆

Isle of Eigg SIBA

Galmisdale, Isle of Eigg, PH42 4RL
⊕ eiggbrewery.com

Crowdfunded during 2020, Isle of Eigg is Scotland's first cooperative brewery. Having built the brewery and installed the kit in 2021, production began in 2022. The brewery uses 100% renewable energy with its water coming from a natural source, and supports the local crofting community by reusing its raw materials.

Isle of Harris

Croft No 6, Borrisdale, Outer Hebrides, HS5 3UE
☎ 07584 354144 ⊕ isleofharrisbrewery.com

Established in 2020, small batch, limited edition beers are produced in a tiny brewshed overlooking the Sound of Harris. Beers are bottled and labelled by hand. LIVE

Isle of Purbeck SIBA

🖺 Bankes Arms Hotel, Manor Road, Studland, Dorset, BH19 3AU
☎ (01929) 450227 ⊕ isleofpurbeckbrewery.com

Founded in 2003, and situated in the grounds of the Bankes Arms Inn, in the heart of the magical Isle of Purbeck. The pub and brewery overlook the sea at Studland and Old Harry Rocks on the Dorset section of the Jurassic World Heritage Coast. This 10-barrel plant produces five core beers, several seasonal beers and Purbeck Pommes cider, available locally, and also nationwide via exchange swaps with other micros, and at beer festivals. ◆LIVE

Best Bitter (ABV 3.6%) BITTER
A classic malty best bitter with rich malt aroma and taste and smooth, malty, bitter finish.
Fossil Fuel (ABV 4.1%) BITTER
Amber bitter with complex aroma with a hint of pepper; rich malt dominates the taste, leading to a smooth dry finish.
Solar Power (ABV 4.3%) GOLD
Tawny mid-range ale brewed using Continental hops. Well-balanced flavours combine to provide a strong bitter taste but short, dry finish.
Studland Bay – Wrecked (ABV 4.5%) BITTER
Deep red ale with slightly sweet aroma reflecting a mixture of caramel, malt and hops that lead to a dry, malty finish.
Full Steam Ahead (ABV 4.8%) BITTER
Mid-brown beer with hop/malt balance in the flavour and a long dry aftertaste.

Isle of Skye SIBA

The Pier, Uig, Isle of Skye, IV51 9XP
☎ (01470) 542477 ⊕ skyeale.com

⊚The Isle of Skye Brewery was established in 1995. Originally a 10-barrel plant, it was upgraded to 20 barrels in 2004. ♯♯➹♦

Tarasgeir (ABV 4%) SPECIALITY
YP (Young Pretender) (ABV 4%) BITTER
A refreshing, amber, hoppy grapefruit bitter. Some sweetness in the taste but continuing into a lingering bitter finish.
Skye Red (ABV 4.2%) BITTER
A light, fruity nose with a hint of caramel leads to a hoppy, malty, fruity flavour and a dry, bittersweet finish.
Skye Gold (ABV 4.3%) SPECIALITY
Porridge oats are used to produce this delicious speciality beer. Nicely-balanced, it has a refreshingly soft lemon, bitter flavour with an oaty background.
Skye Black (ABV 4.5%) OLD
Full-bodied with a malty richness. Malt holds sway but there are plenty of hops and fruit to be discovered in its varied character. A delicious Scottish old ale.
Skye IPA (ABV 4.5%) PALE

It's Quicker by Ale

Harrogate

IVO SIBA

10 Church Street, Somersham, Cambridgeshire, PE28 3EG ⊕ ivobrewery.co.uk

Established in 2020, IVO Brewery is run by two friends and neighbours, Charlie Abbott and Jason Jones, both successful homebrewers. Every beer is naturally fined and vegan-friendly. Despite being a small brewery, a core range is brewed with occasional and on-demand specials. The core range of nine beers varies from a Kolsh-style lager to porters. All are available as bottle-conditioned, with some also in cask and the remainder in keg (dependent on style). ♦LIVE V

Car Park Cuddle (ABV 3.8%) PALE
You've Sean'd It (ABV 4.2%) BITTER
No Man (ABV 4.5%) STOUT
She Keeps It Nice (ABV 4.5%) PALE
Evening Brown (ABV 5%) BROWN
Heavy On The Chips (ABV 6%) PORTER

Ivybridge

Unit 3, Glanvilles Mill, Ivybridge, PL21 9PS
☎ (01752) 894295 ☎ 07512 961085
⊕ ivybridgebrewing.co.uk

Established in 2018, Ivybridge Brewing Company is a social enterprise brewery that provides training and paid work for people from the local area with learning disabilities. It upgraded to a 2.5-barrel kit in 2021 and set up a taproom and shop where its trainees serve its four core beers on draught and bottle-conditioned. It also supplies local outlets. All profits from beer sales are reinvested in the business to create more opportunities for trainees. ➹LIVE♦

Jacaranda

Brinkley, Southwell

Office: 7 St John Street, Mansfield, NG18 1QH
✉ jacarandabc@outlook.com

Brewing began in 2022 producing various beer styles in both cask and bottle. The core beers are named after assorted bird species. ♦

Warbler (ABV 4%) RED
Jackdaw (ABV 4.2%) PALE
Wagtail (ABV 4.2%) PALE
Goldfinch (ABV 4.5%) GOLD

JackRabbit

Prettyfields, Dead Lane, Ardleigh, Essex, CO7 7PF
☎ 07506 596597 ⊕ jackrabbitbrewing.co.uk

JackRabbit Brewing Co was founded in 2019 by two beer lovers with an aim to bring modern craft beer to the Essex & Suffolk border. It offers a popular core range consisting of craft lager, New England pale, and hazy IPA (available in can and keg). New and special releases all year round. ➹

College Hop-Out (ABV 4%) PALE
Roasted Stout (ABV 4.3%) STOUT
Way to Amberillo (ABV 4.5%) BITTER

James Street

See Bath Brew House

Jaw

🏠 **26 Crossveggate, Milngavie, G62 6RA**
☎ (0141) 237 5840 ⊕ jawbrew.co.uk

An independent, family-run, craft microbrewery from Glasgow. Committed to producing the absolute pinnacle of high quality beer. Brewing is currently suspended. LIVE

Jawbone

Unit C, 1 Strawberry Vale, Twickenham, TW1 4RY
⊕ jawbonebrewing.com

Brewing commenced in 2020. Beer was initially available in cans, joined soon after by keg. The range of beers is available at the BrewDock taproom (Thursday-Saturday) located next to a working boatyard by the River Thames. ♦

Jiddlers Tipple

Office: Hornsey Park Road, Wood Green, London, N8 0JY ☎ 07966 527902 ⊕ jiddlerstipple.com

After using UBrew, 2019 saw output scaled up with brewing first at Birmingham Brewery and more recently at By The Horns and Goodness. The wide range of styles is available in keg and cans, sometimes on cask.

Jimbrew SIBA

Provender House, Clifton Fields, Lytham Road, Clifton, PR4 0XG ☎ 07739 859300 ⊕ jimbrew.co.uk

Brewing commenced in late 2022. All beers are unfiltered, unfined and gluten-free. No cask ale is regularly produced but the brewery is experimenting and it may be available during the currency of this Guide. GF V♦

John O'Groats

Last House, County Road, John O'Groats, KW1 4YR
☎ (01955) 611220 ☎ 07842 401571
⊕ johnogroatsbrewery.co.uk

⊚Brewing began in 2015 with a four-barrel plant. Originally housed in the old fire station, in 2019 the brewery expanded when a new three-barrel plant was installed in the Last House, up by the harbour. This enabled the opening of a visitor centre complete with shop and bar, together with offering brewery tours. A bottling facility was added in 2022. Its beers are also available in the brewery tap, the Seaview Hotel. ♯♯➹♦

Swelkie (ABV 4%) BITTER
Slight honey taste in this citrus, hoppy brew.
Duncansby (ABV 4.2%) BITTER

Deep Groat (ABV 4.8%) STOUT
Nearly black brew full of chocolate and coffee with some background roast.

John of Gaunt (NEW)

The Old Barn, Beechfield Farm, Otley Road, Beckwithshaw, North Yorkshire, HG3 1QL ☎ 07798 838105 ✉ andrew.scott393@gmail.com

Andrew Scott, a merchant seaman, who only brews when he is on leave, established the brewery in 2024. The plant is homemade from converted Grundy tanks with an approximate brew length of three barrels. Beers are available locally at Blind Jacks, Knaresborough.

Jolly Boys

Unit 16A, Redbrook Business Park, off Wilthorpe Road, Redbrook, S75 1JN ☎ 07808 085214 ⊕ jollyboysbrewery.co.uk

⊕Jolly Boys started brewing in 2016 using spare capacity at another local brewery before moving to its own site in the same year. The Jolly Tap on the Arcade, Barnsley, has now been joined with a second pub that opened in 2023, the Mallard, Moorthorpe train station. The Jolly Tap in Wakefield closed in 2022. !!♦V✿

Jolly Yorkshire Bitter (ABV 3.8%) BITTER
Blonde (ABV 4%) BLOND
Jolly Cascade Blonde (ABV 4%) BLOND
La Joll'a Blonde (ABV 4%) BLOND
Golden Best (ABV 4.5%) GOLD
Yorkshire Pale Ale (ABV 4.8%) PALE
Jolly Collier Porter (ABV 5%) PORTER
Jolly IPA (ABV 5.8%) IPA

Jolly Sailor SIBA

🍺 **Olympia Hotel Tap House, 77 Barlby Road, Selby, North Yorkshire, YO8 5AB** ☎ (01757) 707564 ☎ 07923 635755 ⊕ jollysailorbrewery.uk

⊕The Jolly Sailor Brewery is an independent, family-run microbrewery established in 2013 in the grounds of the Olympia Hotel Tap House in Selby, on the nearby River Ouse and close to the 11th century abbey. Beers are brewed on a six-barrel plant and available at the brewery's Jolly Sailor Inn, Cawood, and extensively in the free trade. !!🍺♦V✿

Selby Bitter (ABV 3.8%) BITTER
Selby Blonde (ABV 3.8%) BLOND
Selby Pale (ABV 3.9%) PALE
Selby Mild (ABV 4%) MILD
Milk Stout (ABV 4.5%) STOUT
Dark Nights Porter (ABV 5%) PORTER

Joule's

The Brewery, Great Hales Street, Market Drayton, Shropshire, TF9 1JP ☎ (01630) 654400 ⊕ joulesbrewery.co.uk

Re-established in 2010, following a break of 40 years. Joule's is situated in Market Drayton, and has access to pure mineral water drawn from the same aquifer as the original brewery. It runs a collection of over 40 taphouses across its heartland of Shropshire, Staffordshire and Cheshire. !!♦V

Pure Blonde (ABV 3.8%) BLOND
Pale Ale (ABV 4.1%) PALE
Slumbering Monk (ABV 4.5%) BITTER

Jura

7 Keills Croft, Craighouse, Isle of Jura, PA60 7XG ☎ 07817 456347 ✉ jurabrewery2017@gmail.com

Microbrewery that opened in 2021. Jura bottles the majority of its produce with some available in keg.

Kaneen's

Kaneen's Garage, Main Road, Union Mills, Isle of Man, IM4 4AE ☎ 07624 302245 ⊕ kaneensbrewery.com

⊠ Launched in 2021, head brewer Peter Kaneen was originally fixing vehicles in a garage on the Isle of Man, which he inherited from his father John Kaneen. After attending Brewing School and applying to the Isle of Man Small Business Scheme, he converted the workshop into a small artisan brewery. ♦V

Lhune Airh (ABV 4.8%) PALE
Gentle sweet malt and fruit, with hops present to give bitterness throughout.

Keep

🍺 **Village Inn, The Cross, Nailsworth, Gloucestershire, GL6 0HH** ☎ (01453) 835715 ☎ 07877 569586 ✉ paul@dropinpubs.com

After a break of 96 years, brewing returned to Nailsworth in 2004, at the Village Inn. The pub and brewery were sold in 2016 to Paul Sugden and Adam Pavey, who changed the brewery name from Nailsworth to Keep Brewing. Brewing takes place on a six-barrel kit below the bar, with new recipes trialled on a 40-litre pilot plant. ♦LIVE

Keith

Malcomburn, Mulben, Keith, AB55 5DD ☎ (01542) 488006 ⊕ keithbrewery.co.uk

Formerly known as Brewmeister and established in 2012, the brewery was renamed Keith Brewery in 2015. It moved production to Malcolmburn, Mulben, sharing facilities with Spey Valley Brewery (qv). Keith Brewery is part of the Consolidated Craft Breweries Group. !!🍺♦LIVE

Kelburn SIBA

10 Muriel Lane, Barrhead, G78 1QB ☎ (0141) 881 2138 ⊕ kelburnbrewery.com

⊠ Kelburn is an award-winning family business established in 2002. !!♦

Goldihops (ABV 3.8%) GOLD
Well-hopped session ale with a fruity taste and a bitter finish.
Pivo Estivo (ABV 3.9%) GOLD
A pale, dry, citrus, hoppy session ale.
Misty Law (ABV 4%) BITTER
Red Smiddy (ABV 4.1%) BITTER
This bittersweet ale predominantly features an intense citrus hop character balanced perfectly with fruity malt.
Dark Moor (ABV 4.5%) MILD
A dark, fruity ale with undertones of liquorice and blackcurrant.
Jaguar (ABV 4.5%) GOLD
A golden, full-bodied ale with undertones of grapefruit and a long lasting citrus, hoppy aftertaste.
Cart Noir (ABV 4.8%) STOUT
Cart Blanche (ABV 5%) GOLD
A golden, full-bodied ale. The assault of fruit and hop camouflages the strength of this easy-drinking ale.

Kelchner SIBA

Unit D, The Sidings, Station Road, Ampthill, Bedfordshire, MK45 2QY ☎ 07508 305754
✉ kelchnerbrewery@gmail.com

⊗ Kelchner Brewery was set up in 2018 and currently supplies cask, bottles and polypins for trade and retail. Distribution is mainly via sports clubs including a Luton Town FC match day bar, Bedfordshire pubs and bottle retailers. It also attends many local farmers markets and craft fayres. Brewing capacity is between 900 and 1,200 litres. ‼ ☞ ♦ LIVE

Half Nelson (ABV 3.8%) GOLD
Ampthill Gold (ABV 4.1%) GOLD
Hat Trick (ABV 4.1%) GOLD
Curse of the Red (ABV 4.3%) RED
Full Nelson (ABV 4.5%) GOLD
IPA (ABV 4.5%) PALE
Parklife (ABV 4.5%) BITTER
After Dark (ABV 4.8%) PALE
Ammetelle (ABV 5%) STOUT

Kelham Island

See Thornbridge

Keller

🏛 23-27 Broughton Street Lane, Edinburgh, EH39 5NG
⊕ kellertaproom.com

This in-house brewery operates from a space next to, and visible from, the Keller Taproom. There is also a distillery. The first unfiltered craft lager appeared in mid-2021.

Keltek SIBA

Candela House, Cardrew Way, Redruth, TR15 1SS
☎ (01209) 313620 ⊕ keltekbrewery.co.uk

⊙ Keltek (Celtic in Cornish) began brewing award-winning ales in 1997, and was founded by Stuart Heath. It started as a 2.5-barrel plant in Stuart's disused stable block on the Roseland Peninsula. Several moves and expansions mean it is now based in Redruth, and can brew more than 250 barrels a week. In 2013 Keltek acquired four pubs in south-west Cornwall (the second brewery in Cornwall to own an estate of pubs). Two more were acquired in 2016. ☞ ♦

Pool of Mist (ABV 3.4%) BITTER
Amber bitter with apple aroma. Light malt and hop flavour with apple and tangerine. Distinctly bitter, dry finish with apples.
Big Tackle (ABV 4%) GOLD
Engine House (ABV 4%) BITTER
Pale brown bitter with faint aroma. Light malt taste balanced by tangerine hops with earthy notes and esters. Bitter finish.
Panning for Gold (ABV 4%) PALE
Gold pale ale with light fruity aroma. Biscuit malt flavour balanced by grassy citrus hop bitterness and pineapple. Long finish.
Heart of Kernow (ABV 4.5%) BITTER
Golden best bitter. Powerful fruity hops with high bitterness but backed with solid malt which lingers well on the finish.
Mines Gold (ABV 5.1%) BITTER
Copper-coloured, premium bitter with malt and fruit aromas. Biscuit malt balanced by earthy hops and tropical and citrus fruit.
Pilot Gig (ABV 5.2%) PORTER
Grim Reaper (ABV 6%) BITTER

Tawny winter bitter with full malt, molasses, resinous hops and vine fruit flavours. Toffee, liquorice, fruitcake hints. Lingering malt finish.
Beheaded (ABV 7.5%) STRONG
Tawny strong ale with balanced malt and hops. Sherry sweet with honey, toffee and fruit notes and a bittersweet finish.

Kent SIBA

The Long Barn, Birling Place Farm, Stangate Road, Birling, Kent, ME19 5JN
☎ (01634) 780037 ⊕ kentbrewery.com

⊗ Kent Brewery was founded in 2010 by Toby Simmonds (ex Dark Star brewer) and Paul Herbert. A 10-barrel plant has been in operation at the Birling site since 2011. Outlets (500+) are supplied direct, mainly in Kent, Sussex, and London. A dozen regular beers are produced, constantly changing specials, and house beers for the Craft Beer Co pubs. Casks are also sold throughout the UK and abroad, particularly in Sweden and Finland. Kegs are also produced, all of which are unfined, naturally-carbonated live beer. ☞ ♦

Session Pale (ABV 3.7%) PALE
Black Gold (ABV 4%) PALE
Pale (ABV 4%) PALE
Cobnut (ABV 4.1%) BITTER
Kent Golding Bitter (ABV 4.1%) BITTER
Zingiber (ABV 4.1%) SPECIALITY
Quiet American (ABV 4.2%) GOLD
Single Hop (ABV 4.5%) GOLD
Stout (ABV 4.5%) STOUT
Prohibition (ABV 4.8%) PALE
Hops and citrusy bitter grapefruit dominate all the way through then finishes dry and clean.
The New Black (ABV 4.8%) PALE
TropicAle (ABV 4.9%) PALE

Kernel SIBA

Arch 11, Dockley Road Industrial Estate, Dockley Road, Bermondsey, London, SE16 3SF

Office: 1 Spa Business Park, Spa Road, Bermondsey, London, SE16 4QT ⊕ thekernelbrewery.com

Kernel was established in 2009 by Evin O'Riordain and moved to larger premises in 2012 to keep up with demand. The brewery produces cask, keg and bottle-conditioned beers, and has won many awards for its wide, ever-changing range. A new brewery tap, a few arches along, opened in 2020 and cask ale, introduced in 2022, is now widely available to much acclaim. ☞ LIVE V

Kerr's (NEW)

The Engine Shed, Rosemains Steading, Pathhead, EH37 5UQ

Family-owned brewery founded in 2022, fusing traditional beers styles with modern ingredients and rigorous scientific approach. The owner scours historic brewery records for beer recipes, looks far and wide for flavourful hops and source British barley varieties, resulting in uniquely flavoured, beautifully balanced beers that owe much to the past.

Kerroo (NEW)

Former Commissioner's Depot, Droghadfayle Road, Port Erin, Isle of Man, IM9 6EE ⊕ kerroobrewing.com

Brewing began in 2024 using a 100-hectolitre plant. Initially only producing live beer in kegs, cask beer is planned later in 2024. The brewery and taproom is located a short stroll from the Isle of Man Steam Railway station. ◆

Keswick SIBA

The Old Brewery, Brewery Lane, Keswick, Cumbria, CA12 5BY
☎ (01768) 780700 ⊕ keswickbrewery.co.uk

Keswick, owned by Sue Jefferson, began brewing in 2006 using a 10-barrel plant on the site of a brewery that closed in 1897. The brewery is set up to be environmentally-friendly using sheeps wool insulation, and reducing its environmental impact. Outlets include the Fox bar at the brewery, the Dog & Gun, Keswick, and many other pubs across Cumbria. !! ⬌ ◆ ⚫

Black Star (ABV 3.5%) BITTER
Gold (ABV 3.6%) PALE
Predominantly hoppy bitter with malts, sweetness and fruit and a dry, bitter finish.
Bitter (ABV 3.7%) BITTER
A ruby brown beer with fruity aromas, sweet fruity caramel flavours, light dry bitterness and a light, fruity, roast finish.
Thirst Rescue (ABV 3.8%) BITTER
Bitter beer with some fruitiness, full-bodied and a lasting bitter finish.
Fox Dark (ABV 4%) MILD
Fox Pale (ABV 4%) BLOND
Sweet, fruity, blond beer with fruity citrus aromas rounded up with a crisp and lasting hop bitter finish.
Thirst Run (ABV 4.2%) PALE
A well-balanced, golden-coloured beer that maintains its fruitiness from start to finish.
Thirst Quencher (ABV 4.3%) BLOND
Light-bodied fresh hoppy beer with fruit in the middle and a balancing sweetness.
Pale Ale (ABV 4.4%) PALE
KSB (Keswick Special Bitter) (ABV 4.8%) BITTER
Dark Horse (ABV 6%) BROWN
Malty sweet and fruity robust brown ale with gentle hop bittering and a lasting finish.
K4 (ABV 6%) IPA
Thirst Celebration (ABV 7%) STRONG

Kettlesmith SIBA

Unit 16, Treenwood Industrial Estate, Bradford-On-Avon, Wiltshire, BA15 2AU
☎ (01225) 864839 ⊕ kettlesmithbrewing.com

⊠ Kettlesmith is an independent microbrewery established in 2016. It brews modern interpretations of a wide variety of beer styles, drawing inspiration from the brewer's background in America and England, as well as a love of Belgian beer. !! ⬌ ◆ LIVE GF V ⚫

Streamline (ABV 1.2%) SPECIALITY
Outline (ABV 3.8%) BITTER
Faultline (ABV 4.1%) PALE
Plotline (ABV 4.4%) STOUT
Fogline (ABV 4.7%) SPECIALITY
Coastline (ABV 4.9%) SPECIALITY
Ridgeline (ABV 5%) RED
Timeline (ABV 5.4%) PALE
Skyline (ABV 5.6%) SPECIALITY

Kibble

Rear of Crystal Palace, 11 Towngate, Thurlstone, South Yorkshire, S36 9RH ☎ 07952 790245

⊛ Brewing began in 2021 in the former stable block of the Crystal Palace pub. The owner (an ex miner) on seeing the mash tun exclaimed it looked like a kibble (a

big bucket used in pit shafts to move men and machinery) and the brewery name was born. A 2.5-barrel kit is used to produce mining-themed beers mostly named after local coal seams. The beers are rarely found outside the pub. ◆

Kickabo

Unit 7B, Harvey Works, Lingard Street, Stoke On Trent, ST6 1ED ⊕ kickabobrewery.com

A small, three-barrel brewery set up in Burslem in the Potteries in 2020. Its aim is to recreate beers that will feature styles from across the world. Currently available in keg or cans. ◆

Kiln

Chiddinglye Farm, West Hoathly, RH19 4QS ☎ 07800 556729

Office: 1st Floor, 30 Church Road, Burgess Hill, RH15 9AE ⊕ thekilnbrewery.co.uk

Kiln brewery was set up by two friends in 2014. Following a search for new premises, it has joined forces with Missing Link brewery. Although Kiln's website is focusing on keg and canned beer, they are continuing to produce cask beers, but are no longer sticking with a core range.

King Aelle

Delaval Arms, Old Hartley, Seaton Sluice, NE26 4RL ☎ (0191) 237 0489

Brewing commenced in 2021 on a 2.5-barrel plant which was originally based at the Hop & Cleaver, Newcastle upon Tyne. The brewery is based in an outbuilding at the Grade II-listed Delaval Arms, Old Hartley, on the Northumberland coast. Beers are available in both cask and five litre mini casks. Brewing is currently suspended.

King Street SIBA

Riverside House, Welsh Back, Bristol, BS1 4RR ☎ (0117) 405 8948

Office: City Pub Group, 2nd Floor, Essel House, London, W1W 7TH ⊕ kingstreetbrewhouse.co.uk

⊠ The King Street Brew House is owned by the City Pub Group, which has several pubs and brewpubs around the country. The compact brewery is on the ground floor, with the fermenting vessels and conditioning tanks in the basement. The enthusiastic onsite brewer produces a wide range of beers, from regular favourites (all year), to one off/seasonal specials. Guest beers are also available. !! ◆ LIVE V

King's Cliffe

Unit 10, Kingsmead, Station Road, King's Cliffe, Northamptonshire, PE8 6YH ☎ 07843 288088
⊕ kcbales.co.uk

⊠ In 2014, exactly 100 years after the last brewery in King's Cliffe ceased brewing, village resident Jeremy O'Neill set up this venture. It currently produces five barrels a week. !! ◆

5C (ABV 3.8%) GOLD
A light bitter with balanced taste of malt and hops and a refreshing bitter finish.
No. 10 (ABV 4%) PALE
Amber beer with a clean malty taste and a long bitter finish.
66 Degrees (ABV 4.6%) BITTER

Amber beer with a floral aroma, a balanced taste of malt and hops, and a long bitter finish.
B5 (ABV 4.6%) PALE
P51 (ABV 5.1%) PORTER
A rich dark porter with a smooth roast and chocolate taste and a malt, fruit and bitter chocolate finish.

Kingstone

Tintern, NP16 7NX
☎ (01291) 680111 ⊕ kingstonebrewery.co.uk

Kingstone Brewery is located in the Wye Valley close to Tintern Abbey. Brewing began on a four-barrel plant in 2005. ‼ ☰ LIVE

Tewdric's Tipple (ABV 3.8%) BITTER
Challenger (ABV 4%) BITTER
Gold (ABV 4%) GOLD
Llandogo Trow (ABV 4.2%) BITTER
No.1 Premium Stout (ABV 4.4%) STOUT
Classic (ABV 4.5%) BITTER
1503 (ABV 4.8%) BITTER
Abbey Ale (ABV 5.1%) BITTER
Humpty's Fuddle IPA (ABV 5.8%) IPA

Kinver SIBA

Unit 1, Britch Farm, Rocky Wall, Kinver, Staffordshire, DY7 5NW ☎ 07715 842676 ⊕ kinverbrewery.co.uk

⊛Established in 2004, Kinver brewery produces a wide range of different beer styles including one-off specials. The brewery relocated in 2012 to a new 10-barrel plant on the edge of Kinver due to increased demand. An ever-increasing number of pubs, mainly in the Midlands, and beer festivals, are supplied with the award-winning ales. ‼ ♦ LIVE

Light Railway (ABV 3.8%) BLOND
Straw-coloured session beer. A fruity and malty start quickly gives way to well-hopped bitterness and lingering hoppy aftertaste.
Cavegirl Bitter (ABV 4%) BLOND
Edge (ABV 4.2%) BITTER
Amber with a malty aroma. Sweet fruity start with a hint of citrus marmalade in the spicy edged malt; lasting hoppy finish that is satisfyingly bitter.
Noble (ABV 4.5%) GOLD
Fruity hop aroma. Very fruity start then the grassy hops give a sharp bitter finish with malt support.
Maybug (ABV 4.8%) BLOND
Half Centurion (ABV 5%) BITTER
A golden best bitter; malty before the hops take command to give a balanced hoppy finish and provide the great aftertaste.
Black Ram Stout (ABV 5.2%) STOUT
Witchfinder General (ABV 5.5%) PORTER
Khyber (ABV 5.8%) BITTER
Golden strong bitter with a Centennial hop bite that overwhelms the fleeting malty sweetness and drives through to the long dry finish.

Kirkby Lonsdale SIBA

Unit 2F, Old Station Yard, Kirkby Lonsdale, Cumbria, LA6 2HP
☎ (01524) 272221 ⊕ klbrewery.com

⊛Kirkby Lonsdale is a family-run business established in 2009 on a six-barrel plant. It has expanded brewing capacity with the installation of a 24-barrel plant at Old Station Yard and consolidated all its brewing to one site. ‼ ♦ GF ✦

Crafty Mild (ABV 3.6%) MILD

A typical mild with powerful malty aromas and some caramel, which follows through in the taste and finish.
Tiffin Gold (ABV 3.6%) BLOND
A full-flavoured, grapefruit, hoppy and bitter beer with a dry finish.
Stanley's (ABV 3.8%) PALE
Hops dominate this sweet and fruity, well-balanced beer.
Ruskin's (ABV 3.9%) PALE
A bitter with aromas of fruit and malt. Hop flavours are balanced with fruity sweetness and a sustained bittersweet finish.
Singletrack (ABV 4%) GOLD
Crisp citrus hops predominate in a well-balanced beer with a pleasant bitter finish.
Pennine Ambler (ABV 4.1%) BITTER
Radical (ABV 4.2%) RED
Malty beer with a caramel sweetness that is balanced by a bitter finish.
1822 (ABV 4.3%) BITTER
Monumental (ABV 4.5%) BLOND
Distinctly hoppy, a fruity, sweet, pale-coloured, full-bodied bitter beer.
Devil's Bridge IPA (ABV 5.2%) PALE
Jubilee (ABV 5.5%) STOUT
Rich, well-balanced stout with dark chocolate and roast coffee aromas, increasing bitterness with strong roast aftertaste

Kirkstall SIBA

100 Kirkstall Road, Leeds, LS3 1HJ
☎ (0113) 898 0280

Second site: Midland Mills, Station Road, Cross Hills, BD20 7DT ⊕ kirkstallbrewery.com

⊛Established in 2011, a few yards from the original Kirkstall Brewery beside the Leeds-Liverpool canal. In 2017 it moved to a new state-of-the-art brewery incorporating a 60-barrel plant, malting unit and canning line. Nearby Kirkstall Abbey and lost local industries are the inspiration for beer names. A secondary site, the former Naylor's brewery in Cross Hills, was purchased and began operation in 2022. In 2023 Kirkstall began brewing the former Leeds Brewery beers. The Kirkstall Bridge Inn is the brewery tap. ‼ ♦ ✦

Bitter (ABV 3.6%) BITTER
Pale Ale (ABV 4%) GOLD
A refreshing, golden-coloured bitter beer with citric hop flavours, zesty bitterness especially in the finish.
Three Swords (ABV 4.5%) GOLD
Good quantities of hops and juicy fruit define this yellow beer, a bitter taste and a tenacious pithy bitter finish.
Dissolution IPA (ABV 5%) PALE
Hops define this gold beer from the massive aroma, through the orange and fruity taste, finishing with yet more hops.
Black Band Porter (ABV 5.5%) PORTER
Dark smooth and rich with roasty smokiness, dried fruit and soft caramel balance the bitterness.

Brewed under the Leeds Brewery brand name:
Pale (ABV 3.8%) PALE
Yorkshire Gold (ABV 4%) GOLD
Best (ABV 4.3%) BITTER
Midnight Bell (ABV 4.8%) MILD

Kissingate

Pole Barn, Church Lane Farm Estate, Church Lane, Lower Beeding, West Sussex, RH13 6LU
☎ (01403) 891335

Office: 2 Drury Close, Maidenbower, Crawley
⊕ kissingate.co.uk

⊠ Kissingate Brewery was founded in 2010 by husband-and-wife team Gary and Bunny Lucas. Current production capacity is eight barrels. The brewery building is a converted barn set in a wooded valley near the village of Mannings Heath. It has a taproom and minstrels gallery. The brewery is available to hire for private events. ‼️ ☞ ◆ LIVE V ✦

Storyteller (ABV 3.5%) GOLD
Sussex (ABV 4%) BITTER
Black Cherry Mild (ABV 4.2%) SPECIALITY
Moon (ABV 4.5%) BITTER
Old Tale Porter (ABV 4.5%) PORTER
Chocolate & Vanilla Oatmeal Stout (ABV 4.8%) SPECIALITY
Chennai (ABV 5%) BITTER
Nooksack (ABV 5%) GOLD
Pernickety Pale (ABV 5%) BITTER
Smelter's Stout (ABV 5.1%) STOUT
Powder Blue (ABV 5.5%) PORTER
Stout Extreme Jamaica (ABV 6%) STOUT
Six Crows (ABV 6.6%) STOUT
Blackeyed Susan (ABV 7%) STRONG
Murder of Crows (ABV 10%) STOUT

Knight Life

27 Feversham Avenue, Queenspark, Bournemouth, Dorset, BH8 9NH ☎ 07722 564444
⊕ knightlifebrewing.com

Established in 2018, Knight Life has a three-barrel system, with six three-barrel fermenters. Canning machine is in-house. It now has its own tap house, with 12 lines in the heart of busy Ashley Cross, in Poole.

Knockout

Unit 10, Alanbrooke Park, Alexander Road, Belfast, BT6 9HB

Founded in 2009 by Joseph McMullan, Knockout produces a range of bottle-conditioned beers. Each brew is usually in small 900-litre batches. LIVE

Knoydart

St. Agatha's Chapel & Manse, Inverie, Knoydart, PH41 4PL
☎ (01687) 462372 ⊕ knoydartbrewery.co.uk

Knoydart is one of the most remote breweries on mainland Britain. There are no road links so access is by ferry, or on foot over mountain passes. Beers are brewed in part of an old chapel using a 60-litre electric brewery and a five-barrel plant with four fermenters.

Krafty Braumeister SIBA

Unit 4a, Eastlands Industrial Estate, Leiston, Suffolk, IP16 4LL ☎ 07508 435893 ⊕ kraftybraumeister.co.uk

Krafty Braumeister was established in 2018 and produces historic German beer styles, matured naturally in bottles and kegs.

LabRat

Office: 33 Bernham Avenue, Stonehaven, AB39 2WD
☎ 07542 072774

Commercial nanobrewer Peter Mackenzie started brewing in 2019, producing beers based on international styles.

Lacada SIBA

7a Victoria Street, Portrush, BT56 8DL

☎ (028) 7082 5684 ⊕ lacadabrewery.com

Lacada is a co-operative brewery founded in 2015. It produces a wide variety of styles. It is situated on the scenic north coast of Northern Ireland, and each beer is named after a feature of the coast line (along with a picture of the feature on the cans and bottles). **V**

Lacons SIBA

Falcon Brewery, Main Cross Road, Great Yarmouth, Norfolk, NR30 3NZ
☎ (01493) 850578

Office: Cooke Road, Lowestoft, NR33 7NA
⊕ lacons.co.uk

⊠ Lacons Brewery has a rich history dating back to 1760. In the 1960s it was acquired by a giant metropolitan brewer and reclaimed independence in 2013. To this day it brews with original Lacons yeast, frozen at the National Yeast Bank for almost 50 years, endowing its beer with centuries of brewing heritage. ‼️ ☞ ◆ LIVE

Norfolk Gem (ABV 3.6%)
Smooth, malty brew with sweetness and a fruity mix of orange and kiwi. Well-balanced with a long, mellow finish.

Encore (ABV 3.8%) BITTER
A solid hop backbone with strong citrus support. Sweetness subsides as a crisp dryness emerges in the long, strong finale.

Falcon Ale (ABV 4.2%) BITTER
Complex, with malt, caramel, hop and plum vying for supremacy. Both smooth and grainy with a well-rounded, bittersweet finale.

Legacy (ABV 4.4%) GOLD
Grapefruit and lemon nose and first taste where a crisp bitterness is also encountered. Some malt in a bitter finish.

Audit (ABV 8%) BARLEY
Honey, orange marmalade and maltiness define this full-bodied ale. Damson, toffee and a refreshing bitterness sharpens the palate.

Lacuna

Unit 19, Kernick Industrial Estate, Penryn, TR10 9EP
⊕ lacunabrewing.com

Owners Tristan and Ben's ethos for Lacuna Brewing is simple and sustainable, being committed to reaching zero carbon brewing as soon as possible. Three canned beers are available. Its taproom is open every Saturday. No real ale. ✦

Lady Luck

🍺 Little Angel, 18 Flowergate, Whitby, YO21 3BA
☎ (01947) 820475 ☎ 07920 282506

⊛Lady Luck is a 0.5-barrel brewery situated at the back of the Little Angel, Whitby. Brewing began in 2018 and takes place four times a week. In addition to the core range, a wide variety of other beers are produced in small batches, both cask and in cans. Beers are distributed across North Yorkshire as well as at beer festivals. ◆

Laine @ Ram

🍺 Ram, 68 Wandsworth High Street, Wandsworth, London, SW18 4LB
☎ (0208) 871 9752 ⊕ theraminnsw18.co.uk

Laine Pub Company, the new owner of the Ram, revived the former SlyBeast brewery in 2023 and it was used by the Coalition Brewery. This ceased in early 2024 and the kit has remained unused since then. No real ale.

Laine

🍺 North Laine Bar & Brewhouse, 27 Gloucester Place, Brighton, East Sussex, BN1 4AA
☎ (01273) 683666

Second site: Adversane, West Sussex, RH14
⊕ laine.co.uk

⊗ Laine launched its first brewery in 2012, in Brighton, using a five-barrel plant based within the North Laine pub. The brewing equipment and process can be viewed from the bar. A number of sister breweries in pubs in Acton, Hackney and Battersea in London were established between 2013 and 2015 but have since been closed. In 2016 a 45-barrel brewing hub was established in Adversane near Billingshurst in order to supply its sister company's growing pub estate. In 2022 Laine Brew Co acquired Redchurch Brewery in Harlow. A sister brewery in Wandsworth opened in 2023, but brewing is currently suspended at that site. ‼🍺

Lakedown SIBA

Lakedown Farm, Swife Lane, Burwash, East Sussex, TN21 8UX
☎ (01435) 685001 ⊕ lakedownbrewing.com

Lakedown Brewing Co was established in 2020. Beers are available in can, bottle, keg and cask. 🍺GFV❤

Off the Hook (ABV 3.8%) PALE
Sussex Pale (ABV 4.2%) PALE
Kicking Donkey (ABV 4.4%) BITTER
American Red (ABV 4.8%) RED
IPA (ABV 5%) PALE

Lakes SIBA

Mintsfeet Road South, Kendal, Cumbria, LA9 6ND
☎ (01539) 324005 ⊕ lakesbrewco.com

Brewery opened in 2021 by former employees of Hawkshead brewery. ❤

Pale Ale (ABV 3.5%) GOLD
A powerful aroma of citrus hops follows through to bitterness which builds upon drinking. There is balancing sweetness and fruit.

LAMB

Queens Arms, Litton, North Yorkshire, BD23 5QJ
☎ 07900 013245 ⊕ lambbrewing.com

⊕The LAMB Brewing Company brews on a 600-litre plant behind the Queen's Arms in Litton. Independently-owned, the beer is served in the pub, as well as a few other outlets in the local area. Cask beers are available. ❤

X Mild (ABV 3.2%) MILD
Bitter (ABV 3.7%) BITTER
Brown bitter with malt, hops in the aroma. Fruit and subtle nuttiness in the taste, lead to a bitter finish.
Pale (ABV 3.9%) GOLD
Golden pale ale. Citrus hops dominate with a subtle grassiness and light bitter finish.

Lancaster SIBA

Lancaster Leisure Park, Wyresdale Road, Lancaster, LA1 3LA
☎ (01524) 848537 ⊕ lancasterbrewery.co.uk

⊕Lancaster began brewing in 2005. The brewery moved to new premises in 2010 and installed a larger 60-barrel brewing plant. ‼🍺❤

Junction 34 (ABV 3.4%) PALE
Amber (ABV 3.6%) BITTER
Amber malt flavours lead to an increasingly astringent bitter finish.
Blonde (ABV 4%) BLOND
Session blonde ale, sweet biscuit malt and citrus hop aroma. Gentle malt and lemon hop flavour, bitter dry astringent finish.
IPA (ABV 4.2%) BLOND
Black (ABV 4.5%) STOUT
Dark ruby ale with hoppy roast bitterness, coffee and hint of caramel. Dry malt bitterness in the mouth.
Red (ABV 4.8%) RED
A characterful beer with plenty of fruits, roast malt and hops, well-balanced with a lasting finish.

Langdale

Cross Houses Farm, Docker, Cumbria, LA8 0DE
☎ 07876 838051 ⊕ langdalebrewing.co.uk

⊕Langdale Brewing was formed in 2018 by Steve Mitchell, formerly of Eden Brewery, and Paul Fry of the Britannia Inn, Elterwater. The brewery produces a range of cask ales using water harvested from a Langdale spring.

Bowfell Bitter (ABV 3.5%) BITTER
Elterwater Gold (ABV 3.8%) GOLD
Pikes Pale (ABV 3.9%) PALE
Bowfell Blonde (ABV 4.2%) BLOND
Bowfell Amber (ABV 4.3%) BITTER
Weiss Ghyll (ABV 4.5%) SPECIALITY

Langham SIBA

Old Granary, Langham Lane, Lodsworth, West Sussex, GU28 9BU
☎ (01798) 860861 ⊕ langhambrewery.co.uk

⊗ Langham Brewery was established in 2006 in an 18th century granary barn and is set in the heart of West Sussex with fine views of the rolling South Downs. It is owned by Lesley Foulkes and James Berrow who brew and run the business. The brewery is a 10-barrel, steam-heated plant and more than 200 outlets are supplied. ‼🍺❤V

Session Bitter (ABV 3.5%) BITTER
Saison (ABV 3.9%) SPECIALITY
Hip Hop (ABV 4%) GOLD
Golden ale packed full of hops. Crisp bitterness with hint of sweetness leading to an enticing dry and sharp finish.
Triple XXX (ABV 4.4%) MILD
Best (ABV 4.5%) BITTER
Arapaho (ABV 4.9%) PALE
Langham Special Draught/ LSD (ABV 5.2%) BITTER

Langton SIBA

Grange Farm, Welham Road, Thorpe Langton, Leicestershire, LE16 7TU
☎ (01858) 540116 ☎ 07840 532826
⊕ langtonbrewery.co.uk

Established in 1999 in outbuildings behind the Bell Inn, East Langton, the brewery relocated in 2005 to a converted barn at Thorpe Langton, where a four-barrel plant was installed. Further expansion in 2010 and 2016 significantly increased capacity. ‼❤LIVE

Rainbow Bridge (ABV 3.8%) GOLD
Caudle Bitter (ABV 3.9%) BITTER

Copper-coloured session bitter that is close to pale ale in style. Flavours are relatively well-balanced throughout with hops slightly to the fore.

Union Wharf (ABV 4%) BITTER
Inclined Plane Bitter (ABV 4.2%) BLOND
Thomas Lift (ABV 4.4%) BITTER
Bullseye (ABV 4.8%) STOUT

Larkins SIBA

Larkins Farm, Hampkins Hill Road, Chiddingstone, Kent, TN8 7BB
☎ (01892) 870328 ⊕ larkinsbrewery.co.uk

⊠ Larkins brewery was founded by the Dockerty family in Rusthall in Kent in 1986, on the site of the original Royal Tunbridge Wells Brewery. In 1988 the brewery relocated to Larkins Farm in Chiddingstone. All beers include hops grown on a four-acre site near Larkins Farm and are brewed with its own yeast strain. The brewery delivers direct to around 40-50 pubs and restaurants within a 20-mile radius. !!♦

Traditional Ale (ABV 3.4%) BITTER
Pale (ABV 4.2%) PALE
Best (ABV 4.4%) BITTER
Full-bodied, slightly fruity and unusually bitter for its gravity.
Porter (ABV 5.4%) PORTER
Potent black winter beer. An explosion of roasted malt, bitter and fruity flavours leaves a bittersweet aftertaste.

Larrikin

🍺 Urchin, 15-17 Belfast Street, Hove, West Sussex, BN3 3YS
☎ (01273) 241881 ✉ hello@urchinpub.co.uk

Following two years of homebrewing research, commercial brewing began in 2018 in the Urchin, Hove – a shellfish and craft beer pub. Beer is only available in the pub, mainly in keg, with cask-conditioned beer available infrequently.

Law

Unit 17, Mid Wynd, Dundee, DD1 4JG ☎ 07893 538277 ⊕ lawbrewing.co

Law was established in 2016 and is named after Dundee's most distinctive landmark; the volcano-like slopes of the Law.

Leadmill

Unit 3, Heanor Small Business Centre, Adams Close, Heanor, Derbyshire, DE75 7SW ☎ 07971 189915
✉ leadmill@fsmail.net

⊠ Set up in Selston in 1999, Leadmill moved to Denby in 2001 and again in 2010 to Heanor. A sister brewery to Bottle Brook (qv), the brewery tap is at the Old Oak, Horsley Woodhouse. ♦

Langley Best (ABV 3.6%) BITTER
Mash Tun Bitter (ABV 3.6%) BITTER
Old Oak Bitter (ABV 3.7%) BITTER
Dream Weaver (ABV 4.3%) GOLD
Linebacker (ABV 4.6%) BLOND
B52 (ABV 5.2%) BITTER
American Girl (ABV 5.6%) IPA
Rajah Brooke (ABV 5.6%) BLOND
Mellow Yellow (ABV 5.7%) BITTER
Slumdog (ABV 5.9%) GOLD

Leatherbritches

Brewery Yard, Tap House, Annwell Lane, Smisby, Leicestershire, LE65 2TA ☎ 07976 279253
⊕ leatherbritches.co.uk

☺The brewery, founded in 1993 in Fenny Bentley, has relocated and expanded over the years. It moved to its current address in 2011, where it effectively took over the existing Tap House Brewery (established 2010) but continued to brew the latter's beers. Since 2015, however, Tap House beers have become rebadged Leatherbritches products. !!♦LIVE

Goldings (ABV 3.6%) BITTER
Bounder (ABV 3.8%) GOLD
Lemongrass & Ginger (ABV 3.8%) SPECIALITY
Ashbourne Ale (ABV 4%) PALE
Cad (ABV 4%) BITTER
Dr Johnson (ABV 4%) BITTER
Scoundrel (ABV 4.1%) PORTER
Mad Ruby (ABV 4.4%) BITTER
Raspberry Belter (ABV 4.4%) SPECIALITY
Ashbourne IPA (ABV 4.7%) PALE
Hairy Helmet (ABV 4.7%) GOLD
Spitting Feathers (ABV 4.8%) BITTER
Bespoke (ABV 5%) BITTER
Game Over (ABV 5%) BITTER
Porter (ABV 5.5%) PORTER
Scary Hairy Export (ABV 7.2%) IPA

Ledbury SIBA

Gazerdine House, Hereford Road, Ledbury, Herefordshire, HR8 2PZ
☎ (01531) 671184 ☎ 07957 428070
⊕ ledburyrealales.co.uk

☺Established in 2012, Ledbury Real Ales uses hops grown in Herefordshire and Worcestershire with other materials sourced locally, where possible. The beers are sold mainly within a 15-mile radius of the brewery. !!♦

Bitter (ABV 3.8%) BITTER
Dark (ABV 3.9%) MILD
Gold (ABV 4%) GOLD
Ledbury Pale Ale (ABV 4%) PALE

Leeds

See Kirkstall

JW Lees IFBB

Greengate Brewery, Middleton Junction, Manchester, M24 2AX
☎ (0161) 643 2487 ⊕ jwlees.co.uk

☺Family-owned since its foundation by John Lees in 1828, the brewery has a tied estate of around 150 pubs, mostly in North Manchester, Cheshire, Lancashire and North Wales. The vast majority serve cask beer. The current Brewing Director is a family member. An in-house microbrewery, Boilerhouse, also produces a wide range of cask beers. !!♦

Dark (ABV 3.5%) MILD
A malt and caramel aroma. A creamy mouthfeel with malt, caramel and fruit flavours and a malty finish.
Manchester Pale Ale (ABV 3.7%) PALE
Some fruity aromas. A moderately-hopped beer with gentle bitterness, which dominates the lasting dry finish.
Bitter (ABV 4%) BITTER
Earthy hops and biscuit malt aroma. Bittersweet and biscuit malt flavours, drying throughout to the finish.
Dragon's Fire (ABV 4%) BITTER
Stout (ABV 4.2%) STOUT

Founder's (ABV 4.5%) BITTER
Moonraker (ABV 6.5%) STRONG
Strong malty, fruity toffee aromas. Sweet with burnt sugars and a rising dry roast bitter finish.

Brewed under the Boilerhouse brand name:
Craft Pale (ABV 4.2%) PALE

Left Bank SIBA

Ty Newydd Farm, Llangorse, LD3 7UA ☎ 07815 849523 ⊕ leftbankbrewery.co.uk

After a spell brewing in various London locations, brewing has now relocated to what are the former premises of the Lithic brewery. Production is in bottle and cask form.

Hopla (ABV 4.2%) BITTER
Ty Coch (ABV 4.2%) RED

Left Handed Giant

Unit 3, Wadehurst Industrial Estate, St Philips Road, St Philips, Bristol, BS2 0JE

Second Site: Compressor Building, Hawkins Lane, Finzels Reach, Bristol, BS1 6EU
⊕ lefthandedgiant.com

Left Handed Giant started in 2015 as a cuckoo brewery using spare capacity at other local breweries. The St Philips brewery and taproom opened in 2017. Two years later the brewpub in Bristol city centre opened. The St Philips brewery site is mainly responsible for the new beers and collaborations (released on a regular basis). LHG own Small Bar in King Street, Bristol (brewing began here in 2014). Typically these are single-batch brews. A small amount of the output goes into cask. !!♦V✦

Legitimate Industries

10 Weaver Street, Leeds, West Yorkshire, LS4 2AU
⊕ legitimateworldwide.com

Founded in 2016, the 30-barrel plant mainly brews keg beer for the company's Red's True Barbecue restaurant chain. Under new ownership, a wider portfolio of non-permanent beers are being produced, with canned output substantially increasing too, aided by the installation of a 200-litre pilot kit. A limited amount of cask beer is sometimes available in the local free-trade.

Leigh on Sea SIBA

35 Progress Road, Leigh-on-Sea, Essex, SS9 5PR
☎ (01702) 817255 ⊕ leighonseabrewery.co.uk

⊠ Established in 2017 to produce vegan-friendly beer, which is unfiltered, unpasteurised and unfined (except for Renown). Initially brewing on a one-barrel kit, it rapidly progressed to a 10-barrel plant. Many of the names of the beers are based on Leigh's maritime heritage, which is also reflected in the branding, by a local artist and graphic designer. The brewery has a taproom, and it has now opened a pub, Legra Tap & Kitchen. !!ᴇ♦V✦

Bawley Bitter (ABV 3.4%) BITTER
Legra Pale (ABV 3.8%) PALE
Kursaal Gold (ABV 3.9%) GOLD
Six Little Ships (ABV 4.2%) BITTER
Beach Hut Brew (ABV 4.5%) PALE
Boatyard IPA (ABV 5%) PALE
Cockle Row Spit (ABV 5.6%) IPA

Leighton Buzzard SIBA

Unit 23, Harmill Industrial Estate, Grovebury Road, Leighton Buzzard, Bedfordshire, LU7 4FF
☎ (01525) 839153 ☎ 07538 903753
⊕ leightonbuzzardbrewing.co.uk

The first brewery to operate in Leighton Buzzard for more than 100 years. Established in 2014, the brewery changed hands in 2019. !!ᴇ♦

Leighton Gold (ABV 3.6%) GOLD
Golden Buzzard (ABV 4.1%) GOLD
Bavarian Dragon (ABV 4.2%) GOLD
Best Buzzard (ABV 4.3%) BITTER
Restoration Ale (ABV 4.6%) BITTER

Leila Cottage

See 8 Sail

Leith Hill

🏠 c/o Plough Inn, Coldharbour Lane, Coldharbour, Surrey, RH5 6HD
☎ (01306) 711793 ⊕ ploughinn.com

⊠ Leith Hill was established in 1996 at the Plough Inn and was moved to converted storerooms at the rear in 2001, increasing capacity to 2.5 barrels in 2005. New owners took over in 2016. !!LIVE V

Lenton Lane

Unit 5G, The Midway, Lenton Industrial Estate, Nottingham, NG7 2TS
☎ (0333) 003 5008 ⊕ lentonlane.co.uk

⊠ Lenton Lane began brewing in 2014 under the name Frontier, after taking over the brewing plant at the Flower Pot pub, Derby. Lenton Lane changed its name in 2016 and relocated to a purpose-built brewery in Nottingham using a 10-barrel plant. The brewery produces a range of Single Malt & Single Hop beers (SM&SH), along with various other regular beers including award-winning 200 Not Out. ᴇ♦LIVE V

Newbird (ABV 3.7%) PALE
Pale Moonlight (ABV 3.7%) PALE
Pale ale with hints of lemon, and lingering bitterness.
36 North (ABV 3.9%) BITTER
A malty, well-balanced session bitter.
Gold Rush (ABV 4.2%) GOLD
Outpost (ABV 4.5%) BITTER
Cloudburst (ABV 4.6%) PALE
Escape (ABV 5%) GOLD
Twist & Stout (ABV 5%) STOUT
A strong, dry stout with hints of liquorice and coffee.
200 Not Out (ABV 6%) IPA
A strong IPA with hop punch, tempered with a little sweetness.

Lerwick SIBA

Staneyhill, North Road, Lerwick, Shetland, ZE1 0NA
☎ (01595) 694552 ☎ 07738 948336
⊕ lerwickbrewery.co.uk

Lerwick Brewery was established in 2011 using a 12-barrel plant and sits at the very edge of the North Atlantic. Originally only brewing keg beer, a cask-conditioned range was launched in 2015. ᴇ♦V✦

Skipper's Ticket (ABV 4%) BITTER
Azure (ABV 4.3%) GOLD
Refreshing, grapefruity/peachy, hoppy, golden bitter.
Lerwick IPA (ABV 5%) PALE

Grapefruity, hoppy bitter with a slight biscuit background.
Tushkar (ABV 5.5%) STOUT
Very good dark brown roasted malty stout with chocolate, coffee and liquorice.

Leviathan

Unit 4, 17 Reddicap Trading Estate, Sutton Coldfield, West Midlands, B75 7BU ☎ 07983 256979
⊕ leviathanbrewing.co.uk

Established in 2018 by Chris Hodgetts, Leviathan is a microbrewer of unique, small-batch craft beers. There is now a taproom (Thursday-Sunday). Opening times on website/ Facebook. It normally has at least twelve beers (including guests), mostly keg, but some cask available, as is cider. There are plans to start bottling again and home deliveries are available (see website). ☎◆

Libatory

Altrincham ☎ 07957 227540

Office: Unit 3, Peel House, 30 The Downs, Altrincham, WA14 2PX ⊕ libatory.co.uk

A nanobrewery, home-based, started brewing in early 2022. A 150-litre plant is used. Beer is mostly available in cans, but the brewery can do cask or keg by request. LIVE V

Liberation

Tregar House, Longueville Road, St Saviour, Jersey, JE2 7WF
☎ (01534) 764089 ☎ 07911 744568
⊕ liberationgroup.com

⊠ The Liberation Brewery (owned by the Liberation Group, which also owns Butcombe Brewery) is located at Longueville, just outside St Helier. Its multi-award-winning flagship beer Liberation Ale can be found in many of the Group's freehold and partner pubs in the Channel Islands (39 in Jersey, 17 in Guernsey and three in Alderney) and 60 in the UK. !!☎◆

Ale (ABV 4%) GOLD
Herm Gold (ABV 4.2%) GOLD
IPA (ABV 4.8%) PALE

Libertalia (NEW)

Arch 142, Tilbury Road, Leyton, London, E10 6RE
☎ 07706 946372 ✉ info@libertaliabrewing.co.uk

During 2023, Libertalia took on the arch formerly used by Gravilty Well, installing its own kit with keg beers appearing by the end of the year, and cask in early 2024. The owners have a good brewing pedigree having met when working in a Greek brewpub and most recently at 3 Locks in Camden Town. Its taproom is open Friday to Sunday, serving keg beers with a cask weekend once a month. ◆

Lincoln Green SIBA

Unit 5, Enterprise Park, Wigwam Lane, Hucknall, Nottingham, NG15 7SZ
☎ (0115) 963 4233 ☎ 07748 111457
⊕ lincolngreenbrewing.co.uk

⊛Anthony Hughes established the Lincoln Green Brewing Company in 2012 using a 10-barrel plant. The brewery takes its name from the colour of dyed woollen cloth associated with the legend of Robin Hood. Beers are named with a respectful nod towards the Nottinghamshire legend. A range of craft beers is available in KeyKeg. Bottled beers are available online

and in supermarkets, including limited edition, special bottle-aged, bottle-conditioned beers. ☎◆LIVE

Marion (ABV 3.8%) PALE
Subtly-hopped golden ale with citrus aroma and a dry, bitter finish.
Archer (ABV 4%) PALE
Citrus golden ale with American hops and a moderately bitter finish.
Hood (ABV 4.2%) BITTER
Tawny-coloured ale with balanced hops and bitterness.
Bowman (ABV 4.3%) BITTER
Fountain Dale (ABV 4.3%) BLOND
Little John (ABV 4.3%) BITTER
Malty best bitter, well-balanced with hops and bitterness throughout.
Arrow (ABV 4.5%) PALE
Shot Firer (ABV 4.5%) STOUT
Tuck (ABV 4.7%) PORTER
Full-bodied and rich dark ale with roast and malt flavours throughout.
Scarlett (ABV 4.8%) BITTER
Gin And Beer It (ABV 5%) SPECIALITY
Longbow (ABV 5%) GOLD
A malty golden ale with caramel and citrus aroma and a strong citrus hop finish.
Quarterstaff (ABV 5%) STOUT
Black in colour with roasty aromas and taste, leading to a dry coffee and bitter finish.
Shackler (ABV 5%) PALE
Buttermuch (ABV 5.5%) STOUT
Dark brown beer with strong butterscotch caramel taste throughout and a gentle, bitter finish.
Sheriff (ABV 5.5%) IPA
Golden, full-bodied IPA, citrus hop taste and bitterness balanced throughout.

Lincolnshire Craft

Race Lane, Melton Ross, DN38 6AA
☎ (01652) 680001 ⊕ lincolnshirecraftbeers.com

Lincolnshire Craft Beers is the company formed by Mark Smith who bought the Tom Wood Brewery in 2017. It continues to brew the Tom Wood range of beers on the 60-barrel Melton Ross plant. ◆

Best Bitter (ABV 3.7%) BITTER
A good citrus, passion fruit hop dominates the nose and taste, with background malt. A lingering hoppy and bitter finish.
Melton Mild (ABV 3.7%) MILD
Lincoln Gold (ABV 4%) GOLD
Bomber County (ABV 4.8%) BITTER
An earthy malt aroma but with a complex underlying mix of coffee, hops, caramel and apple fruit. The beer starts bitter and intensifies to the end.

Linear

Bingham, Nottinghamshire, NG13 8EU ⊕ linear.beer

Small-scale, 50-litre brewery, started production in 2016 and is located at the owner's home. Primarily produces a range of bottle-conditioned beers, on occasion it supplies casks for selected local stockists. Also collaborates with other nanobreweries for local beer festivals and events. LIVE

Lines

⧉ 37a Bridge Street, Usk, NP15 1BQ
⊕ linesbrewco.com

Established in 2020, Lines is located to the centre of Usk and is a brewpub on the High Street. The brewery, led by the former Celt Experience head brewer, occupies the ground floor through which you pass to access the rustic upper taproom serving beer and pizza. No Real Ale.

Linfit

Moor End Farm, South Crosland, Huddersfield, HD4 7BZ ☎ 07850 621516

😊The brewery has relocated from the Sair Inn to new premises. It is using the same equipment to brew the original Linfit beer recipes.

Bitter (ABV 3.7%) BITTER
A refreshing session beer. A dry-hopped aroma leads to a clean-tasting, hoppy bitterness, then a long, bitter finish with a hint of malt.
Gold Medal (ABV 4.2%) GOLD
Janet Street Porter (ABV 4.2%) PORTER
Special (ABV 4.3%) BITTER
Dry-hopping provides the aroma for this rich and mellow bitter, which has a very soft profile and character: it fills the mouth with texture rather than taste. Clean, rounded finish.
Autumn Gold (ABV 4.7%) GOLD
Straw-coloured best bitter with hop and fruit aromas, then the bittersweetness of autumn fruit in the taste and the finish.
English Guineas Stout (ABV 4.7%) STOUT
Old Eli (ABV 5.3%) BITTER

Liquid Light SIBA

Unit 9, Robin Hood Industrial Estate, Alfred Street South, Nottingham, NG3 1GE
⊕ liquidlightbrewco.com

A strong ethos of community and inclusiveness at its core, with beers influenced by rock and psychedelic music. Moving to its own premises in 2021, with a taproom (open weekends) featuring many visual and music-oriented events throughout the year. A popular inclusion at tap takeovers and craft beer festivals across the country. Vegan food, hot and cold, available all year round. ♦V⥊

Day Tripper (ABV 4.3%) PALE
A hazy session pale, fruity and hoppy

Lithic

See Cold Black Label

Little Brewing SIBA

Unit 23, Northedge Business Park, Alfreton Road, Derby, DE21 4BN
☎ (01332) 987100 ⊕ littlebrewing.co.uk

Established in 2015 as Littleover Brewery, in 2020 it changed hands and in 2022 rebranded as Little Brewing Company. It brews three days a week on a ten-barrel plant. It supplies direct to local outlets and nationally through specialist wholesalers. It recently moved to a bigger purpose-built brewing facility with its own large taproom. ☒♦GFV⥊

Loop (ABV 3.7%) PALE
King George's Bitter (ABV 4%) BITTER
Epiphany Pale Ale (ABV 4.1%) PALE
The Panther Oatmeal Stout (ABV 4.2%) STOUT
Hush (ABV 4.4%) PALE
Taj Session IPA (ABV 4.6%) PALE
Rambler (ABV 5.6%) IPA

Contract brewed for Boot Beer Ltd:
Clod Hopper (ABV 3.9%) GOLD
Bitter (ABV 4.3%) BITTER

Little Big SIBA

23 St George's Esplanade, St Peter Port, Guernsey, GY1 2BG
☎ (01481) 728149 ⊕ littlebigbrewco.com

😊Little Big Brew Co was founded in 2020. ‼☒♦V⥊

Alan (ABV 4%) PALE
Betty (ABV 4%) RED

Little Big Dog

Barrow-Upon-Humber, Lincolnshire, DN19 7SH
⊕ littlebigdogbeer.co.uk

Commercial home-based brewery, first brewed in 2020. Beers are available in cask, keg and can.

Pantiles (ABV 3.8%) BITTER
Make it Real Pale (ABV 4.2%) GOLD
Watchmaker (ABV 4.2%) PALE
Fog on the Humber (ABV 4.8%) GOLD

Little Black Dog

Carlton Brewery, Duddings Farm, Carlton, North Yorkshire, DN14 9LU ☎ 07495 026173
⊕ littleblackdogbeer.com

Established in 2015, Little Black Dog is a small batch, family-run brewery. All beer is unfined, unpasteurised and unfiltered. The brewery tap is the Doghouse, Selby. ☒♦V

Yorkshire Bitter (ABV 3.8%) BITTER
Big Red American Amber (ABV 4.5%)
Oatmeal Stout (ABV 4.5%) STOUT

Little Creatures

See Babel

Little Critters SIBA

80 Parkwood Road, Sheffield, South Yorkshire, S3 8AG
☎ (0114) 276 3171

Office: Horizon House, 2 Whiting Street, Sheffield, S8 9QR ⊕ littlecrittersbrewery.com

A small batch, family-owned microbrewery. It opened in 2016, and operates on a 10-barrel brewing plant. Pubs are supplied throughout Yorkshire, the East Midlands and nationally. Brewery improvements took place in 2020 and the core range expanded. It also supplies beer in cans through a number of bottle shops and via its online shop. ♦LIVE

Little Hopper (ABV 3.6%) GOLD
Blonde Bear (ABV 4.2%) BLOND
Shire Horse (ABV 4.3%) BITTER
Raspberry Blonde (ABV 4.5%) BLOND
Sleepy Badger (ABV 4.5%) SPECIALITY
Malty Python (ABV 4.8%) BITTER
White Wolf (ABV 5%) PALE
Nutty Ambassador (ABV 6%) STOUT

Little Earth Project

Mill Green, Edwardstone, Sudbury, Suffolk, CO10 5PX
☎ (01787) 211118 ⊕ littleearthproject.com

Mill Green Brewery started in 2008, becoming Little Earth Project in 2016. Built on an old stable site, using local wood, reclaimed bricks, sheep wool and lime plaster. It has its own borehole, brewing liquor is heated using bio and solar power, and its 3,000-litre storage is heated by solar panels, and a wood boiler. It creates innovative beers and sours. Most use local ingredients, and age in old wine barrels. About half is KeyKeg, the rest is bottled, with some cask available.

Little Eaton

See Black Hole

Little Goat

Ynysmeudwy, Pontardawe, SA8 4PP ☎ 07590 520457 ⊕ littlegoatbrewery.co.uk

A 2.5-barrel brewery in an outbuilding of owner's private houise. The main output goes into bottles but as pub trade picks up, there will be greater concentration on the range of cask beers. All beers are suitable for vegans (unfined and unfiltered). Brewery sets up stalls at local markets for sale of bottles. Distribution of beers is to local areas as wholesalers are not used. **V**

Siencyn (ABV 4%) RED
Scapegoat (ABV 4.3%) BITTER
Golden Goat (ABV 4.4%) GOLD
Jumping Jack (ABV 4.9%) BITTER
Yankee Doodle Nanny (ABV 6.5%) SPECIALITY
Satan's Little Helper (ABV 6.6%) STOUT

Little London

**Unit 6B, Ash Park Business Centre, Ash Lane, Little London, Hampshire, RG26 5FL
☎ (01256) 533044 ☎ 07785 225468
⊕ littlelondonbrewery.com**

⊠ Brewing began in 2015 using a six-barrel plant. Three fermentation vessels ensure a production capability of 60 firkins per week, with capacity for expansion.

Doreen's Dark (ABV 3.2%) MILD
Blacksmith's Gold (ABV 3.5%) GOLD
Red Boy (ABV 3.7%) BITTER
Hoppy Hilda (ABV 3.8%) GOLD
Luvly (ABV 3.9%) BITTER
Pryde (ABV 4.2%) BITTER
Ash Park Special (ABV 4.9%) BITTER

Little Martha

**23 Oxford Street, St Phillips, Bristol, BS2 0QT
⊕ littlemarthabrewing.co.uk**

This brewery is tucked under a railway arch close to Bristol Temple Meads Station. Brewing commenced in late 2021 prior to the official tap opening at the end of the year. Four core beers are brewed, along with a range of specials. ➽♦V◈

Little Mesters

**352 Meadowhead, Sheffield, S8 7UJ ☎ 07859 889547
⊕ littlemestersbrewing.co.uk**

Microbrewery and taproom established in 2020 producing beers in cask, keg and can. ◈

Little Monster

Office: Burton Warren, Burton Park Road, Petworth, West Sussex, GU28 0JS ⊕ littlemonsterbrew.com

Brewing began in 2018. Owner Brenden collaborates with other breweries to produce the beers.

Little Ox SIBA

Unit 6, Wroslyn Road Industrial Estate, Freeland, Oxfordshire, OX29 8HZ

☎ (01993) 881941 ☎ 07730 496525

**Office: 25 Castle Road, Wootton, OX20 1EQ
⊕ littleoxbrewery.co.uk**

Little Ox began production in 2016 and uses its 17-hectolitre (10 barrel) plant to produce beer in cask, keg and can. It offers a small core range, a larger range of seasonal and occasional beers, and also brews an experimental beer every month (which includes a barrel-aged project released at the end of the year). It supplies more than 50 pubs, restaurants and off-licences and offers free delivery to homes around Oxfordshire. All beer is gluten free and vegan. ➽♦GF V

Hufflepuff (ABV 3.8%) GOLD
Wipeout (ABV 4.2%) GOLD
Ox Blood (ABV 4.3%) RED
Yabba Dabba Doo (ABV 4.8%) BITTER

Little Valley

See Great Newsome

Live

Hudswell ⊠ livebrewco@gmail.com

Four-barrel microbrewery set up by the team behind the 2016 National Pub of the Year, the George & Dragon, Hudswell. It specialises in small-scale one-off brews utilising traditional techniques and locally-foraged ingredients. Brewing is currently suspended.

Liverpool Brewing

**39 Brasenose Road, Liverpool, L20 8HL
☎ (0151) 933 9660
⊕ liverpoolbrewingcompany.com**

⊕Liverpool Brewing Company was established in 2018. A 20-hectolitre Vince Johnson brewkit with a fermenting volume of 200-hectolitres is used with extensive cold storage capacity to produce a range of traditional and new-wave beers. In 2022 it opened two venues, one of which is its brewery taproom on Lime Street, Liverpool. ⏚➽

Little IPA (ABV 3.6%) PALE
Dark Mode (ABV 3.7%) MILD
Balanced, rewarding, nutty, lightly-hopped session dark mild with raisin undertones. Caramel and fruit aromas and sweetness in the finish.
Cascade (ABV 3.8%) GOLD
Honeyed flowery citrus hop aromas, dry bitter citrus hops flavours and a dry fruity bitter finish with some light pine.
Pale Ale (ABV 4%) BLOND
A pale golden beer with light fruity hop aromas, sweet bitter flavours and a light malty finish.
24 Carat Gold (ABV 4.1%) GOLD
Hoppy citrus fruity aromas, sweet fruity, slightly honeyed flavours and a dry fruity hop bitterness, which follows into the finish.
Bier Head (ABV 4.1%) BITTER
Light amber beer with malt/roast and hop aromas, bitter hop and roasted malt flavours and a peppery hop finish.
Syren's Call (ABV 4.2%) BITTER
Tropical Pale (ABV 4.2%) PALE
Pudding Lane (ABV 4.4%) SPECIALITY
Stout (ABV 4.7%) STOUT
Aromas of biscuity caramel, vanilla and light fruit. Vanilla flavours with bitter coffee on tasting and a lasting, fruity, dry bitter roast.
Shipwreck (ABV 6.5%) IPA

Fruity resiny hop aromas, some malt, big hop bitterness with fruity sweetness on tasting and lasting hop bitterness to finish.

Lizard

The Old Nuclear Bunker, Pednavounder, Coverack, Cornwall, TR12 6SE
☎ (01326) 281135 ⊕ lizardales.co.uk

⊠ Launched in 2004 in St Keverne, Lizard Ales is now based at former RAF Treleaver, a massive, disused nuclear bunker in the countryside near Coverack on the Lizard Peninsula. Specialising in bottle-conditioned ales, it mainly supplies local shops and pubs. !!LIVE

Llangollen

🛏 **Abbey Grange Hotel, Horseshoe Pass Road, Llantysilio, Llangollen, LL20 8DD**
☎ (01978) 861916 ⊕ llangollenbrewery.com

Brewing began in 2010 on a 2.5-barrel plant. The brewery was updated and upgraded in 2014 to a 10-barrel plant. !! ☗LIVE

Lleu SIBA

Penygroes Industrial Estate, Caernarfon, LL54 6DB
☎ (01286) 875910 ☎ 07840 910460
⊕ bragdylleu.cymru

⊗Brewing began in 2014 using a 1.25-barrel plant and was upgraded to six barrels in 2016 to meet demand. In 2022 it moved to larger premises. The four beers are named after Welsh folklore characters of the Mabinogi. !!☗

Blodeuwedd (ABV 3.6%) GOLD
Lleu (ABV 4%) BITTER
Gwydion (ABV 4.7%) BITTER
Bendigeidfran (ABV 5%) PALE

Llyn

1 Parc Eithyn, Ffordd Dewi Sant, Nefyn, Gwynedd, LL53 6EG
☎ (01758) 721981 ☎ 07792 050134
⊕ cwrwllyn.cymru

⊗Brewing began in 2011 in an old converted barn. In 2016 the brewing moved into a new, purpose-built, 15-barrel brewery that includes a brewery taproom and shop. It is based in the seaside town of Nefyn on the Llyn Peninsula, and the cask and keg beers and distributed throughout the North West of Wales. Bottled beer is distributed throughout Wales. !!☗◆

Y Brawd Houdini (ABV 3.5%) PALE
Brenin Enlli (ABV 4%) BITTER
Cwrw Glyndwr (ABV 4%) GOLD
Seithenyn (ABV 4.2%) GOLD
Porth Neigwl (ABV 4.5%) PALE

Loch Leven SIBA

The Muirs, Kinross, KY13 8AS
☎ (01577) 864881 ⊕ lochleven.beer

Based opposite the Green Hotel in Kinross, the brewery started production in 2017. Four cask-conditioned beers are produced and available throughout Tayside, with availability spreading westwards through Scotland's central belt. !!☗◆

Warrior Queen (ABV 3.8%) PALE
Shining Knight (ABV 4%) SPECIALITY
Outlaw King (ABV 5%) MILD

King Slayer (ABV 5.2%) OLD

Loch Lomond SIBA

Vale of Leven Industrial Estate, Unit 11, Block 2, Renton, G82 3PD
☎ (01389) 755698 ☎ 07891 920213
⊕ lochlomondbrewery.com

⊗Established in 2011 by Fiona and Euan MacEachern, Loch Lomond was the first brewery to be established in the area. Having reached brewing capacity at its original site in Alexandria, it moved to a new purpose-built, 35-hectolitre brewery in Renton in 2019. This site also houses a canning line and taproom. ☗◆LIVE◆

West Highland Way (ABV 3.7%) BITTER
A light ale with fruity flavours.
Bonnie & Blonde (ABV 4%) BITTER
Maris Otter and Caragold malts give a light, refreshing ale and a blend of hops produces a well-rounded citrus flavour.
Southern Summit (ABV 4%) BLOND
The palate is fresh and fruity, with hints of grapefruit and lemon which lead on to a crisp, light bitter finish.
Silkie Stout (ABV 5%) STOUT
Award-winning black stout with chocolate-orange spicy notes.

Loch Ness

See Cairngorm

Lock 81

c/o Wishful Drinking, 124 High Street, Rickmansworth, WD3 1AB ☎ 07768 320229
⊕ wishfuldrinking.co.uk

Named after the Batchworth lock on the Grand Union Canal at Rickmansworth. Name and beer recipes now owned by the owners of the Wishful Drinking bar in Rickmansworth and is currently nomad brewing canned and KeyKeg beers at various sites.

Loddon SIBA

Dunsden Green Farm, Church Lane, Dunsden, Oxfordshire, RG4 9QD
☎ (0118) 948 1111 ⊕ loddonbrewery.com

⊗This family-run brewery was established in 2002 in a brick-and-flint barn (originally a grain store). The custom-built, 17-barrel plant typically produces 120 barrels per week and supplies more than 700 outlets far and wide. To complement the existing taproom, an onsite farm shop opened in late 2021. Some beers are gluten-free. !!☗◆GF V◆

Hoppit (ABV 3.5%) BITTER
Pale session bitter with hops dominating the aroma. Malt and hops in the balanced taste followed by a bitter aftertaste.
Hullabaloo (ABV 4.2%) BITTER
Session bitter with fruit in the initial taste. This develops into a balance of hops and malt in the mouth followed by a bitter aftertaste.
Citra Quad (ABV 4.4%) GOLD
Ferryman's Gold (ABV 4.4%) GOLD
Premium golden ale with a strong hoppy character throughout, accompanied by fruit in the taste and aftertaste.
Hocus Pocus (ABV 4.6%) OLD
New Wave (ABV 5%) PALE
Dragonfly (ABV 5.2%) PALE

Logan Beck SIBA

The Barn at Beckfoot Farm, Duddon Bridge, Cumbria, LA20 6EU ☎ 07926 179749
✉ loganbeckbrewing@gmail.com

The brewery has expanded from a 0.75-barrel to a 5.5-barrel plant (formerly Chadwicks). Cans and bottles are planned. Beer availability is limited but there are frequent seasonal specials and 'cupboard' brews. Regular beers use mainly locally-sourced ingredients.

Phoenix Pale (ABV 3.5%) PALE
Subterfuge (ABV 3.8%) MILD
Gentle mild with some roast malt and sweetness with enough bitterness to give balance.
Swinside Single Hop (ABV 3.8%) BITTER
Nine Cara Gold (ABV 3.9%) BLOND
Proper (ABV 4%) BITTER
Sweet malty start with some roast pleasant hops and a lasting bitter finish.
Navigator (ABV 4.3%) PALE
BlackMail (ABV 4.4%) STOUT
Proper XB (ABV 4.4%) PALE
Damage Control (ABV 5.8%) STOUT

Lola Rose

🏠 Wanlockhead Inn, Wanlockhead, ML12 6UZ
☎ (01659) 74535 ☎ 07500 663405
🌐 wanlockheadinn.co.uk/lola-rose-brewery

Lola Rose is based in the family-run Wanlockhead Inn, situated in the scenic Lowther Hills of the Scottish Lowlands. Brewing occurs for special occasions and events. LIVE

London Beer Factory

c/o The Barrel Project, 80 Druid Street, Bermondsey, London, SE1 2HQ
☎ (020) 7394 6763 🌐 thelondonbeerfactory.com

London Beer Factory started brewing in 2014 on the same estate and at the same time as Gipsy Hill. This site was vacated during 2022 and brewing now takes place at an unknown location in Norfolk. The Barrel Project, along the Bermondsey Beer Mile, remains in use for fermenting and ageing beer. No cask ale. ◆

London Beer Lab SIBA

Arch 283, Belinda Road, Loughborough Junction, London, SW9 7DT

Second Site: Arch 41, Nursery Road, Brixton, London, SW9 8BP ☎ (020) 8396 6517 🌐 londonbeerlab.com

Opened in Brixton in 2013 as a bottle shop and homebrew supplies outlet, also offering brewing workshops and tastings. Commercial brewing began in Loughborough Junction in 2015 for larger batches of the core range with the shop at Arch 41 focusing on small-batch production and collaborations, available downstairs at the 14-line taproom.

Session IPA (ABV 4.2%) GOLD
Tip Top Citra (ABV 5%) PALE
Amber beer with citrus nose and flavour with some biscuity sweetness. The pithy bitter astringency builds in the bitter finish.

London Brewing SIBA

🏠 Bohemia, 762-764 High Road, North Finchley, London, N12 9QH
☎ (020) 8446 0294 🌐 londonbrewing.com

⊠ London Brewing began in 2011 at the Bull in Highgate. In 2014 it acquired its second pub, the Bohemia in North Finchley. It began brewing there in 2015 in a new, 6.5-barrel brewhouse visible from the pub, becoming its sole location when the Bull was sold in 2016. The range of award-winning beers is now widely available with an emphasis on cask including monthly specials in the pub. ◆V

Flying the Mags (ABV 3.8%) MILD
Chocolate, damsons and treacle throughout. Orange and toffee on the palate with a peppery, dryish, spicy, roasty, bitter finish.
London Lush (ABV 3.8%) GOLD
Easy-drinking, hazy golden ale with tropical fruits, lemons and floral hops on a sweet biscuit base. Dry bitter aftertaste.
Beer Street (ABV 4%) BITTER
Malty, toasty aromas with a toffee, stone fruit, nutty red rye flavour. Aftertaste moves from slightly sweet to dry bitter.
100 Oysters Stout (ABV 4.6%) STOUT
Dark chocolate and raisins on nose and palate, which has roasty notes, liquorice, dark plums and a hint of sweetness.

Long Arm

🏠 Long Arm, 20-26 Worship Street, Shoreditch, London, EC2A 2DX
☎ (020) 3873 4065 🌐 longarmpub.co.uk

Opened in 2017, this brewery took over all Long Arm beers when brewing at the Ealing Park Tavern stopped. Beers are served onsite from tanks and in keg in the other 12 pubs in the ETM chain, the brewery's owners. Some beers may be brewed elsewhere in larger batches. No cask ale.

Long Man SIBA

Church Farm, Litlington, East Sussex, BN26 5RA
☎ (01323) 871850 🌐 longmanbrewery.com

⊠ Long Man began brewing in 2012 using a 20-barrel stainless steel plant. Hops and grain are sourced-locally alongside homegrown barley and locally-drawn water. A traditional strain of Sussex yeast is used. ‼🍺◆✦

Long Blonde (ABV 3.8%) BLOND
Best Bitter (ABV 4%) BITTER
Copper Hop (ABV 4.2%) BITTER
Old Man (ABV 4.3%) OLD
Sussex Pride (ABV 4.5%) BITTER
Rising Giant (ABV 4.8%) PALE

Longdog

Unit A1, Moniton Trading Estate, West Ham Lane, Basingstoke, Hampshire, RG22 6NQ
☎ (01256) 324286 ☎ 07579 801982
🌐 longdogbrewery.co.uk

⊠ Established in 2011, the Longdog Brewery is named after a type of Lurcher used for hare coursing – once a popular pastime in the North Hampshire downs. ‼🍺◆LIVE✦

Skinny Dog (ABV 1.5%) BITTER
Refreshing low alcohol bitter. Predominantly malty, fruity aroma continues into the taste combined with some dry bitterness. A short finish.
Bunny Chaser (ABV 3.6%) BITTER
Malt dominates this amber-coloured session bitter throughout. Some hops come through with growing bitterness and a fading background sweetness.
Golden Poacher (ABV 3.9%) BLOND

Light, refreshing, blond with lemony nose and honeyed taste. Lingering malty sweetness with some hops and residual bitterness in finish.

Basingstoke Pride (ABV 4.2%) BITTER
Predominantly malty and rather sweet session bitter. Decent level of English hops in the taste combined with some subtle fruitiness.

Red Runner (ABV 4.2%) BITTER
Satisfying, mahogany-coloured red ale, with solid malt backbone. Hedgerow fruits and hops, with peppery tones and lasting dry hop bitterness.

Lovely Nancy (ABV 4.8%) PALE
Full-bodied, golden straw-coloured pale ale. Hints of honey, lemon and pineapple, with malty sweetness that diminishes into increasingly bitter finish.

Lamplight Porter (ABV 5%) PORTER
Splendid porter, smoky and drier than many, with strong roast flavours giving way to blackberry taste and slightly vinous finish.

Longdog IPA (ABV 6%) IPA
Classic English IPA; rich and earthy with hops pushed hard. Lemony notes, hints of spice lead to a bittersweet finish.

Longhill

Longhill Cottage, Whitstone, Cornwall, EX22 6UG ☎ (01288) 341466

Longhill began brewing in 2011 using a 0.5-barrel plant, upgraded in 2012 to a four-barrel plant to meet demand. Paul and Sue brew one beer, available in the bar at the rear of the brewery.

Hurricane (ABV 4.8%) BITTER
Full-bodied, tawny, premium bitter with an earthy malt aroma. Quite bitter with fruit and resinous hop flavours. Refreshing and persistent bitterness.

Loomshed

Unit 3, Lomairt an Obain, Tarbert, Isle of Harris, HS3 3DS ☎ 07808 098860 ⊕ loomshed.scot

Brewing commenced in 2019 on the outskirts of Tarbert. The brewery backs onto the Minch, with views of the Scottish mainland. An eco-friendly approach to brewing extends to the onsite taproom. Following a period of inactivity the brewery resumed production in 2022. No real ale. ◆

Loose Cannon SIBA

Unit 6, Suffolk Way, Abingdon, Oxfordshire, OX14 5JX ☎ (01235) 531141 ⊕ lcbeers.co.uk

Brewing began in 2010 using a 15-barrel plant, reviving Abingdon's brewing history after the Morland Brewery closed in 2000. Beers can be found in an increasing number of local pubs and within 50 miles of the brewery. Loose Cannon operates an attractive taproom and a membership scheme enables customers to buy beer at a 10% discount. ‼️≡◆

Gunners Gold (ABV 3.5%) GOLD
Abingdon Bridge (ABV 4.1%) BITTER
Detonator (ABV 4.4%) BITTER
Porter (ABV 5%) PORTER
India Pale Ale (ABV 5.4%) PALE

Lord Conrad's

Unit 21, Dry Drayton Industrial Estate, Scotland Road, Dry Drayton, Cambridge, Cambridgeshire, CB23 8AT ☎ 07736 739700 ⊕ lordconradsbrewery.co.uk

Lord Conrad's was established in 2007 and moved to Dry Drayton in 2011, using a 2.5-barrel plant. One permanent outlet is supplied, the Black Horse, Dry Drayton, along with other local free houses and beer festivals. The brewery adheres strongly to green principles, using low energy systems, recycled materials and local ingredients. All beers are available cask-conditoned and bottle-conditioned with a varying selection available in keg. ‼️≡

Hedgerow Hop (ABV 3.7%) BITTER
Spiffing Wheeze (ABV 3.9%) PALE
A-Bomb (ABV 4%) GOLD
Big Bad Wolf (ABV 4%) PALE
Fools Gold (ABV 4%) PALE
Slap N'Tickle (ABV 4.3%) BLOND
Horny Goat (ABV 4.8%) SPECIALITY
Self Isolation (ABV 5%) PALE
Stubble Burner (ABV 5%) BLOND

Lord Randalls

Holme View Farm, High Street, Laxton, Newark, Nottinghamshire, NG22 0NX ☎ 07712 078346 ✉ randallig@aol.com

The five-barrel brewery equipment was purchased in 2018 from the defunct Market Harborough Brewery. Brewing commenced 2020. The proprietors are the Randall family and the head brewer is Dean Penny.

Huntsman Best Bitter (ABV 4%) BITTER
Laxton Original (ABV 4%)
Tally-Ho Light Ale (ABV 4%) PALE
Landlords De-Light (ABV 4.9%) GOLD

Lords SIBA

Unit 15, Heath House Mill, Heath House Lane, Golcar, West Yorkshire, HD7 4JW ☎ 07881 204628 ⊕ lordsbrewing.com

Established in 2015, Lords Brewing Co is set in picturesque 19th century mill houses. An eight-barrel plant is used. The brewery changed ownership in 2023 and a rebranding took place. ◆V

Brock (ABV 3.6%) MILD
Fell Runner (ABV 3.8%) PALE
Corax (ABV 4%) STOUT
Reynard (ABV 4%) BLOND
Sanglier (ABV 4%) PALE
Sharecropper (ABV 4.2%) SPECIALITY
Malamute (ABV 4.5%) PALE
Buckwild (ABV 5%) BITTER

Lost

Unit 12, Lantague Studios, Scotland Road, Zelah, TR6 9JG ☎ (01637) 876873 ⊕ lostbrewing.co

Established by brothers Daniel and Jamie in 2018, they provide a small range of craft keg beers for their own bar, which is a café by day and a bar in the evenings. In 2023 a joint brewery with Newquay Brewing Project opened in Zelah. No real ale. ◆

Lost & Grounded SIBA

91 Whitby Road, Bristol, BS4 4AR ☎ (0117) 332 7690 ⊕ lostandgrounded.co.uk

Established in mid-2016, L&G brew a range of German and Belgian-inspired beers on its state-of-the-art German-built brewhouse. Beer styles include Helles and Pils lagers, tripels, pale ales and Baltic porters. All beers are unfiltered and vegan-friendly. ‼️≡V◆

Lost Industry

14a Nutwood Trading Estate, Sheffield, South
Yorkshire, S6 1NJ
☎ (0114) 231 6393
✉ beer@lostindustrybrewing.com

Lost Industry is a craft beer brewery run by a family of
beer enthusiasts, which opened in 2015. Pushing
boundaries and brewing a wide range of creative beers,
it is becoming well known, in particular, for its sours.
There is no core range, although favourites may be
repeated. A barrel-ageing programme began in 2018.
Spare brewing capacity is utilised by Steel City (qv).

Lost Pier

Office: 28 Fourth Avenue, Hove, BN3 2PJ
⊕ lostpier.com

Launched in 2017, the three founders transferred more
than 50 years of joint experience in the wine industry to
brewing. Cuckoo brewing at two local breweries, the
beer is unpasteurised, unfiltered and vegan-friendly. The
Assemblage series blends beer and wine. V

Loud Shirt SIBA

Unit 5, Bell Tower Industrial Estate, Roedean Road,
Brighton, East Sussex, BN2 5RU
☎ (01273) 087077 ☎ 07979 087945
⊕ loudshirtbeer.co.uk

⊗ The brewery was established in 2016 using a 10-barrel plant in
the Kemptown area of Brighton. The current owner, Elias, took over in
2021, and since the beer range has been completely revamped. The
taproom has been refurbished (check for times). Production is split
between cask, keg, bottles and cans, the brewery having recently
acquired its own canning machine. Beers are available at selected
Sussex pubs and bottle shops, and at the Whitehawk football club
during home matches. ‼️🍺◆◆

Hazed & Confused (ABV 4.5%) PALE
El Dorado American Pale Ale (ABV 5.5%) PALE

Love Lane

🏠 62-64 Bridgewater Street, Liverpool, Merseyside,
L1 0AY
☎ (0151) 317 8215 ⊕ lovelanebrewery.com

Established in 2017 in the Baltic Triangle area of
Liverpool, the 30-barrel plant can be seen from the Love
Lane Bar & Kitchen pub. Craft beers are produced under
this name, some cask-conditioned beers are badged as
Higsons. The brewery went into administration twice but
sold in 2024 to TJ Morris, owners of Home Bargains
discount stores, so expect to see Love Lane and Higsons
beers in their stores. ‼️◆

LoveBeer SIBA

95 High Street, Milton, Oxfordshire, OX14 4EJ
☎ 07434 595145 ⊕ lovebeerbrewery.com

Starting as a small-scale passion project in 2013,
LoveBeer quickly outgrew its original 0.5-barrel plant and
expanded to six barrels in 2017. The family-run brewery
supplies pubs around Oxfordshire and Berkshire as well
as beer festivals and farm shops. In addition to its core
and seasonal range, LoveBeer brews bespoke beers for
special occasions. 🍺◆LIVE

Doctor Roo (ABV 3.7%) BITTER
Molly's (ABV 4%) BITTER
Not on Your Nelly (ABV 4%) GOLD
OG (ABV 4.1%) PALE
Spotted Dog (ABV 4.1%) GOLD

Skyfall (ABV 4.3%) GOLD
Bonnie Hops (ABV 4.6%) PALE

Lovibonds

Friar Park Stables, Badgemore, Henley-on-Thames,
Oxfordshire, RG9 4NR
☎ (01491) 576596 ⊕ lovibonds.com

Founded by Jeff Rosenmeier, Lovibonds has been
brewing American-style craft beer since 2005. Named
after Joseph William Lovibond (inventor of the
Tintometer to measure beer colour). Beers are unfiltered
and unpasteurised. In 2017, a purpose-built brewery was
established on the outskirts of Henley, with a steam-
heated mash tun and copper. Beers are available at a
number of local outlets. It has added a new range to its
limited release beers called Hold Our Beer. This is
intended to explore historic styles and develop new
ideas.

Loxley

🏠 539 Loxley Road, Sheffield, South Yorkshire, S6 6RR
☎ (0114) 233 4310 ⊕ loxleybrewery.co.uk

Established in 2018, Loxley use a five-barrel plant located
at the Wisewood Inn, partner pub to the Raven in nearby
Walkley. Six regular cask beers, brewed with natural
spring water, complement an ever-changing range of
specials. The beers are increasingly available locally, with
more than 30 pubs supplied. Live beers are bottled
onsite, and all brews (except milk stout) are vegan-
friendly. A growing range of keg beer, including cans, is
also available. Branded merchandise is on sale at both
pubs. LIVE V

Fearn (ABV 3.8%) PALE
Halliday (ABV 4%) BITTER
Revill (ABV 4%) BLOND
Lomas (ABV 4.4%) PALE
Gunson (ABV 4.8%) PALE
Black Dog (ABV 5%) STOUT

Lucifer

9 Ellerncroft Road, Wotton-Under-Edge,
Gloucestershire, GL12 7AX ☎ 07886 604690
⊕ luciferbrewhouse.co.uk

Lucifer Brewhouse was established in 2019 using a one-
barrel plant. It produces a growing number of small-
batch beers for pubs in the local area. Some of the cask-
conditioned beers are also available bottle-conditioned,
mainly for local outlets. ◆LIVE

Double Fuggle (ABV 4.1%) BITTER
Clive (ABV 4.2%) PALE
Gold Star (ABV 4.2%) GOLD
Fallen Angel Bitter (ABV 4.3%) BITTER
Wotton Hop Project (ABV 4.4%) GOLD
Big Dipper (ABV 4.5%) BITTER
GL12 (ABV 4.7%) PALE

Lucky 7

Unit 4, Hay On Wye, HR3 5EW
☎ (01497) 822778 ☎ 07815 853353
⊕ lucky7beer.co.uk

A four-barrel brewery offering unfined beers suitable for
vegans, but no real ale. V

Luda (NEW)

6 Bollingbroke Court, Bollingbroke Road, Louth,
Lincolnshire, LN11 0ZW

Setup in 2021 to brew craft beers and lagers, now with a taproom onsite. Cask versions of some beers available on request. Tap on the Line in Louth town centre is the brewery tap. ◆

Luddite

▤ Calder Vale Hotel, Millfield Road, Horbury Junction, Wakefield, West Yorkshire, WF4 5EB
☎ (01924) 277658

Brewing began in 2019 at the Calder Vale pub in Horbury Junction. The pub was shut for five years until being reopened by a group of three former Horbury school friends, Ian Sizer, Tim Murphy and Gary Portman. The six-barrel plant brews, on average, once per week.

Ludlow SIBA

The Railway Shed, Station Drive, Ludlow, Shropshire, SY8 2PQ
☎ (01584) 873291
⊕ theludlowbrewingcompany.co.uk

☺Established in 2006, the brewery occupies a converted railway sidings shed. Beers are produced using a 20-barrel plant and a microplant called the Derailed Brewing Co for one-off beers. The site has a taproom (which now has regularly-changing beer from the micro plant, including some experimental keg beers), a visitor centre, and event area. ‼🍽◆

Best (ABV 3.7%) BITTER
Blonde (ABV 4%) BLOND
Gold (ABV 4.2%) GOLD
Black Knight (ABV 4.5%) STOUT
Red Dawn (ABV 4.5%) RED
Stairway (ABV 5%) GOLD

Lune (NEW)

Units 1D & 2A, Galgate Mill, Lancaster, LA2 0PR

New brewery, opened summer 2023. ◆

Lydbrook Valley

▤ Forge Row, Lydbrook, Gloucestershire, GL17 9NP
☎ (01594) 860310 ✉ andy@theforgehammer.co.uk

⊗ Brewing commenced in 2018 in the Forge Hammer pub in Lydbrook. Alison and Andrew Jopson use full mash to produce beers for sale in the pub. V

Lyme Regis SIBA

Slape Hill, Netherbury, Dorset, DT6 5LH
☎ (01297) 444354

Office: Malt House, Mill Lane, Lyme Regis, Dorset, DT7 3PU ⊕ lymeregisbrewery.com

⊗ Lyme Regis Brewery, the trading name of Lyme Bay Brewery Ltd (formerly Town Mill Brewery), was incorporated in 2007 and is now situated in a barn north of Bridport. The former brewery site was at the taproom, which is located in Lyme Regis. The taproom previously housed the Lyme Regis electricity generator and has in the past been a brewer's malthouse. ◆LIVE GF V

Moonrise (ABV 3.4%) STOUT
Cobb (ABV 3.9%) BITTER
Lyme Gold (ABV 4.2%) GOLD
Black Ven (ABV 5%) PORTER
Revenge (ABV 5.3%) PALE

Lymestone SIBA

The Brewery, Mount Road, Stone, Staffordshire, ST15 8LL
☎ (01785) 305102 ⊕ lymestonebrewery.net

☺Lymestone commenced brewing in 2008. Based in the old Bents Brewery, it uses a 10-barrel plant. A family-run business, daughter Sarah joined the brew team as one of the UK's youngest brewsters. The brewery delivers in a 50-mile radius, works with national wholesalers and has its own pub adjacent to the brewery. ‼🍽◆

Stone Cutter (ABV 3.7%) BITTER
Hoppy and grassy aroma, clean, sharp and refreshing. A hint of caramel start then intense bitterness emerges with a good bitter aftertaste and touch of mouth-watering astringency.

Stone Faced (ABV 4%) BITTER
Foundation Stone (ABV 4.5%) BITTER
An IPA-style beer with pale and crystal malts. Faint biscuit and chewy, juicy fruits burst on to the palate then the spicy Boadicea and Pilot hops pepper the taste buds to leave a dry bitter finish.

Ein Stein (ABV 5%) GOLD
Stone the Crows (ABV 5.4%) STOUT
A rich dark beer from chocolate malts. Fruit, roasts and hops abound to leave a deep lingering bitterness from the Styrian Goldings and Millennium hop mix.

Abdominal Stoneman (ABV 7%) STRONG

Lymm

18 Bridgewater Street, Lymm, Cheshire, WA13 0AB
☎ (0161) 929 0663 ⊕ lymmbrewing.co.uk

☺Lymm is a small, family-run brewery, launched in 2013. Located in an old post office, the brewing equipment is downstairs in what used to be the mess rooms with a brewery tap upstairs in what was the sorting office/post office counter. A sister brewery to Dunham Massey (qv). Costello's Bars located in: Altrincham (opened 2010), Stockton Heath (opened 2013), and Warrington (opened 2022) are all tied to both breweries. ◆LIVE ◆

Bitter (ABV 3.8%) BITTER
Gold Leaf (ABV 4.5%) BITTER
Heritage Trail Ale (ABV 4.5%) BITTER
IPA (ABV 4.8%) PALE
Dam Strong Ale (ABV 7.2%) STRONG

Lynn

5 Hayfield Road, North Wootton, Norfolk, PE30 3PR
☎ 07706 187894 ⊕ lynnbrewery.co.uk

Lynn Brewery is an independent, family-owned brewery based in King's Lynn, making small-batch, hand-bottled craft beer. It is passionately local, the grain used comes from a local malting group and all the beers are inspired by, and named after, the people and places of Lynn. V

Lytham

See Brewhouse

Mabby

▤ Mabby Brew Pub & Kitchen, Forest Road, Trefforest, CF37 1SY
☎ (01443) 402033

Brewpub in the cellar of the Otley Arms supplying the pub and few other outlets. The name is derived from a partnership between brewer Matt Otley and his wife Gabby. The beers have no names as such and each recipe is referred to as a colour, with that colour being reflected on the pumpclip. More recently, a series of Single Hop brews have been produced. All beers are available in five litre casks. V

McCanns

Haffenden Farm, Bugglesden Road, St Michaels, Kent, TN30 6TG
☎ (01303) 760957 ☎ 07894 013271
⊕ mccanns.beer

⊠ Brewing began in 2016 using a 20-barrel plant. Capacity increased to 30 barrels in 2023 when it moved into the old oast house at Hukins Hop farm. The oast house also has a 60-seat taproom brasserie and 120-seat patio, with stunning Weald views. Onsite glamping is available. Two brands are brewed, the McCanns range of traditional ales, and the Angels & Demons range of craft keg beer. Keg and cask beers are sold nationally. ♦

Straight Red (ABV 4%) RED
Hukins (ABV 4.1%) PALE
Ernest (ABV 4.5%) RED
Janet Street (ABV 4.5%) PORTER
The Troubadour (ABV 4.5%) BITTER

McColl's

Unit 4, Randolph Industrial Estate, Evenwood, Bishop Auckland, DL14 9SJ
☎ (01388) 417250 ⊕ mccollsbrewery.co.uk

Brewing commenced in 2017 using a 20-barrel plant. Outlets are supplied across the North-East and further afield. A brewery tap is open fortnightly.

McCracken's

Derryall Road, Portadown, BT62 1PL
⊕ mccrackensrealale.com

Currently Co Armagh's only real ale brewery, established in 2018. Producing a range of bottle-conditioned beers. LIVE V

McGivern

⊟ c/o The Bridge End Inn, 5 Bridge Street, Ruabon, LL14 6DA
☎ (01978) 810881 ☎ 07891 676614
⊕ mcgivernales.co.uk

☺The brewery was established in 2008 and was originally based at the brewer's home in Wrexham, but moved in 2011 to the award-winning Bridge End Inn, Ruabon using a 2.5-barrel plant. Production is continuing on an occasional basis. ♦

McMullen SIBA IFBB

26 Old Cross, Hertford, SG14 1RD
☎ (01992) 584911 ⊕ mcmullens.co.uk

☺McMullen, Hertfordshire's oldest, independent brewery, was founded in 1827. Its famous brew, AK, is traceable back to the 19th century. The 'Authentic Heritage' tag promotes its core beers. Additional seasonal ales are produced throughout the year, sometimes produced under the Rivertown Brewing name. A microbrewery supplements the main plant. Almost all 125 tied pubs, spread across South-East England, serve cask beer. ☕♦

AK Original Mild (ABV 3.7%) MILD
A pleasant mix of malt and hops leads to a distinctive, dry aftertaste.
Country Bitter (ABV 4.3%) BITTER

A full-bodied beer with a well-balanced mix of malt, hops and fruit throughout.
IPA (ABV 4.8%) PALE

Macintosh

1 Bouverie Road, Stoke Newington, London, N16 0AH
⊕ macintoshales.com

Starting in a garage in Stamford Brook, 2023 saw a brewery tap open in Stoke Newington. Charlie now cuckoo brews his beers at Orbit in Walworth. Beers are available in cask, keg and bottles, with plans to extend the range. LIVE

Best Bitter (ABV 4.6%) BITTER
Pale Ale (ABV 4.6%) PALE

Mad Bush

Office: 136 Gardner Drive, Aberdeen, AB12 5SA
⊕ madbushbeer.com

Mad Bush Beer is a small brewery based in Aberdeen producing bottled beers.

Mad Cat SIBA

Brogdale Farm, Brogdale Road, Faversham, Kent, ME13 8XZ
☎ (01795) 597743 ☎ 07960 263615
⊕ madcatbrewery.co.uk

⊠ Established in 2012 by Peter Meaney in a refurbished cold store using an eight-barrel plant. Beers are distributed to local pubs. Bottles and polypins are available from the brewery and Peter often attends local markets, festivals and events. ‼♦

Red Ale (ABV 3.9%) RED
Crispin Ale (ABV 4%) BLOND
Golden IPA (ABV 4.2%) PALE
Platinum Blonde (ABV 4.2%) BLOND
Emotional Blackmail (ABV 4.5%) SPECIALITY
Jet Black Stout (ABV 4.6%) STOUT

Mad Dog SIBA

17-19 Castle Street, Cardiff, CF10 1BS ☎ 07864 923231 ⊕ maddogbrew.co.uk

The brewery has relocated to the centre of Cardiff, opposite the Castle in a street corner plot. Its new premises include a taproom. A new brewer has been appointed. After a spell of offering cask and keg beers, the brewery has settled into producing a wide range of keg beers. ♦

Mad Scientist

⊟ c/o The Quakerhouse, 2-3 Mechanics Yard, Darlington, DL3 7QF
☎ (01325) 245052

Brewing commenced in 2017 on a half-barrel plant situated in the cellar of the Quakerhouse.

Mad Squirrel SIBA

Unit 18, Boxted Farm, Berkhamsted Road, Potten End, Hertfordshire, HP1 2SG
☎ (01442) 256970 ⊕ madsquirrelbrew.co.uk

⊠ Originally based in Hertford, brewing began in 2010 near Hemel Hempstead. Since 2017 it has used a custom brew kit from the US, using water from an onsite borehole. The brewery maintains an innovative outlook, introducing many specialised craft beers, while also having a range of traditional cask ales with a modern twist. Output is distributed throughout London, the South-East and to a wider area via distribution links. Though finings are used in the cask ales, most other beers are suitable for vegans. **!! ♦ V ⚫**

Resolution (ABV 4.2%) GOLD
London Porter (ABV 5%) PORTER

Made of Stone

🏠 **8 Woodford Road, Bramhall, Stockport, SK7 2JJ**

Nanobrewery situated at the back of the Mounting Stone micropub in Bramhall. Brewing began in 2018 on a one-barrel plant at the rear of the pub. The brewery specialises in twice monthly, one-off brews and collaborations with local brewers. Beers are usually supplied to the pub and the Chiverton Tap, Cheadle Hulme.

Magic Dragon

Plassey Brewery, Eyton, LL13 0SP
☎ **(01978) 781675** ⊕ **magicdragonbrewing.co.uk**

Originally named Plassey, and later New Plassey, another new owner, brewer and personnel took over in 2017. Some beer replicates the old Plassey range but others are new recipes. There is a plan to open a new pub in Whitchurch.

Burning Dragon (ABV 3.6%) PALE
Old Magic (ABV 3.6%) MILD
Border Bitter (ABV 3.8%) BITTER
Eyton Gold (ABV 4%) GOLD
Green One (ABV 4.2%) GOLD
Obsidian (ABV 4.2%) STOUT
Hoppy Jester (ABV 4.5%) PALE

Magic Rock SIBA

Units 1-4, Willow Park Business Centre, Willow Lane, Huddersfield, West Yorkshire, HD1 5EB
☎ **(01484) 649823** ⊕ **magicrockbrewing.com**

Magic Rock began brewing in 2011. The brewery is located about half a mile walk from Huddersfield town centre on an industrial estate. The 50hl brewhouse site also houses a taproom and distribution centre. In 2022 Magic Rock was purchased by Odyssey Inns Ltd along with the Magic Rock Tap at Holmfirth. The brewery specialises in barrel-aged ales, vegan beers and gluten-free beers. **!! ♦ GF V ⚫**

Hat Trick (ABV 3.7%) BITTER
Ringmaster (ABV 3.9%) GOLD
Inhaler (ABV 4.5%) GOLD
Common Grounds (ABV 5.4%) PORTER
High Wire (ABV 5.5%) IPA
Dark Arts (ABV 6%) STOUT

Magic Spells

c/o 22-24 Rigg Approach, Leyton, London, E10 7QN
☎ **(020) 3475 1781** ⊕ **magicspellsbrewery.co.uk**

Magic Spells is owned and operated by Hare Wines. The onsite brewery was removed during 2021, with the beers now being brewed at an unknown brewery. Beer is available in cans and bottles. No cask ale.

Magpie SIBA

Unit 4, Ashling Court, Iremonger Road, Nottingham, NG2 3JA
☎ **(0115) 874 8467** ☎ **07419 991310**
⊕ **magpiebrewery.com**

⚫ Launched in 2006 using a six-barrel plant, the brewery upgraded to 17.5-barrels in 2017. Only British hops and malt are used in the core range, with the Wanderlust range taking more worldly influences and ingredients. A 2.5-barrel plant is used for small batch brews and trials. Beers also appear under the Mardy Bum and Flipside brand names. Its shop and tap opened in 2019 at the brewery (see website for details). **!! ➡ ♦ ⚫**

Hoppily Ever After (ABV 3.8%) BLOND
Golden bitter, gently-hopped with biscuit malt flavours and a bitter finish.
Best (ABV 4.2%) BITTER
A malty, traditional pale brown best bitter, with balancing hops giving a bitter finish.
Cherry Raven (ABV 4.4%) SPECIALITY
Stout flavoured with cherry. Sweet, fruity aroma, malty with a hint of vanilla. Cherry isn't overpowering.
Raven Stout (ABV 4.4%) STOUT
Dark stout with roast coffee aroma and taste leading to a dry, bitter finish.
Thieving Rogue (ABV 4.5%) GOLD
A hoppy golden ale with a long-lasting, bitter finish.
Jay IPA (ABV 5.2%) PALE
Amber-coloured premium pale with a hop aroma. Bitter, malty taste with a peppery, roasted finish.

Brewed under the Flipside brand name:
Sterling Pale (ABV 3.9%) PALE
Golden ale with a citrus aroma and hoppy taste, leading to a bitter and peppery finish.
Franc in Stein (ABV 4.3%) BLOND
Golden ale with a floral hop aroma, leading to a hoppy bitter finish.
Flipping Best (ABV 4.6%) BITTER
Brown-coloured, malty strong bitter with lasting malt, bitterness and subtle hop flavours.

Brewed under the Navigation Brewery brand name:
New Dawn (ABV 3.9%) PALE

Mains

Office: 45a Alderman Road, Glasgow, G13 3YG
✉ **mainsbrewco@gmail.com**

Mains is a small-batch brewery, producing farmhouse-inspired beers.

Makemake

Unit 1.2, Central Point, Kirpal Road, Portsmouth, PO3 6FH
☎ **(023) 9273 5939**
⊕ **makemakebeer.myshopify.com**

Makemake Brewing has been producing modern craft beers since 2019. Originally based in the Greenwich Brewpub, Southsea, the brewery moved to Central Point in 2022. The new premises house a state-of-the-art brewery plus taproom. No real ale. ⚫

Mallinsons

Unit 1, Waterhouse Mill, 65-71 Lockwood Road, Huddersfield, West Yorkshire, HD1 3QU
☎ **(01484) 654301** ☎ **07850 446571**
⊕ **drinkmallinsons.co.uk**

⚫ Mallinsons was originally set up in 2008 on a six-barrel plant by CAMRA members Tara Mallinson and Elaine Yendall. The company moved to its current premises in 2012 with a 15-barrel plant and brewery shop. It specialises in hop-forward and single hop beers and has a permanent presence in numerous Huddersfield pubs. It holds an annual Mallytoberfest in October. **!! ➡ ♦ LIVE**

Wappy Nick (ABV 3.9%) BLOND
The aroma is lemony. Fruity citrus flavours develop on the palate giving way to smooth, soft, bitter aftertaste.

Malt Coast

Branthill Farm, Wells-next-the-Sea, Norfolk, NR23 1SB ☎ 07881 378900 🌐 maltcoast.com

Brewing began in 2016. It grows its own barley on the farm. ‼ ⛿

Malton

5 Navigation Wharf, Off Yorkersgate, Malton, YO17 7AA ☎ 07946 776613 🌐 maltonbrewery.com

Microbrewery situated on the banks of the Derwent, operating since 2018. Owner Howard Kinder had previously launched Horsetown Beers in 2016 with a donation to Racing Welfare made for each sale. LIVE

Mammoth

Units DG02 3 & 4, Hackney Bridge, East Bay Lane, Hackney Wick, London, E15 2SJ ☎ 07970 927272 🌐 mammothbeer.com

Mammoth began brewing in 2021 and is located at the canal-side Hackney Bridge development for local enterprises. A taproom opened in Leytonstone in 2022 providing an outlet for the beers alongside regular appearances at the Hangar Bar at Hackney Bridge and the Rosemary Branch pub in Hoxton. No cask ale.

Manchester Union

96d North Western Street, Manchester, M12 6JL 🌐 manchesterunionbrewery.com

⊗ Manchester Union is a Central European-style, lager brewery co-founded by former Six O'Clock brewer Ian Johnson. It uses a decoction technique in the mash and German lager malts. The beers undergo several weeks conditioning in tanks. Beers are unfiltered and unpasteurised and available across Greater Manchester. ◆

Mansfield

See Banks's

Mantle

**Unit 16, Pentood Industrial Estate, Cardigan, SA43 3AG
☎ (01239) 623898 ☎ 07552 609909
🌐 mantlebrewery.com**

From start-up in 2013 on a 10-barrel plant, Mantle has become a major player in the West Wales area. Engineer Ian Kimber and his scientist wife Dominique, formerly homebrewers, have built a solid reputation for consistent quality. More than 200 outlets are supplied direct with wider distribution via carefully selected wholesalers. ‼ ⛿ ♦

Rock Steady (ABV 3.8%) GOLD
MOHO (ABV 4.3%) PALE
Cwrw Teifi (ABV 4.5%) BITTER
Dark Heart (ABV 5.2%) PORTER

Manual SIBA

c/o 36-40 Bellfield Street, Dundee, DD1 5HZ 🌐 manualbrewing.co.uk

Launched in 2018, Manual Brewing Co uses spare capacity at 71 Brewing (qv) in Dundee.

Many Hands SIBA

Dunkeswell Airfield, Dunkeswell, Devon, EX14 4LF ☎ (01404) 892100 🌐 manyhandsbrew.com

Many Hands Brew Co began brewing in 2017 to produce small-batch, bottled beers. It now brews unfiltered keg beers in a wide range of styles, from two-hectolitre brew runs. **V**

Marble SIBA

Unit 7, Boston Court, Salford, M50 2GN 🌐 marblebeers.com

Originally founded at the Marble Arch pub in 1997, Marble Beers moved to a 15-barrel plant in Salford and opened an onsite taproom. Vegetarian beers are available in both its core and speciality ranges. It supplies its own Marble Arch and more than 70 other outlets. ‼ ♦ V ◆

Hindmarsh (ABV 3.7%) PALE
Manchester Bitter (ABV 4.2%) BITTER
Biscuity aroma with floral hops. Balanced bitter hop and malt in taste. Full, fruity palate. Dry bitter finish.
North South (ABV 4.2%) PALE
Prominent citrus aroma. Bitter citrus hop flavour balanced with moderate sweetness. Bitterness dominates after the initial taste, with drying mouthfeel.
Lagonda (ABV 5%) GOLD
Golden beer with a fruity nose. Powerful citrus and bitter hops backed by pale malt, and a bitter aftertaste.
Alf (ABV 5.4%) PALE
Extra Special Marble (ABV 5.5%) BITTER
Stout (ABV 5.7%) STOUT
Rich aroma of coffee and chocolate. Complex, bittersweet, roasted flavour with fruit and caramel. Smooth mouthfeel, with a drying finish.
Earl Grey IPA (ABV 6.8%) SPECIALITY
Sweet citrus aroma. Full-bodied, creamy mouthfeel. Bold Bergamont flavour balanced with sweetness and pronounced bitterness. Lasting hoppy taste.

March Hare

▮ 34 High Street, Dunton, Bedfordshire, SG18 8RN ☎ (01767) 318121

Brewing commenced in 2022. Head brewer John is an award-winning homebrewer and has been brewing since he was 15. Beer styles include traditional bitters, stouts, porters, milds and golden ales with occasional specials recreated from historic recipes.

Mardy Bum

See Magpie

Marko Paulo

**▮ Owl & The Pussycat, 106 Northfield Avenue, Northfields, London, W13 9RT
☎ (020) 8810 0880 🌐 markopaulo.co.uk**

A 1.25-barrel brewpub opened in 2016 in a former bookshop by two ex-teachers. Brewing ceased in 2020 but was resurrected in 2023 on the demise of Ealing Brewery. The beer travels about 20 feet from mash tun to glass. Cask-conditioned beers are complemented by a wide range of European-style keg beers. **V**

Marlix

Berger Close, Petts Wood, BR5 1HR ⊕ **marlix.co.uk**

⊠ Longtime friends Mark and Alex built a sizable garden shed to contain the brewery, after brewing beer together for the past 20 years, going commercial in 2020. Beers are available in cask, keg and bottles, with names based on the TV show The Young Ones. The range can be found in local micropubs and clubs. ◆

TPP (The People's Poet) (ABV 3.5%) BITTER
Kebab & Calculator (ABV 4.2%) PALE
Hazy light brown pale ale. Stone fruit on the nose with a building bitter taste. A lingering complex bitter/sweet aftertaste.
SPG (ABV 4.2%) SPECIALITY
Shut Up (ABV 4.7%) STOUT

Marlowe

Office: 1 Mount Pisgah, Otley, LS21 3DX

One-barrel, small-batch brewery based in Otley, West Yorkshire. Sister brewery to Chevin Brew Co (qv) and brewing at the same premises. Most of the beer produced goes into bottles. The interesting beer range has included a fruited saison and an imperial stout.

Marlpool

目 5 Breach Road, Marlpool, Heanor, Derbyshire, DE75 7NJ
☎ (01773) 711285 ☎ 07963 511855
⊕ **marlpoolbrewing.co.uk**

Marlpool was founded in 2010 by brothers Andy and Chris McAuley. The two-barrel brewery is situated behind the Marlpool Ale House. The brewery yard doubles up as a beer garden and the majority of the beer is sold through the Ale House and served unfined. The remainder is sold to reputable outlets. ‼◆LIVE

Marston's

Shobnall Road, Burton upon Trent, Staffordshire, DE14 2BW
☎ (0345) 758 5685

Office: Carlsberg Marston's Brewing Co Ltd, Wolverhampton, WV1 4JT ⊕ **carlsbergmarstons.co.uk**

⊛Brewing began in Burton in 1834. A nanobrewery within the visitors centre (DE14) is used for small-batch brews. Contract brewing includes Draught Bass brewed for Budweiser UK. A joint venture with Carlsberg in 2020 led to the company being renamed Carlsberg Marston's Brewing Company. ‼🍺◆LIVE

EPA (ABV 3.6%) PALE
Fever Pitch (ABV 4.2%) PALE
Pedigree (ABV 4.5%) BITTER
Pale brown to amber with a sweet hoppy aroma and hint of sulphur. Malt with a dash of hop flavours give a satisfying tasty finish.
Old Empire (ABV 5.7%) IPA
Sulphur dominates the gentle malt aroma. Malty and sweet to start but developing bitterness with fruit and a touch of sweetness. A balanced aftertaste of hops and fruit leads to a lingering bitterness.

Brewed for Budweiser UK:
Draught Bass (ABV 4.4%) BITTER

Brewed under the Courage brand name:
Best Bitter (ABV 4%) BITTER
Directors (ABV 4.8%) BITTER

Brewed under the Jennings brand name:
Cumberland Ale (ABV 4%) BITTER

Brewed under the Wychwood brand name:
Hobgoblin Ruby (ABV 4.5%) RED
King Goblin (ABV 6.6%) STRONG

Mash Paddle

92 Enid Street, Bermondsey, London, SE16 3RA
⊕ **mashpaddlebrewery.com**

Mash Paddle opened in 2022 in a railway arch along the Bermondsey Beer Mile as an incubator for startup brewers. A collection of small brewing kits allows customers to brew their own beers using supplied ingredients, tapping into the expert guidance onsite. Its own beers are also available from the taproom although larger batches are sometimes brewed elsewhere. No cask ale. ◆

Mashdown

Castlewellan Road, Banbridge, BT32 4JF

Mashdown began brewing on its own nanobrewery in 2018, with brewing formerly taking place in collaboration with other breweries. Although cask is available on occasion the majority of production is bottled. A range of bottled-conditioned beers, Half Bap Pour, is produced for Commercial Court Inns. LIVE

Mashionistas

Coventry, CV5 6AF ☎ 07960 196204
⊕ **mashionistas.com**

Mashionistas was formed in 2018 by Flo, Jon and Simon with several years of home brewing experience between them. It brews on a one-barrel plant in a garage, and all output is vegan-friendly. Being smaller than most other commercial breweries it has the ability to brew anything it likes because it will only ever be in a small batch. Since its inception, a wide variety of well-received KeyKeg beers have been produced. V

Mason (NEW)

Unit D, Cedar Units, Threemilestone Industrial Estate, Threemilestone, Cornwall, TR4 9LD
⊕ **masonbrewing.co**

Established in 2024 by Mike Mason, brewing on a six-barrel plant. Mike was previously the head brewer at the Driftwood Spars, St Agnes, and Brewhouse & Kitchen, Lichfield. ◆

Three Spires (ABV 4%) BLOND

Matheson (NEW)

Office: Burns Cottage, Cornhill, Banff, AB45 2DL
☎ 07801 983598 ⊕ **mathesonbrewers.co.uk**

A farm brewery led by a father and son team dedicated to brewing quality beer using the best locally sourced ingredients. Bottle-conditioned beers are produced on a small scale using a system capable of 100 litres. LIVE

Mauldons SIBA

13 Church Field Road, Sudbury, Suffolk, CO10 2YA
☎ (01787) 311055 ⊕ **mauldons.co.uk**

Mauldons started brewing in Sudbury in 1795, was taken over by Greene King in the 1960s, and reopened by the Sims family in 2000. A new 30-barrel plant and brewery were built. After 19 years they retired and sold to local farming-based company, Heathpatch. It is planned that its barley and hops will be used in production. A new website was launched in 2020 (bottled and draught beer available online). Three pubs are owned, and over 200 outlets supplied. ‼️🍺♦LIVE🍂

Pale Ale (ABV 3.6%) BITTER
Moletrap Bitter (ABV 3.8%) BITTER
Plum and toffee on the nose. A good balance of malt, hops and fruit, leading to an increasingly bitter aftertaste.
Ploughmans (ABV 3.9%) GOLD
Silver Adder (ABV 4.2%) BITTER
Light fruity aroma, dry hoppiness and citrus fruit with rich honey in the taste, and a long, fruity, sweet aftertaste. Refreshing and well-balanced.
225 (ABV 4.5%) PALE
Blackberry Porter (ABV 4.8%) SPECIALITY
Cherry Porter (ABV 4.8%) SPECIALITY
Suffolk Pride (ABV 4.8%) BITTER
A full-bodied, copper-coloured beer. A bubblegum nose leads to a spicy taste, with mild astringency in the aftertaste.
Black Adder (ABV 5.3%) STOUT
Full-bodied reddish black stout with roast malt throughout and, in the mouth, soft fruit with a scattering of caramel.

Maule SIBA

Rothersthorpe Trading Estate, Northampton, NN4 8JH
🌐 maulebrewing.com

Brewing began in 2014 on a self-built plant. Production is mainly unfiltered keg and bottle-conditioned beers, but cask-conditioned ales are occasionally produced for festivals. The beers are available from various local stockists, including its tap in Northampton, as well as featuring on the London craft beer scene. LIVE

Maverick

Ganders Business Park, Forge Road, Kingsley, GU35 9LU 🌐 maverickbrewingco.com

This small-batch craft brewery and taproom opened in 2023 in a farm building in the village of Kingsley. The beers, mainly heavily-hopped pale ales and IPAs, are unfined and unfiltered. The taproom is open at weekends and bank holidays and features live music and food trucks. 🍂

Maxim SIBA

1 Gadwall Road, Rainton Bridge South, Houghton le Spring, Tyne & Wear, DH4 5NL
☎ (0191) 584 8844 🌐 maximbrewery.co.uk

😊Rising from the ashes of Sunderland brewer Vaux, Maxim was set up with a 20-barrel plant in Houghton-le-Spring in 2007. More than 100 outlets are supplied direct and two pubs are owned. A weekday phone and collect service is available for bottled beers and a brewery open night is held on the first Friday of every month. 🍺♦🍂

Lambtons (ABV 3.8%) GOLD
Samson (ABV 4%) BITTER
Ward's Best Bitter (ABV 4%) BITTER
Swedish Blonde (ABV 4.2%) PALE
Sweet malt and fruit with moderate hop bitterness which lasts to provide a long dry finish.
Double Maxim (ABV 4.7%) BROWN
Hops give a gentle bitterness to the dominant fruit, which reduces on drinking. A complex beer with a butterscotch smell.
Raspberry Porter (ABV 5%) SPECIALITY
Maximus (ABV 6%) OLD

Fruit and sweetness dominate this beer throughout along with crystal malts, hops and alcohol, combining to create a lasting mouthfeel.

Maypole

North Laithes Farm, Wellow Road, Eakring, Nottinghamshire, NG22 0AN ☎ 07971 277598
🌐 maypolebrewery.co.uk

😊The brewery opened in 1995 in a converted 18th-century farm building. After changing hands in 2001 it was bought by the former head brewer, Rob Neil, in 2005. ♦

Midge (ABV 3.5%) PALE
Little Weed (ABV 3.8%) GOLD
Mayfly Bitter (ABV 3.8%) BITTER
Celebration (ABV 4%) BITTER
Gate Hopper (ABV 4%) GOLD
Mayfair (ABV 4.1%) SPECIALITY
Hop Fusion (ABV 4.2%) GOLD
Maybee (ABV 4.3%) SPECIALITY
Major Oak (ABV 4.4%) BITTER
Wellow Gold (ABV 4.6%) BLOND
Platinum Blonde (ABV 5%) BLOND

MBH Beer SIBA

Meadowside Barn, Hulme Lane, Lower Peover, Cheshire, WA16 9QH
☎ (01565) 873601 🌐 mbh.beer

MBH Beer started brewing as Mobberley Fine Ales in 2011 changing the name to the Mobberley Brewhouse (styled MBH Beer) in 2015. Continued expansion has meant it relocated to its third site in 2022. Approximately 25% of output is cask, the remainder kegged or canned. It provides contract brewing and packaging for other breweries. ♦

Bunji (ABV 3.8%) PALE
Cheshire Pale (ABV 3.9%) PALE
Sidekick (ABV 4.2%) PALE
1924 (ABV 4.5%) BITTER
Summit (ABV 4.6%) GOLD
IPA (ABV 5.2%) PALE

Contract brewed for Burton Road Brewery:
The Don (ABV 3.8%) BITTER
These Walls (ABV 3.8%) PALE
Mosaic Pale (ABV 4.2%) PALE
Pale Ale (ABV 4.8%) PALE
IPA (ABV 5.6%) IPA

Meanwood

1 Sandfield View, Leeds, West Yorkshire, LS6 4EU
🌐 themeanwoodbrewery.com

😊The Meanwood Brewery was started by brothers Baz and Graeme Phillips in 2017 and focuses on brewing keg and cask beer styles from around the world. In 2021, installation of an eight-barrel brewkit and canning line expanded production. The Terminus Tap Room & Bottle Shop opened in 2018. V🍂

Herald (ABV 3.9%) PALE
As Above, So Below (ABV 4.5%) PALE
Black Goddess (ABV 4.9%) PORTER
Arecibo Message (ABV 5.7%) PALE

Melbourn

All Saints Brewery, All Saints Street, Stamford, Lincolnshire, PE9 2PA
☎ (01780) 752186

A famous Stamford brewery that opened in 1825 and closed in 1974. It reopened in 1994 and is owned by Samuel Smith of Tadcaster (qv). No real ale. ‼ V

Merakai

Unit 12, Squires Farm, Palehouse Common, Framfield, Uckfield, East Sussex, TN22 5RB
⊕ merkaibrewing.com

Merakai Brewing was established in 2020. It produces cans and one-litre bottles. It now has a tap in Worthing.

Merchant City

See Glasgow Beer Works

Merlin

3 Spring Bank Farm, Congleton Road, Arclid, Cheshire, CW11 2UD
☎ (01477) 500893 ☎ 07812 352590
⊕ merlinbrewing.co.uk

⊕Home brewers David and Sue Peart started Merlin in 2010 using an eight-barrel plant in a modern farm unit just outside Sandbach. The beers are normally supplied to outlets within a 30-mile radius, and bottled-conditioned ales are also produced. The brewery is environmentally-friendly, using power from solar panels and a wind turbine, and spent water soaks away naturally through reed beds on the farm. ‼♦LIVE

Merlin's Gold (ABV 3.8%) PALE
A hoppy bitter beer with a touch of malt sweetness and fruit before dry, lingering hop bitterness dominates
Excalibur (ABV 3.9%) BLOND
Sweet throughout with a hoppy bitterness which takes control of the finish. Malt and fruit flavours add to the mix.
Spellbound (ABV 4%) BLOND
Avalon (ABV 4.1%) PALE
The Wizard (ABV 4.2%) PALE
Sweet, fruity start with building bitterness and malt in the background. Finishes bitter with a long-lasting full mouthfeel.
Castle Black (ABV 4.4%) STOUT
Malts and roast bitterness, balanced with fruit and hops which complement the sweet background. The finale is of lasting bitter.
Dark Magic (ABV 4.8%) MILD
Sweet malty start with plenty of roast malt flavours. Lightly-hopped with the roast bitterness lingering.
Mythic IPA (ABV 5.5%) IPA
Dragonslayer (ABV 5.6%) BITTER

Mersea Island

Rewsalls Lane, East Mersea, Essex, CO5 8SX ☎ 07970 070399 ⊕ merseabrewery.co.uk

⊗ The brewery was established at Mersea Island Vineyard in 2005. It supplies several local pubs on a guest beer basis as well as beer festivals. It holds its own festival of Essex-produced ales over the four-day Easter weekend. The Cork 'n' Cap off sales and gift shop opened in 2020. �📛LIVE

Mersea Mud (ABV 3.8%) MILD
Yo Boy! (ABV 3.8%) BITTER
Gold (ABV 4.4%) SPECIALITY
Skippers (ABV 4.8%) BITTER
Oyster Stout (ABV 5%) STOUT

Metalhead SIBA

Unit 9, Bowes Court, Barrington Industrial Estate, Bedlington, Northumberland, NE22 7DW ☎ 07923 253890 ⊕ metalhead-brewery.co.uk

⊕Metalhead Brewery began life in 2019 following a career change and a love of real ale and music. Beers are available in its micropub, the Lounge in Blyth. LIVE

Hammer Best Bitter (ABV 3.8%) BITTER
Old Knacker (ABV 3.8%) BITTER
Best Mate (ABV 4.2%) BITTER
Simpley Red (ABV 4.6%) BITTER
Axl Gold (ABV 4.8%) GOLD
Archer (ABV 5.1%) BITTER

Mighty Oak

14b West Station Yard, Spital Road, Maldon, Essex, CM9 6TW
☎ (01621) 843713 ⊕ mightyoakbrewing.co.uk

⊗ Established in 1996, the Mighty Oak Brewery produces 5000+ hectolitres of beer each year. Some 450 outlets across East Anglia and the South East are supplied. The brewery shop is open during office hours and a popular festive beer tasting day takes place in early December. The Mighty Oak Tap Room can be found at the top end of picturesque Maldon High Street. ‼📛♦LIVE

Oscar Wilde (ABV 3.7%) MILD
Roasty dark mild with suggestions of forest fruits and dark chocolate. A sweet taste yields to a more bitter finish.
Captain Bob (ABV 3.8%) BITTER
Maldon Gold (ABV 3.8%) GOLD
Pale golden ale with a sharp citrus note, moderated by honey and biscuity malt.
Jake the Snake (ABV 4%) PALE
Old Man and the Sea (ABV 4.1%) STOUT
Flavoursome session stout with bags of roast malt, touches of caramel and a satisfying bittersweet palate.
Gorgeous George (ABV 4.2%) BITTER
Robust, copper-coloured bitter with a satisfying balance of malt and hops, underlying fruitiness and a long bitter finish.
Kings (ABV 4.2%) GOLD
This yellow-gold beer is easy-drinking with a gentle anchor of citrus hops and a slowly tapering malty sweet background.
Cascade IPA (ABV 6.2%) IPA
Saxon Strong (ABV 6.5%) BARLEY

Mikkeller

🍽 37-39 Exmouth Market, Clerkenwell, London, EC1R 4QL
☎ (020) 3940 4991 ⊕ mikkellerbrewpublondon.com

A brewery was opened in Mikkeller of Denmark's second bar in London (sister bar to Mikkeller Shoreditch) in 2020 in collaboration with singer Rick Astley. Regular new beers appear in the brewpub and at the Shoreditch bar but a core range of favourites is emerging. No cask ale.

Milestone SIBA

Great North Road, Cromwell, Newark, Nottinghamshire, NG23 6JE
☎ (01636) 822255 ⊕ milestonebrewery.co.uk

⊕Established in 2005, Milestone currently brew on a 12-barrel plant. More than 150 outlets are supplied. ‼📛♦LIVE ♪

Best Bitter (ABV 3.7%) BITTER

Lion's Pride (ABV 3.8%) BITTER
New World Pale (ABV 3.9%) PALE
Shine On (ABV 4%) BITTER
Azacca Gold (ABV 4.2%) BLOND
Loxley Ale (ABV 4.2%) GOLD
Black Pearl (ABV 4.3%) STOUT
Maid Marian (ABV 4.3%) GOLD
Cromwell Best (ABV 4.4%) BITTER
Crusader (ABV 4.4%) BLOND
Rich Ruby (ABV 4.5%) RED
Honey Porter (ABV 4.9%) PORTER
Little John (ABV 5%) BITTER
Fletcher's Ale (ABV 5.2%) GOLD
Colonial Pale Ale (ABV 5.5%) PALE
Raspberry Wheat Beer (ABV 5.6%) SPECIALITY

Milk Street

See Frome

Mill Hill

Unit 2, King Street Buildings, King Street, Enderby, Leicester, LE19 4NT

Office: 12-14 Mill Hill, Leicester, LE19 4AL
⊕ millhillbrew.co.uk

Established in 2022, Mill Hill Brew Co is an innovative nanobrewery with a focus on brewing creative and flavourful, vegan-friendly ales. These are made available at its nearby family-run taproom (Mill Hill Cask & Coffee) as well as in the wider county area. ♦V

Clives Vibe (ABV 4.2%) PALE
It's A Lesta Thing (ABV 4.2%) PALE
Meet Ya At The Clock Tower (ABV 5.2%) PALE
Wanna Croggeh (ABV 5.2%) IPA

Mill Valley SIBA

Unit 10, Woodroyd Mills, South Parade, Cleckheaton, BD19 3NW
☎ (01274) 032017 ☎ 07565 229560
⊕ millvalleybrewery.co.uk

⊛Launched in 2016 on a three-barrel plant in Cleckheaton, after relocating to Liversedge in 2019 the brewery returned to Cleckheaton in 2022. More than 50 outlets are supplied as well as beer festivals. A taproom is open some Thursdays-Sunday (check for times). Regular events are hosted. ‼♦V♪

Dark Mild (ABV 3.4%) MILD
Luddite Ale (ABV 3.8%) GOLD
White Panther (ABV 3.8%) PALE
Panther Ale (ABV 4%) GOLD
Yorkshire Bitter (ABV 4%) BITTER
Mill Blonde (ABV 4.2%) BLOND
Black Panther (ABV 4.6%) STOUT
XTRA Fudge Stout (ABV 4.6%) SPECIALITY

Mills

Jumpers Lane Yard, Berkeley, Gloucestershire, GL13 9BW ☎ 07848 922558 ⊕ millsbrewing.com

Mills was established in Berkeley in 2016 by husband-and-wife team Genevieve and Jonny Mills. Wort is produced in multiple locations, which is then fermented in wooden vessels at its premises using 100% wild yeasts and bacteria from the local surroundings. The lambic-style bottle-conditioned beers are mostly available via its online store. LIVE

Millstone SIBA

Unit 4, Vale Mill, Micklehurst Road, Mossley, Lancashire, OL5 9JL
☎ (01457) 835835 ⊕ millstonebrewery.co.uk

Established in 2003 by Nick Boughton and Jon Hunt, the brewery is located in an 18th century textile mill and uses an eight-barrel plant. More than 30 regular outlets are supplied. ☞♦

Citra (ABV 4%) BLOND
Tiger Rut (ABV 4%) PALE
Light, fruity beer with hop aroma and gentle bitterness.
Trinnacle (ABV 4.2%) GOLD
Stout (ABV 4.5%) STOUT
Green Bullet (ABV 4.7%) BLOND
True Grit (ABV 5%) GOLD

Milltown SIBA

The Brewery, The Old Railway Goods Yard, Scar Lane, Milnsbridge, West Yorkshire, HD3 4PE ☎ 07946 589645 ⊕ milltownbrewing.co.uk

⊛Milltown began brewing in 2011 using a four-barrel plant. Two pubs are owned, the Dusty Miller at Longwood, which acts as the official brewery tap, and the Traveller's Rest, Meltham. ‼♦LIVE

Spud's (ABV 3.8%) BITTER
Weaver's Bitter (ABV 3.8%) BITTER
American Pale Ale (ABV 3.9%) PALE
Platinum Blonde (ABV 4%) BLOND
Tigers Tail (ABV 4.1%) GOLD
Black Jack Porter (ABV 4.5%) PORTER

Milton SIBA

Pegasus House, Pembroke Avenue, Waterbeach, Cambridgeshire, CB25 9PY
☎ (01223) 862067 ⊕ miltonbrewery.co.uk

⊠ The brewery has grown steadily since it was founded in 1999, moving to larger premises in the village of Waterbeach in 2012. It now operates three pubs in Cambridge through a sister company. In 2016 a separate brand, Beach Brewery, was created to market unpasteurised and unfiltered keg beers. Since 2021 the brewery has an outdoor taproom (open seasonally). ‼V♪

Minotaur (ABV 3.3%) MILD
A dark ruby mild with liquorice and raisin fruit throughout. Light dry finish.
Orion (ABV 3.4%) PALE
Dionysus (ABV 3.6%) BITTER
Justinian (ABV 3.9%) BITTER
Pegasus (ABV 4.1%) BITTER
Malty, amber, medium-bodied bitter with faint hops. Bittersweet aftertaste.
Sparta (ABV 4.3%) BITTER
A yellow/gold bitter with floral hops, kiwi fruit and balancing malt softness which fades to leave a long dry finish.
Minerva (ABV 4.6%) GOLD
Nero (ABV 5%) STOUT
A complex black beer comprising a blend of milk chocolate, raisins and liquorice. Roast malt and fruit completes the experience.
Cyclops (ABV 5.3%) BITTER
Marcus Aurelius (ABV 7.5%) STOUT

Mine

The Brewery, Consols, St Ives, TR26 2HW

☎ (01736) 793001 ☎ 07500 957962
⊕ minebrewing.com

☺Current nanobrewery located in St Ives, Cornwall, brewing small-batch beers available in cask, bottle and keg. There are plans to install a 20-barrel capacity kit during the currency of this Guide. ◆LIVE

Mild (ABV 3.1%) MILD
Consols (ABV 3.7%) BITTER
FeS2 (ABV 4%) PALE
Ransom (ABV 4.2%) PALE
Cousin Jack (ABV 4.6%) PALE
In Vein (ABV 4.6%) STOUT
Mines Best (ABV 4.6%) BITTER
Southwest Coast (ABV 5%) PALE
Adit (ABV 6%) IPA

Missing Link

The Old Dairy, Chiddinglye Farm, West Hoathly, West Sussex, RH19 4QS ⊕ missinglinkbrewing.com

Missing Link was established in 2017 by Jeremy Cook. A state-of-the-art brewery, it welcomes other users, branding itself as a collective of like-minded breweries. Contract brewing and canning are also carried out. Mainly KeyKeg beers. **V**

Mitchell's Hop House

354 Meadowhead, Sheffield, South Yorkshire, S8 7UJ
☎ (0114) 274 5587 ⊕ mitchellswine.co.uk

Brewing began in 2016 in a converted space at the back of Mitchell's Wine Merchants. Beers are available from the brewery shop and a growing number of local pubs and beer retailers. All production is now bottled.

Mithril

Aldbrough St John, North Yorkshire, DL11 7TL
☎ (01325) 374817 ☎ 07889 167128
✉ mithril58@btinternet.com

☺Mithril started brewing in 2010 in old stables opposite the brewer's house on a 2.5-barrel plant. Owner Pete Fenwick, a well-known craft brewer, brews twice a week to supply the local areas of Darlington, Richmond and Teesdale. Up to two new beers are usually brewed every week. ◆

Brigante (ABV 3.8%) GOLD
Dere Street (ABV 3.8%) BITTER
Flower Power (ABV 3.9%) SPECIALITY
A66 (ABV 4%) GOLD
Kingdom of Ovingtonia (ABV 4%) BROWN

Mobberley

See MBH

Modest Beer SIBA

86 Clonkeen Road, Randalstown, BT41 3JJ
⊕ modestbeer.co.uk

Small, independent brewery, originally brewing in a private garage but has now moved to a much larger brewery in Randalstown.

Molson Coors

Molson Coors (Burton): 137 High Street, Burton upon Trent, Staffordshire, DE14 1JZ
☎ (01283) 511000

Molson Coors (Tadcaster): Tower Brewery, Wetherby Road, Tadcaster, LS24 9JR ⊕ molsoncoors.com

Molson Coors is the result of a merger between Molson of Canada and Coors of Colorado, US. Coors established itself in Europe in 2002 by buying part of the former Bass brewing empire, when Interbrew (now A-B InBev) was instructed by the British government to divest itself of some of its interests in Bass. Coors owns several cask ale brands. It brews 110,000 barrels of cask beer a year (under licensing arrangements with other brewers) and also provides a further 50,000 barrels of cask beer for other breweries. In 2011 Molson Coors bought Sharp's brewery in Cornwall (qv) in a bid to increase its stake in the cask beer sector. No cask ale is produced in Burton or Tadcaster.

Mona

Unit 6, Gaerwen Industrial Estate, Gaerwen, Anglesey, LL60 6HR ☎ 07988 698260
✉ info@bragdymona.co.uk

Seven enthusiastic locals got together and set up Mona Brewery, which was launched in 2019. Beers offered from this Porter Installations kit include one cask beer and four keg beers. A significant part of the output is canned.

Pabo (ABV 3.8%) BITTER

Mondo

86-92 Stewarts Road, Battersea, London, SW8 4UG
☎ (020) 7720 0782 ⊕ mondobeer.com

⊗ Mondo began brewing in 2015. Close to the rejuvenated Battersea Power Station complex, the onsite taproom (Wed-Sat) has 15 taps and showcases the wide range of beer styles brewed. The core, seasonal and occasional beers are available in keg and cans. Occasional cask available, usually collaborations. ◆

Monkey

🍺 167 Southampton Road, Lymington, Hampshire, SO41 9HA
☎ (01590) 676754 ⊕ monkeybrewhouse.co.uk

⊗ Monkey Brewhouse is a five-barrel brewery that opened in 2021, producing a wide range of both cask and keg beers. It is housed in an oak-framed extension to the associated pub, with full height windows allowing viewing from both the dining room and outside. **V**

Tollhouse (ABV 3.8%) BITTER
Malt and caramel dominate this copper-coloured bitter. Little aroma, with sweet plum and subtle hop, leading to a surprisingly dry finish.
Sea Wall (ABV 4.2%) GOLD
Unfined golden ale with tropical and citrus fruits dominating a light malt base. Strong hop character and short, dry bitter finish.
Lymington Special Bitter (ABV 4.8%) BITTER
ESB with complex malts entwined and an assertive hop bitterness, balanced with a delicious whack of Goldings in the whirlpool.

Monkey House

Unit 1, Windmill Way West, West Ramparts Business Park, Berwick upon Tweed, TD15 1UN ☎ 07718 489485 ⊕ monkeyhousecider.co.uk

Run by Phil Elliot, a master brewer having had over 30 years experience in brewing and distilling. Primarily a cider producer, a varying range of beers is also brewed.

Beside the range of ciders available in its taproom, the brewery's beers are also available. ✦

Double Citra (ABV 4%) GOLD
Tommy The Miller (ABV 4%) BITTER
Irish Stout (ABV 4.8%) STOUT

Monty's SIBA

Unit 1, Castle Works, Hendomen, SY15 6HA
☎ (01686) 668933 ⊕ montysbrewery.co.uk

Montgomeryshire's longest operating brewery began in 2009 and brews at Hendomen just outside Montgomery. The brewery produces four main cask beers with a large number of seasonal and bottle-conditioned, gluten-free, and low alcohol beers. ✦LIVE GF

Old Jailhouse (ABV 3.9%) BITTER
MPA (ABV 4%) PALE
Navigation (ABV 4%) PALE
Sunshine (ABV 4.2%) GOLD
Mischief (ABV 5%) GOLD

Moody Goose

🍺 **King William IV, 114 London Road, Braintree, Essex, CM77 7PU** ☎ 07595 911046
⊕ moodygoosebrewery.co.uk

A three-barrel brewery, brewing approximately 15 times a year. The beers are currently only available in the King William IV, where the brewery is located, and select beer festivals.

moogBREW

Meads End, Ye Meads, Taplow, SL6 0DH ☎ 07941 241954 ⊕ moogbrew.co.uk

⊗ This nanobrewery was set up in 2016 and moved to new premises in 2019. Most of the production is keg, along with bottle-conditioned beer. Cask is available to local festivals and pubs on request. The focus of the brewery is to serve the local community through the onsite taproom and beer garden. Free home delivery is available locally. Visits to the brewery, and collections of off-sales, are by appointment outside opening times. ‼️🍴✦LIVE ✦

Moon Gazer

Moon Gazer Barn, Harvest Lane, Hindringham, Norfolk, NR21 0PW
☎ (01328) 878495 ⊕ moongazerale.co.uk

⊗ Brewing began in 2012 using a 10-barrel plant. The brewery is owned and run by Rachel and David Holliday. Chalk-filtered water is used from the brewery's own well. ‼️✦GF

Jumper (ABV 3.9%) BITTER
Gentle hop character with supporting sweet malt and bitterness. Caramel swirls in and out as a dry edge develops.
Pintail (ABV 3.9%) PALE
Crisp lemon hoppiness flows through this well-balanced, long-lasting brew. Bitterness and light malty sweetness float in the background.
Jigfoot (ABV 4%) PALE
Orange peel and honey nose. Marmalade intro bolstered by well-defined bitterness. Initial sweetness fades into a sharp astringent bitterness.
Nibbler (ABV 4%) OLD
Roasty dark fruit nose flows through into the first taste. Increasing malt and caramel. Smooth grainy mouthfeel. Short, bitter finish.
Bouchart (ABV 4.9%) MILD

Smoky bacon character throughout. Bittersweet dark chocolate nuances give depth. A smooth and creamy finish with hints of blackcurrant.
Cheeky Jack (ABV 5%) PALE

Moonface

13 Moira Street, Loughborough, LE11 1AU
☎ (01509) 700171 ⊕ moonfacebrewery.co.uk

⊗ Moonface Brewery has been running since 2018, brewing in six-firkin batches. Up to two Moonface beer types are on the bar in the tap at any time, one sometimes served from a wooden cask. ✦

X No.1 (ABV 3.6%) MILD
Best Bitter (ABV 4.2%) BITTER
Citra (ABV 4.5%) PALE
Mid Atlantic Pale (ABV 4.7%) PALE
London Porter (ABV 5.6%) PORTER

Moonraker (NEW)

Unit 17a, Deverill Road Trading Estate, Deverill Road, Sutton Veny, Wiltshire, BA12 7BZ ☎ 07502 207418
✉ moonraker.brewery@gmail.com

Moonraker took over the premises and brew kit of the former award-winning Plain Ales. A 10-barrel plant is used, which was installed in 2011. Its beer range has initially been based on the former Plain Ales range with some rebranding.

Harvest Moon (ABV 3.4%) GOLD
Grafter (ABV 3.8%) BITTER

Moonshine

Hill Farm, Shelford Road, Fulbourn, Cambridgeshire, CB21 5EQ ☎ 07906 066794

Office: 28 Radegund Road, Cambridge, CB1 3RS
✉ mark@moonshinebrewery.co.uk

⊗ Established in 2004, the brewery produces up to 20 barrels a week. Locally-produced ingredients are used, including water from the brewery's own well, and barley grown on the farm where the brewery is based. CAMRA beer festivals are supplied throughout the country, with 30 local outlets supplied direct. ✦LIVE

Moonshine Mild (ABV 3.5%) MILD
Cambridge Pale Ale (ABV 3.8%) PALE
Shelford Crier (ABV 3.9%) BITTER
Cambridge Best Bitter (ABV 4.1%) BITTER
Heavenly Matter (ABV 4.1%) GOLD
Blueberry Ale (ABV 4.2%) SPECIALITY
Frank (Zappa Hopped Pale Ale) (ABV 4.2%) PALE
Motueka Pale Ale (ABV 4.3%) PALE
Black Hole Stout (ABV 5%) STOUT
Cellarman's Stout (ABV 6%) STOUT
Chocolate Orange Stout (ABV 6.7%) SPECIALITY

Moonwake SIBA

6a Tower Street, Leith, Edinburgh, EH6 7BY
☎ (0131) 553 6995 ⊕ moonwakebeer.com

Brewing commenced in 2021 from a site close to the Water of Leith using a 35hl three-vessel brew kit. The range of core beers together with seasonal beers, one-offs and collaborations are produced. Beers are also available in can. 🍴✦

Moor SIBA

Days Road, Bristol, BS2 0QS
☎ (0117) 941 4460 ⊕ moorbeer.co.uk

Starting in Somerset in 2007, Moor is an established part of the Bristol beer scene and exports around the world. The Bristol brewery features a taproom and shop. The Moor London Vaults, Bermondsey, doubles as a tap/venue for gigs. All beers are unfined, naturally hazy, vegan-friendly, and naturally-conditioned with live yeast. Moor's canned beers were the first to be recognised as real ale by CAMRA. It was one of 16 breweries given a CAMRA Gold award during its 50th Anniversary. !! ▄ ♦ LIVE V ✦

Nano Cask (ABV 3.4%) BITTER
Balanced beer that belies its strength. Malty backbone with soft bitterness, dark fruit and trace of caramel. Short bittersweet ending.
Revival (ABV 3.4%) PALE
Cloudy orange colour with some peachy aroma, flavours of slightly resinous hops and a gentle bitterness in the short finish.
Resonance (ABV 4.1%) PALE
Light, refreshing, bittersweet pale ale with generous citrus flavours and subtle pine notes overlaid on a light malt base.
Illumination (ABV 4.3%) BITTER
Fruity aroma, overall bitter flavour with pale malt, yeasty ester and tropical fruit, and a hint of spice all evident.
Feedback (ABV 4.4%) PALE
Distortion (ABV 4.7%) PALE
Stout (ABV 5%) STOUT
Roasted malt aroma, slightly smoky on the palate with liquorice, dark fruit, coffee and dark chocolate all lingering into the complex aftertaste.
PMA (ABV 5.3%) PALE
Aroma and flavours are both well-balanced with biscuity malt, hops and tropical fruit before a short bittersweet ending.
Live IPA (ABV 5.5%) IPA
Hoppiness (ABV 6.5%) IPA
Hop-forward nose with hints of honey. Full-bodied, with tropical fruit flavours and bitterness which increases into the finish.
Old Freddy Walker (ABV 7.3%) STRONG
Roasted malt and dark fruit aromas, flavours balance roasted malt with liquorice treacle and blackberry before a slightly dry finish.

Moorhouse's SIBA

The Brewery, 250 Accrington Road, Burnley, Lancashire, BB11 5EN
☎ (01282) 422864 ⊕ moorhouses.co.uk

Established in 1865 as a soft drinks manufacturer, the brewery started producing cask-conditioned ale in 1978. A new brewhouse and visitor centre opened in 2012. Beers from the former Squawk Brewery are now brewed here. !! ♦

Black Cat (ABV 3.4%) MILD
A dark mild-style beer with delicate chocolate and coffee roast flavours and a crisp, bitter finish.
Premier (ABV 3.7%) BITTER
A clean and satisfying bitter aftertaste rounds off this well-balanced hoppy, amber session bitter.
Sharp Pinz (ABV 4%) GOLD
White Witch (ABV 4%) BLOND
Delicate citrus aroma. Sweet fruity taste balanced with gentle bitterness. Increased bitterness in the citrus finish.
Pride of Pendle (ABV 4.1%) BITTER
Amber session bitter, sweet malt and floral hop aroma. Balanced malt/hop flavour, stone fruit with sustained dry bitter finish.
Straw Dog (ABV 4.2%) GOLD
Witches Cauldon (ABV 4.2%) BITTER
Moonbeam (ABV 4.3%) GOLD

Blonde Witch (ABV 4.4%) BLOND
Pronounced sweet taste with gentle pithy bitterness and touch of citrus fruit. Dry finish. Slight fruity hop aroma.
Pendle Witches Brew (ABV 5.1%) BITTER
Well-balanced, full-bodied, malty beer with a long, complex finish.

Moot

c/o Red Lion Inn, Matlock Green, Matlock, Derbyshire, DE4 3BT ☎ 07886 630985
⊕ mootales.co.uk

Moot Ales Brewery was established in 2018 and all its beers are available in the Red Lion pub to which it is attached. Since 2021, the brewery has expanded its core range to allow most beer styles to be sampled: blonde, traditional best bitter, golden ale, IPA and a porter/stout. All beers are vegan and all are available in bottles. In addition, a craft keg beer is produced. LIVE V

MootBrew

Court Farm, Pilgrims Road, Upper Halling, Rochester, Kent, ME2 1HR ⊕ mootbrew.co.uk

An independent microbrewery, close to Halling Station and the River Medway. The brewery is now fully open with an attached taproom. ✦

MòR

Old Mill, Kellas, DD5 3PD ☎ 07402 900755
⊕ morbeers.co.uk

Established in 2012 and now trading as MòR Beers. Dominic Hughes, an experienced brewer, moved to Scotland from London to take ownership of the brewery in 2018. !! ♦ LIVE

MòR Tea Vicar? (ABV 3.8%) BITTER
MòR Ish! (ABV 4.2%) BITTER
MòR Please! (ABV 4.5%) GOLD

Morgan Brewmasters

Spirit Vaults, 53 Church Street, Melbourne, Derbyshire, DE73 8EJ
☎ (01332) 300542 ☎ 07946 851828
✉ info@thespiritvaults.pub

Fully refurbished in 2020, this brewery is incorporated into the Spirit Vaults, Melbourne (formerly the Blue Bell Inn, brewery tap for Shardlow brewery), and can be viewed from within the pub. It produces regular unique brews from in-house and in collaboration with other specialist breweries, plus the ever popular Reverend. !! LIVE

Morland

See Greene King

Morton Collins

Star, Standbridge Lane, Sandal, Wakefield, West Yorkshire, WF2 7DY
☎ (01226) 728746 ☎ 07812 111960

Office: 49 Willow Garth, Durkar, Wakefield, WF4 3BX
✉ ged.morton@aol.com

Set up in 2016 by Ged Morton and Sam Collins using a 100-litre plant in Ged's garage. The brewery produces to demand but can brew every day if required. It took over the lease of the Star, Sandal, in 2016. Several of the beers are named after the nearby Nature Reserve at

Wintersett. The brewery kit was upgraded to 200 litres per brew in 2017.

Morwellham

Morwellham Quay, Morwellham, Devon, PL19 8JL
☎ **(01822) 832766** ⊕ **morwellham-quay.co.uk/ morwellham_brewery**

Established in 2017 at the Victorian Village tourist attraction by brewer George Lister. Using a 100-litre plant, three bottle-conditioned beers are brewed, which are available in the onsite shop and café, the Ship Inn, and a growing number of local outlets. It also supplies cask beers to the Ship Inn. ▰LIVE

Morwell Adit (ABV 4.2%) BITTER
Refreshing, amber-coloured malted ale with citrus and floral notes.
Morwell Miner (ABV 4.4%) GOLD
Easy-drinking dark golden ale, well-balanced and malty with subtle fruity notes on the finish.
Morwell Hop (ABV 4.8%) PALE

Mote & Bailey

🍺 **Blue Bell Inn, 10 High Street, Annan, DG12 6AG**
☎ **(01461) 202385**

⊗ Brewing began in 2018 in the cellar of the Blue Bell Inn, Annan, using equipment from Andrews Ales. Brewing capacity is one barrel. The range varies and is only available at the pub. ▰♦

Motley Hog

🍺 **Tap House, 1 Millpond Street, Ross-on-Wye, HR9 7AP** ☎ **07510 156708**
✉ **motleyhogbrewery@gmail.com**

Gaining HMRC registration early in 2021, Motley Hog is a 300-litre brewery based at The Tap House, Ross on Wye. The aim is to bring small-scale, commercial brewing back to the town for the first time since 1956, with two core ales, and various specials during the year.

Moulin

🍺 **2 Baledmund Road, Moulin, Pitlochry, PH16 5EL**
☎ **(01796) 472196**

Office: Moulin Hotel, 11-13 Kirkmicheal Road, Moulin, Pitlochry, PH16 5EH ⊕ **moulinhotel.co.uk**

☺The brewery opened in 1995 to celebrate the Moulin Hotel's 300th anniversary. Two pubs are owned and four outlets are supplied. ‼LIVE

Mount St Bernard SIBA

Oaks Road, Coalville, Leicestershire, LE67 5UL
☎ **(01530) 832298** ☎ **07453 760874**
⊕ **mountsaintbernard.org/tynt-meadow**

This Cistercian monastery has been brewing its Trappist beer since 2017. It is the first ever recorded such beer to be brewed in England. Currently its only brew is the bottle-conditioned Tynt Meadow, which is available at the monastery and through outlets around the country. ‼▰LIVE

Mountain Hare

🍺 **Mountain Hare Inn, Brynna Road, Brynnau Gwynion, CF35 6PG**
☎ **(01656) 860453** ⊕ **mountainhare.co.uk**

☺Brewing remains suspended and the plant remains in situ. Licensee/Brewer states that due to overheads etc,

he does not intend to resume brewing in the short to medium term.

Mourne Mountains SIBA

Milltown East Industrial Estate, Upper Dromore Road, Warrenpoint, BT34 3PN
☎ **(028) 4175 2299**
⊕ **mournemountainsbrewery.com**

Mourne Mountains have been brewing with beautifully soft water sourced directly from the Mourne Mountains in County Down, Northern Ireland, since 2015. Five core beers and numerous seasonal and special brews are produced throughout the year, available in cans, kegs and a small volume of casks. All beers are vegan-friendly. ♦V

Mourne Gold (ABV 4%) GOLD

Mr Bees

Unit D, Searsons Farm, Cordys Lane, Trimley, Suffolk, IP11 0UD ☎ **07503 773630** ⊕ **mrbeesbrewery.co.uk**

Mr Bees is based on the beautiful Suffolk Coast. All beers contain honey for conditioning and smoothness. Twelve regular cask beers are produced for local free houses and are also available in bottle-conditioned form from the brewery's online shop. LIVE

Easy Beezy (ABV 3.6%) BITTER
Trimley Bee Air (ABV 3.7%) BLOND
Pollen Power (ABV 3.8%) GOLD
Best Bee-R (ABV 4%) BITTER
Sun Turn (ABV 4.1%) PALE
Beelightful (ABV 4.3%) BITTER
Bee Clipse (ABV 4.5%) MILD
Black Bee (ABV 4.5%) STOUT
Landguard Discoverbee (ABV 4.5%) PALE
Nucleus (ABV 4.6%) BROWN
RuBee (ABV 4.8%) RED
Buzz Lite Beer (ABV 4.9%) PALE

Mr Grundy's

See Black Hole

Mr Winter's

8 Keelan Close, Norwich, NR6 6QZ
☎ **(01603) 787820** ⊕ **mrwintersbeers.co.uk**

⊗ Winter's was established in 2001 by David Winter, who had previous award-winning success as a brewer for both Woodforde's and Chalk Hill breweries. Winter's ales has won many awards, with David now passing his brewing knowledge to his son, Mark, now a regular multi award-winning brewer in his own right. The brewery rebranded as Mr Winter's in 2020; operating at five-15 barrels. Some existing beers have been discontinued or renamed, and new brews commenced. ▰♦LIVE

Fusioneer (ABV 3.6%) MILD
Roast and dried fruit in both aroma and taste. Caramel, hazelnut and arrowroot add to a complex mix of flavours.
Twin Parallel (ABV 3.8%) PALE
Strong hop, grapefruit and apricot presence in aroma and taste. A bittersweet background gives depth and balance. Strong flowing finale.
Evolution APA (ABV 4%) GOLD
Clementine on the nose is followed by lemon and grapefruit in the body. Hoppy bitterness develops in a full-bodied finish.
Quantum Gold (ABV 4.1%) GOLD
A hint of hops in the aroma. Initial taste combines a dry bitterness with fruity apple. Fading dry bitter finish.

Tranquility (ABV 4.2%) BITTER
Sulphurous hoppy nose. Balanced hoppiness throughout with cereal and bitter orange providing contrast. Short ending with a bitter signature.
Rorschach (ABV 4.5%) STOUT
A smooth mouthfeel with a grainy edge. Roast dominates throughout balanced by malt, a bittersweet fruitiness and increasingly nutty finish.
Vanilla Latte (ABV 4.6%) SPECIALITY
Full on mix of coffee, vanilla and lactose with a smooth malty base. Continues to a long coffee crème ending.
Twisted Ladder (ABV 5%) PALE
Citrus Kiss IPA (ABV 6%) IPA
Strong citrus base with hop and malt in the background. Lemon and grapefruit continue as a bittersweet background provides depth.

Muckle SIBA

3 Bellister Close, Park Village, Haltwhistle, Northumberland, NE49 0HA ☎ 07711 980086 ⊕ mucklebrewing.co.uk

Established in 2016, Muckle Brewing is a tiny brewery in rural Northumberland, close to Hadrian's Wall. Beers are influenced by the local landscape. V

Whin Sill Blonde (ABV 3.5%) BITTER
Tickle (ABV 4%) GOLD
Chuckle (ABV 4.2%) GOLD
Buster (ABV 4.5%) BITTER
Kings Crag (ABV 5.4%) PALE

Muirhouse

Unit 1, Enterprise Court, Manners Avenue, Manners Industrial Estate, Ilkeston, Derbyshire, DE7 8EW ☎ 07916 590525 ⊕ muirhousebrewery.co.uk

Muirhouse was established in 2009 in a domestic garage in Long Eaton. It expanded in 2011 to its present location in Ilkeston and the plant was upgraded in 2016 to 7.5 barrels. ‼◆

Ruby Jewel (ABV 3.8%) RED
Shunters Pole (ABV 3.8%) BLOND
Shopping for Hops (ABV 3.9%) PALE
Fully Fitted Freight (ABV 4%) GOLD
Summit Hoppy (ABV 4%) PALE
Blueberry Porter (ABV 4.1%) PORTER
Magnum Mild (ABV 4.5%) MILD
Pirate's Gold (ABV 4.5%) GOLD
Tick Tock Boom (ABV 4.5%) BITTER
Hat Trick IPA (ABV 5.2%) PALE
Stumbling Around (ABV 5.2%) RED

Mumbles SIBA

Unit 14, Worcester Court, Swansea Enterprise Park, Swansea, SA7 9FD ☎ (01792) 792612 ☎ 07757 109938 ⊕ mumblesbrewery.co.uk

⊠ Mumbles Brewery Limited was established in 2011 and began brewing in 2013 in the district of the Mumbles. As of 2015, the brewery has a new permanent location, with a 10-barrel plant installation. Beers are available in numerous pubs in South Wales and the Bristol area. Seasonal and one-off beers are produced. 🛒◆V

Hop Kick (ABV 4%) PALE
Mile (ABV 4%) PALE
Malt Bitter (ABV 4.1%) BITTER
Murmelt (ABV 4.2%) SPECIALITY
Gold (ABV 4.3%) PALE
Beyond The Pale (ABV 4.4%) SPECIALITY

Oystermouth Stout (ABV 4.4%) STOUT
Lifesaver Strong Bitter (ABV 4.9%) BITTER
India Pale Ale (ABV 5.3%) PALE
Albina New World Pale (ABV 5.7%) IPA
Chocolate Vanilla Porter (ABV 6.2%) PORTER

Munro

Devonian Lodge, Logie, Kirriemuir, DD8 5PG ☎ (01575) 572232 ⊕ munrobrewingco.com

A family-owned business founded in 2020 in Kirriemuir, the final resting place of the Scottish mounaineer, Sir Hugh Munro. Beer is available in cans.

Munson's

🛱 Chequers, The Green, Gazeley, Newmarket, Suffolk, CB8 8RF ☎ (01638) 551511 ⊕ munsons.co.uk

Microbrewery at the Chequers in Gazeley, specialising in small-batch hoppy IPAs and Belgian-style beers.

Munyard (NEW) SIBA

Unit 5, Alnwick Court, Louth, Lincolnshire, LN11 0YB

Father and son brewery set up in 2019 to brew local craft lagers. Cask ales are also occasionally produced. ◆

Patchwork (ABV 3.9%)
My Father (ABV 4.2%) BITTER

Musket SIBA

Loddington Farm, Loddington Lane, Linton, Kent, ME17 4AG ☎ (01622) 749931 ☎ 07967 127278 ⊕ musketbrewery.co.uk

⊠ Launched in 2013 with a five-barrel plant, this family-owned brewery is based at Loddington Farm, Linton, in the heart of the Kent countryside. Expanding to a 15-barrel plant with onsite brewery tap, Musket Brewery now supplies more than 450 pubs, micropubs and clubs throughout Kent and Medway. ◆LIVE◆

Trigger (ABV 3.6%) BLOND
Fife & Drum (ABV 3.8%) BLOND
Matchlock (ABV 3.8%) MILD
Ball Puller (ABV 4%) BITTER
Flintlock (ABV 4.2%) BITTER
Muzzleloader (ABV 4.5%) SPECIALITY

Muswell Hillbilly

4 Avenue Mews, Muswell Hill, London, N10 3NP ☎ 07920 554812 ⊕ muswellhillbillybrewers.co.uk

⊠ The founders of Muswell Hillbilly, originally homebrewers, acquired Mews premises in 2017. Brewing is in small batches, incorporating locally-grown hops, with beers named after the local area. After the successful launch of a taproom in 2018, it took possession of a nearby unit in 2020, using a 500-litre brew kit. A recently acquired fermenter has increased cask ale output. ‼V◆

Mutineers

London Lane, Bromley, BR1 4HE ⊕ mutineers.beer

Established in 2018 in the heart of Bromley. Mutineers creates small batches of traditional English ales as well as a range of European styles not often found in cask. Beers can be found locally and at beer festivals in cask and bottles.

Bill Stickers is Innocent (ABV 3.4%) PALE
Mild Thing (ABV 3.4%) MILD
Filibuster (ABV 4.2%) BITTER
Hazy amber bitter with sweet toffee on the nose. Hoppy, full-bodied flavour alongside caramelised fruit lingering in the bitter aftertaste.
You Don't Know Jack (ABV 4.2%) PALE
Black Flag (ABV 4.8%) STOUT
Camberwell Kolsch (ABV 4.8%) PALE

Myrddins

Church Street, Barmouth, LL42 1EH
☎ (01341) 388060 ☎ 07732 967853
⊕ myddinsbrewery.com

Established in 2016 within a café bar in the centre of Barmouth, the brewery relocated a short distance away in 2018. Now known as Myrddins Tap & Brewery Shop, the brewery is in Barmouth but not on the same site as the shop. There are six different beers on the bar (changing daily). The brewery produces 1968 litres maximum per week; twelve batches of 164 litres, using four nine gallon casks.

Mysterious (NEW)

Unit 6B, Tadley, RG26 5FL

A small independent brewery located near Reading producing hop-forward modern beers in cask, keg and can. Installing their own fermentation vessels at Little London Brewery allowed Adam and Ken to brew commercially, having emerged from the Reading Amateur Brewers ranks.

Nailmaker

Unit 9, Darton Business Park, Barnsley Road, Darton, South Yorkshire, S75 5NH
☎ (01226) 380893 ☎ 07973 824790
⊕ nailmakerbrewing.co

☺Nailmaker Brewery is located in an old carpet mill by the River Dearne, using an eight-barrel plant. The extensive list of draught cask ales is supplemented by bottles, cans, pouches, and beer in a box. The onsite taproom is open Fridays and Saturdays with food and music, and also on Sundays on Bank Holiday weekends. The taproom is available to hire for private parties. Its pubs are the Anvil Arms, Darton, the Talbot Inn and Wentworth Arms, Mapplewell, and the recent addition of Tap 2, Barnsley, the Wharf, Wakefield, and the Ark, Flockton. Brewery and distillery tours are available by arrangement. ‼️☎♦♦

Yorkshire Bitter (ABV 3.6%) BITTER
Wapentake (ABV 3.8%) GOLD
Auckland (ABV 4%) BITTER
Cascade (ABV 4%) PALE
Chinook (ABV 4%) PALE
Jester Pale Ale (ABV 4%) PALE
Mango Magic Pale Ale (ABV 4%) PALE
Mosaic (ABV 4%) PALE
Paleton Pale Ale (ABV 4%) PALE
Citra Grapefruit Pale Ale (ABV 4.1%) PALE
Citra Pale Ale (ABV 4.1%) PALE
Anvil Porter (ABV 4.4%) PORTER
Cardinal Sin (ABV 4.4%) PALE
Plum Porter (ABV 4.4%) PORTER
Wentworth (ABV 4.8%) BITTER
Clout Stout (ABV 5%) STOUT
Chocolate Safari Stout (ABV 5.5%) STOUT
Triple Chocolate Stout (ABV 5.5%) STOUT
Imperial Stout (ABV 8.8%) STOUT

Nant SIBA

Y Felin, Pentrefoelas, LL24 0HU

Cwrw Nant began brewing in 2021 at a 16th century mill that was last operational in 1984. The brew plant was acquired from the former Bragdy'r Nant.

Nat 20

Hut 53, Cultybraggan Camp, Comrie, PH6 2AB
☎ 07754 093561

A microbrewery producing traditional ales plus mead, brewed using old family and historic recipes.

Neatishead

See Pell & Co

Neckstamper SIBA

Unit 3, Cromwell Industrial Estate, Staffa Road, Leyton, London, E10 7QZ
☎ (020) 7018 1760 ☎ 07968 150075
⊕ neckstamper.com

Neckstamper began brewing in 2016 using a 10-barrel plant. Beers are all vegan-friendly and are available in keg and cans either at the taproom or locally. Cask ale may be produced for local beer festivals. V♦

Neepsend

Unit 13, 92 Burton Road, Sheffield, South Yorkshire, S3 8BX
☎ (0114) 276 3406 ⊕ neepsendbrewco.com

☺Established in 2015 by James Birkett and Gavin Martin, after taking over Little Ale Cart Brewery, and moving to new premises in Sheffield's Valley of Beer. A 10-barrel plant is used, supplying beers locally, including to its own pubs; Sheaf View, Blake Hotel and Wellington. Despite only having one core beer, the brewery produces an ever-changing range of hop-forward seasonal ales. There is an onsite taproom that opens occasionally. ♦♦

Blonde (ABV 4%) BITTER

Neighbourhood

Royal British Legion Club, St George's Road West, Poynton, Cheshire, SK12 1JY ☎ 07944 618869
✉ sales@neighbourhoodbrewco.com

☺Neighbourhood Brew Co was founded in 2022. It opened on the same site using the same brewing kit that had been used by Poynton Brewery up until that date. It began as a partnership between Dre Scuglia and Jake Astbury, but in 2023 Dre left, and Corinne Goode became joint owner. Around 30 pubs, clubs and bars are supplied in the Stockport, Altrincham, Macclesfield and East Cheshire areas. ☎♦V

Telegram (ABV 3.8%) BITTER
Slow Sundays (ABV 4%) BLOND
Salem (ABV 5%) GOLD
Dark North (ABV 5.5%) STOUT

Nene Valley

Oundle Wharf, Station Road, Oundle, Northamptonshire, PE8 4DE
☎ (01832) 272776 ⊕ nenevalleybrewery.com

⊠ Nene Valley Brewery was established in 2011. A bespoke 15-barrel plant was installed in former Water Board premises in 2012. Further expansion in 2016 has doubled the floorspace. A brewery tap, Tap & Kitchen, opened on the same site in 2014. !! ▆ ◆ LIVE GF V◢

Simple Pleasures Ale (ABV 3.6%) GOLD
A light, clean and refreshing beer with a pleasing citrus hop aroma and flavour.

Blonde Session Ale (ABV 3.8%) GOLD
Grain and fruit aroma with a bitter fruit flavour with some burnt malt which predominates in the aftertaste.

Manhattan Project (ABV 4%) BITTER
Grapefruit and New World hops aroma is followed by grapefruit and tropical fruits flavour, and a dry bitter aftertaste.

Bitter (ABV 4.1%) BITTER
Floral hop and malt aroma introduces a full clean biscuit malt taste balanced by bitterness and some fruit, ending with a long malt and bitter finish.

Woodcock's Relish (ABV 4.3%) BITTER

Australian Pale (ABV 4.4%) BITTER

Release the Chimps (ABV 4.4%) PALE
Rich, malty aroma with grapefruit notes, dry bitter hoppy and grapefruit flavour, and a lingering, slightly astringent aftertaste.

Egyptian Cream (ABV 4.5%) STOUT

Pulping on Your Stereo (ABV 4.5%) SPECIALITY

Hop Stash (ABV 5%) PALE

Big Bang Theory (ABV 5.3%) PALE
Well-balanced pale ale with a huge hop aroma giving way to malty sweetness and a gentle bitter finish.

A Beer Named LEEROY (ABV 5.5%) IPA

Supersonic (ABV 6%) SPECIALITY
A pale wheat beer brewed with gin & tonic botanicals including lemons, juniper and cardamom.

Bible Black (ABV 6.5%) PORTER
An inviting aroma of malt and fruit leads to a rich tasting beer where blackberry dominates but is balanced by malt, hops and some bitterness. The lingering finish is bittersweet, with fruit assertive.

Mid-week Bender (ABV 7.4%) STRONG

Neolithic

Bradwell, CM0 7PS ⊕ neolithicbrew.co.uk

Nanobrewery producing bottled beers and naturally-carbonated keg using hand-milled malt.

Neon Raptor

Unit 14, Avenue A, Sneinton Market, Nottingham, NG1 1DT ☎ 07367 358661
⊕ neonraptorbrewingco.com

Neon Raptor is a small independent brewery producing modern and traditional beer styles from its central Nottingham site, in the heart of the city's creative quarter, since 2018. Beers are available in cask, keg and can and can be found in the taproom at the brewery or in bars, pubs and shops locally and across the country. ◢

Neptune SIBA

Unit A, Arnos House, Wakefield Road, Liverpool, L30 6TZ
☎ (0151) 222 3908 ⊕ neptunebrewery.com

⊕Neptune began brewing in 2015 and was originally based in Maghull but expansion in 2023 led to a move to the outskirts of Liverpool. The beers are unfined and unfiltered, and in keeping with the brewery name, the majority of beers are named to a water theme (fish, the sea and mythological creatures). 2023 saw the opening of a licenced premises in Maghull. V

Forecast (ABV 3.9%) BITTER

Medium-bodied, light amber beer, caramel malt aromas, sweet caramel on tasting, dry hop bitterness, light caramel, dry hop finish.

Ezili (ABV 4%) PALE
Lemon/grapefruit hoppiness dominates the aroma and initial taste. Peachy sweetness, smooth creamy feel. Long soft finish with increasing sweetness.

Sea of Dreams (ABV 4.2%) PALE

Shifting Sands (ABV 4.3%) PALE

Mosaic (ABV 4.5%) PALE
Fruity grapefruit and mango aromas, light malty sweetness, fruity flavours with dry hop bitterness and a light fruity finish.

Wooden Ships (ABV 4.7%) PALE

Abyss (ABV 5%) STOUT
Premium stout, sweet roast caramel malt aroma, chocolate and coffee. Smooth, creamy, malt sweetness and a light hop, gentle bitter, dry finish.

Nessie

Westoaks, Fort William Road, Fort Augusus, PH32 4BH

Set up in 2017 Nessie Brew is a nanobrewery that markets a range of bottled beers to the tourist trade around Fort Augustus.

Nethergate SIBA

Rodbridge Corner, Long Melford, Suffolk, CO10 9HJ
☎ (01787) 377087 ⊕ nethergate.co.uk

⊠ Nethergate was formed in 1986 in Clare, Suffolk and moved to its current site in 2017. It produces both traditional recipes and more modern beers and has recently added craft lager and low alcohol beer to its range. The establishment of a borehole means all the water comes directly from the chalk bed. In 2021 a still was added and local craft gins are now produced. Nethergate have now opened a shop and taproom in nearby Bury St Edmunds. !! ▆ ◆ V◢

Melford Mild (ABV 3.7%) MILD

Venture (ABV 3.7%) GOLD
Refreshingly crisp golden ale with a firm citrus hop base throughout and a tapering soft sweet maltiness adding depth.

Umbel Ale (ABV 3.8%) SPECIALITY
Pleasant, easy-drinking bitter, infused with coriander, which dominates.

Suffolk County Best Bitter (ABV 4%) BITTER
Dark bitter with roast grain tones off-setting biscuity malt and powerful hoppy, bitter notes.

Stour Valley Gold (ABV 4.2%) GOLD
Quaffable golden ale with gentle zingy citrus hop, a scattering of malt and an expanding bitterness in a mellow finish.

Augustinian Ale (ABV 4.5%) BITTER
A pale, refreshing, complex premium bitter. A fruity aroma leads to a bittersweet flavour and aftertaste with a predominance of citrus tones.

Old Growler (ABV 5%) PORTER
Robust dark brown porter with appealing bittersweet meld of roast malt, hop and caramel; sustained finish with developing hop bitterness.

Umbel Magna (ABV 5%) SPECIALITY
Old Growler flavoured with coriander. The spice is less dominant than in Umbel Ale, with some of the weight and body of the beer coming through.

New Bristol SIBA

20a Wilson Street, Bristol, BS2 9HH ☎ 07837 976871
⊕ newbristolbrewery.co.uk

⊠ Having started out in 2013 with his brother Tom, Noel James, wife Maria and assistants now brew on a fifteen-barrel plant. Year-round beers are supplemented by regularly released brews based on progressive and modern themes, which include IPAs and stouts. All beers are unfined and unfiltered, with some oak barrel-aged and many available in cans. The premises house a shop, brewery tap and kitchen (Thu-Sun). !! 〓 ♦ LIVE V ♦

Bristol Bitter (ABV 4%) BITTER
Cinder Toffee Stout (ABV 4%) SPECIALITY
Caramelised honey and roasted malt aromas, sweet flavours of honeycomb and chocolate, some hop bitterness in the slightly dry finish.
Wonderland IPA (ABV 4.1%) PALE
Tropical fruit aroma and juicy fruit hop burst of pineapple and mango flavours with some bitterness in the short finish.
Joy of Sesh (ABV 4.2%) BITTER
Powerfully-hopped, naturally hazy, unfined beer with citrus and tropical fruits on the palate and a long bitter finish.
Irish Cream Stout (ABV 7%) SPECIALITY
Super Deluxe Stout (ABV 7%) SPECIALITY
Banana and vanilla aromas. The taste and mouthfeel is like vanilla ice cream, but this sweetness contrasts with an assertive bitterness.

New Buildings SIBA

Unit 3, Southways Industrial Estate, Coventry Road, Hinckley, Leicestershire, LE10 0NJ
☎ (01455) 635239 ☎ 07795 954392

Office: 24 Leicester Road, Hinckley, LE10 1LS
⊕ newbuildingsbrewery.com

⊙New Buildings Brewery brew using the David Porter 5.5-barrel system and also have an 18-gallon system. The smaller kit is used for trialling new recipes and specials. The eight regular beers are sold predominantly in the Midlands to freehouses and some 35 Wetherspoon pubs.

Lighthouse Pale Ale (ABV 3.9%) PALE
Windmill Best Bitter (ABV 4.1%) BITTER
Farmhouse (ABV 4.2%) GOLD
Treehouse Marmalade IPA (ABV 4.2%) GOLD
Courthouse Porter (ABV 4.5%) PORTER
Cruckhouse (ABV 4.5%) RED
Manorhouse (ABV 4.5%) RED
Summerhouse Pale Ale (ABV 5.5%) PALE

New Invention

Unit 2, Pinfold Industrial Estate, Walsall, WS3 3JS
☎ 07955 629538 ⊕ newinventionbrewery.co.uk

Opened in 2020, the brewery produces a wide range of beer styles, mainly in keg and can for its own taproom, and distribution into the local free trade. ♦

New River SIBA

Unit 47, Hoddesdon Industrial Centre, Pindar Road, Hoddesdon, Hertfordshire, EN11 0FF
☎ (01992) 446200 ⊕ newriverbrewery.co.uk

⊠ New River commenced brewing in 2015 on the banks of the New River in Hoddesdon, using a new 10-barrel plant. Many of its beer names are themed around the river. Its core range of ales is complemented by seasonal beers and one-off specials. 〓 ♦

London Tap (ABV 3.8%) PALE
Twin Spring (ABV 4%) GOLD
Chadwell (ABV 4.2%) BITTER

Blind Poet (ABV 4.5%) PORTER
Impressive, easy-drinking porter. Light roast malt, chocolate, liquorice, a satisfying bittersweet palate and a light, dry, smoky finish.
Five Inch Drop (ABV 4.6%) PALE
Crisp, gold-yellow premium pale ale. Bittersweet palate with hops, malt and hints of caramel.
Isle of Rye Pale Ale (ABV 5.2%) PALE

New Street

Volunteer Tavern, 9 New Street, Old Market, Bristol, BS2 9DX
☎ (0117) 955 8498 ⊕ sites.google.com/view/volunteertavern/home

⊠ New Street Brewing is located in the building next door to the 17th century Volunteer Tavern. Currently, one regular beer is brewed onsite, with seasonal specials also available from time to time. ♦ V

Volly Pale (ABV 4%) PALE
Slightly hazy, powerfully-hopped (American) pale ale. Fruity aroma, sharp, pithy, citrus flavour and bitterness that lingers in the aftertaste.

New Wharf SIBA

Hyde Farm, Marlow Road, Maidenhead, Berkshire, SL6 6PQ
☎ (01628) 634535 ⊕ newwharfbrewing.co.uk

A 20-barrel brewery, founded in 2017. It has a core range of three cask beers, plus seasonal ales. These and other beers, including a Helles lager, Lost Soul, are also available in cans. The beer names are taken from tales of travel and exploration. There are plans to produce live keg beers. ♦

Voyager (ABV 4%) BITTER
Explorer (ABV 4.3%) PALE

Newbarns

13 Jane Street, Leith, Edinburgh, EH6 5HE
☎ (0131) 554 4363 ⊕ newbarnsbrewery.com

The four founders moved north from London (having worked at Kernel and Siren breweries in the past decade), and opened Newbarns in 2020. Real ale production commenced at the end of 2021. An adjacent taproom was opened in 2022 and collaborations on cask ale with Donzoko, which formerly brewed at the site, as well as other brewers, has been a recent feature. ♦

Table Beer (ABV 3%) PALE
Sparkling Ale (ABV 3.8%) PALE
Pale Ale (ABV 4.8%) PALE
Stout (ABV 5%) STOUT

Newbridge

Unit 3, Tudor House, Moseley Road, Bilston, West Midlands, WV14 6JD ☎ 07970 456052
⊕ newbridgebrewery.co.uk

First established in 2014, the five-barrel plant incorporates six original Grundy cellar tanks. Occasional specials are brewed to complement the regular beers. The beers are permanently available at the Hail to the Ale micropub in Wolverhampton and can also be found in other pubs and clubs around the city.

Little Fox (ABV 4.2%) BITTER
Solaris (ABV 4.5%) BITTER
Indian Empire (ABV 5%) BITTER

Newby Wyke SIBA

Unit 24, Limesquare Business Park, Alma Park Road, Grantham, Lincolnshire, NG31 9SN
☎ (01476) 565682 ⊕ newbywyke.co.uk

⊗ The brewery is named after a Hull trawler skippered by brewer Rob March's grandfather. It started life in 1998 as a 2.5-barrel plant in a converted garage then moved to premises behind the Willoughby Arms, Little Bytham. In 2009 it moved back to Grantham. ‼♦

Banquo (ABV 3.8%) BLOND
Summer Session Bitter (ABV 3.8%) BITTER
Orsino (ABV 4%) BLOND
Comet (ABV 4.1%) BITTER
Kingston Topaz (ABV 4.2%) GOLD
Bear Island (ABV 4.6%) BLOND
Black Squall (ABV 4.6%) PORTER
White Squall (ABV 4.8%) BLOND
Blonde-hued with a hoppy aroma. Generous amounts of hop are well-supported by a solid malty undercurrent. An increasingly bittersweet tang makes itself known towards the finish.
White Sea (ABV 5.2%) BITTER
Chesapeake (ABV 5.5%) BITTER

Newquay Brewing Project

Unit 12, Lantague Studios, Scotland Road, Zelah, Cornwall, TR6 9JG ☎ 07720 399942
⊕ newquaybrewingproject.com

After travelling the world, owners Ash and Kez purchased the eight-barrel former Fowey brewplant to make a range of beer styles similar to those they enjoyed while travelling. In 2023, it relocated and the joint brewery and taproom, with Lost Brewing, opened in Zelah. It is trying to be as carbon neutral and environmentally-friendly as possible, without compromising on flavour. A small but growing range of beers are all vegan-friendly, unfined and unpasteurised and are available can-conditioned or in kegs. LIVE V

Newquay Steam

New Inn, Newquay Road, Goonhavern, Cornwall, TR4 9QD

Newquay Steam Brewery commenced in 2020. Three beers, one cider, a rum and gin are currently produced under the name.

Newt SIBA

Unit 1, Block 4, Inveresk Industrial Estate, Musselburgh, EH21 7UL ☎ 07979 905055

Office: 7 / 7 Cornwallis Place, Edinburgh, EH3 6NG
⊕ newtbrew.com

Originally set up at the ecological organic farm, East Coast Organics in Pencaitland, Newt Brew has moved to new premises at Eskbank, Musselburgh, just outside Edinburgh. Beers are produced in 100-1,000 litre batches, usually using the 1,000 litre kit or the 200 litre pilot. All beers are certified organic, unfined and are vegan. The range is available in bottles and cask, with expansion into cans and kegs planned. LIVE V

Thirsty Dog (ABV 4%) PALE
Cascade Karma Pale Ale (ABV 4.7%) PALE
Organic Pale Ale (ABV 5%) PALE
Gold/yellow with medium citrus hop aroma increasing in the flavour and aftertaste, balanced by a light malt sweetness.
Sunshine Pale (ABV 5%) PALE
Night Porter (ABV 5.5%) PORTER

Black, lightly malty and roasty aroma, increasing on the palate with sweetness and fruit notes and a light hop bitterness.

Newtown

25 Victoria Street, Gosport, Hampshire, PO12 4TX
☎ (023) 9250 4294 ⊕ newtownbrewery.co.uk

Newtown is one of the smallest UK breweries with just a half-barrel plant. Full mash beers are produced on demand for local pubs and beer festivals. V

Nightjar

2 Richmond House, Caldene Business Park, Mytholmroyd, West Yorkshire, HX7 5QL ☎ 07778 620800 ⊕ nightjarbrew.co.uk

☺Nightjar Brew Co was initially established in 2011 and was rebranded in 2018. This 10-barrel brewer, located in Mytholmroyd, has occasional open brewery nights and supplies hundreds of free trade outlets across the UK. It combines a core range with around 20 new beers a year, in both cask and keg. Nightjar beers are always available in its two brewery taps: Nightjar, Hebden Bridge, and the Exchange Craft Beer House, Bradford. ♦GF V

At One With Citra (ABV 3.9%) GOLD
Naturally cloudy, pale yellow, single-hopped ale. Citrus flavours dominate the aroma and taste. This is followed by a mellow aftertaste.
Come As You Are (ABV 4%) PALE
Hermit Crab of Hope (ABV 4%) PALE
Dr Dray (ABV 4.1%) BLOND
Release the Pressure (ABV 4.1%) GOLD
Lost in Ikea (ABV 4.2%) PALE
Cosmonaut (ABV 4.4%) STOUT
Dark creamy stout with roasted malt dominating the aroma and taste. A liquorice flavour develops in the dry, bitter aftertaste.
Mosaic, Lollipops & Rainbows (ABV 4.4%) PALE
To the Winchester (ABV 4.4%) BITTER
Can I Pet That Dawg? (ABV 4.6%) PALE
Dua NEIPA (ABV 5.1%) PALE
You Had Me at Hazy (ABV 5.9%) IPA
Don't Over Think Your Socks (ABV 6.2%) IPA
Emotional Support Hamster (ABV 7%) IPA

Nine Standards

See Settle

No Frills Joe

50 Wakefield Road, Greenhithe, Kent, DA9 9JE
☎ 07516 725577

⊗ Unpasteurised, unfiltered, and unfined vegan beers are produced on a small five-barrel plant, and may be cloudy. The range is available in pubs nationwide. Up to eight different beers are available in cans. LIVE V

Joe Solo Pale Ale (ABV 5.5%) GOLD

No Limits

25 Lime Road, Dumbarton, G82 2RP

After two years trialling and refining beers, Henry Boswell and Andy Logan opened No Limits Brewing at the end of 2022 in the former Lennox brewery premises. A craft nanobrewery, 120L per brew, beers are sold direct from the brewery. After four months, expansion was marked with the purchase of a new 300L fermenter.

Noa

Peveril Building, Peveril Square, Douglas, Isle of Man, IM1 2BS

Brewing started in early 2023 based directly opposite the ferry terminal in Douglas. The beers use leftover sourdough bread as yeast from the associated bakehouse. No cask ale is currently produced. ◆

Noble Craft (NEW) SIBA

Little Acorns, Spoonley, Shropshire, TF9 3SR
☎ (01630) 659777 ⊕ noblecraftbrewing.co.uk

Founded in 2020, with beers available in 2021, Noble Craft Brewing is a microbrewery based in the Market Drayton area in Shropshire. It brews a range of cask and bottled beers for the free trade.

Nook SIBA

🏠 Riverside, 7b Victoria Square, Holmfirth, West Yorkshire, HD9 2DN
☎ (01484) 682373 ⊕ thenookbrewhouse.co.uk

☺The Nook Brewhouse is built on the foundations of a previous brewhouse dating back to 1754, next to the River Ribble. Three brewery taps are supplied, two being restaurants with dishes matched to the beer, plus the onsite pub that rotates the 22 different ales. ‼◆LIVE

Norfolk Broads

See Humpty Dumpty

Norn Iron

Unit 30, The Cutts, Dunmurry, Belfast, BT17 9HN
⊕ nornironbrewco.com

Proudly brewing beer on the outskirts of Belfast since 2018 using quality local ingredients. V

North

Springwell, Buslingthorpe Lane, Leeds, West Yorkshire, LS7 2DF
☎ (0113) 345 3290

Office: Regents Court, 39A Harrogate Road, Leeds, LS7 3PD ⊕ northbrewing.com

☺Having opened in 2015, the brewery initially supplied the North Bar group of bars in and around Leeds. Expansion to 15-barrels on the original site quickly followed as the number of other outlets supplied increased. Due to substantially increased canned production, including national availability in supermarkets, further expansion was required, with the current premises opening in 2021. ‼◆V◆

Session Pale (Action Against Hunger) (ABV 3.8%) PALE
Vanishing Point (ABV 3.8%) PALE
Atlantis (ABV 4.1%) PALE
Seasons Reverse (ABV 4.3%) BITTER
Shadow Play (ABV 4.8%) PORTER

North Cotswold SIBA

Unit 3, Ditchford Farm, Stretton-on-Fosse, Warwickshire, GL56 9RD
☎ (01608) 663947 ⊕ northcotswoldbrewery.co.uk

☺North Cotswold started in 1999 as a family run 2.5-barrel plant, which has since been upgraded to 10-barrel capacity. Beers are also produced under the Shakespeare brand name, available in cask and bottles. 🚲◆LIVE

Windrush Ale (ABV 3.6%) BITTER
Jumping Jack Flash (ABV 3.8%) GOLD
Moreton Mild (ABV 3.8%) MILD
Cotswold Best (ABV 4%) BITTER
Green Man IPA (ABV 4%) PALE
Shagweaver (ABV 4.5%) BITTER
Hung, Drawn 'n' Portered (ABV 5%) PORTER
Freedom IDA7 (ABV 5.2%) IPA

Brewed under the Shakespeare Brewery brand name:
Bard's Best (ABV 4.2%)
Falstaff's Folly (ABV 4.2%) BITTER

North Garden (NEW)

Unit 5, 33 Victoria Road, Burgess Hill, West Sussex, RH15 9LH

Founded in 2023 by James Harley, previously with Bestens Brewery, North Garden now shares the same Burgess Hill site as Bestens, with the aim of serving the community by producing a range of beers using high quality ingredients.

North Pier SIBA

Queen Victoria Hotel, Harbour View, Sunderland, SR6 0PQ ⊕ northpierbrew.co.uk

Brewing commenced in 2020 at Tow Law in County Durham with beers available in both the County Durham and Wearside areas. The brewery then moved to share premises with Great North Eastern (qv), however, in 2024 it found new premises in Sunderland formerly used by Blockyard (qv).

Rokerite (ABV 4%) PALE
Pale (ABV 4.2%) PALE
Cold Brew (ABV 4.7%) PORTER
Bounty Hunter (ABV 4.8%) STOUT

North Riding (Brewery)

Unit 6, Barker's Lane, Snainton, North Yorkshire, YO13 9BD
☎ (01723) 864845 ⊕ northridingbrewery.com

☺Having outgrown the brewpub in Scarborough, Stuart Neilson established a 10-barrel brewery in East Ayton on the outskirts of Scarborough in 2015. In early 2019 operations moved to a much larger premises in Snainton, enabling further expansion of brewing capacity. Concentrating on hop-forward beers, distribution is throughout the North of England and the Midlands. ◆LIVE

Mosaic Pale Ale (ABV 4.3%) PALE
Citra Pale Ale (ABV 4.5%) PALE

North Riding (Brewpub)

🏠 North Marine Road, Scarborough, North Yorkshire, YO12 7HU
☎ (01723) 370004 ⊕ northridingbrewpub.com

☺Brewing commenced in 2011 using a two-barrel plant situated in the cellar of the pub, which is now brewing to capacity with three fermenting vessels. ◆

Northbound

Campsie Industrial Estate, McLean Road, Eglinton, BT47 3XX ☎ 07512 198686
⊕ northboundbrewery.com

Established in 2015, Northbound produce a range of bottle-conditioned beers primarily named after their measurement of bitterness (IBUs). ◆LIVE

Northdown SIBA IFBB

Unit no J1C/A, Channel Road, Westwood Industrial Estate, Margate, Kent, CT9 4JS ☎ 07791 441219
⊕ northdownbrewery.co.uk

⊠ Northdown began brewing in 2018 using a seven-barrel plant. It is run by Jonny and Katie Spanjar and takes its name from the original intention to operate out of the Northdown area of Margate. The origins of a Northdown brewery date back to the 1600s. ‼☲♦LIVE ✦

Bright Island (ABV 3.8%) BLOND
Dune Buggy (ABV 3.8%) PALE
Bitter Seas (ABV 4%) BITTER
Pale Ale Mary (ABV 4%) BITTER
Reginald Perrin (ABV 4%) BLOND
Tidal Pool (ABV 4.6%) PALE

Northern Alchemy

The Old Coal Yard, Elizabeth Street, Byker, Newcastle upon Tyne, NE6 1JS ☎ 07834 386333
⊕ wearenorthernalchemy.com

Brewing began in 2014. The brewery was situated in a converted shipping container, known as the Lab, just behind the Cumberland Arms. In 2017 it moved to larger premises in a former coal depot. All beers are unfined and unfiltered. Beers are always available in the Cumberland Arms, and the brewery opens a tap on Friday and Saturday evenings. ♦V✦

Be Curious (ABV 4.1%) PALE

Northern Monk SIBA

Unit 7, Sydenham Road, Leeds, West Yorkshire, LS11 9RU
☎ (0113) 243 6430

Secondary site: The Old Flax Store, Marshalls Mill, Holbeck, Leeds, LS11 9YJ
⊕ northernmonkbrewco.com

☺After using spare capacity at other breweries in 2013, a 10-barrel plant was established in 2014 in a Grade II-listed mill. In 2017, a much larger second site with canning line was opened. 2019 saw further expansion into the adjacent former Leeds Brewery site, with a new 50-hectolitre brewkit installed in 2021. The mill hosts a taproom and events space. Most production is keg but cask-conditioned beer is available. ‼GF✦

Eternal (ABV 4.1%) GOLD
A pleasing mix of hops, citrus and other fruits combine to produce a bittersweet, gold-coloured beer.

Northern Monkey

68 Chorley Street, Bolton, BL1 4AL ☎ 07825 814631
⊕ northernmonkeybrew.co.uk

Established in 2016 and relocated in 2021, Northern Monkey Brew Co is a six-barrel brewery with an onsite tap bar. The original brewpub remains a town centre outlet. It brews a variety of ales, maintaining a traditional edge but with a modern twist. The ales rotate regularly so no core range is available. ♦✦

The Last Drop (ABV 3.6%) PALE
Winter Hill (ABV 3.8%) GOLD
Reenys Beans (ABV 4%) SPECIALITY
Sheephouse (ABV 4.2%) PALE
Dirty Harry (ABV 4.5%) BITTER
Funky Monkey (ABV 5.5%) IPA
Underdog (ABV 6%) MILD
Malt, hops, fruit and caramel aromas. A sweet beer with roast, fruit and some gentle hop in the lingering finish.

Northern Whisper

Hill End Mill, Hill End Lane, Cloughfold, Lancashire, BB4 7RN
☎ (01706) 230082
⊕ northernwhisperbrewingco.uk

First brewing in 2017, the brewery's beers are widely available in East Lancashire and northern Greater Manchester. ♦

Soft Mick (ABV 3.8%) PALE
Oppenchops (ABV 4%) GOLD
Yammerhouse (ABV 4.5%) PALE
Beltie (ABV 4.8%) STOUT
Chinwag (ABV 5.6%) IPA

Norton

Norton Priory, Tudor Road, Manor Park, Runcorn, Cheshire, WA7 1SX
☎ (01928) 577199 ☎ 07775 761114
⊕ nortonbrewing.com

Situated within the grounds of Norton Priory, the brewery was created as a social enterprise by Halton Borough Council to provide employment opportunities for people with learning disabilities, autism and other disabilities. It opened in 2011 with a 2.5-barrel plant. Beers in bottles, mini-kegs and casks are available for collection from the brewery only. ☲

Noss Beer Works SIBA

Unit 6, Ash Court, Pennant Way, Lee Mill, Devon, PL21 9GE ☎ 07977 479634 ⊕ nossbeerworks.co.uk

⊠ Noss Beer Works was formed in 2012 using a six-barrel plant. The beers are made from only the finest locally-sourced hops and malts. ‼♦LIVE

Black Rock (ABV 4%) PALE
Church Ledge (ABV 4%) BITTER
Bitter dominated by hops and fruit throughout. Hoppy and citrusy, slight caramel balances bitter dryness. Slight kick at the end.
Mew Stone (ABV 4.3%) BITTER
Malty biscuit aroma which follows on taste. Quaffable session bitter.
Ebb Rock (ABV 4.9%) BITTER
A dark copper-coloured, full-bodied strong bitter.

Not That California SIBA

Braeview, California, Falkirk, FK1 2DH ☎ 07972 574949 ⊕ notthatcalifornia.com

⊠ A microbrewery in the heart of Scotland, in a small village called California. Run by former homebrewers that moved into commercial brewing in 2022, it brews modern takes on traditional styles of beer. ♦

Farmers Ale (ABV 4%) GOLD
Bitter Tomorrows (ABV 4.3%) PALE
Goldrush (ABV 4.3%) BROWN
Pale Viking (ABV 4.3%) PALE
West Coast IPA (ABV 4.7%) IPA
Filthy B***ard (ABV 6%) STOUT

Nothing Bound (NEW)

The Brewery at Chapel Farm, Heightington, Worcestershire, DY12 2XY ☎ 07989 304331
⊕ nothingbound.co.uk

Brewing began in 2021 in farm premises near Bewdley, Worcestershire. The brewery currently produces a wide range of modern styles in small pack and keg form.

Nottingham SIBA

Plough Inn, 17 St Peter's Street, Radford, Nottingham, NG7 3EN
☎ (0115) 942 2649 ☎ 07815 073447
⊕ thenottinghambrewery.co.uk

Re-established in 2000 after post-war closure by Whitbread of the original Nottingham Brewery in the 1950s. Investment by a new majority shareholder meant a site move for the brewery was planned during the currency of this Guide, to allow space for expansion and updating the brewery plant. The ethos of the brewery remains the same; traditional cask ales, serving the local market and beyond. ‼♦✦

Rock Bitter (ABV 3.8%) BITTER
A pale and bitter, thirst-quenching hoppy beer with a dry finish.
Rock Mild (ABV 3.8%) MILD
A reddish-black malty mild with some refreshing bitterness in the finish.
Trent Bridge Inn Ale (ABV 3.8%) BITTER
A gold-coloured, hoppy session ale with a long bitter finish.
Legend (ABV 4%) BITTER
A fruity and malty pale brown bitter with a touch of sweetness and bitterness.
Citra (ABV 4.2%) PALE
Extra Pale Ale (ABV 4.2%) PALE
A hoppy and fruity golden ale with a hint of sweetness and a long-lasting bitter finish.
Dreadnought (ABV 4.5%) BITTER
Well-balanced best bitter. Blend of malt and hops give a rounded fruity finish.
Trentsman (ABV 4.5%) BITTER
Bullion (ABV 4.7%) GOLD
A refreshing premium golden ale. Brewed with a single malt variety, it is triple-hopped and exceptionally bitter.
Supreme (ABV 5.2%) GOLD
A strong, amber, fruity ale. A touch of malt in the taste is followed by a sweet and slightly hoppy finish.

Nuttycombe SIBA

Ford Road, Wiveliscombe, Somerset, TA4 2RE
☎ (01823) 802400 ⊕ nuttycombebrewery.co.uk

Cotleigh Brewery closed in 2021 and was purchaed by a well-respected and long-established local publican, Ross Nuttycombe, in 2022. Production of its own core range of beers commenced that year. At the end of 2022, it purchased the rights to brew the former Cotleigh beers, followed in 2023 by the rights to also brew the former RCH/Pitchfork brands, all to the original recipes. ♦✦

Cheers! (ABV 3.7%) BITTER
Just One More! (ABV 4%) BITTER
Doonicans (ABV 4.2%) PALE

Brewed under the Cotleigh Brewery brand name:
Golden Seahawk (ABV 3.4%) GOLD
Tawny Owl (ABV 3.8%) BITTER
Barn Owl (ABV 4.5%) BITTER

Brewed under the RCH Brewery brand name:
Pitchfork (ABV 4.5%) GOLD
East Street Cream (ABV 5%) BITTER
Old Slug (ABV 5%) PORTER

O'Connor

12 Lime Road, Faughanvale, Greysteel, BT47 3EH
☎ 07748 004065 ⊕ oconnorbrewing.com

Brewing began in 2013. No real ale.

Oakham SIBA

2 Maxwell Road, Woodston, Peterborough, Cambridgeshire, PE2 7JB
☎ (01733) 370500

Second Site: 80 Westgate, Peterborough, PE2 7JB
⊕ oakhamales.com

⊠ The brewery was established in 1993 in Oakham (Rutland) and moved to Peterborough in 1998. The brewery's main production site is a 75-barrel plant in the Woodston area of the city. The six-barrel 'Westgate' plant at the Brewery Tap pub recommenced brewing in 2023. Five permanent beers are supplied along with monthly seasonals. Additionally around eight 'cask aged' beers are brewed every year. ‼▦♦LIVE

JHB (ABV 3.8%) GOLD
Hoppy yellow golden ale with bags of citrus hop. An underlying sweet maltiness ebbs away as the citrus hop prevails.
Inferno (ABV 4%) GOLD
The citrus hop character of this straw-coloured brew begins on the nose and builds in intensity on the palate. Clean dry citrus finish.
Citra (ABV 4.2%) GOLD
Robust golden ale with explosive grapefruit and lemony hop. A scattering of sweet malt provides contrast to the hop bitterness.
Bishops Farewell (ABV 4.6%) GOLD
Mouth-filling yellow beer with uncompromising zesty citrus hop, softened by undertones of malt, delivering a big-hearted bittersweet palate.
Green Devil (ABV 6%) IPA
Powerful premium golden ale with soaring citrus hop deepening in the mouth progressing into an unrelenting dry hoppy finish.

Oaks SIBA

Unit 6, Stanney Mill Industrial Estate, Dutton Green, Ellesmere Port, Cheshire, CH2 4SA ☎ 07526 437098
⊕ theoaksbrewing.co

Founded as Cheshire Brew Brothers in 2013 and taken into new ownership in 2017. The beers can be found in free and tied trade across North-West England and West Yorkshire. An ever-changing range of beers is produced to satisfy customer demand. ♦V

Bernstein Bitter (ABV 3.4%) BITTER
Chester Gold (ABV 3.5%) BLOND
A fruity, hoppy bitter with a pleasant sweet finish.
Dark Matter (ABV 3.7%) MILD
Delamere Blonde (ABV 4%) GOLD
East Coast Pale (ABV 4.4%) PALE

Oddly

Office: Galla House, 695 High Road, North Finchley, London, N12 0BT ⊕ oddly.beer

⊠ Originally founded on an island in the Thames at Hampton, it moved to be one of the three breweries in the Tottenham Brewery location during 2019 until later that year. Since then it has been using spare capacity at other breweries such as Muswell Hillbilly. ♦V

Odin SIBA

Unit 25 & 26, Snugborough Trading Estate, Union Mills, Isle of Man, IM4 4LH ☎ 07624 266664

Established in 2019 using the 2.5-barrel brewery from Betteridge's of Hampshire. Founder and brewer Rob Storey brews six core beers in cask. The brewery expanded and relocated in 2024 to larger premises in

Union Mills, just off the TT course. A taproom is planned. LIVE

Manx Mild (ABV 3.4%) MILD
Well-balanced mild, malt and caramel sweetness along with roast bitterness in the taste is followed by a sweeter malty finish.

Rhumsaa Bitter (ABV 3.7%) BITTER

Laksaa Pale (ABV 3.8%) PALE
Hoppy beer with some supporting sweet malts. The sweetness fades a little in the finish leaving a drier hoppy bitterness.

Asgard Bitter (ABV 4.2%) BITTER
Gentle malty and caramel aromas move to a sweet, malty bitter with a long dry hop finish.

Black Claw (ABV 4.5%) STOUT
Full-bodied stout, roast builds along with some hop and caramel leading into a lasting, slightly drier finish.

Oyster Stout (ABV 4.8%) STOUT

Odyssey

Brockhampton Brewery, Oast House Barn, Bromyard, Herefordshire, WR6 5SH
☎ (01885) 483496 ☎ 07918 553152
⊕ odysseybrewco.com

☒ This six-barrel brewery was established in 2014 by Alison and Mitchell Evans, who previously owned the Beer in Hand, Hereford. The original building, a restored barn on a National Trust estate, has been retained. A wide range of beers is brewed, predominantly served in keg and can and occasionally bottled for special release.

Oil Basin Brewhouse

See Wintrip

Okell's

Kewaigue, Douglas, Isle of Man, IM2 1QG
☎ (01624) 699400 ⊕ okells.co.uk

☺ Founded in 1874 by Dr Okell, this is the main brewery on the island and moved in 1994 to a new, purpose-built plant at Kewaigue. All the beers are produced under the Manx Brewers' Act. !!♦

MPA (Manx Pale Ale) (ABV 3.6%) PALE
A golden fruity, session beer with background sweetness and a rising hoppy finish.

Bitter (ABV 3.7%) BITTER
Classic traditional bitter with sweet malt and hops in balance. Some fruit and caramel throughout and an even bitter finish.

Dr Okell's IPA (ABV 4.5%) BLOND
A clean, fruity, sweetish bitter with an alcoholic bite.

Old Cannon

🍴 86 Cannon Street, Bury St Edmunds, Suffolk, IP33 1JR
☎ (01284) 768769 ⊕ oldcannonbrewery.co.uk

☒ The St Edmunds Head pub opened in 1845 with its own brewery. Brewing ceased in 1917, and Greene King closed the pub in 1995. It reopened in 1999 as the Old Cannon Brewery, complete with a unique, state-of-the-art brewery housed in the bar area. Other pubs in the chain are also supplied. At least six beers available at any one time. !!♦

Old Chimneys

Office: Old Chimneys, The Street, Market Weston, Suffolk, IP22 2NZ

☎ (01359) 221411 ⊕ oldchimneysbrewery.com

Old Chimneys was established in 1995, moving to a converted farm building in 2001. In 2019 Alan Thomson ceased brewing at Market Weston to concentrate on collaborative brewing projects with other breweries. !!♦LIVE

Old Felixstowe

30 Falkenham Road, Kirton, Ipswich, Suffolk, IP10 0NW ☎ 07889 238784 ⊕ tofbc.co.uk

Brewing began in 2018 in an outhouse in Old Felixstowe. Following a move to Kirton, the brewery was upgraded to a two-barrel plant in 2020. Seven core beers are produced, with seasonal specials. Beer is mostly available bottle-conditioned, but cask beers are produced for bars and events run by the brewery and upon request. Beers can be found at most local farmers markets and a selection of food and drink festivals. Free local delivery is also available. LIVE V

Old Friends

🍴 Old Friends Inn, 49 Soutergate, Ulverston, Cumbria, LA12 7ES
☎ (01229) 208195 ☎ 07563 521575
⊕ oldfriendsulverston.co.uk

☺ Brewing began in 2019 in a room to the rear of the Old Friends pub in Ulverston. Beers are currently only available at the pub.

Old Goat (NEW)

🍴 Compasses, Sudbury, Suffolk, CO10 8LN

☒ The Old Goat brewery is located at the Stansfield Compasses. Crafting fine ales in small batches and offering them in a 16th-century farmhouse pub creates a unique experience for ale enthusiasts. Roy Elder, the owner and brewer, and partner Alexis Rudd, took over the Compasses to establish the brewery. Their vision is to breathe new life into the once-neglected Compasses and restore it as the heart of the community while serving as the flagship pub for the Old Goat brand.

Old Luxters

Old Luxters Vineyard, Dudley Lane, Hambleden, Buckinghamshire, RG9 6JW
☎ (01491) 638330 ⊕ chilternvalley.co.uk

Situated in a 17th century barn beside the Chiltern Valley Vineyard, Old Luxters is a traditional brewery established in 1990 and awarded a Royal Warrant of Appointment in 2007. It produces a range of bottle-conditioned beers. !!🍴♦LIVE

Old Mill SIBA

Mill Street, Snaith, East Yorkshire, DN14 9HU
☎ (01405) 861813 ⊕ oldmillbrewery.co.uk

☺ Established in 1983 in a 240-year-old Maltings and clog mill, the brew length is 60 barrels. The brewery works with its 18 tied estate public houses all around Yorkshire. The beers are delivered direct to the tied estate and free trade by its own fleet of drays (one being horse-drawn). Beers can also be found nationally via wholesalers. Over the past two years extensive improvements in equipment and quality assurance have been installed and implemented to ensure the brewery is in good shape for the next 40 years. !!♦🗡

Styrian Dragon (ABV 3.8%) GOLD
Cask (ABV 3.9%) BITTER

Blonde (ABV 4%) BLOND

Old School SIBA

Holly Bank Barn, Crag Road, Warton, Lancashire, LA5 9PL
☎ (01524) 740888 ⊕ oldschoolbrewery.co.uk

A 12-barrel brewery, founded in 2012, located in a renovated 400-year-old former school outbuilding overlooking the picturesque village of Warton. Beer is mainly sold to free houses within a 40-mile radius. An onsite bar, the Detention Centre, opens daily. ♯♦⬥

Junior (ABV 3.6%) PALE
Hopscotch (ABV 3.7%) GOLD
Initially hoppy, astringency builds in this satisfying beer, ending with a bitter finish.
Textbook (ABV 3.9%) BLOND
Pale beer with malt and hops in the taste, creamy texture and a dry bitter finish.
Detention (ABV 4.1%) PALE
Light amber-coloured, hoppy bitter with a lingering aftertaste.
Headmaster (ABV 4.5%) BITTER

Old Street

Unit 1, Queens Yard, White Post Lane, Hackney Wick, London, E9 5EN
☎ (020) 8525 9731 ✉ oldstreetbrewery@gmail.com

Brewing began in 2013 at the Queen's Head pub in King's Cross. In 2018, the brewery moved to a railway arch near Bethnal Green underground station, with an onsite taproom. A second brewing site and onsite taproom was installed in Queens Yard, Hackney Wick in 2020. The Bethnal Green site was closed in late 2021. No cask ale. Brewing is currently suspended. ⬥

Old Tree

Old Tree, Yachtwerks, 28-29 Richmond Place, Brighton, East Sussex, BN2 9NA ☎ 07413 064346
⊕ oldtree.house

A co-operative based in Brighton producing a unique range of small-batch, probiotic and celebration drinks. It supplies its own zero-waste Silo restaurant. Brewing and gardening are combined, and a production process is used that contributes to land regeneration. LIVE

Old Vicarage

Old Vicarage, Walton, Cumbria, CA8 2DH
☎ (01697) 543002 ⊕ oldvicaragebrewery.co.uk

A microbrewery, bar and B&B accommodation in North Cumbria. Brewing experience days are offered. ⬥

OVB (ABV 4%) BITTER
Coachman (ABV 4.6%) BLOND
SB Special (ABV 5%) BLOND

Olde England

See Potbelly

Olde Swan

Olde Swan, 89 Halesowen Road, Dudley, DY2 9PY
☎ (01384) 253075

A famous brewpub best known as Ma Pardoe's after the matriarch who ruled it for years. The pub has been licensed since 1835 and the present brewery and pub were built in 1863. Brewing continued until 1988 and restarted in 2001. More than 30 outlets are supplied through distributors. ♯♦

Original (ABV 3.5%) MILD
Straw-coloured light mild, smooth but tangy, and sweetly refreshing with a faint hoppiness.
Dark Swan (ABV 4.2%) MILD
Smooth, sweet dark mild with late roast malt in the finish.
Entire (ABV 4.4%) BITTER
Faintly hoppy, amber, premium bitter with sweetness persistent throughout.
NPA (Netherton Pale Ale) (ABV 4.8%) PALE
Bumble Hole Bitter (ABV 5.2%) BITTER
Sweet, smooth amber ale with hints of astringency in the finish.

Oldershaw

See Zest

On Point (NEW)

14 Herbert Street, Bristol, BS3 1FJ

On Point is a new brewery which is testing around six different ales and lagers (of which 25% is cask). The brewery predominantly produces lighter ales, session beers and lagers. Several local Bristol pubs serve the trial brews. ☛⬥

On the Edge

Sheffield, South Yorkshire ☎ 07854 983197
⊕ ontheedgebrew.com

On the Edge started brewing commercially in 2012 using a 0.5-barrel plant in the brewer's home. Brewing takes place once a week. Three local pubs are supplied as well as beer festivals. There is no regular beer list as new brews are constantly being tried.

On The Level (NEW)

Unit 3, Wrantage Mill, Wrantage, Taunton, TA3 6DG
☎ 07476 062662

Office: Woodlawns, Tiverton, EX16 8BE
⊕ onthelevelbrew.co

A new family-run brewery nestled in the scenic Somerset Levels, in full production since 2023. Led by a dedicated son and father team, it specialises in crafting traditional cask ales. Brewed for quality and flavour, OTL started with a six-barrel capacity and eagerly anticipate expanding its reach. ♦

Pale (ABV 4%) PALE
Amber (ABV 4.2%) BITTER

Only With Love

Little Goldsmiths Farm, Beechy Road, Uckfield, East Sussex, TN22 5JG
☎ (01825) 608410 ☎ 07786 830368
⊕ onlywithlove.co

Only With Love was founded in 2020 by Steve Keegan and Roger Warner. It produces kombucha and beer in the heart of Sussex with all products sustainably created, packaged and delivered.

Opa Hay's

Glencot, Wood Lane, Aldeby, Norfolk, NR34 0DA
☎ (01502) 679144 ☎ 07916 282729
✉ arnthengel@hotmail.co.uk

⊠ Opa Hay's began brewing in 2008. It is a small, family-run, award-wining brewery, taking its name from the brewer's great grandfather – a Brewmeister of Schleswig Holstein (northern Germany). Only traditional brewing methods are used, with ingredients that are, where possible, sourced locally. ◆LIVE

ORA

Unit 16a, Rosebery Industrial Park, Rosebery Avenue, Tottenham, London, N17 9SR ☎ 07703 563559 ⊕ orabeer.com

Originally split between Italy and cuckoo brewing at Ubrew, ORA took over Brewheadz in Tottenham in 2019. A variety of hop-forward beers are brewed complemented by styles incorporating classic Italian ingredients such as lemons, balsamic vinegar and vanilla. No cask ale. ◆

Orbit SIBA

Arches 225 & 228, Fielding Street, Walworth, London, SE17 3HD **☎ (020) 7703 9092** ⊕ orbitbeers.com

Established in 2014 in a railway arch in Walworth, Orbit produces keg and bottled beers, focusing on traditional styles, especially continental European styles, supplemented by White Label specials. The design work and beer names relate to the founder's love of vinyl records. Cask is sometimes available in the new taproom in another railway arch across the street. LIVE V

Orkney SIBA

Orkney Brewery, Quoyloo, Orkney, KW16 3LT **☎ (01667) 404555 ☎ 07721 013227**

Office: Sinclair Breweries Ltd, Unit 10B, Balmakeith Industrial Estate, Nairn, IV12 5QW ⊕ orkneybrewery.co.uk

☺The Orkney Brewery was established in 1988, in an old schoolhouse on mainland Orkney. Having incorporated sister brewery Atlas in 2012, brewing capacity was increased, and a brewery shop and a visitor centre, which received Five Star status by VisitScotland, was added. More recently, in 2023, the brewery opened a bottle shop in Kirkwall, Orkney's main town. ‼▉◆✦

Island Life (ABV 3.7%) GOLD
Light golden, citrus hoppy ale with grapefruit and peach flavours leading to a bitter finish.
Raven (ABV 3.8%) BITTER
A well-balanced, quaffable bitter. Malty fruitiness and bitter hops last through to the long, dry aftertaste.
Northern Light (ABV 4%) BITTER
A well-balanced, clean, crisp amber ale with a good mix of malt, citrus hops in the taste and an increasing bitter aftertaste.
Red MacGregor (ABV 4%) BITTER
This tawny red ale has a well-balanced mix of red fruit, malt and hops. Slight sweetness throughout.
Corncrake (ABV 4.1%) GOLD
A straw-coloured beer with soft citrus fruits and a floral aroma.
Man O'Hoy (ABV 4.2%) GOLD
Dark Island (ABV 4.6%) MILD
A sweetish roast chocolate malt taste leads to a long-lasting roasted, slightly bitter, dry finish. Has won many awards.
Cliff Edge IPA (ABV 4.7%) PALE
Full of grapefruit citrus and and mixed red fruit but a dry, astringent finish.
Skull Splitter (ABV 8.5%) BARLEY

An intense velvet malt nose with hints of apple, prune and plum. The hoppy taste is balanced by satiny smooth malt with sweet fruity spicy edges, leading to a long, dry finish with a hint of nut.

Ormeau

Knock Eden Park, Belfast, Northern Ireland, BT6 0JF

Launched in 2022 this nano-brewery, based in South Belfast, delivers quality, internationally-inspired beer at a local level in a sustainable way. Available in can and keg.

Oscars

Unit 1, Riverside Works, Brunswick Street, Nelson, Lancashire, BB9 0HZ **☎ (01282) 616192** ⊕ oscarsbrewery.co.uk

☺Originally based in Preston, the brewery was taken over in 2017 by the Lancashire Beer Co, a pub supplies wholesaler in Nelson. In 2018 the brewery name was changed to Oscars and a new range of beers introduced. Production moved to purpose-built premises in Nelson at the parent company in 2019.

Notorious D.O.G. (ABV 3.8%) PALE
Top Dog (ABV 3.8%) PALE
Dog Father (ABV 3.9%) BITTER
Gun Dog (ABV 4%) BLOND
Space Dog (ABV 4.2%) PALE

Ossett SIBA

Kings Yard, Low Mill Road, Ossett, West Yorkshire, WF5 8ND **☎ (01924) 261333** ⊕ ossett-brewery.co.uk

☺Ossett is an independent brewery established in 1998, located in the heart of Yorkshire. Ossett Pub Company was formed in 2003 and now consists of more than 30 sites across Yorkshire. ‼▉◆GF✦

Butterley (ABV 3.8%) PALE
Yorkshire Blonde (ABV 3.9%) BLOND
Sweet beer with peachy fruity flavours and gentle bitter finish.
White Rat (ABV 4%) GOLD
Inviting citrus hops and fruit last throughout. Hop bitterness rises in the slightly drier finish.
Silver King (ABV 4.3%) GOLD
Citrus aromas lead to a hoppy golden ale with a lengthy bitter finish.
Voodoo (ABV 5%) SPECIALITY
A sweet, fruity stout with vanilla and a long dry roast finish.
Excelsius (ABV 5.2%) PALE
Fruity aromas lead to a sweet hoppy bitter beer with a long bitter aftertaste.

Ostlers

▉ **White Horse, 2 York Street, Harborne, West Midlands, B17 0HG** **☎ (0121) 427 8004** ⊕ whitehorseharborne.com

Started up at the rear of the White Horse pub in Harborne, the brewery was in occasional production for a few years. It now has a 4.5-barrel plant, brewing a small range of core beers alongside frequent specials and seasonal beers, many available in KeyKeg as well as cask. The beer is mainly found in the White Horse pub but can be found in other free houses in the Birmingham area.

Other Monkey SIBA

5-6 St Nicholas Street, Colchester, Essex, CO1 1LB
☎ (01206) 986446 ⊕ othermonkeybrewing.com

⊠ Other Monkey is located in the rear portion of Other Monkey Taproom and is visible to users of the pub. The beer brewed is predominantly served on draft, but cask is produced alongside this and served at the taproom and Three Wise Monkeys pub next door. V✦

Pale Ale (ABV 4.4%) PALE

Otherworld

27 / 1 Hardengreen Estate, Eskbank, Dalkeith,
EH22 3NX ⊕ otherworldbrewing.com

Otherworld Brewing Ltd was established in 2022 and specialises in producing modern sour and mixed fermentation beers. There is a quarterly cask release of special beers, however, beers are mostly available in cans.

Otley SIBA

⯄ Ynysangharad Road, Pontypridd, CF37 4DA

This is a new venture, new premises and new plant. The brewery is built on part of the car park at the Bunch of Grapes. Both are operated by Nick Otley, who was involved in the previous Otley brewery, but now brewing is intended just for the pub. Some beers will be based on the recipes of the previous brewery. Cwrw Otley soft launched with a new beer. Since, recipes of previous Otley beers have been replicated. At present there is no permanent range. ♦

Otter SIBA

Mathayes, Luppitt, Honiton, Devon, EX14 4SA
☎ (01404) 891285 ⊕ otterbrewery.com

⊠ A family-run brewery set high up in the Blackdown Hills. Environmental responsibility lies at the heart of its ethos. Otter's eco cellar has been built underground and is naturally chilled. The beers are made from the brewery's own spring water and locally-sourced ingredients. ♦✦

Bitter (ABV 3.6%) BITTER
Well-balanced session bitter with a fruity nose. Biscuity overtones, hop, lemon and apricot with bitter taste and dry aftertaste.
Amber (ABV 4%) BITTER
Light, refreshing and mellow with hints of citrus hoppiness. Creamy and delicate with hops and fruit.
Bright (ABV 4.3%) GOLD
A light and refreshing golden ale with delicate malt, and fruit leading through hops to a lingering bitter aftertaste.
Ale (ABV 4.5%) BITTER
Malt dominates from nose to throat. Sweet fruit, toffee and caramel with a dry aftertaste, full of flavour.
Head (ABV 5.8%) BITTER
Smooth strong ale. Caramel malt throughout. Full-bodied with rich malty fruitiness and a chocolate hint, leaving a bitter aftertaste.

Our

86 Clonkeen Road, Randalstown, Northern Ireland,
BT41 3JJ
☎ (0800) 228 9433

Energy efficient brewery launched in 2022, which is a passion project from the team at Get Er Brewed, overlooking Lough Neagh.

Out of Office

⯄ Ulster Sports Club, 96-98 High Street, Belfast,
Northern Ireland, BT1 2BG
☎ (028) 9023 0771 ⊕ outofofficebrewing.co.uk

Located on the 2nd floor of the Ulster Sports Club, the brewery opened in 2021 producing modern craft beers. The onsite taproom is open Thursday to Sunday. No real ale. ‼

Out There

Unit 4, Foundry Lane Industrial Estate, Newcastle
upon Tyne, NE6 1LH ☎ 07946 579534
⊕ outtherebrewing.com

Out There was established in 2012 by Steve Pickthall. Branding and beer names are themed around the 1950s space race.

Space is the Place (ABV 3.5%) BITTER
Laika (ABV 4.8%) SPECIALITY
Celestial Love (ABV 5.1%) BITTER

Outhouse

4 Southgate House, Alexandra Court, Denmark Street,
Wokingham, Berkshire, RG40 2SL
⊕ theouthousebrewery.com

⊠ A nanobrewery established in 2021, using a 300-litre (1.8-barrel) plant, situated within the onsite taproom. Beers are supplied in KeyKegs, are unfiltered and unpasteurised, and can be purchased from the taproom. The majority of production is dispensed onsite, with occasional KeyKegs on sale at local pubs or beer festivals. New recipes are constantly being brewed and older recipes tweaked. ⯇✦

Outlandish

Woodend Hayloft, Birkenshaw Road, Glenboig,
ML5 2QH

Established in 2020, brewing traditional and contemporary craft beers with names inspired by local lingo.

Outlaw

See Rooster's

Outpost

See Three Hills

Outwoods (NEW)

⯄ Unit 21-22, Station Street Yard, Burton upon Trent,
Staffordshire, DE14 1AZ ☎ 07737 617496
✉ outwoodsbrewco@gmail.com

Colin Trowell realised his dream by converting two railway arches into a pub and 0.5-barrel brewery producing cask and keg beers.

Overtone

Unit 19, New Albion Industrial Estate, Halley Street,
Glasgow, G13 4DJ
☎ (0141) 952 7772

Established in 2018, Overtone produce hop-forward craft beers with an emphasis on quality and flavour. It specialises in New England-style IPAs but also brews a number of other styles such as fruit sours and stouts.

Oxford

Unit 1, Coopers Yard, Manor Farm Road, Horspath, Oxfordshire, OX33 1SD
☎ (01865) 604620 ☎ 07710 883273
⊕ oxfordbrewery.co.uk

⊠ A family-owned and run brewery, it began brewing in 2009 and supplies outlets in the Oxford area. All beers are suitable for vegans. !! 🍺 ♦ LIVE V 🌿

Prospect (ABV 3.7%) BITTER
Trinity (ABV 4.2%) PALE
Vivid Dreams (ABV 4.2%) GOLD
Let the Dragon See the Wolf (ABV 4.5%) BITTER
Scholar (ABV 4.5%) BITTER
Matilda's Tears (ABV 5%) PALE

Oxhey Village (OVB)

14 Maxwell Rise, Watford, Hertfordshire, WD19 4DX
☎ 07470 422842 ✉ shaun@ruthandshaun.co.uk

Oxhey Village Brewery (OVB) is a nanobrewery set up by five drinking companions, which began commercial brewing in 2019. Currently producing real ale in cask and craft beer in keg for a few local pubs and clubs. Additionally, small batches are available on request for events and beer festivals.

P-Noot

Office: 373 Stockport Road, Denton, M34 6EP
☎ 07931 986794 ⊕ p-nootbrewco.com

⊛P-Noot commenced brewing in 2021, in the cellar of the Lowes Arms, moving to cuckoo brew at Four Kings Brewery in Hyde in 2022. It has now moved to full outsourced contract brewing at unnamed breweries. Its full range of cask and keg products are still available. ♦

APEX EGA (ABV 3.8%) GOLD
Into the Light (ABV 4%) PALE
Stark BA (ABV 4.1%) PALE
Force 8 SB (ABV 4.3%) BITTER

Padstow SIBA

Unit 4a, Trecerus Industrial Estate, Padstow, Cornwall, PL28 8RW
☎ (01841) 532169 ☎ 07834 924312
⊕ padstowbrewing.co.uk

⊠ Owners Des and Caron Archer established the brewery in 2013, using a 0.5-barrel plant, which has since been upgraded to 10 barrels. Besides the integral brewery shop, two licenced town-centre tasting rooms have been established. !! 🍺 ♦ LIVE V

Pale Ale (ABV 3.6%) PALE
Thin golden beer. Citrus hops dominate flavours with bitter grapefruit, sweet tropical fruits and a trace of malt. Lingering finish.
Padstow Local (ABV 4%) BITTER
Amber session bitter with a fruity aroma. Dominant apricot and bitter flavour with some biscuit malt. Long sweet, fruity finish.
Windjammer (ABV 4.3%) BROWN
American brown ale with dominant malt plus summer and citrus fruits. Distinct malt aroma. Bitter and sweet throughout. Dry finish.
IPA (ABV 4.8%) PALE
Golden pale ale with hop, oranges and faint malt aroma. Malt is minimal, but oranges, lemons, grapefruit and peaches dominate.
Padstow May Day (ABV 5%) PALE

Golden pale ale with grapefruit and mango aroma. Mixture of citrus and tropical fruits leads the taste with minimal malt.

Palmers SIBA IFBB

Old Brewery, West Bay Road, Bridport, Dorset, DT6 4JA
☎ (01308) 422396 ⊕ palmersbrewery.com

⊠ Palmers is one of Britain's only thatched breweries and dates from 1794. It is situated in Bridport, the heart of the Jurassic Coast in south-west Dorset. The company continues to make substantial investment in its 54 tenanted pubs, all serving cask ale. An additional 400 outlets are supplied within the free trade. !! 🍺

Copper Ale (ABV 3.7%) BITTER
Beautifully-balanced, copper-coloured light bitter with a hoppy aroma.
IPA (ABV 4.2%) PALE
Hop aroma and bitterness stay in the background in this predominately malty best bitter, with some fruit on the aroma.
Dorset Gold (ABV 4.5%) GOLD
More complex than many golden ales thanks to a pleasant banana and mango fruitiness on the aroma that carries on into the taste and aftertaste.
200 (ABV 5%) BITTER
This is a big beer with a touch of caramel sweetness adding to a complex hoppy, fruit taste that lasts from the aroma well into the aftertaste.
Tally Ho! (ABV 5.5%) OLD
A complex dark old ale. Roast malts and treacle toffee on the palate lead in to a long, lingering finish with more than a hint of coffee.

Panther

Unit 1, Collers Way, Reepham, Norfolk, NR10 4SW
☎ 07766 558215 ⊕ pantherbrewery.co.uk

⊠ Panther began brewing in 2010 on an industrial estate near the old railway station, formerly the home of Reepham Brewery. !! 🍺 ♦ LIVE GF

Mild Panther (ABV 3.3%) MILD
Smooth, sweet base with contrasting dry cobnut notes and a gentle roastiness. Short, clean finish with biscuit airs.
Ginger Panther (ABV 3.7%) SPECIALITY
Refreshingly clean ginger wheat beer with a distinct fiery kick. Contains all the ingredients of a Thai Curry.
Golden Panther (ABV 3.7%) GOLD
Refreshing orange and malt notes flow through this well-balanced, easy-drinking bitter. Hops and a soft bitterness add depth.
Honey Panther (ABV 4%) SPECIALITY
A gentle flowing brew with honey and malt throughout. Amber-coloured with a tapering bittersweet finale.
Red Panther (ABV 4.1%) RED
A distinctly malty nose with a nutty, bittersweet beginning. Rye, plum and caramel appear before a full-bodied hoppiness emerges.
American Pale Ale (ABV 4.4%) BLOND
Zesty lemon and hop character with a gentle sweet counterpoint. Light grapefruit notes bolster a short crisp finish.
Black Panther (ABV 4.5%) PORTER
Vanilla rum and raisin throughout. Strong supporting mix of caramel, malt and robust roastiness. Mellow and complex finish slowly sweetens.
Beast of the East (ABV 5.5%) IPA
A hoppy resinous bouquet with hints of sweetness. Earthy, peppery beginning with a hoppy backdrop. Long drying, bitter, citrus finish.

Papworth SIBA

**24 Earith Business Park, Meadow Drove, Earith,
Cambridgeshire, PE28 3QF**
☎ (01487) 842442 ☎ 07835 845797
🌐 papworthbrewery.com

Brewing began in 2014 in Papworth Everard. The
brewery moved to new premises in Earith in 2017 and
acquired an 11-barrel plant, significantly increasing its
production. A brewery tap and bottle shop, the Crystal
Ship, opened in 2020 and can be found at Unit 32, Earith
Business Park. ⏰ 🍺 ♦ LIVE V

Mild Thing (ABV 3.5%) MILD
Mad Jack (ABV 3.8%) BITTER
The Whitfield Citrabolt (ABV 3.8%) GOLD
Whispering Grass (ABV 3.8%) BITTER
Fen Skater (ABV 4%) PALE
Crystal Ship (ABV 4.2%) BITTER
Half Nelson (ABV 4.2%) PALE
Old Riverport Stout (ABV 4.5%) STOUT
Red Kite (ABV 4.7%) BITTER
Off the Lip (ABV 5%) PALE
Robin Goodfellow (ABV 5.4%) BITTER
Pass the Porter (ABV 5.5%) PORTER
Koura (ABV 5.7%) SPECIALITY
Saison d'Etre (ABV 6%) SPECIALITY

Parachute (NEW)

**Unit 16, Old Yarn Mills, Westbury, Sherborne, Dorset,
DT9 3RQ**
☎ (01935) 509187 🌐 parachutebrewing.co.uk

Opened in 2023, Parachute Tap Room & Bar brews using
traditional methods and natural processes in open-top
fermenters. Beers are naturally carbonated in the kegs.
♦

Parish

**6 Main Street, Burrough on the Hill, Leicestershire,
LE14 2JQ**
☎ (0116) 430 0020 🌐 parishbrewery.co.uk

Parish began brewing in 1983 and is now operating on a
20-barrel plant, with capacity to brew a further 12
barrels. The brewery is located in a 400-year-old building
next to the Stag & Hounds, supplying real ale in cask to
many pubs across Leicestershire & Derbyshire and is
always available at the Melton & District Indoor Bowls
Club. One-off brews are produced for beer festivals both
locally and across surrounding counties. ⏰ LIVE

Proper Charlie (ABV 3.9%) GOLD
PSB (ABV 3.9%) BITTER
A refreshing pale session ale. Distinctive floral aroma
with mild hints of pine. Sharp hop bitterness balanced
with crisp malt flavours in the taste giving way to a
lovely lingering floral finish.
Fruits of the Parish (ABV 4.2%) SPECIALITY
A refreshing fruity amber ale with hints of black cherry,
strawberry, raspberry and blackberry.

Park SIBA

Unit 7, Hampden Road, Norbiton, KT1 3LG
☎ (020) 8541 1887

**Office: 38 St Georges Road, Kingston upon Thames,
KT2 6DN** 🌐 theparkbrewery.com

⊠ Founded in 2014, Park moved to larger premises in
2018. A wide variety of beers is now produced in cask,
keg and cans, named after sites in nearby Richmond
Park. The beers are unfined and sometimes experimental
in their range of hops. ♦ LIVE V ♦

Killcat Pale (ABV 3.7%) GOLD
Easy-drinking, straw-coloured golden ale. Citrus on nose
and palate with the biscuity sweetness providing balance
to the hoppy bitterness.
Amelia (ABV 4.2%) PALE
Pale gold. Aromas of biscuity malt and spicy hops. Dry-
bitter and light with a grassy bitterness and a slight
sweetness.
Gallows (ABV 4.5%) GOLD
Tropical fruit, orange and hop notes dominate. Malt is
restrained with a gentle biscuit presence and growing
bitterness. Well-balanced.
Spankers Hill IPA (ABV 6%) IPA
An amber-coloured, hoppy, citrus, dry golden ale with a
similar finish and a touch of dry bitterness.

Parker

Unit 3, Gravel Lane, Banks, Lancashire, PR9 8BY
☎ (01704) 620718 ☎ 07949 797889
✉ theparkerbrewery@gmail.com

⊛ Parker was established in 2014 using a 25-litre plant,
but quickly expanded to a five-barrel plant. In 2018 the
brewery opened its own micropub, the Beer Den,
Southport. Three Years later, in 2021, it opened another
micropub, Beer Den 2, on Rufford Road, Crossens. ⏰ LIVE

Centurion Pale Ale (ABV 3.9%) PALE
Barbarian Bitter (ABV 4.1%) BITTER
Saxon Red Ale (ABV 4.5%) RED
Viking Blonde (ABV 4.7%) BLOND
Dark Spartan Stout (ABV 5%) STOUT
Well-balanced stout with a smoky roast aroma, roast
strong on tasting, a little sweetness and some bitterness
to finish.

Parkway

**Unit 11, Wessex Park, Somerton Business Park,
Bancombe Road, Somerton, Somerset, TA11 6SB**
☎ (01458) 897240 🌐 parkwaybrewing.co.uk

Parkway began its journey into brewing in 2018, having
purchased the former Glastonbury Ales plant and
equipment. Although located in the small market town
of Somerton, Parkway is named after a road in North
London's Camden Town. The brewery also contract brew
for others under license. LIVE

Giggle & Titter (ABV 3.8%) BITTER
Cheeky Monkey (ABV 4%) BLOND
Norwegian Blue (ABV 4.2%) BITTER

Contract brewed for Tanners Ales:
Box of Frogs (ABV 4%) GOLD

Parlour

Chadwick Farm, Garford, Nr Abingdon, OX13 5PD
☎ (01865) 392227 ☎ 07799 183119

Office: Ock Barn, Garford, OX13 5PD
✉ ben@milletsfarmcentre.com

Run by three brothers-in-law, this small brewery was set
up in a converted milking parlour in 2020. It brews beer
in 240L batches, which can be bottle-conditioned or
kegged. LIVE

Partizan

Grange Farm, Thorpe Langon, Leicestershire, LE16 7TU
☎ 07443 168191 🌐 partizanbrewing.co.uk

Started in 2012, using an ex-Kernel kit in a taproom on
the Bermondsey Beer Mile, the brewery moved its
production out of London in 2023 to a farm in Thorpe

Langton in rural Leicestershire, locating it at long-time friends, Langton Brewery. Expansion is taking place with a new fermenter hall and greater capacity than at its London plant. ☒♦V

Pastore SIBA

Unit 2, Convent Drive, Waterbeach, Cambridgeshire, CB25 9QT ⊕ pastorebrewing.com

⊠ Founded in 2019, Pastore Brewing & Blending specialise in mixed-fermentation sour and wild ales. Pastore (Pas-tor-ray) is Italian for shepherd, in honour of the brewer's Italian family. It ties rustic, wild brewing with a modern, semi-urban setting, making new-age fresh, fruited weisses, as well as barrel-aged old saisons. ‼☒♦LIVE V✦

Pathfinder

See Exmoor

Patrons Tap (NEW)

☗ Patrons Tap, 3 School Lane, Blackburn, Lancashire, BB1 2LW

Patrons Tap is a new brewery that first brewed in the summer of 2023.

Patten

☗ Patten Arms, Park Lane, Winmarleigh, PR3 0JU
☎ (01524) 791484
✉ thepattenarmswinmarleigh@gmail.com

Brewing started in 2019 using a small plant in the cellar of the Patten Arms. Five different beers are brewed on rotation and only on sale at the pub. Brewing is currently suspended.

Peak SIBA

Unit 3-6, Park Farm Industrial Units, Longstone Lane, Ashford in the Water, Derbyshire, DE45 1NH
☎ (01246) 583737 ⊕ peakales.co.uk

⊕Peak Ales opened 2005 in a former derelict farm building on the Chatsworth estate, aided by a DEFRA Rural Enterprise Scheme grant and support from trustees of Chatsworth Settlement. The main production moved to a new facility at Ashford in the Water in 2014 to increase capacity. A new shop has opened on site for sales of Peak Ales to take home, Chatsworth gin and merchandise. ‼☒♦

Swift Nick (ABV 3.8%) BITTER
Bakewell Best Bitter (ABV 4.2%) BITTER
Chatsworth Gold (ABV 4.6%) SPECIALITY
Speciality beer made with honey, which gives a pleasant sweetness leading to a hop and malt finish.
Black Stag (ABV 4.8%) STOUT
DPA (Derbyshire Pale Ale) (ABV 5%) PALE
IPA (ABV 6%) IPA

Peakstones Rock SIBA

Peakstones Farm, Cheadle Road, Alton, Staffordshire, ST10 4DH ☎ 07891 350908

Office: 1 Tape Street, Cheadle, ST10 1BB
⊕ peakstonesrock.co.uk

⊠ Peakstones Rock are a family-run brewery established in 2005 with a five-barrel plant located on a farm in the Peak District National Park. The brewery was expanded to 10-barrel capacity in 2009. It supplies an expanding

free trade market in the North Midlands and surrounding areas. ‼♦LIVE

Nemesis (ABV 3.8%) BITTER
Biscuity aroma with some hop background. Sweet start, sweetish body then hops emerge to give a fruity middle. Bitterness develops slowly to a tongue-tingling finish.
Pugin's Gold (ABV 4%) GOLD
Chained Oak (ABV 4.2%) BITTER
Alton Abbey (ABV 4.5%) BITTER
Black Hole (ABV 4.8%) OLD
Grassy aroma with malt background. Hops hit the mouth and intensify. Bitterness lingers with some mouth-watering astringency
Oblivion (ABV 5.5%) BITTER

Peerless SIBA

The Brewery, 8 Pool Street, Birkenhead, Merseyside, CH41 3NL
☎ (0151) 647 7688 ⊕ peerlessbrewing.co.uk

Peerless began brewing in 2009 and is under the directorship of Steve Briscoe. Beers are sold through festivals, local pubs and the free trade. ‼♦✦

Triple Blond (ABV 4%) BLOND
Skyline (ABV 4.2%) BITTER
Full-bodied traditional bitter, well-balanced and fruity/hoppy. Plenty of malt, some roast and sweetness, hops rise in the finish.
Langton Spin (ABV 4.4%) GOLD
Oatmeal Stout (ABV 5%) STOUT
Roast malts, burnt sugar/toffee aroma. Smooth, full-bodied mouthfeel, sweet caramel/chocolate flavour, light hop, roast, dry bitter finish.
Knee-Buckler IPA (ABV 5.2%) PALE
Full Whack (ABV 6%) IPA

Pell & Co

White Horse Inn, The Street, Neatishead, Norfolk, NR12 8AD
☎ (01692) 630828
⊕ thewhitehorseinnneatishead.com

⊠ Formerly known as Neatishead Brewery, production began in 2015 at the White Horse Inn. The brew kit can be viewed through glass from the restaurant. Beer is only available in the White Horse and the owner's other pub, the Lion, Thurne. A range of semi-regular beers is brewed with at least one ever-changing ale. The range is currently being contract brewed by an unknown brewery. V

Pennine SIBA

Well Hall Farm, Well, Bedale, North Yorkshire, DL8 2PX
☎ (01677) 470111 ⊕ pennine-brewing.co.uk

⊕Located in the village of Well near Masham, the brewery has been in production on this site since 2013 using an 18-barrel plant complete with lauter tun. Beer is supplied to pubs throughout the North of England as well as to beer festivals and local outdoor events. ‼♦

Amber Necker (ABV 3.9%) BITTER
Hair of the Dog (ABV 3.9%) BITTER
Heartland (ABV 3.9%) BITTER
Millie George (ABV 4.1%) PALE
Scapegoat (ABV 4.2%) GOLD
IPA (ABV 4.4%) PALE

Pentrich SIBA

Unit B, Asher Lane Business Park, Asher Lane,
Pentrich, Derbyshire, DE5 3RB
☎ (01773) 741700 ⊕ pentrichbrewing.com

⊠ Two former homebrewers began producing beer in
their garage in Pentrich before moving to share the plant
at the Beehive Inn, Ripley, in 2014. In 2016, the brewery
moved to its own premises using second-hand
equipment. In 2019, it purchased a made-to-order 16-
barrel plant. Every brew produced is a special brew (no
regular beers). Local free trade outlets are supplied while
a wholesaler distributes more widely. ♦

Penzance

🗏 Star Inn, Crowlas, Cornwall, TR20 8DX
☎ (01736) 740375 ☎ 07763 956333
⊕ penzancebrewingcompany.co.uk

⊠ Family-run brewery, established in 2008 by the then
owner, the late Peter Elvin, who designed and built the
five-barrel plant in the old stable block of the Star Inn. In
full production the brewery now exceeds 1,400 barrels a
year, supplying well over 25 selected outlets. ‼♦

Mild (ABV 3.6%) MILD
Smooth auburn mild. Grainy malt, coffee and chocolate
dominate the taste with dried fruit notes. Fading sweet
roast malt finish.
Crowlas Bitter (ABV 3.8%) BITTER
Refreshing copper session bitter with light malt aroma.
Light biscuit maltiness and hops. Lingering finish of malty
bitterness with dryness.
Potion No 9 (ABV 4%) PALE
Refreshing pale ale. Grapefruit hops and tropical fruit
flavours dominate with pine resin notes, malt and
bubblegum flashes. Lasting bitterness.
Crows-an-Wra (ABV 4.3%) BLOND
Yellow blond ale with citrus hoppy aroma. Grapefruit
bitter hops dominate the long-lasting taste with a light
hoppy, dry finish.
Brisons Bitter (ABV 4.5%) BITTER
Full-bodied, tawny bitter with malt aroma. Biscuit malt
dominates the taste with robust sweetness, fruit esters
and hop bitterness.
Trink (ABV 5.2%) BLOND
Blond ale with grapefruit nose. Punchy pine-resin hop
flavours with grapefruit, marmalade and mango. Dry,
bittersweet and hoppy finish.
Zythos (ABV 5.3%) PALE
Golden pale ale with fruity hop nose. Bitter grapefruit
and apricot fruity hop flavours dominate with a light malt
balance.
IPA (ABV 6%) IPA
Smooth, golden, genuine IPA with hoppy aroma.
Powerful hop bitterness with light malt and tropical
fruits, finishing bitter and dry.

People's

Mill House, Mill Lane, Thorpe-Next-Haddiscoe,
Norwich, Norfolk, NR14 6PA
☎ (01508) 548706 ✉ peoplesbrewery@mail.com

⊠ A one-barrel brewery associated with the Queen's
Head pub in Thurlton, which takes most of its draught
output. Bottled beers are also available at Thurlton
Community Shop.

Northdown Bitter (ABV 3.8%) BITTER
Raveningham Bitter (ABV 3.9%) BITTER
Thurlton Gold (ABV 4.2%) PALE
Norfolk Cascade (ABV 4.5%) GOLD
Northern Brewers (ABV 4.6%) BITTER

People's Captain

39 Sackville Road, Hove, East Sussex, BN3 3WD
⊕ peoplescaptain.co.uk

People's Captain was an idea conceived by Greg
Bateman, a professional Rugby player. Along with friends
Stewart Beale and Jason Reeves, the company was
established to brew craft beer while also contributing to
positive mental health. Every beer sold raises money via
the People's Captain Foundation.

Peregrine

Unit 27, Richmond Industrial Estate, Richmond Street,
Accrington, Lancashire, BB5 0RJ ☎ 07757 404231
⊕ peregrinebrewingltd.com

Started brewing in late 2020 using a 1.5-barrel plant. ♦V

What What? (ABV 3.6%) BITTER
Flight of the Falcon (ABV 3.7%) GOLD
Atomic (ABV 3.9%) BLOND
Gold (ABV 3.9%) GOLD
Cream Stout (ABV 4%) STOUT
Próst! (ABV 4%) PALE
BRUT IPA (ABV 4.5%) PALE
Hayabusa (ABV 4.5%) PALE
Mutiny (ABV 4.8%) PORTER
Serendipity (ABV 4.8%) PALE

Pererin (NEW)

Ty Brew House, Llansteffan, SA33 5HH

Brewery established in 2022 producing cask and bottled
beers with a Welsh theme.

Pure Pale Ale (ABV 5%) PALE

Perivale

Horsenden Farm, Horsenden Lane North, Perivale,
UB6 7PQ ☎ 07892 409392 ⊕ perivale.beer

Established in 2019, the brewery is based at a farm
looked after by the Friends of Horsenden Hill. As well as
other events, weekly Saturday taproom openings are
hosted, selling beers brewed with hops grown on the
farm, and other local foraged ingredients, available in
keg and bottles. Cask ale is now available to trusted
outlets and at the taproom openings. 🍺♦

Phantom

Unit 3, Meadow Road, Reading, Berkshire, RG1 8LB
⊕ phantombrew.com

A brewery located on the outskirts of Reading town
centre, brewing an ever-changing range of KeyKeg beers
in a variety of styles including hoppy pales, fruit sours
and stouts. No beer is brewed all the time, but favourites
turn up at regular intervals. ‼♦

Pheasantry SIBA

High Brecks Farm, Lincoln Road, East Markham,
Nottinghamshire, NG22 0SN
☎ (01777) 872728 ☎ 07948 976749
⊕ pheasantrybrewery.co.uk

⊛ Pheasantry began brewing in 2012 using a new 10-
barrel plant from Canada. The brewery is situated in a
listed barn on a Nottinghamshire farm and incorporates a
wedding and events venue. It supplies more than 200
pubs, restaurants, venues and bottle shops across
Nottinghamshire, Lincolnshire, Derbyshire and South
Yorkshire. In addition to the core range a different artisan
beer is brewed every 2-3 weeks. The bottling line,

installed in 2018, has capacity for contract bottling.
🍴♦LIVE

Best Bitter (ABV 3.8%) BITTER
Pale Ale (ABV 4%) PALE
Ringneck Amber Ale (ABV 4.1%) BITTER
Amber-coloured best bitter, initial malt and caramel
leading to a brief, bitter, dry finish.
Black Pheasant Dark Ale (ABV 4.2%) PORTER
Lincoln Tank Ale (ABV 4.2%) BITTER
Excitra (ABV 4.5%) GOLD
Dancing Dragonfly (ABV 5%) BLOND

Phipps NBC SIBA

**Albion Brewery, 54 Kingswell Street, Northampton,
NN1 1PR**
☎ (01604) 946606 ☎ 07717 078402
⊕ phipps-nbc.co.uk

Founded initially in Towcester in 1801, Phipps had been
brewing in Northampton since 1817. Following a
takeover by Watney Mann in 1960, the brewery closed in
1974. The company name, trademark and recipes were
acquired and Phipps beers reappeared in 2008. The
founding Phipps family rejoined the company in 2014,
allowing the historic Albion Brewery and its associated
bar to be restored, and Phipps brewing to return to the
town after a 40-year absence. ‼♦LIVE ⚘

Foundry Mild (ABV 3.5%) MILD
Sweet malt aroma with hints of dried fruit continuing
into the slightly sweet, spicy, liquorice flavour which
follows into the aftertaste.
Thrupenny Bitter (ABV 3.6%) BITTER
Diamond Ale (ABV 3.7%) BITTER
Rich honey sweetish aroma, a full bitter flavour with
citrus notes and a bitter aftertaste with hints of
grapefruit.
Red Star (ABV 3.8%) BITTER
Honey malt aroma, a flavour of rye, some sweetness and
hints of dark cherry and a dry bitter aftertaste.
Steam Roller (ABV 3.8%) BITTER
Biscuity aroma with some sweetness followed by earthy
spiced bitterness with hints of plum which continue in
the dry aftertaste.
Midsummer Meadow (ABV 3.9%) BITTER
Malty, slightly sweet and fruity aroma followed by a
hoppy flavour with lemon and grapefruit notes and a
lingering bitter aftertaste with hints of apple.
Cobbler's Ale (ABV 4%) BITTER
Strong malty aroma with hints of candied orange,
followed by a strong bitter flavour with dried fruit notes
and a long, bitter, biscuity finish.
Phipps IPA (ABV 4.3%) GOLD
Sweet, malty aroma with orange notes followed by a
bitter flavour balanced by malt and fruit and a dry bitter
aftertaste.
Ratliffe's Celebrated Stout (ABV 4.3%) STOUT
Becket's Ale (ABV 4.5%) BITTER
Sweetish malty aroma with a slight spicy bite and orange
dried fruit notes followed by a dry earthy flavour and a
bitter, slightly astringent finish with hints of dried fruit.
Bison Brown (ABV 4.6%) MILD
Black Star (ABV 4.8%) BITTER
Roasted malt aromas with liquorice notes followed by a
bitter coffee chocolate flavour and a dry bitter coffee
aftertaste.
Last Orders (ABV 4.8%) BITTER
Kinky Boots (ABV 4.9%) SPECIALITY
Gold Star (ABV 5.2%) PALE

Phoenix SIBA

Green Lane, Heywood, OL10 2EP

☎ (01706) 367359 ✉ cheers@phoenixbrewery.co.uk

☺Phoenix Brewery (Oak Brewing Co Ltd) was founded
in 1982 by Tony Allen. It relocated to the imposing red
brick Heywood site (built in 1898) and changed name in
1991. The first microbrewery in Manchester, it gained a
strong following in the North West. Tony Allen died in
2021, and the brewery was saved by a family team (now
run by two sisters). It continues to brew the classics, and
also new brews and bottled beers. The site boasts a
shop, and tap with a large outdoor area. ♦⚘

Hopsack (ABV 3.8%) BLOND
Light citrus aroma, gentle bitterness, sweet body with
hops lasting in the finish.
Monkeytown Mild (ABV 3.9%) MILD
Light roast aroma. Mild creamy roast flavour with sweet
malt and some astringency. Lasting dry bitter finish.
Phoenix (ABV 4%) GOLD
Arizona (ABV 4.1%) BLOND
Yellow in colour. This gentle beer with fruity aromas, has
hops, a good bitterness and a short dry finish.
Heywood Pale (ABV 4.1%) PALE
Spotland Gold (ABV 4.1%) BLOND
Pale Moonlight (ABV 4.2%) PALE
Black Bee (ABV 4.5%) SPECIALITY
White Monk (ABV 4.5%) GOLD
Yellow with a citrus fruit aroma, plenty of fruit, hops and
bitterness in the taste and a hoppy, bitter finish.
Thirsty Moon (ABV 4.6%) BITTER
Tawny beer with a fresh citrus aroma. Hoppy, fruity and
malty with a dry, hoppy finish.
West Coast IPA (ABV 4.6%) PALE
Golden in colour with a hoppy, fruity nose. Strong hoppy
and fruity taste and aftertaste with good bitterness
throughout.
Double Gold (ABV 5%) PALE
Initial fruit and sweet flavours gradually give way to an
increasing hop presence in the slightly drier finish.
Wobbly Bob (ABV 6%) BITTER
A beer with malty, fruity aromas. Malty and fruity in
flavour with hops. Both sweetness and bitterness are
evident throughout.

Pictish

**Unit 9, Canalside Industrial Estate, Woodbine Street
East, Rochdale, OL16 5LB**
☎ (01706) 522227 ⊕ pictish-brewing.co.uk

☺The brewery was established in 2000 and supplies
free trade outlets in the North West and West Yorkshire.
Famed for the consistency and clarity of its brews and its
ever-changing single hop series of beers. ♦

Brewers Gold (ABV 3.8%) BITTER
Session pale ale with moderate levels of sweetness,
malty character and hops
Talisman IPA (ABV 4.2%) PALE
Alchemists Ale (ABV 4.3%) BITTER
A bitter beer with resiny hops. Malt aromas to start some
sweetness ending with hoppy bitterness.

Piddle

**Unit 24, Enterprise Park, Piddlehinton, Dorchester,
Dorset, DT2 7UA**
☎ (01305) 849336 ☎ 07730 436343
⊕ piddlebrewery.co.uk

⊗ Established in 2007, with new owners in 2014. The
brewery produces a broad range of beers from its
location in the Piddle Valley in Dorset. Some beer names
reflect this unusual name. Beers are available in pubs
and retail outlets across Dorset and beyond. ♦

Dorset Rogue (ABV 3.9%) BITTER

Piddle (ABV 4.1%) BITTER
Cocky (ABV 4.3%) PALE
Bent Copper (ABV 4.8%) BITTER
Slasher (ABV 5.1%) BLOND

Pied Bull

▤ Pied Bull Hotel, 57 Northgate Street, Chester, CH1 2HQ
☎ (01244) 325829 ⊕ piedbull.co.uk

☺Pied Bull began brewing in 2011 using a one-barrel plant. Beer is mainly for in-house consumption but local beer festivals are supplied and occasional brewery swaps occur. ◆

Pig & Porter

9 Chapman Way, Tunbridge Wells, Kent, TN2 3EF
☎ (01892) 615071 ⊕ pigandporter.co.uk

⊠ Originally brewing at several microbreweries in Sussex and Kent, brewing has taken place on its own plant in Tunbridge Wells since 2013, using a 10-barrel plant. ◆V

Bipperty Boppity (ABV 3.6%) PALE
Caravan (ABV 3.6%) BITTER
Blackbird (ABV 4%) STOUT
Skylarking (ABV 4%) PALE
Slave to the Money (ABV 4.1%) BITTER
Stone Free (ABV 4.3%) PALE
Got the Face On (ABV 4.5%) PALE
Jumping Frog (ABV 4.5%) GOLD
Forever Lost (ABV 5.5%) IPA

Pig Barn

Low Hall Road, East Lound, Lincolnshire, DN9 2LU
☎ (01427) 754339

Located in a converted piggery, this is one of the smaller breweries in the UK. Brewing commenced in late 2019, with the first cask beers launched in local pubs in spring 2020. During lockdown the brewer was forced to concentrate on the production of bottle-conditioned ales. Brewing of cask ales recommence and Pig Barn ales are available in both forms. Pig Barn ales are available in pubs and at festivals in and around the Isle of Axholme, Lincolnshire LIVE V

Pig Beer SIBA

Hop House, Setley Ridge, Brockenhurst, Hampshire, SO42 7UF
☎ (01590) 607237 ☎ 07747 462139 ⊕ pigbeer.com

Pig Beer, launched in 2021, is an 18-barrel brewery located on a former pig farm in the heart of the New Forest. The sustainable, environmentally responsible brewery was founded by two brothers and their cousin. Seven beers are brewed for bottle and keg using homegrown hops, available from shop or onsite tented tap, with pizza oven. ▤◆

Pig Pub

▤ Pig In Muck, Manor Road, Claybrooke Magna, Leicestershire, LE17 5AY
☎ (01455) 202859 ⊕ piginmuck.com/brewery

Brewing began in 2013 using a two-barrel plant, upgraded to a five-barrel plant built by head brewer Kev Featherstone. ▤◆LIVE◆

Piglove

Unit 6, Cross Green Lane, Leeds, West Yorkshire, LS9 8LJ ☎ 07718 630467 ⊕ piglovebrewing.com

Piglove is a small craft brewery based in Leeds. Inspired by the heritage of craft brewing in the UK and influenced by its co-founders' Venezuelan roots, its beers are bold, fragrant, unusual and exotic. Beers are organic and vegetarian. No real ale. ◆

Pilgrim SIBA

11 West Street, Reigate, Surrey, RH2 9BL
☎ (01737) 222651 ⊕ pilgrim.co.uk

⊠ Pilgrim was the first microbrewery in Surrey, set up in 1982 in Woldingham before moving to its current premises in Reigate in 1984. Many original recipes are still being brewed in the traditional manner, while there is also a range of craft ales inspired by worldwide styles, which can all be enjoyed in the onsite taproom, numerous local outlets and the only tied pub, the Hatch, Redhill. !!▤◆GFV◆

Surrey (ABV 3.7%) BITTER
Pineapple, grapefruit and spicy aromas. Biscuity maltiness with a hint of vanilla, balanced by a hoppy bitterness and refreshing bittersweet finish.
Session IPA (ABV 3.9%) PALE
Progress (ABV 4%) BITTER
Well-rounded, tawny-coloured bitter. Predominantly sweet and malty with an underlying fruitiness and hint of toffee, balanced with a subdued bitterness.
Quest (ABV 4.3%) GOLD
Saracen (ABV 4.5%) STOUT
Exile (ABV 5%) PALE

Pillars SIBA

Unit 2, Ravenswood Industrial Estate, Shernhall Street, Walthamstow, London, E17 9HQ
☎ (020) 8521 5552 ⊕ pillarsbrewery.com

Brewing began in 2016 as an exclusively keg lager brewery. The range has been expanded over the years but still sticks to its lager roots. 2021 saw the introduction of 330ml stubby bottles. As well as the taproom, it runs the Untraditional Pub in the Crate development by St James Street station. No cask ale. ◆

Pilot Beer SIBA

4B Stewartfield, Edinburgh, EH6 5RQ
☎ (0131) 561 4267 ⊕ pilotbeer.co.uk

Pilot began brewing in 2013 in an industrial unit in Leith using a five-barrel plant. A move to larger premises has allowed for expansion. Beers are unfined and unfiltered, some vegan and gluten-free. Most output is keg or can, but cask-conditioned ale is making a regular return to selected pubs in Edinburgh by means of a subscription scheme. Traditional styles are being brewed monthly, with a Pilot twist. There is a brewery shop, with beers and other merchandise available. !!▤GFV

Pilot Brewery

▤ 726 Mumbles Road, Mumbles, Swansea, SA3 4EL
☎ 07897 895511 ⊕ thepilotbrewery.co.uk

☺The Pilot Brewery began production on its 2.5 barrel plant in 2013. It is located at the rear of The Pilot Inn on the Mumbles sea front. The output is mainly for the Pilot Inn but can also be supplied to festivals and other select outlets. The proprietors have also set up Beer Riff brewery (qv). V

Pin-Up

Unit 3, Block 3, Chalex Industrial Estate, Manor Hall
Road, Southwick, West Sussex, BN42 4NH
☎ (01273) 411127 ☎ 07888 836892
⊕ pinupbrewingco.com

⊠ Pin-Up began brewing in 2011, initially having its
beers contract brewed at an Essex brewery. In 2014 it
obtained its own plant and began brewing in Southwick,
and expanded from a five-barrel to a 10-barrel plant in
2015. Its first pub, the United Brethren, Chelmsford,
opened in 2016. ◆LIVE

Honey Brown (ABV 4%) BITTER
Session IPA (ABV 4.1%) PALE
Summer Pale (ABV 4.1%) PALE
Red Head (ABV 4.2%) RED
Milk Stout (ABV 4.5%) STOUT

Pinkers

148, Quantock Road, Weston-Super-Mare, Somerset,
BS23 4DP ☎ 07775 746300
⊕ pinkerscraftbrewery.co.uk

Small-batch microbrewery brewing all grain craft beers
using fresh ingredients from British suppliers. V

Pinnora SIBA

Unit 2, Rear of Jubilee Parade, Marsh Road, Pinner,
HA5 1BB
☎ (0845) 474 2337 ⊕ pinnorabrewing.com

Family-run, craft brewery based in North West London.
Refurbishment took place in 2021. The short four-
hectolitre brew length allows for seasonal brews and an
evolving series of craft beers. No cask ale.

Pipeline

Great Western Railway Yard, St Agnes, Cornwall,
TR5 0PD ☎ 07973 178877 ⊕ pipelinebrewing.co.uk

Pipeline Brewing Co crafts small batches of vibrant,
hoppy beers on the North Cornwall coast. Using fresh
ingredients and Cornish water, it creates craft beers that
showcase the best of New World hops. All beers are
vegan-friendly. No live beer. V◆

Pipes

183A Kings Road, Cardiff, CF11 9DF ☎ 07776 382244
⊕ pipesbeer.co.uk

Pipes create examples of some of the unique and least
known beer styles from around the globe with no
preservatives or additives used in production. The main
output is bottled and keg beers although the occasional
cask beer is produced by special request. 🛒◆GF V

Pit Top

See Wrytree

Pitchfork

See Nuttycombe

Plan B

Audley Avenue Enterprise Park, Audley Avenue,
Newport, TF10 7DW
☎ (01952) 810091 ⊕ newbrew.co.uk

⊕Plan B is a family-run brewery set up in 2016 using a
10-barrel plant. Cask-conditioned ale is available within a
30-mile radius of the brewery. It has its own bottling
plant and all beers are available from the shop or online.
‼🛒LIVE

New Alchemy (ABV 3.9%) BITTER
New Session IPA (ABV 4%) PALE
American Pale Ale (ABV 4.1%) IPA
New Tun (ABV 4.2%) IPA
Boscobel Bitter (ABV 4.3%) BITTER
Newport Pale Ale (ABV 4.4%) PALE

Play

8 Cannon Park Way, Middlesbrough, North Yorkshire,
TS1 5JU
☎ (01642) 244769 ⊕ playbrewco.com

Launched in 2019, Play Brew is a brewery, taproom and
event space. The 20-hectolitre plant produces unfiltered
beers available in keg, cans and occasionally in cask,
distributed throughout the north. ◆◆

Plockton

5 Bank Street, Plockton, IV52 8TP
☎ (01599) 544276 ☎ 07823 322043
⊕ theplocktonbrewery.com

The brewery started trading in 2007 and expanded to a
2.5-barrel plant in 2009. Bottle-conditioned beers are
available and are suitable for vegetarians. ‼◆LIVE

Yarrowale (ABV 4.2%)
Plockton Bay (ABV 4.6%) BITTER
A well-balanced, tawny-coloured, premium bitter with
plenty of hops and malt which give a bittersweet, fruity
flavour.
Starboard! (ABV 5.1%) GOLD
A fine, fruity golden ale with a light citrus bitterness. Hop
and spicy fruit feature in the nose with a smack of
grapefruit in the taste. The bitterness holds well into the
aftertaste.
Ring Tong (ABV 5.6%) IPA

Poachers

439 Newark Road, North Hykeham, Lincolnshire,
LN6 9SP
☎ (01522) 807404 ☎ 07954 131972
⊕ poachersbrewery.co.uk

⊕The brewery was founded in 2001 in buildings on the
former RAF Swinderby site. In 2006 the plant was
relocated to outbuildings at the rear of the brewer's
home. Regular outlets in Lincolnshire and surrounding
counties are supplied direct; outlets further afield, via
beer swaps with other breweries. An onsite bar is open
to the public on a Friday evening and for groups at other
times by prior arrangement. ‼🛒◆◆

Trembling Rabbit Mild (ABV 3.4%) MILD
Shy Talk Bitter (ABV 3.7%) BITTER
Rock Ape (ABV 3.8%) BITTER
Poachers Pride (ABV 4%) BITTER
Tedi Boy (ABV 4%) PALE
Bog Trotter (ABV 4.2%) BITTER
Lincoln Best (ABV 4.2%) BITTER
Billy Boy (ABV 4.4%) BITTER
Imp Ale (ABV 4.4%) BITTER
Black Crow Stout (ABV 4.5%) STOUT
Hykeham Gold (ABV 4.5%) SPECIALITY
Monkey Hanger (ABV 4.5%) BITTER
Jock's Trap (ABV 5%) BITTER
Trout Tickler (ABV 5.5%) BITTER

Polly's

Holland Farm, Blackbrook, Mold, CH7 6LU
☎ (01244) 940621 ⊕ pollysbrew.co

Polly's Brew Co was established in 2016, originally as Black Brook, inside the stable of an old horse called Polly, and has continuously expanded to what is currently a 23-hectolitre plant. It concentrates on KeyKeg and canned beer, widely distributed throughout the UK and further afield. The beer range changes constantly.

Pomona Island

Unit 33, Waybridge Enterprise Centre, Daniel Adamson Road, Salford, M50 1DS
☎ (0161) 637 2140 ☎ 07972 445474
⊕ pomonaislandbrew.co.uk

Brewery set up in 2017, close to Salford's Media City. Part owned by the people behind the Gas Lamp in Manchester city centre. Head brewer James Dyer is formerly of Tempest Brew Co (qv). Its brewery tap opened in 2021 at Escape to Freight Island. ◼V✦

Pale (ABV 3.8%) PALE
Pungent fruity hop aroma. Sweet fruity taste with some bitterness. Gentle and balanced. Lasting delicate bitter finish.

Stout (ABV 4.5%) STOUT

APA (ABV 5.3%) PALE
Hoppy beer with fruit and moderate bitterness, leading to a rising bitter finish. Brewed with variable hops.

Poole Hill SIBA

41-43 Poole Hill, Bournemouth, Dorset, BH2 5PW
☎ (01202) 557583 ☎ 07469 172568
⊕ poolehillbrewery.com

⊠ Award-winning Poole Hill Brewery was created by Jennifer Tingay, head brewer, CEO and creator of Southbourne Ales and Tingay's craft beer. Originally a cuckoo brewery, the 20-barrel brewery and taproom was created in a Victorian ironmongers and latterly a disused car showroom after attracting £280K from crowdfunding. Southbourne Ales comprise fine traditional styles from light ale to oatmeal stout. The Tingay's brand features styles from American pale ale, and floral, to smoked, doppelboch and punchy low alcohol beers. ‼ ◼ ✦ LIVE V✦

Brewed under the Southbourne Ales brand name:

Paddler (ABV 3.4%) BITTER
Easy-drinking bitter with subtle malt flavour and hints of hop bitterness in the aftertaste.

Sunbather (ABV 4%) RED
Dry red ale with some caramel sweetness and a lingering, nutty aftertaste.

Headlander (ABV 4.2%) BITTER
Traditional best bitter with intense malt aroma and sweet flavour. Complex and moreish with hop bitterness in aftertaste.

Grockles (ABV 4.5%) GOLD
Refreshing, well-balanced golden ale with subtle sweet aromas and gentle hop finish.

Stroller (ABV 4.6%) STOUT
Strong mild crossed with old ale, complex flavours of hop malt and fruit, but well balanced.

Brewed under the Tingay's brand name:

Armed with Flowers (ABV 4.5%) SPECIALITY

Digies (ABV 5%) PALE

Pope's Yard

Unit 12, Paramount Industrial Estate, Sandown Road, Watford, Hertfordshire, WD24 7XA
☎ (01923) 224182 ⊕ popesyard.co.uk

Pope's Yard began commercial brewing in 2012 using a one-barrel plant. Two expansions since then, and three relocations, means it now operates a five-barrel plant for production and a one-barrel pilot plant. Some beers may be suitable for vegans. LIVE V

Lacerta (ABV 3.9%) PALE
Luminaire (ABV 3.9%) PALE
Bright Star (ABV 4.1%) PALE
Quartermaster (ABV 4.4%) BITTER
Club Hammer Stout (ABV 5.5%) STOUT

Poppyland

46 West Street, Cromer, Norfolk, NR27 9DS
☎ (01263) 515214 ☎ 07802 160558
⊕ poppylandbrewery.com

Established in 2012, the 2.5-barrel brewery specialises in unusual and innovative brews mainly using Norfolk malt. Foraged saisons are a speciality. Beers are on sale at the brewery and at numerous specialist beer shops across East Anglia. Cask ales are available in some Norfolk and Norwich pubs. ◼LIVE GF V✦

Portishead

⊟ **Unit 3, The Precinct, Portishead, BS20 6AH**
☎ 07526 636167 ⊕ portisheadbrewing.com

Brewing started in 2018 before relocating the following year into its permanent home in Portishead town centre. In 2020, it expanded into the adjacent unit. It continues to supply a small number of local businesses. Around ten beers are regularly brewed, ranging from lagers to stouts, available as draught keg and bottle-conditioned. The majority of the beer is sold through the brewpub and also online sales. Brewing equipment is visible from the brewpub. Guest beers and food available. ◼ ✦ LIVE V

Portobello SIBA

Unit 6, Mitre Bridge Industrial Estate, Mitre Way, North Kensington, London, W10 6AU
☎ (020) 8969 2269 ⊕ portobellobrewing.com

⊠ Established in 2012, Portobello has since expanded into an adjacent unit and has a 7,500-hl capacity. The range of beers is available in cask with a similar range in keg, all widely available around London. The management of some pubs has been taken on in recent years. ✦

Westway Pale Ale (ABV 3.8%) PALE
Easy-drinking pale ale with bitter grapefruit and tropical flavours overlaying a digestive biscuit sweetness. Finish is astringent and bitter.

VPA (ABV 4%) PALE
Refreshing yellow pale ale with citrus fruit throughout and a little peppery hop and biscuit notes. Bitterness builds on drinking.

Star (ABV 4.3%) BITTER
Chocolate roasty notes, sweet caramel with floral hops are noticeable throughout overlaid with orange fruit. Finish is spicy and bitter.

Central Line Red (ABV 4.4%) RED
Ruby red beer. Creamy banana toffee base with caramel and hop bitterness. Long, tapering finish with a nutty character.

Market Porter (ABV 4.6%) SPECIALITY

Malt and roast aromas, a balanced blend of roast, chocolate, rye, coffee with a lingering sweet to dry finish.
APA (ABV 5%) PALE
Orange and apricot notes on a sweet biscuity base. A spicy hop on the finish, which becomes dry and bitter.
Stiff Lip IPA (ABV 5%) BITTER
Fruity with sweet caramel and earthy hops aroma. Pink grapefruit, sweet biscuit and apricot flavours, with a building dry bitterness.

Portpatrick

24 Main Street, Kirkcolm, Stranraer, DG9 0NN
☎ 07713 114844 ✉ portpatrickbrewery@gmail.com

☺Established in 2015, the brewery changed ownership in 2022. Its core range is available both cask and bottle conditioned. ◆LIVE

All Day Breakfast (ABV 3.9%) PALE
Meilleur Point (ABV 4.9%) BITTER

Potbelly SIBA

31-44 Sydney Street, Kettering, Northamptonshire, NN16 0HY
☎ (01536) 410818 ☎ 07834 867825
⊕ potbelly-brewery.co.uk

Potbelly started brewing in 2005 on a 10-barrel plant and supplies around 200 outlets. A craft brand called 'A Bloke Down the Pub' was launched in 2021. Beers are also contract brewed for the Olde England Ales estate under the Olde England name. ‼🍴◆LIVE

Piggin' Proud Ale (ABV 3.7%) BITTER
Best (ABV 3.8%) BITTER
Sweet malty aroma with a delicately spiced raisiny dried fruit flavour and a light bitter aftertaste
Lager Brau (ABV 3.9%) SPECIALITY
A Piggin' IPA (ABV 4%) PALE
Hop Trotter (ABV 4.1%) GOLD
Beijing Black (ABV 4.4%) MILD
Pigs Do Fly (ABV 4.4%) GOLD
Hedonism (ABV 4.5%) BITTER
Slightly sweet aroma with citrus notes, followed by a sharp, hoppy flavour with hints of grapefruit and a bitter aftertaste.
Black Sun (ABV 5%) BITTER
SOAB (ABV 5%) BITTER
Crazy Daze (ABV 5.5%) BITTER
Slightly sweetish aroma followed by a sharp bitter flavour with hints of dried fruit and a lingering bitter aftertaste.

Brewed under the A Bloke Down the Pub brand name:
Clever Colin (ABV 4%) GOLD
Handy Andy (ABV 4.2%) GOLD
Dangerous Darren (ABV 4.3%) BROWN
Gorgeous Gary (ABV 4.5%) GOLD
Philanthropist Phil (ABV 5.2%) BITTER
Incredible Ian (ABV 5.6%) BLOND

Contract brewed for the Olde England Ales estate:
Gold Testament (ABV 3.9%)
Black Prince (ABV 6%) PORTER

Potton

Unit 3, 8 Market Square, Potton, Bedfordshire, SG19 2NP ☎ 07957 534688
⊕ pottonbrewingcompany.com

⊠ Potton Brewing Company was founded in 2017 in order to return brewing to the community after the previous local brewery shut down a few years before.

The brewery uses a 2.5-barrel plant, brewing 1-2 times a fortnight. All bottled beers are unfined and suitable for vegans, cask beers are fined with isinglass. Under new ownership since 2023. 🍴LIVE GF V

Shannon (ABV 3.5%) BITTER
Holly Pup (ABV 3.8%) MILD
Transmitter (ABV 4%) GOLD
Village Recycler (ABV 4.3%) BITTER
Crow (ABV 4.5%) STOUT
Sunny Days (ABV 4.8%) PALE

Powder Monkey SIBA IFBB

Priddy's Hard, Heritage Way, Gosport, Hampshire, PO12 4FL
☎ (023) 9252 2126 ⊕ powdermonkeybrewing.com

Powder Monkey, situated in a former gunpowder magazine, started brewing in 2021. There is a visitors' centre on the premises, and a nearby pub which serves as a brewery tap. During 2022 the brewery acquired an extra nearby building and consequently extra brewing capacity. The emphasis is on keg and canned beer, but occasionally cask beer is produced for nearby pubs and beer festivals. ‼🍴◆V

Powderkeg SIBA

10 Hogsbrook Units, Woodbury Salterton, Devon, EX5 1PY
☎ (01395) 488181 ⊕ powderkegbeer.co.uk

⊠ Powderkeg was established in 2015 brewing small batches of beer. It combines international beer styles with new ingredients sourced from around the world.
◆GF V

Idler (ABV 3.9%) BITTER
Speak Easy Pale Ale (ABV 4.3%) BITTER

Prescott

See Hanlons

Pressure Drop SIBA

Unit 6, Lockwood Industrial Park, Mill Mead Road, Tottenham Hale, London, N17 9QP
⊕ pressuredropbrewing.co.uk

The three owners began with home brewing before starting to brew commercially in Stoke Newington in 2012. A move to Hackney in 2013 was followed by a move in 2017 to Tottenham Hale with a new brewhouse and taproom. Beers are available in keg and cans with some cask produced for local beer festivals. LIVE ✿

Pretty Decent SIBA

Unit 10, Uplands Business Park, Blackhorse Lane, Walthamstow, London, E17 5QJ
⊕ prettydecentbeer.co

Brewing began in 2017 in a railway arch in Forest Gate, expanding into an adjacent taproom in 2021. Production now takes place in a new brewery and taproom in Walthamstow (opened 2022), part of the newly organised Blackhorse Beer Mile. Output is mostly keg and cans in a wide range of styles and includes alcohol-free options. Cask beer is available for local pubs and festivals on demand. A portion of profits is donated to local and international charities. ‼◆LIVE ✿

Problem Child

🏠 **Wayfarer Inn, 1 Alder Lane, Parbold, Lancashire, WN8 7NL**
☎ (01257) 464600 ☎ 07588 736926
⊕ problemchildbrewing.co.uk

Problem Child began brewing in 2013 using a five-barrel plant at the Wayfarer Inn, Parbold, where four beers from the range are usually available. ‼

Pumphouse Brewing

Unit 10D, Twydale Business Park, Skerne Road, Driffield, East Yorkshire, YO25 6JX ☎ 07811 180195
✉ david@pumphousebrewing.co.uk

Launched in 2019, Pumphouse Brewing are a craft brewery producing small-batch, one-off beers available in keg and bottle. The constantly-changing range is unfined and unfiltered. ♦

Pumphouse Community

Green Man Barn, Church Lane, Toppesfield, Essex, CO9 4DR ☎ 07934 126592
⊕ pumphousebrewery.co.uk

⊠ Pumphouse is a community-owned brewery. Established in 2015, it uses a two-barrel plant and specialises in session beers with occasional one-off, experimental brews. Pubs, clubs, special events and festivals are supplied within a 20-mile radius as well as its Green Man brewery tap outlet. ⬛♦LIVE

Allied Amber (ABV 3.8%) BITTER
St Margaret's Ale (ABV 3.8%) BLOND
Gold (ABV 4.2%) GOLD
19 Elms (ABV 4.3%) BROWN
9th Havocs (ABV 4.3%) PALE

Purity

The Brewery, Upper Spernal Farm, Spernal Lane, Great Alne, Warwickshire, B49 6JF
☎ (01789) 488007 ⊕ puritybrewing.com

☺ Brewing began in 2005 in a purpose-designed plant housed in converted barns. The brewery prides itself on its eco-friendly credentials. It supplies its award-winning beers into the free trade within a 70-mile radius (plus London postcodes), delivering to more than 500 outlets. Recently sold to equity finance company BREAL, although it is continuing production. Beers are also contract brewed for Crate Brewery. ‼⬛♦

Bunny Hop (ABV 3.5%) PALE
Pure Gold (ABV 3.8%) GOLD
Mad Goose (ABV 4.2%) BITTER
Pure UBU (ABV 4.5%) BITTER

Purple Moose SIBA

Madoc Street, Porthmadog, LL49 9DB
☎ (01766) 515571 ⊕ purplemoose.co.uk

A 40-barrel plant housed in a former iron works in the coastal town of Porthmadog. It owns the 'Australia' pub and the Station Inn, both Porthmadog, plus two shops. The names of the beers reflect local history and geography. ‼⬛♦

Cwrw Eryri / Snowdonia Ale (ABV 3.6%) GOLD
Golden, refreshing bitter with citrus fruit hoppiness in aroma and taste. The full mouthfeel leads to a long-lasting, dry, bitter finish.
Cwrw Madog / Madog's Ale (ABV 3.7%) BITTER
Full-bodied session bitter. Malty nose and an initial nutty flavour but bitterness dominates. Well-balanced and refreshing with a dry roastiness on the taste and a good dry finish.
Cwrw Ysgawen / Elderflower Ale (ABV 4%) SPECIALITY
Cwrw Glaslyn / Glaslyn Ale (ABV 4.2%) BITTER
Refreshing, light, malty, amber-coloured ale. Plenty of hop in the aroma and taste. Good, smooth mouthfeel leading to a slightly chewy finish.
Whakahari (ABV 4.3%) BITTER
Ochr Dywyll y Mws / Dark Side of the Moose (ABV 4.6%) OLD

Q Brew

58 Lower North Road, Carnforth, Lancashire, LA5 9LJ
☎ (01524) 903105 ⊕ qbrew.co.uk

☺Q Brew started brewing in 2019 and is Carnforth's first microbrewery.

Quantock SIBA

Westridge Way, Broadgauge Business Park, Bishops Lydeard, Somerset, TA4 3RU
☎ (01823) 433812 ⊕ quantockbrewery.co.uk

⊠ Quantock is a family-run brewery that started trading in Wellington in 2007 on an eight-barrel plant. It has since expanded and moved to its current location in 2015. The brewery supplies beer to outlets throughout the South West, and further afield via wholesalers. The brewery taproom and shop are open five days and three evenings a week, with the taproom regularly playing host to live bands and comedy nights. An annual beer festival is held in July. ⬛♦V♦

QPA (ABV 4%) PALE
Wills Neck (ABV 4.3%) GOLD
Stout (ABV 4.5%) STOUT
Plastered Pheasant (ABV 4.8%) PORTER
Titanium (ABV 5.1%) PALE

Quartz SIBA

Archers, Alrewas Road, Kings Bromley, Staffordshire, DE13 7HW
☎ (01543) 473965 ⊕ quartzbrewing.co.uk

☺Quartz is a small craft brewery which was established in 2005 by Scott and Julia Barnett. Around 50 outlets are supplied direct. ‼⬛♦

Blonde (ABV 3.8%) BLOND
Little aroma, gentle hop and background malt. Sweet with unsophisticated sweetshop tastes.
Crystal (ABV 4.2%) BITTER
Sweet aroma with some fruit and yeasty Marmite hints. Hoppiness begins but dwindles to a bittersweet finish.
Extra Blonde (ABV 4.4%) BITTER
Sweet malty aroma with a touch of fruit. Sweet start, smooth with a hint of hops in the sugary finish.
Heart (ABV 4.6%) BITTER
Pale brown with some aroma of fruit and malt. Gentle tastes of fruit and hops eventually appear to leave a bitter finish.
Cracker (ABV 5%) BITTER

Queen Inn

🏠 **28 Kingsgate Road, Winchester, Hampshire, SO23 9PG**
☎ (01962) 853898 ⊕ thequeeninnwinchester.com

⊠ The three-barrel brewery replaced earlier kit and was installed in 2022. Currently brewing three to four beers twice a week, mainly for the pub, but other local pubs are supplied. One-off brews use new variety hops.

Queer (NEW)

Office: Unit D2, Leyton Industrial Village, Argall Avenue, London, E10 7QP
☎ (020) 3089 0829 ⊕ thequeerbrewingproject.com

Queer Brewing is a queer and trans-owned brewery whose aim is to increase visibility and representation for LGBTQ+ people through beer. Founded in 2019, the first two years saw founder Lily Waite raising thousands of pounds for LGBTQ+ charities in numerous countries by brewing collaborations all over the world. Since 2021 Lily has been joined by Charlotte and Beth, expanding the team to three. It has been brewing its own beers since 2021, a core range of four through to a range of specials, with 10p from every pint and can being donated to a quarterly-rotating charity. A pop-up taproom opens sporadically. V◆

Quiet

🍴 Woodend Barn, Burn O Bennie, Banchory, AB31 5QA
☎ (01330) 826530 ⊕ buchananfood.com

Quiet Brewery produces bottle-conditioned beers, supplied to Buchanan's Bistro, Banchory. ◆LIVE

Quirky

Unit 3, Ash Lane, Garforth, Leeds, West Yorkshire, LS25 2HG
☎ (0113) 286 2072 ⊕ quirkyales.com

☺Established in 2015, Quirky Ales brews two or three times a week on its 2.5-barrel plant. Simon Mustill and Richard Scott acquired the brewery in 2019 with Dean Sanderson replacing Richard Scott as a director in 2023. Aaron Getliffe is the full-time brewer. The onsite taproom is open every weekend from Thursday evening, with occasional live music. Most beers are also available in bottles, and are available in the taproom, delicatessens and farm shops. Brewing schools are frequently held, and available on request. 🍴◆

Porter (ABV 3.5%) PORTER
Blonde Ale (ABV 3.8%) BLOND
Two Islands (ABV 3.8%) GOLD
Bitter (ABV 4%) BITTER
Ruby (ABV 4%) BITTER
1 Hop Wonder (ABV 4.1%) GOLD
ITA (ABV 4.8%) BITTER
Hip Hop (ABV 5.5%) IPA
Classic (ABV 5.7%) MILD

Radical

Oak Hill, Port Sodderick, Isle of Man, IM4 1AN
☎ 07624 493304 ⊕ radicalbrewing.im

Dr Mike Cowbourne, who was in charge of brewing at Okell's Brewery, has set up this small brewery in his garage. The beers are available to the free trade and the most likely venue to have them is the Falcon Hotel, Port Erin. This brewery only produces pins so no firkins are used and usually there's one brew a week (could be one of four beers).

Ironic Rye (ABV 3.8%) PALE
Radical Bitter (ABV 3.8%) BITTER
Amarillo Dreaming (ABV 4.4%) PALE
Supernova Sunshine (ABV 4.6%) PALE

Radio City (NEW)

Horsfrith Park Farm, Old Barns Lane, Radley Green, Essex, CM4 0LR

Founded in 2017 and now brewing off a 30-hectolitre kit. The beer is all fermented and conditioned in unitanks before being cold-crashed and carbonated, then kegged and canned. There is a tap in central Chelmsford that has been open since 2022.

Radnorshire

Timberworks, Brookside Farm, Mutton Dingle, New Radnor, LD8 2SU
☎ (01544) 350456 ☎ 07789 909748
⊕ radnorhillsholidaycottages.com

☺Set up in 2012 in a barn on the grounds of a farm offering holiday cottage accommodation, Radnorshire uses its own spring water. Drinkers staying at the cottages are supplied as well as a few local pubs. 🍴🍺

Whimble Gold (ABV 3.8%) GOLD
Four Stones (ABV 4%) BITTER
Smatcher Tawny (ABV 4.2%) BITTER
Water-Break-Its-Neck (ABV 5.7%) PALE

Ralf + Alf

See Hydes

Ralph's Ruin

🍴 c/o Royal Oak, Lower Bristol Road, Bath, BA2 3BW
☎ (01225) 481409 ⊕ ralphsruin.co.uk

Brewing commenced in 2017 using a two-barrel plant in the old kitchen of the Royal Oak. The beer is only available in the pub. ◆V

Ramsbury SIBA

Stockclose Farm, Aldbourne, Wiltshire, SN8 2NN
☎ (01672) 541407 ⊕ ramsburybrewery.co.uk

⊠ Ramsbury Brewing & Distilling Company started in 2004 using a 10-barrel plant, situated high on the Marlborough Downs, Wiltshire. The brewery uses home-grown barley from the Ramsbury Estate. Expansion in 2014 saw an upgrade to a 30-barrel plant with a visitor centre and a borehole to provide water. A distillery that uses estate-grown grains became operational in 2015. A beer garden was added in 2020. An automated bottling machine for gin/ vodka was installed in 2021. A gin school opened in 2023. 🍴🍺◆LIVE

Farmer's Best (ABV 3.6%) BITTER
Deerstalker (ABV 4%) BITTER
RPA (Ramsbury Pale Ale) (ABV 4%) PALE
Gold (ABV 4.5%) GOLD
Red Ram (ABV 4.5%) SPECIALITY
Chalk Stream (ABV 5%) PALE

Ramsgate (Gadds') SIBA

1 Hornet Close, Pyson's Road Industrial Estate, Broadstairs, Kent, CT10 2YD
☎ (01843) 868453 ⊕ ramsgatebrewery.co.uk

Ramsgate was established in 2002 at the back of a Ramsgate seafront pub. In 2006 the brewery moved to its current location, allowing for increased capacity and bottling. A 25-hectolitre brew plant is used. 🍴🍺◆

Gadds' Hoppy Pale (ABV 3.6%) BLOND
Gadds' No.7 Bitter Ale (ABV 3.8%) BITTER
Gadds' Seasider (ABV 4.3%) BITTER
Gadds' No.5 Best Bitter Ale (ABV 4.4%) BITTER
Light brown bitter. The robust biscuit malt, caramel, and stone fruit smell, carries through to the taste, and softens

in the aftertaste. Bitter and dry balance the sweet malts and finish long.

Gadds' SheSells SeaShells (ABV 4.7%) GOLD
Gadds' No.3 Kent Pale Ale (ABV 5%) BLOND
Gadds' Faithful Dogbolter Porter (ABV 5.6%) PORTER
Gadds' Black Pearl (ABV 6.2%) STOUT

Randalls

La Piette Brewery, St Georges Esplanade, St Peter Port, Guernsey, GY1 3JG
☎ (01481) 720134

Office: PO Box 154, Guernsey, GY1 3JG ⊕ randalls.gg

Randalls has been brewing in Guernsey since 1868. The company was bought out in 2006 and moved into a modern, purpose-built brewery in 2008. 20 pubs are owned and a further 70 outlets are supplied. ‼◆

Patois (ABV 4.5%) BITTER

Rascality (NEW)

🍺 Bull, Bury St Edmunds, Suffolk, IP31 1EW

A brewery at the Bull, which started production as Wilde Bull Brewery in 2017. It closed down along with the pub in 2018, but brewing was subsequently restarted under the Rascality name when the pub reopened.

Rat

🍺 Rat & Ratchet, 40 Chapel Hill, Huddersfield, West Yorkshire, HD1 3EB
☎ (01484) 542400 ✉ ratandratchet@ossett-brewery.co.uk

⊕The Rat & Ratchet was originally established as a brewpub in 1994. Brewing ceased and it was purchased by Ossett Brewery (qv) in 2004. Brewing restarted in 2011 with a capacity of 30 barrels per week. A wide range of occasional brews with rat-themed names supplement the regular beers. ◆

Raven Hill

19 Manor Court, Scarborough Business Park, Scarborough, North Yorkshire, YO11 3TU
⊕ ravenhillbrewery.com

Formerly a farm-based company, Raven Hill Brewery relocated in mid 2024 to a business park on the edge of Scarborough following its sale to new owners. Beers are available in cans. No real ale.

RBA

Oswestry Close, Oakwood, Derby, DE21 2RT ☎ 07943 367765 ✉ rbabrewery@gmail.com

In 2015 two friends, Richard Burton and Colin Fryer, began homebrewing in a back garden shed. Five years later they decided to sell commercially, and production increased accordingly. The 0.25-barrel plant brews once a week with occasional brews being bottled. There are plans to increase production further.

RCH

See Nuttycombe

Reaction

47 Erw Goch, Ruthin, LL15 1RS
✉ reactionbrewery@gmail.com

Brewing returned to Ruthin after many years when keen homebrewer and CAMRA member Clwyd Roberts made his cask and KeyKeg beers available commercially in 2019. One-off beers are produced on a monthly basis with most of the output going to Mold Alehouse, which acts as the brewery tap.

Reality

127 High Road, Chilwell, Beeston, Nottingham, NG9 4AT ☎ 07801 539523
✉ alandenismonaghan@hotmail.com

⊠ Since starting in 2010, the brewery has built up a loyal following of pubs locally, while supplying beer festivals across the country, functions and individual customers. ◆

Virtuale Reality (ABV 3.8%) PALE
No Escape (ABV 4.2%) PALE
Bitter Reality (ABV 4.3%) BITTER
Stark Reality (ABV 4.5%) SPECIALITY
Reality Czech (ABV 4.6%) SPECIALITY

Rebel

See Dynamite Valley

Rebellion SIBA

Bencombe Farm, Marlow Bottom, Buckinghamshire, SL7 3LT
☎ (01628) 476594 ⊕ rebellionbeer.co.uk

⊠ Established in 1993, Rebellion has grown steadily and relocated to its current site in 1999. It brews up to 100,000 pints per week, supplying around 600 trade customers within 30 miles alongside its retail shop, online store, drive-through and onsite Tap Yard. A three-barrel development brewery was installed in 2022, which enables small batches of a wider range of craft beer styles. The membership club has around 4,500 active members. ‼🚲◆🍃

IPA (ABV 3.4%) BITTER
Copper-coloured bitter, sweet and malty, with resinous and red apple flavours. Caramel and fruit decline to leave a dry, bitter and malty finish.
Smuggler (ABV 4.2%) BITTER
A red-brown beer, well-bodied and bitter with an uncompromisingly dry, bitter finish.
Hazy Pale (ABV 4.3%) PALE
Overthrow (ABV 4.3%) BLOND
Roasted Nuts (ABV 4.6%) BITTER
Black (ABV 5.2%) STOUT

Reckless Dweeb

Forest Link, Bilsthorpe, Nottinghamshire, NG22 8PR
☎ 07969 779763 ⊕ recklessdweeb.com

Established in 2020 and upgraded in 2022 to a 200-litre plant with two 150-litre fermenting vessels and a 120-litre bright tank, Reckless Dweeb Brew Co is a nanobrewery nestled in a quiet village in the heart of Nottinghamshire. ◆LIVE

Son of My Brother (ABV 5.1%) GOLD
Did You See That Ludicrous Display Last Night!? (ABV 8.2%) IPA

Recoil

See Copper Dragon

Red Dog

Unit 6, Gallows Industrial Park, off Furnace Road, Ilkeston, Derbyshire, DE7 5EP

A 10-barrel microbrewey located on the Nottinghamshire/Derbyshire border producing a modern take on traditional cask ales.

Rose Tattoo (ABV 4.1%) PALE
Campbell's Best Bitter (ABV 4.4%) BITTER
Old Saxon (ABV 4.9%) PALE

Red Fox

See WHARF

Red Moon

See Fosse Way

Red Rock

Higher Humber Farm, Bishopsteignton, Devon, TQ14 9TD
☎ (01626) 879738

Office: Unit 3, Woodlands Business Park, Burlescombe, Tiverton, Devon, EX16 7LL
⊕ redrockbrewery.co.uk

⊗ Red Rock first started brewing in 2006 using a four-barrel plant and upgraded in 2011 to a 7.5-barrel one. It is based in a converted barn on a working farm using locally-sourced malt, fresh hops and the farm's own spring water. It has a bar and can accommodate private functions. Brewing is currently suspended. !! ╦ ♦ LIVE V♣

Red Rose SIBA

Unit 4, Brookmill Complex, Branch Road, Darwen, Lancashire, BB3 0PR
☎ (01254) 738194

Office: 2 Hameldon View, Great Harwood, BB6 7BL
⊕ redrosebrewery.co.uk

Brewing began in 2020 initially based in Ramsbottom. The brewery relocated to Darwen at the beginning of 2024.

Treacle Miners' Tipple (ABV 3.6%) MILD
Roast malt and caramel aromas lead to a sweet tasting beer and a lasting finish of sweet roast malt bitterness.
Czeckmate (ABV 3.8%) PALE
Too Wet to Woo (ABV 3.8%) BITTER
Mystick (ABV 3.9%) PALE
Harlequin (ABV 4%) PALE
Gladrags (ABV 4.1%) PALE
Rat Trap (ABV 4.3%) BLOND
Paddy O'Hacker's (ABV 4.6%) STOUT
Roasty malty start, smooth, full-bodied stout with a centre of sweet caramel and a long dry roast finish.
Likely More Bar Tat (ABV 6.1%) IPA

Redchurch

15-16 Mead Park Industrial Estate, Harlow, Essex, CM20 2SE
☎ (01279) 626895 ☎ 07836 762173
⊕ redchurch.beer

⊗ Established in 2011 using an eight-barrel plant in Bethnal Green railway arches. Most production moved to Harlow in 2016, leaving only the taproom. It was purchased by new management in 2019, who closed the Bethnal Green taproom. In late 2022 Redchurch was purchased by the Laine Brewing Company. The current range of ten core beers and seasonal specials is available

in keg and bottles only. Its taproom also hosts events (see website for details and tickets). !! ╦ ♦ V♣

Redemption SIBA

Unit 16, Compass West Industrial Estate, 33 West Road, Tottenham, London, N17 0XL
☎ (020) 8885 5227 ☎ 07919 416046
⊕ redemptionbrewing.co.uk

⊗ Redemption began brewing in 2010 on a 12-barrel plant. In 2016 it moved into a larger unit with a 30-barrel plant. Most of the beer is supplied in cask to pubs in north and central London and to beer festivals. Keg, cans and bottles are also available, some being found in North London supermarket chains. Its taproom opens before home games at the Tottenham Hotspur Stadium.
!! ╦ ♦ LIVE ♣

Trinity (ABV 3%) GOLD
Fruity, caramel sweet nose with caramel, orange and a hint of apricot. Bitterness builds and lingers with a faint spicy note.
Pale Ale (ABV 3.8%) PALE
Earthy hops, orange and apricot overlaid with a caramel sweetness on the palate lingering in the dry, increasingly bitter finish.
Kazbek (ABV 4%) BLOND
Fruit and lemon in the aroma and biscuity citrus flavour. Spicy hops in the lingering, dry bitter finish that builds.
Hopspur (ABV 4.5%) BITTER
Nicely-balanced, dark amber-coloured premium bitter. Smooth with spicy hops, caramelised toffee and orange marmalade. Dry bitter finish.
Urban Dusk (ABV 4.6%) BITTER
Chocolate notes throughout. Orange and sultana notes, a hint of apricot overlaid with roasty notes. Long, dry, spicy bitter finish.
Fellowship Porter (ABV 5.1%) PORTER
Roasty sweet nose with caramelised fruit, raisins, plums on the sweet palate and cocoa. Finish has dry roasty bitter notes.
Big Chief (ABV 5.5%) IPA
Aroma is sweet and earthy with apricot and orange fruits on the palate. Growing dry bitter finish with earthy hops.

Redscar SIBA

▤ c/o Cleveland Hotel, 9-11 High Street West, Redcar, North Yorkshire, TS10 1SQ
☎ (01642) 513727 ☎ 07828 855146
⊕ redscar-brewery.co.uk

☺Redscar first brewed in 2008. In 2014 it increased its capacity to a five-barrel plant. The brewery supplies the hotel, local pubs and beer festivals. !! ♦

Blonde (ABV 3.8%) BLOND
Poison (ABV 4%) BITTER
Beach (ABV 5%) BITTER

Redwell SIBA

Under the Arches, Bracondale, Trowse Millgate, Norwich, NR1 2EF
☎ (01603) 904990 ⊕ redwellbrewing.com

⊗ Redwell was started in 2013 by a group of beer lovers, tracing their beery influences from around the world. Ownership and control has changed a few times throughout the years. From mid 2024 it is again under new control by a local hospitality entrepreneur, with the intention to maintain standards while looking to extend the range. Its Polish head brewer is Marcel Liput. The taproom accommodates up to 150 guests, and the beer garden up to 300. Food is available most of the time. The brews are unfined and unfiltered, certified vegan and audited gluten-free. ‼ ☕ GF V♦

RedWillow SIBA

The Lodge, Sutton Garrison, Byrons Lane, Macclesfield, Cheshire, SK11 7JW
☎ (01625) 502315 ⊕ redwillowbrewery.com

⊛Established in 2010 by homebrewer Toby McKenzie and his wife Caroline. In 2015 brewing moved to a larger, purpose-built unit on the same site. The award-winning beers are distributed nationwide and are available from the brewery's own RedWillow bars in Macclesfield and Buxton. ♦ V

Headless (ABV 3.9%) PALE
Nicely-balanced with some malty sweetness. Fruit and hops show in the drinking with hop bitterness lasting to the end.
Feckless (ABV 4.1%) BITTER
Well-balanced best bitter, malt and hop in the taste with some fruit and roast flavours.
Weightless (ABV 4.2%) PALE
Balanced with a promise of fruit and hop at the start, full-bodied bitter, sweet fruity middle and lasting finish.
Wreckless (ABV 4.8%) PALE
Hoppy, fruity, sweet pale ale that finishes on the drier side.
Heritage Porter (ABV 5.3%) PORTER
Sweet malts and caramel aromas. Rich fruity tasting beer, sweetness at first then finishing with a dry roast bitterness.
Sleepless (ABV 5.4%) RED
Breakfast Stout (ABV 5.6%) STOUT
Strong aromas of chocolate, coffee and hazelnut alongside expected malt and roast. Composed to give a long, smooth mouthfeel.
Smokeless (ABV 5.7%) SPECIALITY
Shameless (ABV 5.9%) IPA
Fruit and hops throughout with full-bodied sweetness and a long finish.

Reedley Hallows SIBA

Unit B3, Farrington Close, Farrington Road Industrial Estate, Burnley, Lancashire, BB11 5SH ☎ 07749 414513 ⊕ reedleyhallows.co.uk

⊛Brewing started on this four-barrel plant in 2012. Having moved to larger premises, the brewery now has nine fermenters to cope with demand. ‼

Beer O'Clock (ABV 3.8%) BLOND
Old Laund Bitter (ABV 3.8%) BITTER
Filly Close Blonde (ABV 3.9%) BLOND
Pendleside (ABV 4%) GOLD
Gentle malt and hops in the aroma lead to a fruity and peppery bitterness which continues to a dry finish.
Monkholme Premium (ABV 4.2%) BLOND
New Laund Dark (ABV 4.4%) STOUT
Griffin IPA (ABV 4.5%) PALE
Fruity, hoppy bitter with sweet fruity flavours and a light bitter finish
New Zealand Pale (ABV 4.5%) PALE
Nook of Pendle (ABV 5%) BITTER
Balanced smooth malt and hop bitterness, raisin and peach flavours leading to a growing hop bitter and dry finish.

Reids Gold

61 Provost Barclay Drive, Stonehaven, AB39 2GE
⊕ reidsgold.com

The brewery was established in 2018. It is a small-batch microbrewery with an average weekly production of five barrels. Beers are unfiltered and unpasteurised and available in cans and mini-kegs.

Remedy Oak SIBA

Horton Road, Wimborne, Dorset, BH21 8ND
☎ (01202) 612509 ⊕ remedyoakbrewery.co.uk

The Remedy Oak Brewing Company was established commercially in 2020. It is based in a redeveloped barn in the grounds of the Remedy Oak Golf Club. Traditional styles as well as hop-forward craft beers are produced. An onsite taproom opened in 2021. ☕ ♦

Renegade SIBA

The Old Dairy, Frilsham Farm, Yattendon, Berkshire, RG18 0XT
☎ (01635) 767090 ⊕ renegadebrewery.co.uk

⊗ Formerly known as West Berkshire and under new ownership since late 2021, the brewery rebranded to Renegade in 2022. Originally established in 1995, it moved to new, purpose-built facilities in 2018 in a former dairy farm building covering 68,000sq ft (its fourth expansion). Capacity was increased tenfold to 60,000 hectolitres, complemented by a fully-automated bottling and canning line. The site includes a shop, taproom and kitchen. ‼ ☕ ♦ ♦

Mister Chubb's (ABV 3.4%) BITTER
A drinkable, balanced, session bitter. A malty caramel note dominates aroma and taste and is accompanied by a nutty bittersweetness and a hoppy aftertaste.
Maggs' Mild (ABV 3.5%) MILD
Silky, full-bodied, dark mild with a creamy head. Roast malt aroma is joined in the taste by caramel, sweetness and mild, fruity hoppiness. Aftertaste of roast malt with balancing bitterness.
Good Old Boy (ABV 4%) BITTER
Tawny-coloured session bitter with malty aroma, then a balanced flavour with hops and fruit, leading to a long, dry, bitter aftertaste.
Maharaja IPA (ABV 5.1%) PALE

Republic of Liverpool

See Stamps

Resting Devil SIBA

🍺 **Chesterfield Arms, 40 Newbold Street, Chesterfield, Derbyshire, S41 7PH**
☎ (01246) 236634 ⊕ restingdevil.co.uk

⊛Established in 2022 at the Chesterfield Arms, producing cask ales for the pub and occasionally for beer festivals. Bottled beers are also available. ♦ LIVE GF V

Rhymney

Gilchrist Thomas Industrial Estate, Blaenavon, NP4 9RL
☎ (01495) 790456 ☎ 07831 350635
⊕ rhymneybreweryltd.com

⊛Established in 2005, the brewery is going from strength to strength. A range of beers are available in the 11 tied houses, and widely available in free houses throughout South Wales. It is unashamedly traditional in its range of beers. Situated in the heart of a UNESCO World Heritage Site, close to the National Mining Museum and the Blaenavon Iron Works (first place to make commercial steel worldwide). Ideal to include when visiting the adjacent Pontypool & Blaenavon Preserved Railway. ‼ ᴱ ♦ LIVE

Hobby Horse (ABV 3.8%) BITTER
Dark (ABV 4%) MILD
Bevans Bitter (ABV 4.2%) BITTER
Golden Ale (ABV 4.2%) GOLD
General Picton (ABV 4.3%) BITTER
Export Light (ABV 4.4%) BITTER
Bitter (ABV 4.5%) BITTER
King's Ale (ABV 4.7%) BITTER
Export (ABV 5%) BITTER

Rhythm & Brews (NEW)

🏠 Doghouse, 8 Park Street, Selby, North Yorkshire, YO8 4PW ✉ thebigorangecateringco@gmail.com

Microbrewery established in the Doghouse, Selby, in 2023.

Ridgeway

Stane Street, North Heath, Pulborough, West Sussex, RH20 1DJ
☎ (01491) 873474

Office: Ridgeway Brewing Ltd, South Stoke, RG8 0JW
⊕ ridgewaybrewery.co.uk

Set up by ex-Brakspear head brewer Peter Scholey, Ridgeway specialises in bottle-conditioned beers, although cask beers are occasionally available at beer festivals and locally. A new brewery has been operational since 2016, located within Hepworth Brewery's new premises near Pulborough, sharing some facilities. LIVE

Rigg & Furrow

Acklington Park Farm, Acklington, Morpeth, Northumberland, NE65 9AA ⊕ riggandfurrow.co.uk

Brewing commenced in 2017 in a former milking parlour. It is a family-run business celebrating the best of home-grown Northumbrian and British produce, creating exciting and innovative beers. A brewery tap is open on selected dates (see website for details). ♦

Running Bier (ABV 4%) BITTER
Run Hop Run (ABV 4.2%) PALE
Land Bier (ABV 4.8%) SPECIALITY
Crown of Gorse (ABV 5.6%) IPA

Ringwood

See Banks's

Rising Sun

🏠 Rising Sun, 235 Stockport Road, Mossley, OL5 0RQ
☎ (01457) 238236 ⊕ risingsunmossley.co.uk

⊕Brewing since 2016 using a two-barrel plant at the side of the Rising Sun. The beers are produced occasionally and are only available for sale in the pub. Beers of differing styles and strengths are available throughout the year.

River Leven SIBA

Lab Road, Kinlochleven, PH50 4SG
☎ (01855) 424224 ⊕ riverlevenales.co.uk

First established in 2011, the brewery is under new ownership from 2023. Beers are produced using the pure Kinlochleven water with no added sugars or unmalted grain.

Blonde (ABV 4%) GOLD
IPA (ABV 4%) PALE
Scooby Dubh (ABV 4%) PORTER
Trans-Atlantic (ABV 4.4%) PALE

Riverhead

🏠 2 Peel Street, Marsden, West Yorkshire, HD7 6BR
☎ (01484) 841270 (pub) ⊕ ossett-brewery.co.uk

⊕Riverhead is a brewpub that opened in 1995, with an upstairs dining room. Ossett Brewing (qv) purchased the site in 2006 but runs it as a separate brewery. Many different beers are produced on a rotating basis. ‼♦

Rivertown

See McMullen

Riviera

4 Yonder Meadow, Stoke Gabriel, Totnes, Devon, TQ9 6QE ☎ 07857 850110 ⊕ rivierabrewing.co.uk

⊕Riviera started brewing commercially in 2015 using a one-barrel plant. European and New World hops are used in addition to various British varieties. ♦

RBC Best (ABV 3.8%) BITTER
Riviera Pale Ale / RPA (ABV 3.9%) PALE
Devonian (ABV 4.1%) BITTER
Riviera Gold (ABV 4.2%) GOLD

Rivington

Home Farm, Horrobin Lane, Rivington, Lancashire, PR6 9HE ☎ 07859 248779 ⊕ rivingtonbrewing.co.uk

⊕Established in 2015 using a three-barrel plant, the brewery moved to its current address in 2020. A 12-barrel plant is now used. A number of local outlets are supplied direct from the brewery. Approximately 20 per cent of production is supplied in cask form, but all beers are unpasteurised, unfiltered and unfined. Experimental brews and collaborations are regularly available. ‼ ᴱ ♦ LIVE V ♦

Beach House (ABV 3.8%) GOLD
Clouded Eyes (ABV 4.2%) PALE
Moving South (ABV 4.2%) PALE
Walking in Circles (ABV 4.2%) PALE

Roam

New Victoria House, Weston Park Road, Plymouth, Devon, PL3 4NU
☎ (01752) 251059 ☎ 07971 411727
⊕ roambrewco.uk

⊠ Roam produce small-batch beers using a combination of traditional and modern brewing techniques and local ingredients. A six-barrel plant is used. ‼ ᴱ ♦ LIVE ♦

Tavy IPA (ABV 4.8%) PALE
Gold ale dominated by hops and fruit from start to finish. Slight fruit/straw aroma. Citrus/hoppy dry taste. Dry bitter finish.

Robinsons SIBA IFBB

Unicorn Brewery, Lower Hillgate, Stockport, SK1 1JJ
☎ (0161) 612 4061 ⊕ robinsonsbrewery.com

⊕The sixth generation of the Robinson family now run the brewery, founded in 1838. Following a significant reduction in the tied estate in recent years, there is now gradual expansion. The core range, bi-monthly seasonals, and other one-off beers are brewed, notably the Trooper range, in conjunction with Iron Maiden's Bruce Dickinson. In 2022 Robinsons announced plans to relocate brewing from the town centre site to the botting plant in nearby Bredbury. This move should complete during the currency of this Guide. 🍴🍺♦

Citra Pale (ABV 3.4%) BLOND
Dizzy Blonde (ABV 3.8%) BLOND
Aromas and tastes of malt, fruit and hop. The malt and fruit recedes leaving a dryer, more bitter conclusion.
Cumbria Way (ABV 4.1%) BITTER
A malty aroma and taste with some hops, a little fruit and sweetness and a maintained bitterness throughout.
Cwrw'r Ddraig Aur (ABV 4.1%) GOLD
Unicorn (ABV 4.2%) BITTER
Amber beer with malt, hops and fruit in the taste along with a gentle bitterness which lasts.
Cascade IPA (ABV 4.8%) PALE
Pale brown beer with malt and fruit aromas. Hoppy taste with malt and fruit, leading to a hoppy, bitter finish.
Trooper (ABV 4.8%) BITTER
Balanced amber beer with sweet malts and hops in aroma and taste.
Old Tom (ABV 8.5%) STRONG
Full-bodied with chocolate malt and fruit aromas. Complex flavours of dark chocolate maltiness, port and fruits, with a bittersweet aftertaste.

Rock & Roll

19 Hall Street, Jewellery Quarter, Birmingham, West Midlands, B18 6BS ☎ 07922 554181 ✉ rnrbrewhouse@outlook.com

⊠ The Rock & Roll brewery started as Birmingham's only rooftop pub brewery, set up by experienced brewer Mark Shepherd. In 2014 brewster Lynn Crossland joined and now does all of the brewing. In 2016 the brewery moved and expanded to a six-barrel plant. In 2020 it moved to its current location in the Jewellery Quarter. Specials and experimental beers are regularly available. A brewhouse bar is open at weekends. All beers are suitable for vegans. 🍴♦V✿

Brew Springsteen (ABV 4.2%) PALE
Thirst Aid Kit (ABV 4.2%) PALE
Mash City Rocker (ABV 4.5%) PALE
Voodoo Mild (ABV 5%) MILD

Rock Leopard (NEW)

Office: 81 Bellegrove Road, Welling, DA16 3PG ☎ (020) 3633 5693 ⊕ rockleopardbrewing.com

Rock Leopard started brewing in 2019 at other breweries and that continues to this day. Crowdfunding was started in 2022 for a new brewery and taproom in Thamesmead and it is hoped that the necessary permissions for this will be in place soon.

Rock the Boat SIBA

6 Little Crosby Village, Little Crosby, Merseyside, L23 4TS
☎ (0151) 924 7936 ☎ 07727 959356
⊕ rocktheboatbrewery.co.uk

Rock the Boat began brewing in 2015 in a converted 16th century wheelwright's workshop and old blacksmiths. All draught beers are cask-conditioned, bottled versions are bottle-conditioned, as the brewery does not use cold conditioning tanks. Beer names relate to local themes, often reflecting the brewer's musical tastes and local landmarks. The beers are increasingly available in central and north Lancashire. Specials are

brewed for Market Town Taverns pubs in Liverpool, and a green hop beer is produced each year. **LIVE**

Liverpool Light (ABV 3.4%) BLOND
Light hoppy aromas on this refreshing straw bitter with a delicate hop flavour and a dry, bitter finish.
(Sittin' on) The Dock (ABV 3.5%) MILD
Rich chocolate malt aromas, with caramel roast flavours and light sweetness with a mellow caramel roast finish.
Bootle Bull (ABV 3.8%) BITTER
Yellow Submarine Special (ABV 3.9%) GOLD
Waterloo Sunset (ABV 4.2%) BITTER
Malt and fruity aromas, sweet malt and caramel flavours, fruity with light hop bitterness and a fruit and malt finish.
Fab Four Liverpool IPA (ABV 4.4%) BLOND
A medium-bodied beer with fruity hop aromas, sweet fruity flavours and dry hop bitterness, finishing with light hop bitterness.

Rocket

The Orchard, Garden Farm, The Town, Great Staughton, Cambridgeshire, PE19 5BE ☎ 07747 617527 ✉ info@rocket-ales.com

Originally using spare capacity at King's Cliffe Brewery, Rocket Ales relocated to its own site in 2017 and currently brews five core ales, and a changing range of specials.

Black Knight (ABV 3.7%) MILD
Congreve IPA (ABV 3.9%) IPA
Rapier (ABV 3.9%) IPA
Sidewinder (ABV 3.9%) PALE
Bloodhound (ABV 4.2%) PALE

Rockingham SIBA

1 Kingsmead, Station Road, King's Cliffe, Northamptonshire, PE8 6YH
☎ (01832) 280722

Office: 25 Wansford Road, Elton, Cambridgeshire, PE8 6RZ ⊕ rockinghamales.co.uk

⊠ Rockingham is a small brewery established in 1997 that operated from a converted farm building near Blatherwycke, Northamptonshire, with a two-barrel plant producing a wide range of beers. It moved to a new site at King's Cliffe in 2023. Half a dozen local outlets are supplied. ♦

Forest Gold (ABV 3.9%) BLOND
Hop Devil (ABV 3.9%) GOLD
White Rabbit (ABV 4%) GOLD
Fruits of the Forest (ABV 4.3%) BITTER
After Dark Stout (ABV 5%) STOUT

Roebuck SIBA

Roebuck, Tobys Hill, Draycott-in-the-Clay, Staffordshire, DE6 5BT ☎ 07903 396885 ⊕ roebuckdraycott.co.uk

☺Brewing began in 2017 using a six-barrel plant, in a purpose-built, English oak-framed, new building behind the Roebuck Inn. Master Brewer Steve Topliss was Carlsberg Tetley's last head brewer in Burton. The brewery is now managed by his son-in-law Jon Hardwick. Enquiries welcomed for brewery visits and tasting tutorials, with good food at the family-owned adjacent pub. 🍴

Blonde (ABV 3.7%) BLOND
Hopzester (ABV 4.2%) BITTER
Roebuck Bitter (ABV 4.5%) BITTER
Roebuck IPA (ABV 5.2%) PALE

Roman Way

Building 79, The Old Depot, Bridge Street, Weedon
Bec, Northamptonshire, NN7 4PS
⊕ romanwaybrewery.co.uk

Roman Way Brewery was established in 2019. It has built
up an interesting and extensive list of beers which is now
in double figures. Its shop and taproom are usually open
to the public on Fridays and Saturdays with pop up food
and regular events. 🍽♦

Barbarian Best (ABV 3.8%) BITTER
Carpe Diem (ABV 3.9%) PALE
Tribune (ABV 3.9%) PALE
Senate Gold (ABV 4.1%) GOLD
Hints of orange throughout. Dry earthy aroma, a bitter
flavour with orchard fruits, and a lingering bitter
aftertaste.
Claudius IPA (ABV 4.7%) GOLD
Boudicca (ABV 5.5%) IPA
Pantheon (ABV 6%) PALE

Romney Marsh

Unit 7, Jacks Park, Cinque Ports Road, New Romney,
Kent, TN28 8AN
☎ (01797) 362333 ⊕ romneymarshbrewery.com

⊗ Romney Marsh Brewery launched in 2015. The team
consists of husband and wife, Matt Calais and Cathy
Koester, plus Matt's dad, Brian Calais. The barley, wheat
and oats used for the beers are sourced in Britain, and
hops are worldwide. Beer is supplied to outlets
throughout Kent and East Sussex, plus cases of bottled
beers can also be ordered online for nationwide delivery.
🍴🍽LIVE

Romney Best Bitter (ABV 4%) BITTER
Romney Amber Ale (ABV 4.4%) PALE
Marsh Sunset (ABV 4.8%) RED
Romney APA (ABV 5%) PALE

Rook & Gaskill (NEW)

🍽 Rook & Gaskill, York, YO10 3WP

From the ashes of 3 Non Beards brewery comes Rook &
Gaskill, founded by Paul Marshall in 2024. This brewpub
produces beer predominantly for the eponymous pub.

Rooster's SIBA

Unit H5, Fifth Avenue, Hornbeam Park, Harrogate,
North Yorkshire, HG2 8QT
☎ (01423) 865959 ⊕ roosters.co.uk

⊕Roosters is an independent, family-owned brewery
and taproom which celebrated its 30th anniversary in
2023. Weekly production capacity is 200 barrels, which
includes one-off experimental beers, brewed as part of
the brewery's Outlaw Project. As well as the permanent
beer range, Roosters' produces over 30 limited release
beers each year. 🍽♦GF V♦

Buckeye (ABV 3.4%) GOLD
Highway 51 (ABV 3.7%) GOLD
Pale, bitter and hoppy beer where the citrus tastes,
especially of grapefruit, have the upper hand, finishing
bittersweet.
Capability Brown (ABV 4%) BITTER
YPA (Yorkshire Pale Ale) (ABV 4.1%) PALE
London Thunder (ABV 4.2%) PORTER
A very dark beer with a predominantly roast aroma
which continues into the surprisingly light taste, finish is
subtle.
Easy Going Assassin (ABV 4.3%) PALE
Yankee (ABV 4.3%) PALE

Hops and gentle fruitiness make this is an easy-drinking,
well-balanced, light gold beer, some grapefruit present,
finishing dry.
Thousand Yard Stare (ABV 5.4%) PALE
Baby-Faced Assassin (ABV 6.1%) IPA
Tropical Assassin (ABV 6.1%) IPA

Rossendale

🍽 Griffin Inn, 84 Hud Rake, Haslingden, Lancashire,
BB4 5AF
☎ (01706) 214021 ⊕ rossendalebrewery.co.uk

⊕The brewery acquired the brew plant previously used
by Porter Brewing Co in 2007 and is based in the cellar of
the Griffin Inn in Haslingden. The Sportsman in Hyde and
many other local outlets are also supplied. 🍽

Rother Valley

Gate Court Farm, Station Road, Northiam, East Sussex,
TN31 6QT
☎ (01797) 252922 ☎ 07798 877551
⊕ rothervalleybrewery.co.uk

⊗ Rother Valley Brewey was established in Northiam in
1993, overlooking the Rother Levels and the Kent & East
Sussex Railway. Brewing on a 10-barrel plant, around
100 outlets are supplied direct. Established and new hop
varieties are sourced locally. ♦

Black Ops (ABV 3.8%) PALE
Valley Bitter (ABV 3.8%) BITTER
Level Best (ABV 4%) BITTER
Full-bodied, tawny session bitter with a malt and fruit
aroma, malty taste and a dry, hoppy finish.
Copper Ale (ABV 4.1%) BITTER
Hoppers Ale (ABV 4.4%) BITTER
Boadicea (ABV 4.5%) BLOND
Blues (ABV 5%) OLD
NIPA (ABV 5%) GOLD

Rough Brothers SIBA

Unit 2D, Altnagelvin Industrial Estate, Derry /
Londonderry, Northern Ireland, BT47 2ED ☎ 07946
638513

A family-run microbrewery producing handmade beer in
Derry/Londonderry. A number of tie-in beers are brewed
with local restaurants.

Roughacre

Clare Hall Barns, Cavendish Road, Clare, Suffolk,
CO10 8PJ ☎ 07801 930091 ⊕ roughacre.com

⊗ Established in 2018 by a passionate home brewer in
Castle Camps, East Cambridgeshire. The brewery moved
to Clare in West Suffolk in 2021. The brewery is run by a
two-person team and now has a taproom and shop. It
brews high quality, fine ales of character which range
from classic amber ales and golden IPA, to Belgian-style
Abbey Ale, and a dark coffee porter. The beers are now
available in several local pubs. 🍴🍽♦LIVE V♦

Cavendish Red (ABV 3.8%) MILD
Ashdon Amber (ABV 4.4%) BITTER
Nighthawker Coffee Porter (ABV 4.6%) SPECIALITY
Three Counties East Anglian Best
Bitter (ABV 4.6%) BITTER
Abbey Gold (ABV 5.2%) SPECIALITY
Mosquito (ABV 5.2%) PALE
Saffron Sun (ABV 5.4%) SPECIALITY
Saints Reserve (ABV 6.2%) BITTER

Round Corner SIBA

Melton Mowbray Market, Scalford Road (Gate 2), Melton Mowbray, Leicestershire, LE13 1JY
☎ (01664) 569855 ⊕ roundcornerbrewing.com

Round Corner Brewing was launched in 2018. The state-of-the-art brewery and its taproom are in the old sheep shed in the historic Melton Mowbray Market. Multi award-winning, it produces a range of keg beers covering a variety of styles. There is normally one cask beer in the taproom and available to pubs. The cask range varies. ‼ ◆

Roundwood Project

Unit 24, Excelsior Studios, 17-19 Sunbeam Road, North Acton, London, NW10 6JP ☎ 07815 784704
⊕ theroundwoodproject.com

Brewing began in 2022 on a small scale selling bottled beers. The site is sometimes open for special events. No cask ale.

Route21

145 Bridgemere Road, Eastbourne, East Sussex, BN22 8TY ✉ wordpress@route21brewing.co.uk

Established in 2020 Route 21 produces hoppy, hazy and juicy, unfiltered and unfined vegan craft beers. **V**

Rowton SIBA

🍺 **Pheasant, 56 Market Street, Wellington, Telford, Shropshire, TF1 1DT ☎ 07854 885870**
⊕ rowtonbrewery.com

Rowton Brewery is an independent, family-run brewery which was established in 2008. The brew length of the brewery is six barrels. ◆

Wrekin No. 1 (ABV 3.9%) GOLD
Shropshire Star (ABV 4%) PALE
Meteorite (ABV 4.2%) BITTER
Ironbridge Gold (ABV 4.4%) GOLD
Area 51 (ABV 5.1%) BITTER
Full Moon (ABV 6.2%) MILD

Ruddles

See Greene King

Rude Giant SIBA

Great Bathampton Farm, Wylye, Wiltshire, BA12 0QD

Brewery set up in 2023 following the take over of the former Blonde Brothers site in Wiltshire. There are currently two live beers and three craft beers brewed.

Rudgate SIBA

2 Centre Park, Marston Moor Business Park, Tockwith, York, North Yorkshire, YO26 7QF
☎ (01423) 358382 ⊕ rudgatebrewery.co.uk

☺Rudgate Brewery is in its 33rd year in 2025. It is situated in the heart of Yorkshire, in the Vale of York, on the old RAF Marston Moor airfield. The old Roman road of Rudgate runs through the airfield and led the Vikings into Jorvik (York), which is what inspires many of the beer names. It brews six core cask beers and two seasonals each month. ◆

Jorvik Blonde (ABV 3.8%) BLOND
Viking (ABV 3.8%) BITTER
An initially warming and malty, full-bodied beer, with hops and fruit lingering into the aftertaste.

Battleaxe (ABV 4.2%) BITTER
A well-hopped bitter with slightly sweet initial taste and light bitterness. Complex fruit character gives a memorable aftertaste.
Ruby Mild (ABV 4.4%) MILD
Nutty, rich ruby ale, stronger than usual for a mild.
Valkyrie APA (ABV 5%) PALE
York Chocolate Stout (ABV 5%) STOUT

Runaway

9-11 Astley Street, Stockport, SK4 1AW
☎ (0161) 480 1359 ⊕ therunawaybrewery.com

Runaway is located in a renovated and converted sheet metal fabrication unit close to Stockport's bus and rail stations. It began brewing in 2014, producing KeyKeg and bottle-conditioned beers. However, when production was moved to Stockport, cask-conditioned ales were added to the range in response to local demand. All core range beers are unfiltered and unpasteurised, with many available locally, including in its own taproom. ‼ 🍴 ◆ LIVE ◆

IPA (ABV 5.5%) IPA
ESB (ABV 5.8%) BITTER

Running Man

26 Greenway, Davis Estate, Chatham, Kent, ME5 9UX

⊗ Running Man was established in 2018 by Chris Mildren, with assistance from a relative. It is a small-batch craft brewery with occasional bottling.

Rural (NEW)

Inglenook, Hurstons Lane, Alton, Staffordshire, ST10 4AP ☎ 07794 321364 ⊕ ruralbrew.co.uk

Established in 2021 in a converted shed, Rural Brewing Co has since expanded to double its original size. Available in cans, a core range is available along with seasonal specials and collaboration brews such as ones brewed for Alton Towers theme park.

Rusty Garage

Unit 115, Rivermead Business Centre, Westlea, Swindon, Wiltshire, SN5 7EX ☎ 07889 928241
⊕ rustygaragecraftbrewery.com

Microbrewery established in Swindon in 2020, producing a range of small-batch beers available in canned and bottle formats, all named after a motoring theme and all are unfined. ◆

St Andrews Brewhouse SIBA

🍺 **41 Saint Andrews Street, Norwich, NR2 4TP**
☎ (0117) 405 8948

Office: 2nd Floor, Essel House, London, W1W 7TH
⊕ kingstreetbrewhouse.co.uk

⊗ A city centre brewpub opened in 2015 in the premises formerly occupied by Delaney's Irish Bar. ‼ ◆ GF

St Andrews Brewing

Unit 7, Bassaguard Business Park, St Andrews, KY16 8AL
☎ (01334) 208586
⊕ standrewsbrewingcompany.com

Established in 2012 as a four-barrel brewery it was upgraded in 2019 to a thirty-barrel plant producing bottle-conditioned, cask and eco keg beers. In addition to its own three outlets (two in St Andrews, and one in

Dundee), beers are supplied to a number of supermarket chains, local retailers and outlets. ‼ LIVE

Oatmeal Stout (ABV 4.5%) STOUT
Mocha Porter (ABV 6%) SPECIALITY
Notorious BIPA (ABV 6%) SPECIALITY
Yippie IPA (ABV 6%) IPA

St Annes

St Annes Church, Shorthill, Lea Cross, Shrewsbury, SY5 8JE
☎ (01743) 860296 ☎ 07530 556951
Office: 38 Hafren Road, Shrewsbury, SY3 8NQ
⊕ shropshirebeers.co.uk

⊠ Brewing began in 2017. This independent brewery is in the quirky location of a restored and occasionally functioning church. Recipes are Scandinavian-influenced but traditional British real ales. A broad range of beer styles is produced. ‼ ♦

Three Erics (ABV 3.7%) BITTER
Golden Dart (ABV 3.8%) GOLD
Lea Cross Dark (ABV 3.9%) MILD
Tumbledown Dick (ABV 4.2%) BITTER
Round The Wrekin (ABV 4.7%) BITTER
Iron And Fire (ABV 7.5%) STOUT

St Austell SIBA IFBB

63 Trevarthian Road, St Austell, Cornwall, PL25 4BY
☎ (0345) 241 1122 ⊕ staustellbrewery.co.uk

☺Founded in 1851, St Austell brewery remains fully independent and family-owned. Cask ale is available in all its pubs, and is widely available nationally. St Austell also brews limited edition cask beers throughout the year as well as a range of keg and bottled beers. A ten-barrel, small-batch plant is used to brew regular beers for its Cask Club (available in 40 selected outlets, and at its Hicks Bar), and to make a range of experimental bottle beers. In 2016 it purchased Bath Ales (qv). ‼ ♦ LIVE V ✦

Cornish Best Bitter (ABV 3.4%) BITTER
Light, refreshing bitter with little aroma. Gentle biscuit malt and hops flavour with fruity bitterness. Malty, bitter, faintly dry finish.

Anthem (ABV 3.8%) PALE
Smooth, refreshing, amber ale. Fruity hop aroma. Citrus and peach fruits dominate the taste. Sweet malt. Dry and bitter throughout.

Nicholson's Pale Ale (ABV 4%) PALE
Copper bitter. Hops dominate the taste with citrus and tropical fruits and malt. Dry bitterness rises in the finish.

Tribute (ABV 4.2%) PALE
Gold bitter with malt and citrus hop aroma. Dominant marmalade hop bitterness balanced by sweet malt, ending bitter and fruity.

Proper Job (ABV 4.5%) GOLD
Smooth premium golden ale with citrus hop aroma. Copious citrus fruits with bitterness, dryness and crisp hop bitter and grapefruit finish.

Hicks (ABV 5%) BITTER
Tawny premium bitter with malt nose. Powerful malt and vine fruit flavour with balancing bitterness. Long malty and floral finish.

Brewed for Brunning & Price Pub Co:
Traditional (ABV 3.4%) BITTER

St Botolphs

8 Gladwin Road, Colchester, Essex, CO2 7HS
☎ (01206) 511835 ⊠ info@stbotolphsbrewery.co.uk

Brewing began in 2014. Its Belgian-style bottled beers can be found in pubs, farm shops, specialist beer shops, markets and food festivals in Essex and Suffolk.

St Davids

Grange, Porthgain, Haverfordwest, SA62 5BJ
Office: Lecha Farm, SOLVA, Haverfordwest, SA62 6YD

Long-established trading concern which owns a number of pubs in far West Wales. It has no brewery and its range of bottled beers are contract brewed at Felinfoel.

St David's Old Farmhouse SIBA

Upper Harglodd, St Davids, SA62 6BX
☎ (01437) 729248 ⊕ oldfarmhousebrewery.co.uk

⊠ With a planned brewery name of St David's, later changed, Mark and Emma Evans commenced brewing in 2021 in a renovated farmhouse. The brewery uses home-grown grain and its own well water in the process.

St Ives SIBA

Unit 5, Marsh Lane Industrial Estate, Hayle Industrial Park, Hayle, Cornwall, TR27 5JR
☎ (01736) 793467 ☎ 07702 311595
⊕ stives-brewery.co.uk

⊠ Originally located in St Ives, it purchased a larger site in Hayle with a state-of-the-art, 25-barrel plant as the main brewery. The new site also incorporates a taproom, bar and café. The original two-story site in St Ives has been retained as a café and tourist attraction. The brewery has also established a St Ives town centre tasting room and shop. ‼ ♥ ♦ LIVE ✦

Hella Pale (ABV 4.2%) PALE
Porth Pilsner (ABV 4.4%) SPECIALITY
Meor IPA (ABV 4.8%) PALE
Pale/blond ale with fruity hop nose. Hop-forward with bitterness and sweetness but minimal malt. Tropical more than citrus fruits.
Slipway (ABV 5%) PALE
Alba IPA (ABV 5.2%) PALE
Creamy pale ale with fruity aroma, bitter spicy hop flavour, citrus and tropical fruits but minimal malt. Bitter, dry finish.
Zennor Oatmeal Stout (ABV 5.2%) STOUT
Back Road West (ABV 6.5%) IPA

St John at Hackney

See Hackney Church

St Judes

🍺 2 Cardigan Street, Ipswich, Suffolk, IP1 3PF
☎ (01473) 413334 ☎ 07879 360879
⊕ stjudestavern.com

⊠ The 10-barrel brewery produces beer for the St Judes Brewery Tavern in Ipswich. It can also be found at some local festivals.

St Mars of the Desert

90 Stevenson Road, Attercliffe, Sheffield, South Yorkshire, S9 3XG ☎ 07365 222101
⊕ beerofsmod.co.uk

A family-run brewery, recognised as one of the 'top ten new breweries in the world' by Rate Beer in 2020. Dann, Martha and Scarlet brew a range of beers inspired by many regional brewing cultures (American IPAs, or lagers inspired by Franconia and the Czech Republic, for example). The taproom is open most weekends between March and December for drinks and cans to take away. The brewery also ships cans to many independent retailers nationwide. ⬛◆

St Peter's SIBA

St Peter's Hall, St Peter South Elmham, Suffolk, NR35 1NQ
☎ (01986) 782322 ⊕ stpetersbrewery.co.uk

⊠ The brewery, built in 1996, is housed in traditional former agricultural buildings adjacent to the moated, medieval St Peters Hall, dating from 1280. Brewing makes use of the water from an onsite borehole combined with locally-malted barley. Beer is distributed nationally across the UK and exported to more than 40 countries worldwide. ‼⬛◆◆

Organic Best (ABV 4.1%) BITTER
A dry and bitter beer with a growing astringency. Pale brown in colour, it has a gentle hop aroma which makes the definitive bitterness surprising.
Ruby Red (ABV 4.3%) BITTER
Gold Dust (ABV 4.5%) GOLD
Plum Porter (ABV 4.6%) SPECIALITY
Citrus (ABV 4.7%) PALE
Fudge as well as grapefruit on the nose. A refreshing fruit flavour, with hints of grapefruit peel in the aftertaste.

Sabrina

Worcester

Saint Monday (NEW)

365-366 Warburton Street, London Fields, London, E8 3RR
☎ (020) 3011 1323 ⊕ saintmondaybrewery.uk

The Grace Land chain of pubs purchased the former London Fields Brewery and taproom from Carlsberg UK in early 2023, with the first beers appearing at the taproom by late summer 2023. The range of beers is now quite extensive and are available at the taproom and the eight pubs run by Grace Land. No cask ale. ◆

Salamander

See Stubbee

Salcombe SIBA

Estuary View, Ledstone, Devon, TQ7 4BL
☎ (01548) 854888 ⊕ salcombebrewery.com

⊠ Established in 2016 and built on the site of a decommissioned reservoir overlooking the Kingsbridge-Salcombe estuary, Salcombe Brewery craft award-winning beers using sustainable brewing methods. Locally-sourced ingredients are used where possible. ‼⬛GFV◆

Devon Amber (ABV 3.8%) BITTER
Amber-coloured bitter, using British hops. This easy-drinking malt driven bitter has a dry, yet sweet aftertaste backed up by the traditional British hop aromas.
Gold (ABV 4.2%) GOLD
Citrus aroma coming from the fruity hops. Tastes of apricot, peach and melon in with a mellow biscuit touch in the background. A refreshing ale.
Shingle Bay (ABV 4.2%) BITTER
A light, easy-drinking ale, with a fruity aroma and flavour. Smooth to the taste with a crisp revitalising finish.
Seahorse (ABV 4.4%) BITTER

Toffee malt is evident throughout this complex yet subtle mix of everything you would expect from a best bitter.
Lifesaver (ABV 4.8%) BITTER
A refreshing ale, deep copper in colour, with a smack of citrus and orange peel and luscious malty flavour. A dry citrus finish with a taste of liquorice.
Island Street Porter (ABV 5.9%) PORTER
Creamy head, aroma of chocolate/coffee and cherries giving a black forest gateau taste. Flavours linger on tongue during aftertaste.

Salopian SIBA

The Old Station Yard, Station Road, Hadnall, Shropshire, SY4 3DD
☎ (01743) 248414 ⊕ salopianbrewery.co.uk

⊕The brewery was established in 1995 in an old dairy on the outskirts of Shrewsbury but moved in 2014 to its new location in an industrial unit in the village of Hadnall, where it now produces more than 150 barrels a week of its multi award-winning ales, for distribution throughout the midlands, and further afield. To capitalise on the small pack market, the brewery has invested in its own canning plant. ‼⬛◆LIVE

Shropshire Gold (ABV 3.8%) GOLD
Auric (ABV 4%) PALE
Oracle (ABV 4%) GOLD
Citrus aromas lead to an impressive dry and increasing citrusy taste.
Darwins Origin (ABV 4.3%) BITTER
Pale brown in which hops and fruit are dominant. Hops top the aftertaste with a pleasing lingering bitterness. Well-balanced with a moreish demand.
Hop Twister (ABV 4.5%) GOLD
Lemon Dream (ABV 4.5%) SPECIALITY
Paper Planes (ABV 4.6%) IPA
Golden Thread (ABV 5%) GOLD
Kashmir (ABV 5.5%) BITTER
Automaton (ABV 7%) STRONG
Gold with pine forest aromas and peaches! Syrup with a kick. Dry hints and exotic astringency as hops give a dry finish but sweet balance.

Salt

🏛 **199 Bingley Road, Shipley, West Yorkshire, BD18 4DH**
☎ (01274) 533848

Second Site: Unit 35.9, Cobalt, White Hart Triangle Estate, White Hart Avenue, Thamesmead, SE28 0GU
⊕ saltbeerfactory.co.uk

Housed in a Grade II-listed Edwardian tramshed, Salt is a state-of-the-art, 200-hectolitre brewplant and one of the Ossett group of independently-run breweries. The site includes a taproom and live music space. Two bars, branded as Craft Asylum, are operated. It bought the Hop Stuff brewery in Thamesmead when it was put up for sale by Molson Coors in 2021. ‼◆

Salt Steel

Office: 24 St Cuthberts Way, Darlington, DL1 1GB
⊕ saltsteelbrewing.com

Established in 2020 and forged from the industrial landscapes of Teeside and Cheshire, Salt Steel Brewing have been collaborating with other brewers in the North East.

Saltaire SIBA

Unit 7, County Works, Dockfield Road, Shipley, West Yorkshire, BD17 7AR

☎ (01274) 594959 ⊕ saltairebrewery.com

☺Saltaire Brewery opened in a converted gasworks by the River Aire in 2006 and has established itself as a leading independent brewer of cask ales. There is a stated emphasis on providing quality of product, whilst maintaining a steadfast commitment to an expanding range of cask and KeyKeg beers. Supplies pubs and retail outlets throughout the UK and worldwide. 🍺♦⬧

South Island (ABV 3.5%) PALE
Titus (ABV 3.9%) BITTER
Blonde (ABV 4%) BITTER
Citra (ABV 4.2%) PALE
Best (ABV 4.4%) BITTER
Amarillo (ABV 4.5%) PALE
Cascade (ABV 4.8%) PALE
Triple Choc (ABV 4.8%) SPECIALITY
Unity (ABV 6%) IPA

SaltRock SIBA

Lochend Farm, Dunfermline, KY12 0RY
⊕ saltrockbrewing.co.uk

SaltRock Brewing began brewing in 2021. Born of a desire to re-awaken a celebration of malt over the hop, it produces malt-forward beers.

Sambrook's SIBA

Unit 11.09, Bellwether Lane, The Ram Quarter, Ram Street, Wandsworth, London, SW18 1UR
☎ (020) 7228 0598 ⊕ sambrooksbrewery.co.uk

⊠ Sambrook's was founded in 2008 and supplies its award-winning ales throughout London. The range of beers is traditional in style and available in all formats but cask is the key focus. A move in 2021 saw a new brewery built in the redeveloped Young's Brewery complex in central Wandsworth. The Ram brewery, which had been brewing on site since the closure of Young's Brewery, is now part of Sambrook's, although it still brews its own range of beers. ‼♦LIVE⬧

Wandle (ABV 3.8%) BITTER
Amber bitter with a biscuity sweetness and orange on nose and palate, with apricot. A spicy bitter hop lingering finish.
Pumphouse Pale (ABV 4.2%) PALE
Aromas and flavours of malt, honey, hops, citrus and apricot. Sweetness is balanced by a dry, slight spicy, lingering bitterness.
Junction (ABV 4.5%) BITTER
Aroma is roasty, and slightly sweet with caramelised citrus, toffee, sultanas, hints of roasty chocolate throughout. Dry, spicy, bitter finish.
Lavender Hill (ABV 4.5%) SPECIALITY
Honey and orange floral nose and a malty palate gives way to a slightly dry hoppy bitter finish with orange peel.
Powerhouse Porter (ABV 4.9%) PORTER
Sweet fruity chocolate nose with sweet toffee, chocolate, caramelised fruit and a hint of orange peel. Roasty bitter finish.

Sandbanks SIBA

Unit 6, 4-6 Abingdon Road, Nuffield Industrial Estate, Poole, Dorset, BH17 0UG
☎ (01202) 671950 ⊕ sandbanksbrewery.net

⊠ Opened in 2018 on a local industrial estate with a five-barrel plant plus a one-barrel plant for one off-brews. The beer is becoming increasingly available in the local free trade with one-off and special beers available in the taproom. 🍺♦⬧

Bitter (ABV 3.9%) BITTER
Refreshing session bitter with pleasant malt character.
Free Bird (ABV 4.2%) PALE
Golden Years (ABV 4.3%) GOLD
Back in Black (ABV 5%) STOUT
Easy-drinking stout with roast malt on tongue and hints of liquorice and coffee, lingering rich fruit aftertaste.
Wayward Son IPA (ABV 5%) PALE

Sandstone

Unit 5a, Wrexham Enterprise Park, Preston Road, off Ash Road, North Wrexham Industrial Estate, Wrexham, LL13 9JT
☎ (01978) 664805 ☎ 07415 409625
⊕ sandstonebrewery.co.uk

☺Sandstone Brewery was established as a four-barrel plant in 2008. The brewery was taken over by the current owners in 2013. The beers are available at around 50 outlets in North-West England and North Wales. ‼🍺♦

Edge (ABV 3.8%) BITTER
A satisfying session ale, this pale, dry, bitter beer has a full mouthfeel and a lingering hoppy finish that belies its modest strength.
Onyx Dragon (ABV 4%) MILD
Morillo (ABV 4.2%) BITTER
Twisted Dragon (ABV 5.8%) BITTER

Scarborough SIBA

Unit 21B, Stadium Works, Barry's Lane, Scarborough, North Yorkshire, YO12 4HA
☎ (01723) 367506 ⊕ scarboroughbrewery.co.uk

☺Scarborough is a family-run brewery established in 2010, now using a 10-barrel plant. Beers can be found in the family-owned Valley Bar and Rivelyn Hotel as well as being the sole suppliers to Merchant Bar, Scarborough. ♦

Trident (ABV 3.8%) PALE
Citra (ABV 4.2%) GOLD
Sealord (ABV 4.3%) GOLD
Stout (ABV 4.6%) STOUT
Hello Darkness (ABV 5%) PORTER

Scruffy Dog

🏠 94 Station Road, Sutton-in-Ashfield, Nottinghamshire, NG17 5HF
☎ (01623) 550826 ⊕ thescruffydog.co.uk

Microbrewery at the Scruffy Dog pub in Sutton-in-Ashfield. Open since 2017, it is family-run and produces a wide range of beer styles. It started on a one-barrel plant, but is hoping to expand capacity.

Seagate

Seagate, Lamlash, Isle of Arran, KA27 8JN
☎ (01770) 600110 ☎ 07798 854295
⊕ seagatebrewery.co.uk

In 2020 Stephen Sparshott progressed from homebrewing in his kitchen into commercial brewing in a purpose-built shed on the shores of Lamlash Bay. Concentrating on Belgian and Scottish ales, a small range of core beers are brewed on his 30-litre and 50-litre kits, with further ales produced on a separate installation at Arran Botanical Drinks, Cladach, Brodick. All bottled beers are bottle-conditioned, but the brewery hopes to produce them all as can-conditioned. All beers are accredited under CAMRA's One to Try scheme but only sold locally. ‼♦LIVE

Rise Above 80/- (ABV 4.5%) BITTER
RYIPA (ABV 5%) SPECIALITY

789

Saorsa Blond Ale (ABV 5%) SPECIALITY
Scottie Stout (ABV 5%) STOUT

Second Sun (NEW)

Quaker Yard, Rear of 24 Newgate, Barnard Castle, County Durham, DL12 8NG ⊕ secondsunbrewing.com

Brewing commenced in 2023 on a kit previously owned by Barnard Castle Brewery. The brewery is run by Chris Corr, owner of Crafty Merlin's micropub in Darlington.

Secret Project

March Road, Turves, Cambridgeshire, PE7 2DW
☎ 07429 185333 ✉ secretprojectbrew@gmail.com

A microbrewery in Cambridgeshire, specialising in hoppy craft beer. Only limited run, single batches are brewed (contact the brewery for details of current brews).

Selby Middlebrough SIBA

131 Millgate, Selby, North Yorkshire, YO8 3LL
☎ (01757) 702826 ✉ martinsykesuk@yahoo.com

Small batch brewery launched in 2022.

Serious SIBA

Unit C5, Fieldhouse Industrial Estate, Fieldhouse Road, Rochdale, OL12 0AA ☎ 07840 301797 ⊕ seriousbrewing.co.uk

🅖Established in 2015 and run by husband-and-wife team, Ken and Jenny Lynch. The beers are brewed in Rochdale on a six-barrel plant supplied by Vincent Johnson. The focus is on producing top quality beers drawing on influences from traditional British ales, US craft beers and artisinal Belgian beers. Many outlets are supplied direct and the beers are available nationwide through wholesalers. A tap, The Whitewell in Waterfoot, Rossendale is a new addition. ♦ LIVE V

Prime (ABV 4.2%) PALE
Evergreen (ABV 4.5%) BITTER
Hoppy aroma. Taste of fruit and bitter hops, with lasting bitterness. Crisp and bitter throughout. Background of sweet malt.
Moonlight (ABV 4.5%) STOUT
Medium-bodied dry stout with roast character that develops into a crisp bitter finish.
Redsmith (ABV 4.5%) BITTER
Goldrush (ABV 5.6%) SPECIALITY

Settle SIBA

Unit 2B, The Sidings, Settle, North Yorkshire, BD24 9RP
☎ (01729) 824936 ⊕ settlebrewery.co.uk

🅖Settle Brewery is located in an industrial unit adjacent to Settle Railway Station. Brewing started in 2013 using a 12-barrel plant. It supplies more than 40 outlets across Cumbria, North and West Yorkshire and Lancashire. The beers are also available through wholesalers. Beers are occasionally branded as Nine Standards. ‼♦

Jericho Blonde (ABV 3.6%) BLOND
Citrus hops lead to a soft malt background and a slightly bitter finish.
Ribblehead Bitter (ABV 3.8%) BITTER
Full-bodied bitter is malty in aroma and taste. Subtle hints of citrus lead to a long bitter finish.
Hoffman Gold (ABV 4.1%) GOLD
Attermire Pale (ABV 4.3%) PALE
Epic IPA (ABV 4.4%) PALE

Hop-led pale ale with citrus aroma. A soft maltiness leads into a lingering bitter finish.
Ernie's Milk Stout (ABV 4.5%) STOUT
Ruby red beer, fruity roasted malt and caramel aromas. Roast malt, vine fruits and dark chocolate give a bitter finish.
Old Smithy Porter (ABV 4.7%) PORTER
Roasty porter with coffee and dark fruits. Hints of liquorice and plums in the aroma. The finish is bitter and roasty.

Seven Bro7hers

Unit 63, Waybridge Enterprise Centre, Daniel Adamson Road, Salford, M50 1DS
☎ (0161) 228 2404 ⊕ sevenbro7hers.com

Brewing began in 2014 using a 10-barrel plant. A new brewhouse, incorporating a brewery tap, plus new fermentation tanks, doubled brewing capacity in 2017, and allowed for the brewing of speciality and one-off beers. The Seven Bro7hers Beerhouse in Ancoats opened in 2016, and a Beerhouse opened in 2019 in the Middlewood Locks area, near Salford Central Station. Further venues have opened in Halifax, Liverpool and at Manchester Airport. ‼🍺♦

Session (ABV 3.8%) PALE
Fruity hop taste of tropical fruit, well-balanced with bitter and pale malt. Citrus hop aroma. Refreshing bitter finish.

Seven Stars

See Hidden

Severn Valley

The Stables, Hollow Ash Lane, Bridgnorth, Shropshire, WV15 6ET ☎ 07402 636482
✉ beer@severnvalleyales.co.uk

The trading name of Bridgnorth Brewery Ltd, Severn Valley Ales started brewing in 2019 producing a range of beers in different packaging formats. The main outlet is Bridgnorth Rugby Club, but beers can be found in other pubs in Bridgnorth. Brewing is currently suspended.

Shadow

98 Boroughgate, Otley, West Yorkshire, LS21 1AE
☎ 07792 690536 ⊕ shadowbrewing.co.uk

Set up in 2019, originally in the owner's garage, Shadow Brewing moved to Otley in 2021 and now has its own taproom. A range of cask beers is produced on its one-barrel kit and via contract brewing with larger breweries. ♦

Shadow Bridge

Unit 1, Humber Bridge Garden Centre, Barton-upon-Humber, Lincolnshire, DN18 5RF

Brewery located in the shadow of the Humber Bridge, hence the name which opened in 2022. The core beers plus seasonals are available in cask and bottle and available in the taproom and shop. The spent grains are used by the neighbouring farm for livestock. ♦

Battle Standard (ABV 3.8%) BITTER
Dragon Slayer (ABV 4.1%) GOLD
Elvish Fury (ABV 4.3%) RED
Wrath of the Gods (ABV 4.5%) PALE

Shakespeare

See North Cotswold

Sharp's

Pityme Business Centre, Rock, Cornwall, PL27 6NU
☎ (01208) 862121 ⊕ sharpsbrewery.co.uk

⊗ Sharp's was founded in 1994 and within 15 years had grown from producing 1,500 barrels a year, to 60,000. It was bought by Molson Coors in 2011. Heavy investment has brought the capacity up to 200,000 barrels a year. The company owns no pubs and delivers beer to more than 1,200 outlets across South England via temperature-controlled depots in Bristol and London. Part of Molson Coors PLC. ⌷♦LIVE

Doom Bar (ABV 4%) BITTER
Amber bitter with sweet taste, balanced malt, pine hops and toffee. Broad mixture of fruit flavours. Gentle sweet, malty finish.
Atlantic (ABV 4.2%) BITTER
Golden light bitter with citrus hop and fruit aroma. Malt, elderflower and caramel sweetness balanced by grapefruit and resinous hops.
Solar Wave (ABV 4.6%) PALE
Gold hazy pale ale with faint sweet fruit aroma. Sweet tropical fruit cocktail dominates the taste with malt and bitterness.
Sea Fury (ABV 5%) BITTER
Smooth auburn premium bitter with malt and caramel aromas. Dominant sweet malt with berry, stone and dried fruits with spice hints.

Shaws of Grange

12 Station Yard, Grange-over-Sands, Cumbria, LA11 6DW
☎ (01539) 555349 ☎ 07951 009607
⊕ shawsofgrange.co.uk

This 0.5-barrel brewery began producing beers for sale in 2019. A range of four beers has been developed for sale in cask and by hand bottling. Virtually all the production has been sold in bottles since 2020, although the brewery will supply a cask on demand.

Shed

Thornton Cleveleys, Lancashire ⊕ shedbeer.co.uk

⊙Shed Beer was established in 2019 as a commercial home-based brewery producing occasional beer for events. Brewing became more regular following the opening of its own micropub in Fleetwood towards the end of 2022, although the popularity of the beers means that production is now carried out at Ben's Brewery in Chorley.

Shed 35

Chapman Drive, Carnoustie, DD7 6DX ☎ 07530 430579 ⊕ shed35brewery.co.uk

Now run solely by John Wilson, brewing began in 2016. Although mainly producing bottle-conditioned beers for sale locally at farmers' markets and other outlets in Angus and the surrounding area, the brewery occasionally produces cask beer.

Sheelin

178 Derrylin Road, Bellanaleck, Enniskillen, Northern Ireland, BT92 2BA ☎ 07730 432232
⊕ sheelinbrewery.com

Sheelin was established by brewer and chemist Dr George Cathcart in 2013. Beer is mainly available in bottles.

Blonde (ABV 4.5%) BLOND

IPA (ABV 4.5%) PALE
Red (ABV 4.5%) RED
Stout (ABV 4.5%) STOUT

Shepherd Neame IFBB

17 Court Street, Faversham, Kent, ME13 7AX
☎ (01795) 532206 ⊕ shepherdneame.co.uk

⊗ Shepherd Neame traces its history back to at least 1698, making it the oldest continuous brewer in the country. The company has around 300 tied houses in the South-East, nearly all selling cask ale. More than 2,000 other outlets are also supplied by this independent family brewer. The cask beers are made with mostly Kentish hops, and water from the brewery's own artsian well. The Cask Club offers a new and different cask ale every month or so. ⌷⌷⌷♦LIVE

Master Brew (ABV 3.7%) BITTER
A distinctive bitter, mid-brown in colour, with a hoppy aroma. Well-balanced, with a nicely aggressive bitter taste from its hops, it leaves a hoppy/bitter finish, tinged with sweetness.
Whitstable Bay Pale Ale (ABV 3.9%) PALE
Spitfire Gold (ABV 4.1%) GOLD
Spitfire (ABV 4.2%) BITTER
Malty caramel with bitter hops and caramelised fruit and citrus flavours. Spiciness builds and remains in the hoppy dry finish.
Bishops Finger (ABV 5%) BITTER

Sherfield Village

Goddards Farm, Goddards Lane, Sherfield on Loddon, Hampshire, RG27 0EL ☎ 07906 060429
⊕ sherfieldvillagebrewery.co.uk

Production started in 2011 in a converted barn on a working dairy farm. Using a five-barrel plant, the brewery supplies local pubs and regional festivals. Extensive use is made of New World hops, particularly those from New Zealand. All beers are unfined. ♦LIVE V

Southern Gold (ABV 4%) GOLD
Green Bullet (ABV 4.3%) GOLD
Strong lemony nose, with hops dominating the taste building to a strong aftertaste and big astringent hit at the end.
Single Hop (ABV 4.3%) GOLD
Pioneer Stout (ABV 5%) STOUT
Dark roast malts dominate this jet black stout, with hints of autumnal fruits. Bitter, with a long dry finish.

Shilling

92 West George Street, Glasgow, G2 1PJ
☎ (0141) 353 1654 ⊕ shillingbrewingcompany.co.uk
Brewing began in 2016.

Shiny

Unit 10, Old Hall Mill Business Centre, Little Eaton, Derbyshire, DE21 5EJ
☎ (01332) 902809 ⊕ shinybrewing.com

Brewing commenced in 2012 using a six-barrel plant sited in the beer garden of the Furnace Inn, Derby. After initially brewing solely for the pub, 2014 saw an increase in scale and output, with beers distributed across most of the country. A second 12-barrel brew plant was built in 2015 to increase capacity and host a visitor centre, taproom and shop. ⌷♦LIVE GF V♦

Thunder Bridge (ABV 3.7%) PALE
NZ Pale (ABV 3.9%) PALE
Rocky (ABV 4.1%) PALE

Afterglow (ABV 4.2%) PALE
Wrench (ABV 4.4%) STOUT
4 Wood (ABV 4.5%) BITTER
Lil Wingman (ABV 4.5%) PALE
Affinity (ABV 4.6%) GOLD
Disco Balls (ABV 5.3%) GOLD
Glamour Muscles (ABV 5.3%) PALE

Ship Inn

🏠 Ship Inn, Newton Square, Low Newton-by-the-Sea, Northumberland, NE66 3EL
☎ (01665) 576262 ⊕ shipinnnewton.co.uk

☺Brewing commenced in 2008 on a 2.5-barrel plant. The brewery now brews three times a week producing 7.5 barrels. Sixteen beers are brewed in constant rotation but are only available on the premises. A special beer is brewed for every 100 brews. Some beers are now available in cans but again only available from The Ship Inn. ◆LIVE

Shipstone's SIBA

Fox & Crown, 33 Church Street, Old Basford, Nottingham, NG6 0GA
☎ (0115) 837 4200 ⊕ shipstones.com

☺A full-mash, 10-barrel brewery, it is located behind the Fox & Crown. Established in 1996 as Fiddlers Ales, becoming Alcazar Brewery on change of ownership in 1999. It changed hands in 2016, the name changed again, and a new portfolio of beers was established, but was short-lived. It soon reverted back to Alcazar. In late 2016 Shipstone's took over brewing, producing its range of beers previously contract brewed at Belvoir Brewery (qv). Beers are also brewed under the Hollow Stone Brewing Co brand name. ‼◆

Original (ABV 3.8%) BITTER
Pale brown malty traditional bitter, well-balanced in both hops and bitterness without either becoming overpowering.
Nut Brown (ABV 4%) BITTER
A dark, ruby brown session bitter; sweet and malty with a fruity nose and subtle roast aftertaste.
Gold Star (ABV 4.2%) GOLD
Golden in colour with a delicate citrus hop and slight dry bitter finish.
IPA (ABV 5.5%) IPA
Hop bitterness with a slight citrus aroma and malty aftertaste.

Brewed under the Hollow Stone Brewing Co brand name:
Oligo Nunk (ABV 4%) GOLD
This golden ale has pronounced bitterness and grapefruit flavour.
Pale Ale (ABV 4.2%) PALE
Bitter hop flavour with a fresh citrus finish.
Waitomo (ABV 4.5%) PALE
Aruru (ABV 4.7%) BITTER

Shivering Sands

91 Maple Leaf Business Park, Manston, Kent, CT12 5GD ☎ 07805 061343
⊕ shivering-sands-brewery.business.site

☒ Established in 2020, it is situated in an industrial estate outside the airfield at Manston, near Ramsgate, and uses an eight-barrel plant, brewing once a week. Its onsite taproom is open on Saturdays and at other times by arrangement. ♪

Spring Tide (ABV 3.8%) PALE
Maunsell (ABV 4%) BITTER

Estuary Porter (ABV 4.1%) PORTER
Golden Sands (ABV 4.5%) PALE
Knock John (ABV 4.5%) BITTER
Ribersborg Stout (ABV 4.7%) STOUT
Warden Black IPA (ABV 5.2%) PALE

Shoals

The Shipyard, Porthleven, TR13 9JY ☎ 07817 241024
⊕ shoalsbrewery.com

☒ Opened in early 2022, the brewery is located in an historic central Porthleven venue occupying the buildings of the old shipyard. The taproom is open to the public Thursday-Sunday. V♪

Harbinger Pale Ale (ABV 4.2%) PALE

Shortts SIBA

Shortts Farm, Thorndon, Suffolk, IP23 7LS ☎ 07900 268100 ⊕ shorttsfarmbrewery.com

An award-winning brewery established in 2012 by Matt Hammond on what has been the family farm for over a century. Ales are produced using carefully selected ingredients to create both traditional and more complex contemporary flavours. The beer names are based around a musical theme and can be found throughout East Anglia. LIVE V

The Cure (ABV 3.6%) BITTER
Clean-tasting, copper-coloured, malty bitter. Sweetish malt and caramel with hints of fruit and a background hop bitterness.
Strummer (ABV 3.8%) BITTER
Amber bitter with hops supported by sweetish nutty malt and a gentle bitterness.
Two Tone (ABV 3.8%) MILD
Enjoyable, well-rounded, dark brown mild with a sweet maltiness tempered by gentle roast flavours and a touch of caramel.
Blondie (ABV 4%) PALE
Satisfying gold-coloured ale with sweet malt and a gentle citrus hoppiness. The malty sweetness lingers as a light bitterness develops.
Hunky Dory (ABV 4.1%) GOLD
Rockabilly (ABV 4.3%) PALE
Skiffle (ABV 4.5%) BITTER
Copper-coloured premium bitter with light hop flavours jostling with sweet malt and a counterbalance of berry fruit.
Black Volt (ABV 4.8%) STOUT
Powerful smooth stout with full roast malt flavours, hints of caramel and a sweetish palate.
Indie (ABV 4.8%) PALE
Mouth-filling amber-hued ale with a fruity aroma and fruity hop with hints of malt in the sweetish palate.
Darkside (ABV 5%) PORTER
Powerful porter with inviting roast malt and hop aroma then a booming roasty taste with biscuity caramel sweetness and hops.

Shottle Farm

Office: School House Farm, Lodge Lane, Shottle, Derbyshire, DE56 2DS
☎ (01773) 550056 ☎ 07877 723075
⊕ shottlefarmbrewery.co.uk

Located in the hills above Belper, the Grade II-listed farm is part of the Chatsworth Estate. Established in 2011 with a 10-barrel plant, beers are now contract brewed elsewhere. Shottle Farm has an onsite bar (limited opening hours), the Bull Shed, which is the only outlet for its beers. ◆LIVE

Shottlecock (ABV 3.6%) BITTER
Black Peggy (ABV 3.9%) MILD
Pale Ale (ABV 4%) PALE
BOB (Best of Both) (ABV 4.1%) SPECIALITY
Eight Shilling (ABV 4.1%) BITTER
Gold (ABV 4.3%) GOLD
Dilks (ABV 5%) BITTER

Shugborough

Shugborough Estate, Milford, Staffordshire, ST17 0XB
☎ (01782) 823447 ⊕ shugborough.org.uk

Brewing in the original brewhouse at Shugborough (home of the Earls of Lichfield) restarted in 1990, but a lack of expertise led to the brewery being a static museum piece until Titanic Brewery of Stoke-on-Trent (qv) began helping in 1996. Brewing is currently suspended. ‼

Signal SIBA

Unit 8, Stirling Way, Beddington Farm Road, Beddington, CR0 4XN
☎ (020) 8684 6111 ⊕ signalbeerco.com

Starting in 2016, Signal's lager was the staple product in keg and cans. 2018 saw a refresh and a range of cask ale is now produced along with an increased variety of keg. Available at the taproom, its Cloud Nine bar at the O2 in North Greenwich, and now regionally. ◆

Absolutely Fuggled (ABV 4%) BITTER
Perfumed hops aroma with hops and a bitter orange character throughout. A developing dry spiciness fading in the bitterish finish.
Sticky Hoppy Pudding (ABV 4.3%) SPECIALITY
Distinct caramel and biscuit aroma and flavour with a little hop and fruit. Dry, bitter finish with some lingering sweetness.

Signature SIBA

Unit 15, Uplands Business Park, Blackhorse Lane, Walthamstow, London, E17 5QJ
☎ (020) 7684 4664 ⊕ signaturebrew.co.uk

Starting off cuckoo brewing in 2011, crowdfunding saw brewing start in Leyton in 2015 followed by a move to Walthamstow in 2019. Aside from the core range, specials are brewed in collaboration with music artists. These are available in the onsite taproom and its bars in Walthamstow and Haggerston. ◆LIVE◆

Roadie All-Night IPA (ABV 4.3%) GOLD
Hop-forward golden ale with lemon and grapefruit in aroma and flavour with a biscuity sweetness. Lingering dry, bitter finish.
Backstage IPA (ABV 5.6%) IPA
Hoppy aroma. Palate of strong hops with biscuit, grapefruit, tropical and a little apricot fruits. Aftertaste becomes spicy and bitter.
Nightliner Coffee Porter (ABV 5.7%) SPECIALITY
Smoky black porter with dark roast coffee dominating with hints of dark fruit, dark treacle and a dry toasty bitterness.

Silent Mill (NEW)

Unit 9, Coppice Business Park, West Moss Lane, Lytham St Annes, Lancashire, FY8 4SH ☎ 07961 228089 ⊕ silentmillbrew.co

Brewing began in late spring 2024.

Silhill

44 Bracebridge Street, Aston, Birmingham, West Midlands, B6 4PE
☎ (0845) 519 5101 ☎ 07977 444564

Office: PO Box 15739, Solihull, B93 3FW
⊕ silhillbrewery.co.uk

⊠ Established in 2010, Silhill was, until recently, a small, independent brewery. Originally based in premises just outside Solihull town centre using a 10-barrel plant, it moved in 2024 to a new location in Aston, Birmingham, with an onsite taproom. Beers are available in Solihull, Birmingham and Stratford-upon-Avon. ‼LIVE◆

Gold Star (ABV 3.9%) SPECIALITY
Blonde Star (ABV 4.1%) BLOND
Hop Star (ABV 4.2%) PALE
Pure Star (ABV 4.3%) BITTER
Super Star (ABV 5.1%) GOLD

Silver

Units 3 & 4, Silver House, Adelphi Way, Staveley, Chesterfield, Derbyshire, S43 3LJ
☎ (01246) 470074 ☎ 07496 757619
⊕ silverbrewhouse.com

⊠ Silver Brewhouse is a 12-barrel brewery producing hop-forward and traditional ales. It also brews under the brand names Industrial Ales and Funky Hop Donkey including a range of single-hopped ales under the Arkwright Pal label. ☟◆LIVE GF V

West Coast Pale Ale (ABV 3.7%) PALE
Baby Ghost IPA (ABV 3.9%) GOLD
Independence APA (ABV 4.1%) PALE
Eyup Cocka! (ABV 4.3%) GOLD
Anubis Porter (ABV 5.2%) PORTER
Grey Ghost IPA (ABV 5.9%) IPA

Brewed under the Industrial Ales brand name:
Brickworks Bitter (ABV 4%) BITTER
Stephensons Pale (ABV 4%) PALE
Arkwrights Pale (ABV 4.1%) PALE
Coal Face Stout (ABV 4.5%) STOUT
Iron Ore IPA (ABV 5%) PALE

Silverstone SIBA

Kingshill Farm, Syresham, Northamptonshire, NN13 5TH ☎ 07835 279400
⊕ silverstonebrewery.co.uk

Established in 2008 Silverstone Brewery is a traditional tower brewery located near the celebrated motor racing circuit. The brewery has won multiple awards for its beers, which are supplied mainly in bottles but also cask or KeyKeg. ‼◆

Ignition (ABV 3.4%) BLOND
Pitstop (ABV 3.9%) BITTER
Polestar (ABV 4.1%) STOUT
Chequered Flag (ABV 4.3%) BITTER
Octane (ABV 4.8%) BITTER
Classic IPA (ABV 5.6%) IPA

Simple Things Fermentations SIBA

The Bakehouse, 6 Hazel Avenue Lane, Glasgow, G44 3LJ
☎ (0141) 237 2202
⊕ simplethingsfermentations.com

Opened in 2019 beer is produced in can, bottle, keg and cask. All beer is naturally carbonated through re-fermentation in package. ‼LIVE

Simpsons

🏠 White Swan, Eardisland, Herefordshire, HR6 9BD
☎ (01544) 388635 ⊕ thewhiteswaneardisland.com

Tim Simpson acquired the White Swan in 2011 and set up the brewery at the rear of the pub in 2013. All beers are brewed for consumption in the White Swan. ◆

Siren SIBA

Unit 1, Hogwood Lane Industrial Estate, Weller Drive, Finchampstead, RG40 4QZ
☎ (0118) 973 0929

Office: Siren Tap Yard, Alberto House, 18 Marino Way, Hogwood Lane Industrial Estate, Finchampstead, RG40 4RF ⊕ sirencraftbrew.com

⊠ Established in 2013, this is a state-of-the-art, 40-barrel craft brewery, which produces 70-100 unique beers every year. Beers are produced in cask, keg, KeyKeg, bottles and cans, and are distributed throughout the UK and Europe. The tap yard serves freshly-brewed beers, pizzas and hosts special events. Siren also own a country pub nearby in Swallowfield and is due to open a bar in Reading, to be called the 'Siren City Bar'.
!! ☷ ◆ GF V✓

Yu Lu (ABV 3.6%) SPECIALITY
Memento (ABV 3.8%) BITTER
Lumina (ABV 4.2%) PALE
Broken Dream Breakfast Stout (ABV 6.5%) SPECIALITY

Six° North

Reekie House, Aberdeen Road, Laurencekirk, AB30 1AG
☎ (01561) 377047 ☎ 07840 678243
⊕ sixdnorth.co.uk

⊠ Established in 2013, the brewery brews beers in the Belgian tradition, using a purpose-built 472-hectolitre plant. Depending on beer style, the beers are supplied as cask or keg and can. !! ◆ LIVE GF

Omnium (ABV 4.3%) PALE
Motion Honey Stout (ABV 4.7%) STOUT

Six Hills SIBA

Rear of 29b High Street, Stevenage, Hertfordshire, SG1 3BG ☎ 07973 673040 ⊕ sixhillsbrewing.co.uk

⊠ Previously known as Bog Brew, Six Hills Brewing was established in 2017 and renamed in 2021. Beers are available at local beer festivals, freehouses, and the brewery tap located next to the brewery. It has expanded from a two-barrel plant to 2,500 litres per month capacity. There are several regular beers as well as seasonal specials. All beers are unfined and vegan. The brewery holds regular events (festivals/ takeovers) throughout the year. !! ☷ ◆ LIVE V✓

Running with the Big Dog (ABV 4.8%) PALE

Sixpenny SIBA

The Old Dairy, Holwell Farm, Cranborne, Dorset, BH21 5QP
☎ (01725) 762006 ⊕ sixpennybrewery.co.uk

⊠ Founded in 2007, Sixpenny moved into its present home of renovated Victorian farm buildings near Cranborne, in 2016. This allowed for the expansion of the brewery bar and shop (Sixpenny Tap), in converted stables next door. Sixpenny has been brewing to its 20-barrel plant capacity for some while now to meet

demand. Fortnightly music events are held on a Saturday (see website for information). !! ☷ ◆ ◆

6d Best Bitter (ABV 3.8%) BITTER
Traditional, well-balanced session bitter with good malt flavours and a pleasant bittersweet finish.
6d Gold (ABV 4%) GOLD
Earthy golden ale with green hop character on the nose and lingering hop aftertaste.
6d IPA (ABV 5.2%) PALE
Flavoursome premium pale ale that tastes like a classic IPA but without the full strength. A strong hop character and solid malt backbone with lingering hop aftertaste.

Skinner's

Riverside, Newham Road, Truro, TR1 2DP
☎ (01872) 271885 ⊕ skinnersbrewery.com

⊠ Following the change of ownership in 2023, the new owners, local brewer Goodh Brewing Co (qv), continue to operate the brewery independently from its other brewery. Now in full production, the reintroduction of Skinner's iconic beers continues. The production of all core beers and some of the seasonal beers has already been achieved. The revamped Tapyard Bar & Kitchen is popular. !! ☷ ◆ ◆

Cornish Trawler (ABV 3.8%) BITTER
Balanced amber bitter with light malt and hop aroma. Malt complements the fresh grassy hops with floral notes. Refreshing finish.
Betty Stogs (ABV 4%) BITTER
Amber/gold bitter. Bitter resinous hops balanced by sweet malt, grapefruit and tropical fruits. Malt fades into the long bitter finish.
Lushingtons (ABV 4.2%) BLOND
Refreshing blond beer. Mango, spicy hops and orange aroma. Tropical fruits dominate the flavour. Long fruity, bitter finish with rising dryness.
Cornish Knocker (ABV 4.5%) PALE
Smooth golden pale ale. Blend of citrus, floral, piney and earthy hops with biscuit malt with hints of toffee and honey.
Pennycomequick (ABV 4.5%) STOUT
Creamy, ruby, sweet stout with roast grain aroma. Heavy bitter roast coffee, malt, fig and cherry flavours. Roast malt finish.
Porthleven (ABV 4.8%) PALE
Robust pale ale with citrus hop aroma. Assertive citrus bitterness with sweet fruity flavours and light malt. Bitter citrus finish.

Slaughterhouse SIBA

Bridge Street, Warwick, CV34 5PD
☎ (01926) 490986 ☎ 07951 842690

Second site: Wild Boar, 27 Larkin Road, Warwick, CV34 5BU ⊕ slaughterhousebrewery.com

☺ Production began in 2003 on a four-barrel plant in a former slaughterhouse. Around 30 outlets are supplied, mostly within five miles of the brewery. The brewery premises are licensed for off-sales direct to the public. In 2010 Slaughterhouse opened its first pub, the Wild Boar in Warwick, adding a two-barrel brew plant that brews specials for the pub. !!

Saddleback Best Bitter (ABV 3.8%) BITTER
Extra Stout Snout (ABV 4.4%) STOUT
Boar D'eau (ABV 4.5%) GOLD
Wild Boar (ABV 5.2%) BITTER

SLOPEmeisteR

Oak House, Airth Castle Estate, Airth, FK2 8JF
☎ 07895 734867 ⊕ slopemeister.com

SLOPEmeisteR started brewing in 2018, initially at Hybrid Brewery in Grangemouth, then setting up a nanobrewery in a garage in Airth. Cask-conditioned beer is supplied to festivals. SLOPEmeisterR recently purchased brewing equipment from the now closed Tryst Brewery. V

Small Beer SIBA

70-72 Verney Road, South Bermondsey, London, SE16 3DH
☎ (020) 7096 2353 ⊕ theoriginalsmallbeer.com

Small Beer was set up in 2017 as the world's first to specialise exclusively in the production of low strength beers (1.0%-2.7% ABV). The core range of five beers is widely available in keg, 350ml stubby bottles and now cans. One cask ale was introduced during 2022, including a green-hopped version, and a range of cask beers is now available in pubs (see map on website) and usually one in the taproom. ◆

Mild (ABV 2.4%) MILD
Session Pale (ABV 2.5%) GOLD
Steam (ABV 2.7%) SPECIALITY

Small Beer (Lincoln)

See Black Hole

Small Paul's

Gillingham, Dorset, SP8 4SS
☎ (01747) 823574 ✉ smallbrewer@btinternet.com

⊠ Launched in 2006, this half-barrel brewery is located in the owner's garage. Brewing is now reduced to about once a month and on demand. A small number of local pubs, clubs and beer festivals are supplied direct and beers can be brewed to order.

Small World SIBA

Unit 10, Barncliffe Business Park, Near Bank, Shelley, West Yorkshire, HD8 8LU
☎ (01484) 602805 ⊕ smallworldbeers.com

☺The brewery is situated in the former Barncliffe Mill near the picturesque village of Shelley. The beers are brewed on a 20-barrel Moeschle plant using spring water from an onsite borehole. SALSA+ Beer approved. !!◆

Barncliffe Bitter (ABV 3.7%) BITTER
A traditional Yorkshire bitter. Malty and fruity with a long bitter farewell.
Long Moor Pale (ABV 3.9%) PALE
It's Never One (ABV 4%) GOLD
Port Nelson (ABV 4%) PALE
Spike's Gold (ABV 4.4%) GOLD
Thunderbridge Stout (ABV 5.2%) STOUT
Twin Falls (ABV 5.2%) PALE

Samuel Smith

The Old Brewery, High Street, Tadcaster, North Yorkshire, LS24 9SB
☎ (01937) 832225 ⊕ samuelsmithsbrewery.co.uk

☺Fiercely independent, family-owned company. Tradition, quality and value are important, resulting in brewing without any artificial additives. The majority of products are vegan-friendly, with the exception of Old Brewery Bitter and Yorkshire Stingo. All real ale is supplied in traditional wooden casks. LIVE V

Old Brewery Bitter (ABV 4%) BITTER

John Smith

The Brewery, Tadcaster, North Yorkshire, LS24 9SA
Office: 3-4 Broadway Park, Edinburgh, EH12 9JZ
☎ (0131) 528 1000 ⊕ heineken.com

The brewery was built in 1879 by a relative of Samuel Smith (qv). John Smith's became part of the Courage group in 1970 before being taken over by S&N and now Heineken UK. John Smith's cask Magnet has been discontinued. The brewery does not produce any real ales. John Smith's Bitter is brewed elsewhere.

John Smith's Bitter (ABV 3.5%) BITTER

Snaggletooth

Office: Rear of 11 Pole Lane, Darwen, Lancashire, BB3 3LD ☎ 07810 365701
⊕ snaggletoothbrewing.com

Snaggletooth was established in 2012 by three beer geeks with a passion for crafting ales. A 2.5-barrel plant is used at the Hopstar Brewery (qv) in Darwen, Lancashire. Beers are available throughout East Lancashire and Manchester. ◆

Allotropic (ABV 3.8%) PALE
BeEr (ABV 3.9%) PALE
I Ain't Afraid of Noh Ghost (ABV 3.9%) GOLD
Three Amigos (ABV 3.9%) GOLD
Déjà Brewed (ABV 4%) PALE
Rolling Maul (ABV 4.1%) PALE
'Cos I'm a Lobster (ABV 4.2%) RED
Avonaco (ABV 4.3%) PALE

Snowdon Craft

Quinton Hazell Enterprise Parc, 55 Glan-y-Wern Road, Mochdre, LL28 5BS
☎ (01492) 545143 ⊕ snowdoncraftbeer.co.uk

☺Snowdon Craft, is located in Mochdre near Llandudno, and uses an 18-barrel plant for its latest core range and seasonal beers. Suppling the local area and the Albion in Conwy, which it part owns, also the Johnny Dough's restaurant chain. Brewing is currently suspended. !!◆

Snowdonia Parc

⌗ Snowdonia Parc Brewpub & Campsite, Waunfawr, Caernarfon, LL55 4AQ
☎ (01286) 650409 ⊕ snowdonia-park.co.uk

Snowdonia Parc started brewing in 1998 in a two-barrel brewhouse. The brewing is now carried out by the owner, Carmen Pierce. The beer is brewed solely for the Snowdonia Parc pub and campsite.

Snowhill

Snow Hill Cottage, Snow Hill Lane, Scorton, Lancashire, PR3 1BA
☎ (01524) 791352

☺Snowhill was established in 2015. A one-man operation which occasionally brews on a 1.5-barrel plant, it supplies pubs mostly within a 20-mile radius of the brewery. An environmentally-friendly set-up sees the spent grain feeding local cattle and wastewater treated through a small reed bed. ◆

Pale (ABV 3.7%) GOLD
Copy Cat (ABV 3.8%) BITTER
Target (ABV 3.8%) BLOND
Amberling (ABV 3.9%) BITTER

Blonded (ABV 3.9%) BLOND
Gold (ABV 3.9%) GOLD
Black Magic IPA (ABV 4.2%) PALE
Golden Bitter (ABV 4.2%) PALE
Porter (ABV 4.8%) PORTER
Winter Porter (ABV 4.8%) PORTER

So What

🍴 Bull & Finch, 126 Gipsy Hill, London, SE19 1PL
⊕ thebullandfinch.square.site

A nanobrewery was installed in the Bull & Finch in early 2022, a bar run by the Bullfinch brewery of Herne Hill. The house beers are occasionally available in cask and keg in the pub.

Soar

🍴 Swan Inn, 10 Loughborough Road, Mountsorrel, Leicestershire, LE12 7AT
☎ (0116) 230 2340 ⊕ theswaninn.online

A small onsite brewery supplying the Swan Inn and local beer festivals. ♦

Sociable

6-8 Britannia Road, Worcester, WR1 3BQ ☎ 07957 583984 ⊕ thesociablebeercompany.com

☺A small craft brewery just outside Worcester city centre, established in 2017. An onsite taproom is open Friday to Sunday. A small range of core beers is brewed, mainly for sale in the local area. ✦

Shindig (ABV 3.6%) BITTER
Bash (ABV 4%) BITTER
Wingding (ABV 4.2%) GOLD

Somer Valley (NEW) SIBA

Knoll Farm, White Ox Mead, Peasedown St John, Bath, BA2 8PL ☎ 07984 352070
✉ chester.ellis@somervalleyfarms.com

From the refreshing core range to contemporary seasonal releases, Somer Valley Brewery aims to have a beer for everyone in the Somer Valley and beyond. All beers are brewed using local ingredients, including water from below the brewery, thereby supporting nearby farms and businesses.

Sommar

Unit 3B, Utilia Arena Birmingham, Canal Side, King Edwards Road, Utilita Arena, Birmingham, B1 2AA

Office: 41 St Marks Crescent, Ladywood, Birmingham, B1 2PY ⊕ sommar.co.uk

⊗ Started in 2019, this microbrewery brews a wide range of strengths and styles for its taproom and several others around the region. Beers are keg and KeyKeg. The taproom has up to 18 taps in use, including guest beers from smaller breweries and collaborations. It now has three outlets in the Birmingham area. Located on the canalside near Utilia Arena, brewery masterclass tours are available (see website). Limited outside seating area available when weather allows. It holds quizzes and live music events. ✦

Son of Sid

🍴 Chequers, 71 Main Road, Little Gransden, Cambridgeshire, SG19 3DW
☎ (01767) 677348 ⊕ sonofsid.co.uk

⊗ Son of Sid was established in 2007. The three-barrel plant is situated in a room at the back of the pub and can be viewed from a window in the lounge bar. It is named after the father of the current landlord, who ran the pub for over 40 years. His son has carried the business on as a family-run enterprise. Beer is sold in the pub and at local beer festivals. Brewing is currently suspended. 🍴 🍺 LIVE

Source House

Cross Cottage, Clifton Road, Clifton, Ashbourne, Derbyshire, DE6 2DH ☎ 07834 722481
⊕ sourcehouse.co.uk

Established in 2021. Source House brew beers using only British malts and hops, experimenting with local and homegrown ingredients.

South Hams SIBA

Stokeley Barton, Stokenham, Kingsbridge, Devon, TQ7 2SE
☎ (01548) 581151 ⊕ southhamsbrewery.co.uk

⊗ South Hams has been brewing ales for 20 years in Start Bay, Devon. A family-run brewery, it supplies more than 350 outlets in Plymouth and South Devon with wholesalers distributing further afield. 🍴 🍺 ♦ LIVE

Devon Pride (ABV 3.8%) BITTER
A surprisingly full-bodied ale for a session beer. Fruity malty aroma, with a malty biscuit taste and mixed fruits.
Stumble Bee (ABV 4.2%) SPECIALITY
Light amber colour beer with flowery and fruity aroma. Full-bodied, smooth drink, honey adds its bit with a nice hoppy after taste. A pleasing blend between bitter and sweet.
Wild Blonde (ABV 4.4%) BLOND
Subtle notes of malt, roast and caramel, dominated by fruity hops. These persist to a refreshing hint of lemon.
Eddystone (ABV 4.8%) BITTER
Strong, amber, summery ale. Hoppy, caramel, slightly citrus nose. Dryer taste with light fruit and hops. Dry yet fruity finish.
Sherman (ABV 6.4%) IPA
A strong American pale ale, a thick-flavoured beer, very fruity and sweet on aroma/taste and aftertaste.

South Oxfordshire (SOX)

Office: Windrush Innovation Centre, Howbery Business Park, Benson Lane, Wallingford, Oxfordshire, OX10 8BA ☎ 07704 307182
⊕ soxbrewery.co.uk

South Oxfordshire Brewery (aka SOX) began brewing cask ales in 2022 at White Horse Brewery (qv). SOX beers are currently being contract brewed by another brewery. 🍺

SOX Pale Ale (ABV 3.5%) PALE
Mr Toad's (ABV 3.9%) BITTER
Midnight Belle (ABV 4%) BITTER

Southbourne

See Poole Hill

Southey

21 Southey Street, Penge, London, SE20 7JD
⊕ southeybrewing.co.uk

⊗ Southey took over the Late Knights brewery in 2016 in an old warehouse that has been an abattior and a candle factory. The vegan and unfiltered beers are available in the other Beer Dispensary bars and in the taproom at the brewery which has recently been expanded including an upstairs meeting room. Part of the Local Brewery Loop. ♦V✦

Best Bitter (ABV 4.5%) BITTER
Hazy, well-balanced, pale brown premium bitter. Sweet caramel, malty biscuit overlaying tangerine, and some earthy hops. Dry, lingering bitter finish.

Southport SIBA

Unit 3, Enterprise Business Park, Russell Road, Southport, Merseyside, PR9 7RF ☎ 07748 387652 ⊕ southportbrewery.co.uk

☺Southport Brewery was established in 2004 on a five-barrel plant. Outlets are supplied in Southport, North-West England and nationally. ♦

IPA (ABV 3.6%) PALE
Sandgrounder Bitter (ABV 3.8%) PALE
Dark Night (ABV 3.9%) MILD
Full-bodied mild with fruity malt aromas dominating, lasting roast bitterness and hop, lots of flavour for the strength.
Golden Sands (ABV 4%) GOLD

Southsea

Southsea Castle, Clarence Esplanade, Southsea, Portsmouth, Hampshire, PO5 3PA ☎ 07939 063970 ⊕ southseabrewing.co.uk

⊠ Launched in 2016, Southsea Brewing is located in an old ammunition storage room within the walls of a coastal defence fort built by Henry VIII in 1544. All beers are unfined, unfiltered and unpasteurised, and bottled onsite. ⬛LIVE

Low Tide (ABV 3.8%) PALE
Casemate IPA (ABV 5.4%) PALE

Southwark SIBA

46 Druid Street, Bermondsey, London, SE1 2EZ ☎ (020) 3302 4190 ⊕ southwarkbrewing.co.uk

⊠ Southwark opened in 2014 as the first cask-orientated brewery on the Bermondsey Beer Mile. The range of beers brings modern styles to cask, including a regularly changing, single-hop beer, and is complemented by a small keg range. ♦LIVEV✦

Bankside Blonde (ABV 3.8%) BLOND
Grapefruit and sweet biscuit in the aroma and flavour. Dry bitterness with peppery hops and a lingering, bitter, dry aftertaste.
Routemaster Red (ABV 3.8%) RED
Malt aromas and flavour of chocolate and caramelised fruits, with notes of bitter lemon, red berries and sweet toffee.
London Pale Ale (ABV 4%) PALE
Lime and melon, caramelised biscuit aroma and palate with hints of citrus and fruit. Dry, fruity and spicy bitter aftertaste.
Potters' Fields Porter (ABV 4%) PORTER
Chocolate, roasty and malt aroma, complex bitter, prunes and caramel flavour with hint of raisins. Long roast bitter dry finish.
Mayflower (ABV 4.2%) GOLD
Citrus and tropical fruit dominates the flavour with honey and some spicy floral hop, which is also on the nose.
Bermondsey Best (ABV 4.4%) BITTER
Milk chocolate, earthy hoppy aroma and palate with caramelised fruit and hazelnuts. Dry roasty chocolate finish and some hoppy bitterness.
Single Hop (ABV 5%) GOLD

The resinous hops balance the malty sweetness on nose, palate and aftertaste. A little bitterness and some flavour of grapefruit.
Harvard (ABV 5.5%) IPA
Orange, grapefruit marmalade aromas with earthy hops, peach and orange flavours prominent, becoming bitter, spicy, dry and lingering.

Spa Town

See Harrogate

SpadeTown

25 Silverwood Industrial Estate, Lurgan, BT66 6LN

Established in Lurgan in 2021, a group of brewers are producing a range of craft beers available in bottle and can and also on draft.

Spartan

Office: Lewis Mews, Ravens Dene, Chislehurst West, BR7 5FJ ⊕ spartanbrewery.com

Spartan started brewing at UBrew in 2017, before moving in 2018 to premises on the Bermondsey Beer Mile vacated by Partizan Brewery. Brewing ceased here, as well as the taproom, in 2023 and now takes place from time to time at local breweries. V

Spectra

Office: 33 Highfield Drive, Clarkston, G76 7SW ⊕ spectrabrewing.co.uk

Established in 2021, Spectra Brewing came about from founder Alex's love of hop-forward craft beer, coupled with an appreciation of the proper ales that he had always enjoyed during his years of experience visiting the pubs and bars of Scotland and beyond. Its beers are heavily influenced by the US-led IPA revolution, with the East Coast style being the 'go-to', while also taking influences from classic UK and US beers. Based in Clarkston, East Renfrewshire, Spectra currently produces beer using 'nomad brewing' around the south side of Glasgow. Beers are available in cask, keg and cans.

Visible Light (ABV 3.9%) PALE

Spenside Stables (NEW)

Office: 51 Ramsay Street, Rowlands Gill, NE39 2EJ

Established in 2023 using the brewing kit from "TOPS" (The Old Potting Shed (qv). It is located in what are the only existing original pit pony stables remaining in North East England, and the stables at Beamish Museum are actual replicas of these buildings.

Pit Pony (ABV 4%) PALE
Top Marks (ABV 4.2%) BLOND
Victoria Seam (ABV 4.3%) BITTER
More Dogs Than Men (ABV 4.4%) BLOND

Sperrin

⬛ Lord Nelson Inn, Birmingham Road, Ansley, Warwickshire, CV10 9PQ ☎ (024) 7639 2305 ☎ 07917 772208 ⊕ sperrinbrewery.co.uk

Sperrin began brewing in 2012 on a six-barrel plant at the side of the Lord Nelson Inn. The pub always has five of its beers available and two or three at its sister pub, the Blue Boar, Mancetter. Around 25 other outlets are supplied direct. ‼♦LIVE

Ansley Mild (ABV 3.5%) MILD
Head Hunter (ABV 3.8%) BITTER
Band of Brothers (ABV 4.2%) GOLD
Third Party (ABV 4.8%) RED
Thick as Thieves (ABV 6.8%) STOUT

Spey Valley

Malcolmburn, Mulben, Keith, AB55 6YH
☎ (01542) 488006 ☎ 07780 655199
⊕ speyvalleybrewery.co.uk

⊗ Founded in 2007, Spey Valley Brewery merged with Keith Brewery in 2018 and is part of the Consolidated Craft Breweries Group, along with Alechemy Brewing (qv). It brews on a 20-barrel plant on a purpose-built site at Mulben. Brewing capacity was increased in 2022. ‼🍷◆

Sunshine on Keith (ABV 3.5%) BITTER
Golden, light citrus bitter hop with a malty background. Name is a play on Proclaimers song.
Any Time / Winter Time (ABV 4%) BLOND
David's Not So Bitter (ABV 4.4%) BITTER
Light brown with a good mix of malts, hops and red fruits.
Stillman's IPA (ABV 4.6%) SPECIALITY
Amber hoppy bitter with a whisky background.
Spey's Hopper (ABV 5%) SPECIALITY
Spey Stout (ABV 5.4%) STOUT
Good, thick, dark, malty stout with a smoky blackcurrant background.

Speyside

10-11 West Road, Forres, IV36 2GW
☎ (01309) 763041 ☎ 07854 053277
⊕ speysidecraftbrewery.com

Based in a traditional whisky-producing area, Speyside Brewery uses the same water that goes into the region's whisky. A number of local outlets are supplied. Following suspension of brewing during 2020, the brewery resumed production in 2023 just yards from its previous home – in bigger premises with a larger, eight-hectolitre plant. Beers are available in bottle and membrane keg. ◆

Bow Fiddle Blonde (ABV 3.8%) BLOND
Bottlenose Bitter (ABV 4.1%) BITTER
Randolph's Leap (ABV 4.9%) GOLD
Moray IPA (ABV 5.5%) IPA
Findhorn Killer Red IPA (ABV 5.6%) IPA
ScotcHop IPA (ABV 8.5%) SPECIALITY

Spilsbury & Jones

Orleton Court Farm, Orleton, Worcestershire, WR6 6SU
⊕ spilsburyandjones.co.uk

Launched in 2018, this brewery produces beer in small batches from hops grown within a few hundred yards of the brewery. ◆

Spitting Feathers SIBA

Common Farm, Waverton, Cheshire, CH3 7QT
☎ (01244) 332052 ☎ 07974 348325
⊕ spittingfeathers.co.uk

☺ Spitting Feathers was established in 2005. The brewery is located in a sandstone building set around a cobbled yard. Around 200 local outlets are supplied. Monthly Brewbarn sessions throughout the year include a brewery tour but tickets must be purchased in advance. All beers are vegan-friendly and gluten-free. ‼◆GF V

Session Beer (ABV 3.6%) PALE

Sweet malts have a consistent presence in this hoppy bitter beer.
Thirstquencher (ABV 3.9%) BLOND
A hoppy blond with citrus notes and some sweetness to balance.
Special Ale (ABV 4.2%) BITTER
A traditional amber bitter consisting of gentle sweet malt, hops and some fruit. Balanced centre and a hoppy bitter finish.
Old Wavertonian (ABV 4.4%) STOUT
Creamy and smooth stout. Full-flavoured with coffee notes in aroma and taste. Roast flavours throughout, finishing with hoppy bitterness.
Empire IPA (ABV 5.2%) PALE
Sweet beer with hop bitterness that builds in the mouth to dominate the finish.
Little Donker (ABV 6%) STRONG

Spookton (NEW)

The Mill, St Thomas Pathway, Chester, CH1 3LQ

Launched in 2022 as a cuckoo brewery, Spookton opened its own microbrewery and tap in the centre of Chester in 2024. ◆

Spotlight

The Goddards, Goole Road, Goole, West Cowick, East Yorkshire, DN14 9DJ ☎ 07713 477069
⊕ spotlightbrewing.co.uk

☺ Spotlight is a social enterprise that is passionate about good beer. All beers are brewed, packaged and delivered by people with learning disabilities. The beer names reference medical conditions. Brewing is currently suspended. ‼🍷◆

Spring Hill Farm (NEW)

Springhill Farm, Belthorn Road, Belthorn, Lancashire, BB1 2NY

A new brewery launched in spring 2024.

Squawk

See Moorhouses

Staffordshire

12 Churnet Court, Cheddleton, Staffordshire, ST13 7EF
☎ (01538) 361919 ☎ 07971 808370
⊕ staffordshirebrewery.co.uk

Brewing started in 2002. The brewery was renamed from Leek Brewery in 2013 at which time cask production ceased, being replaced by filtered, pasteurised bottled beers only. A small pilot plant is sometimes used to contract brew for Wicked Hathern (qv) when time permits. ‼

Stag

Little Engeham Farm, Bethersden Road, Woodchurch, Kent, TN26 3QY ☎ 07539 974068
⊕ stagbrewery.co.uk

⊗ Operating since 2016 at Engeham Farm also home to Kent's largest steam rally. All brews are dry-hopped and unfiltered before leaving the five-barrel commercial plant. Stag beer can be bought at the rally, in local pubs and mini kegs online. ◆LIVE

Magic Muntjac (ABV 4%) PALE
Screaming Sika (ABV 5%) GOLD

Staggeringly Good SIBA

Unit 10, St Georges Industrial Estate, Rodney Road, Southsea, Hampshire, PO4 8SS
☎ (023) 9229 7033 ⊕ staggeringlygood.com

This Dino-centric brewery began production in 2014 and is now a 20-barrel facility producing 140K hectolitres per annum with a core circulation of three regularly brewed beers and a bevy of cutting edge, boundary pushing ales with a strong focus on heavily-hopped IPAs and extreme sours. All beers are real ales and available in KeyKeg and cans. With an onsite shop and taproom hosting festivals, DJ sets, live music and more, there is always a good reason to stop by. !! ▪ ♦ LIVE V✦

Staggersaurus (ABV 4%) PALE
Prehistoric Creatures: Best Bitter (ABV 4.2%) BITTER
Little Arms, Big Ambitions (ABV 5%) PALE
Post Impact Porter (ABV 5.4%) PORTER

Stamps SIBA

St Mary's Complex, Waverley Street, Bootle, L20 4AP
☎ 07913 025319 ⊕ stampsbrewery.co.uk

☺Brewing began in 2012, with beers named after famous world postage stamps. The brewery moved to its current site in 2017. The beers can be found regularly in Stamps Bar, Crosby, the Lock & Quay, Bootle, and the Caledonia, and the Vernon Arms, Liverpool. Beers may appear with the Republic of Liverpool brand name. There are plans to build a new brewery and pub as part of a local regeneration project alongside the Leeds-Liverpool canal in Bootle. !! ▪ V

Blond Moment (ABV 3.6%) GOLD
Ahtanum (ABV 3.9%) GOLD
First Class (ABV 3.9%) PALE
Mail Train (ABV 4.2%) BITTER
Inverted Jenny (ABV 4.6%) BITTER
Rum Porter (ABV 4.6%) PORTER
Cascade (ABV 5%) PALE
Penny Black (ABV 5.5%) PORTER

Stancill SIBA

Unit 2, Oakham Drive, off Rutland Road, Sheffield, South Yorkshire, S3 9QX
☎ (0114) 275 2788 ☎ 07809 427716

☺Stancill began brewing in 2014 and is named after the first head brewer and co-owner. It is situated on the doorstep of the late Stones' Cannon Brewery, taking advantage of the soft Yorkshire water. !!

Barnsley Bitter (ABV 3.8%) BITTER
Blonde (ABV 3.9%) BLOND
India (ABV 4%) BITTER
No.7 (ABV 4.3%) BITTER
Stainless (ABV 4.3%) BITTER
Porter (ABV 4.4%) PORTER
Black Gold (ABV 5%) STOUT

Stannary SIBA

Unit 6, Pixon Trading Centre, Tavistock, Devon, PL19 8DH
☎ (01822) 258130 ⊕ stannarybrewing.shop

Stannary began operating in 2016 using a 2.5-barrel plant, moving to larger premises with a six-barrel plant in 2018 and again in 2023 with room to expand. The brewery tap is open on Friday-Saturday showcasing its many unfined and unfiltered craft beers with sports events and occasional live entertainment. Street food is

available on Friday evenings. The shop is open Monday-Thursday (see website for times). ▪ ♦ V✦

Life Goes On (ABV 4.4%) SPECIALITY
Fat Head (ABV 7.4%) STRONG
Strong American brown ale, slightly red in colour, tastes of caramel, liquorice, biscuits and orange peel. Sweet ale similar to a barleywine with tropical overtones.

Stardust SIBA

Unit 5, Howe Lane Farm Estate, Howe Lane, White Waltham, Berkshire, SL6 3JP
☎ (01628) 947325 ⊕ stardustbrewery.co.uk

⊗ An independent, family-owned and run brewery, Stardust was established in 2016 and capacity was increased to 12 barrels in 2023. Located in a unit on a small farm estate, there is a brewery shop and a small bar onsite plus an online shop offering delivery. It supplies direct to trade outlets in Berkshire and surrounding counties, and further afield via distributors. !! ▪ ♦ ✦

English Bitter (ABV 4%) BITTER
Just Stout (ABV 4.2%) STOUT
Optic (ABV 4.2%) GOLD
Red Rocket (ABV 4.4%) BITTER
PK3 (ABV 5.6%) IPA

State of Kind

Unit 4, Hemfield Court, Wigan, WN2 2ER ☎ 07765 808889 ⊕ stateofkindbrew.co

Launched in 2021, initially as a nomad brewery. State of Kind now has its own brewery and taproom. ✦

Stay Wild (NEW) SIBA

12 Boakes Meadow, Shoreham, TN14 7SH

Office: Russell House, Edgware, HA8 7LW

⊗ Nanobrewery surrounded by woodland that commenced brewing in 2023 in the Darent Valley village of Shoreham, near Sevenoaks. Its beer is frequently found in the Samuel Palmer pub in the same village, as well as other local outlets and beer festivals. The beers are titled after different names for Bigfoot. Each brew run fills six casks.

Stealth

Unit 3, Intercity Industrial Estate, Melksham, Wiltshire, SN12 8DE
☎ (01225) 707111 ☎ 07917 272482
⊕ stealthbrew.co

Business commenced in 2014 and under the current name since 2018. Moved to present premises in 2021. Most beers are unfined and the range changes frequently. The brewery tap is the Hiding Place in Melksham town centre owned by an associated company which also owns the Piggy Bank micropub in Calne. In addition to sales through those two outlets the beers also go into the free trade. !! ♦ GF V

Covert (ABV 3.9%) PALE
Tiptoe (ABV 4.2%) BITTER
Huggermuggery Coffee Porter (ABV 5.9%) SPECIALITY

Steam Machine SIBA

Unit 14, The IES Centre, Horndale Avenue, Newton Aycliffe, DL5 6DS ☎ 07415 759945
⊕ steammachinebrew.com

Founded by a husband and wife team with a homebrewing background of more than 10 years. Since opening in 2015 production has expanded. Beers are available mainly in keg but KeyKegs are occasionally supplied to beer festivals.

Steam-Shed

The Old Train Shed, Station Street, Swaffham, Norfolk, PE37 7HP ☎ 07813 005424

Production began in 2021 and currently beer is available in casks, polypins and bottles. Distribution is via local pubs and farmers' markets. Brew capacity is circa 600 litres per brew.

Steam Town SIBA

⊟ 1 Bishopstoke Road, Eastleigh, Hampshire, SO50 6AD
☎ (023) 8235 9130 ⊕ steamtownbrewco.co.uk

⊗ Steam Town is a six-barrel microbrewery with its own attached pub-restaurant, established in 2017. Many other local pubs, clubs and micropubs within a 10-mile radius also sell its ales, as well as beer festivals and outlets further afield by arrangement. Steam Town beers are available in many formats: cask, keg, mini-cask/keg, bottles and cans. ‼ ☲ LIVE

Stoke Pale (ABV 3.8%) GOLD
Light golden ale with hops dominating but complemented by some light pineapple notes and sweetness, with a short dry bitter finish.
Barton (ABV 4%) BITTER
Traditional light brown bitter with some toffee notes leading to malty sweetness balanced by bitterness and a lingering dry finish.
NZ Pale (ABV 4.2%) PALE
Reefer (ABV 4.2%) PALE
Modern pale ale, with an aroma of citrus fruits and grapefruit flavours leading to a smooth and predominantly bitter finish.
Salus Populi (Suprema Lex) (ABV 4.5%) BLOND
Steam Stout (ABV 4.5%) STOUT
Firebox (ABV 4.6%) RED
Complex American red with distinctive aroma of redcurrants and jelly, leading to full-bodied malty sweetness and a refreshing hop bite.
Bishop's APA (ABV 4.8%) PALE
West Coast IPA (ABV 5.4%) PALE

Steamin' Billy

Office: 5 The Oval, Oadby, Leicestershire, LE2 5JB
☎ (0116) 271 2616 ⊕ steamin-billy.co.uk

⊕ Pub Company that has a range of beers contract brewed for its pubs. ‼

Tipsy Fisherman (ABV 3.6%) BITTER
Bitter (ABV 4.3%) GOLD
1485 (ABV 5%) BITTER
Skydiver (ABV 5%) BITTER

Steel Brew

Mills Bakery Building, Royal William Yard, Plymouth, Devon, PL1 3GD
☎ (01752) 987728

Office: 4, 219 Kensington High Street, London, W8 6BD

Brewing began in a garage in 2018 on a six-barrel plant. The brewery relocated to the Grade 1* listed Melville Building, Royal William Yard in 2020, and relocated again to Mills Bakery within Royal William Yard in 2021. Four core beers and numerous one-off specials are brewed, available in its onsite taproom. Bottled beers are also sold in the Plymouth Gin Distillery, Barbican, Plymouth. Brewing recommenced onsite in 2023, with all brewing undertaken by Patrick Lawrence of Bulletproof Brewery. ‼ ☲ V✦

Steel City

c/o Lost Industry Brewing, 14a Nutwood Trading Estate, Sheffield, South Yorkshire, S6 1NJ

⊗ Steel City was established in 2009 and operates as a cuckoo brewery, brewing on an occasional basis and when inspired. Brewing currently takes place at Lost Industry Brewing (qv). Much of the Steel City output is collaborations with other like-minded brewers, having a little fun producing interesting and experimental beers. ✦V

Steelfish

c/o 78b Temperance Street, Ardwick, Manchester, M12 6HU ⊠ steelfishbrewing@gmail.com

Steelfish started brewing in 2020 as a cuckoo brewer based at Beer Nouveau in Ardwick, Manchester. From early 2022 to late 2023 it relocated the brewing operation to Ventile Brew Co's Spur Mill site in Reddish, Stockport. From late 2023 it returned to Ardwick to share location with Courier Brewing Co.

Stewart SIBA

26a Dryden Road, Bilston Glen Industrial Estate, Loanhead, EH20 9LZ
☎ (0131) 440 2442 ⊕ stewartbrewing.co.uk

☺ Established in 2004 by Steve and Jo Stewart, Stewart Brewing is Edinburgh's original craft brewery. It has been innovating and brewing award-winning beers for 20 years, now from a custom-built 20,000-hectolitre brewhouse just outside of Edinburgh. As well as producing a wide range of beers there is a varied retail offering including an onsite Brew-It-Yourself Experience, a well-stocked brewery shop with growler fill station, weekly brewery tours, and a Bar & Pizza Kitchen with cask-conditioned, tank and kegged beers. ‼ ☲ ✦LIVE V✦

Jack Back (ABV 3.7%) PALE
A pale hoppy beer with strong citrus and tropical fruit aromas. The taste is light, crisp and refreshing.
Pentland IPA (ABV 3.9%) PALE
A delicately-hopped, deep golden-coloured session ale. The dry bitter taste is well-balanced by sweetness from the malt, and fruit flavours.
80/- (ABV 4.4%) MILD
Superb traditional Scottish heavy. The complex profile is dominated by malt with fruit flavours giving the sweetish character typical of this beer style. Hops provide a gentle balancing bitterness that intensifies in the dry finish.
Citra Blonde (ABV 4.5%) BLOND
A lean, citrus yellow/gold session ale. Refreshing and light-bodied with medium hop bitterness that fades quickly.
Edinburgh Gold (ABV 4.8%) GOLD
Lightly malty golden beer with hops and fruit providing balance. A slight grainy character with a lasting gentle hop bitterness.

Stinky Bay

La Grand Route, St Lawrence, Jersey, JE3 1NH
☎ 07797 781703 ⊕ stinkybay.com

Named after a rugged bay on the North-Western tip of Jersey, Stinky Bay Brewing Co was established in 2017.

Stocks

See Welbeck Abbey

Stod Fold

Stod Fold, Ogden, Halifax, HX2 8XL ☎ **07789 998775** ⊕ **stodfoldbrewing.com**

☺The 10-barrel Stod Fold Brewery is located on the edge of the moors in a renovated farm building. It supplies around 50 free trade outlets each year, mainly in Yorkshire, and occasionally does beer swaps with other brewing companies. Beers can always be sampled at the Stod Fold Brewery Tap at Dean Clough Mills, Halifax. ♦V

Gold (ABV 3.8%) PALE
Refreshing, light, malty, fruity session ale with a smooth hoppy aftertaste.
Blonde+ (ABV 4.3%) BLOND
A fruity beer with a lingering dry finish. The main hop changes monthly so the fruit flavour can be citrusy or tropical.
Dark Porter (ABV 4.8%) PORTER
Easy-drinking, well-balanced, dark brown porter. Smooth and mellow with roast to the fore.
Dr Harris (ABV 5.7%) IPA
An amber-coloured traditional IPA with earthy/floral English hop flavours.

Stone Daisy

The Old Carpenters Workshop, Berwick St Leonard, Wiltshire, SP3 5SN
☎ **(01747) 356108** ☎ **07887 847057**
⊕ **stonedaisy.co.uk**

Stone Daisy Brewery takes its name from the medieval 'witch marks', in the shape of daisy wheels, carved into the stone of its buildings. Traditonal equipment and methodology, coupled with some modern techniques, produce beers available in cask, bottle and can. Beers can be found across Wiltshire and beyond.

Cow Down (ABV 3.8%) PALE
Snail Creep Hanging (ABV 4.2%) BITTER
Park Bottom (ABV 4.5%) PALE

Stonehenge SIBA

The Old Mill, Mill Road, Netheravon, Wiltshire, SP4 9QB
☎ **(01980) 670631** ⊕ **stonehengeales.co.uk**

⊗ Stonehenge Ales was established in 1984 in the Old Mill, Netheravon, a Grade II-listed building originally serving as an electricity generator for the Netheravon Airfield in 1914. The brewery stands in a distinctive location alongside the River Avon. Nestled in the heart of Wiltshire, it distinguishes itself by crafting traditional English cask ale brewed using spring water drawn from its own well. In 2022, James and Nicola Robinson took over the reins to continue its legacy as one of Wiltshire's oldest breweries. ‼♦

Spire Ale (ABV 3.8%) PALE
A golden-coloured session bitter with an initial bitterness giving way to a well-rounded aftertaste with discernible fruit balance.
Pigswill (ABV 4%) BITTER
Medium-bodied, malty bitter, some fruit and caramel on the aroma and taste, balanced bittersweet finish with hops throughout.

Heel Stone (ABV 4.3%) BITTER
Complex and interesting aroma of resinous hops and stoned fruit, sweet malty taste with developing hops bitterness and fruity finish.
Great Bustard (ABV 4.8%) BITTER
Rich peppery aroma, full taste of malt, hops, with slight floral and peppery notes. Dry fruity finish with good bitterness.
Danish Dynamite (ABV 5%) GOLD
A sweet aromatic aroma, complex malty taste with bitterness and fruit, medium finish with a mix of hops and fruit.

Stonehouse SIBA

Stonehouse, Weston, Oswestry, SY10 9ES
☎ **(01691) 676457** ⊕ **stonehousebrewery.co.uk**

Stonehouse is a family-run brewery, distillery and cider maker. Established in 2007, it operates a 22-barrel plant. It is next to the Cambrian Heritage Railways line and includes a shop, bar and restaurant. Direct delivery is within 30 miles of the brewery. ‼🍴♦

Wrangler (ABV 3.8%) IPA
Station Bitter (ABV 3.9%) BITTER
Cambrian Gold (ABV 4.2%) GOLD

Stoney Ford

See Grainstore

Storm

2 Waterside, Macclesfield, Cheshire, SK11 7HJ
☎ **(01625) 431234** ⊕ **stormbrewing.co.uk**

☺Storm Brewing was founded in 1998. In 2001 it moved to its current location, an old riverside pub building, which until 1937, was called the Mechanics Arms. Many local pubs are supplied, as well as beer being distributed further afield. Now run by a brother and sister team. ♦LIVE

Beauforts Ale (ABV 3.8%) BITTER
Desert Storm (ABV 3.9%) BITTER
Bosley Cloud (ABV 4.1%) BLOND
Ale Force (ABV 4.2%) BITTER
Amber, smooth-tasting, complex beer that balances malt, hop and fruit on the taste, leading to a roasty, slightly sweet aftertaste.
Dexter (ABV 4.2%) GOLD
Downpour (ABV 4.3%) PALE
PGA (ABV 4.4%) SPECIALITY
Light, crisp, lager-style beer with a balance of malt, hops and fruit. Moderately bitter and slight dry aftertaste.
Silk of Amnesia (ABV 4.7%) BITTER
Smooth, premium, easy-drinking bitter. Fruit and hops dominate throughout. Not too sweet, with a good, lasting finish.
Isobar IPA (ABV 4.8%) PALE
Fruity (peach and apricot) aromas and taste in this sweet-bodied beer that finishes with plenty of hops.
Red Mist (ABV 4.8%) BITTER

Stow

Plenploth House, Old Stage Road, Stow, TD1 2SU
☎ **07834 396991** ⊕ **dhubrew.com**

Stow is a small-batch nanobrewery in the Scottish Borders that produces four core cask beers available in the Borders and the central belt, sold under the name Dhu Brew. The beers (all but the stout), are also available in can, bottle and keg. The business has plans for significant growth over the next 2-3 years, with contract brewing for larger volumes already underway.

Brewed under the Dhu Brew brand name:
IPA (ABV 3.8%) IPA
80/- (ABV 4%) BITTER
Pils (ABV 4.2%) SPECIALITY
Stowt (ABV 4.5%) STOUT

Stow Fen

Fenview, Flixton Road, Bungay, Suffolk, NR35 1PD
☎ 07775 279181 ✉ stowfenbrewingco@gmail.com

⊗ Stow Fen Brewing Co Ltd was established in 2020 by Paul Holland and Philip Gilham, the head brewer. Malts are from Branthill Farms in Wells-next-the-Sea, and all hops are from the UK.

Broad Water Gold (ABV 4.2%) GOLD
Angels Way Amber (ABV 4.4%) BITTER
Stock Bridge Best (ABV 4.6%) BITTER
Twisted Oak IPA (ABV 5%) IPA
Wolds ESB (ABV 5.8%) BITTER
Mouldings Porter (ABV 6.5%) PORTER

Stowey

Old Cider House, 25 Castle Street, Nether Stowey, Somerset, TA5 1LN
☎ (01278) 732228 ⊕ stoweybrewery.co.uk

Somerset's smallest brewery was established in 2006, primarily to supply the owners' guesthouse and to provide beer to participants at events run from the accommodation. The small quantities of beer produced are also supplied to the George, Nether Stowey. ‼◆

Strands

🏠 Strands Inn, Nether Wasdale, Cumbria, CA20 1ET
☎ (01946) 726237 ⊕ strandshotel.com

☺Strands Brewery is a ten-barrel plant with a 5,000-litre fermentation capacity. Six of the beers are available on the bar of the Strands Inn at all times or in the Screes, across the road. ‼◆LIVE

Green Bullet (ABV 3.5%) GOLD
High impact hops dominate this low strength golden-coloured ale. Loads of hop bitterness in the finish.
Responsibly (ABV 3.7%) BITTER
Brown Bitter (ABV 3.8%) BITTER
A complex tasting brown beer with a lingering bitter aftertaste.
Errmmm... (ABV 3.8%) BITTER
A bitter with a fruity aroma and taste, hop bitterness and some sweetness which continues through to the finish.
Best Bitter (ABV 4.3%) BITTER
Red Screes (ABV 4.5%) RED
An interesting, rich-tasting, smooth, strong bitter; full-flavoured with plenty of roast and malt tastes.
T'errmmm-inator (ABV 4.9%) PORTER
A smooth, dark brown, roast-led beer. Full-bodied and well-balanced.
Traditional IPA (ABV 6%) IPA

Contract brewed for Independent Lakeland Breweries:
Gold Wing (ABV 4%) BITTER

Strangers SIBA

Narrowboat Farm, Linlithgow, EH49 6QY
⊕ strangersbrewing.co.uk

Commencing brewing in 2022, Strangers Brewing Co brew hand-crafted beer in small batches from quality local ingredients. Three core beers are available, as well as seasonal specials that take flavours from what's growing on the farm and the surrounding Scottish countryside. ◆

Strathcarron

Arinackaig, Strathcarron, IV54 8YN
☎ (01599) 577236 ⊕ strathcarronbrewery.com

⊗ Brewing since 2016 with a 2.5-barrel plant using its own onsite water supply. All beer is cask and bottle-conditioned, and is usually available on draught at seven or eight local pubs, and in bottles at a dozen or so local shops and restaurants (see website). Bottles available from the website. Labels are available in Gaelic or English. LIVE

Golden Cow (ABV 3.8%) GOLD
Black Cow (ABV 4.2%) STOUT
Red Cow (ABV 4.2%) BITTER
Highland Cow (ABV 5.4%) BITTER

Stroud SIBA

Kingfisher Business Park, London Road, Thrupp, Stroud, GL5 2BY
☎ (01453) 887122 ⊕ stroudbrewery.co.uk

⊗ Established in 2006, Stroud Brewery supports the local ecomony and its ales are available in 40-50 pubs, independent retailers and its brewery shop. All beers have full organic status and are available in cask or keg as well as in cans. ‼🍴◆V✦

Tom Long (ABV 3.8%) BITTER
OPA (Organic Pale Ale) (ABV 4%) PALE
Big Cat (ABV 4.5%) STOUT
Budding (ABV 4.5%) PALE

Stu Brew SIBA

Newcastle University, Merz Court, Newcastle upon Tyne, NE1 7RU ⊕ stubrew.com

Stu Brew is Europe's first student-run microbrewery based at Newcastle University. The brewery produces a wide range of beers including many seasonal and one-off beers while enabling students to run research projects on a range of brewing issues including reducing environmental impact and waste. ◆V

Lab Session (ABV 4.3%) PALE
Exam Room Tears (ABV 5%) SPECIALITY

Stubbee SIBA

22 Harry Street, Dudley Hill, Bradford, BD4 9PH
☎ (01274) 933444 ⊕ stubbee.co

⊗ Launched as Salamander Brewery in 2000, the 40-barrel brewery was purchased by the McKenna Group and renamed Stubbee in 2021. Founder, Daniel Gent, remains head brewer and its cask ales retain the Salamander imagery on the pump clips. ‼◆✦

Blondie (ABV 4%) BITTER
Mudpuppy (ABV 4.2%) BITTER
Golden Salamander (ABV 4.3%) GOLD
Spectre Stout (ABV 4.5%) STOUT
Bright Black Porter (ABV 4.8%) PORTER

Stubborn Mule

Unit 1, Skelton Road, Timperley, Altrincham, WA14 1SJ ☎ 07730 515251
⊕ stubbornmulebrewery.com

Brewing began in 2015. In 2022 the brewery moved to larger premises allowing it to increase production capacity. Brewer Ed Bright continues to brew the core beers with occasional one-off specials. The additional space also allows it to offer more frequent brew taps, with more seating than previously. See website for full details and dates. ‼◆LIVE GF V◆

Mandarin Candidate (ABV 3.4%) SPECIALITY
Li'l Napoleon (ABV 3.9%) GOLD
Hazy Afternoon (ABV 4%) PALE
Absolute Banker (ABV 4.7%) BITTER
Pils, Thrills & Bellyaches (ABV 4.8%) SPECIALITY
Donkey Punch (ABV 5.5%) SPECIALITY
Pre-Prohibition Cream Ale (ABV 5.5%) BLOND
The initial hop presence is balanced by a sweet honeyed body, followed with a gentle, lasting, drier hop bitterness.
Single Hop IPA (ABV 5.7%) IPA
Chocolate Stout (ABV 5.8%) STOUT

Stumptail

North Street, Great Dunham, Kings Lynn, Norfolk, PE32 2LR
☎ (01328) 701042 ✉ stumptail@btinternet.com

Stumptail began commercial homebrewing in 2011 using a 100-litre plant. Bottle-conditioned beers are produced with cask-conditioned versions brewed to order, all to bespoke recipes. LIVE

Sulwath SIBA

The Brewery, 209 King Street, Castle Douglas, DG7 1DT
☎ (01556) 504525 ⊕ sulwathbrewers.co.uk

Sulwath started brewing in 1995. Its award-winning beers are supplied to around 100 outlets and four wholesalers as far away as Devon and Aberdeen. The brewery has a popular, fully-licensed taproom. ‼ 🍽◆LIVE◆

Cuil Hill (ABV 3.6%) BLOND
Distinctively fruity session ale with malt and hop undertones. The taste is bittersweet with a long-lasting, dry finish.
Tri-ball (ABV 3.9%) GOLD
Brewed with three hops, it is fresh, crisp and blond – the ideal session ale.
The Grace (ABV 4.3%) MILD
A refreshing, rich ale with a full-bodied flavour that balances the caramel undertones.
Black Galloway (ABV 4.4%) PORTER
A robust porter that derives its colour from the abundance of chocolate malts.
Criffel (ABV 4.6%) BITTER
Full-bodied beer with a distinctive bitterness. Fruit is to the fore with hops becoming increasingly dominant in the finish.
Galloway Gold (ABV 5%) GOLD
A cask-conditioned lager that will be too sweet for many despite being heavily-hopped.
Knockendoch (ABV 5%) BITTER
Dark, copper-coloured, reflecting a roast malt content, with bitterness from Challenger hops.
Solway Mist (ABV 5.5%) SPECIALITY
A naturally cloudy wheat beer. Sweetish and fruity.

Summerskills SIBA

15 Pomphlett Farm Industrial Estate, Broxton Drive, Billacombe, Plymouth, Devon, PL9 7BG
☎ (01752) 481283 ⊕ summerskills.co.uk

Established in a vineyard in 1983 at Bigbury-on-Sea, Summerskills moved to its present site in 1985. It is the oldest brewery in Plymouth. Wholesalers and pub companies provide national distribution and the beers regularly appear in a growing selection of local outlets. ◆LIVE

Start Point (ABV 3.7%) GOLD
Golden with a clean and fresh nose. Sweet upfront with a delicate bitter finish. An excellent session ale.
Westward Ho! (ABV 4.1%) BITTER
Malt dominates a light nose. Gentle bitterness introduces its malty-fruit friends. Malt and bitterness remain, with bitterness dominating the conversation.
Tamar (ABV 4.3%) BITTER
A sweet malty taste, with a slight bitter finish. A refreshing, easy-drinking, traditional best bitter.
Stout (ABV 4.4%) STOUT
Strong coffee aroma, slight sweetness on the taste with coffee/chocolates on tongue. Bitter finish.
Devon Dew (ABV 4.5%) GOLD
Malty aroma but not too hoppy on the nose. A sweet lemon taste comes through followed by grapefruit. An easy, drinkable golden bitter.
Devon Frost (ABV 4.5%) GOLD
A slight nutty roast on the nose and also on taste with grapefruit flavours on the tongue.
Bolt Head (ABV 4.7%) BITTER
Fruit-hop nose has roast-malt hints. Bitter flavours with sweet malt, roast and hoppiness. Lingering bitter finish with background malt and fruit.
Whistle Belly Vengeance (ABV 4.7%) RED
Strong aroma of rich malts, tastes of dates and liquorice sweetness in this strong ale. When served in good condition it's a top beer in the red ales section.
Dragon Pioneer (ABV 4.8%) PALE
A floral citrus aroma, grapefruit on taste with a floral tang and crispiness to it. Slightly herbal finish to a refreshing beer.
Plymouth Porter (ABV 5%) PORTER
Strong, sweet, chocolate aroma, tastes of chocolate and toffee. Aftertaste dies off quickly, a nice drinkable sweet Porter.
Bunker Hill (ABV 5.1%) BITTER
Light, amber-coloured traditional bitter, hoppy upfront with a sweet aftertaste. Brewed with English hops grown in Herefordshire and Worcestershire.
Indiana's Bones (ABV 5.6%) OLD
Old ale with good body. Rich malty roasts aroma bursting with strong sweet flavours on the tongue. Slightly dryer finish.

Sun Bear (NEW)

17 Cheltenham Crescent, Moreton, Merseyside, CH46 1PU

A nanobrewery based in Morton, Wirral.

Pale (ABV 3.8%) PALE

Sunbeam

52 Fernbank Road, Leeds, West Yorkshire, LS13 1BU
☎ 07772 002437 ⊕ sunbeamales.co.uk

Sunbeam Ales was established in a house in Leeds in 2009, with commercial brewing beginning in 2011. Since moving, capacity has increased to a two-barrel plant based in a garage. The core range of ales (available in West and North Yorkshire at present) is brewed on rotation up to twice weekly, with occasional brews every six weeks or so. ◆

Bottoms Up (ABV 3.7%) PALE
Polka Hop (ABV 3.8%) PALE

Sun Beamer (ABV 3.8%) PALE
Bright Day (ABV 4.2%) PALE
Rain Stops Play (ABV 4.5%) BITTER

Sunken Knave (NEW)

Office: 172 Tarring Road, Worthing, West Sussex,
BN11 4HG ☎ 07920 590936 ⊕ sunkenknave.com

A new Worthing-based brewery started by the former
Head Brewer of Darkstar, specialising in recreations of
historical British styles. Currently operating out of Hand
Brew Co (qv) but with aspirations of opening a brewery
in Worthing.

Supercute

Unit G1, Coldharbour Works, 245a Coldharbour Lane,
Loughborough Junction, London, SW9 8RR

Former Friendship Adventure brewery bought by
Supercute bar in Brixton Market in mid 2024. The
brewery relaunched as Supercute soon after. The original
onsite taproom (open Wed-Sun) remains open under the
new owners as well as the original Friendship Adventure
bar in Brixton Market. No cask ale. ✦

Sureshot

5 Sheffield Street, Manchester, M1 2ND
⊕ sureshotbrew.com

Established by James Campbell (Ex-Cloudwater founder)
and started brewing in 2022. Located in the arches below
Piccadily Station, in the premises vacated by Track the
previous year. 🛒✦

Surrey Hills SIBA

Denbies Wine Estate, London Road, Dorking, Surrey,
RH5 6AA

☎ (01306) 883603 ⊕ surreyhills.co.uk

⊠ Surrey Hills began brewing in 2005 near Shere,
moving to Dorking in 2011. Nearly 95% of production is
sold within 15 miles of the brewery. The beers have won
several local and national awards. The brewery is open
Mon-Sat for sales of cask ale to drink onsite, or take
away. ‼🛒✦🏵

Ranmore (ABV 3.8%) GOLD
Glorious, light, flavoursome session beer. An earthy
hoppy nose leads into a grapefruit and hoppy taste and a
clean, bitter finish.
Shere Drop (ABV 4.2%) PALE
Hoppy with some balancing malt. Pleasant citrus aroma
and noticeable fruitiness in taste with some sweetness.
Gilt Complex (ABV 4.6%) GOLD
Initial citrus fruitiness quickly gives way to a piercing hit
of bitter hops fading slowly in a big dry finish.
Gilt Trip (ABV 4.6%) GOLD
Greensand IPA (ABV 4.6%) PALE
A strong-flavoured and easily-drinkable IPA, with intense
grapefruit and hops in the aroma and taste and soft
citrusy finish.
Collusion (ABV 5.2%) GOLD
Golden ale with a changing hop mix. A pale malt
backbone with citrus and tropical flavours combined with
characteristics of marmalade.

Suspect

34 Jane Street, Leith, Edinburgh, EH6 5HD ☎ 07468
436652 ⊕ suspectbrewing.co.uk

A gluten-free brewery set up in the former Liquid
Brewing premises. No real ale. GF

Sussex Small Batch

23 The Vinery, Poling, Arundel, West Sussex,
BN18 9PY ☎ 07718 222425

Office: 48 Henty Road, Worthing, BN14 7HE
✉ ssbbrewery@outlook.com

⊠ Jim Brown started the Sussex Small Batch Brewery in
2018, focusing on producing quality stouts with a
difference. Brewing takes place using spare capacity at
Goldmark Brewery (qv). Cask stout is available from
time-to-time in a few select pubs in Worthing, but most
production is canned (available throughout the UK via
Eebria). Collaboration brews are sometimes available.
More recently it has produced KeyKeg stouts (supplied to
a few select pubs).

Tiramisu Stout (ABV 5.5%) SPECIALITY
Zucotto Stout (Chocolate &
Raspberry) (ABV 5.5%) SPECIALITY
Smoked Chilli Chocolate Stout (ABV 5.8%)
SPECIALITY

Swannay

Birsay, Swannay by Evie, Orkney, KW17 2NP
☎ (01856) 721700 ⊕ swannaybrewery.com

🏵Brewing began in 2006 in the redundant Swannay
dairy on Orkney mainland's exposed North-Western tip.
Two brewing plants are utilised, a five and a twenty
barrel. Founder Rob is assisted by son Lewis plus a small
team of passionate beer lovers. The cask ales are widely
available within Orkney and also distributed on the
mainland of Scotland and to the north of England. ‼🛒✦

Orkney Best (ABV 3.6%) GOLD
A refreshing, light-bodied, low gravity golden beer
bursting with hop, peach and sweet malt flavours. The
long, hoppy finish leaves a dry bitterness.
Island Hopping (ABV 3.9%) GOLD
Passionfruit hoppiness with some caramel and a lasting
bitter aftertaste.
Dark Munro (ABV 4%) MILD
The nose presents an intense roast hit which is followed
by plums and blackcurrant in the mouth. The strong roast
malt continues into the aftertaste.
Scapa Special (ABV 4.2%) BITTER
A good copy of a typical Lancashire bitter, full of
bitterness and background hops, leaving your mouth
tingling in the lingering aftertaste.
Sneaky Wee Orkney Stout (ABV 4.2%) STOUT
Bags of malt and roast with a mixed fruit berry
background. Dry bitter finish.
Pale Ale (ABV 4.7%) PALE
Orkney IPA (ABV 4.8%) PALE
A traditional bitter, with light hop and fruit flavour
throughout.
Duke IPA (ABV 5.2%) PALE
Good refreshing citrus-fruited IPA with background malt.
Orkney Blast (ABV 6%) BITTER
Plenty of alcohol in this warming strong bitter/barley
wine. A mushroom and woody aroma blossoms into a
well-balanced smack of malt and hop in the taste.

Swansea

🍺 Railway Inn, 533 Gower Road, Upper Killay,
Swansea, SA2 7DS
☎ (01792) 203946

🏵Opened in 1996, with beers brewed at the Joiners
Arms, Bishopston. During the building and
commissioning of a brand new facility at the Railway Inn,
the owner and brewer, Rory Gowland, sadly passed
away and brewing was suspended. This has now

recommenced, brewing to the original recipes, and the old favourites are back on tap at the Railway. ‼♦

Taddington

Blackwell Hall, Blackwell, Buxton, Derbyshire, SK17 9TQ
☎ (01298) 85734

Taddington started brewing in 2007, and brews one Czech-style, unpasteurised lager in two different strengths. No real ale

Tally Ho!

🏠 14 Market Street, Hatherleigh, Devon, EX20 3JN
☎ 07779 339089 ⊕ tallyhohatherleigh.co.uk

⊠ Having stood idle at the rear of the Tally Ho! pub for 14 years, the brewery was resurrected in 2015, and then sold in 2018. The current owner and brewer took over in 2020. As well as the pub, several local free houses and other establishments are supplied. ♦

Tamworth

29 Market Street, Tamworth, Staffordshire, B79 7LR
☎ (01827) 319872 ☎ 07712 893353
⊕ tamworthbrewing.co.uk

Owner/brewer George Greenaway brought brewing back to Tamworth town centre after a gap of 70 years. Brewing started in 2017 in a former shop, which dates back to Tudor times and also serves as a tap. In 2020 brewing moved into the adjacent building, which records indicate was a brewhouse in the 1750s. The move allowed production on its five-barrel plant to double, and included the provision of an off-licence. Local outlets and festivals are supplied ‼ 🍴♦🔧

Hopmaster (ABV 4.2%) GOLD
Big Game (ABV 4.5%) BITTER
Amber-hued with a malty aroma. Generous malt taste with spicy sides. Hints of pepper and lemon lurk under the hop bitterness which emerges with a mouth-watering bite.
Ethelfleda (ABV 4.5%) BITTER
Full malt aroma from this golden beer. Sweet and grassy mix to start, developing to a bitter finish.
Hoppy Poppy (ABV 4.6%) GOLD
Our Aethel (ABV 4.8%) STOUT
Whopper (ABV 6.5%) IPA

Tangled Web (NEW)

Fermor Road, Preston, Lancashire, PR4 6AP ☎ 07840 599890 ⊕ tangledweb.uk

Commercial home-based brewery that started in 2023.

Tankleys

Beech Avenue, Sidcup, DA15 8NH ☎ 07901 333273
⊕ tankleysbrewery.com

Tankleys is a home-based brewery in Sidcup and has brewed larger batches at other breweries. Its Australian brewer brews styles from modern takes on traditional through to avant garde, the Hawaiian Pizza Beer being particularly notable. Available in bottles and in cask locally and at beer festivals. V

Tanners

See Parkway

Tap East SIBA

🏠 7 International Square, Westfield Stratford City, Montfichet Road, Stratford, London, E20 1EE
☎ (020) 8555 4467 ⊕ tapeast.co.uk

⊠ Tap East is located in Westfield Stratford City shopping centre, opposite the entrance to Stratford International Station. Brewing began in 2011 using a 2.5-barrel plant. One-off and collaborative beers with other breweries are also produced. Beers are available onsite or at the Utobeer stall and the Rake, both at Borough Market. ♦V

Tap It

Unit 6, Muira Industrial Estate, William Street, Southampton, SO14 5QH ⊕ tapitbrew.co.uk

The first brew by enthusiastic homebrewer Rob Colmer was in 2018. Tap It is an eight-barrel plant producing eight regular beers, mainly in KeyKeg and bottles. Occasional cask-conditioned beers are available. There is an onsite brewery tap and a bar in Southampton is planned. ‼ 🍺🔧

Tap Social Movement SIBA

Unit 16A, Station Field Industrial Estate, Rowles Way, Kidlington, Oxfordshire, OX5 1JD
☎ (01865) 236330

Office: 27 Curtis Industrial Estate, North Hinksey Lane, Botley, Oxfordshire, OX2 0LX
⊕ tapsocialmovement.com

The three founders (with criminal justice backgrounds) established the brewery in 2016 to provide training and work opportunities for those serving sentences. Brewing is on its 6,000-litre plant, which produces beer in kegs, cans and increasingly cask (appearing as guests at White House, Oxford, and Lock 29, Banbury). The original Botley site is a brewery tap and events venue. The former LAM brewery, in Kennington is now a bakery, coffee bar and takeaway outlet for its cans. A new Market Tap is now open in Oxford's covered market. 🔧

Tapestry By Props

Unit B, Totterdown Bridge Industrial Estate, Albert Road, St Philips, Bristol, BS2 0XH
⊕ tapestrybrewery.com

Previously known as Cocksure, this 10-barrel brewery was established in 2017, and moved from the Severn Vale to Bristol in 2018. Tapestry is a social enterprise brewery that provides training and employment for people with learning disabilities. ♦LIVE V🔧

Raconteur Amber Session (ABV 3.9%) BITTER
Slight citrus aroma, background sweet biscuit flavours overlaid with pine and citrus hoppiness which fade during the short finish.
Propeller Pale Ale (ABV 4.2%) PALE
African Hibiscus + Honey Golden Ale (ABV 4.8%) SPECIALITY
Initial hit of hoppy bitterness then the tart flavour of hibiscus combines with honey sweetness which lingers on the palate.
Swingball Session IPA (ABV 4.8%) PALE
Fruity hops on the nose combining on the palate with light malt and tropical fruit hints, lingering, dry bitter ending.
African Mango + Orange Pale Ale (ABV 5%) SPECIALITY
Definitely not a traditionalist's beer. The aroma, flavours and aftertaste are loaded with mango with an additional citrus orange punch.

Night Ride Cold Brew Stout (ABV 5%) SPECIALITY
Roasted malt and coffee aroma and flavours to match with hints of dark fruit before a slightly dry finish.
Topline IPA (ABV 6.5%) IPA

Tapped

🍺 Sheffield: Sheffield Tap, Platform 1b, Sheffield Station, Sheaf Street, Sheffield, South Yorkshire, S1 2BP
☎ (0114) 273 7558

Leeds: Boar Street, Leeds, West Yorkshire, LS1 5EL
☎ (0113) 244 1953 ⊕ tappedbrewco.com

Brewing began in 2013 after the old station Edwardian dining rooms were converted into an four-barrel, onsite brewery with a viewing gallery at the Sheffield Tap pub. The beer is mostly sold onsite and via the company's specialist beer wholesale business, Pivovar, to its other outlets, and occasionally the free trade. A further onsite brewery was opened at the Leeds Tap in 2014 which supplies that pub. Part of the Pivovar group that also includes the Elvington brewery. **V**

Tapstone

11 Bartlett Park, Millfield, Chard, Somerset, TA20 2BB
☎ (01460) 929156 ⊕ tapstone.co.uk

⊠ Founded in 2015, the brewery was custom built around a brewing process that preserves delicate hop oils, thus making beers with a saturated hop flavour. It is growing its own hops two miles from the brewery. There is a small onsite taproom. All beers are unfined and hazy.
🍴 ☰ V✦

Tarn 51

🍺 Robin Hood, 10 Church Road, Altofts, Normanton, West Yorkshire, WF6 2NJ
☎ (01924) 892911 ✉ realale@tarn51brewing.co.uk

Tarn 51 uses a three-barrel plant situated at the Robin Hood in Altofts. Five other outlets are supplied.

Tartan Shark

5 Bangholm Park, Edinburgh, EH5 3BA ☎ 07746 432512 ⊕ tartanshark.co.uk

This self-styled 'smallest brewery in Edinburgh' began production in early 2020, brewing bottle-conditioned, can-conditioned and keg beers (often delivered by pushbike). LIVE

Tartarus

Office: New Road Site, Horsforth, LS18 4NR
✉ tartarus.brewing@gmail.com

Nanobrewery based in Horsforth, Leeds, launched commercially in 2020. Producing small-batch, craft beers on a 100-litre kit.

Tatton

Unit 7, Longridge Trading Estate, Knutsford, Cheshire, WA16 8PR

Office: Kent Barn, St Nicholas Court Farm, St Nicholas at Wade, Kent, CT7 0PT
✉ info@wantsumbrewery.co.uk

Tatton is based in the heart of Cheshire, brewing since 2010 using a steam-fired, custom-built 15-barrel brewhouse. It supplies pubs throughout Cheshire and the North-West. After a short period of closure in 2024, the brewery was acquired by Wantsum Brewery, Kent. 🍴 ☰ ✦

Lazy Haze (ABV 3.7%) SPECIALITY
Blonde (ABV 4%) BLOND
Best (ABV 4.2%) BITTER
Black (ABV 4.5%) PORTER
Gold (ABV 4.5%) BITTER

Tavernale

🍺 Bridge Tavern, 7 Akenside Hill, Newcastle upon Tyne, NE1 3UF
☎ (0191) 232 1122 ⊕ thebridgetavern.com

A two-barrel plant supplying beers to the Bridge Tavern only. All beers brewed are one-offs. Brewing is currently suspended. ✦

Tavistock

The Old Root House, Harragrove Farm, Peter Tavy, Devon, PL19 9JR ☎ 07564 869198
⊕ tavistockbrewery.co.uk

Located in Dartmoor National Park, and overlooking Peter Tavy, Tavistock Brewery is a family-run business which was five years in the planning and design. It is set in a renovated farm building previously used as an old dairy. Brewing commenced 2022. Three beers are brewed on the four-barrel plant and are currently available in a small but growing number of local pubs and bars.

Golden Ale (ABV 4.3%) GOLD
English Ale (ABV 4.5%) BITTER
Master Ale (ABV 4.9%) BITTER
Deep ruby colour, rich, well-balanced flavour. Very drinkable leaves you wanting more.

Taw Valley

Westacott Farm, Westacott Lane, North Tawton, Devon, EX20 2BS ☎ 07900 002299
⊕ tawvalleybrewery.com

Established in 2017 in a Grade-II listed, 17th century barn and the UK's only fully thatched brewery building with water drawn from it's own spring. Beer is delivered in the brewery dray, a converted minibus. A taproom has been added, with seasonal opening times. ✦LIVE V✦

Black Ops (ABV 3.9%) MILD
Tawton Session Ale (ABV 4%) GOLD
Devon Jester (ABV 4.2%) PALE
Kennard's Steam (ABV 4.3%) BITTER
Copper Best (ABV 4.4%) BITTER

Tay Brew (NEW)

56 Warmingham Lane, Middlewich, CW10 0DJ

A nanobrewery based in Middlewich, Cheshire, which opened in 2023.

Timothy Taylor SIBA IFBB

Knowle Spring Brewery, Keighley, West Yorkshire, BD21 1AW
☎ (01535) 603139 ⊕ timothy-taylor.co.uk

☺An independent, family-owned company established in 1858, it has occupied the Knowle Spring site since 1863. Pennine spring water is used to brew its award-winning ales on both the established main plant and a 10-barrel plant used to develop new beers, including occasional specials. 19 pubs are operated. ✦V

Dark Mild (ABV 3.4%) MILD
Malt and caramel dominate throughout in this sweetish beer with background hop and fruit notes.
Golden Best (ABV 3.4%) MILD

Refreshing, amber-coloured mild. A delicate fruit hoppy aroma leads to a fruity taste with underlying hops and malt. Fruity finish.

Boltmaker (ABV 4%) BITTER
Tawny bitter combining hops, fruit and biscuity malt. Lingering, increasingly bitter aftertaste. Formerly, and sometimes still sold as, Best Bitter.

Knowle Spring (ABV 4.2%) BLOND
Tropical fruitiness on the nose leads to a bittersweetness that carries through into the finish.

Landlord (ABV 4.3%) BITTER
A moreish bitter combining citrus peel aromas, malt and grassy hops with marmalade sweetness and a long, bitter finish.

Landlord Dark (ABV 4.3%) BROWN
A black beer with coffee-coloured head. Burnt caramel aroma. Dark fruits with caramel in the taste and a light bitter finish.

Taylor Walker

See Greene King

Teifi

See Cardigan

Teignmouth SIBA

Warehouse 1, Old Quay Street, Teignmouth, TQ14 8ES
☎ (01626) 770846 ⊕ teignmouthbrewery.co.uk

Teignmouth Brewery is a family-run business based in the iconic port town of Teignmouth. Brewing commenced in 2019 with the brewery growing from strength to strength, picking up a number of SIBA awards. A range of three core beers is offered as well as seasonals, supplied to Devon and further afield. ♦LIVE

Templer (ABV 4%) BITTER
Portside (ABV 4.3%) BITTER
Proper old English-style bitter – a mixture of biscuit malt tones and sweet caramel almost a nutty coffee amaretto tone, very enjoyable.

Deckhand (ABV 4.5%) GOLD
A refreshing, golden-coloured best bitter, brewed with pale malt and a blend of citrusy hops. A good summer time beer.

Teignworthy

The Maltings, Teign Road, Newton Abbot, Devon, TQ12 4AA
☎ (01626) 332066 ⊕ teignworthybrewery.com

⊠ Teignworthy Brewery opened in 1994 within the historic Tucker's Maltings building and remains family run. Based on a tower system with open squares the 20-barrel plant produces up to 50 barrels a week and supplies around 150 outlets in Devon and Somerset plus wholesalers further afield on a pre-arranged basis. It diversified in 2017 with the addition of the Dartmoor gin distillery. !! ▱ ♦LIVE V

Neap Tide (ABV 3.8%) PALE
Clear amber colour. Malt, caramel, and English hops aroma. Light to moderate sweet and bitter, hedgerow fruits, berry hints. Medium body, soft carbonation, and dry, bitter finish.

Reel Ale (ABV 4%) BITTER
Subtle aromas. Gentle with malt and fruit dominating the hops, and a dry aftertaste.

Thirsty Blonde (ABV 4.2%) BLOND
Gun Dog (ABV 4.3%) BITTER

Easy-drinking, session best bitter. Fruity throughout. Dry aftertaste lingers; sweetness and fruit over malt and caramel, progressing into hoppiness.

Old Moggie (ABV 4.4%) BITTER
Hoppy and bitter with fruity undertones. Complex aftertaste with a balance of malt, hops and fruit.

Teme Valley SIBA

☷ Talbot, Bromyard Road, Knightwick, Worcestershire, WR6 5PH
☎ (01886) 821235 ☎ 07792 394151
⊕ temevalleybrewery.co.uk

☺Teme Valley was established in 1997 to brew beer for the Talbot, Knightwick. Only hops grown in Herefordshire and Worcestershire are used in brewing, including Green Hop specials during the season. Beers are supplied throughout the West Midlands and Marches. All beers are gluten-free. !! ♦LIVE GF ✿

T'Other (ABV 3.5%) PALE
This (ABV 3.7%) BITTER
That (ABV 4.1%) BITTER
Talbot Blonde (ABV 4.4%) BLOND
Wotever Next? (ABV 5%) BITTER
Roasted malt and toffee aromas lead to a complex taste of stone fruits, dark malt, hops and melon. The finish is, at first, of slightly smoky malt and fruits, fading into lingering dry hops.

Temper

☷ Dronfield Arms, 91 Chesterfield Road, Dronfield, Derbyshire, S18 2XE ☎ 07725 639648

Office: 18 Egerton Road, Dronfield, Derbyshire, S18 2LG ⊕ temperbrewing.com

⊠ Situated in the basement of the Dronfield Arms, this 5.5-barrel plant is run by Chris Wigg, who began brewing there in 2021. The beers are mainly brewed for the upstairs Arms bar, in both cask and KeyKeg, but are also available wholesale. V

Resolve (ABV 4%) PALE
Sky Trails (ABV 4%) PALE
Wild Light (ABV 4.6%) GOLD
Relacite (ABV 4.8%) RED
Valleys (ABV 5.2%) PALE

Temperance Street

75 North Western Street, Manchester, M12 6DY
☎ 07595 493462 ⊕ temperancestreet.co.uk

Community-focused brewery and taproom in the centre of Manchester. As well as producing its own beer, it makes its brewkit available to customers to trial their own recipes on a larger scale. !! ✿

Tempest SIBA

Block 11, Units 1 & 2 Tweedbank Industrial Estate, Tweedbank, TD1 3RS
☎ (01896) 759500 ⊕ tempestbrewco.com

Well-established in its premises at Tweedbank, Gavin Meiklejohn's brewery continues to evolve with specialised brews, many using lesser known hop varieties. Beers are both cask and keg form, along with an expanding bottle and canning production. There are plans to move the entire operation along the road to new premises in Tweedside Park, which will also include the shop and the ever popular weekend tap sessions, as well as occasional music sessions. !! ▱ ♦LIVE GF V✿

Armadillo (ABV 3.8%) GOLD

Modern Helles (ABV 4.1%) PALE
Elemental Porter (ABV 5.1%) PORTER

Temple Brew House SIBA

▤ Temple Brew House, 46 Essex Street, Temple,
London, WC2R 3JF
☎ (020) 7936 2536

Office: City Pub Group, 2nd Floor, Essel House,
London, W1W 7TH ⊕ templebrewhouse.com/
brewery

☺Originally opened in 2014 as the Essex Street Brewery,
it reopened during 2022 after a two-year closure, and
rebranded to Temple Brew House, the name of the pub.
Owned by the City Pub Group, the beers are available on
cask and in keg at the pub. Future of the brewery
uncertain after sale of the City Pub Group to Youngs in
early 2024. ♦⚷

Ten Tun (NEW)

▤ 3 Westbrook Walk, Alton, Hampshire, GU34 1HZ
⊕ tentuntaphouse.beer/brewery

A new brewery in Hampshire focussing on progressive
beers using modern ingredients. V

Tenby

Unit 15, The Salterns, Tenby, SA70 7NJ
☎ (01834) 218090 ☎ 07410 169447
⊕ tenbybrewingco.com

Tenby Brewing Co has been brewing a diverse range of
full-flavoured beers in South Pembrokeshire since 2015.
90%+ of the energy used at the brewery is sustainable,
the majority coming from the onsite solar array. There is
a 150 capacity onsite tap (open Fri/Sat in Spring/
Summer). Two brewery bars, 'Tap & Tan', Tenby town
centre, and 'Hwb Food Hall', Narberth. KeyKegs are a
significant part of the output. Cask beers are no longer
produced. LIVE GF V⚷

Tenby Harbour

See Harbwr Tenby

Tennent Caledonian

Wellpark Brewery, 161 Duke Street, Glasgow, G31 1JD
Home of Tennent's beers including the best-selling lager.
No real ale. ‼

Terra Tempo (NEW)

The Hanger, Manor Farm, Tongham, Surrey, GU10 1DE

Established in 2023, this small brewery operates from
Hogs Back Brewery and has produced six beers, which
are conditioned in old Portugese wine casks. Hops grown
at Hogs Back are often used along with seasonal fruits to
produce interesting beers with complex flavour profiles.
The beers are available direct from the brewery and at
the Hogs Back shop. ▰

Tewkesbury SIBA

Unit 29, Highfield Business Park, Tewkesbury Road,
Deerhurst, GL19 4BP ☎ 07415 118197
✉ info@tewksbrew.co.uk

Formed in 2020, cask brewing commenced in 2022, currently brewing
once a month. Three ales have been launched so far. Plans have been
put in place to bring in bottling and canning capability, as well as
several new brews during the currency of this Guide. ♦V

Gold (ABV 4.1%) PALE
Dark Knight (ABV 4.8%) STOUT

Thame

c/o XT Brewing, Unit 27, Notley Farm, Chearsley
Road, Long Crendon, Buckinghamshire, HP18 9ER
☎ (01844) 218202
✉ thamebrewery@btinternet.com

⊠ The one-barrel brewery at the Cross Keys, Thame, is
no longer in use. The long-standing publican, Peter
Lambert also works at XT (qv) and brews Thame beers
there from time to time.

Thames Ditton

Office: PO Box 1037A, Thames Ditton, KT1 9BS
☎ 07761 473621
✉ thamesdittonbrewery@gmail.com

Established in 2020, it produces two regular cask beers,
available in selected local outlets, one bottled lager, and
occasional, limited edition cask ale. All beers currently
contract brewed elsewhere.

Henry's Alt (ABV 4.5%) BITTER
Screaming Queen (ABV 5%) GOLD

Thames Side SIBA

1 Hale Street, Staines-upon-Thames, TW18 4SU
☎ 07703 518956 ⊕ thamessidebrewery.co.uk

⊠ Founded in 2015 by CAMRA member Andy Hayward
using a four-barrel plant. In 2020 a one-barrel pilot brew
kit for experimental and developmental brews was
added. In late 2022 it moved to its current brewery and
taproom by the entrance to the Two Rivers retail park. A
full range of beers are named after birds found on or
near the nearby river, while specials follow a musical
theme. ‼▰♦⚷

Harrier Bitter (ABV 3.4%) BITTER
Heron Ale (ABV 3.7%) BITTER
Malty traditional English bitter with a tangerine fruit
flavour. Well-balanced with an impressive dry finish and
loads of flavour for its strength.
White Swan Pale Ale (ABV 4.2%) PALE
New World pale ale. Grapefruit pith and grassy hops
almost overpowering biscuit maltiness. Some sweetness
in the finish with a crisp biscuitiness.
Egyptian Goose India Pale Ale (ABV 4.8%) PALE
English IPA with initial floral aroma leading to an earthy
mango fruitiness as sweetness builds and a balanced
bitter finish.
Wryneck Rye IPA (ABV 5.6%) IPA
Spicy rye IPA with lychees and increasing lemony taste
balanced by rye and New World hops. Short, dry, bitter
finish.

Theakston SIBA

The Brewery, Masham, North Yorkshire, HG4 4YD
☎ (01765) 680000 ⊕ theakstons.co.uk

☺An independent, family business, established in 1827
by Robert Theakston. From 1984, for 19 years the
brewery was in non-family hands. Following a successful
buy back in 2003, the company returned to family
control, managed by Simon Theakston and his three
brothers (great-great grandsons of the founder).
Significant investment in the brewery since then has
provided additional capacity and flexibility to meet
growing demand and variety of beers brewed. ‼♦⚷

Best Bitter (ABV 3.8%) BITTER

Easy-drinking, light amber ale with a good malty fruity taste with some bitterness.

Black Bull Bitter (ABV 3.9%) BITTER
Lightfoot (ABV 4.1%) PALE
XB (ABV 4.5%) BITTER
Malt-forward, slightly sweet beer rounded out by some fruitiness, light brown in colour.
Old Peculier (ABV 5.6%) OLD
A complex, full-bodied, ruby brown strong ale. Expect plenty of malt and especially dried fruits, finishing sweet and fruity.

Thirsty Moose SIBA

Unit 5c, Galaxy Business Park, Newburn Bridge Road, Ryton, NE21 4SQ ☎ **07862 087087**
⊕ **thirstymoosebrewingco.com**

Brewing commenced in 2022 by two partners with Canadian heritage and a passion for brewing.

Northern 22 (ABV 4.4%) PALE
Canny Canuck (ABV 4.5%) BROWN
Oot n' Aboot (ABV 5.6%) PALE

Thornbridge SIBA

Riverside Business Park, Buxton Road, Bakewell, Derbyshire, DE45 1GS
☎ **(01629) 815999** ⊕ **thornbridgebrewery.co.uk**

⊙The first Thornbridge craft beers were produced in 2005, using a 10-barrel brewery housed in the grounds of Thornbridge Hall. The beers have gained considerable success with more than 300 consumer and industry awards won. A 30-barrel brewery opened in Bakewell in 2009. The original brewing plant, having been relocated to the Riveside site, continues to develop new, seasonal and speciality beers. In 2022, Thornbridge were part of a group who saved Sheffield's famous beer, Kelham Island Pale Rider. 200 outlets are supplied direct. 12 pubs are managed and owned. ‼ ☛ ♦LIVE GF V

Wild Swan (ABV 3.5%) BLOND
Extremely pale yet flavoursome and refreshing beer. Plenty of lemony citrus hop flavour, becoming increasingly dry and bitter in the finish and aftertaste.
Astryd (ABV 3.8%) PALE
Brother Rabbit (ABV 4%) GOLD
Lord Marples (ABV 4%) BITTER
Smooth, traditional, easy-drinking bitter. Caramel, malt and coffee flavours fall away to leave a long, bitter finish.
The Wednesday (ABV 4%) BLOND
Ashford (ABV 4.2%) BITTER
AM:PM (ABV 4.5%) GOLD
Market Porter (ABV 4.5%) PORTER
Crackendale (ABV 5.2%) PALE
Kipling (ABV 5.2%) GOLD
Golden pale bitter with aromas of grapefruit and passion fruit. Intense fruit flavours continue throughout, leading to a long bitter aftertaste.
Britannic (ABV 5.3%) PALE
Jaipur (ABV 5.9%) IPA
Full-bodied gold IPA with a backbone of malt but with an abundance of hops giving citrus and tropical fruit flavours.
Cocoa Wonderland (ABV 6.8%) SPECIALITY

Contract brewed for Kelham Island Brewery:
Pale Rider (ABV 5.2%) PALE

Thornsett

Thornsett Fields Farm, Briargrove Road, Thornsett, Birch Vale, Derbyshire, SK22 1AX ☎ **07803 477812**
⊕ **thornsettbrewery.co.uk**

⊕Located on Thornsett Fields Farm in Thornsett, High Peak, the brewery uses a one-barrel plant with three fermenters. The brewery is off-grid, and is as sustainable and eco-friendly as possible, relying on renewable energy sources. Alongside the brewery is an organic hop yard with eight different hop varieties. Its onsite taphouse has open days with local food traders on most weekends from spring to late summer. ☛ ♦

Blue Ron's Ale (ABV 3.4%) BLOND
Home Sweet Home (ABV 3.6%) MILD
He's Behind You (ABV 4.2%) PALE
Best Bitter (ABV 4.5%) BITTER
Beep Beep Corner (ABV 5%) STOUT
New Mills Madness (ABV 5%) PALE

Three Acre SIBA

Dairy Yard, Little Goldsmiths Farm, Beechy Road, Uckfield, East Sussex, TN22 5JG ☎ **07450 315960**
⊕ **threeacrebrewery.co.uk**

⊠ Founded in 2019 by three lifelong friends, on a rural Sussex farm, this award-winning brewery almost doubled fermentation capacity in 2023, primarily due to increased demand for its cask beers and more contract customers, including Wetherspoons. Apart from the core range, the fourteen-barrel brew plant produces seasonal and new beers. Several are offered bottle-conditioned, or in cans, with home delivery available. A new Uckfield taproom was opened in 2024 while a mobile bar attends outside events. ♦LIVE V

Session Pale (ABV 3.7%) PALE
Best Bitter (ABV 4%) BITTER
Blood Orange Pale (ABV 4.9%) SPECIALITY
IPA (ABV 5%) GOLD

Three B's

⊟ **Black Bull, Brokenstone Road, Blackburn, Lancashire, BB3 0LL**
☎ **(01254) 581381** ⊕ **threebsbrewery.co.uk**

Robert Bell acquired the Black Bull in 2011 and the brewpub now supplies 50 outlets. ‼ ♦LIVE

Stoker's Slake (ABV 3.6%) MILD
Lightly roasted coffee flavours are in the aroma and taste. A mild with dried fruit flavours in the long finish.
Bee's Knees (ABV 3.7%) PALE
Honey Bee (ABV 3.7%) SPECIALITY
Bobbin's Bitter (ABV 3.8%) BITTER
Bee Blonde (ABV 4%) BLOND
Black Bull (ABV 4%) BITTER
Ju-bee-lation (ABV 4.1%) PALE
Black Bull Lager (ABV 4.5%) SPECIALITY
Doff Cocker (ABV 4.5%) BLOND
Knocker Up (ABV 4.8%) PORTER
A smooth, rich, creamy porter. The roast flavour is foremost without dominating and is balanced by fruit and hop notes.
Old Bee (ABV 5.8%) OLD

Three Blind Mice SIBA

Unit W10, Black Bank Business Park, Black Bank Road, Little Downham, Cambridgeshire, CB6 2UA
☎ **(01353) 864438** ☎ **07912 875825**
✉ **mice@threeblindmicebrewery.com**

Award-winning 16-barrel brewery, established in 2014. The name comes from the three owners/brewers, who reckoned they didn't have a clue what they were doing when they first started brewing. Beer is supplied regularly to the Drayman's Son micropub, Ely, plus other outlets in Ely, Cambridgeshire and further afield. Beers are also supplied canned to outlets. ◆

Lonely Snake (ABV 3.5%) GOLD
Gold session ale with a fruity aroma, a sustained sweet fruitiness and a short-lived gentle balance of hops and malt.

Old Brown Mouse (ABV 4.2%) BITTER
A ruby brown beer with light fruity malt aromas, a sweetish malty palate and a light malt finish.

Juice Rocket (ABV 4.5%) PALE
Hazy pale ale with citrus hop aroma supported by sweet malt in the mouth. Sweet fruity finish with mellow hop.

Milk Worm (ABV 5.3%) PORTER

Rocket Nun (ABV 5.5%) IPA

Three Brothers SIBA

Unit 4, Clayton Court, Bowesfield Crescent, Stockton-on-Tees, TS18 3QX
☎ (01642) 678084 ⊕ threebrothersbrewing.co.uk

The vision of Kit Dodd, after brewing for five years with another local brewery. Working with his brother David and brother-in-law Chris, the brewery was established in 2016. It is situated on an industrial estate within the southern outskirts of Stockton-On-Tees. With backgrounds in chemical and mechanical engineering, the family use these skills to create their own recipes and ensure quality is maintained at the highest level. Beers are traditional with some American-inspired beers.
‼ ▰ ◆ LIVE V ⌀

The Bitter Ex (ABV 3.7%) BITTER

Trilogy (ABV 3.9%) BLOND
Pale hoppy citrus-flavoured blond with a bitter aftertaste.

Northern Pale Ale (ABV 4%) PALE

Au (ABV 4.2%) PALE

Session IPA (ABV 4.5%) PALE

Ruby Revolution (ABV 4.6%) RED

S'more Porter (ABV 4.8%) SPECIALITY

Three Daggers SIBA

47 Westbury Road, Edington, Westbury, Wiltshire, BA13 4PG
☎ (01380) 830940 ⊕ threedaggersbrewery.com

⊠ The brewery consists of a 2.5-barrel plant in a building used as a farm shop beside the Three Daggers pub. The brewing area can be viewed from outside and from the shop. Beer is supplied to the pub, the shop and the local free trade. ‼ ◆

Daggers Ale (ABV 4.1%) BITTER

Daggers Edge (ABV 4.7%) BITTER

Three Fiends

Brookfield Farm, 148 Mill Moor Road, Meltham, Holmfirth, West Yorkshire, HD9 5LN ☎ 07810 370430
⊕ threefiends.co.uk

The brewery was set up by three friends in 2015 and is based in one of the outbuildings at Brookfield Farm. The original two-barrel kit was upgraded to an eight-barrel plant in 2019. Beers are available around Huddersfield, and at CAMRA beer festivals. The Fourth Fiend, Meltham, is the brewery tap.

Stelfox (ABV 4%) IPA

Bad Uncle Barry (ABV 4.2%) PALE

Bandito (ABV 4.5%) PALE

Fudge Unit (ABV 4.8%) STOUT

Super Sharp Shooter (ABV 5.2%) IPA

Dark Side (ABV 5.3%) PALE

Punch Drunk (ABV 5.5%) PALE

Voodoo (ABV 6%) SPECIALITY

Panic Attack Espresso Stout (ABV 6.8%) SPECIALITY

Stelfoxed (ABV 7.5%) IPA

Three Hills

3 & 5 Cosy Nook, Thrapston, Northamptonshire, NN14 4PS ☎ 07400 706884

Office: 4 Thrapston Road, Woodford, Northamptonshire, NN14 4HY
⊕ threehillsbrewing.com

Named after the ancient communal tombs on the outskirts of the village of Woodford, Three Hills is a small-batch brewery established in 2016. Initially bottle, can and KeyKeg, it now produces occasional cask beers. It purchased the Affinity brewery site and kit in 2020 and brewed in London under the Outpost name in Bermondsey. Production is now in Cosy Nook, Thrapston. In late 2022, Three Hills opened The Way Station Taproom in the warehouse adjacent to the production site in Thrapston. ◆

Three Hounds

Office: Three Hounds, 57 Beckenham Road, Beckenham, BR3 4PR
☎ (020) 3976 0028 ⊕ threehoundsbeerco.com

The long term ambition to open a brewery (either onsite or elsewhere) is still being worked on. Until then, the staff from the Three Hounds Beer Café & Bottle Shop help to brew their own beers at Drop Project. Available in the bottle shop (in cask and keg), including the Brewhouse Experiments range. ◆

Three Kings SIBA

14 Prospect Terrace, North Shields, NE30 1DX
☎ 07580 004565 ✉ ewan@threekingsbrewery.co.uk

Three Kings started in 2012 using a 2.5-barrel plant, and have steadily upgraded it to its current 25-barrel capacity. Two house beers are brewed for local pubs. As well as the regular beers it typically brews two one-off beers each month. ◆

Shieldsman (ABV 3.8%) BITTER

Billy Mill Ale (ABV 4%) BITTER

Dark Side of the Toon (ABV 4.1%) STOUT
Dark roast malts and a sweet creamy body last through to a drier finish of roast bitter.

Ring of Fire (ABV 4.5%) PALE

Silver Darling (ABV 5.6%) IPA

Three Legs

Unit 1, Burnt House Farm, Udimore Road, Broad Oak, East Sussex, TN31 6BX ☎ 07939 997622
⊕ thethreelegs.co.uk

⊠ The Three Legs was started in 2014 by two friends who met studying winemaking and viticulture at university. It has grown from a nanobrewery to a 10-barrel plant in a converted farm barn. Beers can be found in most free-houses and bottle shops across the South East as well as its brewery tap. Beers are ever changing with the majority modern, hop-forward and unfined.
‼ ▰ LIVE V ⌀

Pale (ABV 3.7%) PALE

Session IPA (ABV 4.5%) GOLD

Three Peaks

Kelbrook, Lancashire ☎ 07790 539867
⊕ threepeaksbrewery.co.uk

⊛Named after the three Yorkshire Dales mountains and established in 2006, owners Chris and Jennifer Holt moved the five-barrel plant to new modern premises while retaining the services of previous owner/brewer, Colin Ashwell. Its philosophy is to produce quality ales using premium ingredients to celebrate the great outdoors. Beers are currently supplied to outlets in the Dales, West Yorkshire and East Lancashire. ‼◆V

Fell Walker (ABV 3.6%) PALE
Pen-y-Ghent Bitter (ABV 3.8%) BITTER
This malty mid-brown session bitter is balanced by fruit in the aroma and taste. The finish is malty and hoppy.
Ingleborough Gold (ABV 4%) GOLD
Whernside Pale Ale (ABV 4.2%) PALE
Blea Moor Porter (ABV 4.5%) PORTER
Plum Porter (ABV 4.5%) SPECIALITY
Malham Tarn Stout (ABV 5%) STOUT

Three Tuns SIBA

▤ Salop Street, Bishop's Castle, Shropshire, SY9 5BN
☎ (01588) 638392 ☎ 07973 301099

Office: 16 Market Square, Bishops Castle, SY9 5BW
⊕ threetunsbrewery.co.uk

Brewing on this site started in the 16th century and was licensed in 1642. A small-scale tower brewery from the late 19th century survives. Three Tuns was one of only four pub breweries still running in the 1970s. Today its beers can be found throughout the Midlands at selected free houses. ‼▛◆LIVE

Thurstons

The Courtyard, 102c High Street, Horsell, Surrey, GU21 4ST
☎ (01483) 729555 ☎ 07789 936784
⊕ thurstonsbrewery.co.uk

⊗ Originally based in the Crown, Horsell, Thurstons moved next door in 2014 when the brewery upgraded to a 4.5-barrel plant. The brewery supplies pubs across Surrey. ◆LIVE V

Small IPA (ABV 3%) PALE
Horsell Best (ABV 3.8%) BITTER
Traditional, well-balanced bitter, initially malty with strong caramel and redcurrant flavours throughout and balancing bitterness, becoming drier in finish.
Horsell Gold (ABV 3.8%) PALE
Light fruit and slightly nutty aroma, lead to some bitterness and malt, which soon fades into a light bitter finish.
Milk Stout (ABV 4.5%) STOUT
Smooth, sweet stout, with chocolatey and sweet malt flavour. Pleasant sharpness as lactose comes through leading to slightly dry finish.
Un-American Pale Ale (ABV 4.6%) PALE
Well-hopped, American-style pale using English grown hops. Grapefruit and pineapple grow into full-bodied sweetness and lingering bitterness.

Thwaites IFBB

Myerscough Road, Mellor Brook, Lancashire, BB2 7LB
☎ (01254) 686868 ⊕ thwaites.co.uk

⊛Founded in 1807, Thwaites moved from Blackburn to a rural site in the Ribble Valley in 2018. Brewing is exclusively for the company's 210 tenanted pubs, 13 managed Inns of Character, eight hotels and two lodges. Annual cask output includes 10 seasonals and six small batch brews which range from mild to stronger, specialist beers. ◆

Original (ABV 3.6%) BITTER
TBC (Thwaites Best Cask) (ABV 3.8%) BITTER
IPA (ABV 4%) PALE
Gold (ABV 4.1%) GOLD
A golden beer with citrus and mango aromas, well-balanced citrus flavours, hop bitterness on tasting and a bitter hop finish.
Amber (ABV 4.4%) BITTER

Tigertops SIBA

22 Oakes Street, Flanshaw, Wakefield, West Yorkshire, WF2 9LN
☎ (01229) 716238 ☎ 07951 812986
✉ tigertopsbrewery@hotmail.com

⊛Tigertops was established in 1995 by Stuart Johnson and his wife Lynda who, as well as owning the brewery, ran the Foxfield brewpub in Cumbria (qv). After retiring, the brewery is now run on their behalf by Barry Smith, supplying five regular outlets. ◆

Cass 2CV (ABV 4.6%) BITTER

Tiley's

▤ Salutation Inn, Ham, Gloucestershire, GL13 9QH
☎ (01453) 810284 ⊕ sallyatham.com

⊗ This 2.5-barrel microbrewery was established in an outbuilding of the award-winning Salutation Inn in 2015. It concentrates on producing small batches of beer, predominantly in cask, some in KeyKeg. Some of the brewery's output is sold onsite at the Salutation Inn. The rest goes to more than 25 selected local pubs.

Ordinary Bitter (ABV 3.8%) BITTER
Ordinary Pale (ABV 3.8%) PALE
Special Bitter (ABV 4.3%) BITTER
Special Pale (ABV 4.5%) PALE
ESB (ABV 5.2%) BITTER
IPA (ABV 6.5%) IPA

Tilford

Duke of Cambridge, Tilford Road, Farnham, Surrey, GU10 2DD ☎ 07710 500967
✉ mark@tilfordbrewery.beer

⊗ Tilford Brewery has been brewing for eight years. Using a 2.5-barrel plant situated in an old coaching house adjacent to the Duke of Cambridge Pub, it supplies its award-winning cask ales to pubs and clubs in Surrey, Sussex and Hampshire plus beer festivals. ‼▛◆

Punchbowl (ABV 3.7%) BITTER
Hankley Gold (ABV 3.9%) BLOND
Rushmoor Ripper (ABV 4.4%) BITTER
IPA (ABV 4.6%) PALE

Tillingbourne

Old Scotland Farm, Staple Lane, Shere, Surrey, GU5 9TE
☎ (01483) 222228 ⊕ tillybeer.co.uk

⊗ Tillingbourne was established in 2011 on a farm site previously used by Surrey Hills Brewery using its old 17-barrel plant. Around 25 local outlets are supplied. ‼▛◆

The Source (ABV 3.3%) GOLD
Light and crisp golden ale with strong grapefruit flavours. Packed full of Citra hops and drinking well above its strength.
Black Troll (ABV 3.7%) PALE
A black IPA in which initial roast notes are eventually overpowered by citrus hop through to the finish.
Dormouse (ABV 3.8%) BITTER

Predominately sweet & malty, with strong toffee notes and a short, fruity finish.

AONB (ABV 4%) GOLD
Golden ale in which Cascade hop dominates throughout. Some balancing malt in the aroma and taste.

Falls Gold (ABV 4.2%) GOLD
Whilst hops dominate, balancing malt is evident throughout. Hints of grapefruit in aroma and taste lead to a dry finish.

Whakahari (ABV 4.6%) PALE
Hop Troll (ABV 4.8%) PALE
Big hop flavours together with peach and apricot. Sweet, fruity taste leads to a floral bitter finish.

Summit (ABV 6%) IPA

Tilt & Pour SIBA

Belfast ⊕ tiltnpour.com

After ten years informing and promoting the Northern Ireland beer scene, Tilt & Pour has collaborated with Heaney Farmhouse Brewery to produce its own canned beer.

Time & Tide

Statenborough Farm, Felderland Lane, Eastry, Deal, CT14 0BX ☎ 07739 868256
⊕ timeandtidebrewing.co.uk

Time & Tide Brewery was founded in 2013 and is based on Statenborough Farm just outside Deal. Specialising in hoppy IPAs, it has a core range of five beers, with regular new releases. The taproom is open from Easter to December, with draught and small pack options, including guest beers. It also has a summer pop up bar at Macknade's Food Village in Faversham. ⌚♦LIVE V♦

Tin Head

Unit 22F, Bradley Fold Trading Estate, Radcliffe Moor Road, Radcliffe, Bolton, BL2 6RT ☎ 07980 262766
⊕ tinheadbrewery.co.uk

⊕Established in 2017, run by a father and son who are passionate about beers. Popular with locals, the 60-seater taproom is dog-friendly, and the rear section offers music from solo artists. Generally eight craft keg beers are dispensed on font taps at the bar, together with gins. Beers are brewed as per real ale but dispensed as chilled keg type. ⚑♦

Tindall

Toad Lane, Seething, Norfolk, NR35 2EQ ☎ 07703 379116 ⊕ tindallbrewery.com

⊠ Tindall Ales began brewing in 1998. It was originally based in Ditchingham but moved to its current location in 2001. Mike is passionate about brewing a new generation of cask beer using the finest local ingredients, whenever possible, and live yeast. ⚑⌚♦LIVE V

Best Bitter (ABV 3.7%) BITTER
Mild (ABV 3.7%) MILD
Soft malty, dark fruit bouquet. Balanced, with fig roll, roast and a crisp, bitterness leading to a strong savoury finish.

Liberator (ABV 3.8%) PALE
Golden-hued with a grapefruit and lemon hoppiness that floats over a subtle maltiness. A bittersweet finish with citrus notes.

Galaxy Dream (ABV 4%) BLOND
Seething Pint (ABV 4.3%) BITTER
Caramel Stout (ABV 4.5%) STOUT

Full on roast coffee and vanilla with caramel. Crisp, well-defined taste with toffee adding complexity. Long finish becomes dryer.

Tingay

See Poole Hill

Tintagel SIBA

Condolden Farm, Tintagel, Cornwall, PL34 0HJ ☎ (01840) 213371 ⊕ tintagelbrewery.co.uk

⊠ Established in 2009 in a redundant milking parlour on the highest farm in Cornwall using a 7.5-barrel plant and water from its own spring. A new purpose-built brewery, shop, restaurant and visitor centre opened in 2017. The brewery is powered by a wind turbine and uses only wet yeast and English malt and hops. ⚑⌚♦

Castle Gold (ABV 3.8%) PALE
Refreshing pale ale with malt aroma. Citrus hop, tropical fruits, cherries, sweet malt and dry, bitter flavour. Hop bitter finish.

Cornwall's Pride (ABV 4%) BROWN
Pale brown bitter with malt aroma. Sweet, grainy malt with toffee and summer fruits. Late dried fruit and coffee hints.

Sir Lancelot (ABV 4.2%) PALE
Gold pale ale. Bitter, grassy hops dominate the taste with citrus and tropical fruit mixture. Light biscuit malt. Lingering grapefruit finish.

Arthur's Ale (ABV 4.4%) BITTER
Light brown, complex beer with balance of sweet toffee, malt and bitter, earthy hops. Hints of honey and vine fruits.

Pendragon (ABV 4.5%) PALE
Golden beer with citrus hop nose. Refreshing, strong grapefruit citrus and pine hop bitterness. Hints of toffee, honey and malt.

Harbour Special (ABV 4.8%) OLD
Tawny old ale with ripe fruity, malty aroma. Rich nutty malt, stone fruits and esters taste, finishing bitter and malty.

Merlins Muddle (ABV 5.2%) BITTER
Auburn, creamy premium bitter. Spicy hop bitterness balanced by bread malt flavours and a mixture of marmalade and summer fruits.

Caliburn (ABV 5.8%) OLD
Dark old ale. Smoky, roast malt and Christmas pudding fruits with rich and complex flavours including treacle and earthy hops.

Tinworks SIBA

Unit 20.1, Trostre Industrial Park, Llanelli, SA14 9UU ☎ 07595 841958 ⊕ tinworksbrewery.co.uk

Brewery commenced operations on a rural farm but relocated and upgraded to a 10-barrel kit in 2019. Cask, bottle and keg beers are produced. ⚑♦

Cwrw Grav (ABV 3.9%) BITTER
Old Castle Pale (ABV 4.6%) PALE
Marshfield Red (ABV 4.7%) RED
Ashburnham Porter (ABV 5%) PORTER
Dafen IPA (ABV 6.3%) IPA

Tiny Rebel

Wern Industrial Estate, Rogerstone, Newport, NP10 9FQ

Office: Sunnybank, St Brides, Wentlooge, Newport, NP10 8SQ ⊕ tinyrebel.co.uk

⊙Tiny Rebel is one of the leading craft breweries in the UK. Founded in Newport, Wales in 2012, by brothers-in-law Brad and Gazz. Beers vary from one-offs to seasonals to supplement the more established range. There is an increasing incidence of unfined beers. ‼🍺♦⬧

Peloton Pale (ABV 4.2%) PALE
Cwtch (ABV 4.6%) RED

Tiny Vessel

Unit 505, Platts Eyot, Hampton, TW12 2HF ☎ 07888 730210 ⊕ tinyvessel.co.uk

⊠ Tiny Vessel is a 1.5-barrel brewery established in 2016 on Platts Eyot, an island on the River Thames near Hampton. All beers are unfiltered and unfined, mostly available bottled or in keg. At least one beer is usually available in bottle and keg (and sometimes in cask) in the Northumberland Arms, Brentford. LIVE

Tipple's

Unit 3, The Mill, Wood Green, Salhouse, Norfolk, NR13 6NY
☎ (01603) 721310 ⊕ tipplesbrewery.com

⊠ Tipple's was established in 2004 on a six-barrel brew plant. In addition to a full range of cask ales, an extensive range of bottled beers is produced, which can be found in some farmers markets and supermarkets in Norfolk. Bottled beers can now be ordered direct from the brewery for delivery or collection. 🍺♦LIVE

Bowline (ABV 3.8%) BITTER
Malten Copper (ABV 4.4%) BITTER
Moonrocket (ABV 5%) BITTER
A complex golden brew. Malt, hop bitterness and a fruity sweetness swirl around in an ever-changing kaleidoscope of flavours.

Tirril SIBA

Red House, Long Marton, Cumbria, CA16 6BN
☎ (01768) 361846 ⊕ tirrilbrewery.uk

⊙Established in 1999, Tirril Brewery has twice outgrown its premises. It delivers to more than 170 outlets, 100 of which regularly stock the beer. Contract brewing is also carried out for Bitter End Brewery. ‼♦GF

Grasmere IPA (ABV 3.6%) PALE
Ullswater Blonde (ABV 3.8%) BLOND
Grasmere Gold (ABV 3.9%) PALE
Kirkstone Gold (ABV 3.9%) GOLD
Old Faithful (ABV 4%) BITTER
Initially bitter, gold-coloured ale with an astringent finish.
1823 (ABV 4.1%) BROWN
Borrowdale Bitter (ABV 4.2%) BITTER
Castlerigg Blonde (ABV 4.2%) BLOND
Hardknott Ale (ABV 4.2%) BITTER
Red Barn Ale (ABV 4.4%) RED
Dungeon Ghyll Stout (ABV 5%) SPECIALITY

Titanic SIBA

Callender Place, Burslem, Stoke-on-Trent, Staffordshire, ST6 1JL
☎ (01782) 823447 ⊕ titanicbrewery.co.uk

⊙One of the earliest microbreweries, founded in 1985. Now owned by two local beer loving brothers, it has grown from a small, seven-barrel brewery, to producing over four million pints of its award-winning ales per year. With an expanding fleet of tied pubs and the Bod chain of café bars, it also supplies free trade customers in the Midlands, North West and further afield. Captain Smith,

captain of the Titanic was born in Stoke on Trent, hence the name. ‼♦LIVE

Classic Mild (ABV 3.5%) MILD
Fresh, fruity hop aroma leads to a caramel start then a rush of bitter hoppiness ending with a lingering dry finish.
First Class (ABV 3.8%) BITTER
Steerage (ABV 3.8%) BITTER
Pale yellow bitter. Flavours start with hops and fruit but become zesty and refreshing in this light session beer with a long, dry finish.
Lifeboat (ABV 4%) BITTER
Dark brown with fruit, malt and caramel aromas. Sweet start, malty and caramel middle with hoppiness developing into a fruity and dry, lingering finish.
Anchor Bitter (ABV 4.1%) BITTER
Amber beer with a spicy hint to the fruity start that says go to the rush of hops for the dry bitter finish.
Black Ice (ABV 4.1%) PALE
Iceberg (ABV 4.1%) SPECIALITY
Yellow gold sparkling wheat beer with a flowery start leading to a great hop crescendo.
Cappuccino Stout (ABV 4.5%) SPECIALITY
Black with a vanilla and strong coffee nose leading to a sweet taste again with strong coffee. Aftertaste is sweet.
Chocolate and Vanilla Stout (ABV 4.5%) SPECIALITY
Chocoholic paradise with real chocolate and vanilla support. Cocoa, sherry and almonds lend depth to this creamy, drinkable "Heaven in a glass" stout.
Stout (ABV 4.5%) STOUT
Roasty, toasty with tobacco, autumn bonfires, chocolate and hints of liquorice; perfectly balanced with a bitter, dry finish reminiscent of real coffee.
White Star (ABV 4.5%) BITTER
Hints of cinnamon apple pie are found before the hops take over to give a bitter edge to this well-balanced, refreshing, fruity beer.
Raspberry Pale (ABV 4.7%) SPECIALITY
Cherry Porter (ABV 4.9%) SPECIALITY
Last Porter Call (ABV 4.9%) PORTER
Plum Porter (ABV 4.9%) SPECIALITY
Dark brown with a powerful fruity aroma. A sweet plum fruitiness gives way to a gentle bitter finish.
Captain Smith's Strong Ale (ABV 5.2%) BITTER
Red brown and full-bodied, lots of malt and roast with a hint of honey but a strong bittersweet finish.

Titsey SIBA

Clarks Lane Farm, Tatsfield, Surrey, TN16 2JU
☎ (01959) 528535 ⊕ titseybrewingco.com

⊠ A microbrewery established in 2017 on the Titsey Estate, after which some of the beers are named. In 2023, it moved to larger premises on the outskirts of Tatsfield but still within the Titsey Estate. The new premises has allowed the brewing plant to be doubled in size and a taproom to be opened onsite. In addition a borehole has been sunk. It supplies the associated Botley Hill Farmhouse and increasingly other local outlets. Innes Lager and all the bottles are suitable for vegans. ♦LIVE V⬧

Gresham Hopper (ABV 3.7%) GOLD
Leveson Buck (ABV 3.7%) PALE
Gower Wolf (ABV 4%) BITTER

Toast

Ground Floor, Unity Place, 200 Grafton Gate East, Milton Keynes, Buckinghamshire, MK9 1UP

Office: 7-19 Triton Street, London, NW1 3BF

Established in 2015 and moved to new premises in 2024, this three-barrel brewery uses surplus bread to brew beer. Some of the output is also contract brewed at Curious Brewery (qv) in Ashford, Kent. No real ale.

Toll End

■ c/o Waggon and Horses, 131 Toll End Road, Tipton, West Midlands, DY4 0ET
☎ (0121) 502 6453 ☎ 07903 725574

The four-barrel brewery opened in 2004. With the exception of Phoebe's Ale, named after the brewer's daughter, all brews commemorate local landmarks, events and people. Nearly all of the brewery's output is sold in the Waggon & Horses. !! LIVE

Tollgate SIBA

Unit 1, Southwood House Farm, Staunton Lane, Calke, Derbyshire, LE65 1RG
☎ (01283) 229194 ⊕ tollgatebrewery.co.uk

⊗ This six-barrel brewery was founded in 2005 on the site of the former Brunt & Bucknall Brewery in nearby Woodville, but relocated to new premises on the National Trust's Calke Abbey Estate in 2012. Around 20 outlets are supplied direct, mainly in the North Midlands, with most cask production directed to the brewery's three micropubs: Queens Road Tap, Leicester, Tap at No.76, Ashby-de-la-Zouch, and Town Street Tap, Duffield, plus the onsite tap, the Milking Parlour. !! ☒ ♦ LIVE V ♦

Hackney Blonde (ABV 3.9%) SPECIALITY
Duffield Amber (ABV 4.4%) BITTER
Ashby Pale (ABV 4.5%) PALE
Old Rasputin (ABV 4.5%) STOUT
Red Star IPA (ABV 4.5%) PALE
Billy's Best Bitter (ABV 4.6%) BITTER
Super QSB (ABV 5.6%) IPA

Tolly Cobbold

See Greene King

Tom's Tap

4-6 Thomas Street, Crewe, Cheshire, CW1 2BD
☎ 07931 573425
⊕ tomstapandbrewhouse.wordpress.com

Tom's Tap & Brewhouse consists of three units; brewery equipment in the first, live music and special events in the middle (including meet the brewer events), and a taproom in the third (open to the public Thu-Sun). Tom's Tap cask ale is now delivered to many outlets far and wide, not just locally, but it is still mostly keg only in its own outlet, although one changing cask ale per week is occasionally brewed for consumption on the premises. !! ♦

Tombstone

■ 6 George Street, Great Yarmouth, Norfolk, NR30 1HR ☎ 07584 504444
⊕ tombstonebrewery.co.uk

⊗ Established in 2013, the brewery is run by former homebrewer Paul Hodgson. The original brewery backed onto the town cemetery, inspiring the name, but it has now relocated to the rear of its brewery tap, the Tombstone Saloon. Around 30 outlets are supplied around Norwich. ☒ ♦ V

Ale (ABV 3.7%) GOLD
Banana toffee aroma. Piquant, bitter, hoppy beginning softened by a biscuity maltiness. Dry, bitter finish.
Amarillo (ABV 3.8%) BITTER
Arizona (ABV 3.9%) BITTER

Malt and lemon nose. Initial lemongrass and sweet biscuit beginning quickly fades. Sweet watery finish enhanced by malt.
Texas Jack (ABV 4%) BROWN
Toffee apple and vanilla aroma. Caramel leads the smooth complex mix of flavours. A bittersweet fruitiness continues to the end.
Regulators (ABV 4.1%) GOLD
Gunslinger (ABV 4.3%) BITTER
Lone Rider (ABV 4.3%) OLD
Stagecoach (ABV 4.4%) OLD
A rich caramel and treacle aroma. Malt, roast and caramel dominate a hoppy bittersweet foundation. Short, increasingly dry finish.
Cherokee (ABV 4.5%) BITTER
Malty nose with plum and cherry. Initial mix of biscuit and roasty bitterness gently changes to a slightly spicy maltiness.
Santa Fe (ABV 5%) BITTER
Big Nose Kate (ABV 5.2%) BITTER
6 Shooter (ABV 6.6%) IPA

Tomos & Lilford SIBA

Unit 11b, Vale Business Park, Llandow, Cowbridge, CF71 7PF
☎ (01446) 677757 ☎ 07747 858514

Office: 117 Boverton Road, Llantwit Major, CF61 1YA
✉ info@tomosandlilford.com

⊗ Tomos & Lilford was launched in 2013 by homebrewers Rolant Tomos, and brothers Rob and James Lilford. The brewery supplies pubs and clubs across the Vale of Glamorgan and further afield. ☒ ♦ LIVE GF

Summerhouse (ABV 3.6%) GOLD
High Brown Fritillary (ABV 3.9%) BROWN
Gwenith Du (ABV 4%) SPECIALITY
Nash Point (ABV 4%) BITTER
An amber gold-coloured beer with gentle malt aromas in the initial taste. The flavour develops giving a hoppy bitterness with hints of lime leading to astringency in the aftertaste.
Grizzled Skipper (ABV 4.2%) PALE
Vale Pale Ale (ABV 4.3%) PALE
Life's a Peach (ABV 4.5%) SPECIALITY
Tropic of Jones (ABV 4.5%) GOLD
Southerndown Gold (ABV 4.6%) GOLD
Big Boot (ABV 4.8%) BROWN
Irreverent James (ABV 4.8%) BITTER
Lemon Soul (ABV 5%) BLOND

Tonbridge SIBA

Unit 19, Branbridges Industrial Estate, East Peckham, Kent, TN12 5HF
☎ (01622) 871239 ⊕ tonbridgebrewery.co.uk

⊗ Tonbridge Brewery was launched in 2010 using a four-barrel plant, expanding to a 12-barrel. Spring 2023 it expanded again with a new 20-barrel plant and additional warehousing. It supplies pubs, clubs, restaurants and shops throughout Kent, East Sussex, and South East London, with a large range of beers (all gluten-free and vegan). The same strain of live yeast has always been used (originated from the Barclay Perkins Brewery in Southwark). It has also started canning, expanding its keg range. GF V

Golden Rule (ABV 3.5%) GOLD
Traditional Ale (ABV 3.6%) BITTER
Coppernob (ABV 3.8%) BITTER
Countryman (ABV 4%) BITTER
Rustic (ABV 4%) MILD
Blonde Ambition (ABV 4.2%) BLOND

Old Chestnut (ABV 4.4%) BITTER
American Pale (ABV 5%) PALE
Velvet Raven (ABV 5.2%) STOUT

Toolmakers SIBA

6-8 Botsford Street, Sheffield, South Yorkshire, S3 9PF
☎ 07956 235332 ⊕ toolmakersbrewery.com

Toolmakers is a family-run brewery established in 2013 in an old tool-making factory, with the names of the beers reflecting this history. The regular brews are supplemented by a varying range of different styles and strengths and are available in the adjoining Forest pub, which is owned. The function room at the brewery also doubles as the brewery taproom. !! ✦

Lynch Pin (ABV 4%) BITTER
Razmataz (ABV 4.2%) BLOND
Flange Noir (ABV 5.2%) STOUT

Tooth & Claw

See Camerons

Top-Notch

Office: 60 Wickham Way, Haywards Heath, West Sussex, RH16 1UQ ☎ 07963 829368
✉ topnotchbrewing@hotmail.com

A one-barrel brewery situated in a converted residential outbuilding in Haywards Heath. Beer styles change with each brew. LIVE

Top Rope SIBA

Unit 6, Lipton Close, Bootle, Liverpool, L20 8PU
⊕ topropebrewing.com

☺Top Rope commenced brewing on a small scale in Merseyside in 2016. It expanded in 2018, moving to Sandycroft Industrial Estate, Deeside, North Wales. Further expansion in 2021 led to a return to its current location in Bootle, Liverpool, which coincided with the opening of its taproom. Output is mainly keg, but the supply ratio is approximately 45% cask beers, which are often named on a wrestling theme. It was saved from closure in mid-2024 due to a partnership with Legends Whiskey. !! ☷ V ✦

Topsham

The Warehouse, Haven Road, Exeter, Devon, EX2 8GR
☎ 07735 591557

The brewery was established in 2018 and moved to its current location at the popular Exeter Quay in 2019. A new 1,200-litre plant was commissioned in early 2023. The taproom, with an outside drinking area, is next to the brewery, which is visible from the bar. There are frequent one-off brews, normally available as keg, with some appearing as cask along with the regular and seasonal beers at the brewery tap. ✦ ✦

Serenity (ABV 3.8%) BLOND
Ask Your Dad (ABV 4.3%) BITTER
Goat Walk (ABV 4.6%) PALE

Torrside

New Mills Marina, Hibbert Street, New Mills, Derbyshire, SK22 3JJ
☎ (01663) 745219 ☎ 07539 149175
⊕ torrside.co.uk

☺Established in 2015, Torrside brews a wide range on a 10-barrel plant, under the tagline Hops, Smoke,

Monsters. A changing line-up of largely hop-driven, smoked and strong, all unfined, beers are sold within a 50-mile radius. Brewery tap events usually take place at least one weekend each month (Mar-Sep). A smoked beer festival is held in September. The brewery runs the Beer Shed pub, New Mills (not as a tap). Torr Vale Tap, permanently serves five Torrside beers (KeyKeg). !! ☷ LIVE V

Candlewick (ABV 4%) STOUT
Yellow Peak (ABV 4.2%) PALE
Franconia (ABV 5.2%) SPECIALITY
I'm Spartacus (ABV 6.8%) IPA

Totnes

🖪 **The Barrel House, 59a High Street, Totnes, Devon, TQ9 5PB** ☎ 07974 828971 ⊕ barrelhousetotnes.co.uk

⊗ The Barrel House, home to Totnes Brewery since 2014, is a family-run brewpub, brewing for consumption on the premises only. Brewing takes place on a 300-litre kit, positioned behind the bar. Output has increased to six beers permanently on tap at the bar. ✦ V ✦

Towcester Mill SIBA

The Mill, Chantry Lane, Towcester, Northamptonshire, NN12 6AD
☎ (01327) 437060 ⊕ towcestermillbrewery.co.uk

⊗ A five-barrel brewery situated at the Grade-II listed Old Mill in Towcester. There is a brewery tap and beer garden onsite together with off-sale facilities. !! ☷ ✦ V ✦

Crooked Hooker (ABV 3.8%) BITTER
Golden/amber in colour with a honeyed fruit aroma, a slightly earthy taste with some fruit and a bitter finish.
Mill Race (ABV 3.9%) BLOND
Slightly citrus aroma followed by a dry citrus taste with hints of grapefruit and a long bitter aftertaste.
Bell Ringer (ABV 4.4%) PALE
Sweetish malty aroma followed by a bitter flavour with zesty orange marmalade notes and an earth and spicy aftertaste.
Steam Ale (ABV 4.5%) BITTER
Sweetish aroma with fruit and citrus, complex, well-balanced flavours with passionfruit and citrus notes persisting in the lingering aftertaste.
Black Fire (ABV 5.2%) STOUT
Treacle and vanilla aftertaste with roast malt notes, a dry bitter dark chocolate flavour and a dark prune aftertaste.
Roman Road (ABV 5.2%) PALE
Tropical fruit aroma followed by a good balance of malt and hops with pineapple notes and a long bitter aftertaste.

Tower

Old Water Tower, Walsitch Maltings, Glensyl Way, Burton upon Trent, Staffordshire, DE14 1PZ
☎ (01283) 562888 ☎ 07771 926323
⊕ towerbrewery.co.uk

☺Tower was established in 2001 by John Mills in a converted derelict water tower, originally built for Thomas Salt's Brewery in the 1870s. The conversion was given a Burton Civic Society award for the restoration of an industrial building. The premises incorporate a public bar, open Friday evenings only, plus an outside bar on a patio in summer. Tower has around 20 regular outlets. !! ☷ ✦ ✦

Bitter (ABV 4.2%) BITTER
Gold-coloured with a malty, caramel and hoppy aroma. A full hop and fruit taste with the fruit lingering. A bitter and astringent finish.
Gone for a Burton (ABV 4.6%) BITTER

Imperial IPA (ABV 5%) PALE

Townes

🍺 **Speedwell Inn, Lowgates, Staveley, Chesterfield, Derbyshire, S43 3TT**
☎ (01246) 472252

Townes Brewery was started by Alan Wood in 1994 at an old ice cream factory and moved to its present site, the Speedwell Inn at Staveley, in 1997. The brewery and pub were taken over by Lawrie and Nicoleta Evans on Alan's retirement in 2013. They continue to use Alan's recipes at the five-barrel brewery. Townes beers are rarely found outside the pub, other than occasional swaps and at beer festivals.

Townhouse

35 Chapel Street, Dalton-in-Furness, Cumbria, LA15 8BY ☎ 07812 035143

Office: 52 Steel Street, Askam-in-Furness, LA16 7BP
✉ townhousebrewery@gmail.com

☺Townhouse was setup in 2002 in Audley, Staffordshire with a 2.5-barrel plant that expanded to five barrels in 2004. In 2006 two further fermenting vessels were added producing the bulk of its beer for the Potteries. In 2021 the brewery relocated to Dalton-in-Furness, Cumbria. All cask beers have been vegan since 2005. Canning is planned. V

Meg's Mild (ABV 3.9%) MILD
Flowerdew (ABV 4%) PALE
Floral aroma and flowery hop taste delivering a crisp hoppy bite and a lingering taste of flowery citrus hops.
Barney's Stout (ABV 4.5%) STOUT
Furness IPA (ABV 4.9%) PALE

TQ Beerworks SIBA

Unit 6, Kingswood Court, Long Meadow, South Brent, Devon, TQ10 9YS ⊕ tqbeerworks.com

TQ is a small, family-run brewery dedicated to bringing craft beer to Torbay and the surrounding area. It produced 29 different keg beers in 2022. It does not have a core range. All beers are unfined, unfiltered and vegan-friendly. LIVE V♦

Track SIBA

Units 17 & 18, Piccadilly Trading Estate, Manchester, M1 2ND
☎ (0161) 536 3975 ⊕ trackbrewing.co

☺Track Brewing Co was established in 2014, and are based in the Piccadilly Trading Estate close to Piccadilly Station. It produces a wide range of beer styles, as well a growing barrel-ageing program. There is an onsite taproom with a beer garden and it has started to give tours. ‼♦V♦

Sonoma (ABV 3.8%) GOLD
An unfined, well-balanced sweet, fruity beer with moderate bitterness and plenty of citrus hops.

Tractor Shed SIBA

The Tractor Shed, Calva Brow, Workington, Cumbria, CA14 1DB
☎ (01900) 68860 ⊕ tractor-shed.co.uk

☺Renamed from Mitchell Krause in 2014 and having previously had its beers brewed under contract, brewing started in an old tractor shed on the family farm in 2013. After initially focusing on bottled and kegged continental-style beers, the first cask-conditioned beer

was produced in 2014. The brewery contract brews for various other brewing companies. ‼♦

Mowdy Pale Ale (ABV 3.9%) BITTER
An interesting, well-balanced beer with persistent fruitiness, sweet and hoppy centre giving way nicely to hop in the finish.
Clocker Stout (ABV 4%) STOUT
Tasty, easy-drinking start with malt and roast, a fruity centre, some hop joining in at the end.

Traquair House SIBA

Traquair House, Innerleithen, EH44 6PW
☎ (01896) 830323 ⊕ traquair.co.uk/traquair-house-brewery

The 18th century brewhouse is based in one of the wings of the 1,000-year-old Traquair House, Scotland's oldest inhabited house. All the beers are oak-fermented and 60% of production is exported. ‼🚚♦

Bear Ale (ABV 5%) BITTER
Malty aroma and a complex taste of malts, citrus fruit, sweetness and bitterness, all lasting into the aftertaste.

Treehouse

Cavendish Bridge, Shardlow, Leicestershire, DE72 2HL

Treehouse Brewery was established in 2022 and is based in Cavendish Bridge. All beers have a tree-themed name and are available at several pubs in the area.

Treen's SIBA

Unit 3, Viaduct Works, Frog Hill, Ponsanooth, Cornwall, TR3 7JW
☎ (01872) 719633 ☎ 07552 218788
⊕ treensbrewery.co.uk

⊠ This family-run brewery was founded in 2016, initially using spare capacity at another local brewery. It now has its own premises using a 12-barrel plant. Bottling was introduced in 2018. An additional 12-barrel fermentation vessel was acquired in 2021. ♦

Essential (ABV 3.8%) PALE
Bitter golden pale ale with grassy, peppery hops and biscuit malt flavours. Citrus and stone fruit notes. Long, bitter finish.
Classic (ABV 4.3%) BITTER
Tawny bitter with malt aroma. Robust malt balanced by spicy hop bitterness. Coffee, molasses with light summer and stone fruits.
Local (ABV 4.3%) PALE
Amber pale ale with malty and hoppy aroma. Balanced malt and bitter hops with stone fruit, oranges and bitter finish.
Sunbeam (ABV 4.8%) PALE
Smooth gold pale ale. Refreshing citrus, spicy, bitter hop and malt flavours with fruit and caramel hints. Long, bitter finish.
Resolve (ABV 5.2%) STOUT
Dark brown, strong, sweet stout with dark chocolate aroma. Dominant smoky coffee, bitter chocolate, molasses flavours with malt and stone fruit.

Tremethick

Grampound, Cornwall, TR2 4QY ☎ 07726 427775
⊕ tremethick.co.uk

⊠ Tremethick began brewing in 2015, and are now well established as a small, village brewery with strong community support. Bottle sales dominate but casks are supplied to a few pubs and to all-important beer festivals. Monthly brewery open evenings are popular with locals. ‼ LIVE

Gwella (ABV 3.7%) BITTER
Amber bitter with bready malt and citrus hop aroma. Assertive malt is balanced by citrus hops with candied peel fruit.

Pale Ale (ABV 4.3%) PALE
Gold pale ale with light aroma. Dominant bitter grapefruit and apples, grassy hops and underlying malt. Long, bitter, citrus finish.

Dark Ale (ABV 4.6%) MILD
Complex dark brown ale. Nutty malt with kaleidoscope of fruit flavours. Quite sweet with hints of coffee-roast. Faintly bitter and hoppy.

Red IPA (ABV 4.8%) PALE
Auburn bitter with light grapefruit and malt aroma. Grapefruit and marmalade flavours masking malt and other fruits. Long bitter, dry finish.

Trig (NEW) SIBA

Main Street, Sutton on Derwent, North Yorkshire, YO41 4BN

Family-run brewery based near York, established in 2023. It currently brews in small batches producing four core beers as well as seasonals and one-offs. Beers are available in cask, keg and can. ♦

Interloper (ABV 5%) PORTER

Tring SIBA

Dunsley Farm, London Road, Tring, Hertfordshire, HP23 6HA
☎ (01442) 890721 ⊕ tringbrewery.co.uk

Founded in 1992, Tring Brewery revived the traditional art of brewing in the market town of Tring, which had been without a brewery for more than 50 years. It moved to its present site in 2010. It brews more than 130 barrels a week, producing an extensive core range of beers augmented by monthly and seasonal specials, most taking names from local myths and legends. ‼ ⛾ ♦ LIVE V

Side Pocket for a Toad (ABV 3.6%) BITTER
Mansion Mild (ABV 3.7%) MILD
Piggeries (ABV 3.8%) BITTER
Ridgeway (ABV 4%) BITTER
Liberator (ABV 4.1%) PALE
Moongazing (ABV 4.2%) BITTER
Tea Kettle Stout (ABV 4.7%) STOUT
Colley's Dog (ABV 5.2%) BITTER
Death or Glory (ABV 7.2%) BARLEY

Trinity

Unit 4, The Shires, Essington Close, Lichfield, Staffordshire, WS14 9AZ ☎ 07886 809835
⊕ trinitybrewco.com

Set up in 2021, the name refers both to the three spires of Lichfield's Cathedral and the three owners. An eight-barrel brew kit is used, along with a pilot plant for trial brews. A wide range of styles is produced, mainly for can and keg, but cask output is growing. Barrel-aged beers are planned. There is an onsite taproom, generally open at weekends. Beers are widely available in the local free trade. ♦

Triple fff SIBA

Magpie Works, Station Approach, Four Marks, Hampshire, GU34 5HN
☎ (01420) 561422 ⊕ triplefff.com

⊠ Established in 1997 close to a stop on the Watercress Line Heritage Steam Railway, the brewery and all the beers (except Alton's Pride) are named following a musical theme. The fff refers to fortissimo, meaning louder or stronger. Brewing on a 50-barrel plant since 2006, multiple CAMRA awards have been won. Two pubs are owned: the Railway Arms, Alton, and the Artillery Arms, Southsea. ‼ ⛾ ♦ LIVE

Alton's Pride (ABV 3.8%) BITTER
Full-bodied, brown session bitter. Initial maltiness fades as some citrus notes and hoppiness take over, leading to lasting bitter finish.

Pressed Rat & Warthog (ABV 3.8%) MILD
Toffee aroma, hints of blackcurrant and chocolate lead to well-balanced flavour with roast, fruit and malt vying with hoppy bitterness.

Moondance (ABV 4.2%) PALE
An aromatic citrus hop nose, balanced by bitterness and sweetness in the mouth. Bitterness increases in finish as fruit declines.

Sundown (ABV 4.3%) GOLD
Goldfinger (ABV 5%) SPECIALITY

Triple Goat

See Hornes

Triple Point SIBA

178 Shoreham Street, Sheffield, South Yorkshire, S1 4SQ
☎ (0114) 229 4769 ☎ 07828 131423
⊕ triplepointbrewing.co.uk

A modern brewery and bar conversion, owned by a father and son. The brewery is clearly visible from the drinking area which operates as the taproom for the brewery. Convenient for Sheffield Station and Bramall Lane football ground. ‼ ♦

Gold (ABV 4%) GOLD
Cryo (ABV 4.2%) IPA
Porter (ABV 4.4%) PORTER
Debut (ABV 5.5%) IPA

Triumph

🮮 **33 Parkside, Coventry, West Midlands, CV1 2NE**
☎ 07903 131512 ✉ triumphbrewing@aol.com

Small, keg only craft brewery based at the rear of Triumph Brewhouse micropub and café, which is open every day. Beers are named after significant dates in the history of Coventry. V

True North SIBA

47 Eldon Street, Sheffield, South Yorkshire, S1 4GY
☎ (0114) 272 0569

Office: 127-129 Devonshire Street, Sheffield, S3 7SB
⊕ truenorthbrewco.uk

True North began brewing in 2012 using spare capacity at Welbeck Abbey Brewery (qv). It opened its own plant in Sheffield in 2016. Dean Hollingworth is head brewer, supplying 11 pubs owned by the company plus other independent outlets.

Best Bitter (ABV 3.8%) BITTER
Blonde (ABV 4%) GOLD
Polaris (ABV 4.3%) BITTER

True Story

7 Curtis Centre, Kingdom Avenue, Northacre Industrial Park, Westbury, BA13 4EW

☎ (01225) 800153

Office: 3 Lyme Avenue, Warminster, BA12 8LN
⊕ truestorybrewing.com

This nanobrewery commenced brewing in 2022. It aims to brew beers of exceptional quality that blur boundaries and reassess conventional techniques. It only uses the freshest hops, only the best malted grains, real fruit, time and more hops. V✦

Truman's

See Big Penny

Truth Hurts

c/o MSS, City Mills, Peel Street, Morley, Leeds, West Yorkshire, LS27 8QL ☎ 07700 153300 / 07873 556041 ⊕ truthhurts.co.uk

☺Established in 2016 as Blue Square Brewery and rebranded as Truth Hurts in 2019. It produces one-off brews from its four-barrel plant in a split-level building that is part of a mill complex. ☛✦

Tucks (NEW) SIBA

Tucks Brewery & Tap, Unit 16, Thoresby Park, Thoresby, Nottinghamshire, NG22 9EP
⊕ tucksbrewery.co.uk

Created by three friends, each with a particular set of skills, Tucks Brewery was established in 2020. Situated in the picturesque grounds of Thoresby Park, the brewery also has an onsite taproom. ✦

Tudor

Unit A, Llanhilleth Industrial Estate, Llanhilleth, NP13 2RX
☎ (01495) 214808 ☎ 07498 734896
⊕ tudorbrewery.co.uk

☺Tudor began brewing in 2007 in Abergavenny and moved to Llanilleth in 2012. Several local pubs are supplied, in addition to others further afield. There is a bar and function room in the office suite above the brewery, for which it has acquired a full license. It brews 700 litres at a time, five times a week. LIVE ✦

Blorenge (ABV 3.8%) PALE
Black Mountain Stout (ABV 4%) STOUT
IPA (ABV 4%) PALE
Skirrid (ABV 4.2%) MILD
Super Hero (ABV 4.5%) PALE
Sugarloaf (ABV 4.7%) BITTER
Black Rock (ABV 5.6%) PORTER

Turk's Head SIBA

▤ **202 High Street, Exeter, EX4 3EB**
☎ (01392) 706013

Office: City Pub Group, 2nd Floor, Essel House, London, W1W 7TH ⊕ turksheadexeter.com

A historic public house, refurbished by City Pub Group during 2020/2021, brewing a range of up to five live beers. The range is expected to increase. ‼V

Turning Point SIBA

Unit 3, Grimbald Park, Wetherby Road, Knaresborough, North Yorkshire, HG5 8LJ
☎ (01423) 869967 ⊕ turningpointbrewco.com

⊠ Two friends, Cameron Brown and Aron McMahon, began brewing in Kirkbymoorside in 2017, before relocating to the former Roosters brewery in Knaresborough in 2019. All beers are unfined and unfiltered. The Falcon, Micklegate, is the brewery tap with the Outpost, Piccadilly, York, a secondary outlet. ✦V✦

Wavelength (ABV 4.5%) PALE
Orange, mango and other tropical fruit sit over a hoppy base, bitterness coming through at the finish.
Lucid Dream (ABV 5%) SPECIALITY
Disco King (ABV 5.1%) PALE

Turnstone

The Old Post Office, Vicarage Road, Wingfield, Suffolk, IP21 5RB ☎ 07807 262662
✉ turnstoneales@outlook.com

⊠ Turnstone Ales is a small home-based brewery set up in Kent in 2014 and relocated to Suffolk in 2020. Fining or filtering are not used, and bottle-conditioned ales are available at local markets including Framlingham and Bury St Edmunds. LIVE V

Turpin

Turpins Lodge, Lodge Farm, Tadmarton Heath Road, Hook Norton, Oxfordshire, OX15 5DQ
☎ (01608) 737033 ⊕ turpinslodge.co.uk/turpin-brewery

⊠ Brewing started in 2013, with brewing capacity extended in 2019. A number of local pubs are supplied regularly, as well as a few pubs further afield in Oxford, Rugby and Birmingham. Brewing is temporarily suspended and is expected to restart soon. ✦

Twice Brewed SIBA

▤ **Twice Brewed Brewhouse, Bardon Mill, Hexham, NE47 7AN**
☎ (01434) 344534 ⊕ twicebrewed.co.uk

☺Originally set up Summer 2017, The Twice Brewed Brewery has since doubled its production capacity, with a wide variety of brewing styles. These are available from the taproom, the adjoining Twice Brewed inn, and other local pubs. ‼☛✦V✦

Best Bitter (ABV 3.8%) BITTER
Sycamore Gap (ABV 4.1%) PALE
Ale Caesar (ABV 4.4%) BITTER
Steel Rigg (ABV 4.9%) PORTER
Vindolana (ABV 5.3%) PALE

Twickenham SIBA

Unit 6, 18 Mereway Road, Twickenham, TW2 6RG
☎ (020) 8241 1825 ⊕ twickenham-fine-ales.co.uk

⊠ Established in 2004, Twickenham Fine Ales is London's oldest, independent, stand-alone brewery. Operating a 25-barrel plant, the styles are traditional with a modern twist and output is predominantly cask. It opens on match days for the rugby fans going to the nearby stadium. ‼☛✦✦

Grandstand Bitter (ABV 3.8%) BITTER
Sweet caramelised orange aromas. Flavours of apricot, toffee and hints of orange fruits. Balanced growing bittersweet, dry finish.
Red Sky (ABV 4.1%) RED
Sweet caramel, hazelnut aromas. Sweet citrus marmalade, caramel and sultana flavours. Increasing dryness and gentle peppery spiciness in the finish.
Naked Ladies (ABV 4.4%) BLOND

Fruit and biscuity malt aromas with honey sweetness throughout. Sweet grapefruit fading in the dryish finish with spicy hoppy bitterness.

Twin Taff

8 Jenkins Place, Twynrodyn, Merthyr Tydfil, CF47 0ND
☎ **07564 187945** ✉ **twintaffbrewery@outlook.com**

☺ Twin Taff was established in 2018 by twin brothers Darryl and Daniel Williams. It is Merthyr Tydfil's first town centre microbrewery. Brewing is currently suspended.

Twisted SIBA

Unit 8, Commerce Business Centre, Commerce Close, Westbury, BA13 4LS
☎ **(01373) 864441** ⊕ **twisted-brewing.com**

⊗ Twisted began brewing in 2014. It is an independent brewery producing traditional ales with a modern twist. ◆ LIVE

Heritage Mild (ABV 3.4%) SPECIALITY
Three & Sixpence (ABV 3.6%) PALE
Bittersweet citrus and tropical fruits, light malt and a hint of caramel all combine in this easy-drinking pale ale.
Rider / Three Lions (ABV 4%) BITTER
Malty biscuit and fruit aroma, impressions of mango and tangerine balance the biscuit malt flavours before a dry, bitter ending.
Pirate (ABV 4.2%) BITTER
Aroma has floral hints, flavours combine malt with some spice, ripe fruit and earthy hop bitterness, fading short aftertaste.
Urban Legend (ABV 4.3%) GOLD
Light malt background overlaid with soft citrus and tropical fruits and a dry bitterness that continues into the aftertaste.
Finnegan's No. 1 (ABV 4.4%) SPECIALITY
Distinctive aroma and flavour of coffee with dark roast malt and hop bitterness. Coffee also evident in the dry aftertaste.
Canteen Cowboy (ABV 4.5%) GOLD
Slightly sweet cocktail of malt and fresh fruit on both the nose and tongue, with bitterness increasing towards the finish.
Gaucho / Fly Half (ABV 4.6%) BITTER
A solid malty backbone supports the background hop bitterness and forest fruit flavours in this full-bodied, premium bitter.

Twisted Ankle

The Old Mill Of Kincraigie, Aboyne, AB34 4TT
☎ **07814 922442**
✉ **twistedanklebrewco@gmail.com**

Twisted Ankle is a small-batch microbrewery situated in the Howe of Cromar, Aberdeenshire, using home grown hops. Beer is available in bottles at local farmers markets in Aboyne and Ballater. It regularly produces cask and bottle-conditioned ale. LIVE

Twisted Barrel

Unit 11, FarGo Village, Far Gosford Street, Coventry, CV1 5ED
☎ **(024) 7610 1701** ⊕ **twistedbarrelale.co.uk**

⊗ Founded in 2013 in a garage, the brewery moved to FarGo Village in 2015. It has since relocated to larger premises on the same site. With a capacity of 5,200 litres, and an onsite brewery, the brewery hosts a vibrant homebrew club, and a variety of regular events. A canning machine purchased in 2021 has given greater flexibility. Although a significant amount of production is

kegged, the brewery is committed to cask, and one cask beer is always available at the Taphouse bar. ‼ 🍴 ◆ LIVE V

Detroit Sour City (ABV 4.5%) SPECIALITY
God's Twisted Sister (ABV 4.5%) STOUT
A well-balanced, easy-drinking stout with hints of malt, coffee and fruit undertones finishing with a bitter aftertaste.
Sine Qua Non (ABV 4.5%) PALE
A hazy pale, unfined vegan ale with hints of grapefruit and apricot which linger on the aftertaste.
Kazan (ABV 5.5%) IPA

Twisted Kettle

25 Ballyblack Road East, Donaghadee, BT21 0NA

An independent nanobrewery producing small-batch beers.

Twisted Oak SIBA

Yeowood Farm, Iwood Lane, Wrington, BS40 5NU
☎ **(01934) 310515** ⊕ **twistedoakbrewery.co.uk**

⊗ This multi award-winning small microbrewery is based on a farm just outside Wrington in North Somerset. Brewing since 2012, it uses traditional brewing techniques and 100% renewable energy to create small batches of unique vegan-friendly ales. The beers are available in several local outlets. ◆ LIVE V

Fallen Tree (ABV 3.8%) BITTER
Superb bittersweet session bitter. Aroma and flavour of hops and ripe fruit. Complex and satisfying, bitter, astringent finish.
Wild Wood (ABV 4%) BITTER
Little aroma. Very smooth, with flavours of hops and fruit and a little malt. Minimal aftertaste.
Crack Hops (ABV 4.2%) PALE
Hops on the nose, pale malt with fruity orange and grapefruit hints on the palate, leaving a bittersweet aftertaste.
Junction Lock IPA (ABV 4.2%) PALE
Slightly floral aroma, powerful hop bitterness and spice on the palate with a long dry bitter finish.
Code Red (ABV 4.3%) RED
Initial malty sweetness, then spicy hop character comes forward with some tart bitterness continuing into the slightly dry finish.
Old Barn (ABV 4.5%) RED
Fruity red ale. Well-balanced flavour with a very long bitter finish.
Spun Gold (ABV 4.5%) GOLD
Light fruit aroma, sweet soft fruit flavours balance a light malt background before bitterness comes through in the finish.
Leveret (ABV 4.6%) BITTER
Light hop aroma, some pale malt on the palate with sweet fruit and hop bitterness before a lingering dry aftertaste.
Citra Blass (ABV 4.7%) PALE
Solstice (ABV 4.7%) BITTER
Nicely-balanced ale with English hop bitterness and impressions of dark fruit overlaid on a rich and smooth malty background.
Sheriff Fatman (ABV 5%) GOLD
Amber-coloured ale with hops dominant on both the nose and the slightly citrus palate, also in the bitter finish.
Slippery Slope (ABV 5.3%) PORTER
Rich velvety porter with roasted malt, chocolate, coffee, vanilla, dark berries and gentle hop bitterness all combining on the palate.
Ghost Town (ABV 5.7%) SPECIALITY

THE BREWERIES

Rich, creamy, sweet stout with roast malt, dark fruit, chocolate and vanilla on the palate, bitterness increases in the finish.

Twisted Wheel

Haffenden Farm, Bugglesden Road, St Michaels, Tenterden, Kent, TN20 6TG ☎ 07507 928971 ⊕ twistedwheelbrewco.co.uk

☺Twisted Wheel began brewing in 2020 using a 10-barrel brew plant. In 2020 it moved from Standish to Warrington and subsequently, in 2023, across the Pennines to Cropton, North Yorkshire. In 2024 it moved again to share premises with McCanns in Tenterden, Kent, under the umbrella company United Craft Beverages. An extensive range of beer is available in cask, can and keg. ☞♦GFV♦

Sunday Sessions (ABV 3.8%) PALE
Moral Panic (ABV 4.3%) PALE
Speed Wobble (ABV 4.7%) PALE
Hoodoo Voodoo (ABV 6.5%) IPA

Two Bob

Oaklands, AL6 9SG ☎ 07966 159643
✉ twobobbrewco@gmail.com

⊗ Two Bob Brewing Co is a nanobrewery in North East Hertfordshire producing small-batch, hand-crafted ales using traditional methods and natural ingredients. ♦LIVE V

Gold (ABV 4.3%) GOLD
EPA (ABV 4.6%) IPA

Two by Two

Unit 8, Morley's Yard, Byker, Newcastle upon Tyne, NE6 1PQ ☎ 07723 959168

Office: 14 Albany Gardens, Whitley Bay, NE26 2DY
✉ twobytwobrewing@gmail.com

Brewing began in 2014 using a five-barrel plant in Wallsend on Tyneside. At the end of 2018 an additional five-barrel plant was installed, increasing capacity to 10 barrels. In 2022, the brewery moved to Byker, thus becoming another addition to this already burgeoning area for microbreweries. LIVE

Session IPA (ABV 4%) GOLD
Citrus hops to the fore in this cleverly balanced hoppy ale with fruity sweetness. Hop bitterness persists in the finish.
Leap Frog (ABV 4.1%) PALE
Foxtrot Pale (ABV 4.5%) PALE
Snake Eyes Pale (ABV 4.6%) GOLD
Significant citrus and fruit aromas lead to a sweet, hoppy, full-bodied ale. Hops dominate the lasting fruity finish.
Citra Idaho 7 Azacca (ABV 5%) PALE
Dragonfly (ABV 5.5%) IPA
Sitting Duck (ABV 5.7%) STOUT
American Pale Ale (ABV 5.8%) IPA
Citra Simcoe Ekuanot (ABV 6%) PALE
South Paw IPA (ABV 6.2%) IPA

Two Flints

25-26 The Arches, Alma Road, Windsor, SL4 1QZ
☎ 07827 915308 ⊕ twoflintsbrewery.com

Brewery and taproom in a railway arch directly below Windsor & Eton Central Station. The 20-hectolitre plant opened in 2022 and brews a range of keg and canned beers with cask occasionally available. It is now a key stop on the 'Windsor Brewery Mile'. The taproom is on two floors, with food trucks often outside. ‼♦

Two Matts (NEW)

Unit 1A, Craster Street, Sutton-in-Ashfield, Nottinghamshire, NG17 5AG
⊕ twomattsbrewing.co.uk

☺Two Matts Brewery was founded in 2023 by two school friends (who you may have guessed are both called Matt). They share a passion for developing exciting new beers and tastes using a selection of quality ingredients. Currently a four-barrel plant is used to brew a core range, alongside special one-offs and trials, all of which are available to the trade in casks. Plans are to increase the scale of operation, and make canned beer available to the wider public online. ♦V

The Hoptimist (ABV 3.9%) PALE
Audacity of Hops (ABV 4.9%) GOLD
Dawn of the NEIPA (ABV 5.2%) GOLD

Two Rivers SIBA

2 Sluice Bank, Denver, Downham Market, Norfolk, PE38 0EQ ☎ 07518 099868 ⊕ denverbrewery.co.uk

⊗ Established in 2012, bottled-conditioned ales have been available since then, with cask ales being produced since 2013. The brewery now has nine established production ales. Experimental brews are also available on an ad-hoc basis. The brewery also brews three house ales for the Wellington at Feltwell and will brew bottled or cask ale on commission. The Blackstone Engine Bar (micropub) and beer gardens at Denver Windmill is the breweries' popular brewery tap. ‼☞♦LIVE V

Miners Mild (ABV 3.1%) MILD
Hares Hopping (ABV 4.1%) BITTER
Kiwi Kick (ABV 4.1%) GOLD
Denver Diamond (ABV 4.4%) BITTER
Happy Hopper (ABV 4.5%) PALE
Light citrus airs introduce a hop-based beginning with grapefruit notes. Biscuit arrives as a long dry finish takes command.
Captain Manby (ABV 5%) BITTER
Porters Pride (ABV 5%) PORTER
Windmill Wheat (ABV 5%) SPECIALITY
Norfolk Stoat (ABV 5.8%) STOUT

Two Thirsty Men

76 High Street, Grantown on Spey, PH26 3EL
☎ 07779 227795 ⊕ twothirstymen.com

Brewing began in 2016 in a garage at the back of a café bar.

Spey IPA (ABV 3.5%) PALE
No. 74 (ABV 4.5%) BITTER

Two Tinkers

Aylburton, Gloucestershire, GL15 6DW
☎ (01594) 840100 ☎ 07711 368397
⊕ twotinkers.co.uk

The Two Tinkers are husband and wife Tim and Esther Kearsey, who established the brewery in 2020. They try to be as low impact on the environment as possible and make everything in as sustainable way as possible. All spent malt goes to feed local farm animals, and hops and yeast are composted. There are three core beers, and a growing number of seasonal ales. All beers produced are can-conditioned and vegan-friendly, and are available in more than 20 local shops. V

Two Towers SIBA

29 Shadwell Street, Birmingham, B4 6HB

☎ (0121) 439 3738 ☎ 07795 247059
🌐 twotowersbrewery.co.uk

⊠ Originally established in 2010 on a site in the Jewellery Quarter, the 10-barrel brewery is now located behind its taphouse, the Gunmakers Arms, and is visible from the beer garden. Frequent specials and bespoke beers supplement the core range. The beers can be found in cask at the Gunmakers, and a range of beers in bottles are widely available in restaurants and other local outlets. ‼ ⬛ ♦ LIVE V

Baskerville Bitter (ABV 3.8%) BITTER
Hockley Gold (ABV 4.1%) GOLD
Complete Muppetry (ABV 4.3%) BITTER
Chamberlain Pale Ale (ABV 4.5%) PALE
Peaky Blinders Mild (ABV 4.5%) MILD
Jewellery Porter (ABV 5%) STOUT

Two Towns Down

47 Back Sneddon Street, Paisley, PA3 2DD
🌐 twotownsdown.com

Two Towns Down Brewery was founded in Paisley in 2019 by Sandy McKelvie, formerly of Black Isle Brewery and Fallen Brewing. The brewery is currently doubling its brew length from 1,000 to 2,000 litres per day and increasing its fermenting capacity from 3,000 to 7,000 litres. It brews four core beers and numerous limited editions. Each of its cans feature an examle of the famous paisley pattern. The brewery's taproom is open every Saturday. Beers available in kegs and cans.

Two Tribes

Unit 4, Tileyard Studios, Tileyard Road, Barnsbury, London, N7 9AH
☎ (020) 3955 6782 🌐 twotribes.co.uk

Brewing started in Horsham in 2015, moving to its current London brewery north of King's Cross in 2018. It brews both onsite and using third parties. The name is based on the idea of collaboration. Currently, the beers are mostly sold around London or through its online shop, which offers regular promotions. There are plans for major expansion, including overseas. Adjacent outdoor taproom with camp fires and 'live-fire' food plus music events. No cask ale. GF ✦

Twt Lol SIBA

Unit B27, Trefforest Industrial Estate, Pontypridd, CF37 5YB ☎ 07966 467295 🌐 twtlol.com

Established in 2015 using a 10-barrel plant, the brewery has a capacity of 80 firkins a week, with the potential to expand to 160. All of its branding is produced in both Welsh and English. The brewery is now open on the first weekend of each month. Check website, Facebook, or Twitter for details. ‼ ⬛ ♦

Bwgan Brain/ Scarecrow (ABV 3.5%) BITTER
Buwch Goch Gota/ Little Red Cow (ABV 3.7%) RED
Glog (ABV 4%) BITTER
Twti Ffrwti (ABV 4%) GOLD
Cwrw'r Afr Serchog/ Horny Goat Ale (ABV 4.2%) GOLD
Cymryd y Pyst (ABV 4.4%) BITTER
Lol! (ABV 4.4%) GOLD
Glo in the Dark (ABV 4.5%) PORTER
Blŵbri (ABV 4.6%) SPECIALITY
Pewin Ynfytyn/ Crazy Peacock (ABV 4.8%) PALE
Pyncio Pioden IPA/ Pretty Fly For A Magpie (ABV 5%) PALE
Dreigiau'r Diafol/ Diablo Dragons (ABV 5.5%) IPA

Ty Mo

Old Market Hall, Palace Street, Caernarfon, LL55 1RR
☎ 07391 696575

Brewing commenced in 2020 in a 19th century former market hall building using equipment formerly used by the Old Market Brewery. Output is cask, keg and bottle, supplying local pubs and the market hall bar.

Tydd Steam SIBA

Manor Barn, Kirkgate, Tydd Saint Giles, Cambridgeshire, PE13 5NE
☎ (01945) 871020 ☎ 07932 726552
🌐 tyddsteam.co.uk

⊠ Established in 2007 in a converted agricultural barn, the brewery is named after two farm steam engines. A 15-barrel plant was installed in 2011. Around 70 outlets are supplied direct. ‼ ♦ LIVE

Barn Ale (ABV 3.9%) BITTER
A golden bitter that has good biscuity malt aroma and flavour, balanced by spicy hops. Long, dry, fairly astringent finish.
Scoundrel (ABV 4%) BITTER
A dry pale amber bitter with a gentle malty and hoppy aroma, plenty of hop bitterness with fruity hints in the taste and a persistent dry aftertaste.
Piston Bob (ABV 4.6%) BITTER
Amber bitter with malt and faint hop aroma, a malty flavour balanced by hops and fruit then a dry finish.

Tyne Bank

375 Walker Road, Newcastle upon Tyne, NE6 2AB
☎ (0191) 265 2828 🌐 tynebankbrewery.co.uk

⊠ Major changes have happened at the brewery with new ownership in 2023 and a focus on producing quality real ales and craft beers together with hosting events in its industrial taproom. The beer range has been reviewed with refreshed versions of Monument Bitter and West Coast IPA. A new range is now becoming available. V

Monument Bitter (ABV 4.1%) BITTER

Uffa

🍺 **White Lion Inn, Lower Street, Lower Ufford, Suffolk, IP13 6DW**
☎ (01394) 460770 🌐 uffabrewery.co.uk

Uffa began brewing in 2011 using a 2.5-barrel plant. It is situated next to the White Lion pub in a converted coach house. ♦

Uley

The Old Brewery, 31 The Street, Uley, GL11 5TB
☎ (01453) 860120 🌐 uleybrewery.com

⊠ Brewing at Uley began in 1833 as Price's brewery. After a long gap, the premises were restored and Uley Brewery opened in 1985. Now operating a 10-barrel plant, it uses its own spring water. Uley delivers to 40-50 outlets in the Cotswolds area. ‼ ⬛ ♦ ✦

Uley Pale (ABV 3.8%) PALE
Bitter (ABV 4%) BITTER
Copper-coloured beer with hops and fruit in the aroma and a malty, fruity taste, underscored by a hoppy bitterness. The finish is dry, with a balance of hops and malt.
Hussar (ABV 4.2%) GOLD
Old Ric (ABV 4.5%) BITTER

Full-flavoured, hoppy bitter with some fruitiness and a smooth, balanced finish. Distinctively copper-coloured, this is the house beer for the Old Spot Inn, Dursley.
Taverner (ABV 4.5%) BITTER
Old Spot Prize Strong Ale (ABV 5%) BITTER
A ruby ale with an initial strong malty sweetness that develops into a smooth, dry, malty finish. A beer that is deceptively easy to drink.
Pigs Ear (ABV 5%) PALE
A golden pale ale with an initial refreshing taste with a hint of fruitiness that develops into a light malty finish. A smooth, quaffable, strong ale.

Ulverston

Lightburn Road, Ulverston, Cumbria, LA12 0AU
☎ (01229) 586870 ☎ 07840 192022
⊕ ulverstonbrewingcompany.co.uk

☺The brewery occupies the octagonal bull ring of the old livestock market. There is a bar that overlooks the brew plant, which opens by prior arrangement and during some local festivals. Some beers have a Laurel and Hardy theme (Stan Laurel was born in Ulverston). ⊮⊠♦⊘

Flying Elephants (ABV 3.7%) PALE
Well-balanced pale session beer with malt, hops and some fruit and a lasting finish.
Celebration Ale (ABV 3.9%) PALE
Yellow, fruity bitter beer with hints of tangerine and a notably sustained dry finish.
Harvest Moon (ABV 3.9%) BLOND
A well-balanced blond beer. Hoppy with sweetness and a lasting finish.
Laughing Gravy (ABV 4%) BITTER
Malt and hops in the aroma. Balanced sweet malt, hops and fruit in the taste with a long finish.
Lonesome Pine (ABV 4.2%) BLOND
A fresh and fruity blond beer; honeyed, lemony and resiny with an increasingly bitter finish.
Fra Diavolo (ABV 4.3%) MILD

UnBarred SIBA

UnBarred Brewery & Taproom, Elder Place, Brighton, East Sussex, BN1 4GF
☎ (01273) 894563 ⊕ unbarredbrewery.com

☺UnBarred was born and bred in Brighton and Hove, established in 2014 in the shed of founder and head brewer, Jordan, before establishing its own brewery and taproom in the heart of Brighton in 2019. Beers are inspired by the creative nature of the city. It is passionate in its commitment to quality and adventurous in approach, with no styles out of bounds. ♦LIVE⊘

Unbound SIBA

Lenches Road, Colne, BB8 8EU ☎ 07886 062825
⊕ unboundbrew.co.uk

Brewing commenced in early 2021 on a 12-barrel new brewhouse. ♦⊘

Supernova (ABV 3.4%) PALE
Origin (ABV 4.2%) PALE
Nocturnal (ABV 6.5%) STOUT

Underground Medicine

Upper Eastern Green Lane, Coventry, CV5 7DN
☎ 07921 120932

A Coventry nanobrewery producing a wide range of craft beers in keg/KeyKeg.

Unity

23-27 Princes Street, Northam, Southampton, SO14 5RP
☎ (023) 8178 2627 ⊕ unitybrewingco.com

Founded in 2016, Unity was taken over in 2023 after a brief closure. A modern taproom and bottle shop, it houses 12 lines of Unity beer with fridges of guest beers, local wine and cider. ⊠V⊘

Unsworth's Yard SIBA

4 Unsworth's Yard, Ford Road, Cartmel, Cumbria, LA11 6PG ☎ 07810 461313 ⊕ unsworthsyard.co.uk

☺Unsworth's Yard opened in 2011, brewing on a five-barrel plant. The brewery produces beers named after historic figures and legends associated with the Cartmel area. Beers are available in Cartmel pubs and other local outlets as well as the brewery's tap bar. ⊮⊠⊘

Cartmel Thoroughbred (ABV 3.5%) GOLD
Cartmel Pale (ABV 3.7%) PALE
Peninsula Best (ABV 3.8%) BITTER
Crusader Gold (ABV 4.1%) GOLD
Eel River IPA (ABV 4.3%) PALE
Sir Edgar Harrington's Last Wolf (ABV 4.5%) BROWN
Well-balanced, rich, fruity, tawny ale with gentle bitterness.
The Flookburgh Cockler (ABV 5.5%) PORTER

Up Front SIBA

Office: 1 / 1, 27, Skirving Street, Glasgow, G41 3AB
☎ 07526 088973 ⊕ upfrontbrewing

Founded in 2015 by former homebrewer Jake Griffin, Up Front is a nomad brewery primarily using spare capacity at Overtone Brewing Co (qv), plus other local breweries. Predominantly producing canned beers and speciality bottles, cask-conditioned beers are available on rare occasions.

Up The Creek

⊟ Up The Creek Comedy Club, 302 Creek Road, Greenwich, London, SE10 9SW
☎ (020) 8858 4581 ⊕ up-the-creek.com/visiting-us/up-the-creek-brewery

Up The Creek began brewing in 2018 (as Greenwich Brewery) using a three-barrel plant and is situated in the front part of the bar area of the Up the Creek Comedy Club. The beers are available in the bar. Entrance to the bar is usually restricted to event ticket holders only, but it may be possible to obtain access by phoning beforehand. LIVE V

Uprising

See Windsor & Eton

Urban Chicken

Ilkeston, Derbyshire, DE7 5EH ☎ 07976 913395
⊕ urbanchickenale.co.uk

Upgraded in 2022 to a 2.5-barrel brewery, producing small batch beer for local pubs, restaurants, bottle shops and beer festivals. Registered as a commercial brewery in 2016. Cask and can, unfined. ♦V

Hop A Doodle Brew (ABV 4.2%) PALE
Pit Pony Stout (ABV 4.9%) STOUT
Benno Bitter (ABV 5.4%) BITTER
Subliminal Vision (ABV 6.3%) IPA

The Day Is My Enemy (ABV 6.7%) IPA

Urban Island SIBA

Unit 28, Limberline Spur, Limberline Industrial Estate, Portsmouth, Hampshire, PO3 5DZ
☎ (023) 9266 8726 ⊕ urbanislandbrewing.uk

⊗ Urban Island began production in 2015 and now has a capacity of 12 barrels. The range is distributed throughout Hampshire and neighbouring counties. In addition to cask it also has a range of beer available in cans and keg. Canned beers can be ordered online and delivered nationwide. !! ☴ ♦ V ♦

Mosaic (ABV 4%) GOLD
Great use of Mosaic hops. Dry and hoppy with pronounced citrus, tropical fruit and grapefruit throughout. Lingering, bitter finish. Unfined.
DSB (Dolly's Special Beer) (ABV 4.6%) PALE
Unfined yellow ale. Aroma of orange, pink grapefruit and tangerine, leading to a robust hoppy taste and softer bittersweet finish.

Utopian SIBA

Unit 4, Clannaborough Business Units, Bow, Devon, EX17 6DA
☎ (01392) 769765 ⊕ utopianbrewing.com

Utopian began brewing in 2019, producing craft lagers using all British ingredients. While being a predominantly lager brewery, cask ales are now brewed, mainly on an occasional and one-off basis. Aiming for sustainability the brewery has the facility to store and re-use naturally produced CO2. ♦ V

British Pale Ale (ABV 4.4%) PALE

Uttoxeter SIBA

26b Carter Street, Uttoxeter, Staffordshire, ST14 8EU
☎ 07789 476817 ⊕ uttoxeterbrewingcompany.com

Established in 2016, The Uttoxeter Brewing Company is a microbrewery producing hand-crafted real ales. A combination of passion, knowledge and hard work produces ales demonstrating distinctive aromas and delicious flavours, exploiting the famous Burton-Upon-Trent hard water. ☴ ♦

Bunting's Blonde (ABV 3.7%) BLOND
Dark Horse Mild (ABV 3.7%) MILD
Ground Breaker (ABV 4%) GOLD
Bartley Bitter (ABV 4.1%) BITTER
? (Question Mark) (ABV 4.5%) PALE
Admiral Gardner (ABV 4.5%) GOLD
Dr Johnson's Contrafibularity (ABV 4.5%) PALE
Earthmover (ABV 4.5%) GOLD
Final Furlong (ABV 4.5%) BITTER
Sargeant's Special Ale (ABV 4.6%) PALE
Chinook (ABV 4.7%) PALE
Earthmover Gold (ABV 4.7%) PALE
Full Gallop (ABV 4.7%) BROWN
Paddock Porter (ABV 4.8%) PORTER
Uxonian (ABV 4.9%) BITTER
American IPA (ABV 5.2%) PALE

Vaguely

15 Lune Way, Bingham, Nottinghamshire, NG13 8YX
☎ 07969 137248 ⊕ vaguelybrewing.co.uk

⊗ Vaguely Brewing launched as a commercial nanobrewery in 2019 following four years of homebrewing and recipe development. It produces vaguely traditional beers that are naturally-conditioned, unfiltered and unfined. LIVE V

Bitter (ABV 4.2%) BITTER
Hazy (ABV 4.5%) PALE
Porter (ABV 4.7%) STOUT
Pale Ale (ABV 6%) IPA

Vale SIBA

Tramway Business Park, Ludgershall Road, Brill, Buckinghamshire, HP18 9TY
☎ (01844) 239237 ⊕ valebrewery.co.uk

⊗ Founded in 1995 in Haddenham, Vale moved to Brill in 2007. Brothers Joe and Jimmy Brouder bought the brewery in 2021 and head brewer David has been with Vale since 1999. Seven beers are permanently available, as well as seasonal brews and one-offs from the experimental ABC range. Distribution is direct to free trade pubs and off-trade outlets and via wholesale partners across the country. There is an onsite taproom and shop, with regular brewery tours, street food and live music. !! ☴ ♦ LIVE ♦

Brill Gold (ABV 3.5%) GOLD
Best IPA (ABV 3.7%) BITTER
This pale amber beer starts with a slight fruit aroma. This leads to a clean, bitter taste where hops and fruit dominate. The finish is long and bitter with a slight hop note.
Wychert (ABV 3.9%) BITTER
VPA (Vale Pale Ale) (ABV 4.2%) PALE
Red Kite (ABV 4.3%) BITTER
Black Beauty (ABV 4.4%) PORTER
A very dark ale, the initial aroma is malty. Roast malt dominates initially and is followed by a rich fruitiness, with some sweetness. The finish is increasingly hoppy and dry.
Gravitas (ABV 4.8%) PALE

Vale of Glamorgan SIBA

Unit 42, Atlantic Business Park, Barry, CF64 5AB
☎ (01446) 730757 ⊕ vogbrewery.co.uk

☺ Established in 2005 and is now in its third generation of ownership, this 10-barrel brewery opened a bigger site on the same estate in Barry in 2023. It has two brands – Vale of Glamorgan (heritage brand, using British hops and celebrating classic styles), and VOG (mostly US hops). The brewery has a bottleshop and a taproom (restricted open times – usually Fridays from 3pm-9pm). It also brews seasonals, plus collaborations with others. Beers are sold over the UK. ☴ ♦ LIVE ♦

Dark (ABV 3.5%) MILD
Oh! What's Occurring? (ABV 3.8%) PALE
VPA (Vale Pale Ale) (ABV 3.8%) PALE
Dancing in the Streets (ABV 4.1%) PALE
This Time Next Year Rodney (ABV 4.1%) PALE
Maverick (ABV 4.2%) PALE
Paradigm Shift (ABV 4.2%) BITTER
Best (ABV 4.4%) BITTER

Brewed under the VOG brand name:
Hotel Barrifornia (ABV 4%) PALE
South Island (ABV 4.2%) PALE
Dark Matter (ABV 4.4%) SPECIALITY

Vault City SIBA

Unit 2, A1 Industrial Park, Sir Harry Lauder Road, Edinburgh, EH15 2QA ⊕ vaultcity.co.uk

Launched as a kitchen brewery in Edinburgh in 2018, Vault City Brewing relocated to share facilities at 71 Brewing in Dundee in 2019 before moving back to Edinburgh. Making fruit-forward, modern sour beers, the monthly Farm to Fermenter series utilises local fruits. Available in bottles and kegs.

Vaux

Unit 2, Monk Street, Sunderland, Tyne & Wear,
SR6 0DB
☎ (0191) 580 5770 ⊕ vaux.beer

Opened in 2020, Vaux is a five-barrel microbrewery resurrecting the old Vaux Brewery name. Vaux was a major regional brewer, which closed in 1999. Its taproom is open Friday, Saturday and Sunday. The brewery is moving and doubling its capacity, but the taproom will stay where it is. During the currency of this Guide it plans to welcome the return of 1899, which is an old Vaux recipe for a 7% ABV bottle-conditioned stout. ■◆

Black Wave (ABV 5%) STOUT

Ventile

Unit 4, Spur Mill, Broadstone Hall Road South,
Stockport, SK5 7BY ⊕ ventilebrew.co

Ventile Brew Co began brewing in 2021 and is a modern, small-batch microbrewery. As of mid-2022 Ventile have been running the Station Hop Bar, Levenshulme, with a range of Ventile beers featuring. The taproom at the Spur Mill site therefore temporarily remains closed. The Ventile name is a nod to WWII history in Manchester. It was a cotton fabric invented in the city that found favour for fighter pilot's flying suits that extended their survival chances should they ditch in water.

Verdant

Unit 30, Parkengue, Kernick Road, Penryn, Cornwall,
TR10 9EP
☎ (01326) 619117 ⊕ verdantbrewing.co

Verdant Brewing Co was established by keen homebrewers in 2014 near Falmouth. It moved to new premises in 2020 and upgraded from an 18-hectolitre kit to a new 40-hectolitre brewhouse. The brewery started producing cask ale in 2022 and has now settled on a regular rotation of four, along with one-off specials. ■◆

Penpol (ABV 3.8%) PALE
Lamanva (ABV 4%) BITTER
Light brown bitter with malty aroma. Hit of biscuit malt, minimal hops and dried fruits. Bitter finish with raspberry fruit.
Burnthouse (ABV 4.6%) PORTER
Creamy dark porter with roast coffee aroma. Dominant roast malt coffee flavour masking any hops. Dried fruits with bubblegum flashes.
Bissoe (ABV 5.3%) PALE

ViBish

Unit 95, Basepoint Business Park, Rivermead Drive,
Swindon, Wiltshire, SN5 7EX ⊕ vibishbrewing.co.uk

Established by three friends in mid-2023 to brew the craft beers they enjoy drinking themselves. Cask beers are brewed occasionally. ◆

Vibrant Forest

The Purlieu Centre, Units 3-6, Hardley Industrial
Estate, Hardley, Hampshire, SO45 3NQ
☎ (023) 8200 2200 ☎ 07921 753109
⊕ vibrantforest.co.uk

⊗ In 2019 Vibrant Forest Brewery relocated to a four-unit brewery at Hardley and increased in size to a 12-barrel plant, with its own canning machine, plus taproom. A mezzanine floor has been added, with its own bar, increasing the capacity of the taproom, which can be hired for functions. ‼■◆GF V◆

Summerlands (ABV 3.5%) PALE

PUPA (ABV 4.5%) PALE
Hazy pale with tropical fruits and resinous hops to fore. Soft and creamy complemented by slight sweetness and some bitterness.
Farmhouse (ABV 5%) SPECIALITY
Single Hop Pale Ale (ABV 5%) PALE
Kick-Start (ABV 5.7%) SPECIALITY
Metropolis (ABV 6%) IPA
Intense resinous hoppiness dominate this black IPA. Complex with chocolate notes and tropical fruits lead to a dry hoppy finish.
Kaleidoscope (ABV 6.5%) IPA
Umbral Abyss (ABV 8.8%) SPECIALITY

Victoria Inn

🏠 Victoria Inn, Roch, Haverfordwest, SA62 6AW
☎ (01437) 710426 ☎ 07814 684975
⊕ thevictoriainnroch.com

⊗ A small brewery on the site of the pub which also offers B&B. Good food, family-friendly, dogs welcome. In addition to the mainstay beers, occasional seasonals are produced. Please check website for opening hours and special events as these may vary according to season. ‼◆V

Village Brewer Brew 22

🏠 22 Coniscliffe Road, Darlington, DL3 7RG
☎ (01325) 354590 ⊕ villagebrewer.co.uk

☺One-barrel microbrewery, established in 2013, which has been brewing on a regular basis since 2015. The plant is also used to produce the malt wash for the distilling of gin and vodka onsite. The beer strength and style varies from brew to brew.

Village Brewer

See Hambleton

Villages

21-22 Resolution Way, Deptford, London, SE8 4NT
☎ 07308 969667 ⊕ villagesbrewery.com

Established in 2016 by brothers Archie and Louis Village who sold the business in 2022 and it is now a sister company to Backyard, Grasshopper and Warwickshire breweries. Predominantly keg and canned beers, although a Villages cask beer is sometimes available at the taproom and a few local pubs. V◆

Vine Inn

🏠 Vine Inn & Brewery, Sheep Fair, Rugeley,
Staffordshire, WS15 2AT
☎ (01889) 574443 ✉ chris@thevinebrewery.com

⊗ The Vine Brewery is based in Rugeley, within the Vine Inn public house, parts of which date back to the 16th century. The brewery's beers can be found in a number of pubs in the Cannock Chase area.

Session Ale (ABV 3.8%) BITTER
EPA (ABV 4%) PALE
Vanilla Porter (ABV 4.5%) SPECIALITY
Grapefruit IPA (ABV 4.8%) SPECIALITY

Virtue

The Old Forge, Alfred Groves Industrial Estate, Shipton
Road, Milton-under-Wychwood, Oxfordshire, OX7 6JP
☎ 0330 223 6801 ⊕ virtuebrewing.co.uk

Established in 2022, this microbrewery produces craft beers in cans and kegs. All beers are unfined, unfiltered and are suitable for vegans. Beers can be ordered online with free delivery to the UK mainland. V✿

Vocation SIBA

Unit 8, Craggs Country Business Park, New Road, Cragg Vale, Hebden Bridge, West Yorkshire, HX7 5TT
☎ (01422) 410810 ⊕ vocationbrewery.com

☺Vocation began brewing in 2015 and is located high above Hebden Bridge. Brewing capacity continues to increase at pace as it expands UK and Worldwide markets with a wide range of beer styles. This includes barrel-aged and a single hop series, as well as collaboration brews. It has local bars in Hebden Bridge called Vocation & Co, and Assembly Underground in Leeds. ⟐♦V

Bread & Butter (ABV 3.9%) GOLD
A feast of floral hops with citrus aroma and taste. Robust bitter aftertaste.
Heart & Soul (ABV 4.4%) GOLD
A golden ale with a strong citrus aroma. Hops dominate taste and aftertaste.
Pride & Joy (ABV 4.8%) PALE
Flavoursome IPA packed with citrus hoppiness. A hint of sweetness gives way to a mellow aftertaste.
Life & Death (ABV 5.5%) IPA
Naughty & Nice (ABV 5.9%) STOUT
A rich and smooth velvety stout. A combination of chocolate and roasted barley develops on the palate.

VOG

See Vale of Glamorgan

Volden

74 Malham Road, Forest Hill, London, SE23 1AG
☎ (020) 8699 1398 ⊕ volden.co.uk

⊠ Volden produces beer for the remaining Antic Collective pubs. Originally taking over the Clarence & Fredericks brewery in Croydon in 2015, a brewery was installed in Forest Hill in 2020, comprising various kits Antic owned and this remains to be commissioned. Meanwhile, the beers, available in cask and keg, are contract brewed at Wimbledon. ♦

Volunteer Tavern

See New Street

Wadworth SIBA IFBB

Folly Road Brewhouse, Folly Road, Devizes, Wiltshire, SN10 2HT
☎ (01380) 723361 ⊕ wadworth.co.uk

⊠ Established in 1875 by Henry Alfred Wadworth, this impressive, family-owned brewery has a modern brewhouse and a microbrewery, which enables it to create unique, small-batch beers. Its traditional horse-drawn drays deliver beer daily around Devizes. Wadworth has more than 150 pubs in the South West of England. ‼⟐♦LIVE GF

Henry's IPA (ABV 3.6%) BITTER
Horizon (ABV 4%) BITTER
6X (ABV 4.1%) BITTER
Copper-coloured ale with a malty and fruity nose, and some balancing hop character. The flavour is similar, with some bitterness and a lingering malty, but bitter finish.
Swordfish (ABV 5%) SPECIALITY

Wagtail

New Barn Farm, Wilby Warrens, Old Buckenham, Norfolk, NR17 1PF
☎ (01953) 887133
✉ wagtailbrewery@btinternet.com

Wagtail Brewery went into full-time production in 2006. All beers are only available bottle-conditioned. This is a chemical-free brewery. No chemicals are onsite and all cleaning is done with hot water and 'elbow grease'. LIVE

Wakey Wakey

⟐ **Flying Horse Hotel & Brewhouse, 9 Packer Street, Rochdale, OL14 5PU**
✉ wakeywakeybrewingcompany@gmail.com

☺Its journey began as a nanobrewery in 2022, supplying cask ales to local pubs and several beer festivals. At the start of 2024 it moved to bigger premises in the heart of Rochdale – the Flying Horse Hotel & Brewhouse. The core range covers both modern and traditional styles. ♦

Bunk (ABV 3.8%) BITTER
Bright & Early (ABV 4%) PALE
Fever Dream (ABV 5%) PALE

Walkie Talky

10 Whitecraig Road, Whitecraig, EH21 8PG
⊕ walkietalkybrewing.com

A craft brewery set up in 2021 by Michael Johnstone and Joel Saunderson amplifying classic beer styles with a post-punk mindset.

Walled City

⟐ **Ebrington Square & Parade Ground, 70 Ebrington Square, Derry, BT47 6FA**
☎ (028) 7134 3336 ⊕ walledcitybrewery.com

Restaurant-based brewery established in Derry in 2015. Beers are brewed onsite, and a member of staff is usually happy to show you around. The taproom has restricted opening times due to NIs licensing (see Facebook page for opening times).

Izaak Walton

⟐ **Railway Inn, Station Road, Norton Bridge, Staffordshire, ST15 0NT** ☎ 07496 097883
✉ steve@iwbrewhouse.co.uk

Originally on a small trading estate, the brewery relocated to a new building to the rear of the Railway public house, reused and upgraded equipment. Core beer range with seasonal beers, all with an angling/fly fishing theme, as Izaak Walton resided in the vicinity during the 17th century. ‼

Wander Beyond

98 North Western Street, Manchester, M12 6JL
☎ (0161) 661 3676 ⊕ wanderbeyondbrewing.com

Wander Beyond launched in 2017 in a railway arch under Piccadilly Station. The range of beer available can vary, each beer is brewed for only a short period so the range is constantly changing. Styles and ingredients are unusual and sometimes unique. ⟐V✿

Peak (ABV 3.8%) PALE

Wanderlust

See Magpie

THE BREWERIES

Wantsum SIBA

Kent Barn, St Nicholas Court Farm, Court Road, St Nicholas at Wade, Kent, CT7 0PT
☎ (01227) 910135 ⊕ wantsumbrewery.co.uk

⊗ Wantsum Brewery, established by James Sandy in 2009, takes its name from the nearby Wantsum Channel. Located in St Nicholas at Wade just outside Canterbury. Wantsum brews a wide range of traditional and modern craft ale styles packaged in cask, keg, minikegs, polypins, bottles and cans, supplied to outlets throughout the south of England. An onsite taproom and shop showcases a wide selection of the beers. Wantsum acquired Tatton Brewery in mid-2024. !! ☲ ◆ LIVE ⌀

More's Head (ABV 3.7%) BITTER
Ruby golden brown beer with fruity American hops and rye.
1381 (ABV 3.8%) BLOND
Black Prince (ABV 3.9%) MILD
Imperium (ABV 4%) BITTER
Montgomery (ABV 4%) PALE
An amber-coloured, light, easy, summer session beer with American hops that are light and refreshing. Spicy finish.
One Hop (ABV 4.2%) GOLD
Dynamo (ABV 4.3%) GOLD
Hurricane (ABV 4.5%) GOLD
Fortitude (ABV 4.6%) BITTER
Black Pig (ABV 4.8%) PORTER
Black porter with sweet aroma. The flavour is of sweet malt, roasty chocolate and fruit that fade in the finish.
Golgotha (ABV 5.5%) STOUT
Smooth, rich dry roasty stout with dark fruits and malt throughout.
Ravening Wolf (ABV 5.9%) SPECIALITY

Ward & Houldsworth

Office: 62 Drakehouse Lane West, Beighton, Sheffield, South Yorkshire, S20 1FX ☎ 07912 028880
⊕ ifinfused.com

Former Kelham Island brewer Paul Ward together with Darren Houldsworth established the company in 2019. Beers are contract brewed at Pheasantry (qv) and distributed from storage in Sheffield.

Warwickshire

Bakehouse Brewery, Queen Street, Cubbington, Warwickshire, CV32 7NA ⊕ 52degreesbrewing.com

A six-barrel brewery in a former village bakery, which has been in operation since 1998. More unusual craft beers are available under the Bakehouse Brewery brand name. It came under the 52 Degrees Brewing umbrella in 2023. ◆ LIVE

Wasted Degrees SIBA

Unit 11, Sawmill Yard, Blair Atholl, PH18 5TL
⊕ wasteddegrees.com

Owned by two local brothers, brewing began commercially in 2016 before a move to the current site, in Blair Atholl, in 2019. Production capacity doubled in 2022 and output grew to 35,200 litres, including the first export of 12,500 cans to Europe. Cask ales can be found in local pubs. Its taproom is open from April to October. !! ☲ V⌀

Atholl Light (ABV 3.2%) PALE
Atholl Gold (ABV 3.5%)
Drookit Session (ABV 3.9%) PALE

Watchmaker's Arms

▤ **84 Goldstone Villas, Hove, East Sussex, BN3 3RU**

⊗ Hove's first micropub has its own 100-litre microbrewery, producing under the Watchmakers Arms (TWA) name. Beer is primarily for the Watchmakers but is available in other local pubs.

Waterworks (NEW) SIBA

Playden Oasts, Rye, East Sussex, TN31 7UL

Founded in 2022 as an adjunct and supplier to the Waterworks micropub in the nearby historic Cinque Ports town of Rye, the brewery has a six-barrel capacity. Brewing started with the signature URYEnal Best Bitter which has since been joined by an increasing range of ales of different styles. All current brews are available in cask at the taproom, the Waterworks pub and in addition local pubs and a club are now supplied. There is an onsite taproom, open at weekends. ⌀

URYEnal Best Bitter (ABV 3.6%) BITTER
Pissoir (ABV 5.3%) PORTER

Watson's

Old Heath, Colchester, Essex, CO1 2HD ☎ 07804 641267 ⊕ watsonsbrewery.co.uk

⊗ Small-batch home brewery, three firkins at a time, supplying local pubs and beer festivals with many one-off beers and a few regulars.

Watts & Co

Gardeners Road, Debenham, Suffolk, IP14 6RX
☎ 07764 906886 ⊕ watts.fm

Watts and Co was established in 2015 and brew a range of traditional and modern beers from its tiny brewhouse in the heart of Suffolk. Each brew produces just 300 pints, with a range of traditional and modern beers, all handcrafted.

Waveney

▤ **Queen's Head, Station Road, Earsham, Norfolk, NR35 2TS**
☎ (01986) 892623 ✉ lyndahamps@aol.com

⊗ Established at the Queen's Head in 2004, the five-barrel brewery produces three beers, regularly available at the pub along with other free trade outlets. ◆

Way Outback

146 Seabourne Road, Southbourne, Bournemouth, Dorset, BH5 2HZ

Office: 144 Seabourne Road, Southbourne, Bournemouth, BH5 2HZ ⊕ thewayoutback.co.uk

Started in 2017 and born in a shed, Way Outback is based in Southbourne. Now located in a modern brewery run by owner and head brewer Richard Brown, it specialises in beers using high quality ingredients, using 100% green energy, and recycling the grain and yeast. V⌀

We Are Wolf (NEW)

Uppermill, OL3 6LW

Set in an idyllic location near St Chad's Church, Saddleworth Brewery started brewing in 1997 in a 120-year old brewhouse at the Church Inn, in a valley overlooking Saddleworth Moor. By mid 2023 Saddleworth was closed and the brewing facilities have been taken over by We Are Wolf Brewing, who initially make four core beers.

It's Proper Pale (ABV 4%) PALE
West Coast Pale (ABV 4.5%) PALE
New World Red Ale (ABV 4.8%) RED
Lunar Stout (ABV 5.5%) STOUT

Weal

Unit 6, Newpark Business Park, London Road, Chesterton, Staffordshire, ST5 7HT
☎ (01782) 565635 ✉ weal.ales2023@gmail.com

Weal Ales was established in 2014 by Paul and Andrea Wealleans and was sold to new owners in 2023. It uses a six-barrel plant and bottles many of its beers, supplying independent outlets and events both locally and nationally. LIVE V✦

Wear (NEW)

26 Silksworth Row, Sunderland, Tyne & Wear, SR1 3QJ

Wear Beer was launched in 2023 in the cellar of the Ship Isis in Sunderland by Julio Romero Johnson, following nine years as project and brewing assistant at Sunderland brewing institution Brewlab. A core range of traditional styles has now become established in the local area for cask, keg and bottled beer. Seasonal and one-off beers are available throughout the year, including a fresh hop lager, English IPA and a Christmas chocolate orange stout. V

Weard'ALE

🍺 Hare and Hounds, 24 Front Street, Westgate, DL13 1RX
☎ (01388) 517212

⊕Brewing commenced in the Hare & Hounds in 2010. The beers are only sold on the premises

Weatheroak

Unit 7, Victoria Works, Birmingham Road, Studley, Warwickshire, B80 7AS ☎ 07771 860645
⊕ weatheroakbrewery.co.uk

⊠ The brewery was set up in 1997 at Weatheroak Hill. It is now in a spacious factory unit in Studley. Weatheroak supplies 20 outlets. Off-sales available for all beers at the Tap House on the High Street in Studley. 18 and 36 pint polypins are available with notice. ‼♦

Bees Knees (ABV 3.7%) BITTER
This straw-coloured quaffing ale has lots of hoppy notes on the tongue and nose, and a fleetingly sweet aftertaste.
Victoria Works (ABV 4.3%) PALE
Redwood (ABV 4.4%) BITTER

Weatheroak Hill

🍺 Coach & Horses, Weatheroak Hill, Worcestershire, B48 7EA
☎ (01564) 823386 ☎ 07496 289924
✉ weatheroakhillbrewery@gmail.com

Established in 2008, Weatheroak Hill Brewery has been supplying the Coach & Horses with quality beers brewed onsite on its six-barrel brewery for over a decade, travelling a mere 50 metres from grain to glass. The free trade and CAMRA festivals are also supplied, and customers can order online for collection and delivery. ‼♦

IPA (Icknield Pale Ale) (ABV 3.8%) PALE

Impossible IPA (ABV 4.1%) PALE
Slow Lane (ABV 4.4%) PALE
Cofton Common (ABV 4.9%) SPECIALITY

Weekend Project

Meadowside Barn, Hulme Lane, Lower Peover, Cheshire, WA16 9QH
☎ (01565) 873601 ⊕ weekendproject.beer

Opened in 2023 by one of the directors of MBH Beer (qv) it operates as a nomad brewery utilising both MBH's kit and other breweries plants as required. It is focussed on stronger, full-flavoured craft ales, usually in keg format.

Weetwood SIBA

The Brewery, Common Lane, Kelsall, Cheshire, CW6 0PY
☎ (01829) 752377 ⊕ weetwoodales.co.uk

⊕Weetwood Ales, originally starting out in a barn back in 1992, now operate out of a modern 30-barrel plant close to Kelsall. The broad range of beers is available across the North West and North Wales. Besides regular brewery tours and modifying the onsite shop into a taproom, it also distills its own spirits from grain on a purpose-built sustainable site. ‼ 🍺♦

Southern Cross (ABV 3.6%) PALE
Well-balanced pale ale with a lasting hoppy bitter finish.
Best Bitter (ABV 3.8%) BITTER
Traditional bitter with a malty sweetness and a dash of fruit. The hop presence increases slightly providing a drier finish.
Mad Hatter (ABV 3.9%) RED
A typical red beer, malty aromas lead to a fruity sweet middle backed up with a bitter finish.
Cheshire Cat (ABV 4%) BLOND
Gentle hoppy blond beer with dominating sweetness.
Turncoat (ABV 4%) PALE
Eastgate (ABV 4.2%) BITTER
Well-balanced and refreshing clean amber beer. Fruit and some malt flavours in the taste with a dry aftertaste.
Oregon Pale (ABV 4.3%) BITTER
Malty, fruity and hoppy mouthfeel with a sweet centre and a lasting finish of hop bitterness.
Old Dog (ABV 4.5%) BITTER
Well-balanced amber beer. Malt, roast and fruit flavours are balanced by bitterness and sweetness.
Jester IPA (ABV 4.8%) PALE

Weird Dad

🍺 Filling Station, 23-23A Caerleon Road, Newport, NP19 7BU
☎ (01633) 244238 ⊕ weirddad.co.uk

⊠ Now well-established, Weird Dad continues to augment its core beer range with infrequent brews and one-offs in a wide variety of styles. All product is live beer with about a third being cask-conditioned, half in keg and the remainder canned. The majority is dispensed in the pub and bottleshop, while some is sold to free houses around South Wales. It brews 120 litres weekly. ‼🍺♦V

Welbeck Abbey SIBA

Brewery Yard, Welbeck, Nottinghamshire, S80 3LT
☎ (01909) 512539 ☎ 07921 066274
⊕ welbeckabbeybrewery.co.uk

Starting in 2011, General Manager Claire Monk has grown the brewery to focus on supplying just over 17,000 pints of quality beer into local pubs, bottled beer shops and restaurants. Produce from the brewery, bakehouse and dairy can all be found under one roof in the Welbeck Farm Shop. Welbeck is one of the historic Nottinghamshire estates. Beer is also brewed for Stocks Brewing Co, Doncaster. !!

Georgiana (ABV 3.7%) BLOND
Red Feather (ABV 3.9%) RED
Skylight (ABV 4.1%) PALE
Atlas (ABV 5%) PALE
Cavendish (ABV 5%) BLOND
Golden in colour with a smooth, hoppy and malt mouthfeel and a lingering hoppy bitter finish.

Brewed for Stocks Brewing Co:
St Leger Gold (ABV 4.1%) BLOND
Select (ABV 4.3%) BITTER
Old Horizontal (ABV 5.3%) OLD

Weldon

Bencroft Grange, Bedford Road, Rushden, Northamptonshire, NN10 0SE
☎ (01536) 601016
Office: 12 Chapel Road, Weldon, NN17 3HP
⊕ weldonbrewery.co.uk

Weldon Brewery originally started brewing in 2014 on a two-barrel plant at the Shoulder of Mutton, after which the brewery was originally named. In 2016 the brewery acquired the premises and 3.5-barrel kit of the former Copper Kettle brewery in Rushden and became the main production facility, with the brewery being renamed Weldon. ♦V

Diab-Lo (ABV 3.7%) PALE
Dragline (ABV 3.9%) GOLD
Stahlstadt (ABV 4%) BLOND
Galvy Stout (ABV 4.2%) STOUT
Windmill (ABV 4.2%) BITTER
Mad Max (ABV 4.4%) PALE
Paradisium (ABV 4.4%) PALE
Turbine (ABV 5.9%) BITTER
It Takes All Sorts (ABV 7.2%) STOUT

Wensleydale SIBA

Unit 4, Badger Court, Harmby Road, Leyburn, North Yorkshire, DL8 5BF
☎ (01969) 622463 ☎ 07765 596666
⊕ wensleydalebrewery.co.uk

☺Wensleydale was set up in 2003 and moved to larger premises in Leyburn in 2018 utilising a 12-barrel plant. More than 500 outlets are supplied direct in Northern England. It has an onsite shop and special events bar. Along with the core range of four beers, two new specials are brewed every week. !!▤♦✦

Falconer (ABV 3.9%) BITTER
Semer Water (ABV 4.1%) BLOND
Gamekeeper (ABV 4.3%) BITTER
Well-balanced, hoppy, bitter, malty start with some fruitiness. All flavours linger until the hop bitterness dominates the finish.
Black Dub (ABV 4.4%) STOUT
Roast and malt flavours, caramel sweetness and hints of fruit and coffee. Roast bitter finish with other flavours also persisting.

Weobley

Jules Restaurant, Portland Street, Weobley, Herefordshire, HR4 8SB
☎ (01544) 318206 ☎ 07493 269189
⊕ theweobleybrewing.co

Commercial brewing began in 2019 at this nanobrewery, which is part of Jules restaurant in the village of Weobley and is run by chef and head brewer Tom Evans. Four beers are regularly brewed along with two occasional beers, available from the brewery, restaurant and other local outlets and pubs. The bulk of the production is bottled, cask is a rare bonus.

Werewolf SIBA

Arch 87, Randolph Street, Camden Town, London, NW1 0SR ⊕ werewolfbeer.com

Starting at Little Creatures in Kings Cross and then on its own nanobrewery in Kentish Town, 2022 saw the brewery open in a railway arch in Camden Town. The "American brewery in London" includes a quirky theme park taproom with its own ghost train. No cask ale. ✦

WEST

▤ **Binnie Place, Glasgow Green, Glasgow, G40 1AW**
☎ (0141) 550 0135 ⊕ westbeer.com

Brewery producing artisan lagers and ales in strict accordance with the German Purity Law of 1516, which also has an onsite beer hall, restaurant and events venue. All beers are unpasteurised. !!♦V

West Coast Rock

▤ **Rhythm & Brew Room, 137-139 Church Street, Blackpool, Lancashire, FY1 3NX**
☎ (01253) 319165 ⊕ thebrewroom1887.co.uk

☺Historic Blackpool pub, reopened as a specialist beer outlet in 2017 and first brewed in 2018 using a six-barrel plant. Some beers have a Blackpool Football Club theme, the club being founded in the pub in 1887. !!♦

West Coast

See Conwy

Westerham SIBA

Beggars Lane, Westerham, Kent, TN16 1QP
☎ (01732) 864427 ⊕ westerhambrewery.co.uk

⊗ Having moved in 2017 to a new, purpose-built brewery, Westerham opened a taproom with 12 taps serving beer straight from the maturation tank. The brewery benefits from the supply of Greensand aquifer water from an onsite borehole. It also utilises original heritage yeasts from the former Black Eagle Brewery, thus maintaining a link to the Kent style of the past. More than 500 outlets are supplied in Kent, Surrey, Sussex and London. !!▤♦V✦

Grasshopper Kentish Bitter (ABV 3.8%) BITTER
Summer Perle (ABV 3.8%) GOLD
Spirit of Kent (ABV 4%) GOLD
British Bulldog (ABV 4.1%) BITTER
1965 – Special Bitter Ale (ABV 4.8%) BITTER
Audit Ale (ABV 6.2%) BITTER

Westgate

See Clark's

Westmorland

Mint Street, Kendal, Cumbria ☎ 07554 562662
✉ westmorlandbrewery@gmail.com

Westmorland began brewing in 2016 using a one-barrel plant. A continuously changing range of beers is brewed.

Wetherby

Beer Station, York Road Industrial Estate, York Road, Wetherby, West Yorkshire, LS22 7SU
☎ (01937) 584637 ☎ 07725 850654
⊕ wetherbybrewco.com

⊙Wetherby Brew Co was established in 2017, and is a short walk from the town centre. It is independently-owned and operated from a three-barrel plant. ▅♦◈

Bitter (ABV 3.8%) BITTER
Blonde (ABV 3.9%) BLOND
Gold (ABV 4%) GOLD
Porter (ABV 4.3%) PORTER
Classic (ABV 4.4%) OLD
IPA (ABV 4.4%) GOLD

WHARF

Upp Hall Farm, Salmons Lane, Coggeshall, Essex, CO6 1RY

WHARF Brewery was founded in 2023 with the merger of three breweries, Red Fox, Harwich Town and Witham. WHARF brews at the former Red Fox brewery premises (Witham and Harwich Town were cuckoo breweries using the same plant), and have a beer range derived from all three constituent parts. WHARF sells to pubs across the combined catchment area, many beer festivals, and puts on the Coggeshall Beer Festival (beginning of September), and the Harwich Redoubt Beer Festival (end of July).

IPA (ABV 3.7%) BITTER
EPA 100 (ABV 3.8%) PALE
Leading Lights (ABV 3.8%) BITTER
Scruffy Mild (ABV 3.9%) MILD
Best Bitter (ABV 4%) BITTER
Pucks Folly (ABV 4.2%) GOLD
Redoubt Stout (ABV 4.2%) STOUT
No Name (ABV 4.3%) BITTER
Stone Pier (ABV 4.3%) GOLD
Parkeston Porter (ABV 4.5%) PORTER
Golden Boar (ABV 5%) GOLD
Wily Ol' Fox (ABV 5.2%) PALE

Wharfe

See Hambleton

Wharfedale SIBA

⊟ Back Barn, 16 Church Street, Ilkley, West Yorkshire, LS29 9DS
☎ (01943) 609587 ⊕ wharfedalebrewery.com

⊙Wharfedale began brewing in 2012 using spare capacity at Five Towns brewery in Wakefield. Brewing moved to Ilkley in 2013 using a 2.5-barrel plant located at the rear of the Flying Duck pub, creating Wharfedale's first brewpub.

What the Hush

See Hush

Wheatsheaf SIBA

17 Halcyon Court, St Margarets Way, Huntingdon, Cambridgeshire, PE29 6DG
⊕ wheatsheafbrewery.co.uk

Founded in 2022, Wheatsheaf Brewery is a microbrewery making hand-crafted real ales. All the beer is unfined and made in small batches using only quality natural ingredients. A mix of traditional and modern brewing

techniques are used to create the beers. The onsite taproom is generally open the last Saturday of each month and there is also a bottle shop (see website for details). ▅LIVE V◈

Supernova (ABV 4%) GOLD
Isolation (ABV 4.5%) BITTER
Prognosis (ABV 4.5%) BROWN
Unlocked (ABV 4.5%) BITTER
Oracle (ABV 4.8%) GOLD
Mockingbird (ABV 5%) STOUT

Whim SIBA

Whim Farm, Hartington, Derbyshire, SK17 0AX
☎ (01298) 84991 ⊕ whimales.co.uk

Whim Ales began brewing in 1993 in an outstanding location at Whim Farm near Hartington in the Derbyshire Dales, Peak District. It produces cask ales using the finest ingredients, Derbyshire hill water and its own yeast. The beers are available in 50-70 outlets and the brewery's tied house, Wilkes Head, Leek. ♦

Marynka (ABV 3.3%) GOLD
Arbor Light (ABV 3.6%) GOLD
Hartington Bitter (ABV 4%) PALE
Earl Grey Bitter (ABV 4.2%) BITTER
Hartington IPA (ABV 4.5%) PALE
Flower Power (ABV 5.3%) GOLD

Whitby SIBA

East Cliff, Whitby, North Yorkshire, YO22 4JR
☎ (01947) 228871 ☎ 07516 116377
⊕ whitby-brewery.com

Whitby Brewery was established in 2012 under the Conquest name. It expanded in 2016 to a new site in the shadow of Whitby Abbey, with a 20-barrel capacity. Music events are hosted occasionally at weekends. In addition to the core range, small-batch beers (cask and keg) are produced from time to time and are available at the brewery tap. Due to local demand, most of the beer is only distributed in the Whitby area ‼▅♦V◈

Abbey Blonde (ABV 3.8%) BLOND
Whaler (ABV 4%) PALE
Saltwick Nab (ABV 4.2%) RED
Smugglers Gold (ABV 4.2%) BITTER
Jet Black (ABV 4.5%) PORTER
IPA (ABV 5.2%) BITTER

White Hart

⊟ White Hart Hotel & Restaurant, 15 High Street, Halstead, Essex, CO9 2AP
☎ (01787) 475657 ⊕ whitehartbrewery.co.uk

⊠ Brewing began in 2017 in old stables at the back of the White Hart. Both the brewery and pub are owned by father and son, Charles and Hugo Townsend. Beers are available in the pub and at local beer festivals.

White Hart Tap

⊟ White Hart Tap, 4 Keyfield Terrace, St Albans, Hertfordshire, AL1 1QJ
☎ (01727) 860974 ⊕ whiteharttap.co.uk

Brewing began in 2015. Beers are only available in the pub. Brewing is currently suspended.

White Label

See Orbit

White Rose

Premises R/0, 7 Doncaster Road, Mexborough, South Yorkshire, S64 0HL
☎ (0114) 246 6334

Office: 119 Chapel Road, Burncross, Chapeltown, Sheffield, S35 1QL
✉ whiterose.brewery@btinternet.com

☺Established in 2007 by Gary Sheriff, former head brewer at Wentworth Brewery. Formerly sharing premises with Little Ale Cart, White Rose then brewed in Mexborough, sharing premises with Imperial Brewery (qv). In 2018 it moved to its own premises using a new seven-barrel plant. ‼♦

Original Blonde (ABV 4%) BLOND
Stairlift to Heaven (ABV 4.2%) BLOND
Raven (ABV 4.9%) STOUT

Whitechapel

See Farmers

Whitewater

Lakeside Brae, Clarkhill Road, Castlewellan, Northern Ireland, BT31 9RH
☎ (028) 4377 8900 ⊕ whitewaterbrewery.com

Established in 1996, Whitewater is now the biggest brewery in Northern Ireland. ‼♦

Copperhead (ABV 3.7%) BITTER
Belfast Black (ABV 4.2%) STOUT
Belfast Ale (ABV 4.5%) BITTER
Maggie's Leap IPA (ABV 4.7%) PALE
Clotworthy Dobbin (ABV 5%) PORTER

Whitley Bay

2-4 South Parade, Whitley Bay, NE26 2RG ☎ 07392 823480 ⊕ whitleybaybrew.com

☺Brewing commenced in 2016 on a five-barrel plant and was relocated to much larger premises in the centre of Whitley Bay in 2018. The brewery was expanded in 2022 in order to supply a local wholesaler as well as direct sales to approximately 30 pubs. V

137 Steps (ABV 3.9%) BLOND
A Dog Called Mouse (ABV 3.9%) BITTER
Warrior (ABV 3.9%) PALE
Remembrance (ABV 4%) PORTER
Kangaroo (ABV 4.2%) PALE
Spanish City Blonde (ABV 4.2%) BLOND
Ghost Ships (ABV 4.3%) PALE
Dark Knight (ABV 4.5%) STOUT
Texas Cleggy (ABV 5%) BITTER
Equinox (ABV 6.2%) IPA

Whitstable SIBA

Little Telpits Farm, Woodcock Lane, Grafty Green, Kent, ME17 2AY
☎ (01622) 851007 ⊕ whitstablebrewery.co.uk

Whitstable Brewery was founded in 2003. It currently provides all the beer for the Whitstable Oyster Company's three restaurants, its hotel and a brewery tap, as well as supplying pubs all over Kent, London and Surrey. ♦

Native Bitter (ABV 3.7%) BITTER
A classic copper-coloured Kentish session bitter with hoppy aroma and a long, dry bitter hop finish.
Renaissance Ruby Mild (ABV 3.7%) MILD
East India Pale Ale (ABV 4.1%) PALE

A well-hopped golden IPA with good grapefruit aroma hop character and lingering bitter finish.
Oyster Stout (ABV 4.5%) STOUT
Pearl of Kent (ABV 4.5%) BLOND
Winkle Picker (ABV 4.5%) BITTER
Kentish Reserve (ABV 5%) BITTER

Whitworth Valley (NEW)

Unit 4, Daniel Street, Whitworth, Lancashire, OL12 8BX ⊕ whitworthvalleybrewing.co.uk

Taking over the former site of Medicine Brewery, Whitworth Valley Brewing launched towards the end of 2023. Taproom events occur on the last Friday of many months. ✦

Brew Got the Love (ABV 4%) BLOND
Don't Look Back in Amber (ABV 4.2%) BITTER
Shake a Pale Feather (ABV 4.2%) PALE
Drop It Like It's Hop (ABV 4.5%) PALE
I Wanna Beer-dored (ABV 4.5%) PALE
Stout to the Top (ABV 5%) STOUT

Whyte Bar

Office: 7 White Oak Square, London Road, Swanley, Kent, BR8 7AG ⊕ whytebarbrew.com

☺Whyte Bar, pronounced 'White Bear', was founded in 2018 as a cuckoo brewery by Andy Whyte and Joel Barnard. Brewing has taken place at local breweries, such as Many Hands and Topsham (qv). Its own outlet, Cuckoo Bar, Exeter, is now open.

Wibblers SIBA

Goldsands Road, Southminster, Essex, CM0 7JW
☎ (01621) 772044 ⊕ wibblers.com

⊠ Established in 2007, Wibblers expanded to a 20-barrel plant, and in 2016 moved to new premises, housed in a medieval barn in Southminster with its own taproom. Craft beers and ciders are now produced, as well as seasonal specials. Numerous outlets are supplied throughout East Anglia in addition to exporting to Europe. It runs an annual Flocculation brewing event each August and hosts 'Be the Brewer' and brewery experience days plus bespoke events for individuals, groups and the local community. ‼☰♦LIVE GF V✦

Dengie IPA (ABV 3.6%) PALE
Apprentice (ABV 3.9%) BITTER
Dengie Dark (ABV 4%) MILD
Dengie Gold (ABV 4%) GOLD
Hop Black (ABV 4%) BITTER
Beneath the Embers (ABV 4.7%) PALE
Crafty Stoat (ABV 5.3%) STOUT

Wicked Hathern

See Staffordshire

Wickham House

1 Kiln Yard, Queen Street, Louth, Lincolnshire, LN11 9BL ☎ 07817 467303
✉ bearplumb64@gmail.com

☺Wickham House is a small artesian brewery producing traditional ales. In 2024 the brewery moved to the old Soulby, Sons & Winch Ltd site in Louth, which is part of one of the last remaining finishing tanneries in the country.

Grimsby Mild (ABV 3.5%) MILD
Blonde Jester (ABV 4%) BLOND

Tanner & Hyde (ABV 4%) PALE

Wickham

目 Five Bells, Baydon Road, Wickham, Berkshire, RG20 8HH

☎ (01488) 657300 ⊕ fivebellswickham.co.uk

A brewpub which started in 2020, on the same site and using the kit as previously used by INNformal brewery, which moved to Hungerford in 2019. The brewhouse was built by the previous owners behind the Five Bells in 2015. A borehole in the pub garden supplies water for the 2.5-barrel plant and 0.5-barrel test kit.

Wickwar

See Butcombe and Hanlons

Wickwar

See Butcombe and Hanlons

Wigan Brewhouse

Old Brewery, Brewery Yard, off Wallgate, Wigan, WN1 1JQ ☎ 07534 945821
✉ beckie@wiganbrewhouse.co.uk

☺Wigan Brewhouse make fine crafted cask ale in the heart of Wigan in a fully-restored 19th century, Grade II-listed tower brewery. Combining heritage with imagination it puts true 'Northern Soul' into its award-winning beers. The Provost family took ownership of the brewery in 2023, with Jonny having been Head Brewer at Wigan Brewhouse and previously Allgates Brewery for more than a decade. ‼♦

California (ABV 3.8%) BLOND
A yellow beer with a restrained hoppy, fruity aroma. Hops malt and fruit in the mouth ending with hoppy dryness.
Junction (ABV 3.9%) BITTER
Sweet malty beer with caramel in the nose and gentle hops providing a drier bitter finish.
Dry Bones (ABV 4%) BLOND
Old Boston Plum Porter (ABV 4.4%) SPECIALITY
Porteresque (ABV 4.4%) PORTER

Wight Knuckle SIBA

New Farm, West Lane, Brading, Isle of Wight, PO36 0JG ⊕ wightknucklebrewery.com

Wight Knuckle Brewery was founded in 2021 by two brothers and their father and was originally based at their pub, the Pilot Boat Inn, Bembridge. It uses natural British ingredients and is brewed in a sustainable way. All beers are unfined, unfiltered, unpasteurised and 100% vegan. In 2023, the brewery moved to its current location, a farm near Brading. V♦

Wigtown

Carleton, Bladnoch, DG8 9AB ☎ 07981 925629
⊕ wigtownbrewery.co.uk

Family owned and run, small-batch microbrewery set up by the Kitson family, that first commercially brewed in 2019. Four core beers are available in bottles with limited availability.

Wild Barn

Unit 1, Caol Industrial Estate, Kilmallie Road, Caol, PH33 7PH ⊕ wildbarnbeer.com

Wild Barn was originally launched in 2019, rebranded in 2020 and then sold in 2021 and relocated. The brewery was purchased again in late 2023 and has set about building on the recipes inherited from the original Belgian owner with production currently focused on cans. ➤V

Wild Beer

See Curious

Wild Boar SIBA

目 Wild Boar, Crook Road, Bowness-on-Windermere, Cumbria, LA23 3NF
☎ (0845) 850 4604 ⊕ englishlakes.co.uk/the-wild-boar

⊠ Brewing began in 2013 at the Wild Boar, a large, traditional Lakeland luxury hotel. The hotel is part of the English Lakes Hotels group and supplies beers to hotels within the group. ♦

Wild Card SIBA

Unit 2, Lockwood Way, Blackhorse Lane, Walthamstow, London, E17 5RB
⊕ wildcardbrewery.co.uk

⊠ Wild Card began brewing in 2013, initially using spare capacity at several breweries in and around London. After brewing since 2014 at its Ravenswood site, production moved to its Lockwood site in 2018. Cask ale was reintroduced during 2021 with great success. ♦

Best (ABV 4.2%) BITTER
Malt aroma with plum and earthy hop flavours overlaid with caramel and sultanas. Spicy, hoppy dry finish with lingering bitterness.
Pale (ABV 4.3%) GOLD
Fruity nose and tropical grapefruit and peach flavours. Sweet biscuit throughout becoming spicy and bitter in the peppery sweet finish.

Wild Horse SIBA

Unit 4, Cae Bach Builder Street, Llandudno, LL30 1DR
☎ (01492) 868292 ⊕ wildhorsebrewing.co.uk

Small brewery that initially concentrated on supplying keg, bottled and canned beers to local bars and off-licences but now also produces regular but one-off cask ales. All products are unfiltered and unpasteurised. ♦♦

Wildcraft SIBA

Church Farm, Smallburgh, Norfolk, NR12 9NB
☎ (01603) 278054 ☎ 07584 308850
⊕ wildcraftbrewery.co.uk

⊠ Wildcraft was set up in 2016 and uses as much foraged and locally sourced ingredients as possible to produce its beers resulting in innovative and intriguing brews. Continuing success resulted in a move in 2022 to much larger premises in the nearby village of Smallburgh. Its own malting barley (Laurate) is grown within 50 meters of the brewery. Beers are gluten-free and vegan. A new taproom including a café selling local produce opened 2023. ‼➤GFV♦

Wild Eye P.A (ABV 3.8%) PALE
Wild Steamer (ABV 4%) BITTER
Wild Norfolk (ABV 4.2%) PALE
Strong cut grass and citrus hop aroma. Full-bodied with lemon, sweet biscuit and a dry bitterness. Increasingly astringent finish.
Wild Caribbean (ABV 4.3%) GOLD

Wild Anchor (ABV 4.4%) PALE
Wild Bill Hiccup (ABV 4.5%) BITTER
Wild Summer (ABV 4.5%) PALE
Wild Hopster (ABV 5%) PALE
Wild Ride (ABV 5%) GOLD
Wild Stallion (ABV 5%) STOUT
Full on roastiness with black cherry, vanilla and burnt chestnut. A subtle sweet maltiness adds to the richness of flavour.
Wild Wood (ABV 5.2%) STOUT
Wild Un-Bongo (ABV 5.8%) PALE
Wild One (ABV 8%) STOUT

Wilde Child SIBA

Unit 5, Armley Road, Leeds, West Yorkshire, LS12 2DR
☎ **(0113) 244 6549** ☎ **07908 419028**
⊕ **wildechildbrewing.co.uk**

Established as one of the smallest breweries in Leeds in 2016, Keir McAllister-Wilde took his operation from a one-barrel plant in a garage to a 10-barrel operation in a 2,000 sq ft unit, within two years. There are a large number of different ales in Wilde Child's portfolio. As well as distributing nationwide, beers are being sent to Holland, Spain and Finland. ✦

Resplendent Perspective (ABV 3.8%) BLOND
Dutiful Supremacy (ABV 4%) BITTER
Shamrocks & Shenanigans (ABV 4.4%) STOUT
Brownie Hunter (ABV 4.9%) SPECIALITY

Wilderness

Unit 54, Mochdre Industrial Estate, Newtown, SY16 4LE
☎ **(01686) 961501** ⊕ **wildernessbrew,co.uk**

The five-barrel brewery focuses on seasonal, barrel-aged and mixed fermentation beers. Belgian and farmhouse-style beers make up the majority of the range. As such, there are no regular beers.

Williams Bros SIBA

New Alloa Brewery, Kelliebank, Alloa, FK10 1NT
☎ **(01259) 725511** ⊕ **williamsbrosbrew.com**

A brotherhood of brewers, creating unique beers. Bruce and Scott Williams started brewing Heather Ale in 1988. A range of indigenous, historic ales have been added since. Three cask ales are produced all year round. The ales are regularly found in pubs in Central Scotland. !!₹♦

Fraoch Heather Ale (ABV 4.1%) SPECIALITY
The unique taste of heather flowers is noticeable in this beer. A fine floral aroma and spicy taste give character to this drinkable speciality beer.
Birds & Bees (ABV 4.3%) GOLD
Joker IPA (ABV 5%) PALE

Willy's

🍺 **17 High Cliff Road, Cleethorpes, Lincolnshire, DN35 8RQ**
☎ **(01472) 602145**

The brewery opened in 1989 to provide beer mainly for its in-house pub in Cleethorpes, although some beer is sold in the free trade. It has a five-barrel plant with maximum capacity of 15 barrels a week. The brewery can be viewed at any time from the pub or street. !!♦

Wilsons of Warslow

🍺 **Greyhound Inn, Leek Road, Warslow, SK17 0JN**
☎ **(01298) 84782** ⊕ **thegreyhoundinnwarslow.co.uk**

Started brewing commercially at the beginning of 2023 on a two-barrel plant alongside the Greyhound Inn in Warslow. Beers find their way into the trade throughout the Staffordshire Moorlands and the Peak District.

Wily Fox SIBA

1 Kellet Close, Wigan, WN5 0LP
☎ **(01942) 215525** ⊕ **wilyfoxbrewery.co.uk**

A bespoke 20-barrel brewery, set up in 2016. Head brewer Dave Goodwin previously worked for Thwaites and Samuel Smith. !!

Blonde Vixen (ABV 3.8%) BLOND
Lightly-hopped with fruity grapefruit aromas, dry hop bitterness and fruity on tasting with a lasting dry finish.
Prohibition APA (ABV 3.9%) PALE
Hoppy beer with citrus character throughout.
Crafty Fox (ABV 4%) BITTER
Well-balanced bitter and malty sweetness, with fruity hops. Creamy mouthfeel, and bitter finish.
Karma Citra (ABV 4.3%) GOLD
Citrus fruit in aroma and taste with balanced bitterness, and a dry finish.
Dark Flagon (ABV 4.4%) SPECIALITY
Flavoured with plums, vanilla and chocolate, smooth texture and thick-bodied, a beer packed with roast malts and sweet balance.

Wimbledon SIBA

Unit 8, College Fields Business Centre, 19 Prince Georges Road, Colliers Wood, London, SW19 2PT
☎ **(020) 3674 9786** ⊕ **wimbledonbrewery.com**

⊠ Wimbledon Brewery began production in SW19 in 2015 with master brewer Derek Prentice (previously at Young's and Fuller's) at the helm of a brand new 30-barrel plant. By 2018 the brewery had added 180 barrels of extra fermenting capacity. The brewery has won multiple global and national awards including the International Brewing Awards Overall Champion Beer 2019. Some beers are inspired by the original Wimbledon Brewery (destroyed by fire, 1889). Keg and canned beer are unfiltered, live, unpasteurised and vegan. !!₹♦LIVE V✦

Common Pale Ale (ABV 3.7%) BITTER
Hops, orange, biscuit and caramel on the nose and on the palate. A bitter, citrussy, slightly dry finish.
Copper Leaf (ABV 4%) RED
Strong hoppy nose with sweet chocolate, dry roasty notes balanced by under-ripe plums, sultanas and burnt citrus. Gentle bitter dry finish.
SW19 (ABV 4%) BLOND
Biscuit and fruit aromas. Well-hopped, with hints of orange and apricot, balanced by malt flavours. A dry aftertaste develops.

Contract brewed for Volden Brewery:
Session Ale (ABV 3.8%) BITTER
Amber bitter with caramel malt and orange aroma. Fruit, hops and sweetish malty biscuit fading to a bitter dryish finish.
Pale Ale (ABV 4.6%) GOLD
Gold beer with floral hop flavour and a slight hint of fresh orange peel and biscuit, becoming more bitter on drinking.

Wincle SIBA

Tolls Farm Barn, Dane Bridge, Wincle, Cheshire, SK11 0QE
☎ **(01260) 227777** ⊕ **winclebeer.co.uk**

Wincle Beer Co was set up in 2008 on a farm, close to its present location. It now has a 15-barrel plant in Wincle. The beers are brewed using water from its own borehole. The brewery shop is housed in a converted stable next to the brewery. Monthly tap nights are hosted (Apr-Oct) on the evening of the first Friday, plus a beer festival on the first weekend of July. Please check the website for other events. ‼⬛♦GFV⚫

Straight Furrow (ABV 3.5%) BITTER
Waller (ABV 3.8%) BLOND
Hen Cloud (ABV 3.9%) BLOND
Sir Philip (ABV 4.2%) BITTER
Malty aromas with some caramel. Hops come forward in the taste providing a dry finish.
Wibbly Wallaby (ABV 4.4%) GOLD
Life Of Riley (ABV 4.8%) BITTER
Burke's Special (ABV 5%) BITTER

Windermere SIBA

⬛ Watermill Inn, Ings, Cumbria, LA8 9PY
☎ (01539) 821309 ⊕ lakelandpub.co.uk

Originally known as Watermill, the brewery was established in 2006 in a purpose-built extension to the inn. The beers have a doggy theme (dogs are allowed in the main bar). Windermere Brewing was originally a separate brand but all beers are now brewed under the name. ‼♦

Windmill Hill SIBA

Unit 14, Victoria Business Centre, Neilston Street, Leamington Spa, Warwickshire, CV31 2AZ
☎ (01926) 355450 ⊕ whbrewery.co.uk

Windmill Hill is an independent microbrewery using an eight-barrel plant brewing small-batch beers. Around 30 outlets are supplied direct. Beers are available in cask and keg formats as well as small package. ‼

Table Beer (ABV 2.9%) BITTER
Porter (ABV 4%) PORTER
Bitter (ABV 4.2%) BITTER
Lager (ABV 4.2%) BITTER
Pale (ABV 4.5%) GOLD

Windsor & Eton SIBA

Unit 1-4, Vansittart Estate, Duke Street, Windsor, Berkshire, SL4 1SE
☎ (01753) 854075 ⊕ webrew.co.uk

⊠ Founded in 2010 by ex-Courage brewers, Windsor & Eton Brewery produces approximately 5,000 barrels per year, mainly for the pubs of London and Thames Valley, from its 18-barrel, Burton-fabricated brewing plant. It has a Royal Warrant and strong sustainability credentials. In 2021, it opened a new taproom, featuring up to 22 different draft beers. Beers are also produced under the Uprising brand name. ‼⬛♦LIVE⚫

Knight of the Garter (ABV 3.8%) GOLD
Session golden ale with a citrus hop aroma, joined by some sweetness in the taste, followed by bitterness in the finish.
Windsor Knot (ABV 4%) BITTER
Guardsman (ABV 4.2%) BITTER
Eton Boatman (ABV 4.3%) GOLD
Session golden ale with tropical fruit and citrus hop aroma, continuing into the taste with some sweetness and subtle bitter finish.
Father Thames (ABV 4.8%) BITTER
Conqueror (ABV 5%) PALE
Dark brown ale with an aroma of dark malts and citrus hops. Malt dominates the taste with citrus and spice. Dry malty finish.

Windy

⬛ Volunteer Inn, New Road, Seavington St Michael, Somerset, TA19 0QE
☎ (01460) 240126 ⊕ thevolly.co.uk

The brewery was established at the Volunteer Inn in 2011 using a four-barrel plant. The name stems from the time when alterations were carried out to the back of the pub and the workmen suffered extremes of varying weather conditions. All beers are named with a weather theme. ‼♦

Wingtip

The Grain Shed, Ford Lane, Ashurst, West Sussex, BN44 3AT
☎ (0333) 224 4888 ⊕ wingtipbrewing.com

⊠ Established in 2015, Wingtip is influenced by the history of Shoreham Airport and its founders experience of aviation and travel. Beers are available in pubs and bars around Sussex and London.

Autopilot (ABV 3.9%) BLOND

Winton

10 Station Yard Industrial Estate, Hospital Road, Haddington, EH41 3PP
☎ (01620) 826854 ⊕ wintonbrewery.com

After a spell brewing at Top Out (qv), and a site adjacent to Thistly Cross Cider in West Barns, Winton relocated to Haddington in 2021. It produces a range of distinctive beers in keg, cask and can. It took over the Station Yard micropub, Dunbar, in 2020 before opening a brewery tap room (The Haddy Tap) in 2022. ♦

Peelywally (ABV 5%) GOLD
Barry Swally (ABV 5.5%) PALE

Wintrip

7 Copenhagen Street, Worcester, WR1 2HB
☎ (01905) 612808 ☎ 07964 196194
✉ rob@wintripbrew.co

Wintrip began brewing in 2014 as Three Shires Brewery on a hand-built plant in Worcester before moving to new premises at the Oil Basin Brewhouse and subsequent name change. Local outlets are supplied.

Butchers Beastly Best (ABV 4%) BITTER
A russet-coloured, best bitter, dry-hopped with Chinook giving it a punchy fruit aroma.
Salt Mine Stout (ABV 4.6%) SPECIALITY

Wiper & True SIBA

Units 11-15, City Business Park, Easton Road, Bristol, BS5 0SP
☎ (0117) 941 2501 ⊕ wiperandtrue.com

Originally launched in 2012 by Michael Wiper as a nomad brewery, Wiper & True has operated since 2015 using its own 20-barrel plant. Producing an ever-changing range of seasonal specials along with several core beers. A proportion of its output goes into cask. The beers are available locally in Bristol and Bath, nationally and internationally. ‼⬛♦LIVE⚫

Wishbone

2A Worth Bridge Industrial Estate, Chesham Street, Keighley, West Yorkshire, BD21 4NS
☎ (01535) 600412 ☎ 07867 419445
⊕ wishbonebrewery.co.uk

Established in 2015 and run by a husband and wife team with many years experience in the brewing industry. Beers are brewed on a modern 10-barrel plant. GF V✦

Blonde (ABV 3.6%) BLOND
A hoppy golden ale with with a strong citrus character. A bitter hoppy and slightly astringent finish.
Eezee (ABV 3.8%)
Two Lapels (ABV 4%)
Flux (ABV 4.1%) PALE
Drover (ABV 4.2%) BITTER
Session bitter, malty aroma. Taste hints of citrus peel with cocoa in the background. Bittersweet finish.
Tiller Pin (ABV 4.2%) GOLD
Yellow session beer, citrus and hops in the aroma and dominating the flavour, leading to a long citrus finish.
Tiny Pixie (ABV 4.2%)
Abyss (ABV 4.3%) STOUT
Caramel and coffee bean aroma in a stout of chocolate and liquorice leading into a malty finish.
Gumption (ABV 4.5%) BITTER
Balanced amber bitter. Hints of dried fruit, biscuit and nuts, underpinned by dry hoppiness, leading to a bitter finish.

Witham

See WHARF

Wobbly

Unit 22c, Beech Business Park, Tillington Road, Hereford, HR4 9QJ
☎ (01432) 355496 ✉ sales@wobblybrewing.co

Wobbly began brewing in 2013 in a small business park in Hereford and is closely linked with its sister canning company, BPS. The brewery has a refurbished tap house open every day selling its cask-conditioned beers, cider and street food, plus an onsite shop. A new canning line has greatly increased capacity. Core beers are now available in several pubs throughout Herefordshire. Wobbly are now brewing its signature series of craft ales on draught. ‼ ➓ ✦LIVE ✦

Wabbit (ABV 4%) PALE
Gold (ABV 4.2%) GOLD
American Amber Ale (ABV 4.5%) BITTER
Crow (ABV 4.5%) STOUT
Welder (ABV 4.8%) BITTER
IPA No. 3 (ABV 6%) IPA

Wold Top SIBA

Hunmanby Grange, Wold Newton, Driffield, East Yorkshire, YO25 3HS
☎ (01723) 892222 ⊕ woldtopbrewery.co.uk

☺Family-owned, farm-based brewery Wold Top has been creating exceptional beer on the Yorkshire Coast since 2003. Using sustainably home-grown malting barley, chalk-filtered water, and powered by renewable energy, the brewery's range includes bitters, pale ales, golden ales, porters and IPAs, of which five are gluten-free. All beers are produced and packaged in-house using a modern 40-barrel brew kit. It also has the facility to contract package for other breweries too. ‼ ➓ ✦GF

Bitter (ABV 3.7%) BITTER
Anglers Reward (ABV 4%) PALE
Wolds Way (ABV 4%) PALE
Headland Red (ABV 4.3%) BITTER
Against The Grain (ABV 4.5%) BLOND
Wold Gold (ABV 4.8%) GOLD
Marmalade Porter (ABV 5%) SPECIALITY
Scarborough Fair IPA (ABV 6%) IPA

Wolf SIBA

Decoy Farm, Old Norwich Road, Besthorpe, Attleborough, Norfolk, NR17 2LA
☎ (01953) 457775 ⊕ wolfbrewery.com

⊠ The brewery was founded in 1995 on a 20-barrel plant, which was upgraded to a 25-barrel plant in 2006. It moved to its current site in 2013. More than 300 outlets are supplied. ➓✦

Edith Cavell (ABV 3.7%) GOLD
Hoppy, peppery nose flows into taste. Malt, caramel and bitterness give depth and complexity. Crisp finish with a hoppy edge.
Golden Jackal (ABV 3.7%) GOLD
Gentle lemon citrus aroma. A balanced mix of malt and hop with a crisp bitter tang. Burgeoning bitter swansong.
Wolf in Sheep's Clothing (ABV 3.7%) MILD
Robust mix of malt and caramel with crisp blackcurrant notes adding focus. Soft bittersweet undertones contribute to a smooth ending.
Lavender Honey (ABV 3.8%) SPECIALITY
Malty caramel aroma leads into a bittersweet beginning with background honey notes. A long drying finish.
Battle of Britain (ABV 3.9%) BITTER
Wolf Ale (ABV 3.9%) BITTER
Copper-coloured with a smooth mix of biscuit and hop. A growing grainy bitterness gives contrast to the long finale.
Lupus Lupus (ABV 4.2%) PALE
Hoppy throughout with malt and lemon. Increasing bitterness overcomes the initial sweetness although the beer is easy-drinking and balanced.
Sirius Dog Star (ABV 4.4%) RED
Rich tapestry of malt, roast and caramel with interwoven hop hints. Sweetness and bitterness provide a light but growing undercurrent.
Sly Wolf (ABV 4.4%) BLOND
Mad Wolf (ABV 4.7%) RED
Well-rounded malty foundation with chocolate and chestnut support. A bittersweet hoppiness provides depth and balance. Full-bodied and lasting.
Granny Wouldn't Like It (ABV 4.8%) RED
Complex, with a malty bouquet. Increasing bitterness is softened by malt as a gentle, fruity sweetness adds depth.
Woild Moild (ABV 4.8%) MILD
Heavy and complex with malt, vine fruit, bitterness and roast notes vying for dominance. Increasingly dry finish.

Brewed under the City of Cambridge Brewery name:
Boathouse (ABV 3.7%) BITTER
Hobson's Choice (ABV 4.2%) GOLD
Atom Splitter (ABV 4.5%) GOLD
Parkers Piece (ABV 5%) PORTER

Tom Wood

See Lincolnshire Craft

Woodcote SIBA

Woodland Road, Dodford, Bromsgrove, Worcestershire, B61 9BT ☎ 07779 166174
⊕ woodcotebrewery.co.uk

⊠ Opened in 2015 as Woodcote Manor in former dairy outbuildings attached to the brewer's house, the name was shortened to Woodcote in 2020. The original one-barrel plant has now expanded to seven barrels at new premises nearby, with a new mash tun and copper. The regular beers are distributed to a number of local pubs. ✦LIVE V

SSS (ABV 3.8%) GOLD
XPA (ABV 3.9%) BLOND
Half Cut (ABV 4.2%) PALE
Weavers Exclusive (ABV 4.4%) GOLD
Squires Gold (ABV 4.5%) BITTER
Oatmeal Stout (ABV 4.7%) STOUT
Dark in colour, roasted malt, chocolate and coffee tones are evident in the aroma and flavour, leading to a satisfying slightly bitter finish.
IPA (ABV 5%) GOLD
Golden, well-balanced and hoppy, grapefruit aromas are followed by a pronounced hop and slightly spicy taste, with a lingering bitter finish.

Woodforde's SIBA

Broadland Brewery, Woodbastwick, Norfolk, NR13 6SW
☎ (01603) 720353 ⊕ woodfordes.co.uk

⊠ Founded in 1981 by two members of the Homebrewers' Society, Woodforde's is named after Parson Woodforde, the 18th century Norfolk diarist with a penchant for real ale. In 1989 the brewery moved to its current home at Woodbastwick. It has its own boreholes and brews using locally-grown Maris Otter. Further investment has increased the capacity and the brewery tap (Fur & Feather) is located next door to the brewery, along with the Lord Nelson at Burnham Thorpe.
!! ☰ ♦ LIVE ♦

Wherry (ABV 3.8%) BITTER
A sweet biscuit base with strawberry and a contrasting hoppy bitterness. Long and well-balanced with a noticeable citrusy encore.
Old Bittern (ABV 4%) BITTER
Reedlighter (ABV 4%) PALE
Well-balanced hop and grapefruit backbone with a sweet biscuity undercurrent. Full-bodied with a pronounced bittersweet ending.
Sundew (ABV 4.1%) GOLD
Hops emerge from a mix of malt, fruit and bitterness to provide a cutting edge to both taste and aroma.
Albion Stout (ABV 4.2%) STOUT
Bure Gold (ABV 4.3%) PALE
Singularly citrus throughout with a succinct hop garland. Sweet biscuit floats in the background over a bitter footing.
Nelson's (ABV 4.5%) BITTER
Malt, hop and vine fruits dominate this full-bodied, well-balanced brew. Caramel and bitterness add depth and contrast.
Volt (ABV 4.5%) PALE
Rollicking mix of lemon, lime, hop and biscuit. Slightly astringent resinous notes add crispness and character at the end.
Nog (ABV 4.6%) OLD
Full-bodied, with dark chocolate and roast provide the dominant aroma and taste. Hints of black cherry, raisin and caramel.
New England (ABV 5%) PALE

Woodland

14 Market Street, Penistone, Sheffield, South Yorkshire, S36 6BZ ☎ 07894 532456

Established in 2017 producing bottled and keg beers, the brewery moved into cask production in 2019, winning CAMRA awards the same year. Cans were introduced in 2020. Originally brewing from his residence, owner/brewer David Hampshaw soon relocated the two-barrel brewery into a tap house in Penistone town centre. The brewery has been expanded to a five-barrel system, allowing for an increased range, a greater focus on cask

ale, and wider distribution. The brewery is named after the highly-prized local whitefaced woodland sheep.
♦ LIVE ♦

Painted Tiles (ABV 4%) PALE
First Flight (ABV 6%) PALE

Woodshedding (NEW)

Westcombe Dairy, Lower Westcombe Farm, Westcombe, Somerset, BA4 6ER
☎ (01749) 705729

Office: 20-22 Wenlock Road, London, N1 7GU
⊕ woodsheddingbrew.com

Woodshedding commenced brewing in 2024 in premises formerly occupied by Wild Beer. It has local food and drink as well as the local community at its core. It is looking to connect to local farmers who use sustainable and regenerative practices and, where possible, use their grains in its beers. Planning permission for a taproom has been granted.

Woodstock

24 Shipton Road, Woodstock, Oxfordshire, OX20 1LL
☎ 07481 569419 ⊕ woodstockbrewery.co.uk

A nanobrewery which started in 2021 on 70-litre brewing kit. A range of bottle-conditioned beers are produced, which are sold online, at local pubs and shops and at local markets through the Thames Valley Farmers' Market cooperative. LIVE

Woofy's

Strangford, Herefordshire, HR9 6QT
⊕ woofysbrewery.com

Established in 2020 and based near Ross-on-Wye, the brewery produces handcrafted beers inspired by the owner's boxer dog, Sir Woofy Woofington.

Wookey

9 Sadler Street, Wells, Somerset, BA5 2RR ☎ 07417 544175 ⊕ wookeyale.co.uk

Wookey Brewing was established in 2020 by Samuel Mills and a fellow beer connoisseur to create a local beer for the famous village of Wookey Hole. It is the long term aim to eventually produce the beers from a new brewery in the Wookey area. It supplies a number of trade outlets in the South West. ☰ ♦ GF V

Deer Leap (ABV 4.4%) GOLD

Woolybutt

Hull, East Yorkshire, HU5 2NS ☎ 07966 511242
✉ woolybuttbrewshed@hotmail.com

⊛ Woolybutt Brew Shed is a two-barrel brewery. Rob Sutherland moved to commercial brewing after years of homebrewing experience.

English Pale Ale (ABV 4.4%)

Worcester

Arch 49, Cherry Tree Walk, Worcester, WR1 3AU
☎ 07906 432049
✉ worcesterbrewingcompany@gmail.com

A small brewery in the heart of Worcester and home to Sabrina Ales. A range of beers is brewed in rotation using traditional British hops, named with a loose association to the English Civil War. V

Holy Ground (ABV 4.2%) BITTER
Powick Porter (ABV 4.5%) PORTER
1651 (ABV 5.1%) BITTER

Brewed under the Sabrina Ales brand name:
Dark Ruby Ale (ABV 5.5%) BITTER

Workshy

Cardigan Road, Richmond, TW10 6BW
⊕ workshybrewing.co.uk

Workshy started using the facilities at UBrew in 2018 and brewed elsewhere when UBrew closed in 2019. The home kit was upgraded to 200L during 2021 and this is now used for small batches with larger runs cuckoo-brewed at an undisclosed brewery. Available locally in keg and wider afield in cans. No cask ale.

World's End

🍴 Crown Inn, 60 Wilcot Road, Pewsey, Wiltshire, SN9 5EL

☎ (01672) 562653 ⊕ thecrowninnpewsey.com

⊠ World's End Ales was established in 2009 on a one-barrel plant at the rear of the Crown Inn, Pewsey. World's End is the 18th century name for the area in which the brewery is located. Three regular beers are available, plus seasonal specials. ‼◆

Wrexham Lager

42 St Georges Crescent, Wrexham, LL13 8DB
☎ (01978) 266222 ⊕ wrexhamlager.co.uk

Lager was first brewed in Wrexham in 1882. It returned to the town in 2011 with a 50-hectolitre brewery following the closure of the original brewery in 2000. The brewery produces a range of bottled and keg beers, some of which are available in Tesco and Aldi supermarkets.

Wrong Side of the Tracks

South Park Crescent, Catford, London, SE6 1JW
⊕ wrongsideofthetracks.beer

A small-scale home brewer selling bottled beers commercially to local bottle shops and from its webshop with delivery to the local area. After brewing was suspended in 2020, larger scale brewing was tried at other breweries with the beer available on keg and in cans. No cask ale.

Wrytree

Unit 1, Wrytree Park, Greenhead, Northumberland, CA8 7JA

Brewing commenced in 2015 as Pit Top Brewery. The name changed to Wrytree in 2019.

Gold (ABV 3.9%) GOLD
Copper (ABV 4%) BITTER

Wychwood

See Banks's

Wye Valley Meadery

See Hive Mind

Wye Valley SIBA IFBB

Stoke Lacy, Herefordshire, HR7 4HG

☎ (01885) 490505 ☎ 07970 597937
⊕ wyevalleybrewery.co.uk

Founded in 1985 in the back of a village pub, this award-winning brewery is now producing around 250,000 pints per week and delivers direct to more than 1,200 pubs, including eight of its own. Its products are also available through selected wholesale and retail stockists. ‼🍴◆LIVE

Bitter (ABV 3.7%) BITTER
A beer whose aroma gives little hint of the bitter hoppiness that follows right through to the aftertaste.
The Hopfather (ABV 3.9%) BITTER
HPA (ABV 4%) PALE
A pale, hoppy, malty brew with a hint of sweetness before a dry finish.
Butty Bach (ABV 4.5%) BITTER
Wholesome Stout (ABV 4.6%) STOUT
A smooth and satisfying stout with a bitter edge to its roast flavours. The finish combines roast grain and malt.

Wylam

Palace of Arts, Exhibition Park, Newcastle upon Tyne, NE2 4PZ
☎ (0191) 650 0651 ⊕ wylambrewery.co.uk

⊛Wylam commenced brewing in 2000 on a 4.5-barrel plant. In 2016 the brewery moved to Newcastle upon Tyne, and a new 30-barrel kit was installed at the Palace of the Arts, in the city's Exhibition Park. It hosts regular events and concerts in the main hall and has a separate taproom area (open Fri-Sun). ◆◈

Gold (ABV 4%) GOLD
Fresh, clean flavour, full of hops. This golden ale has a hint of citrus in the finish.
Fleek (ABV 4.2%) PALE

Wylde Sky SIBA

Unit 8a, The Grip, Hadstock Road, Linton, Cambridgeshire, CB21 4XN
☎ (01223) 778350 ⊕ wyldeskybrewing.com

⊠ Established in 2018, the brewery has a purpose-built, 10-barrel plant, brewing small batches of innovative beers in a range of styles from around the world. All beers are unfined, unfiltered and unpasteurised. A number of outlets are supplied in the area and an onsite taproom is open Thursday-Sunday (some seasonal variations.) ‼🍴◆V◈

Wyre Piddle

See Ambridge

XT SIBA

Unit 27, Notley Farm, Chearsley Road, Long Crendon, Buckinghamshire, HP18 9ER
☎ (01844) 208310 ⊕ xtbrewing.com

⊠ XT started brewing in 2011 using an 18-barrel plant. It supplies direct to pubs across southern England and the Midlands. The taproom and shop sell draught and bottled beers to drink in or take out. A range of limited edition, but ever-changing, one-off brews is produced under the Animal Brewing Co name. ‼🍴◈

Four (ABV 3.8%) BITTER
Hop Kitty (ABV 3.9%) PALE
Three (ABV 4.2%) PALE
Eight (ABV 4.5%) PORTER

Xtreme

Unit 21-22, Alfric Square, Peterborough, Cambridgeshire, PE2 7JP ☎ 07825 680932
⊕ xtremeales.com

⊠ The Hunt brothers took over Xtreme Ales in 2020. The core range of ales is retained, along with some of the popular seasonals, but a number of new brews have also been added. The award-winning beers can be found locally and at national beer festivals. ‼♦

PiXie APA (ABV 3.7%) PALE
BeXt Bitter (ABV 3.9%) BITTER
ChinooX (ABV 4.3%) PALE
Pigeon Ale (ABV 4.3%) PALE
BlaX Forest (ABV 4.5%) STOUT
Red FoX (ABV 4.5%) RED
Strawberry Xtreme (ABV 4.5%) STOUT
Christopher ColumbuX (ABV 4.6%) PALE
OatiX Stout (ABV 4.6%) STOUT
Triple Hop Xtra-IPA (ABV 5%) GOLD
Xtreme Special Bitter (ABV 5%) BITTER
Rhubarb X Custard (ABV 6%) PORTER
Xporter (ABV 6%) PORTER
SaXquatch (ABV 8.6%) OLD

XYLO

▤ Unit 1, 2-14 High Street, Margate, Kent, CT9 1AT
☎ (01843) 229403 ⊕ xylobrew.com

Neil Wright and Ben Atkins set up the XYLO brewery and pub in 2019 using a four-barrel brew plant built in the pub cellar. Keg and canned beer only at the moment. ‼

Yard of Ale

▤ Surtees Arms, Chilton Lane, Ferryhill Station, DL17 0DH
☎ (01740) 655933 ☎ 07540 733513
⊕ thesurteesarms.co.uk

⊕Established in 2008, the 2.5-barrel microbrewery supplies ales to its tap, the Surtees Arms, beer festivals, and to a growing number of pubs. Produces a range of core beers with monthly specials (both keg and cask).
‼☲♦LIVE

Yardsman

See Hercules

Yates' SIBA

Unit 4C, Langbridge Business Centre, Newchurch, Isle of Wight, PO36 0NP
☎ (01983) 867878 ⊕ yates-brewery.co.uk

Brewing started in 2000 on a five-barrel plant at the Inn at St Lawrence. In 2009 it moved to Newchurch and upgraded to a 10-barrel plant. The brewery was moved on the same site in 2015 to sit alongside the wholesale unit at Newchurch. In 2022 the old kit was replaced with a newly-commissioned 15-barrel plant, including five fermenting vessels. ♦

Islander (ABV 4%) BITTER
Plum Porter (ABV 4%) SPECIALITY
Sea Dog (ABV 4%) GOLD
Beachcomber (ABV 4.3%) BLOND
Don't Look Back in Amber (ABV 4.4%) BITTER
Dark Side of the Wight (ABV 5%) SPECIALITY

Yelland Manor

Lower Yelland Farm, Yelland, Barnstaple, Devon, EX31 3EN ☎ 07770 267592
✉ yellandmanor@gmail.com

⊠ Located on the Taw Estuary and close to the Tarka Trail, this five-barrel plant in a converted milking parlour, was established in 2013. It supplies a small number of local pubs and hotels, although the majority of sales are now made from the premises, either as takeaways or for consumption as part of a 'brewery experience'. Small functions are also catered for. ‼☲♦↗

English Standard (ABV 4.1%) BITTER

Yikes

13 New Broompark, Granton, Edinburgh, EH5 1RS
⊕ yikesbrew.co

The original plan for Yikes Brew Co was to borrow ideas from the world of soda and add them to fruited sours but that has expanded to encompass traditional beers and historical farmhouse brewing. Beers are available canned.

Yonder SIBA

The Workshop, Rookery Farm, Binegar, Radstock, Somerset, BA3 4UL
☎ (01749) 681378 ⊕ brewyonder.co.uk

⊠ A farmhouse-style brewery founded by Stuart Winstone and Jasper Tupman, formally of Wild Beer fame, in 2018. Yonder focuses on wild yeasts, foraged ingredients and barrel-ageing. All ingredients are sourced locally, within about 40 minutes of the brewery. V

Yorkshire Brewhouse

Matrich House, Goulton Street, Hull, East Yorkshire, HU3 4DD
☎ (01482) 755199 ⊕ yorkshirebrewhouse.com

⊕Founded in 2017 by friends Jon Constable and Simon Cooke as a weekend family venture. The brewery started with a 200-litre capacity and has now expanded to 2,500 litre per batch. It supplies cask, bag in box and bottle-conditioned ale to East Yorkshire outlets, and online. Most of the beers are given names that mirror Yorkshire dialect or have a local connection. LIVE V

1904 (ABV 3.8%) BITTER
Reet (ABV 3.8%) BITTER
EYPA (ABV 3.9%) PALE
Tenfoot (ABV 3.9%)
Ey Up (ABV 4%) BITTER
Faithful (ABV 4.5%) STOUT
Flippin Eck (ABV 4.6%) OLD
Red Robin (ABV 4.6%) STOUT
Well Chuffed (ABV 4.9%) PALE

Yorkshire Dales

Abbey Works, Askrigg, North Yorkshire, DL8 4LP
☎ (01969) 622027 ☎ 07818 035592
⊕ yorkshiredalesbrewery.com

⊕Situated in the heart of the Yorkshire Dales, brewing started in a converted milking parlour in 2005. In 2016 the brewery moved to larger premises. More than 150 pubs are supplied throughout the north of England. A tap and bottle shop opened at the brewery in 2017.
‼♦LIVE↗

Butter Tubs (ABV 3.7%) GOLD

Askrigg Bitter (ABV 3.8%) BITTER
Aysgarth Falls (ABV 3.8%) GOLD
Bainbridge Blonde (ABV 3.8%) BLOND
Buckden Pike (ABV 3.9%) BLOND
Drovers Arms (ABV 3.9%) MILD
A rich, full-bodied mild full of malt and chocolate with a
gentle roastiness some fruit and sweet to balance.
Nappa Scar (ABV 4%) GOLD
Muker Silver (ABV 4.1%) BLOND
Askrigg Ale (ABV 4.3%) PALE
Garsdale Smokebox (ABV 5.6%) SPECIALITY

Yorkshire Heart SIBA

The Vineyard, Pool Lane, Nun Monkton, North
Yorkshire, YO26 8EL
☎ (01423) 330716 ☎ 07838 030067
⊕ yorkshireheart.com

☺ Established in 2011, Yorkshire Heart is based at Nun Monkton,
which is near York. Adjacent to the Yorkshire Heart vineyard and
winery, run by the same family, it has its own natural spring. The
brewery utilises a 12-barrel plant to produce cask and bottled ales,
which can be found around pubs in Yorkshire. ‼🍴♦

Hearty Bitter (ABV 3.7%) BITTER
Rhubarbeer (ABV 3.7%) SPECIALITY
Blonde (ABV 3.9%) BLOND
Silverheart IPA (ABV 4%) PALE
Blackheart Stout (ABV 4.8%) STOUT
Platinum EPA (ABV 5%) PALE
Ghost Porter (ABV 5.4%) PORTER

Young's

See Banks's

Zapato

Unit 1a, Holme Mills, West Slaithwaite Road,
Marsden, West Yorkshire, HD7 6LS
☎ (01484) 841201 ☎ 07788 513432
⊕ zapatobrewery.co.uk

Small company, established in 2016, that nomad-brewed
in the Leeds and Manchester areas prior to establishing a
permanent home in Marsden. It produces innovative
beers based on traditional European styles. Collaboration
brews are a staple part of its output. 🍴V♦

Pale (ABV 3.5%) GOLD
A light-bodied, refreshing golden ale. It has a hoppy
aroma. Flavours of citrus fruits develop on the palate and
the beer slips down easily.
Bothy (ABV 4.5%) BITTER
Tent (ABV 4.5%) PALE

Zepto

Graig Fawr Lodge, Blackbrook Road, Caerphilly,
CF83 1NF ☎ 07951 505524 ⊕ zeptobrew.co.uk

Established in 2016, Zepto is a 100-litre brewery set up by CAMRA
member Chris Sweet. Although production is mainly bottled, cask-
conditioned beers are occasionally brewed. Brewing is currently
suspended.

Zero Six

16a High Street, Lutterworth, Leicestershire, LE17 4AY
⊕ zerosixbrew.co.uk

Zero Six Brew launched in 2021. It focuses on small batch
beers in bottle, can, keg and cask. The brewery shares
premises with the Cork & Hop, a tasting venue and bottle
shop dedicated to local and hard to find award-winning
beers from across the UK and Europe.

Zerodegrees SIBA

🏠 Blackheath: 29-33 Montpelier Vale, Blackheath,
London, SE3 0TJ

Bristol: 53 Coniston Street, Bristol, BS1 5BA

Cardiff: 27 Westgate Street, Cardiff, CF10 1DD

Reading: 9 Bridge Street, Reading, RG1 2LR
⊕ zerodegrees.co.uk

Brewing started in 2000 in Blackheath, and now four
brewpubs are owned. Each incorporates a German
computer-controlled plant producing unfiltered and
unfined ales and lager served from storage tanks using
air pressure. The core range remains a Czech pilsner, an
American pale, a mango golden ale, and a changing
monthly speciality. No cask ale. ♦

Zest SIBA

Heath Lane, Barkston Heath, Grantham, Lincolnshire,
NG32 2DE
☎ (01476) 572135 ⊕ zest-brewery.com

☺ In 2020 Zest was rebranded from Oldershaw Brewery,
which had been brewing since 1997. Owned and run by
brewster Kathy Britton, Zest produces a core range of
beers in both traditional and contemporary styles, as well
as seasonal ales. Bespoke bottled and cask beers can be
created to order and a mobile bar service (Bar Zest) is
also available. ‼🍴♦

Heavenly Blonde (ABV 3.8%) BLOND
Newton's Drop (ABV 4.1%) BITTER
Balanced malt and hops but with a strong bitter,
lingering taste in this mid-brown beer.
Mosaic Blonde (ABV 4.3%) BLOND
Atomic IPA (ABV 4.5%) BLOND

Zoo SIBA

ExCAL House, Capel Hendre Industrial Estate,
Ammanford, SA18 3SJ ☎ 07889 592614
⊕ zoo-brew.com

⊠ Zoo Brew was established in 2019. It produces a small
range of cask-conditioned and bottled ales. Beer is
mainly supplied to local pubs plus home deliveries. The
company has recently diversified into distilling.

Amman Eagle (ABV 4.4%) GOLD
Towy Tiger (ABV 5%) BITTER
Merlin's Own (ABV 5.2%) PALE

Zulu Alpha

51b Symondscliffe Way, Caldicot, Gwent, NP26 5PW
☎ 07578 196275/ 07899 794294
⊠ info@zulualphabrewing.co.uk

Brewing since 2018, Zulu Alpha has a seven-barrel plant
and six fermenters in the brewery. It has an onsite
taproom (open Fri-Sat), and an online shop. ♦🍴

New Horizon (ABV 4%) SPECIALITY
Caldi-kolsch (ABV 4.6%) SPECIALITY
Coco Loco (ABV 4.6%) SPECIALITY
Poco Loco (ABV 4.6%) PORTER
Voyager (ABV 4.8%) PALE
Citra IPA (ABV 5%) PALE
Freedom (ABV 5%) PALE
Evolution (ABV 5.2%) PALE

Signature Brew, Walthamstow, hosted the launch of the *Good Beer Guide* 2024

National Pub of the Year, Tamworth Tap (p385)

Closed Breweries

The following breweries have closed or gone out of business since the 2024 Guide was published:

12 Steps, Darwen, Lancashire
3 Non Beards, York, North Yorkshire
Ad Hop, Liverpool, Merseyside
Alechemy, Livingston,
   Edinburgh & the Lothians
Ales of Scilly, St Mary's: Isles
   of Scilly, Cornwall
Alpha Delta, Newburn,
   Tyne & Wear
Anglesey, Llangefni,
   North-West Wales
Art Brew, Reading, Berkshire
Ascot, Camberley, Surrey
Ayr, Ayr, Ayrshire & Arran
Balcombe, Balcombe, West Sussex
Baldy, Southwater, West Sussex
Barefaced, Blandford, Dorset
Beavertown (Tottenham),
   Greater London
Bedlam, Plumpton Green,
   East Sussex
Beer Ink, Huddersfield,
   West Yorkshire
Beer Nouveau, Manchester,
   Greater Manchester
Bent Barrel, Heanor, Derbyshire
Black Storm, Percy Main,
   Tyne & Wear
Bliss, St Helier: Jersey,
   Channel Islands
Block, London, Greater London
Blockyard, Sunderland,
   Tyne & Wear
Blue, Gateshead, Tyne & Wear
Bone Machine, Hull, East Yorkshire
Boojum & Snark, Sandown,
   Isle of Wight
Boutilliers, Faversham, Kent
Boxcar, London, Greater London
Brack 'n' Brew, Penrith, Cumbria
Brakspear, Witney, Oxfordshire
Brew By Numbers, London,
   Greater London
Brew Monster, Caerphilly,
   Glamorgan
Brew Studio, Sompting,
   West Sussex
Brewhouse & Kitchen, Bedford,
   Bedfordshire
Brewhouse & Kitchen, Islington,
   London, Greater London
Brewhouse & Kitchen, Milton
   Keynes, Buckinghamshire
Brick, London, Greater London
Bricknell, Hulll, East Yorkshire
BritHop, London, Greater London

Britt, Rowley Regis, West Midlands
Bucklebury, Upper Bucklebury,
   Berkshire
Bungo, Glasgow,
   Greater Glasgow & Clyde Valley
Burtonwood, Burtonwood, Cheshire
Butts, Great Shefford, Berkshire
By the Mile, Broadstairs, Kent
Cains, Liverpool, Merseyside
Calvors, Ipswich, Suffolk
Camel, Aberaeron, West Wales
Castor, Castor, Cambridgeshire
Chadkirk, Romiley,
   Greater Manchester
Cliff Quay, Debenham, Suffolk
Coastal, Crewe, Cheshire
Concrete Cow, Milton Keynes,
   Buckinghamshire
Copper Fox, Rhynie,
   Aberdeen & Grampian
Corless, Scorton, Lancashire
Corvedale, Corfton, Shropshire
Crafty Little, Hull, East Yorkshire
Crop, Portsmouth, Hampshire
Cross Bay, Morecambe, Lancashire
Dargavel, Langbank,
   Glasgow & Clyde Valley
Deviant & Dandy, London,
   Greater London
Devon Earth, Paignton, Devon
Dog's Grandad, London,
   Greater London
Dovedale, Stanshope, Derbyshire
Draycott, Dale Abbey, Derbyshire
Eden Mill, Guardbridge,
   Kingdom of Fife
Elland, Elland, West Yorkshire
Endangered, Ditchling Common,
   West Sussex
Ethical, Mauchline, Ayrshire & Arran
Fallen Acorn, Gosport, Hampshire
Fallen Angel, Writtle, Essex
Fat Belly, Ilfracombe, Devon
Fearless Nomad, Brentford,
   Greater London
Flagship, Liverpool, Merseyside
Folly, Clayton le Dale, Lancashire
Four Kings, Hyde,
   Greater Manchester
Frank's Head, Leeds, West Yorkshire
Fownes, Sedgley, West Midlands
Freewheelin', Peebles, Borders
Furnace Brook, Trolliloes,
   East Sussex
Grafham, Great Staughton,
   Cambridgeshire

Grafton, Worksop, Nottinghamshire
Great British Breworks, Pickering,
   North Yorkshire
Great Central, Leicester,
   Leicestershire
Greg's, Scampton, Lincolnshire
Greyhound, West Chiltington,
   West Sussex
Gritchie, Ashmore, Wiltshire
Growling Gibbon, Hursley,
   Hampshire
Halton Turner, Birmingham,
   West Midlands
Hartshorns, Derby, Derbyshire
Hidden Lane, Glasgow,
   Glasgow & Clyde Valley
High House Barn, Matfen,
   Northumberland
Hilltop, Conisbrough,
   South Yorkshire
Hopdaemon, Newnham, Kent
Hopshackle, Market Deeping,
   Lincolnshire
Instant Karma, Clay Cross,
   Derbyshire
Irving, Portsmouth, Hampshire
Koomor, Dartford, Kent
Krow, Redruth, Cornwall
Lakehouse, Malvern, Worcestershire
Lazy Lizard, Cleadon, Tyne & Wear
Leeds, Leeds, West Yorkshire
Lister's, Lower Barpham,
   West Sussex
Little Beer, Evesham,
   Worcestershire
Little Valley, Hebden Bridge,
   West Yorkshire
London Road Brew House,
   Southampton, Hampshire
Lost + Found, Brighton, East Sussex
Lowland, Lockerbie,
   Dumfries & Galloway
Malt, Prestwood, Buckinghamshire
Matlock Wolds Farm, Matlock,
   Derbyshire
Meantime, London, Greater London
Mellors, London, Greater London
Melwood, Knowsley Park,
   Merseyside
Mighty Medicine, Whitworth,
   Lancashire
Mile Tree, Peterborough,
   Cambridgeshire
Monstex, Loughborough,
   Leicestershire
Moody Fox, Hilcote, Derbyshire

Moon, Brighton, East Sussex
Mosaik, Fintry, Loch Lomond, Stirling & the Trossachs
Navigation, Nottingham, Nottinghamshire
Nelson, Chatham, Kent
New Devon, Woodbury Salterton, Devon
New Lion, Dartington, Devon
Newark, Newark, Nottinghamshire
North Sea, Rosyth, Kingdom of Fife
Old Inn, Gairloch, Highlands & Western Isles
Old Pie Factory, Warwick, Warwickshire
Old Sawley, Sawley, Derbyshire
Out of Town, Cumbernauld, Greater Glasgow & Clyde Valley
Outhouse Brewing, Carlton, South Yorkshire
Ovenstone 109, Ovenstone, Kingdom of Fife
Paradigm, Sarratt, Hertfordshire
Plain, Sutton Veny, Wiltshire
Popeye, Heanor, Derbyshire
Posh Boys, Wickford, Essex
Priest Town, Preston, Lancashire
Printworks, Lye, West Midlands
Prior's Well, Mansfield, Nottinghamshire
Q Brewery, Queniborough, Leicestershire
Radiant, Leeds, West Yorkshire
Red Cat, Winchester, Hampshire

Red Moon, Solihull, West Midlands
Redcastle, Arbroath, Tayside
Richmond, Richmond, North Yorkshire
Ridgeside, Leeds, West Yorkshire
Ringwood, Ringwood, Hampshire
Rock Mill, New Mills, Derbyshire
Rock Solid, Blackpool, Lancashire
Rufford Abbey, Boughton, Nottinghamshire
S&P, Horsford, Norfolk
St Mary's, London, Greater London
Saddleworth, Oldham, Greater Manchester
SALT London, London, Greater London
Shalford, Shalford, Essex
Shed Ales, Pewsey, Wiltshire
Six Towns, Tunstall, Staffordshire
Squawk, Manchester, Greater Manchester.
Star Wing, Redgrave, Suffolk
Stenroth, Edinburgh, Edinburgh & the Lothians
Stockport, Stockport, Greater Manchester
Strange Times, Salford, Greater Manchester
Stripey Cat, Bridport, Dorset
Swamp Bog, Enborne, Berkshire
Swan on the Green, West Peckham, Kent
Team Toxic, Liverpool, Merseyside
Thirst Class, Stockport, Greater Manchester

Three Engineers, Winterbourne, Gloucestershire & Bristol
Tir Dha Ghlas, Dover, Kent
ToBEERmory, Tobermory: Isle of Mull, Argyll & the Isles
TOPS (The Olde Potting Shed), High Spen, Durham
Trailhead, Dorking, Surrey
Two Cocks, Enborne, Berkshire
Tyton, Liverpool, Merseyside
Untapped, Gwent
Urban Alchemy, New Barnet, Hertfordshire
Verse, Bath, Somerset
Vine, Tarring, West Sussex
Vittles, Hull, East Yorkshire
Tomos Watkin, Swansea, Glamorgan
Weird Sisters, Great Barton, Suffolk
Well Drawn, Caerphilly, Glamorgan
Welland, Spalding, Lincolnshire
Wessex, Longbridge Deverill, Wiltshire
White Horse, Stanford in the Vale, Oxfordshire
Why Not, Norwich, Norfolk
Windswept, Lossiemouth, Aberdeen & Grampian
Wreck Creation, Scalloway: Shetland, Northern Isles
Wriggle Valley, Stalbridge, Dorset
Wriggly Monkey, Launton, Oxfordshire
Wychwood, Witney, Oxfordshire
York, Masham, North Yorkshire

Future Breweries

The following new breweries have been notified to the Guide and will start to produce beer during 2024/2025. In a few cases they were in production during the summer of 2024 but were too late for a full listing:

Bad Dragon, Greenfield, North-East Wales
Common Rioters, London, Greater London
Deirge, Castlederg, Northern Ireland

Drum & Monkey, Stamford, Lincolnshire
Fintry Brew Crew, Fintry, Greater Glasgow & Clyde Valley
Heathen Soul, Kelly Bray, Cornwall

Tanat, Llanrhaeadr-ym-Mochnant, Mid Wales
West Walls, Carlisle, Cumbria

Breweries for Sale

The following breweries are reported as being for sale:

Battledown, Cheltenham, Gloucestershire & Bristol
Big Bog, Speke, Merseyside
Burton Bridge, Burton upon Trent, Staffordshire
Cellar Head, Flimwell, East Sussex

Chapter, Sutton Weaver, Cheshire
Church Aston, Church Aston, Shropshire
Ial, Eryrys, North-East Wales
Irwell Works, Bury, Greater Manchester

Kings Clipstone, Kings Clipstone, Nottinghamshire
Shropshire Brewer, Longden Common, Shropshire
Slater's, Stafford, Staffordshire
Thorley & Sons, Ilkeston, Derbyshire

Indexes & Further Information

Places
Index

Places index

Beers
Index

Beers index

These beers refer to those in bold type in the brewery listings (beers in regular production) and so therefore do not include seasonal, special or occasional beers that may be mentioned elsewhere in the text.

BEERS INDEX

Caldi-kolsch Zulu Alpha *838*
Caliburn Tintagel *812*
California Dreaming Hemlock *718*
California Wigan Brewhouse *831*
Call Out First & Last *697*
Calm Before The Storm Five Kingdoms *698*
Calmer Chameleon Brew York *657*
Camberwell Kolsch Mutineers *758*
Cambrian Gold Stonehouse *801*
Cambridge Best Bitter Moonshine *754*
Cambridge Bitter Elgood's *690*
Cambridge Gold Elgood's *690*
Cambridge Pale Ale Moonshine *754*
Campbell's Best Bitter Red Dog *781*
Campfire Hophurst *723*
Can I Pet That Dawg? Nightjar *761*
Candelriggs Drone Valley *687*
Candlewick Torrside *815*
Canny Canuck Thirsty Moose *809*
Canteen Cowboy Twisted *819*
The Cap Bitter Ampersand *632*
CAPA Elmesthorpe *691*
Capability Brown Rooster's *785*
Cappuccino Stout Titanic *813*
Capt. Lawrence Oates Gilbert White's *705*
Captain Bob Mighty Oak *751*
Captain Manby Two Rivers *820*
Captain Morrison's IPA Five Kingdoms *698*
Captain Smith's Strong Ale Titanic *813*
Car Park Cuddle IVO *729*
Caradog Grey Trees *711*
Caramel Stout Tindall *812*
Caravan Pig & Porter *774*
Cardinal Sin Nailmaker *758*
Carfax Horsham *724*
Carlisle Bell Carlisle *668*
Carmen Carnival *668*
Carpe Diem Roman Way *785*
Cart Blanche Kelburn *730*
Cart Noir Kelburn *730*
Cartmel Pale Unsworth's Yard *822*
Cartmel Thoroughbred Unsworth's Yard *822*
Cascade IPA Mighty Oak *751* Robinsons *784*
Cascade Karma Pale Ale Newt *761*
Cascade Blackedge *649* Gloucester *706* Gwaun Valley *712* Liverpool Brewing *740* Nailmaker *758* Saltaire *789* Stamps *799*
Casemate IPA Southsea *797*
Cask Ale Mansfield (Banks's) *638*
Cask Old Mill *765*
Cass 2CV Tigertops *811*
Cast Iron Stout Iron Pier *728*
Castle Black Merlin *751*
Castle Gold Tintagel *812*
Castle Hill Dunham Massey *688*
Castle Arundel *635*
Castlerigg Blonde Tirril *813*
Castletown Bitter Bushy's *665*
Cat Nap Barngates *639*
Catalyst Atom *636*
Catbells Hesket Newmarket *719*
Catcher Flack Manor *698*

Cat's Whiskers Colchester *673*
Caudle Bitter Langton *735*
Causeway Cornish Crown *676* Horsham *724*
Cavegirl Bitter Kinver *733*
Cavendish Red Roughacre *785*
Cavendish Welbeck Abbey *828*
Celebration Ale Ulverston *822*
Celebration Maypole *750*
Celestial Love Out There *768*
Cellarman's Stout Moonshine *754*
Celtic Gold Hereford *719*
Celtic Pride Felinfoel *695*
Cemetery Gates Crafty Monkey *678*
Centennial Bingley *647*
Central Line Red Portobello *776*
Centurion II Corinium *676*
Centurion Pale Ale Parker *770*
Centurion Dow Bridge *686*
Cerberus Stout Fox *700*
Chadwell New River *760*
Chaff Farm Yard *694*
Chain & Anchor Burnside *664*
Chain Ale Black Country *648*
Chain Reaction Pale Ale Fixed Wheel *698*
Chained Oak Peakstones Rock *771*
Chairman Dave Amwell Springs *632*
Chalk Stream Ramsbury *779*
Challenger Kingstone *733*
Chamberlain Pale Ale Two Towers *821*
Chaos More Chaos Disruption is Brewing *684*
Chapel Street Porter Billericay *646*
Chapter 1 New Beginnings Fuggle Bunny *702*
Chapter 2 Cotton Tail Fuggle Bunny *702*
Chapter 3 Orchard Gold Fuggle Bunny *702*
Chapter 4 24 Carrot Fuggle Bunny *702*
Chapter 5 Oh Crumbs Fuggle Bunny *702*
Chapter 6 Hazy Summer Daze Fuggle Bunny *702*
Chapter 7 Russian Rare-Bit Fuggle Bunny *702*
Chapter 8 Jammy Dodger Fuggle Bunny *702*
Chapter 9 La La Land Fuggle Bunny *702*
Charismatic Beermats *642*
Charlie Don't Surf Empire *691*
Charrington IPA Heritage (Burton Bridge) *665*
Chase Buster Beowulf *644*
Chasewater Bitter Beowulf *644*
Chatsworth Gold Peak *771*
Cheeky Blonde Bridgetown *660*
Cheeky Jack Moon Gazer *754*
Cheeky Monkey Parkway *770*
Cheers! Nuttycombe *764*
Cheltenham Flyer Humpty Dumpty *724*
Cheltenham Gold Goff's *706*
Chennai Kissingate *734*
Chequered Flag Prescott (Hanlons) *715* Silverstone *793*
Cheriton Porter Flower Pots *699*
Cherokee Tombstone *814*

Cherry Porter Mauldons *750* Titanic *813*
Cherry Raven Magpie *747*
Chesapeake Newby Wyke *761*
Cheshire Cat Weetwood *827*
Cheshire Gold Coach House *673*
Cheshire IPA Dunham Massey *688*
Cheshire Oak Coach House *673*
Cheshire Pale MBH Beer *750*
Chesn't Cabin *666*
Chester Gold Oaks *764*
Cheswold Doncaster *685*
Chief Jester Farr Brew *694*
Chiffchaff Digfield *683*
Child of the Jago Hop Monster (George's) *704*
Chilli Beer Hopstar *723*
Chilli Porter Billericay *646*
Chiltern Black Chiltern *671*
Chiltern Pale Ale Chiltern *671*
Chimera IPA Downton *686*
Chinook & Grapefruit Bollington *652*
Chinook Blonde Goose Eye *708*
Chinook Nailmaker *758* Uttoxeter *823*
ChinooX Xtreme *837*
Chinwag Indigenous *726* Northern Whisper *763*
Chockwork Orange Brentwood *656*
Choco-lots Brolly *662*
Chocolate & Cherry Mild Empire *691*
Chocolate & Vanilla Oatmeal Stout Kissingate *734*
Chocolate Amaretto Blue Monkey *651*
Chocolate Cherry Mild Dunham Massey *688*
Chocolate Guerilla Blue Monkey *651*
Chocolate Milk Porter Brewers Folly *657*
Chocolate Orange Stout Moonshine *754*
Chocolate Orange Blue Monkey *651*
Chocolate Porter Beowulf *644*
Chocolate Safari Stout Nailmaker *758*
Chocolate Stout Stubborn Mule *803*
Chocolate Vanilla Porter Mumbles *757*
Chocolate and Vanilla Stout Titanic *813*
Chorlton Pale Ale Bootleg (Joseph Holt) *721*
Christopher ColumbuX Xtreme *837*
Chub IPA Brolly *662*
Chuckle Muckle *757*
Chummy Bluster Best Bitter Gun *712*
Church Ledge Noss Beer Works *763*
Churches Pale Ale FILO *696*
Cinder Stout Inferno *727*
Cinder Toffee Stout New Bristol *762*
Citadel Carlisle *668* Clun *673*
Citra Ass Down Botley *653*
Citra Blass Twisted Oak *819*

Cwrw Eryri / Snowdonia Ale Purple Moose *778*
Cwrw Glaslyn / Glaslyn Ale Purple Moose *778*
Cwrw Glyndwr Llyn *741*
Cwrw Gorslas/ Bluestone Bitter Glamorgan *705*
Cwrw Grav Tinworks *812*
Cwrw Gwyn Gwaun Valley *712*
Cwrw Madog / Madog's Ale Purple Moose *778*
Cwrw Melyn Gwaun Valley *712*
Cwrw Teifi Mantle *748*
Cwrw Ysgawen / Elderflower Ale Purple Moose *778*
Cwrw Evan Evans *692*
Cwrw'r Afr Serchog/ Horny Goat Ale Twt Lol *821*
Cwrw'r Ddraig Aur Robinsons *784*
Cwtch Tiny Rebel *813*
Cyclops Milton *752*
Cygnet Captain Cook *667*
Cymryd y Pyst Twt Lol *821*
Czeckmate Red Rose *781*

D _____

Déjà Brewed Snaggletooth *795*
Dafen IPA Tinworks *812*
Daggerbill Great Oakley *710*
Daggers Ale Three Daggers *810*
Daggers Edge Three Daggers *810*
Daily Bread Abbeydale *629*
Dainty Eight Arch *690*
Daisy Gold Brightwater *660*
Dam Strong Ale Lymm *745*
Damage Control Logan Beck *742*
Dambusters Ale Beermats *642*
Damn Gates Burton *704*
Damson Porter Burton Bridge *664*
Dancing Dragonfly Pheasantry *773*
Dancing in the Streets Vale of Glamorgan *823*
Danefield Pale Chevin *670*
Dangerous Brian Guisborough *712*
Dangerous Darren A Bloke Down the Pub (Potbelly) *777*
Danish Dynamite Stonehenge *801*
The Dankness Bullhouse *663*
Danny's Brew Cerne Abbas *669*
Dark Ages Copper Street *676*
Dark Ale Tremethick *817*
Dark Angel Durham *688*
Dark Arts Magic Rock *747*
Dark Destroyer CrackleRock *677*
Dark Drake Dancing Duck *681*
Dark Dunkel Barnaby's *638*
Dark Flagon Wily Fox *832*
Dark Fox Hornes *723*
Dark Habit Guisborough *712*
Dark Heart Mantle *748*
Dark Horse Mild Uttoxeter *823*
Dark Horse Stout Elmtree *691*
Dark Horse Blythe *651*
　　Hepworth *718*
　　Keswick *732*
Dark Island Orkney *767*
Dark Knight Hopstar *723*
　　Tewkesbury *808*
　　Whitley Bay *830*
Dark M Batemans *640*
Dark Magic Merlin *751*
Dark Masquerade Half Moon *713*

Dark Matter Bridge *659*
　　Oaks *764*
　　VOG (Vale of Glamorgan) *823*
Dark Mild Artefact *635*
　　Bank Top *637*
　　Blackedge *649*
　　Harvey's *716*
　　Mill Valley *752*
　　Timothy Taylor *806*
Dark Mode Liverpool Brewing *740*
Dark Moor Kelburn *730*
Dark Munro Swannay *804*
Dark Night Southport *797*
Dark Nights Porter Jolly Sailor *730*
Dark North Neighbourhood *758*
Dark Porter Fuddy Duck *702*
　　Stod Fold *801*
Dark Raven Beowulf *644*
Dark Ruby Ale Sabrina (Worcester) *836*
Dark Ruby Mild Bridge *659*
　　Consall Forge *675*
　　Sarah Hughes *724*
Dark Ruby Blythe *651*
　　Hydes *725*
Dark Rum Blackedge *649*
Dark Side of the Toon Three Kings *810*
Dark Side of the Wight Yates' *837*
Dark Side Fosse Way *700*
　　Three Fiends *810*
Dark Spartan Stout Parker *770*
Dark Storm Stout Five Kingdoms *698*
Dark and Stormy Combe *674*
Dark Swan Olde Swan *766*
Dark Wave Porter Big Smoke *646*
Dark 9 Lives *628*
　　Arran *634*
　　Brains *655*
　　Courtyard *677*
　　Hereford *719*
　　JW Lees *736*
　　Ledbury *736*
　　Rhymney *783*
　　Vale of Glamorgan *823*
Darkest Ennerdale *692*
Darkness Exeter *693*
Darkside Bushy's *665*
　　Falstaff *694*
　　Shortts *792*
Dartmoor IPA Dartmoor *682*
Darwins Origin Salopian *788*
Dashingly Dark Derby *683*
Dave Goldmark *707*
David's Not So Bitter Spey Valley *798*
Davy Dark Chelmsford *670*
Dawlish Bitter Isca *728*
Dawlish Pale Isca *728*
Dawlish Summer Isca *728*
Dawn of the NEIPA Two Matts *820*
The Day Is My Enemy Urban Chicken *823*
Day Trip to Bangor Escape *692*
Day Tripper Liquid Light *739*
Daymark Castle *668*
Daze Guisborough *712*
DB Dark Dow Bridge *686*
DB One Dorking *685*
DCUK Dancing Duck *681*
Death of a Cowboy Chelmsford *670*
Death or Glory Tring *817*
Debbie Does Elmesthorpe *691*

Debonair Hophurst *723*
Debut Triple Point *817*
Decadence Brewster's *659*
Deception Abbeydale *629*
Deckhand Teignmouth *807*
Deep Groat John O'Groats *730*
Deepdale Buxton *665*
Deer Beer Dunham Massey *688*
Deer Leap Wookey *835*
Deer Stalker Bowland *654*
Deerstalker Ramsbury *779*
Delamere Blonde Oaks *764*
Delapre Dark Great Oakley *710*
Delight Guisborough *712*
Delta APA Great North Eastern *710*
Delver's Drop IPA Litte Eaton (Black Hole) *648*
Demockracy Disruption is Brewing *684*
Dengie Dark Wibblers *830*
Dengie Gold Wibblers *830*
Dengie IPA Wibblers *830*
Denver Diamond Two Rivers *820*
Derbyshire Blonde Drone Valley *687*
Dere Street Mithril *753*
Desert Storm Storm *801*
Desperately Seeking Dopamine Big Trip *646*
Detention Old School *766*
Detonator Loose Cannon *743*
Detroit Sour City Twisted Barrel *819*
Deuchars IPA Caledonian (Belhaven) *643*
Devil's Bridge IPA Kirkby Lonsdale *733*
Devil's Elbow Hexhamshire *719*
Devils Dyke Porter Downlands *686*
Devils Dyke Salted Caramel Downlands *686*
Devil's Water Hexhamshire *719*
Devon Amber Salcombe *788*
Devon Dew Summerskills *803*
Devon Dumpling Bays *641*
Devon Frost Summerskills *803*
Devon Jester Taw Valley *806*
Devon Pale Isca *728*
Devon Pride South Hams *796*
Devonian Riviera *783*
Devout Bishop Nick *647*
Dexter Storm *801*
DHB (Dave's Hoppy Beer) Facer's *694*
Diab-Lo Weldon *828*
Diamond Ale Phipps NBC *773*
Diamond Black Stout Chantry *669*
Dick Turpin Best Bitter Coach House *673*
Dickie Billericay *646*
Did You See That Ludicrous Display Last Night!? Reckless Dweeb *780*
Diggers Gold Grey Trees *711*
Digies Tingay's (Poole Hill) *776*
Dilks Shottle Farm *793*
Dimpus Big Stone *646*
Dionysus Milton *752*
Diplomat Beermats *642*
Directors Courage (Marston's) *749*
The Dirt Bat Country *639*
Dirty Deeds Allendale *631*
Dirty Harry Northern Monkey *763*
Disco Balls Shiny *792*
Disco King Turning Point *818*

Endeavour Bingley 646
   Captain Cook 667
Endike Black Aitcheson's 630
Endless Summer Black Iris 648
Engine House Keltek 731
Englands Finest hour
   Consortium 675
English Ale Tavistock 806
English Bitter Stardust 799
English Guineas Stout Linfit 739
English IPA Barnaby's 638
   Botley 653
English Pale Ale Woolybutt 835
English Standard Yelland
   Manor 837
English Stout 4Ts 628
English Hop Fuzz 722
Entire Stout Hop Back 722
Entire Cronx 678
   Olde Swan 766
EPA 100 WHARF 829
EPA Marston's 749
   Two Bob 820
   Vine Inn 824
Epic IPA Settle 790
Epic Prang Apex 633
Epiphany Pale Ale Little
   Brewing 739
Equilibrium Consall Forge 675
   Deeply Vale 682
Equinox Aither 630
   First & Last 697
   Whitley Bay 830
Eric's ESB Clearwater 672
Erik Weiss Escape 692
Ernest Brightwater 660
   McCanns 746
Ernie's Milk Stout Settle 790
Errmmm... Strands 802
ESB Fuller's 702
   Runaway 786
   Tiley's 811
Escape Lenton Lane 737
Essential Treen's 816
Essex Boys Best Bitter Crouch
   Vale 679
Esthwaite Bitter Cumbrian 680
Estuary Porter Shivering Sands 792
ETale Cheviot 671
Eternal Northern Monk 763
Ethelfleda Tamworth 805
Eton Boatman Windsor & Eton 833
Evening Brown IVO 729
Evening Star Hop Kettle 722
Evergreen Serious 790
Evolution APA Mr Winter's 756
Evolution Darwin 682
   Zulu Alpha 838
Exam Room Tears Stu Brew 802
Excalibur Merlin 751
Excelsius Ossett 767
Excitra Pheasantry 773
Executioners Assistant
   Consortium 675
Exile Pilgrim 774
Expedition Ale Clearwater 672
Expedition Darwin 682
Explorer New Wharf 760
Export Light Rhymney 783
Export Stout Boundary 654
Export Rhymney 783
Extra Blonde Quartz 778
Extra Double Stout Fengate 695
Extra Fine Ale Craven 678
Extra Pale Ale Nottingham 764

Extra Special Marble Marble 748
Extra Stout Snout
   Slaughterhouse 794
Ey Up Yorkshire Brewhouse 837
EYPA Yorkshire Brewhouse 837
Eyton Gold Magic Dragon 747
Eyup Cocka! Silver 793
Ezili Neptune 759

F

F'Hops Sake Half Moon 713
Fab Four Liverpool IPA Rock the
   Boat 784
The Fabrick Ashover 635
Fair Lady Dhillon's 683
Faithful Yorkshire Brewhouse 837
Falcon Ale Lacons 734
Falconer Wensleydale 828
Fallen Angel Bitter Lucifer 744
Fallen Angel Church End 671
Fallen Tree Twisted Oak 819
Falling Star Wickwar (Hanlons) 715
Fallout Coalshed 673
Falls Gold Tillingbourne 812
Falstaff's Folly Shakespeare (North
   Cotswold) 762
Fanshaw Blonde Drone Valley 687
Far Out Capitalist Hippy (Gyle
   59) 713
Far-Fetched Pale Ale Hairy
   Dog 713
Farmer's Best Ramsbury 779
Farmers 5K Bradfield 655
Farmers Ale Drinkstone 687
   Not That California 763
Farmers Bitter Bradfield 655
Farmers Blonde Bradfield 655
Farmers Brown Cow Bradfield 655
Farmers Pale Ale Bradfield 655
Farmers Sixer Bradfield 655
Farmers Steel Cow Bradfield 655
Farmers Stout Bradfield 655
Farmhouse New Buildings 760
   Vibrant Forest 824
Farming County Consortium 675
Farne Island Pale Ale Hadrian
   Border 713
Farr & Away Farr Brew 694
Farr Afield Farr Brew 694
Farr Apart Farr Brew 694
Fastback Pale Ale 360° 627
Fat Cat Fuller Consortium 675
Fat Head Stannary 799
Father Thames Windsor & Eton 833
Faultline Kettlesmith 732
The Favourite Gyle 59 713
Fearn Loxley 744
Featherbed Buxton 665
Featherstone Amber Ale
   Hornes 723
Feckless RedWillow 782
Feedback Moor 755
Fell Explorer Bowness Bay 654
Fell Runner Bowness Bay 655
   Lords 743
Fell Walker Bowness Bay 654
   Three Peaks 811
Fellowship Porter Redemption 781
Fen Skater Papworth 770
Fenman 8 Sail 628
Ferryman Exeter 693
Ferryman's Gold Loddon 741
FeS2 Mine 753
Festival Ale Burton Bridge 665

Fettler's Finest Broadtown 661
Fever Dream Wakey Wakey 825
Fever Pitch Marston's 749
FGB Firehouse 697
Fife & Drum Musket 757
Filibuster Mutineers 758
Filly Close Blonde Reedley
   Hallows 782
Filthy B***ard Not That
   California 763
Final Furlong Uttoxeter 823
Finally an ESB Artefact 635
Findhorn Killer Red IPA
   Speyside 798
Fine Light Ale Goacher's 706
Fine Soft Day Iceni 725
Finnegan's No. 1 Twisted 819
Finn's Hall Porter Beowulf 644
Fire Cracker CrackleRock 677
Firebird VI Corinium 676
Firebox Steam Town 800
Firefly Hanlons 715
Firemore Ewebrew 693
Fireside Black Country 648
First Aviation Doncaster 685
First Class Black Box 647
   Stamps 799
   Titanic 813
First Flight Woodland 835
First Light Brew Foundation 657
   Horbury 723
First Voyage Captain Cook 667
Fist Full of Hops Falstaff 694
Fistral Pilsner Atlantic 636
Five Claw Dorking 685
Five Inch Drop New River 760
Flack's Double Drop Flack
   Manor 698
Flange Noir Toolmakers 815
Flapjack Marmalade Hop
   Kettle 722
Flat Cap Bank Top 637
Flaxen Carlisle 668
   Hophurst 723
Fleek Wylam 836
Fletcher's Ale Milestone 752
Flight of the Falcon Peregrine 772
Flint's Gold Burnside 664
Flintlock Musket 757
Flintshire Bitter Facer's 693
Flippin Eck Yorkshire
   Brewhouse 837
Flipping Best Flipside
   (Magpie) 747
The Flookburgh Cockler
   Unsworth's Yard 822
Flora Daze Blue Anchor 650
Flower Power Capitalist Hippy
   (Gyle 59) 713
   Mithril 753
   Whim 829
Flowerdew Townhouse 816
Fluffy Bunny Beer Hut 642
Flummoxed Farmer Ainsty 630
Flux Wishbone 834
Flying Elephants Ulverston 822
Flying the Mags London
   Brewing 742
Fog on the Humber Little Big
   Dog 739
Fogline Kettlesmith 732
Folded Cross Beowulf 644
Font Ashover 635
Fools Gold Brinkburn Street 661
   Lord Conrad's 743

BEERS INDEX

Hops & Dreams Brew Foundation 657
Hopsack Phoenix 773
Hopscotch Old School 766
Hopspur Redemption 781
Hopster Hydes 725
Hoptical Illusion Brass Castle 656
The Hoptimist Two Matts 820
Hoptimystic Hemlock 718
Hopzester Roebuck 784
Horizon Wadworth 825
Hornswoggle Froth Blowers 702
Horny Goat Lord Conrad's 743
Horse & Jockey Full Mash 702
Horse Brass Fresh Standard 701
Horsell Best Thurstons 811
Horsell Gold Thurstons 811
Horsforth Pale Horsforth 724
Hot Lap Apex 633
Hot Wired Tuk Tuk Caps Off 667
Hotel Barrifornia VOG (Vale of Glamorgan) 823
Hound Handsome 714
Hounded Best Bitter Hairy Dog 713
How Now Brolly 662
Howardian Gold Helmsley 718
An Howl Firebrand 697
HPA Botley 653
Wye Valley 836
HSB Gale's (Fuller's) 703
Hudson's Bitter Fengate 695
Hufflepuff Little Ox 740
Huggermuggery Coffee Porter Stealth 799
On the Huh Beeston 643
Hukins McCanns 746
Hullabaloo Loddon 741
Humpty's Fuddle IPA Kingstone 733
Hung, Drawn 'n' Portered North Cotswold 762
Hunky Dory Shortts 792
Huntsman Best Bitter Lord Randalls 743
Hurricane Jack Fyne 703
Hurricane Beowulf 644
Buntingford 664
Longhill 743
Wantsum 826
Hush Little Brewing 739
Hussar Uley 821
Hykeham Gold Poachers 775

I

I Ain't Afraid of Noh Ghost Snaggletooth 795
I Wanna Beer-dored Whitworth Valley 830
I'm Spartacus Torrside 815
Icarus Blindmans 650
Iceberg Titanic 813
Idaho 7 Harrison's 716
Idler Powderkeg 777
If the Caravan's A Rockin' Escape 692
Ignition Silverstone 793
Illicit Black Market 649
Illuminati Full Mash 702
Illumination Moor 755
Imp Ale Poachers 775
Imperial Drake Dancing Duck 681
Imperial IPA Tower 816
Imperial Stout Nailmaker 758

Imperium Wantsum 826
Impossible IPA Weatheroak Hill 827
Impy Dark Brampton 655
In Vein Mine 753
Inca Gold Bull of the Woods 663
Inclined Plane Bitter Langton 736
Incognito Alter Ego 632
Incredible Ian A Bloke Down the Pub (Potbelly) 777
Incredible Pale Ale Fat Cat 695
Incredible Taste Fantastic Clarity Dove Street 686
Independence APA Silver 793
Independence Bristol Beer Factory 661
India Pale Ale Loose Cannon 743
Mumbles 757
India Stancill 799
Indian Empire Newbridge 760
Indian Porter Dancing Duck 681
Indiana's Bones Summerskills 803
Indie Shortts 792
Inferno Oakham 764
Infinity IPA Blue Monkey 651
Coniston 674
Infinity Plus 1 Blue Monkey 651
Ingleborough Gold Three Peaks 811
Inhaler Magic Rock 747
INN Alcatraz INNformal 727
INN Darkness INNformal 727
INN Deep INNformal 727
INN House Bitter INNformal 727
INN Session INNformal 727
Inner Sound Applecross 633
INNspiration Cabin 666
Interloper Trig 817
Into the Light P-Noot 769
Into the Wild Aleworks 630
Inverted Jenny Stamps 799
An Invisible Hand Five Kingdoms 698
IPA (Icknield Pale Ale) Weatheroak Hill 827
IPA No. 3 Wobbly 834
IPA 3 Brewers of St Albans 627
4Ts 628
AJ's 630
Alnwick 632
The IPA Anspach & Hobday 633
IPA Black Cloak 648
Black Hole 648
Blackedge 649
Born 653
Bosun's 653
Boundary 654
Brentwood 656
Brewster's 659
Brighton Bier 660
Brimstage 661
Burton Road (MBH Beer) 750
Caps Off 667
Church Farm 671
Clevedon 672
Courtyard 677
Cross Borders 679
Davenports 682
Dhu Brew (Stow) 802
Drone Valley 687
Eagle (Banks's) 638
First Chop 697
Flower Pots 699
Forge 700
Fox 700

Glasgow Beer Works 705
Grasmere 709
Greene King 711
Gyle 59 712
Handyman 715
Indian 726
Joseph Holt 721
Kelchner 731
Lakedown 735
Lancaster 735
Liberation 738
Lymm 745
MBH Beer 750
McMullen 746
Padstow 769
Palmers 769
Peak 771
Pennine 771
Penzance 772
Rebellion 780
River Leven 783
Runaway 786
Sheelin 792
Shipstone's 792
Southport 797
Three Acre 809
Thwaites 811
Tiley's 811
Tilford 811
Tudor 818
Wetherby 829
WHARF 829
Whitby 829
Woodcote 835
Yardsman (Hercules) 718
Irish Cream Stout New Bristol 760
Irish Stout Hilden 720
Monkey House 754
Irk Street Pale Ale Blackjack 650
Iron & Steel Bitter Chantry 669
Iron And Fire St Annes 787
Iron Horse Hepworth 718
Iron Ore IPA Industrial Ales (Silver) 793
Ironbridge Gold Rowton 786
Ironic Rye Radical 779
Ironsand Consett 675
Irreverent James Tomos & Lilford 814
Is This a Joke Dungeon 688
Isambard Chapel-en-le-Frith 670
Island Hopping Swannay 804
Island Life Orkney 767
Island Street Porter Salcombe 788
Islander Exmoor 693
Yates' 837
Isle of Rye Pale Ale New River 760
Isobar IPA Storm 801
Isolation Wheatsheaf 829
It Takes All Sorts Weldon 828
It's Never One Small World 795
It's A Lesta Thing Mill Hill 752
ITA Quirky 779
Iti Hawkshead 717
It's My Shadow Drop The Anchor 687
It's Proper Pale We Are Wolf 827
Ixworth Blonde Artefact 635

J

Jack Back Stewart 800
Jack the Devil Cullercoats 680
Jack in the Box Blackjack 650

BEERS INDEX

Legra Pale Leigh on Sea *737*
Leighton Gold Leighton
Buzzard *737*
Leila's Lazy Days Leila Cottage (8 Sail) *628*
Leila's One Off Leila Cottage (8 Sail) *628*
Lemon & Ginger Humpty Dumpty *724*
Lemon Dream Salopian *788*
Lemon Soul Tomos & Lilford *814*
Lemongrass & Ginger Leatherbritches *736*
Lemonhead Hemlock *718*
Leningrad Chapel-en-le-Frith *670*
Lerwick IPA Lerwick *737*
Let the Dragon See the Wolf Oxford *769*
Level Best Rother Valley *785*
Level Crossing Delphic *683*
Level Up Elusive *691*
Leveret Twisted Oak *819*
Leveson Buck Titsey *813*
LFB (Lunns First Brew) Golden Duck *707*
LGM1 Green Jack *711*
Lhune Airh Kaneen's *730*
Li'l Napoleon Stubborn Mule *803*
Lia Fail Inveralmond *727*
Liberator Tindall *812*
Tring *817*
Life & Death Vocation *825*
Life Goes On Stannary *799*
Life Of Riley Wincle *833*
Life's a Peach Tomos & Lilford *814*
Lifeboat Titanic *813*
Lifeline Brolly *662*
Lifesaver Strong Bitter Mumbles *757*
Lifesaver Salcombe *788*
Lift & Shift Burnside *664*
The Light Brigade Ben's *644*
Light Railway Kinver *733*
Light Rale Ashover *635*
Light Wait Beeston *643*
Lighterman Exeter *693*
Lightfoot Theakston *809*
Lighthouse Pale Ale New Buildings *760*
Lightning Pale Ale Axholme (Docks) *684*
Lignum Vitae Grain *709*
Likely More Bar Tat Red Rose *781*
Lil Wingman Shiny *792*
Lincoln Best Poachers *775*
Lincoln Gold Lincolnshire Craft *738*
Lincoln Imperial Ale Small Beer (Black Hole) *648*
Lincoln Tank Ale Pheasantry *773*
Lincolnshire Country Bitter Firehouse *697*
Lincolnshire Traditional Bitter Consortium *675*
Line of Sight Broadtown *661*
Linebacker Leadmill *736*
Lion's Pride Milestone *752*
Lip Smacker Brightwater *660*
Liquid Gold Goldmark *707*
Liquorice Lads Stout Great Newsome *710*
Lit Beartown *641*
Litehouse Forge *700*
Little Arms, Big Ambitions Staggeringly Good *799*
Little Belgium Firebrick *697*

Little Bitter That Brew Foundation *657*
Little Black S Big Hand *645*
Little Bollington Bitter Dunham Massey *688*
Little Citra Single Hop Pale Basement Beer *639*
Little Donker Spitting Feathers *798*
Little Dragon Eight Arch *690*
Little Fox Newbridge *760*
Little Hopper Little Critters *739*
Little IPA Liverpool Brewing *740*
Little John Lincoln Green *738*
Milestone *752*
Little Marvel Hafod *713*
Little Monkey Big Hand *645*
Little Nipper Brightwater *660*
Little Pearl Brolly *662*
Little Sharpie Humpty Dumpty *724*
Little Weed Maypole *750*
Littlemoor Citra Ashover *635*
Live IPA Moor *755*
Liverpool Light Rock the Boat *784*
Llandogo Trow Kingstone *733*
Lleu Lleu *741*
Loaded Bull of the Woods *663*
Local Treen's *816*
Lochan Cairngorm *666*
Lock N Load BOA (Brothers of Ale) *652*
Locomotion No 1 George Samuel *704*
Lode Star Hop Kettle *722*
LOHAG (Land of Hops & Glory) Front Row *701*
Lol! Twt Lol *821*
Lomas Loxley *744*
London Glory Greene King *711*
London Lush London Brewing *742*
London Original Young's (Banks's) *638*
London Pale Ale Southwark *797*
London Pale Hafod *713*
London Porter Mad Squirrel *747*
Moonface *754*
London Pride Fuller's *702*
London Special Young's (Banks's) *638*
London Tap New River *760*
London Thunder Rooster's *785*
Lone Rider Tombstone *814*
Lonely Snake Three Blind Mice *810*
Lonesome Pine Ulverston *822*
Long Blonde Long Man *742*
Long Hop Bollington *652*
Long Lane Austendyke *636*
Long Moor Pale Small World *795*
Longbow Lincoln Green *738*
Longdog IPA Longdog *743*
Loop Pale Ale Barney's *638*
Loop Little Brewing *739*
Looper Full Circle *702*
Loophole Clun *673*
Lord Cullens Ruby Elmesthorpe *691*
Lord Kitchener Mr Grundy's (Black Hole) *648*
Lord Marples Thornbridge *809*
Lost Horizon Basement Beer *639*
Lost in Ikea Nightjar *761*
Lost Luggage Black Box *648*
Lost Shadow Burnside *664*
Lou's Brew Driftwood Spars *687*
Loud Mouth BOA (Brothers of Ale) *652*

Louis Louis Harrogate *716*
Lovely Nancy Longdog *743*
Lovely Nelly Cullercoats *680*
Lover's Leap Hwgga *725*
Low Tide Southsea *797*
Loweswater Gold Cumbrian *680*
Lowry Hydes *725*
Loxhill Biscuit Crafty *677*
Loxley Ale Milestone *752*
Lucid Dream Turning Point *818*
Lucky Spence Pale Bellfield *643*
Luddite Ale Mill Valley *752*
Lumberjack Brentwood *656*
Lumina Siren *794*
Luminaire Pope's Yard *776*
Lunar Stout We Are Wolf *827*
Lunnys No. 8 Golden Duck *707*
Lupus Lupus Wolf *834*
Lurcher Stout Green Jack *711*
Lush Hopstar *723*
Lushingtons Skinner's *794*
Luvly Little London *740*
Luxury Porter Chelmsford *670*
Lyme Gold Lyme Regis *745*
Lyme Regis Ammonite Gyle 59 *712*
Lymington Special Bitter Monkey *753*
Lynch Pin Toolmakers *815*

M

MòR Ish! MòR *755*
MòR Please! MòR *755*
MòR Tea Vicar? MòR *755*
Mad Gaz Amwell Springs *632*
Mad Goose Purity *778*
Mad Hatter Weetwood *827*
Mad Jack Ha' First & Last *697*
Mad Jack Papworth *770*
Mad Max Weldon *828*
Mad Monk Digfield *683*
Mad Ruby Leatherbritches *736*
Mad Wolf Wolf *834*
Mad World Beath *641*
Madagascan Vanilla Porter Cornish Crown *676*
Madre Brolly *662*
Maggie's Leap IPA Whitewater *830*
Maggs' Mild Renegade *782*
Magic Muntjac Stag *798*
Magic Number Carlisle *668*
Magic Potion Bakers Dozen *637*
Magnitude Axholme (Docks) *684*
Magnum Mild Muirhouse *757*
Magus Durham *688*
Maharaja IPA Renegade *782*
Mahseer IPA Green Jack *711*
Maid Marian Milestone *752*
Maiden Voyage Bosun's *653*
Hop Union *722*
Mail Train Stamps *799*
Main Street Citra Downham Isle *686*
Mainwarings Mild Firehouse *697*
Major Oak Maypole *750*
Make it Real Pale Little Big Dog *739*
Malamute Lords *743*
Maldon Gold Mighty Oak *751*
Malham Tarn Stout Three Peaks *811*
Malt Bitter Mumbles *757*
Malten Copper Tipple's *813*

BEERS INDEX

EERS
NDEX

Papworth 770
Vale 823
Red Knocker Fox 700
Red Lion Ashover 635
Red MacGregor Orkney 767
Red Mild Fresh Standard 701
Red Mill Humpty Dumpty 724
Red Mist Storm 801
Red Nek Cabin 666
Red Nelson Grain 709
Red Panther Panther 769
The Red Queen Boudicca 654
Red Ram Ramsbury 779
Red Rebel IPA Dhillon's 683
Red Revival Glen Spean 705
Red Robin Yorkshire
  Brewhouse 837
Red Rocker Cromarty 678
Red Rocket Stardust 799
Red Roses Front Row 701
Red Rowan First & Last 697
Red Runner Longdog 743
Red Rye Barney's 638
Red Screes Strands 802
Red Sky Twickenham 818
Red Smiddy Kelburn 730
Red Star IPA Tollgate 814
Red Star Hop Kettle 722
  Phipps NBC 773
Red Bushy's 665
  Castle Eden 668
  Hawkshead 717
  Lancaster 735
  Sheelin 791
Redgate Godstone 706
Redhouse Premium Bexley 645
Redoubt Stout WHARF 829
Redsmith Serious 790
Redwood Weatheroak 827
Reedcutter Humpty Dumpty 724
Reedlighter Woodforde's 835
Reef Break Country Life 677
Reefer Steam Town 800
Reel Ale Teignworthy 807
Reenys Beans Northern
  Monkey 763
Reet Pale Blue Bee 650
Reet Yorkshire Brewhouse 837
The Reeve's Ale Canterbury
  Ales 667
Regal Blond Byatt's 666
Reginald Perrin Northdown 763
Regulators Tombstone 814
Reiver First & Last 697
Relacite Temper 807
Release the Chimps Nene
  Valley 759
Release the Pressure Nightjar 761
Release the Quacken Dancing
  Duck 681
Reliance Pale Ale Brixton 661
Remembrance Whitley Bay 830
Renaissance Ruby Mild
  Whitstable 830
Renton Five Kingdoms 698
Repeater Full Circle 702
Reprazent! Furnace 703
Reservoir Gold Gates Burton 704
Reservoir Gates Burton 704
Resolute Bitter Andwell 632
Resolution Mad Squirrel 747
Resolve Temper 807
  Treen's 816
Resonance Moor 755
Respire Black Sheep 649

Resplendent Perspective Wilde
  Child 832
Responsibly Strands 802
Restoration Ale Leighton
  Buzzard 737
Restormel Gold Castle 668
Rev Hawker Forge 700
Rev James Original Brains 655
Revenge Lyme Regis 745
Reverend Green Golden Duck 707
Revill Loxley 744
Revival Moor 755
Reward IPA Crafty Monkey 678
Reynard Lords 743
RFA Sir Galahad Harbwr Tenby 715
Rhatas Black Dog (Hambleton) 714
Rhode Island Red Brimstage 661
Rhubarb X Custard Xtreme 837
Rhubarbeer Yorkshire Heart 838
Rhumsaa Bitter Odin 765
Rhythm Stick Billericay 646
Ribblehead Bitter Settle 790
Ribersborg Stout Shivering
  Sands 792
Rich Ruby Milestone 752
Rider / Three Lions Twisted 819
Ridgeline Kettlesmith 732
Ridgeway Tring 817
Ridley's Rite Bishop Nick 647
Ridware Pale Blythe 651
Riff IPA Clearwater 672
Riggwelter Black Sheep 649
Right to Roam Buxton 665
Right On Bluntrock 651
Ring of Fire Three Kings 810
Ring Tong Plockton 775
Ringmaster Magic Rock 747
Ringneck Amber Ale
  Pheasantry 773
Ripchord BrewBoard 657
Ripper Green Jack 711
Rise Above 80/- Seagate 789
Rising Giant Long Man 742
Rising Star Hop Kettle 722
Rising Sun Crich 678
Rivet Catcher Great North
  Eastern 710
Riviera Gold Riviera 783
Riviera Pale Ale / RPA Riviera 783
Riwaka Station Buntingford 664
Road Apple Strong Drinkstone 687
Road Crew Camerons 667
Road Kill Apex 633
Road Trip Bullhouse 663
Roadie All-Night IPA
  Signature 793
Roadrunner Bottle Brook 653
Roan Aldwark Artisan 630
Roasted Nuts Rebellion 780
Roasted Stout JackRabbit 729
Robbie's Red Adur 629
Robin Goodfellow Papworth 770
Rock & Roll Briggs Signature 660
Rock Ape Poachers 775
Rock Bitter Nottingham 764
Rock Mild Nottingham 764
Rock Steady Bull of the Woods 663
  Mantle 748
Rockabilly Shortts 792
Rocket Nun Three Blind Mice 810
Rocket Brunswick 662
Rocketeer Bluestone 651
Rocky Shiny 791
Roebuck Bitter Roebuck 784
Roebuck IPA Roebuck 784

Rogue Wave Cromarty 678
Rokerite North Pier 762
Rolling Hitch Darwin 682
Rolling Maul Snaggletooth 795
Roman Road Towcester Mill 815
Romney Amber Ale Romney
  Marsh 785
Romney APA Romney Marsh 785
Romney Best Bitter Romney
  Marsh 785
Romsey Gold Flack Manor 698
Root Thirteen Downlands 686
Ropetackle Golden Ale Adur 629
Rorschach Mr Winter's 757
Rose Tattoo Red Dog 781
Rosherville Red Iron Pier 728
Rough Rock Big Stone 646
Round The Wrekin St Annes 787
Routemaster Red Southwark 797
RPA (Ramsbury Pale Ale)
  Ramsbury 779
RuBee Mr Bees 756
Rubis Horsforth 724
Ruby Duck Fuzzy Duck 703
Ruby Jewel Muirhouse 757
Ruby Mild Harrison's 716
  Rudgate 786
Ruby Red St Peter's 788
Ruby Revolution Three
  Brothers 810
Ruby Ruby Ruby Ruby Crafty
  Monkey 677
Ruby Sunset Combe 674
Ruby AJ's 630
  Quirky 779
Rucked Front Row 701
Rude Not To Amwell Springs 632
Rufus Crooked 679
Rum Porter Stamps 799
Rumour Gower 708
Run Hop Run Rigg & Furrow 783
Rundle Beck Bitter Brewster's 659
Running Bier Rigg & Furrow 783
Running with the Big Dog Six
  Hills 794
Rushmoor Ripper Tilford 811
Ruskin's Kirkby Lonsdale 733
Rustic Tonbridge 814
Rusty Stag Farr Brew 694
Rusty's Ale Godstone 706
Rutland Beast Grainstore 709
Rutland Osprey Grainstore 709
Rutland Panther Grainstore 709
Ryestone Hornes 723
RYIPA Seagate 789

S

Séance Full Mash 702
S'more Fire Alter Ego 632
S'more Porter Three Brothers 810
SA Gold Brains 655
SA Brains 655
Sabro IPA Brewers Folly 657
Sabro Harrison's 716
Saddleback Best Bitter
  Slaughterhouse 794
Saffron Sun Roughacre 785
St Andrew's Amber Ale
  Belhaven 643
St Edmunds Greene King 711
St George Holsworthy 721
St Leger Gold Stocks (Welbeck
  Abbey) 828

Table Beer Newbarns 760
Windmill Hill 833
Tag Lag Barngates 639
Taiheke Sun Great North
Eastern 710
Tailshaker Great Oakley 710
Taiphoon Hop Back 722
Taj Session IPA Little Brewing 739
Take It Easy Gyle 59 712
Taking the Biscuit
Elmesthorpe 691
Talbot Blonde Teme Valley 807
Talisman IPA Pictish 773
Tally Ho! Palmers 769
Tally-Ho Light Ale Lord
Randalls 743
Tamar Black Holsworthy 721
Tamar Source Forge 700
Tamar Summerskills 803
Tanglefoot Hall & Woodhouse
(Badger) 714
Tanner & Hyde Wickham
House 831
TAR Gan Yam 703
Tarasgeir Isle of Skye 729
Target Snowhill 795
Taverner Uley 822
Tavy IPA Roam 783
Tawny Owl Cotleigh
(Nuttycombe) 764
Tawton Session Ale Taw
Valley 806
TBC (Thwaites Best Cask)
Thwaites 811
Tea Kettle Stout Tring 817
TEA Hogs Back 720
Team Mates Beermats 642
Techno Briggs Signature 660
Tedi Boy Poachers 775
Telegram Neighbourhood 758
Telegraph Session IPA Crafty
Monkey 677
Tell No Tales Bosun's 653
Tempest Bosun's 653
Templer Teignmouth 807
Ten Fifty Grainstore 709
Tenfoot Yorkshire Brewhouse 837
Tent Zapato 838
Tequila Blonde Bridgehouse 659
Terminus George Samuel 704
Tern IPA Bowness Bay 655
Tether Blond Wharfe
(Hambleton) 714
Tetley Bitter Carlsberg Marston's
(Banks's) 638
Tewdric's Tipple Kingstone 733
Texas Cleggy Whitley Bay 830
Texas Jack Tombstone 814
Textbook Old School 766
Thanks Pa Consortium 675
That Teme Valley 807
There's Something in the Water
Beer Hut 642
These Walls Burton Road (MBH
Beer) 750
Thick as Thieves Sperrin 798
Thieving Rogue Magpie 747
Third Party Sperrin 798
Thirst Aid Kit Rock & Roll 784
Thirst Celebration Keswick 732
Thirst of Many GT 712
Thirst Quencher Keswick 732
Thirst Rescue Keswick 732
Thirst Run Keswick 732

Thirstquencher Spitting
Feathers 798
Thirsty Blonde Teignworthy 807
Thirsty Dog Newt 761
Thirsty Moon Phoenix 773
Thirsty Walker Dove Street 686
Thirty Three Brighton Bier 660
This Splendid Ale Facer's 694
This Time Next Year Rodney Vale
of Glamorgan 823
This Teme Valley 807
Thomas Lift Langton 736
Thomas Sykes Burton Bridge 665
Thoroughbred IPA Hambleton 714
Thousand Yard Stare Rooster's 785
Three & Sixpence Twisted 819
Three Amigos Snaggletooth 795
Three Brewers Blonde 3 Brewers
of St Albans 627
Three Counties East Anglian Best
Bitter Roughacre 785
Three Erics St Annes 787
Three Spires Mason 749
Three Swords Kirkstall 733
Three Tails Bitter Boudicca 654
Three XT 836
ThreeOneSix Grain 708
Through and Off Fixed Wheel 698
Thrupenny Bitter Phipps NBC 773
Thunder Bridge Shiny 791
Thunderbird Glamorgan 705
Thunderbridge Stout Small
World 795
Thunderstruck Durty 688
Thurlton Gold People's 772
Thurstein Pilsner Coniston 674
Tick Tock Boom Muirhouse 757
Tickety-Boo Indigenous 726
Tickle Muckle 757
Tidal Pool Northdown 763
Tiffield Thunderbolt Great
Oakley 710
Tiffin Gold Kirkby Lonsdale 733
Tiger Rut Millstone 752
Tiger Tom Ruby Mild Cerne
Abbas 669
Tiger Everards 692
Tigers Tail Milltown 752
Tight Bar Steward
Elmesthorpe 691
Tiller Pin Wishbone 834
Time Lapse Good Chemistry 707
Timeline Kettlesmith 732
Tinder Box Inferno 727
Tinderbox IPA Fell 695
Tinners Tipple Golden Duck 707
Tiny Pixie Wishbone 834
Tip Top Citra London Beer Lab 742
Tipsy Fisherman Steamin' Billy 800
Tiptoe Stealth 799
Tiramisu Stout Sussex Small
Batch 804
Tiramisu Horbury 723
Titanium Quantock 778
Titus Saltaire 789
Tizzie Whizie Great Corby 709
TNT IPA Dynamite Valley 689
Tod's Blonde Little Valley (Great
Newsome) 710
Together Brolly 662
Tollhouse Monkey 753
Tom Cat Fat Cat 695
Tom, Dick & Harry Escape 692
Tom Long Stroud 802
Tomahawk Exeter 693

Tommy The Miller Monkey
House 754
Tonkoko Brew York 657
Too Wet to Woo Red Rose 781
Toon Broon Firebrick 697
Top Dog Oscars 767
Top Knot Handsome 714
Top Marks Spenside Stables 797
Top Notch Brightwater 660
Topline IPA Tapestry By Props 806
Topsail Bays 641
Totty Pot Cheddar 670
Touch Front Row 701
Toujours Gyle 59 712
Tournament Goff's 706
Tower Blonde Darkland 681
Town Crier Hobsons 720
Towy Tiger Zoo 838
TPL Brightwater 660
TPP (The People's Poet)
Marlix 749
Trade Star Firebrick 697
Trade Winds Cairngorm 666
Traditional Ale Larkins 736
Tonbridge 814
Traditional IPA Strands 802
Traditional Porter Gwaun
Valley 712
Traditional Sussex Bitter
Hepworth 718
Traditional Brunning & Price (St
Austell) 787
Trafalgar Horsham 724
Tranquility Mr Winter's 757
Trans-Atlantic River Leven 783
Transmitter Potton 777
Trapper's Hat Bitter Brimstage 661
Travelling Light George
Samuel 704
Trawlerboys Best Bitter Green
Jack 711
Treacle Miners' Tipple Red
Rose 781
Treehouse Marmalade IPA New
Buildings 760
Trembling Rabbit Mild
Poachers 775
Trenchman's Hop Godstone 706
Trent Bridge Inn Ale
Nottingham 764
Trentsman Nottingham 764
Tri State Bingley 647
Tri-ball Sulwath 803
Tribune Roman Way 785
Tribute St Austell 787
Trident Scarborough 789
Trig Point Cheviot 671
Trigger Musket 757
Trilogy Three Brothers 810
Trimley Bee Air Mr Bees 756
Trinity Oxford 769
Redemption 781
Trink Penzance 772
Trinnacle Millstone 752
Triple B Grainstore 709
Triple Blond Peerless 771
Triple C Brewhouse 658
Triple Champion 1648 627
Triple Choc Saltaire 789
Triple Chocolate Stout
Nailmaker 758
Triple Goat IPA Hornes 723
Triple Goat Pale Ale Hornes 723
Triple Goat Porter Hornes 723
Triple Hop Xtra-IPA Xtreme 837

Well Chuffed Yorkshire Brewhouse 837
Welland Valley Mild Great Oakley 710
Wellington Ben's 644
Wellingtonian Froth Blowers 702
Wellow Gold Maypole 750
Welsh ESB Felinfoel 695
Welsh Pale Ale Glamorgan 705
Welsh Pride Conwy 675
Wentworth Nailmaker 758
West Coast IPA Fengate 695
Not That California 763
Phoenix 773
Steam Town 800
West Coast Pale Ale Silver 793
West Coast Pale Empire 691
We Are Wolf 827
West Coast Session IPA Firebrand 697
West Coast Blackedge 649
West Highland Way Loch Lomond 741
West Pier Brighton Bier 660
Westcountry IPA Bridgetown 660
Westward Ho! Summerskills 803
Westway Pale Ale Portobello 776
Wet Pocket Consortium 675
Wey-Aye PA Firebrick 697
Whakahari Purple Moose 778
Tillingbourne 812
Whaler Whitby 829
Whapweasel Hexhamshire 719
What the Fox's Hat Church End 671
What Makes Larry Happy Bang The Elephant 637
What What? Peregrine 772
Wheat Ear Full Mash 702
Wheat Storm Inferno 727
Wheelie Pale Fixed Wheel 698
Wheres My Fiorucci Consortium 675
Whernside Pale Ale Three Peaks 811
Wherry Woodforde's 835
Whimble Gold Radnorshire 779
Whin Sill Blonde Muckle 757
Whispering Grass Papworth 770
Whistle Belly Vengeance Summerskills 803
Whistlin' Dixie Full Mash 702
Whitby Abbey Ale Black Dog (Hambleton) 714
White Boar Village Brewer (Hambleton) 714
White Feather Brunswick 662
White Gold Durham 688
White Hot Consett 675
White Knight Goff's 707
White Lion Empire 691
White Monk Phoenix 773
White Nancy Bollington 652
White Panther Mill Valley 752
White Rabbit Rockingham 784
White Rat Ossett 767
White Sea Newby Wyke 761
White Squall Newby Wyke 761
White Star Titanic 813
White Swan Pale Ale Thames Side 808
White Witch Moorhouse's 755
White Wolf Deeply Vale 682
Little Critters 739
White Enville 692
Whiteout Cromarty 678

The Whitfield Citrabolt Papworth 770
Whitstable Bay Pale Ale Shepherd Neame 791
Wholesome Stout Wye Valley 836
Whopper Tamworth 805
Why Kick a Moo Cow? Arbor 634
Wibbly Wallaby Wincle 833
Wide to Gauge Broadtown 661
The Wife of Bath's Ale Canterbury Ales 667
Wight Gold Island 728
Wight Knight Island 728
Wight Squirrel Goddards 706
Wild Anchor Wildcraft 832
Wild Bill Hiccup Wildcraft 832
Wild Blonde South Hams 796
Wild Boar Buxton 665
Slaughterhouse 794
Wild Caribbean Wildcraft 831
Wild Cat IPA Fat Cat 695
Wild Coast Chelmsford 670
Wild Eye P.A Wildcraft 831
Wild Heaven Arundel 635
Wild Hopster Wildcraft 832
Wild Light Temper 807
Wild Norfolk Wildcraft 831
Wild One Wildcraft 832
Wild Orchid Brightwater 660
Wild Rhino Burnside 664
Wild Ride Wildcraft 832
Wild Stallion Wildcraft 832
Wild Steamer Wildcraft 831
Wild Summer Wildcraft 832
Wild Swan Thornbridge 809
Wild Un-Bongo Wildcraft 832
Wild Wood Twisted Oak 819
Wildcraft 832
Wild Ennerdale 692
Wildcat Cairngorm 666
Wildern Botley 653
Wildfire Darkland 681
Will-o'-the-Wisp Black Metal 649
William Mucklow's Dark Mild Bewdley 645
Wills Neck Quantock 778
Willy Wickams Posthumous Ale Consortium 675
Wiltshire Gold Arkell's 634
Wily Ol' Fox WHARF 829
To the Winchester Nightjar 761
Windermere Pale Hawkshead 717
Windjammer Padstow 769
Windmill Best Bitter New Buildings 760
Windmill Bitter 8 Sail 628
Windmill Stout Birch Cottage 647
Windmill Wheat Two Rivers 820
Windmill Weldon 828
Windrush Ale North Cotswold 762
Windsor Knot Windsor & Eton 833
Windy Gyle Cheviot 671
On the Wing Ampersand 632
Wingding Sociable 796
Winkle Picker Whitstable 830
Winter Hill Northern Monkey 763
Winter Porter Snowhill 796
Wipeout Little Ox 740
Witches Cauldron Moorhouse's 755
Witchfinder General Kinver 733
Withens Pale Little Valley (Great Newsome) 710
The Wizard Merlin 751
Wobbly Bob Phoenix 773
Wobbly Weasel Firehouse 697

Woild Moild Wolf 834
Wold Gold Wold Top 834
Wolds ESB Stow Fen 802
Wolds Way Wold Top 834
Wolf Ale Wolf 834
Wolf in Sheep's Clothing Wolf 834
Wolf Allendale 631
Wonderland IPA New Bristol 760
Woodcock's Relish Nene Valley 759
Wooden Ships Neptune 759
Woodman Pale Ale Firehouse 697
Woodstock Bull of the Woods 663
Woody's Bark Billericay 646
Worcestershire Sway/ 2857 Bewdley 645
Worcestershire Way Bewdley 645
World's End Delphic 683
Worth the Wait Beeston 643
Worthog Green Jack 711
Wot No Cheyz Front Row 701
Wot's Occurring Great Oakley 710
Wotever Next? Teme Valley 807
Wotton Hop Project Lucifer 744
WPA (Welsh Pale Ale) Evan Evans 692
Wrangler Stonehouse 801
Wrath of the Gods Shadow Bridge 790
Wrecker Evan Evans 692
Wreckless RedWillow 782
Wrekin No. 1 Rowton 786
Wrench Shiny 792
Wryneck Rye IPA Thames Side 808
WSB 4Ts 628
Wuffa Beowulf 644
Wybar Hop Shed 722
Wychert Vale 823

X

X Mild LAMB 735
X No.1 Moonface 754
XB Batemans 640
Theakston 809
XL Bitter Burton Bridge 664
XL Mild Burton Bridge 664
XPA Five Points 698
Woodcote 835
Xporter Xtreme 837
XTRA Fudge Stout Mill Valley 752
Xtreme Special Bitter Xtreme 837
XX Crooked 679
XXXB Batemans 640

Y

Y Brawd Houdini Llyn 741
Yabba Dabba Doo Little Ox 740
Yachtsmans Ale Island 728
Yakima Gold Crouch Vale 679
Yakima Valley Arbor 634
Yammerhouse Northern Whisper 763
Yankee Doodle Nanny Little Goat 740
Yankee Rooster's 785
Yardbird Greene King 711
Yarrowale Plockton 775
Yellow Hammer Hanlons 715
Yellow Peak Torrside 815
Yellow Submarine Special Rock the Boat 784
Yellowhammer Black Isle 648
Yggdrasil Black Metal 649

Readers' recommendations

Suggestions for pubs to be included or excluded

All pubs are regularly surveyed by local branches of the Campaign for Real Ale to ensure they meet the standards required by the *Good Beer Guide*. If you would like to comment on a pub already featured, or on any you think should be featured, please fill in the form below (or a copy of it), and send it to the address indicated. Alternatively, email **gbgeditor@camra.org.uk**. Your views will be passed on to the branch concerned. Please mark your envelope/email with the county where the pub is, which will help us to direct your comments efficiently.

Pub name:

Address:

Reason for recommendation/criticism:

Pub name:

Address:

Reason for recommendation/criticism:

Pub name:

Address:

Reason for recommendation/criticism:

Your name and address:

Please send to: [Name of county] Section, Good Beer Guide, 230 Hatfield Road, St Albans, Hertfordshire AL1 4LW

Readers' recommendations
Suggestions for pubs to be included or excluded

All pubs are regularly surveyed by local branches of the Campaign for Real Ale to ensure they meet the standards required by the *Good Beer Guide*. If you would like to comment on a pub already featured, or on any you think should be featured, please fill in the form below (or a copy of it), and send it to the address indicated. Alternatively, email **gbgeditor@camra.org.uk**. Your views will be passed on to the branch concerned. Please mark your envelope/email with the county where the pub is, which will help us to direct your comments efficiently.

Pub name:

Address:

Reason for recommendation/criticism:

Pub name:

Address:

Reason for recommendation/criticism:

Pub name:

Address:

Reason for recommendation/criticism:

Your name and address:

Please send to: [Name of county] Section, Good Beer Guide,
230 Hatfield Road, St Albans, Hertfordshire AL1 4LW

Readers' recommendations

Suggestions for pubs to be included or excluded

All pubs are regularly surveyed by local branches of the Campaign for Real Ale to ensure they meet the standards required by the *Good Beer Guide*. If you would like to comment on a pub already featured, or on any you think should be featured, please fill in the form below (or a copy of it), and send it to the address indicated. Alternatively, email **gbgeditor@camra.org.uk**. Your views will be passed on to the branch concerned. Please mark your envelope/email with the county where the pub is, which will help us to direct your comments efficiently.

Pub name:

Address:

Reason for recommendation/criticism:

Pub name:

Address:

Reason for recommendation/criticism:

Pub name:

Address:

Reason for recommendation/criticism:

Your name and address:

Please send to: [Name of county] Section, Good Beer Guide,
230 Hatfield Road, St Albans, Hertfordshire AL1 4LW

HOW BEER IS BREWED

The brewer's art sees raw ingredients transformed into a wide variety of styles of beer. Follow their journey from field to glass with this general look at how beer is brewed.

THE KEY INGREDIENTS OF BEER

While brewers will experiment and make use of the cornucopia of ingredients available to them, there are four key elements most beers have in common: water, yeast, malt and hops, although, increasingly brewers are playing with extra ingredients that impart unusual and exciting flavours, aromas or consistency into a beer. Lactose, and heather, for example, have historically been used as additions, but more and more brewers are now employing honey, flowers, spices, fruits, and even meat in specialty ales.

Differing preparation methods, and varietals can create a spectrum of beer – from the very pale, to the near black; from clean, simple aromas, to deep coffee notes, or a fruity punch on the nose; and gentle, sessionable flavours that comfort the palate, to those that assault and challenge your taste buds.

Some breweries will have their own specific way of doing things, and each brewery set-up is individual, but the process is broadly the same. Use the flow chart overleaf to discover how brewers take the four key ingredients below and use them to create one of the most diverse drinks on the planet.

 ## MALT

The mix of malts used in making a beer contribute to the colour, flavour and strength of the beer. Malted barley is most common, but other grains, such as wheat, oats or rye can be used. Once harvested, maltsters steep barley in water to absorb moisture, then spread it on heated floors or inside rotating drums where it will start to germinate. It is then kilned to dry. The temperature determines the type of malt produced – from pale, through to black. Common flavours and aromas derived include Ovaltine, oatmeal biscuits, Ryvita, almonds/nuts, honey, butterscotch, caramel, tobacco and vanilla.

 ## HOPS

Hops can be used either as dried whole flowers or ground and compressed into pellets. Hops – via their oils and resins – impart aroma and flavour (including bitterness) into a beer, and are added into the copper/kettle, but can also be added later in the process. 'Dry-hopping', for example, is the process of adding a small amount of hops to a cask before it leaves the brewery en route to the pub, for additional aroma. Delicate aromas that can be destroyed during the boil can be retained in this way. While New World hops have become increasingly popular for their tropical fruit explosion in recent decades, UK hops provide the basis of more traditional beers.

WATER

Water used for the brewing process is called liquor. Pure water can come from springs, bore holes or from the public supply. And while some breweries will treat their water to achieve a certain profile (adding sulphates such as gypsum and magnesium), or to remove potential off-flavour-causing compounds, others have embraced the natural, distinct quality of the local water – such as world-renowned Burton water. This water trickles through bands of gypsum and gives the resulting beer the world-famous, sought-after 'Burton snatch'.

YEAST

Every brewery will have its own yeast culture and often this will be a closely guarded asset. Yeast are living organisms that consume sugars, turning them into alcohol and carbon dioxide. Traditionally most yeast used in UK beer production would have been 'ale yeast' which rises to the surface during fermentation and is therefore known as 'top-fermenting'. Other commonly-used yeasts are lager yeast, known as 'bottom-fermenting', and wild yeasts which create 'spontaneous fermentation', when beer in open vats is exposed to wild yeast in the air. Yeast produces natural chemical compounds called esters that give off aromas reminiscent of apples, oranges, pear drops, banana, liquorice, molasses and, in especially strong beers, fresh leather.

START

When malted barley reaches the brewery, it's ground in a mill into a powder called grist.

Grist and pure hot water, also called liquor, flow into the mash tun, where the porridge-like mixture of grain and water starts the brewing process.
The mixture is left to stand in the mash tun for around two hours, and during that time enzymes in the malt convert the remaining starch into fermentable sugar.

Malt mill

Mash tun   Liquor tank

Casks have to be vented to allow some of the natural gas to escape. A cask has two openings: a bung at the flat end where a tap is inserted to serve the beer; and a shive hole on top. A soft porous peg of wood, known as a spile or peg, is knocked into the shive, enabling some of the CO_2 to escape. As fermentation dies down, the soft spile is replaced after 24 hours by a hard one that leaves some gas in the cask: this gives the beer its natural sparkle, known as 'condition'.
Inside the cask, finings sink to the bottom, attracting the yeast in suspension.

When the publican is satisfied that the beer has 'dropped bright', plastic tubes or 'lines' are attached to the tap and the beer is drawn by a suction pump activated by a handpump on the bar. Some pubs and beer festivals may serve the beer straight from the cask.

FINISH

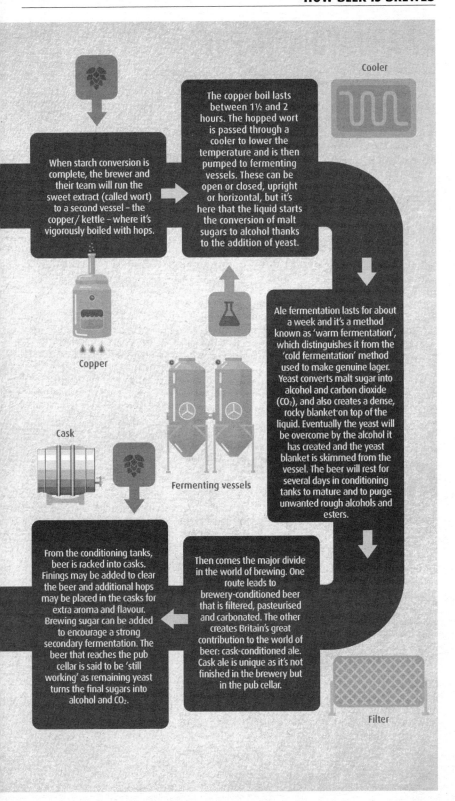

Cooler

When starch conversion is complete, the brewer and their team will run the sweet extract (called wort) to a second vessel – the copper/ kettle – where it's vigorously boiled with hops.

The copper boil lasts between 1½ and 2 hours. The hopped wort is passed through a cooler to lower the temperature and is then pumped to fermenting vessels. These can be open or closed, upright or horizontal, but it's here that the liquid starts the conversion of malt sugars to alcohol thanks to the addition of yeast.

Copper

Cask

Fermenting vessels

Ale fermentation lasts for about a week and it's a method known as 'warm fermentation', which distinguishes it from the 'cold fermentation' method used to make genuine lager. Yeast converts malt sugar into alcohol and carbon dioxide (CO_2), and also creates a dense, rocky blanket on top of the liquid. Eventually the yeast will be overcome by the alcohol it has created and the yeast blanket is skimmed from the vessel. The beer will rest for several days in conditioning tanks to mature and to purge unwanted rough alcohols and esters.

From the conditioning tanks, beer is racked into casks. Finings may be added to clear the beer and additional hops may be placed in the casks for extra aroma and flavour. Brewing sugar can be added to encourage a strong secondary fermentation. The beer that reaches the pub cellar is said to be 'still working' as remaining yeast turns the final sugars into alcohol and CO_2.

Then comes the major divide in the world of brewing. One route leads to brewery-conditioned beer that is filtered, pasteurised and carbonated. The other creates Britain's great contribution to the world of beer: cask-conditioned ale. Cask ale is unique as it's not finished in the brewery but in the pub cellar.

Filter

AWARD-WINNING PUBS

The Pub of the Year competition is judged by CAMRA members. Each of the CAMRA branches votes for its favourite pub: criteria include the quality and choice of real ale, atmosphere, customer service, community offering, and value. The pubs listed below are the current winners of the title, look out for the ♥ next to the entries in the Guide.

ENGLAND

Bedfordshire
Devonshire Arms, Bedford
Fox, Carlton
Stone Jug, Clophill
Engineers Arms, Henlow
Bricklayers Arms, Luton

Fox, Carlton

Berkshire
Bell Inn, Aldworth
Newtown Pippin, Bracknell
Fox & Hounds, Caversham
A Hoppy Place Maidenhead, Maidenhead

Buckinghamshire
Victoria Inn, Milton Keynes: Bradwell Village

Cambridgeshire
Champion of the Thames, Cambridge
West End House, Ely
King of the Belgians, Hartford
Bumble Inn, Peterborough

Cheshire
Lodge Inn, Alsager
Cavern of the Curious Gnome, Chester
Brewery Tap, Lymm
Norton Arms, Runcorn
Bull's Head, Smallwood

Cornwall
Hole in the Wall, Bodmin

Cumbria
Fox Tap, Keswick
Drovers Rest, Monkhill
Swan Inn, Ulverston

Derbyshire
Rose & Crown, Chesterfield
Red Lion at Kniveton, Kniveton

Devon
Thatched House Inn, Exeter
Grove Inn, Kings Nympton
Fortescue Hotel, Plymouth
Walkhampton Inn, Walkhampton

Dorset
Woodman Inn, Bridport
Barking Cat Alehouse, Poole
Horse & Groom, Wareham

Durham
Grey Horse, Consett
Quakerhouse, Darlington
Old Elm Tree, Durham
Surtees Arms, Ferryhill Station
Golden Smog, Stockton-on-Tees

Grey Horse, Consett

Essex
Victoria Arms, Brentwood
Ale House, Colchester
Maybush Inn, Great Oakley
Queen Victoria, Maldon
Railway Arms, Saffron Walden
Endeavour, Springfield
Cap & Feathers, Tillingham
Mile & a Third, Westcliff-on-Sea

Gloucestershire & Bristol
Beehive Inn, Cheltenham
Horseshoe, Chipping Sodbury
Hearts of Oak, Drybrook
Old Spot Inn, Dursley
Inn at Fossebridge, Fossebridge
Cross House Tavern, Tewkesbury

Hampshire
Eight Bells, Alton
Andover Tap at the Lamb, Andover
Junction Tavern, Gosport
Park Inn, Southampton

Herefordshire
Alma Inn, Linton

Hertfordshire
Queen's Head, Allens Green
Orange Tree, Baldock
Robin Hood, St Albans
King's Arms, Tring
Two Trees Micro, Watford

Isle of Wight
Newport Ale House, Newport

Kent
Halfway House, Brenchley
Royston, Broadstairs
Thomas Becket, Canterbury
Larkins' Alehouse, Cranbrook
Compass Alehouse, Gravesend
Three Tuns, Lower Halstow
Coopers Arms, Rochester
Dog House Pub, Smeeth
Nelson Arms, Tonbridge
Berry, Walmer

Leicestershire
New Plough Inn, Hinckley
Blue Boar, Leicester
Organ Grinder, Loughborough
Anchor, Plungar
Stilton Cheese, Somerby

Lincolnshire
Railway Tavern, Aby
Thirsty Giraffe, Deeping St James
Lord Harrowby, Grantham
Yarborough Hotel, Grimsby
Tiny Tavern, Lincoln
Clickem Inn, Swinhope

London, Greater
North Star, E11: Leytonstone
Little Green Dragon, N21: Winchmore Hill
Southampton Arms, NW5: Kentish Town
River Ale House, SE10: East Greenwich
Trafalgar, SW19: South Wimbledon
Victoria, W2: Paddington
Owl & the Pussycat, W13: Northfields
Claret & Ale, Addiscombe
Robin Hood & Little John, Bexleyheath
Cockpit, Chislehurst
Gidea Park Micropub, Gidea Park
Lamb, Surbiton
Masons Arms, Teddington

Nelson Arms, Tonbridge

Cockpit, Chislehurst

Lancashire
Ralph's Wife's, Banks
Old England Forever, Clayton le Moors
Little Bare, Morecambe
Black Horse, Preston
Fifteens of St Annes, St Annes

Manchester, Greater
Beer House, Chorlton-cum-Hardy
Heaton Hops, Heaton Chapel
Bank Top Brewery Ale House, Horwich

Travellers Rest, Lowton
City Arms, Manchester
Northumberland Arms, Marple Bridge
Fox & Pine, Oldham
New Oxford, Salford
Wigan Central, Wigan

Merseyside
Roscoe Head, Liverpool: City Centre
Magazine Hotel, New Brighton
Turk's Head, St Helens
Grasshopper, Southport: Hillside

Norfolk
Blackfriars Tavern, Great Yarmouth
Red Lion, Kenninghall
Angel, Larling
White Lion, Norwich

Blackfriars Tavern, Great Yarmouth

Northamptonshire
Three Horseshoes, Ecton

Nottinghamshire
Wheatsheaf, Bingham
Just Beer Micropub, Newark
Final Whistle, Southwell
Horse & Jockey, Stapleford
Mallard, Worksop

Oxfordshire
Brewery Tap, Abingdon
White Horse, Banbury
Royal Blenheim, Oxford
Cross Keys, Thame
Cross Keys, Wallingford
King's Arms, Wantage

King's Arms, Wantage

Rutland
Railway, Ketton

Shropshire
Three Horseshoes Inn, Alveley
Bailey Head, Oswestry
Pheasant Inn, Telford: Wellington

Somerset
Old Green Tree, Bath
Crossways Inn, West Huntspill

Staffordshire
Devonshire Arms, Burton upon Trent
Newhall Arms, Cannock
Black Lion, Cheddleton
Cross Inn, Kinver
Holy Inadequate, Stoke-on-Trent: Etruria
Borehole, Stone
Tamworth Tap, Tamworth
Night Inn, Uttoxeter

Tamworth Tap, Tamworth

Suffolk
Dove, Bury St Edmunds
Fat Cat, Ipswich
Greyhound, Ixworth
Buck, Rumburgh

Surrey
Three Horseshoes, Cranleigh
Star Inn, Godalming
Thames Side Brewery, Staines-upon-Thames
Walton Village, Walton on Thames

Sussex, East
Brickmaker's Alehouse, Bexhill on Sea
Foghorn, Hove
King's Arms, Rotherfield

Sussex, West
Engine Room, East Grinstead
Inglenook, Pagham
Five Bells, West Chiltington

Tyne & Wear
Microbus, Gateshead
Marine, South Shields

Warwickshire
Three Tuns, Henley-in-Arden
Old Bakery, Kenilworth
Church End Brewery Tap, Ridge Lane
Seven Stars, Rugby
Thirst Edition, Shipston-on-Stour
Griffin Inn, Shustoke
Four Penny Pub, Warwick

West Midlands
Robin Hood, Amblecote
Hop & Scotch, Birmingham: Kings Heath
Hops d'Amour, Coventry: City Centre
Beacon Hotel, Sedgley
Pup & Duckling, Solihull
Robin Hood, Willenhall
Hail to the Ale, Wolverhampton

Wiltshire
Flemish Weaver, Corsham
Cuckoo Inn, Hamptworth
Five Bells, Royal Wootton Bassett

Worcestershire
Weighbridge, Alvechurch
Bewdley Brewery Tap, Bewdley
Fleece Inn, Bretforton
Weavers, Malvern

Yorkshire, East
Three B's Micropub, Bridlington
Centurion Arms, Brough
Hugh Fitz-Baldric, Cottingham
Hop & Vine, Hull
Jemmy Hirst, Rawcliffe

Three B's Micropub, Bridlington

Yorkshire, North
Harrogate Tap, Harrogate
Countryman's Inn, Hunton
Chapel @ Whitehouse Street, Middlesbrough
Sun Inn, Pickering
Scholars Bar, Scarborough
Beer Engine, Skipton
Buck Inn, Thornton Watlass
Swan, York

Beer Engine, Skipton

Kelham Island Tavern, Sheffield: Kelham Island

Yorkshire, South
Heaven & Ale, Barnsley
Doncaster Brewery Tap, Doncaster
Dragon's Tap, Rotherham
Kelham Island Tavern, Sheffield: Kelham Island

Yorkshire, West
Corn Dolly, Bradford
Victorian Craft Beer Café, Halifax: Town Centre
County Beerhouse, Huddersfield
Black Bull, Liversedge
Travellers Rest, Meltham

WALES

Glamorgan
Griffin Inn, Hendreforgan
Beaufort Arms, Mumbles
Pilot, Penarth

Gwent
Queen's Head, Chepstow

Mid-Wales
Arvon Ale House, Llandrindod Wells
Royal Oak, Pencelli

North-East Wales
Mold Alehouse, Mold
Magic Dragon Brewery Tap, Wrexham

North-West Wales
Myrddins Tap, Barmouth
Bay Hop, Colwyn Bay

West Wales
Stag & Pheasant, Carmarthen
Cresselly Arms, Cresswell Quay
Rhos yr Hafod Inn, Cross Inn (Llanon)

SCOTLAND

Aberdeen & Grampian
Globe Inn, Aberdeen

Argyll & the Isles
Oban Inn, Oban

Borders
Cobbles Freehouse & Dining, Kelso

Dumfries & Galloway
Blue Bell Inn, Annan
Clachan Inn, Dalry
Cavens Arms, Dumfries
Harbour Inn, Garlieston

Edinburgh & the Lothians
Jolly Judge, Edinburgh: Central
Four Marys, Linlithgow
Volunteer Arms (Staggs), Musselburgh

Harbour Inn, Garlieston

Jolly Judge, Edinburgh: Central

Greater Glasgow & Clyde Valley
Bull Inn, Paisley

Highlands & Western Isles
Bandstand, Nairn

Kingdom of Fife
Hillend Tavern, Hillend

Northern Isles
Helgi's Bar, Kirkwall: Orkney

Tayside
Speedwell Bar, Dundee

NORTHERN IRELAND

Northern Ireland
Dog & Duck Inn, Lisbellaw

CHANNEL ISLANDS

Channel Islands
Thomas de la Rue, St Peter Port, Guernsey

Bandstand, Nairn

ADDITIONAL RESOURCES

Please see below for information about other digital formats for the *Good Beer Guide* as well as details about how entries are chosen each year and how to get the best deal when purchasing the Guide with an annual subscription.

POINTS OF INTEREST (POI) FILES

The *Good Beer Guide* is also available as a sat-nav Points of Interest (POI) download.
See **shop1.camra.org.uk** for further information.

CAMRA'S NATIONAL BEER SCORING SYSTEM

CAMRA's National Beer Scoring System (NBSS) is used by members across the country to help them identify outlets that serve consistently good beer. The system uses a 0–5 scale that can be submitted online.

The NBSS is also used to select beers for the annual Champion Beer of Britain competition.
See **camra.org.uk/NBSS** for details.

JOIN CAMRA'S GOOD BEER GUIDE PRIVILEGE CLUB

CAMRA members can take advantage of an even bigger discount on the *Good Beer Guide*, and get further benefits, by joining the Good Beer Guide Privilege Club.

- Pay just £12 (RRP £16.99) for your copy, with free p&p

- Receive your copy hot off the press and in advance of other purchasers

- Receive occasional special Club offers and discounts on other CAMRA books and merchandise

- Stay up-to-date every year with the *Good Beer Guide* as everything is taken care of with one simple Direct Debit

- Help to fund CAMRA directly, allowing us to continue to campaign for real ale and community pubs

For further details and to sign up visit **camra.org.uk/gbg-privilege-club** and follow the online instructions.

THE GOOD BEER GUIDE

BOOKS AND MERCHANDISE

CAMRA's online shop is the ideal place to visit for anyone looking for beer- and pub-related books, clothing or merchandise for themselves or fellow beer lovers.

Books on beer, brewing, pubs, and breweries have been exploding onto our bookshelves in more numbers than ever before in recent years. Alongside a rise in the 'craft' beer movement the books on beer have taken on a much more eclectic and varied approach to the subject. Beer and cooking, brewing your own with a myriad of ingredients and the most exotic places to drink beer, have all been covered in one form or another. CAMRA books are keen to embrace this new-found desire to explore the quirky and exciting aspects of beer but with more than 50 years of publishing and a combined membership life experience of over 9 million years, we are much more inclined to approach these subjects with the long term in mind. As an authority on beer, we are very much concerned with preserving it in its purest form and celebrating the changes and innovations for their benefits.

- Browse the full range of CAMRA Books titles within categories including beer knowledge; beer travel; history & culture, heritage, home brewing and pub walks & travel

- Discover our growing selection of beer-related titles from other publishers

- Shop our expanding range of clothing and merchandise

- Get upcoming CAMRA titles in advance of publication at special pre-order prices

- As a CAMRA member, log in to receive further discounts

Visit us at: **shop1.camra.org.uk**

Desi Pubs

David Jesudason

The Desi Pub began as a story of resistance. First established in the 1960s to break the racist colour bar, which saw many non-white customers refused service, they have since evolved into a modern-day celebration of multiculturalism. This is how 'desis' – people with Indian heritage – saved failing pubs and turned them into a joyful festival of mixed grills, naans and curries all washed down with plenty of beer.

In this new book, the first of its kind, award-winning British-Asian journalist and beer writer David Jesudason travels the length and breadth of the country, visiting over 200 'desi pubs' run by British-Indian landlords who have stamped their unique identity on a beloved institution and helped to challenge our preconceptions of the pub customer: from rowdy cricket fans to vibrant bhangra nights via football supporters enjoying pre-match mixed grills and beers.

Desi Pubs will take you on a journey to parts of Britain that are seldom visited. This is a celebration of 21st-century Britain and the forgotten people who created our modern multicultural country.

RRP: £14.99   **ISBN**: 978-1-85249-385-1

For this and other books on beer and pubs, visit CAMRA's online bookshop at **shop1.camra.org.uk** or call 01727 867201.

Discounts are available for CAMRA members.

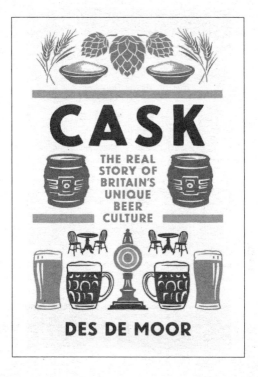

London's Best Beer, Pubs & Bars

Des De Moor

The essential guide to beer drinking in London, completely revised for 2022. Laid out by area, the book makes it simple to find the best London pubs and bars – serving the best British and world beers – and to explore the growing number of London breweries offering tours, taprooms and direct sales. Features tell you more about London's rich history of brewing and the city's vibrant modern brewing scene. The venue listings are fully illustrated, with detailed information on opening hours, local landmarks, and public transport links to make planning any excursion quick and easy. The book also includes a comprehensive listing of London breweries.

RRP: £16.99   **ISBN**: 978-1-85249-360-8

For this and other books on beer and pubs, visit CAMRA's online bookshop at **shop1.camra.org.uk** or call 01727 867201.

Discounts are available for CAMRA members.

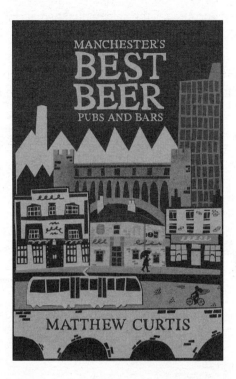

AWARD-WINNING CIDER PUBS

The National Cider & Perry Pub of the Year recognises the best pub or club that promotes and encourages the sale of quality real cider and perry across the country.

There are four stages to the competition and the winner is usually announced in October as part of CAMRA's Cider & Perry month.

Listed below are the current regional winners. Please note that not all feature in this edition of the Guide.

ENGLAND

East Anglia
Frothblowers, Peterborough

East Midlands
Red Lion at Kniveton, Kniveton

Greater London
Hop Inn, Hornchurch

Greater Manchester
Petersgate Tap, Stockport

Kent
Old House, Ightham Common

Merseyside & Cheshire
That Beer Place, Chester

North East
Station House, Durham

South West
Tom Cobley Tavern, Spreyton

Surrey & Sussex
Robin Hood, Icklesham

Wessex
Woodman Inn, Bridport

West Midlands
Bailey Head, Oswestry

West Pennines
Black Horse, Preston

Yorkshire
Nan Moor's, Todmorden

WALES

Flute & Tankard, Cardiff: City Centre

SCOTLAND

Jolly Judge, Edinburgh: Central

NORTHERN IRELAND

Dog & Duck Inn, Lisbellaw

AWARD-WINNING CLUBS

CAMRA campaigns to protect and promote clubs, which are important community assets that promote the social wellbeing of their local area.

The Club of the Year competition is run in conjunction with Club Mirror magazine, with the simple aim of finding the best clubs with the greatest commitment to quality real ale – those which offer a fantastic atmosphere, welcoming surroundings and most importantly, top quality real ale served in great condition.

The clubs listed below are the current CAMRA branch winners of the title. Please note that not all of these are listed in this edition of the Guide.

ENGLAND

Bedfordshire
Stewartby Club, Stewartby

Berkshire
Hungerford Club, Hungerford
Wargrave Snooker Club, Wargrave

Buckinghamshire
Marlow RBL, Marlow

Cambridgeshire
Comrades Club, Godmanchester

Cheshire
Appleton Thorn Village Hall, Appleton Thorn
Elworth Cricket Club, Elworth

Derbyshire
Osmaston Mens Social Club, Alvaston
Hasland WMC, Chesterfield
Dronfield Pioneer Club, Dronfield
Parwich RBL, Parwich

Devon
Hartland British Legion Club, Hartland
Paignton Conservative Club, Paignton
Fawn Member's Club, Plymouth

Dorset
Corfe Castle Club, Corfe Castle

Durham
Darlington Snooker Club, Darlington
Tanfield Lea WMC, Tanfield

Essex
South Benfleet Social Club, South Benfleet
Wethersfield Club, Wethersfield

Gloucestershire & Bristol
Cheltenham Motor Club, Cheltenham
Chalford Sports and Social Club, France Lynch

Hampshire
Dockyard Club, Portsmouth
Whitchurch Sports & Social Club, Whitchurch

Hertfordshire
Bishop's Stortford Sports Trust, Bishop's Stortford
Hitchin Rugby Club, Hitchin
Royston Social Club, St Albans

Isle of Wight
Island Sailing Club, Cowes

Kent
Dartford WMC, Dartford
Marden Village Club, Marden
Orpington Liberal Club, Orpington
Tunbridge Wells Constitutional Club, Tunbridge Wells

Lancashire
Blackpool Cricket Club, Blackpool
Garstang Club, Garstang
St Wilfrid's Terrace Members Club, Longridge
Whitworth Vale & Healey Band Club, Whitworth

Leicestershire
Sapcote Club, Sapcote

Marden Village Club in Marden, Kent, has been named the best club in the UK for the second consecutive year in CAMRA's National Club of the Year competition

Lincolnshire
Grantham Railway Club, Grantham

London, Greater
Questors Theatre Grapevine Bar, Ealing
Leyton Orient Supporters Trust, Leyton

Manchester, Greater
Bolton Ukrainian Club, Bolton
Flixton Conservative Club, Flixton
Standish Unity Club, Standish
Dobcross Band Social Club, Stockport
Ladybarn Social Club, Stockport

Merseyside
Haydock Reading Room, Haydock
Fleetwood Hesketh Sports & Social Club,
   Southport

Norfolk
Aylsham Social Club, Aylsham
Carleton Rode Social Club, Carleton Rode
Ferry Lane Social Club, King's Lynn

Northamptonshire
Midland Band Club, Kettering
Rushden Historical Transport Society, Rushden

Rutland
Empingham Cricket & Social Club, Empingham

Shropshire
Chelmarsh Sports & Social Club, Chelmarsh
St Georges Sports & Social Club, Telford

Somerset
G.W.R.S.A., Exmouth
Esplanade Club, Watchet

Staffordshire
Firs Club, Codsall
Rolleston Club, Rolleston on Dove
Uttoxeter Golf Club, Uttoxeter
Porthill Park Cricket Club, Wolstanton

Suffolk
Constitutional Club, Bury St Edmunds

Surrey
United Services Club, Egham
Kingswood Village Club, Kingswood
Woking Railway Athletic Club, Woking

Sussex, East
Albatross Club, Bexhill on Sea

Sussex, West
Keymer & Hassocks Sports & Social Club,
    Hassocks

Tyne & Wear
Mid Boldon Club, East Boldon
Heaton Stannington Football Club,
    Newcastle upon Tyne

West Midlands
Kings Heath Cricket & Sports Club, Birmingham
Knowle & Dorridge Cricket Club, Dorridge
Walsall Cricket Club, Walsall
Pennfields Bowling & Social Club,
    Wolverhampton

Wiltshire
Salisbury Rugby Club, Salisbury
Ashford Road Club, Swindon

Worcestershire
Cookley Village Hall & Sports Club, Cookley

Yorkshire, North
Crossing Club, Grosmont
Corporation Club, Scarborough
York Sports Club, York

Yorkshire, South
Coronation Club, Norton
Crookes Social Club, Sheffield
Sitwell Park Golf Club, Sitwell
Wortley Men's Club, Wortley

Yorkshire, West
Armitage Bridge Monkey Club, Armitage Bridge
Barkisland Cricket Club, Barkisland
Oatlands Club, Harrogate
Knowl Club, Mirfield
Applegarth Club, Riddlesden
Caroline Street Social Club, Saltaire
Labour Club (Red Shed), Wakefield

WALES

North-East Wales
Esplanade Club, Rhyl

North-West Wales
Royal St David's Golf Club, Harlech

West Wales
Pembroke Rugby Football Club, Pembroke
Pontyberem WMC, Pontyberem

SCOTLAND

Aberdeen & Grampian
Ravenswood British Legion Club, Banchory

Ayrshire & Arran
Ardrossan Academicals RFC, Ardrossan

JOIN THE CAMRA STORY

People from all walks of life join CAMRA. They're brought together by a love of real ale, cider and perry, the traditions of the pub and a desire to protect them. Be part of the story and seek out your local branch. Keep real ale alive and share tasting notes. Volunteer at a festival or campaign to protect everything you love for the future. Discover the many ways to celebrate our shared passions.

Join as a member from only £30.50† today – as a thank you for being a hero in the CAMRA story, your membership gets you...

- A **welcome pack**, including membership card, to help you make the most of your membership

- Access to award-winning, quarterly *BEER* magazine and **What's Brewing** online news

- £30* worth of **CAMRA real ale** vouchers

- Access to the **Real Ale Discount Scheme**, where you receive discounts on pints at over 3,500 participating pubs nationwide

- **Learn & Discover** online resources to help you discover more about beer and brewing

- **Free or reduced entry** to CAMRA beer festivals

- The opportunity to **campaign for great real ale, cider and perry**, and to save pubs under threat from closure

- **Discounts on CAMRA books** including our best-selling *Good Beer Guide*

- Complete access to our **beer**, **pub and brewery database**, as well as trip planning functionality and **member discounts online** with our new website

Whether you're a dedicated campaigner, a beer enthusiast looking to learn more about beer, or you just love beer and pubs, CAMRA membership is for you. Join us today!

Join the campaign at
camra.org.uk/join

CAMRA, 230 Hatfield Road, St Albans, Herts AL1 4LW.
Tel: 01727 798440 Email: camra@camra.org.uk

Rates and benefits are subject to change.
† Concessionary rates may be lower.
* Joint members receive £40 worth of vouchers.
** real ale, cider and perry, subject to terms and conditions.

Campaign
for
Real Ale